A Multidisciplinary Science Program for High School

Level 2

BSCS SCIENCE

AN INQUIRY APPROACH

TEACHER EDITION

EXPLORING THE BUILDING BLOCKS OF THE UNIVERSE

KENDALL/HUNT PUBLISHING COMPANY
4050 Westmark Drive Dubuque, Iowa 52002

BSCS Development Team

Rodger W. Bybee, PhD, *Co-Principal Investigator*
Pamela Van Scotter, *Co-Principal Investigator, Project Director*
Nicole Knapp, *Curriculum Developer, Professional Development Coordinator*
Betty Stennett, *Curriculum Developer, Professional Development Coordinator*
Steve Getty, PhD, *Curriculum Developer, Classroom-Based Research Associate*
K. David Pinkerton, PhD, *Curriculum Developer*
Cyndi Long, *Curriculum Developer, Professional Development Coordinator*
Sandy Smith, *Curriculum Developer*
C. Jane Wilson, *Curriculum Developer*
Debra Hannigan, *Curriculum Developer, Curriculum Coordinator*
David Hanych, PhD, *Curriculum Developer*
Steve Williams, PhD, *Curriculum Developer*
Hedi Baxter, *Curriculum Developer*
Molly McGarrigle, *Internal Evaluator*
Theodore Lamb, PhD, *Co-Director, Center for Research and Evaluation*
Ann Lanari, *Research Assistant*
Raphaela Conner, *Project Assistant*
Susan Hawkins, *Project Assistant*
Terry Redmond, *Project Assistant*
Pamela S. Warren, *Project Assistant*

BSCS Production Team

Barbara Perrin, *Director of Publications*
Dottie Watkins, *Production Coordinator*
Stacey Luce, *Manuscript Specialist, Permissions*
Lisa Rasmussen, *Graphic Artist*
Diane Gionfriddo, *Photo Researcher*
Angela Paoleti, *Production Assistant*

BSCS Administration

Rodger W. Bybee, PhD, *Executive Director*
Janet Carlson Powell, PhD, *Associate Director*
Pamela Van Scotter, *Director, BSCS Center for Curriculum Development*
Marcia Mitchell, *Director of Finance*
Carlo Parravano, PhD, *Merck Institute for Science Education; Chairman, BSCS Board of Directors*

Editors

Barbara Resch, Colorado Springs, CO
Francelia Sevin, *Education Editor,* Crestone, CO

External Evaluator

Doug Coulson, PhD, PS International, Arnold, MD

Artists, Designers, Photographers, Photo Researchers

David Ball, Illustrator, Colorado Springs, CO
Rick Bickhart, Peaceful Solutions Design, Albuquerque, NM
Natalie Giboney, Freelance Permissions, Fort Worth, TX
Joe Hartman, Photographer, Branding Iron Media and Design, L.L.C., Colorado Springs, CO
Jane McBee, Photographer, Colorado Springs, CO
Barbara Perrin, Ibis Production Management, Colorado Springs, CO
Rick Simonson, Illustrator, Kearney, NE
Paige Thomas, Illustrator, Colorado Springs, CO
Nina Whitney, Picture Vision, Falmouth, MA

ISBN: 978-0-7575-1735-8

The development of this material was funded by the National Science Foundation under Grant Numbers ESI 9911614 and ESI 0242596. Any opinions, findings, conclusions, or recommendations expressed in this publication are those of the authors and do not necessarily reflect the views of the granting agency.

Printed in the United States of America
1 2 3 4 5 6 7 8 9 10 12 11 10 09 08 07

Acknowledgments

Advisory Board Members

Marshall Berman, PhD, New Mexico State Board of Education
Kathy Comfort, PhD, Partnership for the Assessment of Standards-Based Science, WestEd, San Francisco, CA
Ginger Davis, Brevard Public Schools, FL
Melissa DeWitt, East Fairmont High School, Fairmont, WV
Christine Funk, Douglas County High School, Castle Rock, CO
Steve Getty, PhD, Colorado College, Colorado Springs, CO
Michael Hanson, Tahoma High School, Kent, WA
Jerrie Mallicoat, Titusville High School, Titusville, FL
M. Patricia Morse, PhD, University of Washington, Seattle, WA
Susan Mundry, PhD, WestEd, Stoneham, MA
Harold Pratt, PhD, Educational Consultants, Inc., Littleton, CO
Rochelle Rubin, PhD, Waterford School District, Waterford, MI
Gary Scott, San Pedro Math, Science, and Technology Center, San Pedro, CA
Ethan Smith, Tahoma High School, Kent, WA

Contributors and Reviewers

Gary Axen, PhD, New Mexico Tech, Socorro, NM
Marshall Berman, PhD, New Mexico State Board of Education
Robert Blake, PhD, Texas Tech University, Lubbock, TX
Mark Bloom, PhD, BSCS, Colorado Springs, CO
Cathy Box, Tahoka Middle School, Tahoka, TX
Heidi Carlone, PhD, University of North Carolina, Greensboro, NC
Steven Clemmens, PhD, Brown University, Providence, RI
Rocky Coleman, PhD, Colorado State University, Fort Collins, CO
George Davis, PhD, Minnesota State University, Moorehead, MN
Edward Drexler, Pius XI High School, Milwaukee, WI
Ellen Friedman, PhD, San Diego, CA
James Garrett Davis, Albuquerque, NM
Steve Getty, PhD, Colorado College, Colorado Springs, CO
Anne Haley-Mackenzie, PhD, Miami University of Ohio, Oxford, OH
David Hanych, PhD, BSCS, VA
Mary Kay Hemmenway, PhD, University of Texas, Austin, TX
William Hoyt, PhD, University of Northern Colorado, Greeley, CO
Barbara Hug, PhD, University of Michigan, Ann Arbor, MI
Jay Kauffman, PhD, University of Maryland, College Park, MD
Laura Laughran, PhD, New Directions, Tucson, AZ
Toby Merlin, MD, Centers for Disease Control and Prevention, Atlanta, GA
Samuel Milazzo, University of Colorado, Colorado Springs, CO
Gary Morgan, New Mexico Museum of Nature and Science
Jerry Phillips, PhD, BSCS, Colorado Springs, CO
Harold Pratt, PhD, Educational Consultants, Inc., Littleton, CO
Richard Reynolds, PhD, USDA Forest Service, Rocky Mountain Research Station, Fort Collins, CO
Carol Sheriff, Albuquerque, NM
Ray Tschillard, BSCS, Colorado Springs, CO
Anne Westbrook, PhD, BSCS, Colorado Springs, CO
Lawrence Woolf, PhD, General Atomics, San Diego, CA
Ted Yeshion, Cluefinders, Erie, PA

Field-Test Teachers and Leaders

Arizona

Abigail Moore, Desert View High School, Tucson, AZ

California

Dlunari Edirisinghe, Narbonne High School, Harbor City, CA
Carolyn Higuchi, Narbonne High School, Harbor City, CA
Roger Mataumoto, Narbonne High School, Harbor City, CA
Gary Scott, San Pedro Math, Science, and Technology Center, San Pedro, CA

Colorado

Kerry Adams, Alamosa High School, Alamosa, CO
Christine Funk, Douglas County High School, Castle Rock, CO
Sharon Harter, Coronado High School, Colorado Springs, CO
Dennis Lopez, District Representative, Alamosa High School, Alamosa, CO
Jim Street, Alamosa High School, Alamosa, CO
Jodi Vine Schlang, University of Denver High School, Denver, CO

Florida

Lori Braga, Melbourne High School, Melbourne, FL
Kim Bragg, District Representative, Brevard Public Schools, FL
Ginger Davis, Science Supervisor, Brevard Public Schools, FL
Elizabeth Hickey, Cocoa High School, Cocoa, FL
Catherine Hoffman, Satellite High School, Satellite Beach, FL
Edward Johnson, Cocoa High School, Cocoa, FL
Jerri Mallicoat, Titusville High School, Titusville, FL
Kip Mapstone, Eau Gallie High School, Melbourne, FL
James Meegan, Melbourne High School, Melbourne, FL
Raul Montes, Cocoa High School, Cocoa, FL
Melindy Myrick-Lupo, Eau Gallie High School, Melbourne, FL
Jon Nelson, Titusville High School, Titusville, FL
Cheryl Reve, Cocoa High School, Cocoa, FL
Lisa Scott, Satellite High School, Satellite Beach, FL
Nelson Salazar, Eau Gallie High School, Melbourne, FL
Michelle Walker, Eau Gallie High School, Melbourne, FL
Lisa Wall-Campeau, Eau Gallie High School, Melbourne, FL

Illinois

Shannon Edwards, Centennial High School, Champaign, IL
Kevin Kuppler, District Representative, Champaign, IL
Shirley Ma, Centennial High School, Champaign, IL

Indiana

Kristy Slaby, Kankakee Valley High School, Wheatfield, IN

Massachusetts

Alan Murphy, Pioneer Valley Regional High School, Northfield, MA
Lawrence Poirier, Pioneer Valley Regional High School, Northfield, MA
Jo Anne Pullen, Science Supervisor, Pioneer Valley Region School District, Northfield, MA

Michigan

John Bayerl, Fordson High School, Dearborn, MI
Herm Boatin, Science Supervisor, Dearborn Public Schools, MI
Mary Beth Henry, Dearborn High School, Dearborn, MI
Richard Klee, Science Supervisor, Dearborn Public Schools, MI
David Mayoros, Edsel Ford High School, Dearborn, MI
Robert Tyler, Dearborn High School, Dearborn, MI

Missouri

LaurAnn Robertson, Lamar High School, Lamar, MO

New Hampshire

Lise Bofinger, Concord High School, Concord, NH
Sarah Carson, Concord High School, Concord, NH
Charles Swift, Concord High School, Concord, NH

Pennsylvania

Stephen Garstka, Ridley High School, Folsom, PA

Paul McGibney, Ridley High School, Folsom, PA
Thomas Pfleger, Ridley High School, Folsom, PA

Tennessee

Laura Kile, Webb School of Knoxville, Knoxville, TN

Vermont

Merribelle Coles, Brattleboro Union High School, Brattleboro, VT
Bruce Holloway, Brattleboro Union High School, Brattleboro, VT
James Maland, District Representative, Brattleboro Union High School, VT
Katherine Martin, Brattleboro Union High School, Brattleboro, VT
Scott Noren, Brattleboro Union High School, Brattleboro, VT
Julie Wheeler, Brattleboro Union High School, Brattleboro, VT

Washington

Aanika DeVries, Spring Street School, Friday Harbor, WA
Ken Loomis, Tahoma Senior High School, Covington, WA
James McLean, Science Supervisor, Kennewick School District, WA
Jim Ramsey, Kamiakin High School, Kennewick, WA
Ethan Smith, Tahoma Senior High School, Covington, WA
Walt Szklarski, Tahoma Senior High School, Covington, WA
Allison Winward, Kamiakin High School, Kennewick, WA

West Virginia

Jules Adam, Oak Glen High School, New Cumberland, WV
Melissa DeWitt, East Fairmont High School, Fairmont, WV
Joyce Duvall, Parkersburg High School, Parkersburg, WV
Diane Furman, Science Supervisor, Marion County Schools, WV
Sally Morgan, East Fairmont High School, Fairmont, WV
Joyce Pitrolo, Parkersburg High School, Parkersburg, WV
Mary Lynn Westfall, East Fairmont High School, Fairmont, WV

Wisconsin

Sue Alberti, Science Supervisor, Ashwaubenon School District, Ashwaubenon, WI
Michael Lyga, Ashwaubenon High School, Green Bay, WI
Kylie Werner, Ashwaubenon High School, Green Bay, WI
Joelle Zuengler, Ashwaubenon High School, Green Bay, WI

Contents

Welcome to

BSCS Science: An Inquiry Approach

This multidisciplinary program is designed to promote enduring understandings of fundamental concepts in physical science, life science, and earth and space science while using scientific inquiry as the integrating theme.

Every time BSCS develops a new program, it is a reflection of a collaborative effort among teachers, scientists, and science educators. Our goal is to create a highly teachable program with scientific integrity as its foundation. BSCS developed this program with effective, student-centered learning as a central focus. We could not do this without input from the many teachers who have field-tested the program as well as input from teachers who use the program in their classrooms after it is in print.

Our work does not end when the program is published, so we invite you to join the Inquiry team at BSCS by sending your thoughts, experiences, and questions to us at info@bscs.org.

Sincerely,

Carlo Parravano	Rodger W. Bybee	Janet Carlson Powell
BSCS Board of Directors, Chair	Executive Director, BSCS	Associate Director, BSCS

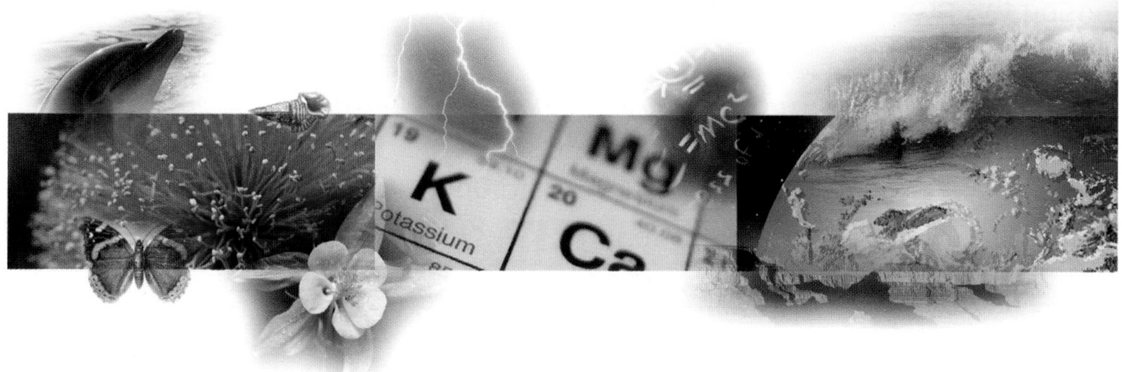

Dear Colleague,

Do you think about teaching during your commute to school? At BSCS, we're the same way. Teaching and learning are always on our minds. That's because we all know that teaching and learning are so important for today's students. It's why you teach. And it's why we wrote this teacher edition of *BSCS Science: An Inquiry Approach*.

You want a teacher edition that respects your time, trusts your judgment, and partners in your success. To respect your time, we designed this book so you could find, use, and understand what you need for each lesson in an efficient way. For example, the wraparound text saves you time by matching student text and procedures for investigations with teaching strategies and sample answers. Extensive background information sections save you time if you're teaching out of field. Clear learning goals and standards help you plan. The *Teacher Resource CD* provides ready access to copymasters and other related resources. Also, detailed materials lists and preparation advice help you manage the investigations efficiently.

We respect your judgment. So, at times, we offer you a variety of suggestions and alternatives, trusting you to select what's best for your students. For example, some answers are given according to levels of performance, so you can individualize instruction. This feature helps you with ongoing assessment—monitoring the daily changes that add up to a year's worth of growth. We present creative alternatives for beginning a lesson, explicit connections among science disciplines, and extensive resources for additional exploration so you can tailor lesson plans for your students.

BSCS wants to be a partner in your success. That means we share our professional experience and insights toward a common end—helping students think, learn, and problem solve. Like you, we want students to be better prepared to participate effectively in an increasingly complex world. It's one of many steps in the long journey to a satisfying adulthood. And it's a journey we are honored to take with you.

The staff at BSCS wrote this teacher edition to meet the needs of your demanding position. Please share your thoughts with us. Finally, thank you for choosing this program.

BSCS Science: An Inquiry Approach
BSCS
5415 Mark Dabling Boulevard
Colorado Springs, CO 80918-3842
info@bscs.org

Sincerely,
The *BSCS Science: An Inquiry Approach* Team

Getting to Know *BSCS Science: An Inquiry Approach*

Program Overview

BSCS Science: An Inquiry Approach represents a new generation of instructional materials for high school science. As with all BSCS programs, *An Inquiry Approach* is an innovative, student-centered science program. This three-year program for high school is funded by the National Science Foundation. It introduces students to the core concepts in inquiry, the physical sciences, the life sciences, and the earth and space sciences as articulated in the *National Science Education Standards* (National Research Council [NRC], 1996). In addition, the curriculum engages students in integration across the disciplines in relevant contexts that explore the standards related to science in a personal and social perspective and to science and technology. When students complete all three years of the program, they will have been introduced to all of the national standards for grades nine through 12. *BSCS Science: An Inquiry Approach* provides high school students nationwide with a rigorous, coherent alternative to the traditional sequence of biology, chemistry, and physics, and covers earth and space science as well.

As states establish science standards for all students that span the disciplines, high schools must rethink their science programs and requirements. From 1997 to 1999, BSCS conducted an important design study to examine the need for such a program (BSCS, 2000). The findings were clear. Teachers across the country seek a coherent alternative to the traditional sequence of biology, chemistry, and physics. A multidisciplinary program is now an essential offering. *BSCS Science: An Inquiry Approach* represents a high-quality response to this need.

Foremost among the program's innovative features is a comprehensive emphasis on inquiry and the big ideas of science. We developed this program with a team of scientists, teachers, science educators, and many students in field-test classrooms across the country. As we developed this program, we focused on the following goals for students:

- To increase students' enduring understanding of fundamental concepts across the disciplines of science
- To present science in a context that is relevant to students
- To increase students' interest and achievement in science
- To enhance their critical-thinking and problem-solving skills

To meet the needs of teachers who must facilitate learning in classrooms characterized by student populations with multiple abilities and learning styles, our goal was to develop a flexible curriculum that can be individualized to suit particular teaching styles and unique classroom settings. An explicit instructional model, collaborative learning opportunities, ongoing assessment, optional activities, and a variety of educational technologies all can be used to adapt the curriculum to virtually any learning situation.

The Framework

The framework for *BSCS Science: An Inquiry Approach* presents a coherent articulation of concepts through each year and across the years.

Each of the core units comprises two to three chapters that expose the students to fundamental concepts in each of the disciplines. The last chapter in each core unit allows students to apply what they have learned thus far in a compelling, integrated context. This approach of providing students with a foundation of knowledge with which to build an in-depth understanding across time, as well as providing the students with a compelling context within which to learn, is supported by recent research in learning (Bransford, Brown, & Cocking, 2000; Pellegrino, Chudowsky, & Glaser, 2001).

BSCS Science: An Inquiry Approach, High School Framework

	Major concepts addressed at each level		
Units	**Level 1**	**Level 2**	**Level 3**
	Abilities necessary to do and understandings about scientific inquiry with a focus on:		
Science As Inquiry	• Questions and concepts that guide scientific investigations	• Design of scientific investigations • Communicating scientific results	• Evidence as the basis for explanations and models • Alternative explanations and models
Physical Science	• Structure and properties of matter • Structure of atoms • Integrating chapter	• Motions and forces • Chemical reactions • Integrating chapter	• Interactions of energy and matter • Conservation of energy and increase in disorder • Integrating chapter
Life Science	• The cell • Behavior of organisms • Integrating chapter	• Biological evolution • Molecular basis of heredity • Integrating chapter	• Matter, energy, and organization in living systems • Interdependence of organisms • Integrating chapter
Earth-Space Science	• Origin and evolution of the universe • Origin and evolution of the Earth system • Integrating chapter	• Geochemical cycles • Integrating chapter	• Energy in the Earth system • Integrating chapter
Science in a Personal and Social Perspective, Science and Technology	• Personal and community health • Natural and human-induced hazards • Abilities of technological design	• Population growth • Natural resources • Environmental quality	• Science and technology in local, national, and global challenges • Understandings about science and technology
	History and Nature of Science addressed throughout grade levels and units • Science as a human endeavour • Nature of science • History of Science		

Components of the Program

BSCS Science: An Inquiry Approach is a comprehensive program that includes the following components:

- Student Edition
- Student Edition on CD
- *Student Resource CD*
- Teacher Wraparound Edition
- *Teacher Resource CD*
- *Test Bank*
- Transparencies
- Web site

Student Edition

The student book is designed with 10th graders in mind. Each chapter and unit draws the students into an engaging learning experience. The BSCS 5Es structure the learning experience for the students through each chapter. In addition to being conceptually appealing, the book is visually appealing. Features such as the chapter organizers and openers, special reading sections, FYIs, sidebars, interesting art, the *How To* section at the back of the book, and National Science Teachers Association SciLinks keep the students interested and focused on their learning journey.

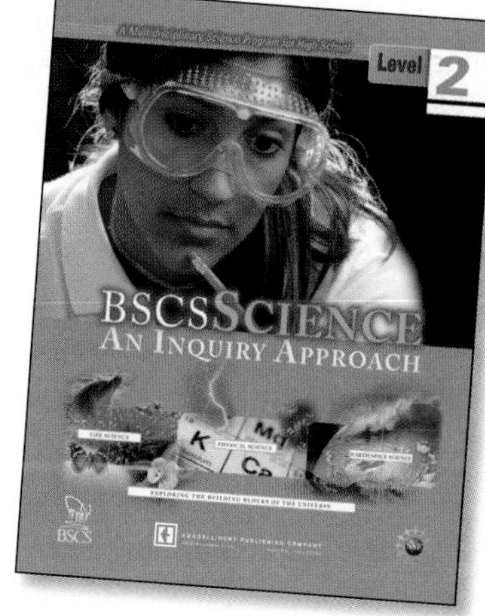

Student Resource CD

The *Student Resource CD* (*SRCD*) provides students with concept maps for each chapter. From the concept maps, students can link to the additional resources on the *SRCD*. For example, from a specific concept on a specific map, the students might link to an interesting video clip, animation, or simulation. This visually rich resource is a powerful learning tool for students.

Teacher Wraparound Edition

The Teacher Wraparound Edition is an invaluable tool for teachers. It includes reduced student pages with wraparound teaching strategies. This means teachers are on the same page as the students and still have access to the strategies and answers. The teacher edition provides teachers with the important background information for each chapter, strategies for guiding the students through each activity using an inquiry-based approach, answers to the questions posed, and outcomes and indicators of success for each activity. The teacher edition also includes a chapter organizer, a comprehensive list of materials, reminders about advance preparations and safety, and important reminders about misconceptions students might have.

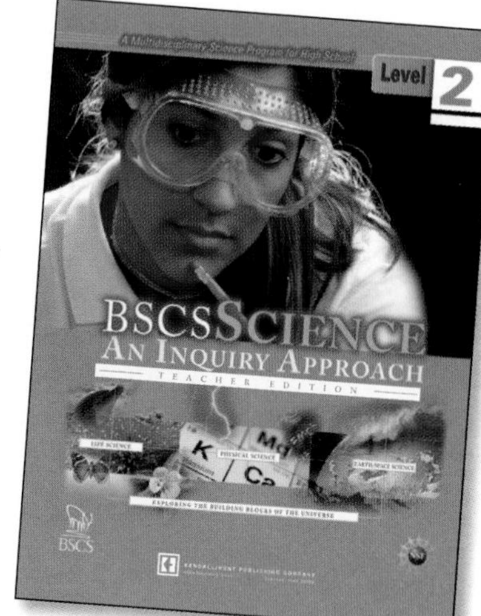

Teacher Resource CD

The *Teacher Resource CD* (*TRCD*) provides additional resources that teachers will find useful. The *TRCD* includes the following:

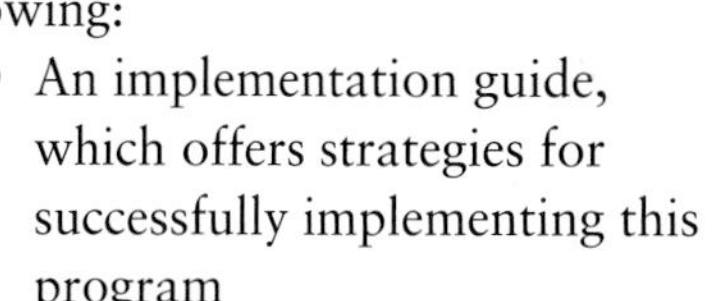

- An implementation guide, which offers strategies for successfully implementing this program
- A guide to assessment, which includes a complete set of assessment instruments

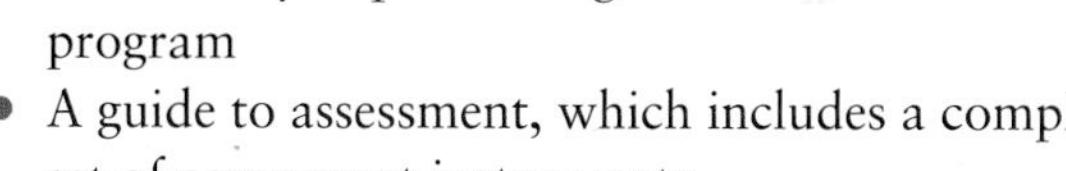

- A guide to collaborative learning
- A correlation of *An Inquiry Approach* to the *National Science Education Standards*
- Copymasters for all activities that require them
- Optional activities
- *Toolbox* activities

Test Generator

The *Test Bank* for the program includes questions for each chapter in the program. The *Test Bank* is part of the comprehensive assessment package and includes the central evaluate activities as well as opportunities for ongoing assessment. The *Test Bank* is a flexible resource that allows you to design your own test that emphasizes the concepts and content you want to emphasize. The test questions are modeled after state and national tests for high school science and, as such, provide students with important opportunities to practice taking tests.

Transparencies

The transparency book is a collection of the salient pieces of art from the program that convey concepts visually. These transparencies provide you with an important teaching tool when reviewing concepts with the whole class.

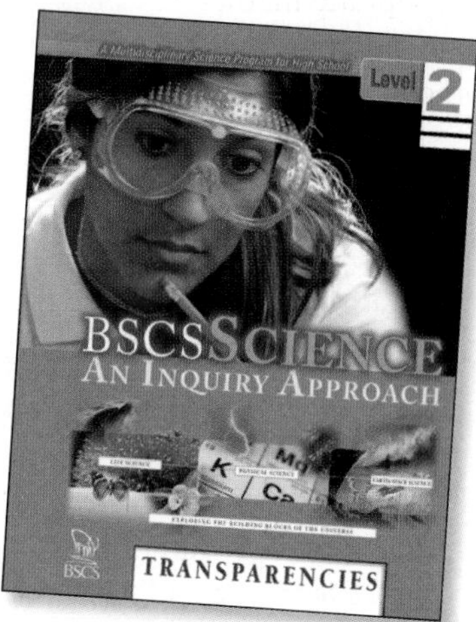

Web Site

The Web site keeps teachers up to date on the program. From time to time, BSCS provides updates to content, shares new resources with teachers, and helps create a network of teachers who are using the program.

Distinguishing Features of the Program

As our BSCS team developed *An Inquiry Approach*, we thought carefully about the following features that distinguish the program:

- Rigorous, standards-based content
- Inquiry as the overarching theme
- Multidisciplinary science content
- Content background for teachers who teach out of field
- Activity-centered lessons
- Opportunities for structured and open inquiry in relevant contexts
- Opportunities for students to design and conduct their own investigations
- Opportunities for students to consider recent research
- A constructivist, student-centered approach
- The use of literacy strategies to help students monitor their own learning
- The integration of mathematics
- The use of chapter organizers, science notebooks, and *How Tos*
- The BSCS 5E instructional model
- A collaborative learning environment
- A comprehensive, multifaceted assessment package

Rigorous, Standards-Based Content

The content for the program is defined by the *National Science Education Standards* for grades nine through 12. This includes the standards related to inquiry, physical science, life science, earth and space science, science and technology, science in personal and social perspectives, and the history and nature of science. This specific focus allows for an in-depth, rigorous exploration of the central ideas in the sciences.

Inquiry as the Overarching Theme

Science as inquiry is a hallmark of the program. Ideas that students encounter in chapter 1, *Investigations by Design*, will be central to every chapter that follows. Both an understanding of inquiry and the abilities related to inquiry provide the overarching theme and foundation for the program. Each lesson approaches the content from the perspective of experiencing science as a way of knowing.

Multidisciplinary Science Content

In the natural world, science is not divided into disciplines, so we feel that students' study of science should not be either. The program includes many opportunities to explore interdisciplinary concepts and areas in science that reflect the unity of the natural world. Indeed, the last chapter of each unit and the final unit of the program are specifically devoted to such studies. Our work with teachers and students across the country has shown us that more students are engaged and interested in science when the content is integrated.

Content Background for Teachers Who Teach Out of Field

We know that many teachers who teach *An Inquiry Approach* find themselves teaching out of field for parts of the program. That is exactly why we thought carefully about this situation as we developed the program. Our field-test teachers, many of whom were teaching out of field, helped us identify the types of things that would be the most helpful. In the teacher edition, we provide extensive background information for each activity. We provide detailed answers for the *Stop and Think* questions and the *Reflect and Connect* questions. A special section on misconceptions helps teachers understand and effectively address misconceptions with which they might not be as familiar. In addition, BSCS has a Web site for the program that we update and add to as we come across important new resources for teachers.

Activity-Centered Lessons

The lessons in the program are centered on activities that provide students with meaningful experiences that are conceptually organized. The conceptual flow builds throughout each chapter, each unit, and across the entire program, encouraging students to continuously seek a greater understanding.

Opportunities for Structured and Open Inquiry in Relevant Contexts

Each chapter provides a range of opportunities for inquiry. Our approach is to place inquiry in the hands and minds of the students, encouraging their scientific habits of mind. As the students construct their understanding across time, they take charge of their learning journey. As they explore specific contexts or try to solve specific problems, they encounter situations where they need to know more. At these points, they design and conduct investigations and use other resources in the program to answer their questions.

Opportunities for Students to Design and Conduct Their Own Investigations

Our development team knows that it is vital to provide students with specific opportunities to design and conduct their own investigations. Each chapter presents such opportunities related to one or more of the central ideas. The students ask questions, design and conduct investigations, make predictions, and analyze results, all of which help them develop and better understand a broad range of scientific explanations. After the students have experienced each of the core units, we provide the structure for an optional full inquiry that students conduct across a number of weeks. The full inquiry takes place alongside their regular classroom work and allows them to explore one compelling question in greater depth.

Opportunities for Students to Consider Recent Research

Our development team also felt that it was important to expose students to some recent research in science. These experiences allow students to better understand and appreciate the nature of science and to see science as an ongoing human endeavor rather than as a static body of knowledge. Each chapter in the program presents at least one such opportunity.

A Constructivist, Student-Centered Approach

The BSCS philosophy is that students learn best when they are provided with significant opportunities to construct their own understanding of the concepts across time. This philosophy is supported by current research in learning (Bransford, Brown, & Cocking, 2000). The BSCS 5E instructional model is based on this constructivist learning theory.

The Use of Literacy Strategies to Help Students Monitor Their Own Learning

Much of what students learn comes in the form of printed text or graphic images such as charts, tables, graphs, and diagrams. A literate student is able to use these forms of information effectively to acquire, interpiret, and apply knowledge. Most students, however, need to learn about and practice these skills in order to be effective.

This program includes rresearch-based literacy strategies in the day-to-day progress through each chapter.

The Integration of Mathematics

Mathematics is integral to the program. Throughout the chapters and units, mathematical concepts are presented when it is appropriate or necessary for the science concepts being developed. In addition to including the appropriate mathematics, the program includes *Toolbox* activities that provide students with more support and practice with a range of mathematical ideas, if necessary.

The Use of Chapter Organizers, Science Notebooks, and *How Tos*

At the beginning of each chapter, we provide students with a chapter organizer that helps them visualize the central concepts, the sequence of activities, and the questions that link one activity to the next. These organizers provide students with the context and structure for learning. In the teacher edition, we provide a simplified version of the organizer along with an indication of how much time each lesson might take to complete. Science notebooks help students organize and articulate their growing understanding. In this way, throughout the program, they are responsible for monitoring their own learning.

Students use a science notebook throughout the course as a key piece in developing metacognitive skills that lead to conceptual continuity and depth. The use of the science notebook is integral to student participation and growth. At different times, students will use their science notebooks in the following ways:

- Record data
- Take notes
- Make sketches
- Organize their ideas through concept maps or other visuals
- Respond to questions in the activities
- Complete homework
- Keep track of questions they may have
- Complete other assignments

The *How To* section at the back of the Student Edition provides students with guidance for completing some key activities and improving skills that are required throughout the program. These *How Tos* include a range of skills such as how to construct different types of graphs, how to use a microscope, and how to conduct research on the Web. In addition, there is a set of *How Tos* related to specific literacy strategies that the students will find useful throughout the year.

The BSCS 5E Instructional Model

In *BSCS Science: An Inquiry Approach*, each chapter proceeds through a cycle of activities based on the BSCS 5Es:

ENGAGE | EXPLORE | EXPLAIN | EVALUATE | ELABORATE

According to the BSCS 5E model, each *E* represents an important part of the sequence through which students progress to develop their understanding. First, students are *engaged* by an event or a question related to a concept, and they have opportunities to express their current understanding. Then they participate in one or more activities to *explore* the concept and share ideas with others before beginning to construct an *explanation*. Following the initial development of an explanation, students have the opportunity to *elaborate* and deepen their

Stage of the Instructional Model	The BSCS 5E Instructional Model What the Teacher Does	
	that is consistent with this model	**that is inconsistent with this model**
Engage	• Creates interest • Generates curiosity • Raises questions • Elicits responses that uncover what the students know or think bout the concept/ topic	• Explains concepts • Provides definitions and answers • States conclusions • Provides closure • Lectures
Explore	• Encourages the students to work together without direction instruction from the teacher • Observes and listens to the students as they interact • Asks probing questions to redirect the students' investigations when necessary • Provides time for the students to puzzle through problems • Acts as a consultant for students	• Provides answers • Tells or explains how to work through the problem • Provides closure • Tells the students that they are wrong • Gives information or facts that solve the problem • Leads the students step-by-step to a solution
Explain	• Encourages the students to explain concepts and definitions in their own words • Asks for justification (evidence) and clarification from students • Formally provides definitions, explanations, and new labels • Uses students' previous experiences as basis for explaining concepts	• Accepts explanations that have no justification • Neglects to solicit the students' explanations • Introduces unrelated concepts or skills
Elaborate	• Expects the students to use formal labels, definitions, and explanations provided previously • Encourages the students to apply or extend the concepts and skills in new situations • Reminds the students of alternate explanations • Refers the student to existing data and evidence and asks: What do you already know? Why do you think . . . ? (Strategies from Explore apply here also)	• Provides definitive answers • Tells the students that they are wrong • Lectures • Leads students step-by-step to a solution • Explains how to work through the problem
Evaluate	• Observes the students as they apply new concepts and skills • Assesses students' knowledge and/or skills • Looks for evidence that the students have changed their thinking or behaviors • Allows students to assess for their own learning and group-process skills • Asks open-ended questions such as, Why do you think . . . ? What evidence do you have? What do you know about x? How would you explain x?	• Tests vocabulary words, terms, and isolated facts • Introduces new ideas or concepts • Creates ambiguity • Promotes open-ended discussion unrelated to the concept or skill

understanding of the concept in a new situation. Finally, students *evaluate* their growing understanding of the concept before encountering a new one. The combination of the 5E model with a strong assessment-oriented design provides opportunities for learning and conceptual change in students, which leads to an improved understanding of science (Bransford, Brown, & Cocking, 2000).

The 5E instructional model naturally supports the program's inquiry focus. Research on learning indicates that students need to know more than just scientific concepts and information. They need to develop both the understandings and abilities of inquiry and learn strategies for scientific thinking (NRC, 1996; NRC, 2000; Linn et al., 1989). With the 5E instructional model, lessons are sequenced so that students have opportunities to study the natural world, propose explanations based on evidence, and increase their understanding of scientific ideas and the nature of science.

Stage of the Instructional Model	The BSCS 5E Instructional Model What the Student Does	
	that is consistent with this model	**that is inconsistent with this model**
Engage	• Asks questions such as Why did this happen? What do I already know about this? What can I find out about this? • Shows interest in the topic	• Asks for the "right" answer • Offers the "right" answer • Insists on answers or explanations • Seeks one solution
Explore	• Thinks freely, but within the limits of the activity • Tests predictions and hypotheses • Tries alternatives and discusses them with others • Records observations and ideas • Suspends judgment	• Lets others do the thinking and exploring (passive involvement) • Works quietly with little or no interaction with others (only appropriate when exploring ideas or feelings) • "Plays around" indiscriminately with no goal in mind • Stops with one solution
Explain	• Explains possible solutions or answers to others • Listens critically to others' explanations • Questions others' explanations • Listens to and tries to comprehend explanations that the teacher offers • Refers to previous activities • Uses recorded observations in explanations	• Proposes explanations from "thin air" with no relationship to previous experiences • Brings up irrelevant experiences and examples • Accept explanations without justification • Does not attend to other plausible explanations
Elaborate	• Applies new labels, definitions, explanations, and skills in new but similar situations • Uses previous information to ask questions, propose solutions, make decisions, and design experiments • Draws reasonable conclusions from evidence • Records observations and explanations • Checks for understanding among peers	• "Plays around" with no goal in mind • Ignores previous information or evidence • Draws conclusions from "thin air" • In discussion, uses only those labels that the teacher provided
Evaluate	• Answers open-ended questions by using observations, evidence, and previously accepted explanations • Demonstrates an understanding or knowledge of the concept or skill • Evaluates his or her own progress and knowledge • Asks related questions that would encourage future investigations	• Draws conclusions, not using evidence or previously accepted explanations • Offers only yes-or-no answers and memorized definitions or explanations as answers • Fails to express satisfactory explanations in his or her own words • Introduces new, irrelevant topics

A Collaborative Learning Environment

Collaborative learning is an important strategy that helps decrease students' dependence on the teacher as the sole repository of information and increase their responsibility for their own learning. Collaborative learning in this program also models the processes that scientists use when working together and helps teach the working-relationship skills necessary in today's team-based workforce.

In *BSCS Science: An Inquiry Approach*, you can use collaborative learning strategies in a significant number of the activities. These strategies enhance the setting in which the best learning occurs in the following ways:

- Collaborative learning empowers the learners, making them responsible for seeking information and achieving a particular task.
- Collaborative learning strategies model one feature of the nature of the scientific endeavor.
- Research has shown that collaborative learning is an effective technique for involving students from groups that are underrepresented in science, such as females and ethnic minority students.
- Collaborative learning can be a powerful way to interest and motivate students who might not otherwise excel or even be interested in science.

The *Guide to Collaborative Learning* on the *TRCD* provides additional background information.

A Comprehensive, Multifaceted Assessment Package

Our development team knows how important assessment is, and we wanted to provide a comprehensive and useful package. As a result, this assessment package includes the following:

- Test bank assessments at the unit level
- Performance-based assessments at the chapter level
- Embedded assessments at the activity level
- Scoring rubrics for students and teachers
- Guidelines for portfolio development

Specific assessment opportunities, which allow you to evaluate your students' progress on an ongoing basis, are embedded throughout the program and are based on the philosophy that assessment itself should be a learning experience. The following strategies, which include both formal and informal assessment techniques, are included in the program:

- Performance-based assessments such as investigations
- Written tests with a variety of multiple-choice and short-answer questions
- The use of our *Learn from Mistakes Protocol*
- Presentations, both team and individual
- Written assignments related to both short-term and long-term work
- Special projects
- Full inquiry
- Discussions, both team and whole class
- Opportunities for self-assessment and peer assessment
- Debates
- Portfolios

You will find more information on assessment in the *Guide to Assessment* on the *TRCD*.

National Field Test Demonstrates Effectiveness

As with anything new, we need evidence that it works. A semester-long national field test of *BSCS Science: An Inquiry Approach* was conducted from January through June 2002. The field test comprised urban, suburban, and rural classrooms across 10 states (Vermont, Massachusetts, West Virginia, Florida, Tennessee, Michigan, Illinois, Wisconsin, Washington, and Colorado), 31 teachers, 64 classes, and nearly 1,600 students, representing significant diversity.

The assessment instruments included student surveys, teacher surveys, pre- and post-tests, an end-of-field-test survey, and classroom observations by an external evaluator and BSCS project staff. Among the findings, two major results stand out with respect to the quality and effectiveness of the instructional materials and student achievement (Coulson, 2002).

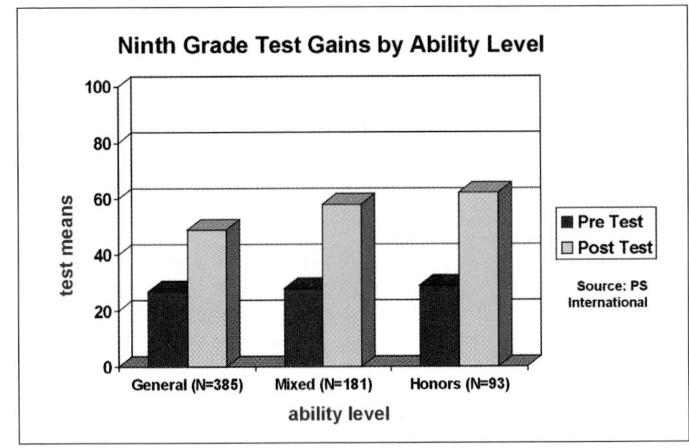

Level 1 test score means by ability level

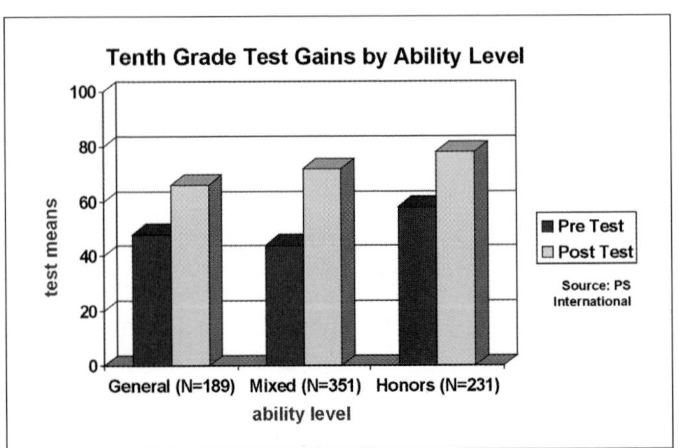

Level 2 test score means by ability level.

First, overall results from pre- and post-tests were tracked per student in a total of 1,550 paired results. These tests were developed for 14 chapters, seven per grade level. The results demonstrate strong and statistically significant gains in student achievement. Average student gains at both Level 1 and Level 2 were between 20 and 25 percent.

Second, a key goal was to evaluate whether students of different ability levels benefited from the curriculum. Results show that for both grade levels, classes characterized as having students with "general ability" and "high ability" and classes where these abilities were "mixed" each demonstrated a significant increase from pretest to post-test, independent of the ability level of students.

Background for *An Inquiry Approach*

As we developed our vision for a new generation of instructional materials, we used the following criteria: the program will be based on the *Standards*; our work will be informed by the most recent research on learning and assessment; our design will be informed by the Trends in International Mathematics and Science Study (TIMSS) results; and the development process and strategies for teachers will be guided by principles from *Understanding by Design* (Wiggins & McTighe, 1998).

The *National Science Education Standards*

As we began our discussions of what characteristics our new generation of materials should embrace, it was clear that our materials should provide students with high-quality opportunities for learning science across the disciplines. Indeed, the *Standards* are clear about the concepts that students in high school science should understand. These concepts include the disciplines of physical science, life science, and earth and space science, as well as science as inquiry, science and technology, and science in a personal and social perspective. Most states and school districts across the country have based their own standards on the work at the national level. They, too, include core concepts from each of these areas. We hope that this experience with our multidisciplinary program and levels of exposure will translate into higher test scores on standards-based state and national tests of science.

Recent Research in Learning and Assessment

While the *Standards* informed our approach to content, *How People Learn* (Bransford, Brown, & Cocking, 2000) informed our development and presentation of the content in ways that should increase student learning. *How People Learn* is a synthesis of research on learning with three key findings: (1) students come to the classroom with preconceptions about how the world works; (2) to develop competence in an area of inquiry, students must develop a core foundation of knowledge within a coherent framework and be able to organize that information in ways that help them retrieve it and apply it; and (3) students learn more effectively when they monitor their own progress.

A recent study focusing on the best ways of assessing what students know, *Knowing What Students Know* (Pellegrino, Chudowski, & Glaser, 2001), complements the work above on learning and also informed the design and development of our materials. The study articulates several principles for assessing what students know: (1) instruction should be organized around meaningful problems and goals; (2) instruction must provide scaffolds for solving meaningful problems in order to promote understanding; (3) instruction must provide opportunities for practice with feedback, revision, and reflection; (4) the social arrangement of instruction must promote collaboration and distributed expertise, as well as independent learning (Pellegrino, Chudowski, & Glaser, 2001; Pellegrino, 2002).

The TIMSS Results

In a continuing analysis of the TIMSS results, William Schmidt and his colleagues at Michigan State (2001) uncovered patterns as they compared curricular content in the top-achieving countries with countries performing near the bottom. In general, U.S. science students do not perform as well as students in other countries similar to the United States (National Center for Education Statistics, 2001). This emerging pattern informed our work on the program design. Although cultural differences play a significant role in establishing the learning environment in the schools, and consequently in playing into the differences in the cross-nation results, some significant patterns with respect to other differences that focus on the curricular materials themselves are emerging. Schmidt and his colleagues (2001) summarized four distinctive features of curricular materials that set the top-achieving countries apart: coherence, rigor, focus, and persistence. To summarize briefly: the materials from top-achieving countries are coherent in presentation across the years and through the years (both vertically and horizontally); the materials are carefully focused through the introduction of fewer concepts each year; the materials are rigorous in that they present in-depth coverage of these concepts; and the materials demonstrate persistence in that concepts are introduced at the appropriate grade level and remain in the curriculum with a spiral effect that provides the context for rigor. Schmidt also has concluded that there is a high correlation between what is in the instructional materials and what students learn; said differently: instructional materials make a difference (Schmidt, 2003).

Principles from *Understanding by Design*

As we developed this new generation of materials, we used principles from Wiggins and McTighe's (1998) *Understanding by Design*. This process, which complements the BSCS 5E model, is divided into three main stages. In *Stage I, Desired Results*, we carefully articulated what it is that we want students to understand.

We began with the standards and identified the enduring understandings we want students to acquire and the essential questions we want them to explore related to these standards. In *Stage II, Assessment Evidence*, we developed the assessment tasks that will serve as evidence that the students have gained the targeted understandings. In the BSCS 5E model, the fifth *E* (the evaluate activity) and the unit-level assessments represent these tasks. In *Stage III, Learning Plan*, we developed the sequence of learning experiences that will ensure students' ability to construct the targeted understandings and be successful on the assessments. In this stage, we focused first on the outcomes we seek for the explain activities as well as the evaluate activities. With these outcomes clearly in mind, we developed the engage, explore, explain, and elaborate activities, focusing on the knowledge and skills that will be required for a sound understanding of the concepts and success with the assessments.

Indeed, our team believes that curriculum materials make a difference, and we know you believe that as well. With *BSCS Science: An Inquiry Approach*, we have the opportunity to provide you with high-quality materials to help your students develop a fundamental understanding of central ideas across the sciences.

References for the Front Matter

Bransford, J., Brown, A., & Cocking, R. (Eds.). (2000). *How people learn: Brain, mind, experience, and school.* Washington, DC: National Academies Press.

BSCS. (2000). *Making sense of integrated science: A guide for high schools.* Colorado Springs, CO: Author.

Coulson, D. (2002). BSCS Science: An Inquiry Approach—*2002 interim evaluation findings.* Arnold, MD: Author.

Linn, M. C., Clement, C., Pulos, S., & Sullivan, P. (1989). Scientific reasoning in adolescence: The influence of instruction in science knowledge and reasoning strategies. *Journal of Research in Science Teaching, 26*(2), 171–187.

National Center for Education Statistics. (2001). *Pursuing excellence: Comparisons of international eighth grade mathematics and science achievement from an international perspective, 1995–1999.* Washington, DC: Author.

National Research Council. (1996). *National science education standards.* Washington, DC: National Academy of Sciences.

National Research Council. (2000). *Inquiry and the national science education standards.* Washington, DC: National Academy Press.

Pellegrino, J. (2002, February). *Understanding how students learn and inferring what they know: Implications for the design of curriculum, instructions, and assessment.* Paper presented at the National Science Foundation Instructional Materials Development Conference, Washington, DC.

Pellegrino, J., Chudowsky, N., & Glaser, R. (Eds.). (2001). *Knowing what students know.* Washington, DC: National Academies Press.

Schmidt, W., McKnight, C. C., Houang, R. T., Wang, H., Wiley, D. E., Cogan, L. S., et al. (2001). *Why schools matter: A cross-national comparison of curriculum and learning.* San Francisco: Jossey-Bass.

Schmidt, W. (2003). National Science Foundation–supported instructional materials: Something new and something old. In the NSF K–12 *Mathematics and Science Curricula and Implementation Centers 2003 Conference*, Alexandria, VA: American Geological Institute.

Wiggins, G., & McTighe, J. (1998). *Understanding by design.* Alexandria, VA: Association for Supervision and Curriculum Development.

CHAPTER 1

Investigations by Design

Chapter Overview

As you begin this first chapter of *BSCS Science: An Inquiry Approach*, take advantage of all that we have designed to help you guide your students throughout the year. There is valuable material included for you in the front of this Teacher Edition as well as on the *Teacher Resource CD* (*TRCD*). The degree of success that your students will experience this year rests on a combination of their efforts as well as your willingness to guide them in an inquiry approach to learning. There are many tools that we have provided to help you with this task. The Teacher Edition is your primary guide. This is not just a place for you to find the right answers to each question; it is also a resource for teaching and learning strategies, questioning strategies, misconceptions, advance preparation, and many other valuable resources. We encourage you to take advantage of the entire package of resources provided for you and your students.

During chapter 1, *Investigations by Design*, students will build upon their fundamental abilities and understandings about inquiry. By the 10th grade, students should know how to ask scientifically testable questions, how to formulate hypotheses, and how to use evidence to form explanations. In this chapter, students review asking scientifically testable questions and learn how to design their own scientific investigation to answer a question.

The chapter focuses on scientific inquiry. It does this by engaging students in the current phenomenon of antimicrobial resistance. Scientific inquiry and science content are taught in parallel. This makes the investigations more relevant to students. Students will be challenged to discover ways to investigate current problems. They will learn the importance of design in scientific investigation and will use the processes of inquiry. By the end of the chapter, students will understand the significant role experimental design plays in scientists' study of the world. By designing and conducting their own investigations, students gain a greater understanding of science content and scientific inquiry.

You will notice that this chapter, as well as all others in the book, is based on the BSCS 5E instructional model. This model structures the learning for students in a way that supports enduring understandings. It provides opportunities for students to explore the essential features of scientific inquiry in five stages of classroom activity—the 5Es. Take time to review the information on using this model in both the front matter in the Teacher Edition and in additional information provided for you on the *TRCD*. The success of this program to provide the best mechanism for student learning hinges on your abilities to foster inquiry in the classroom. These resources will support you in this task.

Goals for the Chapter

Your students are engaged in several activities as they learn about designing scientific investigations. By the end of chapter 1, they will understand

- what characterizes a scientifically testable question,
- how to design and conduct a scientific investigation,
- what measures are used to evaluate the design of others, and
- how to communicate the results of a scientific investigation to others.

Look at the chapter organizer each day to remind yourself of where students are in the overall sequence of events in the chapter.

Chapter 1 Organizer

INVESTIGATIONS BY DESIGN

Major Concepts

- **Scientific investigations include**
  - A testable question
  - A design that leads to valid and reliable results
  - An appropriate way of communicating and defending a scientific argument.
- **Scientific inquiry is a systematic, nonlinear process.**

ENGAGE — A Clean Design ★

Key Ideas:
- Careful design of scientific investigations is essential to ensure that the investigation answers the question.
- Scientific investigations include careful control of variables.

Activity: Students use the act of hand washing to analyze different investigation designs. They decide on the best design that answers the proposed question.

Linking Question: How can I use what I have learned to design a scientific investigation of my own?

EXPLORE / EXPLAIN — Small Problem? ★ ★ ★ ★ ★

Key Ideas:
- All questions are not testable in science.
- Valid results can only be obtained with careful design and implementation of a scientific investigation.
- Communicating scientific results is important to the design.

Activity: Students design and conduct their own investigation. They learn about testable questions, control of variables, valid results, and communicating their findings.

Linking Question: How does my design reflect the process of scientific inquiry?

EXPLAIN — Why and How Do We Inquire? ★ ★ ★

Key Idea:
- Scientific inquiry is a systematic, nonlinear process.

Activity: Students analyze their investigation and compare it to the process of scientific inquiry. They also analyze a historical scientific discovery and relate it to the process of inquiry.

Linking Question: How can the process of scientific inquiry help me to evaluate scientific claims in the media?

ELABORATE — Valid or Deceptive? ★ ★

Key Ideas:
- All "science" that is reported in the media is not valid.
- Researchers and scientists must be able to defend their arguments and show valid and reliable data to claim scientific discoveries.

Activity: Students take on the roles of a journalist and a researcher. They propose a set of interview questions and the answers designed to determine if a "scientific claim" is supported by valid and reliable results.

Linking Question: How can I demonstrate what I have learned about the process of scientific inquiry?

EVALUATE — Killing Germs? Digging Deeper ★ ★ ★ ★ ★

Key Idea:
- Scientific investigations include
  - a testable question
  - a design that leads to valid and reliable results
  - an appropriate way of communicating and defending a scientific argument.

Activity: Students' understandings are evaluated as they design and investigation to determine the effectiveness of antibacterial products.

★ = One Class Period ☆ = ½ Class Period *Note:* Based on a 50-minute class period.

Standards Covered by Chapter 1

INVESTIGATIONS BY DESIGN

STANDARD A: Science as Inquiry. As a result of activities in grades 9–12, all students should develop

abilities to do scientific inquiry

- Identify questions and concepts that guide scientific investigations. Students should formulate a testable hypothesis and demonstrate the logical connections between the scientific concepts guiding a hypothesis and the design of an experiment. They should demonstrate appropriate procedures, a knowledge base, and conceptual understanding of scientific investigations.
- Design and conduct scientific investigations. Designing and conducting a scientific investigation requires introduction to the major concepts in the area being investigated, proper equipment, safety precautions, assistance with methodological problems, recommendations for use of technologies, clarification of ideas that guide the inquiry, and scientific knowledge obtained from sources other than the actual investigation. The investigation may also require student clarification of the question, method, controls, and variables; student organization and display of data; student revision of methods and explanations; and a public presentation of the results with a critical response from peers. Regardless of the scientific investigation performed, students must use evidence, apply logic, and construct an argument for their proposed explanations.
- Use technology and mathematics to improve investigations and communications. A variety of technologies, such as hand tools, measuring instruments, and calculators, should be an integral component of scientific investigations. The use of computers for the collection, analysis, and display of data is also a part of this standard. Mathematics plays an essential role in all aspects of an inquiry. For example, measurement is used for posing questions, formulas are used for developing explanations, and charts and graphs are used for communicating results.
- Communicate and defend a scientific argument. Students in school science programs should develop the abilities associated with accurate and effective communication. These include writing and following procedures, expressing concepts, reviewing information, summarizing data, using language appropriately, developing diagrams and charts, explaining statistical analysis, speaking clearly and logically, constructing a reasoned argument, and responding appropriately to critical comments.

understandings about scientific inquiry

- Scientists usually inquire about how physical, living, or designed systems function. Conceptual principles and knowledge guide scientific inquiries. Historical and current scientific knowledge influence the design and interpretation of investigations and the evaluation of proposed explanations made by other scientists.
- Scientists conduct investigations for a wide variety of reasons. For example, they may wish to discover new aspects of the natural world, explain recently observed phenomena, or test the conclusions of prior investigations or the problems of current theories.
- Scientists rely on technology to enhance the gathering and manipulation of data. New techniques and tools provide new evidence to guide inquiry and new methods to gather data, thereby contributing to the advance of science. The accuracy and precision of the data, and therefore the quality of the exploration, depends on the technology used.
- Mathematics is essential in scientific inquiry. Mathematical tools and models guide and improve the posing of questions, gathering data, constructing explanations and communicating results.
- Results of scientific inquiry—new knowledge and methods—emerge from different types of investigations and public communication among scientists in communicating and defending the results of scientific inquiry, arguments must be logical and demonstrate connections between natural phenomena, investigations, and the historical body of scientific knowledge. In addition, the methods and procedures that scientists used to obtain evidence must be clearly reported to enhance opportunities for further investigation.

Standard G: History and Nature of Science. As a result of their activities in grades 9–12, all students should develop an understanding of

science as a human endeavor

- Individuals and teams have contributed and will continue to contribute to the scientific enterprise. Doing science or engineering can be as simple as an individual conducting field studies or as complex as hundreds of people working on a major scientific question or technological problem. Pursuing science as a career or as a hobby can be both fascinating and intellectually rewarding.

nature of scientific knowledge

- Science distinguishes itself from other ways of knowing and from other bodies of knowledge through the use of empirical standards, logical arguments, and skepticism, as scientists strive for the best possible explanations about the natural world.
- Scientific explanations must meet certain criteria. First and foremost, they must be consistent with experimental and observational evidence about nature, and must make accurate predictions, when appropriate, about systems being studied. They should also be logical, respect the rules of evidence, be open to criticism, report methods and procedures, and make knowledge public. Explanations on how the natural world changes based on myths, personal beliefs, religious values, mystical inspiration, superstition, or authority may be personally useful and socially relevant, but they are not scientific.

historical perspectives

- Usually changes in science occur as small modifications in extant knowledge. The daily work of science and engineering results in incremental advances in our understanding of the world and our ability to meet human needs and aspirations. Much can be learned about the internal workings of science and the nature of science from the study of individual scientists, their daily work, and their efforts to advance scientific knowledge in their area of study.

  Occasionally, there are advances in science and technology that have important and long-lasting effects on science and society. Examples of such advances include the following:
  - Copernican revolution
  - Newtonian mechanics
  - Relativity
  - Geologic time scale
  - Plate tectonics
  - Atomic theory
  - Nuclear physics
  - Biological evolution
  - Germ theory
  - Industrial revolution
  - Molecular biology
  - Information and communication
  - Quantum theory
  - Galactic universe
  - Medical and health technology
- The historical perspective of scientific explanations demonstrates how scientific knowledge changes by evolving over time, almost always building on earlier knowledge.

Prerequisite Knowledge

From Level 1 of *BSCS Science: An Inquiry Approach*, students should have an understanding of the difference between evidence and inference. Students should know about variables and controls. If they are having difficulty with these terms, then take time as needed to review. It would be helpful, but not essential, if students had some practice in designing parts of a scientific investigation.

Commonly Held Misconceptions

Often students have learned the "scientific method" as a linear plan to solve problems in science. They may think that all science is conducted in this sequential, step-by-step manner. They will learn that the process is far from linear and is one that evolves depending on where students are in the investigation.

Students may think that all questions can be answered by science. They will learn in this chapter that there are testable questions that science can answer but there are other questions that are often unanswerable by science.

Students may also think that if a claim is reported and published, it is based on scientific investigations and evidence. Students learn in this chapter to look for evidence and experimental designs that make these claims either valid or invalid.

NOTES:

ENGAGE

A Clean Design

Activity Overview

In *A Clean Design*, students will work in teams to engage in the process of scientific inquiry by investigating how effectively they wash their hands. By participating in this activity, students will begin to learn the components of scientific investigations. This activity engages students in thinking about the process of inquiry by giving them the opportunity to explore a simple problem. Students will investigate the effectiveness of their own hand-washing techniques by using germ simulator. Germ simulator is a lotion, powder, or gel-like product that glows when exposed to ultraviolet (UV) light. Students will then look critically at three different investigations and determine which investigation will lead to answering the question, "Does the length of time you spend washing your hands affect the amount of germs that remain?"

The "hook" of this activity is the presence of germs in daily life. The purpose of the activity, however, is to get the students thinking about the process of scientific inquiry, specifically in designing scientific investigations.

Before You Teach

Background Information

Your students will learn the process of designing a scientific investigation in this chapter. Students have questions and are naturally curious. They often want to test various methods that would provide answers to their questions. Often, these tests do not attend to the control of variables. In a scientific investigation, the investigator controls the variables and tests how one factor depends on (correlates with) another. Students also will need to learn to measure the effect of a variable. For example, to study the effect of temperature on plants, students would change only the temperature and decide how they were going to measure the effect (for example, the rate of growth, maximum growth, number of leaves). Students can also see cause-and-effect relationships by conducting scientific investigations in this way.

In a lab setting, it is easier for the investigator to control the variables. In reality, it can be difficult to control the variables. For example, when investigating a new heart medicine, similar test subjects are chosen (same age, gender, health, medical history, etc.), but it is difficult to keep everything identical (diet, exercise, sleep, etc.). The important idea for students is that scientists control the variables as much as possible so that the results can be attributed to the one variable they are testing.

Materials

For each team of 2 students

access to germ simulator
access to an ultraviolet light source
access to hand soap and a sink

Advance Preparation

Take time to read the student pages for this activity and the corresponding teacher information in this guide.

Purchase germ simulator (ordering information is available on the *TRCD*). The germ simulator is a lotion, powder, or gel-like substance that glows when exposed to UV light. There are several brands of germ simulator on the market. This substance is commonly used to examine the effectiveness of hand washing, usually at organizations such as hospitals and restaurants. Typically, people spread the simulator on their hands and then look at their hands under an ultraviolet light. They then try to wash the substance off in incandescent light. They do not know how thorough their hand washing is until they place their hands under ultraviolet light again.

Schools often have a portable UV light. Check with the physics or geology teacher as UV lights are often used in those courses. If you need to purchase a UV light, they are available from lab supply companies. The portable, hand-held models are relatively inexpensive and easy to use. Pet stores even sell UV lights as a way to detect animal urine.

Make as many sinks and as much hand soap as possible accessible to students; many of them will wash their hands at the same time.

You will also need to darken the room. Results are more vivid in a very dark room. Cover windows or secure a room that can be darkened.

Educational Technologies

Students may want to record their results with a digital camera. Have students bring theirs from home or have one available for student use.

Cautions

Although germ simulator poses no particular hazards, make sure students use caution when using any chemical in the laboratory. Students should not ingest the germ simulator or any other chemical. Make sure students do not look directly into the ultraviolet light source or shine the light into other students' eyes. Looking directly at ultraviolet light can damage the corneas, lenses, and retinas of the eyes. Have students wash their hands thoroughly before leaving the lab.

As You Teach

Outcomes and Indicators of Success

By the end of this activity, students should

1. reveal their prior knowledge of high-quality designs for a scientific investigation.

   They will reveal their prior knowledge by

   - examining three investigations that attempt to answer the question, "Does the length of time you spend washing your hands affect the amount of germs that remain?"
   - comparing the investigations and determining which investigation answers the posed question, and

- communicating reasons why each investigation is or is not a valid design.

2. begin to become aware of what criteria make a scientific investigation.

   They will demonstrate their awareness by describing in their answers to the *Reflect and Connect* questions the need for controls in an investigation and that the investigation attempts to answer the question posed.

3. be aware of how germ simulator can be used as a tool to investigate the effectiveness of hand washing.

   They will demonstrate their awareness by
   - making observations about what their hands look like under ultraviolet light after putting on the germ simulator and after they wash their hands and
   - discussing possible reasons why the germ simulator might not have been completely washed off, including hand-washing techniques, the soap used, and the length of time they washed their hands.

4. begin to recognize the differences and usefulness of both qualitative and quantitative data.

   They will communicate this recognition by
   - identifying if their experience with the germ simulator produced quantitative or qualitative results and
   - explaining that if their results included observations, they are qualitative, and if they measured the amount of germ simulator present, they are quantitative, and that both types of data are useful.

Strategies

Getting Started

Ask the class if anyone has a job that requires frequent hand washing. Discuss why students think hand washing might be necessary. Listen as students share their knowledge about germs. Ask if they think washing their hands removes all the germs. Read the introduction to *A Clean Design* as a class.

Cautions

Although germ simulator poses no particular hazards, make sure students use caution when using any chemical in the laboratory. Students should not ingest the germ simulator or any other chemical. Make sure students do not look directly into the ultraviolet light source or shine the light into other students' eyes. Looking directly at ultraviolet light can damage the corneas, lenses, and retinas of the eyes. Have students wash their hands thoroughly before leaving the lab.

Process and Procedure

Pair off students and ask them to follow the procedures in Step 1. Provide all students with equal amounts of germ simulator, telling them to spread it on their hands like lotion. Turn off the lights and ask the students to shine the ultraviolet light on each student's hands. Remind students not to look directly into the UV light. Ask students to make observations and discuss what they see with their partners. You may want to try to photograph their hands with a digital camera when they are illuminated with the UV light. This photograph will have to be taken without the flash, so students should lay their hands on the desk to keep them still. In addition, the photographs will be of better quality if the camera is mounted on a tripod. Turn on the classroom lights and ask students to follow Steps 1c–d. Students might ask whether they should use soap when washing their hands in Step 1d. Tell them to wash their hands as they normally would.

ENGAGE

A Clean Design

A successful restaurant system depends on many parts working together successfully. From the production of french fries to the cleanliness of the work area and workers, everyone and every part works together to make the restaurant successful. Have you ever worked in a restaurant? If so, you know that all employees are required to wash their hands frequently (figure 1.1). If you spread disease by not washing your hands properly, then the system breaks down and the success of the restaurant suffers.

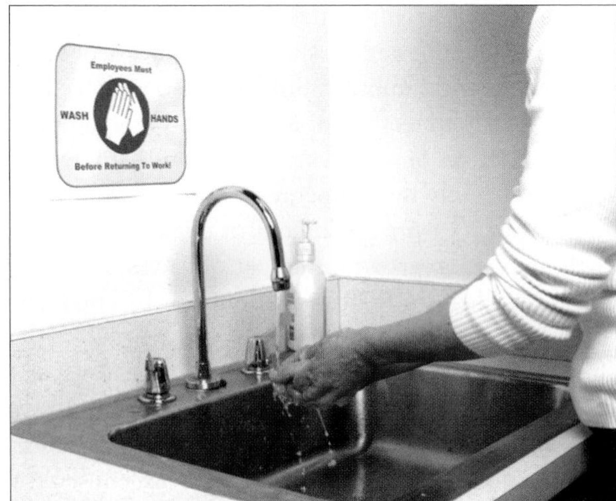

▲ **Figure 1.1 Hand washing.** Why is it so important to wash your hands regularly?

When you were younger, your parents may have reminded you to wash your hands before dinner. An important safety practice in science class and in any science laboratory is to wash your hands before leaving the lab. It should be clear to you why washing your hands in both of these situations is so important. In *A Clean Design*, you will work with a partner to investigate hand washing. You will use the simple act of hand washing as a way to think about the criteria of a good scientific investigation.

Student	Glo Germ	Soap	Time	Temp. of Water	Way to Measure Data

▲ **Figure T1.1 Example data table.** Your students could make a table similar to this to represent factors present in each design.

After students have washed their hands, darken the room and direct them to shine the UV light on their hands again. If you were successful in getting quality photographs of their hands before, take another set of photographs after they have washed their hands. Have students complete the remainder of Step 1. Discuss students' observations by questioning several students. Have students share what they see. Ask them to look at each other's hands and note any similarities or differences. Students should observe that most of the surface of their hands glows under UV light before using the germ simulator. After washing their hands as they normally would, they should still see some spots where the germ simulator is present. Students should begin to ask questions about how well hand washing removes germs (as modeled by the germ simulator). If students do not volunteer their questions, ask them specifically to think of questions they might have about their observations.

Ask the class to discuss the factors that might affect how clean their hands get. Listen to their ideas. Factors they might suggest are the use of soap, the type of soap, the length of time spent washing, the water temperature, and how they dry their hands. Ask students if they think that all the factors they mentioned can be tested by conducting a scientific investigation.

Instruct students to read the scenario in Step 2 and investigations A, B, and C with their partners. Give them time to discuss each investigation with their partners. They are instructed to scan the investigations first. This is to give them an idea of what they need to record. Encourage students to develop a way to organize the information from the three investigations. Allow time for students to develop their own ways of organizing the data. Many students struggle with this skill. Help them develop this skill by making them think about the factors that should be compared in each investigation. In this way, you are not simply giving them the table and their only exercise is to fill in the blanks. It takes thought and planning to develop a good way to organize this information, and this skill, if perfected, will serve your students in many aspects of their education and life. When they have developed their method of organization, they are instructed to read the investigations and record the information in their notebooks.

An example of what students might develop to keep track of factors present in each design is shown in figure T1.1. Once students have developed their method, direct them to record the information in their science notebooks.

If some students are struggling, create a transparency of the tables in this guide. Fill them in with the students.

Materials

For each team of 2 students

access to germ simulator

access to an ultraviolet light source

access to hand soap and a sink

Cautions

Always use caution when using any chemical in the laboratory. Only apply the germ simulator to your hands—do not ingest it. Do not look directly into the ultraviolet light source. Looking at ultraviolet light directly can damage the corneas, lenses, and retinas of your eyes.

Process and Procedure

Germ simulator is a substance that glows when exposed to ultraviolet (UV) light (see figure 1.2). In this activity, the germ simulator represents germs (the substance is not manufactured to contain germs). This simulator is used for many applications, such as determining how well restaurant employees wash their hands.

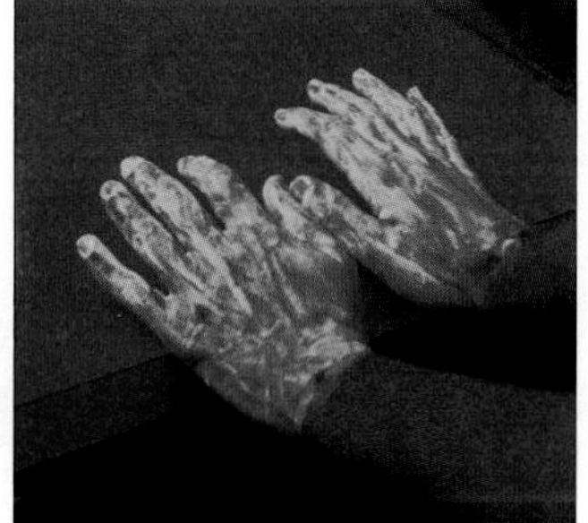

▲ **Figure 1.2 Germ simulator.** Does simple hand washing remove all the bacteria on your hands?

1. Experiment with the germ simulator and make some observations by completing Steps 1a–f.
   a. Apply a small amount of germ simulator to your hands and rub it in like lotion.
   b. When your teacher darkens the room, take turns placing your hands under the UV light. Discuss your observations with your partner.
   c. Record your observations with words and detailed drawings in your science notebook.
   d. Wash and dry your hands as you normally do.
   e. When your teacher darkens the room, place your hands under the UV light again. What do you see? Discuss your observations with your partner.
   f. Record your results in your science notebook with words and drawings.
2. Imagine that students in another high school science class observed the same phenomenon that you just witnessed. They wondered if the length of time that people spent washing their hands made a significant difference in how clean their hands got. Three lab groups, A, B, and C, designed investigations to answer the question, "Does the length of time you spend washing your hands affect the amount of germs that remain?" Use this focus question as you complete Steps 2a–c.

Answers to Step 3, SE page 10

3. Investigation B demonstrated the best design for answering the question, "Does the length of time you spend washing your hands affect the amount of germs that remain?" The design of investigation A was not a bad design in itself, but the students did not design it to answer the question. Instead, it answers a question about water temperature and germ removal. The students in investigation C intentionally changed 3 variables: the length of time washing, the amount of soap, and the student who was washing.

The data from the scenarios are organized in tables in figures T1.2, T1.3, and T1.4. A discussion of each investigation appears in the caption.

In Step 4, discuss the three investigations and the teams' choices for the best one. Did everyone agree on which investigation was the best design to answer the question? If so, why? If not, ask teams about what differences they saw among the investigations. Prompt the class by asking what it has learned in the past about scientific investigations and how it applied its prior knowledge to this activity. Ask students what criteria they used to determine if the investigation provided meaningful results. If students do not understand the term *meaningful* in the question, ask them to think about if the investigation answered the question and if they can use the results to explain the data. Lead the discussion to define the word *valid*. This term will be used many times in this chapter and throughout the units, so it is important that your students understand that valid results are those that measure what you really want to measure. In other words, the results can answer the question that the investigation is trying to answer. Valid results are also those that control for bias and error. A valid investigation will be designed in a way to control for these factors and answer the investigational question.

NOTES:

a. Review all the investigations and look for differences.
b. Think of a way to organize the differences in each investigation so that you can easily compare the 3 investigations. Consider using a table or a chart. Record this information in your science notebook as you read the investigations.
c. Read the investigations designed by each lab group: investigation A, investigation B, and investigation C.

Remember, germ simulator is used to *represent* germs; it is not manufactured to contain germs.

3. Discuss with your partner which investigation (A, B, or C) is most likely to give you meaningful results and answers the question, "Does the length of time you spend washing your hands affect the amount of germs that remain?"
   a. Record the investigation you chose and the reasons why you chose it in your science notebook.
   b. Record the reasons you did *not* choose the other 2 investigations.
4. Discuss the investigations and your answers as a class.

Investigation A

Procedure

1. Ask for 3 student volunteers.
2. Apply exactly 1 milliliter (mL) of germ simulator to the hands of each volunteer. Spread the germ simulator very evenly, covering both the top and bottom of their hands. Make sure that they do not touch anything.
3. Shine the ultraviolet (UV) light on the hands of each student. Identify where the germ simulator is present. Take a photograph of both the top and the bottom of their hands.
4. Label the photographs "before washing."
5. Ask all 3 students to wash their hands.
   - The first student should wash for 1 minute under warm water using exactly 2 mL of hand soap.
   - The second student should wash for 1 minute under cold water using exactly 2 mL of the same hand soap.
   - The third student should wash for 1 minute under hot water using exactly 2 mL of the same hand soap.
6. Do not let the students touch anything. Allow their hands to dry in the air completely.
7. Shine the UV light on the hands of each student. Identify where the germ simulator is present. Take a photograph of both the top and the bottom of their hands.
8. Compare the before and after photographs, looking carefully for places that glow.
9. Count the number of spots that still glow in the after photographs.
10. Compare the number of spots present on each student's hands. The hands with the fewest number of spots that glow are the cleanest.

10

Student	Germ Simulator	Hand Soap	Time Spent Washing	Temp. of Water	Way to Measure Data
1	1 mL	2 mL	1 min.	warm	Photo before & after
2	1 mL	2 mL	1 min.	cold	Photo before & after
3	1 mL	2 mL	1 min.	hot	Photo before & after

▲ **Figure T1.2** **Investigation A.** This investigation may look well designed. The students paid attention to detail and measured exact quantities. However, they did not attempt to answer the question, "Does the length of time you spend washing your hands affect the amount of germs that remain?" They actually tested the impact of water temperature on hand washing in this investigation.

Student	Germ Simulator	Hand Soap	Time Spent Washing	Temp. of Water	Way to Measure Data
1	1 mL	2 mL	10 secs.	30°C	Photo before & after
1 (same as above)	1 mL	2 mL	15 secs.	30°C	Photo before & after
1 (same as above)	1 mL	2 mL	30 secs.	30°C	Photo before & after

▲ **Figure T1.3** **Investigation B.** This investigation is the best of the three. The students tested only one variable, which is the amount of time spent washing hands. Even the student subject is the same. As long as she washes all the germ simulator off between trials, this is the best design. Some students might think it is better to use different students. For the time being, it is all right that they think this. As you get into the explore and explain activities, you will have the opportunity to explain how scientists try to control as many variables as possible.

Student	Germ Simulator	Hand Soap	Time Spent Washing	Temp. of Water	Way to Measure Data
1	1 mL	3 mL	10 secs.	27°C	Photo before & after
2	1 mL	2 mL	15 secs.	27°C	Photo before & after
3	1 mL	1 mL	30 secs.	27°C	Photo before & after

▲ **Figure T1.4** **Investigation C.** At first glance, this investigation looks good, but the students changed three variables: the amount of soap, the amount of time spent washing hands, and the students.

Answers to Reflect and Connect, SE page 12

Students are instructed to discuss these questions with the class and record their answers in their science notebooks. Monitor this discussion so that one student in a group does not dominate the discussion or give out all the answers. Question students' responses and ask questions of those students who are reluctant to participate.

1. Students should indicate that they compared the investigations by examining the variables, or factors, in each investigation. These factors include the number of student volunteers, the amount of germ simulator used, the amount of soap used, the amount of time the student spent washing his or her hands, the water temperature, and the method of data collection. By looking at the data, students should be able to determine the variables and controls in the investigations and thus determine which investigation is the best design in this activity. If students cannot make these comparisons, take time to analyze each investigation, perhaps using the data table in figure T1.1 to guide your discussion. Students are instructed to use the terms *variable*, *control*, and *constant* in their answers. Use their answers to assess their understanding of these terms. Review the terms with the class if necessary. Remember that this is the chance for you to assess students' prior knowledge. The purpose of the activity is for students to *begin* to build an understanding of scientific investigational design. They will have multiple opportunities to get it right throughout the chapter.
2. Results from students' experience with the germ simulator can be measured both qualitatively and quantitatively. Students should recognize that if they actually counted spots or measured areas of their hands that glowed under ultraviolet light, they collected quantitative data. If students recorded observations, such as what their hands looked like visually under UV light before and after they washed their hands, they collected qualitative data. Students should begin to understand the different ways to gather and record data.
3. Students should *begin* to recognize what a scientific investigation looks like, based on prior knowledge and their experience looking at the 3 investigations in this activity. As students proceed through the rest of the chapter, their understanding should deepen and become refined. An effective scientific investigation addresses the following criteria. Students might list some or all of the following:
   - The investigation addresses the question being tested.
   - It tests only one factor (variable).
   - It keeps all other variables as constant as possible.
   - It has controls.
   - It contains multiple trials and samples.
   - It is clear, concise, and well planned.
   - It incorporates an organized method for recording data.
   - It uses appropriate tools, technology, and mathematics.
   - It is safe.
   - It potentially provides evidence that will support (or refute) an explanation or lead to new questions.

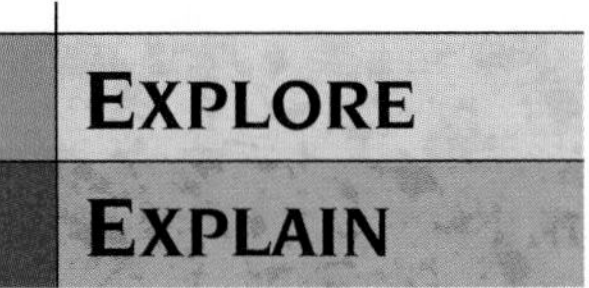

Small Problem?

Activity Overview

Germ simulator mimics microorganisms. We cannot see microorganisms easily, but we experience their presence through disease and infection. This lack of visibility frustrated scientists for many years. We now have the technology to see individual bacterial cells and even virus particles, which are extremely small. We now know how to grow and culture hundreds of species of bacteria. In this investigation, students consider scientifically testable questions and focus on designing and conducting a scientific investigation to learn more about the invisible world of microorganisms.

Small Problem? is divided into three parts: in Part I, students will read a scenario and develop scientifically testable questions based on that scenario; in Part II, students will work in teams to design an investigation to test their question; and in Part III, they will conduct the investigation as a class and collect data by teams. Each team will share data, and the class determines evidence that supports an explanation based on its original question.

Before You Teach

Background Information

Microorganisms (microbes) are organisms that are too small to see without a microscope. Examples of microbes include protists, viruses, fungi, and bacteria. Microbes are everywhere but we cannot easily see them. Like other organisms, each type of microbe has a niche. Viruses require a living host cell in order to replicate. Protists, fungi, and bacteria have their own environmental requirements. Some of them cause disease and others are beneficial. Still others simply live among us.

Bacteria are very adaptable and reproduce rapidly when nutrients, moisture, and temperature are conducive to growth. *Escherichia coli* (*E. coli*), for example, double approximately every 20 minutes. When conditions are unfavorable (lack of food, water, or desired temperature), some bacteria can form spores. Spores are dormant cells that contain genetic material surrounded by a tough outer covering. When conditions become favorable for bacterial growth, the bacteria become active. They begin growing, reproducing, and forming colonies of varying sizes, shapes, and colors, depending on the species.

Bacteria and bacterial spores are microscopic and are everywhere; any surface can have some bacteria on it.

Some locations may harbor greater quantities or more types of bacteria than other areas. This is often because some areas provide better nutrients for growing bacteria.

Bacteria tend to be specific to food sources. Some types of bacteria will only grow in the presence of certain nutrients. For example, when scientists study bacteria that parasitize animal tissue, they culture them on agar with a blood base and nutrients found in the animal tissue. Bacteria that require that type of food source will not grow on agar if it does not contain the nutrients it requires.

Included on the *TRCD* is a list and description of common bacteria. You may want to use this for your own reference or allow your students to use it for further research.

Keep in mind that this chapter focuses on the process of scientific inquiry, specifically on designing a scientific investigation. Students will apply their understanding and abilities in inquiry to an investigation into the presence of microorganisms in their school. Remember to keep in the foreground the process of inquiry: making observations and asking testable questions, designing and conducting investigations, and proposing explanations based on evidence and logic. As they practice inquiry in the context of bacteria in their school, students also will learn concepts about microorganisms.

Materials—Part I

none

Materials—Part II

none

Materials—Part III

For the entire class

37°C incubator or source of warmth
30% bleach solution in a large container (for waste)
biohazard disposal bags

For each team of 3 students

3 pairs of safety goggles
3 pairs of gloves
2 petri dishes with nutrient agar
2 sterile cotton swabs
1 permanent marker
tape (to tape petri dishes closed)
2 index cards
other materials as needed
3 copies of copymaster 1.1, *Scientific Investigation Report*

Advance Preparation

Take time to read the student pages for this activity and the corresponding teacher information.

You can purchase sterile swabs from laboratory supply companies or drugstores.

Make 1 copy of copymaster 1.1, *Scientific Investigation Report* for each student.

Purchase prepoured agar petri dishes that contain nutrient agar. Nutrient agar is a good medium for growth of many types of bacteria. Tryptic Soy Agar also works well. Prepoured dishes are available from science supply companies. For a less expensive alternative, you can prepare your own nutrient agar plates as follows.

Investigation B

Procedure

1. Ask for 1 student volunteer.
2. Set the water temperature of the sink at 30° Celsius (C).
3. Have the volunteer apply 1 mL of germ simulator to his or her hands and spread it evenly.
4. Shine the UV light on the hands of the volunteer. Take photographs of both the top and the bottom of the volunteer's hands. Label the photographs "before washing."
5. Have the volunteer wash his or her hands with water for 10 seconds using 2 mL of hand soap.
6. Let the volunteer's hands air-dry.
7. Shine the UV light on the hands of the volunteer. Identify where the germ simulator is present. Take a photograph of both the top and the bottom of the hands. Label the photographs "after washing."
8. Compare the photographs and record the results.
9. Have the student remove all the germ simulator by washing his or her hands.
10. Have the student repeat Steps 2–9, but increase the washing time to 15 seconds.
11. Repeat Steps 2–9 again, increasing the washing to 30 seconds.
12. Compare all the before and after photographs. The set of photographs that shows the least amount of germ simulator after washing indicates the amount of time you need to wash your hands in order to get rid of most germs.

Investigation C

Procedure

1. Ask for 3 student volunteers.
2. Ask all the volunteers to apply 1 mL of germ simulator to their hands and spread it evenly on both the top and the bottom of their hands.
3. Shine the UV light on the hands of each student. Identify where the germ simulator is present. Take a picture of both the top and the bottom of their hands. Label these photographs "before washing."
4. Have one of the students wash his or her hands in 27°C water for 15 seconds using 3 mL of hand soap.
5. Have a second student wash his or her hands in 27°C water for 30 seconds using 2 mL of the same hand soap.
6. Have the third student wash his or her hands in 27°C water for 45 seconds using 1 mL of the same hand soap.
7. Shine the UV light on each student's hands. Take photographs and label each "after washing."
8. Compare all the photographs. The set of photographs that shows the least amount of germ simulator after washing indicates the amount of time you need to wash your hands in order to get rid of most germs.

Chapter 1 Investigations by Design 11

To Make Your Own Nutrient Agar Petri Dishes

You can prepare your own petri dishes in one of two ways.

1. You can use premixed nutrient agar by following these steps.
   a. Purchase ready-made nutrient agar that comes in a bottle. Also, purchase *sterile* petri dishes separately.
   b. Liquefy the agar either in a microwave or in a hot water bath. You will need to loosen the cap of the agar bottle before placing it in the micro-wave. Heat it at a medium power setting until the agar is in liquid form. Monitor closely, as the pressure may cause the lid to pop off. If you choose to use a hot water bath, place the agar bottle in a boiling water bath until the agar liquefies. Once the agar melts, allow it to cool until the bottle is warm to the touch.
   c. Pour the agar. Only open the petri dishes right before you are ready to pour the agar. Pour enough agar in the bottom of the petri dishes to cover the bottom. Approximately 20–25 milliliters (mL) of nutrient agar fills 1 plate. Put the lid on the dish immediately after you pour the agar. Stacking the plates and letting them sit at room temperature overnight will help reduce condensation.
   d. Store plates at 4° Celsius (C) (e.g., in the refrigerator).

   Or

2. You can make your own agar by following these steps.

   One liter of agar will be enough to make approximately 40–50 petri dishes.

   a. In a clean flask, add 20 grams of nutrient agar powder to 1 liter of distilled water.
   b. Cover the top of the flask with foil and autoclave the solution for 20 minutes at 121°C.

   If an autoclave is not available, you can use a pressure cooker. Sterilize the mixture at 15 psi for 20 minutes at 121°C.

   c. Remove flask from the autoclave or pressure cooker and let cool until the bottom of the flask is warm to the touch.

Cautions

The flask and its contents will be hot: handle with care.

   d. Pour enough agar in the bottom of the petri dish to cover the bottom of the dish. Approximately 20–25 mL of nutrient agar fills 1 plate. Put the lid on the dish immediately after you pour the agar. Stacking the plates and letting them sit at room temperature overnight will help reduce condensation.
   e. Store the plates at 4°C (e.g., in the refrigerator).

Educational Technologies

Students may want to use a digital camera to record changes in their bacterial plates. Either ask students to bring their own or acquire a digital camera for classroom use.

Cautions

Students should wear safety goggles and gloves during their investigations. All materials that come into contact with bacteria should be disposed of properly. Soak

Answers to Reflect and Connect are on TE page 10b.

Reflect and Connect

Discuss the following questions with your class. Record your own answers in your science notebook.

1. What information did you and your partner use about each investigation (A, B, and C) to determine which one gave valid results? Use the terms *variable*, *control*, and *constant* in your answer.
2. Were the results from your experience with germ simulator qualitative or quantitative? Give examples to support your answer.

Results from investigations are quantitative **if the data represent measurements or specific numbers or amounts. Results are** qualitative **if the data describe features, characteristics, observations, or relative comparisons.**

3. Consider your experience with the germ simulator and the investigation procedures you examined (A, B, and C). What criteria do you think are important for designing a scientific investigation that will give valid results? Explain your criteria.

EXPLORE
EXPLAIN

Small Problem?

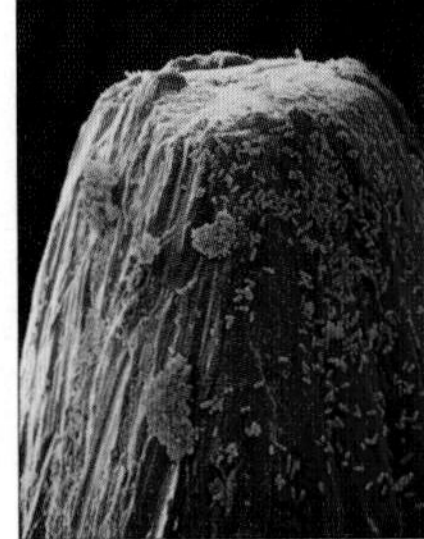

▲ **Figure 1.3**
SEM image of bacteria. This image taken with a scanning electron microscope (SEM) magnifies the structures 290 times. It shows the small size and large numbers of bacteria that are present on the point of a pin.

In *A Clean Design*, the germ simulator represented common bacteria or other microorganisms that might have been on your hands. Bacteria are virtually everywhere. Figure 1.3 shows a number of bacteria on the point of a pin. These tiny organisms might or might not cause disease. If the microorganisms do cause disease, they are called **pathogenic**. If they do not cause disease, they are nonpathogenic. Many types of bacteria are even helpful. For example, a certain type of *Escherichia coli* (*E. coli*) resides in our intestines to aid the process of digestion.

Through years of study, scientists have learned a lot about bacteria. They have answered many questions by conducting scientific investigations. They carefully design the investigations so that they can collect the best possible data. Scientists then use the data as evidence to support explanations. In *Small Problem?*, you will work in a team to ask a scientifically testable question and design and conduct a scientific investigation to explore the world of bacteria through inquiry.

them in a 30% bleach solution, drain, and throw away in the regular trash. Have students wash their hands after the investigation. Once the petri dishes have been exposed to bacteria, they should be taped shut and never opened by the students. Students should make their observations only by looking at the sealed plates. Since the nutrient agar is a basic food source for nonpathogenic bacteria, the growth of disease-causing bacteria is unlikely, but it is wise not to take chances. Clean up any broken dishes with a 30% bleach solution.

When the class is finished with its investigation, carefully clean and dispose of materials. If you are using disposable petri dishes, soak them in a 30% bleach solution, drain them and wrap them in plastic bags. Discard them in a trash can. If you want to reuse the dishes for other reasons, soak them in a 30% bleach solution, scrape out the agar, and dispose of it down a garbage disposal (or wrap it in plastic bags and discard in a trash can). Wash the empty petri dishes in warm, soapy water. Properly wipe down work areas in the classroom with a mild (10%) bleach solution. Make sure students wash their hands before leaving the classroom.

Biohazard!

When working with bacteria from the environment, use caution. There is the potential of pathogenicity of the organisms involved (especially in the case of organisms cultured from humans). The problem is that pathogenic, or potentially pathogenic, bacteria that are present in small amounts in the environment (or someone's throat!) could be cultured into a very large population in the laboratory, endangering those who are working with them. This is especially true for students, who are just learning how to maintain aseptic technique. Because of this, once the students' samples are taken, seal the dishes and do not let students open them when the colonies are growing. They can make all their observations from a dish that is taped shut. Follow the disposal instructions when students have completed their investigations.

As You Teach

Outcomes and Indicators of Success

By the end of this activity, students should

1. be able to develop a question that can be answered using science.

   They will demonstrate their ability by

   - listing questions they have about bacteria,
   - discussing the criteria for scientifically testable questions, and
   - determining which questions are scientifically testable.

2. be able to design a scientific investigation.

   They will demonstrate their ability by

   - determining a scientific question to investigate that focuses on where bacteria are found in their school and
   - writing a step-by-step procedure that describes the investigation, which includes
     - listing the tools and materials necessary to conduct the investigation,
     - describing the type of data they will collect and how they will organize those data,
     - describing what type of safety precautions they will take,
     - describing constants and variables present in their design, and
     - identifying and including controls in the investigation.

Part I: Developing a Question

Materials

none

Process and Procedure

When you think about what scientists do, what thoughts come to mind? If "scientists ask questions" popped into your head, then you're right. Asking questions is part of the process of scientific inquiry. But scientists are not the only people who ask questions. On a daily basis, you probably ask a few questions as well. Does that make you a scientist? Of course it does. But can you always answer your questions using science? In other words, are your questions scientifically testable? In Part I of this activity, you will work individually and with a partner to develop a scientifically testable question about bacteria.

1. Read the following fictitious story.

   Health Inspector!

   You and your friends are having lunch when there is an announcement over the intercom. The principal informs you that a health inspector will be at the school next week. The health inspector's job is to make sure the school is clean not only on the surface, but also beneath the surface in areas that we cannot see. While your principal says that everyone has done a very good job keeping the school clean, it is important to know where the health inspector might find problems. The principal asks for your help as scientists. After talking with your friends and your science teacher, you decide that there might be microorganisms like bacteria that general cleaning missed. You decide that this might be something your science class could investigate.

▲ **Figure 1.4** Can you and your classmates investigate the presence of microorganisms in your school?

3. be able to develop and practice skills associated with conducting a scientific investigation.

   They will demonstrate their ability by

   - working effectively in groups to perform the steps in the investigational design,
   - using equipment and supplies appropriately,
   - attending to safety precautions, and
   - documenting data and results.

4. begin to understand the significance of gathering and interpreting evidence.

   They will demonstrate their understanding by

   - organizing their data collection,
   - attending to the control of variables,
   - analyzing the data, and
   - using their data analysis to form a conclusion.

5. develop skills to analyze and communicate a scientific investigation.

   They will demonstrate their skills by

   - presenting the design of the investigation about bacteria in the school to their classmates,
   - presenting the results of the investigation to their classmates,
   - developing conclusions based on evidence gathered during the investigation,
   - writing a laboratory report that includes their rationale, procedure, results, and conclusion about where bacteria are found in the school, and
   - writing a cover letter to the principal describing the investigation and including suggestions for next steps.

Strategies

Getting Started

Ask a student to read the introduction to *Small Problem?* aloud for the class. After he or she is finished, ask your class what it might already know about bacteria. Ask students for ideas about what types of investigations scientists might conduct about bacteria and other microorganisms. Listen to student responses and explain that in this activity they will have an opportunity to learn more about microorganisms by attempting to solve a problem through scientific investigation.

Cautions

Students should wear safety goggles and gloves during their investigations. All materials that come into contact with bacteria should be disposed of properly. Soak them in a 30% bleach solution, drain, and throw away in the regular trash. Have students wash their hands after the investigation. Once the petri dishes have been exposed to bacteria, they should be taped shut and never opened by the students. Students should make their observations only by looking at the sealed plates. Since the nutrient agar is a basic food source for nonpathogenic bacteria, the growth of disease-causing bacteria is unlikely, but it is wise not to take chances. Clean up any broken dishes with a 30% bleach solution.

When the class is finished with its investigation, carefully clean and dispose of materials. If you are using disposable petri dishes, soak them in a 30% bleach solution, drain them and wrap them in plastic bags. Discard them in a trash can. If you want to reuse the dishes for other reasons, soak them in a 30% bleach solution, scrape out the agar, and dispose of it down a garbage disposal (or wrap it in plastic bags and discard in a trash can). Wash the empty petri dishes in warm, soapy water.

2. Make a table similar to figure 1.5 in your science notebook. This will help you organize the information you already have.

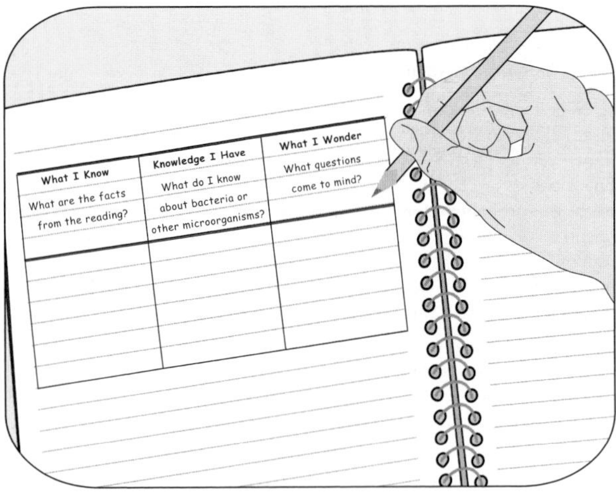

▲ **Figure 1.5 Organization table.** Make a table like this in your science notebook to organize your information.

3. Fill in your table by completing these steps.
   a. Think about what you know about the situation in *Health Inspector!* Record your ideas in the "what I know" column.
   b. Think about what you already know about bacteria. Record your ideas in the "knowledge I have" column.
   c. Think about any questions that come to mind that you could investigate. Record your questions in the "what I wonder" column.
4. Meet with a partner and share and revise your table using Steps 4a–d as a guide.
   a. *Share* your table with your partner and discuss your responses in each column. Read these responses aloud to your partner.
   b. Ask for *advice* on how to make your table more complete.
   c. *Revise* your table if you think your partner's advice is better than yours.

Properly wipe down work areas in the classroom with a mild (10%) bleach solution. Make sure students wash their hands before leaving the classroom.

When working with bacteria from the environment, use caution. There **Biohazard!** is the potential of pathogenicity of the organisms involved (especially in the case of organisms cultured from humans). The problem is that pathogenic, or potentially pathogenic, bacteria that are present in small amounts in the environment (or someone's throat!) could be cultured into a very large population in the laboratory, endangering those who are working with them. This is especially true for students, who are just learning how to maintain aseptic technique. Because of this, once the students' samples are taken, seal the dishes and do not let students open them when the colonies are growing. They can make all their observations from a dish that is taped shut. Follow the disposal instructions when students have completed their investigations.

Process and Procedure

Part I: Developing a Question

Materials

none

Answers to Stop & Think are on TE pages 16–17.

d. Switch roles and listen carefully to your partner.

This process of first thinking (Step 3), sharing (Step 4a), advising (Step 4b), and revising (Step 4c) is called the think-share-advise-revise (TSAR) strategy. You will use this throughout the year in every science subject area.

5. As a class, determine which questions in the "what I wonder" column are scientifically testable in your science class. Agree on which question your class will investigate.

A scientifically testable question is a question addressed and likely answered by designing and conducting a scientific investigation. Evidence gathered in the investigation supports a scientific explanation.

Stop & THINK

PART I

Answer the following questions with your class. Make notes of the class discussion of each answer in your science notebook.

1. Deciding on a scientifically testable question is the first step in designing a good investigation. Answer Questions 1a–b about these questions.
   a. How did you determine which questions were scientifically testable?
   b. Give an example of a question that is testable and one that is not. Explain your choices.
2. Describe how you think research scientists determine scientifically testable questions they will pursue. In your description, consider how this task by a research scientist is similar to or different from your task of choosing a testable question.

Instruct students to read the opening to Part I and the scenario presented in Step 1, *Health Inspector!* Tell students that they are going to be scientists who investigate microorganisms around the school. Direct students to work in teams of two or three and to follow Steps 1–3.

Step 3 begins a strategy called think-share-advise-revise (TSAR). This strategy is used numerous times throughout this program. The strategy allows students to first think about what they are doing or about answers they are formulating. The next step is to share with their partner or team. They should do this by verbalizing what they wrote down or drew in a sketch. The third step is for the other team members to offer advice for corrections, changes, or deletions to what was shared. The final step is for the students to think critically about the advice and revise their work based on what advice they think is acceptable. Students are taken through this process in Steps 3 and 4. The first few times your students use the strategy, they may feel uncomfortable sharing their ideas with others. It is important that you monitor the class and make sure *each* student participates in the process. More information about using this strategy can be found

in the *How To* section at the back of the book.

Circulate around the room, listening as students discuss their ideas and fill in the table. An example of what their tables might look like is shown in figure T1.5.

In Step 5, have a class discussion, eliciting ideas that teams had for each column. At the board in the front of the room, compile a list of questions each team has developed. Go through the list, asking the students which questions they think are scientifically testable in the school using the equipment and supplies in their science class. Ask them to support their answers. If you discover that your students struggle with composing a scientifically testable question,

you may want to use the optional activity *Testable Questions* located on the *TRCD*.

What You Know	Knowledge You Have	Questions That Arise
What are the facts from the reading?	*What do you know about bacteria or other microorganisms?*	*What questions come to mind?*
• Microorganisms might be around the school. • General cleaning might not get rid of microorganisms. • Health inspector arrives in a week.	• They are small—too small to see without a microscope. • They could be everywhere. • They are single-celled organisms. • They might or might not be pathogenic. • They could grow if the environment is right. • If bacteria multiply, you might see them.	• Where are the bacteria? • How did the bacteria get in the school? • What kinds of bacteria are there? • Are certain bacteria, or microorganisms, in certain places?

▲ **Figure T1.5 Sample answers to Step 3.** This is an example of your students' responses to the table in Step 3.

Explain to students that, *as a class*, they will focus on only one question to investigate. Because materials are limited, each team will contribute to the overall investigation. Discuss the importance of collaboration among scientists and how this leads to scientific discoveries, treatments of disease, and many other advancements in science. Collaboration, in the scientific use of the word, certainly involves working together on an agreed-upon set of actions. But collaboration is much more. In science, to collaborate also means to vigorously exchange ideas, sometimes disagreeing and arguing in defense of one's position or interpretation and setting out on a completely different path from other scientists. The clashing of ideas is the cornerstone of scientific advancement. Encourage your students to question one another and voice their own thoughts and opinions. Too often, some students only agree with the students that always seem to have the correct answer. They never offer or defend their own personal opinions.

Guide students to select a question that the whole class can investigate that is scientifically testable. Most likely, the question that your class will explore will be something like, "What locations in the school have the most bacteria?" The remainder of the activity is fashioned around this question. If you allow your students to choose a different question, you will have to adjust some of the instructions and questions that follow.

Answers to Stop and Think—Part I, SE page 15

Students are instructed to answer these questions as part of a class discussion. You should make sure that students do not use this exercise to simply copy down the correct answer from the first student who responds. Ask probing questions that ensure that the class understands the basis of the answers. Ask students to justify their responses. When a student offers an answer, don't immediately indicate if the answer is right or wrong. Instead, ask students if they agree or disagree with the response and have them share their reasons.

Part II: Design Time

Materials

none

Process and Procedure

In Part I of this investigation, you read about a fictional situation at your school and the possible presence of microorganisms. You developed a scientifically testable question based on the situation. In Part II, you will focus on designing a scientific investigation to answer your question. As you design your investigation, you will continue to engage in the process of scientific inquiry. What are the criteria for designing a good investigation? What evidence do you need to collect to answer the question your class is asking? Think about the three investigations you examined in *A Clean Design*. Remember that the design of the investigation leads you to either valid or invalid results (figure 1.6). You and two other students will make up one team of scientists for this activity.

▲ **Figure 1.6 Planning an investigation.** What are the criteria for a good scientific investigation? You will consider these criteria as you and your team plan a scientific investigation.

16

Ask students if they can modify an incorrect answer to make it correct or if they can modify a correct answer to add more information that is also correct. In this way, you lead the class in a valuable discussion of these questions.

1a. Students should indicate that they considered each question and chose the ones that could be answered by doing a scientific investigation. They may also indicate that they must have the materials available to perform these investigations. A question that is answerable by science in a university laboratory may not be answerable in a high school laboratory.

1b. Student answers will vary but an example of a scientifically testable question is, "What locations in the school have the most bacteria?" This is a scientifically testable question because it can be answered by science and by an investigation. The school has adequate materials to perform this investigation. An example of a question that is not testable in your school is, "Where do the bacteria come from?" While this is a good question, and it could be answered by a pathologist, it cannot be answered by your students. To trace the origin of the bacteria that are on doorknobs, for example, would be beyond the scope of a high school science investigation.

2. Students should indicate that a research scientist goes about choosing a scientifically testable question in much the same way as they did. The same rules apply; the question must be able to be answered by science. Students may indicate that a research scientist will have more sophisticated equipment and materials available and could investigate a wider range of questions.

Answers to Step 6 are on TE pages 19–20.

1. As a class, review what you think are the important criteria of a good scientific investigation. Take notes on your class discussion and record these ideas in your science notebook.
2. Read the protocol *Culturing Bacteria* to find out how scientists investigate bacteria. Then look at the materials that are available in your classroom.
3. With your team of scientists, design an investigation that will answer the class question from Part I. To make sure your investigation answers your question with valid results, use the following in your design.
   a. What is your rationale? How will this investigation test your question?
   b. How can you keep the investigation fair? In other words, how will you try to keep all factors or variables constant except for the one you are testing?

A well-controlled investigation only tests one factor at a time and keeps all other factors the same. Factors that are kept the same in each group are called constants. The one factor that changes is called the variable.

   c. How will you set up a control?

In an investigation, the control receives no treatment. All other groups are compared against the control.

   d. What type of data will you collect to answer the question?
   e. What tools will you use and what materials will you need?
   f. What safety precautions will you take?
   g. How will you organize your data? Will your data be qualitative or quantitative?
   h. How will you analyze your data? How will you develop an explanation and how will you support this explanation?
   i. How will you validate your investigation?
4. Write a step-by-step procedure for your investigation. Include labeled diagrams, charts, or tables.
5. Present your team's design and procedure to the class.
6. As a class, choose 1 procedure that all teams will follow. Record this procedure in your science notebook.

Protocol

Process and Procedure

Part II: Design Time

Materials

none

Begin by discussing effective investigations. Refer back to *A Clean Design*, especially *Reflect and Connect*, Question 3. Briefly review what criteria might be important when designing a scientific investigation. Review control of variables and constants and introduce the concept of a "fair" test. Make an analogy of a running race. Ask students if it is fair if one person in the race starts ahead of another person. Explain that in scientific investigations, all components, or factors being tested, must be treated as evenly as possible if the conclusions that are drawn from the investigation are to be valid.

Remind students that an effective scientific investigation addresses the following criteria:

- The investigation addresses the question being tested.
- It tests only one factor (variable).
- It keeps all other variables as constant as possible.
- It has controls.
- It contains multiple trials and samples.
- It is clear, concise, and well planned.
- It incorporates an organized method for recording data.
- It uses appropriate tools, technology, and mathematics.
- It is safe.

Location	Amount of Growth (no growth, light, medium, heavy)	Number of different types of bacteria (or other microorganisms)	Size of colonies	Observations and Descriptions (sketches)

▲ **Figure T1.6 Sample student data table.** Your students' data tables should look similar to this.

- It potentially provides evidence that will support (or refute) an explanation or lead to new questions.

In Step 2, read the protocol *Culturing Bacteria* with your students. Then display the materials scientists use to study bacteria. Show students a petri dish with nutrient agar and explain that the medium has nutrients that are particularly good for bacteria growth. Discuss with the class how to collect bacteria samples; listen to students' ideas and make sure that they are on the right track.

As a class, verify that the question from Part I that the class will investigate can be answered using the materials available.

Direct students to get with their team and follow Steps 3 and 4. Allow time for teams to discuss how to develop a procedure that might answer the question, "What locations in the school have the most bacteria?" Facilitate the process by circulating among the teams to see that they are controlling variables, identifying constants, and thinking of a way to prove that bacteria were at a particular location and not on the dish already (by setting up a control group). Also, make sure students are including in their design ways to organize their data. One example of a way to organize data is the table in figure T1.6.

In Step 5, let each team briefly present the design of its investigation. Discuss the strengths of each team's plan, asking the class for its input.

In Step 6, students choose 1 class procedure that all the teams will follow.

Make sure students have included at least one control group in their investigation. The purpose of a control group is to provide a point of comparison. Each team can set up a control by swabbing a nutrient agar plate with a new sterile swab that has not touched a surface. Bacterial growth should occur when students collect bacteria from a specific location and should not grow on the control plates if all the materials they use are sterile and they use proper techniques.

Have students use the *Culturing Bacteria* protocol to decide how they will obtain samples of bacteria. Explain that each team will test one location and share its information with the rest of the class. Later, the class will determine where in the school the bacteria are located based on the results of the investigation.

Explain to the class that all good investigators try to keep variables as controlled as possible, so if students

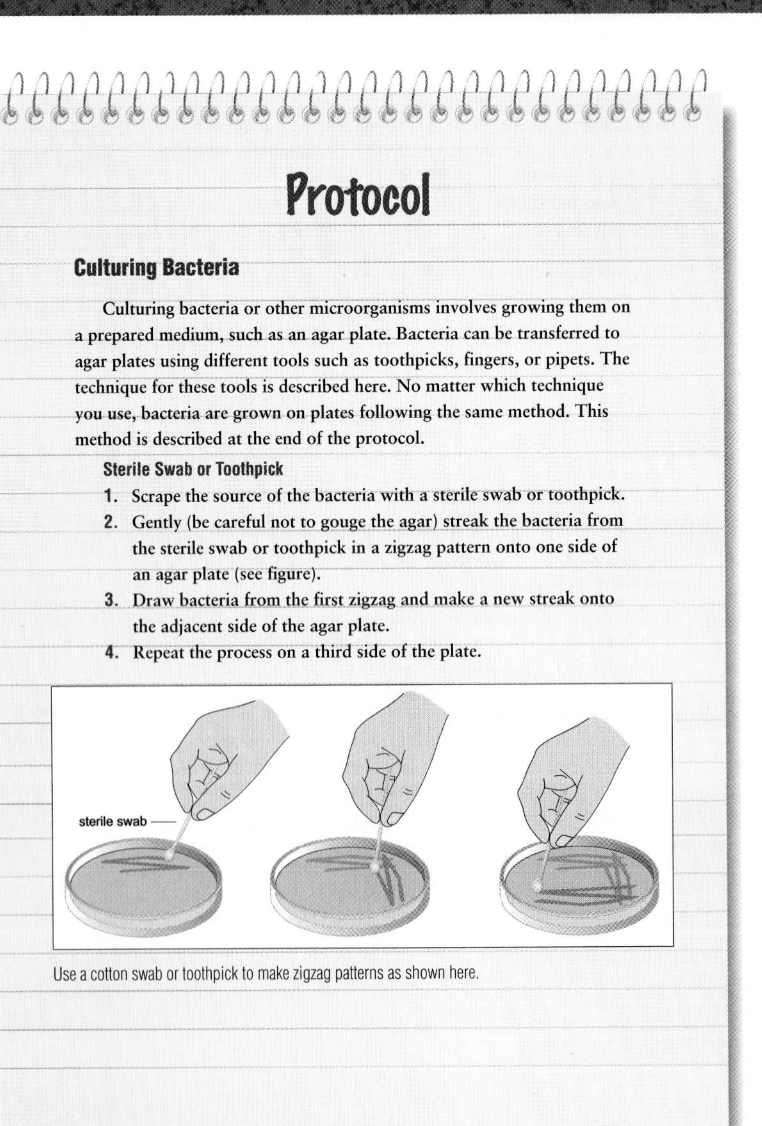

Protocol

Culturing Bacteria

Culturing bacteria or other microorganisms involves growing them on a prepared medium, such as an agar plate. Bacteria can be transferred to agar plates using different tools such as toothpicks, fingers, or pipets. The technique for these tools is described here. No matter which technique you use, bacteria are grown on plates following the same method. This method is described at the end of the protocol.

Sterile Swab or Toothpick

1. Scrape the source of the bacteria with a sterile swab or toothpick.
2. Gently (be careful not to gouge the agar) streak the bacteria from the sterile swab or toothpick in a zigzag pattern onto one side of an agar plate (see figure).
3. Draw bacteria from the first zigzag and make a new streak onto the adjacent side of the agar plate.
4. Repeat the process on a third side of the plate.

Use a cotton swab or toothpick to make zigzag patterns as shown here.

18

follow the technique very similarly, they are following good investigative practices. Make it clear that each team must collect its sample using the exact same procedure. Demonstrate how to swab a petri dish correctly. As a class, agree that each student who is taking the sample will swab the plate back and forth a certain number of times and agree on the number of times. Students can get very specific about how to follow a prescribed technique (i.e., swab the area for 10 seconds, swab the agar back and forth five times, etc.), which indicates their knowledge of control of variables.

Stress that it would be ideal if all factors were kept the same (same student swabbing all dishes, same technique, same time, etc.). To keep materials to a minimum, however, each team will test one location. You can introduce multiple trials by having two or three teams investigate the same location. Comparing these results would give students an idea of why multiple trials are necessary in an investigation.

Answers to Step 6, SE page 17

6. The procedure that the class chooses should be student generated. A sample procedure follows, but avoid giving this out as a procedure to use or to compare it with the students' own procedures. There are many ways to design this investigation effectively; this is only one example.

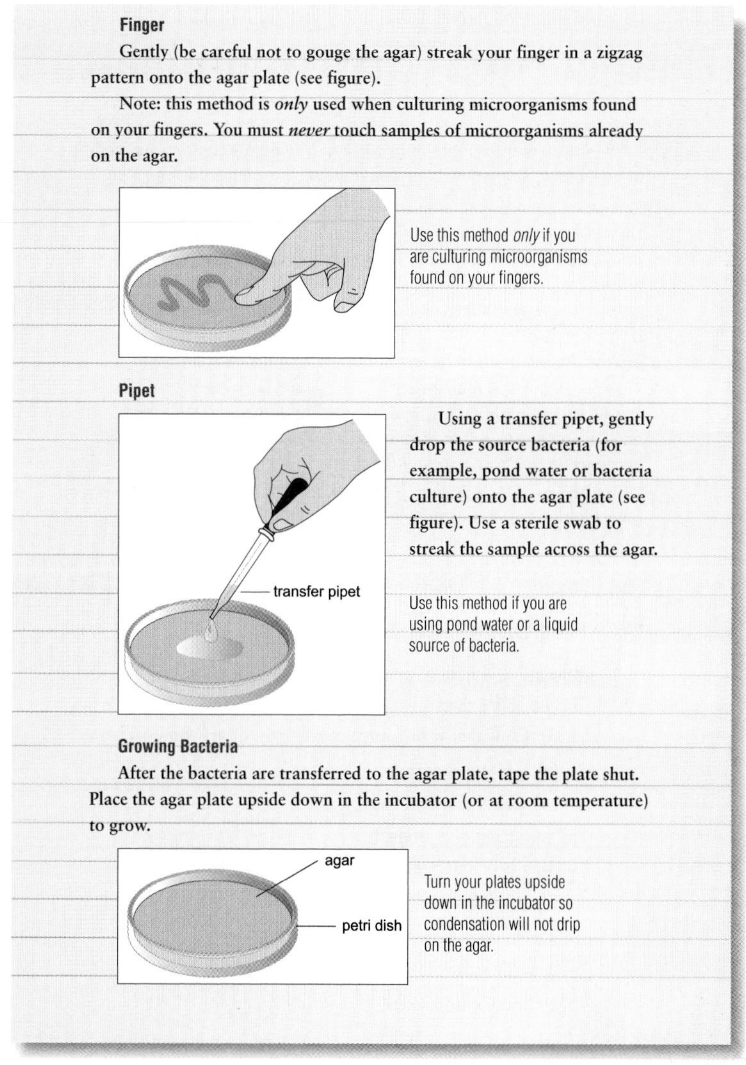
Finger

Gently (be careful not to gouge the agar) streak your finger in a zigzag pattern onto the agar plate (see figure).

Note: this method is *only* used when culturing microorganisms found on your fingers. You must *never* touch samples of microorganisms already on the agar.

Use this method *only* if you are culturing microorganisms found on your fingers.

Pipet

Using a transfer pipet, gently drop the source bacteria (for example, pond water or bacteria culture) onto the agar plate (see figure). Use a sterile swab to streak the sample across the agar.

Use this method if you are using pond water or a liquid source of bacteria.

Growing Bacteria

After the bacteria are transferred to the agar plate, tape the plate shut. Place the agar plate upside down in the incubator (or at room temperature) to grow.

Turn your plates upside down in the incubator so condensation will not drip on the agar.

Chapter 1 Investigations by Design 19

1. Obtain a sterile petri dish with nutrient agar and a sterile swab.
2. Label your petri dish on the bottom with the location from which you are taking a sample.
3. Go to the location that you are sampling. Take the swab and rub it back and forth over the sample location for 30 seconds.
4. Open the petri dish about 30°–45°.
5. Gently swab the sample back and forth 10 times across the agar on the dish in a Z-shaped pattern, turning the dish as you gently swab. (This allows bacteria to come off on different areas of the plate.)
6. Close the dish immediately and tape it shut.
7. Discard the swab appropriately.
8. Store the dish upside down in an incubator at 37°C for 24–48 hours.
9. Check for growth on the plates from all the locations and compare them.
10. Record the growth as light, medium, or heavy when compared with the control groups.
11. Record your other observations such as the color of bacteria, the relative size of colonies, and the shape of colonies.

To get ready to conduct the investigation in Part III, have teams come up with ideas for sampling locations or you can use the following list. Teams should sign up for one sampling location. If appropriate, some teams may collect samples from outside the classroom, but common locations within the classroom work also. Possible locations to sample within the classroom include

- desktop,
- pencil sharpener handle,
- doorknob,
- pencil,
- countertop,
- computer keyboards.

Possible locations outside the classroom include

- stair rail,
- drinking fountain handle or button,
- locker handle,
- bathroom area,
- cafeteria,
- shower bottom in the gym.

Answers to Stop and Think—Part II, SE page 20

1a. Students should describe the constants in the investigation as factors that are kept the same throughout the experiment. For example, the nutrient agar petri dishes, sterile swabs, techniques for obtaining samples, and growth time and temperature are all kept constant.

1b. The variable, the factor that changes, is the location where samples are collected. This is the factor that is being tested.

1c. It is important to test or change only 1 variable in an experiment so that students can see the cause-and-effect relationships. If more than 1 variable is changed, then the students will not know which variable caused the results to be different.

1d. The nutrient agar petri dish that is swabbed with a sterile swab is the control in the investigation.

1e. Students should indicate that a control is needed to use as a comparison. This control also will show them that the bacteria that they grow on their plates comes from their location and not from the agar plate and sterile swab.

2. Both investigations A and B do present certain aspects of sound scientific investigations. Investigation A presents a detailed investigation with constant quantities of soap, constant time of washing, and a description of how to collect evidence. However, the investigation did not attempt to answer the question, which was, "Does the length of time you spend washing your hands affect the amount of germs that remain?" The investigation actually tests a different variable: the temperature of the water.

Investigation B is the best of the 3. The students tested only 1 variable, which is the amount of time spent washing hands. The investigation would guide students to collect evidence that would support an explanation that linked the length of time washing hands to getting rid of germs.

Investigation C includes 3 variables: the amount of soap, the amount of time spent washing hands, and the students. It is difficult to compare results when more than 1 variable is being tested. Many ideas are being tested simultaneously and without proper controls. This is a poor design that would not give fair and valid evidence to support an explanation.

3. Scientists make observations and ask questions that can be answered using scientific research. These questions or ideas are then tested through investigation. For an idea to be tested, the investigation must be sound and logical. In the investigation, scientists try to manipulate only 1 variable. In that way, scientists can focus on 1 idea and keep as many other factors in the investigation as constant

Answers to Stop & Think are on TE pages 20–21.

Stop & THINK

PART II

Answer the following questions with your team of scientists. Make notes of your discussion of each answer in your science notebook.

1. Consider your investigation design and the variables involved to answer Questions 1a–e.
   - **a.** What variables are held constant in your investigation?
   - **b.** What is the variable in your investigation?
   - **c.** Why is it important to test only 1 variable at a time?
   - **d.** What is your control?
   - **e.** Why do you need to have a control?
2. Think back to the 3 investigations presented in the activity A *Clean Design*. Did all of these represent sound scientific investigations? Would each investigation guide scientists to collect evidence? Would that evidence support an explanation for the question asked?
3. Describe why it is important for scientists to design scientifically sound investigations.

Part III: Conducting an Investigation

Materials

For the entire class

37°C incubator or source of warmth for growing bacteria

30% bleach solution

biohazard disposal bags

For each team of 3 students

3 pairs of safety goggles

3 pairs of gloves

2 petri dishes containing nutrient agar

2 sterile swabs

1 permanent marker

20

as possible. It is also important that controls are present; this eliminates false results that might occur from overlooking these controls. For a scientist to collect the best evidence to support (or refute) an explanation, his investigation must be as accurate, straightforward, and fair as possible. Other scientists can then review the research and ask probing, thoughtful questions. They critique one another's research. Scientists must be able to communicate and defend their results using concrete methods and evidence.

Process and Procedure

Part III: Conducting an Investigation

Materials

For the entire class

37°C incubator or source of warmth
30% bleach solution in a large container (for waste)
biohazard disposal bags

For each team of 3 students

3 pairs of safety goggles
3 pairs of gloves
2 petri dishes with nutrient agar
2 sterile cotton swabs
1 permanent marker
tape (to tape petri dishes closed)
2 index cards
other materials as needed

3 copies of copymaster 1.1, *Scientific Investigation Report*

Cautions

Students should wear goggles and gloves while conducting the investigation. Make sure they do not open petri dishes until they are ready to use them and that they tape the petri dishes shut after collecting their sample. Soak the contaminated petri dishes in a 30% bleach solution after observations are complete. Properly wipe down work areas in your classroom and discard disposable items. Be sure students wash their hands before leaving your science class.

Day 1

Students should conduct their investigation early in the week so that bacteria can grow over a 24–48-hour period without interruption. Alternatively, you could conduct the investigation on a Friday and the bacteria could grow over the weekend.

Before students begin the investigation, have them work through Step 1 and predict where the bacteria will be present in the school. Students should already know how to write a hypothesis, but you might need to review the format you would like them to use. An example of a hypothesis is "I think the most bacteria will be found on the drinking fountain handle."

It is helpful to post the locations students plan to test so that students know where samples will be obtained.

Instruct students to work with their teammates and follow Steps 2–4. Teams should conduct the investigation following the procedure they wrote as a class in Part II, Step 6.

Observe as the teams collect their samples. Remind them to only open the petri dish lid when they are ready to swab. Have them close the lid as soon as the swabbing is complete. Make sure they follow the class procedure so that the teams can compare results from all the

tape
other materials as needed
2 index cards
3 *Scientific Investigation Report* handouts

Cautions

Wear safety goggles and gloves while conducting the investigation. Do not open petri dishes until you are ready to use them. Tape the petri dishes shut after you collect your sample. Soak the contaminated petri dishes in a 30% bleach solution after you are finished making your observations. Properly wipe down work areas in your classroom and discard disposable items as directed by your teacher. Be sure to wash your hands before you leave your science class.

Process and Procedure

Most of the time, scientists work collaboratively to gather as much information and data as possible. Your class will now work together to conduct an investigation to answer the question you asked in Part I. The time you spent designing a scientific investigation will help you conduct a valid investigation with reliable, and interesting results. Like the student scientists in figure 1.7, it is time to put your plan to work.

▲ **Figure 1.7**
Students at work. These students have planned their investigation well and have gotten their teacher's approval. Now they are following their plan. What do you think they will find on this doorknob?

Day 1

1. Before you begin your investigation, reread the question your class is attempting to answer. Based on what you already know, what do you think the results of your investigation will show? Record your prediction as a **hypothesis** in your science notebook.

Remember, a hypothesis is a statement that suggests an explanation for an observation or an answer to a scientific problem. Your hypothesis suggests a causal relationship or an if/then relationship. You base your hypothesis on your prior knowledge.

2. Review the investigation agreed upon by your class. Verify your understanding of the procedures with your team.
3. Obtain the materials your team needs. Remember to take safety precautions.

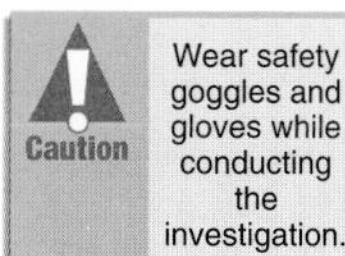

locations. Circulate among the teams, asking questions such as these:

- "How are you recording information in your science notebook?"
- "Do you think there will be bacteria present at this location? Why?"
- "Are you finding the class procedure easy to follow?"
- "How would you improve the class procedure?"

Ask students what they think the bacteria will look like if they grow on the media. Make sure students understand that the "colonies" they might see are actually millions of bacteria that started from a single bacterium. Each colony represents one original bacterial cell that replicated.

After students collect samples, direct them to tape their petri dishes shut and store their dishes upside down in the 37°C incubator or other source of warmth.

Plates are stored upside down in the incubator to reduce condensation dripping on bacteria colonies and causing smears. Also, gravity allows the colonies to grow so that you can see the colonies better.

If using another source of warmth, make sure the temperature is not above 37°C and that the temperature is even for the entire set of class samples. Record the temperature and have students make a note of it in their science notebooks. Explain to students that at lower temperatures, bacteria grow (reproduce) more slowly. It would take longer for the students to see results if they grew their plates at room temperature or at a temperature below 37°C.

Encourage students to try an experiment at home. Have them compare bacteria or other microorganisms growing on old food in the refrigerator with bacteria or other microorganisms growing on the same food at room temperature. They most likely will see faster growth at room temperature.

Day 2

Check your students' plates after 24 hours. If you do not see significant growth, allow another 12–24 hours of growth time. If you are waiting for results, students can begin writing up their lab reports and cover letters that are assigned in the *Reflect and Connect* questions. They will not be able to complete them but could get started. Also, you may want students to draw a map of the school or the area that they tested. This map could be a class-sized map or individual maps.

After the growing period, direct students to continue following the procedure in their student books, Day 2, Step 1. Each team should display its petri dishes with clearly labeled index cards, one for its sample and one for its control. You might choose to display only one or two controls as all the controls should have zero growth. If any of the controls show growth, this would be a good time to remind students about why it is important to have controls in the investigation. Ask students questions such as

- "If the control shows growth, and it is not supposed to, what does that mean about the variable you are testing?"
- "What does that mean about the investigation?"
- "Can you rely on the validity of the investigation?"
- "What might have happened so that bacteria could grow on the plate?"

4. Carry out the investigation carefully; obey all safety precautions. To complete your team's part, do Steps 4a–e.
   a. Obtain a sample from the location that your team is testing. Prepare a petri dish with the sample by following the class procedure.

Remember, the investigation needs to be as controlled as possible.

   b. Properly dispose of all materials as directed by your teacher.
   c. Tape the petri dish shut and do not open the dish again. You can make all your observations through the lid.
   d. Label your dish with the location, date, and team name.

Write on the bottom of the petri dish (the bottom contains the agar).

   e. Store your petri dish upside down in the incubator at 37°C or as your teacher directs.

Day 2

1. On an index card, write a brief description of your team's assigned test location. Retrieve your petri dish and place it next to your index card on display (figure 1.8).

▶ **Figure 1.8 Day 2.** Your bacteria have grown in the incubator. Now it's time to share your results with the rest of the class. Mark your test location on an index card.

22

In Step 2, allow time for students to set up a data table to record the results in their science notebooks. Students should draw sketches of representative dishes as one way of recording their data. Alternatively, students may want to take digital pictures of the dishes. They could then use the photographs in their lab reports and or cover letters. These sketches or photographs should be properly labeled.

In addition to bacteria, students might also have fungi growing on their nutrient agar. Fungal colonies appear as fuzzy colonies. Remind students to record quantitative and qualitative data.

Ask students to complete Step 3. After teams have viewed all the petri dishes, have them analyze the data, concentrating on the evidence and developing an explanation based on that evidence. Ask if they have enough evidence to support an explanation. How confident are they about the explanation? Discuss how well they controlled the factors of the investigation. This is an ideal time to discuss multiple trials (repeating the investigation many times). In this investigation, there may have been only one sample taken from each location. Ask students if they think that is adequate. If a new drug that prevented cancer was tested on only five people, would they try it? Explain that scientists conduct multiple trials using many samples in their studies.

Copymaster 1.1, *Scientific Investigation Report* describes one example of what the lab report might look like. Hand out this report and ask students to use it to guide them when they write up their own report as instructed in the *Reflect and Connect* questions.

Answers to Reflect and Connect, SE page 23

1. Students are instructed to review the handout *Scientific Investigation Report* with their team and analyze their results from the investigation. Monitor this task to ensure that students are talking about each of the requirements in the report. Tell the students that after this discussion, they will be working on their own to write the report. Now is their opportunity to discuss the results and work on explanations and conclusions.
2. Students write a lab report for this step. Use the handout *Scientific Investigation Report* as a rubric for their reports.
3. Student cover letters should include all the criteria listed in the step. Look for clear, concise letters. These letters should not be a reproduction of the lab report.

2. Make a data table according to the class design for recording your results in the investigation. Record the table in your science notebook.
3. Examine all the petri dishes from the other teams in your class. Record your observations and results in your data table as well as those of the other teams of scientists.
4. Listen as your teacher leads a class discussion of these investigations. Make notes in your science notebook of all explanations given for the different results.

Reflect and Connect

Work first with your team and then individually to complete the following tasks.

1. Work with your team to analyze your investigation using the handout *Scientific Investigation Report*. Look at the requirements for your report and discuss with your team how you will answer each section from your investigation.
2. Write a lab report on your own of your investigation. Refer to the *Scientific Investigation Report* handout to guide you.
3. Write a cover letter to your principal that provides an overview of your investigation. This cover letter will go with your lab report. In the letter, tell your principal about your class investigation. Include the following components in the letter:
   a. An introduction about yourself and your science class
   b. Why you are doing this investigation
   c. An abstract of your investigation

An abstract is a brief summary of your investigation. It should include the problem you are trying to solve, observations, explanations, and conclusions based on evidence.

   d. Recommendations based on evidence from your results
   e. What new questions you have

Chapter 1 Investigations by Design 23

EXPLAIN

Why and How Do We Inquire?

Activity Overview

In *Why and How Do We Inquire?*, students will identify how they have been using the process of scientific inquiry in the chapter. They will read about scientific inquiry and apply what they have learned by comparing their investigation with a diagram showing the nonlinear process of scientific inquiry. They will discuss how the results from their investigation either provided evidence for their explanation or led them in a new direction.

Before You Teach

Background Information

"Scientific inquiry refers to the diverse ways in which scientists study the natural world and propose explanations based on the evidence derived from their work. Inquiry also refers to the activities of students in which they develop knowledge and understanding of scientific ideas, as well as an understanding of how scientists study the natural world" (*National Science Education Standards*, National Research Council, 1996, p. 23). Your students have been and will continue to be involved in the types of inquiry activities described by the *National Science Education Standards*. For additional background, see the reading *It's about Inquiry* in the student book.

Materials—Part I

For each team of 3 students

1 sheet of chart paper
1 set of markers (2–3 colors per set)
3 copies of copymaster 1.2, *Process of Inquiry*

TRCD

Materials—Part II

For each student

1 copy of copymaster 1.2, *Process of Inquiry* from Part I

Advance Preparation

Make copies of copymaster 1.2, *Process of Inquiry* for each student.

As You Teach

Outcomes and Indicators of Success

By the end of this activity, students should

1. be able to identify the processes and pathways of scientific inquiry.

   They will show their understanding by

   - creating a diagram or flowchart depicting the general scientific path they took during their investigation of bacteria in their school;
   - comparing the diagram they created with the *Process of Inquiry* handout;
   - identifying points on the inquiry diagram that they followed during their investigation and making appropriate additions or changes to their diagram;
   - reading about Ignaz Semmelweis and explaining how he followed the process of scientific inquiry in his study of the transmission of "cadaver particles"; and
   - describing why the process of scientific inquiry is not always linear, due to new information, unexpected results, flawed design, alternative questions or explanations, and so on.

2. understand that the process of inquiry is a continuous process and recognize alternative models or explanations.

   They will indicate their understanding and recognition by

   - describing ways to improve the scientific investigation of bacteria in their school,
   - developing new questions as a result of their investigation, and
   - analyzing Ignaz Semmelweis's scientific inquiry in the reading and describing how Semmelweis could have convinced the world of his discovery.

EXPLAIN

Why and How Do We Inquire?

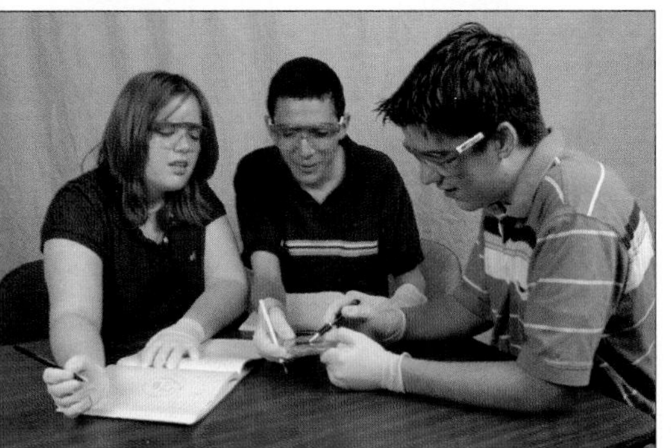

▲ **Figure 1.9 Conducting an investigation.** You have been acting as a scientist as you conducted your investigation. Now you will compare your investigation with the process of inquiry.

You have just been immersed in the process of scientific inquiry (figure 1.9). In *Small Problem?*, you developed a scientifically testable question based on a given situation. You then designed an investigation to answer that question, and you conducted that investigation. Did your investigation go smoothly? Were you able to answer your question? Do you have more questions because of the results you got from your investigation? These are all part of the process called scientific inquiry. In *Why and How Do We Inquire?*, you will identify the process you experienced as a scientist in your own school. You will work in teams for this activity.

Part I: The Process of Inquiry

Materials

For each team of 3 students

1 sheet of chart paper

1 set of markers

3 *Process of Inquiry* handouts

Process and Procedure

1. Get together with the same team of scientists you were working with in *Small Problem?* Using markers, create a flowchart or diagram on chart paper that describes the general process of scientific inquiry your team went through in Parts I, II, and III of *Small Problem?*

Do not repeat the steps in your procedure. Instead, describe in general terms what you did. For example, the first thing you might have done is make an observation or ask a question.

2. When your team has completed its flowchart or diagram, copy it into your science notebook. Then post it in your classroom.
3. Compare your chart with those of your classmates by following Steps 3a–d.
   a. Explain each step in your diagram to another team.

Strategies

Getting Started

Ask the class if it thought its investigation followed a specific path and if it thinks that path is consistent with a good scientific investigation. Allow students to respond candidly but guide them to be specific about components. Keep the discussion focused on what a good scientific investigation includes. Explain that they are going to capture the path they followed in a diagram and then they will read about scientific inquiry. Ask them to think about their investigation as they are reading. Do not pass out copies of copymaster 1.2, *Process of Inquiry* until Step 4.

Process and Procedure

Part I: The Process of Inquiry

Materials

For each team of 3 students

1 sheet of chart paper

1 set of markers (2–3 colors per set)

3 copies of copymaster 1.2, *Process of Inquiry* (obtain for Step 4)

Instruct students to get into their teams from *Small Problem?*, gather their materials, and follow Steps 1 and 2. Remind students to make a chart or diagram that describes in general terms what they did. For example, students might have a flowchart that looks like this:

"Collect evidence (from scenario) ⇨ Ask a scientifically testable question ⇨ Design an investigation to test the question ⇨ Conduct the investigation ⇨ Analyze data ⇨ Answer the question"

Try to get the students to look at the "big picture" of their investigation. Circulate around the room, asking probing questions such as the following:

- "When did you think about the evidence you would be collecting?"
- "Did you consider revising your investigation? When?"
- "Do you think this is how research scientists think about their investigations? Why?"

In Step 3, after all teams have copied their diagrams into their science notebooks and posted their charts around the room, have each team follow Steps 3a–d with another team. Then lead the class in a discussion of these steps. Have students note the similarities and the differences in the diagrams. This is good for discussion because it allows you to focus on the nonlinearity of scientific inquiry. Even though each team was following the same investigation design, slight differences might have occurred.

In Step 4, distribute copymaster 1.2, *Process of Inquiry*. Have students discuss the handout and place Xs along the path that they took during their investigation. Is the diagram on the handout similar to student charts?

---

b. Listen as the other team explains its diagram.
c. Discuss the similarities and differences in your diagrams.
d. You all followed the same procedure. Are your charts similar? List at least 2 similarities and 2 differences.

4. With your team, study the handout *Process of Inquiry*. Compare your chart with the handout. Identify the stages on the handout that you experienced. Place an *X* along the paths on the handout that you experienced in your inquiry.
5. Based on information presented in the *Process of Inquiry* handout and your classmates' charts, make any additions to your chart that you feel are necessary. Make the same adjustments to the diagram in your science notebook, too.

Your diagram should depict the investigation you did in *Small Problem?* Not all scientific inquiries proceed down the same path.

6. Read *It's about Inquiry* to learn more about the process of scientific inquiry.

READING

It's about Inquiry

Asking a question and seeking answers is an obvious path to take when inquiring about the natural world. In *Small Problem?*, you developed a question and then set out to answer your question by carefully designing an investigation. You then conducted your investigation and recorded and analyzed your results. Your results might have helped you answer your question and might have presented you with new questions. You gained some knowledge and understanding of the world of bacteria and possibly identified locations in your school where bacteria were widespread. Was your scientific investigation sound? Did you collect adequate evidence? Were your results valid? Based on your experience, you can see why the design of an investigation is so important.

Scientists propose explanations based on the evidence they collect during their research. This dynamic practice of wondering and asking questions, of making detailed observations, and of developing explanations based on those observations and evidence is the process of **scientific inquiry**. It is not a linear process. Look at figure 1.10 to see the different paths scientific inquiry can take. This is how scientists study the natural world.

The Process

In your investigation of bacteria, or microorganisms, in your school, you used the fundamental process of scientific inquiry. This process is composed of the following methods:

- Make observations and ask questions that can be answered by scientific inquiry.
- Check your current knowledge and the knowledge of other scientists.
- Make a prediction or propose an answer that you can test (hypothesis).

Answers to Step 4, SE page 25

4. Students should place Xs in the following locations:
   - "Access prior knowledge"
   - "Generate testable question"
   - "Design investigation"
   - "Make observations"
   - "Gather evidence"
   - "Propose explanation"
   - "Communicate explanation"

Students might put Xs in other places, depending on the process of inquiry they feel they followed.

Based on the class discussion, ask students to complete Step 5 and then read *It's about Inquiry*.

NOTES:

It's about Inquiry, continued

- Test your prediction by conducting your investigation and gathering evidence through observation.
- Propose explanations based on evidence.
- Consider alternative explanations.
- Test explanations by gathering more evidence or seeing if new predictions are supported based on that explanation.
- Report (or communicate) your findings and proposed explanation.

It is important to realize that inquiry is not a prescribed, sequential process. When scientists do science, they do not just march through the steps in this order. For example, while a scientist is designing an investigation, she might come across new information that causes her to go back to her original question and change it slightly. This might lead her to make changes in the design. Or a scientist collecting data while conducting an investigation might discover a flaw in the design. This might lead him to change the design before he continues. A scientist might not only discover a flaw but might make a new discovery that also generates new questions.

In your investigation, you probably answered, or partially answered, your original question. It is likely that you also came up with new questions. If you had time, you might revise and test your explanations to be satisfied that you answered your question completely. In this way, you are "doing" science.

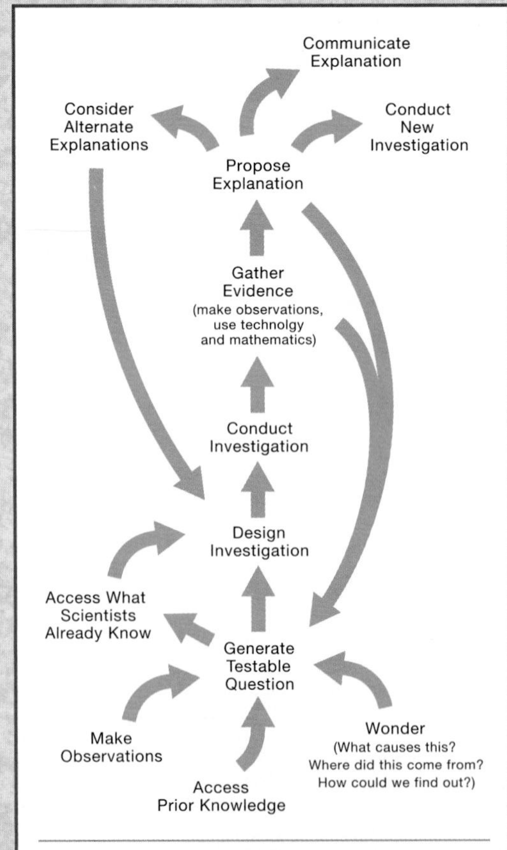

▲ **Figure 1.10 Process of inquiry.** Inquiry is a dynamic practice used to study the world around you. How did you use this process to conduct your investigation?

NOTES:

The Design

When scientists focus on the design of an investigation, they have to make sure that the design itself guides them to the answer to their question and controls for error (figure 1.11). If the design is poor, the results are not valid. Proper design of an investigation includes the following considerations:

- Design an investigation that answers the question in the most appropriate and direct manner.
- Control as many variables as possible. The scientist changes only the variable being tested.
- Set up a control group. Sometimes one group is not exposed to the tested variable. This group serves as a comparison group to determine that the results were due to the tested variable and not to some other factor. For example, if scientists are studying the effectiveness of a new arthritis medicine, one group does not take the medicine. Scientists compare this group with the group taking the medicine.
- Use mathematics and technology tools appropriately to collect and analyze data.
- Collect and organize data appropriately.
- Include numerous trials, samples, or subjects in each investigation.

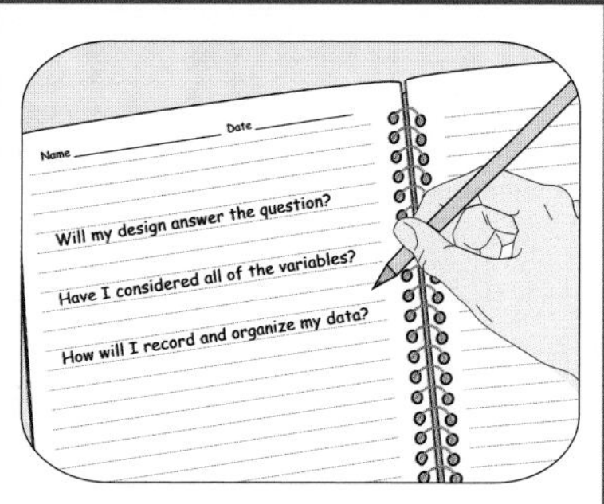

▲ **Figure 1.11 Investigation design.** What should you think about first when designing an investigation?

Stop & THINK

Answer the following questions in your science notebook.

1. What makes the design of an investigation useful and valid?
2. Now that you've learned more about the process of scientific inquiry and about designing scientific investigations, think back to your investigation in *Small Problem?* as you answer Questions 2a–b.
   - **a.** Suggest additional adjustments to the design of your investigation in *Small Problem?* Describe why you feel these adjustments are necessary.
   - **b.** How would these adjustments make the design of your investigation more valid?

Answers to Stop and Think, SE page 27

1. Students should convey their understanding about the importance of investigational design by discussing that the question asked needs to be scientifically testable; the design needs to address that question; the procedure needs to include controls, constants, a variable (related to the question asked), multiple trials, and appropriate tools and technology; and the data collected must provide solid evidence to support an explanation.
2. Students should adjust their investigations by using what they have learned about the process of scientific inquiry. They should recognize that looking at the work of other scientists and accessing their own prior knowledge will help them in their investigations. They should understand that looking for alternative explanations is a part of the process, as is asking new questions. They should also add that communicating their results is an important part of the process. Scientists constantly reflect on the design of their investigations and make adjustments as necessary.

NOTES:

Process and Procedure

Part II: Observations Leading to Discoveries

Materials

For each student

1 copy of copymaster 1.2, *Process of Inquiry* from Part I

Ask students to read *Observations Leading to Discoveries*, a story weaving in the history and nature of science by describing how a doctor, Ignaz Semmelweis, discovered the transmission of disease-causing organisms. Students are introduced to the turn-and-talk literacy strategy in Step 1. Move about the room as they are reading to ensure that they are incorporating the strategy to help them understand the reading. Instruct students to answer Step 2 in their science notebooks after they have completed the reading.

Part II: Observations Leading to Discoveries

Materials

For each student

1 *Process of Inquiry* handout from Part I

Process and Procedure

1. Read *Observations Leading to Discoveries*. Use the turn-and-talk literacy strategy to help you understand the reading by following Steps 1a–h.
   - **a.** Choose a partner to work with during this reading.
   - **b.** Read the first paragraph of the reading silently.
   - **c.** When both you and your partner finish the paragraph, decide which one of you will go first to complete Step 1d.
   - **d.** Turn to your partner and summarize what you read. Relay your summary aloud as your partner listens.
   - **e.** Listen as your partner gives you feedback on your summary. Discuss anything that is confusing to you.
   - **f.** Each of you will read the next paragraph silently.
   - **g.** Switch roles; this time your partner will summarize verbally and you will offer feedback.
   - **h.** Continue this process. Read each paragraph silently and alternate roles as you summarize and offer feedback aloud.

This strategy is the turn-and-talk strategy. You will use this literacy strategy throughout the year to help you understand what you are reading.

READING

Observations Leading to Discoveries

> **"One's mind, once stretched by a new idea, never regains its original dimensions."**
> —*Oliver Wendell Holmes*

In your scientific investigation, you made discoveries about bacteria around your school by beginning with a question. Scientists learn and make discoveries by observing and asking "Why" or "What if" questions. In this reading, you will learn about a man who, when faced with a problem, helped change our way of life. He did this by making observations, asking questions, and engaging in scientific inquiry.

It was the 1840s—a time before scientists had discovered disease-causing organisms. A young Hungarian doctor, Ignaz Semmelweis (figure 1.12), worked in a hospital in Vienna, Austria. As part of his studies, he dissected cadavers (performed autopsies) in one part of the hospital. He also worked in the same hospital delivering babies in the division I ward.

▲ **Figure 1.12 Ignaz Semmelweis (1818–1865).** Semmelweis used the process of inquiry to solve a lethal problem in a Vienna hospital.

Results of Semmelweis's studies revealed that 13 percent of the women giving birth in the division I ward were dying of a disease called "childbed fever" (known scientifically as puerperal fever). Only about 2 percent of the women in the other division of the hospital were dying of childbed fever. The divisions were right next to each other, and pregnant women were cared for similarly in all ways except one: in division I, physicians and their students delivered the babies; in the other division, midwives and their students delivered the babies.

Semmelweis began to investigate. He noticed that when the hospital experienced a violent epidemic of childbed fever, no such epidemic was seen elsewhere in the city of Vienna. He observed that the death rate in home deliveries was much lower than at the hospital in which he worked. He noticed that even homeless mothers too poor to go to the hospital did not contract the fever even after delivering babies themselves in back alleys.

Semmelweis continued his inquiry. Two major correlations came to the surface. First, if the birth was especially traumatic, the mother had a greater chance of contracting childbed fever. Second, closing down division I always stopped the deaths caused by childbed fever.

Chapter 1 Investigations by Design 29

Answers to Step 2, SE page 31

2a. Using what they have learned, students should describe that the cadaver particles might have been bacteria or other microorganisms that were on the cadavers. When the doctors examined the cadavers, they picked up the disease-causing bacteria on their hands. The doctors did not wash their hands after examining the cadavers, so the microorganisms were still there. When the doctors treated the women giving birth, they transmitted the bacteria to them. The bacteria that caused the disease began replicating and infected the women. The women then died from the disease. (Childbed fever is actually caused by a virus, but transmission from sick or dead people to healthy individuals is the same.)

2b. Student answers to Step 2b may vary when identifying the different parts to the process of inquiry using the chart. Students should identify some or most of the processes of inquiry from the chart. This account of Semmelweis's discovery incorporates virtually every piece of the chart. Look for reasoning and examples from the story to support the different aspects of the process of inquiry in the students' answers. If students simply list the aspects of the chart without any correlation from the story, have the students redo their work and give a more complete answer.

Answers to Reflect and Connect, SE page 31

1a. Answers will vary here, but students may suggest that Semmelweis may not have communicated his explanation well. This is not discussed in the story. This is an important part of the process. You may want to take the time here to discuss how the scientific community today communicates its findings. Use this information to guide your discussion.

The scientific community looks for a sound scientific investigation in others' research. It makes sure that the results can be replicated by conducting the same investigations and looking for similar results. It makes sure that the explanations are supported with solid evidence. It reviews the design of the investigations and looks for appropriate controls, techniques and tools, and analysis.

When a scientist wants to publish his or her research, the research is first reviewed by a panel of other scientists critiquing the work. Scientists call this peer review. Your students will have the opportunity several times this year to participate in peer reviews. After the research is published, the entire scientific community can look critically at another researcher's work.

1b. Again, answers will vary, but students may consider that when a discovery is made that is very new and different, it may take time for experts to change their way of thinking. Semmelweis's discovery was a very new idea, one that went against the scientific thinking of the time. Scientists likely wanted to test his theory and repeat the experiment to verify that his conclusions were sound.

1c. Students may mention Galileo and his teachings that the Sun was the center of the universe (Copernican model) and against the model of Aristotle and

Observations Leading to Discoveries, continued

Semmelweis continued to seek the cause of the high death rates from childbed fever. One day, Semmelweis's former professor of forensic pathology, a man he admired greatly, sliced his finger with a scalpel as he performed an autopsy in division I of the hospital. A few days later, the man was dead. He had become severely ill of sepsis (blood poisoning) and showed symptoms that were very similar to those seen in women with childbed fever. Devastated by his former professor's death, Semmelweis resolved to work harder to understand and prevent childbed fever.

Semmelweis hypothesized that the cause of his professor's sepsis was the same as that of childbed fever. He proposed that the source was "cadaver particles." Semmelweis thought that the attending physicians in division I transmitted these particles from cadavers to mothers during childbirth.

People could not see cadaver particles, but they could smell them. Semmelweis thought that when the invisible particles from a cadaver came in contact with an exposed surface on a patient, such as a wound, the particles were transmitted and caused the disease.

Semmelweis instituted a strict hand-washing policy (figure 1.13) for those physicians and medical students who worked in division I. Before attending patients, all medical personnel were required to wash their hands with chlorinated limewater until their skin was slippery and the smell of the cadaver was gone. Some found this practice a great inconvenience. In the first year of this policy, however, death rates dropped from about 18 percent to about 1 percent in division I. Moreover, not a single woman died from childbed fever between March and August 1848 in Semmelweis's division. Semmelweis felt he had evidence to support his idea that cadaver particles were responsible for the deaths in division I.

The connection Semmelweis made, that medical personnel were passing infection from their hands to mothers, was an incredible discovery. He made an observation, asked questions, and discovered a pattern. Observing patterns and asking questions are the guiding elements of much of science, historically and today.

Semmelweis lectured publicly in 1850 about his results and wrote a book about his discoveries in 1861. However, the medical community did not accept Semmelweis's discoveries. In fact, people criticized him both personally and professionally. It was not until 1865 that Joseph Lister (the namesake for Listerine) continued in the vein of Semmelweis's work and introduced

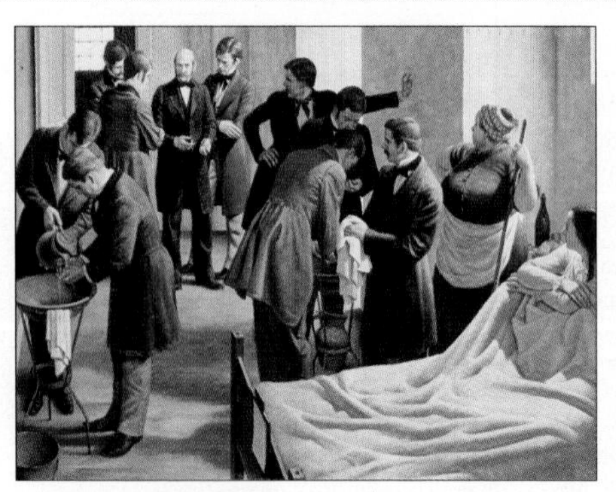

▲ **Figure 1.13 Semmelweis's hospital.** Semmelweis instituted a strict hand-washing policy to stop the spread of "cadaver particles." How did Semmelweis use the process of inquiry to solve a problem?

30

Ptolemy that postulated that Earth was the center of the universe. Galileo was banished from the Church for his radical views. It was hundreds of years before scientists accepted the fact that Earth was not the center of the universe. Students might also mention evolution. Like the Copernican model was, evolution is often seen as contrary to religious beliefs and not accepted by many. Other examples include many of Albert Einstein's theories. Many of his theories could not be tested at the time and were not widely accepted until the technology was developed to test and prove his ideas.

2. Students should understand and explain that the way scientists go about answering a question might not be in a linear, step-by-step manner. In fact, science is conducted to help answer a question. To answer a question, scientists might need to back up and redesign an investigation, gather more data from other scientists' work, or ask a new question that they then attempt to answer. Students should realize that there are not discrete "right steps" to follow to practice inquiry, but instead an iterative process that helps them answer their question.

Answers to Step 2 are on TE page 30.
Answers to Reflect and Connect are on TE pages 30–31.

the use of antiseptics to kill germs and reduce infection and disease. Lister said, "Without Semmelweis, my achievements would be nothing." It is now well known that hand washing is important as a way to reduce the transmission of disease. It is so important, in fact, that the Centers for Disease Control have released this statement: "Hand-washing is the single most important means of preventing the spread of infection."

Today, hand washing is part of American culture. You probably have seen signs posted in restaurant and retail restrooms stating, "Employees must wash their hands before returning to work." Schools also have programs that teach students about hand washing. There are even monitors above sinks in hospital intensive-care units to promote hand washing. The convenience of indoor plumbing, energy to heat water, special soaps, and health awareness makes hand washing part of our everyday regime. Semmelweis's work left a legacy of health and hygiene that has improved our way of life today.

SCI LINKS NSTA
Topic: antiseptics
Go to: www.scilinks.org
Code: 2Inquiry31

2. Consider what you have learned about the process of science as inquiry. Follow Steps 2a–b to explain to members of the scientific community in the 1840s what was happening in division I of the hospital.
   a. Summarize the reading as part of your explanation.
   b. Use the handout *Process of Inquiry* in your explanation. Describe the steps that Semmelweis used to solve his problem. You may use diagrams in your explanations.

Reflect and Connect

Answer the following questions on your own in your science notebook.

1. Initially, the medical community did not accept Semmelweis's discovery. Think about this as you answer Questions 1a–c.
   a. Propose an improvement to Semmelweis's process of inquiry that might have made his discoveries more readily accepted.

   Use the *Process of Inquiry* handout as your guide.

   b. Assume that Semmelweis followed the process of inquiry. Why do you think the medical profession was so reluctant to accept his ideas?
   c. Think of other examples in science where a new discovery was made and the scientific community did not immediately accept the new information. Or think of a discovery that took time to prove and demonstrate that the suggestion was correct. Record at least 1 example in your science notebook.
2. Describe why the process of scientific inquiry is not linear.

ELABORATE

Valid or Deceptive?

Activity Overview

In *Valid or Deceptive?*, students will review a list of claims made by "scientists" and form questions that will inform them about the validity of the claim. They work through the thought process that critical consumers of knowledge should use and develop questions that are important to ask. They then will answer these questions in a way that they would expect a scientist to answer them if the claim was based on solid science.

Before You Teach

Background Information

To develop a scientifically literate society, educators want students to ask questions, think critically about scientific claims that are made in newspapers and on the news, and determine the accuracy of those claims. Scientific claims and informational articles are in newspapers, magazines, and on the Web every day. Understanding and behaving in terms of "Do not always believe what you read" is something that we have been struggling with as a society.

Having a scientifically literate society improves the lives of people in areas such as voting, health, and human impact on the environment. Your students will undoubtedly face legislation that deals with environmental, health, or other scientific issues. They will be the voters who approve or defeat these legislative issues. Their understanding of the process of inquiry will make them a more informed citizenry.

Unfortunately, most (or all) articles in lay journals are slanted. Some people try to get the results they want by manipulating their investigations. Students should learn that the results are only valid if the researcher conducted the investigation properly. They should be able to identify a proper investigation that is controlled and tests for only one variable. When this is not possible (for example, when working with humans or animals as test subjects), students should see that good scientists conduct numerous trials. These trials provide more data on which to base conclusions.

Students should recognize the importance of communicating the results of an investigation and peer review from the scientific community. Claims made without review cannot be considered valid until they have been thoroughly reviewed.

Materials

For the entire class

magazines, newspapers, tabloids, access to the Web

For each student

1 copy of copymaster 1.2, *Process of Inquiry*

Advance Preparation

Obtain copies of tabloid magazine articles that make interesting claims. Cut out specific articles so that students are not distracted by unrelated stories. Also bring in newspapers and magazines that might have science-related articles (local newspaper science section, *Time*, *Newsweek*).

As You Teach

Outcomes and Indicators of Success

By the end of this activity, students should

1. be able to apply their knowledge of the characteristics of a scientific investigation to critique and analyze other investigations.

   They will demonstrate their ability by

   - analyzing headlines that state scientific claims made by a researcher,
   - developing questions focused on the researcher's investigation, and
   - developing answers to those questions that would validate the researcher's claim.

2. be able to recognize and analyze alternative explanations.

   They will demonstrate their ability by

   - analyzing the validity of claims in an article and
   - using scientific criteria to develop logical questions and explanations for scientific claims in an article.

Strategies

Getting Started

Ask the class if it has ever read headlines that make outrageous claims. These articles often appear in tabloid magazines found at checkout stands in supermarkets. Ask students to share a few examples of what types of claims they have seen. Ask why they think the authors can make such claims.

Process and Procedure

Ask students to read the opening paragraph of the activity *Valid or Deceptive?* Make sure students have

a copy of copymaster 1.2, *Process of Inquiry* from the previous activity. Ask students to imagine that they are reporters and instruct them to work through Steps 1 and 2 on their own. Circulate around the room, asking students to share the questions they are developing. Guide them to base their questions on what they have learned about the process of scientific inquiry, specifically on designing an investigation.

In Step 3, read the 5 headlines from Step 1 and ask for a show of hands to see who chose each headline. Instruct students to get into groups with the other students who chose the same headline. Ask students to complete Step 4 with their group.

ELABORATE

Valid or Deceptive?

In the last several activities, you thought carefully about how to design investigations that will answer the scientific questions you have posed. Your understanding of the important criteria for scientific design is expanding. In *Valid or Deceptive?*, you will have an opportunity to extend your understanding by evaluating some claims made by scientists.

Have you ever read a headline that makes claims that sound too absurd to be true, like those shown in figure 1.14? You might wonder if these claims are real. Often, the writer of these articles or whoever is being interviewed makes the claim based on "scientific evidence." But how did the researcher gather evidence? Did the researcher conduct his investigation in a scientifically sound manner? Are the results of the investigation valid? You will work individually as you complete this activity, so think carefully.

▲ **Figure 1.14 Headlines in the news.** Did the researcher making these claims design an investigation that gives valid results?

Materials

For each student

1 *Process of Inquiry* handout

Process and Procedure

There are many decisions you'll make throughout life, as a consumer and as a part of society. Things you learn, information to which you have access, and the community that surrounds you inform your decisions. If you understand the process of scientific inquiry, you can use it to help interpret information you get from many different sources. Read the sidebar *Public Health Careers* to learn more about how a good background in science is important to reporting scientific issues.

1. Read the following headlines:
   - "Skin Patch Cuts Cravings for Sweets"
   - "Sweeteners Cause Memory Loss"
   - "Pizza Protects against Sunburn and Skin Cancer"
   - "Aspirin Cuts Risk of Ovarian Cancer"
   - "Showering Daily Increases Life Span"

Answers to Step 3, SE page 33

3. Students should ask questions that relate to the science of the investigation, for example:
   - "How many subjects did the scientist sample?"
   - "What were the variables?"
   - "What did the scientist keep constant and how?"
   - "What tools or technology did the scientist use?"
   - "How long did the study last?"
   - "How did the scientist gather data? What are the data?"
   - "Were the results published and peer-reviewed?"
   - "What were the limitations of the experimental design?"

Answers to Reflect and Connect, SE pages 33–34

1. Student answers will vary depending on their questions. Look for answers that reflect their understanding of the process of inquiry and the conditions that make the results of an investigation valid. Look for answers that attend to the conditions of a scientific investigation such as control of variables, consistent methods, and all data reported in the report.

Answers to Reflect and Connect are on TE pages 33–34.

2. Imagine you are a reporter assigned to interview the researcher who posted one of the claims in Step 1. It is your goal as a reporter to provide information to other citizens so that they can make informed decisions. As you think about your interview, complete Steps 2a–d.
   a. Review the *Process of Inquiry* handout and Steps 2b–d before you begin.
   b. Develop at least 10 questions that you would ask the researcher making the claim in the headline. Record these questions in your science notebook.
   c. At least 3 of your questions should focus on the "design investigation" stage of the *Process of Inquiry* handout. Address the other stages on the handout with your remaining questions.
   d. When developing your questions, consider the criteria you used when you designed the investigation in the activity *Small Problem?* Be sure that your questions help you determine the following:
      - There is evidence that supports the claim.
      - All the information is presented. Nothing seems to be ignored or deleted from the data.
      - The data are reliable and appropriate.
      - The research is reasonable and the investigation is fair.
      - The researcher or group of researchers is credible and reliable.
3. Get together with other students in your class who chose the same headline. Share your questions. Are they similar?
4. Compile a list of the 10 best questions from the discussion in Step 3 and record them in your science notebook.

Reflect and Connect

Work individually and answer the following questions in your science notebook.

1. Use what you've learned in this chapter to write answers to the 10 best questions you recorded in your science notebook. Imagine that you are the researcher. Keep in mind the characteristics of a scientific investigation and how this type of investigation resulted in the claim the researcher made.

Base your answers on your understanding about the process of scientific inquiry and designing scientific investigations. For example, the question you developed might be for the researcher who claimed that showering daily increases life span. Suppose your question was, "How many people were involved in the study?" The answer could be, "One thousand people were involved in the study over the past 20 years." This addresses a large sample size.

NOTES:

NOTES:

2. Student reviews will vary depending on the article they choose. Look for a demonstration of students' understanding of investigational design and the process of inquiry. The answers here will parallel the answers they gave in Question 1. Use these 2 questions to assess your students' understanding of inquiry and give them feedback before they begin the evaluate activity.

2. Find a science-related article in your local newspaper, a tabloid, or a magazine. Use the article and perform the tasks in Questions 2a–c.
   a. Critically review the article.
   b. Describe whether the article presents a scientific and valid argument.
   c. Do you believe the article? Why or why not?

SIDEBAR

Public Health Careers

How has public health influenced the areas you see in this collage?

When you wake up in the morning, you may hear the radio announcer tell you that it is a clear day. The public health department is around to monitor air quality and the pollution level. It also develops programs to address air quality.

Next, you step into the shower. It is good to know that public health employees monitor the quality of the water you use for your shower and especially the water you drink. Did you know that one of the top 10 great achievements in public health began in 1945 when fluoride was added to drinking water in the United States? This simple act safely and inexpensively benefits both children and adults. Fluoridation prevents tooth decay in both children and adults as well as reduces tooth loss in adults. You get a fluoride treatment on your teeth every time you drink water from a tap that is monitored by public health employees.

As you get in the car to ride to school, you buckle your seat belt to keep you safe en route. Public health efforts have been successful in changing personal behavior in vehicles. These include widespread use

EVALUATE

Killing Germs? Digging Deeper

Activity Overview

In this chapter, students have learned about the process of inquiry, especially the design of investigations. They also learned about the ubiquity of bacteria in the explore-explain activity, *Small Problem?* In *Killing Germs? Digging Deeper*, students demonstrate their understanding of the process of inquiry as they investigate antibacterial products. Students will work with a team to design, conduct, and communicate the results of their investigation.

Before You Teach

Background Information

Much of the background information you need is contained in the previous activities. Keep in mind that the purpose of this activity is to assess your students' understanding of the process of scientific inquiry and investigation design. It is not an assessment on their understanding of microbes or antibacterial products.

Superbugs, or drug-resistant bacteria, are a real threat to hospitals and patients. These bacteria are examples of evolution or natural selection at work. When drugs are used to kill bacteria, some bacteria may survive the drug treatment. These bacteria live and reproduce, passing on the genetic information that makes them drug resistant. You can see the problems doctors and hospitals face in dealing with these bacteria. In Corpus Christi, Texas, doctors at a children's hospital saw fewer than 10 cases a year of community-acquired resistant staph infections (a superbug) in the 1990s. In 2003, they saw 459 cases, with 90 percent of them in healthy children. Have your students read the sidebar *Antibiotics* in the student book to learn how to help decrease the number of bacteria that become resistant.

Materials

For each team of 3 students

3 pairs of safety goggles
3 pairs of safety gloves
30% bleach solution
access to a variety of antibacterial products (students might bring from home)
access to laboratory materials for investigations
materials for visual presentations (such as poster paper, scissors, glue, markers, computer)
sticky notes (3 different colors, e.g., white, blue, yellow)
3 copies of copymaster 1.1, *Scientific Investigation Report*
3 copies of copymaster 1.3, *Scoring Rubric for Killing Germs? Digging Deeper*

Advance Preparation

Arrange to have students work in the same groups of 3 that they worked in during the activity *Small Problem?*

Prepare petri dishes as you did for the investigation *Small Problem?* (Most student teams will investigate bacteria and antibacterial products using techniques similar to those they used in the earlier investigations.)

Have additional materials for the investigations available for students such as

- latex gloves
- 37°C incubator
- petri dishes
- petri dishes with nutrient agar
- test tubes
- sterile swabs

of seat belts, child safety restraints, and motorcycle helmet use. On your ride to school, you pick up breakfast from your favorite fast-food chain. You see a sign posted that indicates the restaurant was rewarded 95 out of a possible 100 points by local public health inspectors, so you know the food is prepared safely.

Public health is important to many facets of our lives. We see the work of public health officials in regulations protecting us, from unsafe food preparation to smoke-free environments, to the safe water that we drink every day.

Because public health is involved in the safety of so many different parts of our lives, many career opportunities are available. These career choices range from research scientists to nurses to journalists. Have you ever thought of being a journalist working in the area of public health?

Can you work under very tight deadlines? Can you write well? Do you think you would enjoy "chasing a story," which involves some basic research as well as tracking down and interviewing the experts? If so, you may want to consider a career as a health communications journalist.

George Strait (no, not the country-and-western singer!) is an award-winning health and science reporter. His undergraduate degree in science helped in his understanding of the scientific process and method and how to interpret data from scientific studies. This is exactly what you are learning in this chapter.

In 1984, George Strait was named the chief medical reporter for *World News Tonight*. At that time, there were no other specialized medical reporters on any television network. Strait appeared regularly on ABC's *World News Tonight* and *Nightline*. During that time, he received broadcast journalism's highest award, the Alfred I. duPont Award, two times. He was presented the awards for his groundbreaking series on women's health and a documentary on AIDS in minority communities.

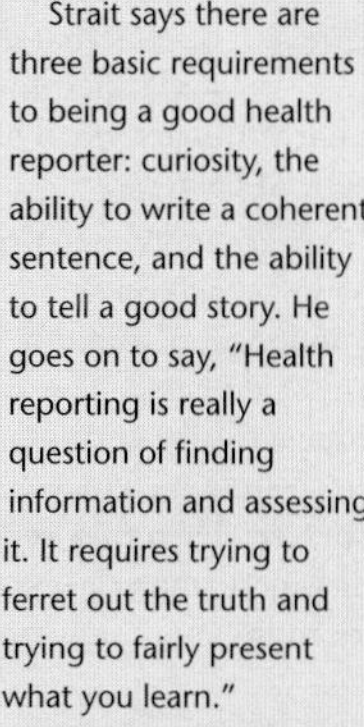
George Strait is a broadcast journalist with a background in science. Can you determine if the science claims from research are valid or deceptive?

Strait says there are three basic requirements to being a good health reporter: curiosity, the ability to write a coherent sentence, and the ability to tell a good story. He goes on to say, "Health reporting is really a question of finding information and assessing it. It requires trying to ferret out the truth and trying to fairly present what you learn."

Can you look at a scientific report and tell if the data are valid? Do you know the right questions to ask a scientist so that you can decide if her claims are believable? If so, you are on your way to being a good health and science journalist.

SCI LINKS NSTA
Topic: public health careers
Go to: www.scilinks.org
Code: 2Inquiry35

- selected antibacterial or disinfectant products
- source of bacteria
- filter paper
- water
- scissors
- permanent markers

Students should design their investigations before getting any visible clues for ideas, so do not put out all the materials beforehand. If your students have trouble getting started, try setting materials out on the table. They will then know in advance which materials they can use.

Student investigations might use bacteria. You can purchase nonpathogenic bacteria or use bacteria from a person (on hands or scraped from the mouth) or from the environment (pond water or other source). Do not allow students to use the contaminated dishes from the *Small Problem?* activity.

Prepare a poster like the one in figure T1.7 for students to post their critiques of each team's investigation.

Cautions

Students should wear safety gloves and goggles during their investigations. All materials that have come into contact with bacteria should be disposed of properly. Soak materials in 30% bleach solution, drain, and throw in the regular trash. Have students wash their hands after the investigation. Wipe work surfaces with a 10% bleach solution before and after the investigation.

Triclosan, the chemical ingredient in most antibacterial products, is not known to be dangerous. However, unwanted trace by-products are a concern because of possible toxicity. The presence or absence of by-products depends on the type and the purity of the materials used to synthesize triclosan. By the time products reach the market, most by-products have been eliminated.

Once students have collected bacteria, swabbed their dishes, and taped them shut, they should not reopen the petri dishes.

As You Teach

Outcomes and Indicators of Success

By the end of this activity, students should

1. demonstrate their understanding of the process of scientific inquiry.

   They will demonstrate their understanding by

   - developing a scientifically testable question focused on antibacterial products,
   - researching background information for an investigation,
   - gathering the information and materials they need to design and conduct the investigation,
   - documenting information relevant to the investigation,
   - conducting the investigation,
   - analyzing the results of the investigation,
   - providing an explanation based on evidence from the investigation, and
   - communicating their results.

2. demonstrate their ability to design a scientific investigation.

   They will demonstrate their ability by introducing parameters in their design, including

   - a clearly stated question and rationale,
   - a hypothesis,
   - variables and controls,
   - process and procedures including data collection,
   - safety precautions, and
   - results and analysis.

EVALUATE

Killing Germs? Digging Deeper

As you discovered in the investigation *Small Problem?*, bacteria and other microorganisms are everywhere. Some of these bacteria cause disease. Scientists have made great strides in developing products that kill bacteria (figure 1.15). The death rate due to infection has decreased as the use of antibiotics increased. People now know about good hygiene and the importance of sterilizing medical supplies. All these seem like great advances in medical science. But are they? Are there problems that could arise from using antibacterial products?

Figure 1.15 Antibacterial products. These products are used to get rid of unwanted bacteria. Is there some danger in this?

Not all bacteria are harmful. For example, *E. coli* bacteria live in the intestinal tract of humans and other organisms. These bacteria aid digestion by helping break down foods. We use another bacteria, *Streptococcus thermophilus*, to culture yogurt. However, a specific strain of *E. coli* found in contaminated beef and other products is often lethal and group A *Streptococcus* causes strep throat and other illnesses. Antibacterial products cannot single out harmful bacteria. These products kill both the harmful and the beneficial bacteria.

Our attempts to get rid of unwanted bacteria are creating a new situation. Bacteria that are sensitive to antibiotics die. But some bacteria are no longer affected by antibiotics. They are *resistant* to antibiotics. Many scientists believe our overuse of antibiotics and antibacterial products causes antibiotic-resistant strains of bacteria to evolve. This means random changes in these bacteria's genetic material allow them to survive. Then they reproduce and pass on their resistance through their genetic material. (See figure 1.16.) Read the sidebar *Antibiotics* to learn more about how antibiotics work and how people misuse them.

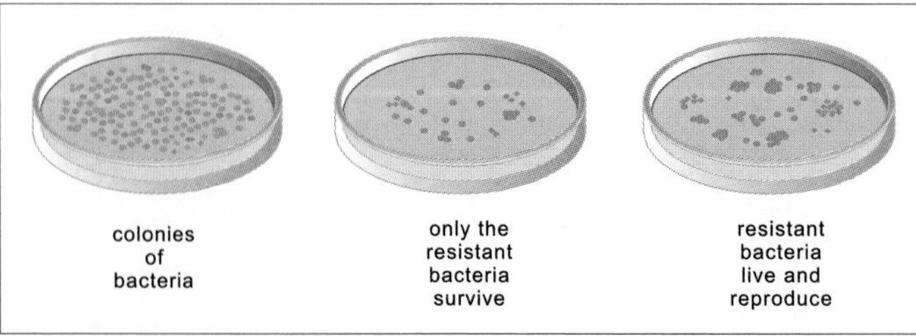

Figure 1.16 Antibiotic-resistant bacteria. The bacteria that are sensitive to antibiotics die out. What happens to the bacteria that survive?

Team	Strength	Improvement	Question

▲ **Figure T1.7 Table for sticky notes.** Make a table similar to this for students to post their sticky notes for the critiques of each team's investigation.

3. demonstrate skills needed to conduct a scientific investigation.

   They will demonstrate their ability by

   - working effectively in groups to perform the steps in the investigational design,
   - using scientific inquiry to obtain evidence,
   - taking appropriate safety precautions during the investigation,
   - collecting data,
   - communicating with others about the data,
   - discussing questions that arise during the investigation and thinking of possible ways to change the investigation to answer those new questions, and
   - developing explanations based on evidence.

4. communicate a scientific argument.

   They will demonstrate their ability by

   - presenting their investigation to their classmates and
   - defending their explanation by showing evidence based on the results of the investigation.

Strategies

Getting Started

Remind students of the investigation in *Small Problem?* Review the major criteria of a scientific investigation. Suggest students refer back to their science notebooks for the lists that they generated in previous activities. The criteria include the following:

- The investigation addresses the question being tested.
- It tests only one factor (variable).
- It keeps all other variables as constant as possible.
- It has controls.
- It contains multiple trials and samples.
- It is clear, concise, and well planned.
- It incorporates an organized method for recording data.
- It uses appropriate tools, technology, and mathematics.
- It is safe.
- It potentially provides evidence that will support (or refute) an explanation or lead to new questions.

Cautions

Students should wear safety gloves and goggles during their investigations. All materials that have come into contact with bacteria should be disposed of properly. Soak materials in 30% bleach solution, drain, and throw in the regular trash.

Is our everyday use of antibacterial products contributing to the evolution of resistant bacteria? Advertisers claim we need these products to stop the spread of disease. Do these products do what advertisers claim?

In *Killing Germs? Digging Deeper*, you will have an opportunity to demonstrate your understanding of scientific inquiry. You do this by designing and conducting a scientific investigation using antibacterial products. What you have learned throughout this chapter will help you decide what questions to ask, what tools to use, how to design a scientific investigation, how to organize your data, and how to answer your question using evidence. You will then present your findings to the rest of the class. You will work with a team for this activity.

Materials

For each team of 3 students

materials as needed to conduct an investigation focusing on antibacterial products, such as the following:

- access to an incubator or warm location
- 3 pairs of latex gloves
- 3 pairs of safety goggles
- petri dishes
- petri dishes with nutrient agar
- test tubes
- sterile swabs
- selected antibacterial or disinfectant products
- source of bacteria
- filter paper
- water
- scissors
- permanent markers

10% bleach solution

30% bleach solution

sticky notes (3 different colors)

3 *Scientific Investigation Report* handouts

3 *Killing Germs? Digging Deeper Scoring Rubric* handouts

Have students wash their hands after the investigation. Wipe work surfaces with a 10% bleach solution before and after the investigation.

Triclosan, the chemical ingredient in most antibacterial products, is not known to be dangerous. However, unwanted trace by-products are a concern because of possible toxicity. The presence or absence of by-products depends on the type and the purity of the materials used to synthesize triclosan. By the time products reach the market, most by-products have been eliminated.

Once students have collected bacteria, swabbed their dishes, and taped them shut, they should not reopen the petri dishes.

Process and Procedure

Ask student teams to follow Steps 1–4. Circulate among teams and listen as students discuss the names of antibacterial products and the claims the manufacturers of these products make. Monitor each team as it is developing its questions. Check that each team poses a scientifically testable question to answer. Distribute

copymaster 1.3, *Scoring Rubric for Killing Germs? Digging Deeper*, and encourage students to look it over so that they know how you will grade them.

Students will design an investigation on their own. Step 5 provides questions that students should answer as they formulate their designs. In Step 6, check each team's design. Be sure teams have written the answers to questions from Step 5 that can be answered at this time.

As you review each team's design, think about the materials required for its investigation. Make sure the materials are available and if they are not, suggest alternative materials or designs. If there are flaws in the design, allow students to discover this in the process of their investigation (as long as it is not a safety concern).

Following are three possible investigations that might be similar to those students design. These investigation ideas are provided as a resource for you; do not use them as protocols for students.

Investigation 1

1. Soak small disks of filter paper (pea size) in the products (1 per product).
2. Mark the bottom of the plate where each disk will be placed with the name of the product.
3. Streak an agar plate with bacteria.
4. Place each disk in its corresponding section on the agar.
5. Close the plate and tape it shut.
6. Turn the plate *upside down* and allow the bacteria to grow. (If you do not have a 37°C incubator, grow the bacteria at room temperature. At lower temperatures, however, the bacteria will take longer to grow.)
7. Determine which, if any, of the products inhibited bacterial growth (look for zone of inhibition—an area around the disks in which no bacteria grow).

Investigation 2

1. Label the bottom of one agar plate "unwashed hand." Label the bottom of a second agar plate "soap- or product-washed hand."
2. Streak an agar plate with an unwashed hand.
3. Wash hands in regular soap or other products.
4. Streak another plate with the soap- or product-washed hand.
5. Tape the plates shut.
6. Turn the plates *upside down* and allow the bacteria to grow.
7. Compare plates (unwashed versus washed with soap or product).

 **Cautions**

Wear safety goggles and gloves during your investigations. All materials that have come into contact with bacteria should be disposed of properly. Soak materials in 30% bleach solution, drain, and throw in the regular trash. Wipe down your work area with 10% bleach solution before and after the investigation. Wash your hands after the investigation.

Process and Procedure

Manufacturers have introduced many products to the market recently that they claim "kill germs," such as antibacterial and disinfectant products.

1. With your team, think of as many products as you can that have claims similar to those of the antibacterial products pictured in figure 1.15. Write your list in your science notebook.
2. Identify scientifically testable questions you might ask about the products on your list.

Think of as many questions as you can and record them in your science notebook.

3. Choose 1 question from your list in Step 2 for your team to investigate.

Your team must agree on the question to investigate. Discuss the options and justify why you would choose that particular question. Consider how you would design an investigation to answer that question, what background information you need, and if you have access to the necessary equipment and supplies.

4. Review the handout *Killing Germs? Digging Deeper Scoring Rubric* so that you understand how your teacher will grade your investigation. Discuss any questions you have with your team and your teacher.
5. In your science notebook, answer the following questions:
   a. What is the question you are investigating?
   b. What is your rationale? How will this investigation test your question?
   c. What is your hypothesis?
   d. What is the design of your investigation?

Record this as a step-by-step procedure. As a team, determine 1 design for your investigation. If you have several ideas, discuss the pros and cons of each design and make sure each member of your team agrees. Justify why you made each decision in your design. Include a list of materials you will use and safety precautions you will take.

Investigation 3

1. Collect pond water that contains microorganisms (check under a microscope).
2. Add 1 product to each container of pond water.
3. Check microbial survival.

Students can read the sidebar *Antibiotics* while they wait for results. Use the sidebar to prompt discussion about the overuse and misuse of antibiotics, which leads to strains of bacteria that are resistant to treatment with antibiotics. If a strain of bacteria is resistant to products that contain antibiotics, does that mean the product does not work anymore? In addition, students can begin working on their presentations and their lab reports.

The students will write an individual lab report in Step 9 based on their investigation. If you are rushed for time, consider assigning this for homework. You may want to use *How To Write a Lab Report* found in the *How To* section at the back of the student and teacher book.

In Step 10, have students prepare a visual presentation of their investigations. They can get started on ideas and preliminary work for this as they are waiting for their bacteria to grow. This is likely to be a poster but can be a slide show, computer presentation, model, or other creative medium. Remind students to review the scoring rubric to help guide them in preparation for their visual presentation.

In Step 11, have students present their investigations. Allow time for the teams to respond to the presentations immediately after each one. Direct teams to post their sticky notes from Step 12 on the poster you prepared. In Step 13, discuss the types of comments the teams made about each presentation. Assess your students on this critique; they should offer good advice and suggestions for others' work as well as their own.

e. What type of data will you collect?
f. How will you organize and analyze your data?
g. What is your explanation (conclusion) and what evidence supports your explanation?
h. What new questions or ideas do you have? Which might you pursue?

6. After you have designed your investigation, show your teacher your procedure for approval.
7. After you have approval from your teacher, conduct your investigation. Record your observations and data in an organized and useful way.
8. Analyze and discuss the results with your teammates. As you discuss your results, answer Questions 8a–d.
   a. How can you explain the results of your investigation?
   b. Did the results help you answer your question?
   c. What conclusion can you reach based on your investigation?
   d. How confident are you that your results answer the question you chose? Explain your answer.

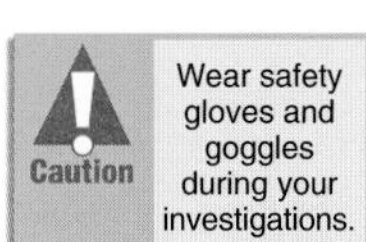

Remember, to answer this question, consider how well you controlled the variables in the investigation. Discuss any sources of error.

9. Write a lab report on your own of your investigation.

Use what you learned about writing a lab report from the explore/explain activity. You may want to review the *Scientific Investigation Report* handout.

10. Prepare a visual presentation of your investigation with your team to share with the class. This could be a poster, a computer presentation, or a slide show. Look at the rubric to guide you.
11. Present your investigation to the class. Your classmates will be looking for good qualities of your investigation, ways to improve your investigation, and questions to ask you.
12. After each group presents, get together with your team for a research critique. Decide on 1 strength of the investigation, 1 way to improve it, and 1 question you have about it. Write the "strength" comment on 1 color of sticky note (designated by your teacher), the "improvement" comment on another color, and the "question" on a third color. Post your notes in the area designated by your teacher.
13. At the conclusion of each presentation, discuss the critique statements as a class. The presenters should answer questions from their classmates and address ways to improve their investigation with their own ideas.

NOTES:

NOTES:

SIDEBAR

Antibiotics

Why is it that sometimes when you feel awful, and you go to the doctor, the doctor does not give you an antibiotic? It could be that you have a virus. Antibiotics do not work on viruses.

Both bacterial and viral infections can make you sick, but bacteria and viruses are very different. Bacteria are single-celled microscopic organisms about 1/100th the size of a human cell, or 1 micrometer long. Bacteria are normally found in our bodies and in our environment, including in plants, animals, soil, and water. Most bacteria are helpful, but some harmful bacteria can cause infections. Common bacterial infections include strep throat, urinary tract infections, and diarrhea that is caused by *Escherichia coli* bacteria. Bacteria also cause diseases, such as tuberculosis and anthrax. See the figure for the three most common shapes of bacteria.

a.

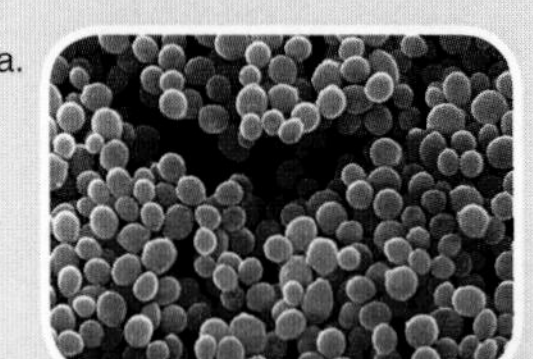

b.

c.

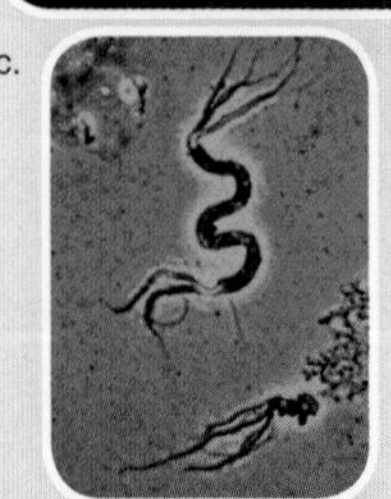

▲ **Bacterial cells.** These are the three most common shapes of bacterial cells. (a) Cocci (spheres) 51,000×; (b) bacilli (rods) 24,000×; and (c) spirochetes (corkscrew) 700×.

A virus is 20–100 times smaller than a bacterium. Viruses consist only of a particle of DNA or RNA surrounded by a protective protein coat, or capsid (see figure on p. 41). Viruses survive only by infecting living cells. Most biologists classify viruses as infectious particles rather than living organisms. Common viral infections are colds, flu (influenza), and mono (mononucleosis). Other examples of viruses include chicken pox, herpes, rabies, Ebola, Asian bird flu, and AIDS.

Antibiotics kill or inhibit the growth of bacteria by interfering with the normal functions of bacteria. Antibiotics do this without harming the host organism (humans or other animals). Each antibiotic affects a unique site within a bacterial cell. Penicillin kills bacteria by attaching to their cell walls and destroying a key part of the wall. Erythromycin attacks the cell components responsible for making proteins. Other similar antibiotics include tetracycline, streptomycin, and gentamicin. Antibiotics do not work on viruses because they work on parts of bacteria that viruses do not have, such as a cell wall.

SciLinks NSTA
Topic: antibiotics
Go to: www.scilinks.org
Code: 2Inquiry40

NOTES:

Viruses only exist within the host cell and do not carry out their own biochemical reactions.

Unfortunately, doctors and patients misuse antibiotics. Doctors sometimes prescribe antibiotics when they are not needed, such as at a patient's request or for a cold (viral infection). Patients may make the mistake of using only part of their antibiotic prescription and saving the remaining doses for later use.

Misuse of antibiotics can lead to the evolution of new strains of bacteria that cannot be killed by currently used antibiotics. These bacteria are called antibiotic-resistant bacteria. Antibiotic resistance occurs when bacterial DNA spontaneously mutate. Out of the millions of bacteria living in your body, one might acquire a mutation that makes it resistant to an antibiotic. If you take an antibiotic, the susceptible bacteria will die, but the resistant bacteria might survive. A resistant bacteria cell will multiply without competition from susceptible bacteria. If the bacteria causing your illness are antibiotic resistant, an antibiotic will not cure you. Antibiotic resistance is a major health care problem.

Antibiotic resistance is inevitable because mutations allow bacteria to evolve. However, people can do things to help decrease the number of bacteria that become resistant. For example, people can reduce the spread of resistant bacteria by washing their hands. Doctors can prescribe antibiotics only when absolutely necessary, and patients can use them appropriately. People also can avoid overusing antibacterial products. By limiting the situations in which antibiotic-resistant bacteria thrive, people can use antibiotics to treat disease-causing bacterial infections successfully.

a.

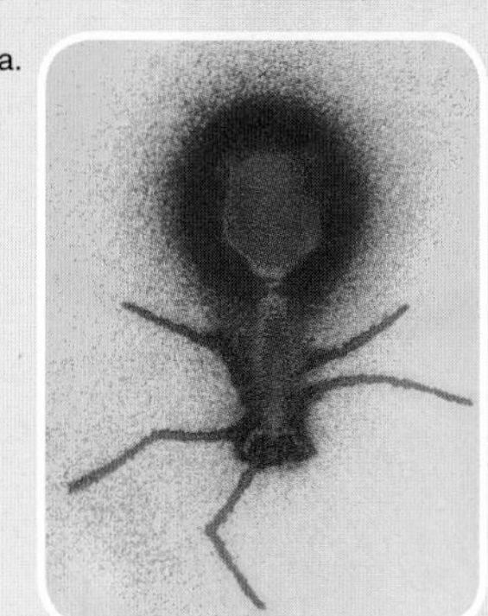

b.

▲ **Structure of a virus.** Viruses are made of DNA or RNA and a protein coat. The electron micrograph (a) shows a virus that infects bacteria magnified 94,500 times. The diagram shown in (b) is of the same type of virus.

Go to: www.scilinks.org
Topic: antibiotic resistance
Code: 2Inquiry41a
Topic: super bugs
Code: 2Inquiry41b

Chapter 1 Investigations by Design 41

UNIT 1

Interactions Are Interesting

Unit Introduction

Unit Overview

When two objects approach each other closely enough, they interact. Often, the interaction leads to change. And change is what scientists study to understand the nature of interactions. That's what makes interactions of all types interesting.

In unit 1, *Interactions Are Interesting*, students study how systems of objects interact by focusing on the changes resulting from interactions. The unit asks students to think about interactions from two viewpoints: (1) large-scale interactions associated with everyday motions such as springs, pendulums, projectiles, and orbits, and (2) small-scale interactions associated with chemical reactions such as acid-base and oxidation-reduction reactions. In both viewpoints, students establish a cause-and-effect connection between forces involved in interactions and the effect of those forces on objects in a system. Throughout the unit, a single question focuses the orchestration of activities: "How does recognizing and evaluating change help us understand interactions in nature?"

The unit begins with an emphasis on force. Specifically, chapter 2, *Collision Course* asks students to think about interactions between macroscopic objects as they collide. Collisions often result in changes (both in motion and physical appearance). Those changes are the result of forces. Thus, students connect change within a system to the forces that brought about that change. They use this unifying principle as they gain understanding of the forces required to produce various common motions (spring, pendulum, projectile, and circular motion) and how forces influence chemical systems (rates of reactions, heat of reactions, acid-base reactions, oxidation-reduction reactions).

Throughout this unit, students look for evidence of change, then link that evidence to the forces causing change. The unit helps students develop an understanding of how one unifying principle, the cause-and-effect link between force and change, explains a myriad of natural phenomena common in everyday life. In this way, we are respecting students by conveying trust in their ability to make sense of what they are learning, as opposed to just memorizing information. Our trust increases students' intrinsic motivation because they begin to view themselves as the primary agent of what they learn, not factors outside their control.

Goals for the Unit

By the end of unit 1, students should understand the following:

- All physical interactions between objects consist of a pair of forces, equal in size and opposite in direction. In these interactions, one force acts on one object and the other force acts on the second object.
- Changes in velocity result from net forces; no net force results in zero or constant velocity (assuming constant mass).
- Many chemical reactions involve the transfer of either electrons or protons.
- Chemical reactions involve changes in energy.
- The laws of conservation allow us to understand complex interactions.
- Investigations are guided by scientific principles and are performed to test ideas and answer questions.
- Mathematical tools and models guide and improve scientific inquiry.

Names of Chapters

Chapter 2: Collision Course

Chapter 3: Collisions—Atomic Style

Chapter 4: Physics Is Moving

Chapter 5: Forces of Attraction

Strategies for the Unit Engage

Use these strategies to get your students thinking about the contents of the unit. Much of what we do as teachers involves motivating students. Research suggests that students who understand *why* they are learning something are more motivated to learn it. Of course, coming up with a classroom full of answers to "Why do we have to learn this?" can be difficult. One method is to link students' everyday experiences (and motivations) to the experiences they are about to study in the lesson.

Unit 1, for example, asks students to learn and understand interactions between objects, both large and small. But why should they want to learn about interactions? Consider using the photograph of the boy presenting a bouquet of balloons as a way to connect students' everyday sense of interaction to interactions in physics and chemistry. Ask students to write in their science notebooks the features of the situation in the photograph that make them think an interaction is taking place. Use the questions posed in the caption to prompt their responses.

Collect as many ideas as possible on the board or on an overhead.

Lead a class discussion toward viewing interactions as any event in which *change* might occur. Then ask the students to anticipate the changes that might happen in this social interaction. When they are done, help them see how studying physical interactions requires the same observation and prediction skills as studying social situations. Thinking about social interactions helps students understand physical interactions. That means that learning about cars colliding, molecules breaking apart, and planets orbiting the Sun is mostly a matter of taking what they already know how to do and applying it to other everyday situations. Connecting prior knowledge and new knowledge actually makes learning new content easier. The notion of making things easier by linking what they already know to what they are about to learn is very motivational and engaging to students.

NOTES:

CHAPTER 2

Collision Course

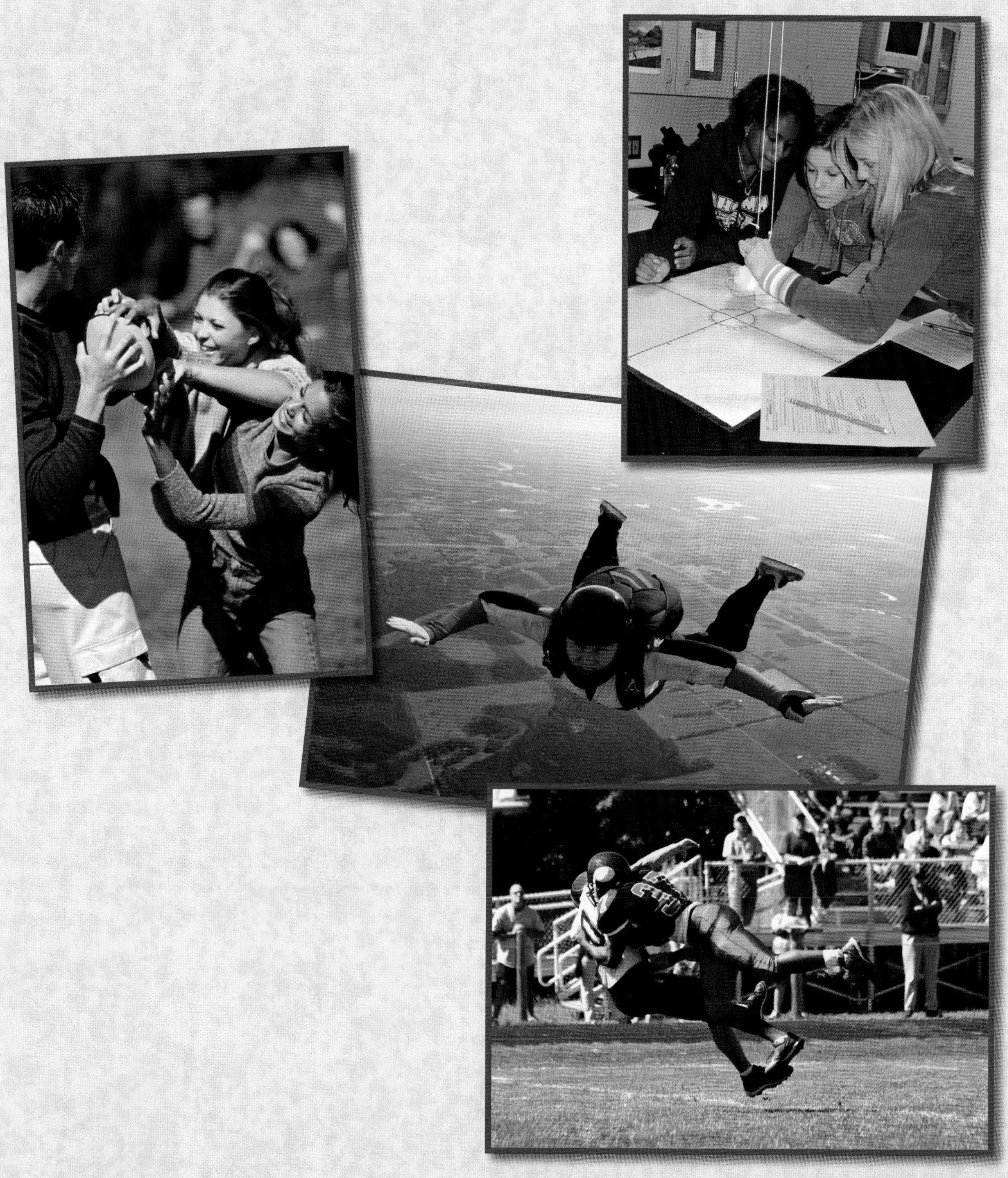

Chapter Overview

In chapter 2, *Collision Course*, students will think about large-scale interactions common in their everyday world and learn to link changes in the system of objects involved in interactions to evidence for forces. Students will observe how objects "bump" into each other, watch for changes, and learn what forces caused those changes. In other words, forces cause change. This chapter focuses on helping students observe and make meaningful connections between observed changes within systems of interacting objects and the forces that caused them. These changes often result in acceleration; however, you will *not* see the term acceleration mentioned in this chapter. Students develop an understanding of the observable changes that result from net forces. The term acceleration is introduced in chapter 4, *Physics Is Moving* after students have had many experiences observing changes in velocity and momentum.

This chapter is the first content chapter of Level 2. In this chapter, several learning strategies will be introduced as well as several tools you and your students can use to be more successful this year. You saw some of these in chapter 1. These tools are located in the How To section in the back of the book. You will find valuable information to promote deeper understandings in your classroom.

Chapter 2 opens with a two-activity study of the most quoted, but least understood law of motion, often called Newton's third law. The version of this law used is, "Forces occur in pairs, equal in size, and opposite in direction, with these forces acting on different objects, no exceptions." Students will use a small ball of clay to prove to themselves that the third law of motion is true regardless of the amount of mass, direction of motion, or frame of reference.

From the beginning of this chapter, students will learn to represent force with arrows for which length and direction have meaning. These arrows are called vectors. Students will use vector representations of forces involved in one-dimensional collisions between tennis balls to develop the idea that force is equal to the time rate of change of momentum. From this idea, students will develop the law of conservation of momentum and then apply this law to two-dimensional collisions. As students study collisions of all types, they will learn that Newton's third law is equivalent to the conservation of momentum. They connect Newton's third law and conservation of momentum as they develop the mathematical relationships that relate the two laws.

After students learn how to identify forces based on observed changes in a system of interacting objects, they will apply their knowledge to two common motions: the brakes in a car slowing it and a falling object reaching terminal velocity. Along the way, they will learn how laws of motion relate a balance of forces to two motion conditions: zero velocity and constant velocity.

Finally, you will assess student understanding by asking them to design an experiment to mimic a car running out of gasoline on top of a hill. Students will use a ball and ramp plus knowledge about forces to graph and understand the motions they observe. In addition, students will analyze a simulated car-crash scene and use their knowledge of conservation of momentum and vectors to determine which driver ran a stop sign and caused the accident.

Goals for the Chapter

By the end of the activities in the chapter, your students should understand

- that all forces occur in pairs, equal in size and opposite in direction. These forces act on two different objects.
- how impulse and change in momentum are related.
- that momentum is conserved.

The chapter organizer uses graphic design principles to help students connect one activity to another. It uses reminders of key concepts, linking questions, and the spatial arrangement of activity titles to foster the sense of a conceptual flow, which connects each activity. Explicitly ask students to locate their position within its flow at the beginning of each activity. This action reinforces the connection among the activities, thus enhancing long-term memory.

Chapter 2 Organizer

COLLISION COURSE

Major Concepts

- **All forces occur in pairs, equal in size but opposite in direction.**
- **Changing velocity indicates net forces.**
- **Momentum is conserved.**
- **Force, velocity, and momentum as well as changes in these qualities behave as vectors.**
- **Force is the rate change of momentum.**

ENGAGE — Forces Make a Lovely Pair ★★

Key Idea: • Interaction forces can be measured directly with a clay ball.

Activity: Students use a clay ball to determine the amount of force in a moving interaction in Part I. In Part II students examine a static interaction of masses in an Atwood's machine.

LINKING QUESTION: How can I determine what variables are important in finding the amount of force in an interaction?

EXPLORE — Controlling Forces ★★★

Key Idea: • The variables that determine the amount of force are change in velocity, mass, and/or time of interaction.

Activity: Students participate in and design investigations to determine what factors influence the amount of force acting on objects.

LINKING QUESTION: In a closed system, how do data from linear collisions support the law of conservation of momentum?

EXPLAIN — In-Line Interactions ★★★

Key Idea: • Both elastic and inelastic collisions exhibit conservation of momentum.

Activity: Students use a tennis ball apparatus to investigate both elastic and inelastic collisions. While doing so, students use their knowledge of action reaction forces to generalize to the law of conservation of momentum.

LINKING QUESTION: Is momentum conserved in two dimensions?

EXPLAIN — Getting Real: Collisions in Two Dimensions ★★

Key Idea: • Momentum is conserved in all collisions.

Activity: Students once again use the tennis ball collision apparatus to apply what they have learned about collisions and momentum in one dimension to collisions in two dimensions.

LINKING QUESTION: What kinds of changes m momentum occcw with and without net forces?

★ = One Class Period ☆ = ½ Class Period *Note:* Based on a 50-minute class period.

ELABORATE With and Without a Net ★★

Key Idea: • Objects in motion tend to stay in motion unless they experience a net force.
Activity: Students use free falling coffee filters to investigate the results of zero and nonzero net forces.

LINKING QUESTION: What happens to the motion of an object when net forces acting on it change?

EVALUATE Forces to Go; Forces to Stop ★★★

Key Idea: • The motion of an object changes depending on changes in the net forces acting on the object.
Activity: Part I of this activity has students design an investigation to mimic a car running out of gas at the top of a hill, rolling down the hill, and coming to a stop at some distance from the bottom of the hill. Students demonstrate their understanding of momentum and forces as they construct a graph of this motion. In part II of the activity, students analyze a car crash scene to determine which car ran a stop sign and caused the collision.

★ = One Class Period ☆ = ½ Class Period *Note:* Based on a 50-minute class period.

Standards Covered by Chapter 2

COLLISION COURSE

STANDARD A: Science as Inquiry. As a result of activities in grades 9–12, all students should develop

abilities necessary to do scientific inquiry

- Identify questions and concepts that guide scientific investigations. Students should formulate a testable hypothesis and demonstrate the logical connections between the scientific concepts guiding a hypothesis and the design of an experiment. They should demonstrate appropriate procedures, a knowledge base, and conceptual understanding of scientific investigations.
- Design and conduct scientific investigations. Designing and conducting a scientific investigation requires introduction to the major concepts in the area being investigated, proper equipment, safety precautions, assistance with methodological problems, recommendations for use of technologies, clarification of ideas that guide the inquiry, and scientific knowledge obtained from sources other than the actual investigation. The investigation may also require student clarification of the question, method, controls, and variables; student organization and display of data; student revision of methods and explanations; and a public presentation of the results with a critical response from peers. Regardless of the scientific investigation performed, students must use evidence, apply logic, and construct an argument for their proposed explanations.
- Use technology and mathematics to improve investigations and communications. A variety of technologies, such as hand tools, measuring instruments, and calculators, should be an integral component of scientific investigations. The use of computers for the collection, analysis, and display of data is also a part of this standard. Mathematics plays an essential role in all aspects of an inquiry. For example, measurement is used for posing questions, formulas are used for developing explanations, and charts and graphs are used for communicating results.
- Formulate and revise scientific explanations and models using logic and evidence. Student inquiries should culminate in formulating an explanation or model. Models should be physical, conceptual, and mathematical. In the process of answering the questions, the students should engage in discussions and arguments

that result in the revision of their explanations. These discussions should be based on scientific knowledge, the use of logic, and evidence from their investigation.

- Recognize and analyze alternative explanations and models. This aspect of the standard emphasizes the critical abilities of analyzing an argument by reviewing current scientific understanding, weighing the evidence, and examining the logic so as to decide which explanations and models are best. In other words, although there may be several plausible explanations, they do not all have equal weight. Students should be able to use scientific criteria to find the preferred explanations.
- Communicate and defend a scientific argument. Students in school science programs should develop the abilities associated with accurate and effective communication. These include writing and following procedures, expressing concepts, reviewing information, summarizing data, using language appropriately, developing diagrams and charts, explaining statistical analysis, speaking clearly and logically, constructing a reasoned argument, and responding appropriately to critical comments.

understandings about scientific inquiry

- Scientists conduct investigations for a wide variety of reasons. For example, they may wish to discover new aspects of the natural world, explain recently observed phenomena, or test the conclusions of prior investigations or the predictions of current theories.
- Mathematics is essential in scientific inquiry. Mathematical tools and models guide and improve the posing of questions, gathering data, constructing explanations and communicating results,
- Scientific explanations must adhere to criteria such as: a proposed explanation must be logically consistent; it must abide by the rules of evidence; it must be open to questions and possible modification; and it must be based on historical and current scientific knowledge.
- Results of scientific inquiry—new knowledge and methods—emerge from different types of investigations and public communication among scientists. In communicating and defending the results of scientific inquiry, arguments must be logical and demonstrate connections between natural phenomena, investigations, and the historical body of scientific knowledge. In addition, the methods and procedures that scientists used to obtain evidence must be clearly reported to enhance opportunities for further investigation.

Standard B: Physical Science. As a result of activities in grades 9–12, all students should develop an understanding of

motions and forces

- Objects change their motion only when a net force is applied. Laws of motion are used to calculate precisely the effects of forces on the motion of objects. The magnitude of the change in motion can be calculated using the relationship $F = ma$, which is independent of the nature of the force. Whenever one object exerts force on another, a force equal in magnitude and opposite in direction is exerted on the first object.
- The electric force is a universal force that exists between any two charged objects. Opposite charges attract while like charges repel. The strength of the force is proportional to the charges, and, as with gravitation, inversely proportional to the square of the distance between them.

Prerequisite Knowledge

This program assumes a full school year of science and mathematics instruction before the beginning of this level. Students should know how to solve simple, one-variable algebraic equations and be comfortable manipulating a variable equation to solve for any one of the variables. In addition, students should know how to inspect a simple two-variable data set and generate an appropriate *xy* plot to represent the data.

Requirements of prerequisite science knowledge are minimal in this chapter. More important is students' ability to observe and analyze everyday interactions. Thus, the skill of making careful and accurate observations, then linking those observations to meaningful results through analysis is crucial. The actual number of new facts, vocabulary words, or skills to learn in this chapter is small.

Commonly Held Misconceptions

The best predictor of what students learn as a result of being in your class is what they know *before* coming to your class. Students come to your classroom with a set of ideas about the way the physical universe operates. They are convinced, at some level, that their explanations are sufficient because their working explanations help them negotiate everyday life successfully. When we make careful observations and conduct thoughtful analysis, however, we find that many of these explanations are contrary to the way nature actually behaves.

What can you do about the entrenched set of misconceptions common to almost all high school students? First, be aware of the most common misconceptions. Review the following list and actively observe when students exhibit these ways of thinking. Second, address the misconception explicitly with a variety of counterexamples, many of which are part of this chapter. Third, orchestrate how students generate new explanations based on careful observations and laws of nature. From there, help students understand that most new situations are actually applications or further examples of the laws they learned.

- Students have many misconceptions regarding Newton's third law.

Many students can quote a grade-school definition of Newton's third law of motion and can apply it to static situations. For example, when discussing the action-reaction forces involved between a stationary chair and the floor, they correctly say, "The force of the floor on the chair (up) is equal to and opposite in direction to the force of the chair on the floor (down)." But when they push the chair across the floor horizontally at a *constant velocity*, they say the pushing force is greater than the force of friction between the chair and floor. This is not true. There is *no* situation, moving or static, in which there is an imbalance of forces between action-reaction pairs. *All* forces occur in pairs, equal in size, opposite in direction, and acting on two different objects.

- Many students believe that the force applied is always in the direction of the final velocity.

Many students think that the force, which caused a motion, acted in the same direction as the final motion. For example, students might think a car turning sharply from east to west must have experienced a force in the west direction. That is, a force toward the west was the agent of the change of motion. Actually, the force is in the same direction as the change in velocity (or momentum), not the final velocity.

- Many students use velocity and momentum interchangeably. They see an object moving fast and say its momentum is greater than an object whose mass is large, but whose velocity is low.

Change in velocity and change in momentum are in the same directions, but are not the same magnitude, nor do they represent the same feature of an object's motion.

ENGAGE

Forces Make a Lovely Pair

Activity Overview

The activity *Forces Make a Lovely Pair* proceeds in three phases: prediction, realization, and learning. In the prediction phase, you will ask students to access their prior knowledge about the action-reaction forces during a collision between unequal masses. Do not be surprised if a large percentage of your students predict that the larger mass exerts a larger force during the collision. As you know, telling them they are incorrect at this point will be largely ineffective. Students learn best when they realize their mistakes based on clear, unambiguous evidence from nature. That is what the realization phase provides them.

In the realization phase, students will place a small ball of clay between two colliding "objects" (finger and thumb) to infer about the forces during collisions. The clay deforms an *equal amount* regardless of the circumstances. Students will realize that no matter the mass or velocity, each object exerts equal forces on the other but in opposite directions. In the learning phase, you will ask students to transfer this realization to new situations.

Before You Teach

Background Information

If you have ever stood still on the floor, stepped on the gas pedal after a green light, or blown up a balloon, you know these action-reaction forces. You (and your students) do not need any mathematical formulas, specialized equipment, or memorized definitions to understand and apply Newton's third law of motion. The background for this activity is common life experience.

There is no such thing as an isolated force. Forces always occur in pairs, equal in size and opposite in direction, each force acting on one of the objects. There are no exceptions. Ever.

But many students will offer articulate explanations suggesting exceptions to this law of the universe—Newton's third law. Commonly, students might explain how they cause a chair to move across the room by saying, "When I first push on the chair, it pushes back on me with an equal but opposite force. But to get it moving, I have to push with a greater force on it than the chair can push back on me or else the chair would never move."

This student response might sound reasonable (although it is not) if the person and the chair forces were the only forces involved in this interaction. But other forces are in play and one must consider on which objects the forces act. Both the chair and the person interact with the floor, through frictional forces. These frictional forces can be either static friction (when the chair is not moving) or sliding friction (when the chair is moving). If the chair is not moving, the static frictional force only acts when there is an opposing force, and it matches the applied force until the maximum value of the static frictional force is exceeded. When the chair is moving, the sliding frictional force is a horizontal force in a direction opposite the motion of the chair. So the chair "pushes" on the floor (horizontally), and the floor "pushes" back (in the form of a horizontal friction force). These interaction forces are independent of the person-chair interaction. For the chair to move, the person must push with a force at least equal to the sliding frictional force. If the person pushes with a greater force than the sliding frictional force, the chair will accelerate (figure T2.1).

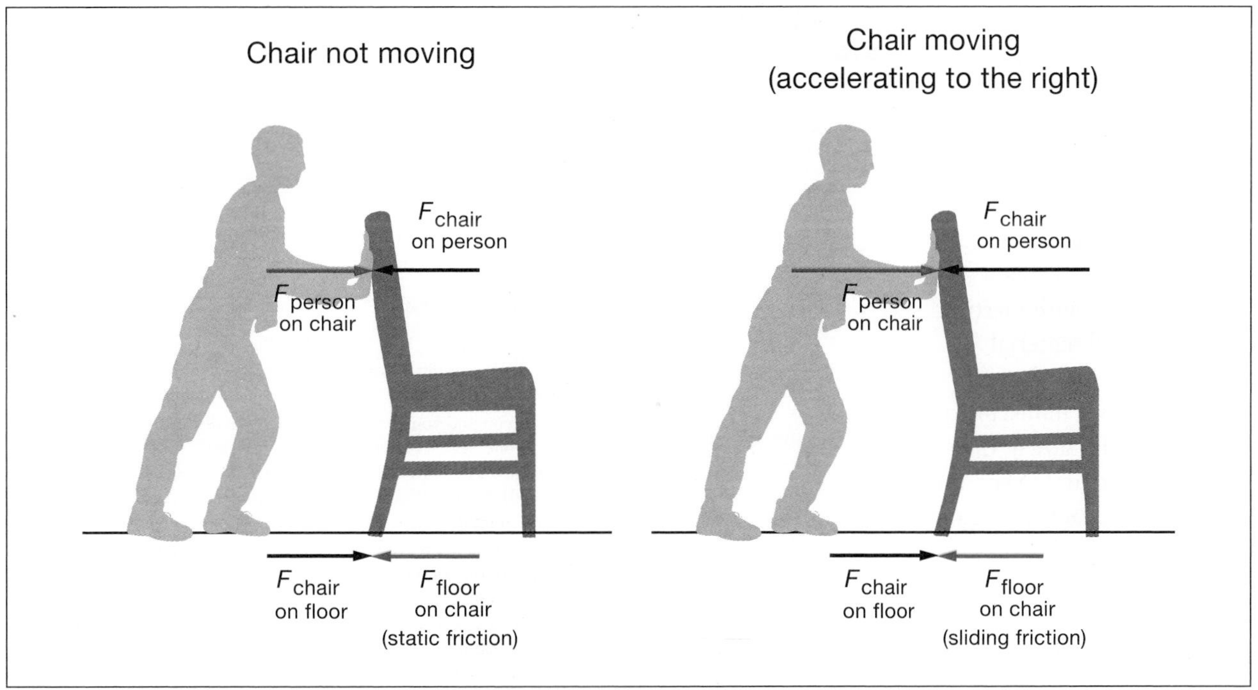

▲ **Figure T2.1 Forces on a chair.** The motion of the chair depends only on the forces that act on the chair. The chair will not move until the force of the person on the chair exceeds the force of the floor on the chair. Then the chair will accelerate to the right. The forces on the chair (shown with red arrows) are the only forces that determine the motion of the chair according to Newton's second law, $F_{net} = ma$.

In summary, Newton's third law says that the horizontal forces are:

- the force of the chair on the floor,
- the force of the floor on the chair (this force is equal and opposite to the force of the chair on the floor),
- the force of the person on the chair, and
- the force of the chair on the person (this force is equal and opposite to the force of the person on the chair).

Then Newton's second law enters the picture. It is only the forces on the chair that affect the chair's motion. Those forces are

- the force of the floor on the chair, and
- the force of the person on the chair.

The motion of the chair depends on the forces on the chair, according to $F_{net} = ma$. Newton's second law forces are a subset of Newton's third law forces.

The push-back force is nature's way of telling you that there is an object with mass in front of you. This property of matter to resist changes in motion is called inertial mass. Thus, the push-back force of any object is an indication of how much mass is there. When objects are difficult to move (even when in frictionless environments such as space), we say those objects have large inertial mass. Likewise, when objects with large inertial mass are moving and their course is difficult to change, we say that a large force is needed to effect a change in motion.

Newton's so-called third law of motion has a lot to do with inertial mass, a property of all material objects, from planets to protons. Whether gargantuan or miniscule or speeding up or slowing down, only pairs of forces exist, equal in size and opposite in direction, each acting on a different object.

Materials—Part I

For each team of 2 students

1 small ball of nontoxic modeling clay

Materials—Part II

For the teacher

2 ring stands (base and upright rod)
2 90° clamps
1 crossing rod (metal rod from extra ring stand will work)
2 pulleys
1 newton scale with easy-to-read numbering
1 small spring scale (calibrated in newtons)
2 identical, hooked masses about 1 kg each
string
colored pens or pencils

Advance Preparation

Be sure to read the teacher material at the beginning of this chapter. It is essential that you understand the big picture for this chapter and see where your students are headed. It would also benefit you to read the entire chapter, both teacher and student materials.

Set out small samples of modeling clay for Part I, preferably in different sections of the room to lower congestion. Be vigilant about picking up clay balls in the carpet or placed in secret places around the room. The size of the ball is very important to the success of the activity. See figure 2.3 in the student book for an example.

Look ahead to figure 2.5 in the student book and assemble the Atwood's machine using ring stands, pulleys, identical weights, string, and a spring scale with large display. Don't attach the weights until you are ready to do the demonstration or students will know what the scale

ENGAGE

Forces Make a Lovely Pair

Collisions result in forces. Just think about the last time you stubbed your toe on a big rock or kicked a soccer ball (figure 2.2). Was the rock or soccer ball the only object to apply a force? How do you know? What's the evidence?

Interactions that produce change involve forces in some way. Scientists study change to determine how large those forces are. That way they can determine the effect of forces on objects. If a large truck and a small car collide, for example, what would the forces of the interactions be? How would those forces affect each vehicle? With the right answers, you could design a safer interior for vehicles. And a safer vehicle interior is a good application of what you learn in school.

In *Forces Make a Lovely Pair*, you and your partner will track, think about, and reach conclusions regarding two interactions, one a collision and the other a kind of tug-of-war. With a scientific mind-set, you will focus on analyzing the changes you observe and sharing what you learn so that others can understand. In this way, you will lay the groundwork for all the interactions you will study in this unit.

▲ **Figure 2.2 Collisions are interactions that result in forces.** Has your big toe ever collided with a soccer ball? Did your toe apply a force to the ball? Did the ball apply a force to your toe?

Part I: Moving Interactions

Materials

For each team of 2 students

1 small ball of modeling clay

Process and Procedure

Look at the two vehicles in figure 2.1. Each vehicle is about to experience a force. Will the forces be the same? Imagine what changes those forces would make.

In Part I, you and your partner will use a small ball of clay to model the forces of interaction between a large truck and a small car. But first, you will draw from previous experiences to answer a question about the forces *during* the collision. Then you will determine if your answer makes sense in light of the changes you observe.

1. Draw a sketch representing the 2 vehicles in figure 2.1 and indicate the following variables in the sketch.
   a. Relative mass of the vehicles
   b. Relative velocity of the vehicles immediately before the collision
   c. Forces acting on each vehicle during the collision

will read. Try to pace Part I of the activity to end with just enough time to pose the question about the scale reading when the identical weights are allowed to dangle from the scale. Students can answer the question and supply a justification in their science notebooks for homework.

Educational Technologies

Some students keep an electronic notebook, which comes equipped with drawing programs. Allow students to use this technology for recording their impressions and observations, especially the sketches of the clay ball before and after the collision. Students may also want to use a digital camera to record their results.

Cautions

Use nontoxic modeling clay.

As You Teach

Outcomes and Indicators of Success

By the end of this activity, students should

1. be able to model the forces of interaction between colliding objects with a clay ball.

   They will demonstrate their ability by

   - placing a ball of clay between a variety of colliding objects,
   - observing symmetrical deformation in the clay ball regardless of collision conditions, and
   - connecting the amount of clay deformation to the amount of force.

2. be able to formulate and revise their explanations using logic and evidence from an investigation.

   They will demonstrate their ability by

   - predicting the forces acting on two different masses during a collision,
   - justifying their predictions,
   - revising their predictions and thinking based on evidence from the activity, and
   - developing new questions from their activity.

3. be able to transfer their knowledge of reaction pairs to other collisions.

   They will demonstrate their knowledge by answering *Stop and Think* questions regarding collisions other than car collisions.

You only have to represent the *relative* sizes of these variables. In other words, simply show in some way which mass is larger or smaller. Or you may decide that some variables are equal. You do not necessarily have to use numbers.

2. Record your answer to the following question under your sketch:

   "During the collision, which force is greater, the force of the truck on the car or the force of the car on the truck?"

Draw from your previous experiences and use the words *force*, *velocity*, *time*, *momentum*, and *mass* as you state reasons for your answer. Underline these words when they appear in your sentences to help your teacher assess what you are thinking now. Remember, in science you get to change your mind based on new evidence and further thinking about a scientific question.

3. Meet with a partner and share your answer using Steps 3a–f as a guide.
   a. Review silently and *think* about the connection between what you sketched and what you wrote. Look for the most important ideas you represented.
   b. *Share* your sketch with your partner and discuss each feature of it, including labels.
   c. Read your answer aloud as you wrote it.
   d. Ask for *advice* on how to make either the sketch or the answer better.
   e. *Revise* your work if you think your partner's understanding is better than yours.
   f. Switch roles and listen carefully to your partner.

This is called the think-share-advise-revise (TSAR) strategy. You will use this throughout the year in every science subject area.

4. Participate in a class discussion and record the thoughts of other teams.
5. Model the forces of interaction between a truck and a car with a clay ball by conducting Steps 5a–d.
   a. Roll a small piece of modeling clay into a sphere about the size of a small pea (figure 2.3).
   b. Pretend your thumb is the truck and your finger is the small car shown in figure 2.1.
   c. Hold the clay ball directly between your "truck" and "car" and model the brief moment of collision by squeezing quickly, just once.
   d. Remove the clay ball carefully from your collision to preserve the changes in the shape of the sphere.

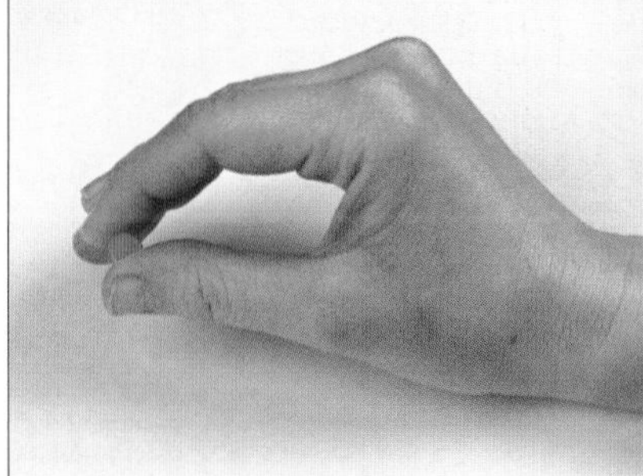

▲ **Figure 2.3**
Clay ball. The size of the clay ball is important to the success of your activity. It should only be the size of a small pea. If the clay squishes out beyond your fingers or curls on the edges, it is too big.

Strategies

Getting Started

Link the idea of interactions between two students, as shown in the photograph of a boy presenting balloons to a girl in the unit 1 opening photograph, to the interactions involved with stubbing your toe or two vehicles colliding. Each requires at least two objects. Each requires objects approaching each other. But most important, each interaction results in some sort of change. What you want students to focus on is the cause of that change.

Use question prompts to help them focus on the forces that cause the changes evident in car collisions or stubbed toes. For example, you can ask, "What do you think will happen when the truck hits the small car?" Follow with, "What evidence supports what you said?" Often, students say the small car is more dented. When you ask them why, they say it's because of a larger force (which is incorrect). Then ask them if the amount of denting is an indication of the amount of force. Once they say yes, you are ready to introduce the clay ball.

Tell them the clay ball records the amount of "denting force" from collisions. Demonstrate how the clay material is easy to squish. Explain that the amount of deformation on the clay is an indication of the amount of force. Then let them proceed through the activity as written. Be careful to monitor the size of the clay ball. If the ball is too large, it curls, masking the effect you want students to observe. The ball of clay should be no larger than a small green pea, preferably smaller. Walk around the room and inspect each ball before you allow students to model the truck–small car collision. See figure 2.3 in the student book as an example of the correct size of the clay ball.

Allow plenty of time for small-group and class debriefing regarding students' predictions about forces. Be certain to elicit justifications for each response but do not indicate the correctness (or incorrectness) of any answer. After students have shared their prior knowledge, tell them that you will not give them the answer. Instead, the laws of nature will provide them with evidence of the answer.

Reminder of Possible Misconceptions

Most students think the large truck exerts the largest force. But this is a violation of Newton's third law. The misconception stems from a common tendency of humans to assign primary agency to the object that is most active or is largest. This misconception is very difficult to dislodge. Only after patient, persistent, and explicit instruction do students change their views about reaction pairs.

Cautions

Use nontoxic modeling clay.

Process and Procedure

Part I: Moving Interactions

Materials

For each team of 2 students

1 small ball of nontoxic modeling clay

colored pens or pencils

In Step 1, students sketch the vehicles and reveal their preconceptions about the collision. Use this sketch to assess students' initial thinking about what is important in collisions. Look for indications of the relative size of any of the variables mentioned in Steps 1a–c. For example, students who draw velocity arrows showing only direction, but not magnitude, will require more time when learning how to represent vector quantities. Mostly focus on how students represent force. Look to see what percentage of the class shows the truck with a longer force arrow (vector). If the percent is near 100 percent, you have a very normal set of teenagers. The majority of students as well as adults will think that the force of the truck on the car is larger than the force of the car on the truck, when in fact the forces are equal. The activity will help them through this misconception.

Students represent what they are thinking in question form in Step 2. Use this question as a language-rich alternative representation of Step 1. In particular, look for evidence that students are reading the hints by looking for descriptions of previous experiences in their writing. In this way, you monitor how much students engage their prior knowledge and link that prior knowledge to new experiences in this activity. Emphasize the incorporation of the words listed in the hint (*force*, *velocity*, *time*, *momentum*, and *mass*). Don't expect students to use the words correctly at this stage but monitor their developing understanding through the chapter.

6. Represent your thinking about changes to the clay ball by performing Steps 6a–e.
   a. Make a before-and-after sketch of the clay ball similar to figure 2.4.

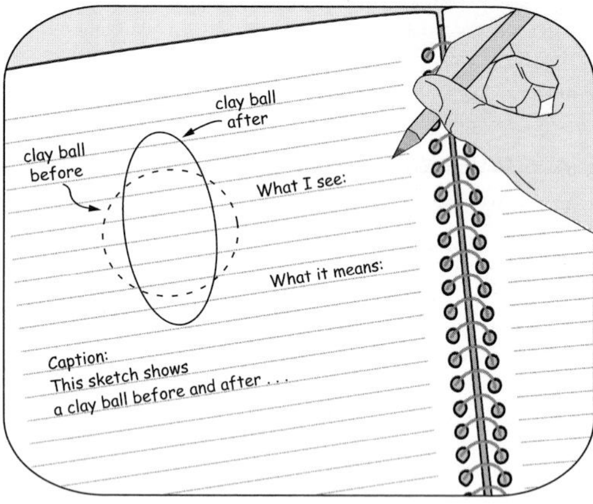

Figure 2.4 Before-and-after sketches help you make sense of change. How you organize your observations affects your ability to make sense of the changes you record. What role do labels play in your effort to understand?

   b. Write the phrase "What I see" near the change you observe on one side of your before-and-after sketch. Then describe the squishing that the clay ball experienced.
   c. Write the phrase "What it means" just under the previous phrase. Then write what the squishing suggests about force.

These 2 phrases together are called *highlight comments* since they represent the essence, or the highlights, of your experience. You used highlight comments in Level 1 of this program to help you better understand graphs.

   d. Write additional highlight comments for the other side of your clay ball.
   e. Use the TSAR strategy with your sketches and highlight comments.

7. Write a caption under your sketch.

Captions tell the reader what is important about the sketch or figure. They convey the essential features of the figure by putting much of the highlight comments into sentence form. You will include captions on many entries in your science notebook throughout the year.

8. How do your highlight comments and caption compare with the answer you gave to the question in Step 2? Write a statement about how your thinking has changed or remained the same.

In Step 3, students use the think-share-advise-revise (TSAR) strategy with a partner to analyze their answers. More information about using this strategy can be found in the *How To* section at the back of the book.

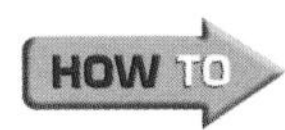

Lead your class in a brief discussion for Step 4. Use this discussion to broaden the TSAR strategy, making it more public. This gives you an opportunity to model the technique, thus reinforcing what you want, and gives students practice verbalizing ideas for a larger audience, an effective step to increase student confidence.

Students will use the clay ball to detect forces of interaction in Step 5. Remind students that models help scientists study difficult interactions with minimum cost and inconvenience. Models function somewhat like analogies in language class since features of the actual interaction map to features of the model. Thus, a model is a way to represent an interaction. You can study it and understand what causes any changes that you observe without experiencing the actual phenomenon because it might be too small, too large, too far away, or, in this case, happen too quickly.

Do not let the ball of clay exceed about 5 millimeters (mm) in diameter. Larger diameters will "squish" out beyond the fingertips, leading to erroneous conclusions. If you are not confident that your students will make the correct size clay ball, then use a larger clay ball with hardbound books of different masses to represent the truck and car. The use of books is foolproof in that they provide flat, hard surfaces compared with fingertips. Don't let students press and hold the clay; they should give the clay ball a very quick squeeze, then release. You might have to snap your fingers to represent the amount of time during a typical crash. Caution students not to stretch the clay's shape as they remove it from fingers or books.

Answers to Stop & Think are on TE pages 56–57.

9. What questions do you have about pairs of forces that result from colliding objects? List at least 2 questions.

Stop & THINK

PART I

Read each question carefully and think about your experiences before you answer. Then record your answers in your science notebook in a way that helps your teacher find, make sense of, and give you feedback on those answers. You may want to use the TSAR strategy with classmates *before* you hand in your answers.

1. In each of the following cases, determine which (if either) of the 2 objects exerts a larger force during the interaction.
   - **a.** A very fast car hits a slow-moving truck from behind (not head on).
   - **b.** A very fast car hits a stationary (static) truck.
   - **c.** A truck pushes a car up a hill.
   - **d.** A car pushes a truck on a flat road.
   - **e.** A grasshopper hits the windshield of a fast-moving truck.
   - **f.** A baseball bat hits a baseball for a home run.
   - **g.** A north magnet gets close to another north magnet.
2. Use arrows to represent the forces at the time of collision by completing Questions 2a–b.

   Using arrows to represent forces is a common practice in science. An arrow can be any length and it points in a particular direction. The length of the arrow should represent the amount of force (longer arrow = more force). The arrowhead should point in the direction the force is acting.
   - **a.** Sketch your finger and thumb squeezing together (without the clay ball).
   - **b.** Use labeled arrows to indicate the force of your finger on your thumb and the force of your thumb on your finger.
   - **c.** Write a caption for your sketch.
3. Think of the forces involved in Question 2 as you answer 3a–b.
   - **a.** How many forces are involved in the situation described in Question 2a? Describe them in words.
   - **b.** How many objects did these forces act upon?

In Steps 6 and 7, students make before-and-after sketches complete with highlight comments and captions. This is another learning strategy that will be used throughout the text. A detailed description of using highlight comments and captions with sketches and graphs is included in the *How To* section at the back of the book.

Recommend that students hold the "squished" ball vertically, but not in a way to deform it further. A suggested before-and-after sketch is shown in figure T2.2. This figure includes the results of Steps 6a–d.

In Step 8, students compare their highlight comments after using the clay ball, to their predictions of forces in Step 2. Many students undoubtedly answered the questions in Step 2 with the misconception that the car would exert a smaller force on the truck than the truck would on the car. After using the clay ball model, student thinking should begin to change and they should indicate their new ideas in this step. Consider having students record these changes in their thinking or understanding in a different-colored pen or pencil.

Step 9 asks students to form new questions about what they have learned. Depending on your time in class, use these questions as a springboard to test several different situations with the clay ball. Students may think the forces were equal and opposite for their thumb and finger

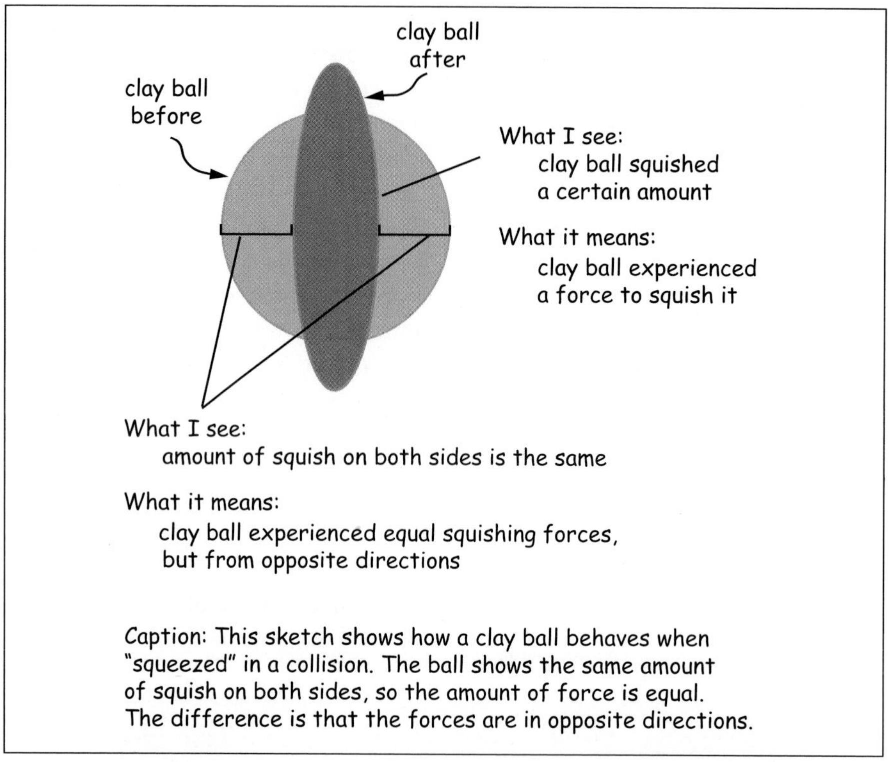

clay ball before

clay ball after

What I see:
clay ball squished
a certain amount

What it means:
clay ball experienced
a force to squish it

What I see:
amount of squish on both sides is the same

What it means:
clay ball experienced equal squishing forces,
but from opposite directions

Caption: This sketch shows how a clay ball behaves when "squeezed" in a collision. The ball shows the same amount of squish on both sides, so the amount of force is equal. The difference is that the forces are in opposite directions.

▶ **Figure T2.2 Before-and-after sketches of students' clay ball.** Student sketches should be similar to this. Since this is the first time students are asked to make highlight comments and captions, take extra time to emphasize the importance of these features.

because they thought they were pushing with the same force with both fingers. Encourage them to test different situations such as a person pushing hard with a large book and another remaining stationary with a small book. Students should see that in *every* situation the clay ball shows that the force acting on one object is equal and opposite to the force acting on the other object.

Answers to Stop and Think—Part I, SE page 55

1. In every case (Questions 1a–g), the forces during collision are equal in size and opposite in direction. There are no exceptions. You might ask students to imagine placing a clay ball between objects in each case. The ball will squish the same amount on both sides just as in the truck-car collision.
2. This question asks students to draw arrows to represent forces. This is the introduction to drawing vectors. Emphasize the elegance of using arrows to represent forces—the length indicates the amount, or magnitude, and the arrowhead points in the direction that the force acts. Students only represent relative magnitudes in this question. Be sure they understand what the

Part II: Static Interactions

Materials

For each team of 2 students

colored pens or pencils

Process and Procedure

Interactions result in forces. You have learned a core concept in science: *these forces* always *occur in pairs, equal in size and opposite in direction,* and *they act on two different objects.* But what if objects are not moving? Do stationary objects interact?

In Part II, you and your partner will reflect on your previous experiences with nonmoving objects and think about the forces of interaction between them. Then you will decide whether you see similarities and differences between the way moving and static objects interact.

First, you will watch an interesting interaction. Your teacher will attach two identical masses to opposite sides of a spring scale so that the masses dangle over pulleys. A sample demonstration apparatus is shown in figure 2.5.

1. Observe a 1-kilogram (kg) mass hanging freely from a spring scale. Sketch or describe this setup and record the weight (in newtons, or N) of the 1-kg mass.
2. Use your experiences from Part I to answer the question, "What will the spring scale read in figure 2.5 when the 1-kg masses are allowed to dangle freely?"

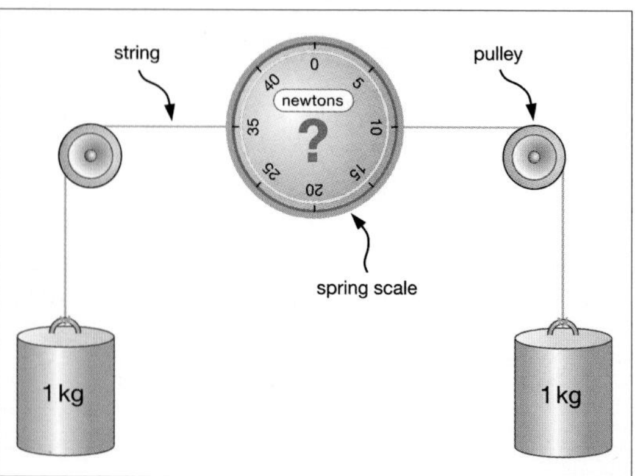

▶ **Figure 2.5 Atwood's machine.** Are forces involved in this apparatus? Will the forces cause the scale dial to move? Will the masses move as well?

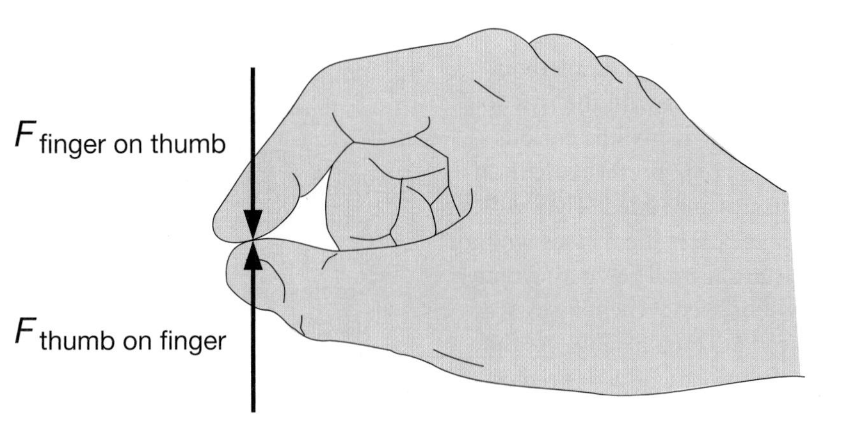

Caption: This sketch shows the forces involved when squeezing your thumb and finger. The forces are equal in size as represented by the same lengths of arrows and opposite in direction.

▲ **Figure T2.3 Forces on thumb and finger.** Your students' sketches should be similar to this.

Answers to Reflect and Connect are on TE pages 58–58b.

3. Observe the demonstration apparatus, sometimes called an Atwood's machine, as your teacher allows the masses to dangle. Record what you see.
4. Modify your answer to the question in Step 2 in light of your observations and class discussion. Use a different-colored pen or pencil to record your changes.
5. Consider other scenarios for the apparatus (different masses, uneven placement of the masses, and so on) and follow Steps 5a–d. Then perform Step 5e.
   a. With your team, make a list of these situations in the form of questions.
   b. Choose 1 scenario and add it to the class list that your teacher has started.
   c. Predict what you think will happen in each of the scenarios on the class list. Record your predictions in your science notebook.
   d. Observe as your teacher demonstrates.
   e. Modify your comments in your science notebook based on your observations and class discussion.

Reflect and Connect

Read each question carefully and think about how your experiences in this activity might lead you to an answer.

1. Copy the table in figure 2.6 into your science notebook. Then complete it to show the similarities and differences between Part I and Part II.

Concept important to interactions	Similarities between Part I and Part II	Differences between Part I and Part II
Velocity		
Mass		
Force		
Time		
Add other concepts based on your current thinking		

▲ **Figure 2.6 Similarities and differences between Part I and Part II.** Use this table or a similar organizer to complete *Reflect and Connect* Question 1.

term relative means, as the term will be used repeatedly in the text. Student sketches should be similar to figure T2.3. If students need more practice, ask them to sketch the forces acting while they are standing on a bathroom scale.

3. There are two forces acting on two different objects. These forces are the force of the thumb on the finger and the force of the finger on the thumb.

Process and Procedure

Part II: Static Interactions

Materials

For the teacher

2 ring stands (base and upright rod)
2 90° clamps
1 crossing rod (metal rod from extra ring stand will work)
2 pulleys
1 newton scale with easy-to-read numbering
1 small spring scale (calibrated in newtons)
2 identical masses about 1 kg each
string
colored pens or pencils

For Step 1, hang one of the 1-kilogram (kg) masses from a spring scale and walk around the room for students to see the reading on the spring scale. They should see that it is about 10 ne wtons (N). Students are to sketch and record this in their science notebooks.

If you have assembled the Atwood's machine ahead of time, you can use the last few minutes of Part I of this activity to conduct this demonstration. Figure 2.5 in the student book shows what a simple Atwood's machine looks like. You will need volunteers to hold the masses in place while you position the scale.

Remember to stage the question *ahead* of your demonstration in Step 3. Assume the masses are identical 1-kg masses (corresponding to a force [or weight] of approximately 10 N). An effective alternative strategy is to place the question from Step 2 on the board along with the following multiple-choice answers:

"What will the spring scale read in figure 2.5 when the 1-kg masses are allowed to dangle freely?"

a. 0 N
b. about 10 N
c. about 20 N
d. about 5 N

Ask students to include one of the answers in their predictions. Then, before you drop the weights, survey the class for its multiple-choice selection. Write the popularity of each choice on the board. Choices a and c will probably be most popular. Ask for classroom feedback on the rationale for those answers. If students hesitate, place a few example force sketches on the board that you observed from walking around the room during the prediction phase of your demonstration. Point to the examples and ask students to respond.

Then say, "Well, let's let the laws of nature decide." Allow the weights to dangle and students to see that the scale reads very close to 10 N. Give them time to record what they see and attempt an explanation. But when you sense a little frustration building, offer a reminder about pairs of forces. You could replace the string attached to one end of the scale with your finger and ask, "With what force am I pulling with my finger?" Many students will connect the scale reading with the correct answer, about 10 N. When you switch to the other string and ask the same question, even more students will answer correctly (about 10 N). Now you can point out that both forces are the same size, but in opposite directions. This effect is universal, for all interactions, for all time, in all places. This knowledge is important for students to understand. If students show signs of confusion, ask them to mentally replace the scale with the clay ball. Ask them to verbalize what they think will happen. Many will say the ball will stretch. Then ask them if the amount of stretch on both sides will be the same. After a short discussion, most will understand that even with pulling-apart forces, the same laws of nature apply.

Students are asked once again to modify their comments and ideas based on new observations and experiences (Step 4).

In Step 5, students think about different scenarios with the Atwood's machine. Students will be curious about the reading on the scale if different masses are added. They will see that in some cases the masses will not remain stationary. They may wonder what will happen if the masses are not placed at equal heights. As time permits, allow students to predict what they think will happen in these situations, record their predictions, and then test them with the Atwood's machine. Always have students record any changes in their thinking or their observations from their predictions to what actually occurred.

Answers to Reflect and Connect, SE pages 57–58

1. Student answers should be similar to figure T2.4.
2. Questions 2 and 3 get students thinking of different situations in which forces are involved. Forces can occur between objects that are not touching, such as those described in Questions 2 and 3. Should you decide to do the alternative activity, *Electrostatic Fanatic*, you can refer back to figures T2.5 and T2.6 for the student answers to these 2 questions.

   Student answers should be similar to figure T2.5.

Answers to Reflect and Connect Questions 2–4 are on pages 58–58b.

2. Imagine another demonstration apparatus similar to the one in Part II. In this apparatus, however, the weights are equal-strength north magnets and the table is a big south magnet (figure 2.7). Generate a labeled sketch of this new apparatus with highlight comments and a caption.

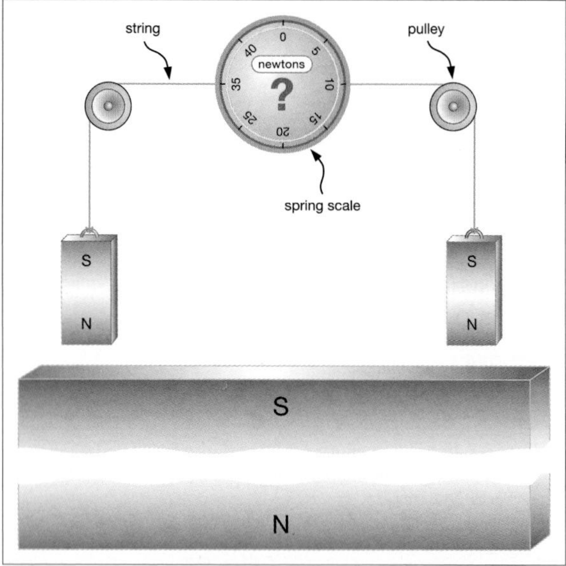

Figure 2.7 Setup with magnets. What will the scale read with the setup pictured here?

3. Repeat Question 2, except replace the weights with electrically charged objects (both with an equal positive charge) and a negatively charged table.
4. Consider the forces you described in Questions 2 and 3 and the forces you considered in Parts I and II of this activity. How are they similar? How are they different? Use a table or a Venn diagram to organize your answers.

See *How to Use and Create Venn Diagrams* in the How To section at the back of the book.

Concept important to interactions	Similarities between Part I and Part II	Differences between Part I and Part II
Velocity	There are no similarities.	Part I objects move, and Part II objects do not move.
Mass	Each object has mass in both parts.	Part I vehicle masses can be different, but Part II masses are equal.
Force	Both Parts I and II have equal-sized forces acting in opposite directions.	Part I forces are much larger than Part II forces.
Time	The interaction has a start and an end.	Part I time is short compared with Part II time.
Add other concepts based on your current thinking.	*Allow students freedom to include a variety of concepts, which you can use as information for planning.*	Part II is static (objects are stationary), Part I is dynamic (objects are moving).

▲ **Figure T2.4 Answer table for *Reflect and Connect* Question 1.** Student answers should be similar to these. This completed table compares the aspects of Part I and Part II.

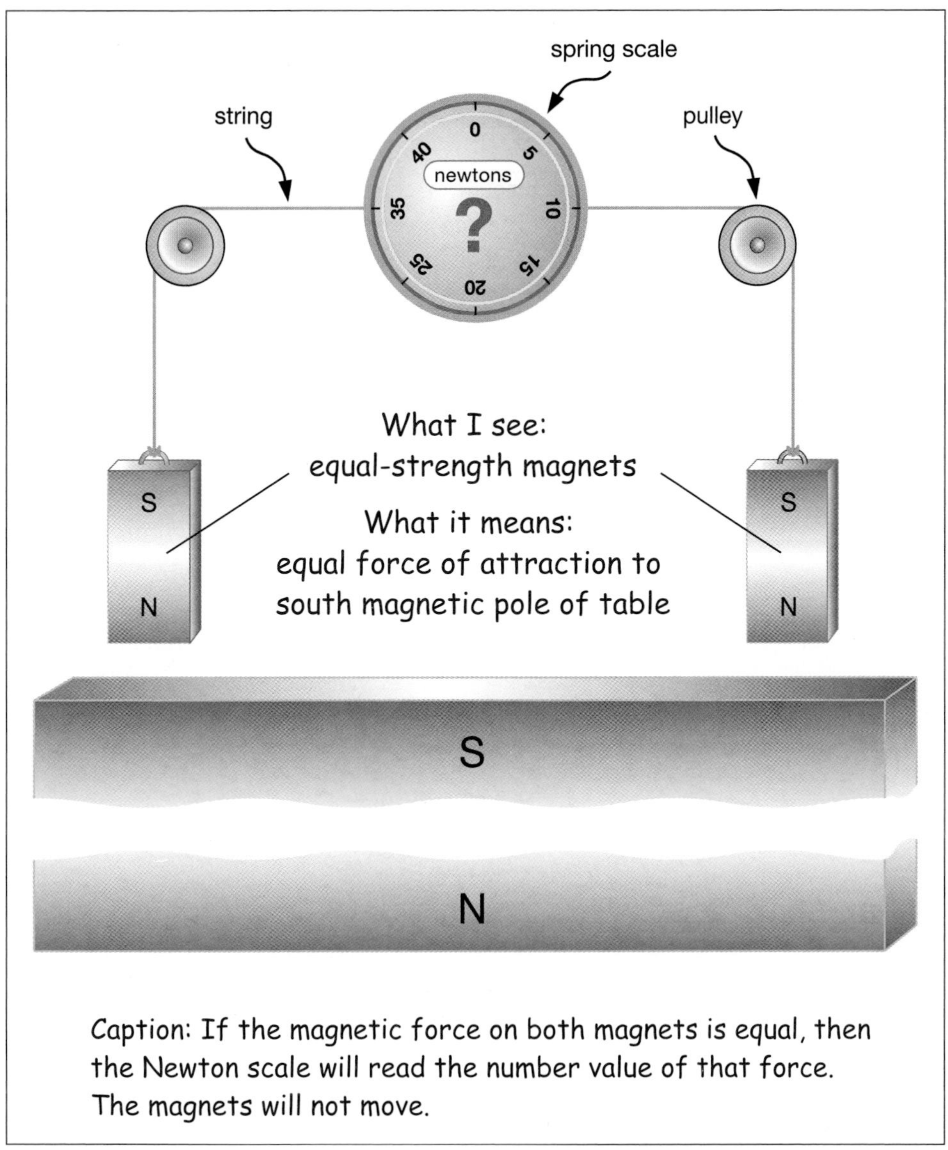

▲ **Figure T2.5 Magnet analogy of Atwood's machine.** This sketch represents an answer to *Reflect and Connect* Question 2.

3. Student answers should be similar to figure T2.6.
4. Students may decide to use a Venn diagram to compare forces. If students are not familiar with this way of organizing comparisons, take some time to teach them the characteristics of a Venn diagram. See *How To Use and Create Venn Diagrams* in the How To section at the back of the book. Student answers should be similar to figure T2.7.

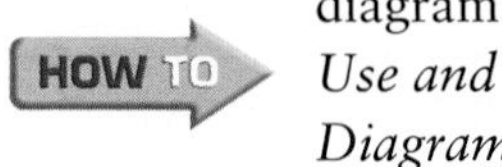

EXPLORE

Controlling Forces

Activity Overview

Many times, students learn a concept in one context and cannot transfer it to a different context. For example, students who perform complex arithmetic to decide on the best deal for clothes or CDs sometimes cannot perform the same operations in the context of homework assignments. Such lack of transfer limits how students use knowledge, thus restricting their access to success. One way to address this problem is to teach students explicitly how to broaden the context of what they know. They do not know how to do this on their own. You have to teach them. Teaching students how to understand the third law of motion in several contexts is the purpose of this explore activity.

Students apply the so-called third law of motion to two different interactions: (1) more horizontal collisions, and (2) vertical interactions. In each case, forces occur in pairs, equal in magnitude, but opposite in direction, and each force acts on a different object.

In *Controlling Forces*, students will explore how new awareness regarding the third law fits into familiar contexts. Then they will find out if the knowledge works for them to understand simple, everyday interactions such as walking down the hall.

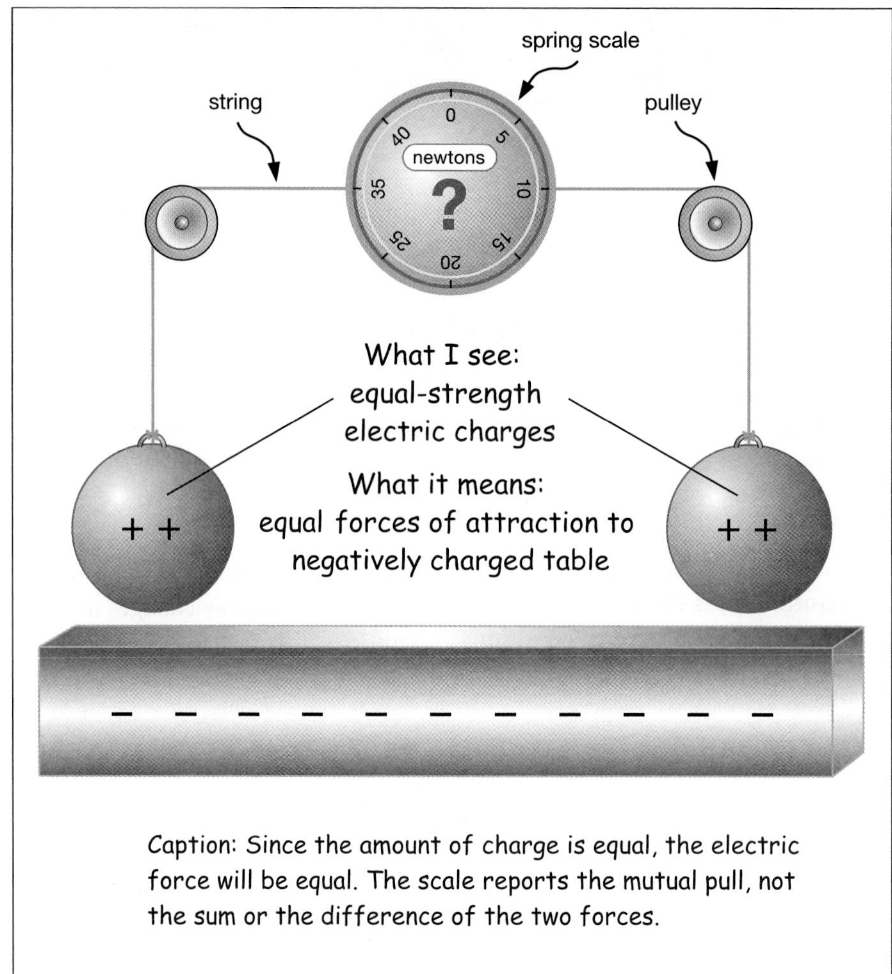

▲ **Figure T2.6 Electrical charge analogy of Atwood's machine.** This sketch represents an answer to *Reflect and Connect* Question 3.

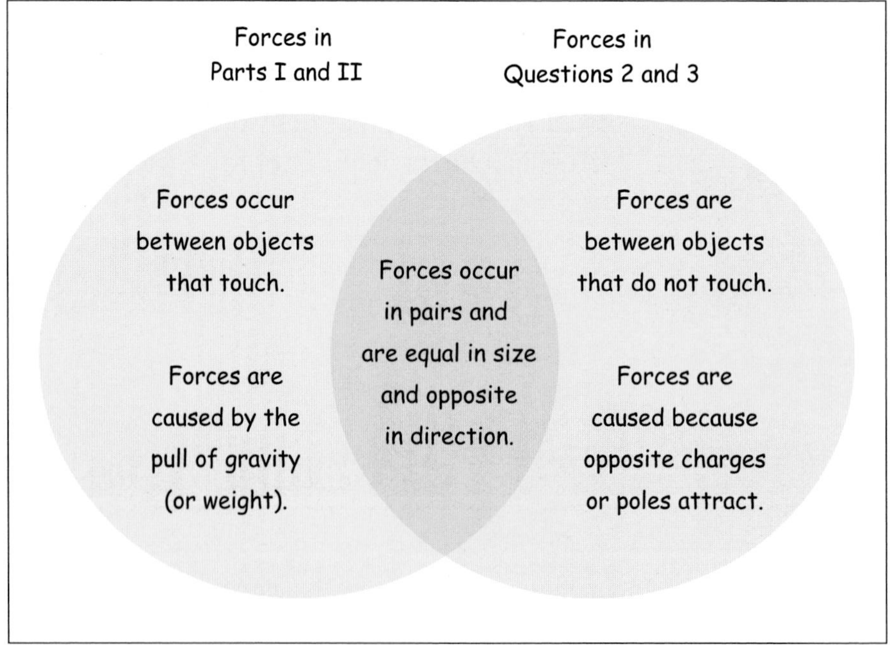

▲ **Figure T2.7 Comparison of forces.** Student answers should be similar to these.

Before You Teach

Background Information

In this activity, students will explore ways to extend their understanding of pairs of forces to more interactions. They will also lay the groundwork for a working mathematical definition of force, which they will develop fully in the first explain activity. That definition is $F = \frac{m\Delta v}{\Delta t}$. This view of force was first proposed by Sir Isaac Newton in the late 18th century. In words it states, "Force is equal to the time rate of change of momentum." Momentum (p) is equal to mv. Since velocity and mass are inherent within the concept of momentum, any change in velocity or mass requires a force. Your students will focus on changes in velocity. Anytime velocity changes, a force has to be involved. Changing velocity becomes the visible observation or indicator of invisible forces. That is, when students observe a change in velocity, they should infer that a force caused that change. Changes in velocity are the concrete manifestation of the rather abstract notion of force.

Note that changes in velocity show up in changes in speed (the time rate of change of position) and change in direction. That is because velocity is a vector quantity along with force, displacement from some reference point, acceleration, momentum, and any changes in these quantities. It is the change in velocity vector that is the most concrete indicator of the direction and magnitude of an applied force (as long as mass does not change). Increases and decreases in speed require a force, and any change in direction requires force. In this activity, students will focus on changes in linear velocity, both in horizontal and vertical motion. This change in velocity is of course called acceleration, but you will *not* see the word acceleration in this chapter. It is important that students focus on the *changes* resulting from an object's acceleration and not the definition of the term or some formula with acceleration as a variable. Students experience the evidence associated with acceleration again and again in this chapter. So by the time the word acceleration appears in chapter 4, it is almost an afterthought. Your students will have developed their own understanding of the concept of acceleration and will be comfortable assigning a name to it.

Also note that the teaching focus of this activity is for students to gain a *qualitative* sense of the relationship between force and changes in velocity. The intent is not for students to be told a formula for later use. Students explore relationships among key variables (force, velocity, and time) mostly from an experiential viewpoint, then they apply these experiences to more formal and quantitative views of force.

Materials—Part I

For each team of 4 students

2 ramps
2 toy cars
various weights
1 small ball of nontoxic modeling clay
tape
1 small piece of stiff cardboard

Materials—Part II

For each team of 2 students

access to a stair

Advance Preparation

Part I asks students to use toy cars, but you could borrow dynamics carts from the physics teacher. Inexpensive plastic dump trucks from the dollar store work well to hold additional mass. The point is

---

Controlling Forces

EXPLORE

Interactions result in pairs of forces. These forces are equal in size, opposite in direction, and act on different objects. And those forces cause all kinds of changes. Is there a way to control those changes? For example, how would you change your walking speed as you move down the hallway in school? Is speeding up different from slowing down? What about sitting at your desk in class? How do forces prevent changes such as falling through your chair to the floor?

Changing your motion is an essential part of the freedom you experience in everyday life. So knowing what factors control the amount of force necessary to move about as you wish is important to you. Are those factors different for objects other than your body? For example, how much force is required to change the speed of a car moving from highway speed to a complete stop?

In *Controlling Forces*, you and your team will explore the factors that allow you to determine how much force is required to accomplish common tasks. First, you will try to understand the variables that affect force *qualitatively* (that is, mostly involving concepts). Later, you will learn about forces *quantitatively* (mostly involving measurement and some calculations). Regardless of the approach to understanding, the relationship among factors important to determining force stays the same. And as you might expect, the most complete understanding of those relationships requires both concepts *and* calculations.

Use the following question to focus your efforts in this activity: "What is the relationship among variables that affect force?" This question will help you monitor the decisions you make about collecting, analyzing, and reporting data. If something doesn't help you answer the focus question, then you should think twice about doing it.

Part I: Speed Bumps

Materials

For each team of 4 students

2 ramps
2 toy cars or trucks
various weights
1 small ball of modeling clay
tape
1 small piece of stiff cardboard

to find carts that will roll down a ramp in a straight line and will easily carry extra weight. Consider asking students to bring in toys from home. If you do this, the cars should be reasonably well matched in height, such that their bumpers or grills will collide easily.

Ramps can be a variety of materials as long as they support the weight of the cars. Stiff cardboard, shelving, or particleboard works well. The ramps should be over 1 meter (m) long and easy for students to manipulate and place books under to increase the slope. Students can fashion a smooth transition from the ramps to the table or floor with notebook paper.

It is important that the cars collide on a flat, vertical surface. Consider demonstrating what you mean by taping a small piece of cardboard to the front bumpers of two cars and showing students how the pieces of cardboard meet upon collision. Then show students where to place the small ball of clay, which students will use as an indicator of the forces during the collision.

If the clay ball falls off the car before the collision, try threading a piece of fishing line or thread through the center of the ball and tying it on the cardboard to hold the ball in place.

Educational Technologies

Force probes can be used instead of the clay ball. These probes are part of computer analysis systems available commercially. If your school has the necessary equipment, consider allowing students to use it if they are interested. Be sure you place a force probe on *each* toy car so that students see that forces come in pairs.

Cautions

In Part II, do not let students with any leg, knee, hip, back, etc. problems jump from the stair to the floor. You might even excuse them from the activity.

As You Teach

Outcomes and Indicators of Success

By the end of this activity, students should

1. be able to design an investigation to explore the effect of velocity and mass on collision forces.

   They will exhibit their ability by

   - discussing procedures with teammates,
   - writing step-by-step procedures in their science notebooks,
   - conducting an approved investigation, and
   - analyzing the results systematically.

2. be able to develop conceptual generalizations regarding the effect of changes in velocity and mass on the amount of force applied during collisions.

   They will show their ability by

   - using sentences and mathematical symbols to state that the force pairs in collisions are directly proportional to the change in velocity of the toy cars,
   - using sentences and mathematical symbols to state that the force pairs in collisions are directly proportional to the mass of the toy cars, and
   - using sentences and mathematical symbols to state that the force pairs in collisions are inversely proportional to the time of collision between toy cars.

Process and Procedure

Head-on collisions can result in significant damage to automobiles and the passengers inside. So finding ways to study the forces occurring from such collisions could help scientists and engineers design better seat belts and air bags. What can you do to understand collisions better, without conducting expensive or dangerous experiments?

One approach is to use a well-designed model. A model is a representation of an actual object that exhibits most of the essential features of the object, but is easier to study. For example, you and your team can use a clay ball and toy cars to study the factors that affect forces in head-on collisions.

1. Meet with your team and develop a list in your science notebook of factors (sometimes called variables) that affect the amount of force each car experiences in a head-on collision.
2. Confer with another team to complete your list of important factors.
3. Read the following paragraph about one of the factors that you may have chosen for your list.

"How fast was I going?" This question is often asked by drivers when they are about to get a speeding ticket. Highway speed limits are in place to protect us and those around us. There is a big difference in a rear-end collision at 5 miles per hour and one at 30 miles per hour.

One of the factors that you listed may have been speed. In science, the speed of an object is often considered along with the direction the object is moving. Speed and direction make up the quantity we call velocity. Velocity is a vector. **Vectors** have both a magnitude (a size) and a direction. So the magnitude of velocity is speed. If you are stopped for speeding by a police officer, you may be concerned with the magnitude of your velocity, or your speed. If the police officer is investigating a car accident, however, she will want to know both how fast the cars were moving (their speed) and in what direction they were moving. She needs to know the velocity of the cars involved in the accident to reconstruct the accident scene.

4. Design a series of investigations to explore the qualitative relationship among velocity, mass, and force. Use the materials provided by your teacher and consider Steps 4a–f.

Design the minimum number of investigations to answer the focus question.

60 | Unit 1 Interactions Are Interesting

Strategies

Getting Started

Seat belts are certainly an important aspect of students' common experience. Ask students if designing seat belts with the proper strength is important. Of course, they will say yes. Then ask what design considerations are important in seat belts. They will probably mention force of impact, mass of the person, velocity of the car, and a variety of ergonomic features, which are not the focus of this activity, but are important. Then mention that scientists determine exact values for these variables by focusing on force. And since students already know something about determining the amount of force involved in collisions (from the clay ball model used in the engage activity), then they will use this prior knowledge to explore how mass and velocity affect force.

Several activities in this chapter include a focus question. The focus question for this activity is, "What is the relationship among variables that affect force?" An effective strategy for keeping this at the forefront of your students' minds as they work through the activity is to write it in a conspicuous place in the room. Discuss what the question means and ways to answer it. Refer back to the question during the activity to remind students of the ultimate goal of the activity.

Reminder of Possible Misconceptions

Part I asks students to apply their understanding of force pairs. A few students will still want to say the fastest or the heaviest car will apply the largest force. Only repeated and consistent explicit evidence will dispel this very persistent misconception.

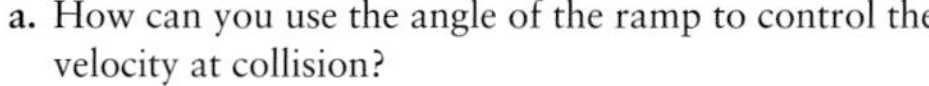

a. How can you use the angle of the ramp to control the velocity at collision?
b. How can you make a smooth transition (without speed bumps) between the ramp and the horizontal surface onto which the cars roll?
c. What can you do to ensure that only flat, vertical surfaces on the fronts of toy vehicles (see figure 2.8) hit the clay ball at the moment of collision?

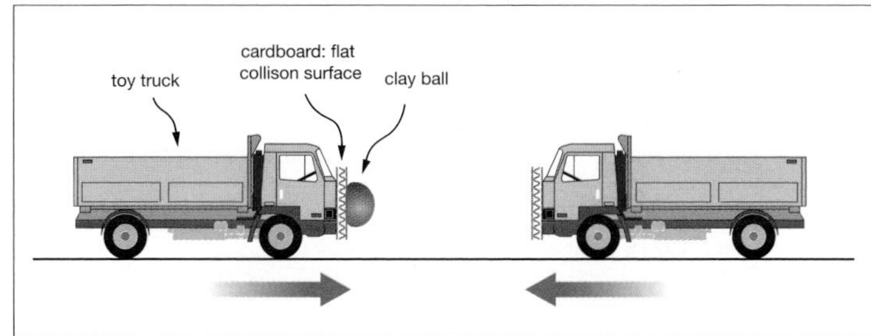

Figure 2.8 Cardboard and clay ball before collision. A flat, vertical surface helps you study the forces involved in head-on collisions.

d. How can you change the mass of the toy vehicles by amounts large enough to make a measurable difference?
e. What variables must be held constant at different times in the activity?
f. What is the best way to organize your observations in an efficient and accurate record of events?

5. Record your investigation in a step-by-step procedure that includes using data tables; obtain your teacher's approval. (Be sure to include units for all measurements.)
6. Carry out your investigation; make sure all team members record observations in their science notebooks.

Process and Procedure

Part I: Speed Bumps

Materials

For each team of 4 students

2 ramps
2 toy cars
various weights
1 small ball of nontoxic modeling clay
tape
1 small piece of stiff cardboard

The first step in this activity asks students to develop a list of factors that affect the amount of force on the cars in a head-on collision. You may choose to lead a class discussion for this step, depending on the needs of your students. Regardless of the approach you use, make sure they at least list the *mass* of the objects involved and the *speed and direction* (the velocity) of colliding objects. You might walk around the room reading a few science notebooks to obtain a quick survey, then stop class and include some variables if key variables are missing. This strategy is an example of formative assessment in which you adjust instruction based on immediate or dynamic feedback.

In Step 2, students confer with another team to complete their lists of important factors. Consider having your students use the TSAR strategy to finish their lists. You can use other sharing strategies, but do not assume students have mastered effective sharing of scientific thoughts in just one activity. Keep them focused by insisting they form effective habits.

Students read a short paragraph in Step 3 that introduces them to vector quantities and specifically velocity. Ensure that students understand the meaning of vector quantities before going on to the next step.

Then in Step 4, students design a series of investigations to answer the focus question. Call attention to the question that you have written on the board or a poster. Remind students that the design is not about finding numerical values for variables; rather, it is about finding the relationship between force, velocity, and mass. Therefore, their designs do not need stopwatches and balances. If you are pressed for time, consider having students do a modified design, paying close attention to the data table. You must decide how much practice your students need in investigation design. They will have multiple opportunities to design investigations and you can shorten the time commitment by specifying the level of detail that you expect. We encourage you, however, to give students multiple opportunities to design entire investigations as described in Step 4.

Steps 4a–f give students guiding questions to help them with their designs. In Step 4a, the steeper the ramp, the faster the car is rolling at the bottom of the ramp and presumably upon collision with the other car. Emphasize that they do not need a protractor. They can refer to angles as large, medium, and small—reinforce what the word "relative" means. Students may use a sheet of notebook paper shaped into a gentle curve to make a smooth transition between the ramp and the floor for Step 4b. Allow students to be creative here.

In Step 4c, it is important that the ball of clay placed between the cars cannot squeeze beyond two flat collision surfaces. Otherwise, the clay will simply conform to the bumper and not reflect the equal and opposite effect, as in the engage activity. Fashion small, flat squares of cardboard and tape them to the front of each car. These will be the impact surfaces. With this design, the clay ball will always be deformed by equal amounts. You may have to attach the clay ball to the cardboard by threading a thin thread or fishing line through the ball and tying it to the back of the cardboard.

Students will have fun adding weight to the cars in Step 4d. If you use small toy cars, it is easy to add mass by taping coins on the hood. If you use dynamics carts that you borrowed from the physics teacher, then add mass with half bricks or standard lab weights. Use qualitative words like "large" and "small" to describe the masses so that students do not get bogged down in exact measurement. Instead, focus their intellectual energy on the relationships among the variables.

Since they are exploring at least 3 variables, one should be held constant as students study the relationship between the remaining variables (Step 4e). If students study velocity and force, for example, they will place a clay ball between the cars and vary the angle of the ramps. This changes the impact velocity. They should keep the masses constant during these investigations. Similarly, when they study the relationship between force and mass, they should keep the ramp angle constant. In each case, the clay ball (if set up properly with flat collision surfaces) will show the same amount of squish on both sides per collision. Of course, for more mass and greater speed, the amount of squish will be more, although still equal on both sides.

Data tables are common ways of organizing data such as these for efficient recording and retrieval (Step 4f). Consider "constant mass" and "constant change in velocity" as 2 examples of data tables. Then set up a grid for the dependent and independent variables.

In Step 5, use the approval process as interim feedback on how students are doing. If their series of steps is disjointed, ill conceived, and

Answers to Stop & Think are on TE page 63.

Stop & THINK

PART I

Read each question carefully before writing your own answers in your science notebook. Then meet with your team and use the TSAR strategy to complete your answers. Keep careful records of what answers you changed, how, and why. This will help you and your teacher see the progress of your learning.

1 What is a general rule governing how changes in velocity affect forces on each car when the masses remain constant? Complete 1a–c to answer this question.

Use the symbols F for force, v for velocity, and m for mass. The delta symbol, Δ, means "the change in." Mathematical symbols you can use are $=$, $<$, $>$, or $\propto$. The $\propto$ symbol means "proportional to." Use this symbol to indicate when one value is directly proportional to another.

a. Complete the following statements:
- As the velocity of the cars at impact increases, the force on each car at collision ________.
- The force of car 1 on car 2 is ________ the force of car 2 on car 1.

b. Using your answers to Question 1a, form the mathematical relationships in this next statement.
F ________ Δv as long as ________ is held constant.

c. What evidence did you observe to form your answer to Question 1a?

2 What is a general rule about how changes in mass affect forces on each car when the velocity at collision remains constant? State this rule in 2 ways.

a. Apply language by writing a sentence using the words *force, mass, velocity*, and *change*.

b. Apply mathematics by writing a relationship using the symbols F, m, v, Δ, and $\propto$.

Use the guided format in Question 1 to help you form your answers to Question 2.

3 How might the relationships you wrote in Questions 1 and 2 change if you replaced the clay ball with a steel ball? A very "squishy" marshmallow? State what factor most affects your answer.

62 Unit 1 Interactions Are Interesting

incomplete, then you know with whom you'll need to spend extra time. Keep moving around the room as students collect data, ensuring each student records all observations in his or her science notebook while completing Step 6.

Answers to Stop and Think—Part I, SE pages 62–63

1a. As the velocity of the cars at impact increases, the force on each car at collision (increases).

The force of car 1 on car 2 is = (equal to) the force of car 2 on car 1.

1b. $F \propto \Delta v$ as long as mass is held constant. Or students may simply say that the change in velocity at impact is proportional to the force at impact.

1c. The clay ball showed more squishing when the velocity, and thus the forces, were greater at impact. The clay ball was squished equally on both sides in all cases, indicating that the forces at impact were equal and opposite.

2. A sentence form of stating the relationship between mass and force for a constant velocity follows:

"As mass increases, so does the force of impact (for constant change in velocity), but the forces are still equal in size and opposite in direction."

A mathematical means of stating the relationship could be the following:

"Mass $\propto$ force with constant velocity, or $m = kF$ with 'k' being a constant of proportionality."

3. This is a transfer question. Use it to determine how far cognitively students can transfer what they know about force pairs. The answer is that regardless of the object replacing the clay ball, impact forces will be equal in size, opposite in direction, and will act on two different objects. What changes is the size or magnitude of the forces in the pair—one pair will have larger forces than the other pair of forces. When the squishy marshmallow replaces the clay ball, the implication is that more time is required during collision. This will decrease the forces at impact.

4. Students think back to the focus question for the activity. They have learned that the variables of mass and change in velocity affect the amount of force in a collision. As the mass or the change in velocity increases, the force during a collision also increases. They have also learned that the forces are equal and opposite. The deformation of the clay ball was the evidence for these relationships as explained in Question 3.

Cautions

In Part II, do not let students with any leg, knee, hip, back, etc. problems jump from the stair to the floor. You might even excuse them from the activity.

Process and Procedure

Part II: Safe Landing

Materials

For each team of 2 students

access to a stair

Students have their first true experience with vectors in Step 1. A *vector* sketch, for now, uses a

Answers to Step 1 are on TE pages 64–65.

4 Think back to the focus question for this activity: "What is the relationship among variables that affect force?" Use the evidence from your investigation to form an answer to this question. Be sure to include *how* each variable affects force.

Part II: Safe Landing

Materials

For each team of 2 students

access to stairs

Cautions

Do not participate in this activity if you have any medical condition that prevents you from engaging in activities like jumping.

Process and Procedure

Some collisions occur horizontally, others vertically. Think about the forces when a skydiver lands on the ground (figure 2.9). How does the skydiver control these forces? Why is controlling forces important?

Safe landings depend, in part, on the ability of skydivers to control forces on their legs when they collide with Earth. How do they do that? What strategies do skydivers use to affect the way their legs respond to impacts? For example, do skydivers change their mass to produce a "softer" landing?

In Part II, you and your partner will explore ways to control forces in vertical interactions by stepping off a stair with both stiff and bent knees.

1. Predict all you can about the relative size of forces acting on you and a stair (or floor) in the following 3 situations. Do this by completing the table in figure 2.10 in your science notebook.

You will be using vectors to represent many quantities in this program. Read *FYI—Vectors in One Dimension* on page 67 to learn more about this way of representing quantities in science.

▼ **Figure 2.9 Skydiver landing.** Why is controlling forces important to this skydiver?

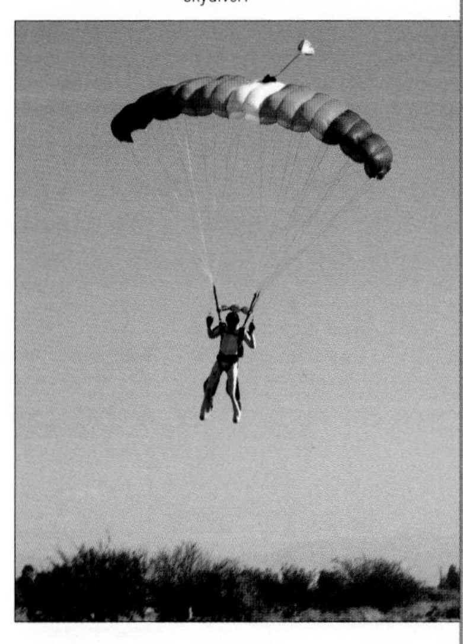

simple arrow to represent a force. The longer the arrow, the greater the force. Also, if an arrow points up, that means you think the force points up (acts in the upward direction). Vectors are an easy way to show what you are thinking without using words. Students are told to read *FYI—Vectors in One Dimension* for more information on using vectors

to represent forces. There is also a *Toolbox* practice set, *Vector Addition in One Dimension*, on the *TRCD* that will give your students more practice with drawing and adding vectors.

Answers to Step 1, SE pages 63–64

Student answers for Step 1 should be similar to figure T2.8. However, this is a prediction step, so expect student answers to change as they progress through the activity. Assess their understanding of these situations only after they have completed the activity.

Answers to Step 2, SE pages 64-65

Cautions

In Step 2, students test their predictions by stepping off a low stair. Don't force students with bad knees, hips, etc. to do this. Rely on those who have healthy knees to report. Students record their observations in a table similar to figure T2.9.

Answers to Step 3, SE page 65

Students are asked a series of questions in Step 3 about their observations. Answers to each should include the following observations.

3a. Each student's mass remained constant, so changing mass had no effect on force. Students would know this because they did not lose any clothes or body parts during the fall.

3b. The velocity of the fall for each instance (bent legs or stiff legs) is the same at impact. The hint suggests that the height of fall is what determines the speed at impact and nothing else, which is true. In both the stiff leg and bent leg cases, the change in velocity was exactly the same.

3c. The amount of *time* that the stopping force was applied is what changed from the stiff leg to bent leg case. Students would know this by the larger amount of time to stop when landing with bent knees compared with stiff legs.

In Steps 4 and 5, students are asked questions to summarize what they have just learned. Students should surmise that if the mass and the change in velocity is constant, then the product, $m\Delta v$, will also be constant. You may need to review what some of the words mean that are mentioned in the hint. Specific ones to note are "independent of" (one factor has no effect on the other), "directly proportional to" (an increase in one factor causes an increase in the other, or a decrease in one factor causes a decrease in the other), and "inversely proportional to" (an increase in one factor causes a decrease in another and vice versa).

a. Situation 1: The forces on your body and the stair or floor as you are standing still
b. Situation 2: The forces on your body and the floor as you land with stiff knees
c. Situation 3: The forces on your body and the floor as you land with bent knees

Remember to label each force. The label "$F_{\text{stair on foot}}$" is one of many appropriate labels that indicate *both* the objects involved in the interaction and *on* which object the force is being applied. The first row of the table is partially completed. Fill in the first row and use it to complete the remainder of the table.

Situation	Forces involved and their magnitude	Vector sketches to represent those forces
1. Standing still	Force of me on the floor is ______ the force of the floor on me, and in the ______ direction.	$F_{\text{me on floor}}$ $F_{\text{floor on me}}$
2. Landng on next stair with stiff knees		
3. Landing on next stair with bent knees		

▲ **Figure 2.10 Predictions table.** Use this table for your predictions in Step 1.

2. Test your predictions in 2 different ways by doing Steps 2a–c. Record all your observations in a table like the one shown in figure 2.11.
   a. Copy the table in figure 2.11 into your science notebook and complete it after doing Steps 2b–c.

Situation	Forces in interaction (in words)	Forces in interaction (in vector sketches at maximum force)
Stiff knees		
Bent legs		

▲ **Figure 2.11 Forces in interaction.** Use this table to complete Steps 2b–c.

Situation	Forces involved and their magnitude	Vector sketches to represent those forces
Standing still	The force of me on the floor is equal to the force of the floor on me, but in opposite directions.	$F_{\text{me on floor}}$ $F_{\text{floor on me}}$
Landing on next stair	The force of me on the stair is equal to the force of the stair on me, and in opposite directions, but larger than just standing still.	$F_{\text{me on stair}}$ $F_{\text{stair on me}}$

▲ **Figure T2.8 Prediction table.** This completed table helps students compare their predictions for standing still versus moving, using two alternative forms of representation: language and mathematics.

Situation	Forces in interaction (in words)	Forces in interaction (in vector sketches at maximum force)
Stiff knees	The force was large enough to be uncomfortable on my knees, certainly larger than standing still on the floor	$F_{\text{me on floor}}$ $F_{\text{floor on me}}$
Bent legs	The force was not as large as in the stiff leg case	$F_{\text{me on floor}}$ $F_{\text{floor on me}}$

▲ **Figure T2.9 Prediction table.** This completed table helps students compare their predictions for the stiff versus bent leg situations, using two alternative forms of representation: language and mathematics.

Answers to Step 3 are on TE page 64.

b. Stand perfectly still on a stair; then step off (with both legs stiff) to the next lower stair.

c. Stand perfectly still on a stair; then step off to the next lower stair, bending your legs as much as possible when you land.

3. What variable changed the amount of force you felt as you stepped off the stair? Complete Steps 3a–c in your science notebook to answer this question.

   a. Did a change of mass affect the forces involved in the interaction between your foot and the stair? How do you know?

   b. Did a change in the velocity *at impact* affect the forces involved in the interaction between your foot and the stair? How do you know?

Remember, the stair height was the same for both situations. So your body fell the same distance in both cases before your feet touched the next lower stair.

   c. What variable did you change (which changed the force you felt) by bending your legs during landing instead of landing with stiff legs? How do you know this variable changed?

4. If your mass (m) and your change in velocity (Δv) remain constant for a given stair, then what must be true about the product of these 2 quantities ($m\Delta v$)?

5. In your science notebook, make 2 complete sentences by joining the phrases in 5a and 5b with the proper connecting term.

Use connecting terms such as "larger than," "smaller than," "equal to," "independent of," "directly proportional to," "inversely proportional to," and "not dependent on." Your final answer in 5a and 5b should result in a complete sentence.

   a. The amount of time to stop when I land on the lower stair ______________ the force I feel when I hit the stair, for a constant mass and change in velocity.

   b. The product of mass and change in velocity ($m\Delta v$) ______________ the product of force and time to stop for a given interaction ($F\Delta t$).

Consider using unit analysis to answer Step 5b. The unit for force is the newton and can be represented by $\frac{\text{kg m}}{\text{sec}^2}$; time is in seconds, mass is in kilograms, and change in velocity is in $\frac{\text{m}}{\text{sec}}$.

   c. Check your answers with other teams. If you are still unsure of your answers, check with your teacher.

Answers to Step 5, SE page 65

Students should complete the sentences in Step 5 as follows.

5a. The amount of time to stop when I land on the lower stair <u>is inversely proportional to</u> the force I feel when I hit the stair, for a constant mass and change in velocity.

5b. The product of mass and change in velocity ($m\Delta v$) <u>is equal to</u> the product of force and time to stop for a given interaction ($F\Delta t$). Instead of "is equal to," students might write "seems related to" or "is proportional to." Students are encouraged to use a unit analysis approach. Though this does not prove the equivalence, it does help students establish a working relationship that they can explore further throughout the remaining activities.

The units of $F\Delta t$ are equal to the units of $m\Delta v$ by the following equation:

$$(\text{N})(\text{sec}) = (\text{kg})\left(\frac{\text{m}}{\text{sec}}\right)$$

$$\left(\frac{(\text{kg})(\text{m})}{\text{sec}^{\not 2}}\right)(\not{\text{sec}}) = (\text{kg})\left(\frac{\text{m}}{\text{sec}}\right)$$

Interaction	Reason it is important to control force	How force is controlled
The car hits the post in the parking lot with and without a 5-miles-per-hour-bumper.	The amount of force a car experiences in a collision relates to the amount of damage.	Bumpers increase the amount of time required for cars to stop in a collision, thus decreasing the force on the car.
The driver hits the steering wheel during a crash with and without deployed air bags.	Too much force could kill a driver.	A driver hitting the steering wheel with and without air bags is like stepping off a chair and landing with stiff legs, then with bent knees. Air bags decrease the force by increasing the time for the driver's body to stop.
The catcher catches a fastball with and without a glove.	Too much force would injure a catcher's hand.	The glove is like padding or a bumper. It decreases the force by increasing the time for the ball to stop.
Hikers hike on a mountain trail with and without hiking boots.	Too much force applied over many steps can injure feet.	Boots act like bumpers, catcher's gloves, or air bags by increasing the time over which the impact force is applied.

▲ **Figure T2.10 Transfer knowledge table.** This completed table helps students transfer what they learned in previous activities to new situations they encounter outside of school. Note that these situations can also increase the surface area in which the force acts, but do not expect your students to know this relationship.

Answers to Reflect and Connect, SE page 66

1. Student answers to Question 1 should be similar to figure T2.10.
2. There are no exceptions to the statement that forces come in pairs, equal in size and opposite in direction, acting on different objects. It is a law of nature.
3. Help students apply algebra skills to this question. Solving for force yields $F = \frac{m\Delta v}{\Delta t}$. This expression says that mass (m) and change in velocity (Δv) are directly proportional to force during an interaction and that the force is inversely proportional to the time interval (Δt) over which the velocity is changing. So force on an object can be increased by increasing mass or change in velocity, or decreasing the time of interaction.
4. Students should use their working relationship, $F = \frac{m\Delta v}{\Delta t}$, to answer this question. They should be able to relate vehicle size (mass) and velocity to increased chance for serious harm from car collisions.

Reflect and Connect

Answer the following questions in your science notebook. Use a learning strategy that maximizes your individual understanding. Check the accuracy of your answers, using a technique that your teacher approves.

1. Explore with your classmates how scientists and engineers adjust the variable change in time (Δt) to control the forces in the following interactions. Record your ideas in your science notebook using a table like the one in figure 2.12.

Interaction	Reason it is important to control force	How force is controlled
Car hits post in parking lot with and without a 5 miles per hour (mph) bumper		
Driver hits steering wheel during crash with and without deployed air bags		
Catcher catches fastball with and without glove		
Hiking on mountain trail with and without hiking boots		

▲ **Figure 2.12 Why and how to control forces.** Use this table to organize your answer to Question 1.

2. Are there any exceptions to the statement, "Forces occur in pairs, equal in size and opposite in direction"? If yes, then give some examples. If no, then explain why there are no exceptions.
3. How do changes in Δt, m, and Δv affect force? You discovered the relationship $F\Delta t = m\Delta v$ in Step 5b. Use specific examples to answer this question.

Mathematical relationships can help you think about how a change in one variable will affect another. It may help you answer the question if you solve the relationship, $F\Delta t = m\Delta v$, for F.

4. Think about the relationships among force, change in time, mass, and change in velocity that you explored in this activity. Assume that the amount of time during which colliding cars are in contact is about the same. How might highway speed limits and vehicle size affect the force of impact in car accidents?

66 Unit 1 Interactions Are Interesting

EXPLAIN

In-Line Interactions

Activity Overview

In-Line Interactions extends what students learn about force pairs in two specific types of collisions: elastic and inelastic collisions. Students use tennis balls suspended on strings hung from the ceiling (long pendulums) as collision objects. The tennis balls are suspended over *xy* axes used as a frame of reference for measurement. Students pull back the tennis balls and release them simultaneously so that the balls meet at the center of the *xy* axes, the origin of the coordinate system. In Part I, the balls hit and bounce (elastic collision), and in Part II, the balls hit and stick together (inelastic collision).

The primary cognitive goal of this activity is for students to use their knowledge of force pairs to relate to the law of conservation of momentum. Once students grasp the law of conservation of momentum, they apply it to a variety of everyday circumstances to broaden the context.

Before You Teach

Background Information

The tennis ball apparatus uses the properties of pendulums to make the measurement of velocity easy for students. For pendulums that do not swing more than about 10° from vertical, the time for one complete back-and-forth swing (period) is the same regardless of the initial amplitude. That is because the ball exhibits simple harmonic motion (spring motion), which says the net force the tennis ball experiences is directly proportional to the amplitude (distance from the lowest point). So the farther from vertical, the greater the force and the faster the ball is moving at the low point. Thus, the ball has farther to move, but is moving faster. The net result is that the period of a pendulum is the same as long as the length remains the same and the pendulum remains on this planet (and is not accelerated).

The amplitude of swing is directly proportional to the velocity. If you released a tennis ball from an amplitude of −3 units of distance, you could say the velocity at the center (point of collision) was 3 units of velocity (only relative values are required in this activity). Also, if a ball rebounds and swings 4 units of distance, then the ball must have had an initial velocity of 4 units immediately after collision.

The law of conservation of momentum states that the momentum of a system does not change during an interaction as long as there are no outside net forces. In this activity, the system of objects is two tennis balls, but the principles gleaned from simplistic systems apply to complex systems as well. The student book asks students to use a working definition of force, $F = \frac{m\Delta v}{\Delta t}$, and Newton's third law to develop the law of conservation of momentum, $\Delta p_{system} = 0$.

Elastic collisions conserve kinetic energy as well as momentum, while inelastic collisions only conserve momentum. The distinction is important as students connect macroscopic collisions (cars and tennis balls) to microscopic collisions (atoms and molecules). Atomic-sized particles collide elastically. That is what allows a balloon filled with gas to maintain its volume at a given temperature and pressure (provided there are no leaks). In most macroscopic interactions, a large amount of heat is generated and the energy lost as heat becomes unavailable for practical use. Therefore, Part I provides a

Vectors in One Dimension

Remember the number lines that you used in elementary school to learn negative numbers? They looked something like the following figure. Drawing vectors in one dimension is as simple as this number line. When drawing vectors, the positive and negative signs indicate the direction of the vectors. Vector quantities are those quantities that have both magnitude and direction. Force, velocity, and momentum are examples of vector quantities. The number represents the magnitude, and the algebraic sign (in one-dimensional motion) represents the direction. Deciding on the direction that will be negative is completely arbitrary. But the custom is to indicate directions to the left or west as negative and to the right or east as positive—just like a number line.

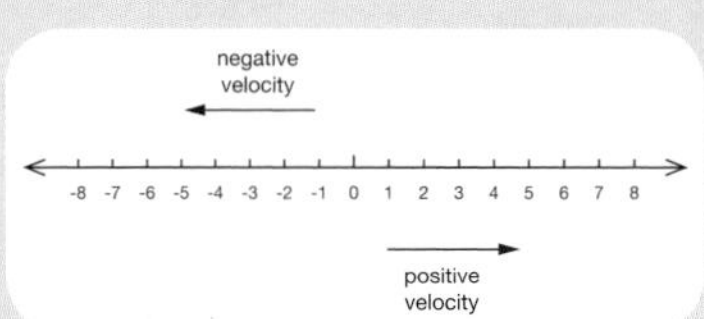

Number line. Use the idea of a number line to help you remember the sign of vectors. The sign indicates the direction of the vector.

When considering one-dimensional vectors that act vertically, positive values are usually assigned to vectors that are directed up, and negative values are usually assigned to vectors that are directed down. Similarly, if the vectors are on a flat plane, as in a map, north would be positive and south would be negative.

Some students mistake the negative values in vectors to be part of the magnitude. But a vector that is −3 is not less than a vector that is +3. These vectors have exactly the same magnitude; they are simply in opposite directions in one-dimensional motion. For example, a force of 3 N has the same magnitude no matter which direction it is applied. A force of −3 N applied to the left is just as much force as a force of +3 N to the right. The sign is only an indication of the direction.

What about adding or subtracting vectors; can it be done? Yes, you can add or subtract vectors easily using two different methods, as long as you are careful about the signs. You add or subtract vector quantities algebraically just as you would add or subtract positive or negative numbers. For example, suppose you wanted to find Δv algebraically. The initial velocity (v_i) is −16 meters per second (m/sec) and a final velocity (v_f) as 11 m/sec. Using the formula for finding Δv,

$$\Delta v = v_f - v_i$$
$$= 11\frac{m}{sec} - \left(-16\frac{m}{sec}\right)$$
$$= 27\frac{m}{sec}$$

You can see how important it is to keep the signs correct. This answer would indicate that the change in velocity (Δv) is 27 m/sec in the positive direction.

The second method to add or subtract vectors is to do it graphically. To do this, carefully draw vectors to scale. To keep this example simple, you will only add vectors. The formula you used before, however, subtracts vectors. How do you turn subtraction into addition? The previous formula, $\Delta v = v_f - v_i$, becomes $\Delta v = v_f + (-v_i)$. Now add the vectors graphically to find Δv. First, draw the two vectors in the appropriate direction and to scale.

v_i
−16 m/sec

v_f
11 m/sec

Draw vectors in the appropriate direction. Begin by drawing the two vectors pointing in the direction dictated by the sign. Always draw the vectors to scale.

Chapter 2 Collision Course 67

good mental picture for students to use as they think about the collisions inherent in chemistry (chapters 3 and 5). Part II more realistically models the interactions students see on a day-to-day basis (this chapter and chapter 4). Additional background material can be found in the student book or any high school physics book.

Materials—Part I

For each team of 4 students

4 pairs of safety goggles

1 tennis ball–collision kit (see *Advance Preparation*), which includes
- 2 tennis balls marked "1 unit of mass," with Velcro strips and a cup hook
- 1 tennis ball marked "2 units of mass," with Velcro strip and a cup hook
- 2 lengths of string long enough to reach from a desk to the ceiling
- 1 collision grid with protractor markings and a center string
- paper clips
- tape

access to computers and *SRCD* (optional)

Materials—Part II

For each team of 4 students

4 pairs of safety goggles

1 tennis ball–collision kit (see *Advance Preparation*), which includes
- 2 tennis balls marked "1 unit of mass," with Velcro strips and cup hook
- 1 tennis ball marked "2 units of mass," with Velcro strip and cup hook
- 2 lengths of string long enough to reach from a desk to the ceiling
- 1 collision grid with protractor markings and a center string
- paper clips
- tape

4 copies, 1 transparency, or both of copymaster 2.1a, *Mathematical Relationships*

TRCD

access to computers and *SRCD* (optional)

For the teacher

1 copy of copymaster 2.1b, *Answer Key for Mathematical Relationships*

Advance Preparation

You need 3 tennis balls for each team. Plan ahead by asking the tennis coach or local tennis club to save old balls. Slice open 1 of the 3 balls and insert enough weight (old nuts and bolts) to make the ball exactly twice the mass of a single ball. If the slice is small, no spills will occur. Label each ball with a large "1" or "2" depending on the relative mass.

Attach 1 cup hook to each ball. Glue a 5-centimeter (cm) Velcro strip around the equator of the tennis ball relative to the cup hook. One of the 1-mass balls will have "male" Velcro and the other "female." The 2-mass ball can have either type. The Velcro strip is not necessary for Part I and in fact may get in the way of the elastic collisions. If you purchase Velcro strips with an adhesive back, you may want to wait until Part II to attach the Velcro. If the adhesive is not strong enough, however, you will have to glue the strips permanently to the ball.

Make several large *xy* axes on butcher paper and laminate it for long-term use. Mark off tick marks every 10 cm on both axes. In addition, use a protractor to mark a circle centered on the origin with tick marks every 10° (figure T2.11). Finally, attach an approximately 50-cm length of string to the origin so that the string rotates freely about the origin. Mark the string every 10 cm. The string will be used to measure the angle of rebound in hit-and-stick collisions in Part II.

Fashion long pendulums of 2 tennis balls that attach to the ceiling

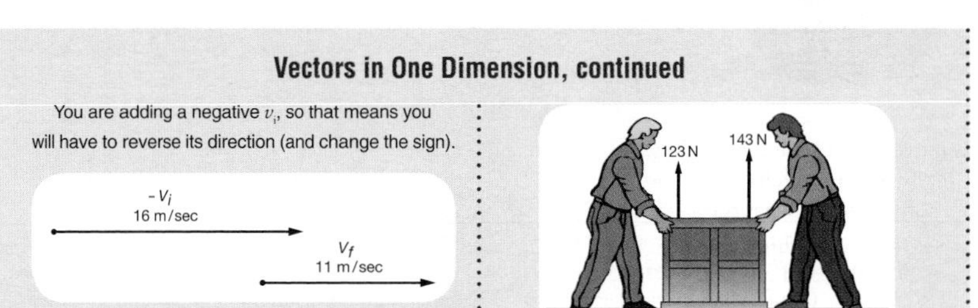

Vectors in One Dimension, continued

You are adding a negative v_i, so that means you will have to reverse its direction (and change the sign).

▲ **Reverse the direction.** To add a negative v_i, you must reverse the vector's direction and change the sign.

To add vectors graphically, place them head to tail. Then draw the resultant vector from the tail of the first vector to the head of the last vector. The resultant is just the result of the vectors you are adding.

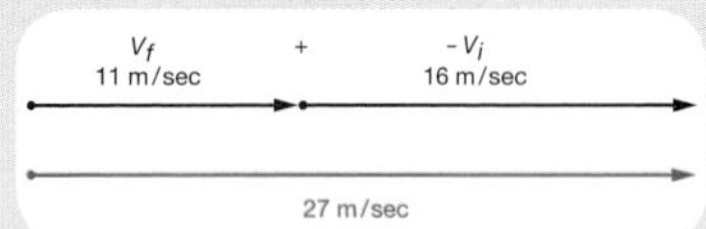

▲ **Adding vectors.** To add the vectors, place them head to tail. The resultant is drawn from the tail of the last vector to the head of the first vector. It does not matter in which order you add vectors—just like in math class.

Notice that, algebraically, the answer was positive, and it was also positive when solved graphically or by using vector math. This indicates that the answer, or the resultant, is in the positive direction, as shown by the direction of the resultant arrow in the example.

Suppose a crate had a weight of 300 N and two workers tried to lift it by the handles on the top. One worker pulled up with a force of 123 N, and the other pulled up with a force of 143 N. What would be the resultant force on the crate? Look at the following diagram, which shows three of the forces on the crate.

The resultant is the sum of these vectors. Graphically, you would solve it by placing the vectors head to tail and drawing the resultant vector from the tail of the first vector to the head of the last

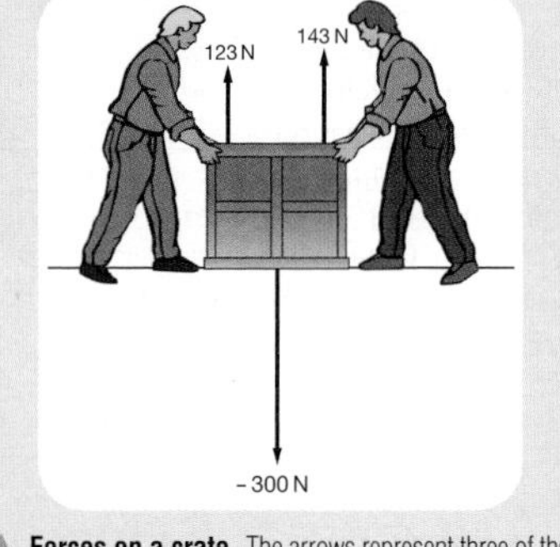

▲ **Forces on a crate.** The arrows represent three of the forces on this crate. Can the two workers lift the crate?

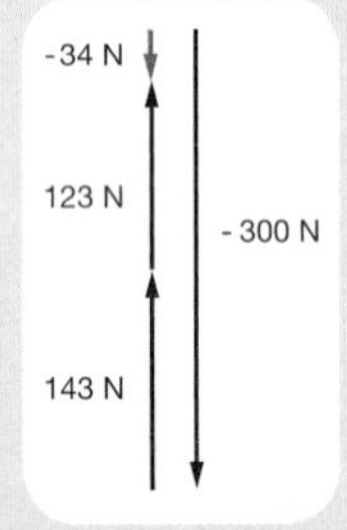

▶ **Adding forces on the crate.** Vectors are placed head to tail when you add them. What is the result of adding these vectors? What direction is the resultant vector pointing? Will the workers be able to lift the crate?

vector. All vectors must be drawn to the same scale, but the order you place them in does not matter. The vectors are placed side by side in the following figure to show overlapping vectors.

To solve for the resultant algebraically, simply add the vectors, making sure to watch the signs.

$-300\text{ N} + 143\text{ N} + 123\text{ N} = -34\text{ N}$

In both cases, the resultant is −34 N, which can be interpreted as 34 N of force in the downward direction. Will the two workers be able to lift the crate? No, the crate's weight of 300 N is too much for the two workers.

68 | Unit 1 Interactions Are Interesting

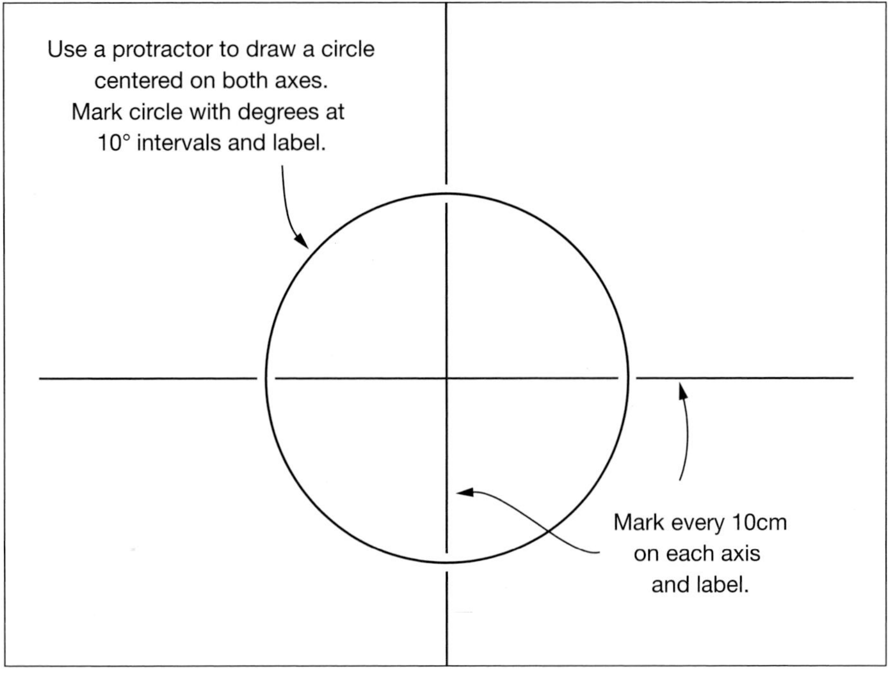

Figure T2.11 Example of axes. Make several large copies of these axes on butcher paper and laminate them for long-term use. You will need one for every team of students.

In-Line Interactions

EXPLAIN

By now you know that when objects interact in a collision, forces are involved. Those forces result in changes. Scientists want to know exactly how much change results from these forces. That is, scientists want to *quantify* what they know about force and change.

For example, think about a chunk of insulation falling from a booster rocket and colliding with the space shuttle wing. Engineers would want to know the impact force of the insulation on the wing. What changes to the wing or insulation would engineers make and what experiments would they perform? Or think about a chlorine radical (Cl·) hitting an ozone molecule (O_3) (figure 2.13). Does the force of collision cause a chemical reaction? The interaction of these atomic species is changing the concentration of the atmosphere's ozone, something you learned in Level 1 of this program. Imagine particles from a sunspot eruption interacting with Earth's magnetic field. Should satellite communications businesses be prepared for changes in the quality of transmission?

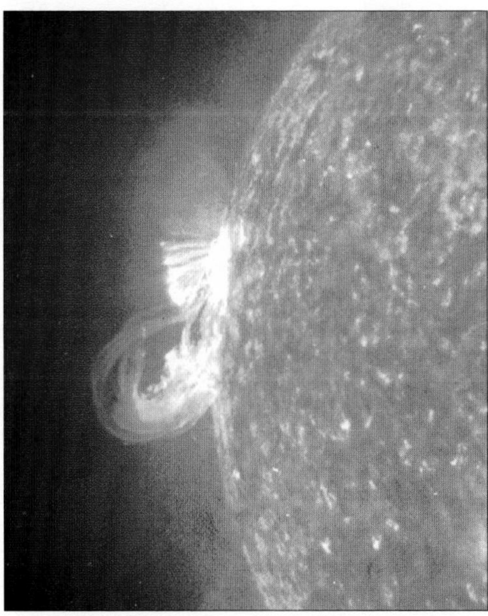

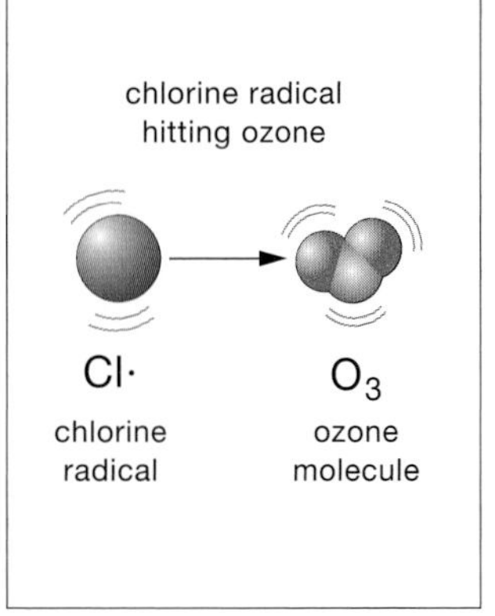

Figure 2.13 Scientists need to know the amount of force resulting from interactions. Find the interaction in each image. Why is the amount of force important to know in each situation?

and hang over the tables at which students work. Cotton string or wrapping ribbon works well. Attach the string or ribbon to the cup hook with paper clips. Another way, which allows for rapid vertical adjustment of the balls, is to loop the string or ribbon through the cup hook and clip the loose end to the remaining string (clips used to bind notebook paper together work well). How you attach the string to the ceiling depends on the type of ceiling. If you have acoustic tiles, students can loop the string over the support frames for the tiles. Ceiling manufacturers also make hooks that attach to the frames; these can be purchased at local hardware stores. The tennis balls should be as close to the table as possible without touching the table.

Familiarize yourself with the material in *Background Information* as well as in the student book for this activity. Read the entire activity so that you will know where the students are going as they build their understanding of these concepts.

TRCD For Part II, make a transparency of copymaster 2.1a, *Mathematical Relationships* and/or enough copies of the copymaster for each student.

Educational Technologies

Consider videotaping a set of collisions and using the stop-action or slow-motion feature of the playback system to help students observe and make the measurements they need.

There is a *Vector Addition* applet available on the *Student Resource CD (SRCD)* for students to practice vector addition and subtraction. If students are careful in drawing the vectors, both one-dimensional and two-dimensional vectors can be manipulated.

As You Teach

Outcomes and Indicators of Success

By the end of this activity, students should

1. be able to make observations important to determining the momentum of a system.

   They will exhibit their ability by

   - adjusting a tennis ball–collision apparatus until it works properly,
   - recording how their tennis ball pendulums keep the same time regardless of the amplitude,
   - associating ending displacement from the origin with maximum velocity, and
   - incorporating measurement uncertainty into relative velocity measurements.

2. be able to design an investigation to verify the law of conservation of momentum for inelastic collisions.

   They will show their ability by

   - discussing procedures with teammates,
   - writing step-by-step procedures in their science notebooks,
   - following their procedures and recording observations in tables, and
   - analyzing the results and confirming conservation of momentum.

3. be able to apply vector math to momentum problems.

   They will show their ability by

   - subtracting velocity vectors to obtain a change in velocity vector;
   - relating change in velocity vectors to net force vectors; and
   - relating change in velocity, force, and change in momentum vectors.

4. be able to use a mathematical model to guide a scientific investigation.

   They will demonstrate their ability by

   - developing quantitative relationships between force and change in velocity,
   - understanding that momentum is conserved in both elastic and inelastic collisions through analysis of quantitative results, and
   - designing an investigation to test the mathematical model $m_1v_{1i} + m_2v_{2i} = (m_1 + m_2)v_{f(1\&2)}$.

Strategies

Getting Started

Consider using a Newton's pendulum (often available in specialty toy stores) to stage this activity. This toy is usually made of five balls suspended from a cradle so that the balls swing and collide with one another. Show students how it works for one and two balls, then ask them to predict what will happen with three balls. Proceed to lifting the two end balls and releasing them simultaneously, ending with two balls on one side and three on the other. Then

Calculating the amount of force is a crucial part of understanding nature. Being able to analyze the result of forces is key to doing well in many businesses and surviving in many sports. To see how scientists have analyzed the forces involved in many sports-related collisions, read the sidebar *Head-On Collisions.*

In *In-Line Interactions*, you will learn how to represent the amount of force and the direction of force resulting from collisions. You also will learn about an important relationship that is constant in collisions. You and your team will model these collisions, or interactions, with tennis balls (see figure 2.14).

Throughout this activity, keep in mind the following focus question: "How do factors such as velocity, mass, and others before a collision compare with the same factors after a collision?" By the end of this activity, you should be able to answer this question.

▲ **Figure 2.14 Tennis ball collisions.** How do factors before a collision of tennis balls compare with the same factors after a collision?

Part I: A Question of Bounces

Materials

For each team of 4 students

1 tennis ball–collision kit, which includes

- 2 tennis balls marked "1 unit of mass," with Velcro strips and cup hook
- 1 tennis ball marked "2 units of mass," with Velcro strips and a cup hook
- 2 lengths of string long enough to reach from a desk to the ceiling
- 1 collision grid with protractor markings and a center string
- paper clips
- tape

Process and Procedure

In Part I, you and your team will use colliding tennis balls as a model to quantify the amount of force resulting from collisions between any two objects.

1. Read *Tools of the Trade,* which summarizes what you have learned so far and the purpose of this activity.

explain to students how they will be doing essentially the same thing on a larger scale and that they will be measuring swing distances. Resist the urge to tell students that the lab is about conservation of momentum. It is best if they make this connection for themselves.

Spend some time up front to ensure that the tennis ball–collision apparatus is set up correctly and that students know how to adjust the height of the balls. This will save you time in the next few days when students have to readjust the apparatus before beginning the activity.

Reminder of Possible Misconceptions

A few students will still want to predict that a tennis ball with a larger initial velocity generates a larger force on the other ball during collision. This prediction is a violation of Newton's third law of motion, and thus cannot be true.

Process and Procedure

Part I: A Question of Bounces

Materials

For each team of 4 students

4 pairs of safety goggles

1 tennis ball–collision kit, which includes

- 2 tennis balls marked "1 unit of mass," with Velcro strips and a cup hook
- 1 tennis ball marked "2 units of mass," with Velcro strip and a cup hook
- 2 lengths of string long enough to reach from a desk to the ceiling
- 1 collision grid with protractor markings and a center string
- paper clips
- tape

access to computer and *SRCD* (optional)

In Step 1, students read *Tools of the Trade*. In this reading, they look back at some of the things that they have learned in previous activities to prepare them for this activity. They will learn about some of the tools that scientists use in their work such as expressing uncertainty in measurement and assigning direction when working with vectors in one dimension. Encourage students to use a literacy strategy that best fits their learning style. They can partner with a classmate, taking turns reading and summarizing paragraphs, taking notes as they read, and so on.

The *Toolbox* exercises *Uncertainty* and *Vector Addition in One Dimension* are for you to use with your students should they need extra practice. You can find these on the *TRCD*. There is also a *Vector Addition* animation on the *SRCD* for practice with vector addition. You should review this program to determine if you want to introduce it at this time. You can use it to add vectors in one dimension, but it is difficult to draw straight lines with the program. You may decide that it is better left for later when the students are learning to work with vectors in two dimensions.

Students are introduced to the tennis ball–collision apparatus in Step 2. They should set it up, align the balls, and see how it works when they are colliding the tennis balls. Use this time to show them the proper setup. The center of mass of the 2-ball system should rest over the origin of the *xy* axis. The tennis balls should be very close to the table but not touching. The tennis ball–collision kit will be new to many students, so giving them guided time to get used to it will pay off later in the activity. You will demonstrate all the key features of the apparatus in Steps 3a–d to give them the best chance of collecting data that lead them to discovery of the law of conservation of momentum.

SIDEBAR

Head-On Collisions

Have you ever bumped your head and "seen stars" or even blacked out? If so, you may have suffered from a mild traumatic brain injury, or MTBI. Brain injuries occur in 1.5 million people in the United States each year. Seventy-five percent of these injuries, like concussions, are classified as MTBIs. Sports-related concussions make up 300,000 of these injuries.

Research scientists are gathering data to determine what can be done to better protect athletes who play contact sports. One tool used to collect real-time data is the use of accelerometers placed in the helmets of football and hockey players. These devices measure the time rate of the change in velocity (or acceleration) experienced when a player collides with another player. The collision may also be with the wall in the case of a hockey player. These measurements are reported as *g*s, which are a comparison of the acceleration to the free fall acceleration due to gravity. For example, an acceleration of 2 *g*s would be two times the free fall acceleration due to gravity.

In recent studies, the average acceleration experienced by high school football, hockey, and soccer players ranged from 29.2 ± 1.0 *g* to 54.7 ± 4.1 *g* (see the table). The soccer measurements were made as a player, wearing an instrumented football helmet, headed a regulation soccer ball. The soccer ball was traveling at an average speed of 39.3 ± 1.8 miles per hour. You might think that soccer would be the sport that was least likely to have a high value for these impact forces. However, you must consider the head-on collisions made with a fast-moving soccer ball in this sport.

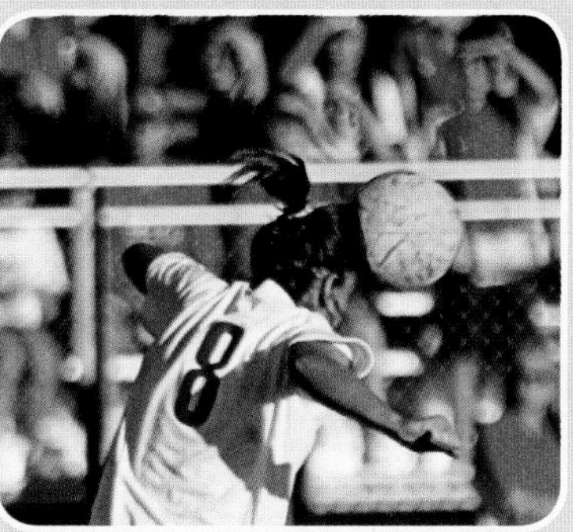

Head-on collision. What do you know about forces that would help you design a better helmet or soccer ball so that this player is not injured?

Table 1 Data collected

Parameter	Football (n = 132)	Hockey (n = 128)	Soccer (n = 23)
Peak *gs*	29.2 ± 1.0	35.0 ± 1.7	54.7[a] ± 4.1

Table of peak *gs*. This table shows the average peak acceleration during the testing of head-on collisions for football, hockey, and soccer.

Data from: Comparison of Impact Data in Hockey, Football, and Soccer from *The Journal of Trauma: Injury, Infection, and Critical Care*, Vol. 48, No. 5 (2000), p. 939 – Table 1.

Chapter 2 Collision Course 71

NOTES:

Head-On Collisions, continued

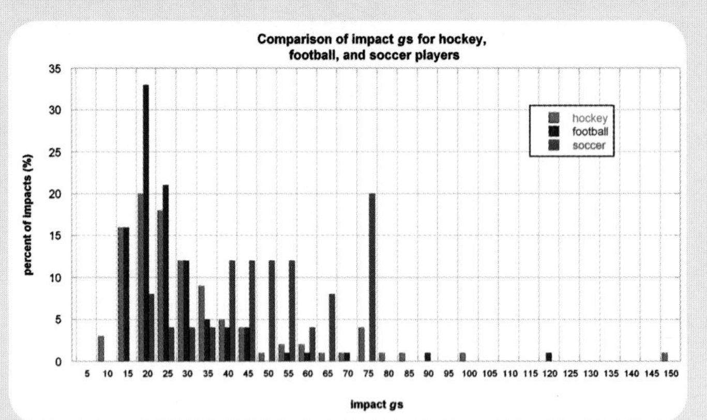

▲ **Comparing the acceleration due to impacts.** This histogram compares the percentage of the impacts occurring at each *g* level for football, hockey, and soccer.

The frequency of head-on collisions in a real soccer game is less than the head-on collisions in a football or hockey game. However, a greater percentage of soccer collisions results in higher *g* values (see the figure) and therefore merits further consideration.

Science has proven that the effects of repeated mild brain injury are cumulative. Repeated low-level injuries may lead to neurological conditions because of these injuries. What can designers of football helmets, hockey helmets, or even soccer balls do to help prevent or lessen these injuries? What have you learned so far in the chapter that can be applied to this technology? Engineers of all types must understand the physics of forces and motion in order to improve our lives.

72 Unit 1 Interactions Are Interesting

NOTES:

READING

Tools of the Trade

How high will a ball bounce when dropped on the floor? The rebound height depends in part on forces the ball experiences. No matter what the size or mass of an object, the forces on each object are equal in size and opposite in direction. The velocity and mass of an object can change the amount of force at impact, but the forces on each object are still equal and opposite (figure 2.15).

Newton's third law is the law of nature that states that forces come in pairs, equal in magnitude and opposite in direction. These forces always act on two *different* objects. You have seen examples of these forces in each of the activities you have completed. The force of your thumb on your finger was one force. The force of your finger on your thumb was the other force. These two forces act on two different objects, your thumb and your finger. The clay ball showed that these forces are equal and opposite as described in Newton's third law. Read more about Sir Isaac Newton and his laws in the sidebar *Newton on the Move* on page 83.

These equal and opposite forces can be represented in a simple mathematical expression: $F_{\text{thumb on finger}} = -F_{\text{finger on thumb}}$. Because force is a vector and thus has direction, forces acting in opposite directions will have opposite signs (+ and −) in algebraic representations. These vectors will point in different directions in graphic representations. Any combination of colliding objects, no matter their mass or velocity at the point of collision, can be represented similarly.

Motions along a straight line are one-dimensional motions. However, things can move in two directions along that line, to the left and to the right.

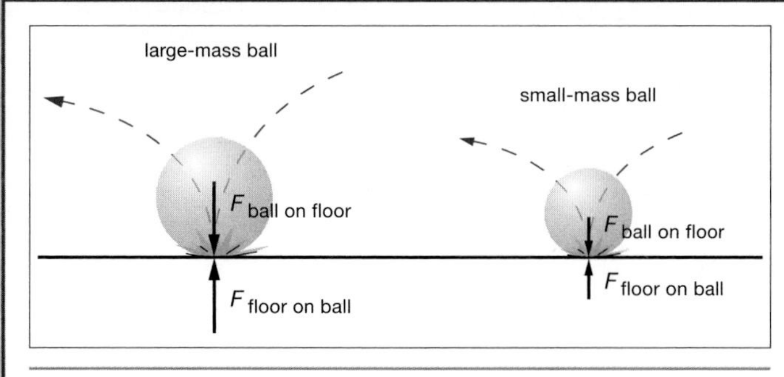

▲ **Figure 2.15 Balls of different mass.** If these balls of different mass bounce off the floor, how do the forces of interaction compare?

NOTES:

Tools of the Trade, continued

In this activity, you will focus on the velocity of a tennis ball. Velocity is a vector, and therefore both the magnitude of the velocity (or the speed) and the direction in which the tennis ball moves are important to consider. You read about how to add these vectors in FYI—*Vectors in One Dimension*.

It is customary to assign positive or negative directions to motions when they are moving along a straight line. Often, objects that move to the right are considered to be moving in the positive direction and objects that move to the left are considered to be moving in the negative direction. This is similar to the number lines you studied in elementary school, where numbers on the left of zero are negative and numbers on the right of zero are positive. However, it does not matter which way these motions are assigned as long as they are consistent and explained.

If you use the directions and signs described here, then velocities to the left (in the negative direction) will have a negative sign assigned to them when they are used in a mathematical equation (figure 2.16). This is the way you will tell in which direction objects are moving. These directions, represented with + and − signs, apply to other vector quantities, like force. Keeping the signs correct in your explanations, labels, and equations is important for understanding the concepts.

Often, you will use Δv, which means the change in velocity. You can calculate this by subtracting the initial velocity (v_i) from the final velocity (v_f). The formula for finding Δv is $\Delta v = v_f - v_i$.

It is very important to assign the correct sign to the velocities when using this formula. Suppose a car that is moving at a speed of 50 kilometers per hour (km/hr) speeds up to 67 km/hr. What would be the car's Δv? Since the car is going in only one direction, you can choose to have it moving in the positive direction. Solving for the car's change in velocity gives us the following:

$$\Delta v = v_f - v_i$$

$$= 67\frac{\text{km}}{\text{hr}} - 50\frac{\text{km}}{\text{hr}}$$

$$= 17\frac{\text{km}}{\text{hr}}$$

You will be swinging tennis balls in the next activity. If the ball moves to the right, it will have a positive velocity. If it moves to the left, it will have a negative velocity.

Remember, good experimental design requires that you repeat a measurement several times, then calculate an average value.

Figure 2.16 Vectors indicate both magnitude and direction. In one dimension (along a line), you can use positive and negative signs to represent the direction that vectors indicate. For example, a tennis ball moving to the left would have a negative velocity if you choose the left direction to be negative. Likewise, a tennis ball moving to the right would have a positive velocity. We will use this method in the examples in this chapter.

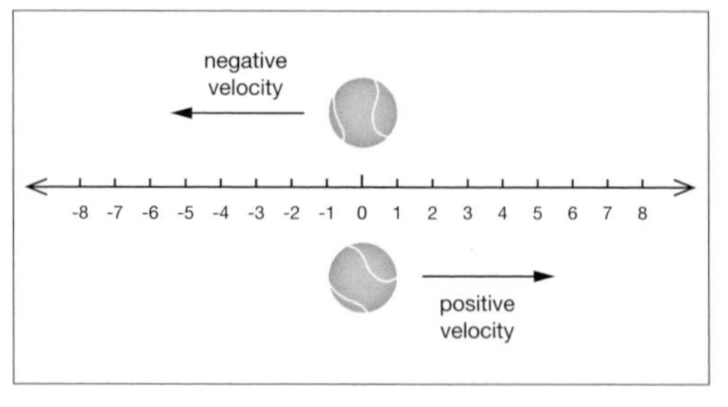

74 Unit 1 Interactions Are Interesting

NOTES:

Experiments are not perfect, and you might observe some uncertainty in your measurements. It is unlikely that you will get the exact same measurement in each of 10 trials. You can calculate the uncertainty associated with a measurement, which will allow you to generalize about scientific laws without worrying about slight variations in measurement.

With sets of measurements, determine the average value ($\bar{x}$) from all of the trials. To estimate your uncertainty, first calculate the range, w. This is the difference between the highest and lowest values. Second, record the number of trials, n. An estimate of uncertainty (error), e, is the range divided by the square root of the number of trials, or

$$e = \frac{w}{\sqrt{n}}$$

It is typical to represent this uncertainty with a ± sign before the uncertainty value, e. This is because uncertainty represents the range of error both above and below the average. For the estimate of uncertainty above, about 60–70 percent of the trials will have values bracketed by $\bar{x} \pm e$.

For example, an average rebound velocity of 7 units to the left was averaged from five trials. The highest rebound velocity was 9 units of velocity, and the lowest rebound velocity was 5 units of velocity. The range (925) was 4 units of velocity. So the uncertainty is calculated by dividing the range of 4 by the square root of 5 (the number of trials). This gives an uncertainty of 1.8. The average value should be reported as −7 ± 1.8 units of velocity (see figure 2.17). This tells you that most of the values lie between −8.8 and −5.2 units of velocity. The negative sign in front of the 7 represents motion in the negative direction (to the left). You can also represent uncertainty in a graph. Figure 2.18 shows how uncertainty is represented on a graph. The bars above and below the point indicate the uncertainty and are called error bars.

Scientists, engineers, and technicians all use these mathematical tools to design and test materials important to their industry. Remember the reference to bouncing balls? Are all balls equally bouncy? Would you want a golf ball to have the same bounce as a softball? What factors do scientists consider when they calculate the exact amount of force required to produce the right bounce? What are the relationships between those factors? These relationships form a law of nature that describes the motion of bouncing balls, crashing cars, and colliding galaxies, as well as any moving system in the universe.

Table of Rebound Velocities

Trial	Units of Velocity
1	-6
2	-9
3	-7
4	-6
5	-5
average	**-7**

▲ **Figure 2.17 Calculating uncertainty.** The uncertainty in your measurements can be calculated. Uncertainty values are reported as a ± value after the average, or mean, of your measurements.

NOTES:

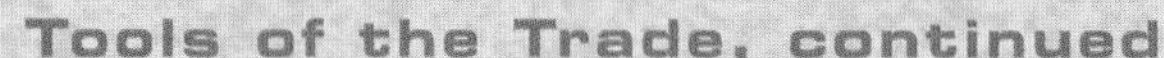

Tools of the Trade, continued

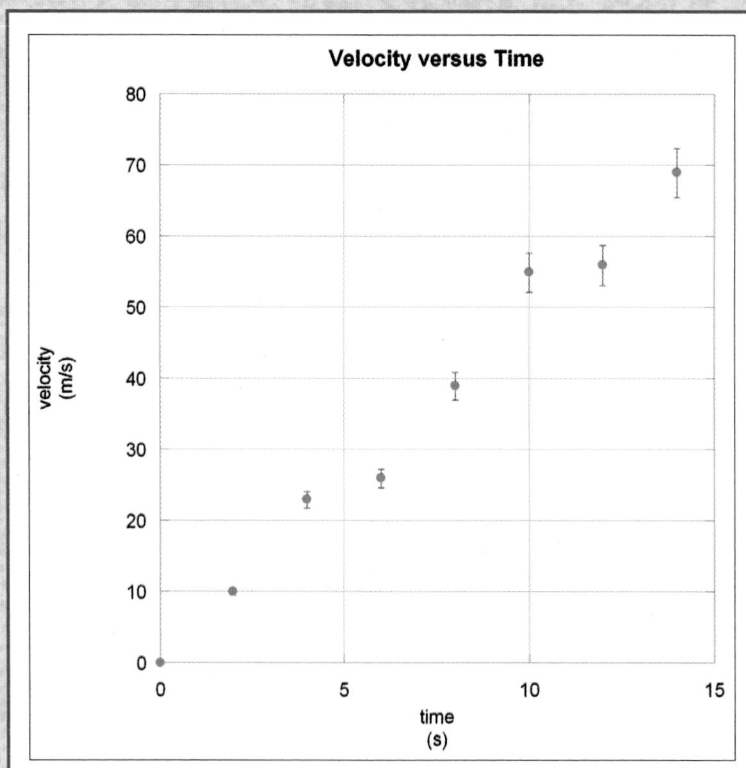

▲ **Figure 2.18 Error bars in graphs.** Uncertainty can be shown in graphs by using error bars with data points. What does the uncertainty tell you about the values shown in this graph?

76 Unit 1 Interactions Are Interesting

NOTES:

Answers to Step 3 are on TE pages 77–78.

2. Explore how the tennis ball–collision apparatus works. In your science notebook, sketch the apparatus and label all the features you think are important.
3. Compare your thoughts from Step 2 with some of the ideas demonstrated by your teacher by answering Steps 3a–d in your science notebook.
   a. Why is it important to adjust the centers of the tennis balls to be at exactly the same level above the table?
   b. Why is it important to position the center of mass of the 2-ball system directly over the origin of your collision axes?
   c. Why is it important that the amount of time for a tennis ball to reach the origin is the same regardless of the position from which it is released (provided the string lengths are the same)?
   d. Why is it important that the speed of the tennis ball at the origin is directly proportional to the swing distance?
4. Determine how to quantify change in velocity (Δv) by doing Steps 4a–g.
   a. Suspend a 1-unit-of-mass tennis ball from each string so that the centers are the same height above the table.
   b. Separate the 2 balls, one at 20 centimeters (cm) to the left of the collision grid's origin and the other 10 cm to the right (figure 2.19).

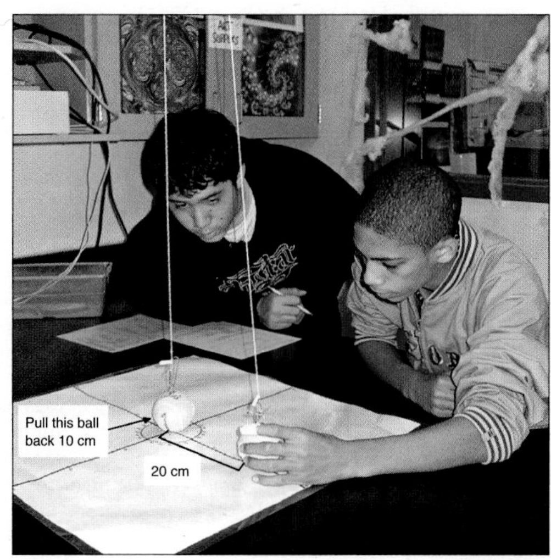

◄ **Figure 2.19 Tennis ball collisions.** Begin your testing with one tennis ball at 20 cm to the left and the other tennis ball 10 cm to the right. How would you represent the swinging with vectors once you release the tennis balls? What signs would you assign to show direction? Remember to use the direction the ball is moving at the point of collision for the initial velocity (v_i) and the direction the ball is moving after collision for the final velocity (v_f).

Answers to Step 3, SE page 77

3a. When the balls collide at the same level, their interaction is in the horizontal plane only. Putting the centers of the tennis balls at the same level simplifies the analysis of collisions by ensuring the forces under investigation are in one dimension. Off-center collisions still exhibit conservation of momentum, but are more difficult for students to analyze, especially early in their exposure to these concepts.

3b. The center of mass of 2 equal-mass balls hanging side by side is the point where they touch. It is the balance point if a rod is attached to the balls. Placing the center of mass directly over the grid origin ensures that rebound displacements after collisions are directly proportional to the velocity after collision, which simplifies the analysis. If the center of mass is off center, one ball will get a "head start" on its eventual rebound distance, which invalidates the simple data analysis.

3c. The time of 1 pendulum swing is independent of amplitude (for amplitudes below about 10°). This property of pendulums makes them important timekeeping devices. Not all students know about this property of pendulums, so you might have to demonstrate it. This property ensures that as long as students release the balls at the same time, the balls will hit the origin at the same time regardless of the amplitude of swing.

3d. This allows students to avoid measuring velocity, a difficult quantity to measure since the ball's velocity is changing at all times.

In Step 4, students begin to use the tennis ball–collision kit to take data.

Help students understand that every measurement involves uncertainty. This uncertainty affects the confidence scientists have in making conclusions from data. Low uncertainty usually increases the confidence, high uncertainty decreases the confidence. Uncertainty is important in this activity because students will eventually compare momentum before and after a collision. These momenta will only be equal on a consistent basis if students include the expected measurement uncertainty in their analysis. Otherwise, they might misinterpret the data and not conclude that momentum is conserved.

Answers to Steps 4 and 5, SE pages 77–78

4f. Using the formula $v_{\text{ball}} = v_f - v_i$, an example of a possible student answer is

$v_{\text{left ball}} = (-6 \pm 2 \text{ velocity units}) - (20 \text{ velocity units})$

$v_{\text{left ball}} = -26 \pm 2 \text{ velocity units}$

$v_{\text{right ball}} = (14 \pm 2 \text{ velocity units}) - (-10 \text{ velocity units})$

$v_{\text{right ball}} = 24 \pm 2 \text{ velocity units.}$

Notice that the initial velocities have no uncertainty since students hold the ball at a prescribed swing distance. Also, notice that the magnitudes of the Δv are equal within the uncertainty of measurement, but opposite in direction.

4g. Student vector drawings should be similar to figure T2.12.

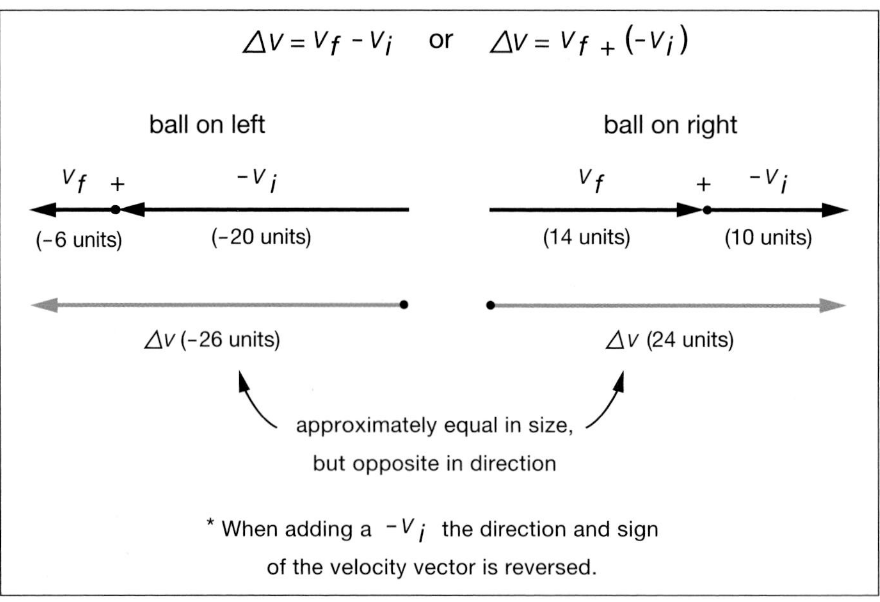

▲ **Figure T2.12 Vector addition.** This sketch is representative of the vector addition required for Step 4g.

Answers to Step 5 are on TE pages 79–80.

For convenience, refer to a ball positioned over the 20-cm mark on the left as having 20 units of velocity going to the right, *at the point of collision*. Represent this velocity with a vector arrow 20 units long, pointing to the right. Call this the initial velocity (v_i). Since this ball is moving to the right, you will assign its value a positive sign to indicate the direction. In which direction and how long should the velocity vector of the other ball be? Will the value have a positive or negative sign?

c. Release both balls simultaneously so that they *bounce* along the original axis.

d. Measure and record the maximum distance each center of mass rebounds.

Remember to record the distance that is directly below the center of mass of the tennis ball.

e. Repeat Steps 4a–d several times to determine the average value and uncertainty.

f. Determine Δv for each ball algebraically. (Use the definition for Δ, $\Delta v = v_f - v_i$, where *f* means "final" and *i* means "initial.")

Don't forget that balls moving to the right have a positive velocity and balls moving to the left have a negative velocity. This is true only because we define the right to be the positive direction.

g. Determine Δv for each ball with vector math. Use the same definition of Δ as in Step 4f, except draw vector sketches as described in *FYI—Vectors in One Dimension.*

5. Determine which velocity vectors (v_i, v_f, or Δv) are the best predictors of the forces that each ball experiences during collision by completing Steps 5a–e.

a. Describe directions and relative magnitudes of the force on each tennis ball.

Remember the clay ball. Imagine a clay ball placed between the colliding tennis balls. What does the amount and direction of squishing tell you about the force acting on each ball?

b. How are the directions and magnitudes of the initial velocity vectors (v_i) related (if at all) to the directions and relative magnitudes of the force each ball experiences during collisions? Provide labeled vector drawings to support your answer.

c. Repeat Step 5a for the final velocities (v_f) of each ball.

d. Repeat Step 5a for the change in velocity vector (Δv).

e. Use your answers from Steps 5a–d to determine which velocity vector (v_i, v_f, or Δv) is the best predictor of the force each ball experiences. Justify your answer.

78 | Unit 1 Interactions Are Interesting

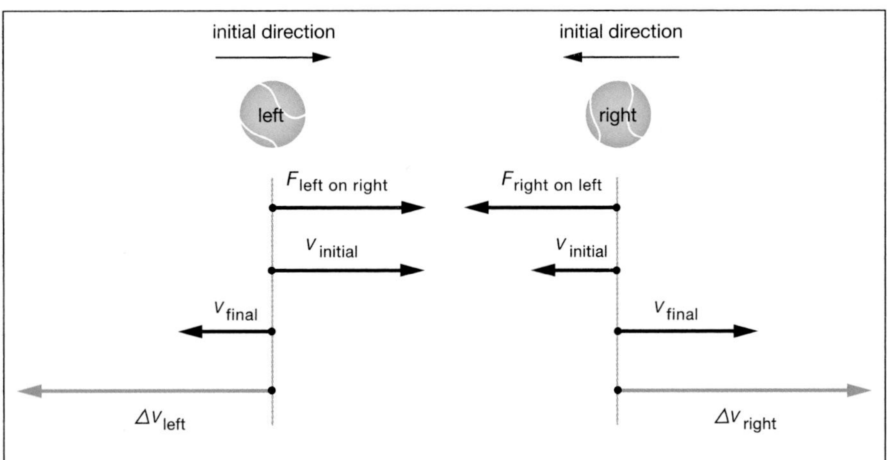

Caption: For the ball on the left, $v_{initial}$ is in the opposite direction to F_{right} on left. v_{final} is in the same direction as F_{right} on left. For each ball, the direction of Δv is the same as the direction of the force on that ball. The Δv for each ball has equal magnitude (within measurement error) and F_{left} on right = $-F_{right}$ on left.

◀ **Figure T2.13 Vector comparison.** This vector sketch helps students compare initial velocity for Step 5.

Answers to Step 6 are on TE page 80.

6. Develop a quantitative relationship between force (F) and change in velocity (Δv) by selecting the most appropriate math symbol or word to complete the following statements in Steps 6a–g. Be prepared to justify your choices with the class.

Possible math symbols are =, >, <, ∝; possible words are *opposite, same, directly proportional to, inversely proportional to*. You can use filler words like *and, as,* and *the*.

a. $F_{\text{ball 2 on ball 1}}$ ______ $-F_{\text{ball 1 on ball 2}}$.

Consider the ball that starts on the left as ball 1 and the ball that starts on the right as ball 2.

b. From previous activities, force is ______ Δt.

Think back to the activity *Safe Landing* where you stepped off a stair with both stiff and bent legs.

c. From previous activities, force is ______ Δv.

Think back to the activity *Speed Bumps* where you changed the velocity and observed the effect on a clay ball.

d. Force is ______ m.

Think back again to *Speed Bumps* where you changed the mass of the toy vehicle and observed the effect on a clay ball.

e. The units for force ______ the units for $\frac{m\Delta v}{\Delta t}$.

f. In general, for each ball, $F_{\text{on ball}}$ ______ $\frac{m\Delta v}{\Delta t}$.

g. As a reasonable statement of cause and effect for each ball, $F\Delta t$ ______ $m\Delta v$.

7. Check your answers with another team. Discuss any differences you have and decide on the best answer. Be prepared to share your answers in a class discussion.
8. Read *Moving on Impulse* to learn more about the valuable relationship that you have just developed.

5a. The force of the left tennis ball on the right tennis ball is equal in magnitude and opposite in direction to the force of the right tennis ball on the left tennis ball.

5b-e. Student vector drawings should be similar to figure T2.13.

The direction of the initial velocity vector is in the opposite direction of the force vector from the other ball. But this is not always the case. If both balls head in the same initial direction when they collide, then one ball's initial velocity is in the same direction as the force from the other ball, and the other ball's initial velocity is in the opposite direction as the force from the first ball. Initial velocity is not a reliable predictor of the direction of force.

Since force and velocity are quantities with different units, their magnitudes cannot be meaningfully compared.

The direction of the final velocity vector is in the same direction as the force vector from the other ball. But this is not always the case. If the initial velocity of one ball is far greater than the other ball, the fastest ball will continue in the same direction and the other ball will rebound in the opposite direction; the first ball experiences a force from the other ball, which is in an opposite direction from its motion. Thus, final velocity is not a good predictor of the direction of force.

The change in velocity vector of a ball is always in the same direction as the force on that ball due to the other ball. Thus, the direction given by the change in velocity of a ball is the most reliable predictor of the direction of force on that ball.

This is a pivotal finding for students. They will use this key, measurable quantity (Δv) to quantify force. Thus, change in velocity is the primary concrete observation used to learn about the abstract and invisible quantity called force.

Answers to Step 6, SE page 79

6. Emphasize to students that, for now, their justification for each statement is just as important as their answer, because the justification helps you assess the way they are linking evidence to relationships. If that process is not going well for students, you must address the problem explicitly. Remind students that class discussion will eventually help them check their answers, but for now, practicing how to link what they see to what it means is most important.
   a. $F_{\text{ball 2 on ball 1}} \underline{\ =\ } -F_{\text{ball 1 on ball 2}}$

      This is according to Newton's third law that states that forces *always* occur in pairs, equal in size and opposite in direction (thus, the negative sign) with each force acting on different objects.
   b. From previous activities, force is <u>inversely proportional to Δt</u>.

      Students saw in the activity *Safe Landing* that as the time during the force interaction between them and the floor increased (with bent legs), the magnitude of the force decreased.
   c. From previous activities, force is <u>$\propto$, or directly proportional to Δv</u>.

      Students saw in the activity *Speed Bumps* that as the velocity of the toy car increased, the force on the car increased.
   d. Force is <u>$\propto$, or directly proportional to m</u>.

      Students saw in *Speed Bumps* that as the mass was increased, the force on the car at impact increased. You can also refer them to figure 2.15 in the student book for added reinforcement.
   e. The units for force <u>are the same as</u> the units for $\frac{m\Delta v}{\Delta t}$.

      The units for force are $\frac{(\text{kg})(\text{m})}{\text{sec}^2}$, which is equivalent to a newton (N). The units for $\frac{m\Delta v}{\Delta t}$ with mass in kilograms (kg) are $\frac{(\text{kg})\left(\frac{\text{m}}{\text{sec}}\right)}{\text{sec}} = \frac{(\text{kg})(\text{m})}{\text{sec}^2}$.
   f. In general, for each ball, $F_{\text{on ball}} \underline{\ =\ } \frac{m\Delta v}{\Delta t}$.

      This comes from a match in the units as well as the relationships stated in Steps 6b–d.
   g. As a reasonable statement of cause and effect for each ball, $F\Delta t \underline{\ =\ } m\Delta v$.

      This is just an algebraic manipulation of the variables in the equation from Step 6f.

READING

Moving on Impulse

Have you ever wondered why coaches always emphasize "follow-through" in the sports of tennis, golf, baseball, and boxing? How is it that a skilled karate athlete can break a board or a stack of cement blocks with a hand or a foot (figure 2.20)? Your knowledge of the relationship of force, time, mass, and velocity can help you answer these questions. Consider the equation that you developed in previous activities:

$$F\Delta t = m\Delta v$$

The product of force and change in time ($F\Delta t$) is known as **impulse**. This is the relationship that explains the need for follow-through in many sports. It is also the scientific reasoning behind air bags and baseball or softball gloves.

▲ **Figure 2.20 Karate kick.** Why does follow-through help this athlete break the boards?

Suppose you hit a fly ball into center field. The ball travels at a certain changing velocity. As it is caught by a softball player, its velocity falls to zero. The mass of the ball, however, does not change in flight. You can determine the change in velocity (Δv) as the ball goes from some initial velocity just before it is caught to zero velocity when it stops. Therefore, the $m\Delta v$ part of the equation, $F\Delta t = m\Delta v$, is constant no matter how the ball stops, in a hand or in a glove.

Now look at the other side of the equation, the $F\Delta t$. You or a ball-glove engineer can manipulate this relationship. When you catch a fly ball, do you want to feel a large force or a small force? If you don't want it to hurt very much, of course you want a small force. What could you do so that you only feel a small force? First, you could wear a padded glove. Second, you could move your hand in the direction the ball is traveling as you catch it. These two actions—using a padded glove and moving with the ball as you catch it—influence the *time* that the force acts on your hand. If you want a small force, then you want the maximum amount of time for the force to act.

This same idea is the explanation for follow-through. There are times when you hit a baseball or a golf ball that you want the ball to go as far as possible. In these cases, you want the ball to have the biggest change in

In Step 7, students check their answers with another team and discuss any differences. Lead the class in a discussion of the concepts in Step 6. Encourage students to record any changes to their thinking and answers in a different color so that you will have a record of their evolving understanding.

Students read *Moving on Impulse* in Step 8. Again, choose a literacy strategy that best fits your student population. A T-table is a good strategy to suggest. Have students write important facts or concepts on one side of the table and questions that they have about what they read on the other.  See *How to Use and Create Organizing Tables* in the How To section at the back of the book. You can use their questions to lead a short discussion after everyone has had a chance to read. You should note that in the example given, catching a softball with a glove not only reduces the force by increasing the time for the ball to stop, but it also increases the surface area. This reduces the pressure on the hand according to the equation: *pressure = force/area*. (This aspect of reducing the pressure by increasing the area is not discussed in this section.)

In Step 9, students test different scenarios using different initial velocities and balls of different mass. Students will need to create a data table to record their observations. Use your judgment regarding the number of examples that your students need to reinforce the relationships developed above. Remember, broadening the context of applicability helps students transfer knowledge. But too many examples can decrease motivation after a while. Consider having students generate another 2 or 3 examples. Emphasize the importance of checking the principles and concept relationships for each example.

Answers to Stop and Think—Part I, SE pages 81–82

1. Student sketches should be similar to figure T2.14. Note that when a ball bounces and changes direction, the change in velocity vector is longer than either the initial velocity vector or the final velocity vector. This can only happen as the result of a relatively large force. That is, a relatively large force is required to change the direction of a moving object, a fact that plays an important role in many motions.

Answers to Stop & Think are on TE pages 81–82.

velocity possible—the biggest Δv. Let's look at the equation again: $F\Delta t = m\Delta v$. You know that the mass of the ball doesn't change when you strike it, so the mass in the equation remains constant. How would you get the biggest change in velocity? You would want to have a large force acting over the greatest amount of time. So when you want a baseball to have a large change in velocity, you would hit it with a great amount of force. And follow-through keeps the bat in contact with the ball for the maximum amount of time.

The product of mass and velocity, mv, is known as **momentum** and is represented by the symbol p. Momentum can be thought of as mass in motion. If an object is in motion, it has momentum—if it has no motion, it has no momentum. We can see from the equation

$$p = mv$$

that an object can have a large momentum if it has a large mass or a large velocity—or both. Could a small car have the same momentum as a large truck? Yes, if the car is moving at a fast speed and the truck is moving at a slow speed, then they could have the same momentum. And, of course, if both the car and the truck were stopped, they would both have zero momentum.

SCI LINKS NSTA
Go to: www.scilinks.org
Topic: momentum
Code: 2Inquiry81a
Topic: impulse
Code: 2Inquiry81b

9. Repeat Step 4 for different tennis ball collisions, some with different mass and some with different velocities, as recommended by your teacher. Record your observations in a data table in your science notebook.

Stop & THINK

PART I

Work out answers to these questions in your science notebook individually, then meet with team members to reach consensus. Keep careful records of any changes in your answers, especially the reason for any change.

1. Consider a tennis ball hitting the floor and bouncing as you answer Questions 1a–d.
   a. Draw a properly scaled and labeled before-and-after sketch representing a 0.05-kg tennis ball hitting the floor at 4.0 meters per second (m/sec), remaining in contact with the floor for 0.10 sec, then rebounding at 3.0 m/sec.
   b. Draw the following 2 scaled vectors: (1) F_{max} of the floor on the ball and (2) F_{max} of the ball on the floor.

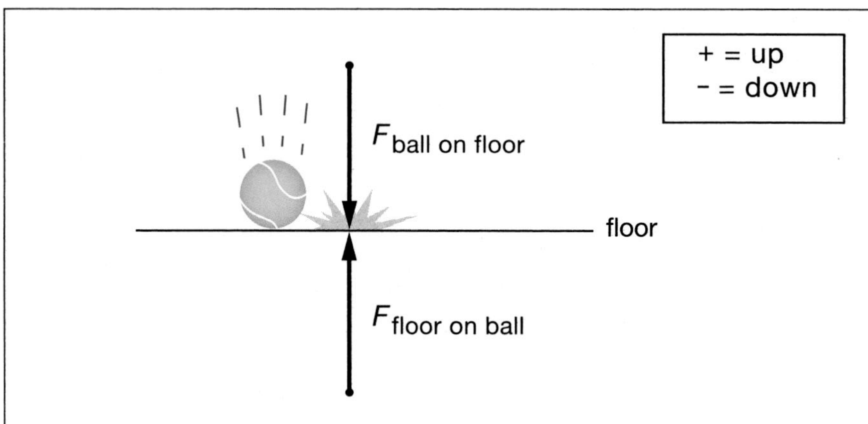

$$F_{\text{floor on ball}} = \frac{m\Delta v}{\Delta t} = \frac{(0.05\ \text{kg})(3.0\ \text{m/sec} - (-4.0\ \text{m/sec})}{(0.10\ \text{s})}$$

$$F_{\text{floor on ball}} = 3.5\ \text{N}$$

Both $F_{\text{floor on ball}}$ and Δv for the ball are positive, which is up.

▶ **Figure T2.14 Sample student sketch.** Student sketches and calculations for Question 1 should be similar to this.

1d. The sign of the force indicates the direction of the force in this case. The direction of the force and the direction of Δv are the same.

2. The magnitude of the momentum is the same before each collision as it is after the collision, as students developed in Step 6d. The sign for momentum is different before and after, indicating the direction of the momentum is different. Momentum of the system is conserved.

STOP & THINK, PART I, continued

Scaled vectors are those in which you use exact measurements and an explanation. For example, you may want to let 1 cm on your paper represent 1 N. You should put a key on your paper indicating 1 cm = 1 N.

c. Calculate the magnitude of force during impact. Show the equation and all your work.

d. What is the significance of the sign of the force and its relationship to Δv?

2 Think about your colliding tennis balls from the previous activity. How does the momentum before and after a collision compare for each tennis ball? Use evidence from your investigation to support your answer.

Part II: Sticky Situation

Materials

For each team of 4 students

1 tennis ball–collision kit, which includes

- 2 tennis balls marked "1 unit of mass," with Velcro strips and a cup hook
- 1 tennis ball marked "2 units of mass," with Velcro strips and a cup hook
- 2 lengths of string long enough to reach from a desk to the ceiling
- 1 collision grid with protractor markings and a center string
- paper clips
- tape

access to a computer for the animation *Elastic and Inelastic Collisions*

4 *Mathematical Relationships* handouts (or transparency)

NOTES:

Newton on the Move

SIDEBAR

Motion—changes in motion—forces. These are concepts that are important to everyday life. How are they connected? Is there a cause-and-effect relationship among these concepts? A famous scientist who lived over 300 years ago first made connections between these concepts. Sir Isaac Newton (1642–1727) summed up motion and the underlying causes of motion in three laws. **Newton's laws** give us the connection between cause and effect.

▲ **Sir Isaac Newton (1642–1727).** The English physicist and mathematician Isaac Newton was born to a poor farming family. Luckily for the scientific community, he did not like farming and turned his attention to studies at the University of Cambridge. He published the *Principia* in 1687, which became one of the most important and influential works on physics of all time.

The law of inertia is often used to describe Newton's first law. It states that there will be no change in an object's motion unless acted upon by an outside force. In other words, if an object is in motion, it will remain in motion (along a straight line) unless some force acts upon it. A passenger in a moving car is pressed up against the seat belt as a car stops suddenly. The body continues in motion, and the force that stops it is the force supplied by the seat belt.

"Force is directly proportional to the time rate of change in velocity" is one way of stating Newton's second law. This chapter introduces this law and it is the focus of chapter 4. Newton's third law, which states, "Forces occur in pairs, equal in magnitude and opposite in direction," is the focus of this chapter. Newton's laws of motion, first published more than 300 years ago, tell us how forces affect the motion of objects. The same laws apply whether you are observing a pesky bee zigzagging through the air or a planet in orbit around the Sun. Newton's laws do not apply to the motions of very small objects like single atoms or electrons or to objects moving near the speed of light. But they apply to almost everything else.

Process and Procedure

Part II: Sticky Situation

Materials

For each team of 4 students

4 pairs of safety goggles

1 tennis ball–collision kit (see *Advance Preparation*), which includes

- 2 tennis balls marked "1 unit of mass," with Velcro strips and cup hook
- 1 tennis ball marked "2 units of mass," with Velcro strip and cup hook
- 2 lengths of string long enough to reach from a desk to the ceiling
- 1 collision grid with protractor markings and a center string
- paper clips
- tape

4 copies, 1 transparency, or both of copymaster 2.1a, *Mathematical Relationships*

TRCD

access to computers and *SRCD* (optional)

For the teacher

1 copy of copymaster 2.1b, *Mathematical Relationships Answer Key*

NOTES:

Have your students read the introduction to Part II. In Step 1, lead a class discussion as students derive and analyze some important mathematical relationships. You can make a copy of copymaster 2.1a, *Mathematical Relationships* for each student or make a transparency so that your students can use it as a guide to write the information in their science notebooks. You might also choose to use the transparency for your discussion and a handout for students to record their work.

Resist talking students through this part. Guide them to think through each step carefully and come up with answers and justifications on their own. Start with a little more guidance to get your students thinking in the right direction, and then gradually allow them to do more on their own. Emphasize to students the importance of writing their justifications by each step. Much of their justifications will be based on algebraic rules. You may have to remind them of some of these rules. Answers are found on copymaster 2.1b, *Answer Key for Mathematical Relationships.*

Students read about the law of conservation of momentum in Step 2. Ask questions after they have read the paragraphs to ensure that they understood what they read.

Newton on the Move, continued

These laws have been tested throughout history. They are as valid today as when they were first written. This is significant because in the physical sciences, changes in theories and understanding are more the rule than the exception.

The laws of motion are only part of the contribution that Newton made to science. He is also known for his contributions in chemistry, light and optics, and even the discovery of calculus. However, the dispute over the person responsible for the discovery of calculus, Newton or Gottfried Wilhelm Leibniz, went on for more than 50 years. This dispute kept the citizens of Newton's country from accepting Newtonian science. Even the British mathematicians would not share the researches of the Continental colleges for over a century.

One of the best known stories about Newton is about his ideas concerning gravity. The story goes that he was sitting under an apple tree when an apple fell, hitting Newton on the head. Some stories go so far as to suggest that the apple's impact somehow made him aware of the force of gravity. Most of this story is just a legend, but there may be some truth to part of it. John Conduitt, Newton's assistant at the royal mint, described the event when he wrote about Newton's life:

"In the year 1666 he retired again from Cambridge . . . to his mother in Lincolnshire and while he was musing in a garden it came into his thought that the power of gravity (which brought an apple from a tree to the ground) was not limited to a certain distance from earth, but that this power must extend much further than was usually thought. Why not as high as the Moon thought he to himself and that if so, that must influence her motion and perhaps retain her in her orbit, whereupon he fell a-calculating what would be the effect of that superposition . . ." (Keesing, R. G. The History of Newton's Apple Tree, *Contemporary Physics*, 39, 377–91, 1998)

Students in physics have been constructing their understanding of these laws of nature for over 300 years. How can these laws of motion explain what we see in nature? What questions are yet to be answered about motion and gravity? Scientific discovery often comes from simple questions and the pursuit to answer those questions.

SCI LINKS NSTA
Topic: Sir Isaac Newton
Go to: www.scilinks.org
Code: 2Inquiry84

Process and Procedure

In Part I, you developed a way to quantify the amount of force an object experiences during a bouncing collision: ($F = \frac{m\Delta v}{\Delta t}$). This type of collision is called an **elastic collision**. Elastic collisions occur when colliding objects rebound or bounce off each other. But not all collisions result in bouncing. Sometimes objects hit and stick together (sometimes called an **inelastic collision**).

In Step 3, students once again derive a mathematical model. Either give each student a copy of copymaster 2.1a, *Mathematical Relationships* or have the students copy the information from the transparency into their science notebooks. Students should be able to work more independently on this step since they have done Step 1 with guidance. You decide how much guidance your class needs, but keep your expectations high and allow the students to struggle some and come up with answers on their own. The payoff for allowing students to work independently is much greater than when they simply copy down answers.

Answers are found on copymaster 2.1b, *Answer Key for Mathematical Relationships*.

In Step 4, students design a step-by-step procedure using the last equation (Question 2d on the handout) as the design equation. The design equation

$$m_{\text{car 1}}\, v_{\text{i, car 1}} = m_{(\text{car 1 + car 2})}\, v_{\text{f, both}}$$

suggests that to predict the final velocity of the 2-car system (as an example investigation), students would have to measure the remaining variables in the design equation, namely

$$m_{\text{car 1}},\ v_{\text{i, car 1}} \text{ and } m_{\text{car 2}}.$$

Students would write steps that show using different initial velocities and masses for the moving ball (car 1) and then predict how far the 2-ball system (car 1 + car 2) swings after collision. Approve their designs in Step 5 before allowing teams to conduct their investigations. Be sure their procedures include the necessary calculations for determining the final velocity and appropriate data tables.

Monitor the progress of each team as it carries out its procedure in Step 6. Make sure each member of the team is recording all the data. In Step 7, students compose a caption for their summary data tables. There is no one correct method of making a data table for this investigation. But many scientists would use a matrix with measured quantities down the left-most column ($m_{\text{car 1}}$, $m_{\text{car 2}}$, v_{i}, $_{\text{car 1}}$, v_{f}, $_{\text{both}}$) and the trial number across the top row.

If students plot the initial momentum versus the final momentum, they will get a straight line passing through the origin. You may want to do this with your class. The line will have a slope of 1. This is one way to verify that momentum is conserved since the equation for the line would be

$$y = mx + b$$
$$p_{\text{i}} = (1)\, p_{\text{f}} + 0$$
$$p_{\text{i}} = p_{\text{f}}.$$

This confirms the law of conservation of momentum.

There is a computer animation of collisions called *Elastic and Inelastic Collisions* on the *SRCD*. You may want your students to have more practice in manipulating the mass and velocity of objects involved in these types of collisions.

Imagine waiting patiently in your car at an intersection. Suddenly, there is a crash from behind! The bumpers lock, and both cars skid forward. Could you determine if the other driver was speeding in addition to not paying attention?

It turns out you can, and so can the police officer investigating the accident scene (figure 2.21). To do this, you will use what you learned about force in Part I to develop a powerful tool for predicting what happens to objects in collisions. Then you and your team will design and conduct activities to test your predictive tool.

1. Participate in a class discussion by completing Question 1 on the handout or recording your thoughts in your science notebook as your teacher directs. Be sure to ask questions if you do not understand.
2. Read the following paragraphs about the important relationship that you just developed at the end of Step 1.

▲ **Figure 2.21 Accident scene.** What mathematical relationships help this police officer reconstruct the accident scene? Can he determine who is at fault?

Recall that the product, mv, is called momentum and is given the symbol p. Momentum is a vector, like force and velocity are, since it has magnitude and direction. If an object experiences a change in velocity, it experiences a change in momentum, Δp. In what ways can you change velocity? You can change either the magnitude (the speed) or the direction of the moving object. If you do, then you change the object's momentum as well.

When a variable does not change in a before-and-after event, then that variable is conserved. Was momentum conserved when you collided two tennis balls in Part I? If you look at your data, you will see that yes, momentum was conserved within the range of uncertainty. Momentum does not change in *any* interaction between two objects even though velocities change. Momentum is conserved in both elastic and inelastic collisions. This result is called the **law of conservation of momentum.**

3. Participate in another class discussion about the *conservation* of momentum. Complete Question 2 on the handout or record your answers in your science notebook as directed by your teacher. Ask questions if you do not understand.
4. Design a step-by-step procedure using Part I as a guide for an experiment to test the design equation in Question 2d of the handout or transparency. Use a variety of masses and initial velocities. Steps 4a–f will help guide you in your design.

Answers to Reflect and Connect, SE pages 86–87

1. Velocity was not conserved: the change in velocity of the system was not zero in all cases. For example, when equal-mass balls hit and stick after one ball is given 10 units of initial velocity (and the other is initially at rest), the resulting 2-ball system has a velocity of 5 units. Clearly, 5 does not equal 10, and therefore velocity is not conserved.

2a. The answers to this problem are below. Δv_A, Δv_B, Δv_{system}

Students must first calculate the final velocity of the system before they can calculate any of the remaining quantities.

$$\Delta p_{system} = (m_A v_{f,A} + m_B v_{f,B}) - (m_A v_{i,A} + m_B v_{i,B}) = 0$$

(conservation of momentum)

Since the particles hit and stick, the combined mass moves at the final velocity. Thus, the equation above can be rewritten, after some simple algebra, as

$$m_A v_{i,A} + m_B v_{i,B} = m_{A+B} v_f$$

$$(0.01\text{ g})(4\frac{\text{m}}{\text{sec}}) + (0.02\text{ g})(-3\frac{\text{m}}{\text{sec}}) = (0.01\text{ g} + 0.02\text{ g})(v_f)$$

$$v_f = -0.67\frac{\text{m}}{\text{sec}}.$$

This means the 2 particles stick together and move to the left at a relatively small velocity.

$$\Delta v_A = (-0.67\frac{\text{m}}{\text{sec}}) - (4\frac{\text{m}}{\text{sec}}) = -4.67\frac{\text{m}}{\text{sec}}$$

$$\Delta v_B = (-0.67\frac{\text{m}}{\text{sec}}) - (3\frac{\text{m}}{\text{sec}}) = 2.33\frac{\text{m}}{\text{sec}}$$

$$\Delta v_{system} = \Delta v_{system,f} - \Delta v_{system,i}$$

$$= (-0.67\frac{\text{m}}{\text{sec}}) - (4\frac{\text{m}}{\text{sec}} + (-3\frac{\text{m}}{\text{sec}}))$$

$$= -1.67\frac{\text{m}}{\text{sec}}$$

Notice that this value is not equal to zero, indicating that change in velocity is not a conserved quantity.

2b. Δp_A, Δp_B, Δp_{system}

p_{system} was calculated in 2a.

$$\Delta p_A = m_A v_{f,A} - m_A v_{i,A} = (0.01\text{g})(-0.67\frac{\text{m}}{\text{sec}}) - (0.01\text{g})(4\frac{\text{m}}{\text{sec}})$$

$$\Delta p_A = -0.047\frac{\text{g m}}{\text{sec}}$$

$$\Delta p_B = m_B v_{f,B} - m_B v_{i,B} = (0.02\text{g})(-0.67\frac{\text{m}}{\text{sec}}) - (0.02\text{g})(-3\frac{\text{m}}{\text{sec}})$$

$$\Delta p_B = 0.047\frac{\text{g m}}{\text{sec}}$$

Note that when you add $\Delta p_A + \Delta p_B$, the result is zero, which confirms the law of conservation of momentum.

Answers to Reflect and Connect are on TE pages 86–87.

a. How can I model the design equation in Question 2d of the handout or transparency with the tennis ball–collision kit?
b. What masses and velocities will I use in each trial?
c. How many trials should I do, and how will I determine the uncertainty associated with my design?
d. How will I control the experiment so that I can be confident in the results?
e. What values and measurements do I need to record in my data table?
f. How can I use a summary table to display all the important relationships that have to be calculated?

5. Have your teacher approve your design and make careful notes regarding any changes you made based on feedback.
6. Carry out your step-by-step procedure; be careful to organize your data into clearly labeled tables and show all important calculations.
7. Compose a caption for your summary data table that communicates the effectiveness (or lack of effectiveness) of the data in confirming the law of conservation of momentum. Use the design equation in Question 2d of the handout or transparency.
8. Use the computer animation *Elastic and Inelastic Collisions* to model these collisions on a computer as your teacher directs.

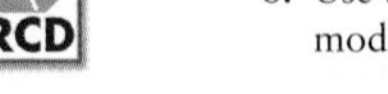

Reflect and Connect

Work by yourself on these questions, then meet with your team and discuss any differences. Record the reasons for any changes to your original answers.

1. Think back to all the interactions you observed in Parts I and II of this activity. Momentum was conserved in each interaction. Was velocity conserved? Prove your point with labeled vector sketches, using at least 1 collision from each part (elastic collision and inelastic collision) as an example.

Use the following information for Questions 2–3.

Clouds form when water vapor condenses on tiny dust particles. Those dust particles form when smaller, electrically charged objects collide to make larger particles. In one such collision, particle A moving at 4 m/sec to the right with a mass of 0.01 grams (g) and +2 charge hits particle B moving at 3 m/sec to the left with a mass of 0.02 g and a charge of −4. They hit head on and stick together to form a larger particle onto which water vapor condenses.

2. Determine the following values for Questions 2a–c using scaled vector sketches and supporting calculations.

2c. F_A and F_B (assuming a 0.01-sec collision)

$$F_A = \frac{m\Delta v_A}{\Delta t} = \frac{(0.01g)(\frac{1\ \text{kg}}{1{,}000\ g})(-4.67\frac{\text{m}}{\text{sec}})}{(0.10\ \text{sec})} = -0.00047\ \text{N}$$ (This is the force of B on A.)

$$F_B = \frac{m\Delta v_B}{\Delta t} = \frac{(0.02g)(\frac{1\ \text{kg}}{1{,}000\ g})(2.33\frac{\text{m}}{\text{sec}})}{(0.10\ \text{sec})} = 0.00047\ \text{N}$$ (This is the force of A on B.)

Notice that the forces are equal in size but opposite in direction, confirming Newton's third law of motion. This is also a confirmation that Newton's third law and conservation of momentum are different ways of stating the same physical law.

3. When you add $\Delta p_A + \Delta p_B$, the result is zero, which supports the law of conservation of momentum. The forces are equal in size but opposite in direction, each force acting on a different object, thus confirming Newton's third law of motion.
4. The players' hands must have had the same amount of momentum in opposite directions. Since momentum is conserved and the ball came to rest (and thus the players' hands) after they hit the ball, the momentum was zero after the hit. Before the hit, the total momentum of the 2 hands also must be zero since momentum is conserved. Players on opposite sides of the net would have hand velocities in opposite directions and so their velocities would have opposite signs, and each velocity would have the same magnitude (same speed) assuming their hands had the same mass.
5. Students should indicate that the mass before and after a collision is the same (at least for the tennis ball collisions). Velocity before and after a collision is not always the same and therefore is not conserved as seen in several previous examples. Momentum is always the same before and after any type of collision. Momentum is always conserved.

EXPLAIN

Getting Real: Collisions in Two Dimensions

Activity Overview

Getting Real: Collisions in Two Dimensions asks students to think about the very same set of conceptual relationships as the last activity, but in two dimensions rather than in one dimension.

The activity asks students to make tennis balls collide, approaching each other from right angles. The balls hit and stick together, and the two-ball system moves off in a new direction and with a new velocity. Therefore, there has been a change in momentum of each of the balls. But the total system momentum is still conserved, something students will design an activity to verify.

You can find the optional activity *Electrostatic Fanatic* on the *TRCD* that uses two-dimensional motion and electrostatic forces. Students use charged balloons instead of tennis balls. Use this activity as a second part for this explain if your state standards require students to know Coulomb's law.

Completion of *Getting Real: Collisions in Two Dimensions* is essential if students are to be successful in Part II of the evaluate activity. Should you decide to omit this activity

You must first find the final velocity of the system before finding the remaining values. Use the law of conservation of momentum in the form,

$$\Delta p_{system} = (m_A v_{f,A} + m_B v_{f,B}) - (m_A v_{i,A} + m_B v_{i,B}) = 0.$$

Since the objects hit and stick together, the equation becomes

$$m_A v_{i,A} + m_B v_{i,B} = m_{A+B} v_f.$$

a. $\Delta v_A, \Delta v_B, \Delta v_{system}$
b. $\Delta p_A, \Delta p_B, \Delta p_{system}$
c. F_A and F_B (assuming a 0.01-sec collision)

3. What is the significance of Δp_{system} that you calculated in Question 2b? What is the significance of the values of F_A and F_B from Question 2c?
4. Two volleyball players on opposite sides of the net jump into the air to hit the ball. They hit the ball at the same time, and the ball does not move but comes to rest in midair. What can you say about the original momentum of each of the player's hands? Explain your answer.
5. Answer the focus question from the beginning of this activity: "How do factors such as velocity, mass, and others before a collision compare with the same factors after a collision?"

Getting Real: Collisions in Two Dimensions

EXPLAIN

One-dimensional interactions are interesting, but not very common in everyday life. It's more common to see objects interact at various angles, not along a straight line. A small rock glances off your windshield, for example, leaving behind the results of its change in momentum. Gas molecules inside a balloon rebound off each other at all angles and hit the balloon wall, causing the inside pressure. A linebacker drives a running back out of bounds with an angled hit (figure 2.22).

To understand these interactions, you need to think in more than one dimension. But that's easy. That's what you do every day as you negotiate the hallway during passing period or try to merge safely into traffic. In *Getting Real: Collisions in Two Dimensions*, you will use the same conceptual relationships and governing principles of nature that you learned in the previous activity, *In-Line Interactions*. Only now you will apply that

▲ **Figure 2.22 A collision in two dimensions.** This linebacker knocks the running back out of bounds with an inelastic collision at an angle. What changes can you observe after a two-dimensional collision? How is a two-dimensional collision different from collisions in one dimension?

Chapter 2 Collision Course 87

because of time constraints or because your state standards do not require an understanding of two-dimensional motion, you will need to adjust Part II of the evaluate to one-dimensional motion or omit it altogether.

Before You Teach

Background Information

Students use right-triangle mathematics to predict and ultimately verify a variety of collision situations. Many students will know the Pythagorean theorem: $a^2 + b^2 = c^2$ for right triangles. You might need to remind them of two special right-triangle relationships. A right triangle with 45° angles has legs in a 1:1 proportion. The hypotenuse is the square root of 2 longer than the side. Another common right triangle has sides in a 3:4 proportion and a hypotenuse of 5 proportionally. The angle between the 3 side and the hypotenuse is approximately 53° and the remaining non-90° angle is approximately 37°.

It is essential that students understand during the activity that only like vectors can be added or subtracted. In other words, they cannot add a velocity vector to a momentum vector. They should understand from the previous activity that velocity is not always conserved in collisions, but momentum is always conserved. It is especially important that you monitor the vector confirmation of the final velocity, through vector sketches of *momentum*, not velocity. This is crucial since it is momentum that is conserved, not velocity. Students must add momentum vectors and use momentum conservation to find the resultant final momentum vector. They can use final momentum to calculate final velocity using the formula $p_f = mv_f$.

Additional background material is included in the student book.

Materials

For each team of 4 students

1 tennis ball–collision kit, which includes

- 2 tennis balls marked "1 unit of mass," with Velcro strips and a cup hook
- 1 tennis ball marked "2 units of mass," with Velcro strip and a cup hook
- 2 lengths of string long enough to reach from a desk to the ceiling
- 1 collision grid with protractor markings and a center string
- paper clips
- tape
- 1 pen cap

access to computers and *SRCD* (optional)

Advance Preparation

Students use the same tennis ball–collision apparatus in this activity that they used in the last activity. For the optional second part (see *Activity Overview*), purchase latex balloons that blow up to about 10 inches in diameter. Sewing thread is sufficient for the pendulum balloon.

Educational Technologies

As with the linear collisions, it is possible to videotape the two-dimensional collisions and use the playback function of the video player to help students analyze the collisions.

As You Teach

Outcomes and Indicators of Success

By the end of this activity, students should

1. be able to design an investigation to verify the law of conservation

Answers to Step 3 are on TE page 90.

knowledge to two-dimensional interactions. You and your team will reach a deeper understanding of everyday events by answering this focus question: "How does conservation of momentum help me understand and predict interactions in two dimensions?"

Materials

For each team of 4 students

1 tennis ball–collision kit, which includes

- 2 tennis balls marked "1 unit of mass," with Velcro strips and a cup hook
- 1 tennis ball marked "2 units of mass," with Velcro strips and a cup hook
- 2 lengths of string long enough to reach from a desk to the ceiling
- 1 collision grid with protractor markings and a center string
- paper clips
- tape
- 1 pen cap

Process and Procedure

In this activity, you and your team will investigate a series of events designed to test the law of conservation of momentum in two dimensions. You will model your experimental design after your experiences with one-dimensional tennis ball collisions from the previous activity. That is, you will use what you already know and understand rather than start from the beginning.

1. Review your results of Steps 2–6 from Part I of the previous activity, *In-Line Interactions*. You can use these same principles in your experimental design for this activity.
2. Assemble the tennis ball–collision kit. Then practice releasing 2 balls simultaneously at right angles along the axes provided. Your goal is to make them hit and stick together.
3. Design a step-by-step procedure to confirm the law of conservation of momentum for 2-dimensional, hit-and-stick collisions. Do this by writing answers to Steps 3a–e in your science notebook.
   a. How and by how much will you vary mass?
   b. How and by how much will you vary initial velocity (v_i) at the point of collision?

Remember, swing distance is directly proportional to the magnitude of the collision velocity.

   c. How will you predict both magnitude and direction of the final velocity (v_f) of the 2-ball system?

of momentum for inelastic collisions in two dimensions.

They will show their ability by

- reviewing previous activities that use similar designs,
- discussing those similar designs with teammates,
- writing step-by-step procedures in their science notebooks,
- following their procedures and recording observations in tables, and
- analyzing the results and confirming conservation of momentum.

2. be able to make observations important to confirming conservation of momentum of a two-dimensional system.

They will exhibit their ability by

- measuring the location of the center of mass of a two-body tennis ball system,
- recording the swing distance of a two-ball system after collision,
- noting the angle of motion of the two-ball system after collision, and
- incorporating measurement uncertainty into relative velocity measurements.

3. be able to transfer vector arithmetic skills involving one-dimensional momentum problems to two-dimensional momentum problems.

They will show their ability by

- using change in momentum to calculate final velocity;
- relating change in velocity vectors and change in momentum vectors to net force vectors; and
- relating force, change in velocity, and change in momentum vectors to algebraic forms of problem solving.

Your design must include a prediction each time you change either mass or velocity in your investigation. Predict the resultant vector (magnitude and direction). You must have a place to record both your prediction and the actual value of the resultant.

To check your prediction, place a pen cap at the point on your grid where you determine the 2-ball system will swing. Then observe whether the system's center of mass knocks over the pen cap.

d. How will you account for measurement uncertainty?
e. How will you organize your data efficiently and clearly? Remember to include labels, units, and a caption of explanation under the table after analyzing your results.

4. Show your design to your teacher for approval before collecting data.
5. Follow your approved, step-by-step procedure. Be sure that each team member records all observations.
6. Determine if momentum was conserved in 2-dimensional collisions, the same as you did for 1-dimensional collisions. Give evidence to support your answer.

Read *FYI—Vector Addition in Two Dimensions* to learn how to manipulate vectors in two dimensions.

Vector Addition in Two Dimensions

Using vectors to determine the result of a collision or a net force is a process that is familiar to you. You used this process in several activities in this chapter. However, the vectors you have used so far have been in a straight line—in one dimension. Now you will work with vectors that interact at angles—in two dimensions. To keep it simple, you will only work with vectors at right angles (90 degrees, or 90°) to each other. In doing this, there are several right-angle relationships that will be helpful.

First, you are familiar with the Pythagorean theorem used to calculate the length of sides in a right triangle. If you know the length of two sides, you can calculate the third by using the formula

$$a^2 + b^2 = c^2$$

In this formula, a and b refer to the two right-angle legs of the triangle and c is the hypotenuse (see figure).

a
c
b

Right triangle. In this right triangle, the letters a and b refer to the two right-angle legs of the triangle. The letter c represents the hypotenuse.

Strategies

Getting Started

Show students how to use the circle marked off in 10° tick marks around the origin of the axes that rest under the tennis ball–collision apparatus. The string you attached to the origin (which is free to rotate about the origin) has tick marks every 10 cm. Swing a tennis ball at an angle that is not along an axis and align the string with the rocking motion. Use the tick marks on the string to measure the magnitude of the amplitude and therefore the relative velocity. Use the 10° tick marks about the origin to report the direction of motion. If you have students use a protractor instead of the 10° tick marks, tape the protractor in place securely.

Reminder of Possible Misconceptions

Students have a tendency to think of velocity and momentum vectors as being equivalent. They are not. Momentum involves mass and velocity. Thus, the vector magnitude of momentum is different since the units of velocity and momentum are different. Also, students tend to think that force is in the same direction as either initial or final velocity rather than the change in velocity.

Process and Procedure

Students begin the activity by reviewing the results of their previous activities so that they can use the same principles in their experimental design for this activity. This would be a good time to review what your students have learned about key concepts in the chapter thus far. Quiz your students about momentum and its conservation, change in velocity, and how they know there is a change in velocity. Ask them what causes a change in velocity and what causes a change in momentum. Since these collisions will not be occurring along a straight line, there will not be positive and negative values. Rather, students will be using angles to identify the direction of vector quantities. Students assemble the tennis ball–collision kit and practice releasing the balls at right angles so that they hit and stick. You might want to demonstrate this, but usually students can operate the apparatus successfully.

Students design their investigations in Step 3 using guiding questions to help them with their designs. Their designs will be very similar to the investigation of 1 -dimensional collisions they just completed. The primary difference is that the tennis balls will approach each other from right angles, along the grid axes. The balls stick together and move off at an angle. Students' general design aim should be to predict and then confirm the final velocity of the *system*. Make sure students do not omit the prediction phase of their design. Check that students have answered the design questions. Sample answers are included here.

Answers to Step 3, SE pages 88–89

3a. The tennis ball–collision kits you prepare contain tennis balls of only 1 and 2 units of mass.

3b. Students should vary the swing distance by at least 5 cm each trial to obtain reproducibly different results.

3c. Students should recommend using vector mathematics to determine final velocity in 2 dimensions.

3d. Students should do several trials and calculate the uncertainty, as in previous activities. Students should see the similarities between this investigation and their investigation of 1-dimensional collisions. In both cases, the uncertainty of the velocity measurements is at least plus or minus 2 units of velocity.

3e. Check that students have appropriate data tables for their investigation.

In Steps 4 and 5, students gain your approval for their designs and then carry out their step-by-step procedures.

In Step 6, students confirm the law of conservation of momentum from their data. They are instructed to read *FYI—Vector Addition in Two Dimensions*. Consider reading this as a class and discussing each example. If your students need more practice with vectors in 2 dimensions, see the

Toolbox activity *Vector Addition II* on the *TRCD*. This would be a good time to coordinate with the math teacher to reinforce these concepts in other classes.

Student answers should confirm the law of conservation of momentum within the uncertainty limits they have calculated. Students may choose to show their answers either by vector math or by calculations. Accept either method. It is especially important that you monitor the vector confirmation of the final velocity, through vector sketches of *momentum*, not velocity. This is crucial since momentum is conserved, not velocity. Thus, drawing final and initial velocity vectors and subtracting them appropriately will still lead to incorrect answers. Students must add momentum vectors and find the resultant final momentum vector. They use the magnitude of the final momentum to calculate the magnitude of the final velocity using the formula $p_f = mv_f$.

Vector Addition in Two Dimensions, continued

In addition, there are two special-sized right triangles that, if you learn their relationships, will save you time. The first is a 45°-45°-90° triangle. In this triangle, the legs are equal lengths. The hypotenuse of this special triangle is equal to the length of a leg times the square root of 2 (see figure).

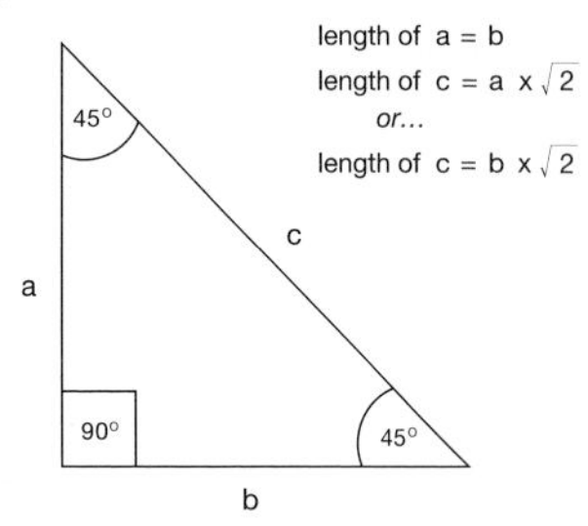

45°-45°-90° right triangle. This special right triangle has angles of 45°, 45°, and 90°. Legs a and b are the same length. The length of the hypotenuse (c) can be calculated by finding the product of the length of one leg and the square root of 2.

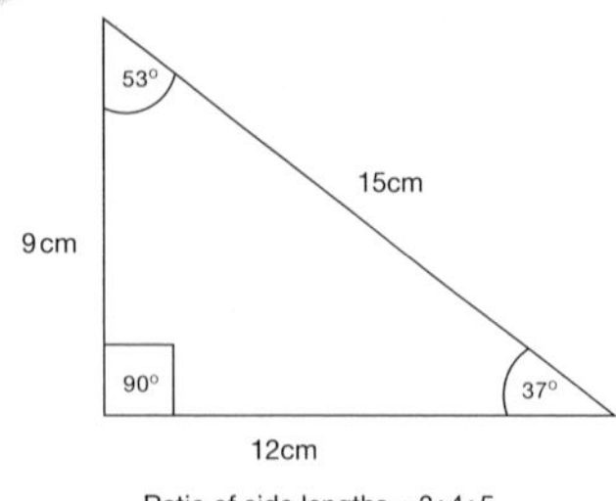

3:4:5 right triangle. This special right triangle has leg lengths in a *ratio* of 3:4:5 with 5 representing the hypotenuse of the right triangle. For example, if the legs of the triangle were 9 cm and 12 cm, then the hypotenuse would be 15 cm long. The angles of this type of right triangle are shown in the figure.

Another special triangle is called a 3-4-5 triangle, where 5 represents the hypotenuse of a right triangle. These numbers refer to the length (or the ratio of the lengths) of each leg. The angle opposite the 4 leg is approximately equal to 53°, and the angle opposite the 3 leg is approximately equal to 37° (see figure). The sum of all the angles in any triangle is 180°. Remembering these special relationships will give you shortcuts in your calculations or vector diagrams because the length of the legs represents the magnitude or the length of the vectors.

How is vector math different in two-dimensional collisions? In one-dimensional motion, you only had to add vectors in a straight line. In two-dimensional collisions, you must consider angles, and the motion that results (the resultant) is not always obvious. But you have some feel for this type of motion because it is something you experience every day. Suppose you are playing billiards and you want the number 13 ball (orange ball) to go into the corner pocket (see figure). You know that you must hit the ball at an angle to give the orange ball the right resultant velocity (both speed and direction) to fall into the corner pocket. In doing this, you are using vector math in two dimensions and you didn't think about science or math at all!

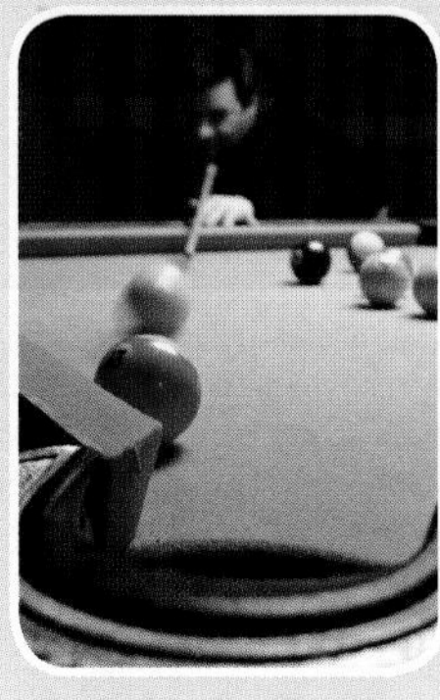

Vector math at work. You must hit the ball at an angle to make it go into the pocket. What are the factors you must consider to make a successful shot?

90 | Unit 1 Interactions Are Interesting

NOTES:

When objects collide at right angles and stick together, they will continue in a path that results from adding the two right-angle momentum vectors. This is because momentum is conserved in all types of collisions.

Suppose a car is moving east with a momentum of 15,000 kg m/sec and collides with a truck moving north with a momentum of 40,000 kg m/sec, figure (a). If the vehicles stick together at impact, what will be the final momentum of the vehicles? Take a look at how to add these vectors, which form a 90° angle. Remember, when adding vectors you place them head to tail. Start by drawing two arrows pointing in the proper direction. The vectors must be drawn to scale and be placed head to tail, figure (b).

Since momentum is conserved, you can use the initial momenta to find the final momentum of the system. The final, or resultant, momentum can be determined graphically by drawing an arrow from the tail of the first arrow to the head of the last arrow, figure (c). Now measure the length of the arrow with a ruler and determine its magnitude by using the scale.

The angle (or direction) of the vector can be found by using a protractor, figure (d).

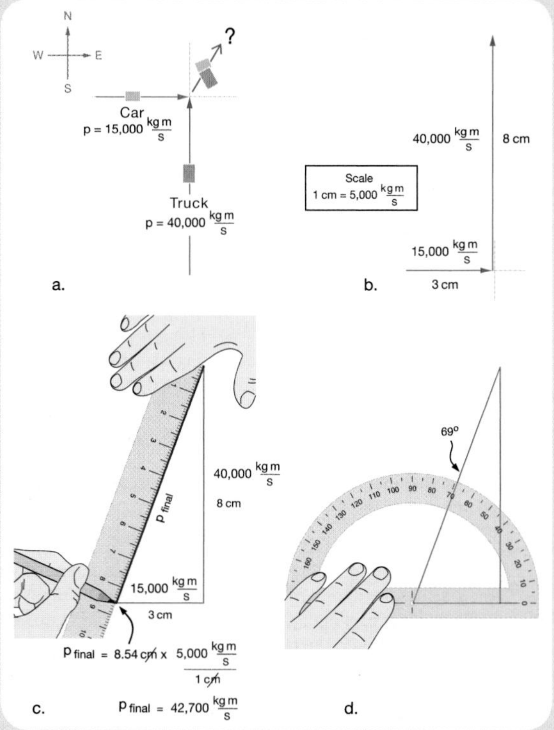

▲ **Initial momenta of the two vehicles.** Two vehicles collide as shown in (a). To add the vectors, draw the initial momenta of the two cars to scale and place the arrows head to tail as shown in (b). To find the magnitude of the final momentum of the two-vehicle system, draw the final momentum (resultant) vector from the tail of the first vector to the head of the last vector (c). Measure the length of this vector and use the scale to determine the magnitude of the vector. Finally, to find the direction of the final momentum, use a protractor to measure the angle (d).

Chapter 2 Collision Course 91

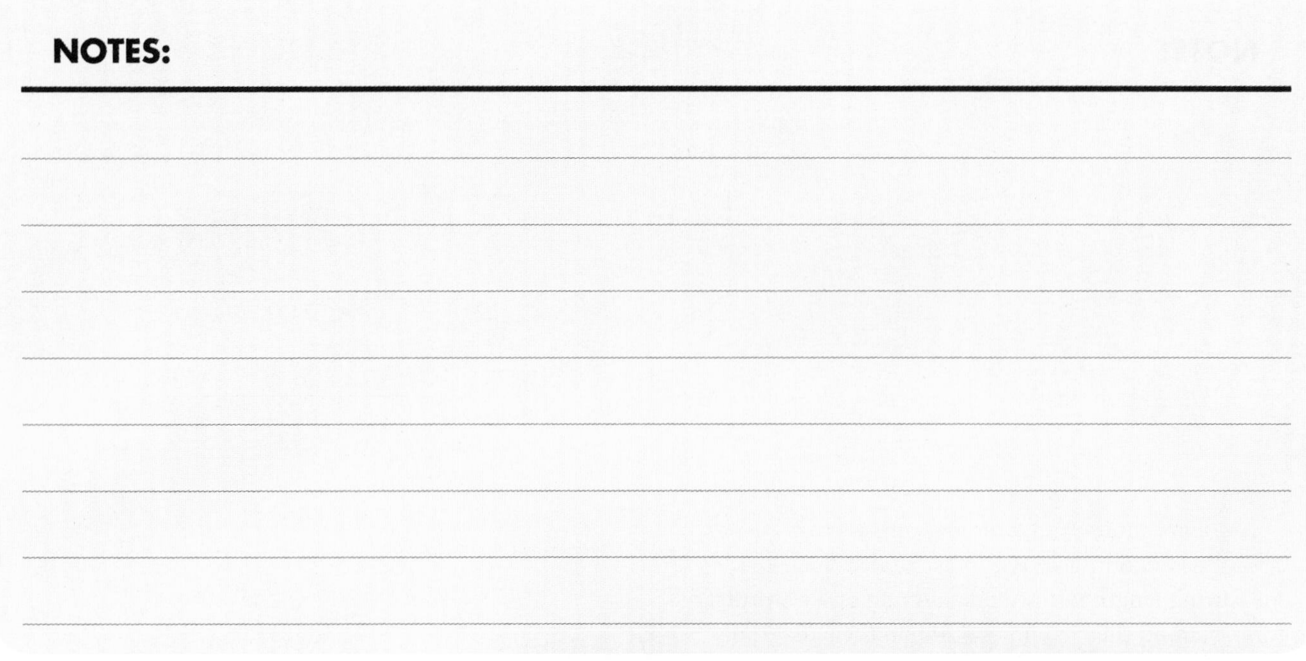

Answers to Reflect and Connect are on TE pages 92a–92b.

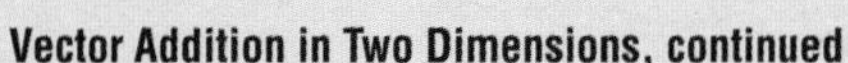

Vector Addition in Two Dimensions, continued

For extra practice with vectors, see *Vector Addition* on the SRCD.

You can also determine its magnitude by using the Pythagorean theorem. Use it to check your answers when using vector math. Using the theorem, the answer of 42,700 kg m/sec confirms the vector math method.

$$a^2 + b^2 = c^2$$

$$\left(15{,}000\,\frac{\text{kg m}}{\text{sec}}\right)^2 + \left(40{,}000\,\frac{\text{kg m}}{\text{sec}}\right)^2 = c^2$$

$$1{,}825{,}000{,}000\,\frac{\text{kg}^2\,\text{m}^2}{\text{sec}^2} = c^2$$

$$\sqrt{1{,}825{,}000{,}000\,\frac{\text{kg}^2\,\text{m}^2}{\text{sec}^2}} = \sqrt{2}$$

$$42{,}700\,\frac{\text{kg m}}{\text{sec}} \approx c$$

Reflect and Connect

Apply your best thinking to these questions individually, and then discuss your answers as directed by your teacher.

1. A 1,300-kg car moving north at 27 m/sec collides with a 2,100-kg car moving east at 20 m/sec. They stick together. In what direction (angle) and with what speed do they move after the collision? Follow Questions 1a–c to find the answer.
   a. Solve for the final momentum using scaled vectors. Measure and label both the magnitude and the direction (angle) for the final momentum.
   b. Check your answer for the magnitude of the momentum by using the Pythagorean theorem.
   c. Use the final momentum of the system to solve for the final velocity of the 2 cars together.

Use the relationship $p_f = (m_1 + m_2)\,v_f$ to find the final velocity of the 2 cars.

2. A high school football player (100-kg mass) is running along the sidelines with a speed of 8.0 m/sec. At the same time, a cheerleader is backing up into the field of play not realizing she is straying out onto the field. She is moving at a speed of 1.0 m/sec and has a mass of 50 kg. They collide at right angles to each other. The football player wants to avoid hurting her. He paid attention in science class and knew that picking her up would be the best plan. He picks up the cheerleader at the point of collision and runs with her as he slows down rather than letting her bounce off him after the collision. How fast will they be going immediately after the collision and in what direction? Use scaled vectors and algebra to answer the question. Explain

Answers to Reflect and Connect, SE pages 92–93

1. Students will have to calculate the magnitude of the initial momentum for the 2 cars first.

car A $p_{\text{car Ai}} = m_{\text{car A}}\, v_{\text{car Ai}}$

$$= 1{,}300 \text{ kg} \times 27.0 \frac{\text{m}}{\text{sec}}$$

$$= 35{,}000 \frac{(\text{kg})(\text{m})}{\text{sec}}$$

car B $p_{\text{car Bi}} = m_{\text{car B}}\, v_{\text{car Bi}}$

$$= 2{,}100 \text{ kg} \times 20.0 \frac{\text{m}}{\text{sec}}$$

$$= 42{,}000 \frac{(\text{kg})(\text{m})}{\text{sec}}$$

Students should draw momentum vectors of the collision. Encourage them to use scaled diagrams, measuring length with rulers and angles with protractors. Remind them to put a scale on their diagrams such as 1 cm = 1,000 units of momentum $\left(\frac{(\text{kg})(\text{m})}{\text{sec}}\right)$. Sample vector diagrams are given in figure T2.15. Students may solve for the final momentum algebraically by using the Pythagorean theorem. They can then use the answer to calculate the final velocity of the 2 cars. They will have to measure the angle directly from their vector drawings for the direction. If students know how to use trigonometry, they can solve for the angle in that manner. Solved algebraically, the final momentum (*c*) is found by the following:

$$a^2 + b^2 = c^2$$

$$\left(35{,}000 \frac{(\text{kg})(\text{m})}{\text{sec}}\right)^2 + \left(42{,}000 \frac{(\text{kg})(\text{m})}{\text{sec}}\right)^2 = c^2$$

$$\sqrt{\left(35{,}000 \frac{(\text{kg})(\text{m})}{\text{sec}}\right)^2 + \left(42{,}000 \frac{(\text{kg})(\text{m})}{\text{sec}}\right)^2} = \sqrt{c^2}$$

$$55{,}000 \frac{(\text{kg})(\text{m})}{\text{sec}} = c$$

The magnitude of the final velocity of the 2-car system can be calculated from the magnitude of the final momentum of the system using the formula $p_f = m_{\text{total}} v_f$.

$$p_f = m_{\text{total}} v_f$$

$$\frac{p_f}{m_{\text{total}}} = v_f$$

$$\frac{55{,}000 \frac{\text{kg m}}{\text{sec}}}{3{,}400 \text{ kg}} = v_f$$

$$16 \frac{\text{m}}{\text{sec}} = v_f$$

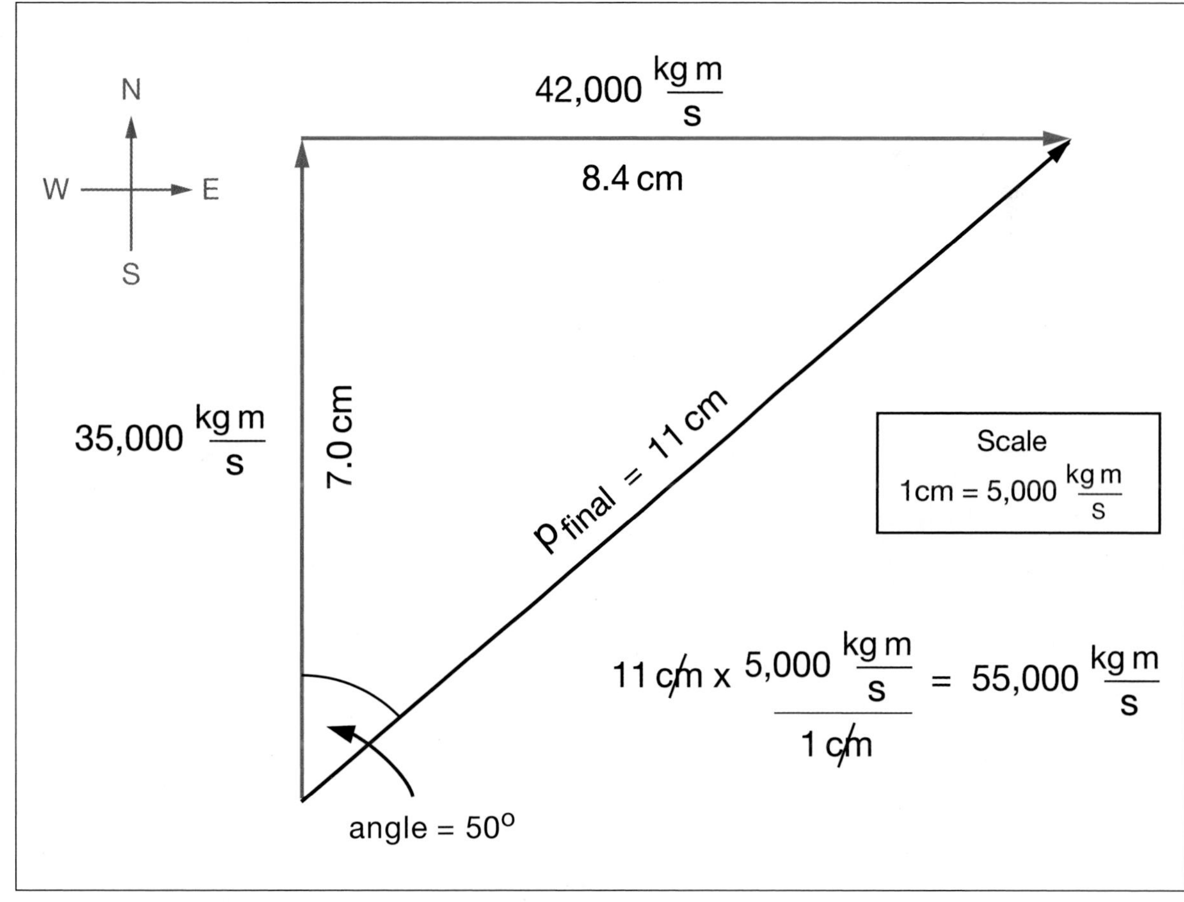

▲ **Figure T2.15 Scaled vectors.** Students can solve for both the magnitude and direction of the final momentum of the car crash by using scaled vectors similar to these.

The direction of the final velocity is about 50° from the horizontal axis. Students will use scaled vectors to obtain this angle and measure it directly with a protractor. To find the angle using trigonometry,

$$\tan\theta = \frac{42{,}000\,\dfrac{\text{kg m}}{\text{sec}}}{35{,}000\,\dfrac{\text{kg m}}{\text{sec}}}$$

$$= 50°.$$

2. Students should calculate the initial momentum of the football player and the cheerleader first. Note: Calculations are carried out to 3 significant figures to show changes due to the very small angle.

football player $p_i = mv_i$

$$= 100.\ \text{kg} \times 8.0\frac{\text{m}}{\text{sec}}$$

$$= 800.\ \frac{\text{kg m}}{\text{sec}}$$

cheerleader $p_i = mv_i$

$$= 50.0\ \text{kg} \times 1.00\frac{\text{m}}{\text{sec}}$$

$$= 50.0\frac{\text{kg m}}{\text{sec}}$$

Using these 2 momenta, students can use the Pythagorean theorem or scaled vectors (figure T2.16) to solve for the final momentum. Using the Pythagorean theorem,

$$a^2 + b^2 = c^2$$

$$\left(800.\frac{\text{kg m}}{\text{sec}}\right)^2 + \left(50.0\frac{\text{kg m}}{\text{sec}}\right)^2 = c^2$$

$$\sqrt{\left(800.\frac{\text{kg m}}{\text{sec}}\right)^2 + \left(50.0\frac{\text{kg m}}{\text{sec}}\right)^2} = \sqrt{c^2}$$

$$802\,\frac{\text{kg m}}{\text{sec}} = c.$$

Using this value for p_f, students can calculate the final velocity of the football player-cheerleader system.

$$p_f = m_{\text{total}}v_f$$

$$\frac{p_f}{m_{\text{total}}} = v_f$$

$$\frac{802\,\dfrac{\text{kg m}}{\text{sec}}}{150.\ \text{kg}} = v_f$$

$$5.35\,\frac{\text{m}}{\text{sec}} = v_f$$

The angle or direction of the final velocity is about 3.5°. Students can find this angle by measuring their scaled vector drawings with a protractor. For your background, the angle can be found by using trigonometry.

$$\tan\theta = \frac{50\,\dfrac{\text{kg m}}{\text{sec}}}{800\,\dfrac{\text{kg m}}{\text{sec}}}$$

$$= 3.6°$$

3. No, you cannot use velocity vectors to find the final velocity of the system since velocity is not conserved. Using velocity vectors in Question 1 would give a final velocity of 34 m/sec ($(20\ \text{m/sec})^2 + (27\ \text{m/sec})^2 = c^2$). If you used this velocity to calculate the final momentum of the system, then it would violate the law of conservation of momentum.

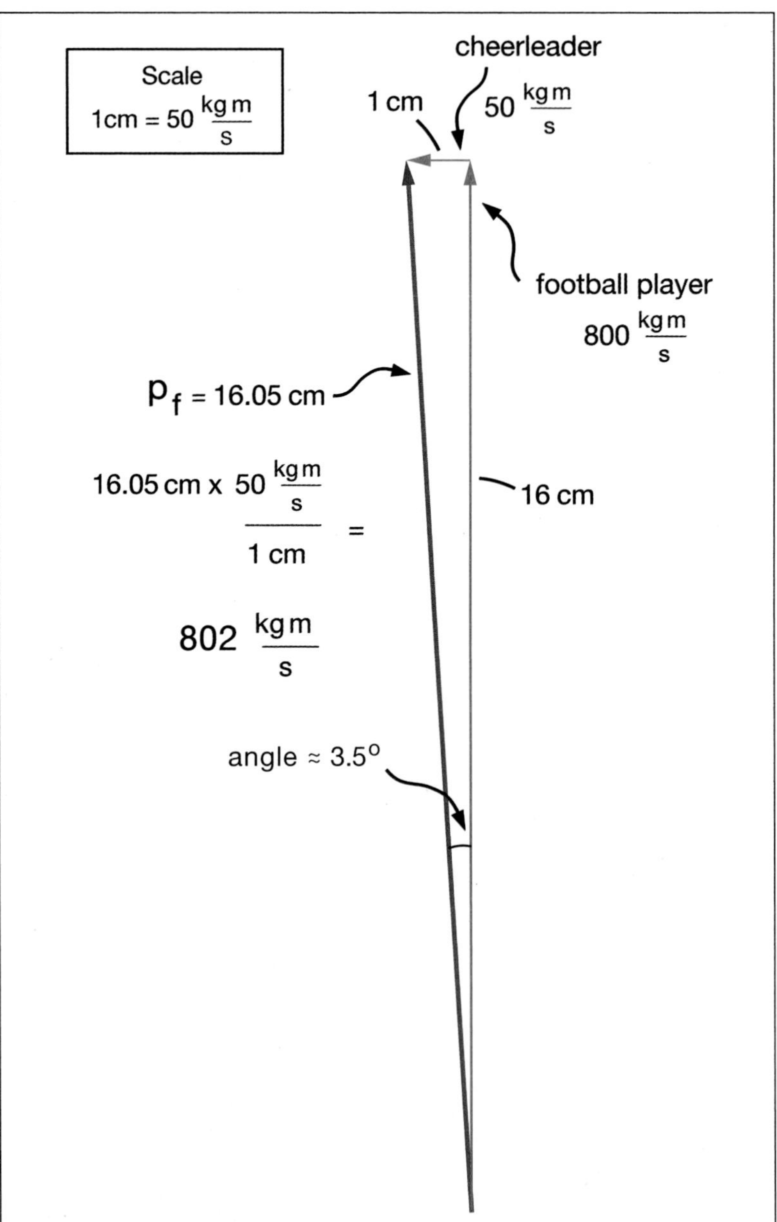

▲ **Figure T2.16 Scaled vectors.** Students can solve for both the magnitude and direction of the final momentum of the football player and cheerleader by using scaled vectors similar to these.

ELABORATE

With and Without a Net

Activity Overview

With and Without a Net helps students think about how the difference between nonzero net forces and balanced forces apply to common motions. The context for this common motion is free fall, the motion resulting when objects are released close to the surface of Earth. The conceptual focus is on the forces required to produce free fall motion for objects that rapidly reach a constant velocity (terminal velocity) and objects whose velocity continues increasing at a steady rate, seemingly until they hit the ground.

The activity is divided into two parts. Part I offers experiences for students to determine some of the variables affecting terminal velocity. They will accomplish this by using a flat-bottomed coffee filter as a model of a parachutist. As students add paper clips, the coffee filter falls farther before reaching terminal velocity. Students will relate constant velocity to nonchanging momentum, and thus zero net force. From there, students will connect a balance of forces to one part of the law of inertia (objects in motion stay in motion unless they experience a net force).

In Part II, students will quantify the relationship between the number of paper clips in the flat-bottomed coffee filter and the time to fall to the floor. They will find that the time to fall does not decrease to zero, but reaches a constant value for a given height. From a graph, students will deduce that all objects fall at the same rate of change of velocity, which for objects close to Earth is approximately 9.8 m/sec^2. This value is often given the symbol g, which stands for the acceleration that all objects close to Earth experience. Students realize that nonzero net forces cause a change of velocity, which leads eventually to Newton's second law of motion, $F_{net} = ma$ (net forces produce accelerated motion).

why picking her up and running with her as he slows down will hurt the cheerleader less than letting her bounce off. Use the equation $F = \frac{m\Delta v}{\Delta t}$ in your answer.

3. Does adding initial velocity vectors give you the correct values for final velocity in the previous problems? Explain your answer using vectors or algebra.

With and Without a Net

ELABORATE

Now that you understand a force is required to change momentum, you can begin to see the applications of what you are learning. You understand how to calculate forces during collisions by considering change in velocity (Δv), time during the collision (Δt), and mass. The key conceptual connection is between force and the effects of force—changing momentum (Δp).

But so far in this unit, you have only looked at forces in two situations. You have seen that forces are either constant or zero. In actual everyday situations, forces change. Now you will be concerned with net forces. Think about a **net force** as the force left over after all forces are added together as vectors. There is a net force if forces on an object are not balanced—or do not all cancel. And if net forces change, so do momentum and velocity.

You can *feel* a net force or a change in velocity. Think about riding in a luxury car with your eyes closed. Or if you have flown on an airplane, think about how it feels once you have reached your cruising altitude. If you have your eyes closed, you cannot tell that you are moving even though you may be moving several hundred kilometers per hour in a plane. You are moving at constant velocity and you know that at constant velocity there is no net force. What you *can* feel is a change in momentum caused by a net force. For example, if the car or plane suddenly speeds up or slows down, you can feel it. What other motions can you feel? You can also feel the change in momentum when the car or plane changes direction. In each of the changes that you can feel, a net force caused a change in momentum.

Think about the changes in force when your heart beats, or the changes in momentum when a hurricane hits shore, or the changes in velocity when the space shuttle reenters Earth's atmosphere (figure 2.23). In each case, the net forces change. But as you have seen, some interactions are the result of a balance of forces (no net force). Yet whether with, or without a net force, the interactions are interesting.

▲ **Figure 2.23 Forces change in everyday interactions.** How do you know that forces are changing in each interaction shown? What is the evidence?

Chapter 2 Collision Course 93

Before You Teach

Background Information

It is difficult to convince students that all objects near the surface of Earth fall with the same time rate of change of velocity. That is because students' eyes tell them a different story. A leaf, for example, does not reach the ground at the same time as a rock when both are released at the same time from the same height. To explain this common observation, students often think that the time rate of change of velocity (called acceleration) is greater for heavy objects by virtue of their "heaviness" and nothing else.

Students often predict that heavier objects fall in less time. The logical result of this thinking is that an infinitely heavy object falls to the ground in zero seconds. This is not the case. Instead, as mass increases, the fall time reaches a constant value. If we increase the mass to a huge number, the fall time (for a certain height) remains the same. The logical conclusion is that all objects fall at the same acceleration and the reason that light objects take more time involves other forces.

The other force (usually) is air resistance (drag). Drag produces an upward force that opposes the downward force of an object's weight. The faster an object moves, the greater the drag force until the weight force down on the object is equal to the drag force up on the object. When this occurs, the object moves at a constant velocity—called terminal velocity. Heavier objects require more fall time before this condition is met, thus the terminal velocity of heavier objects is greater than for lighter objects such as leaves and feathers.

When objects free-fall without opposing forces like air drag, the distance fallen is directly proportional to the fall time squared, or distance $\propto$ time^2. This is an indication that velocity keeps increasing as the object falls. If velocity is increasing, then students know that momentum is changing. If momentum is changing, then there must be a net, nonzero force acting on the falling object. That net force is the mutual gravitational attraction between the object and Earth. This force of gravitational attraction on the object is called weight and is different from planet to planet and, for that matter, slightly different at different places on Earth depending on the amount and type of crust under your feet. More massive objects do experience a greater downward force than less massive objects, but accelerate at the same rate as all other objects because the ratio of force to mass remains constant, a topic we will broach in chapter 4.

Materials—Part I

For each team of 4 students

1 coffee filter (flat bottomed)
1 stopwatch
paper clips
1 chair

Materials—Part II

For each team of 4 students

1 coffee filter (flat bottomed)
1 stopwatch
1 meterstick or tape measure
paper clips

Advance Preparation

Purchase flat-bottomed coffee filters (10-cup size) from a local grocery store. These fall bottom down with very little drift, as with leaves. If you do not have stopwatches, borrow a set from the physics teacher. If you purchase them, buy the kind without alarms since students always find a way to set the alarms, which then go off at inopportune times during class.

Educational Technologies

Computer interface devices such as photo gate timers can be used instead of stopwatches for timing the fall time. This approach allows for convenient storage of data and the rapid formation of data tables.

Cautions

Caution students as they stand on chairs. Make sure the chairs they use are stable. If any students have balance problems or other physical limitations, do not let them stand on an elevated surface.

As You Teach

Outcomes and Indicators of Success

By the end of this activity, students should

1. understand the relationship among variables important to an object attaining terminal velocity.

   They will show their understanding by
   - observing how the addition of paper clips to a coffee filter decreases fall time,
   - developing an analogy between a falling coffee filter and a parachutist, and
   - developing an analogy between a falling coffee filter and a student pushing a chair across the floor at constant velocity.
2. be able to apply the condition of zero net force to two motion conditions: stationary and constant velocity.

In *With and Without a Net*, you and your team will apply what you know about the connection between force and changing momentum to understand everyday situations in which forces are changing. Keep your efforts focused by filtering any actions you take through the following focus question: "How do I recognize when there *is* and *is not* a net force acting on an object?"

Part I: Putting On the Brakes

Materials

For each team of 4 students

1 coffee filter (flat bottomed)

1 stopwatch

paper clips

1 chair

Process and Procedure

A common interaction exerts tremendous influence on our everyday lives. That interaction is gravity. Like all interactions, gravity is the result of a pair of forces, in this case, $F_{\text{Earth } on \text{ us}}$ and $F_{\text{us } on \text{ Earth}}$. But is that mutual force of attraction always constant? Is it the same for all objects? Does the pull of Earth's gravity result in changing or constant momentum?

In Part I, you and your team will investigate the forces acting on a person jumping out of an airplane. Then you will link what you find out to another motion, applying brakes in a car.

 **Cautions**

Make sure the chairs you use are stable. If you have balance problems or other physical limitations, do not stand on an elevated surface.

1. Familiarize yourself with the parachutist model provided by your teacher by performing Steps 1a–b. Then record the results, using sketches with captions in your science notebook.
   a. Stand on a chair, hold a coffee filter above your head, and release it. Focus on whether the filter is speeding up, slowing down, or neither.
   b. Repeat Step 1a with 2, 4, and then 6 paper clips in the filter. Focus on the relative amount of time to hit the floor.

94 Unit 1 Interactions Are Interesting

They will show their ability by

- recognizing that objects in motion stay in motion at constant velocity when the net force is zero;
- recognizing that objects at rest remain at rest when the net force is zero; and
- deduce that when the net force acting on an object is nonzero, the object's velocity changes.

3. be able to design an investigation to test their prediction related to force and motion.

   They will show their ability by

   - writing step-by-step procedures in their science notebooks,
   - following their procedures and recording observations in tables, and
   - analyzing the results and plotting graphs of their data.

4. be able to recognize and analyze alternative explanations.

   They will demonstrate their ability by

   - analyzing three different explanations of falling bodies on Earth and the Moon,
   - choosing the proper explanation, and
   - defending their selection by using their understanding and vector sketches.

Answers to Step 2 are on TE page 96.

2. Copy the table in figure 2.24 into your science notebook. Complete this analogy table to link a parachute jump to the coffee-filter drop. Reading across each row should form a sentence. The first 2 are done for you as a guide.

Feature of a parachute jump	Feature in the coffee-filter drop	Reason
Vertical forces while riding in a plane are like	vertical forces while holding a coffee filter	because the up and down forces balance each other.
The downward velocity at the instant of jumping is like	the downward velocity at the release moment	because both start at 0 m/s.
the downward force on a parachutist is like	the downward force on ____________	because ____________ .
The change in velocity after the parachute opens is like		
The distance fallen before the parachute opens is like		
Continue adding features as your team thinks of them.		

▲ **Figure 2.24 Analogy table for parachute jump and coffee-filter drop.** Use this table in Step 2 to make comparisons between a parachute jump and your coffee-filter drop. Your answers should form a logical sentence when reading across a row.

3. Read *Going Terminal* to prepare for sketching scaled vector diagrams of the forces acting on the coffee filter at several points during its fall.

A good way to get the most out of what you read is to make a T-table with the headings "fact or idea I read" and "question I have" (about the fact or idea). Then fill out the table as you read.

Strategies

Getting Started

If your personality allows, consider starting class with a short theater piece in which you are the only one on stage. Pretend you are riding in an airplane that has run out of fuel and will crash into the mountains. You have to jump. But you don't have a parachute! So you use your creativity and invent one from the materials in the plane. You rush back to the coffeemaker and come out with a coffee filter, hold it over your head, and stand on a chair. Then you ask students, "Will I make it safely? Why or why not? What are the forces I need to analyze to determine my fate?" Then lead students into the introduction of the activity and show them how a coffee filter is in many ways like a parachute.

Reminder of Possible Misconceptions

Many students will think that less massive objects reach terminal velocity only because they are less massive. This is partially true since the weight of an object is a factor. But other forces are involved such as air resistance, which produces an upward force. Therefore, it is the net force acting on an object that determines its motion, not any single force. This fact plays in a common misconception in which students think a net force is required to produce a constant velocity, in this activity, terminal velocity. Actually, a net force of zero results in constant velocity.

Cautions

Caution students as they stand on chairs. Make sure the chairs they use are stable. If any students have balance problems or other physical limitations, do not let them stand on an elevated surface.

Process and Procedure

Part I: Putting On the Brakes

Materials

For each team of 4 students

1 coffee filter (flat bottomed)
1 stopwatch
paper clips
1 chair

Feature of parachute jump	Feature in the coffee-filter drop	Reason
Vertical forces while riding in plane are like	vertical forces while holding a coffee filter	because the up and down forces balance each other.
The downward velocity at the instant of jumping is like	the downward velocity at the release moment	because both start at 0 m/s.
The downward force on a parachutist is like	the downward force on filter paper	because both forces result from mutual gravitational attraction between Earth and the object.
The change in velocity after the parachute opens is like	the velocity of the coffee filter a short distance after dropping	because both are constant (or net force = zero).
The distance fallen before the parachute opens is like	the distance between the hand and the point of constant coffee-filter velocity	because both increase in speed during the initial fall.
The motion before the parachute opens is like	the motion before the coffee filter reaches constant velocity	because both objects accelerate.

▲ **Figure T2.17 Analogy map between a parachute and a coffee filter.** Use this table to help students make an explicit connection between a parachute and a coffee filter.

Demonstrate how a flat-bottomed coffee filter drifts down at a constant velocity while students complete Step 1. Help students see this as a reasonable model (simulation) of a person jumping out of an airplane, then opening a parachute. Students should notice that when more paper clips are added the filter falls a greater distance before attaining a constant velocity.

Answers to Step 2, SE page 95

Student answers to Step 2 should be similar to figure T2.17.

Students read *Going Terminal* in Step 3. Lead a discussion of the reading after all students have had time to process the information. Question the class about its understanding of the concepts presented in the reading. Or you might ask students to summarize what they read.

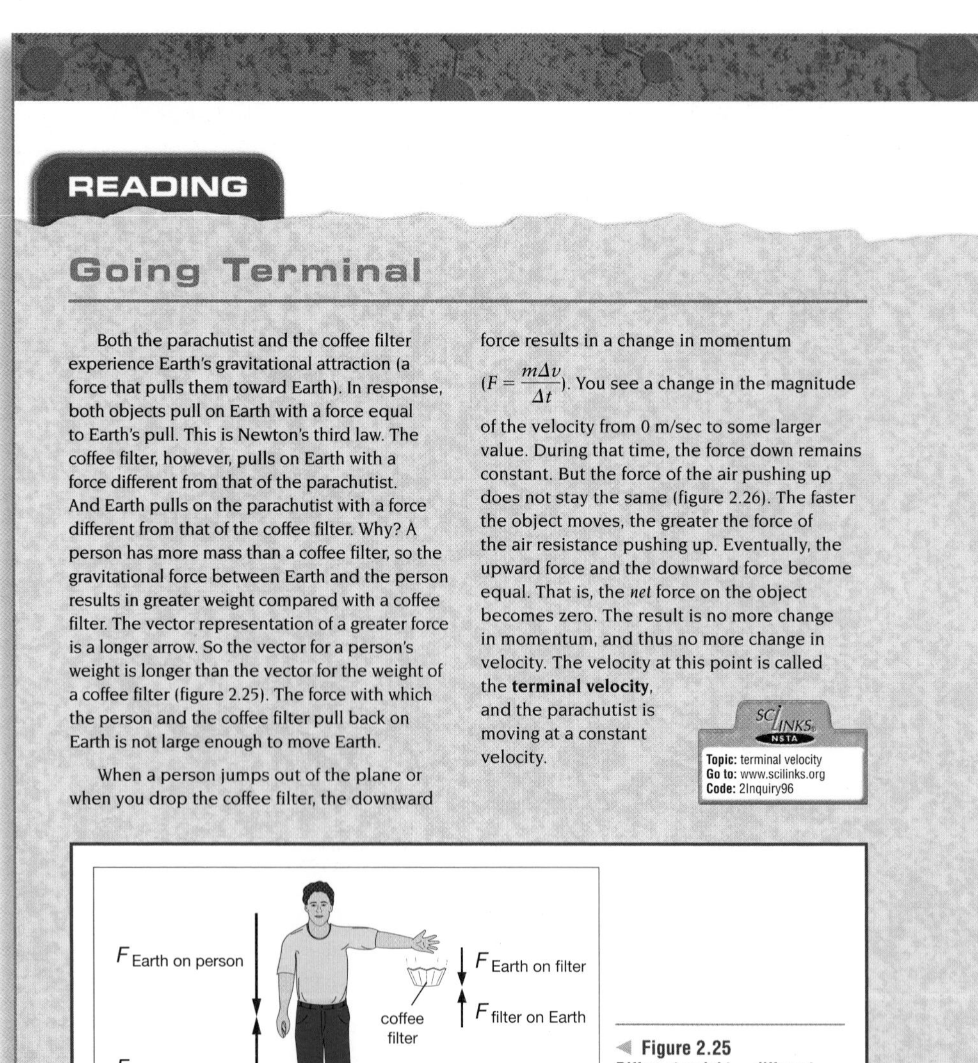

READING

Going Terminal

Both the parachutist and the coffee filter experience Earth's gravitational attraction (a force that pulls them toward Earth). In response, both objects pull on Earth with a force equal to Earth's pull. This is Newton's third law. The coffee filter, however, pulls on Earth with a force different from that of the parachutist. And Earth pulls on the parachutist with a force different from that of the coffee filter. Why? A person has more mass than a coffee filter, so the gravitational force between Earth and the person results in greater weight compared with a coffee filter. The vector representation of a greater force is a longer arrow. So the vector for a person's weight is longer than the vector for the weight of a coffee filter (figure 2.25). The force with which the person and the coffee filter pull back on Earth is not large enough to move Earth.

When a person jumps out of the plane or when you drop the coffee filter, the downward force results in a change in momentum ($F = \frac{m\Delta v}{\Delta t}$). You see a change in the magnitude of the velocity from 0 m/sec to some larger value. During that time, the force down remains constant. But the force of the air pushing up does not stay the same (figure 2.26). The faster the object moves, the greater the force of the air resistance pushing up. Eventually, the upward force and the downward force become equal. That is, the *net* force on the object becomes zero. The result is no more change in momentum, and thus no more change in velocity. The velocity at this point is called the **terminal velocity**, and the parachutist is moving at a constant velocity.

SCILINKS NSTA
Topic: terminal velocity
Go to: www.scilinks.org
Code: 2Inquiry96

◀ **Figure 2.25**
Different weight = different forces. The force that Earth pulls on the filter paper is much less than the force that Earth pulls on a person. Likewise, the force that the coffee filter pulls on Earth is less than the force that the person pulls on Earth.

96 | Unit 1 Interactions Are Interesting

NOTES:

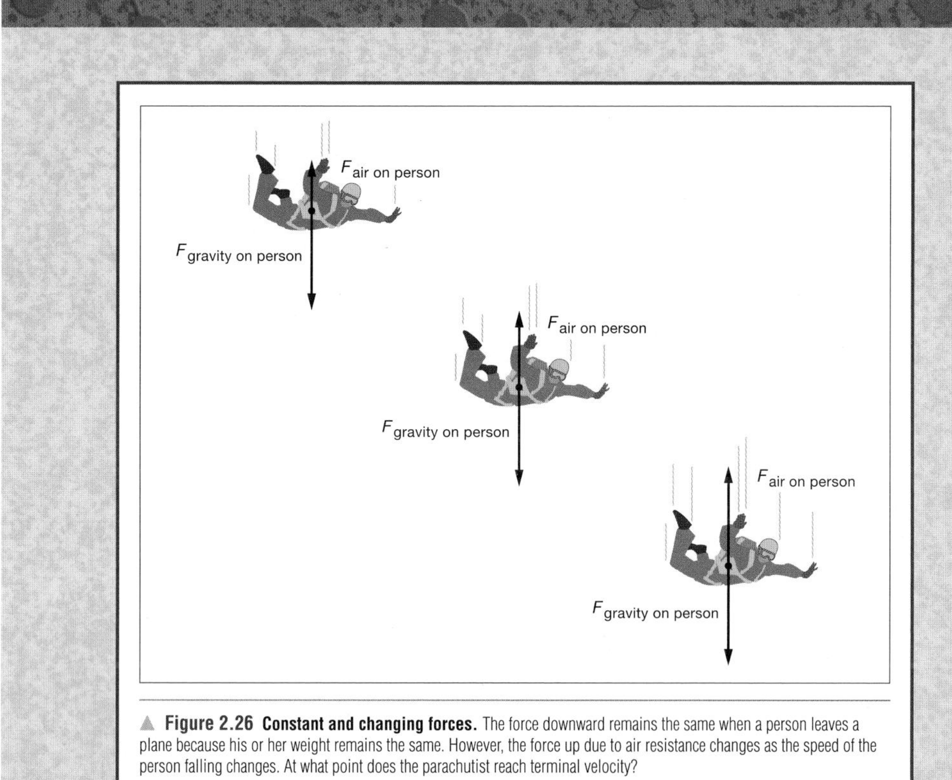

▲ **Figure 2.26 Constant and changing forces.** The force downward remains the same when a person leaves a plane because his or her weight remains the same. However, the force up due to air resistance changes as the speed of the person falling changes. At what point does the parachutist reach terminal velocity?

4. Draw 3 scaled vector sketches showing all the vertical forces acting on the coffee filter. Include sketches that show when the coffee filter is in your hand, when the filter is at some point in midair, and when the filter hits the floor. Include highlight comments and an overall caption.
5. Repeat Step 4 for the filter holding 2, 4, and 6 paper clips while it falls to the floor.
6. Compare the motion of your coffee filter to a chair as you complete Steps 6a–c.

In Step 4, students draw scaled vector sketches of the vertical forces acting on the coffee filter. Student answers should be similar to figure T2.18. Strongly emphasize that students develop a *series* of sketches, showing a gradual set of changes in the forces acting on the filter. This incremental approach to developing an understanding of terminal velocity allows students to bridge what they know (unbalanced forces that cause changes in velocity) and what they are learning about now (balanced forces [no net force] resulting in constant velocity). Use this series of sketches as an interim assessment of students' ideas about equal and unequal forces.

In Step 5, students repeat the process, showing the results when they drop a filter paper with 2, 4, and 6 paper clips. Student sketches should be similar to the first series, except the distance at which the forces become equal is closer to the ground and the amount of both upward and downward forces at that point is greater, reflecting the greater number (mass) of paper clips. Students will complete an analogy map and draw a scaled vector diagram for Step 6. Their answers should be similar to figures T2.19 and T2.20.

Both the analogy map and vector sketch show (in different forms of representation) that constant velocity can result from a balance of forces. A common misconception among students is that a net force is required to produce a constant velocity. This is not true.

Students will complete another analogy map for Step 7. Their answers should be similar to figure T2.21.

Use this task to help students transfer the principles of one physical interaction to another, specifically from a vertical orientation to a horizontal orientation.

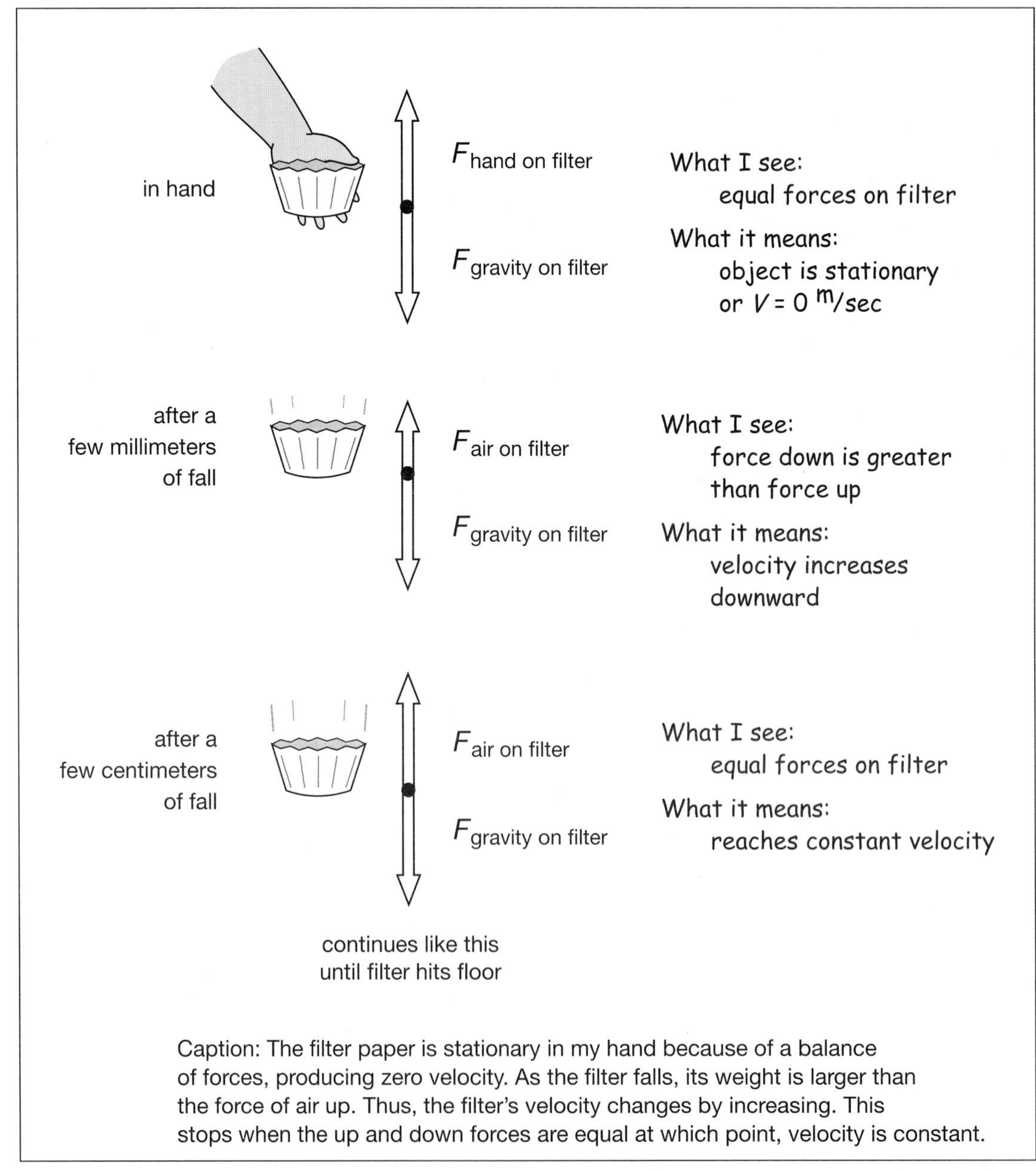

▲ **Figure T2.18 Force vectors for coffee filter.** This vector sketch represents the force vectors on the coffee filter for Step 4.

Feature of coffee filter motion	Feature of chair motion	Reason
Zero velocity in the vertical direction is like	zero velocity in the horizontal direction	because both experience $F_{net} = 0$ in the direction of motion.
Increasing velocity in the first few centimeters of vertical motion is like	increasing velocity in first few centimeters of horizontal motion	because F_{net} exists in the direction of motion.
Frictional force increases in the opposite direction to vertical motion is like	frictional force increasing in the opposite direction of the horizontal forward force	because force increases with speed.
$F_{net} = 0$ at terminal velocity in the vertical direction is like	$F_{net} = 0$ at constant velocity in the horizontal direction	because zero net force results in a nonchanging velocity.

▲ **Figure T2.19 Analogy map between a coffee filter and a chair moving horizontally at constant velocity.** Use this table to help students make an explicit connection in Step 6 between the coffee filter and a chair moving across the floor at a constant velocity.

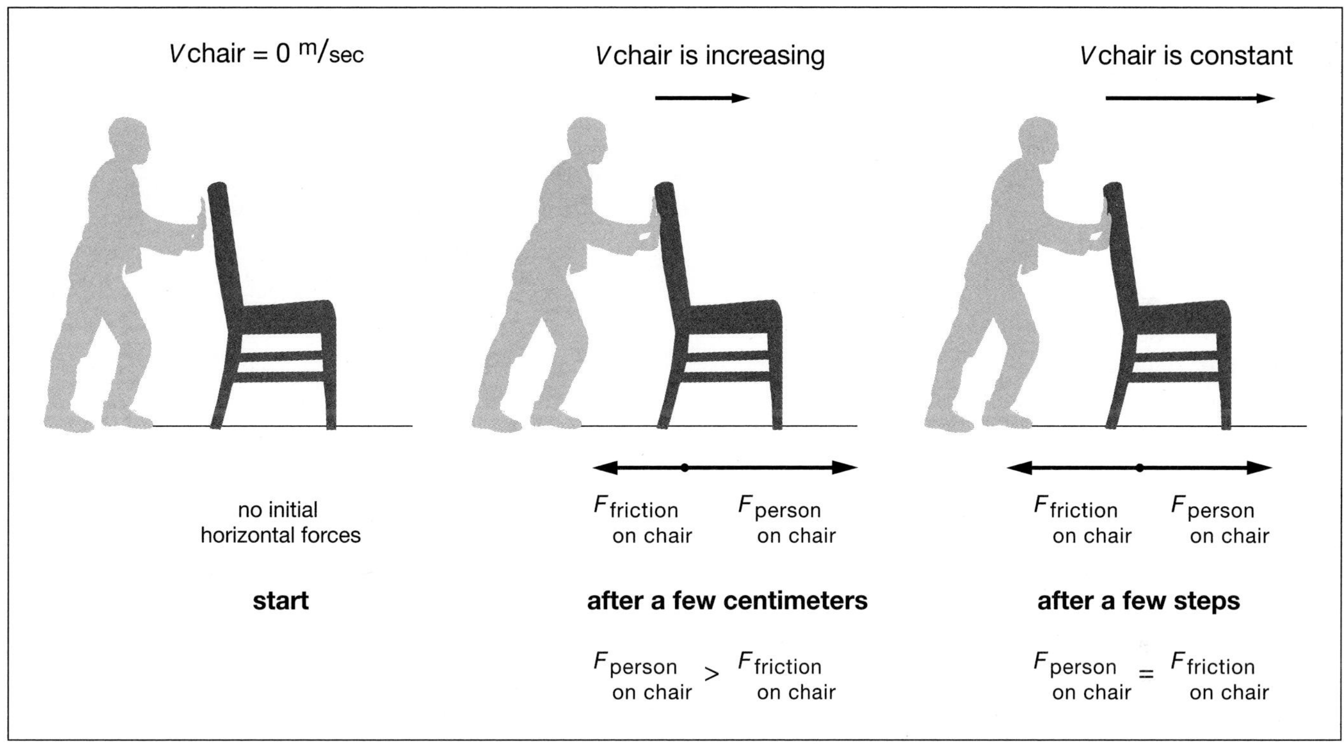

▲ **Figure T2.20 Vector sketch.** This vector sketch represents the force vectors on the chair for Step 6.

Feature in opening a parachute	Feature in applying brakes in car	Reason
Initially moving at constant velocity vertically is like	moving at some constant velocity horizontally	because constant velocity requires F_{net} = zero, and that is true in both cases.
A parachute opening and a person slowing is like	brakes being applied and a car slowing	because both involve a sudden large force in the opposite direction to original motion.

▲ **Figure T2.21 Analogy map between a parachute and the brakes on a car.** Use this table to help students make an explicit connection in Step 7 between a parachute opening and someone applying brakes on a car.

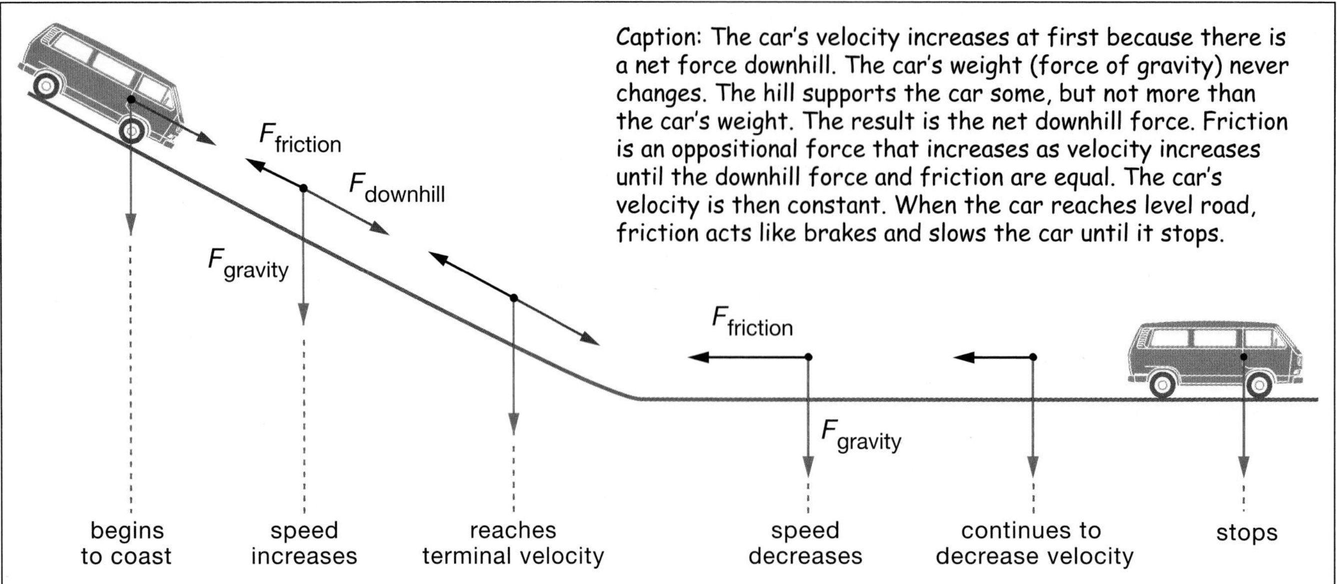

▲ **Figure T2.22 Force vectors on a car coasting downhill.** This vector sketch represents the force vectors for the car coasting downhill in *Stop and Think* Question 3.

Answers to Stop & Think are on TE pages 98–99.

Answers to Stop and Think—Part I, SE page 98

1. A constant force does not automatically result in changing momentum. For example, when a student pushes a chair forward with a constant force across the floor, the chair reaches constant velocity (terminal velocity) because the frictional force equals the pushing force. The net force is zero, thus there is no change in velocity or momentum. Student vector sketches should reflect this.
2. The key idea is net force. If there is a net force acting on an object, then its velocity will change, so there will be a change in momentum. The faster the time rate of momentum changes, the greater the force. Part I supports the law of inertia because the coffee filter's velocity changes during the segment of motion during which there is a net force down and then reaches a constant velocity when the up and down forces balance, resulting in zero net force.
3. Student answers should be similar to figure T2.22. Students should see the similarities between the coffee-filter drop and the car mentioned in this question. As the car coasts downhill, there is a net force downhill, causing an increase in the magnitude

   a. Complete an analogy table like the one in Step 2 to link the filter's motions to pushing a chair across the floor, from rest to some constant velocity.
   b. Draw scaled and labeled vector sketches of all the horizontal forces acting on the chair, from rest to a constant velocity.
   c. Include highlight comments and an overall caption for your sketches.

7. Compare the motion of a parachute opening to applying brakes on a car by completing Steps 7a–c.
   a. Complete an analogy table like the one in Step 2 to link a parachute opening to applying brakes in a car moving at some constant velocity.
   b. Draw scaled and labeled vector sketches of all the horizontal forces acting on the car, from the initial constant velocity to a stop.
   c. Include highlight comments and an overall caption for your sketches.

Stop & THINK

PART I

Answer these questions in your science notebook individually before conferring with classmates. When your discussions cause you to change your answer, document the changes so that you and your teacher can keep track of your ongoing thinking.

1. Does the application of a constant force always result in changing momentum? Support your answer with examples that include vector sketches with labels and captions.
2. Newton's first law (or the law of inertia) states, "Objects in motion stay in motion and objects at rest stay at rest, unless acted upon by an outside net force." Explain whether Part I supports or refutes this statement by providing direct evidence from the activity.
3. A car runs out of gasoline at the top of a hill and coasts down the hill, reaching a flat region. Explain what happens by generating several force vector diagrams at several points in the car's motion downhill. Include a general caption for your sketches describing the significance of the vectors.

of velocity. At some point, the frictional forces equal the downhill force, resulting in constant velocity. When the car reaches flat ground, the car slows (like brakes or a parachute opening) since only the frictional force is acting on the car's motion in the direction opposite to the movement of the car. Understanding the answers to this question will help students be more successful in the evaluate activity.

Cautions

Caution students as they stand on chairs. Make sure the chairs they use are stable. If any students have balance problems or other physical limitations, do not let them stand on an elevated surface.

Process and Procedure

Part II: Fall Time

Materials

For each team of 4 students

1 coffee filter (flat bottomed)
1 stopwatch
1 meterstick or tape measure
paper clips

In Step 1, students predict what a time-to-floor (y-axis) versus number-of-paper-clips (x-axis) graph will look like if they kept adding paper clips to the filter until an entire box of paper clips were added. Answers will vary, but the most common answer will show the time decreasing linearly as the number of paper clips increases, which is indicated with a straight positive-sloping line. This result is not correct, as students will find out through investigation. If it were, this would indicate that with enough paper clips, the time to reach the ground would reach zero. Do not correct your students at this point. The key is to have them access their prior knowledge and then orchestrate an activity in which they want to find out the answer.

Students test their predictions in Steps 2 and 3 by designing and conducting an investigation. Students will continue adding paper clips and timing the total time to the floor. When they graph the data as suggested, the fall time reaches a minimum associated with free fall. That is, the coffee filter and paper clips behave as if they were a dropped cannonball with very little air resistance. When this is the case, the velocity keeps changing at a steady rate during the entire fall. The final student graph will be a curved line starting in the upper left and flattening out at about 1 second.

Students answer a set of true and false questions in Step 4. Monitor your class to ensure that students are writing justifications for their answers.

Answers to Step 4, SE pages 99–100

4a. True. I observe directly the filter increasing velocity for a short period, followed by constant velocity.

4b. True. I observe directly the filter paper starting stationary and then reaching terminal velocity. Thus, the velocity had to change.

Part II: Fall Time

Materials

For each team of 4 students

1 coffee filter (flat bottomed)
1 meterstick or tape measure
1 stopwatch
paper clips

Process and Procedure

You learned in Part I that when the net force acting on an object is zero, two motions are possible: (1) motionless ($v = 0$ m/sec) or (2) constant velocity ($v =$ constant). But what kind of motion results when there is a *constant* net force? To find out, you and your team will use a flat-bottomed coffee filter and paper clips (figure 2.27) to model how an object falls when the only downward force is due to the pull of gravity from Earth.

1. Predict what a time-to-floor (y-axis) versus number-of-paper-clips (x-axis) graph would look like if you continued Step 1 from Part I until there was an entire box of paper clips in the filter.
2. Design an investigation to test your prediction. Your investigation should include the following:
   - A step-by-step procedure
   - Appropriate data tables to record all measurements (including multiple trials)
   - A graph of your results including error bars and highlight comments

Don't write a caption for your graph until you have completed Step 5.

3. Carry out your investigation with your team after your teacher has approved your design and data tables.

▲ **Figure 2.27**
Fall time. You and your team use a flat-bottomed coffee filter and paper clips to model how an object falls. What is the downward force on the coffee filter? Is there an upward force?

Cautions

Make sure the chairs you use are stable. If you have balance problems or other physical limitations, do not stand on an elevated surface.

4. Answer the true or false questions in Steps 4a–e in your science notebook regarding your xy plot of data. Include a justification for your answer (that is, "I answered false because ...")
   a. The filter reaches terminal velocity with zero paper clips. (T or F)
   b. The filter demonstrates a Δv when loaded with no paper clips. (T or F)

4c. False. Past a certain number of paper clips, the time does not change anymore, as shown by the graph flattening.

4d. False. The best fit line on the graph would have to hit the x-axis at some point for this to be true, and my line does not.

4e. True. My graph shows this limit with the flat portion. This section of my graph results from greater and greater mass, yet the amount of time to fall does not change anymore.

After reading *Falling to Earth* in Step 5, students compose a draft caption for their graph from Step 2.

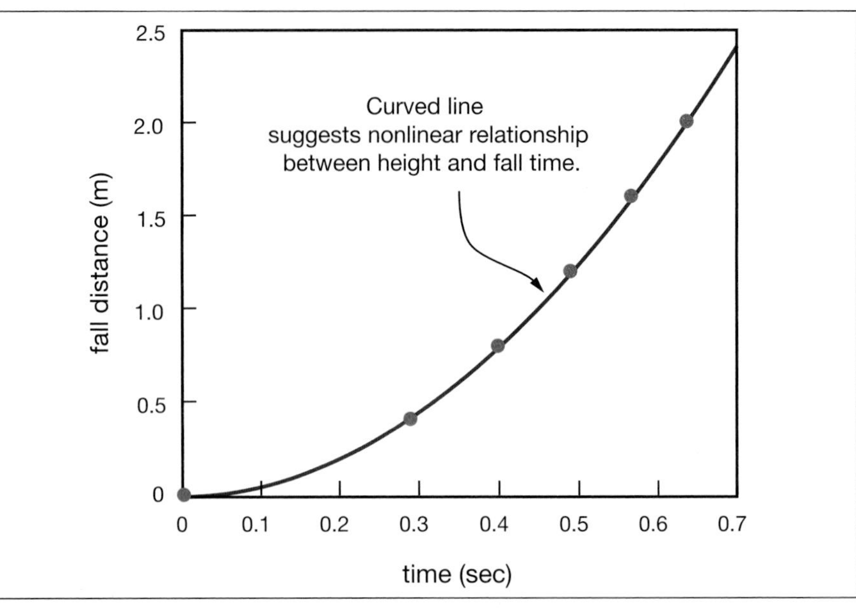

▲ **Figure T2.23 Height versus time.** This plot of height versus time is for Reflect and Connect Question 2.

NOTES:

c. As the number of paper clips increases, the amount of time to reach the floor continues decreasing, no matter how many clips are added. (T or F)

d. Theoretically, if you placed an infinite number of paper clips in the filter, the filter would require 0 seconds to reach the floor. (T or F)

e. For objects falling near the surface of Earth, there is a limit to the amount of time they require to fall a certain distance. (T or F)

5. Read *Falling to Earth* to help you write an effective caption for the time-to-floor versus number-of-paper-clips graph from Step 2.

READING

Falling to Earth

When a parachutist first jumps out of an airplane, the only force down is the pull of gravity. Instantly, air resistance (friction) results in an upward force. The greater the magnitude of the velocity, the greater the upward force, until the force down equals the force up. The average terminal velocity of a parachutist with an unopened parachute is about 125 miles per hour or 56 m/sec. Though terminal velocity is smaller if the upward force is made greater by opening a parachute, even a falling bowling ball with no parachute reaches terminal velocity if it falls long enough. The magnitude of the terminal velocity of the bowling ball would be quite large.

However, there are times when gravitational force (gravity) is the net downward force. Can you think of some examples? What about on the Moon, where there is no atmosphere? There is no air resistance, and when an object falls or is dropped, gravity supplies a constant net force. If there is a very short distance to fall or if there is low air resistance, the fall time is not long enough to produce terminal velocity—so there is a constant net force.

Since the weight remains constant in a fall, so does the net force. And from the mathematical relationship $F = \frac{m\Delta v}{\Delta t}$, if force and mass are constant, so is the rate of change of velocity, $\frac{\Delta v}{\Delta t}$. This rate of change of velocity is the *same* for all objects close to the surface of Earth, regardless of mass, provided no upward forces exist. For the planet we live on, this constant rate of change of velocity has the average numerical value of 9.8 m/sec^2. This number, often called g, means that the maximum change of velocity in 1 second (sec) of free fall near the surface of Earth is 9.8 m/sec. That is, objects dropped from the same height will hit the ground at the same time, regardless of mass. So when either the falling distance is relatively short or air friction is small, the time to hit the ground will reach some constant, nonzero value. This value reflects the mutual gravitational attraction between any two objects near the surface of a particular planet. For Earth, the constant rate of change of velocity that conveys how strong Earth's gravitational field is close to the surface is 9.8 m/sec^2, on average.

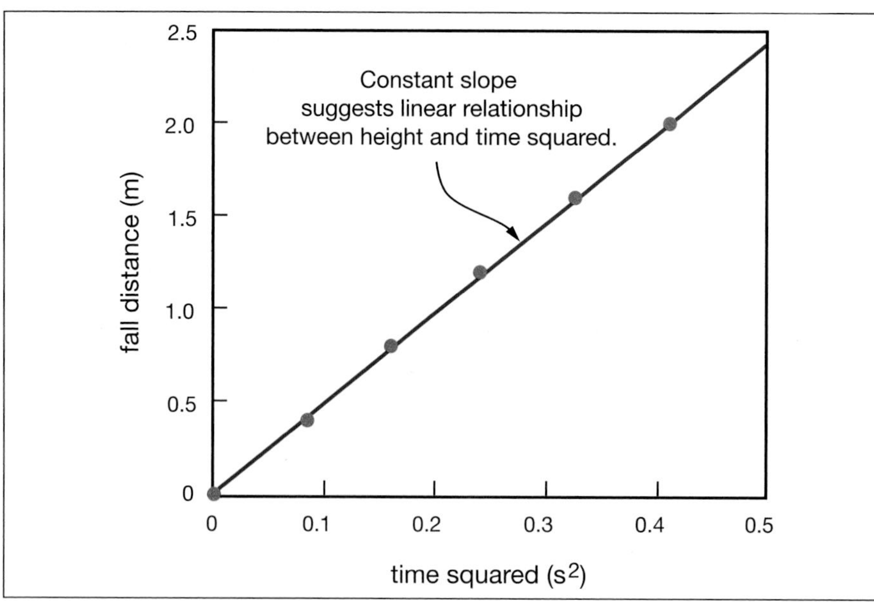

▲ **Figure T2.24 Height versus time squared.** This plot of height versus time squared is for *Reflect and Connect* Question 2.

6. Write a draft caption for your graph from Step 2. Then use the TSAR strategy with your team to finalize your caption.

Reflect and Connect

Think carefully about the answers to the following questions, then write answers in your science notebook. You may discuss your answers with your classmates as directed by your teacher.

1. Three students predict the relative amount of time required for a feather and a hammer, released from the same height on the Moon, to hit the ground.

   Ashley says the hammer hits in less time because the mutual gravitational attraction between the Moon and hammer produces a far greater force than between the feather and the Moon. With a greater force comes a greater change in velocity. Thus, the hammer moves more distance in less time.

   Brandon says they hit at the same time because forces occur in pairs, equal in size and opposite in direction. So the force of gravity is the same on both objects. Since the force is the same, so is the change in velocity. Thus, they hit at the same time.

   Carmella says g on the Moon is constant near the Moon's surface, though less than g on Earth because the gravitational field strength is less on the Moon than on Earth. Since g (the time rate of change of velocity) is constant near the surface, both objects experience the same change in velocity. Thus, they hit at the same time.

   Select a student position to defend and generate labeled vector sketches with highlight comments as your defense. Explain what is incorrect in the other two student explanations.

2. A team of students designed an activity to determine the mathematical relationship between drop height and time to floor for a coffee filter loaded with an entire box of paper clips. The students placed their data in the table in figure 2.28. They generated 2 xy graphs: (1) height (y-axis) versus time (x-axis) and (2) height (y-axis) versus time squared (x-axis).

   a. Generate the same 2 graphs that this team did, using the same height scale for both plots.

   b. Incorporate highlight comments onto both plots, focusing on the best-fit line that the data suggest.

▼ **Figure 2.28 Recorded data for drop height and time.** A team of students recorded the following data from an activity similar to the one you just completed. Use these data for Questions 2a–c.

Drop height (m)	Time to floor (s)
2.0	0.64
1.6	0.57
1.2	0.49
0.80	0.40
0.40	0.29
0.0	0.0

Answers to Reflect and Connect, SE pages 101–103

1. Carmella is correct since the time rate of change of velocity in a constant gravitational field is constant, regardless of mass. Ashley is incorrect, although what she says about the amount of force on the hammer (weight) is true. But the ratio of gravitational force to mass is constant for all objects, so they all have the same acceleration. Brandon is partially correct as well. Forces do occur in pairs, but the force of gravity on both objects is not the same, since the feather has less mass and force = mg.

   The *SRCD* includes a video clip of astronaut Dave Scott from *Apollo 15* as he drops a feather and hammer on the Moon.

2. Student answers are shown in figures T2.23 and T2.24. The height versus time squared graph shows the most linear best-fit line, which suggests that fall time for objects near the surface of Earth (with minimal air friction) is directly proportional to time squared. This graph is linear, so this statement may be confusing to students. As they answer Question 2c, they will see that height is directly proportional to fall time squared. Since the y-intercept equals 0, the value for b in the equation may be omitted. Students should see that the y value is drop height (m) or distance, and the x value is time. Substituting into the equation for a straight line, they get $d = mt^2$. The m value is the slope; students will not realize it now, but this is the setup for the relationship $d = at^2$ that they will study in chapter 4. Resist going into detail about this now as students will build their own understanding in chapter 4.

Objects involved in forces in a pair	Relative size of forces in a pair	Relative size of forces in a pair compared to other two pairs
Teenager and sled	The force of the teenager on the sled equals the force of the sled on the teenager.	The force pair has equal and opposite forces but the forces in this pair are more than the forces between the ground and the sled.
Teenager and ground	These forces are equal to each other.	These forces are equal and opposite and are similar to the other pairs of forces.
Sled and ground	These forces are equal to each other.	The force pair has equal and opposite forces but the forces in this pair are less than the forces between the teenager and the sled.

▲ **Figure T2.25 Identification of force pairs.** This completed table helps students identify and analyze all the action-reaction force pairs in the blocking sled situation.

3. This is a classic question posed in many physics classes. Inspect student diagrams for inclusion of the teenager, the blocking sled, and the ground on which both rest. Students should see that not all the forces shown are the same but should add the missing forces. Each pair of forces must be equal and opposite. Figure T2.25 is a set of correct responses for Question 3c for the teenager pushing from left to right.

3d. Students should recognize that the motion of the sled depends only on the forces on the sled. There is a net force on the sled because the force of the teenager pushing on the sled is greater than the ground pushing on the sled. It is this net force that will cause a change in momentum—the sled will move. So the teenager is clever, but wrong. Newton's third law of motion is not an excuse to get out of football practice!

4. Students should indicate either with words or sketches that a net force on an object results from unbalanced forces—they will not all cancel out. It is important for them to realize that this part of Newton's second law is about forces on one object only. If the forces are not balanced then there is a net force. And if there is a net force, the object will accelerate. Students may also say that a net force will cause a change in velocity or a change in momentum. All of these answers are correct.

Students should also indicate how they would recognize when there is no net force on an object. In this case, the forces on the object balance, or all add to zero. This object will have a constant velocity. That constant velocity can either be zero (motionless) or moving at a constant nonzero velocity.

c. You know from algebra that a straight line with a constant positive slope can be represented by $y = mx + b$. Use this reminder to suggest a mathematical equation that represents the relationship between height and time for falling bodies.

Recall these relationships from the equation:

y = the variable graphed on the y-axis

m = the slope of the line

x = the variable graphed on the x-axis

b = the point where the line crosses the y-axis (the y-intercept)

3. Imagine a "clever" teenager who wanted to avoid a football workout. The conversation with a coach might go like this:

TEENAGER: "It's totally useless for me to try to push the blocking sled."

COACH: "You think so!? Why is that?"

TEENAGER: "Because of a law of nature."

COACH: "This I've got to hear."

TEENAGER: "I have been learning that forces come in pairs, equal in size and opposite in direction. When I push on the sled, the sled pushes back on me with an equal, but opposite, force. The forces cancel. Therefore, I can never get the sled moving. It's useless!"

COACH: "Now I've heard it all! I need to talk to that science teacher . . ."

Follow Questions 3a–d to analyze the motion of the blocking sled.

a. Draw a sketch of a teenager pushing a blocking sled similar to figure 2.29.

b. Use vector arrows to label the pairs of forces that occur at each of the starred areas of the sketch.

EVALUATE

Forces to Go; Forces to Stop

Activity Overview

In *Forces to Go; Forces to Stop*, students will demonstrate what they have learned regarding force, investigation design, and how to document the ongoing process of learning. There are two parts to the activity. In Part I, students will design an investigation to mimic a car running out of gas on top of a hill and rolling to a stop some distance after reaching the bottom. Students will use the data they collect and the graph they generate to demonstrate that they know about what a net positive, net negative, and net zero force does to velocity. Students look for evidence of velocity changes to determine the net force on the ball at various locations in its motion down the ramp.

In Part II, students will analyze the evidence from a car accident scene to decide who is at fault. They will use their understanding of conservation of momentum and collisions in two dimensions to decide which car ran the stop sign.

Before You Teach

Background Information

A ball rolling down a hill behaves the same way as a car coasting down a hill. Initially, both experience a net force directed down the hill, and thus the ball's velocity changes from zero to increasingly larger positive numbers. The net force is less than the ball's weight, so the ball does not experience free-fall acceleration, but some acceleration with a magnitude less than 9.8 m/sec^2. This acceleration shows up as a curved line (second-degree polynomial) in a position versus time graph and as a straight line with a constant positive slope in a velocity versus time graph. This part of the ball's motion is like the coffee filter falling before it reaches terminal velocity, students jumping off chairs, and the first part of a toy car's motion down a ramp.

As the ball rolls, frictional forces increase, retarding the ball's motion. Acceleration decreases until the force down the ramp equals the force of friction. At this point, the ball reaches terminal velocity. If the ramp is steep enough or if the ramp is short, the ball may not reach terminal velocity. If terminal velocity is reached, it shows up as a constant positive slope in the position versus time graph and as a horizontal line on the velocity versus time graph.

When the ball reaches the floor, it no longer experiences a "down-the-ramp" force. The only force affecting the forward motion is the frictional force between the ball and the floor. This force is constant, and so it produces a constant backward acceleration, as when you apply brakes while driving a car. This motion appears as a downward curving line with decreasing slopes in the position versus time graph and a straight line with a constant negative slope in the velocity versus time graph.

Answers to Reflect and Connect Question 4 are on TE page 102.

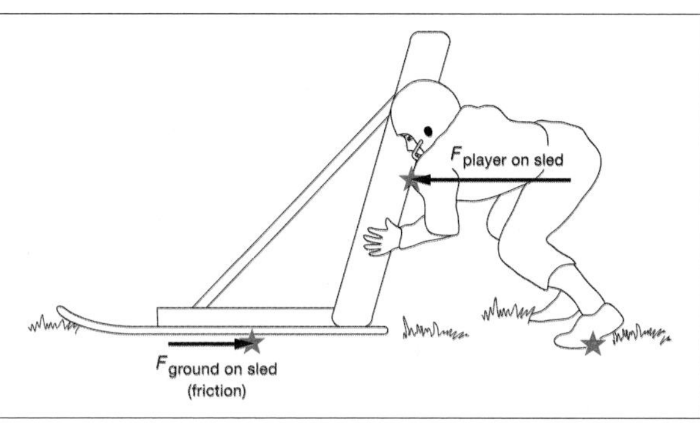

◀ **Figure 2.29 Forces involved in pushing a sled.** Draw this sketch in your science notebook. Place vectors to represent forces at each star. In some cases, one of the forces in the pair has been drawn for you.

c. Complete the table in figure 2.30 in your science notebook. Identify and comment on *all* the horizontal pairs of forces important to the question of whether the teenager can push the sled.

Objects involved in force pair	Relative size of forces in pair	Relative size of force pair compared to other two force pairs
Teenager and sled	The force of the teenager on the sled is equal and opposite to the force of the sled on the teenager.	
Teenager and ground		
Sled and ground		

▲ **Figure 2.30 Table comparing forces.** Complete this table for Question 3c.

d. Decide who is correct in his reasoning. Is it the football player trying to get out of pushing the blocking sled, or the coach who wants the player to complete the workout? Write a statement giving evidence to support your decision. To develop your statement, consider the forces that would cause a change in momentum of the sled.

4. The focus question for this activity was, "How do I recognize when there *is* and *is not* a net force acting on an object?" Use your experiences from this activity to write a short paragraph to answer this question. You may use sketches to illustrate your answer.

Materials—Part I

For each team of 4 students

1 balance
1 ramp
1 stopwatch
balls (same material, different mass)
tape
1 tape measure or meterstick
1 chair or box of similar height
graph paper
1 calculator (optional)

4 copies of copymaster 2.2, *Scoring Rubric for Forces to Go; Forces to Stop*

Materials—Part II

For each team of 4 students

1 ruler
1 protractor
graph paper
1 calculator
4 copies of copymaster 2.3a, *Who's at Fault?*

For the teacher

1 transparency of copymaster 2.3b, *Answer Key for Who's at Fault?*

Advance Preparation

Many items can be used for ramps such as long lengths of cardboard (from refrigerator boxes), shelving, or aluminum tracks from windows or doors (found readily at hardware stores). Each ramp should be at least 1 m long to give students sufficient space for 5 or 6 timing positions down the ramp. Otherwise, their data will be difficult to interpret.

Steel balls and glass marbles of about the same diameter work very well for different masses. It is best to use similar diameters since this decreases the effects of rotational inertia.

Make enough copies of copymaster 2.2, *Scoring Rubric for Forces to Go; Forces to Stop* and copymaster 2.3a, *Who's at Fault?* for all your students. You may want to make a transparency of copymaster 2.3b,

Answer Key for Who's at Fault? to use when students have completed the activity.

Educational Technologies

A sonic motion detector can be used to measure the position versus time behavior of the ball. These devices, when attached to computers with the proper software, can graph the position and velocity versus time graphs. If your school has this equipment, consider allowing some teams to use it as an interesting contrast to paper and pencil methods.

As You Teach

Outcomes and Indicators of Success

By the end of this activity, students should

1. be able to design an investigation intended to determine the relationship between the force and mass of a ball rolling down a ramp, onto the carpet, and coming to a stop.

   They will demonstrate their ability by

   - recording the ongoing results of team discussions, including any changes to design;
   - writing a step-by-step procedure in their science notebooks; and
   - following their step-by-step procedure and recording data in tables.

2. be able to analyze investigation data to establish the relationship between mass and force acting on a ball rolling down a ramp.

   They will show their ability by

   - preparing data tables to organize their experimental data,
   - graphing position versus time and including highlight comments and captions,
   - relating different portions of each graph to different changes in velocity,
   - connecting different changes in velocity to different forces acting on the ball, and
   - relating the differences in motion graphs between the light and heavy balls to differences in the forces each ball experiences on the ramp and on the carpet.

EVALUATE

Forces to Go; Forces to Stop

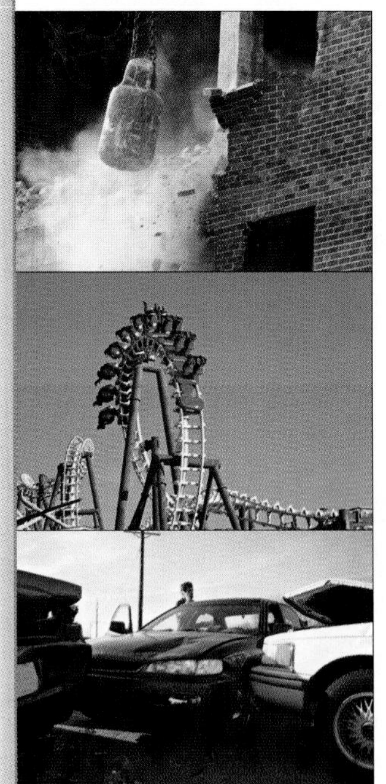

▲ **Figure 2.31 Forces cause changes in momentum.** Look at each photograph and think back to the activities in this chapter. In each activity, what evidence did you collect or observe that indicated a net force?

Forces change things. You saw this happen in each activity so far in this chapter, from colliding cars to parachuting coffee filters. That's because all net forces, *regardless of their origin*, cause changes in momentum (figure 2.31).

In Part I of *Forces to Go; Forces to Stop*, you and your team will demonstrate your understanding of the relationship between force, motion, and changing momentum. To do this, you will focus your planning and interactions on answering the following question: "How are net force and mass related for a ball rolling down a ramp, onto a carpet, and then slowing to a stop?"

Review the rubric for scoring before you start. It will help you get the best performance for the least amount of your team's limited time.

Part I: Out of Gas or Out of Momentum?

Materials

For each team of 4 students

1 balance
1 ramp
1 stopwatch
balls (same material, different mass)
tape
1 tape measure or meterstick
1 chair or box of similar height
graph paper
1 calculator (optional)
4 *Forces to Go; Forces to Stop Scoring Rubric* handouts

Process and Procedure

Imagine you are driving in a car. You glance down at your gasoline gauge and see the needle below E! But luckily, you're on top of a hill. Will you make it to the gasoline station? What factors make a difference when you have no engine force? Are there other forces to think about? What are those forces?

104 Unit 1 Interactions Are Interesting

3. be able to analyze evidence from a crash scene to determine which driver ran a stop sign.

They will show their ability by

- analyzing the forces and velocities involved at the scene;
- drawing vector diagrams of the scene using two scenarios, one with each car running the stop sign;
- using vector math and algebra to solve the problem;
- explaining in words the steps taken and the justifications; and
- drawing diagrams to analyze the scene.

Strategies

Getting Started

Since students have already experienced every aspect of this evaluate in previous activities, you might consider mentioning that this activity asks them to use what they already know, but in a different context. You will be encouraging dialogue and giving feedback to students as they progress through the activity. You will be monitoring how students transfer prior knowledge to new settings based on input from the environment, peers, and yourself.

Review the rubric with students so that they know what to expect. Communicate your standards and how you will assess each part of the activity.

Process and Procedure

Part I: Out of Gas or Out of Momentum?

Materials

For each team of 4 students

1 balance
1 ramp
1 stopwatch
balls (same material, different mass)
tape
1 tape measure or meterstick
1 chair or box of similar height
graph paper
1 calculator (optional)
4 copies of copymaster 2.2, *Scoring Rubric for Forces to Go; Forces to Stop*

Students meet with their teams and design an investigation to answer the focus question. Steps 1a–e help them set up the investigation. The procedure is essentially to measure time and distance for several intervals as the ball rolls down the ramp and onto the carpet to a stop. Students should know they need distance and time data to generate the position graph. This may be the toughest part of the assignment for students. Be sure they understand what data they need to collect and how to graph those data. Discuss what variables should be held constant. Suggest using distance intervals of about 20 cm on the ramp and 1 m on the carpet. This will save them time since the balls roll several meters on the carpet and short intervals become tedious to time repeatedly.

Glass marbles and steel balls of similar diameters work well. Try to get the masses to be in a ratio close to 2:1. Assess whether students can demonstrate the need for multiple trials in scientific investigations. They should record at least three trials for each distance. If the time for a certain distance varies more than 20 percent, students should practice timing until their data are more reproducible. Assess whether students demonstrate quality skills of scientific analysis. Look for margin comments detailing significant team decisions, especially in the context of the decision and the outcome. Assess whether students represent and communicate scientific

---

In this evaluate activity, you will model an out-of-gasoline scenario, using everyday objects (figure 2.32). Then you will analyze evidence and communicate your findings. Along the way, you will document how the design of your study changed due to new information and evolving understandings.

1. Meet with your team and design an experiment to answer the following question. Consider Steps 1a–e as you design your experiment.

   "What do changes in motion tell you about the relationship between force and the mass of balls rolling down a ramp, onto a carpet, and then to a stop?"

   a. Your team must generate a graph of position versus time with highlight comments and captions. You will plot time on the *x*-axis and position on the *y*-axis. This will show the core of your understanding, so be sure to consider the following as you plan your data collection for your graphs:
      - The variables you should measure and how you should control all others
      - The ramp angle you can use so that the speed and distance are easy to measure
      - A method to divide your graph so that you can record highlight comments for both the ramp and the carpet sections
      - The best way to incorporate key concepts such as mass, weight, force, momentum, impulse, vector, change, friction, and force pairs (Newton's third law) in highlight comments, captions, or both

   Create a legend for your graph. Use a different color or different style of data point for each ball. Your graph will have 2 lines on the same graph, one for each ball.

   b. Your team must test at least 2 balls with surfaces of similar smoothness but with different mass.

   c. You must incorporate multiple trials in your analysis of any trends in data. You should include the uncertainty in your measurement and error bars on your graph.

▲ **Figure 2.32 Experimental designs may change.** Answering a scientific question requires discussion and the willingness to change your approach, especially if what you started isn't working. What design will you use to answer the focus question?

information in multiple forms; charts, sketches, graphs, and sentences should be part of the observation process.

Students predict what their graphs will look like in Step 3. Monitor your class to make sure it does not begin the investigation before doing this step. Assess whether students demonstrate ongoing self-evaluation. Again, look for margin comments detailing any changes.

This part of the evaluate will require at least one 50-minute period for data collection. Graphing and analysis will require at least 50 minutes. Use your judgment regarding assigning the graphing task as homework. It is probably most fruitful to focus class time on helping students with the interpretation of the graphs and then allowing them to complete any narrative explanations as homework.

An example of the student graph is shown in figure T2.26, on TE page 108.

Process and Procedure

Part II: Who's at Fault?

Materials

For each team of 4 students

1 ruler
1 protractor
graph paper
1 calculator
4 copies of copymaster 2.3a, *Who's at Fault?*

TRCD

Even though this is an evaluate, students will again be working in teams. You may decide to have them do this part individually. In Step 1, students learn about the evidence collected at a crash scene. The road conditions were icy, so students will not have to worry about friction. Again, students have experienced every part of this evaluate in previous activities, such as inelastic collisions in two dimensions with tennis balls. Consider allowing them to use their science notebooks as a reference during this part. Students who have been diligent in recording all that was asked of them will have a good record of their understanding. Copymaster 2.3a, *Who's at Fault?* includes the crash scene diagram so students can use it for analysis.

Copymaster 2.3b, *Answer Key for Who's at Fault?* shows all the required answers and diagrams. You may want to use this as a transparency as you discuss student answers after they have completed the activity.

d. You must document each design decision and the rationale for making that decision.
e. Your team must document the step-by-step procedure of your design.

2. Show your design to your teacher for approval and incorporate any changes before making your observations.

Be sure to indicate with underlining, highlight markers, or different-colored pens or pencils any changes you made in your design during the course of this entire activity. Record the reasons for your changes in the margin of your science notebook.

3. Before you conduct your investigation, predict what the graph will look like for each ball. Record your prediction on a separate graph. Plot the motion of both balls on the same graph with clearly labeled lines. Give your prediction to your teacher before you go on to Step 4.
4. Conduct your experiment. Then analyze your data by writing highlight comments and captions, and generate your graphs.
5. Hand in your graphs and supporting design documentation as instructed by your teacher.

Part II: Who's at Fault?

Materials

For each student

1 ruler
1 protractor
graph paper
1 calculator
1 *Who's at Fault?* handout

Process and Procedure

When there is a car accident, the drivers in the two cars often do not agree on all the facts. Consider a car accident in which the drivers approached a four-way stop from the south and from the west. The drivers do agree that they both had to stop at the intersection, controlled by stop signs in each direction, before crossing. They do agree that one of them ran through the stop sign at high speed without stopping. As often happens in car accident investigations, the most important thing they don't agree on is who ran the stop sign. The two cars' front ends are smashed; their bumpers are twisted and locked together. After the collision, the two cars came to rest on the sidewalk, where they ran over and destroyed a blue mailbox. Your job, as the

106 | Unit 1 Interactions Are Interesting

NOTES:

investigating officer, is to determine who is telling the truth. Which car ran the stop sign? Was it the SUV or the compact car? You will work with a team to answer these questions.

1. Meet with your team and examine the following evidence and data taken from the scene of the accident:
   - Before the collision, the compact car had been heading east and the SUV had been heading north.
   - The compact car has a mass of 1,160 kg and the SUV has a mass of 3,090 kg.
   - The posted speed limit for the area is 15 mi/hr (24 km/hr).
   - The vehicles moved off together at 14.5 km/hr just after impact.
   - The mailbox that stopped the vehicles is on an angle 36° to the east of north from the center of the intersection.
   - The road conditions at the time of the accident were icy and therefore friction can be ignored.
2. Analyze the crash scene by performing Steps 2a–d. Record your thinking about each of the questions in your science notebook.
   a. What factors control the forces that the objects involved in the collisions experience?
   b. How do the vehicles' velocities change after the cars collide?
   c. What do you need to know to determine which vehicle ran the stop sign?
   d. What vectors can you use to solve the problem?
3. Write a report that provides evidence about which vehicle ran the stop sign and how you know. You should include the following in your report:
   - A description of the problem in words
   - A diagram of the problem, containing all the data from the scene
   - An explanation of the physics involved in collisions as it pertains to this situation
   - The answer to the problem (1 sentence)
   - The vector diagrams and math you used to solve the problem
   - An explanation of the steps you took to solve the problem, and why you took them

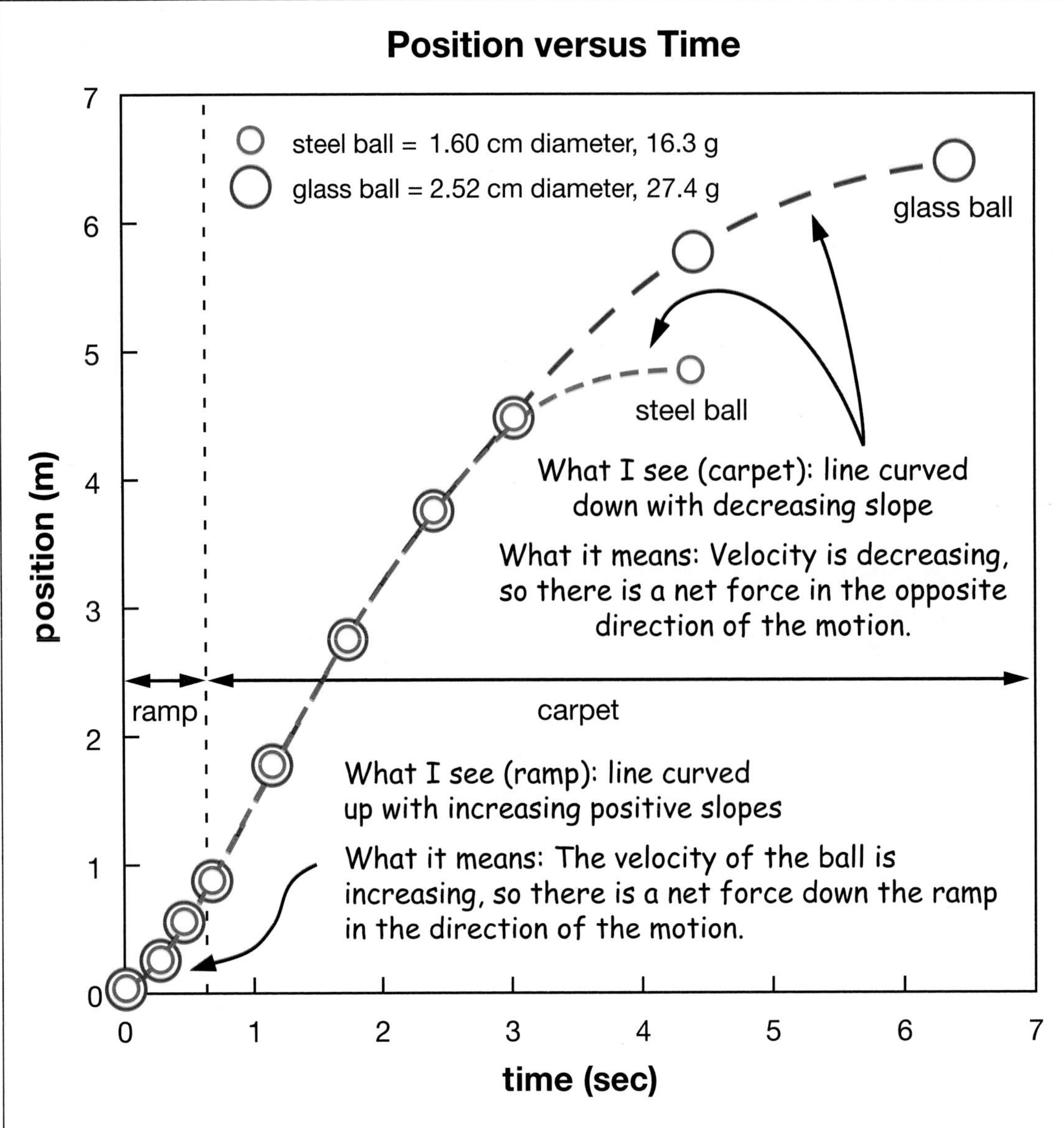

Caption: This graph shows the position versus time behavior of two balls rolling down a ramp, then onto a carpet, to a stop. The velocity of both balls increases down the ramp at the same rate, indicating a change of momentum, and thus a net force down the ramp. But since the mass of the glass ball is greater than the steel ball and the rate of change of velocity is the same, the net force on the glass ball is greater than the net force on the steel ball. The velocity of both balls decreases as they hit the carpet. The velocity of the steel ball decreases faster than the glass ball. The steel ball stops before the glass ball. The net force while on the carpet is in the opposite direction of the motion of the balls.

▲ **Figure T2.26 Sample position versus time graph.** This graph is a possible position versus time graph that students might generate in Part I.

CHAPTER 3

Collisions—Atomic Style

Chapter Overview

Chapter 3, *Collisions—Atomic Style*, will take your students from the large-scale collisions of tennis balls and vehicles to the atomic-scale collisions of molecules and atoms. They will build on their understanding of the physics of these large-scale collisions as they participate in activities in chemistry. Collisions between particles cause change, and your students will study these changes. Students will discover the conditions that are necessary to produce a chemical reaction and what conditions will change the rate of that reaction. Collision theory will be the link from their study of physics to their study of these changes in chemical reactions. This chapter will also introduce students to chemical equilibrium, the phenomena that are constant in the state of equilibrium, and the factors that change equilibrium. They will study Le Châtelier's principle and use it to explain shifts in equilibrium as stresses are introduced to the chemical system.

Along with learning science content, students will have the opportunity to develop their inquiry skills as they design and test their own question related to rates of reaction. Students will also review their classmates' work and offer suggestions for revision.

Goals for the Chapter

As your students focus on the science content and their inquiry skills, they will develop an understanding of

- the role of energy, concentration, catalysts, and kinetics in chemical reactions;
- the changes in energy resulting from chemical reactions;
- the law of conservation of matter and the law of conservation of energy as they relate to chemical reactions;
- systems at equilibrium;
- the similarities in many relationships in the microscopic and the macroscopic world; and
- the abilities necessary to do scientific inquiry.

The chapter organizer uses graphic design principles to help students connect one activity to another. It uses reminders of key concepts, linking questions, and the spatial arrangement of activity titles to foster the sense of a conceptual flow, connecting each activity. Explicitly ask students to locate their position within its flow at the beginning of each activity. This action reinforces the connection among the activities, thus enhancing long-term memory.

Chapter 3 Organizer

COLLISIONS—ATOMIC STYLE

Major Concepts

- **Collisions between particles can lead to reactions.**
- **Energy and concentration play a role in the speed of a reaction.**
- **The laws of conservation of matter and energy can be applied to chemical reactions.**
- **Chemical reactions are systems that can be in equilibrium.**
- **Interactions in the microscopic world are similar to interactions that occur in the macroscopic world.**

ENGAGE — Dish It Up! ★

Key Idea: • Collisions between microscopic particles can be modeled using macroscopic objects.

Activity: Students model particle collisions with a petri dish and BBs. They are asked to manipulate conditions that change the frequency of collisions. They begin to think abut how this might relate to chemical reactions.

LINKING QUESTION: How can I relate collisions between BBs to collisions on an atomic or molecular scale?

EXPLORE — Variable Challenge ★ ★ ★

Key Idea: • Certain factors can influence the rate of a chemical reaction.

Activity: Students develop a testable question then develop and conduct an investigation related to factors that might influence the rate of a chemical reaction.

LINKING QUESTION: What is happening on the atomic scale that can explain the changing rates of chemical reactions?

EXPLAIN — Constructive Collisions ★ ★ ★ ★

Key Ideas:
- Energy, concentration, and the presence of catalysts or inhibitors play vital roles in the frequency of collisions between particles in a chemical reaction. This influences the rate of a chemical reaction.
- The mole is used in chemistry to represent the amount of a substance.

Activity: Students are involved in active reading about the key ideas of this activity. They also participate in activities designed to build their understanding of the mole concept and endothermic and exothermic reactions. Students will also use what they have learned about the mole to calculate stoichiometric quantities.

LINKING QUESTION: What happens when particles in the products of a chemical reaction collide?

ELABORATE — Two-Way Reactions ★ ★

Key Ideas:
- Chemical reactions are reversible and will reach a state of equilibrium under the appropriate conditions.
- Reactions at equilibrium that are subjected to a stress will shift in a direction to relieve the stress.

Activity: Students learn about reversible reactions and chemical reactions at equilibrium through teacher demonstrations and active reading.

LINKING QUESTION: How can I demonstrate what I have learned about collisions between particles at the atomic scale?

EVALUATE — Reaction Rate Readiness ★ ★ ★

Key Idea: • You can explain chemical reactions and reaction rates by understanding collisions between particles.

Activity: Students prepare for a constructed-response test by developing a concept map of important ideas in the chapter. They use this as a means to study for the test. After completing the test, students have the opportunity to learn from their mistakes by applying the *Learn from Mistakes Protocol* to incorrect responses on their tests..

★ = One Class Period ☆ = ½ Class Period *Note:* Based on a 50-minute class period.

Standards Covered by Chapter 3

COLLISIONS—ATOMIC STYLE

STANDARD A: Science as Inquiry. As a result of activities in grades 9–12, all students should develop

abilities necessary to do scientific inquiry

- Identify questions and concepts that guide scientific investigations. Students should formulate a testable hypothesis and demonstrate the logical connections between the scientific concepts guiding a hypothesis and the design of an experiment. They should demonstrate appropriate procedures, a knowledge base, and conceptual understanding of scientific investigations.
- Design and conduct scientific investigations. Designing and conducting a scientific investigation requires introduction to the major concepts in the area being investigated, proper equipment, safety precautions, assistance with methodological problems, recommendations for use of technologies, clarification of ideas that guide the inquiry, and scientific knowledge obtained from sources other than the actual investigation. The investigation may also require student clarification of the question, method, controls, and variables; student organization and display of data; student revision of methods and explanations; and a public presentation of the results with a critical response from peers. Regardless of the scientific investigation performed, students must use evidence, apply logic, and construct an argument for their proposed explanations.
- Use technology and mathematics to improve investigations and communications. A variety of technologies, such as hand tools, measuring instruments, and calculators, should be an integral component of scientific investigations. The use of computers for the collection, analysis, and display of data is also a part of this standard. Mathematics plays an essential role in all aspects of an inquiry. For example, measurement is used for posing questions, formulas are used for developing explanations, and charts and graphs are used for communicating results.
- Formulate and revise scientific explanations and models using logic and evidence. Student inquiries should culminate in formulating an explanation or model. Models should be physical, conceptual, and mathematical. In the process of answering the questions, the students should engage in discussions and arguments that result in the revision of their explanations. These discussions should be based on scientific knowledge, the use of logic, and evidence from their investigation.
- Recognize and analyze alternative explanations and models. This aspect of the standard emphasizes the critical abilities of analyzing an argument by reviewing current scientific understanding, weighing the evidence, and examining the logic so as to decide which explanations and models are best. In other words, although there may be several plausible explanations, they do not all have equal weight. Students should be able to use scientific criteria to find the preferred explanations.
- Communicate and defend a scientific argument. Students in school science programs should develop the abilities associated with accurate and effective communication. These include writing and following procedures, expressing concepts, reviewing information, summarizing data, using language appropriately, developing diagrams and charts, explaining statistical analysis, speaking clearly and logically, constructing a reasoned argument, and responding appropriately to critical comments.

understandings about scientific inquiry

- Scientists usually inquire about how physical, living, or designed systems function. Conceptual principles and knowledge guide scientific inquiries. Historical and current scientific knowledge influence the design and interpretation of investigations and the evaluation of proposed explanations made by other scientists.
- Scientists conduct investigations for a wide variety of reasons. For example, they may wish to discover new aspects of the natural world, explain recently observed phenomena, or test the conclusions of prior investigations or the problems of current theories.
- Mathematics is essential in scientific inquiry. Mathematical tools and models guide and improve the posing of questions, gathering data, constructing explanations and communicating results.

Standard B: Physical Science. As a result of activities in grades 9–12, all students should develop an understanding of

chemical reactions

- Chemical reactions occur all around us, for example in health care, cooking, cosmetics, and automobiles. Complex chemical reactions involving carbon-based molecules take place constantly in every cell in our bodies.
- Chemical reactions may release or consume energy. Some reactions such as the burning of fossil fuels release large amounts of energy by losing heat and by emitting light. Light can initiate many chemical reactions such as photosynthesis and the evolution of urban smog.
- A large number of important reactions involve the transfer of either electrons (oxidation/reduction reactions) or hydrogen ions (acid/base reactions) between reacting ions, molecules, or atoms. In other reactions, chemical bonds are broken by heat or light to form very reactive radicals with electrons ready to form new bonds. Radical reactions control many processes such as the presence of ozone and greenhouse gases in the atmosphere, burning and processing of fossil fuels, the formation of polymers, and explosions.
- Chemical reactions can take place in time periods ranging from the few femtoseconds (10^{-15} seconds) required for an atom to move a fraction of a chemical bond distance to geologic time scales of billions of yars. Reaction rates depend on how often the reacting atoms and molecules encounter one another, on the temperature, and on the properties—including shape—of the reacting species.
- Catalysts, such as metal surfaces, accelerate chemical reactions. Chemical reactions in living systems are catalyzed by protein molecules called enzymes.

conservation of energy and the increase in disorder

- The total energy of the universe is constant. Energy can be transferred by collisions in chemical and nuclear reactions, by light waves and other radiations, and in many other ways. However, it can never be destroyed. As these transfers occur, the matter involved becomes steadily less ordered.
- Heat consists of random motion and the vibrations of atoms, molecules, and ions. The higher the temperature, the greater the atomic or molecular motion.

Prerequisite Knowledge

Students should be familiar with the following concepts taken from middle school standards, standards addressed in Level 1 of this program, and previous chapters in Level 2:

- Substances react chemically in characteristic ways with other substances to form new substances with different characteristic properties.
- Matter is made of minute particles called atoms. Each atom has a positively charged nucleus surrounded by negatively charged electrons.
- Atoms interact with one another by transferring or sharing electrons that are farthest from the nucleus.
- Bonds between atoms are created when electrons are paired up by being transferred or shared.
- Forces are involved in collisions, and collisions cause change.

Students should also be able to do simple conversions using dimensional analysis.

Commonly Held Misconceptions

- Reactions only go in the forward direction.

Students have difficulty thinking of reverse reactions. Common experiences, such as a log burning to ash, tell them reverse reactions do not occur. Though true for the log, many reactions are reversible.

- Because of the reversible nature of reactions, students may have trouble distinguishing between reactants and products.
- The reaction process is not occurring in a chemical reaction that has reached equilibrium.
- Atoms can be seen with a microscope.

"Microscopic" is used several times in this unit, and it is important that you emphasize that that term does not mean to infer that atoms can be seen with a microscope. It is intended to try to get students to look at the particle level of atomic and molecular interactions.

- Bonds store energy, breaking chemical bonds costs energy, and bond making releases energy.
- Physical changes are reversible while chemical changes are not.
- Reactions that proceed more rapidly also proceed further (more completely).
- Chemical reactions will continue until all the reactants are exhausted.
- Chemical equilibrium is a static condition.

NOTES:

ENGAGE

Dish It Up!

Activity Overview

In *Dish It Up!*, your students will work with a model of matter made from BBs of different size and mass. They will look at the motions and behavior of these BBs as they shake the container. They will change the conditions present in the dish and make additional observations. The goal of this activity is to bring out the students' current conceptions about the motion and behavior of particles of matter and relate those motions and behaviors to their understanding from the previous chapter. An additional goal is to get your students thinking about chemical reactions and to set the stage for the explore activity where they must test a question of their choosing related to chemical reaction rate.

Before You Teach

Background Information

Collisions come in all sizes, from the collisions of galaxies to the collisions of atoms. The laws of nature hold true for these collisions on many scales. When BBs collide, their momentum changes. The speed of the BBs changes somewhat, but the most obvious change in momentum is the result of changes in direction. Matter is made up of minute particles of atoms or molecules that are in constant motion. As these atoms or molecules collide, changes often occur.

For a chemical reaction to take place, the reacting particles (reactants) must collide. Not every collision results in a chemical reaction, and so there are variables that can be manipulated to increase the chance that colliding particles will react. Conditions can also be manipulated to increase or decrease the rate at which these colliding particles will react.

Increasing the concentrations of the reacting particles increases the rate. The more particles that are present, the more collisions occur, resulting in a faster reaction rate.

Increasing the temperature of a chemical reaction increases the average kinetic energy of the particles. The particles are moving faster, and thus there are more collisions and the rate increases. Your students will simulate these two variables in this activity. Do not give them this information; it is for your background only. Students will discover these ideas and concepts as they work through this activity and the remainder of the chapter.

It is important to note that when we refer to relationships and motions on a microscopic level, we are referring to interactions between atoms and molecules. The traditional laws of Newtonian mechanics do not always hold true on the subatomic level. There are different laws that govern motions at this level (which include motions of electrons), called quantum mechanics.

Materials

For the teacher

tape or Parafilm

For each team of 2 students

1 petri dish containing 2 different-sized BBs (see *Advance Preparation*)

extra BBs of both sizes

Advance Preparation

Before you begin this activity, prepare the BB dishes. You need 2 different-sized round shots. Copper BBs and lead shot work well; just make sure the larger one is more massive. (Wear disposable laboratory gloves when you handle lead shot.) Put about 20 of each size in a petri dish. You will need to use either tape or Parafilm to secure the lid to the dish. Students will need to open the dish to add more BBs, so do not permanently glue the lid in place. Other small spheres will do as long as they have substantively different masses and they roll well on glass.

Consider preparing 2 sets of petri dishes ahead of time and taping them shut to prevent unwanted spilling. One set will have twice the number of BBs as the other.

Cautions

Spilled BBs pose a slipping danger. Clean up any spills immediately. (Wear disposable laboratory gloves when handling lead shot.)

As You Teach

Outcomes and Indicators of Success

By the end of this activity, students should

1. relate their prior knowledge of collisions on a macroscopic scale to collisions on a microscopic scale.

   They will relate their knowledge by

   - modeling collisions of objects using different-sized BBs in a dish,
   - analyzing the motion of the BBs, and
   - using vector representations in their drawings of the model.

2. realize that certain conditions favor more collisions.

   They will demonstrate their realization by

   - adding more BBs to the model,
   - shaking the model with more vigor, and
   - comparing the results of adding more BBs and shaking the model with more vigor.

3. develop abilities necessary to do scientific inquiry.

   They will develop their abilities by

   - formulating questions related to chemical reactions and
   - comparing different models of molecular motion.

Strategies

Getting Started

Read the chapter introduction with your students and discuss the questions embedded in the introduction. Review the chapter goals with your students. You may want to use questioning strategies to see what they already know about these concepts. But do not answer any questions they may have at this time. Instead, use these questions to help guide instruction; allow students to discover the answers as they work through the chapter.

Look at the chapter organizer together. Remind them that they can use the organizer to review what they have done previously in the chapter. They can also see what is ahead.

Read the introduction to *Dish It Up!* together with your class. There are questions posed in the introduction that students should consider. Allow sufficient time after you read each question to give students the opportunity to formulate their answers. Don't ask for verbal responses from the class at this time. Students will have an opportunity to answer these questions at the end of the activity, so you will want to wait until then to solicit answers.

Cautions

Spilled BBs pose a slipping danger. Clean up any spills immediately. (Wear disposable laboratory gloves when handling lead shot.)

Process and Procedure

Materials

For the teacher

tape or Parafilm

For each team of 2 students

1 petri dish containing 2 different-sized BBs (see *Advance Preparation*)
extra BBs of both sizes

As your students begin this activity, show them the dish of BBs and emphasize that the top of the dish is taped shut. Caution them to keep the lid shut until instructed to open the dish. Tell your students to report any spills to you so that they can be cleaned up immediately.

In Step 1, move about the room and check to see that students are drawing detailed pictures with appropriate labels. It is important for students to note differences, especially in mass, velocity, and changes in velocity.

In Step 2, consider showing students an appropriate "shake frequency" (approximately 2 shakes per second is a good starting point). Make sure the first frequency is low enough for them to increase later. Student should see that the bigger, more massive BBs are moving slower than the smaller, less massive BBs. They can tell how fast the BBs are moving as they make their way across the dish. They should notice that the larger ones take more time to cross the dish than the smaller ones.

Answers to Step 2, SE page 115

2a. Students should see collisions between BBs and with the dish. They can see and hear collisions of the BBs. They should also be able to feel collisions of the BBs with the sides of the dish.

2b. All the BBs are not moving at the same speed. Students' evidence is that each BB moves a different distance in the same time span.

2c. The momentum of the BBs is almost constant as they roll in a straight line since the velocity and mass change very little. There is very little friction between the BBs and the surface of the dish. So the changes in momentum come from changes in velocity due to collisions. The collisions

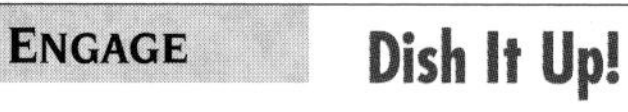

Dish It Up!

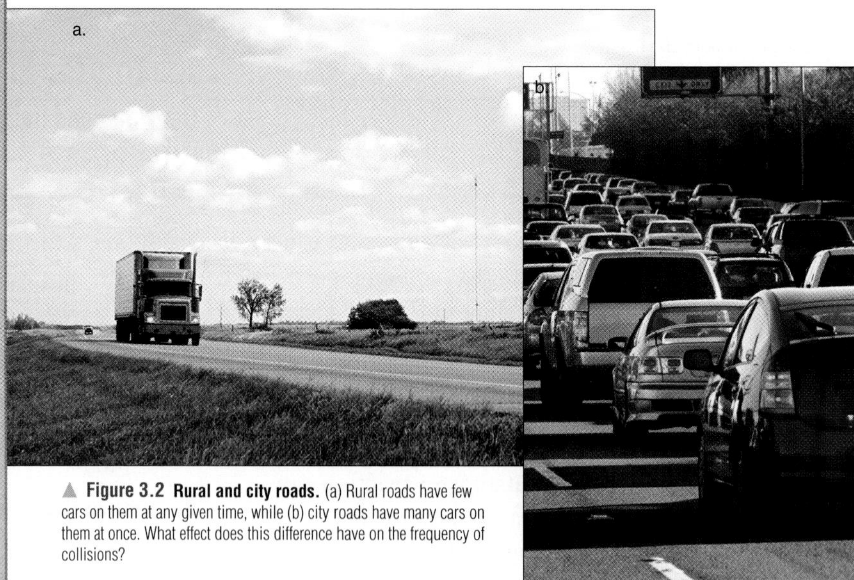

▲ **Figure 3.2 Rural and city roads.** (a) Rural roads have few cars on them at any given time, while (b) city roads have many cars on them at once. What effect does this difference have on the frequency of collisions?

Think about driving down a rural road. You probably feel like you are the only one on the road. Now think about driving on a busy highway. You might worry about your safety because of so many cars. For a particular rural road, officials determined that there were three car accidents in the last 10 years on a 16-kilometer (km, or 10-mile) segment of the road (figure 3.2). On a nearby interstate highway, however, there had been hundreds of collisions during that same time period on a 16-km segment. Can you think of reasons why this is true? Keep those ideas in mind as you work through this activity.

What do car crashes have to do with your study of chemistry? In *Dish It Up!*, you will work with a partner to discover the answer to this question. You also will develop new questions of your own. You will do this by using a petri dish with BBs to model how the atomic world behaves.

114 Unit 1 Interactions Are Interesting

result in changes in speed and direction, both of which change momentum.

In Step 3, students add a few more BBs to their dishes. They should add no more than double the original number. Monitor that students make before-and-after sketches and add proper labels.

Answers to Step 3, SE page115

3c. Collision frequency increases when the number of BBs increases. This is analogous to increasing the concentration of a chemical reactant, which increases reaction rate.

In Steps 4–7, monitor that students make and record observations from increasing the shake frequency. Students should notice more collisions.

Answers to Reflect and Connect, SE page 116

1. The teams changed the number of BBs in the dish and later they shook the dish faster to make more collisions occur. The students may have tried to estimate the number of collisions if the number of BBs was not too great. This question gets students thinking about the properties of the concentration of particles in a reaction mixture and the addition of energy (heat) to a reaction mixture to increase the number of collisions and thus the reaction rate.
2. Students have stated several times that the BBs are not moving at the same speed. They should be able to conclude that the bigger, more massive BBs move slower because the same "shake" was added to both the large and the small BBs. They may say something like, "It takes more energy or force to move a large object than it does a small object. It would be like pushing a bowling ball and a tennis ball with the same force. The tennis ball would move very quickly and the bowling ball would move very slowly."
3. The motions of cars on a highway, BBs in a dish, and molecules are alike in the following ways:
   - All collide.
   - Given the same amount of "energy input," the more massive objects move slower than the less massive objects.
   - An increase in the speed of the objects results in an increase in the frequency of collisions.
   - The faster the objects are moving, the more forceful the collisions.

   The motions are different in the following ways:

   - Cars move along the highway directed by the driver; molecules and BBs move randomly, directed by no driver.
   - Cars and BBs move in two dimensions (mostly); molecules move in three dimensions.
   - Cars dent when they collide; molecules do not dent permanently when they collide.

   There are many more comparisons, but these are typical student responses.

   Help students realize the connection between concentration of BBs and cars. There are many more vehicles on an interstate highway than there are on a rural road. The concentration of vehicles is greater, and thus the chance of collisions is greater. This is like adding more BBs. They may also think about speed limits

Answers to Step 2 are on TE pages 114–115.

Materials

For each team of 2 students

1 petri dish containing 2 different-sized BBs

extra BBs of both sizes

Process and Procedure

1. Represent your dish and BB system in your science notebook by following Steps 1a–b.
   a. Draw a picture of the system as if you were viewing it from above.
   b. Label the BBs "large-mass BBs" and "small-mass BBs."

   Your teacher has confirmed that the larger BBs have a higher mass than the smaller ones.
2. Shake the dish gently at a constant frequency of 1 complete shake (back-and-forth motion) per second. Observe the BBs and record your observations in your science notebook. As you record your observations, be sure to answer the questions in Steps 2a–c.
   a. Are the BBs colliding with one another? With the dish? What is your evidence?

   Think about the evidence you observed when toy cars and tennis balls collided.

   b. Are all the BBs moving at the same speed? What is your evidence?
   c. Is the momentum of the BBs constant or changing? What is your evidence?
3. Add a few more of each type of BB to the dish. Observe what happens when you do Steps 3a–c.
   a. Repeat Steps 1 and 2. Make a new drawing of the system and answer all the questions.

   Use the same "shake frequency" you used in Step 2.

   b. Label your second drawing, "after adding more BBs."
   c. Include highlight comments that help you compare the following:
      - The speed of the BBs from Step 2 with Step 3
      - The frequency of collisions occurring from Step 2 with Step 3 (Are there more, fewer, or about the same?)
4. Now shake the dish with a higher frequency than before.

   Don't shake at such a high frequency that you cannot see what is happening in the dish.

on interstates and rural roads. Typically, the speed limit on an interstate is much higher than on a rural road. Cars on an interstate tend to drive at the speed limit or above, while cars or trucks on a rural road tend to drive at the lower speed limit and often much slower. Students may also state reasons such as slower moving vehicles tend to take less traveled roads since rural roads have no minimum speed limits like interstate highways. Using an analogy, rural roads would be like a petri dish with few BBs, and a busy highway like the petri dish with more BBs. Higher speed limits would be like the higher shake frequency.

Since all the BBs are in the same dish, and your students' hands were shaking the dish and BBs as one unit, the shake (which can represent either force or energy) given to all the BBs was the same. This question sets the stage for future learning in two ways. Students will study Newton's second law and find that, if the force applied is constant, mass and acceleration are inversely proportional. Students will also be learning that adding energy to a system often is done by adding heat. They learn that temperature is a measure of the average kinetic energy of the particles in a system. If the temperature of the system is increased, then the particles will move faster. Just because the entire system is at the same temperature does not mean that all particles are moving at the same speed. The larger, more massive particles will tend to move slower than the smaller, less massive particles—much like the BBs in the petri dish. But even if all particles were exactly the same, they would have different speeds, thus creating a distribution of speeds.

4a. Adding more BBs is like adding more of the atoms or molecules that are involved in the chemical reaction. Don't expect students to use the term concentration now, although some may. It would be a good time to introduce the term if students do not use it in their answers.

4b. Students' responses will reflect the depth of their understanding. Some students may say that the harder and faster shake represents stirring or shaking the chemical mixture. Encourage these students to rethink their answer. Some may say that they were adding more force to the BBs. Ask these students what changes adding more force would cause. Others may say that they were adding more energy. Ask these students what type of energy this could represent. Students may begin thinking about heat energy and what that would do to the speed of the particles in a solution.

4c. If particles are moving around in a beaker, then they are going to collide. If particles are going to react, they must collide.

5. Students should record questions that are related to this activity, for example, questions that deal with adding more particles or energy. Questions like, "What would happen if I mixed chemical A and chemical B?" are not specific to the activity.

Answers to Reflect and Connect are on TE pages 115–116.

5. Record your observations from Step 4 so you can effectively compare all drawings and highlight comments.
6. Write a short caption under your last drawing from Step 5. This caption should summarize what you think is going on when shake frequency and number of BBs change.
7. Exchange captions in your team and read your teammate's summary.

Reflect and Connect

Work with your partner to answer the following questions in your science notebook.

1. What conditions did you change to increase collision frequency? Record evidence that you have to support your answer.
2. Were all BBs moving at the same speed even when the shake frequency was constant? Link evidence from your observations to your explanation.
3. Compare and contrast the motions of cars on a highway, BBs in a dish, and molecules. You may organize your comparisons in a paragraph, a table, or a Venn diagram.
4. Suppose that your dish represents a laboratory beaker and the BBs represent different types of atoms or molecules in the beaker that may react. Turn and talk with your partner. Discuss the following questions. Write your best answers in your science notebook. Be prepared to discuss your reasoning with the class.
   a. What would the addition of more BBs model?
   b. What would increasing the shake frequency model?
   c. What role do collisions play in thinking about atoms and molecules in a beaker?
5. Think about what you know about chemical reactions. With your partner, come up with at least 2 questions that you still have about chemical reactions. Focus your questions on conditions you have modeled in this activity.

EXPLORE

Variable Challenge

In *Dish It Up!*, you began to think about molecules, atoms, and their interactions. BBs helped you model how microscopic objects behave. Then you related BB behavior to the world of atoms and molecules. When atoms and molecules mix together, they collide much like the BBs you saw in your model. Sometimes when molecules collide, they react.

EXPLORE

Variable Challenge

Activity Overview

In *Variable Challenge*, your students will develop a testable question and design and conduct an investigation to answer the question. The students work as a team to develop the question and design. They go through a peer review process and revise their plan based on feedback they receive. This activity strengthens your students' skills in inquiry and helps them to discover some of the conditions that affect reaction rate.

Your role in this activity is to keep the students focused on the goals of the activity. Allow your students to develop their own questions and designs. Facilitate the laboratory in a way that students can conduct their investigations safely and efficiently, and offer guidance to students who are reluctant or unsure of their designs. You should also allow students to test their questions in the method they choose as long as it is safe, even if you can think of a better way to do it. Often, we learn more from our mistakes, and it is good to allow your students to work through theirs. Your students will have the opportunity to suggest ways to improve their plan as they answer the *Reflect and Connect* questions at the end of the activity.

Before You Teach

Background Information

Students will develop a testable question in this activity. This means they must be able to gather evidence to answer the question. If students cannot gather evidence, the question is not scientifically testable.

After they develop a question, your students will design and conduct their own investigation to try to answer the question. Most students are naturally curious and often want to test various methods that would provide answers to the question. Often, however, these tests do not attend to the control of variables. In a sound scientific investigation, the investigator controls the variables so that only one factor is being tested at a time. The investigator must also know how to measure the effect of the variable. To study the effect of temperature on plants, for example, students would change only the temperature and specify the criteria for measuring the effect (for example, the rate of growth, the maximum growth, or the number of leaves).

In a lab setting, an investigator can often control conditions more easily than in non-laboratory settings. For example, when investigating a new heart medicine, researchers choose similar test subjects (same age, gender, health, medical history, etc.). But it is difficult to keep everything in the study identical (diet, exercise, sleep, etc.). It is important for students to understand that scientific investigations must control and measure the variables as much as possible so that the results can be attributed to the variable being tested.

In this activity, students will also learn about factors that affect the rate of a chemical reaction. The area of chemistry that deals with reaction rates is called *chemical kinetics*. Your students will study kinetics throughout the rest of the chapter. Chemical reactions occur because the reacting particles collide. When a reaction occurs, the concentration of the reactants decreases with time as the concentration of the products

How do you know if two chemicals are reacting? You see a change—a chemical change. A chemical reaction results in new substances. Those substances have new chemical and physical properties compared with the original substances.

You see chemical changes, or chemical reactions, every day. Some reactions are slow, like metal rusting on a car. Iron in the car's body is reacting with moisture in the air. The new substance that forms is iron oxide. This is the orange-red rust that you see on the metal. Some reactions are very fast. When gasoline burns in the engine of your car, the gasoline (mostly octane C_8H_{18}) reacts with oxygen gas (O_2). New substances form. Those substances are part of the exhaust of your car and include carbon dioxide and water. This reaction forms new substances, and you know that a chemical reaction is taking place. This reaction is much faster than the iron rusting on your car.

In *Variable Challenge*, you will work as a team to design and conduct a scientific investigation. Your teacher will demonstrate a chemical reaction. Is the reaction fast or slow? How can you determine how long it takes the reaction to occur? Use the following question to focus your activity design: "What factors speed up or slow down chemical reactions?"

Materials

For each student

- 1 pair of safety goggles
- 1 pair of disposable laboratory gloves
- 1 laboratory apron

For each team of 3 or 4 students

- 1 microwell plate
- plastic pipets
- solutions of potassium iodide (KI), sodium thiosulfate ($Na_2S_2O_3 \cdot 5H_2O$), potassium bromate ($KBrO_3$), hydrochloric acid (HCl), and starch
- baking soda ($NaHCO_3$) for acid spills
- toothpicks
- cotton swabs
- 1 sheet of blank, white paper
- additional equipment based on what variable you choose to test

Cautions

Hydrochloric acid is hazardous to skin and eyes. Wash off spills with a lot of cool water. Neutralize spills on countertops with baking soda. Wear chemical splash goggles, disposable laboratory gloves, and a chemical-resistant apron.

increases with time. Chemical kinetics deals with the speed at which these processes occur.

Your students will test different variables, one of which will be the concentration of the reactants. Students will find that, in general, an increase in the concentration of the reactants leads to an increased reaction rate. If you want to take this concept further, then the following information will be helpful. But it is not necessary for your students to understand the order of the reaction to complete this chapter.

Reaction rates and their dependence on the concentrations of reactants must be determined experimentally. When these rates are discovered, chemists find that the rate is not always predictable. For example, the rate of the decomposition of ethane (C_2H_6) at high temperatures and low pressures varies differently from the rate of the decomposition of dinitrogen pentoxide (N_2O_5). In both of these examples, the rate of decomposition varies with the concentrations of the reactant, but not directly proportionately. The equations for the decomposition reactions of these examples are

$$\text{(a) } 2N_2O_{5(g)} \rightarrow 4NO_{2(g)} + O_{2(g)} \text{ and}$$

$$\text{(b) } C_2H_{6(g)} \rightarrow 2CH_{3(g)}.$$

When you double the concentration of N_2O_5 in reaction (a), the rate doubles. Similarly, if the concentration is halved, then the rate is halved as well. This is known as a first-order reaction. In reaction (b), if you double the concentration of ethane (C_2H_6), the reaction rate increases by a factor of four—it is four times faster. We call this a second-order reaction. There are even instances in which an increase in concentration does not affect the reaction rate at all; these are called zeroth-order reactions. You may wish to consult a college general chemistry text for additional background information.

Your students will likely test the effects of temperature on the reaction rate. When heat energy is added to the reaction mixture, the average kinetic energy of the particles increases. The particles are moving faster, and when they move faster, more collisions occur. Chemical reactions speed up when the temperature increases. However, just colliding with another particle does not ensure that a reaction will take place. The rate of reaction is much smaller than the calculated collision frequency. Why is this so?

Svante Arrhenius in the 1880s proposed the existence of a threshold energy, called the activation energy, that must be overcome to produce a chemical reaction. We can visualize the reaction progress as shown in the energy plot of a reaction in figure 3.8 in the student book. The arrangement of atoms found at the top of the potential energy "hill" or barrier is called the activated complex, or transition state. The reaction that produces NO (nitrous oxide) and Br_2 (bromine) from the decomposition of BrNO (activated complex) is exothermic. The products have lower potential energy than the reactant. Students will learn more about exothermic and endothermic reactions in the next activity.

Some of your students may ask, "Can I add anything to the reaction to speed it up?" If they do an investigation to test this question, they will use a catalyst to speed up the reaction. A catalyst speeds up a reaction by lowering the activation energy of the reaction. A catalyzed reaction is shown in figure 3.9 in the student book. Note that a catalyst is not consumed in the reaction.

Materials

For the teacher

1 200-mL beaker
1 overhead projector
20 mL of distilled water
10 mL of starch solution
10 mL sodium thiosulfate ($Na_2S_2O_3$)
10 mL of potassium iodide (KI)
10 mL of hydrochloric acid (HCl)
20 mL of potassium bromate ($KBrO_3$)

For the entire class

0.010 M potassium iodide (KI)
0.040 M potassium bromate ($KBrO_3$)
0.10 M hydrochloric acid (HCl)
0.10 M copper II nitrate ($Cu(NO_3)_2$)
2% starch solution
extra solutions of each of the reactants
tubs for water baths
hot plates or hot pots to heat the water
thermometers
distilled water

For each student

1 pair of safety goggles
1 pair disposable laboratory gloves
1 laboratory apron

For each team of 3 or 4 students

1 microwell plate
plastic pipets
solutions of potassium iodide (KI), sodium thiosulfate ($Na_2S_2O_3 \cdot 5H_2O$), potassium bromate ($KBrO_3$), hydrochloric acid (HCl), and starch
baking soda for acid spills
toothpicks
cotton swabs
1 sheet of blank, white paper
additional equipment based on variables tested
cassette tape box or other container to hold filled pipets

Advance Preparation

You should prepare the solutions ahead of time, as indicated. Each team of students will need approximately 5 mL of each solution. You will need 10–20 mL of each solution for each class demonstration. Increase these preparation amounts to suit your class load.

Potassium Iodide, KI, 0.010 M

To prepare 100 mL of 0.010 M KI, dissolve 0.17 grams (g) of KI in approximately 50 mL of distilled water. Dilute to 100 mL with distilled water and mix. Five mL is enough for a team of students. Potassium iodide solution does not keep well and should be prepared fresh.

Sodium Thiosulfate, $Na_2S_2O_3 \cdot 5H_2O$, 0.0010 M

To prepare 1 L of 0.0010 M $Na_2S_2O_3 \cdot 5H_2O$, dissolve 0.25 g of $Na_2S_2O_3 \cdot 5H_2O$ in 500 mL of distilled water. Dilute to 1 L with distilled water and mix. Five mL is enough for a team of students. You will have much more than you need for your classes, but you must make this amount to maintain the highest accuracy possible.

Potassium Bromate, $KBrO_3$, 0.040 M

Prepare 100 mL of 0.040 M $KBrO_3$ solution by dissolving 0.67 g of $KBrO_3$ in approximately 50 mL of distilled water. Dilute to 100 mL with distilled water and mix. Five mL is sufficient for a team of students.

Hydrochloric Acid, HCl, 0.10 M

Prepare 100 mL of 0.10 HCl by adding 1.7 mL of 6 M HCl to approximately 50 mL of distilled water. Dilute to 100 mL with distilled water and mix. Five mL is sufficient for a team of students.

Copper II Nitrate Solution, $Cu(NO_3)_2$, 0.10 M

Prepare 100 mL of 0.10 M $Cu(NO_3)_2$ solution by adding 2.42 g of $Cu(NO_3)_2 \cdot 3H_2O$ to about 50 mL of distilled water. Stir, dilute to 100 mL with distilled water, and mix. Five mL is enough for a team of students, however, not all teams will use this solution.

Starch Solution, 2%

Use soluble starch from a chemical supply house or cornstarch from the grocery store. Prepare 100 mL of starch solution by making a smooth paste of 2 g soluble starch and 10 mL of distilled water. Pour the paste into 90 mL of boiling water while stirring. Cool to room temperature before using. Starch solution has a poor shelf life. Dispose of it after the experiment, as it will probably form mold if kept too long. Prepare fresh starch solution for each use. Five mL is sufficient for a team of students.

It is convenient to dispense all the solutions in Beral capillary pipets. Prepare the pipets by first labeling each pipet with the solution using a fine-tipped permanent marker. You will need the following solutions for each team:

- KI, 0.010 M
- $Na_2S_2O_3 \cdot 5H_2O$, 0.0010 M
- $KBrO_3$, 0.040 M
- HCl, 0.10 M
- Starch solution, 2%

Have the $Cu(NO_3)_2$, 0.10 M solution available for teams that want to test a catalyst. Do not give this solution to each team.

Next, fill the Beral pipets with the appropriate solution. Prepare the pipets by stretching the tube of the pipet near the bulb and then cutting with a scissors in the stretch area. The solutions will not leak out of the pipets and can be stored upright in a cassette tape box. You may also use micropipets, which already have capillary tips but hold less of the solutions. Prepare a pipet of distilled water for each team. Be sure all pipets are labeled with their contents.

Practice the demonstration before you do it with your class. Set a 200-mL beaker on an overhead projector in view of the entire class. Use the following amounts of each solution and add them in the following order:

1. 20 mL of distilled water
2. 10 mL of starch solution
3. 10 mL $Na_2S_2O_3$
4. 10 mL of KI
5. 10 mL of HCl
6. 20 mL of $KBrO_3$

Stir the mixture well and wait for the reaction. In about 2 minutes, the solution will turn blue as the iodine produced reacts with the starch in the solution.

Educational Technologies

If you have temperature probes that connect to the computer or a graphing calculator, this is a good opportunity for your students to use them if they are testing the effects of temperature on the reaction rate. Also, if students graph their data, they may want to use graphing calculators or computers.

Cautions

Hydrochloric acid is hazardous to skin and eyes. Wash off spills with a lot of cool water. Neutralize spills on countertops with baking soda. Wear chemical splash goggles, disposable gloves, and a chemical-resistant apron.

As You Teach

Outcomes and Indicators of Success

By the end of this activity, students should

1. be able to design a scientific investigation to test variables that affect the rate of a chemical reaction.

   They will demonstrate their ability by

   - generating testable questions,
   - formulating a testable hypothesis,
   - writing a step-by-step procedure that describes their investigation,
   - listing all appropriate materials for their investigation,
   - describing the type of data they will collect and organizing that data appropriately,
   - describing constants and variables present in their design, and
   - identifying ways to control and measure variables.

2. develop and practice skills associated with conducting a scientific investigation.

   They will demonstrate their ability by

   - working effectively in groups to perform the steps in their investigational design and
   - taking appropriate safety precautions during the investigation.

3. begin to understand the significance of gathering and interpreting evidence.

They will demonstrate their understanding by

- organizing their data collection,
- attending to the control and measurement of variables,
- analyzing the data, and
- using their data analysis to formulate a possible explanation.

4. compare the frequency of collisions of reacting particles before and after they manipulate variables in the chemical reaction.

   They will demonstrate their skills by

   - inferring from the rate of reaction the relative frequency of collisions occurring in the chemical reaction and
   - relating collisions in a chemical reaction to collisions of BBs in a model.

5. analyze results of a scientific investigation.

   They will analyze their results by

   - comparing the time it takes for a chemical reaction to occur as they manipulate conditions such as concentration, temperature, and the presence of a catalyst and
   - critiquing the process and results of others.

6. develop skills associated with communicating scientific content.

   They will demonstrate their ability by

   - developing a procedure for a scientific investigation,
   - critiquing other teams' procedures based on a set of criteria, and
   - presenting their results to the class in a way that communicates their explanations based on evidence.

Strategies

Getting Started

The demonstration in Step 1 provides an excellent way to get this activity started. As you perform this demonstration, remind students that designing experiments and controlling variables is very much like what scientists and business people do every day when they need to solve problems.

Cautions

Hydrochloric acid is hazardous to skin and eyes. Wash off spills with a lot of cool water. Neutralize spills on countertops with baking soda. Wear chemical splash goggles, disposable gloves, and a chemical-resistant apron.

Process and Procedure

Materials

For the teacher

1 200-mL beaker
1 overhead projector
20 mL of distilled water
10 mL of starch solution
10 mL sodium thiosulfate ($Na_2S_2O_3$)
10 mL of potassium iodide (KI)
10 mL of hydrochloric acid (HCl)
20 mL of potassium bromate ($KBrO_3$)

For the entire class

0.010 M potassium iodide (KI)
0.040 M potassium bromate ($KBrO_3$)
0.10 M hydrochloric acid (HCl)
0.10 M copper II nitrate ($Cu(NO_3)_2$)
2% starch solution
extra solutions of each of the reactants
tubs for water baths
hot plates or hot pots to heat the water
thermometers
distilled water

For each student

1 pair of safety goggles
1 pair disposable laboratory gloves
1 laboratory apron

For each team of 3 or 4 students

1 microwell plate
plastic pipets

Process and Procedure

1. Make careful observations of the teacher demonstration by following Steps 1a–c.
   a. Draw before-and-after sketches of the reaction.
   b. Write down all the reactants under the appropriate sketches.
   c. Write a caption under each sketch to record the actions your teacher completed.
2. With your team, decide how you would determine how fast this reaction occurred.
   a. Record your best plan in your science notebook.
   b. Share your plan in a class discussion.
   c. Modify your plan based on the best information from the discussion.
3. Meet with your team and read *Reactants, Products, and Indicators*.

READING

Reactants, Products, and Indicators

Chemical reactions occur all around us. Examples include a cake baking in the oven, gasoline burning in the engines of our cars, and even digesting the foods we eat. Complex chemical reactions occur constantly in every cell of our bodies. You just witnessed a complex chemical reaction as your teacher mixed several ingredients, or **reactants**, together to produce the change. Reactants are the starting ingredients for a chemical reaction. **Products** are the new things that are produced as a result of the chemical reaction.

Scientists can determine the rate at which the reaction occurs by measuring how quickly one of the reactants disappears or how quickly one of the products appears. One of the substances used in this reaction is starch. You may have tested for the presence of starch before by dropping iodine on bread or a potato. Iodine turns dark blue to black in the presence of starch. Starch is an **indicator** in this reaction. It forms a starch-iodine substance that is dark blue. Iodine is one of the products of this reaction. When you see the dark blue color, it signals the end of the reaction.

solutions of potassium iodide (KI), sodium thiosulfate ($Na_2S_2O_3 \cdot 5H_2O$), potassium bromate ($KBrO_3$), hydrochloric acid (HCl), and starch
baking soda for acid spills
toothpicks
cotton swabs
1 sheet of blank, white paper
additional equipment based on variables tested
cassette tape box or other container to hold filled pipets

In Step 1, demonstrate the reaction that all teams will use. Students write down all the reactants and make careful observations and sketches of the reaction. To help them do this, write the reactants on the board; use the chemical name and symbols. Conduct the reaction in a 200-mL beaker on top of an overhead projector. This will allow the reaction's progress to be projected onto the screen for the entire class to see. Be sure you are wearing safety goggles to model safe practices. Add the reactants one at a time (see *Advance Preparation*), calling attention to their names and symbols on the board. Students should see the blue color form sometime after the last reactant is added. This signals the end of the reaction. Students may want you to repeat the reaction. Rinse the beaker very well to decrease contamination if you repeat the reaction. All chemicals in this activity can be safely poured down the drain with copious amounts of water.

In Step 2, students will work with their teams to decide the best way to determine how fast the reaction occurred. They will record their ideas in their science notebooks and then share the plans in a class discussion. During this discussion, allow all teams to express their ideas. If some plans have problems, use questioning strategies to help students sort through these problems and come up with a better plan. Teams will revise their plans based on class discussion. The best way to determine how fast the reaction occurred is to use a stopwatch to measure the length of time between the instant the last reactant ($KBrO_3$) is added and the time the blue color first appears.

In Step 3, students read *Reactants, Products, and Indicators*, which will help them formulate a testable question in Step 4. Allow students to come up with their own questions. Some students may have difficulty with this part of the activity. Encourage them to think about the variables that are involved in the reaction and if they could examine one of those to determine the rate. Questions will likely involve adding more of the reactants (changing concentration) and changing the temperature (adding or subtracting energy). Less obvious variables involve adding a catalyst. Hopefully, some group will ask, "Can we add anything to the reaction to speed it up?" If this question arises, talk with the group and allow the students to use this question. You will provide a catalyst for them to add. Do not mention the term catalyst at this time, however; allow them to discover its meaning later.

In Step 4, students work through the think-share-advise-revise (TSAR) strategy that they learned in chapter 2. They wrap up Step 4 by sharing their final questions in a class discussion. Make sure that their questions are testable and safe to test. It is OK for more than one group to test the same question; each group will likely have different methods of investigating the question.

In Step 5, teams make a list of the important criteria of a scientific investigation. They then share their ideas in a class discussion for Step 6. These criteria should include

- only testing the effects of one variable;

4. With your team, formulate a scientifically testable question by following Steps 4a–f.

The question must relate to the speed of the reaction (reaction rate) your teacher just demonstrated.

   a. Think about your question carefully. Are you sure it is scientifically testable?
   b. Share your question with another team.
   c. Ask for advice on how you might improve on your question. Can you make it clearer or easier to test?
   d. Revise your work if your team thinks the advice is good.

Remember from chapter 2 that this process is called think-share-advise-revise (TSAR).

   e. Switch roles with the other team and listen carefully to what it says.
   f. Share your final question with the class as your teacher directs.

5. Work with your team to make a list of important criteria for this scientific investigation.
6. Share your ideas in a class discussion and revise your list based on the ideas proposed by other teams.
7. Read the following information about the investigation you are about to design.

   Now it is time for you to design an investigation to test your question. For this investigation, every team will follow a basic protocol, no matter what question you decide to test. Every team will
   - demonstrate the reaction in a microwell plate,
   - keep the *total* number of drops of the reactants to 20 (you might have to add drops of distilled H_2O to bring the volume to 20 drops),
   - use only 2 drops of the starch indicator and 2 drops of the $Na_2S_2O_3$,
   - add the $KBrO_3$ last, and
   - stir the reaction with a toothpick immediately after the addition of $KBrO_3$.

8. Record the detailed procedure in your science notebook.

Your design should include all the important criteria you listed in the class discussion. Also, construct a data table that outlines the number of drops of each reactant you will use in each test.

9. Choose 1 science notebook from your team to share with other teams. Place this notebook and a blank sheet of paper on your desk.

- measuring all potentially relevant conditions and variables;
- keeping all other variables constant;
- conducting several trials;
- averaging repeated trials;
- using an organized way to record data;
- having a way to analyze data (graphs, charts, etc.);
- creating a list of materials;
- thinking about safety considerations; and
- writing a step-by-step process for conducting and documenting the investigation.

You may want to add additional criteria of your own to this list. Students will revise their lists based on the class discussion in Step 6.

In Step 7, students are given some guidelines for developing their investigation design. Every group will follow the protocol for the basic experiment.

In Step 8, students record their step-by-step plan. Make sure that all students record the procedure in their science notebooks.

In Steps 9 and 10, students conduct a peer review of the investigation designs. Students are instructed to choose one team member's science notebook to represent their team. As an alternative plan, and one which will help keep all team members accountable, you may wish to randomly choose one notebook from each team to display. You and the other teams will then review those notebooks and record comments on a sheet of paper included with each notebook. You may want to set a time limit on the reviews.

Offer advice to teams that chose to vary the concentration in their experiments. Suggest that different teams test different reactants. Students know they must hold all other concentrations the same, so it would be more interesting to test the different reactants. The reactants to test are KI, HCl, and $KBrO_3$. The other reactants are held constant based on the protocol. Water is not a reactant but is simply used to keep the total volume of the reactant solution constant. Students can also use the amount of water as a variable. Make sure teams record the number of drops indicated for their tests in a data table. The moment the blue color appears is subjective. So it is best for teams to repeat their tests several times and record an average of their trials. If your students are confused by more than two variables, then select only two (such as the number of drops of KI and $KBrO_3$). For classes that can handle greater complexity, leave all the variables for students' consideration.

In Step 11, teams revise their plans based on the feedback they have received. This is a very important process—one that is used in scientific research. Call attention to the importance of this step as your students revise their work. Caution them to look carefully at the comments. They must decide which advice to use and which advice to ignore. Use this peer review process as part of your evaluation of their work on this activity.

In Step 12, students record their hypothesis. Review the term *hypothesis* with your class if students are unsure how to formulate a good hypothesis.

In Step 13, students begin their investigations. Students tend to forget their written procedures; remind them to follow their plan. If they find steps where they need to alter their designs, ask them to note those changes in their science notebooks. Students are asked to analyze their data and encouraged to graph their results. It is often easier for them

All team members should have the complete plan recorded in their notebooks.

10. With your team, visit the tables of 2 different teams and read through their designs and detailed procedures.
    a. Note anything that is unclear, that needs to be changed, or that needs to be added or omitted.
    b. Record your suggestions on the blank sheet of paper next to the notebook.
    c. Place your team's initials on the paper with your suggestions so that the team can come to you for clarification if needed.
    d. Rotate around the room until you have reviewed at least 2 plans.
    e. Your teacher will also review your plan and give you feedback.
11. Work with your team to improve the design and procedures for your investigation by completing Steps 11a–c.
    a. Carefully review the comments you received on your design and procedures.
    b. Clarify any misunderstandings with your teacher or with the other teams.
    c. Adjust your plan based on the feedback you received.

You must analyze the feedback and decide what comments to address and what comments to ignore.

    d. Rewrite your procedure if necessary and be sure to have your teacher approve your final procedure.
    e. Keep the paper that includes your peer review. Your teacher will want to look at the reviews to help evaluate your work.
12. Before you begin your investigation, reread the question you are attempting to answer. Based on what you already know, what do you think the results of your investigation will show? Record your prediction as your hypothesis in your science notebook.
13. Conduct your investigation according to your procedure.

Each member of the team is responsible for recording all the data.

14. When you finish your investigation, analyze your data and discuss them with your teammates. You may want to graph your data to see trends and patterns. What patterns do you see in your data?

15. Investigate the *Student Resource CD* (*SRCD*) animation *Kinetics2/Iodine Clock*. This activity lets you control variables to change reaction rates.

to see patterns or trends if they graph their data. This is the part of the investigation that students will struggle with the most. Guide them in the best way to analyze their data using graphs, tables, and so on.

Answers to Reflect and Connect, SE page 121

1. The answer depends on the variable that the team chose to test. Evaluate student answers based on their completeness and the methods students used to control all variables except the one that they tested.
2. Answers will vary based on the variable tested. Those teams that tested changing the concentration or changing the temperature should be able to infer that the frequency of the collisions between particles was also changing. Increased concentration and temperature implies that the collisions would happen more frequently. As evidence, their data should show an increased reaction rate with increased concentration or temperature. The opposite would be true for decreased concentration and temperature. Students testing the addition of a catalyst may infer that the catalyst in some way "helped" the particles collide or react.
3. Again, answers will vary depending on the variable tested. Students testing concentration should remember from the engage activity that when they added more BBs to the dish, there were more collisions. They can explain the increased reaction rate by knowing that particles must collide to react, and thus more collisions will lead to a faster reaction. Similar explanations will come from groups that chose to vary the temperature in their experiment. Students may connect to the BB–petri dish activity and remember that they added more energy to the dish by shaking it more vigorously. The result was more collisions with more energy. Students may know that increasing the temperature increases the speed of the particles, which would lead to more collisions and a faster reaction. This is a good time to assess your students' prior knowledge about heat and temperature. If some students chose to add a catalyst, their explanations may be more vague. Accept all reasonable answers. Students will learn the scientific reasons for their results in a later activity.
4. Students may have noted these changes during the investigation. There is always room for improvement, and you should look for thoughtful answers from your students.
5. This is a very important part of this activity. Students need to understand what happened to the rate of the reaction when various investigations were done. If multiple teams tested the same variable, you can choose only one of the teams to present if you are concerned about time. All teams should prepare for the presentation, so do not tell students until the day of the presentations which team will present. It is important that the class hears results from teams that tested concentration, temperature, and adding a catalyst. If you did not have a team conduct an investigation that tested the addition of a catalyst, you will want to do the test as a demonstration.

Reflect and Connect

Work as a team and use your experimental data to answer the following questions. Record any changes you make to your answers and the reasons for those changes.

1. Describe the variable you tested. Include in your answer how you controlled the other variables.
2. What can you infer from your results? How do your data support your inference?
3. How might you explain these results? Remember to base your explanation on evidence from your investigation. Use a diagram or sketch to help with your explanation. Think back to your experiences with the petri dish of BBs (figure 3.3). Use these experiences and your current understandings about collisions as you draw your sketches and write your explanation.
4. Scientists often repeat the experiments of other scientists. Are your instructions clear enough that another team could follow your procedure exactly? If someone else were going to follow your procedure and repeat your investigation, what changes would you suggest? Describe at least 2 changes you would suggest and why you would make these changes.
5. Everyone in the class needs to understand your results and explanations. Prepare to present your results, inferences, and explanations to the class.

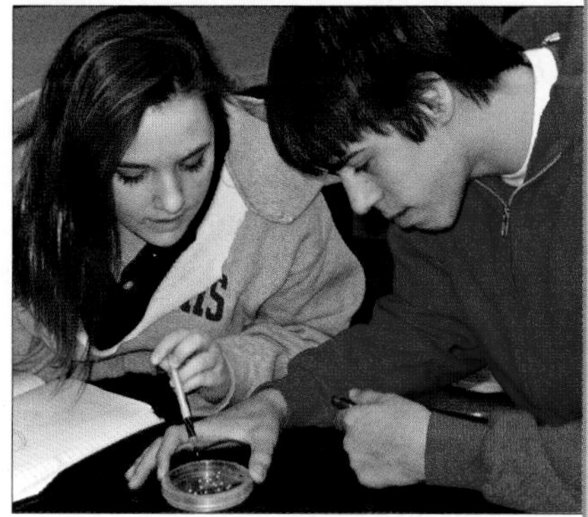

▲ Figure 3.3 Students modeling collisions in chemical reactions. Molecules must collide to react. How does changing the number of BBs model one of the variables you tested in this investigation? How does shaking the petri dish at a greater frequency model one of the variables you may have tested in this investigation?

Constructive Collisions

EXPLAIN

In *Variable Challenge*, you gathered evidence to determine what factors affect how fast chemical reactions occur. Why does adding drops of one reactant solution decrease the amount of time for the solution to turn blue? What happens at the atomic scale when temperature increases? Answers to these questions will help you predict how to speed up or slow down other important chemical reactions. Just imagine inventing a way to slow down rust on a highway bridge. Think of the benefit if you could speed up tumor destruction in cancer patients.

In this activity, *Constructive Collisions*, you and your team will investigate the underlying reasons why chemical reactions speed up or slow down. Those reasons involve something you already know.

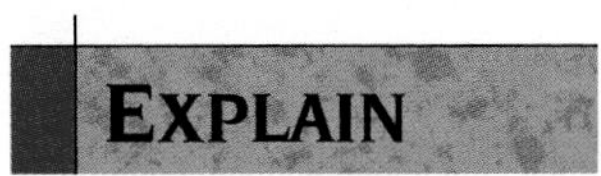

Constructive Collisions

Activity Overview

In *Constructive Collisions*, your students will learn about the molecular view of what they saw macroscopically in their explore investigations. They will learn these things through a series of readings and activities.

In Part I, students will learn how concentration affects the reaction rate. They also will learn about an important chemical quantity, the mole. Students participate in an activity that illustrates how the mole is used and how it is simply a unit that represents a fixed number of items (usually atoms, molecules, or ions). They will also do simple conversions and simple stoichiometry calculations.

Energize Those Reactions is the title for Part II of this activity and, as the title implies, students learn about the role of heat energy in chemical reactions. They will examine and analyze energy plots of different types of reactions. While doing so, they will learn about activation energy and changes in energy that result from a chemical reaction. Students will participate in a simple activity in which they discover the differences between endothermic and exothermic chemical reactions. They then go back to the energy plots and see how these types of reactions are represented on the diagrams. Bond energies are also introduced, and students use these energies to calculate the change in enthalpy (ΔH) for chemical reactions.

Part III explains what is happening in a chemical reaction when a catalyst is added. Students return to the energy plots and see that a catalyst lowers the activation energy to speed up the reaction. Part III includes an optional teacher demonstration of catalysis of hydrogen peroxide.

Before You Teach

Background Information

Some of the background for this section was presented in the background information for the explore activity. Additional details are included here for your benefit. Do not go into this much detail with your students. The information they need is included in the student book.

For chemical reactions to occur, there are two requirements that must be met for the reacting particles to react successfully to produce products.

1. The reacting particles must collide, and the collision must involve enough energy to produce the reaction; that is, the collision energy must equal or exceed the activation energy.
2. The relative orientation of the reactants must allow formation of any new bonds necessary to produce products. See *FYI—Molecular Orientation* in the student book.

Increasing the concentration of reactants increases the probability that a collision will occur and usually increases the reaction rate (see *Background Information* in the explore activity). The concentration of particles in a reaction mixture is related to the number of particles in that mixture. Students will learn about the SI unit for the amount of a substance, the mole. A mole of substance contains 6.02×10^{23} particles of that substance. The molar mass of an element (the number of grams of 1 mole [mol] of that element) is equal to the atomic weight of that element in grams. For example, 1 mol, or 6.02×10^{23} atoms of iron, would have a mass of 55.85 g. Similarly, a mole of water, or 6.02×10^{23} molecules of water, would have a mass of 18.02 g of water (2×1.01 g H + 1×16.00 g O = 18.02 g of H_2O).

A balanced chemical reaction reveals molar ratios as coefficients of the balanced equation. For example, using the equation

$$2N_2O_5 \rightarrow 4NO_2 + O_2$$

2 mol of N_2O_5 react to form 4 mol of NO_2 (nitrogen dioxide) and 1 mol of O_2. The coefficient of 1 is rarely used in a chemical equation; it is simply understood. These ratios can be used in calculations of amounts of reactants and products in a chemical reaction. This quantitative study of chemical changes is known as *stoichiometry*. For example, if you know that you begin with 2.35 g of N_2O_5 in the reaction shown above, you can use these molar ratios (which are constructed from coefficients) to calculate the amounts of each product that can be produced.

First, you must convert 2.35 g of N_2O_5 to moles so that you can use the molar ratios.

$$2N_2O_5 \rightarrow 4NO_2 + O_2$$

Then you must use the molar ratio to convert one of the products to moles.

$$2.35\ \cancel{\text{g } N_2O_5} \times \left(\frac{1 \text{ mol } N_2O_5}{108.02\ \cancel{\text{g } N_2O_5}}\right) = 2.18 \times 10^{-2} \text{ mol } N_2O_5$$

Finally, convert the moles of NO_2 to grams of NO_2 using the molar mass from the periodic table.

$$2.18 \times 10^{-2}\ \cancel{\text{mol } N_2O_5} \times \left(\frac{4 \text{ mol } NO_2}{2\ \cancel{\text{mol } N_2O_5}}\right)$$
$$= 4.36 \times 10^{-2} \text{ mol } NO_2$$

The process is similar if you want to find the number of grams of oxygen gas (O_2) produced from 2.35 g N_2O_5. You can also do it all in one step, like this:

$$4.36 \times 10^{-2}\ \cancel{\text{mol } NO_2} \times \left(\frac{46.01 \text{ g } NO_2}{1\ \cancel{\text{mol } NO_2}}\right) = 2.01 \text{ g } NO_2$$

You can also do it all in one step, like this (if you are comfortable with a one-step process):

$$2.35\ \cancel{g\ N_2O_5} \times \left(\frac{1\ \cancel{mol\ N_2O_5}}{108.02\ \cancel{g\ N_2O_5}}\right) \times \left(\frac{1\ \cancel{mol\ O_2}}{2\ \cancel{mol\ N_2O_5}}\right) \times \left(\frac{32.02\ g\ O_2}{1\ \cancel{mol\ O_2}}\right) = 0.348\ g\ O_2$$

Your students will only do simple conversions and stoichiometry. However, if you wish to add more of these types of calculations, additional practice is included in the *Toolbox* activities *Mole Conversions* and *Stoichiometry.*

Simply increasing the concentration does not ensure that a reaction will take place because the reacting particles may not have sufficient energy during the collision to form the products. This amount of energy is called the activation energy and is best illustrated in the energy plot shown in figure T3.1. Adding energy to a chemical reaction increases the reaction rate. You can add energy in various ways such as adding heat or even light. However, students will only study the details of adding heat to speed up a reaction. Again, review the explore activity for more background information.

Understanding the energy plot for a chemical reaction is important for students. For your background, we include the following details of this plot. The reaction in figure T3.1 shows the energy plot of an exothermic chemical reaction. E_a represents the activation energy of the forward reaction (more about reversible reactions later). ΔH represents the difference in the energies of the reactants and the products and is called the *change in enthalpy.* At constant pressure, the change in enthalpy (ΔH) equals the energy flow as heat. Since the products have lower energy than the reactants, ΔH will be negative and represents an exothermic reaction. At the top of the "hill," an intermediate phase of particles form called the activated complex. Often, these plots will not show the units for the x- and y-axes, but the x-axis always represents some time-oriented sequence of the reaction and is labeled "reaction in progress." The y-axis represents the energy in kilojoules per mole (kJ/mol).

The energy plot in figure T3.2 shows an endothermic reaction. ΔH for this reaction will be positive since the products in the forward reaction have a higher energy than the reactants.

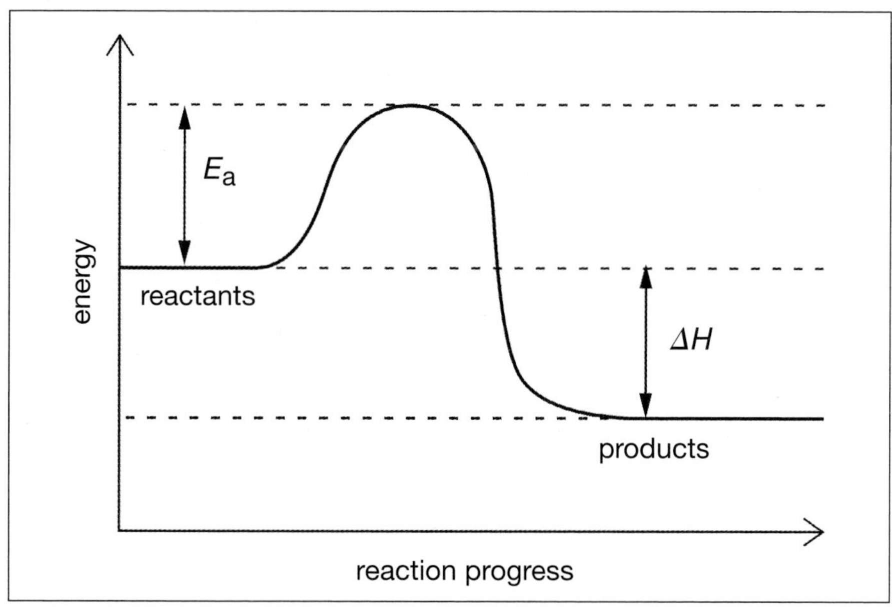

◀ **Figure T3.1 Energy plot for exothermic reaction.** This graph illustrates an exothermic chemical reaction. You can see from the chart that the products have lower energy than the reactants. Therefore, some energy is released as heat.

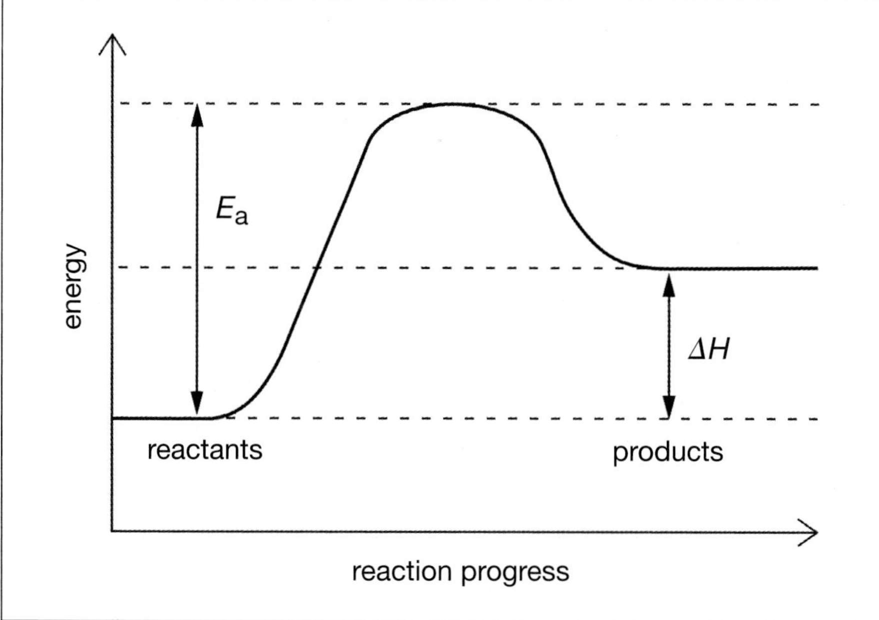

◀ **Figure T3.2 Energy plot for endothermic reaction.** This graph illustrates an endothermic chemical reaction. You can see from the chart that the products have higher energy than the reactants. Therefore, some heat energy is absorbed during the reaction.

Students study bond energies in this explain activity. The value of the bond energy is the energy required to break that bond. Single bonds (one pair of electrons shared), double bonds (two pairs of electrons shared), and triple bonds (three pairs of electrons shared) exist in molecules. The relative strength of bonds increases from single bonds to triple bonds as does the bond energies. For example, carbon has 4 valence electrons and thus can form many different kinds of bonds. As you might expect, it takes less energy to break the single bond between two atoms of carbon C—C (347 kJ/mol) than it would to completely break a double bond between two carbon atoms. The bond energy for the double bond in C==C is 614 kJ/mol. Even more energy is required to break a triple bond between these atoms (839 kJ/mol for a C≡C bond). The bond length also varies with the number of bonds between the atoms. Strong bonds are usually shorter than weak bonds.

You can determine the ΔH of a reaction by calculating the difference in the energies of the bonds broken in the reactants and the new bonds formed in the products. Tables of bond energies are given as *average* bond energies because, in many cases, the amount of energy to break a specific bond will vary with the environment of the bond. For example, chemical reactions often occur in steps, and examining the steps involved in the decomposition of methane into its elements will help you see how average bond energies are determined. See the following example:

Process	**Energy required**
$CH_{4(g)} \rightarrow CH_{3(g)} + H_{(g)}$	435 kJ/mol
$CH_{3(g)} \rightarrow CH_{2(g)} + H_{(g)}$	453 kJ/mol
$CH_{2(g)} \rightarrow CH_{(g)} + H_{(g)}$	425 kJ/mol
$CH_{(g)} \rightarrow C_{(g)} + H_{(g)}$	339 kJ/mol
Total =	1,652 kJ/mol

$$\text{Average} = \frac{1{,}652}{4} = 413 \text{ kJ/mol}$$

A C—H bond is broken in each step, but you can see that the energy required to break each C—H bond is slightly different. The energy needed to break the same kind of C—H bond is sensitive to the environment. Therefore, bond energies reported in tables are *average* bond energies. The average bond energy for a C—H bond in methane is 413 kJ/mol.

The formula for determining ΔH of a reaction using bond energies is

$$\Delta H = \Sigma_{\text{bonds broken}} - \Sigma_{\text{bonds formed}}.$$

The symbol Σ represents the sum of the terms in parentheses. Using the following values for bond strengths (H_2 = 432 kJ/mol, O_2 = 495 kJ/mol, H—O = 467 kJ/mol), ΔH for the reaction $2H_2 + O_2 \rightarrow 2H_2O$ can be calculated using the formula above.

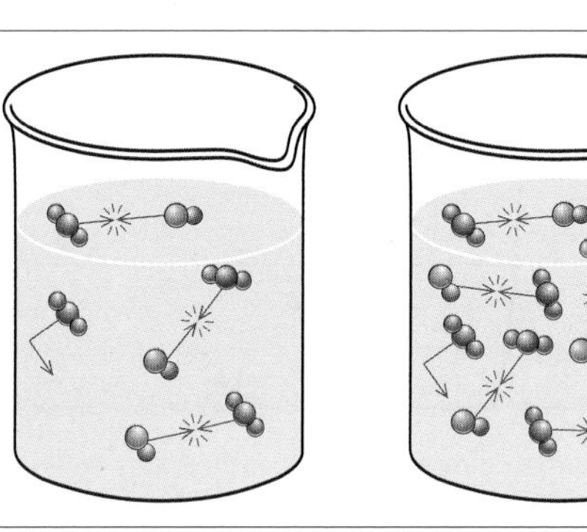

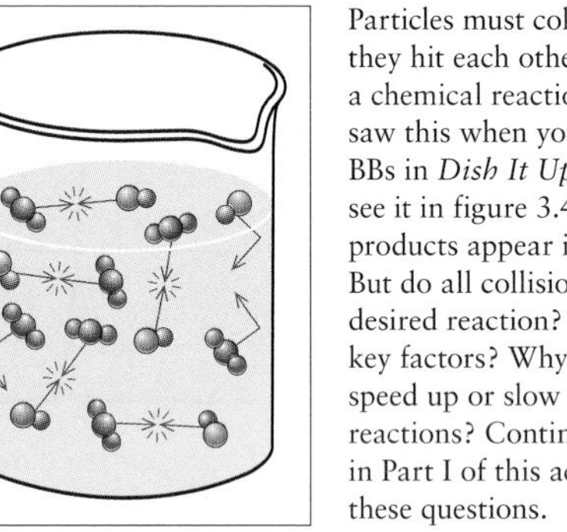

Figure 3.4 Concentrations of particles. The beaker on the right has a higher concentration of particles in the mixture. How does an increased concentration affect the chances of collisions between particles? What does this do to reaction rate?

Particles must collide. And when they hit each other, the chances of a chemical reaction increase. You saw this when you added more BBs in *Dish It Up!* And you can see it in figure 3.4. The result: products appear in less time. But do all collisions result in the desired reaction? What are the key factors? Why do these factors speed up or slow down chemical reactions? Continue your reading in Part I of this activity to answer these questions.

Part I: Frequency Facts

To answer the questions posed in the introduction of this activity, think back to your study of macroscopic objects hitting each other. What affects a system of two tennis balls when they collide? What would happen to the chances of collision if you used three tennis balls? What would happen to a system of many BBs?

Naturally, you answer these questions by using knowledge you already have. For example, three tennis balls swinging instead of two increases the frequency of collisions. The more often collisions occur, the greater chance of a chemical reaction. Think about walking from your science class to your English class through the hallway of your school. When do you have more frequent collisions with students, during passing period or during class when the hallway is almost empty?

In Part I, you and your team will investigate how scientists change the collision frequency involved in a system of atoms or molecules. Focus your activity with this question: "How does collision frequency in macroscopic systems (tennis balls, BBs, cars in busy intersections) compare with collision frequency in microscopic systems (atoms and molecules)?"

Materials

For each team of 3 students

3 pairs of safety goggles

1 small beaker

access to a balance

small, identical items (such as paper clips, corks, pennies, sticky notes, staples)

122 Unit 1 Interactions Are Interesting

$$\Delta H = [2(432\ \text{kJ}) + 495\ \text{kJ}] - [4(467\ \text{kJ})] = -509\ \text{kJ}$$

The negative sign indicates that energy is released and thus is exothermic. Often, you will see the value for ΔH written at the end of an equation, as shown for the previous equation:

$$2H_2 + O_2 \rightarrow 2H_2O \quad \Delta H = -509\ \text{kJ}$$

Adding a catalyst to speed up a reaction alters the pathway of the reaction and lowers the activation energy. The energy plot for a catalyzed reaction is shown in figure 3.9 in the student book. Catalysts will not *cause* a reaction to occur; they only speed up the reaction. A catalyst is not consumed in the chemical reaction. *Enzyme* is the term given to a catalyst in a biological system; many cell functions and processes depend heavily on enzymes.

Materials—Part I

For each team of 3 students

3 pairs of safety goggles
1 small beaker
access to a balance
1 set of small, identical items (paper clips, corks, pennies, sticky notes, staples, etc.)

one of the following:

- aluminum foil
- sulfur
- iron filings
- copper shot
- lead shot
- water

1 pair disposable laboratory gloves
1 wax pencil to label the beaker
1 calculator
markers or chalk

one of the following:

- aluminum foil
- sulfur
- iron filings
- copper shot
- lead shot
- water

1 wax pencil for labeling the beaker

1 pair disposable laboratory gloves

1 calculator

markers or chalk

Cautions

Wear safety goggles when working with the items. Wear disposable laboratory gloves when handling lead shot and copper BBs.

Process and Procedure

1. Read *Mole Patrol I* to learn how chemists quantify the number of particles in a solution.
2. To understand the connection between counting objects you can see and objects that are too small to see, follow Steps 2a–g.

You are making a conceptual connection between counting macroscopic objects and counting microscopic objects.

   a. Your teacher has selected several types of small, identical items. Meet with your team and decide which of these items you will use.
   b. Count out 12 of 1 item and find their total mass.
   c. Record your item name, how many you have of the item, and the total mass on the class chart that your teacher has supplied.
   d. Participate in a class discussion of the importance of this activity. As you participate and listen, take notes in your science notebook. To organize your notes, draw a line vertically down the center of the paper. Use the left side to record important relationships that you learn about in the class discussion, as well as any calculations your teacher writes on the board. You will add notes to the right side of the paper during the next activity. You can also use the left- and right-facing pages for your notes.
   e. Have 1 person from your team get the chemical substance that your teacher has assigned to your team. Place the assigned mass of that substance into a small beaker. Label your beaker with its contents and the mass.

Chapter 3 Collisions—Atomic Style 123

For the teacher

chart paper or space on a board

Materials—Part II

For each student

1 pair of safety goggles
substances A, B, C, and D:

- substance A: baking soda; place 3–5 g in a freezer-type, resealable bag
- substance B: vinegar; 50 mL per team
- substance C: anhydrous calcium chloride, $CaCl_2$; place approximately 5 g in a freezer-type, resealable bag
- substance D: water; 50 mL

Advance Preparation

For Part I, gather several groups of 12 small identical items for teams of students. Ideally, each team would have a different set of items. Suggestions for items include

- Sticky notes
- Paper clips
- Staples
- Tacks
- Corks
- Pencil erasers
- Pencil leads
- Coins (all the same)
- Rubber bands
- Toothpicks

You also need to pull items from your supply room. Examples include

- Lead shot
- Copper BBs
- Sulfur
- Iron filings
- Zinc
- Tin
- Aluminum (may use foil)

These items must be small enough pieces so that students can conveniently measure the molar mass of each. If you use pennies, for example, students will not be able to get close enough (±0.1) to the molar mass. However, copper shot or BBs are acceptable.

The balance should be sensitive to at least a centigram. Have the molar mass of each element written on a piece of paper to give to the students. For the moment, you don't want them to see you looking at a periodic table to get the masses.

Prepare a class-sized chart like figure T3.3 either on large chart paper or on the front board. Make room for each group to record its data. You will add another chart beside this chart, so save some room.

For the second part of the activity, you need to make a second class chart. Place it beside the first one. It should contain the headings shown in figure T3.4. Notice that the last 2 columns are blank. You will title and complete them during the activity.

In Part II, use freezer-type, resealable plastic bags for this activity. It would be best to have a plastic tub or dishpan to catch any spills or leaks that might occur. Instruct students to keep the bag and solutions over or in the pan during the activity. Prepare the substances for the activity as follows:

Substance A: baking soda; place 3–5 g in a freezer-type resealable bag. Label the bag "A."

Substance B: vinegar; 50 mL. Label the container "B."

Substance C: anhydrous calcium chloride, $CaCl_2$; place approximately 5 g in a freezer-type resealable bag. Label the bag "C."

Substance D: water; 50 mL per team. Label the container "D."

Educational Technologies

Electronic balances are good to use for Part I of this activity. Use them if they are available in your lab.

Cautions

Students should wear safety goggles when working with chemicals. Caution students not to touch any chemical and to wash their hands upon completion of the activity.

Group	Type of item	Total mass of the item	Number of the item	Name of this amount of the item

▲ **Figure T3.3 Class chart 1.** Prepare this chart ahead of class and post it at the front of the room. Students will record their data on the chart.

Group	Substance	Chemical symbol or formula	Mass of substance		

▲ **Figure T3.4 Class chart 2.** Prepare this chart ahead of class and post it at the front of the room. Students will record their data on the chart.

READING

Mole Patrol I

You can increase the frequency of collisions by increasing the number of particles in a given space. Chemists call this increase an increase in **concentration**. For example, when you added more of one reactant to the reaction in *Variable Challenge*, you were increasing the concentration of that reactant. The number of particles in solution increased. But how do chemists know exactly how many particles they add to the system of particles?

Chemists know the number of particles by counting them. But counting atomic-sized particles isn't easy. So chemists count atomic-sized particles much like you count numerous small, yet visible, items.

For example, suppose you had the task of getting two dozen doughnuts from the doughnut shop; you would know that there would be 24 doughnuts. You can also count by using the mass. Consider 3,000 grams (g) of pennies. The average mass of one penny is 3 g. About how many pennies would you have? You could "count" the pennies by knowing the mass. You would know that you had about 1,000 pennies and you didn't have to count them all. The same is true for the number of particles in chemical substances.

Chemists use the **mole** (abbreviated *mol*) as a unit that refers to an amount of a substance. A mole contains 6.02×10^{23} particles. This is known as Avogadro's number and is named after Amedeo Avogadro. Chemists use the mole to count particles. If you have a mole of copper atoms, you know that you have 6.02×10^{23} atoms of copper. Chemists know that this amount of copper atoms would have a mass of 63.55 g. Where did this number come from? The average atomic mass of any element (found on the periodic table) *in grams* is known as the **molar mass** of that element. Molar mass is equal to the amount of mass in grams in 1 mol of that element.

If you increase the number of moles in a solution, you increase the concentration and the frequency of collisions. Chemists use the term **molarity** as one way to communicate the concentration of a substance. Molarity has the units of moles per liter (mol/L) and is abbreviated M.

Topic: molarity
Go to: www.scilinks.org
Code: 2Inquiry124

Remember, you must consider the mass of the beaker. The mass assigned to you is only the mass of the substance that your teacher has provided.

Don't forget to think about the connection between the substance you can see and the many millions of invisible particles that constitute the substance.

f. Record the name of your substance and the mass of that substance on the class chart that your teacher has provided. Place the beaker and its contents on a desk at the front of the room.

As You Teach

Outcomes and Indicators of Success

By the end of this activity, students should

1. develop an understanding of collision theory and how it relates to chemical reaction.

   They will demonstrate their understanding by

   - making sense of readings that are presented about collisions and chemical reaction by taking notes as they read and discussing their ideas with a classmate and
   - expressing their ideas about collisions and reactions in response to questions posed in the activity.

2. develop an understanding of collision theory and how it applies to reaction rates.

   They will demonstrate their understanding by

   - explaining how increased concentration or temperature speeds up a chemical reaction based on collisions,
   - drawing models or diagrams of collisions and their effect on reaction rates, and
   - explaining models or diagrams of collisions and their effect on reaction rates.

3. develop an understanding of energy changes in a chemical reaction.

   They will demonstrate their understanding by

   - analyzing energy diagrams depicting energy changes in a chemical reaction,
   - representing energy changes in a chemical reaction by sketching graphs of reactions,
   - analyzing experimental observations for changes in energy,
   - expressing energy changes correctly in a chemical equation,
   - comparing bond energies in a chemical reaction to determine if energy is released or absorbed, and
   - evaluating examples of chemical phenomena and deciding if they represent endo- or exothermic processes.

4. develop an understanding of the mole and its usefulness in chemistry.

   They will demonstrate their understanding by

   - comparing the chemical unit called the mole with more common units like dozen,
   - calculating molar quantities, and
   - using molar ratios to interpret chemical equations and reactions.

5. apply the laws of conservation to chemical reactions.

   They will apply their understanding by

   - explaining how a balanced chemical equation validates the law of conservation of mass and
   - analyzing energy changes in chemical reactions and realizing that they are the result of energy present in the bonds of molecules that is being released or absorbed as heat.

6. learn and practice abilities to conduct a scientific investigation.

   They will learn and practice their abilities by

   - generating and using appropriate data tables and
   - using logic to explain observations.

g. Participate in another class discussion that your teacher leads. Take notes in your science notebook on the right side of the page of your notebook. Record important relationships and calculations as you did before.

3. Read *Mole Patrol II* to find out ways to convert from moles to the number of particles and to units of concentration.

READING

Mole Patrol II

Chemists use the mole concept to do some very important conversions in chemistry. Suppose you had 1.75 mol of water. How many grams of water would that be? You know from the periodic table that 1 mol of water has a mass of 18.02 g. Now start the calculation. Always start the conversion with what you are given in the problem; in this case, it is 1.75 mol of water. Then use the conversion factor: 18.02 g H_2O = 1 mol H_2O. The conversion is set up this way

$$1.75\ \cancel{\text{mol } H_2O} \times \left(\frac{18.02 \text{ g } H_2O}{1\ \cancel{\text{mol } H_2O}}\right) = 31.5 \text{ g } H_2O$$

What would the calculation look like if you measured 6.75 g of water and you wanted to know how many moles of water you had? The conversion would look like this

$$6.75\ \cancel{\text{g } H_2O} \times \left(\frac{1 \text{ mol } H_2O}{18.02\ \cancel{\text{g } H_2O}}\right) = 0.375 \text{ mol } H_2O$$

Could you find out how many molecules are in 0.375 mol of water? What information do you need? For this conversion, you need to use the number of particles in a mole, 6.02×10^{23}. The conversion would look like this

$$0.375\ \cancel{\text{mol } H_2O} \times \left(\frac{6.02 \times 10^{23} \text{ molecules}}{1\ \cancel{\text{mol } H_2O}}\right) = 2.26 \times 10^{23} \text{ molecules}$$

Supposed you dissolved 20 g of sodium hydroxide, NaOH, in water to make 1 liter (L) of solution. What is the molarity of the solution? (Remember, molarity has the units mol/L.) The conversion would look like this

$$20\ \cancel{\text{g NaOH}} \times \left(\frac{1 \text{ mol}}{40\ \cancel{\text{g NaOH}}}\right) \times \left(\frac{}{1\text{L}}\right) = 0.5 \text{ mol/L or } 0.5 \text{ M}$$

Strategies

Getting Started

Much of students' ability to quantify chemical reactions involves the concept of the mole and its applications. Yet this concept involves very large and very small numbers that students may find are beyond their experience. When that happens, student motivation can wane.

Get them started by writing your name on the board and asking, "How many atoms of oxygen are there in my signature?" In various forms, students will express befuddlement. Tell them you are going to show them how they can determine this number by using the concept of a mole. Next, have them read the activity introduction and begin Part I. After students complete the activity, consider asking them to determine the number of oxygen atoms in their signature in chalk ($CaCO_3$) based on what they learned in the activity.

Cautions

Students should wear safety goggles when working with chemicals. Caution students not to touch any chemical and to wash their hands upon completion of the activity.

Process and Procedure

Part I: Frequency Facts

Materials

For each team of 3 students

3 pairs of safety goggles
1 small beaker
access to a balance
1 set of small, identical items (paper clips, corks, pennies, sticky notes, staples, etc.)
one of the following:

- aluminum foil
- sulfur
- iron filings
- copper shot
- lead shot
- water

1 pair disposable laboratory gloves
1 wax pencil to label the beaker
1 calculator

For the teacher

chart paper or space on a board

Read the introduction to this activity together with your class. Stop and answer the questions posed in the reading as they appear. This will give you the opportunity to review and summarize the results of their investigations from the explore activity.

In Step 1, students read *Mole Patrol I*. Encourage students to use a literacy strategy they find helpful. Ask them to think of one that is most beneficial for readings involving mathematical symbols. For example, a T-table with headings of "term" or "equations" and "meaning from term/equation" can help many students focus on important concepts and skills while reading.

In Steps 2a–c, students select the item they want to use for this activity and count out 12 of them. It is important that your students know that this represents 1 dozen. Don't let them spend too much time selecting the item—the type of item is not important to the success of the activity. The point is to have several different types of items to use for comparisons. Students will record their item and its total mass on the class chart.

Step 2d is key for the success of this activity. Students will participate in a class discussion of the activity. It will not be obvious to the students what the purpose of the activity is and they may think that what they have done is very elementary. Express your pleasure that they think it is so simple—it will encourage them to make connections to the mole and perhaps view that as a simple concept as well. Students must understand that 12 items represent a dozen. Make this clear at the beginning. Consider asking questions such as these:

- "How many items did you have?"

Twelve.

- "What do we call 12 items?"

A dozen.

- "Are there always 12 items in a dozen?"

Yes.

Write the word "dozen" in each space in the column titled "name of this amount of the item." Continue the class discussion by using questions similar to the following. Student questioning is the main part of this activity. Make sure that all students are participating and taking notes in their science notebooks. Write key points on the overhead or board as you are involved in the discussion. Sample questions to use for your class discussion follow:

- "Within your group of items, are all the items alike?"

Yes, they are similar but not exactly alike. If a team has a dozen pennies, for example, some pennies may vary in mass, "newness," or color because of age, or other factors. This can lead to a review of isotopes later when you are connecting this activity with the next one, as the items are atoms.

- "Are they similar?"

Yes.

- "Are the masses of each group, each dozen, the same?"

No.

- "Why not?"

Because the individual items in the dozen have different masses, therefore, the different dozens will have different masses.

- "Do all the different dozens take up the same amount of space (have the same volume)?"

No.

- "Why not?"

Because the individual items in the dozen have different volumes, therefore, the different dozens will have different volumes.

- Choose one of the groups that has a mass that would be easy to double and halve. Ask, "What would be the mass of two dozen of item X?"

Answers will vary.

- "How did you get your answer?"

Multiply the mass by two. You may want to set this up on the board using dimensional analysis. This will set the stage for the next activity. Here is an example.

Suppose 12 paper clips had a mass of 13.0 g.

$$2\ \cancel{\text{dozen paper clips}} \times \left(\frac{13.0\text{ g paper clips}}{1\ \cancel{\text{dozen paper clips}}}\right) = 26.0\text{ g paper clips}$$

- "What would be the mass of one-half dozen of item X?"

Answers will vary.

- "How did you get your answer?"

Students may say that they multiplied the mass by one-half or that they divided the mass by two. Some may say they multiplied by 0.5. Set this up on the board as well, using dimensional analysis. Here is one example.

$$2\ \cancel{\text{dozen paper clips}} \times \left(\frac{13.0\text{ g paper clips}}{1\ \cancel{\text{dozen paper clips}}}\right) = 26.0\text{ g paper clips}$$

- "How many items are in a half dozen?"

Six.

- "Is this true no matter what the item?"

Yes.

- Choose another item that has a mass that would be easy to double or halve. Ask,

"How many dozen of item A (use the name of the item that you have chosen) would you have if you had (give them a multiple of the mass of the item you chose) grams of item A?"

Answers will vary.

- "How did you get your answer?"

Answers will vary, but an example is given here.

Suppose that 1 dozen wire clamps had a mass of 100 g and your question was, "How many dozen wire clamps would you have if you had 400 g of wire clamps?"

Students would say that they divided 400 g by 100 g to get their answer of 4 dozen. Set this up on the board and work it out this way.

$$0.5\ \cancel{\text{dozen paper clips}} \times \left(\frac{13.0\text{ g paper clips}}{1\ \cancel{\text{dozen paper clips}}}\right) = 6.5\text{ g paper clips}$$

- "If you had 75 g of wire clamps, how many wire clamps would you have?"

Use your class data to formulate this question. Just use a mass that represents a number of items less than 1 dozen. Students may have more difficulty with this one. Here is the example worked out for you.

$$75\ \cancel{\text{g wire clamps}} \times \left(\frac{1\ \cancel{\text{dozen wire clamps}}}{100\ \cancel{\text{g wire clamps}}}\right) \times \left(\frac{12\text{ wire clamps}}{1\ \cancel{\text{dozen wire clamps}}}\right) = 9\text{ wire clamps}$$

In Steps 2e–f, students are given the element that you have assigned to each team (or they can select their own element). Have students measure the amount of substance as you direct (see suggested list in the materials). Give them the mass to use from the list of molar masses that you have prepared. Give 1 team water. As students finish measuring the mass of the substances, line up the beakers on a desk in front of the class so that everyone can see them. Have the name and mass visible. If this information is written too small on the beaker, consider writing the name of the substance, the chemical symbol, and the mass on a sticky note and placing it with each beaker. Students will also record their data on the class-sized chart that you have prepared. Have this chart near the one that shows their data from the previous activity.

In Step 2g, lead a class discussion and make sure students are recording important information and calculations in their science notebooks. Use a similar line of questions to what you used before. It is important that the students understand that this activity is very similar to the one they just finished. They should recognize that they can use their prior experiences with a dozen to make this quantity (the mole) as simple to understand as the dozen. If students have difficulty answering these new questions, refer them back to the dozen activity and help them to see the relationship.

Use questions and discussions such as these to lead your class.

- "Can you determine the number of atoms by taking the mass of something?"

Students may not think you can do this. But stop and let them think about this question. They should realize that they counted by massing in the previous

activity; the last example illustrates this. Tell your class that chemists have to count by mass because atoms and molecules are too small to count. Tell them that all weighed amounts are approximately 6.02×10^{23} atoms or molecules.

- "Which team or teams had atoms and which team or teams had molecules?"

The teams with the elements had atoms, and the team with water had molecules.

To give students an idea of the scale of this number (6.02×10^{23}), ask them how long it would take their class to count out 6.02×10^{23} atoms if each one in the class counted one atom per second and never stopped for a break. Consider giving a reward to someone coming close (say within 10 percent of the correct answer). Be generous—you will be safe. No one will come close. Record their predictions on the board and then calculate the answer on the board. Suppose you have a class of 30 students; you would count 30 atoms every second. You would set it up like this.

$$6.02 \times 10^{23} \cancel{\text{atoms}} \times \left(\frac{1 \cancel{\text{sec}}}{30 \cancel{\text{atoms}}}\right) \times \left(\frac{1 \cancel{\text{min}}}{60 \cancel{\text{sec}}}\right) \times \left(\frac{1 \cancel{\text{hr}}}{60 \cancel{\text{min}}}\right) \times \left(\frac{1 \cancel{\text{day}}}{24 \cancel{\text{hr}}}\right) \times \left(\frac{1 \text{ yr}}{365.25 \cancel{\text{day}}}\right) = 6.36 \times 10^{14} \text{ yr}$$

That's 636,000,000,000,000, or 636 trillion years! That is much longer than our universe has been in existence.

Students should see very quickly that chemists must "count" by determining the mass of materials. Emphasize that even though this is a very big number, that number of atoms or molecules is the amount contained in their beakers. This should reinforce just how small atoms are. Continue the discussion by labeling the next column on the class chart "number of particles."

Write the number 6.02×10^{23} in the space below this title on each row. Ask your students, "How is this like a dozen?" Indicate the other chart. Tell your students that scientists have a name for this number of particles: the mole. Title the next column on the chart "name of this number of particles" and write the word "mole" in the spaces below the title.

Ask your students if they know where you came up with the mass of each element or compound. Tell them that this mass is significant because it represents 1 mol of the particles. Give them time to think; someone will come up with the average atomic mass that is listed on the periodic table. If not, give them a hint: the number comes from a very important tool that chemists use all the time. Continue the discussion by asking the group with water where its mass came from since water is not listed on the periodic table. With time, students will discover that 18.02 g is equal to two times the molar mass of hydrogen plus the molar mass of oxygen (using the formula for water, H_2O).

Now question your students along a line similar to the way you questioned them about their groups of a dozen items. If students struggle with the calculations, point out that this is just like the calculations they did for a dozen, only with bigger numbers. Sample questions and answers are given here; students might want to use their calculators.

- "How many particles are in your beakers?"

6.02×10^{23}.

- "What do we call this number of particles?"

A mole.

- "Are there always 6.02×10^{23} particles in a mole?"

Yes.

- "Within your beaker of particles, are all particles alike?"

They are similar but not exactly alike. This is a good opportunity to review isotopes with your class. All atoms in the beaker are of the same element (or molecules are of the same compound). But all the atoms are not exactly the same. Some atoms may have more or less neutrons than others. Use this as a review of isotopes and their similarities and differences to other atoms of the same element. This is also a good time to review how the average atomic mass is determined (a weighted average of all the isotopes of the element).

- "Are all the atoms of the same element?"

Yes.

- "Are the masses of each group, each mole, the same?"

No.

- "Why not?"

Because the individual atoms or molecules in the mole have different masses, therefore, the different moles will have different masses. Review with your students what particles make up the mass number of the element. The number of protons and neutrons of each type of atom differ, therefore, the mass of the atom, and the mass of the mole of atoms will be different.

- "Do all the different moles take up the same amount of space (have the same volume)?"

No.

- "Why not?"

Because the individual atoms or molecules in the mole have different volumes; therefore, the different moles will have different volumes.

- Choose one of the groups and ask, "What would be the mass of 2 mol of element X?"

Answers will vary.

- "How did you get your answer?"

Multiply the mass by two. Set this up on the board and make sure students are writing the examples in their science notebooks. Here is an example.

Suppose you use copper with a molar mass of 63.54 g.

$$2 \cancel{\text{mol Cu}} \times \left(\frac{63.54 \text{ g Cu}}{1 \cancel{\text{mol Cu}}}\right) = 127.08 \text{ g Cu}$$

- "What would be the mass of one-half dozen of item X?"

Answers will vary.

- "How did you get your answer?"

Students may say that they multiplied the mass by one-half or that they divided the mass by two. Some may say they multiplied by 0.5. Set this up on the board, as well as using dimensional analysis. Here is one example.

$$2 \cancel{\text{mol Cu}} \times \left(\frac{63.54 \text{ g Cu}}{1 \cancel{\text{mol Cu}}}\right) = 127.08 \text{ g Cu}$$

- "How many items are in half a mole?"

3.01×10^{23}

- "Is this true no matter what the item?"

Yes.

- Choose another element or water. Ask, "How many moles of X (use the name of the substance that you chose before) would you have if you had (give them a multiple of the mass of the substance you chose) grams of substance X?"

Answers will vary.

- "How did you get your answer?"

Answers will vary, but an example is given here. Suppose you asked, "How many moles of water would you have if you had 31.95 g of water?"

$$0.5 \cancel{\text{mol Cu}} \times \left(\frac{63.54 \text{ g Cu}}{1 \cancel{\text{mol Cu}}}\right) = 31.77 \text{ g Cu}$$

- "If you had 25.75 g of sulfur, how many atoms of sulfur would you have?"

Students may have more difficulty with this one. Here is the example worked out for you.

$$31.95 \cancel{\text{g H}_2\text{O}} \times \left(\frac{1 \text{ mol H}_2\text{O}}{18.02 \cancel{\text{g H}_2\text{O}}}\right) = 1.77 \text{ mol H}_2\text{O}$$

Do more examples with your class as necessary. Students will practice some of these conversions in the next *Stop and Think* section. There are also examples in the *Toolbox* activities, if you want to assign your class extra practice.

In Step 3, students read *Mole Patrol II* to learn more about mole conversions. Ask them to take notes and discuss their ideas with a partner as they finish. This represents one of many effective literacy strategies.

NOTES:

Answers to Stop and Think—Part I, SE page 126

1. Lead atoms have more protons and neutrons (82 protons and 125 neutrons for the most common isotope) than aluminum atoms (13 protons and 14 neutrons for the most common isotope). Therefore, the mass of lead will be higher than the mass of the same number of atoms of aluminum.

2a. To determine the number of moles of aluminum, perform the following conversion:

$$7.36\ \cancel{\text{g Al}} \times \left(\frac{1\ \cancel{\text{mol Al}}}{26.98\ \cancel{\text{g Al}}}\right) \times \left(\frac{6.02 \times 10^{23}\ \text{atoms Al}}{1\ \cancel{\text{mol Al}}}\right)$$

$$= 1.64 \times 10^{23}\ \text{atoms Al}$$

2b. $2.55\ \cancel{\text{mol Ca}} \times \left(\frac{6.02 \times 10^{23}\ \text{atoms Ca}}{1\ \cancel{\text{mol Ca}}}\right) = 1.54 \times 10^{24}\ \text{atoms of Ca}$

2c. $1.77\ \cancel{\text{mol NaCl}} \times \left(\frac{58.44\ \text{g NaCl}}{1\ \cancel{\text{mol NaCl}}}\right) = 103\ \text{g NaCl}$

2d. $25.6\ \cancel{\text{g S}} \times \left(\frac{1\ \cancel{\text{mol S}}}{32.06\ \cancel{\text{g S}}}\right) \times \left(\frac{6.02 \times 10^{23}\ \text{atoms S}}{1\ \cancel{\text{mol S}}}\right)$

$$= 4.81 \times 10^{23}\ \text{atoms of S}$$

Answers to Stop and Think—Part I are on TE pages 126–127.

NOTES:

Stop & THINK

PART I

Practice some of these conversions on your own by working through the following questions. Be certain to check your answers and learn from any mistakes.

1. Why does a mole of lead have a higher mass than a mole of aluminum if both have the same number of atoms?
2. Work out the following conversions. Show all your work and cancellation of units.
   - **a.** 7.36 g of aluminum = __________ mol of aluminum.
   - **b.** 2.55 mol of calcium contain __________ atoms of calcium.
   - **c.** 1.77 mol of NaCl would have the mass of ______ g.
   - **d.** If you measured 25.6 g of sulfur, how many atoms of sulfur would you have?
   - **e.** How many grams of sodium chloride are in 0.50 L of 1.5 M NaCl?
3. You use 2 solutions of hydrochloric acid, HCl, to dissolve zinc metal, Zn. Solution A is 1.0 M, and solution B is 2.0 M. Which solution demonstrates the greatest frequency of collisions between HCl and Zn? Explain your answer. Use molecular-level sketches in your explanation.

4. Read *Ratios in Reactions* to discover another important way chemists use moles to account for the number of particles involved in chemical reactions.

READING

Ratios in Reactions

What does the mole have to do with concentrations and chemical reactions? Scientists who construct the living space in the space shuttle certainly must understand the mole. They must remove the buildup of carbon dioxide (CO_2) in the atmosphere of the shuttle. These NASA scientists must make careful predictions about the amount of CO_2 to remove. They base their predictions on the amount each astronaut produces during the time he or she is in the

126 | Unit 1 Interactions Are Interesting

2e. $0.50\ \cancel{L} \times \left(\frac{1.5\ \cancel{mol\ NaCl}}{1\ \cancel{L\ NaCl}}\right) \times \left(\frac{58.45\ g\ NaCl}{1\ \cancel{mol\ NaCl}}\right) = 43.8\ g\ NaCl$

NOTES:

3. The highest concentration produces the greatest number of collisions. Since solution B is 2.0 M, it will lead to the greatest collision frequency and the greatest rate of reaction.

In Step 4, students read *Ratios in Reactions*. This reading might be a review for many students since the main topic is balancing chemical equations. Adjust the amount of time you spend on this reading according your students' background. Consider working through a few examples. Some students will benefit from the use of the table in figure 3.6 in the student book. This table gives students structure for the process of balancing chemical equations. Have students begin working on *Stop and Think* Questions 4–7 immediately after they finish the reading.

shuttle. These scientists understand the mole and use that understanding to determine the amount of the absorber (lithium hydroxide, LiOH) to include on the space shuttle to absorb the CO_2 produced by the astronauts (see figure 3.5).

Look at the following chemical equation, which represents the chemical reaction just described. Remember that reactants are on the left and products are on the right of the arrow.

$$\underbrace{CO_{2(g)} + 2LiOH_{(s)}}_{\text{reactants}} \rightarrow \underbrace{Li_2CO_{3(s)} + H_2O_{(l)}}_{\text{products}}$$

▲ **Figure 3.5 Space shuttle in-flight maintenance.** The crew aboard a 1998 mission of the space shuttle *Columbia* is installing backup lithium hydroxide canisters on the Regenerative Carbon Dioxide Removal System.

A *balanced* chemical equation gives scientists clues to the amounts of reactants that are needed for the reaction to take place. This reaction indicates that *1 mol* of carbon dioxide (CO_2) gas reacts with *2 mol* of solid lithium hydroxide (LiOH) to produce *1 mol* of solid lithium carbonate (Li_2CO_3) and *1 mol* of liquid water (H_2O). The number 2 in front of the reactant, lithium hydroxide (LiOH), is called a coefficient. It works much like coefficients in math equations—it affects everything that it is with. Is there a coefficient in front of CO_2? (One is understood but it is not written.)

The molar ratios of the particles in this reaction are $1CO_2$:2LiOH:$1Li_2CO_3$:$1H_2O$. As scientists prepare for a space shuttle mission, they know that for every 1 mol of carbon dioxide (6.02×10^{23} CO_2 particles) produced by the astronauts, they must provide 2 mol of lithium hydroxide (12.04×10^{23} LiOH units). Knowing these mole ratios is essential to the safety of the astronauts aboard spacecrafts.

This equation is balanced with coefficients. Coefficients show that the same number and kinds of atoms are present at the beginning of the reaction (in the reactants) as at the end of the reaction (in the products). This supports the **law of conservation of matter**, which states that matter is conserved in ordinary chemical and physical changes. Count the atoms in this reaction to verify that it supports this law. Set up a T-table as shown in figure 3.6 to check if this equation is balanced.

$$CO_{2(g)} + 2LiOH_{(s)} \rightarrow Li_2CO_{3(s)} + H_2O_{(l)}$$

If you must balance an equation, only add coefficients to balance it. Never change the subscripts to balance a chemical equation. Look at the reaction of hydrogen (H_2) and oxygen (O_2) to produce water:

$$H_{2(g)} + O_{2(g)} \rightarrow 2H_2O_{(l)}$$

Count the atoms to decide whether the equation is balanced. You should see that it is not balanced. Write down the equation in your science notebook and try to balance it on your own before you continue.

It would be easy to balance the equation by just adding a subscript of 2 at the end of H_2O. Did you try that? If you did, you just turned water (H_2O) into hydrogen peroxide (H_2O_2)! You cannot balance a chemical equation by changing subscripts because that changes the

Answers to Stop and Think—Part I continued, SE pages 128–129

4. When the concentration of the reactants increases, the likelihood of a collision between reacting particles increases. Particles must collide to react, and if there are more collisions, the reaction speeds up. If students struggle with this concept, remind them of the engage activity with the dishes of BBs and the analogy to interstate and rural highways.
5. The balanced chemical reaction is $CH_4 + 2O_2 \rightarrow CO_2 + 2H_2O$. When a chemical reaction is balanced, it shows that the same number and kinds of atoms that you start with in the reactants is equal to the same number and kinds of atoms that you end with as products of the chemical reaction. Therefore, the mass of the reactants will equal the mass of the products, and mass is conserved in the chemical reaction.

6a. The molar mass of sodium is 22.99 g.

6b. The conversion to moles of sodium is shown by

$$2.3 \cancel{\text{mol Na}} \times \left(\frac{22.99 \text{ g Na}}{1 \cancel{\text{mol Na}}}\right) = 53 \text{ g Na}.$$

7a. 1 mol CO_2 : 2 mol H_2O

7b. $3 \cancel{\text{mol CH}_4} \times \left(\frac{2 \text{ mol O}_2}{1 \cancel{\text{mol CH}_4}}\right) = 6 \text{ mol O}_2$

7c. $3 \cancel{\text{mol CH}_4} \times \left(\frac{2 \text{ mol CO}_2}{1 \cancel{\text{mol CH}_4}}\right) = 3 \text{ mol CO}_2;$

$$3 \cancel{\text{mol CH}_4} \times \left(\frac{2 \text{ mol H}_2\text{O}}{1 \cancel{\text{mol CH}_4}}\right) = 6 \text{ mol H}_2\text{O}$$

7d. $25.7 \cancel{\text{g H}_2\text{O}} \times \left(\frac{1 \cancel{\text{mol H}_2\text{O}}}{18.02 \cancel{\text{g H}_2\text{O}}}\right) \times \left(\frac{1 \text{ mol CH}_4}{2 \cancel{\text{mol H}_2\text{O}}}\right) = 0.713 \text{ mol CH}_4$

Ratios in Reactions, continued

substance. Only use coefficients to balance chemical equations. The balanced chemical equation should look like this:

$$2H_{2(g)} + O_{2(g)} \rightarrow 2H_2O_{(l)}$$

The ratio of the reactants and products in this reaction is 2 mol of H_2 to 1 mol of O_2 to 2 mol of H_2O.

The balanced chemical reaction does not tell you anything about the rate at which the reaction will occur. It does, however, give you information about the relative amounts of reactants needed and the amounts of products formed in the reaction.

SCLINKS NSTA
Topic: conservation of matter
Go to: www.scilinks.org
Code: 2Inquiry128

Atoms in reactants	Atoms in products
1C	1C
2Li	2Li
2H	2H
4O	4O
2 O in CO_2 + 2 O in the 2LiOH (remember, the coefficient affects all elements in the compound, LiOH)	3 O in Li_2CO_3 + 1 O in H_2O

▲ **Figure 3.6 Balancing chemical equations.** Use this process as you balance chemical equations to keep track of atoms in the reaction.

Stop & THINK

PART I continued

4. Explain why increasing the concentration of the reactants speeds up a chemical reaction. Use the concept of collisions of particles in your answer.
5. Relate a balanced chemical reaction to the law of conservation of matter. Balance this equation, which shows the combustion of methane (CH_4), and use it in your answer

$$CH_4 + O_2 \rightarrow CO_2 + H_2O$$

128 Unit 1 Interactions Are Interesting

Process and Procedure

Part II: Energize Those Reactions

Materials

For each student

1 pair of safety goggles
substances A, B, C, and D:

- substance A: baking soda; place 3–5 g in a freezer-type, resealable bag
- substance B: vinegar; 50 mL per team
- substance C: anhydrous calcium chloride, $CaCl_2$; place approximately 5 g in a freezer-type, resealable bag
- substance D: water; 50 mL per team

Students begin Part II by reading about the role of energy in the rate of a chemical reaction. Either read this as a class, assign it for homework, or have students read it individually in class. Next, students try to make sense of a puzzling situation involved in gasoline combustion. Try to make sure they see something about the collisions between gasoline and oxygen at room temperature that is insufficient to produce a self-sustaining reaction. Then in the boulder analogy, students connect everyday experiences with macroscopic objects to the probable behavior of microscopic objects in chemical reactions.

NOTES:

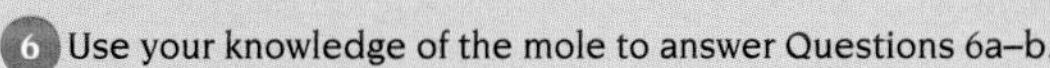

6 Use your knowledge of the mole to answer Questions 6a–b.

a. What is the molar mass of sodium?

b. If you have 2.3 mol of sodium, how many grams of sodium do you have?

7 Molar ratios can be used to determine quantities in chemical reactions. Use these ratios to answer Questions 7a–d.

a. What is the molar ratio of carbon dioxide to water in the reaction in Question 5?

b. If you began the reaction with 3 mol of CH_4, how many moles of O_2 would you need for it to react completely with the CH_4?

c. How many moles of CO_2 and H_2O would be produced?

d. If 25.7 g of water were produced, how many moles of methane were used?

Part II: Energize Those Reactions

Materials

For each student

1 pair of safety goggles

1 resealable plastic bag of substance A, provided by your teacher

1 container of substance B, provided by your teacher

1 resealable plastic bag of substance C, provided by your teacher

1 container of substance D, provided by your teacher

Cautions

You must wear safety goggles during this activity. Do not at any time touch the chemicals.

In Part I, you found out how chemists keep track of the number of particles available for a chemical reaction. You discovered that more moles of reactant particles mean a greater frequency of collision and an increased chance for chemical reaction. But is increased collision frequency the only factor affecting reaction rate? What about how hard particles hit—the energy of collision? After all, a slight bump by a fellow student in the hallway produces a very different reaction than a running crash.

In Step 1, focus students' attention on the questions posed in the last paragraph of the reading *It Only Takes a Spark*. Ask them to generate answers to the questions in their science notebooks. Emphasize that their answers do not need to be correct; rather the answers should be an honest effort to show what they think currently. Encourage students to use sketches of molecules. Walk around the room and interact casually in order to gather ongoing assessment information.

In Step 2, use a class discussion method you find effective. Lead the discussion toward the idea of energy. Gasoline and oxygen collide all the time at room temperature, but not with sufficient energy to cause very many reactions. Sufficient energy is needed to promote the formation of products—carbon dioxide and water. Once a large enough number of successful reactions occur, enough heat is generated from the combustion to provide enough energy for the reaction to be self-sustaining, that is, it continues on its own.

In Step 3, help students compare and contrast their initial ideas about gasoline burning with the boulder analogy. Encourage the use of literacy strategies such as analogy mapping, Venn diagrams, or T-tables to add structure to the compare-and-contrast activity. In narrative form, students might write the following:

"Gasoline and oxygen are reactants. Carbon dioxide and water are the products. The reactants start off with more energy than the products, like a boulder can start on one side of a hill. A match can provide some energy input to the collisions between reactants. That energy can be enough to make the reactants naturally become products. When that happens, energy is given off. That energy can go into the other reactants to get them up the energy hill. Eventually, the gasoline burns on its own."

NOTES:

In Part II, you will investigate the role of energy in chemical reactions. From this core understanding, you will learn in the next activity how energy-producing and energy-consuming reactions affect the rate of chemical reactions.

Process and Procedure

1. Read about the combustion of gasoline in *It Only Takes a Spark* to explore the aspects of energy important to chemical reactions.

READING

It Only Takes a Spark

Gasoline, primarily the hydrocarbon octane (C_8H_{18}), reacts with oxygen gas to produce carbon dioxide and water according to the balanced chemical equation

$$2C_8H_{18} + 25O_2 \rightarrow 16CO_2 + 18H_2O + \text{heat}$$

This reaction occurs in the engine of your car. However, you know that you can have a can of gasoline sitting outside in the air (which contains oxygen gas) and the reaction does not take place, at least not fast enough for you to see the effects. The gasoline does not explode even though there is a high concentration of gasoline and sufficient oxygen present in the air. It does not burn even though octane and oxygen particles are colliding all the time.

What would make this gasoline react quickly? Of course, you must add energy in the form of a spark or fire from a match for it to react. But why? What are the underlying reasons why the relatively small amount of energy in a spark can produce huge amounts of energy in a gasoline explosion?

2. Develop and discuss your ideas about the questions posed at the end of the reading *It Only Takes a Spark*. Be ready to contribute your answers to a class discussion.

Keep a record of your discussion in your science notebook.

3. Compare and contrast your class discussion notes from Step 2 with the following reading, *Boulder Analogy*.

130 Unit 1 Interactions Are Interesting

NOTES:

READING

Boulder Analogy

Energy in chemical reactions, such as burning gasoline, is a lot like pushing a boulder up a hill (see figure 3.7). Once you get the boulder up the hill, the boulder will roll down the hill spontaneously. This is similar to the way chemical reactions take place. Once a molecular collision results in particles with enough energy, the reaction continues on its own.

When the energy into a system is less than the energy out of a system ($E_{in} < E_{out}$), the reaction releases energy to the environment ($E_{in} - E_{out}$ = energy released). Chemists call the net energy associated with a chemical reaction **enthalpy**. Its symbol is ΔH. For a reaction that releases energy to the outside environment, enthalpy is negative ($-\Delta H$). The result you measure directly from $-\Delta H$ is a temperature increase of the surroundings. Reactions with $-\Delta H$ are called **exothermic** reactions. Chemists represent the energy relationships in a heat-producing reaction in an enthalpy diagram such as figure 3.8.

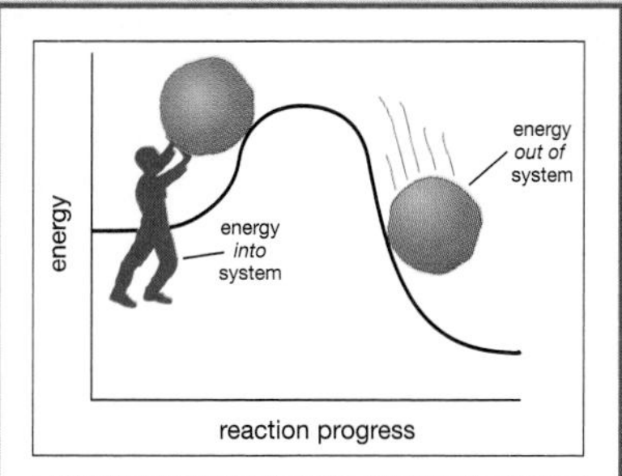

▲ **Figure 3.7 Energy input uphill, energy output downhill.** Why does it take energy input to push a boulder uphill? How would you measure the energy out of the system?

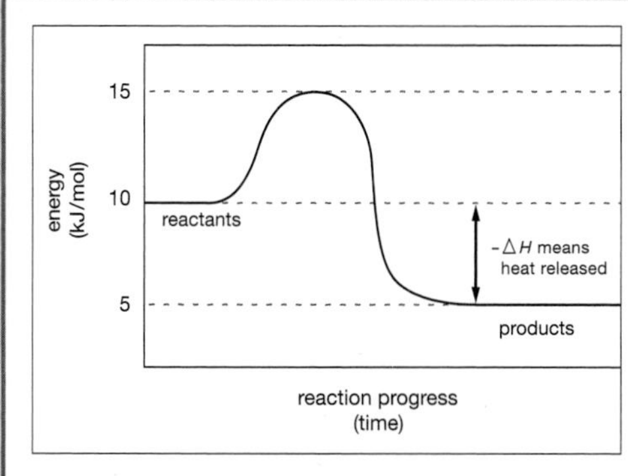

◄ **Figure 3.8 Enthalpy diagram for an exothermic reaction.** Enthalpy diagrams show energy differences between reactants and products. Always subtract the energy of the products from the energy of the reactants. What is always the algebraic sign of ΔH for exothermic reactions?

In Step 4a, students sketch and make observations of substances A and B.

In Step 4b, students mix the substances in the bag and record observations in their science notebooks.

In Step 4c, your students repeat Step 4b using substances C and D. The reaction with substances A and B is the classic baking soda and vinegar reaction. Many will be surprised that the reaction gets cold. Make sure that the bags are vented some if too much CO_2 is produced. Many reactions produce a gas and should not be conducted in a closed container. If you want to take the time, have the students record minimum and maximum temperatures of the reactions. When substance C (anhydrous calcium chloride) comes in contact with water, the dissolution process releases heat and feels quite warm.

In Steps 4d–e, students meet with a classmate and share their observations. They also note any discrepancies.

In Step 4f, lead your students in a class discussion of their results. Ask students to report their observations. If you discover that some groups had conflicting results or missed important observations, consider repeating the activity as a class. Students should observe that the first reaction feels cold and the second reaction feels hot. In the discussion, point out that if the reaction feels cold, it must be absorbing heat. This may be a little counterintuitive to students. But explain that as the reaction is absorbing heat, it is absorbing heat from your hand, or pulling heat from your hand. If your hand is losing heat, it feels cold. Explain that the second reaction releases heat and feels hot. This is always easier for students to understand.

In Step 5, ask students to read *The Ins and Outs of Heat*. Encourage students to think of the chemical bonds during a chemical reaction. Lead them to consider whether bonds must break and form during a reaction. Attempt to get them to see the relationship between the energy to break and the energy to form bonds. The net result is the overall heat of the chemical reaction. This energy can result in cooling the environment or heating it.

NOTES:

4. To feel the energy of a chemical reaction safely, do Steps 4a–g.
   a. Draw a sketch of the substances you are using in this activity. Record the color and state of the substances. Touch their containers to see if the substances feel hot, cold, or about room temperature. Label your sketches with these observations.
   b. Continue to make observations by following Steps i–v.
      i. Carefully open the plastic bag containing substance A.
      ii. Pour substance B into the bag.
      iii. Immediately close the bag and mix the contents by kneading the bag.
      iv. If necessary, open the bag to release the gas produced.
      v. Record all your observations of the bag and its contents in your science notebook.
   c. Repeat the instructions in Step 4b, only this time use substances C and D.
   d. Meet with a classmate and share your observations. Listen as your classmate shares his or her observations.
   e. If you and your classmate disagree on any observations, or you discover that you missed an important observation, be prepared to share this with the class in a discussion.
   f. Listen as your teacher leads a class discussion of these reactions. Share your ideas about the reactions and your observations with the class.
   g. Work with your team to develop an enthalpy diagram for reactions that feel cool. Reactions that cool the outside environment are called **endothermic** reactions.

Label your enthalpy diagram with the following key words: *reactants*, *products*, and $+\Delta H$. Remember that the positive sign means the heat content of the products is greater than the heat content of the reactants.

5. Read *The Ins and Outs of Heat* to understand the reasons at the atomic level for the heat involved in chemical reactions.

READING

The Ins and Outs of Heat

Burning gasoline produces great amounts of heat. At the atomic level, where does that heat come from? It comes from the chemical reaction. Specifically, the energy comes from the energy associated with breaking and forming chemical bonds.

Remember from Level 1 of this program that chemical bonds can be modeled as tiny springs,

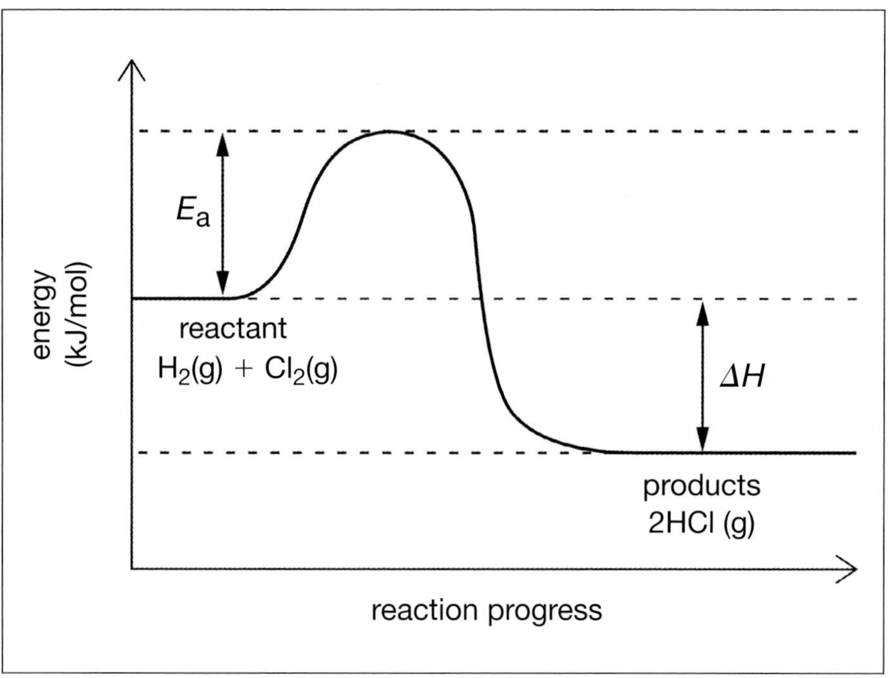

Figure T3.5 Enthalpy diagram for *Stop and Think* Question 1b. Notice that the products are lower than the reactants.

Answers to Stop and Think—Part II are on TE pages 133–134.

holding atoms in molecules together. At different temperatures, the springs make atoms in the molecule vibrate back and forth with different frequencies. Different kinds of atoms are bonded together with springs of different strength.

What must happen to the bonds of reactant molecules to result in product molecules? Indeed, reactant molecule bonds must break before product molecule bonds can form. For bonds to break, the springs must be stretched apart. As with any spring, this requires energy input. This is similar to the energy input required to push a boulder up a hill.

What happens when product molecules form new bonds? This would be like a spring contracting. Energy is released to the environment. The exact amount of energy depends on the spring strength and number of bonds involved. When more energy is released by bonds forming than is required to break bonds, the reaction produces heat and warms the outside environment. You feel the heat and measure a temperature increase.

All chemical reactions involve breaking reactant particle bonds and forming product molecule bonds. The net energy result can be either positive or negative. This results in the outside environment either cooling or heating. Chemists often represent the relationship between bond energy and net energy by

$$\Delta H = \Sigma(\text{bonds broken}) - \Sigma(\text{bonds formed}).$$

In sentence form, this expression reads: "The change in enthalpy (ΔH) equals the sum of all the energy of bonds broken minus the sum of all the energy of the bonds formed."

The Σ symbol (capital of the Greek symbol sigma) means "to find the sum of." For example, $\Sigma(3 + 6)$ equals 9.

Topic: enthalpy
Go to: www.scilinks.org
Code: 2Inquiry133

Stop & THINK

PART II

Read each question carefully before you answer it in your science notebook. Then check your answer and make corrections.

1 Consider the reaction

$$H_{2(g)} + Cl_{2(g)} \rightarrow 2HCl_{(g)}.$$

a. This reaction requires 671 kJ of energy to break all the reactant bonds, and 854 kJ of energy are released when all the product molecules form. Use this information to determine if the reaction warms or cools the outside environment. Show all your work.

Remember, kJ stands for kilojoules, or 1,000 joules of energy.

b. Sketch an enthalpy diagram for this reaction. Clearly indicate the relative energy content of reactants, products, and the ΔH.

Answers to Stop and Think—Part II, SE pages 133–134

1a. $671 \text{ kJ} - (-854 \text{ kJ}) = -183 \text{ kJ}$

The above equation says that $\Delta H = -\Delta 183$ kJ for the reaction. This means the reaction is exothermic, which means the reaction will heat the outside environment.

1b. See figure T3.5.

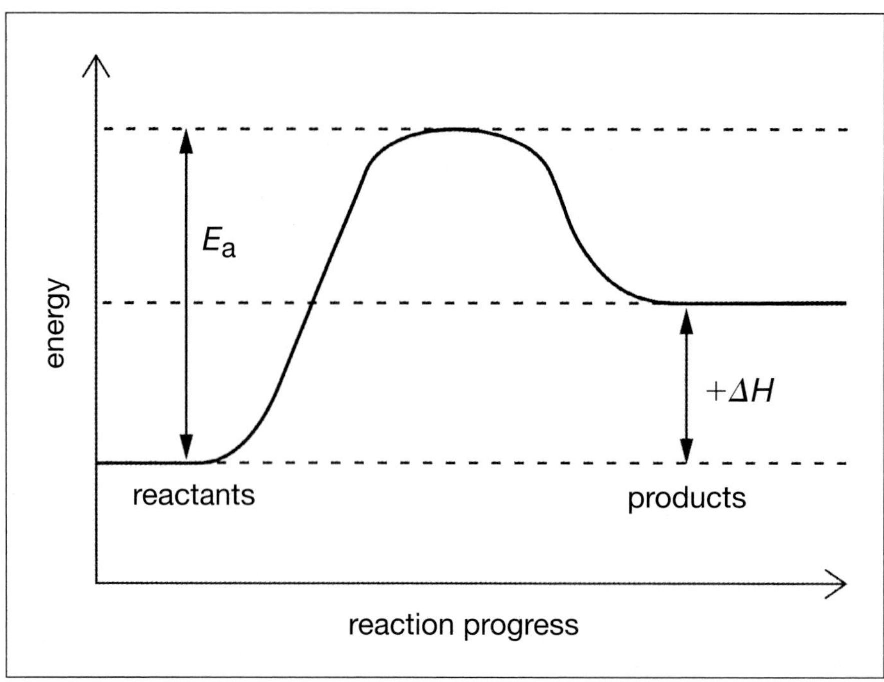

Figure T3.6 Enthalpy diagram for *Stop and Think* Questions 2a–b. Notice that the products are higher than the reactants.

Answers to Step 2 are on TE page 135.

2a–b. See figure T3.6.

3a. Endothermic.

3b. Exothermic.

3c. Endothermic.

3d. Endothermic.

3e. Exothermic.

3f. Exothermic.

3g. Endothermic.

4. There are many examples for these types of reactions. Students may say instant cold packs for injuries (endothermic) and hand warmers and self-heating meals (exothermic).

STOP & THINK, PART II, continued

2. Many chemical reactions cool the outside environment. Remember, these reactions are called endothermic reactions. Consider the generic endothermic reaction, heat + A + B = C + D and answer Questions 2a–b.
   - **a.** What does the enthalpy diagram look like for this reaction? Sketch it in your science notebook.
   - **b.** Label your enthalpy diagram with ΔH along with its correct algebraic sign and the relative energy of reactants and products.
3. Label the following processes as endothermic or exothermic.
   - **a.** Chemical bonds are broken.
   - **b.** New chemical bonds are made.
   - **c.** Heat is absorbed.
   - **d.** The reaction container feels cold.
   - **e.** Heat is released.
   - **f.** ΔH is negative.
   - **g.** Energy of the products is greater than the energy of the reactants.
4. There are many practical uses for endothermic and exothermic reactions. Name 1 practical application for each of these types of chemical reactions.

Process and Procedure

Part III: Economize and Catalyze

Materials

For the teacher (optional)

5 mL of 3% H_2O_2
petri dish
overhead projector
a piece of raw hamburger meat
500-mL graduated cylinder
plastic tub
safety goggles
gloves
apron
50 mL of 30% hydrogen peroxide (H_2O_2)
3 mL of dishwashing detergent
1 drop of food color
1–2 g of solid potassium iodide (KI)

Part III: Economize and Catalyze

Materials

none

Process and Procedure

1. Select an effective literacy strategy and then read *Catalysts Change Reaction Rates.*
2. Apply what you understand from the reading by answering Questions 2a–e in your science notebook.
   - **a.** What is the approximate activation energy in kilojoules per mole of the uncatalyzed reaction in figure 3.9?
   - **b.** From reading the scale in figure 3.9, what is the activation energy of the catalyzed reaction?
   - **c.** Look at the plot in figure 3.9. What effect does adding a catalyst have on the enthalpy of reaction?
   - **d.** How would adding a catalyst speed up a chemical reaction? Use your knowledge of collision frequency to form your answer.

Cautions

Thirty percent hydrogen peroxide is corrosive and will burn your skin. Handle with extreme care. Contact with eyes and skin can cause serious long-term damage. Wear safety goggles and gloves. Wash off spills with large amounts of *cool* water.

Consider beginning Part III with a demonstration of a catalyzed reaction. The reading refers often to the decomposition of hydrogen peroxide. There are a couple of good ways to demonstrate this. You can add 3% H_2O_2 to a petri dish on the overhead projector and add a piece of raw hamburger meat. Students should be able to see the bubbles of oxygen gas forming. Write the decomposition reaction on the board: "$2H_2O_2(l) \rightarrow O_2(g) + 2H_2O\ (l)$."

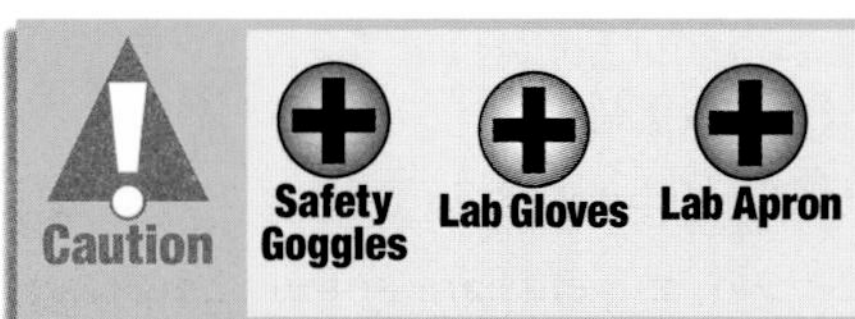

Another demonstration that is quite impressive is to put a 500-mL graduated cylinder in a plastic tub or laboratory sink. Wear safety goggles, gloves, and an apron as you do this demonstration. Add approximately 50 mL of 30% hydrogen peroxide into the cylinder. Add a squirt of dishwashing detergent and a drop of food color. Next add about 1–2 g of solid potassium iodide (KI). KI is a catalyst for this reaction. The reaction produces a vast amount of oxygen gas as seen in the foam that rises out of the cylinder. Also, this reaction is highly exothermic. Be careful handling the glassware as it will be hot. If you choose to do this demonstration, it is a good idea to practice it once before you do it for the class so that you know what to expect. The reaction mixture can be poured down the drain with copious amounts of water if state law permits.

Cautions

Thirty percent hydrogen peroxide is corrosive and will burn your skin. Handle with extreme care. Contact with eyes and skin can cause serious long-term damage. Wear safety goggles and gloves. Wash off spills with large amounts of *cool* water.

Students learn *how* a catalyst speeds up a chemical reaction in the reading for Part III.

In Step 1, help students select an effective literacy strategy (sometimes called reading strategy) for reading the passage. Encourage them to apply their chosen strategy as they read. Walk around the room and assess students' choices and their use of the strategy.

In Step 2, students demonstrate their understanding of what they read about catalysts. Use your judgment on how best to go over the questions in Step 2. Consider assigning them as homework, followed by class discussion.

Answers to Step 2, SE pages 134–136

2a. A reasonable estimate for the activation energy of the uncatalyzed reaction is about 5.0 kJ/mol.

2b. The activation energy for the catalyzed reaction is about 3.5 kJ/mol.

2c. Adding a catalyst lowers the activation energy.

2d. If the activation energy when using a catalyst is lower, then more collisions would occur with at least the proper amount of energy to produce a reaction. This will speed up the reaction.

READING

Catalysts Change Reaction Rates

You know that for a chemical reaction to take place, bonds must be broken and new bonds must form. The energy needed to break the bonds in the reactant is the **activation energy**, E_a, of the reaction. Look at the energy plot in figure 3.8. The hill formed by the solid line is the activation energy in the enthalpy diagram.

There are ways to decrease the height of the energy hill, E_a, without changing the chemical reaction. One way involves adding a substance called a **catalyst**. The dashed line in figure 3.9 represents a reaction with a catalyst. What does adding a catalyst do to the reaction rate?

You see that a catalyst will speed up a chemical reaction by lowering the activation energy. That's because the energy of activation is about 3 kilojoules per mole (kJ/mol) or 2 kJ/mol less than the uncatalyzed reaction. You might think of it this way:

> Suppose you are participating in track at your school. Your event is the high jump. You may be able to clear the bar set to over 1.75 meters (m, or 5 feet, 9 inches), but only with a great deal of energy. However, if they lower the bar to 1 m (about 3 ft), you will be able to jump over the bar with much less energy.

Catalysts that occur in living systems are called **enzymes**. You have witnessed the effects of the enzyme catalase in your body if you have ever poured hydrogen peroxide in a cut. As the hydrogen peroxide interacts with the enzyme in your body, the decomposition of H_2O_2 occurs very rapidly. How do you know that the hydrogen peroxide is decomposing rapidly? You see the formation of oxygen gas bubbles.

Finally, one reason catalysts are so valuable in industry and life is that they are not used up in a chemical reaction. That is, you can add a catalyst and have the reaction speed up without having to add more and more catalyst.

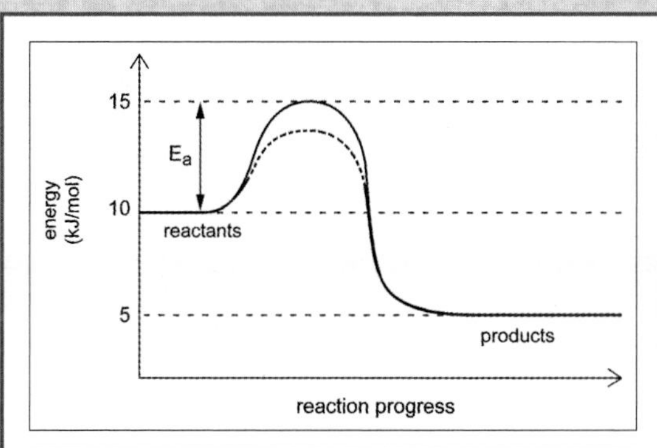

▲ **Figure 3.9 Catalyzed and uncatalyzed reactions.** In which reaction is the energy of activation lower? What effect does this have on the rate of reaction? What evidence would you collect to support your answer?

NOTES:

Answers to Reflect and Connect, SE pages 136–138

1. See figure T3.7.
2. No, students are not in danger. If the H_2O_2 is old that just means that it has probably decomposed. If the H_2O_2 decomposed completely and students poured it on a cut, they would only be pouring water on the cut (the oxygen gas would have escaped). They would see little to no fizzing when it is poured on the cut. The balanced equation for the decomposition of hydrogen peroxide is $2H_2O_2$ $2H_2O + O_2$. Hydrogen peroxide sold in stores is 3% hydrogen peroxide in water. As the hydrogen peroxide ages and decomposes, the percentage of H_2O_2 decreases.
3. These metals are the catalysts in the catalytic converters. Catalysts are not used up in the chemical reactions that they are speeding up. Therefore, they do not need to be replenished or replaced.

Answers to Reflect and Connect are on TE pages 136–138.

e. Collision frequency and energy are not the only factors affecting the rate of a chemical reaction. Read *FYI—Molecular Orientation* to find out more.

Reflect and Connect

Answer the following questions on your own in your science notebook. Then check your answers with several classmates.

1. Copy the table in figure 3.10 into your science notebook. Complete the table by drawing a labeled sketch in the middle column for each of the ways listed that can change the rate of a chemical reaction. You may want to draw a before-and-after sketch to make your point. Your sketch can be a picture or a graph, but it must represent your best understanding. Next, complete the last column with a caption for your sketch or graph and your understanding of the reasons why each of these ways changes the rate of a chemical reaction. Be sure to include *how* the rate changes.
2. There is always an expiration date on a bottle of hydrogen peroxide (H_2O_2). Suppose you just got a paper cut on your finger and you are looking through your medicine cabinet and find an old bottle of H_2O_2. The H_2O_2 expired at least 2 years ago, but you decide to use it on the paper cut anyway. Are you in danger since the hydrogen peroxide has gone "bad"? What would you expect to see as you poured the expired H_2O_2 on your cut? Explain your ideas. Include a balanced equation in your explanation.
3. Catalytic converters on cars use the metals rhodium and platinum as catalysts to convert potentially dangerous exhaust gases to carbon dioxide, nitrogen, and water. Why don't cars need to have the rhodium and platinum replaced after they are used?

Ways to change the rate of a chemical reaction	Sketch or graph	Caption
Increase concentration		
Decrease concentration		
Add a catalyst		

▲ **Figure 3.10 Answer table.** Set up this table in your science notebook. Leave plenty of room for pictures and sketches. To make sure that you will have enough room, you may want to complete one row before you add the next row to your table.

Ways to change the rate of a chemical reaction	Sketch or graph	Caption
Increase concentration	Sketches could include beakers with different numbers of particles colliding. They should show that there are more collisions in a more concentrated solution. The best approach is to show a before-and-after sketch with the concentration increasing in the second sketch.	If students draw a diagram like the example given, their captions should read something like this: "A more concentrated solution will have more particles. The chances of a collision increase with the additional particles; therefore, the reaction will be faster."
Decrease concentration	Sketches could include beakers with different numbers of particles colliding. They should show that there are fewer collisions in a less concentrated solution. The best approach is to show a before-and-after sketch with the concentration decreasing in the second sketch.	If students draw a diagram like the example given, their captions should read something like this: "A less concentrateed solution will have fewer particles. The chances of a collision will decrease with fewer particles; therefore, the reaction will be slower."
Add a catalyst	Students will probably draw a graph similar to figure 3.8. Make sure they clearly indicate the catalyzed reaction.	As a caption for this example, students should say: "Adding a catalyst speeds up a chemical reaction by lowering the activation energy. The reaction plot for the catalyzed reaction is shown by [students will indicate the color or style of the line used to draw the catalyzed reaction]."

▲ **Figure T3.7 Table for *Reflect and Connect* Question 1.** This is a possible answer to *Reflect and Connect* Question 1.

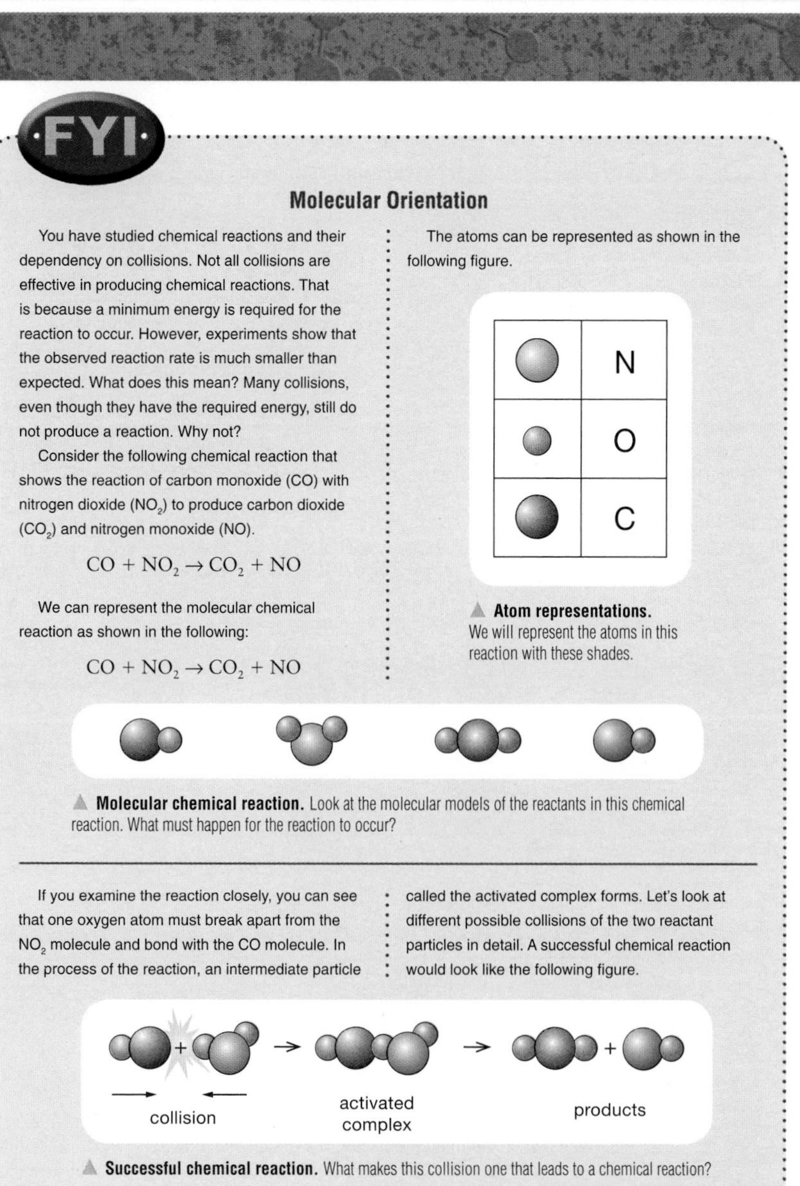

FYI

Molecular Orientation

You have studied chemical reactions and their dependency on collisions. Not all collisions are effective in producing chemical reactions. That is because a minimum energy is required for the reaction to occur. However, experiments show that the observed reaction rate is much smaller than expected. What does this mean? Many collisions, even though they have the required energy, still do not produce a reaction. Why not?

Consider the following chemical reaction that shows the reaction of carbon monoxide (CO) with nitrogen dioxide (NO_2) to produce carbon dioxide (CO_2) and nitrogen monoxide (NO).

$$CO + NO_2 \rightarrow CO_2 + NO$$

We can represent the molecular chemical reaction as shown in the following:

$$CO + NO_2 \rightarrow CO_2 + NO$$

The atoms can be represented as shown in the following figure.

▲ **Atom representations.** We will represent the atoms in this reaction with these shades.

▲ **Molecular chemical reaction.** Look at the molecular models of the reactants in this chemical reaction. What must happen for the reaction to occur?

If you examine the reaction closely, you can see that one oxygen atom must break apart from the NO_2 molecule and bond with the CO molecule. In the process of the reaction, an intermediate particle called the activated complex forms. Let's look at different possible collisions of the two reactant particles in detail. A successful chemical reaction would look like the following figure.

▲ **Successful chemical reaction.** What makes this collision one that leads to a chemical reaction?

Chapter 3 Collisions—Atomic Style 137

4. These conditions will slow down chemical reactions. Light is often the energy needed to speed up a reaction, and cool temperatures will slow down the reaction.
5. There are 6.02×10^{23} particles in a mole. Examples of other words that represent a fixed number of items are couple—2; trio—3; gross—144; and baker's dozen—13.

ELABORATE

Two-Way Reactions

Activity Overview

Students will observe color changes in a chromate solution after substances are added. They will soon see that the observed color changes can be made to occur again and again. That is, the original yellow color changes to orange, then back to yellow depending on what substance is added to the solution. This activity "hooks" students' curiosity for investigating reversible reactions. That is, these observations form an experiential foundation from which students infer what happens at the microscopic level.

After observing the initial color changes, they will read *Switch-A-Roo I* to learn more about reversible reactions and how scientists represent these reactions. They will also consider the rate of both the forward and reverse reactions during the course of the chemical reaction. Next, they will learn about chemical equilibrium and how the rate of the forward reaction equals the rate of the reverse reaction when a reaction is in equilibrium.

Students will represent the inherent changes in concentrations resulting from shifts in equilibrium by making qualitative graphs. They will depict concentration change with line graphs and relate the graphs to the processes in reversible reactions.

Next, students will consider stresses on chemical reactions in equilibrium. They will learn about Le Châtelier's principle and predict shifts in equilibrium from the application of different stresses. Finally, they will see how heat can be a stress and how to make predictions of the direction of the reaction shift.

Before You Teach

Background Information

All chemical reactions are reversible given the right conditions. However, many times one of the products is a gas and it will escape the reaction. Without this product, the reaction cannot reverse. Chemical equilibrium is the state in which the rate of the forward reaction equals the rate of the reverse reaction. Reactants are being consumed to produce the products at the same rate that products are being consumed to produce the reactants. The double arrow, $\rightleftharpoons$, is used to symbolize a reaction at equilibrium.

Chemical equilibrium does not imply that the amounts of reactants *equal* the amounts of products, only that the rate of the forward and reverse reactions is the same. There will be no net change in the concentrations of either the reactants or the products for reactions at equilibrium.

The equilibrium position of a reaction can be far to the right, indicating that the forward reaction is favored and there is a higher concentration of products than there are reactants at equilibrium. Conversely, if the equilibrium position is far to the left, this would indicate that the reverse reaction is favored, and at equilibrium there is a higher concentration of reactants present than products. These can be indicated with a double arrow in which the favored direction is longer.

Molecular Orientation, continued

Other collisions do not result in a chemical reaction. Why not? One possibility that you have studied is that the collision occurs but the reaction does not take place. This may be because the collision does not occur with enough energy. Remember, the particles must collide with at least the activation energy for a reaction to occur. If the particles do not have enough energy, they simply rebound from each other, resulting in no chemical reaction, as seen in the illustration to the right.

Look at the collisions illustrated in the figure below. Neither of these collisions results in a reaction even though the particles collide with more than enough energy in both instances. Compare all the figures and see if you can see why these do not result in a chemical reaction. Can you tell?

Careful study of these examples indicates that in order for a successful collision to occur, the carbon atom in a CO molecule must collide with an oxygen atom in an NO_2 molecule at the moment of impact. Only in that way can a temporary bond between the carbon atom and an oxygen atom form. The collisions shown in the illustration above do not lead to a reaction because the molecules collide with the incorrect orientation. In other words, the carbon atom does not contact an oxygen atom at the moment of impact, and the molecules simply rebound.

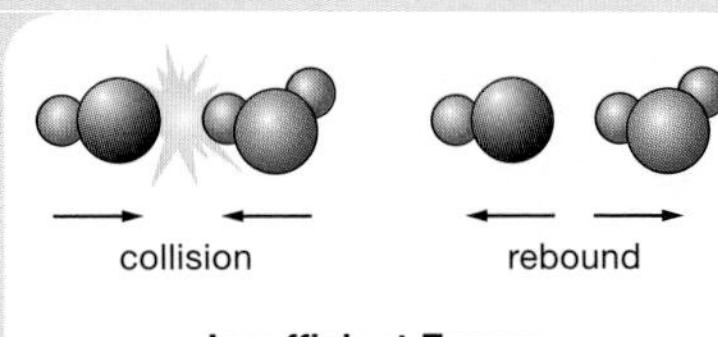

▲ **Unsuccessful collision.** Everything is in place for this reaction to occur. Why doesn't the collision produce a chemical reaction?

Chemical reactions depend on collisions. However, you have seen that all collisions do not result in a successful collision—one that leads to a chemical reaction. These collisions must occur with the appropriate amount of energy and the reacting particles must collide in the proper orientation.

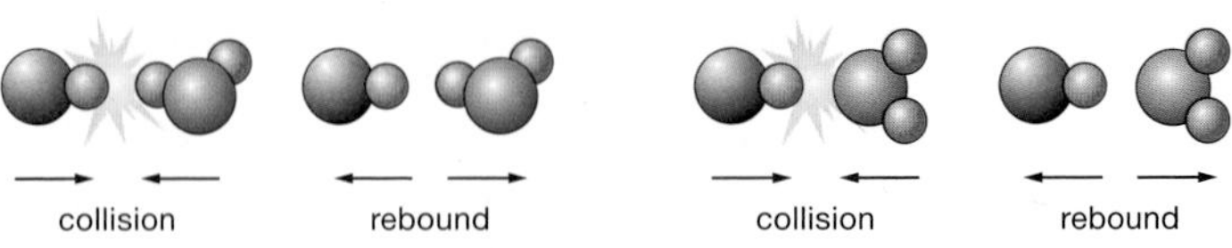

▲ **Two examples of unsuccessful collisions.** Examine these illustrations carefully and compare them with the figure of a successful collision. Why don't these two collisions produce a chemical reaction even though the particles collide with enough energy?

4. Explain why it is best to store chemicals in dark, tightly sealed bottles and in an environment that has cool or moderate temperatures.
5. How many items are in a mole? List at least 3 words other than "mole" and "dozen" that represent a fixed number of items and use them in a sentence.

For example, $\underset{\longleftarrow}{\rightarrow}$ would indicate that the equilibrium position is to the left and that the reverse reaction is favored. The arrows $\overset{\longrightarrow}{\leftarrow}$ would indicate that the forward reaction is favored, the equilibrium position lies to the right, and, at equilibrium, there would be more products present than reactants.

For some reactions, the equilibrium position lies so far to the right and the position so favors the forward reaction that the reaction appears to have gone to completion and there are no reactants left at all. For example, when gaseous hydrogen and oxygen are mixed in stoichiometric quantities and react to form water vapor, the reaction proceeds essentially to completion. When the system reaches equilibrium, the amounts of hydrogen and oxygen gas that are present in the system are negligible. It appears that this reaction does not reach equilibrium but instead goes to completion. However, it does reach equilibrium, but the position is extremely far to the right.

At equilibrium, there are no net, observable changes to the concentration of the reactants or products in the reaction. The reaction may appear to have stopped. However, chemical equilibrium is a dynamic system; the reaction does not stop. Rather, the rates of the forward reaction simply match the rates of the reverse reaction. At the beginning of the reaction when no products are present, the rate of the forward reaction would necessarily be higher than the rate of the reverse reaction. When there are no products, the reaction cannot go in reverse. Once some reactants are consumed, the forward rate would be lower. As more products are produced, the concentration of the product particles increases and more collisions occur, increasing the rate of the reverse reaction. At the same time, the reactants (initially in high concentration) are being consumed and their concentration is decreasing. This slows down the rate of the forward reaction. This rate change finally evens out when the rates become equal and the system has reached chemical equilibrium.

A system at chemical equilibrium will stay at equilibrium unless conditions change. Changing the conditions of a system (known as placing a *stress* on the system) at equilibrium will cause the system to shift in a direction (left or right) to relieve the stress and reestablish equilibrium. This is known as Le Châtelier's principle. Because of this shift, concentrations of reactants and products will change and sometimes the temperature of the system will also change. Examples of stresses and the resulting shifts and changes to the system are detailed in the student book.

For a deeper understanding of chemical equilibrium and the mathematical calculations involved, consult a college general chemistry text.

Materials—Part I

For each team of 4 students

4 pairs of safety goggles
4 pairs of safety gloves
4 laboratory aprons
1 dropper pipet
1 small test tube or microwell plate
1 mL of 1.0 M chromate solution (K_2CrO_4)
3.0 M sulfuric acid (H_2SO_4)
6.0 M sodium hydroxide (NaOH)
colored pencils or markers

Materials—Part II

For each team of 4 students

4 pairs of safety goggles
4 laboratory aprons
1 sealed plastic pipet with cobalt chloride ($CoCl_2 \cdot 6H_2O$) solution
1 ice bath
hot water
colored pencils or markers

SIDEBAR

Careers in Catalysis Research

What would you do if you were a chemist? Mostly, you would try to understand and apply chemical reactions. You would think of better ways to make the chemicals we need for everyday life. And many times, you would apply your knowledge to destroying chemicals. Why would you want to get rid of some chemical substances?

One important reason involves producing safer, cleaner chemical processes. This area of research, sometimes called "green chemistry," seeks environmentally friendly methods of producing the chemical substances we need for everyday living. That's important because many useful products, such as pesticides, detergents, and diesel fuel, produce harmful effects in humans and in the environment.

Researchers from Carnegie Mellon University have developed a catalyst that speeds up several chemical reactions. The name of this catalyst is iron-tetraamido macrocyclic ligand (Fe-TAML). The type of chemical reaction Fe-TAML speeds up is called oxidation. Rusting of metals and burning of fuels are examples of oxidation reactions. In all oxidation reactions, oxidant molecules take electrons from neighboring compounds. Hydrogen peroxide (H_2O_2) and oxygen (O_2) are example oxidants. Oxidation can result in molecules tearing apart.

Why would chemists want to tear apart certain molecules? Some molecules, such as pesticides, do important jobs. But inevitably, they become part of what we eat or of important ecosystems such as estuaries. These molecules oxidize to harmless substances very slowly. Catalysts can speed

Many chemists study how to make better catalysts. What do chemists need to know about enthalpy, activation energy, and reaction rate in order to know when their product is better?

up their destruction by speeding up the oxidation process. This is how Fe-TAML works.

In the next figure, you can see an iron atom at the core of the Fe-TAML molecule in the representation of this catalyst. The iron atom is surrounded by proteinlike molecules. In concentrations as low as 10 parts per million, Fe-TAML speeds up the oxidation of environmentally harmful compounds. When mixed with an oxidant like hydrogen peroxide, Fe-TAML reduces chlorinated pesticides to relatively harmless molecules.

Fe-TAML increases the decomposition rate of other chemical reactions. It catalyzes the cleanup of paper-mill wastewater. The cleaner and clearer water is safer for fish and allows more light to reach underwater plants. Fe-TAML takes the sulfur out of diesel fuel in a two-step process. This saves time and money compared with the current multistep method. Sulfur in fuels fouls

Advance Preparation

Prepare the solutions ahead of time. But do not prepare them more than a few days ahead of time, as some of the solutions need to be fresh. Prepare the solutions as follows.

1. To prepare 500 mL of 1.0 M potassium chromate (K_2CrO_4) (formula weight = 194.21 g/mol) solution, dissolve 97.1 g of solid potassium chromate in a 1-L Erlenmeyer flask and add 500 mL of deionized or distilled water. Decrease amounts proportionally if you need less.
2. To prepare 500 mL of 3.0 M sulfuric acid (H_2SO_4), fill a 500-mL volumetric flask about half full with deionized or distilled water. Then slowly pour 12 mL of concentrated sulfuric acid into the flask, swirling constantly. Wear safety goggles, laboratory gloves, and an apron. Do this under a fume hood. Fill the remaining flask volume to the 500-mL mark and swirl.

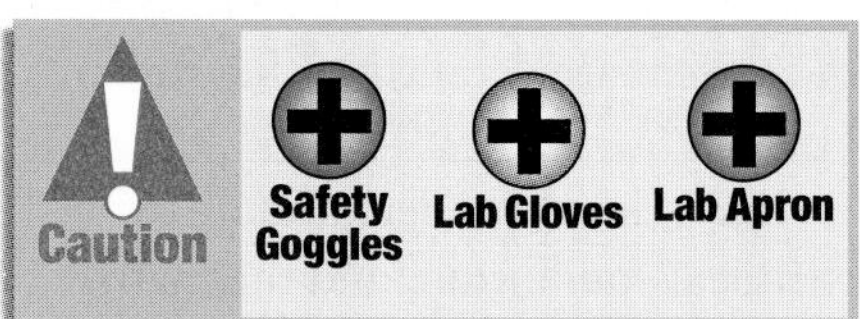

3. To prepare 500 mL of 6.0 M sodium hydroxide (NaOH), dissolve 12 g of sodium hydroxide in 500 mL of water. Wear safety goggles, an apron, and gloves.
4. To prepare the cobalt chloride solution for Part II, dissolve 4 g cobalt II chloride ($CoCl_2{\cdot}6H_2O$) into 40 mL H_2O. Then add concentrated hydrochloric acid (HCl) to 100 mL; put in plastic Beral pipets and seal as mentioned.

Prepare the pipets by first labeling the pipet with the solution name using a fine-tipped permanent marker. Next, fill the Beral pipets with the cobalt chloride solution. Prepare the pipets by stretching the tube of the pipet near the bulb and then cutting with a scissors in the stretched area. The solutions will not leak out of the pipets and can be stored upright in a cassette tape box. You can also use micropipets, which already have capillary tips but hold less of the solutions. You can use these year after year, in which case you do not need to dispose of them.

Cautions

Wear safety goggles, gloves, and an apron at all times. Do not allow any solution to touch your skin. If any solution touches your skin, wash the affected area with large amounts of cool water.

As You Teach

Outcomes and Indicators of Success

By the end of the activity, students should

1. develop a new understanding of collision theory and its significance to reversible chemical reactions. They will develop their new understanding by
   - proposing an explanation of a reversible reaction using their ideas about collisions,
   - applying what they know about collisions to new situations in reversible reactions,
   - creating a graph depicting the rate changes of both the forward and reverse reactions, and
   - revising their graphs of rate changes in a reversible reaction based on new information learned.
2. develop a new understanding of chemical reactions at equilibrium.

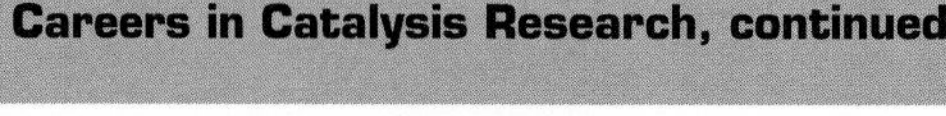

Careers in Catalysis Research, continued

emission-control equipment and produces compounds that contribute to acid rain. Finally, research suggests that Fe-TAML will catalyze the destruction of anthrax spores. Anthrax is a deadly disease used in biological weapons. The spores are very resistant to oxidation in natural environments. But Fe-TAML breaks apart the spores and destroys the disease. Spraying a dilute solution of hydrogen peroxide and a catalyst on military troops could save many lives.

You can see how important knowledge of catalysts is to professional chemists. In high school, these researchers studied math and science each year. After an undergraduate science major, many practicing chemists attain graduate degrees. But learning does not end with formal schooling. These researchers read and study for the rest of their careers. The results speak for themselves. We have access to the chemical substances that make our modern lives possible.

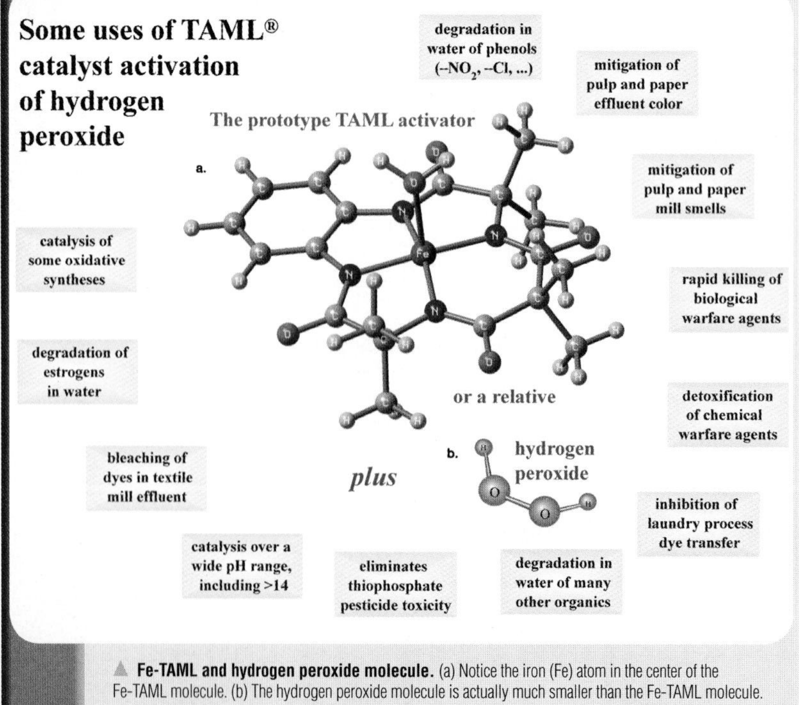

Fe-TAML and hydrogen peroxide molecule. (a) Notice the iron (Fe) atom in the center of the Fe-TAML molecule. (b) The hydrogen peroxide molecule is actually much smaller than the Fe-TAML molecule.

140 | Unit 1 Interactions Are Interesting

They will develop their understandings by

- recognizing systems at equilibrium from graphs and descriptions,
- using their knowledge of collisions to explain changes in the rate of a reaction approaching equilibrium,
- describing equilibrium position,
- analyzing the changes in concentration of a system approaching equilibrium, and
- recognizing the implications of equilibrium state to concentrations of reactants and products at equilibrium.

3. develop an understanding of Le Châtelier's principle in chemical reactions at equilibrium.

They will develop their understanding by

- deciding the direction of equilibrium shift from changes in concentration or temperature,
- describing the changes in concentration of all reactants and products and the temperature when the reaction shifts either left or right due to a stress on a system, and
- justifying their answers to shift and changes in concentration or temperature.

4. acquire greater understanding about the large variety of reasons scientists conduct investigations.

They will show their acquired understanding by

- relating color changes in chemical reactions to understandings about reversible reactions in the natural world and
- testing what they understand about predicting shifts in equilibrium reactions.

Strategies

Getting Started

Read the introduction to the activity with your students. Discuss the questions posed in the introduction.

Cautions

Wear safety goggles, gloves, and an apron at all times. Do not allow any solution to touch your skin. If any solution touches your skin, wash the affected area with large amounts of cool water.

Process and Procedure

Part I: Reversible Reactions

Materials

For each team of 4 students

4 pairs of safety goggles
4 pairs of safety gloves
4 laboratory aprons
1 dropper pipet
1 small test tube or microwell plate
1 mL of 1.0 M chromate solution (K_2CrO_4)
3.0 M sulfuric acid (H_2SO_4)
6.0 M sodium hydroxide (NaOH)
colored pencils or markers
SRCD

In Step 1, students produce color changes in a chromate solution. They accomplish this by adding small amounts of acid and then base. Originally, the chromate solution is yellow. Adding acid makes the solution turn orange due to an equilibrium shift. Adding base in a sufficient amount neutralizes the acid and causes the solution to be yellow again.

Ensure that each student sketches what he or she sees for each step. This process should result in 3 sketches, labeled "beginning," "middle," and "end." Remind students to leave room under each sketch for a caption. Ask that they use colored pencils, if possible.

Two-Way Reactions

ELABORATE

Chemical changes occur when particles collide with the proper amount of energy. You have looked at how different factors can change collision frequency and in turn change the rate of the chemical reaction. You are changing something in the chemical system to produce the results you want. But have you ever thought about the collisions that occur in the system *after* the products have been produced? Do collisions stop at this point? If the particles in the product are also colliding in the system, what might you predict would happen?

Two-Way Reactions helps you answer these questions. You and your team will apply what you already know about concentration and energy to an important class of chemical reactions—equilibrium reactions.

Part I: Reversible Reactions

Materials

For each team of 4 students

- 4 pairs of safety goggles
- 4 pairs of safety gloves
- 4 laboratory aprons
- 1 dropper pipet
- 1 small test tube or microwell plate
- 1 mL of 1.0 M chromate solution (K_2CrO_4)
- 3.0 M sulfuric acid (H_2SO_4)
- 6.0 M sodium hydroxide (NaOH)
- colored pencils or markers

Cautions

Wear safety goggles, gloves, and an apron at all times. Do not allow any solution to touch your skin. If any solution touches your skin, wash the affected area with large amounts of cool water and tell your teacher.

In Part I, you and your team will gather visible evidence, such as color change, for reversible reactions. Then you will think about what might be happening at the invisible level. That is, you will collect macroscopic evidence and infer what occurs at the microscopic level.

Process and Procedure

1. Test for color changes in a chromate ion (CrO_4^{2-}) solution by doing Steps 1a–f.
   a. Put on all safety gear and gather your materials.
   b. Place about 1 mL (15–20 drops) of 1.0 M chromate ion solution in a small test tube.

Chapter 3 Collisions—Atomic Style 141

In Step 2, students read *Switch-A-Roo I* for background information that helps them begin the process of explaining what happened in their test tubes in Step 1.

In Step 3, ask students to apply what they understood from the reading to writing the captions under each sketch. Use the sketches and captions to assess the ongoing development of their thinking.

Possible captions for the 3 sketches are the following:

"Beginning: The chromate solution is naturally yellow. Chromate ions collide with water, but no observable reaction takes place. The concentration of chromate ion is constant."

"Middle: Adding sulfuric acid increases the hydronium ion concentration. It collides with chromate more frequently. This produces more successful reactions. Thus, some dichromate is produced. Its concentration increases to the point we see orange."

"End: Adding sodium hydroxide neutralizes the added acid. This decreases the hydronium ion concentration. This makes the concentration for the reactant molecules temporarily lower on a relative basis. Fewer collisions between reactant molecules occur, producing more reactants. The solution turns back to yellow, indicating an increase in chromate ion concentration."

In Step 4, encourage teams to use the TSAR strategy to manage their own learning. Their performance during this task will help you to assess their ongoing learning.

In Step 5, have students represent the changes they observed in an alternative way from the sketches. Ask them to make a qualitative graph of the concentration changes evident in Step 1. You should only check for the relative positions of each concentration.

Lead a short class discussion once everyone has finished the graphs, highlight comments, and captions. Focus your discussion on the flat sections and the curved sections. The flat sections show how concentrations are not changing. If the flat section for chromate is higher than the flat section for dichromate, the solution is most likely yellow. Naturally, the reverse results in an orange solution. The flat sections represent the system at equilibrium. That is, there is no net, observable change in concentration. Yet collisions occur all the time, resulting in product and reactant molecules being produced.

When acid is added, the concentration of chromate decreases, as shown by the curved line. The decrease is fast at first, and then slows down since the concentration of acid is great at first, then decreases. Soon, a new equilibrium position is created, one in which the dichromate concentration is large enough to turn the solution orange. New flat portions are generated, but at different levels than before. Adding the base decreases the acid concentration rapidly. The curved lines indicate changing concentrations, which reflect a shift in the position of the equilibrium to the left, or reactants, side. This results in a yellow solution. A sample qualitative graph appears in figure T3.8.

c. Sketch what you see in your science notebook, including color.

Label this sketch "beginning" and save room for a caption. Also list the chemicals you think are inside the test tube.

d. Add at least 2 but not more than 10 drops of 3.0 M H_2SO_4 slowly until you see an obvious color change.

Label this sketch "middle" and save room for a caption. Also list the chemicals you think are inside the test tube.

e. Compare the solution from Step 1d with the dichromate solution your teacher shows you. Add comments to your middle sketch based on what you see.

f. Add drops of 6.0 M NaOH until another color change occurs.

Label this sketch "end" and save room for a caption. Also list the chemicals you think are inside the test tube.

2. Read *Switch-A-Roo I* and look for ways to apply your knowledge about collisions to the color changes you saw in Step 1.
3. Use the reading *Switch-A-Roo I* to write captions under each sketch from Step 1. The captions tell the story of what is happening at the atomic level.
4. Use the TSAR strategy with a team member to make your captions the best they can be.
5. Represent the changes you observed in Step 1 in a sketch graph by following Steps 5a–d.

a. Copy the sketch graph in figure 3.12 into your science notebook.

Make the graph large and leave plenty of room for highlight comments and a caption.

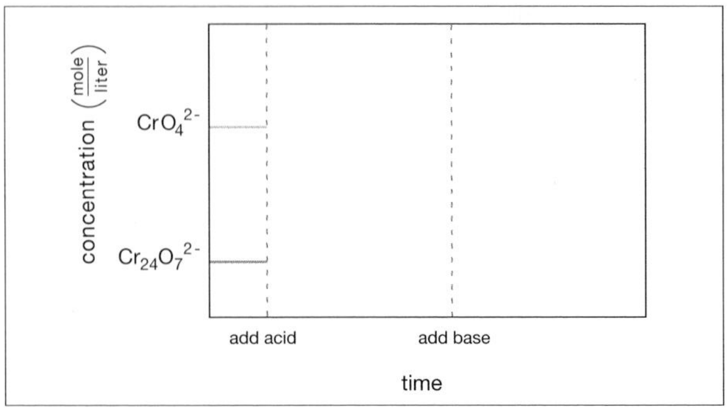

Figure 3.12
Concentration changes. Use these axes as a guide to chart changes in concentration of the chromate and dichromate ions over time. What do the flat regions mean? What happens to the lines when the equilibrium position shifts?

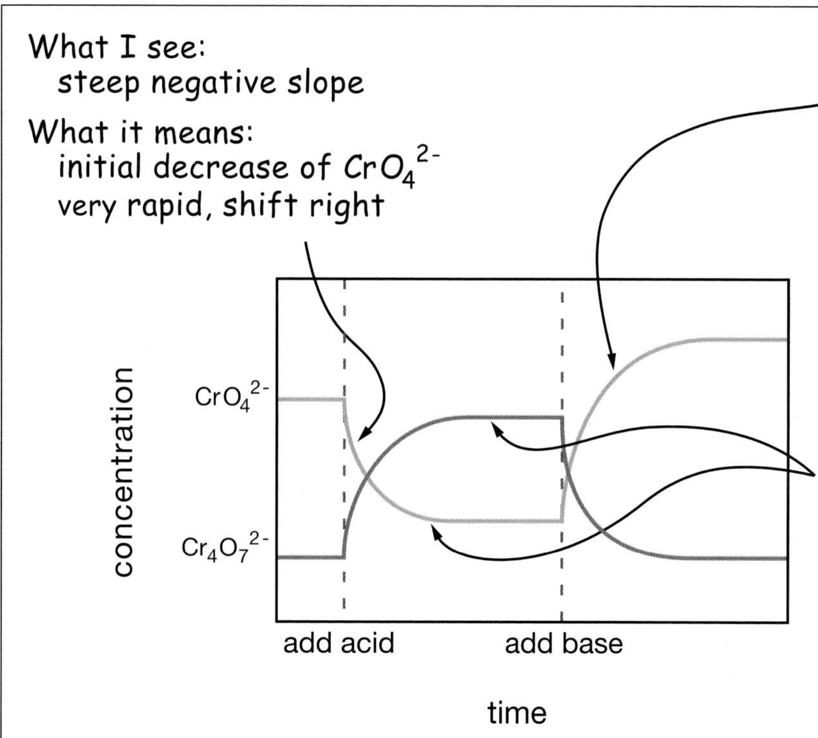

▲ **Figure T3.8 Concentration changes.** This qualitative graph represents an answer to Step 5.

READING

Switch-A-Roo I

Changes are constantly occurring. Scientists try to determine whether these changes are permanent. Can you think of a change that is not permanent? Consider water freezing; is this physical change permanent? Liquid water can freeze and ice can melt. Liquid water can evaporate and then condense back into a liquid state. These processes are examples of reversible reactions as shown in figure 3.11. You should be glad these changes are not permanent; the fact that they are reversible is the focus of the water cycle on Earth. You will learn more about the water cycle in chapter 10, *The Water System*.

▲ **Figure 3.11 A reversible process.** How would you reverse this process? Are chemical reactions reversible?

What about chemical reactions? Can they be reversed? You saw evidence that this was possible in Step 1 of this activity. When particles collide with enough energy, products are formed. The particles of the products also collide and can reverse the original process to form more reactants. Theoretically, all chemical reactions are reversible given certain conditions.

Here is the reversible reaction from Step 1:

$$\underset{\text{yellow chromate}}{2CrO_4^{2-}{}_{(aq)}} + \underset{\text{hydronium ion}}{2H_3O^+_{(aq)}} \rightleftarrows \underset{\text{orange dichromate}}{Cr_2O_7^{2-}{}_{(aq)}} + \underset{\text{water}}{3H_2O_{(aq)}}$$

reactants products

You begin with a yellow solution that is not changing color. That's evidence for no change in concentration—no macroscopic change. Then you add some sulfuric acid (H_2SO_4), which is a source of the hydronium ion, H_3O^+. Hydronium ions are responsible for the acid characteristics of sulfuric acid. The concentration of H_3O^+ increases. What does this do to the collision frequency between the chromate and hydronium ions? What does this do to the rate of the forward reaction?

When reactant concentrations increase, the rate of the forward reaction increases for a moment, resulting in more product. You see the evidence. The chromate solution turns orange. This indicates the formation of dichromate ion ($Cr_2O_7^{2-}$), which is orange. The reaction remains the same color, indicating no change in concentration. Next, you add the base, sodium hydroxide (NaOH). The base neutralizes the acid, decreasing the hydronium ion concentration. There is a relative increase in product concentration. Product molecules collide more frequently and form reactant molecules. The rate of the reverse reaction increases. Within moments, the color stabilizes again, but to a different color.

NOTES:

Answers to Stop and Think—Part I, SE page 144

1. The flat portions represent nonchanging concentrations. This means the color does not appear to be changing on a macroscopic level. But at the microscopic level, collisions occur all the time. But not enough successful collisions occur to change the color.
2. The curved sections of the graph mean that concentrations are changing during a time period. Steep curves mean large amounts of change, and shallow slopes mean small amounts of change.

In Step 6, ask students to read *Switch-A-Roo II*. Encourage them to use a literacy strategy during the reading process to enhance their learning.

b. Use colored pencils to chart the changes in concentration of the chromate and dichromate ions you observed in Steps 1a–f.

You do not need exact concentrations. Remember, flat lines mean no change in concentration. Curving or sloping lines mean the concentration is changing at that moment.

c. Write highlight comments for each section (beginning, middle, and end), and then write an overall caption.

d. Participate in a class discussion about this graph and make changes to your graph as needed.

Interact with the animation titled *Equilibrium* on your *SRCD* to see how reversible reactions affect concentrations of reactants and products.

Stop & THINK

PART I

Answer these questions in your science notebook. Compare your answers with those of a classmate before continuing.

1. What do the flat portions of the graph indicate about what is going on macroscopically? What is going on microscopically?
2. What do the curved or sloped portions of the graph indicate about what is going on macroscopically? What is going on microscopically?

6. Read *Switch-A-Roo II* to find out what your graph tells you about reversible reactions.

READING

Switch-A-Roo II

There is a high concentration of reactants and almost no products at the beginning of a chemical reaction. The forward reaction rate is high, and the reverse reaction rate is low. The concentration of both the reactants and the products changes; thus, the rates change. Eventually, the rate of the forward reaction equals the rate of the reverse reaction. The system is said to be at **equilibrium**. A reversible chemical reaction is in chemical equilibrium when the rate of its

144 Unit 1 Interactions Are Interesting

NOTES:

forward reaction equals the rate of its reverse reaction. A graph showing the rates of forward and reverse reactions at equilibrium would have two horizontal lines. These flat lines would not have to be at the same rate. They would have to indicate nonchanging reaction rates for the forward and reverse reactions.

It may appear that a chemical reaction has stopped when it reaches equilibrium. That's because the concentrations of the reactants and products are not changing. However, this is not the case. On the molecular level, particles are still moving, colliding, and interacting. The equilibrium of chemical reactions is a *dynamic* system. What does that mean? Consider two island cities connected by a bridge. Cars move continuously from one city to the other. At equilibrium, the rate of the cars going in one direction equals the rate of the cars going in the opposite direction. Cars are not stopped (static) but are constantly in motion (dynamic). The cars are also moving both ways at the same time. The number of cars in each city is not changing because the cars leaving each city are equal to the cars entering each city.

Does chemical equilibrium imply anything about the concentrations of the reactants and the products? The answer is yes ... and no. By definition, a chemical reaction reaches equilibrium when the rates of the forward and the reverse reactions are equal. At this point, the concentrations of the reactants and the products are constant. But this does not mean that the concentrations of the reactants and the products are equal, just that there is no *net* change in the concentrations. Think about the analogy of the two cities. The number of cars in each city is not changing, but that does not necessarily mean the number of cars in each city is the same.

Let's summarize conditions of chemical equilibrium:

- The reaction is reversible.
- The forward reaction moves at the same rate as the reverse reaction.
- The forward and reverse reactions happen at the same time.

Here's a specific example in the form of a gas phase chemical reaction

$$H_2O_{(g)} + CO_{(g)} \rightleftarrows H_{2(g)} + CO_{2(g)}$$

What happens when the same concentrations of $H_2O_{(g)}$ and $CO_{(g)}$ are mixed? Notice that the concentrations of the reactants and products change over time and eventually become constant, as shown in figure 3.13.

Since the mole ratio of the reactants is 1:1, the concentrations of both reactants change the same way. The same reasoning is true for the products. Rarely do chemical reactions reach equilibrium and the concentrations of the reactants and products become equal. It is more likely that the forward or the reverse reaction is favored. In a reaction in which the

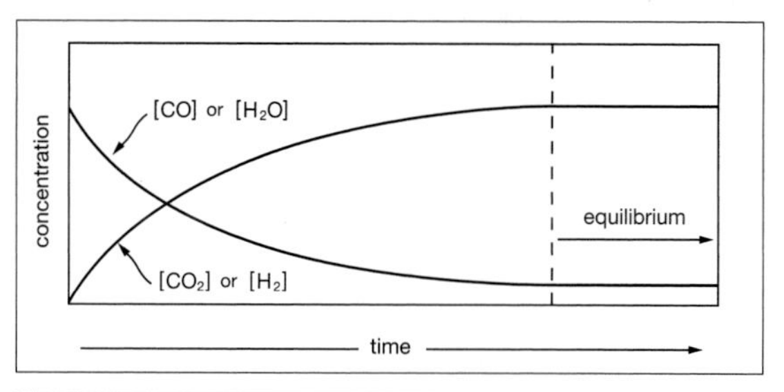

▲ **Figure 3.13 Concentration graph.** The concentrations of both the reactants and the products in this reaction eventually become constant. But are the concentrations equal? What does this say about the equilibrium position of this reaction?

Answers to Stop and Think—Part I continued, SE page 146

3. Students should infer that this would indicate a reaction in which the reverse reaction is favored. This would indicate that the equilibrium position lies to the left. It also would indicate that at equilibrium, the concentration of the reactants is higher than the concentration of the products.
4. At the beginning of the reaction, the concentration of the reactants is high and the concentration of the products is low. As the reaction progresses, the reactants are used up to produce the products and the rate of the forward reaction slows down. As the products are formed, they begin to react to re-form the reactants and the rate of this reverse reaction speeds up.
5. Because the equilibrium position of this reaction is to the left and the reverse reaction is favored, the concentration of the reactants will be higher at equilibrium than the concentration of the products.

In Step 7, work with students so they can generate their own version of *Le Châtelier's Principle*. Emphasize that the exact wording need not read like a textbook. Instead, encourage students to look for the "gist." The gist is that reactions at equilibrium shift or adjust when one of the substances in the equation is added to the system or a substance is removed. The way the reaction shifts is to get rid of the substance that was added or add what was removed. Students will get a chance to test their general rule in Part II.

In Step 8, students read *Stressed Out I*. Consider reviewing the focus question with them before reading. The question serves the function of prereading.

NOTES:

Switch-A-Roo II, continued

forward reaction is favored, the concentration of the products is higher at equilibrium than the concentration of the reactants.

Consider when the reverse reaction is favored. At equilibrium, there will be a higher concentration of reactants than products. Chemists identify these reactions with an **equilibrium position**. If the equilibrium position lies far to the right, it means the forward reaction is favored. What would it mean if the equilibrium position were to the left? The reverse reaction is favored and the reactants (on the left) would be in higher concentration than the products at equilibrium.

Topic: chemical equilibrium
Go to: www.scilinks.org
Code: 2Inquiry146

Stop & THINK

PART I continued

3. Sometimes you may see a chemical equation written this way:

$$A + B \underset{\longleftarrow}{\overset{\longrightarrow}{}} C + D$$

Use your understanding of equilibrium position to explain why the equation is written this way.

4. Describe and explain how the concentrations of each of the reactants and products will change as the system *approaches* equilibrium for this reaction.
5. Describe and explain the concentrations of each reactant and product *at* equilibrium using the equation in Question 3.

7. Develop a general rule for predicting which side of an equilibrium expression is favored when you change concentrations.

Look at the animation *Le Châtelier's Principle* on the *SRCD* to help you understand the general principle.

8. Read *Stressed Out I* and compare your prediction rule with the one from the reading. Do systems at equilibrium stay at equilibrium? Use this as a focus question as you read *Stressed Out I.*

NOTES:

READING

Stressed Out I

You know how to recognize a chemical reaction at equilibrium. Now consider whether all reactions remain at equilibrium. Reactions will stay at equilibrium as long as conditions are constant. Changes to the system may disrupt the equilibrium. Look at an example of a system at equilibrium.

$$N_{2(g)} + 3H_{2(g)} \rightleftarrows 2NH_{3(g)}$$

This is a very important chemical reaction in the agricultural industry. It represents the production of ammonia (NH_3), which is used in large quantities as fertilizer. If you could observe a closed container at room temperature of sufficient concentrations of N_2 and H_2, you would observe no changes. If you could take a sample of gas in the system, you would see that there is no apparent change in the concentrations over time. Why? The reaction is either at equilibrium or the reaction rates are so slow that no changes can be detected. If this system is at equilibrium, then chemists must change the system to drive the reaction to the right. This change produces more NH_3. When we change conditions for a system at equilibrium, it places a stress on the system and upsets the equilibrium. The reaction will shift right to produce more products or shift left to produce more reactants, depending on the stress. The direction that the reaction will shift depends on the stress.

Look at a generic equation for a system at equilibrium

$$A + B \rightleftarrows C + D$$

One condition that can be changed easily is adding or removing either a reactant or a product. If the reaction is at equilibrium, and you increase the concentration of A, this is considered a stress on the system. The system will shift in one direction or the other to relieve the stress. This is known as **Le Châtelier's principle**. If more A is added to the reaction, which way, left or right, will use up this extra A? The forward reaction (shifting to the right) will consume A, so the reaction shifts to the right. Eventually, the system will reach equilibrium again. What if you added some of the product D? Which way would the reaction shift to relieve the stress? The reverse direction or to the left uses D, so the reaction will shift to the left.

What if C were *removed* from the system? You will use the chart in figure 3.14 to look at this situation more closely. The stress was the removal of C as indicated by the down arrow. Since it is the stress, you will put it in parentheses.

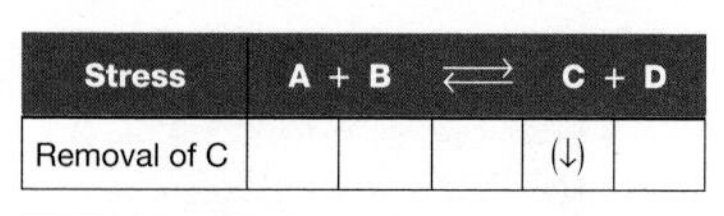

Stress	A	+ B	⇄	C	+ D
Removal of C				(↓)	

▲ **Figure 3.14 Stress chart.** Use this chart to organize your thinking. The stress is indicated in parentheses.

Now decide which direction the reaction will shift to relieve the stress. According to Le Châtelier's principle, the system will shift in a direction to relieve the stress. The stress is too little C since it was removed. To relieve the stress, the system will shift in a direction to make more C. Which direction will it shift? The reaction will shift to the right to relieve the stress and reestablish equilibrium. Place a right

Chapter 3 Collisions—Atomic Style 147

NOTES:

Stress	AB	+ CD	⇄	AD	+ CB
Adding more CD	↓	(↑)	⟶	↑	↑
Removing AB	(↓)	↑	⟵	↓	↓
Increasing AD	↑	↑	⟵	(↑)	↓

▲ **Figure T3.9 Answer table for Questions 6a–b.** Your students will complete a chart similar to this.

Answers to Stop and Think—Part I continued, SE pages 148–149

6a–b. See figure T3.9.

7. Increasing the concentration of AD applies a stress on the system. According to Le Châtelier's principle, a system will shift in a direction to relieve the stress and reestablish equilibrium. Since the stress added extra AD, the system will shift in a direction to consume this extra AD, which is to the left. Shifting to the left consumes the products to produce more of the reactants. Therefore, the concentration of CB will decrease and the concentrations of AB and CD will increase.

Stressed Out I, continued

arrow in the table to indicate the direction of the shift (figure 3.15).

What happens to the concentrations of all the other reactants and products when a shift occurs? The concentrations change. Shifting to the right causes the reactants, A and B, to be consumed and produce the products, C and D. Therefore, the concentrations of the reactants will decrease and the concentrations of the products will increase. Now add arrows to the chart to indicate the change in concentrations of all the other reactants and products (figure 3.16).

The stress on the system was the removal of C, and even though the system shifts in a direction to make more C, equilibrium will be reestablished before the original concentration of C is reached. Therefore, the concentration of C is still lower at the new equilibrium.

Topic: Le Châtelier's Principle
Go to: www.scilinks.org
Code: 2Inquiry148

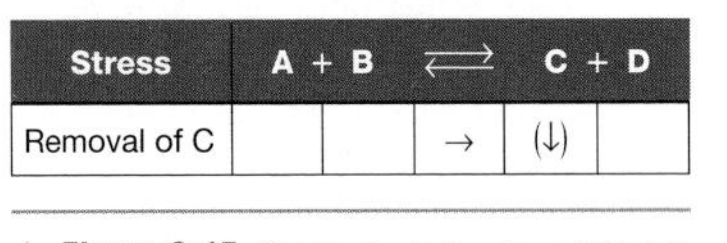

Stress	A	+ B	⇄	C	+ D
Removal of C			→	(↓)	

▲ **Figure 3.15 Stress chart showing shift.** Add an arrow to indicate the direction that the reaction will shift according to Le Châtelier's principle.

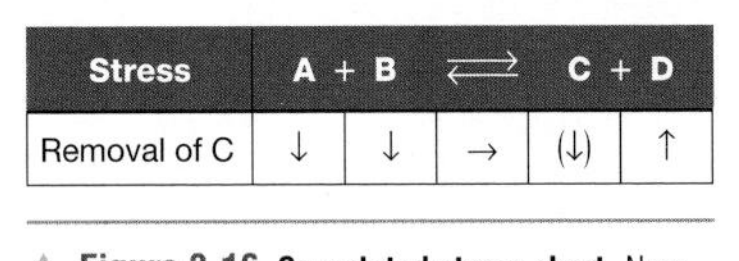

Stress	A	+ B	⇄	C	+ D
Removal of C	↓	↓	→	(↓)	↑

▲ **Figure 3.16 Completed stress chart.** Now add up or down arrows to indicate if the reactant or product will increase or decrease in concentration.

Stop & THINK

PART I continued

6 Consider this reaction and answer Questions 6a–b.

$$AB + CD \rightleftharpoons AD + CB$$

a. Set up a chart similar to figure 3.16 using the equation above.

b. Complete the table by using arrows to represent the stress, the direction of the shift, and the changes of concentrations of all reactants and products. Use the following stresses:

- Adding more CD
- Removing AB
- Increasing the concentration of AD

148 | Unit 1 Interactions Are Interesting

Process and Procedure

Part II: Temperature Shifts

Materials

For each team of 4 students

4 pairs of safety goggles
4 laboratory aprons
1 sealed plastic pipet with cobalt chloride solution ($CoCl_2 \cdot 6H_2O$)
1 ice bath
hot water
colored pencils or markers

Cautions

Wear safety goggles and an apron at all times. Pipets are sealed but should one leak, do not allow any solution to touch your skin. If any solution touches a student's skin, wash the affected area with large amounts of water. Do not put your hand in hot water.

The key to student success in Part II is their ability to transfer what they learned in Part I to the design of an investigation in Part II. Students should understand that solutions at equilibrium can be made to shift. In Part II, they will use changes in temperature instead of changes in concentration to affect shifts in equilibrium.

In Step 1, encourage students to think of heat as either a reactant or product. In this way, adding heat might be like adding acid in the investigation in Part I. From this start, they can predict a shift in the equilibrium position of the cobalt-cobalt chloride equilibrium. Remind students that predictions do not have to be correct, but they do need to be testable, based on logic, and supported by evidence. Consider asking a few teams to share their predictions.

7 Using the last stress described in Question 6b (increasing the concentration of AD), describe in words what happens to the system. Include in your description all the changes in direction and concentration. Use Le Châtelier's principle to support your answer.

Part II: Temperature Shifts

Materials

For each team of 4 students

4 pairs of safety goggles	1 ice bath
4 pairs laboratory gloves	hot water
4 laboratory aprons	colored pencils or markers
1 sealed plastic pipet with cobalt chloride solution	

Cautions

Wear safety goggles and an apron at all times. Pipets are sealed but should one leak, do not allow any solution to touch your skin. If any solution touches your skin, wash the affected area with large amounts of cool water and tell your teacher. Do not use hot water.

In Part I, you applied what you know about particles colliding and concentration to understand chemical systems at equilibrium. You know how to make equilibrium reactions shift in predictable ways. In Part II, you will apply what you know about Le Châtelier's principle and heat to predict shifts in an equilibrium system due to changes in temperature.

Process and Procedure

1. Study the following cobalt chloride equilibrium reaction and predict what will happen when you place the sealed pipet in very hot water and in ice water.

Use the stress chart technique you learned in Part I and your knowledge of enthalpy diagrams.

$$50\text{kJ} + \underset{\text{pink}}{Co(H_2O)_6^{2+}{}_{(aq)}} + 4Cl^-_{(aq)} \rightleftharpoons \underset{\text{blue}}{CoCl_4^{2-}{}_{(aq)}} + 6H_2O_{(l)}$$

NOTES:

In Step 2, walk around the room and offer students advice on their design. Encourage them to reflect on their experiences from Part I. The procedure they create should be close to the following:

i. Keep 1 pipet at room temperature for a control.
ii. Place a pipet into ice water and observe.
iii. Place the same pipet into boiling water and observe.

In Step 4, monitor what teams generate for their graphs. Consider a short class debriefing on the graphs if you think students need it. An example answer is shown in figure T3.10.

In Step 5, the general rule students generate should be very similar to the one they developed in Part I. It might say to treat temperature as though it were a product or reactant. If the reaction is endothermic (heat as a reactant), then increasing the temperature shifts the equilibrium to the right. If the reaction is exothermic (heat as a product), then increasing the temperature shifts the equilibrium to the left.

In Step 6, ask students to use a compare-and-contrast strategy to compare their generalized rule with the rule described in the reading.

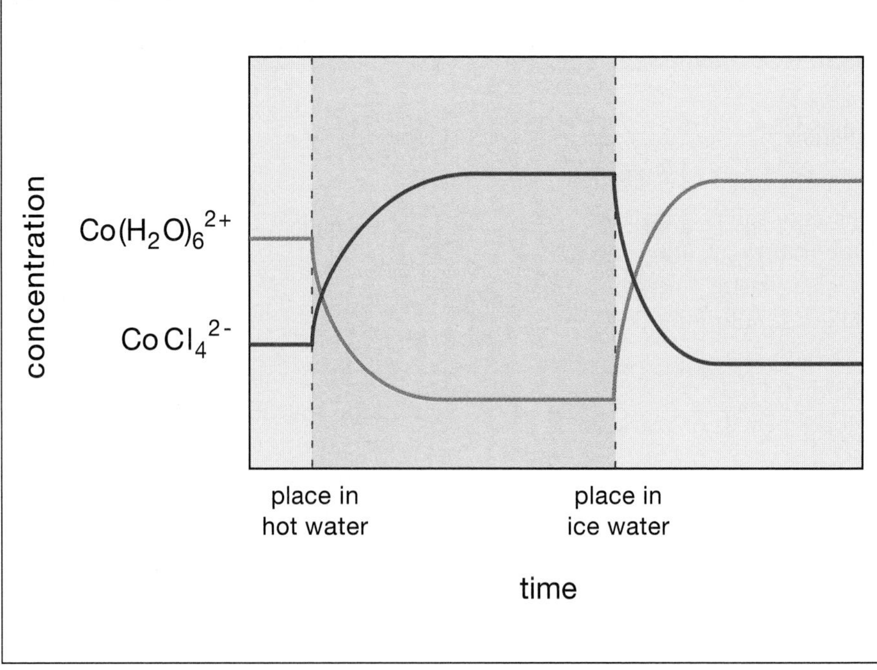

▲ **Figure T3.10 Concentration changes due to temperature changes.** This qualitative graph represents an answer to Step 4.

2. As a team, design an investigation to test your prediction by writing a step-by-step procedure in your science notebook.
3. Gain your teacher's approval of your design, then conduct your investigation.
4. Make a sketch graph like the one from Part I, Step 5 of all the changes you observed by conducting your investigation.
5. Apply what you know about Le Châtelier's principle to write a general rule about equilibrium shifts due to changes in temperature. Write your rule in your science notebook.
6. Compare your rule with what you learn from reading *Stressed Out II* and modify your rule as appropriate.

READING

Stressed Out II

Chemists use Le Châtelier's principle regularly to get the products they want from a chemical reaction. If the desired product is on the right of the chemical reaction, chemists will introduce stresses to shift the reaction to the right to produce more of this product. Is changing the concentration the only way to stress a system? No, changing the temperature will stress the system as well.

Recall that an exothermic reaction releases heat from the reaction. Remember that these reactions feel hot because of the release of heat. This release of heat can be thought of as a product of the chemical reaction. On which side of the reaction should you include the heat if the reaction is an exothermic reaction? It will be included on the right side of the chemical equation with the products.

Since you have been using generic chemical equations, you will continue and just add the word "heat" to the appropriate side of the reaction. In a true chemical reaction, the number of kilojoules would be written in the equation.

$$A + B \rightleftharpoons C + D + \text{heat}$$
exothermic reaction

If the reaction is endothermic, then heat is absorbed in the reaction and the heat is written on the left as part of the reactants

$$A + B + \text{heat} \rightleftharpoons C + D$$
endothermic reaction

Consider the reaction

$$A + B + \text{heat} \rightleftharpoons C + D,$$

an endothermic reaction. How could chemists increase or decrease the temperature of the system to shift the reaction to the right? When you try to answer this question, consider heat as a reactant just as it is written. Then solving the problem is no different than you have learned before. Put this reaction in a table as you did before to organize your thoughts (figure 3.17).

Think about what happens when the temperature decreases. In what direction would the reaction shift? (Remember to think of heat as a reactant.) The reaction would shift in a direction to relieve the stress and attempt to raise the temperature (increase heat). This would shift the reaction to the left. That is not what you want in this case. Instead, if you want to shift the reaction to the right, then you must

Answers to Reflect and Connect, SE pages 151–152

1. First, the reaction must be reversible and the forward and reverse reaction rates are equal. Finally, the forward and reverse reactions will occur simultaneously.
2. Le Châtelier's principle states that when a stress is applied to a system in chemical equilibrium, the system will shift in a direction to relieve the stress and reestablish equilibrium. Students' examples of a stress will vary. Make sure the student explains the direction of the shift and its effect on the concentrations and temperature of the reaction.

3a. This is an example of a system at equilibrium. Suppose the coach wants to substitute 3 players. Three players will go into the game at the same time as 3 players come out of the game.

3b. This is not an example of a system at equilibrium. Students are all entering the school and few if any students are leaving the school.

3c. This is an example of a system at equilibrium. The current is flowing in one direction at the same rate as the person is rowing in the opposite direction.

3d. Students might have to do a little research if they are not familiar with this aquifer. A quick search will tell them that the water level in this aquifer is decreasing. Therefore, this system is not at equilibrium; the water is being

Answers to Reflect and Connect are on TE pages 151–152.

increase the temperature. The reaction will shift in a direction to get rid of this extra heat. That direction is to the right. The completed chart would look like figure 3.18.

Stress	A	+ B	+ heat	⇄	C	+ D
?				→		

▲ **Figure 3.17 Stress chart that includes heat.** This chart includes heat in the equation. Is this simulated reaction an exothermic or an endothermic chemical reaction?

Stress	A	+ B	+ heat	⇄	C	+ D
Increased temperature	↓	↓	(↑)	→	↑	↑

▲ **Figure 3.18 Completed stress chart with heat.** When heat is added to this simulated chemical reaction at equilibrium, the reaction shifts to the right. This decreases the concentration of the reactants and increases the concentration of the products.

Reflect and Connect

Answer each question in your science notebook. Revise your answers after you check them.

1. List all the conditions of a chemical system at equilibrium.
2. Explain Le Châtelier's principle and give an example of a stress and its effect on a chemical system.
3. Consider the following situations. Do they represent a system at equilibrium? Write a sentence for each situation and indicate if it is at equilibrium and how you know.
   a. A coach substituting players in a basketball game
   b. Your school during the beginning of the day when everyone is arriving
   c. A person rowing a boat upstream at the same rate as the current
   d. Irrigation water pumped from the Ogallala Aquifer (an underground water supply)

NOTES:

pumped out faster than the aquifer can be recharged.

4a. The reverse reaction has a higher E_a, or activation energy.

4b. Student diagrams should look like figure T3.11.

4c. The reaction rate for the forward reaction would be faster since the activation energy is lower. More reacting particles would have the necessary energy to collide and react.

5. Answers will vary. Accept all reasonable answers. Some of the scenarios described include
   - disruption of the water cycle or other cycles in nature,
   - failing health if bodily functions or cellular functions could not reach equilibrium, and
   - inability to recharge certain types of batteries.

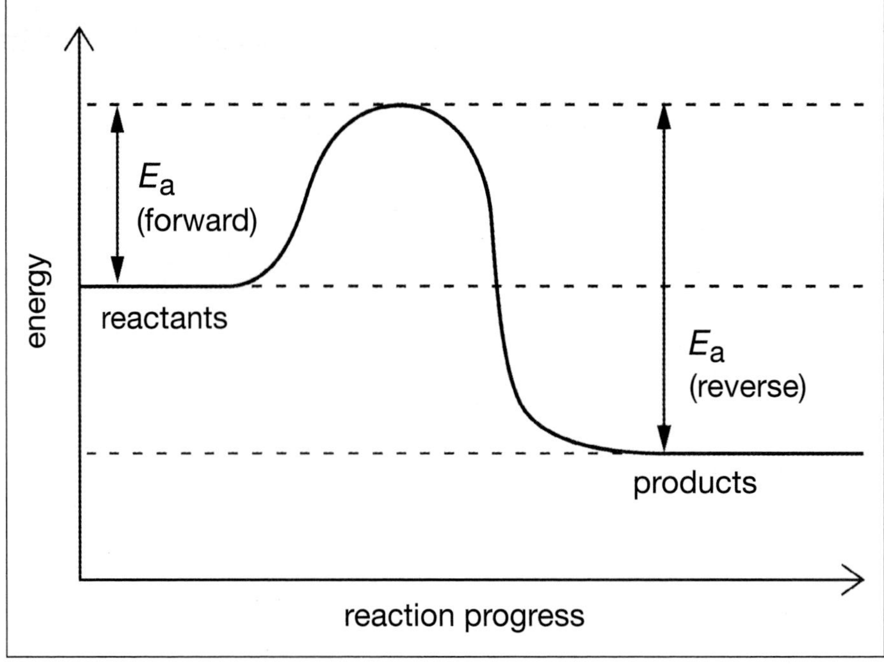

Figure T3.11 Energy plot for Question 4b. Your students should sketch a graph similar to this. Make sure all parts are labeled correctly.

> 4. Consider the enthalpy plot of an exothermic reaction.
>   a. Does the forward or the reverse reaction have a higher activation energy?
>   b. Draw an energy plot of this reaction in your science notebook and label the activation energies for both the forward and reverse reactions ($E_{a(forward)}$ and $E_{a(reverse)}$).
>   c. Which reaction, forward or reverse, would you expect to have a faster reaction rate if concentration and temperature of the reactants were the same? Explain your answer.
> 5. What if chemical reactions did not behave as we know they do? What if they were not reversible? What if they never reached equilibrium? Consider this scenario and write a paragraph that describes how the world would be if chemical processes were not reversible.
>
> EVALUATE
>
> **Reaction Rate Readiness**
>
> Thus far in unit 1, *Interactions Are Interesting*, you have learned a lot about the interactions that occur when collisions take place. In chapter 2, you studied these interactions on a macroscopic scale, and in this chapter you journeyed into the molecular world of chemistry. You saw that there is no fundamental difference in the behavior of large objects such as tennis balls and very small particles in chemical reactions.
>
> In *Reaction Rate Readiness*, you will have the opportunity to demonstrate your understanding of the ideas of moving particles and what factors influence the way that these particles interact. In Part I, you and a partner will begin by organizing your knowledge in a way that will help you review what you have learned. Then in Part II, you will express your understanding individually on a constructed-response test. Your teacher will give you feedback on this part of the activity. In science, it is important that we learn from our mistakes and be able to correct them. You have the opportunity to do this in Part III when you will revise your answers based on your teacher's feedback.
>
> **Part I: Map It!**
>
> **Materials**
>
> **For each team of 3 or 4 students**
>
> note cards
>
> markers
>
> butcher paper
>
> 1 *Reaction Rate Readiness Scoring Rubric* handout
>
> 152 Unit 1 Interactions Are Interesting

EVALUATE

Reaction Rate Readiness

Activity Overview

This evaluate activity is in three parts. In Part I, students will participate in an organized review of the material in this chapter. Students will work with classmates to identify and describe important concepts in the chapter and then construct a graphic organizer. In the process, they will make study cards so that they can continue their preparation at home. This helps students reconfigure their knowledge, which leads to a deeper understanding of the concepts.

In Part II, each student will complete a constructed-response test. In Part III of this activity, students will use the *Learn from Mistakes (LFM) Protocol* to analyze and correct their mistakes on the test. In doing this correctly, students will receive additional credit on their tests.

Before You Teach

Background Information

Background information for this activity is included in previous activities.

Materials—Part I

For each team of 3 or 4 students

note cards
markers
butcher paper
1 copy of copymaster 3.1, *Scoring Rubric for Reaction Rate Readiness*

Materials—Part II

For each student

1 copy of copymaster 3.2a, *Chemical Reaction Rates and Equilibrium*

Materials—Part III

For each student

the scored copy of their test (copymaster 3.2a, *Chemical Reaction Rates and Equilibrium*)
their copy of copymaster 3.1, *Scoring Rubric for Reaction Rate Readiness*

Advance Preparation

For Part I, make enough copies of copymaster 3.1, *Scoring Rubric for Reaction Rate Readiness* for each student. For Part II, make copies of copymaster 3.2a, *Chemical Reaction Rates and Equilibrium* for each student. For Part III, students will need their copies of the scoring rubric and the scored copy of their test. Plan to have these scored by the next class period.

Process and Procedure

1. Organize your learning from this chapter.

Meet with your team and carefully review the rubric for this activity with your partners. Use it to guide your work.

2. Develop a list of words or short phrases that describe the main ideas of the chapter. For example, you should definitely list "chemical reactions" as one of your ideas.
3. Share your team's list with another team. Add any new ideas you hear to your list and omit any ideas you discover that might be included within another concept.
4. List each of these words or phrases on separate note cards. Everyone on your team should have a set.
5. Work with your team to develop summary notes about each topic. These notes can be in the form of a bulleted list of things you think are important to each topic, sentences describing each topic, or diagrams or sketches with labels. Use your book and your science notebook to develop your notes. Put these summary notes on the back of the note cards to make study cards.
6. Use your study cards (topic side up) to construct a concept map on a large piece of butcher paper. Use markers to draw lines between concepts that are connected in some way. Take turns with your teammates and explain the connections and the importance of each word you have on your study cards. Write the connections on your map. Question each other to make sure you understand the material. Be prepared to discuss your concept map with your teacher and with other classmates.
7. As a team, talk through your concept map with your teacher. Listen for anything that you may have forgotten or misunderstood. Make additions or deletions to your map or your study cards based on feedback from your teacher.
8. Take your study cards home and use them to prepare for Part II.

Part II: Test It!

Materials

For each student

1 *Chemical Reaction Rates and Equilibrium* handout

Educational Technologies

Students might need scientific calculators for the test and for Part III.

As You Teach

Outcomes and Indicators of Success

By the end of this activity, students should

1. demonstrate their understanding of the law of conservation of matter and the law of conservation of energy.

   They will demonstrate their understanding by

   - relating the law of conservation of matter to a balanced chemical equation and
   - relating the law of conservation of energy to the change of energy in a chemical reaction.

2. demonstrate their understanding of the role of energy in a chemical reaction.

   They will demonstrate their understanding by

   - describing the change in energy from reactants to products;
   - identifying a reaction as either endothermic or exothermic using a reaction plot, bond energies, and the ΔH of the reaction;
   - determining from a plot the activation energy needed for the reaction to take place; and
   - describing temperature as a measure of the average kinetic energy of the particles in the solution and relating this to reaction rate.

3. demonstrate their understanding of the role of concentration in a chemical reaction.

   They will demonstrate their understanding by

   - highlighting illustrations depicting various concentrations of reactants and
   - relating concentration and collisions in a discussion of the reaction rate.

4. demonstrate their understanding of systems at equilibrium.

   They will demonstrate their understanding by

   - describing what equilibrium position means in a chemical reaction and
   - using Le Châtelier's principle to describe the changes in the system at equilibrium using cause and effect.

5. demonstrate their ability to connect previous learning in the macroscopic world to current learning in the microscopic world.

   They will demonstrate their ability by comparing and contrasting collisions on a macroscopic scale (as in car collisions) to collisions on a microscopic scale (as in chemical reactions).

Strategies

Getting Started

Help students understand that there are many effective techniques for preparing for a test. Generating and discussing concept maps is one such method that they will learn and employ in this chapter.

Process and Procedure

Part I: Map It!

Materials

For each team of 3 or 4 students

note cards

markers

butcher paper

1 copy of copymaster 3.1, *Scoring Rubric for Reaction Rate Readiness*

In Steps 1–2, students meet with a team to review their rubrics and begin to organize their learning. They develop a list of words or short phrases that describe the main ideas of the chapter. Encourage students to refine the list so that it does not get too long. Part of what they should learn is to discern the concepts from trivial vocabulary words. In Step 3, they then meet with another group to refine their lists.

Students prepare study cards in Steps 4–5. To do this, they write the concept or main idea on one side of the card and then list important information on the other side of the card. They can use sketches, graphs, bulleted lists, descriptions, and so forth on their cards. Then in Step 6, students construct a concept map using the topic side of their cards. They work with their teams to explain the connections and importance of each word or phrase that they have used in the map.

In Step 7, the students are instructed to talk through their maps with you. Have the remaining teams practice with another team if they are waiting for you to come to their table. Listen as the students explain their maps. Check for misunderstandings and give suggestions for corrections to their maps. Make sure everyone in the team is participating in the discussion. Encourage students to take the cards home to study for the test.

Process and Procedure

Part II: Test It!

Materials

For each student

1 copy of copymaster 3.2a, *Chemical Reaction Rates and Equilibrium*

Distribute the copy of the test (copymaster 3.2a, *Chemical Reaction Rates and Equilibrium*) and allow students to work individually for the class period to complete the test. Plan to have these tests graded by the next day so that the students will have immediate feedback.

Process and Procedure

1. Obtain a copy of the test and work individually to compose your best answer to the questions. Be sure to answer each question completely and to your best ability.
2. You have 1 class period to answer the questions, so plan your time accordingly.

Part III: Revise It!

Materials

For each student

1 *Reaction Rate Readiness Scoring Rubric* handout

the scored copy of your test

1 sheet of paper

access to stapler

Process and Procedure

1. Look over your scored test. Circle the number of each question for which you did not receive full credit. Working with these questions is the objective for this part of the evaluate activity.
2. Your teacher will provide feedback as a discussion of the concepts that are important to each question. Participate in a class discussion of how to demonstrate that you have learned from your mistakes.
3. Follow the procedures outlined in the *Learn from Mistakes Protocol*. Put all your work on a separate sheet of paper. If you have questions or do not understand how to use the protocol, ask your teacher.
4. When you are finished using the protocol for each question, staple your work to your original test and hand it in to your teacher.

Protocol

Process and Procedure

Part III: Revise It!

Materials

For each student

the scored copy of their test (copymaster 3.2a, *Chemical Reaction Rates and Equilibrium*)

their copy of copymaster 3.1, *Scoring Rubric for Reaction Rate Readiness*

In Step 1, students circle the number to each question for which they did not receive full credit. You must indicate this when you score the tests. In Step 3, students will begin the process of using the *LFM Protocol*. Take some time here to go over the protocol and emphasize your expectations. Give examples of right and wrong ways to correct answers.

In Step 2, you will spend some class time going over each question in the test before students begin the *LFM Protocol*. Avoid simply telling students the answers. Rather, focus your discussion on the essential concepts associated with each question. Refer students to specific sections of the student book or to specific activities to help them find correct answers.

Give the students numerical examples of how successful completion of the *LFM Protocol* will raise their grade. This is often motivation to do better. For example, if a student scored a mere 60 percent on the original test, he or she could earn up to one-half of 40 percent (20 percent) to add to the original score if he or she completes a high-quality *LFM Protocol*.

Students will turn in their work as they finish. Remind them to staple all their work together, including the original test, as they hand in their work. As you score their *LFM Protocols*, focus on Step 2 of the protocol. Students often have difficulty identifying what is incorrect about an answer. When you help them articulate what's wrong, you gradually empower them to become independent learners.

Consider using this protocol each time you give a constructed-response or multiple-choice test. It can greatly enhance your students' learning and give you valuable feedback on their understandings or misunderstandings. Applying this protocol allows you to use these more traditional assessments and still have an assessment technique that is based on inquiry and standards-based reform.

Protocol

Learn from Mistakes (LFM) Protocol

School is not just a place to deposit right answers. Sometimes you make mistakes. In fact, most people make mistakes when they try to learn something, especially when the subject is difficult or new. When you learn to identify and explain what is incorrect about a wrong answer, you have a better chance of avoiding that mistake again.

For each of the questions that you missed or did not receive full credit, perform the following steps. By doing so, you can earn up to 50 percent of the difference between your raw percent score and 100 percent. Before you begin, write your raw percent score at the top of the page along with a list of the numbers of the questions you missed.

1. Represent the original question in a different way than it was represented on the test. For example, if the question was mostly words, represent it as a sketch. If it was mostly a sketch, represent it in words. When you use words, paraphrase the question in your own words. Do not copy the question word for word. Label a sketch with all variables, especially the unknown. If the problem mentions any change in condition, show before-and-after sketches.
2. Identify and explain the mistake you made in the answer you selected. Focus on explaining any conceptual misunderstandings. When you explain what is incorrect, show how the misconception would lead to a contradiction with what you see in nature. Explanations such as "I read the problem wrong" and "I pushed the wrong button on the calculator" will receive no credit.
3. Show the correct solution or answer. When necessary, show all governing equations—first in symbol form, then with number and unit values. Place proper units and labels on your answers. Include an explanation of why the answer is reasonable.

Chapter 3 Collisions—Atomic Style | 155

CHAPTER 4

Physics Is Moving

Chapter Overview

Chapter 4, *Physics Is Moving*, is about motion. This chapter continues the pattern established in this unit of changing the teaching emphasis from the macroscopic scale to the microscopic and back again. For example, unit 1, *Interactions Are Interesting*, began with a large-scale look at forces, with a special focus on the macroscopic evidence always present when a net force is applied to an object. That evidence is a change in velocity, and thus a change in momentum. Chapter 3, *Collisions—Atomic Style*, asked students to shift to a small-scale focus on atoms and molecules interacting. Students applied what they learned about forces to colliding atomic-sized particles, which helped them learn about reaction kinetics and heats of reaction. In chapter 4, the focus is again on large-scale interactions, but this time on what net forces do—they produce various motions. Thus, chapter 2, *Collision Course*, is about cause (force) and chapter 4 is about effect (motion). Together, they form an important, logical, evidence-based connection between what students see and what it means to them.

Chapter 4 asks students to apply what they know about force to several motions they experience almost daily. Thus, students link forces involved in Newton's third law and Newton's second law to free fall, spring motion, pendulum motion, uniform circular motion, and projectile motion. The overarching goal of which is to understand how net force is involved in each motion. Students have very little new information to learn in this chapter. Rather, the primary intellectual effort is to broaden the context of what they already know about force to include its effect on motion and the ways to represent that motion graphically. For example, the engage activity, *Going through the Motions*, asks students to use their prior knowledge of the net force on objects in free fall to investigate *why* all objects fall with the same acceleration near Earth's surface. Students analyze motion graphs and construct graphs of common motions, which allows you to check their current understanding of graphs and the motions the graphs represent.

In the explore activity, *Acceleration Indication*, students gather direct experiences with accelerated motion and begin establishing patterns of motion. Students see that some motions are the result of constant forces and accelerations and some are the result of changing forces and accelerations. There are two explain activities; each addresses one of these two scenarios. The first explain activity, *Constantly Accelerating*, asks students to use graphs and mathematics to begin quantitative descriptions of the motions produced by constant forces and acceleration (i.e., free fall, projectile motion, and circular motion). The second explain, *Back and Forth, Up and Down*, asks students to transfer their ability for describing motion quantitatively to the simple harmonic motion of springs and pendulums. Students apply what they have learned about motions to satellites in orbit during the elaborate activity, *Sky High Motion*. Finally, *Moving toward Understanding*, the evaluate activity, tests students' understanding of motion with a structured review followed by a conceptually based multiple-choice test and the *Learn from Mistakes (LFM) Protocol*.

Goals for the Chapter

There are three broad learning goals for chapter 4:

- Students should learn how the mathematical relationship between force, mass, and acceleration explains motion or lack of motion.
- Students should learn why vertical and horizontal motions are independent of each other.
- Students should learn the similarities and differences among simple harmonic motion, uniform circular motion, projectile motion, and pendulum motion.

Look at the chapter organizer each day to remind yourself of where students are in the overall sequence of events in the chapter.

Chapter 4 Organizer

PHYSICS IS MOVING

Major Concepts

- **All motion graphs for an object describe the same motion, but from different perspectives.**
- **F_{net} and acceleration are constant in some motions and change for others.**
- **F_{net} and acceleration are not always in the same direction as the velocity or displacement.**
- **$F_{net} = ma$**

ENGAGE — Going Through the Motions ★★

Key Ideas:
- Motion can be represented on graphs.
- All objects fall with the same acceleration near Earth's surface.

Activity: In Part I, students model position and velocity time graphs by walking in a straight line. In Part II students drop different shaped objects and find that they hit the ground at the same time.

LINKING QUESTION: What instrument can I use to measure acceleration?

EXPLORE — Acceleration Indication ★★

Key Idea:
- Accelerometers show the direction and relative magnitude of acceleration for many common motions.

Activity: Students construct a soda bottle accelerometer and use it to see the direction and relative magnitude of acceleration in several common motions.

LINKING QUESTION: What motions display constant acceleration?

EXPLAIN — Constantly Accelerating ★★★

Key Idea:
- Free fall and circular motion show a constant acceleration.

Activity: Students study the relationship among force, velocity, and acceleration for the motions where the net force and acceleration remain constant. These motions include a ball tossed into the air and returning to your hand, projectile motion, and uniform circular motion.

LINKING QUESTION: What kind of motion results from changing acceleration?

EXPLAIN — Back and Forth, Up and Down ★★★★

Key Idea:
- Spring and pendulum motion result from varying acceleration.

Activity: Part I helps students connect the vector nature of changing velocities to the forces that cause those changes in spring and pendulum motion. In Part II, students design a series of investigations aimed at determining the variables that influence the period of spring and pendulum motion. In Part III (optional), students translate what they know about force and time to a variety of motion graphs that represent spring and pendulum motion.

LINKING QUESTION: How are these common motions applied to satellites in orbit?

★ = One Class Period ☆ = ½ Class Period *Note:* Based on a 50-minute class period.

ELABORATE Sky High Motion ★★★

Key Idea: • Many satellites mimic circular motion.

Activity: Students use their understanding of motion to investigate one application—satellites. They research types of satellites and their orbits and prepare a report.

LINKING QUESTION: How can I find out what I know about force and motion?

EVALUATE Moving toward Understanding ★★

Key Idea: • The relationship, $F_{net} = ma$, helps explain free fall, spring, pendulum, circular, and projectile motion.

Activity: Students participate in a structured review by analyzing two different concept maps. They take a multiple choice test and then apply the LFM protocol.

★ = One Class Period ☆ = ½ Class Period *Note:* Based on a 50-minute class period.

Standards Covered by Chapter 4

PHYSICS IS MOVING

STANDARD A: Science as Inquiry. As a result of activities in grades 9–12, all students should develop

abilities necessary to do scientific inquiry

- Identify questions and concepts that guide scientific investigations. Students should formulate a testable hypothesis and demonstrate the logical connections between the scientific concepts guiding a hypothesis and the design of an experiment. They should demonstrate appropriate procedures, a knowledge base, and conceptual understanding of scientific investigations.
- Design and conduct scientific investigations. Designing and conducting a scientific investigation requires introduction to the major concepts in the area being investigated, proper equipment, safety precautions, assistance with methodological problems, recommendations for use of technologies, clarification of ideas that guide the inquiry, and scientific knowledge obtained from sources other than the actual investigation. The investigation may also require student clarification of the question, method, controls, and variables; student organization and display of data; student revision of methods and explanations; and a public presentation of the results with a critical response from peers. Regardless of the scientific investigation performed, students must use evidence, apply logic, and construct an argument for their proposed explanations.
- Use technology and mathematics to improve investigations and communications. A variety of technologies, such as hand tools, measuring instruments, and calculators, should be an integral component of scientific investigations. The use of computers for the collection, analysis, and display of data is also a part of this standard. Mathematics plays an essential role in all aspects of an inquiry. For example, measurement is used for posing questions, formulas are used for developing explanations, and charts and graphs are used for communicating results.
- Formulate and revise scientific explanations and models using logic and evidence. Student inquiries should culminate in formulating an explanation or model. Models should be physical, conceptual, and mathematical. In the process of answering the questions, the students should engage in discussions and arguments that result in the revision of their explanations. These discussions should be based on scientific knowledge, the use of logic, and evidence from their investigation.

- Recognize and analyze alternative explanations and models. This aspect of the standard emphasizes the critical abilities of analyzing an argument by reviewing current scientific understanding, weighing the evidence, and examining the logic so as to decide which explanations and models are best. In other words, although there may be several plausible explanations, they do not all have equal weight. Students should be able to use scientific criteria to find the preferred explanations.
- Communicate and defend a scientific argument. Students in school science programs should develop the abilities associated with accurate and effective communication. These include writing and following procedures, expressing concepts, reviewing information, summarizing data, using language appropriately, developing diagrams and charts, explaining statistical analysis, speaking clearly and logically, constructing a reasoned argument, and responding appropriately to critical comments.

understandings about scientific inquiry

- Scientists conduct investigations for a wide variety of reasons. For example, they may wish to discover new aspects of the natural world, explain recently observed phenomena, or test the conclusions of prior investigations or the problems of current theories.
- Scientists rely on technology to enhance the gathering and manipulation of data. New techniques and tools provide new evidence to guide inquiry and new methods to gather data, thereby contributing to the advance of science. The accuracy and precision of the data, and therefore the quality of the exploration, depends on the technology used.
- Mathematics is essential in scientific inquiry. Mathematical tools and models guide and improve the posing of questions, gathering data, constructing explanations and communicating results.
- Results of scientific inquiry—new knowledge and methods—emerge from different types of investigations and public communication among scientists. In communicating and defending the results of scientific inquiry, arguments must be logical and demonstrate connections between natural phenomena, investigations, and the historical body of scientific knowledge. In addition, the methods and procedures that scientists used to obtain evidence must be clearly reported to enhance opportunities for further investigation.

STANDARD B: Physical Science. As a result of activities in grades 9–12, all students should develop an understanding of

motions and forces

- Objects change their motion only when a net force is applied. Laws of motion are used to calculate precisely the effects of forces on the motion of objects. The magnitude of the change in motion can be calculated using the relationship $F = ma$, which is independent of the nature of the force. Whenever one object exerts force on another, a force equal in magnitude and opposite in direction is exerted on the first object.
- Gravitation is a universal force that each mass exerts on any other mass. The strength of the gravitational attractive force between two masses is proportional to the masses and inversely proportional to thee square of the distance between them.
- The electric force is a universal force that exists between any two charged objects. Opposite charges attract while like charges repel. The strength of the force is proportional to the charges, and, as with gravitation, inversely proportional to the square of the distance between them.

Prerequisite Knowledge

The prerequisite knowledge for this chapter is minimal. Some ability and comfort with manipulating simple linear equations in both variable and number form helps, but is not essential. Students will no doubt have working definitions of force, momentum, and acceleration, but rarely are these definitions adequate to explain the motions discussed in this chapter. So it is best to assume that students do not completely understand what these terms mean from a physics perspective.

Students should know how to solve simple, one-variable algebraic equations and be comfortable manipulating a variable equation to solve for any one of the variables.

Students should also know how to inspect a simple two-variable data set and generate an appropriate *xy* plot to represent the data. Students should be familiar with the equation of a line, $y = mx + b$, and slope, $slope = \frac{\Delta y}{\Delta x}$. More important is the ability to observe and connect concepts in a systematic way. Knowing how to keep careful, well-organized records of what they see in an activity and then connecting what they see to plausible explanations goes a long way to ensuring students' success in this chapter. But these skills are developed over the chapter and are not necessarily prerequisite knowledge.

Commonly Held Misconceptions

The following list identifies ideas that many students hold to be valid.

- Heavy objects fall with a greater acceleration than lighter objects near Earth's surface (even in the absence of air resistance).

This misconception stems from everyday observations of falling objects. A leaf and a cannonball reach the ground at vastly different times if dropped from the same height and at the same time. But in the absence of air resistance, the time rate of change of velocity (acceleration) for both objects is identical. This misconception is explicitly addressed in the engage activity.

- Negative velocity does not exist or only exists when the moving object is in a negative position relative to some reference point.

Many students relate negative velocity with negative (backward) time. Negative velocity most commonly refers to an object returning to a starting point of reference, but can be due to an object moving away in a negative direction. Velocity is the time rate of change of position. So whenever the change in position results in a negative number, the velocity is negative. This misconception is addressed primarily in the two explain activities and some in the explore activity.

- When a ball is tossed into the air, the ball is weightless at the top of the path.

This misconception probably results from students' difficulty separating the meanings of velocity and acceleration. Many students use these words interchangeably. This misconception is addressed primarily in the explain activity. The vertical velocity of the ball at the top of its path is zero, but the acceleration remains about 10 meters per second squared (m/sec^2) downward. This is true since the mutual gravitational attraction between Earth and the object (called weight) never ceases during the flight. From $F_{net} = ma$, if there is a net force (F_{net}), then there is an acceleration (a), assuming mass (m) is constant. And, if there is an acceleration, there is also a net force.

- A constant net force is required to make an object maintain constant velocity.

Once again, everyday experiences form the basis for this misconception. For example, a car must provide a forward force in order to maintain a certain speed. The key distinction is "net" force. An object's motion depends on the vector sum of all forces acting on an object, which is the net force. Students tend to neglect forces other than ones directly evident, like a person pushing a chair. A net force results in acceleration, not a constant velocity. The misconception about constant velocity is broached mainly in the explore and explain activities.

- The faster of two objects exhibits the greater acceleration.

Students tend to think that faster-moving objects have a greater magnitude of acceleration. This exemplifies how students often mix the definition of velocity and acceleration. The key is to link the time rate of change of velocity to acceleration, not just the velocity at any moment. The explain activity continues to address this misconception.

- The direction of motion is always the same as the direction of acceleration.

This misconception stems from linking acceleration to either the initial or final velocity rather than the change in velocity. In fact, an object can be moving forward, but experience a backward acceleration. The second explain activity addresses this misconception.

- There are leftover forces when you toss a ball in the air that keep the ball moving until those forces run out.

This misconception is often called impetus. It is linked to the idea that a force is required to produce and maintain motion. In fact, Newton's second law says that an object moving at constant velocity (not accelerating) will have no net force acting on it.

- Vertical and horizontal motions depend on each other.

Students tend to think that an object only moves in the direction of the net force. Actually, an object accelerates in the direction of the net force. If the object already exhibits motion in one direction, then Newton's second law says that the object continues unaltered unless it experiences another force. Thus, an object can experience a net downward force (as in a ball tossed in the air) and yet move forward in an arc. This idea is addressed in the first explain activity.

ENGAGE

Going through the Motions

Activity Overview

In Part I of *Going through the Motions*, students are asked to systematically analyze a position versus time graph. After they discuss the meaning of the features of the graph with their team, they model the motion by walking in a straight line. The students repeat the procedure with a velocity versus time graph. The intent is to engage students in making thoughtful analyses of motion graphs. This activity is designed to help you assess students' current understanding; students are not expected to completely understand the motion. With guided class discussion of the graphs, however, students should be able to develop their own explanations of these motions and their graphical representations by the end of the activity.

In Part II, students will develop a way to act out what their previous experiences help them predict about falling bodies. Students use a book and a sheet of paper to represent two objects of different mass. From the results of the investigations that students design, they link their prior observations to the fact that all objects fall with the same acceleration near the surface of Earth, provided that the only force acting on the object is Earth's gravitational force of attraction. They analyze the relationship $\frac{F_g}{m}$ and see that the value is constant for a given place on Earth.

Before You Teach

Background Information

Galileo Galilei (1564–1642) was among the first to challenge the long-held views about motion proposed by Greek philosopher Aristotle (384 BC–322 BC). Aristotle held that there were two types of motion, natural and unnatural. Natural motion resulted from objects seeking their natural place in the universe, such as a rock dropped from a tower returning to the earth or flames of a fire rising into the air. Unnatural motion resulted from an outside push or pull such as a horse pulling a cart or a hammer hitting a nail. Aristotle believed that for so-called natural motion, such as objects falling near Earth's surface, the speed of fall was proportional to the weight, and inversely proportional to the density of the material through which the body was falling. He thought an object's weight increased as its speed increased. He confirmed none of his thoughts about motion with controlled experiments.

Galileo rejected Aristotle's ideas about motion. While holding a mathematics chair at the University of Pisa in 1589, Galileo demonstrated that the speed of fall of a heavy object is not proportional to its weight, as Aristotle had claimed. Galileo documented his results in the manuscript, *De motu* (*On Motion*) during this period, ushering in the beginning of the scientific exploration of nature.

Galileo also thought there were two types of motion. Horizontal motion resulted in constant velocity in a straight line unless the object experienced an outside force. Vertical motion (called natural motion by Galileo) resulted when objects fell from rest near Earth. Galileo claimed that vertical motion exhibits constant acceleration for all objects, regardless of weight, thus contradicting Aristotle.

Galileo reasoned that if heavy objects fell faster than light objects, then tying two objects together could result logically in either a slower falling rate due to the lighter object slowing the heavier one, or a faster rate due to the combined weight being larger than either object alone. Of course, both slower and faster cannot happen at the same time, thus leading to a contradiction. Galileo reasoned, correctly, that all objects, regardless of their weight, fall with the same constant acceleration, unless there is another force such as air friction acting on the objects.

Students have likely heard the expression "*g*-force" or "*g*s," from either air force pilots or amusement park rides. Information in the student book about the universal law of gravitation relates *g* to what your students will be studying in this chapter. It is important for you to understand that *g* can be thought of in one of two ways:

1. *g* can be the factor relating gravitational force to mass, by

$$F_g = \frac{GmM}{r_{Earth}^2}$$

$$\frac{F_g}{m} = \frac{GM}{r_{Earth}^2}.$$

Since all terms on the right-hand side are constants,

$$\frac{F_g}{m} = \frac{\left(6.67 \times 10^{-11}\frac{\text{m}^3}{\text{kg sec}^2}\right)\left(5.98 \times 10^{24}\text{ kg}\right)}{(6.38 \times 10^6\text{ m})^2}.$$

Canceling units gives us,

$$\frac{F_g}{m} = \frac{\left(6.67 \times 10^{-11}\frac{\cancel{\text{m}^2} \times \text{m}^1}{\cancel{\text{kg}}\text{ sec}^2}\right)\left(5.98 \times 10^{24}\ \cancel{\text{kg}}\right)}{4.07 \times 10^{13}\ \cancel{\text{m}^2}}$$

$$\frac{F_g}{m} = 9.80\ \frac{\text{m}}{\text{sec}^2}.$$

2. Because of Newton's second law, *g* is the acceleration due to gravity for objects in free fall.

$$F_{net} = ma$$

$$F_g = ma$$

$$\frac{GmM}{r_{Earth}^2} = ma$$

$$mg = ma$$

$$g = a$$

See *FYI—Universal Gravitation* in the student book for more information.

Graphs are a means to represent common motions pictorially. Throughout this chapter, students will have experience in analyzing and creating these types of graphs. This activity is structured so that students begin to make careful, systematic analyses of motion, allowing you to see where they are in their understanding. More background for these graphs will be provided in subsequent activities.

Materials—Part I

none

Materials—Part II

For each team of 2 students

1 spring scale
2–4 different-sized hanging masses, 200 grams (g) and greater
1 hardbound book
1 sheet of paper
1 pair of scissors

Advance Preparation

You may want to use multiple motion graphs for Part I so that teams have different motions to mimic. If so, prepare these graphs ahead of time along with overhead transparencies of the graphs for the entire class to see.

Educational Technologies

Consider using motion detectors or range finders for Part I of this activity. Many are available for use with both computers and graphing calculators. If you choose to use this form of technology, ensure that students go through the process of analyzing the graph before they model the motion. Too often, students use a trial-and-error approach, compete with other groups for the best match, and learn little about the graph.

As You Teach

Outcomes and Indicators of Success

By the end of this activity, students should

1. demonstrate their current understanding of graphical representations of motion.

   They will demonstrate their understanding by

   - systematically analyzing features of both a position versus time graph and a velocity versus time graph,
   - modeling the motion represented in the graphs by walking in a straight line, and
   - revising their ideas based on class participation and discussion.

2. design and conduct a scientific investigation.

   They will demonstrate their ability by

   - designing a step-by-step procedure to test the motion of falling objects and
   - using the *Observation Guidelines* to help them in their designs.

3. recognize and analyze alternative explanations and models.

   They will demonstrate their ability by

   - listening to alternative explanations and seeing different graphs for the same motion,
   - offering advice and explanations to other class members, and

ENGAGE

Going through the Motions

Maps are important to our lives. You may have used a map of your school to find your science classroom on the first day of school. Your parents use maps to find the best route for your family vacation or a business trip. Maps such as the one in figure 4.2 tell us locations, distances, and the direction to places around the world. But they do not tell us anything about our velocity as we travel from place to place. In *Going through the Motions*, you will work with graphs that will tell you many things about your motion. Many graphs can tell you locations, distances, and direction, just as a map can. However, with the graphs you will use in this activity, you can find out other information as well—quantities such as velocity and changes in velocity.

In Part I, you will work with a team to go through the motions depicted on two different types of graphs. In Part II, you and your team will examine the motion of falling objects. As you experience the different ways to represent motion graphically, you will learn about important features of motion graphs.

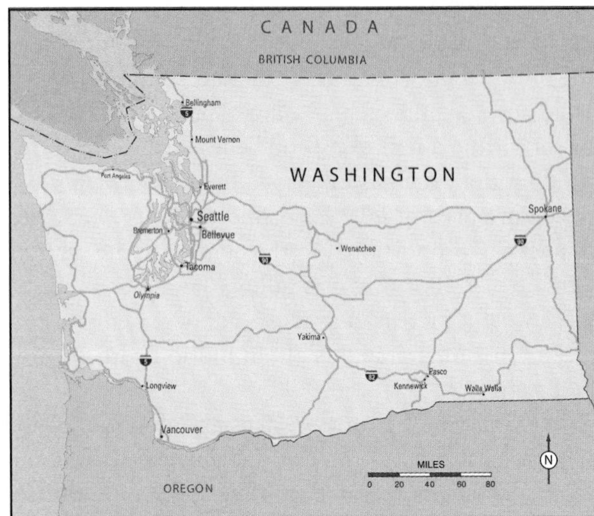

▲ **Figure 4.2 Map of Washington state.** What can you learn from a map? How are maps similar to or different from motion graphs?

- revising their explanations and graphs based on the best ideas from the class.

4. represent their prior knowledge of falling speeds of different-weight objects with a book and a sheet of paper.

   They will represent their prior knowledge by

   - letting a book represent all heavy objects and a sheet of paper represent all light-weight objects,
   - dropping the book and paper and recording what happens relative to their prior experiences, and
   - keeping a written record of what they observe and think in their science notebooks.

Strategies

Getting Started

Have several different maps available so that you can have a prop to go along with the introduction to Part I. Discuss the introduction and the task. If you choose to use motion detectors or range finders connected to computers or graphing calculators, ensure that students follow the analysis procedure *before* they attempt to match the line. Often, students simply see this type of activity as a competition for the best-matched line and only work from a trial-and-error approach. They finish the activity with little more understanding of motion graphs than when they started. Having students systematically analyze the graph *before* they try to model a motion will help them develop their understanding.

Process and Procedure

Part I: Walk the Line

Materials

none

In Step 1, students analyze a position versus time graph for specific characteristics. This is a time for students to talk about their current understanding of this type of graph and for you to assess that understanding. Suggest that students model individual sections of the graph for a feel of that motion. Move about the room and monitor each team's discussion to observe where your students are in their understanding. You will then know where additional help may be needed later in the chapter.

In Step 2, students work within their teams to model the motion by walking in a straight line. Students may not understand that this graph represents motion in a straight line. Remind them that they must define which direction is positive and which direction is negative, along with a position that they will define as the origin. Try to foster this habit for your students every time they are working with motion graphs. You will direct how you want the teams to model their ideas in Step 3. Make sure there is time for discussion during or after a team has modeled the motion. Use this time for other teams to present different ideas and for the modeling team to defend its ideas. Students will most likely revise their ideas based on the ideas of others. In Step 4, students copy the graph into their science notebooks and write a description of the motion that the graph represents.

Part I: Walk the Line

Materials

none

Process and Procedure

1. Meet with your team and study the motions depicted in figure 4.3. Steps 1a–h list characteristics of a motion graph that are significant. Locate these characteristics on the graph and discuss with your team what motion each represents. Record your ideas in your science notebook.
   a. Straight, flat line
   b. Positive sloping line
   c. Negative sloping line
   d. Positive y value
   e. Negative y value
   f. $y = 0$
   g. Steepness or slope of the line
   h. Straight line versus a curved line
2. Model the horizontal motion shown on the graph in figure 4.3. Decide how to model it by walking in a straight line. Prepare to demonstrate your motion to the class.
3. Model your motion for the class as your teacher directs. Watch other teams as they model the motion and explain their ideas.

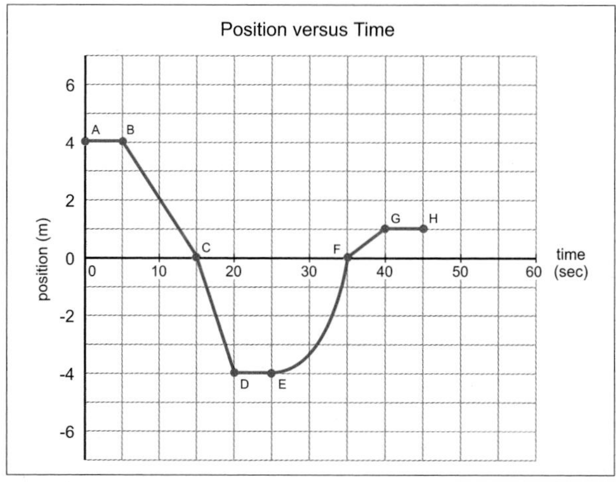

Figure 4.3 Position versus time graph. Use this graph for Part I. What motion does each characteristic of the graph represent?

Chapter 4 Physics Is Moving 163

Answers to Step 4, SE page 164

4. A student modeling the motion in the graph starts at 4 meters (m) in the positive direction from a selected origin (A) and remains in the same position for 5 seconds (sec). The student then moves at a constant velocity of −0.4 meters per second (m/sec) (from B to C), crosses the origin position at C, and moves at −0.8 m/sec for another 5 sec (C to D). At D, the student stops for 5 sec (−4 m from the origin), then moves at a nonconstant velocity in the opposite (positive) direction (speeding up) for 10 seconds (sec). Here he or she crosses the origin point at F and moves at a constant velocity (0.2 m/sec) for 5 sec, and then stops at G (1 m from the origin) and remains stationary for 5 sec.

   Students will not likely know the velocities from the position time graph. These are calculated from the slope of the line and students will discover this later in the activity. These are here for your reference only.

In Step 5, students repeat the activity using a velocity versus time graph. Typically, students have less understanding of this type of graph. This motion is difficult to model accurately, so encourage students to describe verbally what they intend to model as they are doing it. This way, the class has a clear understanding of what each team is trying to do. Again, remind students to define a positive and negative direction along with a reference point.

Answers to Step 5, SE page 164

5. The student starts out at A with a constant positive velocity of 0.5 m/sec for 4 sec. This means that the student will have to define what direction is positive; the motion from A to B will be in that positive direction. Then at B, the student slows down at a constant rate to a stop at C (still going in the same direction). The student remains stationary (0 m/sec velocity) for 4 sec (C to D). The student then begins to move again (in the same positive direction), speeding up at a constant acceleration to 0.5 m/sec from D to E. At E, the student starts to slow down at a constant acceleration from E to F, where the student immediately stops for a moment and changes direction. From F to G, the student speeds up in the negative direction until reaching a velocity of −1.0 m/sec at G. The student (at G) begins to slow down (still moving in the negative direction) at a constant acceleration until the student stops at H.

Answers to Stop and Think—Part I, SE pages 164–165

1. Students should describe the motion from point to point for each student. Remind students to define an origin and the directions for positive and negative motion.

   For Shayla: From A to B, Shayla is stationary (for 1 minute [min]) and is +50 m (in the positive direction) from the origin. From B to C, she moves with a constant positive velocity farther away from the origin, and at C she is +100 m from the origin. At C, Shayla reverses direction and moves at a constant negative velocity toward the origin; she passes the origin and comes to

Answers to Stop & Think—Part I are on TE pages 164–165.

4. Copy the graph into your science notebook and write a description of the motion based on the best ideas from the class.
5. Repeat Steps 1–4 for the graph pictured in figure 4.4. Note that this is a velocity versus time graph.

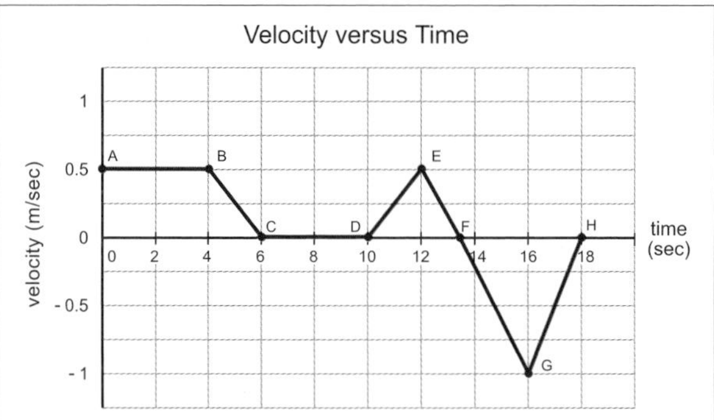

Figure 4.4 Velocity versus time graph. Refer to this graph for Step 5. What motion does each feature of the graph represent? How is this graph different from a position versus time graph?

Stop & THINK

PART I

Work individually and record your answers in your science notebook. Check your answers with a classmate or with your teacher.

1. Examine the graph pictured in figure 4.5. Use the information in the labeled sections to write a description of the motion shown in the graph. Be sure to describe both lines and what happens at the time at position I.
2. Examine the section B–C on the graph shown in figure 4.5 and answer Questions 2a–c.
   a. What feature of this part of the graph is constant?
   b. What is the general formula used to calculate the slope of a line?
   c. Calculate the slope using the values from the graph in figure 4.5.

a stop −100 m past the origin. Shayla remains stationary for 1 min (from D to E).

For Drew: Drew starts at a position that is the opposite direction from where Shayla begins, −100 m from the origin. He moves at a constant positive velocity toward the origin (in the positive direction) until he stops at −50 m from the origin. He remains stationary for 1.5 min and then moves at a constant positive velocity; he passes the origin and comes to rest at +50 m from the origin. He remains at rest for 1 min or until a total of 4 min has passed.

At point I, Shayla and Drew meet, cross paths, and continue in opposite directions.

2a. The slope of the line between B and C is constant.

2b. Students may report the general formula for the slope of a line to either be $slope = \frac{rise}{run}$ or $slope = \frac{\Delta y}{\Delta x}$.

2c. To calculate the slope, students will use the general formula for slope of a line.

$$\begin{aligned} slope &= \frac{100\text{ m} - 50\text{ m}}{1.5\text{ min} - 1\text{ min}} \\ &= \frac{50\text{ m}}{0.5\text{ min}} \\ &= 100\frac{\text{m}}{\text{min}} \end{aligned}$$

Process and Procedure

Part II: All Fall Down

Materials

For each team of 2 students

1 spring scale

2–4 different-sized hanging masses, 200 grams (g) and greater

1 hardbound book

1 sheet of paper

1 pair of scissors

In Step 1, students cut a sheet of paper to match the area of the cover of the hardbound book they will use in the activity. They also construct a table to record their observations for several book-paper scenarios. Check their work to ensure that they have a well-organized table with places for all of their observations. Students are asked to use the *Observation Guidelines* located at the end of the activity to guide them in their step-by-step designs. This tool is a valuable set of guidelines that you may wish to use repeatedly in future investigations. You can also find

How to Make Better Observations in the *How To* section at the back of the student book as well as on the *Teacher Resource CD (TRCD)*.

After you spot-check the students' plans in Step 2, the students will begin their investigations. In Step 3, students draw qualitative graphs (of both position versus time and velocity versus time) of the motion of the falling bodies. Make sure students understand that a qualitative graph only indicates the general shape of the graph. It also includes only enough information to communicate their chosen frame of reference or a sense of the scale of the motion depicted. It might be helpful for your class to use the same direction to indicate a positive direction (such as upward) and the same frame of reference (such as the floor as the origin). The students share their ideas with the class in Step 4. Consider using the think-share-advise-revise (TSAR) strategy to help students with this discussion.

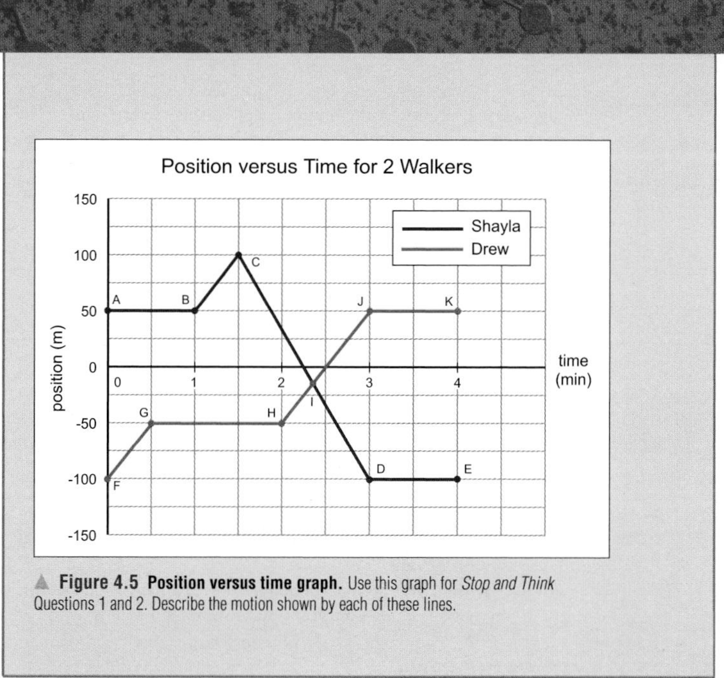

▲ **Figure 4.5 Position versus time graph.** Use this graph for *Stop and Think* Questions 1 and 2. Describe the motion shown by each of these lines.

Part II: All Fall Down

Materials

For each team of 3 students

1 spring scale

2–4 different-sized hanging masses, 200 gram (g) and greater

1 hardbound book

1 sheet of paper

1 pair of scissors

Process and Procedure

Not all motions are horizontal, like those in Part I. Many are vertical. In Part II, you and a team of two other students will use a model to represent two falling objects of different mass (figure 4.6). Then you will design a step-by-step procedure to enact your design and determine what story this tells about forces and motion.

Answers to Steps 3 and 5, SE pages 166–167

3. Student graphs should be similar to those in figure T4.1. Do not expect students to draw these graphs correctly the first time. Allow them to discuss their answers with teammates and the class. Remind them that they must define a negative direction and a reference point for the origin. The answers for their graphs shown in figure T4.1 are based on the floor as the point of origin and down as negative. After the class discussion, students' final answers should be similar to those shown in figure T4.1. Students will have additional opportunities to draw these types of graphs in the chapter.

5a. The heavier an object is, the greater the force between Earth and the object.

5b. The force of gravity (weight) on an object is proportional to (or depends on) the object's mass.

5c. As an object's weight increases, the ratio $\frac{Force_{gravity}}{mass}$ remains the same.

In Step 6, students test their answers to Step 5c by using a spring scale and different masses. Students should find that the ratio of $\frac{Force_{gravity}}{mass}$ is constant and equal to approximately 9.8 newtons per kilogram (N/kg). The value 9.8 N/kg is approximately equal to the average change in velocity due to gravity on Earth's surface. If these units bother students, show how the units are really m/sec/sec or m/sec^2, a common unit for changes in velocity. Students will learn the term acceleration later in the chapter. The unit cancellation is as follows:

$$N = \frac{(kg)(m)}{sec^2}$$

$$\frac{N}{kg} = \frac{\frac{(\not{kg})(m)}{sec^2}}{\not{kg}}$$

$$\frac{N}{kg} = \frac{m}{sec^2}$$

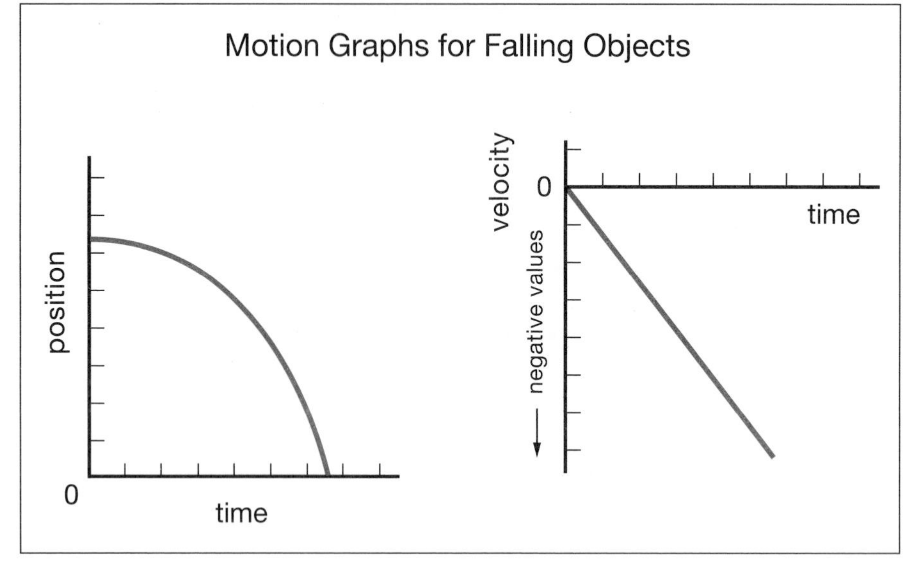

▲ **Figure T4.1 Sample student answers for Step 3.** Student answers should be similar to these.

Finally, you will propose a qualitative graph of this motion that illustrates the story graphically. A qualitative graph is one type of motion graph that you will be working with throughout this chapter.

1. Complete Steps 1a–c as you determine the motion of 2 falling objects.
   a. Trim a sheet of paper so that it has the same area as the cover of your student book.
   b. Prepare a table in your science notebook to record your observations of the 2 falling objects. You will drop these objects as described in the following list:
      - Book and paper falling from identical heights as independent objects
      - Book and paper released at the same time, but with the paper under the book
      - Book and paper released at the same time, but with the paper on top of the book
      - Book and paper released at the same time, but with the paper crumpled into a tight ball that is released at the side of the book
   c. Use the *Observation Guidelines* described at the end of this activity to guide your final, step-by-step procedure.
2. Obtain your teacher's approval and follow your approved design.
3. Draw qualitative graphs of the motion of these falling objects on both a position versus time graph and a velocity versus time graph.

Qualitative graphs are motion graphs that have labeled axes but do not necessarily have numbers on the axes. This type of graph shows only the basic shape of the line without having to plot *xy* ordered pairs.

4. Share your graphs with the class in a class discussion. Modify your graphs based on the best ideas of the class.
5. Work with your team to fill in the missing words for the following sequence of relationships.

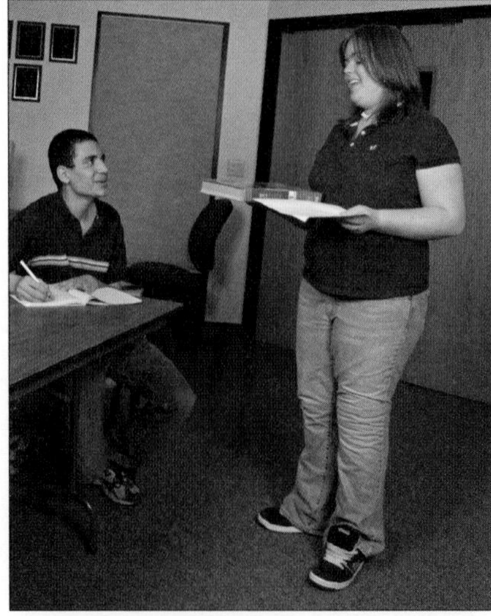

◀ **Figure 4.6 Fall time.** What important observations should you make as you conduct your investigation?

Answers to Step 7, SE page 167

7. Students should have found that the ratio of the force measured by the spring scale and the mass of the object remained the same no matter what the object was. This value is approximately 9.8 N/kg or m/sec^2, as shown in Step 6. This means that the acceleration due to gravity at a given location on Earth is the same for all objects regardless of their mass.

Answers to Reflect and Connect, SE page 167

1. Student answers should be similar to those pictured in figure T4.2. Look for connections to their learning in chapter 2.

2a. On a position versus time graph, the objects will have identical graphs since the acceleration due to gravity is independent of the mass. Therefore, the curve of a position versus time graph will be the same and the slope of the straight line on a velocity versus time graph will be the same. These graphs will be similar to the graphs that students drew in figure T4.1.

2b. For a book falling on Earth and on the Moon, the graphs will be different, as shown in figure T4.3. The acceleration due to gravity on Earth is different from the acceleration due to gravity on the Moon.

3. The ratio of weight to mass for objects of different mass is the same for all objects and is equal to approximately 9.8 N/kg, or g near Earth's surface. In mathematical form, this statement reads as follows:

$$\frac{F_{\text{g, heavy object}}}{m_{\text{heavy object}}} = \frac{F_{\text{g, light object}}}{m_{\text{light object}}} = g$$

Frequently, but not always, g is assigned a negative value to represent the force of gravity *down* toward Earth. It could just as easily be positive if the downward direction were defined as the positive direction.

Answers to Reflect and Connect are on TE pages 167–167b.

a. The heavier an object is, ________ the force between Earth and the object.
b. The force of gravity (weight) on an object is ________ ________ the object's mass.
c. As an object's weight increases, the ratio $\frac{Force_{gravity}}{mass}$ ________ ________.

6. Test your answer to Step 5c by using different masses (to represent the book and the paper) and a spring scale. You may test more than 2 different masses. Organize your data in an appropriate way in your science notebook. Include a column in your data table for the value of the ratio $\frac{Force_{gravity}}{mass}$.
7. What is the significance of the value you found from the ratio of $\frac{Force_{gravity}}{mass}$?

Reflect and Connect

Work alone or with a team as your teacher directs to answer the following questions.

1. Why does the shape of objects that are falling in the air affect the time it takes them to hit the ground? Include force vector sketches with labels and captions in your answer.
2. Draw a position versus time graph and a velocity versus time graph to compare each of the scenarios in Questions 2a–b. Use highlight comments and captions to formulate your answer.
   a. Two objects with different mass falling on Earth
   b. A book falling on Earth and a book falling on the Moon
3. State the relationship between 2 ratios of force to mass, ($\frac{Force_{gravity}}{mass}$ or $\frac{F_g}{m}$), one for a heavy object and one for a lightweight object. Then use what you have learned to write an equation that shows the relationship between this ratio for the heavy object, the light object, and g (the acceleration due to gravity). State this relationship in both a mathematical form and a word sentence.

NOTES:

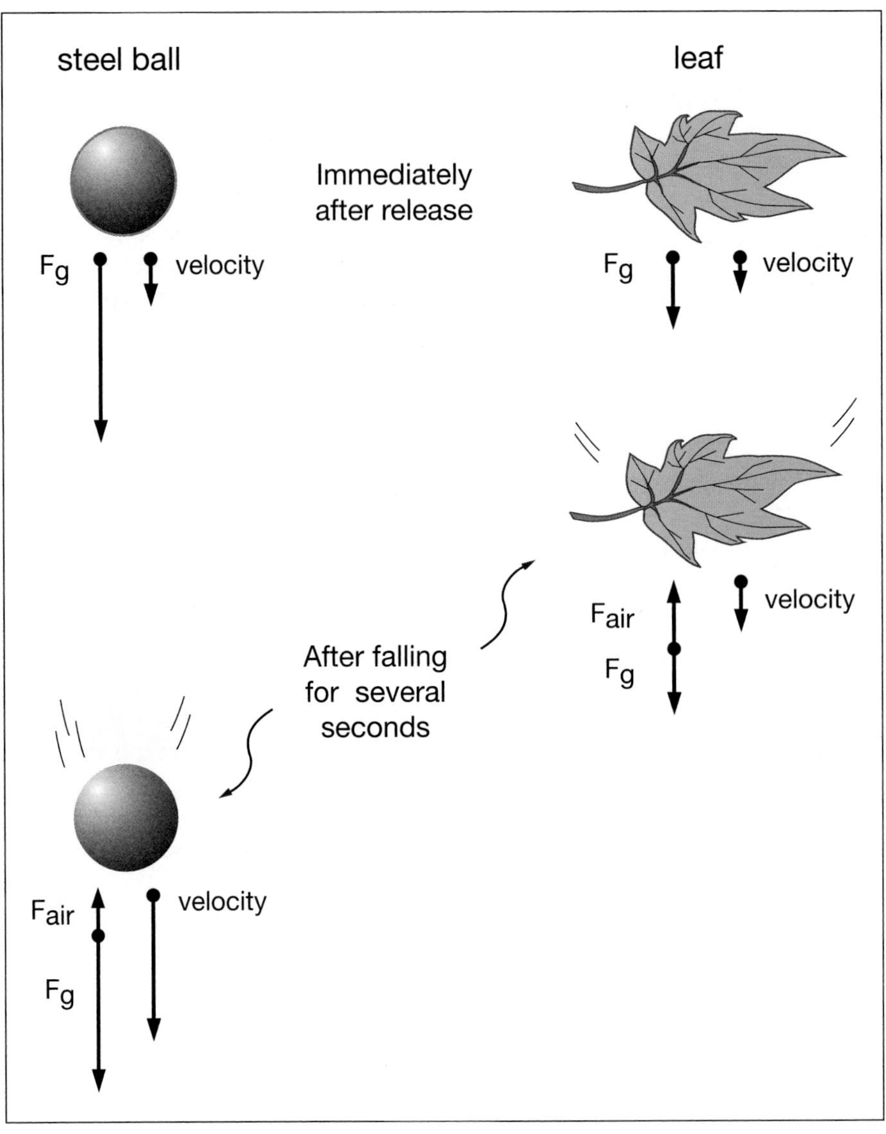

▲ **Figure T4.2 Different-shaped falling objects.** These sample student sketches and vectors will help you evaluate answers to *Reflect and Connect* Question 1.

NOTES:

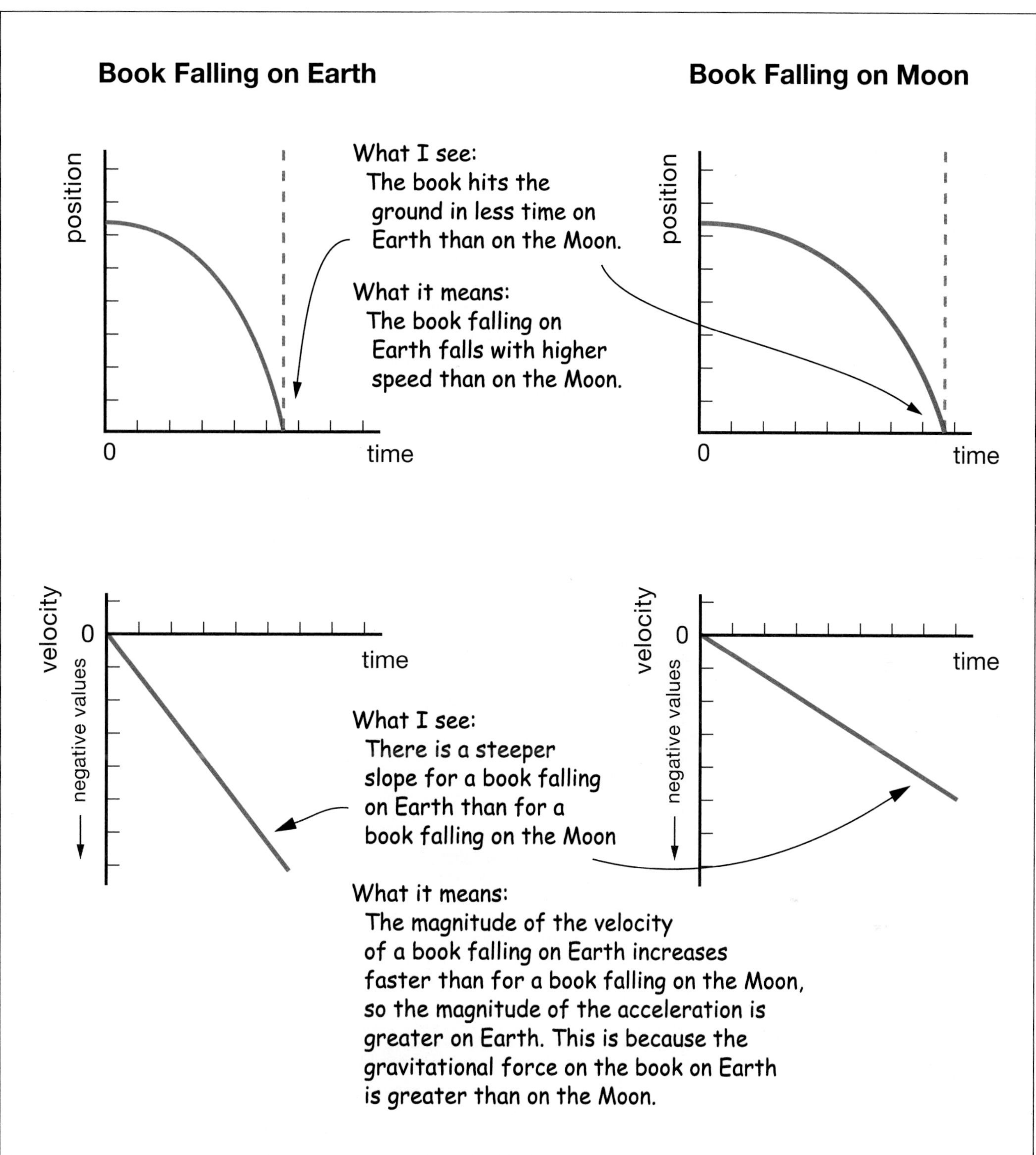

▲ **Figure T4.3 Sample graphs of books falling on Earth and on the Moon.** Student graphs and comments for *Reflect and Connect* Question 2 should be similar to these.

EXPLORE

Acceleration Indication

Activity Overview

In chapter 2, students learned to link changes in velocity to evidence of net force. Changes in velocity are something students can see directly, and thus are reasonably concrete. Forces are invisible. We only see what forces do; thus, they are more abstract than changes in velocity. But for students to acquire a solid understanding of the relationship between force and various types of motion, they must understand the link between force and acceleration. To encourage this link, the engage activity in this chapter got students thinking about the force of gravity on an object and the time rate of change of velocity of that object. In *Acceleration Indication*, students will link what they know about the time rate of change of velocity to acceleration and from acceleration to force. The ultimate goal is a deep understanding of Newton's second law of motion, $F_{net} = ma$.

The first approach to this famous and important relationship ($F_{net} = ma$) used in this activity is qualitative, not quantitative. This activity provides students with opportunities to explore this relationship through a series of investigations that measure acceleration during certain kinds of motions. Students build and use a soda bottle accelerometer to determine whether certain motions are associated with acceleration. If they are, then a net force must be involved. Thus, students gain valuable qualitative understandings of the relationship between net force and acceleration for several common types of motion: they learn that a net force is associated with an acceleration and conversely, that an acceleration is associated with a net force. Newton's third law of motion states another association: that a force of object 1 on object 2 has an associated force of object 2 on object 1—a force pair. In later activities, students will build a bridge between their qualitative experiences and more abstract expressions used to describe and understand motion. These expressions tend to be graphical and mathematical.

Before You Teach

Background Information

Accelerometers are devices used to detect the direction and magnitude of changes in motion that an object experiences. This information helps designers determine changes in an object's path or the kind of forces an object has experienced. Guidance systems in spacecrafts, automobile air bags, oil tankers, and earthquake detectors use accelerometers in various forms. There are mechanical and electronic accelerometers. At least two parts with mass are required that have the ability to move relative to one another in response to the same force. Water in a glass piles up against one side of a glass when you push sharply on the glass because the water tends to remain in one place. The water slopes downward in the direction of the push, therefore indicating the direction of acceleration. If the water had a small toy boat floating on the surface, the boat would move away from the high side of the water. That is, while the water piles up in a direction opposite of the direction of motion, the boat would move in the same direction as acceleration. The more the boat moved, the greater the acceleration and the greater the force causing the acceleration.

The soda bottle accelerometer operates in a similar fashion. A bottle is filled with water and then a floating object, tethered to a string, is suspended in the middle of the bottle.

Observation Guidelines

You were not born knowing how to make good-quality scientific observations. But you can learn. Effective scientists have made good-quality observations for centuries. The following questions related to making observations are not a step-by-step procedure. Rather, they are guidelines (in the form of questions) to help you *think* your way through observations. When done well, observations help you link what you see to what it means. This is the very heart of science.

- How is each procedural step related to the focus question or problem you are investigating?
- What is the best way to represent the initial conditions (with tables, sketches, graphs, equations, or sentences)?
- What is the best way to record the final conditions?
- What is the best way to record what happens *during* the investigation?

You need to focus on what is happening during the investigation, but sometimes changes occur very quickly. In these cases, you must plan carefully so that you are not distracted by writing down your data.

- How do you know that the changes you see are the result of the variable that you are manipulating and not other variables?
- Will multiple trials increase your confidence in what you see?
- What is the best way to keep a record of your initial ideas and how those ideas change during the course of the investigation?

EXPLORE

Acceleration Indication

Graphs tell us many things about the motion they represent. You have seen that you can know the position, direction, and even the velocity of an object by analyzing a simple position versus time graph. When motion is graphed on a velocity versus time graph, there is much more you can learn about the motion. What does a straight line tell you on this type of graph? Slope is calculated the same in all types of graphs as $slope = \frac{\Delta y}{\Delta x}$. Since the y-axis represents velocity and the x-axis represents time in a velocity versus time graph, this formula becomes $slope = \frac{\Delta v}{\Delta t}$. This is the time rate of change in velocity. Sound familiar?

If you push the bottle sharply in one direction, the floating object moves in the direction of acceleration. The more the floating object moves, the greater the acceleration, and thus the greater the net force.

Materials

For each team of 2 students

1 plastic soda bottle with cap (20 oz or larger)
thread
1 packing peanut (nonwater soluble) or cork
water

Advance Preparation

Try to minimize your workload by assigning students the task of bringing a clean, clear soda bottle with cap to class. Plastic pint- or quart-sized jars with widemouthed lids work great, too. The widemouthed jars have the advantage of allowing you to move the accelerometer along the tabletop without toppling over. If you use the widemouthed jars, glue the thread to the center of the lid with a nonwater-soluble glue. Movement of the floating object (cork or packing peanut) is easier to detect in a 2-L bottle than in the 20-oz size, but the 2-L size is more cumbersome. Have an accelerometer assembled so students can see an example.

Be certain to have an assortment of nonwater-soluble packing peanuts or corks that fit into the mouth of soda bottles. Have a few spools of strong thread available. Students tie a length of thread around the packing peanut or cork, put it in the bottle, and allow the other end of the thread to exit the mouth of the soda bottle. Students then fill the bottle with water, cap it tightly, and invert it; the cap holds the floating peanut or cork at the upper one-third of the bottle. A thin diameter of thread will not prevent the cap from forming a tight seal.

Cautions

Students who spin around several times to see how the accelerometer behaves during uniform circular motion will become dizzy. Caution them to stop slowly and to stabilize their position by holding on to a secure object.

It should, because you learned about this in chapter 2. This ratio is commonly called **acceleration** and is represented by the symbol a. You learned in chapter 2 that any time there is a net force, there is a change in momentum. You also learned that if velocity is changing, then there is a net force. Net forces cause accelerations—and an object is accelerating if its velocity is changing. This means speeding up, slowing down, or changing directions are forms of acceleration. Read *FYI—Newton's Third Law Meets Newton's Second Law* for a better understanding of how the forces you have been studying compare.

In *Acceleration Indication*, you and a partner will learn a different means of indicating the direction and size of acceleration. This new approach involves building an instrument called an accelerometer. You will use the accelerometer (figure 4.7) as you design a series of investigations to study the kinds of motions important to everyday life.

▲ **Figure 4.7 Using your accelerometer.** In this activity, you will learn how to use a homemade accelerometer to observe the direction and relative size of acceleration.

During this entire investigation, continue to ask yourself this question: "What is the accelerometer telling me about the relationship between acceleration and force?"

Materials

For each team of 2 students

1 plastic soda bottle with cap (20 oz or larger)

thread

1 packing peanut (nonwater soluble) or cork

water

Process and Procedure

Scientific instruments can help you gain terrific insights into natural events. But their effectiveness is limited in part by the person observing the instrument. So matching accurate and precise observations with quality instruments produces the highest-quality data. From that, scientists have the best opportunity of determining what the data mean.

As you follow the procedure, keep in mind the importance of matching good investigation design, proper instrument use, and careful observations. This match will help you understand more about motions common to your daily life.

As You Teach

Outcomes and Indicators of Success

By the end of this activity, students should

1. be able to construct a functioning soda bottle accelerometer.

   They will show their ability by

   - reading suggestions in the student book and translating those instructions into assembly steps,
   - conferring with a partner about the assembly,
   - checking the assembly during construction with a partner, and
   - practicing with the accelerometer before collecting data for the activity to ensure its proper functioning.

2. be able to use the *Observation Guidelines* to design an investigation to determine the direction of acceleration for various common motions.

   They will show their ability by

   - incorporating steps in their designs to facilitate accurate and efficient data collection;
   - including steps in their designs to study linear, circular, and simple harmonic motion;
   - incorporating steps that tell how data will be displayed graphically and in vector sketches; and
   - including steps that tell how the data will be analyzed relative to the focus question.

3. be able to represent acceleration and force of various common motions with scaled vector sketches.

   They will show their ability by

   - generating scaled vector sketches associated with the motions of their accelerometer and
   - answering *Reflect and Connect* questions involving motions similar to the ones investigated in the activity.

Strategies

Getting Started

Begin this activity by showing the students an assembled acceleromater so that they will have an example to follow. The important part of the activity is not the assembling of the tool but using the tool to make observations about different motions. Encourage students to construct their accelerometers carefully and quickly so that you can proceed to the main part of the activity. You may also want to demonstrate how computer based accelerometers measure accelerations if one is available.

Cautions

Students who spin around several times to see how the accelerometer behaves during uniform circular motion will become dizzy. Caution them to stop slowly and to stabilize their position by holding on to a secure object.

Process and Procedure

Materials

For each team of 2 students

1 plastic soda bottle with cap (20 oz or larger)
thread
1 packing peanut (nonwater soluble) or cork
water

In Step 1, students construct their accelerometers. If they use widemouthed plastic jars, use a nonwater-soluble glue to attach the thread to the center of the lid. This way, the cork or packing peanut will float more toward the center. If students use soda bottles, the opening is small and at the center, so simply tightening the lid with the string hanging out the mouth of the bottle works fine. Be sure to check each team's accelerometer for leaks before the students go on to Step 2.

In Step 2, students practice using the accelerometer. Take the time to ensure that students are seeing the cork or plastic peanut "lean" in different directions depending on the motion. Have students notice the relative amount of lean. Quiz your students so that you know they understand what to look for on their accelerometers. Ask questions such as, "Does it lean a lot, or hardly at all?" "What direction does the cork lean?" "Does the cork lean in the same direction all through the motion?"

In every motion, students should hold the bottle inverted and perpendicular to the floor.

In Step 3, students use the *Observation Guidelines* to design a set of investigations to characterize acceleration in a set of designated motions.

Answers to Step 3, SE pages 170–171

3a. Students must define a positive direction. Once they do, when they speed up in that direction, the cork or plastic peanut will lean in that direction. A graph of this type of motion would look like the graph in figure T4.4.

Answers to Step 3 are on TE pages 170–171a.

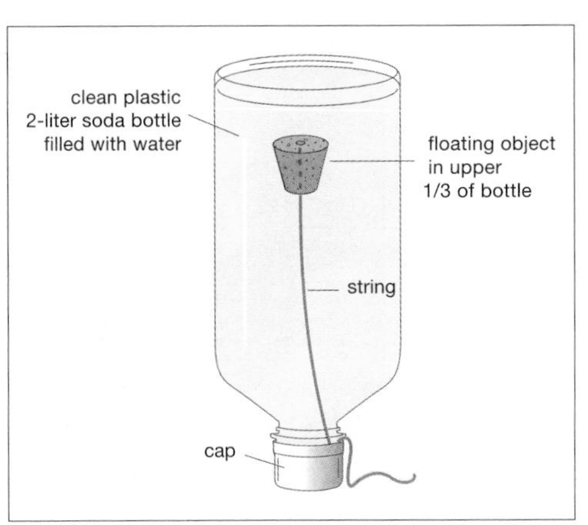

▲ **Figure 4.8 Soda bottle accelerometer.** Make sure that the peanut or cork floats in the upper one-third of the inverted bottle.

1. Obtain the materials used to construct an accelerometer. Then complete Steps 1a–c to assemble it to look like the one in figure 4.8.
   a. Find a piece of packing peanut or a cork that fits into the mouth of a plastic soda bottle. Tie it securely to one end of a piece of strong thread.
   b. Fill the bottle completely with water and place the peanut or cork inside. Be sure to include enough string inside the bottle for the peanut or cork to float in the upper one-third of the bottle when the bottle is inverted.
   c. Cap the bottle securely, invert it, and check for leaks.
2. Practice using your accelerometer before you study certain motions by doing Steps 2a–c.
   a. Stand at arm's length away from your partner, holding the inverted accelerometer at eye level between you.
   b. Holding the bottle far to the left, imagine that the soda bottle is a race car getting ready to start a race. Then accelerate the bottle sharply to the right.
   c. Repeat Steps 2a–b until you and your partner can both reproduce the *direction* and the *magnitude* of the peanut or cork's lean during the speeding up and slowing down process.
3. Use the *Observation Guidelines* from the engage activity, *Going through the Motions,* to devise a set of investigations to characterize acceleration for the motions in Steps 3a–f.

HOW TO

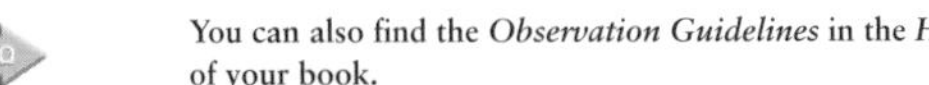

You can also find the *Observation Guidelines* in the *How To* section at the back of your book.

In all tests, keep the accelerometer inverted and perpendicular to the floor.

   a. Positive acceleration starting from rest, then moving along a straight line
   b. Negative acceleration from some constant speed to a stop
   c. Acceleration because of Earth's gravitational field (g)

3b. For negative acceleration from some constant speed to a stop, the students would move in the positive direction and slow down at a constant rate. A graph of this type of motion would look like figure T4.5. Negative acceleration can also be described as speeding up in a negative direction. But based on the directions to begin at a constant speed and slow to a stop, the negative acceleration in this case would be in the positive direction.

3c. The intent is for students to mimic free fall. But dropping the accelerometer will probably result in a watery mess. So show students how to clutch the accelerometer tightly above their heads and then squat extremely quickly. Students should be able to see the cork or plastic peanut move down, albeit briefly.

Note that if students define the drop position as the origin and downward as positive, then the object will accelerate positively and the graph will be shaped like the one from Step 3a. However, if they define the floor as the origin and negative is down, then the graph will look like the one in figure T4.6.

3d. When students spin in a circle and hold the accelerometer perpendicular to the floor, they should observe the cork or plastic peanut leaning into the center of the circle. The students spinning may not see this, but the other members of the team should be able to observe the cork. A graph of this motion would be similar to figure T4.7.

3e. When students move the accelerometer in the motion of a pendulum, they should observe the cork or plastic peanut moving from side to side. The cork should change its direction of lean as the students change the direction of the pendulum's motion. The cork will lean in the direction of motion as the pendulum swings down (speeding up toward the equilibrium position) and lean opposite the motion as the pendulum swings up (slowing down). A graph of this motion would be similar to figure T4.8.

3f. As the students walk with constant velocity, the cork or plastic peanut should not move at all. This graph will look just like the one for circular motion, except it might have a smaller constant speed (magnitude of velocity).

Answers to Step 6 are on TE pages 171 and 171b.
Answers to Reflect and Connect are on TE pages 171b–172.

You may have to exaggerate the downward motion of the soda bottle with a sharp downward pull in order to notice any movement of the peanut or cork.

d. Movement in a circle (with the radius parallel to the floor) at a constant rate
e. Motion of a pendulum
f. A walk across the room at a constant velocity

4. Show your plan to your teacher for approval, then carry out your investigations.
5. Meet with another team. Use an appropriate discussion strategy to reach consensus about the direction and magnitude of acceleration in each motion listed in Step 3.
6. Report your consensus from Step 5 in the form of a sketch of each motion. Include 2 vectors on each sketch: force and acceleration.

Reflect and Connect

Write answers to the following questions in your science notebook. Then meet with 1 or 2 other classmates to check your thinking. If the team cannot reach a consensus, explain to your teacher the key features of any disagreement.

1. What can you say about the net force and the acceleration in each of the motions from Step 3?
2. Sketch what your accelerometer would look like during a bungee jump by completing Steps 2a–d.
   a. Sketch your accelerometer somewhere from the start to the middle of your fall.
   b. Sketch your accelerometer exactly at the middle of your fall.
   c. Sketch your accelerometer somewhere from the middle of your fall to the bottom.
   d. Repeat Steps 2a–c and sketch your return trip to the start of your fall.

For this thought investigation, you'll also have to imagine a stretchy string tied to the peanut or cork.

3. Suppose a particularly athletic cheetah accelerates from rest toward a gazelle at a constant acceleration of 3.0 meters per second squared (m/sec^2).
   a. What is the cheetah's velocity in 2 seconds (sec)? In 6 sec?
   b. How long does it take for the cheetah to obtain a speed of 32 meters per second (m/sec)?
   c. Suppose the cheetah is loping at a constant speed of 1.0 m/sec before accelerating. Answer Questions 3a and b with this new initial condition.

In Step 4, students seek your approval before they conduct their investigations. In Steps 5 and 6, the students meet in their teams and come to a consensus regarding the direction and magnitude of the acceleration in each of the motions listed in Step 3. Consensus building is not an easy task for some students, so monitor the teams carefully and encourage teams that are having trouble coming to a consensus to repeat the task and make additional observations.

Answers to Step 6, SE page 171

6. Student drawings should be similar to figure T4.9. The important part is the direction of the vectors—the net force and acceleration vectors should always point in the same direction.

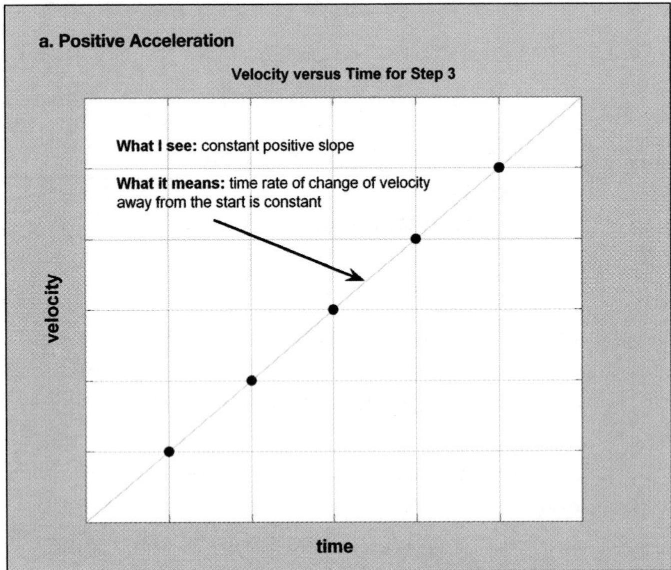

▲ **Figure T4.4 Sample graph of positive acceleration.** This graph shows the motion of an object speeding up in a positive direction.

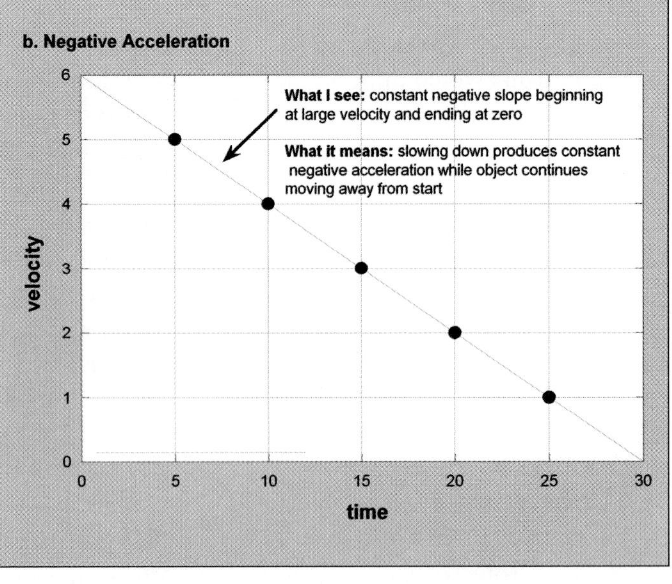

▲ **Figure T4.5 Sample graph of negative acceleration.** This graph shows the motion of an object slowing down in a positive direction. Negative acceleration could also be speeding up in a negative direction.

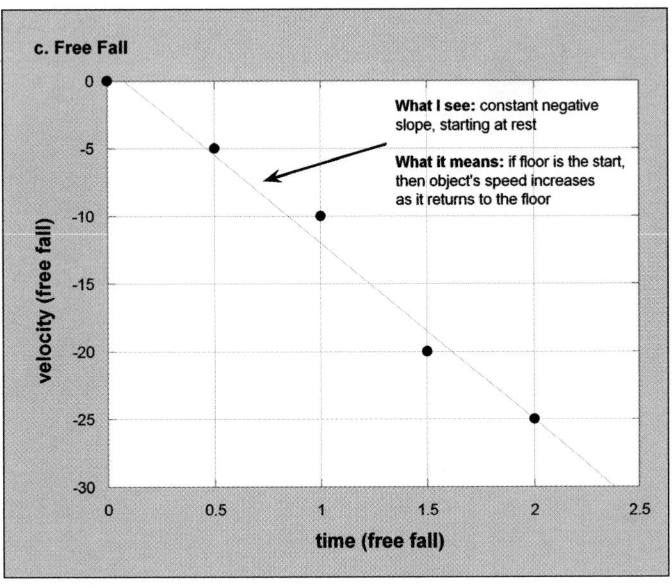

▲ **Figure T4.6 Velocity versus time graph of free fall.** This sample graph is a velocity versus time graph for free fall acceleration along a straight line.

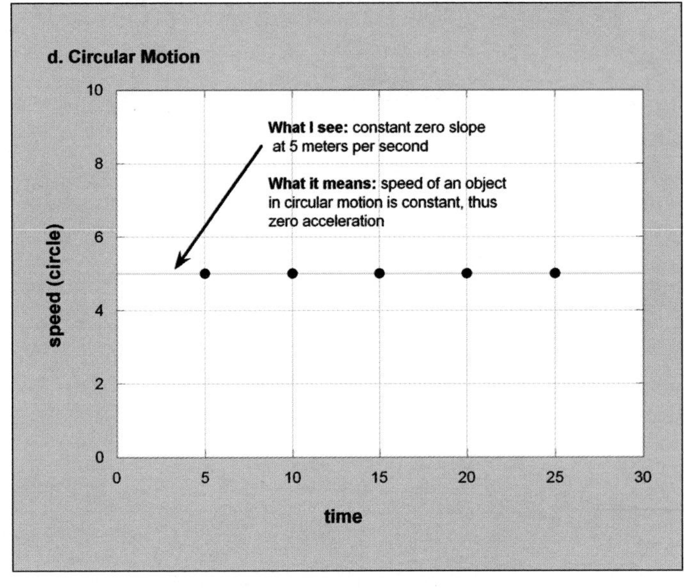

▲ **Figure T4.7 Speed versus time graph for circular motion.** This graph plots speed versus time for uniform circular motion.

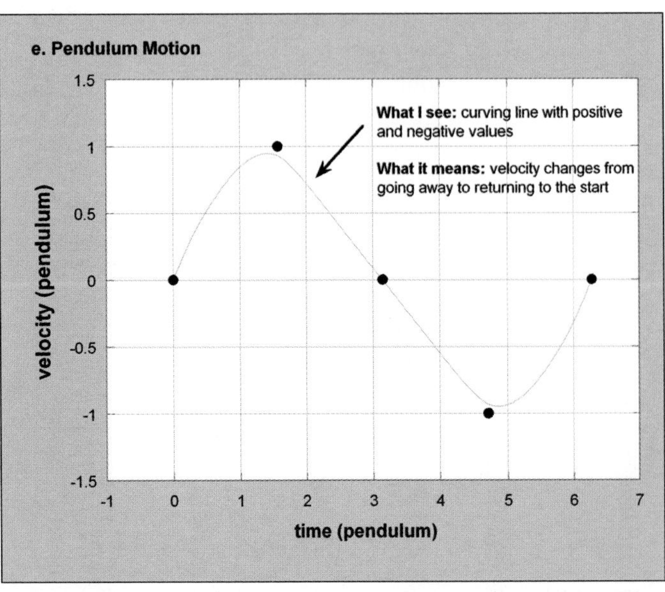

◀ **Figure T4.8 An example of a velocity versus time graph for pendulum motion.** This velocity versus time graph shows the horizontal component of pendulum motion. Motion to the right is defined as positive.

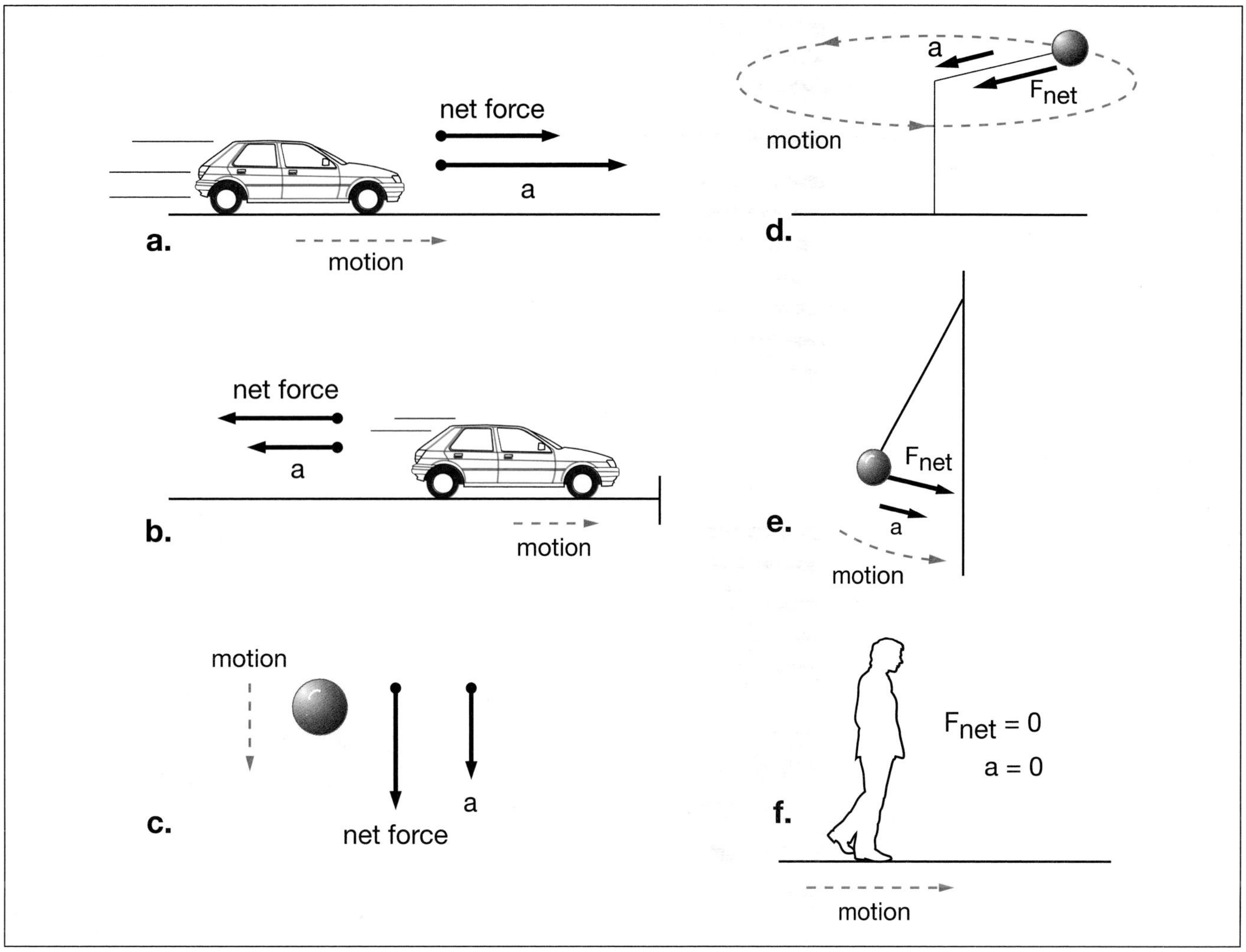

a. net force, a, motion
b. net force, a, motion
c. motion, net force, a
d. a, F_{net}, motion
e. F_{net}, a, motion
f. $F_{net} = 0$, $a = 0$, motion

▲ **Figure T4.9 Student drawings for Step 6.** These sketches represent the motions in Step 3a–f along with force and acceleration vectors.

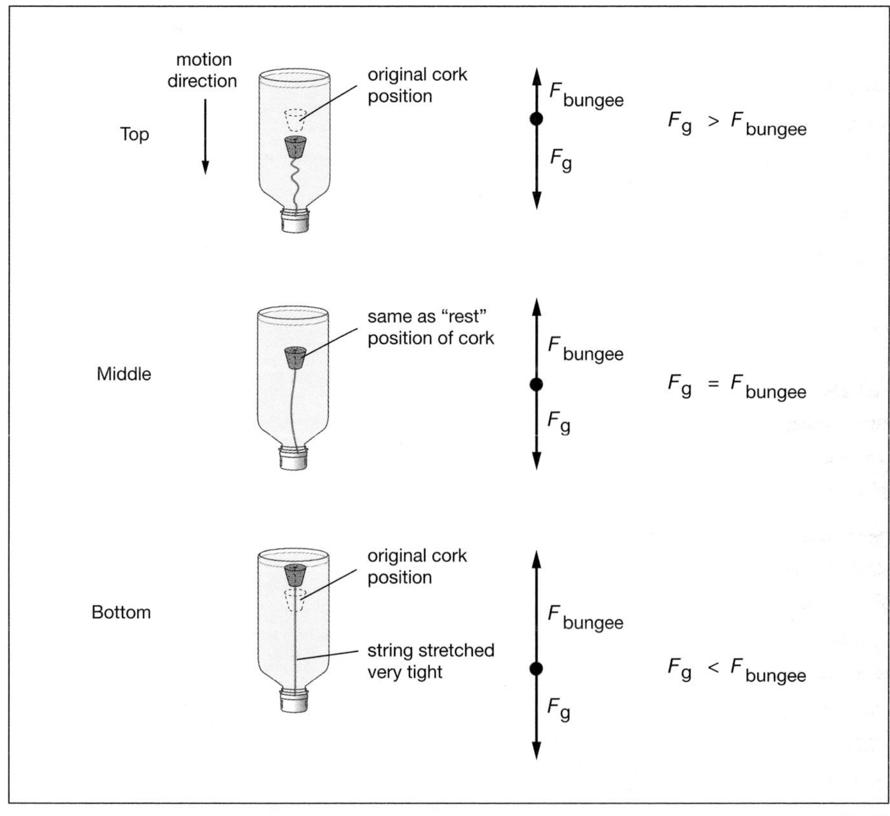

▲ **Figure T4.10 Sketches of accelerometer during bungee jump.** These sketches represent a soda bottle accelerometer in three positions during a bungee jump.

Answers to Reflect and Connect, SE page 171

1. In all cases, the net force and the acceleration are in the same direction. They do not always point in the same direction as the velocity.
2. Student sketches for this question should be similar to figure T4.10.

3a. The following equations show the cheetah's velocity in 2 sec and 6 sec.

$$a = \frac{\Delta v}{\Delta t}$$
$$\Delta v = a\Delta t$$
$$v_f - v_i = a(t_f - t_i)$$
$$v_f - 0\frac{m}{sec} = 3\frac{m}{sec^{\not 2}}(2\ \not{sec} - 0\ sec)$$
$$v_f = 6\frac{m}{sec}\text{(in 2 sec)}$$
$$v_f - 0\frac{m}{sec} = 3\frac{m}{sec^{\not 2}}(6\ \not{sec} - 0\ sec)$$
$$v_f = 18\frac{m}{sec}\text{(in 6 sec)}$$

3b. The answer for a cheetah moving at 32 m/sec follows.

$$a = \frac{\Delta v}{\Delta t}$$

$$\Delta t = \frac{\Delta v}{a}$$

$$\Delta t = \frac{32\,\frac{\cancel{m}}{\cancel{sec}}}{3.0\,\frac{\cancel{m}}{sec^{\cancel{2}}}}$$

$$\Delta t = 11 \text{ sec}$$

(answer to 2 significant figures)

3c. Answers to Questions 3a–b with new initial condition (assuming the initial speed was in the same direction as the acceleration) are shown here.

$$a = \frac{\Delta v}{\Delta t}$$

$$\Delta v = a\Delta t$$

$$v_f - v_i = a(t_f - t_i)$$

$$v_f - 1\frac{m}{sec} = 3\frac{m}{sec^{\cancel{2}}}(2\,\cancel{sec} - 0\,\cancel{sec})$$

$$v_f = 6\frac{m}{sec} + 1\frac{m}{sec}$$

$$v_f = 7\frac{m}{sec} \text{ (assuming only 2 sec of acceleration)}$$

$$v_f = 19\frac{m}{sec} \text{ (assuming only 6 sec of acceleration)}$$

$$a = \frac{\Delta v}{\Delta t}$$

$$\Delta t = \frac{\Delta v}{a}$$

$$\Delta t = \frac{32\,\frac{\cancel{m}}{\cancel{sec}} - 1\,\frac{\cancel{m}}{\cancel{sec}}}{3.0\,\frac{\cancel{m}}{sec^{\cancel{2}}}}$$

$$\Delta t = 10 \text{ sec}$$

NOTES:

Newton's Third Law Meets Newton's Second Law

Forces cause change—sometimes. If all the forces on an object are balanced, then the object's motion will not change. The object could either remain stationary or move along at a constant velocity. The *change* in motion and the forces involved in the changes are the focus of this chapter. This focus is also Newton's second law: a net force causes a mass to accelerate. Net forces cause a change in motion. Newton's third law of motion was the focus of chapter 2: forces occur in pairs—equal in size, opposite in direction—and act on two separate objects. How are these two laws of motion related?

Consider a cart that is not moving (see figure a). This cart is equipped with a digital force meter that will indicate the force produced by the cart. The students in the picture also have digital force meters. Their meters indicate the forces they exert on the cart. Only some of the horizontal forces are shown in order to simplify the diagram.

The force pairs according to Newton's third law are labeled in each figure. All force pairs show forces that are equal in magnitude and opposite in direction. You should also notice that in each force pair, the two forces act on two separate objects. Can you name them?

Will the cart move? To determine if the cart will move, you must consider the forces acting *on the cart* and then use Newton's second law. These forces are a subset of all the force pairs described in Newton's third law. The forces that determine the motion of the cart are only the forces acting *on the cart.* Figure (b) shows those forces in red.

You can tell from the illustration that the forces on the cart are balanced—they are equal in size and opposite in direction. If you added scaled vectors of these two forces, you would get a net force of zero. Newton's second law tells you that if there is no net force on an object, then there is no change in the object's motion—no acceleration according to the formula $F_{net} = ma$. Sometimes the situation of balanced forces is called Newton's first law of motion: objects will remain in their current motion unless outside forces act on that object. Since the forces on the cart are balanced, there will be no acceleration. Can you think of a circumstance where there would be acceleration? Consider figure (c).

If the girl is pushing to the left with 40 newtons (N) and the boy is pushing to the right with 30 N, the forces *on the cart* are unbalanced. There is a net force of 10 N to the left on the cart. According to Newton's second law, the cart will accelerate in the direction of the net force—to the left. You can also find the value of the acceleration by using the formula $F_{net} = ma$. For a cart with a mass of 500 kilograms (kg),

$$F_{net} = ma$$

$$a = \frac{F_{net}}{m}$$

$$= \frac{10\text{N}}{500\text{ kg}}$$

$$= 0.02\,\frac{\text{N}}{\text{kg}} \text{ or } 0.02\,\frac{\text{m}}{\text{s}^2}.$$

This means that the cart will move to the left and speed up 0.02 m/sec every second as long as the net force on the cart remains 10 N.

You can see that Newton's third law and Newton's second law are not two unrelated laws of motion. They are very much connected and are used to explain motion. So how is it that you can lift your backpack from the floor to your back? Aren't the forces involved always in pairs—equal and opposite? This is true, but the force pairs, equal in size and opposite in direction, act on the backpack and on other things. A subset of these force pairs, only the forces on the backpack, determine the motion of the backpack and whether you can lift it from the floor.

EXPLAIN

Constantly Accelerating

Activity Overview

In *Constantly Accelerating*, students will study the relationships among force, velocity, and acceleration for the motions where the net force and acceleration remain constant. These motions include a ball tossed into the air that returns to your hand, projectile motion, and uniform circular motion. Both the ball toss and projectile motion are examples of bodies that are in free fall with the only net force on the body being that of gravity. In circular motion, the net force, and thus the acceleration, is constant and always points toward the center of the circle. In all of these examples, the velocity of the object is changing, but it is changing at a constant rate, which means constant acceleration. This activity continues logically from the engage activity, which asked students to activate their thinking regarding different weights that free-fall, and from the explore activity, *Acceleration Indication*, which gives students a means of analyzing acceleration in free fall as well as other motions. This explain activity helps students make the relationships among force, velocity, and acceleration more concrete and at the same time more mathematical.

In Part I, students will focus on the forces acting on a ball as it is tossed in the air and returns to their hands. Students will use a ball, vector diagrams, and group discussion to determine that once a ball is tossed in the air, the *only* force acting on it is the pull of gravity (disregarding air resistance). Part I pays special attention to the top of the ball's path, where the force and acceleration remain constant, rather than become zero (a common misconception). Students also will learn many relationships among distance, velocity, and acceleration by examining both position versus time graphs and velocity versus time graphs. Students will use the slope of a line and the area under the curve to find these relationships on graphs.

Part II asks students to consider the independence of horizontal and vertical motion by making two pennies fall off a tabletop, one projected horizontally and one dropped vertically. Part II also asks students to design an activity to apply what they learned about the independence of horizontal and vertical motion to a ball projected across a tilted, flat surface. The ball exhibits projectile motion; thus, students will confirm the observations associated with Newton's second law and the independence of vertical and horizontal motion with actual projectile motion. In Part III, students will compare and contrast projectile motion to uniform circular motion using vector representations of force, acceleration, and velocity.

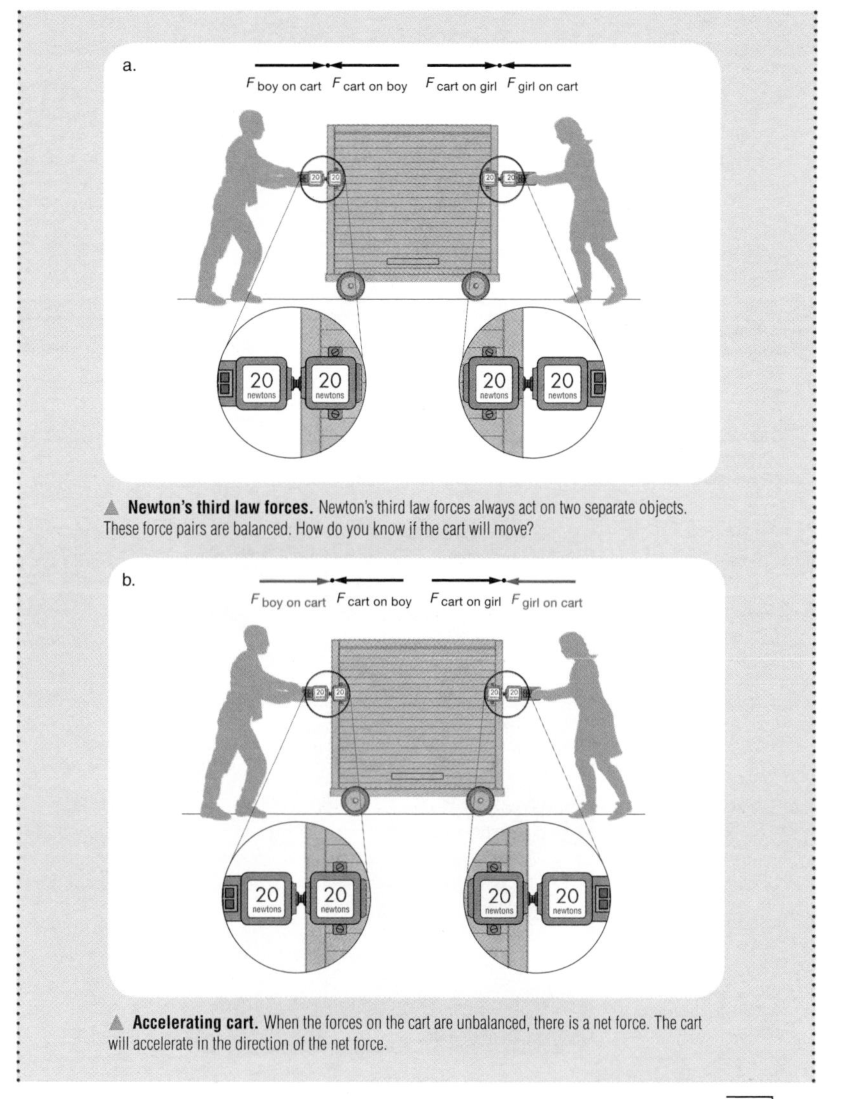

Newton's third law forces. Newton's third law forces always act on two separate objects. These force pairs are balanced. How do you know if the cart will move?

Accelerating cart. When the forces on the cart are unbalanced, there is a net force. The cart will accelerate in the direction of the net force.

Before You Teach

Background Information

Aristotle believed in the impetus theory, which says that so-called violent motion, such as a ball tossed in the air or an arrow shot from a bow, requires a force. As the object progresses in its motion, the cause of the "violence" (a force) decreases steadily until there is none remaining. At the point when the violent force is no longer present, the object returns to its natural location. In the case of a rock tossed in the air, the natural location is with other rocks (Earth). Aristotle, in essence, believed in leftover forces. That is, he thought if you tossed a ball in the air, the ball keeps moving upward because it still experiences a force from your hand. As the ball moves higher, the force decreases. It is as though he envisioned the ball being imparted with a fuel source that propelled the ball forward. When the fuel source becomes depleted, the ball returns to Earth.

Of course, there are *no* leftover forces from your hand. Once the ball leaves your hand, the only force acting on the ball (in the absence of air friction) is the force of gravity (called the ball's weight). This force produces a free fall acceleration of about 9.8 m/sec² on Earth for all objects, regardless of mass. This result can be surprising and counterintuitive since many might think that heavier objects experience a greater acceleration. But consider the relationship developed by equating Newton's second law of motion ($F_{net} = ma$) with his law of universal gravitation ($F_g = G\frac{m_1 m_2}{r^2}$).

Let m_1 be the mass of Earth (m_{Earth}) and m_2 be the mass of some object (m_{object}) falling near Earth's surface. G is the gravitational constant. For an object in free fall, $F_{net} = F_g$, so then Newton's second law ($ma = F_{net}$) becomes

$$\cancel{m}_{object}\, a = G\frac{m_{Earth}\,\cancel{m}_{object}}{r_{Earth}^2}$$

$$a = G\frac{m_{Earth}}{r_{Earth}^2}.$$

substituting the constants into the right side of the equation,

$$a = \frac{\left(6.67 \times 10^{-11}\,\frac{m^3}{kg\ sec^2}\right)\left(5.98 \times 10^{24}\ kg\right)}{(6.38 \times 10^6\ m)^2}$$

canceling units gives us,

$$a = \frac{\left(6.67 \times 10^{-11}\,\frac{\cancel{m^2} \times m^1}{\cancel{kg}\ sec^2}\right)\left(5.98 \times 10^{24}\ \cancel{kg}\right)}{4.07 \times 10^{13}\ \cancel{m^2}}$$

$$a = g = 9.8\,\frac{m}{sec^2}.$$

NOTES:

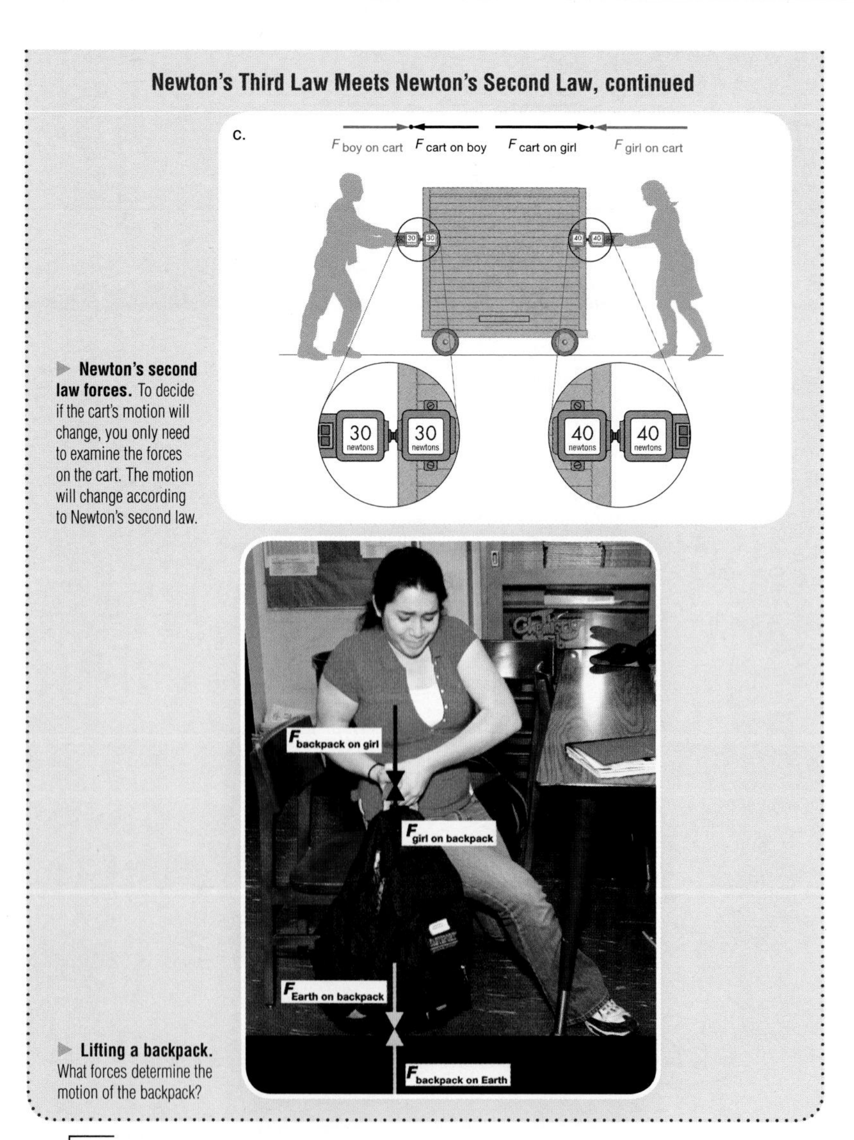

Newton's second law forces. To decide if the cart's motion will change, you only need to examine the forces on the cart. The motion will change according to Newton's second law.

Lifting a backpack. What forces determine the motion of the backpack?

The ball experiences this acceleration vertically (in the downward direction) at all points in the path—even at the top of the path where velocity is zero.

You can determine the velocity of an object by finding the slope of the line on a position versus time graph. If the object moves at a constant velocity, then the graph will be a straight line and the slope will be the same at any point along the line (figure T4.11a). If the object is accelerating, then the graph will be a curved line and the velocity at any instant will be the slope of a line tangent to any point along the curve (figure T4.11b).

The acceleration of an object can be found by finding the slope of the line from a velocity versus time graph. As before, if acceleration is constant, then the graph will be a straight line and the slope will be the same at any point along the line. If the acceleration is not constant, then the graph will have curved lines and the acceleration at any instant will be the slope of a line tangent to any point along the curve.

The area under the curve of a velocity versus time graph will give you the distance the object has traveled. These are simple to calculate provided the graphs are of straight lines. Then finding the area is as simple as finding the area of a rectangle or a triangle. See figure T4.12.

Negative velocities imply that the object is moving either toward a defined origin from a positive position or away from that same origin in increasing negative positions. An object moving at 5 m/sec is moving at the same speed as an object moving at −5 m/sec. The only difference is that they are moving in opposite directions. Negative accelerations can be a little more difficult to understand. Acceleration is calculated by $\frac{v_f - v_i}{t_f - t_i}$ or $\frac{\Delta v}{\Delta t}$. If the object is moving in the positive direction, then positive accelerations occur when the object is speeding up and negative accelerations occur when the object is slowing down. This is the most common use of accelerations. However, if an object is moving in the negative direction, then the object has positive acceleration when it is slowing down and negative acceleration when it is speeding up.

Galileo was credited with stating that the vertical and horizontal components of projectile motion were independent of each other. He said the horizontal motion would continue at a constant velocity unless an outside force was applied in the horizontal direction. Later, this idea formed part of what we know as Newton's second law. For a projectile shot at some angle relative to the ground, the horizontal change in position is determined using $\Delta x = v_x \Delta t$, where v_x is the constant horizontal velocity and Δt is the change in time.

The vertical component of motion is governed by free fall. That is, the vertical position is given by $\Delta y = v_{yi}t - 1/2gt^2$, where v_{yi} is the velocity of the projectile when it first began the motion, but only in the y (vertical) direction; g is the acceleration of objects near Earth's surface and t is the time when $t_i = 0$. Using this equation, assume that downward and g are positive.

If two objects are placed at the same height above the ground and one is dropped while the other is projected horizontally, they both hit the ground at the same time. This is due to the independence of vertical and horizontal motion. For both objects, the only force acting on them is their weight. Thus, both objects hit the ground at the same time.

Constantly Accelerating

EXPLAIN

In the explore activity, *Acceleration Indication*, you learned an instrumental means of determining net forces by measuring acceleration. You found out how an accelerometer helps you characterize changes in velocity (acceleration), and thus changes in momentum. The result was a better understanding of the forces required to produce certain types of common motion.

As you were using your accelerometer, you noticed that some motions produced accelerations that were constant. This was evident during the motion when the cork or peanut leaned in one direction with a constant magnitude, or "lean." This happened when you modeled free fall and circular motion. Would the acceleration of the teenagers on this amusement park ride (figure 4.9) be constant or changing? In *Constantly Accelerating*, you will look at these two motions in detail. In the process, you will learn more about net forces and accelerations that are constant.

▲ **Figure 4.9**
Physics can be fun. Do these teenagers experience a constant or a changing acceleration on this amusement park ride?

Part I: Leftovers

Materials

For each team of 2 students

1 ball

2 rulers for drawing graphs

Process and Procedure

In Part I, you will work individually and in a team to analyze and understand the motion of a ball tossed in the air. (You will not use an accelerometer.) Throughout this activity, use the following focus question to help you stay on track: "What are the relationships among force, position, velocity, time, and acceleration for a ball tossed in the air?"

Chapter 4 Physics Is Moving 175

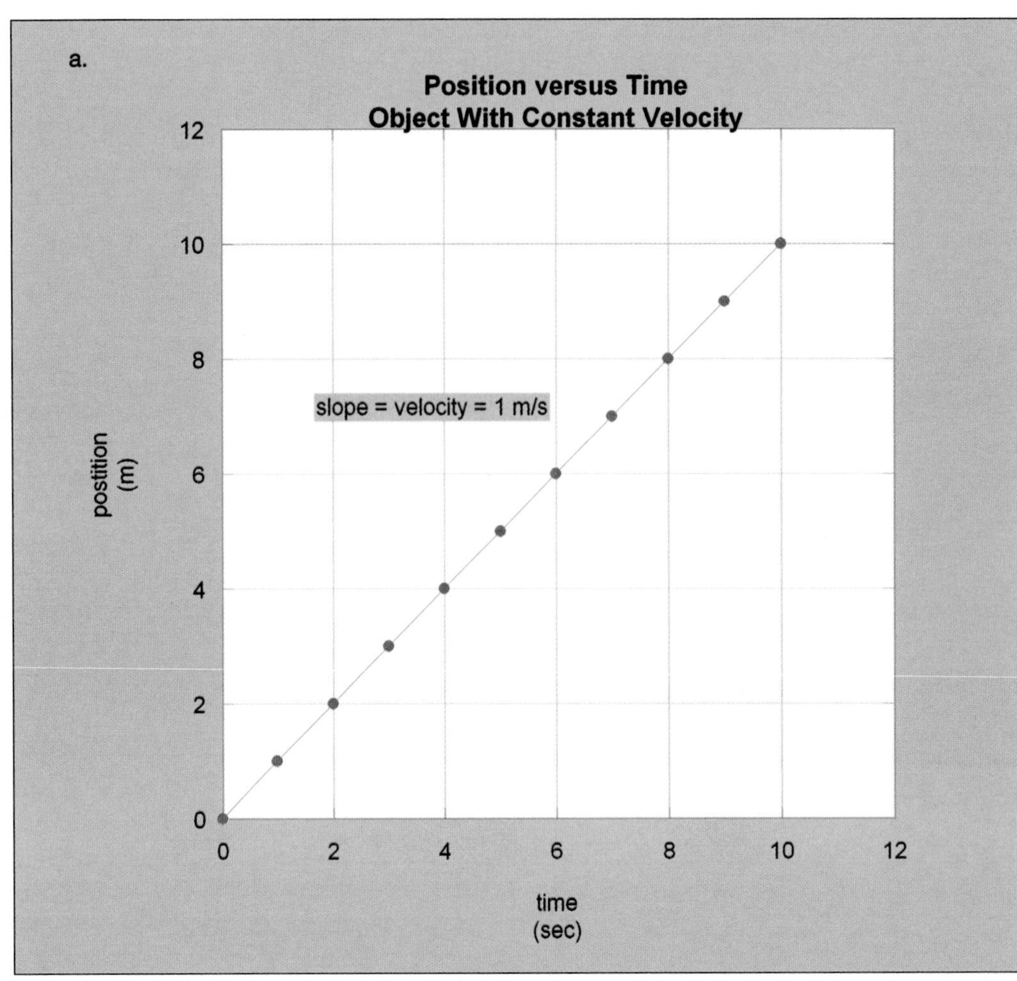

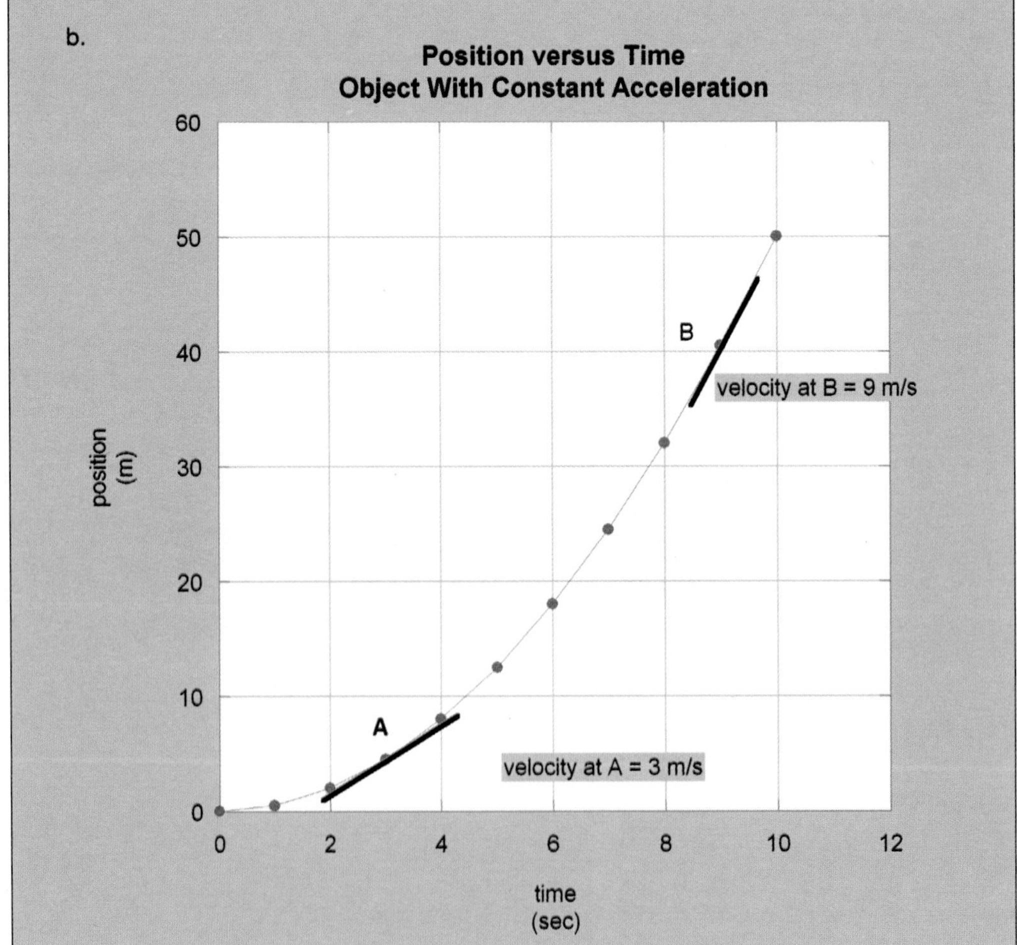

▶ **Figure T4.11 Finding the velocity from a position versus time graph.** If the object is moving at a constant velocity, then the graph of that motion will be a straight line, as in (a). The velocity is the slope of the line. If the object is not moving at a constant velocity (b), then the instantaneous velocity is found by finding the slope of a line that is tangent to any point along the line.

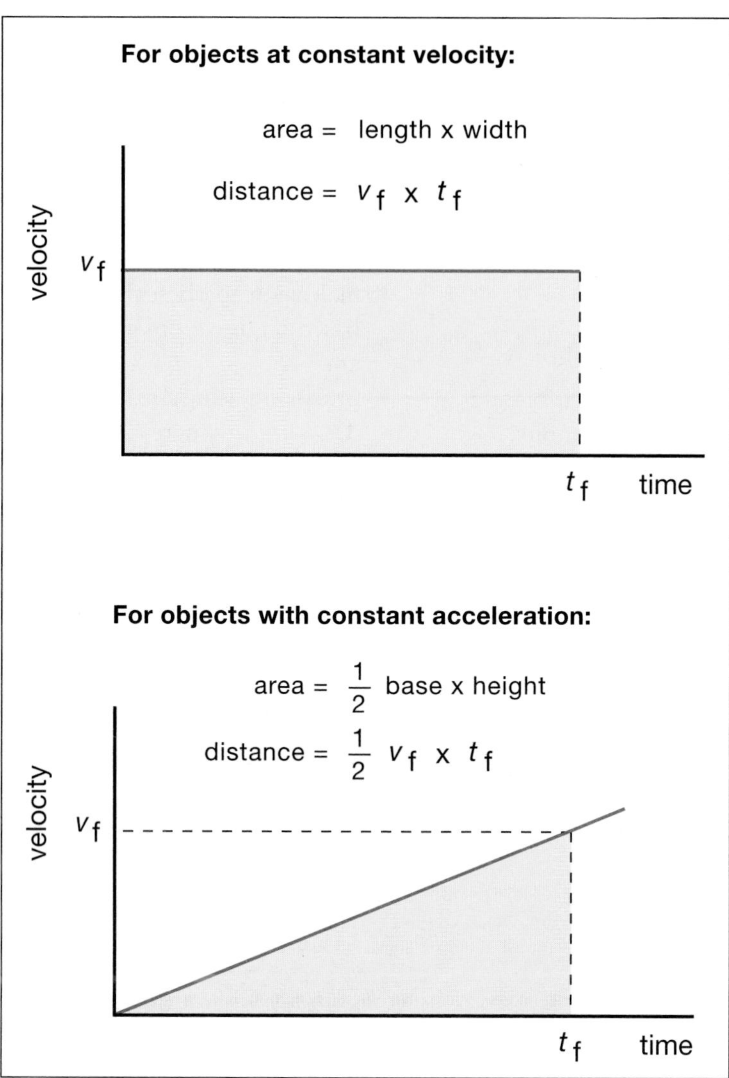

Figure T4.12 Finding the distance traveled using a velocity versus time graph. Finding the distance an object has traveled is as simple as finding the area under the curve on a velocity versus time graph. If the graph is a straight line, then you will find the area of the rectangle or the triangle bound by the times of interest.

The path an object forms while it is in projectile motion is a parabola. We can show this by writing equations for vertical and horizontal motions assuming $t_i = 0$ sec, $y_i = 0$ m, downward is positive, and g is positive.

$x = v_x t$ Horizontal position at any time t; $x_i = 0$

$y = \frac{1}{2}gt^2$ Vertical motion starting from rest at some height

Rearranging the horizontal expression for time and substituting into the vertical expression yields

$$y = \frac{1}{2}g(\frac{x}{v_x})^2.$$

Rearranging into linear form yields

$$y = (\frac{g}{2v_x^2})x^2.$$

Since all terms inside the parentheses are constants, the expression forms the classic equation for a parabola, $y = Ax^2$.

Uniform circular motion requires a constant force to continually change the velocity of an object in orbit. But the magnitude of velocity (speed) does not change in uniform circular motion. Rather, a constant force is required to continually change the *direction* of the velocity vector. As a result, force and acceleration always point to the center of the circle. Velocity is always perpendicular to the acceleration vector.

Materials—Part I

For each team of 2 students

1 ball
1 ramp (optional; see *Advance Preparation*)
2 rulers for drawing graphs

Materials—Part II

For each team of 4 students

1 ring stand assembly
1 plastic ruler
2 coins (same denomination)
2 marbles
1 stopwatch
1 meterstick
tape
flat, rigid surface, approximately 40×100 cm

Materials—Part III

For each team of 4 students

accelerometer from the explore activity

Advance Preparation

In Part I, consider using balls of several sizes and weights so that students do not think any relationships they derive depend on the type of ball used. A baseball, tennis ball, or any rubber ball works very well. Stiff cardboard at least a meter long can be used for ramps as long as students support the middle with books or some other device to prevent sagging. Wide planks of shelving are better for ramps; give yourself time to find these items before the activity, if you choose to use them.

The materials for the activities are typically found in science storerooms or as common materials elsewhere. If you can find plastic rulers with the U-shaped channel down the middle, use them for the ball ramp. If not, tape 2 plastic (bendable) rulers together to create a channel. Otherwise, use a length of garden hose or other such tubing to project the ball onto the ramp's surface.

Educational Technologies

Range finders or motion detectors connected to a computer or a graphing calculator can be beneficial to students who are still struggling with the concepts at the end of the activity. Do not begin the activity with these technologies, however, because if students use them, they will not have to think through the steps and build their own understanding. They may simply copy the graphs from the screen and memorize them, spending little time struggling with the concept and working out explanations on their own.

As You Teach

Outcomes and Indicators of Success

By the end of this activity, students should

1. be able to represent and understand the force acting on a ball tossed in the air at all points in the ball's path.

   They will show their ability by

   - sketching scaled force vectors near the ball's position at several points in the path,
   - writing highlight comments by each vector sketch,
   - modifying initial ideas based on a classroom survey, and
   - correcting false statements posed in *Stop and Think* questions.

2. generate qualitative motion graphs.

   They will show their ability by

   - designing axes for position and velocity versus time graphs,
   - including high-confidence points on graphs for positions they are sure of,
   - filling in the graphs between high-confidence points based on their initial sense of trends, and
   - transferring qualitative motion graphs to other motions.

3. generate quantitative motions graphs.

   They will show their ability by

   - making properly scaled axes based on direct observations and
   - practicing using $\Delta v = a\Delta t$ and $\Delta x = 1/2at^2$ where $t_i = 0$ by answering *Reflect and Connect* questions.

4. be able to analyze three types of motion graphs: position versus time, velocity versus time, and acceleration versus time, for

Answers to Steps 1–4 are on TE pages 177a–177b.

1. Work with your team as you examine the motion of a ball tossed in the air. Steps 1a–c will help you.
   a. Prepare to make a motion graph by drawing and labeling 2 graph axes in your science notebook. Arrange them like figure 4.10.
   b. Toss a ball straight up into the air and catch it at the same level that you released it.
   c. Assume that it takes 2 sec for the ball to complete the round-trip. Plot the motion of the ball on the position versus time graph.

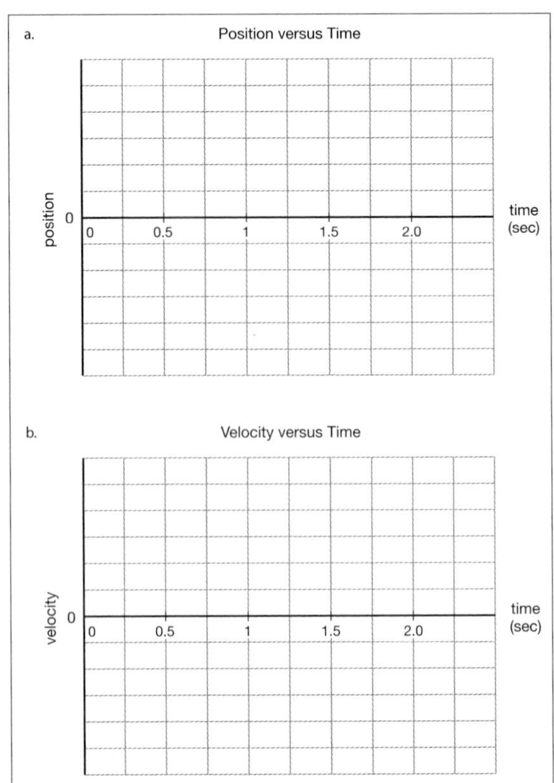

▶ **Figure 4.10 Graph axes for Step 1a.** Copy these axes into your science notebook. Notice that graph (a) plots position versus time and graph (b) plots velocity versus time. Make sure that your time axes (*x*-axes) align vertically.

relationships among the quantities of distance, velocity, and acceleration.

They will demonstrate their ability by

- generating all three types of graphs from observed motions,
- finding the slope of the line on a position versus time graph and relating it to velocity,
- finding the slope of the line on a velocity versus time graph and relating it to acceleration, and
- finding the area under the curve for a velocity versus time graph and relating it to distance.

5. relate the vector nature of $F_{net} = ma$ and falling bodies to the independence of horizontal and vertical motion.

   They will show their ability by

   - conducting a thought experiment about two marbles dropped from the same height, with one projected horizontally;
   - translating the thought experiment into an actual investigation using two pennies and a ruler;
   - sketching the path of both pennies at equal time intervals and comparing the vertical distance traveled; and
   - using the sound of the pennies hitting the floor as evidence for the law of falling bodies.

6. design an investigation to transfer what they learned in the two-penny activity to projectile motion of a ball projected horizontally onto a tilted, flat surface.

   They will show their ability by

   - determining the constant horizontal velocity of the ball,
   - determining the constant vertical acceleration, and
   - predicting where the ball will exit the flat surface for a given set of conditions.

7. understand the vector relationship among force, acceleration, velocity, and position for uniform circular motion.

   They will show their understanding by

   - making scaled vector diagrams of uniform circular motion,
   - writing highlight comments and captions on their scaled vector sketches, and
   - transferring their understanding to other circular motion situations by answering *Reflect and Connect* questions.

8. begin to understand that mathematics is essential to inquiry.

   They will demonstrate their understanding by

   - using mathematics to analyze motion graphs to find relationships among position, velocity, and acceleration;
   - calculating position, velocity, and acceleration from slope and area on motion graphs;
   - practicing calculations to find a missing quantity using $\Delta v = a\Delta t$ and $\Delta x = 1/2at^2$ where $t_i = 0$, and
   - plotting actual positions of a ball at selected intervals based on a series of calculations.

Answers to Steps 2–4 are on TE pages 177a–177b.
Answers to Steps 7–8 are on TE page 178.

Only plot the ball's motion when the ball is *not* touching your hand. Consider the point immediately after the ball leaves your hand to be at time = 0 sec and position at 0 meters (m).

2. Identify the following important features of your graph. Steps 2a–f will help you label them.
   a. Location or locations of maximum height
   b. Location or locations where the ball is moving with the fastest speed
   c. Location or locations where the ball is moving with the slowest speed
   d. Section of the path in which the ball's speed is decreasing
   e. Section of the path in which the ball's speed is increasing
   f. Location or locations where the ball changes direction
3. Mark points on your graph at the following locations.
   a. Beginning of the motion
   b. Middle of the motion
   c. End of the motion
4. Think about the velocity at each of the 3 points you marked in Step 3. Graph these 3 points on the velocity versus time graph and connect your points. Include highlight comments with your graph.

Consider whether you should connect your points with a straight line or a curved line. To make your decision, think about how the velocity is changing.

5. Use a strategy such as think-share-advise-revise (TSAR) to check your answers with another team.

You can find instructions for the TSAR strategy in the *How To* section at the back of your book.

6. Sketch several scaled force vectors to represent the forces acting on the ball at several points in the ball's path. Completing Questions 6a–c will help you.
   a. Resketch the path of the ball so that you have a clean diagram.
   b. Simplify your task by assuming zero air resistance and by only considering ball locations away from the hand, such as the positions from Steps 2a–f.
   c. Write highlight comments for each force vector and a caption under your sketch.
7. Help your teacher plan how to conduct a quick survey of classroom thinking. Record the number of students whose vector sketches showed the following.
   a. The force of gravity (the weight of the ball) always points down.

Strategies

Getting Started

For Part I, begin class by tossing a ball in the air and catching it at the same height from which you threw it. If you can juggle, consider entering the room juggling several balls. This will catch the attention of students for the day's activity. Ask the students to think about the motion of the ball as it travels through its path. Ask them to think about the forces involved, what the velocity is doing, whether the ball is accelerating, what an accelerometer would look like if you could attach it to the ball, and so on. Don't ask students to respond out loud, but simply to start thinking about these things as they prepare for the next activity. Write the focus question on the board: "What are the relationships among force, position, velocity, time, and acceleration for a ball tossed in the air?" The question is also stated in the introduction to Part I; refer to it often throughout Part I. It can be modified to refer to projectile motion and circular motion and used for Parts II and III.

Process and Procedure

Part I: Leftovers

Materials

For each team of 2 students

1 ball
1 ramp (optional; see *Advance Preparation*)
2 rulers for drawing graphs

In Step 1, students work in teams to examine the motion of a ball tossed in the air. They will copy the 2 graphs from student book figure 4.10 into their science notebooks to use throughout the activity. Students should consider only the motion from just after the ball leaves the hand until just before it hits the hand on the return trip. Make sure that students are using the position versus time graph for Steps 1–3. The velocity versus time graph is for Step 4. If students are having trouble seeing the motion that they are graphing because the ball moves too quickly, consider rolling the ball up a ramp and allowing it to roll down. This slows the action and allows for better observations of the motion.

Answers to Steps 1–4, SE pages 176–177

1–3. Student position versus time graphs for Steps 1–3 should be similar to figure T4.13. Wait until students have had a chance to revise their graphs with the TSAR strategy in Step 5 before you assess their graphs.

4. Student velocity versus time graphs should be similar to figure T4.13. Wait until students have had a chance to revise their graphs with the TSAR strategy in Step 5 before you assess their graphs.

In Step 5, students are advised to use the TSAR strategy to check their answers with another team. A detailed description of this strategy is located in the *How To*

section in the back of the student book as well as on the *TRCD*. You may want to conduct a whole-class version of this

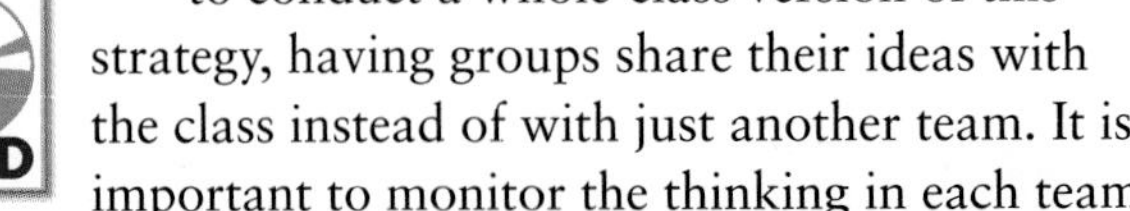

strategy, having groups share their ideas with the class instead of with just another team. It is important to monitor the thinking in each team of students to ensure that they are picking up the important concepts. This is the explain activity, and by this time in the chapter, students should be replacing misconceptions with concepts that are correct or with new concepts, all built on their experiences in the previous activities.

Students will be doing new sketches in Step 6 that include force vectors at several points along the ball's path. This step checks to see if students think there are leftover forces once the ball leaves the hand. Don't be surprised if some students think there are. Use this step to reason with the students about the motions and forces involved.

NOTES:

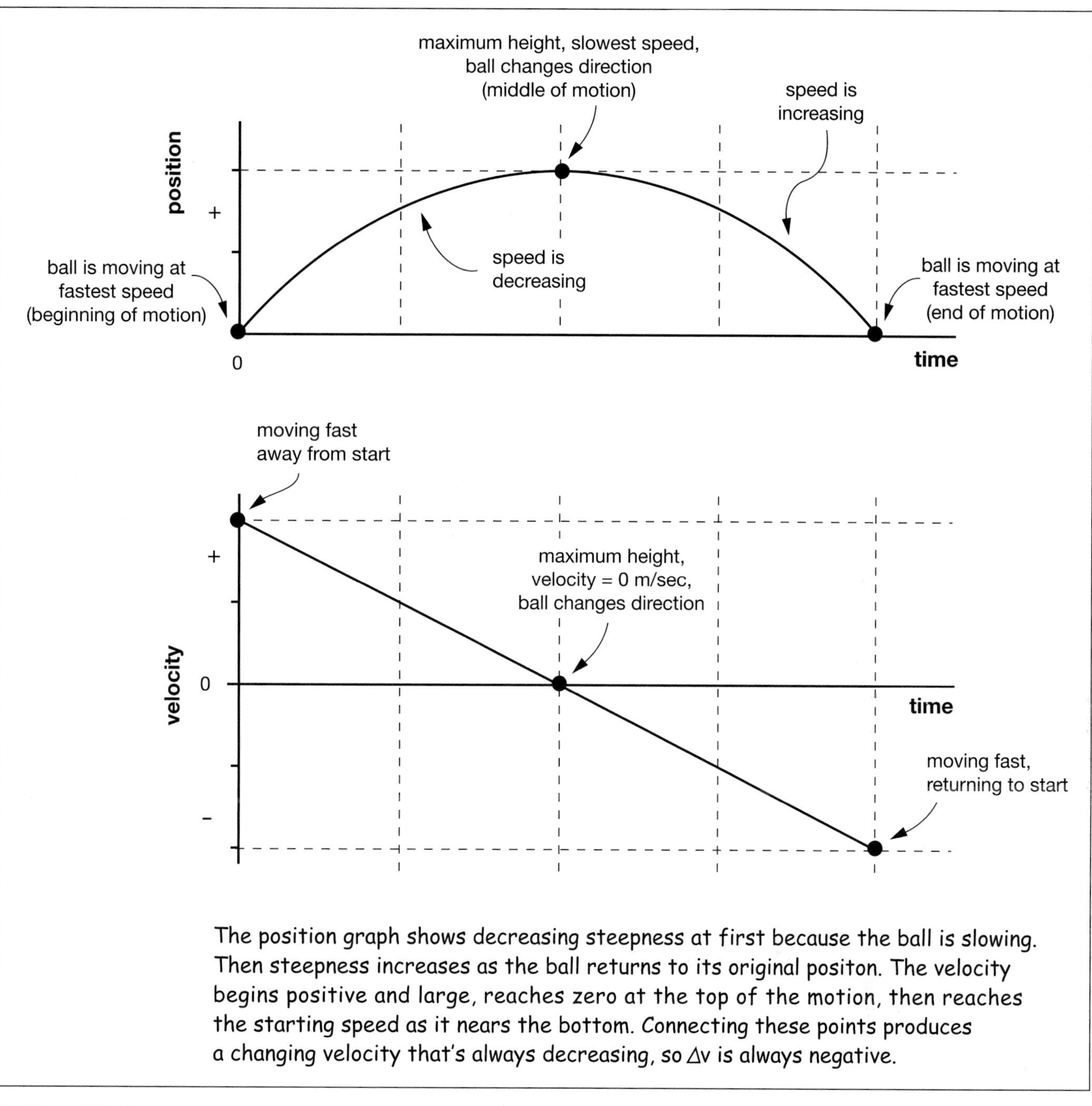

▲ **Figure T4.13** **Student answers.** Student answers for Steps 1-3 should include these graphs with labels.

NOTES:

Students will help you conduct a survey of the class in Step 7 to reveal all the current conceptions about leftover forces. This method is a low-pressure form of feedback that allows for a more open exchange of ideas among students. Any technique you can introduce to foster a natural, nonthreatening exchange of ideas, no matter how unsure a student might be about an answer, will serve students well in developing intellectual independence.

Conduct a class discussion in Step 8 to guide the students to the idea that there are *no* leftover forces from the hand once the ball has left the hand. The only force at this point is the force of gravity. Allow students time to revise their vector diagrams and highlight comments if they have changes to make. Allow students to share with the class their revised comments and sketches.

Answers to Steps 7–8, SE pages 177–178

7. The following answers to Steps 7a–f are for your information as you lead the class discussion in Step 8.
   - **a.** It is true that the force of gravity always points down.
   - **b.** This is also true since the weight of the ball doesn't change in flight.
   - **c.** There are no leftover forces from the hand.
   - **d.** At the highest point, there is still the force of gravity.
   - **e.** Students may think that since the ball slows down, the force must be decreasing. This is not true—the force of gravity is the same at all points.
   - **f.** This is not true—the force of gravity is the same at all points.
8. By the end of Step 8, students should modify their sketches from Step 6 to reflect the information given in figure T4.14. Remember to require students to record in the margin of their science notebooks both what they changed and why they changed it. Consider asking students to record their revisions in a different color.

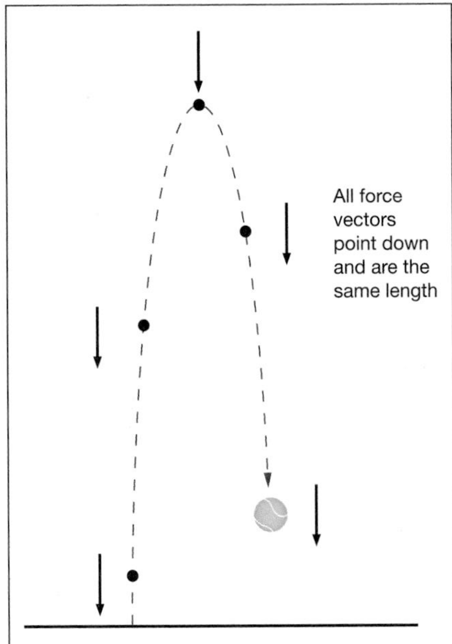

Figure T4.14 Ball toss with force vectors. Student answers should show these vectors. Students should understand that there are no leftover forces from the hand. The only force involved is the constant force of gravity, which is always pointing downward.

In Step 9, students read 2 paragraphs and then begin to analyze a position versus time graph in more detail. They will continue to analyze graphs through Step 13. The analysis will reveal the many details about motion that can be derived from position and velocity versus time graphs. It is important that students become comfortable with both positive and negative positions, velocities, and accelerations, and that they know

Answers to Steps 9–14 are on TE pages 179–181.

b. The force of gravity (the weight of the ball) always is the same length.
c. The force of the hand is left over from the toss.
d. There is zero force at the highest point.
e. The force decreases as the ball approaches the highest point.
f. The force increases as the ball returns to the hand.

8. Modify your force vectors after a classroom discussion of the survey results. Be especially careful to record what and why you changed anything. Revise your caption and highlight comments based on the best ideas of the class.
9. Read the following paragraphs as you prepare to examine figure 4.11 and complete Steps 9a–f.

   Scientists are continuously looking for relationships between variables that they test. You, too, are acting as a scientist when you analyze a motion graph and determine what each part of the graph represents. Many relationships can be discovered while observing motion and representing that motion on different types of graphs. So far in this activity, you have looked at both position versus time graphs and velocity versus time graphs. You also analyzed the forces responsible for the motion of a ball tossed in the air. How are all of these variables related?

   The motion of an object has many characteristics. Think about a car's motion. You can describe the car's velocity, position, or acceleration. The distance the car traveled in a given amount of time is another characteristic to consider. Think about these relationships and characteristics of motion as you complete the next steps in this activity.

   a. Examine the graph in figure 4.11.
   b. Describe the motion the graph represents.
   c. Calculate the slope of the line using the general formula for the slope. Be sure to include units in your calculation.
   d. State the value related to motion that you are calculating when you find the slope of the line on a position versus time graph.
   e. Describe the meaning of the sign (+ or −) assigned to this value.
   f. Write a summary statement that describes what you have learned in Step 9. Include the words *slope*, *position*, *velocity*, *direction*, *time*, *positive*, and *negative* in your description.
10. Find another valuable relationship between position versus time graphs and velocity versus time graphs by completing Steps 10a–e.

what these terms mean regarding motion. If the example they work with reflects positive velocity, give additional examples with negative velocities to make sure they can transfer their understanding to this new situation. Do not let students move to the next step without checking their answers with either another team or with you. Students should be cementing their understanding during this explain activity.

Answers to Steps 9–14, SE pages 178–180

9b. The person starts 50 m from the designated origin and walks toward the origin (in a negative direction), arriving at the origin in 10 sec. The person walks at a constant velocity.

9c. Calculate the slope of the line as follows.

$$slope = \frac{rise}{run} = \frac{\Delta y}{\Delta x} = \frac{\Delta x}{\Delta t}$$
$$= \frac{20\text{ m} - 40\text{ m}}{6\text{ sec} - 2\text{ sec}}$$
$$= -5\frac{\text{m}}{\text{sec}}$$

9d. Students should notice the units of m/sec in the slope and recognize that the value that is being calculated is velocity.

9e. The negative sign (negative velocity) means the person is walking in a negative direction.

9f. The *velocity* of an object in motion can be found by calculating the *slope* of the line on a *position* versus *time* graph of that motion. If the *slope* is negative, then the *velocity* is also negative, meaning the object is moving in a *negative direction*. If the *slope* is positive, then the *velocity* is also positive and the object is moving in a *positive direction*.

10a–c. The velocity versus time graph for the motion depicted in Step 9 is shown in figure T4.15.

10d. The characteristic of motion that this value represents is the object's change in position. The distance an object has traveled can be found by finding the area bound by the graphed line and the *x*-axis.

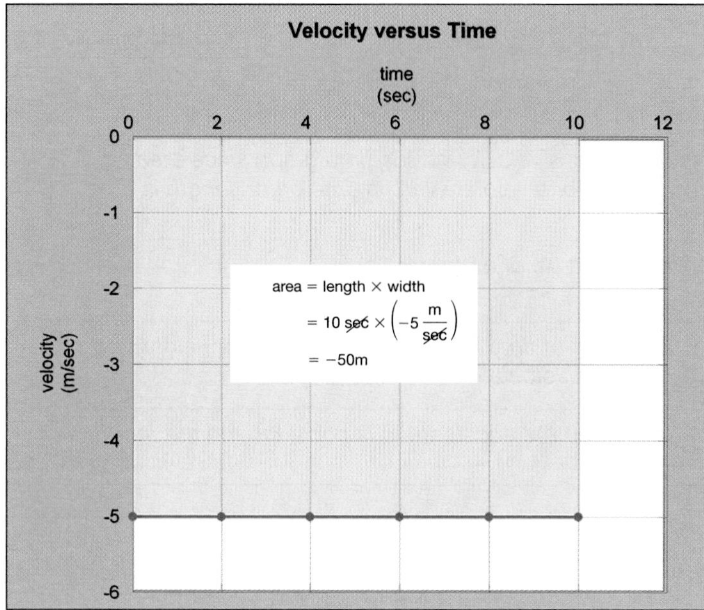

▲ **Figure T4.15 Velocity versus time graph for Step 10.** Students should draw a velocity versus time graph based on the slope they calculated from student book figure 4.11. Since the slope is constant on the position versus time graph, the line will be a straight, horizontal line on the velocity versus time graph.

a. Draw a velocity versus time graph for the motion shown in figure 4.11. Base your graph on the value you calculated in Step 9c.
b. Shade in the rectangle bounded by −5 m/sec and 10 sec.
c. Find the area of this rectangle; pay close attention to the units.
d. What characteristic of motion does this value represent? Write a sentence describing this characteristic and how you determined its value.
e. Calculate the slope of this line. What does that tell you about the object's motion?

Position versus Time

▲ **Figure 4.11 Graph for Step 9.** Use this motion graph to answer Steps 9a–f.

11. Deepen your understanding of graphical relationships by completing Steps 11a–b.
    a. Study the graph in figure 4.12 of a car's motion that starts from rest. Describe the motion of the car using the words *velocity*, *acceleration*, *constant*, *direction*, and *positive* or *negative*.

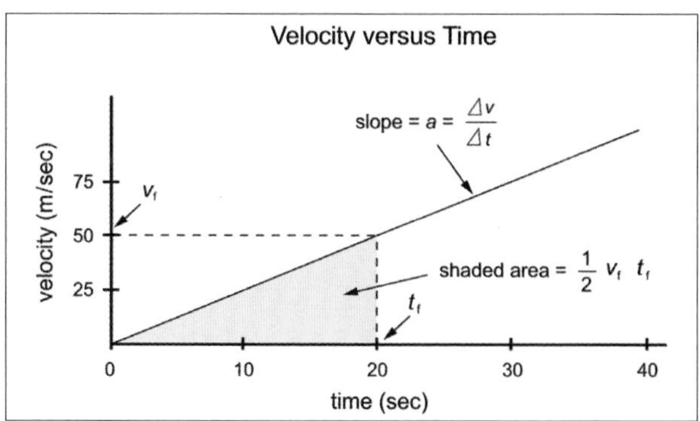

◄ **Figure 4.12 Velocity versus time graph for Step 11.** Refer to this graph as you complete Step 11.

Mathematical equation	Justification for the equation
$\Delta x = \Delta t$	*This is the general statement or relationship to calculate distance when velocity is constant and time is given. change in position = (velocity) × (time)*
x = shaded area	(Think back to Step 10.) *This is true for a velocity versus time graph since area is calculated by length times width and for a velocity versus time graph length is time and width is velocity.*
$A = \frac{1}{2}$ (*base*)(*height*)	*This is a general statement for the area (A) of a triangle.*
$x = \frac{1}{2}(t)(v)$	*This expression conveys a substitution of time for base and velocity for height and x for area where time and velocity refer to a velocity versus time graph.*
$v = at$	*This is a way to calculate velocity when the acceleration is constant and the motion begins at zero velocity at $t_x = 0$.*
$\Delta x = \frac{1}{2}(t)(a)(t)$	*This represents a substitution of $v = at$ into $x = \frac{1}{2}(t)(v)$.*
$\Delta x = \frac{1}{2}at^2$	*This represents combining the two ts into a squared term.*

▲ **Figure T4.16 Answer table for Step 11b.** Student answers should be similar to these. Ensure that students understand the development of these equations because they will use them in future problems.

11a. The car starts from rest at $t = 0$ and $x = 0$ and moves in the *positive direction* with a constantly increasing *velocity* (*constant acceleration* in the *positive direction*) for 40 sec.

11b. Student answers should be similar to those in figure T4.16.

12. Students should see that this represents a time rate of change in velocity (acceleration).

$$slope = \frac{\Delta y}{\Delta x} = \frac{\Delta v}{\Delta t}$$

$$= \frac{50\frac{\text{m}}{\text{sec}} - 25\frac{\text{m}}{\text{sec}}}{20\text{ sec} - 10\text{ sec}}$$

$$= \frac{25\frac{\text{m}}{\text{sec}}}{10\text{ sec}}$$

$$= 2.5\frac{\text{m}}{\text{sec}^2}$$

13. Students should calculate the change in position of the car as follows:

$$\Delta x = \frac{1}{2}at^2$$

$$\Delta x = \frac{1}{2}\left(2.5\frac{\text{m}}{\cancel{\text{sec}^2}}\right)(20\ \cancel{\text{sec}})^2.$$

$$\Delta x = 500\text{ m}$$

Mathematical equation	Justification for the equation
$\Delta x = \Delta t$	*This is the general statement or relationship to calculate distance when velocity is constant and time is given.*
x = shaded area	(Think back to Step 10.)
$A = \frac{1}{2}$ (*base*)(*height*)	
$x = \frac{1}{2}(t)(v)$	
$v = at$	*This is a way to calculate velocity when the acceleration is constant and the motion begins at zero velocity at $t_x = 0$.*
$\Delta x = \frac{1}{2}(t)(a)(t)$	
$\Delta x = \frac{1}{2}at^2$	

▲ **Figure 4.13 Answer table for Step 11b.** Copy this table to help you organize your answers for Step 11b. Some justifications have been filled in for you. Use the graph in figure 4.12 to help you with some of the answers.

b. Copy the table in figure 4.13 into your science notebook. Write detailed explanations or justifications in the table for each of the following mathematical steps. These steps progress in a logical sequence. Some of the justifications have been completed for you.

Each motion begins from rest (or $t_i = 0$) from a position that is defined as the origin (or $x = 0$), and the object moves in the positive direction. For the sake of convenience, let x represent position, v represent velocity, t represent time, and a represent acceleration.

12. Calculate the slope of the line in figure 4.12. Then describe the characteristic of motion that this value represents.
13. Calculate the distance the car in figure 4.12 traveled in 20 sec, starting from rest. Use the relationship you derived in Step 11b and the value you calculated in Step 12 in your calculation.
14. Write a short paragraph summarizing what you have learned about the relationships among force, acceleration, velocity, and position. Use graphs and illustrations to clarify your summary.

180 Unit 1 Interactions Are Interesting

14. If an object is moving at a constant velocity, then there is no acceleration and thus no net force on the object. The position versus time graph of this motion would show a straight, slanted line (with a positive slope for motion in the positive direction and a negative slope for motion in the negative direction). The graph of this motion on a velocity versus time graph would be a straight, horizontal line. The distance traveled (or change in position) can be calculated by finding the area between the graphed line and the x-axis on a velocity versus time graph.

If the object is not traveling at a constant velocity, then the object is accelerating, and the acceleration is the result of a net force. The graph of an object accelerating will be a curved line on a position versus time graph. If the acceleration is constant, then the graph of this motion will be a straight line on a velocity versus time graph and a straight, horizontal line on an acceleration versus time graph.

Answers to Stop and Think—Part I, SE page 181–183

1. Newton's second law does say that an object with zero velocity (and thus no acceleration) for a sustained time experiences no net force. But in the ball toss, the velocity is changing at every instant. Since there is a change in velocity, there must a net force. The classmate is incorrect in saying that zero velocity means zero net force at any point in the ball's path.
2. There is no leftover hand *force* propelling the ball higher. From the moment the ball leaves the hand, it experiences only one *force*, the *force* of gravity down. Since the *force* is down, so is the *acceleration*, the *change* of *velocity*, and the *change* of *momentum*. While the ball is moving up, weight acts like brakes on a car to slow the ball while the ball continues upward. At some point depending on the initial toss *velocity*, the ball reverses direction and begins increasing speed in the downward direction at the same rate it slowed on the way up. At all points in the path, the ball accelerates at a *constant* g, according to Newton's second law.

Answers to Stop and Think—Part I are on TE pages 181–184.

Stop & THINK

PART I

Work individually to answer these questions in your science notebook. Then compare your answers with those of a classmate. If the answers differ, involve a third student or your teacher.

1. A classmate says, "At the highest point, the ball slows to 0 m/sec. Since Newton's second law suggests that objects at rest have no net force acting on them, then the ball has no net force acting on it at the top of the toss. That's why I drew no force vector at the top."

   Respond to your classmate in writing. Carefully detail what you agree and disagree with in this classmate's comments. Be sure to explain why.

   In the elaborate activity from chapter 2, *With and Without a Net*, you learned that there were 2 examples of motion where there was no change in velocity: zero velocity (v = 0 m/sec) and constant velocity ($\frac{\Delta v}{\Delta t} = 0$).

2. A different classmate talks about the forces acting on the ball on the way to the top by saying, "There are 2 forces acting on the ball while it moves to the top—the force of gravity down and the force of my hand up. Since the ball is not moving at a constant speed, there are unbalanced forces. This happens because the hand force is greater than the gravity force at the beginning of the toss and, gradually, the hand force becomes smaller until it becomes zero at the top. Then gravity takes over, making the ball accelerate down."

   Respond to these comments by writing in your science notebook. Use the key concept words *force, velocity, change, constant, acceleration*, and *momentum* in your response.

3. Suppose you stand behind a chair and give it a shove. After a short distance, the chair leaves your hands and coasts to a stop. For the chair's motion *after leaving your hands*, explain the similarities and differences between the ball toss and the coasting chair. Copy and fill out the table in figure 4.14 to list your comparisons.

Feature of motion	Similarity	Difference
Orientation of motion (vertical or horizontal)	*Along one dimension*	*Ball is vertical, chair is horizontal*
Force from person	*Person provides force*	*None*
Force of gravity	*Occurs in both*	*Gravity in same direction (vertical) as motion in ball toss, but perpendicular to motion in chair motion*
Force of friction	*Acts to retard both motions*	*Minimal in ball toss; is the cause of the negative acceleration in chair motion*
Velocity	*Both motions show change in velocity*	*Change in velocity of chair motion results only in lower speeds*
Acceleration	*Both experience constant acceleration*	*Ball toss acceleration is "g"; chair acceleration is much less*
Momentum	*Both experience a change in momentum*	*Change in momentum vector for ball toss always points down and always points in opposite direction to motion for the chair*

▲ **Figure T4.17 Analogy table answers.** Student answers should be similar to these.

3. Student answers should be similar to those in the table in figure T4.17.
4. Justifications for the mathematical relationships follow.

4a. $F_{net} = \frac{m\Delta v}{\Delta t}$: Definition of net force as the time rate of change of momentum where momentum is (constant) mass times the time rate of change of velocity.

4b. $a = \frac{\Delta v}{\Delta t}$: Defines acceleration as the time rate of change of velocity.

4c. $F_{net} = ma$: Substitute acceleration (a) for $\frac{\Delta v}{\Delta t}$ or definition of net force as *mass* × *acceleration*.

5. The direction of the net force is always down the ramp, just like the net force on a ball tossed straight up in the air is always down. The negative sign of the acceleration also shows this. The net force is constant since the acceleration is constant.

$$F_{net} = ma$$
$$= (0.035 \text{ kg})(-2.0 \frac{\text{m}}{\text{sec}^2})$$
$$= -0.070 \frac{\text{kg m}}{\text{sec}^2} \text{ or } -0.070 \text{ N}$$

STOP & THINK, PART I, continued

Feature of motion	Similarity	Difference
Orientation of motion (vertical or horizontal)		
Force from person		
Force of gravity		
Force of friction		
Velocity		
Acceleration		
Momentum		

▲ **Figure 4.14 Comparison table.** Think about the similarities and differences between the motion of a ball tossed in the air and a chair shoved across the floor. Use this table to organize your comparisons.

4. Write justifications or explanations in your science notebook for each of the following mathematical relationships.

   Consider using a table like the one in Step 11b.

   a. $F_{net} = \frac{m\Delta v}{\Delta t}$

   b. $a = \frac{\Delta v}{\Delta t}$

   c. $F_{net} = ma$

5. Suppose you measure a constant acceleration of −2.0 m/sec for a 0.035-kg ball rolling up and down a ramp. What is the net force on the ball (both for direction and magnitude)? How would you determine whether or not the net force is constant?
6. How long does it take a diver to reach the water below a 10-m diving platform?
7. A dragster covers a quarter mile in 6.0 sec, accelerating constantly all the way. What is its acceleration in m/sec²?

182 Unit 1 Interactions Are Interesting

6. Sample student calculations are shown here.

$$\Delta x = \frac{1}{2}at^2$$

$$t = \sqrt{\frac{2\Delta x}{a}}$$

$$= \sqrt{\frac{2(10 \cancel{m})}{9.8 \frac{\cancel{m}}{sec^2}}}$$

$$= 1.4 \text{ sec}$$

7. Student calculations should be similar to these.

$$\Delta x = \frac{1}{2}at^2$$

$$a = \frac{2\Delta x}{t^2}$$

$$= 2\frac{(0.25 \text{ mile})}{(6.0 \text{ sec})^2}$$

$$= \left(14 \times 10^{-2} \frac{\cancel{\text{mile}}}{\text{sec}^2}\right)\left(\frac{1{,}600 \text{ m}}{1 \cancel{\text{mile}}}\right)$$

$$= 22 \frac{\text{m}}{\text{sec}^2}$$

This is a very large acceleration!

8a. Student paragraphs should be similar to the following: "The ball rolls with positive acceleration, then negative acceleration. I can tell from the slope of the velocity versus time line, which is positive at first, then changes to negative and a smaller slope. For positive acceleration, the ball must experience a positive net force. A ball accelerating down a hill would do this as long as friction was less than the force down the hill. For negative acceleration, the ball must experience a net backward force. This could happen if the ball rolls forward on a carpet. The frictional force will act like brakes and slow the ball to a stop. The smaller slope for the negative acceleration section means the frictional force on the ball due to the carpet is smaller than the net force on the ball as it rolls down the hill."

8b. Sample student calculations are shown here.

ramp

$$a = \frac{\Delta v}{\Delta t} = \frac{v_f - v_i}{t_f - t_i}$$

$$= \frac{1\frac{\text{m}}{\text{sec}} - 0\frac{\text{m}}{\text{sec}}}{1 \text{ sec} - 0 \text{ sec}}$$

$$= 1\frac{\text{m}}{\text{sec}^2}$$

carpet

$$a = \frac{0\frac{\text{m}}{\text{sec}} - 1\frac{\text{m}}{\text{sec}}}{10 \text{ sec} - 1 \text{ sec}}$$

$$= -0.11\frac{\text{m}}{\text{sec}^2}$$

8c. The ball rolling on the carpet is moving forward, which is typically called positive velocity. But the acceleration is negative since the slope of the velocity versus time graph is also negative. Since net force and acceleration are always in the same direction, force is also negative. Therefore, any situation like applying brakes on a forward-moving car exhibits positive velocity, negative acceleration, and negative net force.

8d. Both values of acceleration from the ball graph are less than 10 m/sec², or the approximate value (magnitude) of *g*. This is reasonable since neither the ball rolling down the ramp nor the ball rolling on the carpet is the same as free fall. That is, when the ball is on the ramp, some of the force on the

8 Consider the motion of a ball rolling down a ramp, onto the carpet, and finally coming to a stop. The motion is shown on the graph in figure 4.15. Complete Questions 8a–d for this situation.

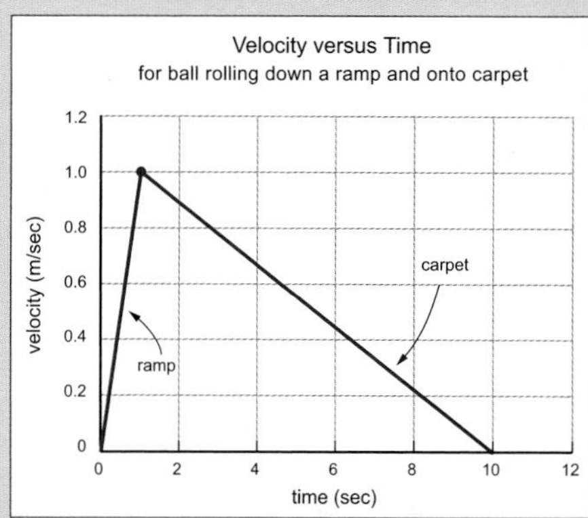

▲ **Figure 4.15 Velocity versus time graph for a ball rolling down a ramp and onto carpet.** What quantities can you determine from this graph? How does the acceleration of the ball compare to *g*?

Think back to the evaluate activity, *Forces to Go; Forces to Stop*, from chapter 2 for a reminder.

a. Write a short paragraph describing the physical conditions necessary to produce this graph of a rolling ball. Pay particular attention to the forces involved.

b. Calculate the acceleration associated with both sections of the graph. Be sure to show the connection between slope and the algebraic definition for acceleration: $a = \frac{\Delta v}{\Delta t}$.

c. Determine which section of the graph, if any, depicts positive velocity, negative acceleration, and a backward force. Explain how 1 ball can have this set of motions at the same time.

d. Compare and contrast your calculated values of acceleration from Question 8b to the constant *g*. Be especially careful to use *g* as a way to determine if your calculated accelerations are reasonable.

Chapter 4 Physics Is Moving 183

ball is due to the ramp supporting the ball, preventing it from falling straight down. Thus, the net force down the ramp is less than g. On the carpet, the net force in the horizontal direction is backward (negative) due to friction and much less than the weight of the ball. Thus, the slow-down acceleration is much less than g.

Process and Procedure

Part II: Projectile Motion

Materials

For each team of 4 students

1 ring stand assembly
1 plastic ruler
2 coins (same denomination)
2 marbles
1 stopwatch
1 meterstick
tape
flat, rigid surface, approximately 40×100 cm

In Step 1, students are asked to think about and predict what they would hear when 2 marbles (one given an initial horizontal velocity and one dropped from the same height) hit the floor. Monitor their predictions, especially how the students represent what they think. Look for an indication of the path of both balls. You can use these initial drawings to assess what students know about projectile motion.

Students will look for your guidance in testing their predictions in Step 2. You will have to show students how to do this. Place the ruler on a tabletop such that about 6 centimeters (cm) hang off the edge close to one corner. Place 1 penny close to one edge of the table and the other on top of the part of the ruler extending off the tabletop. Use one hand placed on the back part of the ruler as a pivot point, then pull back the opposite end of the ruler as if it were a spring. Release the ruler so it simultaneously projects one penny horizontally off the table and allows the other penny to drop vertically. See figure T4.18. Ensure that the students actually hear 1 click when the coins hit the ground at the same time. This may require repeating the step several times.

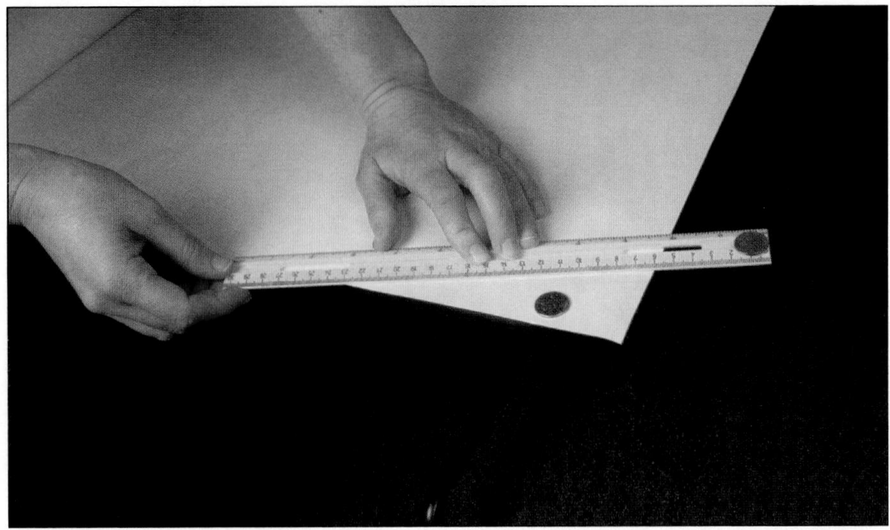

▲ **Figure T4.18 Coin-launching apparatus.** Show students this setup to properly project 1 penny horizontally off the table and drop 1 penny vertically. You may have to repeat the procedure several times to ensure that students actually hear only 1 click as the pennies hit the ground at the same time.

Part II: Projectile Motion

▲ **Figure 4.16 Hitting the bull's-eye.** At what angle and speed would you have to throw the dart to hit the bull's-eye?

One nice thing about analyzing motion is that the same set of principles applies to most motions in our everyday environment. So once you understand those principles, you can describe the motion of everything from mountains to molecules. Now that's a good use of what you learn in school!

What kind of motion would result if you threw a ball horizontally, as fast as you could? Once the ball left your hand, what path would the ball follow? Where would it land? How long would it take to hit the ground? What angle and speed would you have to throw a dart to hit a bull's-eye (figure 4.16)?

As in each of the preceding activities, force is the key. Once you determine what forces act on the ball during flight, you can understand acceleration, velocity, and position. And as before, you can communicate your understanding of motion using a variety of methods.

In Part II, you and your team will apply what you already know about forces and motion to understanding the motion of a ball tossed horizontally. This motion is often called projectile motion.

Materials

For each team of 4 students

1 ring stand assembly
1 plastic ruler
2 coins (same denomination)
2 marbles
1 stopwatch
1 meterstick
tape
flat, rigid surface, approximately 40 × 100 cm

Process and Procedure

Projectile motion involves motion in the horizontal plane (often parallel to the ground) and in the vertical plane (perpendicular to the ground). That is, there is motion in two dimensions. But are there forces in two dimensions?

To answer this question, you and your team will investigate the motion of two objects, both beginning their motion at exactly the same time from the same height. The only difference is that one object drops straight down and the other receives a hit in the horizontal direction.

184 Unit 1 Interactions Are Interesting

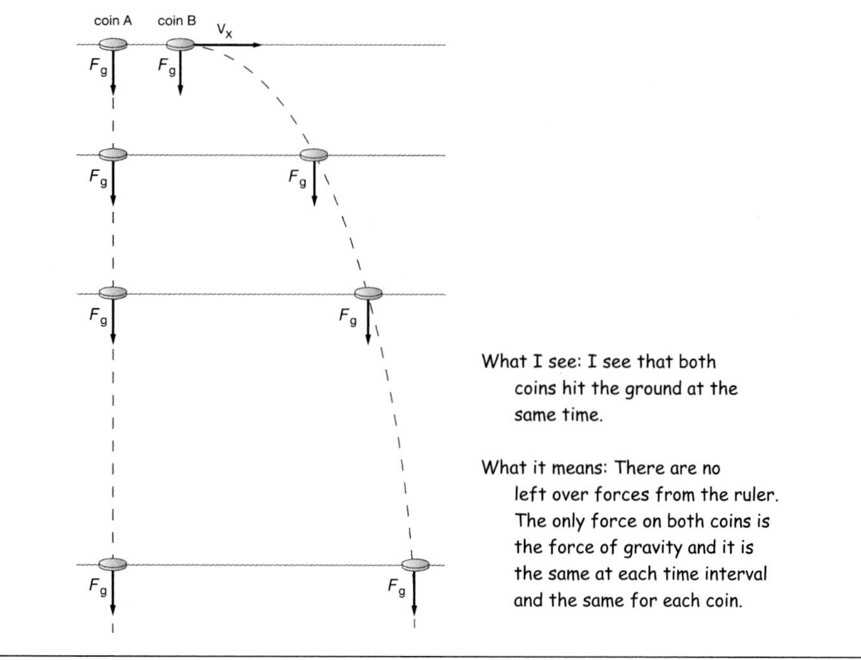

Figure T4.19 Sample sketch of the locations of 2 pennies at several times during Step 3. This sketch shows the pennies at several equal time intervals, along with annotations.

1. Suppose the 2 objects discussed in the preceding paragraph are identical marbles. Predict how many "clicks" you would hear if the horizontally and vertically moving marbles begin motion at the same time (figure 4.17). (A click is the sound of a marble hitting the floor for the first time.) Explain your reasoning.
2. Test your prediction with a plastic ruler and 2 coins, as instructed by your teacher.
3. Sketch the position of each coin at several regular time intervals *after* the motion begins. Include the following in your sketches.
   a. Scaled and labeled force vectors for each position
   b. Highlight comments that focus on the force vectors
4. Explain in your science notebook how you know whether or not there was a leftover plastic ruler force acting on the coin that projected sideways.

Use sketches and words in your answer.

5. Explain how you know whether or not there was a constant net force acting on both coins.

Sometimes motion is difficult to analyze because it happens too fast. If you can slow the motion, yet maintain the relationship among all the key concepts, then you can have time to make better observations. In Step 6, you will slow down the motion so that you can make better observations. You will use rolling marbles to simulate the motion of the pennies.

6. Use the materials recommended by your teacher to assemble a tilted, flat surface and a ball ramp. Your apparatus needs to have the following features.
   a. The tilted surface is very stable and its angle of tilt is less than 10 degrees (°).

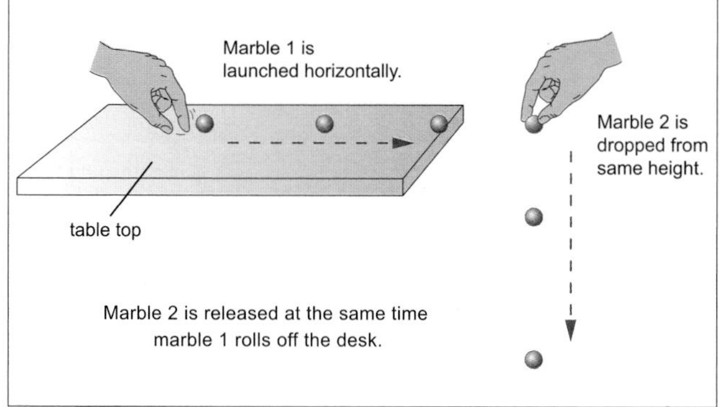

Figure 4.17 Marble launch and drop. If one marble is dropped and another is launched horizontally at the same time, which one will hit the ground first? Or will they hit at the same time?

Answers to Steps 3–5, SE page 185

3. Students sketch the position of each coin and draw scaled and labeled force vectors. They should also include highlight comments. Figure T4.19 shows an example.
4. Use the drawing from Step 3 to address this question. In it, students should find no horizontal forces after the hit. Thus, there is no leftover ruler force.
5. There was a constant net force acting on both pennies. It was the gravitational force (weight) acting vertically in the downward direction.

In Step 6, students construct a tilted, flat surface to slow down the projectile motion so that it is easier to observe. Students can use extra books, ring stands, or boxes to construct the tilted surface. The key to assemble the ball ramp is that the surface should not change while the ball rolls across it. Several arrangements can work to project the ball onto the flat surface horizontally. Reproducibility is very important for this activity. Thus, the ball ramp should be stable. The ball ramp should project the ball exactly parallel to the top of the edge of the large tilted surface. An example setup is shown in figure T4.20.

Students begin using their apparatuses in Step 7. This step allows students to practice with the apparatus before collecting quantitative data. At various flat surface angles and ball ramp angles, students should release a second ball from the top of the tilted, flat surface at the instant the ramp ball hits the tilted surface. Students will observe in all cases that both balls "hit" the bottom of the tilted surface at the same time.

Students summarize their findings and observations in Step 8. Students should conclude that vertical and horizontal motions are independent regardless of the tilt angle of the flat surface or the angle of the ball ramp. This is the important concept for this part of the activity. Use the TSAR strategy or a form of class discussion to ensure that students have gathered evidence that this concept is true and that they can relate the evidence to the concept.

In Step 9, students read *Motion in Two Dimensions, Force in One Dimension*. The student book suggests that students read this with a partner and select a strategy to help with comprehension. Choose from the many strategies listed in the *How To* section in the back of the student book.

In Step 10, students explain the title of the reading. Check that they understand that in projectile motion there is independent motion in 2 dimensions—horizontal and vertical. Also, there is only a force in the vertical direction due to gravity. There is *no* leftover force in the horizontal direction.

Steps 11 and 12 are designated as challenge opportunities. You be the judge of your students' readiness to attempt these 2 steps. However, do not underestimate your students' abilities. They may do quite well on these 2 questions if they have completely grasped the concepts in previous steps and activities.

Answers to Step 11, SE page 186

11a. Student graphs should be similar to figure T4.21.

11b. Figure T4.22 shows sample student work.

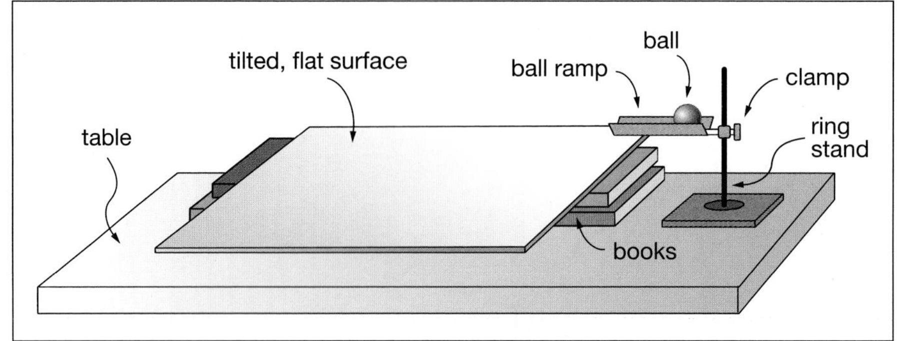

Figure T4.20 Projectile-motion apparatus for Step 6. This sketch represents the equipment arrangement for Part II.

Answers to Step 11 are on TE pages 186–186b.

b. The ball ramp attaches to the top right corner of the tilted surface. It projects the ball horizontally, without bouncing, as the ball moves from the ball ramp to the tilted surface.
c. The ball ramp is very stable and its angle of tilt does not change during a set of trials.

7. Investigate whether the results of your penny experiment transfer to this apparatus. Consider the following during your investigation.
   a. The *Observation Guidelines*

You used the *Observation Guidelines* in the engage activity. You can find the guidelines in that activity or in the *How To* section in the back of your student book.

   b A variety of angles for the ball ramp
   c. A variety of angles for the tilted surface
8. Summarize your findings from Step 7; use at least 2 forms of scientific communication. Then compare your summary with the summaries of at least 2 classmates. Check with your teacher if you have any questions.

Examples of scientific communication that you may want to use are paragraphs, charts or tables, graphs, or mathematical equations or relationships.

9. Relate what you have learned to the information in the reading *Motion in Two Dimensions, Force in One Dimension*. Read the passage with a partner, using a strategy that works best to help you understand the reading.
10. Use what you have learned in this activity to explain the title of the reading, *Motion in Two Dimensions, Force in One Dimension*. Use 2 different types of scientific communication to form your explanation.

Challenge Opportunity

11. Select 1 set of angles for the ball ramp and tilted surface from your investigation in Step 7. Generate qualitative graphs for the criteria in Steps 11a–b.
   a. Motion graphs for position, velocity, acceleration, and force (aligned by time axes): The ball's motion is in the direction parallel to the top edge of the tilted surface (that is, only in the plane of the board).
   b. Motion graphs for position, velocity, acceleration, and force (aligned by time axes): The ball's motion is perpendicular to the top edge of the tilted board (that is, only in the plane of the board).

186 | Unit 1 Interactions Are Interesting

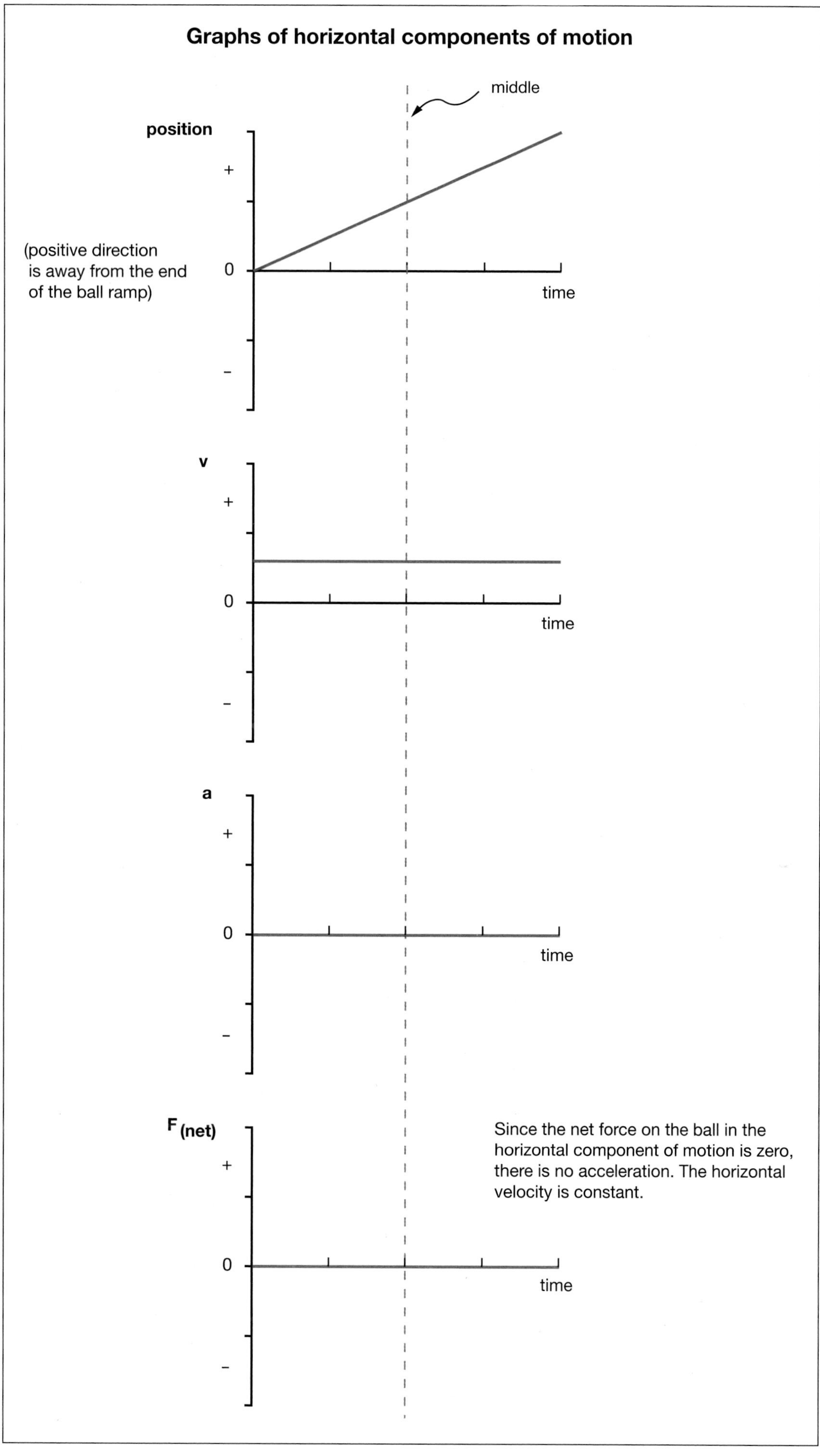

▲ **Figure T4.21 Sample horizontal motion graphs.** These graphs represent possible student answers for Step 11a. This is motion parallel to the top edge of the tilted surface.

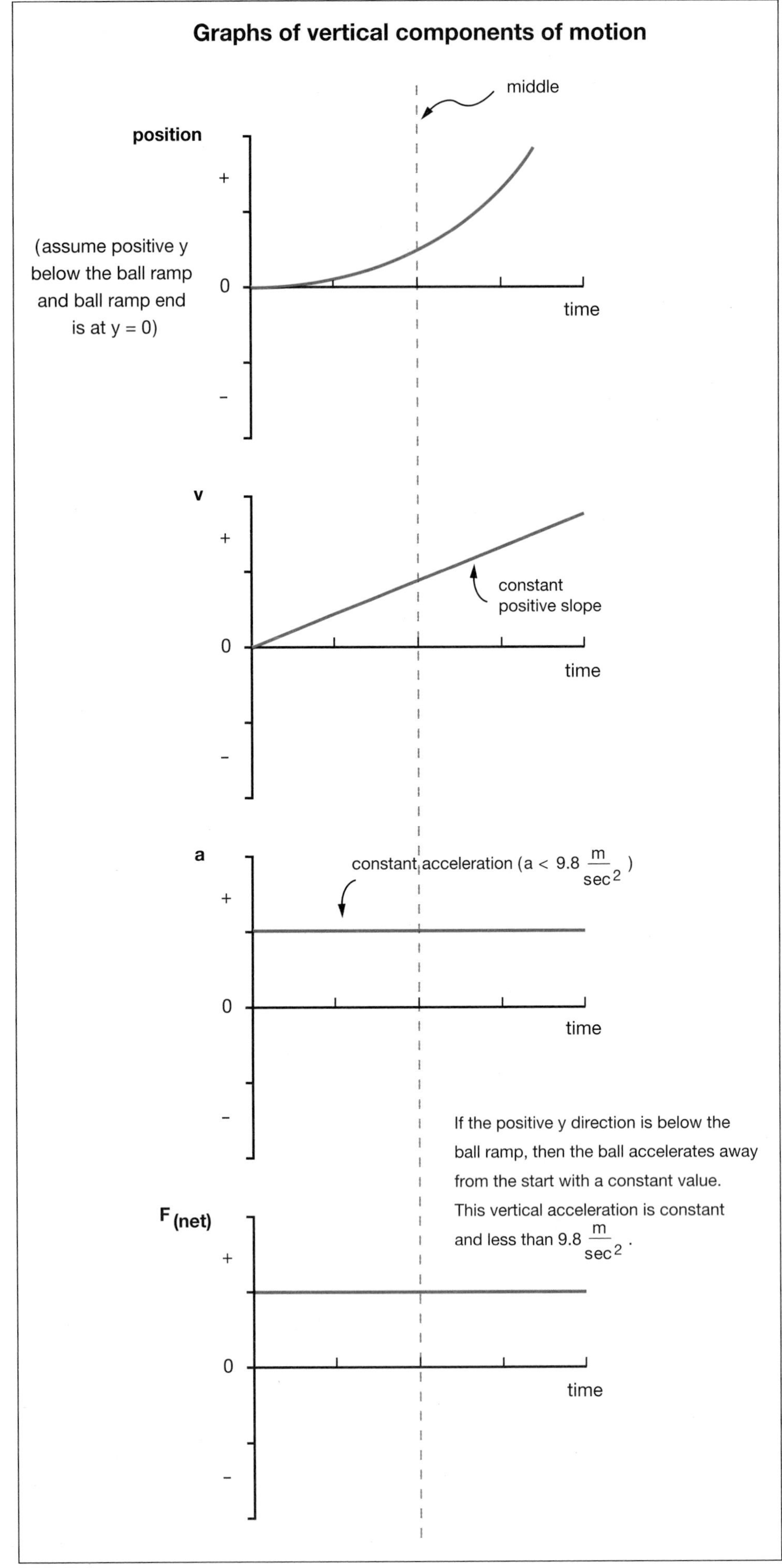

▲ **Figure T4.22 Sample vertical motion graphs.** These graphs represent possible student answers for Step 11b. This is motion perpendicular to the top edge of the tilted surface.

NOTES:

READING

Motion in Two Dimensions, Force in One Dimension

You have learned that when an object is launched horizontally, the motion in the horizontal direction is *independent* of the motion in the vertical direction. (This is also true for objects launched at an angle.) You saw evidence of this when two pennies landed at the same time, although one penny was launched horizontal to the ground. Even though that penny had an initial horizontal velocity, the velocity and acceleration in the vertical direction were unaffected. Because of this, the penny landed at the same time as the one dropped from the same height.

The curved path of a projectile may seem complicated. But we can simplify it by looking at the horizontal and vertical motions separately. We can do this since they act independently of each other. The horizontal component of the motion of a ball thrown off a balcony is the same as the horizontal motion of the ball rolling along a flat surface. (That is, if we can ignore the slowing effect of friction). The ball rolls along the surface at a constant velocity. The ball moves equal distances in the same intervals of time. The ball has no horizontal acceleration. Similarly, a ball thrown as a projectile off a balcony has this same horizontal motion. The horizontal position of the ball at any time can be calculated by using the formula $\Delta x = v_x \Delta t$, where v_x represents the velocity (v) in the x, or horizontal, direction.

The vertical motion of a ball thrown off a balcony is equivalent to the vertical motion of a ball dropped from the same height. The ball accelerates downward in the direction of the force of gravity. You can use the relationship you discovered in Part I, Step 11 to calculate either the vertical position or the time of the fall. This relationship, for vertical motion starting from rest, is represented by $\Delta y = \frac{1}{2}at^2$ when $t_i = 0$. Since the ball is in free fall, the acceleration it experiences is the acceleration due to gravity (g). Thus, the equation becomes $\Delta y = \frac{1}{2}gt^2$ when downward is defined as in the positive direction.

12. Use what you know about the independence of horizontal and vertical motions to plot the actual position of the ball at 0.1-sec time intervals. Follow Steps 12a–d to accomplish this.

Do this for only 1 tilted surface angle and 1 ball ramp angle.

a. Determine the ball's exit speed from the ball ramp.

For Step 12, students plot the actual positions of the ball on the ramp at 0.1-sec time intervals and then check the accuracy of the calculations and measurements. Students may find it difficult to find the ball's exit speed from the ramp. It may take a prompt on your part, but eventually students should place the ball ramp so that it projects the ball off a table onto the floor. If students measure the height of the table, they can calculate the time of flight using the equation $\Delta y = \frac{1}{2}gt^2$. Then if students determine the place where the ball hits the floor, they can calculate the speed of the ball at the bottom of the ball ramp by substituting the time of flight into the equation $\Delta x = v_x \Delta t$. Students must use the same ramp angle in this process as they do on their tilted surfaces for the rest of the step.

To determine the acceleration of the ball on the tilted surface, they can use $\Delta y = \frac{1}{2}at^2$ to solve for the acceleration where $t_i = 0$. Students measure the distance along the flat surface that the ball moves vertically (this distance is along the ramp, not perpendicular to the floor). Then they time the ball's fall. They should calculate the average acceleration for several trials. In Step 12c, students calculate and mark the spots on the tilted surface. For vertical position, use $\Delta y = \frac{1}{2}at^2$, where a is the acceleration calculated in Step 11b and t is every 0.10 sec. For horizontal position, use $\Delta x = v_x \Delta t$, where v_x is the horizontal velocity calculated in Step 11a and t increases in steps of 0.10 sec each. Finally, students mark the surface and check for accuracy in Step 11d.

Answers to Stop and Think—Part II, SE pages 188–189

1a. Answers may be in the form of a sketch similar to figure T4.23.

1b. The horizontal velocity does not influence the vertical acceleration. So free fall governs the time to the ground.

$$\Delta y = \frac{1}{2}gt^2$$

$(y_i = 0; t_i = 0;$ down is positive$)$

$$1{,}500 \text{ m} = \frac{1}{2}\left(9.8 \frac{\text{m}}{\text{sec}^2}\right)t^2$$

$$t = \sqrt{\frac{(1{,}500 \cancel{\text{m}})(2)}{9.8 \frac{\cancel{\text{m}}}{\text{sec}^2}}}$$

$$t = 17.5 \text{ sec.}$$

1c. Since the crate moves with the same constant horizontal velocity as the plane,

$$\Delta x = v_x \Delta t \ (x_i = 0; t_i = 0)$$

$$x = \left(200 \frac{\text{m}}{\text{sec}}\right)(17.5 \text{ sec})$$

$$x = 3{,}500 \text{ m.}$$

1d. The plane and crate shared the same horizontal velocity and still do. Thus, the plane also moves 3,500 m horizontally.

1e. If you looked down to the crate, it would look as though it were falling straight down, with no horizontal movement. This is true since the plane and crate share the same horizontal velocity, with the only movement of the crate being due to freefall (straight down).

2a. As with the plane and crate, the ball hits directly under its release point at the base of the mast.

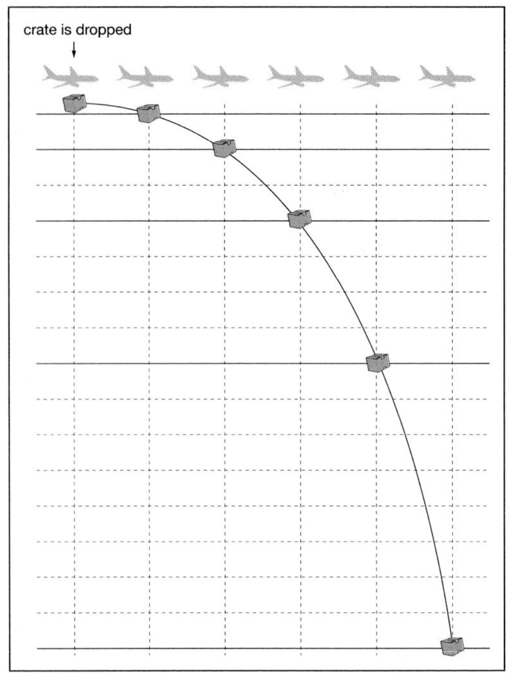

Figure T4.23 Plane and dropped crate. This sketch represents possible student answers for *Stop and Think* Question 1a.

Answers to Stop & Think—Part II are on TE pages 188–189.

b. Determine the vertical acceleration of the ball on the tilted surface.
c. Use the calculated values from Steps 12a–b to determine the horizontal and vertical positions of the ball at 0.1-sec intervals.
d. Check the accuracy of your measurements and calculations by placing a small piece of tape on each position you determined in Step 12c. Then watch how close the ball rolls to those tape marks.

Don't forget to reproduce exactly both the ball ramp and the tilted surface angles from Steps 12a–b.

Stop & THINK

PART II

Read through each question completely before answering it in your science notebook. Check your answers with classmates before proceeding to the next activity.

1. Suppose an airplane carrying a heavy crate of food for flood victims flies parallel to the ground at an altitude of 1,500 m and a speed of 200 m/sec. It then releases the crate of food. Disregard the effect of air resistance when answering Questions 1a–e.
   - **a.** What do the relative positions of the plane and crate look like for equal time intervals? The time intervals start at the moment of release and end when the crate hits the ground.
   - **b.** How many seconds does it take the crate to hit the ground?
   - **c.** How many horizontal meters away from the release point will the crate hit the ground?
   - **d.** How many meters will the plane travel horizontally from the release point until the time the crate hits the ground?
   - **e.** Describe what the crate would look like to you from the airplane.
2. Suppose you rode along on the top part of a ship's mast carrying a heavy ball. (The mast is the tall beam perpendicular to the ship's deck). The ship travels at a constant velocity of 4 m/sec, and you hold the ball 12 m above the deck.
   - **a.** Relative to the mast, where would the ball hit when you dropped it?
   - **b.** Use what you understand about force, acceleration, vertical, and horizontal motion to explain your answer in Question 2a.

2b. The ball experiences no net force in the horizontal direction once it is released, so according to Newton's second law, it keeps its constant horizontal velocity, which is exactly equal to the mast's velocity. The ball accelerates downward in free fall.

3. The ball hits behind the mast. This is true since the ship continues to accelerate after the ball is released, after which the ball no longer experiences any horizontal acceleration.

4. The dock is stationary relative to the ship. Therefore, the ball will travel forward some distance from the dock, but still land at the base of the mast. The ball will appear to fall in a path of projectile motion, also called parabolic motion.

Process and Procedure

Part III: Uniform Circular Motion

Materials

For each team of 4 students

accelerometer from the explore activity

In Step 1, students examine their accelerometers and draw scaled vector diagrams with labels and a caption that depict all the forces acting on the water. The force of the bottle bottom is up on the water and is equal to but in an opposite direction from the force of gravity on the water. For the water to be moving, the forces *on the water* would have to be unbalanced.

The idea in Step 2 is to hold the accelerometer's top at arm's length and spin. Students spin with the accelerometer in a different position than they did in earlier activities. Rather than keeping the long axis of the accelerometer perpendicular to the floor, they grasp it by the neck of the bottle and spin it with the long axis parallel to the floor. The bottom of the bottle will begin to lift, yet the water will remain relatively parallel to the bottom of the bottle. If the accelerometers are completely full of water, you may want students to pour out about half of the water. This allows students to see the movement of the water. Caution students about dizziness.

3 Repeat Questions 2a–b, except answer them for a ship that is accelerating.

4 Repeat Questions 2a–b, except answer them for the ball's landing point relative to a dock directly between the ship and the shore.

Part III: Uniform Circular Motion

Materials

For each team of 4 students

accelerometer from the explore activity

Process and Procedure

In Part II, the force of gravity always points perpendicular to Earth's surface. The force of gravity constantly pulls the object straight down. Then why does a projectile's path curve? It curves because of Newton's second law. When there is a net force, there will be a change in motion. Since there is a net vertical force, the object accelerates toward Earth's surface. The combination of horizontal constant velocity and vertical *changing* velocity results in curved motion.

For a projectile that is thrown horizontally, the horizontal velocity and gravity are perpendicular only at the instant the motion begins. After that, the projectile's velocity vector begins to point increasingly downward. It is no longer perpendicular to the force of gravity (figure 4.18).

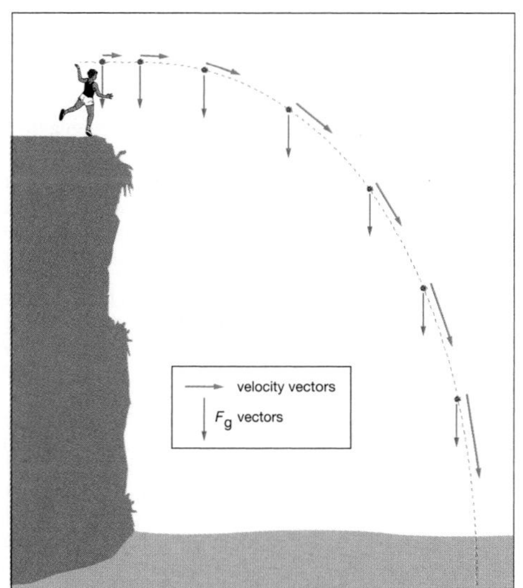

▲ **Figure 4.18 Velocity vectors on a projectile.** At the instant the projectile motion begins, the horizontal velocity vector is perpendicular to the force due to gravity. How does the geometric relationship of these two vectors change as the motion of the projectile continues?

NOTES:

Answers to Steps 3–4 are on TE page 190a.

There is another type of common motion in which the net force is *always* perpendicular to the velocity. And that's the motion you will investigate with your team in Part III.

1. Place your accelerometer on the table in front of you, and then complete Steps 1a–c.

Focus on the water in your accelerometer for these steps. Don't focus on the floating cork or peanut until you are asked specifically about it.

   a. Draw a scaled force vector diagram of all the forces acting on the water.
   b. Label each vector with the source of the force.
   c. Include a caption explaining why the water isn't moving relative to the bottom of the bottle.

2. Use the *Observation Guidelines* in this chapter to focus on your accelerometer. As you stand, hold the bottle by its top, with the long axis of the bottle *parallel* to the ground, and begin to spin it like helicopter blades.

The spinning bottle will form a circle. Be sure each team member observes both the center of the circle and the outside of the circle. Try to keep the spin rate as constant as possible. You may have to pour some water out so it is only half full.

3. Analyze the water's motion by doing Steps 3a–e.
   a. List all the quantities that are constant when the water is not moving relative to the bottom of the bottle during spinning. Include evidence for each item in your list.
   b. Draw scaled and labeled force vector diagrams (viewed from above) of the forces acting on the water when it is not moving relative to the bottom of the bottle during spinning.

Since the water is not falling down during spinning, omit the gravity force vector. Focus only on the force or forces involved with circular motion. Draw diagrams for at least 2 different positions around the circle.

   c. Add a labeled velocity vector of the water to your diagrams from Step 3b.
   d. Add a labeled acceleration vector of the water to your diagrams from Step 3b.

Use your accelerometer to confirm the direction of the acceleration and force vectors you are drawing for uniform circular motion. You will have to spin in a circle while holding the long axis of the accelerometer *perpendicular* to the floor during this step. Observe the lean of the cork or peanut to determine the direction of the acceleration and force. Fill the accelerometer with water if necessary.

   e. Repeat Steps 3b–d for at least 2 other positions of the water as the bottle moves in a circle.

Answers to Steps 3–4, SE pages 190–191

3a. The radius is constant because the arm length did not change. The water's mass did not change because no water escaped. The spin rate remained constant once the final spin rate was established, which suggests the speed of the water remained constant. The amount of pull force on the bottle's top remained constant for a constant spin rate.

3b–e. Sample answers are shown in figure T4.24.

4a. The velocity vector is always perpendicular to the force vector, as shown in the sketch for Step 3. The force is always in the direction of acceleration and the acceleration is toward the center, so the force is toward the center.

The velocity is $\frac{\Delta x}{\Delta t}$ and for any short time interval, the direction of x is close to the tangent of the circle at that point. (Students may just draw a sketch depending on their understanding of the phrase, tangent of the circle.) So the velocity is perpendicular to the force at any point.

4b. The speed of the water in uniform circular motion is constant.

4c. The water is accelerating because the *direction* of the velocity is constantly changing. Acceleration is a change in velocity—that can either be a change in the magnitude (speed), the direction, or both.

4d. Sketches for Step 4d should be similar to figure T4.25.

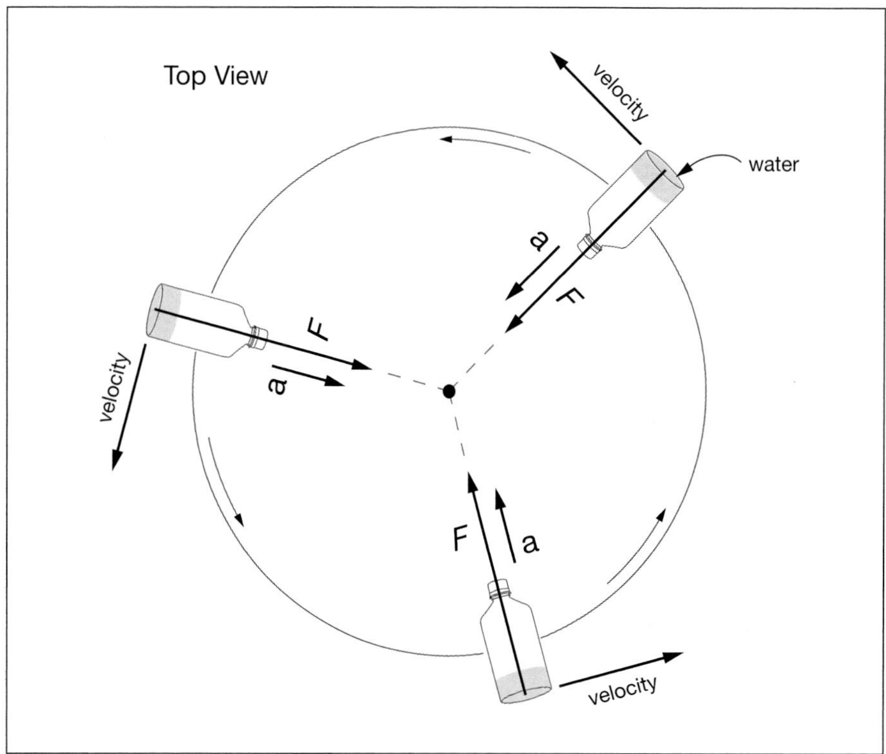

▲ **Figure T4.24 Vector sketches of uniform circular motion.** These sketches show various vectors for uniform circular motion in 3 positions.

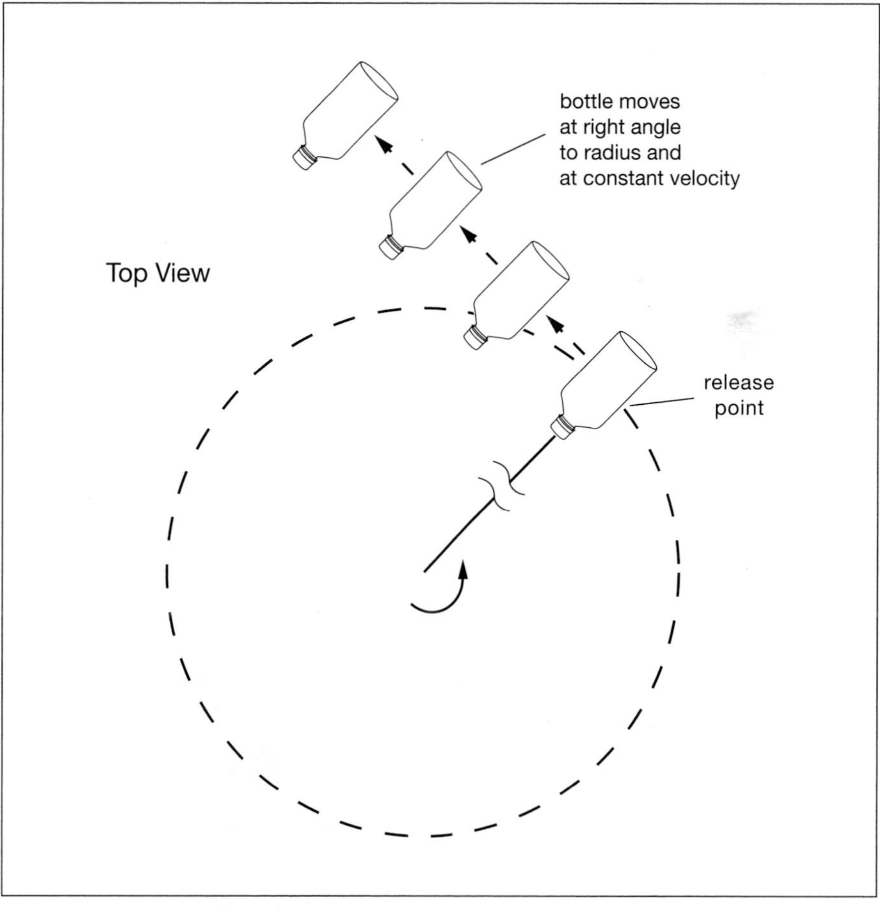

▲ **Figure T4.25 Accelerometer released from circular motion as stated in Step 4d.** This sketch shows how an accelerometer would behave if released from circular motion.

Answers to Reflect and Connect, SE page 191

1. A student might say the projectile accelerates in one direction (vertically) and moves with a constant velocity horizontally. Thus, when the positive direction is down, the position increases vertically proportional to time squared and increases horizontally proportional to time. The result is a curved path.

   A more mathematical answer would reflect the calculations and equations for a parabola as explained in the background section.

2. Student answers should be similar to figure T4.26 if they choose to use a Venn diagram to organize their answer.
3. Answers should be similar to figure T4.27.
4. This is a difficult problem for students who do not feel comfortable connecting concepts from seemingly unrelated content areas. For example, some students might think Earth's rotation has nothing to do with uniform circular motion. But in fact, a person riding on Earth's surface exhibits nearly perfect uniform circular motion. How fast is that person moving (tangentially)? As with all calculations for speed, you need distance and time. The distance is one Earth circumference, given by

$C = \pi D$, where D is Earth's diameter $(2 \times 6.36 \times 10^6 \text{ m})$.

$$C = \pi(2 \times 6.36 \times 10^6 \text{ m})$$
$$C = 4.00 \times 10^7 \text{ m}$$
$$T = \left(24 \frac{\cancel{\text{hr}}}{\text{day}}\right)\left(3{,}600 \frac{\text{sec}}{\cancel{\text{hr}}}\right)$$
$$T = 8.64 \times 10^4 \text{ sec}$$
$$v = \frac{\textit{distance traveled} \text{ (in 1 day)}}{\textit{time} \text{ (1 day)}} = \frac{C}{T} = \frac{4.00 \times 10^7 \text{ m}}{8.64 \times 10^4 \text{ sec}}$$
$$v = 463 \frac{\text{m}}{\text{sec}} \text{ or about } 1{,}042 \frac{\text{miles}}{\text{hr}}$$

5. Students may think of the slosh of the water in their accelerometers as they were spinning in a circle. Or they may think of the amusement park ride described in Question 3. A spinning space station could simulate gravity to astronauts who reside inside a spinning hollow wheel. While it is spinning, the wall of the space station would apply a force on the astronauts that points toward the center of the wheel to keep the astronauts traveling in a circular path. This is similar to the amusement park "salad spinner" ride, only the astronauts would be standing on the wall. The wall of this station has to exert that force because if it didn't, the astronauts would continue moving in straight-line motion. "Up" would be seen as toward the center of the station.

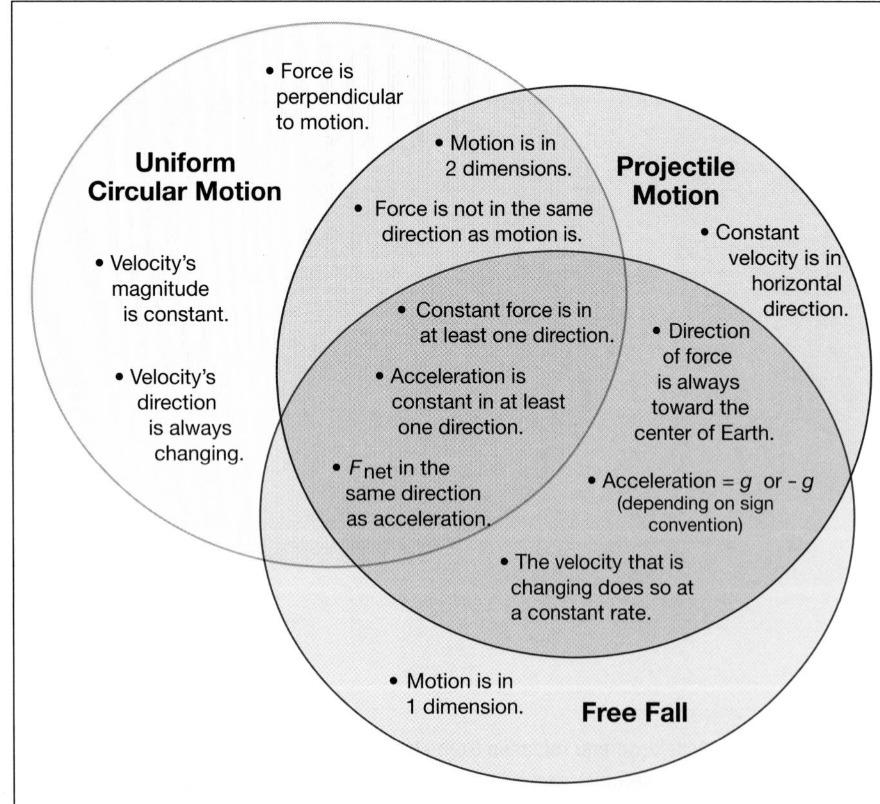

▲ **Figure T4.26 Venn diagram.** Student answers should be similar to these if they choose to answer using this type of diagram.

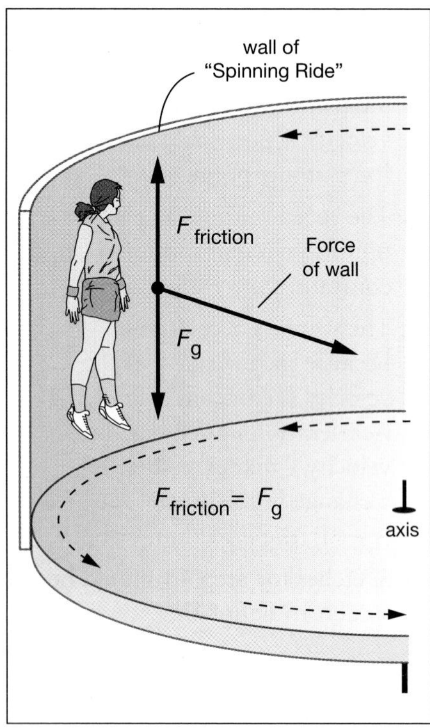

▲ **Figure T4.27 Amusement park "salad spinner."** This sketch shows how the ride mentioned in *Reflect and Connect* Question 3 works.

NOTES:

Answers to Step 4 are on TE page 190a.
Answers to Reflect and Connect are on TE page 190b.

4. Meet with your team and discuss the following questions and tasks. Then write responses in your science notebook.
   a. What is the geometric relationship (perpendicular, parallel, or always at, say, 20°) between force and velocity vectors for uniform circular motion? State the evidence for your answer.
   b. Describe the magnitude of the velocity (the speed) of the water for uniform circular motion.
   c. If the speed is not changing during uniform circular motion and there is a net force, then how can the water accelerate?

Use vector sketches in your answer.

   d. Generate a sketch, as viewed from above, of what would happen to the bottle if you suddenly released it as you were spinning it.

Reflect and Connect

Answer each question in your science notebook, then confer with your teammates to check your thinking. If you change any answer, record what you changed and why.

1. Why is the path of projectile motion curved? Use vectors, words, equations, or all of these in your answer.
2. Compare and contrast uniform circular motion, projectile motion, and the motion of a ball tossed in the air. Choose a method that helps you organize this information. Examples include tables, Venn diagrams, and paragraphs.
3. Some amusement parks have a ride that spins people around in what looks like a huge salad spinner. At a certain spin rate, the floor drops away, yet everyone "sticks" against the wall. Develop a labeled vector sketch with a caption to explain how this happens.

Read the sidebar *Amusement Park Designer* to learn more about careers that involve the physics of amusement park rides.

4. Calculate the speed you are moving due to Earth's rotation. (The radius of Earth = 6.36×10^6 m.)
5. Pretend that you are a NASA scientist and propose a plan to simulate gravity in a space station located in outer space. Use your understanding of circular motion to describe your plan.

EXPLAIN

Back and Forth, Up and Down

Activity Overview

Back and Forth, Up and Down asks students to continue extending what they know about force and motion to different types of motion, in this case, simple harmonic motion. Students do not have to learn any new concepts; rather they use the vector nature of force to understand common oscillatory motions like springs and pendulums. In simple harmonic motion, the force does not remain constant as it did in the previous activity. Instead, it changes as the object oscillates.

The activity occurs in three parts. Part I helps students connect the vector nature of changing velocities to the forces that cause those changes in spring and pendulum motions. In Part II, students will use what they learn about simple harmonic motion to design a series of investigations aimed at determining the variables that influence the period of spring and pendulum motions. Finally, in Part III, students will translate what they know about force and time to a variety of motion graphs that represent spring and pendulum motions. Part III is more challenging and is therefore proposed as a challenge opportunity. Use this activity if your students have a clear understanding of prior concepts and are adept at translating motion to different types of graphs. Many students will embrace the challenge if it is presented as a way for them to demonstrate what they understand and as an activity you are confident they can do.

Before You Teach

Background Information

Many motions are periodic (show repeating patterns over time), but not all of them are simple harmonic motion. Simple harmonic motion requires that the force causing the motion be directly proportional to but in an opposite direction to the displacement from equilibrium. Algebraically, this is represented by $F = -k\Delta x$, where F is the so-called restoring force or the force that causes the object to return to its equilibrium (resting) position. The constant of proportionality, k, is often called the spring constant; Δx is the displacement the object is from equilibrium at any time; and the negative sign means that if the displacement is outward, then the force points inward (to the center). It also means that if the displacement is inward (so a spring would be compressed), then the force points outward. The seasonal movement of clouds is periodic but is not simple harmonic motion. An object bobbing up and down on the end of a spring exhibits simple harmonic motion.

Since force changes in simple harmonic motion, acceleration does as well. As a result, the rate of change of velocity is not constant. This is different from the motion students have studied so far, when force has been constant as in free fall, projectile motion, and uniform circular motion. But what remains the same is the overarching principle of motion, $F_{net} = ma$. Students will continue using this expression in its vector sense to understand simple harmonic motion.

Simple harmonic motion and uniform circular motion are related. For example, the horizontal (as well as the vertical) component of uniform circular motion exhibits simple harmonic motion. From calculus derivations involving angular velocity, we can show that the force required to produce the horizontal component of uniform circular motion is given by $F_x = \dfrac{-m4\pi^2\,\Delta x}{T^2}$, where m is the

SIDEBAR

Amusement Park Designer

Going for a Ride

Do you love the thrill of climbing to great heights and then, seconds later, dropping so fast that your stomach flies up into your throat? Next come the loops, twists and corkscrews, all of which make for an exciting minute or two. Such is the experience of a roller coaster ride—a favorite among vacationers of all ages. These machines of motion are a demonstration of engineering know-how. And designing them can be even better than riding them.

"Everyone has opinions about what makes for a good roller coaster ride, but they don't stop to think that someone actually has to design them," says Scott Andersen, P.E., a structural engineer with Arrow Dynamics in Clearfield, Utah. "It's an uncommon thing that I do for a living."

Roller coasters have been around for more than a century, enticing people's adventurous nature by defying gravity. Andersen carries on that tradition by building coasters that boast multiple loops or sheer, almost 90-degree drops. Thrill seekers today are given the rides of their lives.

Like designing any new product, it all begins with putting an idea on paper.

"We begin with the layout of the ride, whether it will be looping or not and how many loops. Most parks have something in mind when they come to us," he explains. "Then we figure out how long to make the track and how high the lift has to be to get

mass of the moving object, Δx is the change in position on the x-axis, and T is the time for one complete trip in the cycle (one revolution, or the period). Since for a given circle $\frac{m4\pi^2}{T^2}$ are all constants, the expression for the horizontal force in uniform circular motion can be expressed as $F_x = -k\Delta x$, where the constants are collapsed into one value, k. This suggests that $k = \frac{m4\pi^2}{T^2}$ in simple harmonic motion. Solving this expression for T yields $T = 2\pi\sqrt{\frac{m}{k}}$. This expression predicts that the period of an object exhibiting simple harmonic motion depends directly on the square root of the mass and indirectly on the square root of the spring constant. Common experience confirms this relationship qualitatively. For example, if a heavy- and a lightweight person bounce on the end of a diving board independently, the period of oscillation for the heavy person will be longer. Similarly, for the same person, changing the diving board to a stiffer kind (a larger k value) decreases the period of oscillation.

For pendulum motion, we can show that the constant in $F = -k\Delta x$ is equal to $\frac{mg}{l}$, where m is the mass of the object exhibiting pendulum motion, g is the acceleration of all objects near Earth's surface, and l is the length of the pendulum. Using the expanded expression for k from uniform circular motion, $\frac{m4\pi^2}{T^2}$, and setting it equal to $\frac{mg}{l}$, then solving for T, yields $T = 2\pi\sqrt{\frac{l}{g}}$. This expression predicts that for pendulums not swinging more than 10 degrees from equilibrium, their period, T, is directly proportional to the square root of the length of the pendulum and inversely proportional to the square root of g. This makes sense from common experiences since longer objects are more difficult to cause to rotate (longer baseball bats are more difficult to swing than short ones). Thus, longer pendulums exhibit longer periods. The period does not depend on mass since all objects fall with the same acceleration near Earth's surface. But if pendulums operate on a different planet, they will have a different period.

Materials—Part I

For each team of 3 students

1 spring scale (scaled in newtons)
1 spring
1 string
2 weights (approximately the same mass)
1 pair of scissors
access to a computer
Student Resource CD (SRCD)

Materials—Part II

For each team of 3 students

1 spring scale (scaled in newtons)
1 spring
1 string
2 weights (approximately the same mass)
1 pair of scissors
1 stopwatch

Materials—Part III

For each team of 3 students

colored pencils
graph paper
access to a computer
Student Resource CD (SRCD)

Advance Preparation

Assemble the materials and set them out for students. Expansion springs with spring constants between 10 and 30 N/m and about 30 cm long work well in classroom situations.

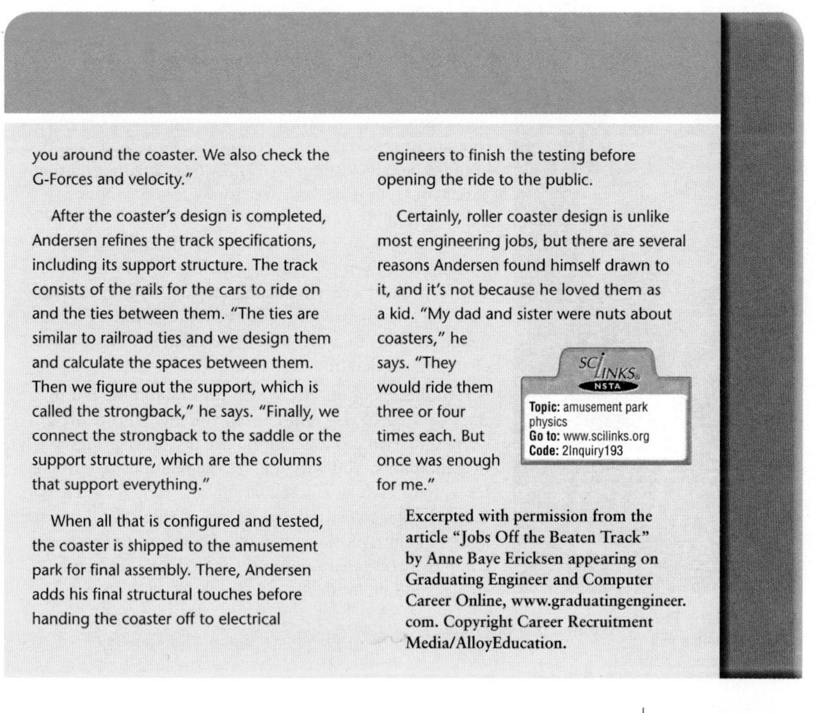
you around the coaster. We also check the G-Forces and velocity."

After the coaster's design is completed, Andersen refines the track specifications, including its support structure. The track consists of the rails for the cars to ride on and the ties between them. "The ties are similar to railroad ties and we design them and calculate the spaces between them. Then we figure out the support, which is called the strongback," he says. "Finally, we connect the strongback to the saddle or the support structure, which are the columns that support everything."

When all that is configured and tested, the coaster is shipped to the amusement park for final assembly. There, Andersen adds his final structural touches before handing the coaster off to electrical engineers to finish the testing before opening the ride to the public.

Certainly, roller coaster design is unlike most engineering jobs, but there are several reasons Andersen found himself drawn to it, and it's not because he loved them as a kid. "My dad and sister were nuts about coasters," he says. "They would ride them three or four times each. But once was enough for me."

SCI LINKS NSTA
Topic: amusement park physics
Go to: www.scilinks.org
Code: 2Inquiry193

Excerpted with permission from the article "Jobs Off the Beaten Track" by Anne Baye Ericksen appearing on Graduating Engineer and Computer Career Online, www.graduatingengineer.com. Copyright Career Recruitment Media/AlloyEducation.

Back and Forth, Up and Down

EXPLAIN

In *Constantly Accelerating*, you applied your ability to observe and analyze motion. You discovered that a ball tossed in the air or thrown horizontally exhibits constant acceleration. Acceleration is also constant in circular motion, although its direction is different. What is the cause of the constant acceleration? A constant net force. The mutual gravitational attraction between the ball and Earth causes constant acceleration in vertical motions. But what kind of motion results when forces change?

At the very least, you would say that changing forces result in changing acceleration. That's because you know the relationship $F_{net} = ma$. This relationship links what you can see (acceleration) to what it means (the object experienced a net force). Can you think of some common motions in which the acceleration is changing?

The newton scales should read up to about 20 N.

Students will be viewing animations on the *Student Resource CD* (*SRCD*) in Parts I and III. Reserve time in the computer lab or have computer stations available for your students to view the animations.

As You Teach

Outcomes and Indicators of Success

By the end of this activity, students should

1. be able to compare and contrast the force requirements to produce simple harmonic (spring) motion and pendulum motion.

   They will show their ability by

   - sketching scaled force vectors near an object's position at several points in the path for both spring and pendulum motion,
   - writing highlight comments by each vector sketch,
   - modifying initial ideas based on peer and teacher discussion, and
   - completing a table that structures the comparison of spring and pendulum forces at similar positions in their motions.

2. design an investigation to determine which variables affect the period of spring and pendulum motions and how they affect the motions.

   They will show their ability by

   - reviewing what they already know regarding the variables that affect force in general;
   - connecting the variables of mass, time, length, and spring constant to a step-by-step procedure;
   - selecting proper control variables; and
   - conferring with teammates.

3. transfer what they learn from conducting their designs to generating motion graphs for spring and pendulum motion.

   They will show their ability by

   - designing proper axes for position and velocity versus time graphs, using estimation skills practiced in prior activities;
   - including high-confidence points on graphs for positions they are very sure of;
   - filling in the graphs between high-confidence points based on their initial sense of trends; and
   - generating qualitative motion graphs for other motions as described in the *Reflect and Connect* questions.

Strategies

Getting Started

As you read the introduction to this activity with your students, ask for examples of periodic motion that they may have experienced. Have students answer the questions posed in the introduction so you can get their ideas before you begin the activity.

Process and Procedure

Part I: Changing Forces

Materials

For each team of 3 students

1 spring scale (scaled in newtons)
1 spring
1 string
2 weights (approximately the same mass)
1 pair of scissors
access to a computer
Student Resource CD (*SRCD*)

In Step 1, students work with a spring and a spring scale. They will connect the spring to the scale and stretch the spring. Remind students to pay attention to what they feel when they stretch the spring. Discuss with students that they will consider

▲ **Figure 4.19 The pendulum motion of a grandfather clock.** Is the acceleration of this pendulum constant or changing?

Perhaps you thought of the motion of car tires as they bounce up and down over a bumpy road. Or you thought of the back and forth motion of a pendulum in a grandfather clock (figure 4.19). In fact, any motion that varies in a repeating way over time (periodic motion) exhibits changing acceleration. So the swaying motion of skyscrapers after an earthquake is due to changing acceleration. Even a vibrating guitar string moves back and forth due to varying acceleration. Oxygen molecules oscillate at a greater frequency when temperature increases. This microscopic motion also represents changing acceleration.

All these motions are worth understanding. But in *Back and Forth, Up and Down*, you and your team will only study two motions: motions caused by springs and by pendulums. You will analyze the relationships among force, mass, velocity, acceleration, and time for these two motions. Once you understand the relationships in spring and pendulum motions, you will be able to understand complex periodic motion, such as earthquakes, guitar strings, and molecules.

Part I: Changing Forces

Materials

For each team of 3 students

1 spring scale (scaled in newtons)
1 spring
1 string
2 weights (approximately the same mass)
1 pair of scissors
access to a computer
animations *Simple Pendulum* and *Spring Pendulum* on the *Student Resource CD* (*SRCD*)

SRCD

Process and Procedure

The key to understanding periodic motion is force. If you know what the net force on an object is at any point in time, you can determine the acceleration. Once you know the acceleration, you can predict the velocity and, ultimately, the object's position. With accurate knowledge of position and time, you can understand that object's motion.

the pull-back force of the spring as the negative direction and the force that they use to pull the scale as the positive direction. Students will be graphing the pull-back force of the spring and will therefore practice graphing negative values.

Answers for Step 1, SE page 195

1c–d. Students' sketches for Step 1c should be similar to figure T4.28, and sample student qualitative graphs for Step 1d are shown in figure T4.29.

In Step 1e, students compare their sketches, graphs, and comments with those of another team. Monitor the class to check for misconceptions. Then have students complete Step 2. If the reading *Changing Forces* doesn't clear up any remaining misconceptions, then help students understand the concept. Student summary statements from Step 1f should give you an idea if students are grasping the concept. Allow them to revise their statements after reading *Changing Forces*. Their summary statements should include the ideas that the force increases proportionally as the stretch of the spring increases. Students may be confused about the negative force. Reiterate that they should assign a negative value to the pull-back force of the spring to indicate the negative direction of this force.

Consider reading or discussing *Changing Forces* as a class. Point out the relationships connected to the equation for a best-fit line. Students will be glad to see that what they have learned in math class has a useful application in their science class.

Answers to Step 1 are on TE pages 195–195a.

In Part I, you and your team will think about the forces acting on similar objects that exhibit periodic motion. You will use force vectors to determine the net force at key locations in the motions of a spring and a pendulum. Then in Parts II and III, you will determine how forces relate to aspects of motion, such as time, position, velocity, and acceleration.

1. Conduct a qualitative investigation of the force a spring applies to a scale that you hold in your hand.
   a. Lay the spring on a table. Have a team member hold one end firmly. Attach the other end to the scale as shown in figure 4.20.

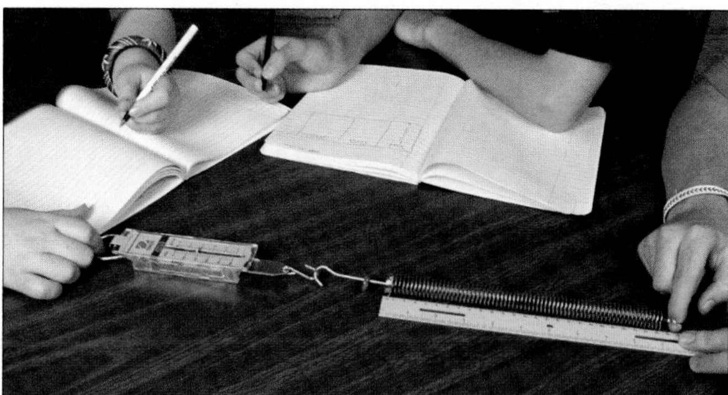

▲ **Figure 4.20 Students with a spring scale and a spring.** Use the scale to stretch and relax the spring. What is the relationship between the amount of force and the amount of stretch of your spring?

   b. Use the scale to stretch and relax the spring.
   c. Sketch the spring, scale, and hand in 2 different "stretch" positions. Include scaled force vector diagrams with labels for those 2 positions.
   d. Generate a qualitative *xy* plot of the force of the spring (vertical axis) versus the position (horizontal axis). Include highlight comments and a caption.
   e. Select an effective technique to compare your sketches, graphs, and comments with team members.
   f. Write a summary statement for what you have learned in Step 1.
2. Connect the results from your qualitative investigation in Step 1 to a quantitative relationship by reading *Changing Forces*.

NOTES:

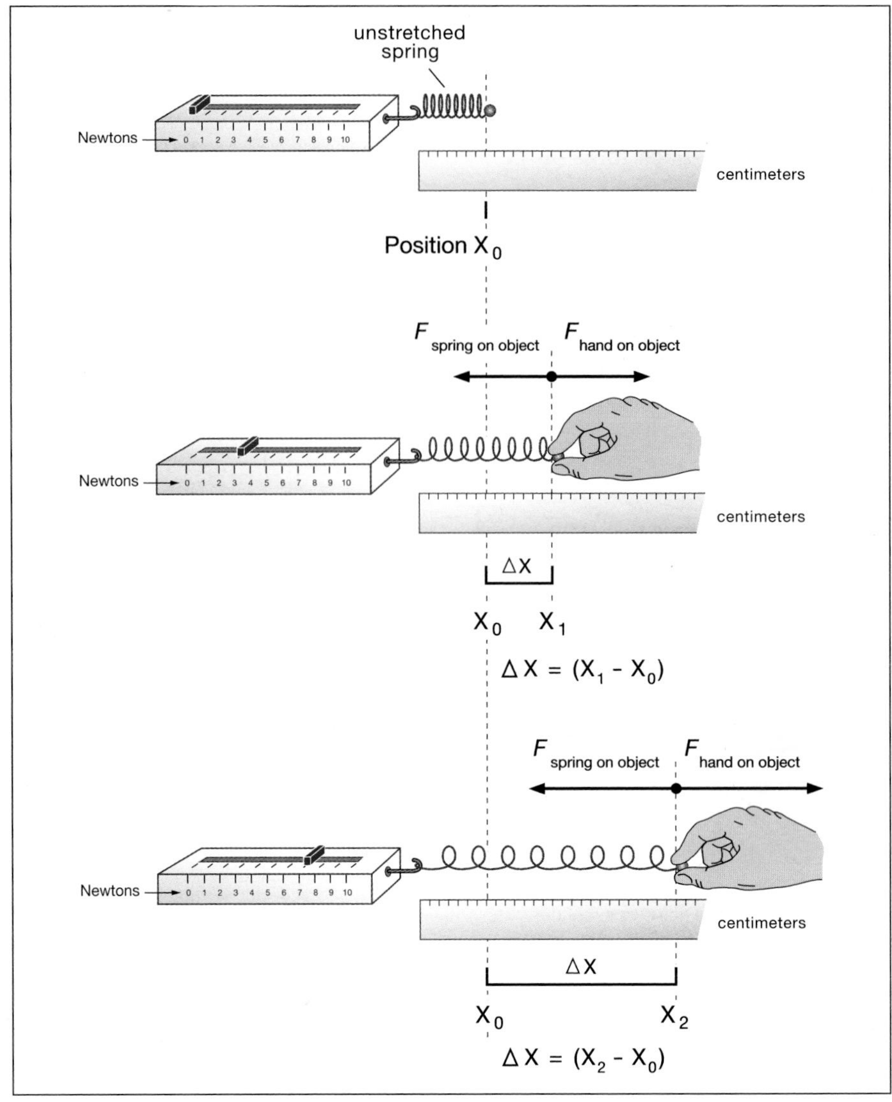

▲ **Figure T4.28 Force vectors for spring as stated in Step 1c.** This sketch represents the forces involved on a spring in 2 positions.

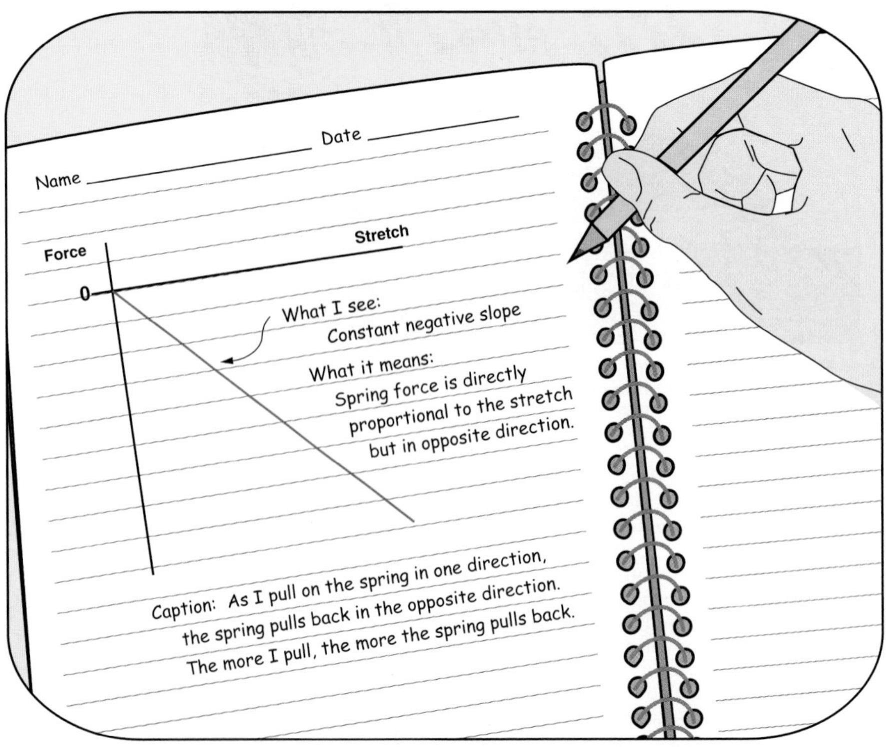

▲ **Figure T4.29 Qualitative graph of force versus stretch as stated in Step 1d.** This graph represents what students might record for the force versus stretch graph. The negative force refers to a pull-back force.

NOTES:

NOTES:

READING

Changing Forces

When you pull on a spring, the spring pulls back on you. What do you remember about the "pull-back" force of the spring as you pull in the opposite direction? Because force always occurs in pairs, equal in size and opposite in direction, the pull-back force is equal to your pulling force. If you pull with a scale, the reading on the scale indicates the numerical value of the mutual forces, but not the direction. You determine direction from observations.

As you pull with a greater force, the scale reading increases. Why? The scale reading increases because the spring force increases, but maintains its opposite direction from your pulling direction. The more you pull on the spring, the more the spring pulls back on you. That is, the spring force changes depending on the amount of stretch. *The force is not constant.*

How can you predict the amount of spring force for a given stretch without using a scale every time you need to know the force? You have already learned how graphs and equations can help you answer this question. Study each feature of figure 4.22 to make the connection between your qualitative investigation and mathematics. The graph in figure 4.22 shows the force of the spring on your hand as you stretch the spring different amounts (figure 4.21).

In your math classes, you may have used the equation for a straight line in a graph: $y = mx + b$. In the equation, x and y are simply the quantities on the x- and y-axes; b is the y-intercept, or where the graphed line crosses the y-axis; and m is the slope of the line. Since the line in figure 4.22 is a straight line, you can apply this equation and discover the mathematical relationship of the stretch of a spring and the force. Because the graphed line appears to cross the y-axis at the origin (0,0), you can omit b from the equation. The equation is now $y = mx$. Can you see how this equation is equivalent to $F = -k\Delta x$?

The symbol Δx represents the stretch of the spring where $\Delta x = x_{stretched} - x_{unstretched}$. The symbol $-k$ represents the slope. This mathematical relationship is the equation for a line. The symbol, k, is called the spring constant. The spring constant is different for

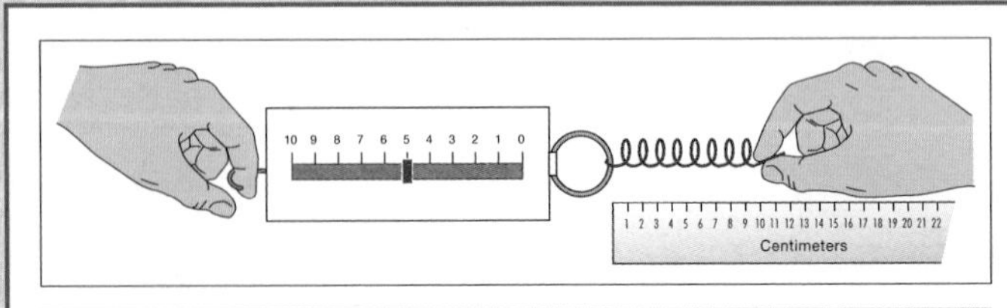

▲ **Figure 4.21 A spring and spring scales.** The graph in figure 4.22 represents the pull-back force of the spring versus the stretch of the spring.

196 Unit 1 Interactions Are Interesting

NOTES:

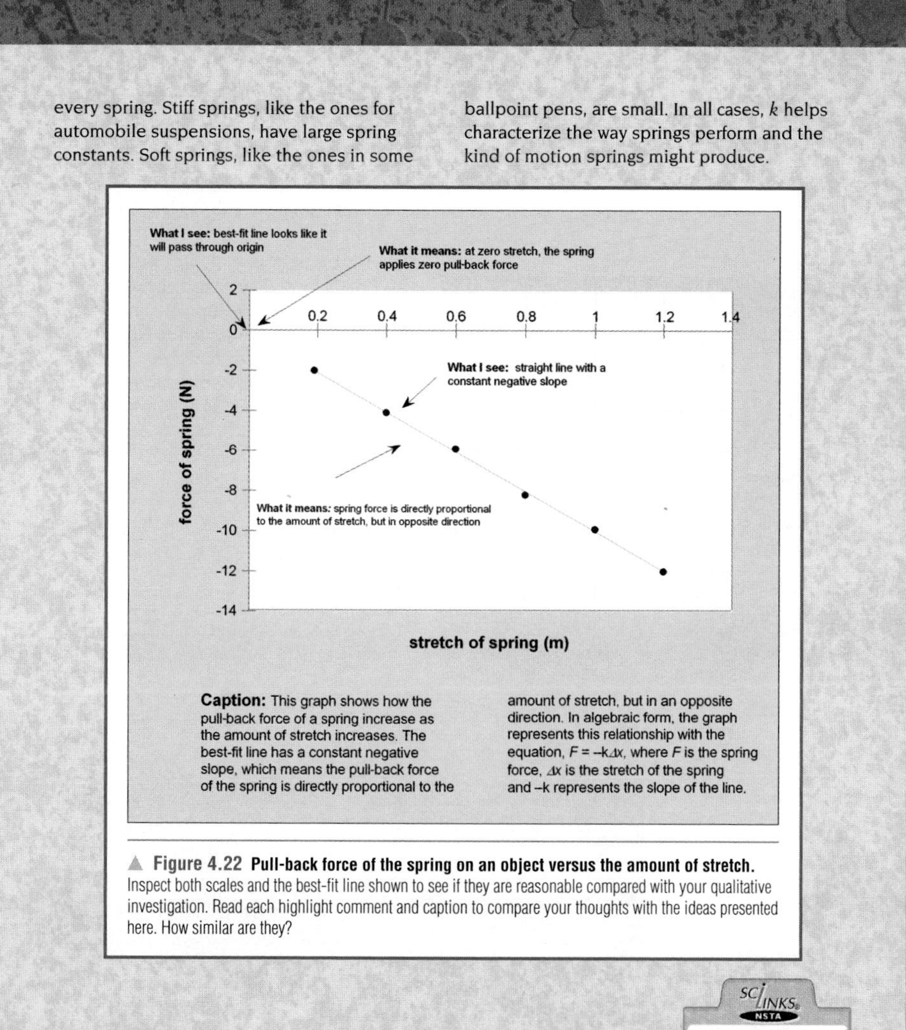

every spring. Stiff springs, like the ones for automobile suspensions, have large spring constants. Soft springs, like the ones in some ballpoint pens, are small. In all cases, k helps characterize the way springs perform and the kind of motion springs might produce.

Caption: This graph shows how the pull-back force of a spring increase as the amount of stretch increases. The best-fit line has a constant negative slope, which means the pull-back force of the spring is directly proportional to the amount of stretch, but in an opposite direction. In algebraic form, the graph represents this relationship with the equation, $F = -k\Delta x$, where F is the spring force, Δx is the stretch of the spring and $-k$ represents the slope of the line.

▲ **Figure 4.22 Pull-back force of the spring on an object versus the amount of stretch.** Inspect both scales and the best-fit line shown to see if they are reasonable compared with your qualitative investigation. Read each highlight comment and caption to compare your thoughts with the ideas presented here. How similar are they?

SciLINKS NSTA
Topic: periodic motion
Go to: www.scilinks.org
Code: 2Inquiry197

NOTES:

Answers to Steps 3–7 are on TE pages 198–200.

In Steps 3–6, students set up pendulums and oscillating springs. They prepare sketches with vectors, labels, and captions. Monitor the progress of each group; question students to assess their understanding. Students have to apply prior learning to a new situation and may struggle at first before they realize that this motion involves forces and accelerations similar to other motions. After students complete Step 6, they should have sketches similar to those in figure T4.30.

Answers to Steps 3–7, SE pages 198–200

3–6. Student sketches, labels, and captions should be similar to figure T4.30. Students have an opportunity to check their sketches for accuracy in Steps 8 and 9.

Acceleration**s** are added to this sketch for the answers to *Stop and Think* Question 2.

3. Connect the relationship between the force and the stretch of a spring, $F = -k\Delta x$, to both spring and pendulum motion by completing Steps 3a–d.
   a. Attach your spring to a fixed object as instructed by your teacher. Then hang a weight from your spring and let it oscillate up and down (figure 4.23).
   b. Construct a pendulum, using a weight similar to the one used in Step 3a. The time required to complete 1 entire swing (1 period) should be close to the time required for the weight on the spring to make 1 oscillation (figure 4.24).
   c. Generate side-by-side sketches similar to figure 4.25 of these 2 motions. Use a blank sheet of paper in your science notebook and be sure to show the weights at 5 positions (A–E) as shown in figure 4.25.

Plan ahead by making these sketches large enough to include highlight comments and captions later.

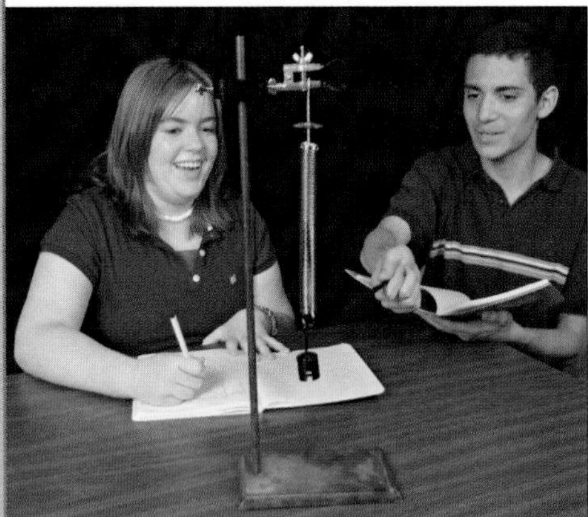

▲ **Figure 4.23 Weight on a spring.** Your weight should oscillate from your spring, as shown in this photograph.

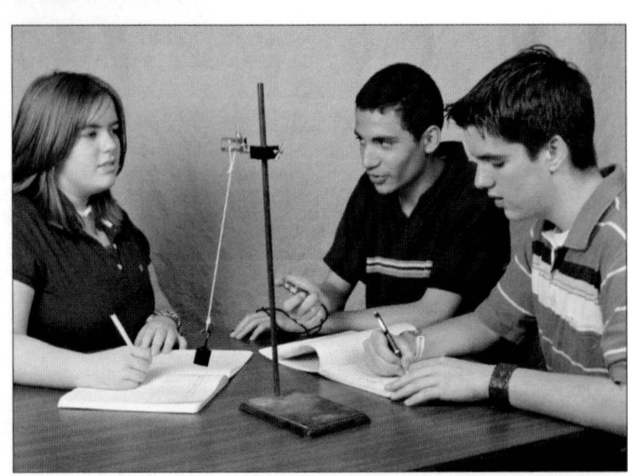

► **Figure 4.24 Weight on a pendulum.** The weight should swing back and forth like a pendulum. Try to manipulate your pendulum so that the time required to complete 1 swing (1 period) is the same as the time required for the weight on the spring to make 1 oscillation.

198 Unit 1 Interactions Are Interesting

NOTES:

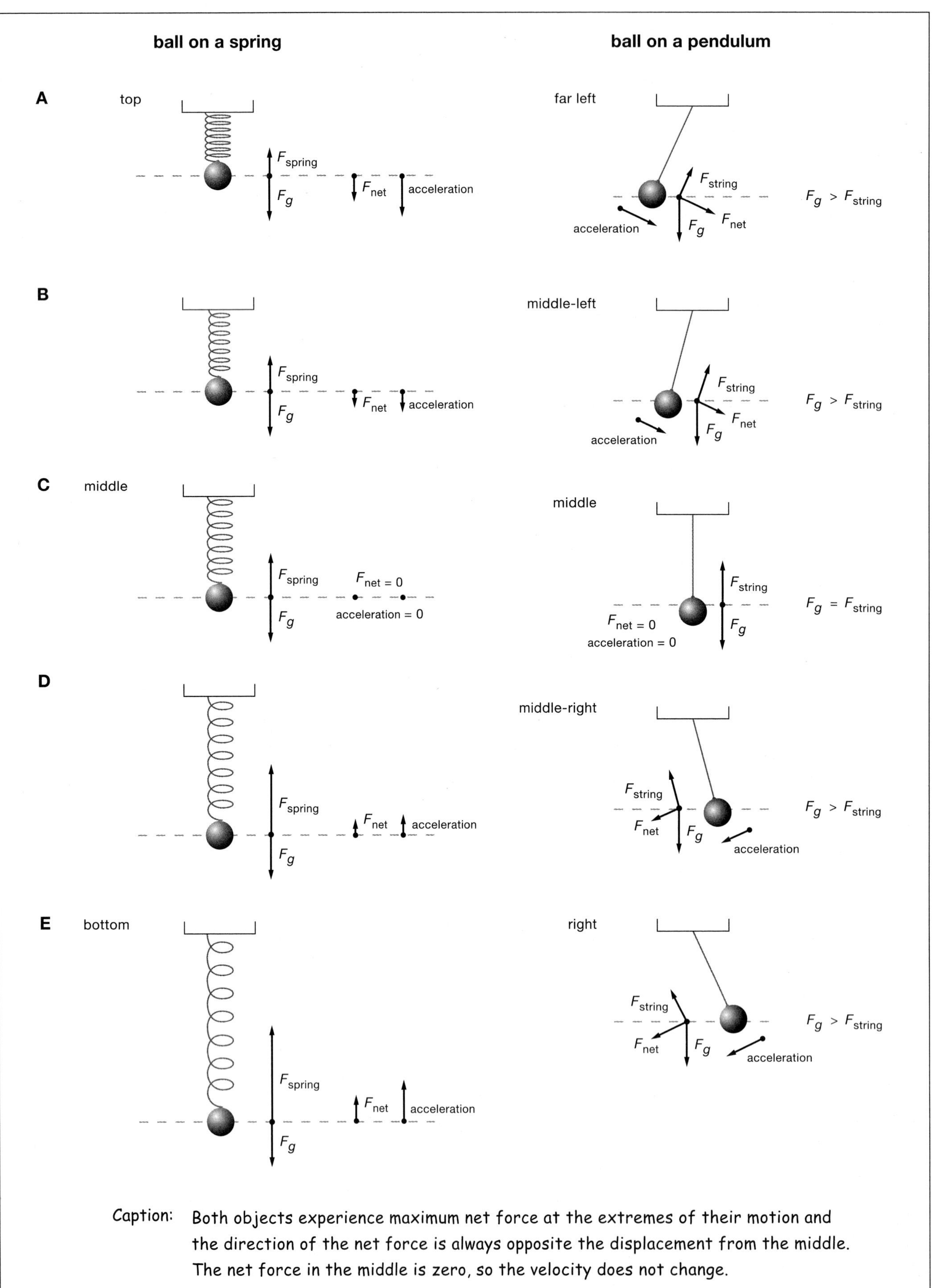

▲ **Figure T4.30 Sample spring and pendulum motions.** This sketch represents possible student answers for Steps 3–6.

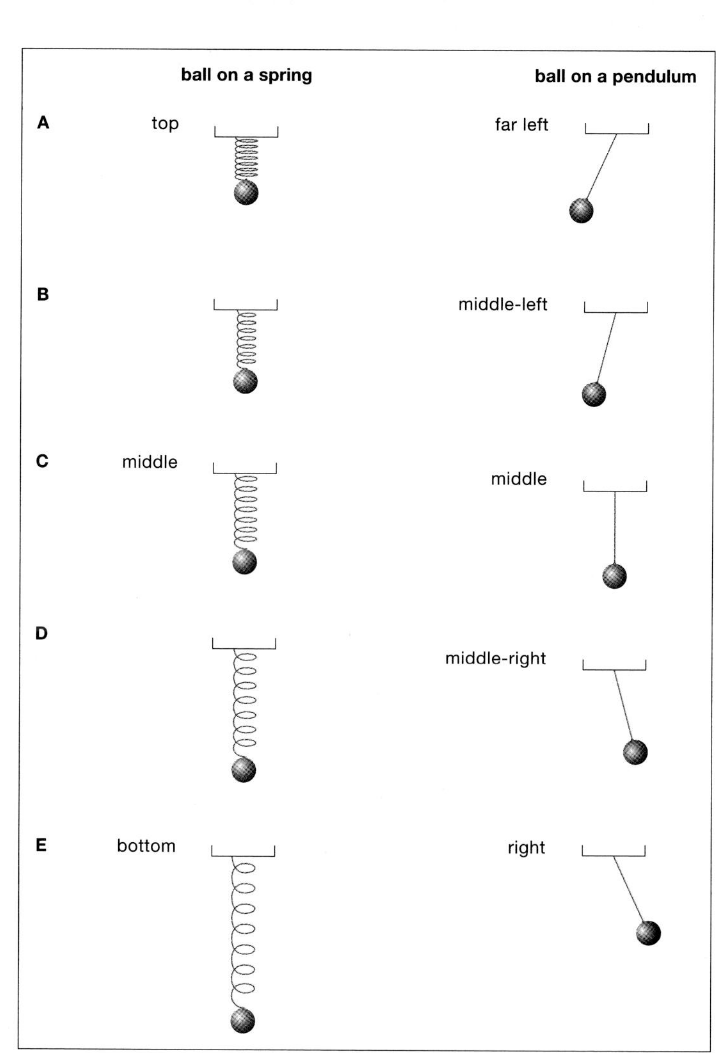

▲ **Figure 4.25 Positions for sketches.** Generate sketches for the 5 positions labeled A to E.

Position (or motion) of the spring	Position (or motion) of the pendulum	Reason
Top	*Far left (or far right)*	*The speed is zero and the weight is reversing direction.*
Bottom	*Far right (or far left)*	*Because the speed is zero and the attached weight is reversing direction.*
Middle	*Lowest position*	*Because the speed is greatest and the acceleration is zero.*
Between top and middle, going down	*Starting at either far left or far right and moving toward the middle*	*Because the speed is increasing since the net force is in the same direction as the motion, even though the net force is decreasing. Thus, the acceleration is decreasing.*
Between middle and bottom, going down	*Starting at the middle and moving to either the far left or far right*	*Because the speed is decreasing since the net force is in the opposite direction to the motion and the net force is increasing. Thus, the acceleration is increasing.*
Between bottom and middle, going up	*Starting at either far left or far right and moving toward the middle*	*Because the speed is increasing since the net force is in the same direction as the motion, even though the net force is decreasing. Thus, the acceleration is decreasing.*
Between middle and top, going up	*Starting at the middle and moving to either the far left or far right*	*Because the speed is decreasing since the net force is in the opposite direction to the motion and the net force is increasing. Thus, the acceleration is increasing.*

▲ **Figure T4.31 Analogy table linking pendulum and spring motions for Step 7.** Use this table to help students make connections between pendulum and spring motions.

7. Student answers to Step 7 should be similar to the table in figure T4.31.

In Steps 8–9, students will check their sketches for accuracy by viewing 2 animations on the *SRCD*. Monitor that your students are grasping the concepts. It is important that they have a good understanding of the forces, accelerations, and velocities involved in these motions before proceeding to the next activity.

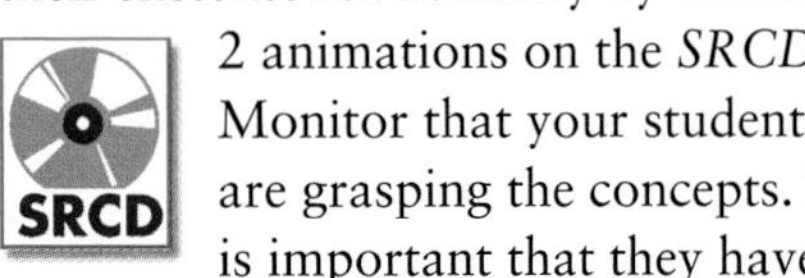

d. Label each position with qualitative descriptions of the motion. Use words like *fastest*, *slowest*, *stationary*, *increasing speed*, and *decreasing speed*.

4. Incorporate scaled force vector diagrams for at least positions A, C, and E of the *spring*. Include the following in your diagrams.
   a. Labeled arrows to represent the direction and relative magnitude of the pull-back force of the spring

Remember that $F = -k\Delta x$ tells you about the amount of pull-back force for each relative stretch position.

   b. Labeled arrows to represent the direction and magnitude of the gravitational force acting on the weight
   c. Labeled arrows to represent the direction and magnitude of the *net* force acting on the oscillating weight

Remember to use vector addition to determine the net force.

5. Meet with your team and decide how to repeat Step 4 for the *pendulum*.
6. Write an overall caption under your sketches. Explain how the sketches, along with vectors, demonstrate changing forces as the weights move back and forth or up and down.

Include the words *momentum*, *net force*, *acceleration*, *velocity*, *position*, and *time* in your caption.

7. Copy the table in figure 4.26 into your science notebook. Complete the table in order to find similarities in 2 examples of periodic motion.

You may choose another form of showing similarities, such as Venn diagrams or a paragraph explanation.

Position (or motion) of the spring	Position (or motion) of the pendulum	Reason
Top	Far left (or far right)	The speed is zero and the weight is reversing direction.
Bottom		
Middle		
Between top and middle, going down		
Between middle and bottom, going down		
Between bottom and middle, going up		
Between middle and top, going up		

▲ **Figure 4.26 Analogy table linking pendulum and spring motions.** This table will help you make connections between pendulum and spring motions.

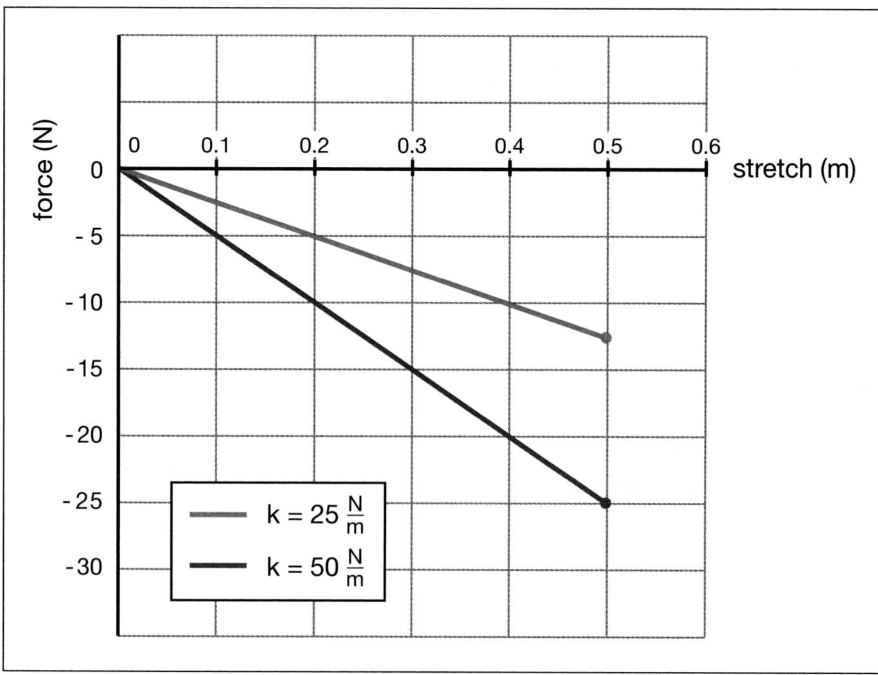

Figure T4.32 Force versus stretch for 2 springs. Use this graph for *Stop and Think* Question 1a.

Answers to Stop and Think—Part I are on TE pages 201–202.

8. Complete Steps 8a–d as you view the animation *Simple Pendulum* on the *Student Resource CD* (*SRCD*).
   a. Select the button for velocity on the bottom right and start the animation.
   b. Note direction of the velocity vector compared with the direction of the motion of the pendulum. Record this comparison in your science notebook.
   c. Repeat Steps 8a–b 2 more times, first choosing the acceleration button and then the force button.
   d. Summarize your findings about the direction of these vectors in relation to the direction of the pendulum motion. Write your summary in a sentence and illustrate it with diagrams.

9. Repeat Steps 8a–d for the animation *Spring Pendulum*, also on the *SRCD*.

Stop & THINK

PART I

Read each question carefully before answering it in your science notebook. Then use an effective learning technique to check and revise your answers.

1. Consider 2 different springs as you answer Questions 1a–e. Spring A has a spring constant of $k = 25$ N/m (newtons per meter), and spring B has a spring constant of $k = 50$ N/m.
   a. Make a qualitative graph in your science notebook of spring force versus stretch for each spring.
   b. Suppose you placed identical weights on the ends of each spring and let them hang. Which weight would hang lower and why? (Assume each spring was originally the same length.)
   c. Suppose you allowed identical masses to oscillate from each spring. Which period would be greatest?
   d. Which spring pulls back with a force of 25 N when stretched 50 centimeters (cm)? Show your justification.
   e. Suppose you were making a bed mattress out of a group of identical springs. Would you use spring A or spring B? Explain the advantages and disadvantages of each. Remember, an average student might weigh 700 N.
2. Include a new set of vectors on your sketches from Steps 4 and 5 to depict the relative acceleration at each position.

Answers to Stop and Think—Part I, SE pages 201–202

1a. Student graphs should be similar to figure T4.32.

1b. Spring A would hang lower since (for this case) it cannot apply the same "hold-back" force as spring B. The mathematical justification for this answer is the following:

$$F = -k_{25}\Delta x_A \text{ and } F = -k_{50}\Delta x_B$$

Since both weights are identical, we can set the forces equal.

$$-k_{25}\Delta x_A = -k_{50}\Delta x_B$$

Solving for the ratio of distances yields

$$\frac{k_{25}}{k_{50}} = \frac{\Delta x_B}{\Delta x_A}$$

$$\frac{25}{50} = \frac{\Delta x_B}{\Delta x_A}.$$

Solving for x_B yields

$$\Delta x_B = \frac{1}{2}\Delta x_A.$$

1c. The period of spring A will be greater than spring B. The mathematical justification is as follows:

$$T = 2\pi\sqrt{\frac{m}{k}}$$

This general relationship is true for A and B, so we can solve for mass and set the two expressions equal.

$$k_A \frac{T_A^2}{4\pi^2} = k_B \frac{T_B^2}{4\pi^2}$$

Eliminating the constants and solving for the ratio of periods yields

$$\frac{T_A}{T_B} = \sqrt{\frac{k_B}{k_A}}.$$

Substituting values yields

$$\frac{T_A}{T_B} = \sqrt{\frac{50}{25}} = 1.41 \text{ or}$$

$$T_A = 1.41T_B.$$

1d. Sample student calculations are shown here.

$$F = -k\Delta x$$

pull-back

$$-25\text{ N} = -k(0.50\text{ m})$$

Note: Negative sign for force reflects the direction of the pull-back force of spring.

$k = 50\frac{\text{N}}{\text{m}}$, so this refers to spring B

1e. A 700-N person would compress each spring, but by different amounts, as shown here.

$$F = -k\Delta x$$

$$700\text{ N} = -(50\frac{\text{N}}{\text{m}})(\Delta x)$$

$$\Delta x = -14\text{ m}$$

This result says the spring *compresses* 14 m (note the negative 14 m), hardly practical for a bed. But one spring does not a bed make. If we estimate a person is lying on 100 of these springs, then each spring experiences 0.01 the original force, and thus 0.01 the compression. This results in 0.14 m or 14 cm—still too much. Increase either the number of springs or the spring constant of the springs, or both.

2. See figure T4.30 for the answer to this question.

3. Students should express their understanding in a clear, concise fashion. Look for summaries that include the following ideas in words, graphs, sketches, or charts:

- The net force and the acceleration are always pointing in the same direction.
- In simple harmonic motion, the direction of the change in velocity vector is in the same direction as the net force and acceleration vector.
- The magnitude of the net force and the acceleration is constantly changing.
- The pull-back force of a spring is directly proportional to the stretch of the spring in simple harmonic motion. The pushing force of a spring is directly proportional to the compression of the spring.

Process and Procedure

Part II: Time Matters

Materials

For each team of 3 students

1 spring scale (scaled in newtons)
1 spring
1 string
2 weights (approximately the same mass)
1 pair of scissors
1 stopwatch

Begin the activity by calling attention to the focus question in the introduction: "What factors affect

STOP & THINK, PART I, continued

3 Summarize what you have learned about changing forces and their affect on velocity and acceleration in periodic motion. Use sentences and sketches to form your summary.

Part II: Time Matters

Materials

For each team of 3 students

1 spring scale (scaled in newtons)	2 weights (approximately the same mass)
1 spring	1 pair of scissors
1 string	1 stopwatch

Process and Procedure

In Part I, you began your in-depth analysis of periodic motion by examining the forces involved in spring and pendulum motions. You learned that a changing net force produces a changing acceleration, which in turn changes velocity and position in a repeating pattern.

The repeating pattern of motion depends on the period of oscillation. This is the time required for one complete cycle of motion. For spring motion, the period is the time from release to the time when the weight returns to the release point. For a pendulum, it is the time from "tick" to "tock" and back to tick. The period of Earth revolving around the Sun is one year, or about 365 days.

So time matters. For example, it would be a big deal if the periodic motion called "one day" changed due to some cosmic force. Because time matters, you and your team will study the factors (sometimes called variables) that affect the time associated with periodic motion (figure 4.27). Focus your efforts in Part II with this question: "What factors affect the period of spring and pendulum motions?"

1. Meet with your team and develop an overall investigation strategy to determine what factors affect the period of oscillation for spring and pendulum motions. Steps 1a–c will help you develop your strategy.
   a. Use appropriate features of the *Observation Guidelines*.

HOW TO

the period of spring and pendulum motions?" Write the question on the board and have students record it in their science notebooks. Remind the students that they will try to answer this question as they plan their investigations.

In Step 1, students meet with their teams to design an investigation to determine what factors affect the period of oscillation for the motion of a spring and a pendulum. Students are given a set of guidelines to help them. Students may already know what affects the period of a pendulum from previous activities or science lessons. However, have them gather evidence to support their ideas.

Exercises to design open-ended investigations can be challenging to students who are used to prescribed procedures that detail every step in the investigation—the so-called recipe approach to science investigations. You might consider leading a short class discussion about the factors students think affect the period. This discussion should identify amplitude, mass, spring constant (for spring), and length (for pendulum). The difficulty for students is twofold: (1) how to design an investigation that produces accurate and reliable quantitative data, and (2) how to communicate the results so that the interpretation is unambiguous.

In Steps 2 and 3, students check their strategies with other teams and get your approval before conducting their investigations. Monitor the teams closely to ensure that all students are recording their data in an organized and concise way. Students are encouraged in Step 3 to reflect on the results of each step as they are doing their investigations. They should stop and examine their data collection techniques to ensure they are doing things right. Such simple "checking as you go" strategies help students think about what they are doing as they are doing it. This is a hallmark of metacognition.

Students formulate an answer to the focus question stated in the introduction based on their data. Actually, they are forming a conclusion to their investigations. Check that students have evidence that the length of the pendulum is the factor that affects the period of a pendulum and the mass of the object affects the period of oscillation for a spring.

b. Use multiple forms of representing and communicating your understanding, including words (in complete sentences), sketches, graphs, and equations.
c. Use a step-by-step procedure that students your age could follow without difficulty.

2. Check with another team and compare your overall strategies. Obtain your teacher's approval before you conduct your investigation.
3. Conduct your overall investigation. Be careful to reflect on the results of each step along the way.
4. Using the data from your investigation, formulate a complete answer to the focus question for Part II.

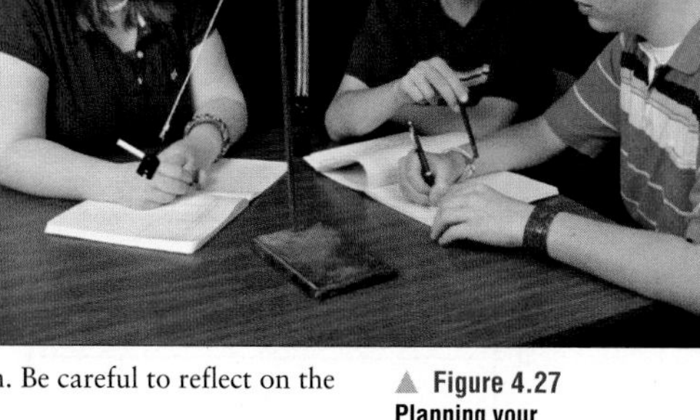

▲ **Figure 4.27 Planning your investigation.** What factors will you investigate to answer the focus question?

Stop & THINK

PART II

Review your observations and results from Part II before writing answers in your science notebook to the following questions.

1. You have become an astronaut for NASA and you are trying out one of your high school experiments on the new colony on the Moon. If you repeated your investigation from this activity using both the pendulum and the spring, how would your results compare?
2. A friend of yours has a grandfather clock that keeps time poorly. It runs slow. Your friend says, "I know how to make it keep proper time. I will decrease the mass of the object at the end of the pendulum. That will speed up the swing rate because the equation $F_{net} = ma$ says lighter objects accelerate faster. Thus, the lighter pendulum mass has less mass and will move faster." Choose a convincing mix of explanation techniques to either confirm or refute your friend's comments.

Answers to Stop and Think—Part II, SE page 203

1. Students should explain that the results and conclusions based on the focus question would be the same. The length of the pendulum (*not* the mass) affects the period of the pendulum, and the mass of the object on a spring affects the period of the oscillating spring. However, they should notice that the time for 1 complete oscillation would change (be longer) since the force of gravity on the Moon is less than the force of gravity on Earth.
2. The student has several incorrect notions. First, mass does not affect the swing rate. Second, while $F_{net} = ma$ does suggest that lighter objects accelerate faster if the same force is applied, it does not say objects in free fall demonstrate different accelerations. That's because the ratio of force to mass does not change near Earth's surface. From the figures that the students drew previously, they should see that the weight is less, but the string force and the net force is also less. Since the mass is less and the net force is less, by $a = \frac{F_{net}}{m}$, the acceleration stays the same.

NOTES:

Process and Procedure

Part III: Graph-o-holic

Materials

For each team of 2 students

colored pencils
graph paper
access to a computer
Student Resource CD (SRCD)

Part III is a challenge opportunity designed for students who require more rigorous activities. Consider offering the opportunity to all students, so that you don't underestimate the skills of your class.

In Step 1, students plot qualitative graphs for either pendulum or spring motion. Be sure to divide the class into approximately equal-sized teams for each motion so that both motions are represented. Ensure that all students are defining the zero position ($x = 0$) as suggested in Step 1b. If not, students will have difficulty comparing their graphs in Step 2. Students will view the same

animations on the *SRCD* as in Part I, Steps 8 and 9, but this time they focus on the graphs. Allow them to revise their graphs based on this check. Ensure that they record their changes in a different color and explain why they are modifying their initial ideas.

Answers to Steps 1–4 are on TE page 204a.

Part III: Graph-o-holic

Materials

For each team of 2 students

colored pencils

graph paper

access to a computer

animations *Simple Pendulum* and *Spring Pendulum* on the *Student Resource CD (SRCD)*

Process and Procedure

Part III is a challenge opportunity. You will use what you have learned to make some connections. You will continue to create and compare graphs because that is a good method to find relationships. You and a partner will construct these graphs by aligning them by their x-axes. That way, it will be easier to compare the motions.

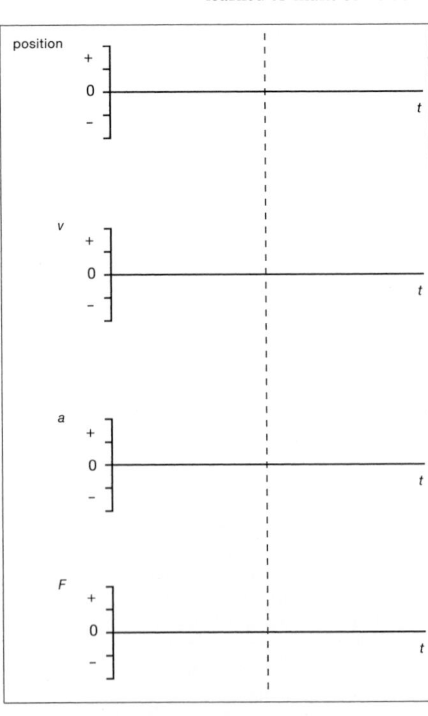

▲ **Figure 4.28 Aligned graph axes.** Draw your graphs on a clean page in your science notebook. Vertically align the time axes for all of the graphs.

1. Draw qualitative graphs of *either* 1 full period of oscillation for spring motion *or* 1 full period of oscillation for pendulum motion. Steps 1a–f will help you organize your graphs.
   a. Use figure 4.28 as a guide to organize your graphs. Note that the time axes are aligned.
   b. Assume that the motion starts to the left for the pendulum and at the top of the oscillation for spring motion. (This is position A on figure 4.25.)
   c. Plot high-confidence points of the motion.

High-confidence points are points for position and velocity that you are sure of. Think about times where position, velocity, acceleration, or force is equal to zero.

Answers to Steps 1–4, SE pages 204–205

1–4. By the end of the activity, student graphs should be similar to figure T4.33. When students compare their graphs with another team's, they should see that the graphs are effectively identical. Thus, spring and pendulum motions are driven by the same relationships among force, velocity, acceleration, and momentum.

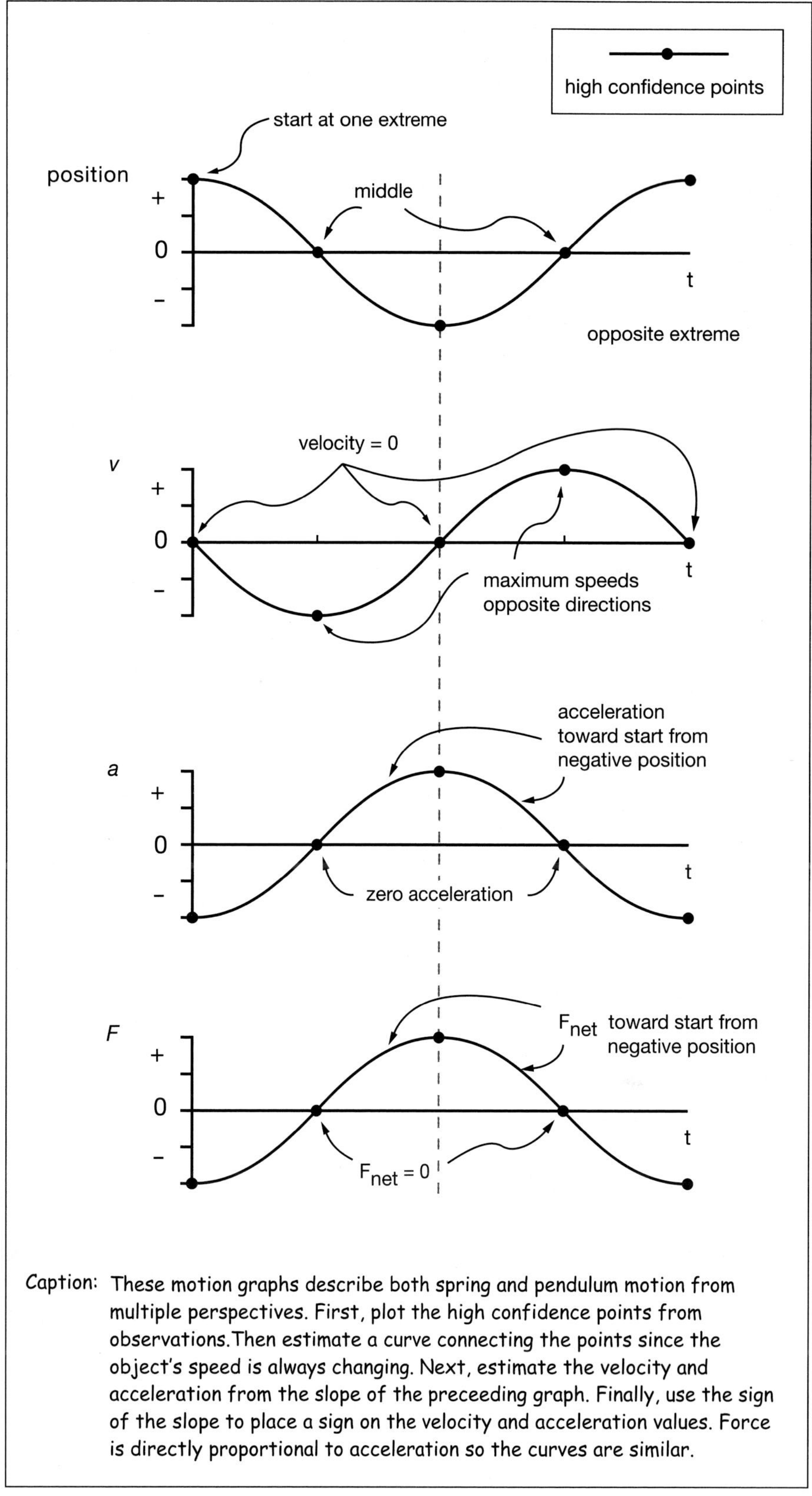

▲ **Figure T4.33 Motion graphs for simple harmonic motion as stated in Step 1.** These graphs represent answers for both spring and pendulum motions.

Answers to Reflect and Connect, SE pages 205–206

1. Student sketches and highlight comments should be similar to figure T4.34.

2a. The key to this question is frame of reference. That is, what place does the motion refer to as a "home base"? For example, in pendulum motion you can arbitrarily assign any position in the swing to the origin (0,0), but usually the middle point (equilibrium position) is the origin. If the middle position is the origin, then using a traditional number line convention, positions on the right side of the origin are positive and positions on the left side of the origin are negative. Motions to the right are then positive and motions to the left are negative, no matter where they are.

2b. Negative velocity describes the direction in which the object is moving. If the object is moving in the negative direction, it will have a negative velocity.

2c. Negative acceleration is not as simple. An object can have a negative acceleration if it is slowing down in a positive direction, or it can have a negative acceleration if it is speeding up in a negative direction. This can be easily determined using the definition of acceleration as, $a = \dfrac{v_f - v_i}{t_f - t_i}$.

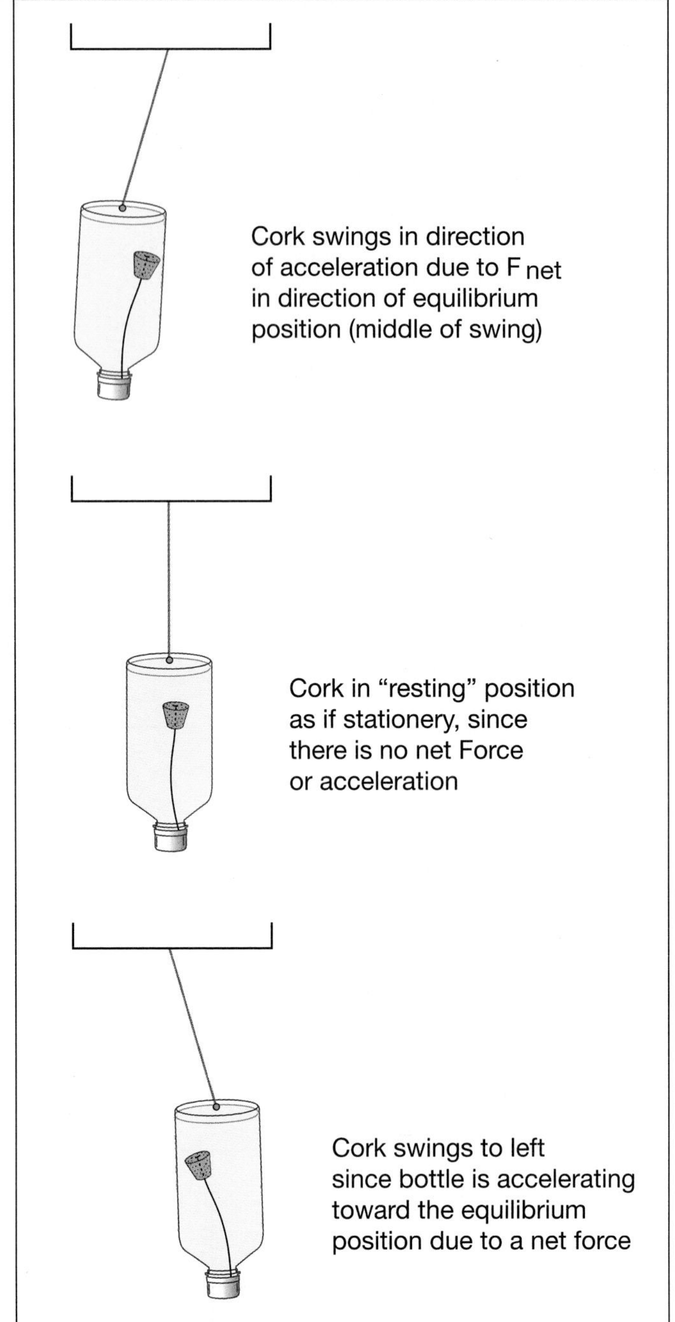

▲ **Figure T4.34 Accelerometer on a playground swing as stated in *Reflect and Connect* Question 1.** These sample sketches show how an accelerometer behaves on a swing.

NOTES:

Answers to Steps 1d–4 are on TE page 204a.
Answers to Reflect and Connect are on TE page 204b–206.

d. Connect the high-confidence points with a line.

Should you use a straight or a curved line?

e. Label each graph with points of maximum and minimum values of position, velocity, acceleration, and force.

f. Write a caption for your set of graphs that communicates the relationships of each graph.

2. Find at least 1 team that analyzed a different motion from your team's and choose an effective strategy to compare and contrast each set of graphs.

Possible strategies include but are not limited to T-tables, paragraphs, Venn diagrams, and annotated sketches.

3. View the animation *Simple Pendulum* on the *SRCD* again. Complete Steps 3a–d as you watch.
   a. Select the button on the bottom right for velocity and start the animation.
   b. What is the direction of the velocity vector compared with the direction of the pendulum's motion?
   c. Repeat Steps 3a–b 2 more times, first choosing the acceleration button and then the force button.
   d. Check your graphs from Step 1 and revise them if necessary. Remember to mark your revisions in a different color.
4. Repeat Steps 3a–d for the animation *Spring Pendulum*, also on the *SRCD*.

SRCD

Reflect and Connect

Answer these questions in your science notebook. Then use a strategy such as TSAR to finish your answers.

1. Imagine holding a soda bottle accelerometer while you swing back and forth on a playground swing. Make a series of 3 sketches similar to figure 4.29. Add the string and cork to show what the side view of your accelerometer would look like at both extremes and at the middle of the swing. Provide highlight comments for each sketch.
2. Answer Questions 2a–e about the meaning of the words "negative" and "positive" when referring to motion and graphs.
   a. What is the physical meaning of negative position?

When thinking about the physical meaning, consider how, where, or in what direction an object is moving.

   b. What is the physical meaning of negative velocity?
   c. What is the physical meaning of negative acceleration?

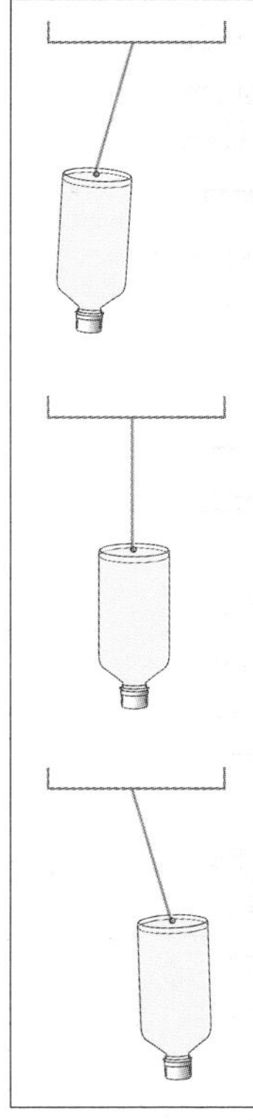

▲ **Figure 4.29**
Swinging accelerometer. Imagine holding a soda bottle accelerometer while you swing back and forth on a playground swing. What would the string and cork look like as you moved like a pendulum?

Idea to compare	Comments regarding circular motion	Comments regarding spring and pendulum motion
Force	Force is constant and always points towards the center.	Force varies and points in a direction opposite to the displacement from equilibrium—always towards the equilibrium point.
Acceleration	Since $F_{net} = ma$, acceleration points in the same direction as force	Since $F_{net} = ma$, acceleration points in the same direction as force.
Velocity	The object maintains constant speed but is always changing direction, so velocity is constantly changing.	The object's velocity and speed are changing at all times.
Position	The circle that the object makes maintains a constant radius and a changing position. Position varies periodically.	The position varies periodically.

▲ **Figure T4.35 Comparison of motions per *Reflect and Connect* Question 4.** This table shows one way to compare circular motion with spring and pendulum motions.

2d. Negative force is a force in the negative direction. Again, the direction is arbitrary and must be defined initially so that the direction of the vectors can be assigned.

2e. Direction is described in words as positive, negative, up, down, to the right, to the left, and so on. Vectors describe direction by pointing in the direction of the quantity. Algebraic equations use signs (+ and −) to represent direction. In 2-dimensional motion, the angle with respect to a reference point represents direction. The position above or below the origin and the slope of the line (whether positive or negative) shows direction on a graph.

3. The lightest one, acetic acid, will oscillate with the shortest period since period squared is directly proportional to the mass for an object on a spring.
4. Examples of possible student answers for Question 4 are shown in figure T4.35.
5. This question gets students to use what they learned in a previous activity to make predictions that start them thinking about ideas in the next activity. Possible student answers include the following:
   - The cannonball will travel a farther distance before hitting the ground.
   - The cannonball will be shot so far that as it falls, the path matches the curvature of Earth. (This will put the ball in orbit around Earth.)
   - The cannonball is shot with such a high initial velocity that it leaves Earth's gravitational pull.

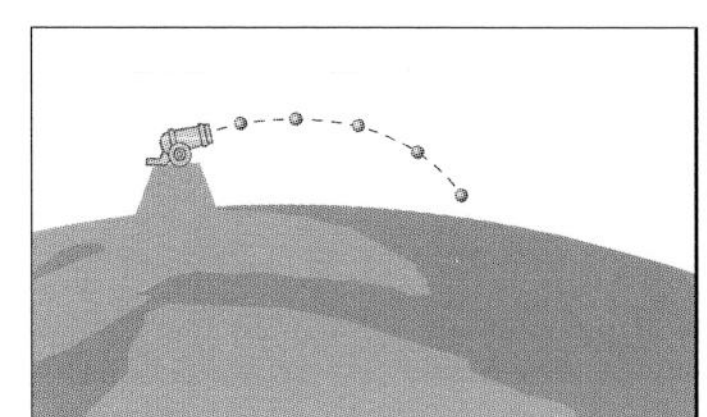

▲ **Figure 4.30 Cannon firing.** What would the path of the cannonball look like if the cannon could fire the ball with higher and higher initial velocity?

d. What is the physical meaning of negative force?
e. How do you convey the meaning of negative relative to positive on graphs? In algebraic equations? In vectors? With words?

3. Chemists often think of chemical bonds as invisible springs connecting atoms. Suppose you were investigating the motion between parts of 2 acid molecules.
   a. Acetic acid: $CH_3COO \xleftrightarrow[bond]{chemical} H$
   b. Propanoic acid: $CH_3CH_2COO \xleftrightarrow[bond]{chemical} H$

   If both acids were at the same temperature, which one would oscillate with the smallest period and why?
4. Think of other periodic motions, like the Moon orbiting Earth or your favorite CD spinning. Choose a method to compare and contrast circular motions like these with pendulum and spring motions. Consider changing or nonchanging force, acceleration, velocity, and position. Find at least 1 classmate who used a comparison technique different from yours. Ask your classmate to explain his or her comparison.
5. Suppose you shot off a cannon from a tall mountain. The path of the cannonball would curve as shown in figure 4.30. Imagine firing the cannon with higher and higher initial velocity. What would the path of the cannonball look like? Describe at least 2 very different scenarios; use both sentences and sketches in your descriptions.

ELABORATE

Sky High Motion

The motions that you have studied in this chapter are all the result of forces. Some of those forces are the result of the force of gravity. Can you think of which motions result from gravity? Is a paintball shot from a paintball gun affected by gravity? The path of the paintball curves as it falls due to its original horizontal velocity after leaving the gun and the force of gravity. Imagine having a super powerful paintball gun that could shoot the ball at extremely high velocities. At some velocity, the paintball would fall in a curved path that matched the curvature of Earth. You have put the paintball in orbit!

The motion of the paintball in an imaginary orbit around Earth is an example of the circular motion that you learned about in a previous activity. However, the circular motion you studied did not result from gravity. Remember twirling around, holding a plastic bottle of water?

ELABORATE

Sky High Motion

Activity Overview

In *Sky High Motion*, students will use their understanding of motion to investigate one application—satellites. Students will research the different types of artificial satellites and their orbits. They will discover that there are many different types of satellites including communication, weather, and navigation satellites. They also will learn that some satellites require a particular type of orbit. Students will apply what they have learned about forces, acceleration, and velocity to satellites as they communicate their learning in sketches, complete with labeled vectors. Students also will prepare a presentation with a visual display to share what they have learned with the class.

Before You Teach

Background Information

The physics background for this activity is simply the background material for previous activities with a concentration on the material for uniform circular motion. Types of artificial (human-made) satellites that students will likely encounter include the following:

- Communication satellites
- Weather satellites
- Astronomical satellites
- Earth observation satellites (for environmental studies)
- Navigation satellites
- Reconnaissance satellites
- Space stations

The different types of orbits that students will find may include the following:

- Low, medium, and high Earth orbits
- Geosynchronous (or geostationary) orbits
- Polar orbits
- Orbits around bodies other than Earth

Reference material on reputable Web sites and in encyclopedias will give you additional background on these satellites and orbits.

Materials

For each team of 3–4 students

access to the Web

access to reference materials in the library

computers or poster materials for visual display

Advance Preparation

Secure a time for students to visit the library, the computer lab, or both to research their satellites.

Educational Technologies

Students will undoubtedly use the Web for some of their reference materials. Ensure that students are doing quality searches and gaining information from reputable Web sites. Consider only allowing references to university or government Web sites such as the NASA site.

Also on the NASA site, students can search for the J-Track 3D. This is an applet that has a database of several hundred satellites. Students may find their satellite and can see its orbit. It is also helpful to see the different orbits compared. The applet shows satellites in real time with positions updated regularly.

As You Teach

Outcomes and Indicators of Success

By the end of this activity, students should

1. apply what they know about forces and motion to satellites in orbit.

The force that kept the bottle moving in a circular motion was the force of your hand on the bottle. And that force pointed toward you.

Think about the motion of the Moon around Earth. The Moon moves in an almost circular path, but what force keeps it in motion around Earth? There is nothing physical holding the Moon in orbit around Earth, but rather, the force of gravity supplies this force. The Moon is a satellite of Earth. A **satellite** is any object that orbits another object. Figure 4.31 shows an example of a satellite that orbits Earth.

In *Sky High Motion*, you will work with a team to investigate different types of satellites and different types of orbits. You will apply your understanding of forces, acceleration, velocity, motion, and direction as you explain your satellite's motion to the class. Your task is to prepare a presentation with a visual display that conveys one application of the understanding you have developed so far in this chapter.

Materials

For each team of 3–4 students

access to the Web

access to reference materials in the library

computers or poster materials for visual display

▲ **Figure 4.31 Satellite in orbit.** What type of satellite will you investigate in this activity? What type of orbit will be appropriate for your satellite? Apply what you have learned about forces to understand how your satellite stays in orbit.

They will demonstrate their ability by

- choosing a type of satellite that interests them and determining what type of orbit would be best for this satellite;
- drawing force, acceleration, and velocity vectors on a sketch of the satellite in at least four different positions in its orbit; and
- presenting what they have learned to the class in a verbal and visual presentation.

2. compare the force of gravity on their satellite to the force of gravity on them.

   They will demonstrate their ability by using the universal law of gravitation to calculate the forces on each body, knowing the distance the satellite is from Earth and the mass of the satellite.

3. understand that science often advances because of the introduction of new technologies.

   They will demonstrate their understanding by

   - considering advances in science that have resulted because of the satellite technology,
   - reporting new scientific knowledge that has resulted from the use of this technology,
   - listing any new problems related to use or ethics that have resulted from satellite technology, and
   - discovering new areas of research that this technology has provided to scientists.

Strategies

Getting Started

Consider beginning this activity with a brainstorming session of technologies that use satellite technology that we use or experience every day. The list may include some cell phones, satellite television or radio, global positioning systems (GPS), and weather reports. If available, bring in a portable navigation unit and demonstrate how it works.

Write the focus question on the board and discuss it with your students: "How can I apply what I have learned about forces and motion to satellite motion?" Remind them of the question often as they are doing research to keep them focused on what is most important. Look at the list of requirements for the activity in Step 4 with your students. Let them know now which part of the presentation will carry the most weight for your assessment of this activity. Emphasize the focus question and the physics behind the satellite as most important. Encourage students to spend the most time and effort on this and not on how the presentation looks.

Process and Procedure

Materials

For each team of 3–4 students

access to the Web

access to reference materials in the library

computers or poster materials for visual display

Students begin investigating different types of satellites in Step 1 and choose one that interests them. They may choose a specific satellite or a general category of satellites such as communication satellites. In Step 2, students research different types of orbits and select one appropriate for their satellite. Students draw a labeled

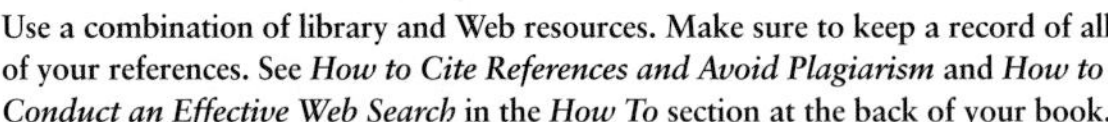

Process and Procedure

Work with your team to complete the following tasks. As you work, focus on this question: "How can I apply what I have learned about forces and motion to satellite motion?"

1. Research different types of artificial satellites and choose one that interests your team.

Use a combination of library and Web resources. Make sure to keep a record of all of your references. See *How to Cite References and Avoid Plagiarism* and *How to Conduct an Effective Web Search* in the *How To* section at the back of your book.

HOW TO

SCILINKS NSTA
Topic: satellites
Go to: www.scilinks.org
Code: 2Inquiry208

2. Research the different types of orbits that satellites make and determine the type of orbit that is best for the satellite your team chose.
3. Individually, draw a carefully labeled illustration of Earth and your satellite in orbit. Use labeled vectors to represent the relative sizes and direction for force, acceleration, and velocity for your satellite. Show at least 4 different positions along the path of the orbit.
4. Decide with your team the best way to communicate your understanding of forces and motion for your satellite. Use the following criteria to prepare your report and presentation for the class. Your final product must include the following.
   a. Verbal presentation by the team
   b. Visual display
   c. Diagram of your satellite in orbit, complete with qualitative scaled vectors for force, acceleration, and velocity

   Revise one of your team's diagrams from Step 3 to reflect the best ideas of the team.

   d. Description of your satellite and its use
   e. Description of advances in science that have resulted from your satellite technology
   f. Description of the type of orbit that your satellite follows and why this type is the best one for your satellite
   g. Comparison of the force of gravity on your satellite and the force of gravity on you

   Read *FYI—Universal Gravitation* to understand how you will make these comparisons. Each member of your team will need to do a separate calculation.

   h. Distance from Earth, the velocity of your satellite, and the period of revolution of your satellite

   Compare satellites that are close to Earth and farther from Earth. Which ones must move faster and why? How do their periods compare?

   i. List of your references with at least 2 references from resources other than the Web.

208 Unit 1 Interactions Are Interesting

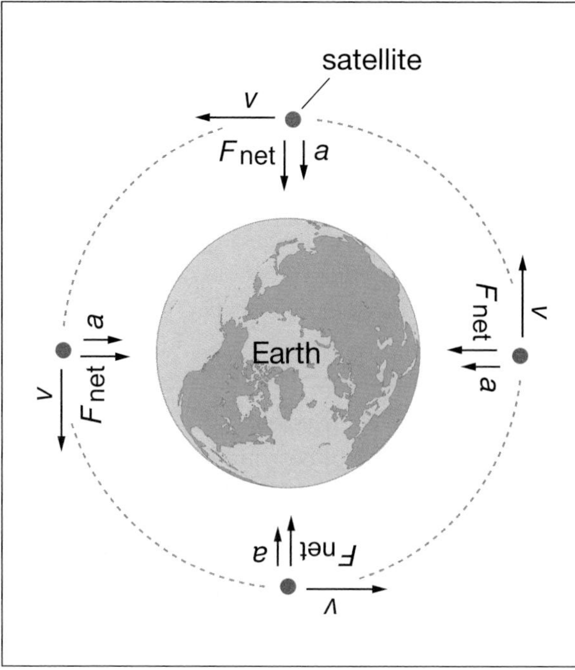

◀ **Figure T4.36 Vector sketches for a satellite in a circular orbit.** Sketches should reflect student learning about uniform circular motion and be similar to these.

Answers to Reflect and Connect are on TE pages 209–210.

5. Divide up the tasks of the project. Make sure everyone on the team has a role gathering information, applying knowledge, preparing the visual display, and presenting the material.
6. Develop at least 3 questions that you will ask other teams during the presentations. These questions should be consistent with the requirements of the activity and should not be meant to "stump" the other teams.

Reflect and Connect

Answer the following questions either individually or with a partner as your teacher directs. Record your answers in your science notebook.

1. If you could somehow stop a satellite from moving, it would simply crash into Earth. Why, then, don't satellites that appear in the same spot above Earth simply crash into Earth?
2. Some satellites follow an elliptical orbit, as shown in figure 4.32. In fact, the orbit of Earth around the Sun is very slightly elliptical. In perfectly circular orbits, the magnitude of the velocity (the speed) of the satellite is constant. Would the speed of the satellite in figure 4.32 be constant or changing? Justify your answer with your understanding of forces.
3. Use figure 4.32 to indicate positions in the orbit where the satellite experiences the following.
   a. Maximum force of gravity
   b. Minimum force of gravity
   c. Maximum speed
   d. Minimum speed
   e. Greatest momentum
   f. Least momentum
   g. Increasing speed
   h. Decreasing speed

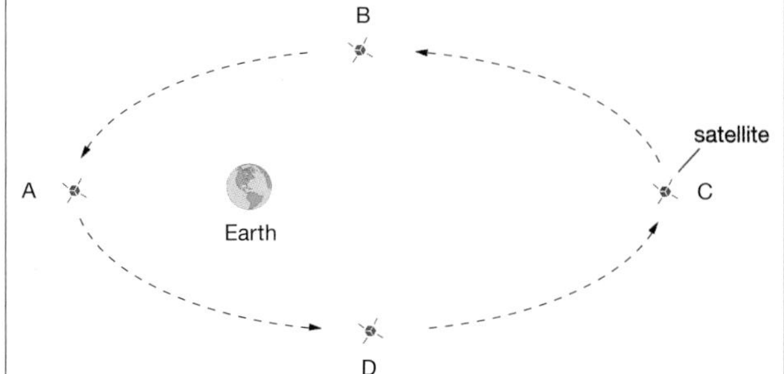

◀ **Figure 4.32 Elliptical satellite path.** Would a satellite in an elliptical orbit have a constant or a changing velocity? Note: Distances are not to scale.

vector diagram of their satellite in orbit. Sample drawings should show the concepts in figure T4.36.

In Step 4, teams begin to put together their information so that they can present it to the class. This step includes a list of requirements for their presentations. Students are also instructed to read *FYI—Universal Gravitation*. Decide on a time limit for each presentation and tell the class. Also, explain to the students how much time they will have for preparation and if the teams can work on the presentations outside of class. Encourage students to read

HOW TO *How to Cite References and Avoid Plagiarism* and *How to Conduct an Effective Web Search*, found in the *How To* section at the back of their student book.

Monitor the teams carefully as they prepare their reports. Hold teams responsible for making sure that all members of the team have a critical role in the completion of the project. In Step 6, students develop 3 questions to ask during the presentations. Check that these questions are well thought out, not superficial or unrelated, and won't stump the other teams.

Answers to Reflect and Connect, SE pages 209–210

1. The satellites described in this question are moving—moving at the same angular speed that Earth is rotating. They only appear motionless to people located on Earth.
2. The speed of a satellite in an elliptical orbit would be changing. As the satellite moves farther away from Earth, its speed would decrease due to the decreasing pull of Earth's gravitational force. As the satellite is moving toward Earth, the speed of the satellite increases, due to the increasing pull of Earth's gravity.
3. Student answers for Question 3 should be as follows:

3a. A	3d. C	3g. B
3b. C	3e. A	3h. D
3c. A	3f. C	

4. Students will list a range of answers. Examples of problems that students may list are, dangers in space from colliding with spacecraft, space trash from old satellites, dangers related to satellites that reenter the atmosphere and fall back to Earth. Ethical issues that students might describe are privacy issues related to reconnaissance or observation satellites as well as others.
5. New research opportunities provided by satellite technology include space science research, research in climate or weather patterns, environmental studies and many others.

EVALUATE

Moving toward Understanding

Activity Overview

Moving toward Understanding occurs in three parts. Part I leads students through a review process in preparation for a multiple-choice test. Since the test is largely concept based, the review focuses on the relationship among concepts important to chapter 4 content. Part II is the multiple-choice test. Part III uses the structured *Learn from Mistakes Protocol.* The protocol is a low-pressure feedback technique in which students learn how to use information from mistakes on tests to improve their understanding and increase achievement.

Before You Teach

Background Information

The Part I review process involves concept maps. Traditionally, teachers ask students to generate concept maps as a way to show the relative importance among concepts within a content area. This approach reflects research that suggests the mental structure among concepts (sometimes called a semantic map) within an expert's mind is vastly different from the mental structure of those same concepts in the mind of a novice. Concept maps represent one method of viewing those structures, albeit indirectly, since the memory nodes are not directly accessible in the brain.

Teachers can infer from analyzing concept maps how students think about a set of concepts and thus infer how students might solve problems. For example, a concept map analyzing motion that has velocity in the center and force toward the perimeter suggests that the student thinks velocity has greater explanatory power than force. This novice would tend to use velocity to explain the cause of motion, rather than to use force as the cause of motion. Thus, velocity alone and not a change in velocity would be sufficient for this student to explain motion. This student might use $F_{net} = mv$ (which is not valid) instead of $F_{net} = ma$ to think about the force on an object moving at constant velocity.

Materials—Part I

For each team of 4 students

4 copies of copymaster 4.1, *Concept Map*

4 copies of copymaster 4.2, *Scoring Rubric for Moving toward Understanding*

TRCD

colored markers

1 large piece of paper

Materials—Part II

For the teacher

1 copy of copymaster 4.3b, *Chapter 4 Test Answer Key*

For each student

1 multiple-choice test booklet made from copymaster 4.3a, *Chapter 4 Test*

4. List any new problems or ethical issues that have resulted from satellite technology.
5. Describe at least one new area of research that satellite technology has provided to scientists.

Universal Gravitation

The force of gravity is something all too familiar to you. As an infant, you "studied" gravity as you adjusted to its effects when you dropped your bowl of cereal off the high chair or when you fell while learning to walk. As you grew older, you naturally learned to compensate for the force and accelerations produced by gravity as you learned to kick a soccer ball, catch a baseball, or shoot a basketball. How would you have to adjust if you were playing these sports on a planet other than Earth? Gravity has influenced the way we do everything on Earth. It has even influenced the course of evolution.

Level 1 of this program introduced the universal law that describes the mutual gravitational force of attraction between any two objects. Every object exerts a force on every other object due to mutual gravitational attraction. This force is directly proportional to the masses of the objects and inversely proportional to the square of the distance between their centers. You can use this relationship to calculate the force of gravity between Earth and a satellite. The equation for this relationship, known as the universal law of gravitation, is

$$F_{gravity} \text{ or } F_g = \frac{Gm_1m_2}{d^2}, \text{ where}$$

G = universal gravitation constant ($6.67 \times 10^{-11} \frac{m^3}{kg\ sec^2}$),

m_1 and m_2 = masses of two objects in kilograms,

d = the distance (in meters) between the centers of mass of the two objects.

In Level 1, this relationship was used to find the force of gravity between galaxies, students, and a student and Earth. In fact, you can use it to calculate the force between any two objects if you know their masses and the distance between their centers of mass. For objects near Earth's surface, the distance between the objects is simply the radius of Earth (6.38×10^6 m). The mass of Earth is 5.98×10^{24} kg.

This universal law of gravitation is related to Newton's second law in the following way. The equation you have learned for Newton's second law is,

$$F_{net} = ma.$$

For an object in free fall, the only force acting on the body is that due to the gravitational force. Then from the universal law of gravitation, the equation becomes,

$$\frac{GmM}{r^2} = ma.$$

In this equation, m represents the mass of the object, and M represents the mass of Earth. So for objects near Earth and canceling the mass on both sides of the equation, the equation becomes,

$$\frac{GM}{r^2} = a.$$

An object that is attracted to Earth by gravity accelerates with constant acceleration of

$$\frac{GM}{r^2}.$$

For ease of writing, we rename the term, $\frac{GM}{r^2}$, g. Thus, the acceleration due to gravity is g.

210 Unit 1 Interactions Are Interesting

Materials—Part III

For each student

the scored copy of the test

Advance Preparation

Make 4 copies per team of copymasters 4.1, *Concept Map* and 4.2, *Scoring Rubric for Moving toward Understanding*. Make 1 copy per student of copymaster 4.3a, *Chapter 4 Test* and staple it into a test booklet.

If you have access to a machine grader that reads graphite pencil marks, then have students answer on the appropriate forms. If not, make a multiple-choice answer sheet, which they can mark instead of marking the test booklet. Plan to score the tests in the same class period.

Block out time to carefully read and comment on students' LFM revisions.

As You Teach

Outcomes and Indicators of Success

By the end of this activity, students should

1. connect the relationship between concepts inherent in a given concept map to a problem-solving approach.

   They will demonstrate their ability by

   - analyzing aspects of two given concept maps for clues regarding the conceptual hierarchy used to generate the map,
   - linking the proposed conceptual hierarchy to a problem-solving style, and
   - producing a solution in the problem-solving style emanating from each given map.

2. demonstrate their content knowledge of how forces are involved in producing the following types of motion: projectile, uniform circular, simple harmonic (spring), and pendulum.

   They will demonstrate their understanding by answering 12 multiple-choice questions regarding the relationship of force to motion.

3. show their ability to assess their own work on a multiple-choice test and articulate both the reasons for a mistake and for the correct answer.

   They will show their ability by

   - following the *LFM Protocol* during the correction phase of the multiple-choice test,
   - identifying the concept-based reason for a given mistake, and
   - detailing the correct solution to an incorrect multiple-choice test question.

All of the values in $\frac{GM}{r^2}$ are constants, so putting in the values for these constants in the expression gives us the following:

$$\frac{GM}{r^2} = a$$

$$\frac{\left(6.67 \times 10^{-11} \frac{m^3}{kg\ s^2}\right)\left(5.98 \times 10^{24}\ kg\right)}{(6.38 \times 10^6\ m)^2} = a$$

$$\frac{\left(6.67 \times 10^{-11} \frac{\cancel{m^2} \times m^1}{\cancel{kg}\ s^2}\right)\left(5.98 \times 10^{24}\ \cancel{kg}\right)}{4.07 \times 10^{13}\ \cancel{m^2}} = a$$

$$9.80\ \frac{m}{s^2} = a$$

This is our familiar acceleration due to gravity near Earth's surface.

Unit 1, *Interactions Are Interesting*, has introduced you to the laws of motion described by Sir Isaac Newton. In fact, he is also responsible for finding the relationships described in the universal law of gravitation. It took Newton 20 years to prove that this law is valid for large objects like the planets as well as very small particles.

Moving toward Understanding

EVALUATE

In this chapter, you have linked net force to many types of motion in a match between cause and effect. The result is your increased ability to explain, understand, and apply motions common to your everyday environment. These are motions such as free fall, spring motion, pendulum motion, projectile motion, and uniform circular motion. That's a lot of understanding.

Now it is time to demonstrate what you know and understand. Of course, learning is ongoing. So the test you will take in this activity is vital feedback that helps you and your teacher make the best plans for your long-term benefit.

First, you will work with team members to review the relationships among concepts important to motion. Then you will take a test on your own to demonstrate your understanding of force and motion. After the test, you will learn how to use feedback to improve your understanding.

Chapter 4 Physics Is Moving 211

Process and Procedure

Part I: Structured Review

Materials

For each team of 4 students

4 copies of copymaster 4.1, *Concept Map*

4 copies of copymaster 4.2, *Scoring Rubric for Moving toward Understanding*

colored markers

1 large piece of paper

In Step 1, students review the scoring rubric to make sure they understand what is expected of them in this activity.

In Step 2, the class develops a list of criteria for a concept map that reflects a complete understanding of concepts. Students should list criteria in this way: the most general or overarching concept should be at the top or in the middle of the map, supporting concepts should be either below or toward the perimeter of the map, and concepts should be connected in a logical sequence. Consider using the information from the background section to inspire students' thinking. Ideally, get students to recognize that the 2 maps in copymaster 4.1, *Concept Map* reflect very different ways of viewing force and motion, thus implying different ways of solving problems. Students choose the map that they think conveys the best understanding of the concepts and write a justification for their selection. Monitor their choices so that they understand that the first concept map on copymaster 4.1 is the best at meeting the criteria established in Step 2a.

Students are asked to redraw the concept map on a large piece of paper in Step 2d. They then add connecting language to the concept map so that they can demonstrate their understanding of the relationships depicted on the map. Students may want to add other concepts to their maps in Step 2f. Students take turns explaining the map and relationships to other team members. Decide if you want them to share with you or the class during this class time. This step works as an effective review for the test in Part II.

NOTES:

Part I: Structured Review

Materials

For each team of 4 students

4 *Concept Map* handouts

4 *Moving toward Understanding Scoring Rubric* handouts

colored markers

1 large piece of paper

Process and Procedure

There are many effective ways to review for a test. One technique is to reexamine what you know about the key concepts of the chapter (figure 4.33). Focusing on the *relationships* among those concepts and how those relationships help you solve problems is particularly effective.

Concept maps are one way to represent and communicate the relationships among concepts important to force and motion. You generated a concept map in chapter 3, *Collisions—Atomic Style*. The map communicated which concept you thought was most important and which concepts are most closely related. Your map showed the concepts you are most likely to use when you solve problems and the ones you tend not to use. Concept maps give you feedback about the way you approach thinking and solving problems in science.

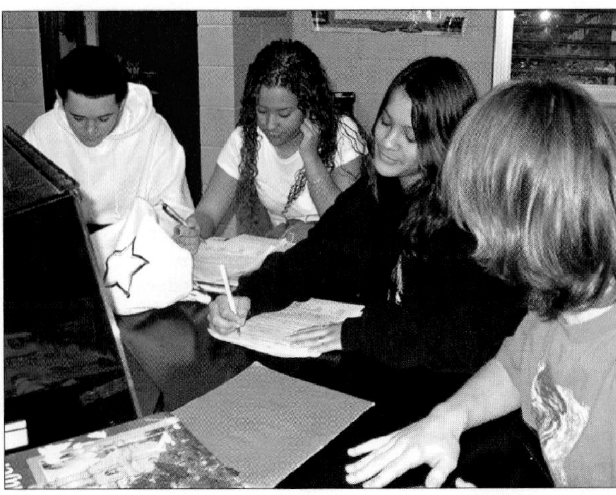

▶ **Figure 4.33** **Structured review.** These students are working together to focus on the relationships among the concepts covered in this chapter. In this way, they will be prepared for the upcoming chapter assessment.

Process and Procedure

Part II: Multiple-Choice Test

Materials

For the teacher

1 copy of copymaster 4.3b, *Chapter 4 Test Answer Key*

For each student

1 multiple-choice test booklet made from copymaster 4.3a, *Chapter 4 Test*

Students begin the test during this part of the activity. This test is not easy. Do not expect many students to score 100 percent. Grade the tests immediately and return them in the same class period. This is a crucial part of the *LFM Protocol.* If you use a machine grader, the scores will be marked already. If you make your own multiple-choice answer sheet, gather all the tests and align the responses. Then place your key on top of the stack and punch through the key with a nail or awl and a hammer. Holes mark correct answers on students' answer sheets.

NOTES:

In Part I, you and your team will use completed concept maps to consider different ways of thinking. In doing so, you will review and strengthen your own understanding about force and motion.

1. Review the *Moving toward Understanding Scoring Rubric* handout to understand what is expected of you for this activity. Ask your teacher for clarification if you do not understand any part of the rubric.
2. Examine the *Concept Map* handout, which shows 2 concept maps created from concepts in this chapter. Use this handout to complete Steps 2a–e.
   a. Develop a list of criteria with your class of the important features of a concept map. List those features that will convey the best understanding of the concepts.
   b. Decide which concept map shows a better understanding of the concepts in this chapter based on the criteria from your class discussion.
   c. Write a justification for your selection of the best concept map.
   d. Redraw the concept map you chose onto a large piece of paper using colored markers.
   e. Add connecting language to your concept map that communicates the relationship of the connected words.
   f. Add other details to your concept map that will help you review the material in this chapter.
   g. Take turns explaining the concepts in your map to your teammates. Use language that explains the relationship between concepts. Be prepared to share your ideas with other teams, the class, or your teacher.

Part II: Multiple-Choice Test

Materials

For each student

1 multiple-choice test booklet

Process and Procedure

1. Obtain a copy of the multiple-choice test from your teacher.
2. Follow your teacher's instructions and work individually to complete the test.
3. Hand in your test when you are finished.

Process and Procedure
Part III: Learn from Mistakes

Materials
For each student
the scored copy of the test

In Step 1, lead a class discussion on how, as scientists, we learn from mistakes. Read through the *Learn from Mistakes* (*LFM*) *Protocol* with the class. Communicate the reasons for and the nature of the *LFM Protocol*. Emphasize the importance of learning how to learn from mistakes.

Then lead a quick discussion on the test questions you think were most frequently missed. Try not to tell students the correct answers. Instead, review the key concepts necessary to solve the problem and point out the common misconceptions, especially in the context of missed questions. Encourage students to take notes on the discussion to use during their LFM revision. Finally, remind them to write their original score on the top of their LFM revisions since you have not recorded it yet. If you worry that students will lose or not turn in the LFM revisions, then quickly record the original scores before you return the scored answer sheets. Try to orchestrate class so that students take the test, you score it and explain some of the questions, and students have at least 15 minutes to begin their LFM work. Assign any remaining LFM work as homework and collect it the next day.

Remember that when you grade the LFM work, marking the correct answer is not the most important feature. Students can obtain the correct answers easily from looking at other tests. Rather, you're looking for evidence of students' ability to identify and articulate the conceptual mistakes inherent in a given incorrect response. This ability helps students monitor their own thinking, thus decreasing their dependence on you.

NOTES:

Part III: Learn from Mistakes

Materials

For each student

the scored copy of your test

Process and Procedure

Now it's time to get feedback on what you know and understand. The feedback is called learning from mistakes. Be prepared to analyze your individual test results for patterns in what you understood and what is still challenging for you. Then use the process of scientific inquiry to learn from mistakes you may have made.

Your teacher will score your test from Part II and give you immediate feedback. Part of that feedback will be a discussion of the concepts important to each question.

1. Participate in a class discussion of how to demonstrate that you have learned from mistakes.
2. Read the *Learn from Mistakes* (*LFM*) *Protocol* carefully before you begin to make corrections.
3. Follow the *LFM Protocol* for each question you missed and turn in your paper as instructed by your teacher.

NOTES:

Protocol

Learn from Mistakes Protocol

School isn't just a place to deposit right answers. Sometimes we make mistakes. In fact, most humans make mistakes when they try to learn something, especially when the subject is difficult or new. When you learn to identify and explain what's incorrect about a wrong answer, you have a better chance of avoiding that mistake next time.

For each of the questions you missed on the test, perform the following steps. If you do, you can earn up to 50 percent of the difference between your raw percent score and 100 percent. Be sure to write your raw percent score at the top of the page along with a list of the numbers you missed.

1. Represent the original question in a different way than it was represented on the test. For example, if the question was mostly words, represent it as a sketch. If it was mostly a sketch, represent it in words. When you use words, paraphrase the question in your own words. Do not copy the question word for word. Label any sketch with all the variables, especially the unknown. If the problem mentions any change in condition, show a before-and-after sketch.
2. Identify and explain the mistake you made in the answer you selected. Focus on explaining any conceptual misunderstandings. When you explain what is incorrect, show how the misconception would lead to a contradiction with what you see in nature. Explanations like, "I read the problem wrong" and "I pushed the wrong button on the calculator" will receive no credit.
3. Show the correct solution or answer. When necessary, show all governing equations, first in symbol form, then with number and unit values. Always place proper units and labels on answers. Include why the answer is reasonable.

Chapter 4 Physics Is Moving 215

CHAPTER 5

Forces of Attraction

Chapter Overview

In Chapter 5, *Forces of Attraction*, students will apply what they have learned in the previous chapters about chemical reactions and forces to specific types of chemical reactions. They will study reactions in which the competitive forces of attraction for charged particles drive the properties and the products of the chemical reaction. They will study acid-base reactions, where the proton is the charged particle of interest, and they will study oxidation-reduction, or redox, reactions, where the charged particle that drives the reaction is the electron.

In their study of these reactions, your students will analyze properties of common substances including pH as they predict results, design experiments, test their predictions, and offer explanations about the substances' properties and chemical behavior. Then they will analyze data about bonds, electronegativity, and reactivity to build their understanding of the reasons behind the substances' behavior and properties. They also will apply what they have learned to the field of electrochemistry, where they will see practical applications of the chemistry they are learning. As you evaluate their understanding of the concepts in this chapter, your students will be engaged in a hands-on evaluation where they must analyze results and make decisions as they take on the role of a corrosion engineer.

Goals for the Chapter

As your students complete chapter 5, they should develop an understanding of

- simple acid-base reactions including neutralization,
- pH and how it relates to the concentration of ions,
- the differences between strong and weak acids and bases,
- the characteristics of redox reactions,
- practical applications of both acid-base and redox chemistry, and
- the competitive forces that drive these types of chemical reactions.

The chapter organizer uses graphic design principles to help students connect one activity to another. It uses reminders of key concepts, linking questions, and the spatial arrangement of activity titles to foster the sense of a conceptual flow, connecting each activity. Explicitly ask students to locate their position within its flow at the beginning of each activity. This action reinforces the connection among the activities, thus enhancing long-term memory.

Chapter 5 Organizer

FORCES OF ATTRACTION

Major Concepts

- **Acids and bases vary in strength and concentration and affect the pH.**
- **Acid-base processes can be explained by the relative attractions for hydrogen ions.**
- **The activity of elements depends on the relative attractions for electrons.**
- **Oxidation-reduction reactions can be manipulated to give the desired results.**

ENGAGE — Ranking Tasks ★

Key Ideas:
- Students can use their experiences to identify acids and bases and rank them according to degrees of acidity and basicity.
- Students can use their experiences to rank metals by their degree of reactivity.

Activity: Students use their prior experiences to classify substances as acids or bases and then rank them according to their degree of acidity and basicity. Then they rank metals on the basis of their reactivity.

LINKING QUESTION: How can I verify my classifications and rankings with evidence?

EXPLORE — Gathering Evidence ★★

Key Ideas:
- Acids and bases have specific ranges of pH values.
- Metal reactivity can be determined based on observable evidence.

Activity: Students measure the pH of the substances from the previous activity to verify their rankings. Students also conduct tests with metals and an acid to determine the metal's degree of reactivity.

LINKING QUESTION: How can I use my knowledge of forces to explain acid base behavior?

EXPLAIN — Acids and Bases ★★★★

Key Ideas:
- Acids and bases vary in strength due to the forces of attraction of ions.
- Both strength and concentration play a role in determining the pH of substances.

Activity: Students build models and participate in active reading on the concepts of dissociation, acid-base strength, bond strength, electronegativity, concentration, pH, and neutralization reactions.

LINKING QUESTION: Can I use my knowledge of forces of attraction to also explain oxidation-reduction reactions?

EXPLAIN — Redox Reactions ★★

Key Idea:
- Reactivity is predictable based on competition for electrons in redox reactions.

Activity: Students investigate redox reactions and learn about the processes involved in these types of reactions through an investigation and active reading.

LINKING QUESTION: Can I use and manipulate redox reactions to produce useful processes and products?

ELABORATE — Electrochemistry ★★

Key Idea:
- By understanding strength of reducing and oxidizing agents, redox reactions can be used and manipulated to produce useful processes and products.

Activity: Students apply what they have learned about redox reactions as they learn about voltaic and electrolytic cells through investigations and readings.

LINKING QUESTION: How can I demonstrate what I have learned about acid-base and oxidation-reduction reactions?

EVALUATE — Nail It Down ★

Key Idea:
- Corrosion is a process that can be controlled by understanding acid-base and redox chemistry.

Activity: Students demonstrate their understanding of acid-base and redox chemistry by determining the best metals to use to prevent corrosion in iron.

★ = One Class Period ☆ = ½ Class Period *Note:* Based on a 50-minute class period.

Standards Covered by Chapter 5

FORCES OF ATTRACTION

STANDARD A: Science as Inquiry. As a result of activities in grades 9–12, all students should develop

abilities necessary to do scientific inquiry

- Identify questions and concepts that guide scientific investigations. Students should formulate a testable hypothesis and demonstrate the logical connections between the scientific concepts guiding a hypothesis and the design of an experiment. They should demonstrate appropriate procedures, a knowledge base, and conceptual understanding of scientific investigations.
- Design and conduct scientific investigations. Designing and conducting a scientific investigation requires introduction to the major concepts in the area being investigated, proper equipment, safety precautions, assistance with methodological problems, recommendations for use of technologies, clarification of ideas that guide the inquiry, and scientific knowledge obtained from sources other than the actual investigation. The investigation may also require student clarification of the question, method, controls, and variables; student organization and display of data; student revision of methods and explanations; and a public presentation of the results with a critical response from peers. Regardless of the scientific investigation performed, students must use evidence, apply logic, and construct an argument for their proposed explanations.
- Use technology and mathematics to improve investigations and communications. A variety of technologies, such as hand tools, measuring instruments, and calculators, should be an integral component of scientific investigations. The use of computers for the collection, analysis, and display of data is also a part of this standard. Mathematics plays an essential role in all aspects of an inquiry. For example, measurement is used for posing questions, formulas are used for developing explanations, and charts and graphs are used for communicating results.
- Formulate and revise scientific explanations and models using logic and evidence. Student inquiries should culminate in formulating an explanation or model. Models should be physical, conceptual, and mathematical. In the process of answering the questions, the students should engage in discussions and arguments that result in the revision of their explanations. These discussions should be based on scientific knowledge, the use of logic, and evidence from their investigation.
- Recognize and analyze alternative explanations and models. This aspect of the standard emphasizes the critical abilities of analyzing an argument by reviewing current scientific understanding, weighing the evidence, and examining the logic so as to decide which explanations and models are best. In other words, although there may be several plausible explanations, they do not all have equal weight. Students should be able to use scientific criteria to find the preferred explanations.
- Communicate and defend a scientific argument. Students in school science programs should develop the abilities associated with accurate and effective communication. These include writing and following procedures, expressing concepts, reviewing information, summarizing data, using language appropriately, developing diagrams and charts, explaining statistical analysis, speaking clearly and logically, constructing a reasoned argument, and responding appropriately to critical comments.

understandings about scientific inquiry

- Scientists conduct investigations for a wide variety of reasons. For example, they may wish to discover new aspects of the natural world, explain recently observed phenomena, or test the conclusions of prior investigations or the prediction of current theories.
- Scientists rely on technology to enhance the gathering and manipulation of data. New techniques and tools provide new evidence to guide inquiry and new methods to gather data, thereby contributing to the advance of science. The accuracy and precision of the data, and therefore the quality of the exploration, depends on the technology used.
- Mathematics is essential in scientific inquiry. Mathematical tools and models guide and improve the posing of questions, gathering data, constructing explanations and communicating results.

- Scientific explanations must adhere to criteria such as: a proposed explanation must be logically consistent; it must abide by the rules of evidence; it must be open to questions and possible modification; and it must be based on historical and current scientific knowledge.
- Results of scientific inquiry—new knowledge and methods—emerge from different types of investigations and public communication among scientists. In communicating and defending the results of scientific inquiry, arguments must be logical and demonstrate connections between natural phenomena, investigations, and the historical body of scientific knowledge. In addition, the methods and procedures that scientistss used to obtain evidence must be clearly reported to enhance opportunities for further investigation.

STANDARD B: Physical Science. As a result of activities in grades 9–12, all students should develop an understanding of

structure of atoms

- Matter is made of minute particles called atoms, and atoms are composed of even smaller components. These components have measurable properties, such as mass and electrical charge. Each atom has a positively charged nucleus surrounded by negatively charged electrons. The electric force between the nucleus and electrons holds the atom together.

structure and properties of matter

- Atoms interact with one another by transferring or sharing electrons that are furthest from the nucleus. These outer electrons govern the chemical properties of the element.
- The physical properties of compounds reflect the nature of the interactions among its molecules. These interactions are determined by the structure of the molecule, including the constituent atoms and the distances and angles between them.

chemical reactions

- Chemical reactions occur all around us, for example in health care, cooking, cosmetics, and automobiles. Complex chemical reactions involving carbon-based molecules take place constantly in every cell in our bodies.
- A large number of important reactions involve the transfer of either electrons (oxidation-reduction reactions) or hydrogen ions (acid-base reactions) between reacting ions, molecules, or atoms. In other reactions, chemical bonds are broken by heat or light to form very reactive radicals with electrons ready to form new bonds. Radical reactions control many processes such as the presence of ozone and greenhouse gases in the atmosphere, burning and processing of fossil fuels, the formation of polymers, and explosions.

motions and forces

- The electric force is a universal force that exists between any two charged objects. Opposite charges attract while like charges repel. The strength of the force is proportional to the charges, and, as with gravitation, inversely proportional to the square of the distance between them.

conservation of energy and the increase in disorder

- The total energy of the universe is constant. Energy can be transferred by collisions in chemical and nuclear reactions, by light waves and other radiations, and in many other ways. However, it can never be destroyed. As these transfers occur, the matter involved becomes steadily less ordered.

Prerequisite Knowledge

To be successful in this chapter, students need the background knowledge provided by the previous chapters in this unit. Students need to be able to use a scientific calculator and do simple algebra in calculations.

Commonly Held Misconceptions

Students may harbor misconceptions about the material they will be studying in this chapter. Some of those are listed here. Do not take time to go through these as a list of lecture topics for your students, but rather use them to inform your evaluation of student discussions and explanations as they emerge. Many activities included in this chapter work to expose and to dispel these misconceptions.

- Atoms "own" their electrons.

There aren't different kinds of electrons for different atoms. Electrons are electrons no matter what atom or molecule they surround and they can be transferred from one atom to another.

- The chemical bond is a physical thing made of matter.

Chemical bonds are not made of a separate form of matter, but result from the arrangement of particles in the molecule and forces of attraction.

- Electron pairs are equally shared in all covalent bonds.

Electron pairs are not shared equally due to differences in the electronegativity of the atoms in the molecule.

- "Strength" of acids and bases and "concentration" mean the same thing.

Concentration reflects the number of particles of solute that are dissolved in a liter of solution. Strength reflects the degree to which acids and molecules dissociate into ions in solution.

- Mixing an acid and a base regardless of concentration and strength always produces a neutral product.

The results of mixing equal concentrations of a strong acid and a strong base will produce a neutral salt and water. However, unequal concentrations or mixing strong acids with weak bases and vice versa will produce either acidic or basic salts.

- Pure water, since it is neutral, contains no hydrogen ion (H^+) or hydroxide ion (OH^-).

Because of the self-ionization of water, water contains 1×10^{-7} M H^+ and 1×10^{-7} M OH^-. Since these concentrations are equal, water is neutral. Even distilled water will register a lower pH than 7 because of dissolved carbon dioxide (CO_2) from the air. To get distilled water to have a neutral pH, you must heat the water to drive off the CO_2 and use it immediately or store it in a CO_2-free container.

- "pH balanced" means the substance is neutral.

Some personal care items and cosmetics often say they are pH balanced. This does not mean they are neutral, but that they are formulated to have a particular pH.

- Strong acids have very low pH values, and strong bases have very high pH values.

A very dilute solution of a strong acid or base can have a pH value near 7.

- Oxidation is only the addition of oxygen in a reaction, and reduction is only the removal of oxygen in a reaction.

Historically, this is how the reactions got their name, but the more modern definitions of these reactions include many more types of reactions.

- Oxidation and reduction can occur independently.

Oxidation and reduction always occur as a pair. If oxidation is the loss of electrons, then there must be a process to take the electrons (reduction). Often, we look at half reactions of the process, but this does not in any way indicate that oxidation takes place separately from reduction.

ENGAGE

Ranking Tasks

Activity Overview

In this activity, students access their prior knowledge and understanding about reactions involving acids, bases, and the activity of metals. They use this knowledge and understanding to develop a ranking system that sorts common materials according to relative strengths and reactivity. Students practice developing a ranking system for acids and bases, then apply what they learn to developing a ranking for the relative reactivity of common metals.

Before You Teach

Background Information

Substances can be considered acidic, basic, or neutral based on their properties and their pH. Cleaners designed to "cut grease" and drain openers for grease and hair clogs tend to be basic. Fruits and fruit juices usually contain ascorbic and citric acids and are acidic. Any number of substances can have a pH of 7 and be considered neutral.

The bulk of the background material will be given in a later section. Your students will be discovering much of this information as they work through the activities. In keeping with the constructivist model, do not give your students information and facts up front. Allow them to build their knowledge throughout the chapter.

Materials—Part I

For the teacher

containers with commercially available products such as

- ammonia
- liquid soap
- antacid (any type)
- lemon juice
- gastric juice (simulated with dilute HCl)
- vinegar
- milk
- distilled water
- rainwater
- contact lens solution
- baking soda solution

For each team of 2–4 students

1 copy of copymaster 5.1, *Card Pack 1*
1 copy of copymaster 5.2, *Property Card Pack*

Materials—Part II

For the teacher

1 pair disposable laboratory gloves
samples of metals such as

- iron nails
- galvanized nails (zinc)
- copper pipe or wire
- lead fishing weights
- a sparkler
- aluminum foil
- tin roofing material
- gold and silver jewelry

Cautions

Wear disposable laboratory gloves when handling leads.

For each team of 2–4 students

1 copy of copymaster 5.3, *Card Pack 2*

TRCD

Advance Preparation

Make enough copies so that each team of students has a set of cards from copymaster 5.1, *Card Pack 1*, copymaster 5.2, *Property Card Pack*, and copymaster 5.3, *Card Pack 2*. Cut them apart. Make enough for your largest class; you can reuse them for each class. Consider copying them on card stock or heavy paper and laminating them. They will last several years if you take this time now. Gather your materials and display them to students. Use commercially available containers to reinforce the "household" nature of these substances.

As You Teach

Outcomes and Indicators of Success

By the end of this activity, students should

1. share their current understanding about acids and bases.

   They will demonstrate their understanding by

   - classifying common substances as acids or bases,
   - ranking the substances in each group of acids or bases,
   - justifying their groupings and rankings, and
   - reevaluating acids and bases according to a set of properties.

2. share their current understanding about the relative activities of metals.

   They will demonstrate their understanding by

   - ranking metals from most reactive to least reactive based on their current ideas and experiences with the metals and
   - justifying their rankings.

3. design a procedure to rank the reactivity of metals.

   They will demonstrate their ability to design by

   - developing a step-by-step procedure to rank a set of metals and
   - applying their procedure to a given set of common metals.

Strategies

Getting Started

It is always good to have students read the chapter introduction and introduction to the specific activity. There are many questions designed to get your students thinking about the topic. In addition, have the original bottles or containers of each of the substances you choose to use in the engage activity in front of the class (see *For the teacher* for Part I and Part II). Since some students may not have used or seen some of these, lead a class discussion about the item and what its uses are. Some of the manufacturers of cleaning products will list the product's uses, ingredients, and cautions on the label. This is good information for the students and will help them in their predictions.

For Part II, show samples of each of the metals you collected and discuss their uses. (See the *Process and Procedure* for Part II for a list of the common uses of some metals.) Students who do not have experience with the metals may be embarrassed to tell you or their teams, so a class discussion will help everyone better understand the metals and their uses.

Reminder of Possible Misconceptions

The activity and the questions that follow are designed to expose some of your students' misconceptions. Use these to inform your teaching.

Process and Procedure

Part I: Acid, Base, or Neutral?

Materials

For the teacher

containers with commercially available products such as

- ammonia
- liquid soap
- antacid (any type)
- lemon juice
- gastric juice (simulated with dilute HCl)
- vinegar
- milk
- distilled water
- rainwater
- contact lens solution
- baking soda solution

For each team of 2–4 students

1 copy of copymaster 5.1, *Card Pack 1*

1 copy of copymaster 5.2, *Property Card Pack*

In Steps 1 and 2, students meet with their teams and discuss each of the substances on the cards. If they have questions about what a substance is or what it is used for, they will ask another team for help. If you have the original containers for some of these substances, provide the container and let students propose a use of the substance.

In Step 3, your students categorize each substance as an acid, a base, or a neutral substance. They make a chart in their science notebooks to record their predictions. They record their reasoning behind the predictions or justifications in a similar chart on the facing page. Encourage your students to use their experiences with these types of substances to give justification for their groupings.

In Step 4, give teams the set of 2 cards in the *Property Card Pack*. Emphasize to your students that scientists are continuously revising their work based on new evidence. Students revise their groupings based on the new evidence contained in these cards. Refrain from giving them any clues to the correct classification at this time. They will develop a classification scheme as they go along. Students again have to justify and record any changes they make in their groupings.

In Step 5, students rank the items they have placed in the acid and base groups according to which substances they think are more or less acidic or basic. Encourage your students to use their experiences to rank these. Some students, especially the A students, may be frustrated because they cannot figure out (and you will not tell them) the correct answer. Emphasize that they will not be graded on their correctness for this task, but on how they justify and document their rankings.

ENGAGE

Ranking Tasks

Life is packed with competitions. There is competition for class rank, to be first in line at the movie theater, or to be first chair in your section of the band. Often, competition results in ranking things from best to worse or strongest to weakest. Sometimes ranking tells you something about the properties of objects. For example, the venom from a brown recluse spider is ranked as one of the most poisonous. A ranking system for how poisonous different spiders are helps you learn what spiders can be potentially deadly and what spiders are virtually harmless. In this activity, you and your team will be ranking items and substances. Understanding how these items rank will help you understand something about their properties.

Does battery acid harm you if it gets on your skin? What about lemon juice? Have you ever accidentally spilled drain cleaner on your hand? What were the results? In Part I of *Ranking Tasks*, you will use your everyday experiences with some common substances to first sort and then rank the substances according to what you currently know about them. Later, you will connect your ranking to the force of attraction between electrically charged objects.

Part II is similar to Part I. You will think about the reactivity of some metals. What might you notice about some nails that are left outside for a long period? Do all nails behave this way? You will think about these things as you work with a partner to rank metals according to how reactive they are with other substances.

Use the following question to focus your thinking and actions in this and the next four activities: "How do forces of attraction and repulsion help me understand chemical reactions?"

Part I: Acid, Base, or Neutral?

As you work through Part I of *Ranking Tasks*, think about your experiences with the substances that are listed on the cards that you will receive. Talk with your teammates and use your current understanding to complete the task.

Materials

For each team of 2–4 students

Card Pack 1

Property Card Pack

222 Unit 1 Interactions Are Interesting

Wrap up Part I of this activity with a class discussion. This is a time for students to express their ideas and for you to listen. You should use this time to evaluate how students are thinking about acids, bases, or both. Do they think one is more harmful than the other? Do they consider everyday products to be mild forms of acids or bases? Again, do not tell students the correct answers or rankings, but instead foster their curiosity by encouraging them to find the answers themselves. They will do this in the next activity.

Answers to Stop and Think—Part I, SE page 224

1. Many answers are acceptable here. Students might use color, the state of matter, or the availability of the item in stores. The point is *not* whether their criteria agree with yours; rather, the point is if they use their criteria consistently. As time goes by, they will develop sorting criteria more closely aligned with your knowledge. This is another opportunity for you to assess your students' current understanding about acids and bases.
2. Students may indicate that after they reviewed the property cards, they had new information that allowed them to make better, more informed decisions about the items.
3. Accept any answers here except, "I have no clue." Students may say something about the antacid canceling out the properties of the stomach acid. Encourage them by saying they do know many things.
4. Again, many answers are acceptable here. Nonetheless, all answers should be justified by the consistent application of some criterion. This is a chance for you to see what your students know about pH. From their answers, you should be able to tell if they know that acids have pH values below 7, bases have pH values above 7, and a pH of 7 is neutral. You can also tell if they know that the farther from 7 the substance appears on the scale, the more acidic or basic the substance is.

Process and Procedure

Part II: Active or Not?

Process and Procedure

1. Meet with your team and obtain *Card Pack 1* from your teacher. Spread the cards face up on your desk or table.
2. Discuss each of the substances on the cards. Talk about your experiences with each of them.

If there is a substance listed on a card that no one on your team recognizes, ask another team for help.

3. Use your everyday experiences and general knowledge about each substance to complete Steps 3a–b.
   a. Make a chart with 3 columns in your science notebook on a blank, left-hand page. Place the substances on each card into 1 of 3 categories: acid, base, or neutral.

Each team member should make a chart in his or her notebook.

   b. Make a chart with the same 3 categories on the right-hand page and record your justifications for placing each substance in one of those categories.

What experiences do you have that led you to classify a substance as acid, base, or neutral? What evidence do you have for your reasoning? Use this evidence for your justifications.

4. Use the *Property Card Pack* to complete Steps 4a–d.
   a. With your team, read through the 2 cards in the *Property Card Pack*.
   b. Summarize these properties in a new chart in your science notebook.

Be sure to use headings that make sense in your chart.

   c. Make any changes to your categories based on new information.

Scientists classify or group things in many different ways, but they are always looking for similarities between things in the same group. If new evidence surfaces, they may change their groups or move items from one group to another.

   d. Record any changes *and* reasons for those changes in your charts.

Consider using a different-colored pen for any change you make. This helps you find and remember what you learned. It also helps you track your thinking.

Materials

For the teacher

samples of metals (such as iron nails, galvanized nails [zinc], copper pipe or wire, lead fishing weights, a sparkler, aluminum foil, tin roofing material, and gold and silver jewelry)

For each team of 2–4 students

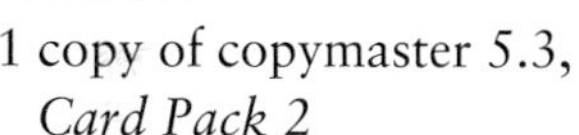

1 copy of copymaster 5.3, *Card Pack 2*

The task for your students in Part II is similar to that in Part I. Based on their experience and some on the class discussion at the start of this activity, students will rank a set of metals based on their reactivity. They will ask another team for help if they are unfamiliar with some of the metals. Circulate among the teams and offer help only if they seem to be unfamiliar with some of the metals. Some common uses for metals are the following:

- Magnesium: Used for the bright sparks in fireworks and flares; also used in old flash photography in flashcubes; its compounds used in medicine
- Iron: Major component used in steel; used in making nails, in construction, and so on
- Copper: Used in coins, electric wire, and pipes

- Aluminum: Used in cans, foils, and kitchen utensils; used some in construction
- Tin: Used in coatings on other metals
- Silver: Used in jewelry and dinnerware, photography, and electrical connections
- Zinc: Used in nail and pipe coatings, coins, and batteries

Don't mention details about galvanizing metals at this time; students will learn about corrosion protection in a later activity.

In Step 2, teams develop a short procedure detailing how they will go about ranking the metals by reactivity. Do not worry about the procedure being exactly what you would do.

In Step 3, look for evidence of a logical sequence of steps that has a reasonable chance of leading to a ranking based on objective criteria such as the amount of bubbling when the metal is placed in acid. Give hints to students regarding their procedures, but do not tell them outright to change their procedures. Allow the interaction with other teams to be a way for teams to see how differences in thinking affect results.

In Step 4, students rank the metals and most likely make a chart in their science notebooks to record their rankings as they did in Part I. They make a similar chart on the facing page to record the justifications for their rankings.

In Step 5, lead a class discussion of their rankings. Initiate the discussion and then allow the students to lead the discussion. Your role is to listen to your students' ideas and make sure that all students are given the chance to share their ideas. Make an extra effort to elicit students' reasoning for their rankings. Help them understand whether or not they have applied their criteria consistently.

Answers to Reflect and Connect, SE pages 225–226

1. Many answers are acceptable, but look for those that indicate that the students understand that this is a chemical reaction and that new substances will be formed in the process.
2. The two most obvious reasons are that gold is much too expensive and too soft to be used as a nail. Other answers include the scarcity of gold versus iron, durability, and weight.
3. Students should see that base A shows a stronger current than base B. They should infer that there are more charged particles or ions in the solution with the brighter light. This question is designed to get students thinking about bases on the molecular level.
4. Students should notice that all of these acids have hydrogen in their chemical formulas. Most have the hydrogen listed as the first element of the formula. The purpose of this question is to get students thinking about acids on the molecular level.

EXPLORE

Gathering Evidence

Activity Overview

In this activity, students translate the paper and pencil experience from the engage activity, *Ranking Tasks*, to a hands-on experience in the explore activity. Here, they will test the actual household materials mentioned in the engage. Their tests are designed

Answers to Stop and Think—Part I are on TE page 223.

5. Rank your acid and base items according to which substances you think are more or less acidic and more or less basic.
6. Participate in a class discussion of your rankings.

As you participate, share your rankings and your reasoning. Listen as others share their ideas about this ranking task.

7. Record any new ideas you hear or questions that you have in your science notebook.

Stop & THINK

PART I

Work individually as you answer these questions about Part I. Then consult with your team and record any changes you make, including the reasons for those changes.

1. What were the main criteria that you used in first grouping the substances?
2. How did your ideas change as you learned new information?
3. Antacids are used to neutralize excess stomach acid. How do you think this works?
4. You may have heard of pH and know that it relates to acids and bases. The scale that measures pH goes from 0 to 14 and is illustrated in figure 5.1. Copy this scale into your science notebook and indicate where you would put each of the substances you just worked with on the scale. Use your current understanding to place these substances on the scale. Don't worry about being exactly correct; you will learn more about the pH scale in the next activity.

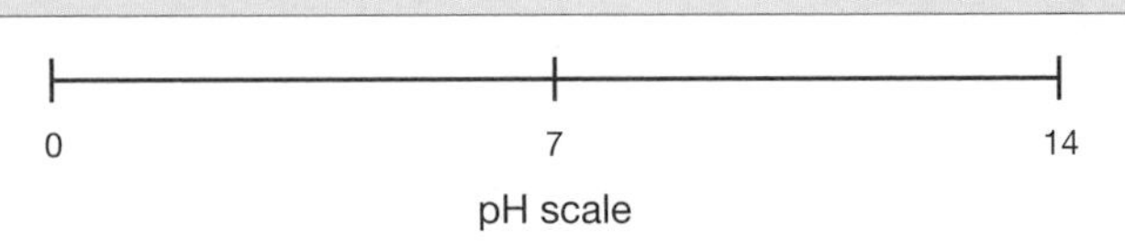

Figure 5.1 pH scale. Copy this scale into your science notebook. Where would the substances you worked with in Part I fall on this scale?

to rank the materials according to their direct observations of chemical reactions.

Before You Teach

Background Information

Acids and bases are very common to our everyday lives. In your kitchen and bathroom cupboards, you will find numerous examples of each. Cleaners designed to dissolve fats and oils are typically bases. Drain cleaners, oven cleaners, soaps, and products containing ammonia are bases. Acids may be more common in your kitchen; fruits and fruit juices, pickled cucumbers, peppers, and okra are in the acid category. Some cleaners will be acidic, especially those designed to dissolve calcium deposits in toilets and showers. Some of these household items may be very dangerous if they come in contact with skin or eyes. In addition, some produce noxious and poisonous gases if mixed.

Your students will be ranking and testing metals. They will place different metals in an acid. One of the properties that they learned earlier is that acids react with some metals to produce a gas. This gas is hydrogen. They will test for this during the activity. The reaction can be represented in this unbalanced generic form where M represents a metal:

$$M_{(s)} + H^{+}_{(aq)} + Cl^{-}_{(aq)} \longrightarrow H_{2(g)} + M^{n+}_{(aq)} + Cl^{-}_{(aq)}$$

Not all metals will react with acids; only the more reactive metals will. Generally, the more active metals are on the left side of the periodic table and those less reactive are on the middle right of the table. See figure 5.8 in the student book.

There is additional background material in the next activity. Consult a college-level general chemistry text for more information.

Answers to Reflect and Connect are on TE page 224.

Part II: Active or Not?

Materials

For each team of 2–4 students

Card Pack 2

Process and Procedure

Many things in our world are made of metals, from our jewelry to huge skyscrapers. Do all metals behave in the same way? What chemical properties are important to consider when choosing which metal to use for a particular application? Some metals react by simply being exposed to the atmosphere. Other metals are very nonreactive. Knowing how metals rank in reactivity is important information to use when deciding the best metal to use for certain purposes. Use your experiences with metals of different kinds as you work with your team to complete another ranking task.

1. Meet with your team and obtain *Card Pack 2*. Spread the cards face up on your desk or table.
2. Design a step-by-step procedure to rank the metals in *Card Pack 2* from "most reactive" to "least reactive."

   Use your experiences with charts from Part I of this investigation to guide your design. Each team member should have a design in his or her science notebook.
3. Agree as a team on your design, then obtain your teacher's approval before conducting your design.
4. Follow your design to obtain a ranking of metal reactivity.
5. Participate in a class discussion of your rankings.

   As you participate, share your rankings and your reasoning. Listen as others share their ideas about this ranking task. Record any new ideas you hear or questions that you have in your science notebook.

Reflect and Connect

Answer these questions in your science notebook based on what you know and understand. Then work with your team members to check your thinking. Make revisions to your answers as needed.

1. How do you know that a metal is reacting with another substance? (That is, what is the evidence?)
2. Iron rusts but gold does not rust. Why don't we use gold to manufacture nails? Give at least 2 reasons why.
3. Electrolytes are substances that, when placed in water, conduct an electric current. For an electric current to flow, some type of charged particle (either ions or electrons) must be free to move.

Materials—Part I

For each team of 2–4 students

2–4 pairs of safety goggles
2–4 pairs of safety gloves
2–4 laboratory aprons
microwell plates or small beakers
disposable plastic pipets
samples of common substances, such as
- drain cleaner
- lemon juice
- baking soda solution
- ammonia
- vinegar
- rainwater
- soap solution
- antacid solution
- simulated stomach acid (0.01 M HCl)

pH meter, universal indicator solution, or pH paper

Cautions

Wear safety goggles, safety gloves, and lab aprons and take care not to touch any of the substances used in this activity. Even though you are working with household solutions, substances such as drain cleaner can be extremely harmful.

Materials—Part II

For the teacher

1 pair of safety goggles
1 laboratory apron
1 pair of safety gloves
test-tube holder
3 large test tubes
distilled water
baking soda ($NaHCO_3$)
vinegar (CH_3COOH in water)
3% hydrogen peroxide (from the grocery store; H_2O_2)

manganese dioxide (MnO_2)
3 M hydrochloric acid (HCl)
zinc shot or powder
wooden splints
matches

For each team of 2–4 students

2–4 pairs of safety goggles
2–4 laboratory aprons
2–4 pairs of safety gloves
test-tube racks
test tubes
samples of the following metals from the previous activity, such as

- iron
- copper
- zinc
- tin
- aluminum
- magnesium

3 M hydrochloric acid (HCl)

Advance Preparation

For Part I, have labeled droppers or small beakers with droppers filled with each of the substances. Keep the original container at the front of the room for students to refer to as they are completing the activity. Have 1 set per team.

Mix simulated stomach acid by making a 0.01 M solution of hydrochloric acid (HCl). Slowly add 0.83 milliliters (mL) of concentrated HCl (12 M) to about 900 mL of distilled water. Stir and bring the volume to 1 liter (L). If you have 1 M HCl in stock, you can dilute it by adding 2.5 mL of 1 M HCl to about 200 mL distilled water as an alternative. Stir and bring the volume to 250 mL.

If you are using pH probes, make sure you are familiar with their operation and you follow instructions for calibrating the probes before class.

For Part II, your list of materials includes some items not shown in the student book. These include steel wool or sandpaper to clean the surface of the metals, as well as other supplies that students may require for their designs. Think ahead to what your students might request.

Cut small strips of each of the metals. Or iron nails (the kind that rust) can be used for iron, galvanized nails can be used for zinc, and copper wire can be used for copper. Don't go into detail about galvanized nails and that they are zinc-coated iron. Your students will learn about corrosion protection in a later activity. Students should be given steel wool or sandpaper to clean the outside of the metals before making them react with the acid.

Prepare the 3 M HCl by slowly adding 250 mL concentrated HCl (12 M) to 900 mL distilled water. Stir and bring the volume to 1 L. You will need about 100 mL per team for each class.

Students will be testing to determine the type of gas produced in their chemical reactions. They will watch you demonstrate how to do this test. Practice this test before class. Prepare carbon dioxide gas (CO_2) in a large test tube by mixing baking soda ($NaHCO_3$) and vinegar (CH_3COOH in water). Light a wooden splint and while holding the test tube at an angle, put the flaming splint in the tube. The flame will go out, indicating the presence of CO_2. This is a good time to bring up the use of CO_2 fire extinguishers.

Prepare oxygen gas (O_2) by adding a small sample of manganese dioxide (MnO_2) to some 3% hydrogen peroxide (H_2O_2). Allow the reaction to fizz for a while, then light a wooden splint as before. However, this time blow the splint out right before you insert it into the tube. A glowing splint will relight, indicating a higher concentration of oxygen gas.

Answers to Reflect and Connect are on TE page 224.

Look at the 2 pictures in figure 5.2. What do the results of these 2 experiments tell you about the 2 bases in the figure?

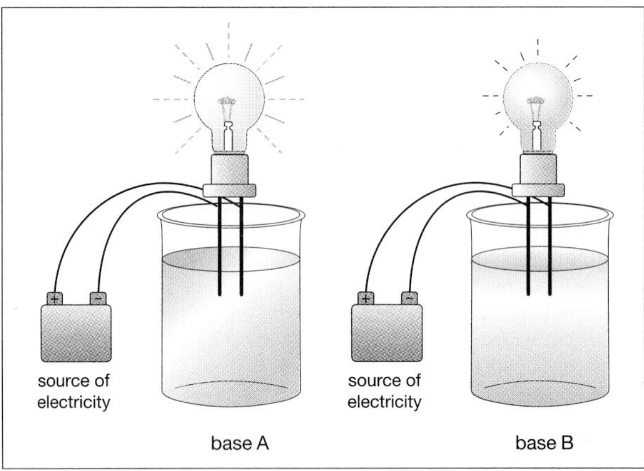

Figure 5.2 Electrolytes in solution. What do the results of these two experiments tell you about the different bases in solution? The concentration of the base in water is the same for both bases.

4. Consider this list of acids and their chemical formulas: hydrochloric acid (HCl), sulfuric acid (H_2SO_4), nitrous acid (HNO_2), and acetic acid (CH_3COOH, also written as $HC_2H_3O_2$). What do all these acids have in common?

EXPLORE

Gathering Evidence

There were certainly different rankings and groupings within your class for the previous activity. Did it frustrate you when your teacher did not give you the accepted answers for the tasks? Scientists often go long periods before they know if their ideas are supported by other evidence. They must wait for more evidence to verify their ideas. You have seen that knowing what spider is most poisonous is important to your safety. When you are ranking things such as poisonous spiders, it is important to have your rankings correct. Otherwise, you may mistake a potentially harmful spider for a harmless one.

But you are lucky. You do not have to wait long to find out if your rankings from the last activity are correct. You will gather your own evidence to develop explanations as you work with a team to verify your rankings.

226 Unit 1 Interactions Are Interesting

To make hydrogen gas (H_2), place some solid magnesium in the hydrochloric acid (HCl) used for this activity. (Do not let the students know how you are generating these gases so that they will not know beforehand what gas they are testing for.) Light a wooden splint and place it in the test tube. You should hear a "pop," indicating the presence of H_2. Have a small beaker of water at each lab station for students to dispose of their burned wooden splints.

Educational Technologies

This activity presents a good opportunity for you to incorporate technology into the lab. pH meters, either the stand-alone type or those that connect to Calculator-Based Laboratories (CBLs), or computers offer the chance for your students to learn to use these pieces of technology. This equipment will give much more precise measurements than pH indicators or papers. Consult the operating manual for instructions on their use and for calibrating these probes. It is important for you to calibrate the pH probes before they are used in your class.

Cautions

Common household substances can be dangerous if not handled properly. Be careful when handling cleaners and all acids and bases. Make sure students do not mix the cleaners as some will produce toxic gases. The substances can be disposed of down the drain but only if done separately and with copious amounts of water. The acid that students will be using is a strong acid and should be treated as such. Students should wear goggles, lab gloves, and lab aprons during this activity. Place burned wooden splints in a beaker of water.

As You Teach

Outcomes and Indicators of Success

By the end of this activity, students should

1. evaluate various common substances based on properties.

   They will demonstrate their ability to evaluate these substances by reexamining their rankings based on their prior knowledge of the properties of acids, bases, and metals.

2. begin to understand the pH scale.

   They will demonstrate their understanding by

   - conducting investigations with common substances using pH indicators or probes,
   - comparing results of their reactions to the pH scale and adjust their rankings, and
   - using the pH scale to compare various substances.

3. begin to understand an activity series of metals.

   They will demonstrate their understanding by

   - conducting investigations with various metals as they react to an acid,
   - comparing their results with a table of oxidizing and reducing agents, and
   - using the table of oxidizing and reducing agents to compare various metals.

4. begin to understand the connection to the strength of acids and bases, the reactivity of metals to the strength of the forces involved in transferring electrons or ions, or both.

   They will demonstrate their understanding by

   - analyzing strong and weak acids and how their molecular structure relates to this property and

Part I: pH Evidence

Materials

For each team of 2–4 students

2–4 pairs of safety goggles

2-4 pairs of safety gloves

2–4 laboratory aprons

microwell plates or small beakers

disposable plastic pipets

samples of common substances such as

- drain cleaner
- lemon juice
- baking soda solution
- ammonia
- vinegar
- rainwater
- soap solution
- antacid solution
- simulated stomach acid

pH meter, universal indicator solution, or pH paper

Cautions

Wear safety goggles, safety gloves, and lab aprons and take care not to touch any of the substances used in this activity. Even though you are working with household solutions, substances such as drain cleaner can be extremely harmful.

Process and Procedure

You began thinking about pH at the conclusion of the last activity. How is it used to rank acids and bases? Work with your team to test your rankings using pH.

1. Determine which end of the scale represents acids and which end represents bases by following the procedures in Steps 1a–f.

You saw in the last activity how pH is used when ranking acids and bases.

   a. Choose one of the substances that you know tastes sour.

Remember, one of the properties of acids is that it tastes sour.

   b. Determine the pH of your substance. Use either a pH probe or an indicator as your teacher directs.

Chapter 5 Forces of Attraction 227

- analyzing metals and their atomic properties and comparing these to their level of reactivity.

5. design and conduct an investigation to gather pH data.

   They will demonstrate their ability to design and conduct an investigation by

   - generating a step-by-step procedure for determining the pH for several household substances and
   - recording data in tables that are organized in their science notebooks.

Strategies

Getting Started

Start this activity by getting your students excited about finding out the "right" answers for their rankings. Some of your students may have been frustrated at the end of the previous activity when they did not know if their answers were correct. Emphasize that scientists often do not know right away if their predictions are correct and must wait for new tests or new evidence. Students have the opportunity to test and verify their predictions right now.

Cautions

Common household substances can be dangerous if not handled properly. Be careful when handling cleaners and all acids and bases. Make sure students do not mix the cleaners as some will produce toxic gases. The substances can be disposed of down the drain but only if done separately and with copious amounts of water. The acid that students will be using is a strong acid and should be treated as such. Students should wear goggles, lab gloves, and lab aprons during this activity. Place burned wooden splints in a beaker of water.

Process and Procedure

Part I: pH Evidence

Materials

For each team of 2–4 students

2–4 pairs of safety goggles
2–4 pairs of safety gloves
2–4 laboratory aprons
microwell plates or small beakers
disposable plastic pipets
samples of common substances used in the previous activity, such as

- drain cleaner
- lemon juice
- baking soda solution
- ammonia
- vinegar
- rainwater
- soap solution
- antacid solution
- simulated stomach acid (0.01 M HCl)

pH meter, universal indicator solution, or pH paper

In Step 1, students verify where acids and bases lie on the pH scale. They use pH probes, pH indicator, or pH paper to test the pH of a substance they know is sour. This will be either lemon juice or vinegar. Make sure students understand that they do not taste or smell (intentionally) substances in the lab.

In Step 2, students identify that bases are the upper range of the pH scale by testing a substance they know is a base since its purpose is to dissolve fats and oils (a property of bases). They use drain cleaner for this test. During these steps, students record their data.

c. Draw another pH scale in your science notebook. Mark the divisions 0–14 from left to right along the scale. Label only 0, 7, and 14 on the scale.

Your scale should look similar to figure 5.1.

d. Record the pH and the name of your substance in your notebook.

e. Is this substance an acid or a base? Record your answer and justification in your notebook.

f. Does the pH value for this substance lie on the left or the right side of your scale? Record your answer in your notebook.

2. Use the drain cleaner to complete Steps 2a–d.

One property of bases is that they react to break down fats and oils. This makes bases good candidates for drain cleaners.

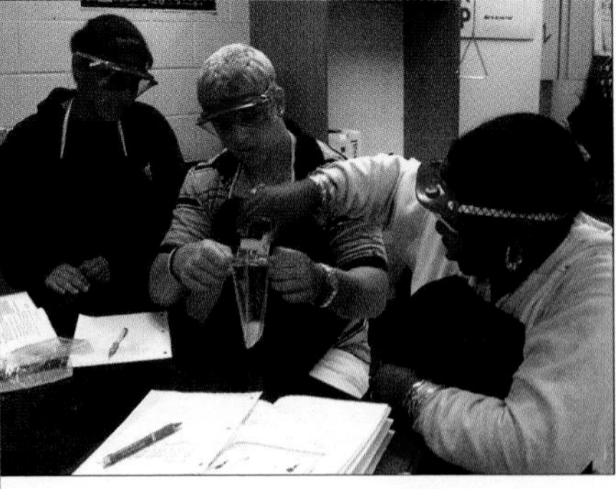

a. Determine the pH of your drain cleaner. Use either a pH probe or an indicator as your teacher directs.

b. Record the pH and the name of the drain cleaner in your science notebook.

c. Is this substance an acid or a base? Record your response in your notebook.

d. Does the pH value for this drain cleaner lie on the left or the right side of your scale? Keep records of your answer.

3. Label your pH scale with "acid" and "base" on the appropriate sides of the scale.

4. What do you think a pH of 7 means about the amount of acid and base present?

5. Design a step-by-step procedure to determine the pH of all your substances. Use your answers to the questions in Steps 5a–f to guide your design.

   a. How will you determine the pH of each substance?
   b. How will you make sure that there is no contamination of the samples?
   c. What is the most efficient and organized way to keep track of all your data?
   d. How will you rank these substances on the pH scale?
   e. What safety precautions do you need to consider?
   f. How will you clean up when you are finished?

228 Unit 1 Interactions Are Interesting

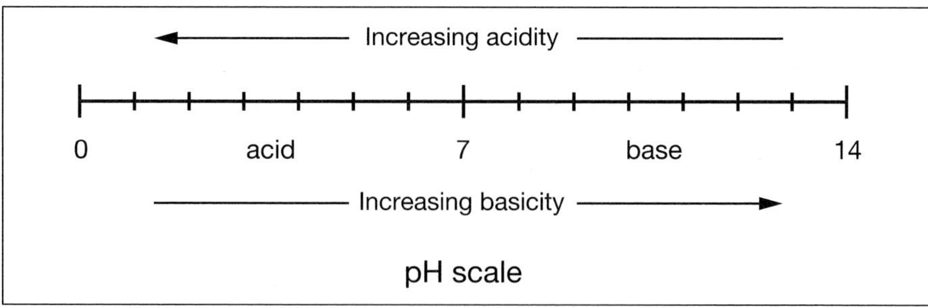

▲ **Figure T5.1 pH scale for *Stop and Think* Question 2.** Your students should add arrows to their diagrams to indicate increasing acidity and basicity.

In Step 3, they label their pH scales, which they have drawn in their science notebooks.

In Step 4, students are asked to think about what it might mean to have a pH of 7. Accept any reasonable answer. Students may not know the term neutral, so they might say that a pH of 7 is between an acid or a base. Assess students' ability to justify their answers and record their thoughts in their science notebooks.

In Step 5, teams design an investigation to test the pH of the remainder of their substances. There are several questions for them to consider as they plan the investigation. Their plans must have your approval before they conduct the investigation. Be sure students have an organized way to keep track of their data before you approve of their plans.

In Step 7, students conduct their investigations. Monitor each team to make sure all students are participating and all students are recording data.

6. After you have answered these questions and designed your tests, compare your design with the design of another team. Finally, have your teacher approve your design.
7. Conduct the tests that you have designed.

Stop & THINK

PART I

1. Suppose you needed a mild base to use as a gentle cleaner. You would not want to use a base that was extremely strong because it might be harmful to certain surfaces or to your skin. Knowing the degree of acidity or basicity (sometimes called alkalinity) is important in this case, and ranking is a way to confirm this. Using your experiences with these substances and the results of your pH tests, rank your acids from most acidic to least acidic. Rank your bases in a similar way.

   Be sure to label your rankings properly so that your teacher can interpret your answers.

2. Use arrows to label the pH scale that you drew in Step 1c to indicate increasing acidity and increasing basicity.

   You will have to use 2 separate arrows, one for acids and one for bases.

3. The cells of your skin contain lipids (or fats). Use what you know about the properties of acids and bases to explain why bases can be harmful to your skin.
4. You predicted the relative degrees of acidity and basicity in the engage activity, *Ranking Tasks*. Compare your results in this activity with your original predictions by answering the following questions.
   a. What substances changed in your rankings based on your tests?
   b. How did their grouping (acid or base) or ranking (more or less acidic or basic) change based on your tests?

Part II: Reactivity Evidence

Materials

For each team of 2–4 students

2–4 pairs of safety goggles

2–4 laboratory aprons

Answers to Stop and Think—Part I, SE page 229

1. Depending on the brands of the substances you choose, answers will vary. The simulated stomach acid should register a pH of about 2, vinegar about 3.5, soft drinks about 3, rainwater about 5.6, household ammonia about 11, oven cleaner 14, and antacids a pH of about 9.5–10.5.
2. Students should have a pH scale similar to the one in figure T5.1.
3. A property of bases is that they dissolve fats and oils. If students get a strong base on their skin, it can be very harmful because it will dissolve the fats in the cells of the skin.
4. Many answers are correct here. Look for thorough and thoughtful responses.

Process and Procedure

Part II: Reactivity Evidence

Materials

For the teacher

1 pair of safety goggles
1 laboratory apron
1 pair of safety gloves
test-tube holder
3 large test tubes
distilled water
baking soda ($NaHCO_3$)
vinegar (CH_3COOH in water)
3% hydrogen peroxide (from the grocery store; H_2O_2)
manganese dioxide (MnO_2)
3 M hydrochloric acid (HCl)
zinc shot or powder
wooden splints
matches

For each team of 2–4 students

2–4 pairs of safety goggles
2–4 lab aprons
2–4 pairs of safety gloves
test-tube racks
test tubes
samples of the following metals from the previous activity, such as

- iron
- copper
- zinc
- tin
- aluminum
- magnesium

3 M hydrochloric acid (HCl)

Cautions

Wear safety goggles, safety gloves, and lab aprons for each part of this experiment. Hydrochloric acid is corrosive; use care when working with acids. Wash your hands at the conclusion of the lab.

In Step 1, students work with their teams and design an investigation to test the reactivity of metals. A list of questions helps them plan the investigation. Your list of materials includes some items not shown in the student book. These include steel wool or sandpaper to clean the surface of the metals and other supplies that students may require for their designs. Think ahead to what your students might request. Often, they will repeat what they have done in the past. If they are used to using microwell plates, for example, they may design an experiment to use this equipment. However, it may be easier for students to see the reaction using small test tubes.

All of these solutions can be disposed of down the drain with copious amounts of water. So that students do not think all chemical wastes may be poured down the drain, you may want to provide a large container in the room labeled "acidic waste." Students can dispose of their solutions in the container and you can properly dispose of the contents at a later time.

In Step 2, students compare their designs to those of other teams. This step reinforces the importance of peer review in science. If some students come directly to you for feedback, ask if they have first carefully compared their procedure to another team's. This should encourage them to solve their own problems instead of depending on you for the answers.

Students must get your approval before beginning their investigations in Step 3. Make sure to check for safety precautions, data tables, and cleanup procedures before giving approval. After students have completed their investigations, they rank their substances from most reactive to least reactive in Step 4. Make sure the students label their rankings with headings so that you will have an easier time grading their work.

In Step 5, students read about 4 common gases produced in chemical reactions: carbon dioxide (CO_2), oxygen (O_2), chlorine (Cl_2), and hydrogen (H_2). They learn how to verify the 3 odorless gases produced using a flaming wooden splint.

In Step 6, students will watch as you demonstrate the procedure to test for each type of gas. Practice this procedure before class so that you are familiar with it. Model proper safety procedures by wearing goggles and a lab apron and keeping the test tube pointed away from you and others. Dispose of burned splints in a beaker of water. Do not let the students know how you are generating these gases so that they do not know beforehand what gas they will test for.

Prepare CO_2 gas in a large test tube by mixing baking soda and vinegar. Light a wooden splint and, while holding the test tube at an angle, put the flaming splint in the tube. The flame will go out, indicat-

2–4 pairs of safety gloves
Test tube racks, test tubes
samples of the following metals:

- iron (Fe)
- copper (Cu)
- zinc (Zn)
- tin (Sn)
- aluminum (Al)
- magnesium (Mg)

3 M hydrochloric acid (HCl)

Cautions

Wear safety goggles, safety gloves, and lab aprons for each part of this experiment. Hydrochloric acid is corrosive; use care when working with acids. Wash your hands at the conclusion of the lab.

Process and Procedure

One of the properties of metals is their reactivity with other substances. Knowing their reactivities is important in making decisions for those who select building materials. Imagine if the supporting materials in your home or school were constructed with a metal that is highly reactive. The metal would disintegrate and the building would no longer be safe.

In the engage activity, you learned that acids react with some metals to produce a gas. You can use this property of acids and metals to determine their relative reactivities. That is, you can rank the chemical reactivity of metals. Work with a team to design and conduct chemical tests to verify your rankings from the previous activity.

Use the following question to focus your thinking and actions in this part of the activity: "How does chemical reactivity help me rank metals?"

1. Design an investigation to test the relative reactivities of the metals provided by your teacher. In planning your design, answer the questions in Steps 1a–f.
   a. Some metals react with air and form a coating on their outer surface. How will you ensure that the reaction is with the metal and not with the coating?
   b. What are some outside variables and how will you control them?
   c. How will you determine the reactivity of each metal?
   d. What is the best, and most organized, way to record your data?
   e. What safety precautions should you consider?
   f. How will you clean up when the investigation is finished?

230 | Unit 1 Interactions Are Interesting

ing the presence of CO_2. This is a good time to bring up the use of CO_2 fire extinguishers.

Prepare O_2 gas by adding a small sample of MnO_2 to some 3% H_2O_2. Allow the reaction to fizz for a while, then light a wooden splint as before. However, this time blow the splint out right before you insert it into the tube. A glowing splint will relight, indicating the presence of O_2.

To make H_2 gas, place some solid Mg in the dilute HCl used for this activity. Light a wooden splint and place it in the test tube. You should hear a "pop," indicating the presence of H_2 gas. Students may ask you if they should use a lighted splint or blow it out as you did for the O_2 test. Advise them to try both. They may get a "pop" with a glowing splint, but they will not get any of the other results. They should then try a lighted splint.

In Step 7, students predict what type of gas is produced. H_2 gas is possible because hydrogen atoms are present in the HCl. Cl_2 gas is possible for the same reason. Students who realize that water is part of the solution will predict that O_2 gas could be the gas that is produced. The only gas that is not reasonable at this stage is CO_2 gas. If students do choose CO_2, ask them to identify the source of carbon (C). There is none.

In Step 8, students test for the gas. If all their reactions have stopped fizzing, allow them to use another piece of metal or additional acid. Students may want to smell to test for chlorine. Demonstrate the safe way to smell a gas by wafting. Students may notice the smell of Cl_2 gas from the HCl, but advise them that the odor could be from the acid and not the gas. Encourage them to do additional tests to verify. This should take little encouragement since students are always excited about using fire in labs. Monitor the class for safe lab practices.

Students begin building a chemical equation for the reaction of a metal and the acid in Step 9. If your students have not had much practice at this, you may choose to have the whole class do the same metal and work through this together. As an example, if students chose magnesium (Mg) to work with, then the reactants of the equation would be

$$Mg_{(s)} + HCl_{(aq)} \longrightarrow$$

or

$$Mg_{(s)} + H^+_{(aq)} + Cl^-_{(aq)} \longrightarrow.$$

2. Compare your design with the design of another team.

Make adjustments in your design based on advice from your classmates. Always have your teacher approve your design before proceeding.

3. Following all safety procedures, conduct your investigation. Wear safety goggles, safety gloves, and lab aprons and don't forget to wash your hands at the conclusion of the lab.
4. Rank your metals from most reactive to least reactive and record your ranking in your science notebook.
5. Read the following 2 paragraphs to learn how you can identify the gas produced in these chemical reactions.

The four typical gases produced in a chemical reaction are carbon dioxide (CO_2), oxygen (O_2), chlorine (Cl_2), and hydrogen (H_2). You can identify chlorine gas by its odor. You will recognize the smell of chlorine gas if you have ever been at a swimming pool. Chlorine kills bacteria in pools. Chlorine gas results when bleach reacts with water and other substances in the pool. Chlorine gas is toxic and should never be smelled directly.

Carbon dioxide, oxygen, and hydrogen are odorless gases. Scientists verify whether these gases are produced in chemical reactions by using a lighted wooden splint. If the gas is carbon dioxide, the flame will extinguish when the splint is placed in the presence of the gas. If the gas is oxygen, a glowing splint will relight when placed near where the gas is produced. If the gas produced is hydrogen, you can identify the gas by the "pop" you hear when you place a lighted splint near the gas that is produced.

6. Record your observations as your teacher demonstrates the procedure to test the type of gas produced.
7. What gas do you think is produced in the tests you conducted with your metals?

Use your knowledge of chemical reactions and the reactants involved to justify your answer.

8. Test the gas produced in the reactions with your metals and hydrochloric acid. Record the results in your science notebook.

You may have to add another small piece of metal if the bubbling has ceased.

9. Choose 1 metal and write the reactants of the chemical reaction that you investigated. Write the reactants in the form of a chemical equation.
10. Does the type of gas produced make sense based on the law of conservation of matter? Explain your answer.

Step 10 asks the students if the gas that they discovered makes sense according to the law of conservation of matter. Take time to review this law if needed. All tests should have verified hydrogen gas as the gas produced in the reaction, and it does make sense since hydrogen was not created or destroyed. Students will complete their chemical equations in Step 11 by adding the hydrogen gas and the other products. It would be good to remind students about diatomic molecules. Hydrogen gas is diatomic and will always appear as H_2 in equations. Completing and balancing the reaction started earlier,

$$Mg_{(s)} + 2HCl_{(aq)} \longrightarrow H_{2(g)} + MgCl_{2(aq)}$$

or

$$Mg_{(s)} + 2H^+_{(aq)} + 2Cl^-_{(aq)} \longrightarrow H_{2(g)} + Mg^{2+}_{(aq)} + 2Cl^-_{(aq)}.$$

As you review balancing with your students, point out that the reaction is not only balanced according to mass but also according to charge. They will use this repeatedly in a later activity.

Answers to Reflect and Connect, SE page 232

1. Answers will vary. Look for students' evidence for changing any rankings from the engage activity.

2a. The balanced equation is

$$2Na + 2HI \rightarrow H_2 + 2NaI.$$

2b. The gas produced is hydrogen and it came from the hydrogen atoms in the HI (hydroiodic acid).

2c. The symbol for the acid is HI. Students should be aware by now that acids contain H and it is usually written at the beginning of the formula.

2d. Students should think this is very acidic since it is toward the left end of the pH scale.

3. Accept a wide range of answers. Two common answers might be (1) "If by result you mean how vigorously the bubbles are produced, then, no, the weak acids would produce less vigorous reactions." (2) "If 'result' means the relative ranking, then yes, the ranking will be the same regardless of the acid strength. The only difference would be the amount of time to produce the results."

Acids and Bases

Activity Overview

In *Acids and Bases*, students combine their previous experiences with acids and bases with new knowledge from readings and model building to explain acid-base reactions. Specifically, students construct models of acids and bases, then use their models to explain dissociation and neutralization. Students learn how the pH scale helps to quantify acid-base strengths.

Before You Teach

Background Information

The essential nature of acids and bases was first recognized by Svante Arrhenius (1859–1927). Based on his work with electrolytes, Arrhenius proposed that acids produce hydrogen ions in aqueous solutions, while bases produce hydroxide ions. This is the acid-base theory that students will work with in this chapter. At the time, the Arrhenius concept of acids and bases was a major step forward in quantifying acid-base chemistry. However, this concept is limited because it applies only to aqueous solutions and allows for only one kind of base—the hydroxide ion. A more general definition of acids and bases was postulated by the Danish chemist Johannes Brønsted (1879–1947) and the English chemist Thomas Lowry (1874–1936). In the Brønsted-Lowry concept, an acid is a proton (H^+) donor and a base is a proton acceptor. For example, when gaseous HCl dissolves in water, each HCl molecule donates a proton to a water molecule, and so qualifies as a Brønsted-Lowry acid. The molecule that accepts the proton, water in this case, is a Brønsted-Lowry base. The proton that is donated by HCl and is accepted by water bonds with water to form the hydronium ion, H_3O^+. Hydrogen ions or protons do not exist alone in aqueous solutions but bond with a water molecule to form H_3O^+.

There is another way to define acids and bases, and this is by the Lewis model named after G. N. Lewis (1875–1946). This is an even more general definition of acid-base behavior. A Lewis acid is an electron-pair acceptor, and a Lewis base is an electron-pair donor. You can think of a Lewis acid as having an empty atomic orbital that it can use to accept or share an electron pair from

11. To complete the chemical reaction you started in Step 8, do Steps 11a–c.
    a. Add the gas that is produced as a product of the chemical reaction.
    b. Is this the only product? Why or why not? Explain your answer based on the law of conservation of matter.
    c. Complete the chemical reaction with all the reactants and products.

Reflect and Connect

Develop answers to these questions on your own. After you have written your best ideas in your science notebook, check your thinking with classmates or your teacher.

1. How did your rankings of metals in the last activity differ from your predictions in the engage activity? What evidence did you use to modify your rankings?
2. You learned how to balance equations in chapter 3. Work through Questions 2a–d, which are related to chemical reactions with metals.
   a. Balance the following equation, which represents the chemical reaction of sodium and an acid.

   $$Na + HI \rightarrow H_2 + NaI$$

   b. What is the gas produced in this reaction and where did it come from?
   c. What is the symbol for the acid in this equation?
   d. A certain concentration of this acid has a pH of 1.3. Would you consider this to be very acidic? Why?
3. You used a strong acid to produce the chemical reactions in Part II of this activity. Would you expect the same results with a weak acid? Explain your reasoning.

EXPLAIN

Acids and Bases

Have you ever been stung by an ant or a bee? If you have, you have personally experienced the effects of formic acid (HCOOH). The sting you feel is the result of an injection of formic acid into your skin. Is formic acid a strong or a weak acid? Judging by what you feel, you may think it is a strong acid, but how do you know? What is it about acids and bases that makes one strong and another weak?

You have learned that you can rank acids and bases according to their pH. This helps identify them as more or less acidic or basic. What

232 Unit 1 Interactions Are Interesting

a molecule that has a lone pair of electrons (a Lewis base).

Acid strength refers to the degree to which the acid dissociates in water to form hydronium ions. There are six common strong acids; the others the students will see are considered weak. These acids are hydrochloric (HCl), hydrobromic (HBr), hydroiodic (HI), sulfuric (H_2SO_4), nitric (HNO_3), and perchloric ($HClO_4$). You can decide if you want to give your students this list of acids to memorize. The approach in the chapter is for them to see *why* the acids are strong or weak determined by the competitive forces of attraction for the proton. Acid dissociation can be represented in the generic form,

$$HA_{(aq)} + H_2O_{(l)} \rightleftharpoons H_3O^+_{(aq)} + A^-_{(aq)}.$$

A strong acid is one for which this equilibrium lies far to the right. This means that almost all the original HA is dissociated at equilibrium. A weak acid is one for which this equilibrium lies far to the left. At equilibrium, there is much of the original acid still present as HA. Notice that one of the strong acids is diprotic (has two acidic protons). This acid is H_2SO_4 and can dissociate two H^+ ions into a solution. However, the first dissociation,

$$H_2SO_{4(aq)} \longrightarrow H^+_{(aq)} + HSO_4^-{}_{(aq)},$$

goes essentially to completion. In the second dissociation,

$$HSO_4^-{}_{(aq)} \rightleftharpoons H^+_{(aq)} + SO_4^{-2}{}_{(aq)},$$

HSO_4^- is a weak acid.

All the hydroxides of group 1 dissolve and dissociate completely when dissolved in water and are all strong bases. The alkaline earth (group 2) hydroxides—calcium hydroxide ($Ca(OH)_2$), barium hydroxide ($Ba(OH)_2$), and strontium hydroxide ($Sr(OH)_2$)—are also strong bases. For these compounds, 2 moles (mol) of hydroxide ion are produced for every mole of metal hydroxide dissolved in aqueous solution. These bases are not very soluble but contribute additional OH^- ions due to their chemical composition. Other bases that students will see in this chapter are considered weak bases.

A discussion of the role of forces in determining acid strength is given in the student book. For a more detailed background on this topic, refer to a college-level general chemistry text.

Concentration as well as strength play a role in the pH of a substance. The concentration of solutions in chemistry is often given in the unit molarity (M) and represents the number of moles of solute in a liter of solution, or $M = \frac{\text{moles of solute}}{\text{liters of solution}}$. This says nothing about the degree to which the solute dissociates. "Strong" or "weak" just refers to the degree of dissociation in an aqueous solution. Therefore, you can have a very concentrated weak acid or a very dilute strong acid. The same goes for bases. pH is a measure of the concentration of hydrogen or hydronium ions in solution. By adjusting concentrations, it is possible to have a strong and a weak acid with the same pH value as long as the desired pH is not too low. A very dilute solution of a strong acid or a strong base can have a pH near 7.

is the difference, on the atomic level, between acids and bases? You may have thought about this as you were working through the previous activities. In *Acids and Bases*, you will have the chance to answer this question. You will determine what it is about the atomic makeup of these substances that makes the difference.

This activity will help you develop your own explanations about the strength of acids and bases. You will work individually and as part of a team while you learn about the pH scale and neutralization reactions.

Materials

For each team of 2 students

- marshmallows
- toothpicks
- markers

Process and Procedure

Acids and bases are an integral part of life and life processes. You have seen that many products that you use every day have properties of acids or bases. But did you know that your body functions best in a very narrow pH range? The acidity or alkalinity of your blood can give clues to doctors about your health. If this balance is disrupted, you can become very ill.

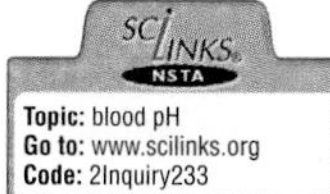

Understanding acids and bases involves understanding protons, charges, and forces. This actually makes your work a lot easier since you have already learned about these three concepts. All you have to do now is understand them in the context of acid-base chemistry.

As with many concepts in science, there are multiple ways to define or think about acids and bases. For the purposes of this chapter, we will use a general description of acids recognized by the Swedish chemist Svante Arrhenius (1859–1927). This model of acids and bases, known as the Arrhenius model, describes an **acid** as a chemical compound that increases the concentration of hydrogen ions (H^+) in solution. A **base** is described as a chemical compound that increases the concentration of hydroxide ions (OH^-) in solution. How do acids and bases increase the number of these ions? Are there differences in the extent to which some acids or bases form these ions? You will work with a partner to understand the chemistry behind acids and bases and what causes one to be strong or weak.

1. Read *Dissociation* to find out where OH^- (hydroxide) and H^+ (hydrogen) ions come from.

Chapter 5 Forces of Attraction 233

The pH scale is a logarithmic scale, and thus each number on the scale represents a factor of 10. For example, a substance with a pH of 1 is 1,000 times more acidic than a substance with a pH of 4. A logarithm is an exponent. Any number N can be expressed as $N = 10^x$.

For example,

$$\begin{aligned} 1{,}000 &= 10^3 \\ 100 &= 10^2 \\ 10 &= 10^1 \\ 1 &= 10^0. \end{aligned}$$

The common, or base 10, logarithm of a number is the power to which 10 must be taken to yield that number. Thus, since $1{,}000 = 10^3$, then

$$\begin{aligned} \log 1{,}000 &= 3. \\ \text{Similarly, } \log 100 &= 2 \\ \log 10 &= 1 \\ \log 1 &= 0. \end{aligned}$$

In calculating pH, the equation is $pH = -\log[H^+]$. If $[H^+] = 1 \times 10^{-5}$, then $pH = -\log 1 \times 10^{-5}$ and $pH = 5$. Students will have to use scientific calculators for values that are not simply a power of 10.

Use your own judgment in sharing this background material about logarithms with your students. Some may want more information than others.

When equimolar amounts of a strong acid and a strong base are mixed, the following reaction occurs. (A^- represents the anion of an acid and M^+ represents the metal of any hydroxide.)

$$H^+_{(aq)} + A^-_{(aq)} + M^+_{(aq)} + OH^-_{(aq)} \longrightarrow H_2O_{(l)} + M^+_{(aq)} + A^-_{(aq)}$$

Canceling out the spectator ions,

$$H^+_{(aq)} + \cancel{A^-_{(aq)}} + \cancel{M^+_{(aq)}} + OH^-_{(aq)} \longrightarrow H_2O_{(l)} + \cancel{M^+_{(aq)}} + \cancel{A^-_{(aq)}},$$

the net ionic equation becomes

$$H^+_{(aq)} + OH^-_{(aq)} \longrightarrow H_2O_{(l)}.$$

Any equimolar combination of a strong acid and a strong base will give the same result, and the solution will have a pH of 7 (provided an equivalent number of H^+ and OH^- in the acid and base molecules, respectfully). However, combinations of weak acids with strong bases, and strong acids with weak bases give different results.

Water has some very interesting properties, many of which are the result of its highly polar nature. A water molecule can actually pull itself apart into H^+ ions and OH^- ions. This dissociation of water always gives equal numbers of H^+ ions and OH^- ions. Experiments show that $[H^+] = [OH^-] = 1.0 \times 10^{-7}$ M. Since $[H^+] = 1.0 \times 10^{-7}$ M, then the $pH = 7$. Solutions with a higher concentration of H^+ ions than water ($> 1.0 \times 10^{-7}$ M) will have lower pH values and be acidic; solutions with a lower concentration of H^+ ions than water ($< 1.0 \times 10^{-7}$ M) will have higher pH values and be basic.

Materials

For the teacher

sodium chloride (NaCl)
sucrose ($C_{12}H_{22}O_{11}$)
conductivity meter
beaker
50 mL each of 1.0 M, 0.10 M, 0.0010 M, 0.00010 M, 0.0000010 M, and 0.00000010 M HCl; 0.10 M NaOH; 0.10 M CH_3COOH; 0.10 M NH_4OH
conductivity meter
universal indicator

Answers to Step 3 are on TE pages 238–239.

READING

Dissociation

You have seen examples of many acids and have examined their chemical formulas. Some examples include hydrochloric acid (HCl), sulfuric acid (H_2SO_4), nitrous acid (HNO_2), and acetic acid (CH_3COOH). Most acids, including these, have hydrogen in them, and often hydrogen is written first in the chemical formula. You may recall studying dissociation in previous science classes. Dissociation occurs when compounds break apart to form charged particles. When these acids are placed in water, the acid molecule dissociates to varying degrees according to the following general acid dissociation equation:

$$HA_{(aq)} \rightleftarrows H^+_{(aq)} + A^-_{(aq)}$$

HA is the general chemical formula to represent an acid.

According to Arrhenius, bases are substances that increase the number of OH^- in solution; thus, many bases contain an OH^- (hydroxide) group. Some chemical equations representing dissociation of bases can be represented generally, like the following:

$$MOH_{(aq)} \rightleftarrows M^+_{(aq)} + OH^-_{(aq)}$$

MOH is the general chemical formula for metal hydroxides such as sodium hydroxide (NaOH) or potassium hydroxide (KOH). Metal hydroxides are bases.

2. Complete Steps 2a–c to develop a model of acids at the atomic level.
   a. Build a model of a general acid (HA) molecule using 2 marshmallows and a toothpick.
   b. With a marker, label one marshmallow "H^+" and the other marshmallow "A^-."
   c. Draw a picture of this molecule on a blank page in your science notebook so that you will have a permanent record. Leave room to add other pictures and labels to the right of this diagram. Label this picture "acid dissociation."
3. Write the dissociation reaction for the following substances. Use the general examples from the reading as your guide.
   a. Hydrochloric acid (HCl)
   b. Acetic acid (CH_3COOH)
   c. Sodium hydroxide (NaOH)
   d. Lithium hydroxide (LiOH)

234 Unit 1 Interactions Are Interesting

For each team of 2 students

marshmallows
toothpicks
markers

Advance Preparation

Read the student book and the background material included for this section before class. If you need further background information, locate a college-level general chemistry text.

Students will use markers to write on the marshmallows. It is best if the marshmallows are not fresh. Leave the bag open or leave the marshmallows out on the counter for a day to allow the outside surface to dry out. This will make it easier to write on and discourage students from eating their experiment!

As You Teach

Outcomes and Indicators of Success

By the end of this activity, students should

1. understand the pH scale.

   They will demonstrate their understanding by

   - describing the level of acidity and basicity related to the substance's position on the pH scale and
   - comparing H^+ and OH^- concentrations to different pH values.

2. relate the strength of attraction for hydrogen ions to acid strength.

   They will demonstrate their ability by

   - comparing forces of attraction of H^+ and other atoms in the acid molecule with the attraction of H^+ to a water molecule and
   - relating the relative strength of these forces to strong and weak acids.

3. develop a basic understanding of acid, base, and neutralization chemistry.

   They will demonstrate their understanding by

   - correctly predicting products and balancing acid-base and neutralization reactions;
   - comparing and contrasting concentration versus strength of acids and bases;
   - calculating concentrations, in molarity, of acids and bases;
   - predicting and completing acid-base reactions that involve water;
   - relating weak acids and bases in solution to chemical equilibrium; and
   - analyzing reactions of an acid and a base and predicting if the resulting solution of a salt will be acidic, basic, or neutral.

4. formulate and revise scientific explanations of acids and bases using models, logic, and evidence.

   They will demonstrate their ability to formulate explanations by

   - modeling acid and base dissociation with marshmallows and
   - comparing chemical equations to their marshmallow models.

Strategies

Getting Started

This is a relatively involved activity with several readings. Decide beforehand what literacy strategies you want to use that will work best with your class. Decide if you want the readings to be done in class or read for homework with discussion to follow in class.

Many of the sections can be introduced with a demonstration and thoughtful questions to follow that will engage the students for the class

4. Complete Steps 4a–c to generate a model of a base.
   a. Build a model of a general hydroxide, represented by MOH.

Use 3 marshmallows instead of 2, along with the correct number of toothpicks.

   b. With a marker, label each atom and charge.

The hydroxide will stay together, and the OH pair has a negative charge. The M (which represents the metal) will always have a positive charge. Put the O and the H very close together in your model—these atoms stay together in the reaction.

   c. Draw a picture of this molecule on a blank page in your science notebook so that you will have a permanent record. Leave room to add other pictures and labels to the right of this diagram. Label this picture "base dissociation."
5. Using your models as props, explain the dissociation of an acid and a base to your partner. Switch roles when you are finished.
6. Read *Water Works* to see what happens to the water molecule in the presence of acids and some bases.

READING

Water Works

When an acid dissociates in water, the acid breaks apart into positive hydrogen ions (H^+, really just protons) and negative hydroxide ions (OH^-). These ions form a solution with water, which is a polar molecule. Recall that water molecules, while being neutral overall, are very polar and have an unequal distribution of charge around the molecule (figure 5.3). When the hydrogen ion is in the presence of a polar water molecule, the ion will be attracted to the water molecule's negative end. This plus-minus attraction results in the formation of the more stable hydronium ion.

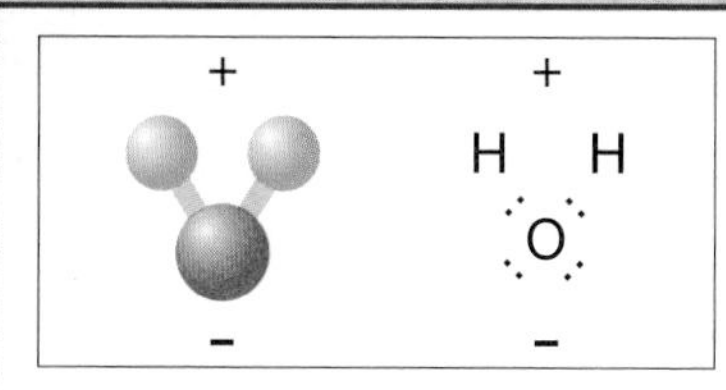

▲ **Figure 5.3 A polar water molecule.** The unequal distribution of the electrons around this neutral water molecule cause one end of the molecule to have a partial negative charge and one end to have a partial positive charge.

Water plays an important role in some base processes as well. According to Arrhenius, a base is a substance that increases the number of hydroxide or OH^- ions in solution. Consider the gas ammonia (NH_3). When ammonia dissolves in water, initially it retains its molecular formula, NH_3. Then it reacts with water to form hydroxide ions. It does not dissociate into ions to any significant amount. So there must be something different occurring besides simple dissociation.

Chapter 5 Forces of Attraction 235

and the topic at hand. For example, the first section is about dissociation. Dissolve salt in one beaker of water and sugar in another. Ask students to describe what has happened. You can pick up on your students' current conceptions about dissolving from simple questions. Write the formula for table salt on the board (NaCl) and the formula for sugar ($C_{12}H_{22}O_{11}$). NaCl dissociates in water, forming the ions Na^+ and Cl^-. Sucrose ($C_{12}H_{22}O_{11}$) simply dissolves in the water; the molecule remains intact. You can ask students if they know how to tell the difference in the salt water and the sugar water without tasting. If no one in your class knows the answer, test the conductivity of the solutions. The salt-water solution will conduct an electric current and the sugar water will not.

A great demonstration to begin the section on acid and base strength is to have equal concentrations of hydrochloric acid (HCl) and acetic acid (CH_3CHOOH). Test the conductivity of these two solutions without telling students which one is a strong acid and which one is a weak acid. Have them describe what is different about the solutions. There are more ions in the solution of HCl. Tell the students which acid is the best conductor but let them figure out why by continuing the reading and activity. Revisit this demonstration after they have completed the reading to check for understanding.

For the reading *A Matter of Concentration*, you can have a range of concentrations of the same acid such as HCl. A 1 M solution will have a pH near 0. You can do a series of dilutions taking 1 mL of the 1 M HCl and mixing it with 9 mL of water to make a 0.1 M HCl solution. This solution would have a pH of 1. Now take 1 mL of 0.1 M HCl and mix it with 9 mL of water to make a 0.001 M solution with a pH of 3. Continue the process a few more times to have several pH values to work with. HCl is a strong acid but can have a range of pH values based on its concentration. This is also a good setup to illustrate the logarithmic nature of the scale.

When your students reach the section on neutralization, it might be helpful to have a solution of a strong base, a strong acid, a weak base, and a weak acid, all of the same concentration. That way you can demonstrate some of the concepts presented in the reading. If you mix equal amounts of the same concentration of these different acids and bases, you should be able to model the results that are described in the reading. These can be done in a microwell plate or a small beaker on the overhead projector using a universal indicator. The entire class can view the color changes as you mix the two chemicals.

Reminder of Possible Misconceptions

Student misconceptions may include the following:

- Atoms "own" their electrons.

There aren't different kinds of electrons for different atoms. Electrons are electrons no matter what atom or molecule they surround and they can be transferred from one atom to another.

- The chemical bond is a physical thing made of matter.

Chemical bonds are not made of a separate form of matter, but result from the arrangement of particles in the molecule and forces of attraction.

Water Works, continued

Ammonia (figure 5.4) is a polar molecule, like water. The ammonia molecule exhibits a force of attraction to hydrogen atoms in water. When ammonia comes close to water, the ammonia molecule "rips off" one of the hydrogens from the water molecule. This happens because the force of attraction between hydrogen and ammonia is stronger than the force of attraction between the hydrogen atom and water. Note that the ammonia molecule takes the hydrogen nucleus only, not the hydrogen's electron.

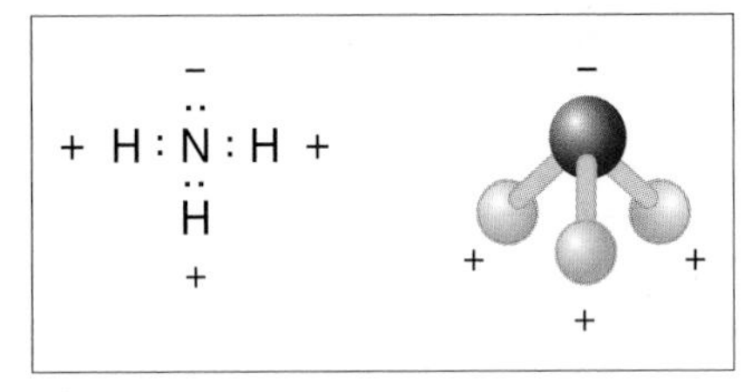

▲ **Figure 5.4 Ammonia molecule.** This molecule produces hydroxide ions in water. What role does water play in this reaction?

7. Follow Steps 7a–e to build 2 water molecule models. You will use these models to learn about acid and base processes.
   a. Assemble 3 marshmallows together in the shape shown in figure 5.3.
   b. Use your marker to label the hydrogen atoms and the oxygen atom.
   c. Place 2 pairs of dots on the top sides of the oxygen atom to represent the 2 pairs of unshared electrons.

   Recall that unshared electrons are electrons that are not shared between 2 atoms.

   d. Use figure 5.3 as your guide and mark the appropriate end of the water molecule with the correct charge.

   The water molecule, as a whole, is neutral, but the distribution of charge is not even. Part of the molecule has a slight positive charge and the opposite end of the molecule has a slight negative charge. This permanent separation of charge makes the molecule polar.

   e. Draw a picture of this molecule beside the acid molecule you drew in Step 2c. Add a plus sign between them to represent the reactants in a chemical equation. Leave room to add the products later.
8. Work with your model and complete Steps 8a–g.

   Working with a model will help you understand the processes in acid-base chemistry that are too small to observe, especially the formation of hydronium ions.

236 Unit 1 Interactions Are Interesting

- Electron pairs are equally shared in all covalent bonds.

Electron pairs are not shared equally due to differences in the electronegativity of the atoms in the molecule.

- "Strength" of acids and bases and "concentration" mean the same thing.

Concentration reflects the number of particles of solute that are dissolved in a liter of solution. Strength reflects the degree to which acids and molecules dissociate into ions in solution.

- Mixing an acid and a base regardless of concentration and strength always produces a neutral product.

The results of mixing equal concentrations of a strong acid and a strong base will produce a neutral salt and water. However, unequal concentrations or mixing strong acids with weak bases and vice versa will produce either acidic or basic salts.

- Pure water, since it is neutral, contains no H^+ or OH^-.

Because of the self-ionization of water, water contains 1×10^{-7} M H^+ and 1×10^{-7} M OH^-. Since these concentrations are equal, water is neutral. Even distilled water will register a lower pH than 7 because of dissolved CO_2 from the air. To get distilled water to have a neutral pH, you must heat the water to drive off the CO_2 and use it immediately or store it in a CO_2-free container.

- "pH balanced" means the substance is neutral.

Some personal care items and cosmetics often say they are pH balanced. This does not mean they are neutral, but that they are formulated to have a particular pH.

- Strong acids have very low pH values, and strong bases have very high pH values.

A very dilute solution of a strong acid or base can have a pH value near 7.

Cautions

If you do some of the suggested demonstrations, model good safety practices by wearing your safety goggles, lab apron, and gloves.

a. Remove the H^+, or proton, from the acid molecule and attach it to the negative portion of the water molecule. Attach it where you have marked 1 of the pairs of unshared electrons.

b. You have just made hydronium. What is the chemical formula for hydronium? Record your answer in your science notebook.

c. Water is a neutral molecule, and you have added a proton, or H^+. What is the charge of hydronium (H_3O^+)? Add it to your formula from Step 8b.

d. Draw your hydronium ion as one of the products of the chemical reaction you started in Step 2c.

e. What is the other product of this reaction? Draw it as part of the chemical reaction. Record your answer in your science notebook.

f. Write the chemical formulas underneath your drawings to complete the chemical reaction.

Don't forget to add charges where appropriate.

g. What is water's role in this reaction? Record your answer in your science notebook.

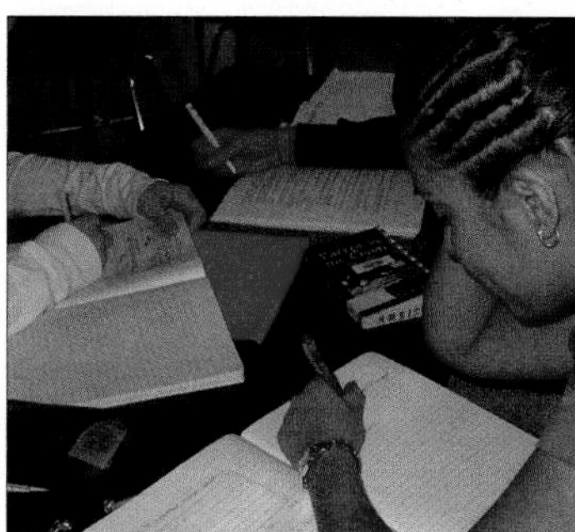

9. Compete the dissociation reaction for the general base that you started in Step 4c by following Steps 9a–d. This reaction is similar to the one you just completed for acids.
   a. Model dissociation by separating the molecule into its 2 ions according to the general equation.

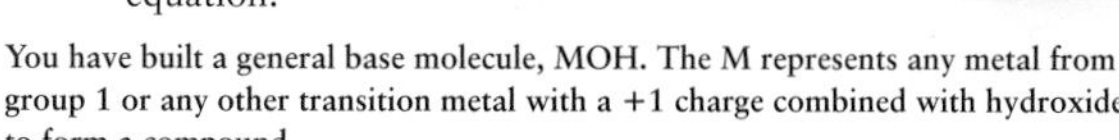

You have built a general base molecule, MOH. The M represents any metal from group 1 or any other transition metal with a +1 charge combined with hydroxide to form a compound.

   b. Draw the 2 resulting ions as the product of the dissociation reaction you started in your science notebook in Step 4c.
   c. Be sure to include the charges of each ion and write the names of each particle underneath the drawing.
   d. What role does water play in this dissociation reaction? Record your answer in your science notebook.

10. Follow Steps 10a–d to model the dissociation of bases like ammonia.
    a. Build a molecule to represent the polar ammonia molecule. It should look similar to figure 5.4.
    b. Draw the ammonia molecule and the water molecule as reactants. Use your second water molecule for this reaction.

Process and Procedure

Materials

For each team of 2 students

marshmallows
toothpicks
markers

In Step 1, students are directed to read a passage about dissociation. They will be building a model throughout this activity in the steps that follow.

In Step 2, students begin their models using marshmallows and toothpicks. When they draw their models in their science notebooks, they should use a new page and begin the drawing on the far left. This will leave room for comments and to add more to the drawing. Drawing and model building will help anchor this learning and help those learners who are visual and kinesthetic. All students will benefit by representing the same material in multiple ways.

Answers to Step 3, SE page 234

3. You may want to have students sketch and model these reactions as well.

3a. $HCl \rightleftharpoons H^+ + Cl^-$

3b. $HC_2H_3O_2 \rightleftharpoons H^+ + CH_3COO^-$

3c. $NaOH \rightleftharpoons Na^+ + OH^-$

3d. $LiOH \rightleftharpoons Li^+ + OH^-$

In Step 4, students continue their model building by making a general hydroxide. Ask your students what metals would have to be represented by having the 1:1 ratio between the metal and the hydroxide. These are the group 1 metals. To model the group 2 metal hydroxides, students would have the formula $M(OH)_2$. Students are encouraged to put the O and H very close together to model the polyatomic ion. As they sketch their models, encourage them to organize their drawings to allow room to add additional diagrams and labels.

Students use their models in Step 5 to explain simple dissociation to their partners. Monitor this step to make sure students both verbalize dissociation and kinesthetically manipulate their models during their explanations. They will read about water's role in dissociation in Step 6.

In Step 7, students continue their model building by making 2 water molecules. They use 1 water molecule now and the other in a later step. They use markers to indicate the 2 unshared pairs of electrons around the central oxygen atom. Verify that they have labeled the charges correctly on their models. The hydrogen atoms should be labeled "positive" and the oxygen should be labeled "negative." They continue to manipulate their models in Step 8 as they remove a hydrogen ion (proton) and move it to a water molecule to form hydronium. As you move about the classroom, question your students to make sure they are grasping the concept. The final equation should be $HA + H_2O \rightleftharpoons H_3O^+ + A^-$. You can see from this generic equation that water is the molecule that accepts the H+ or the proton. The student book does not go into the Brønsted-Lowry model, but students can see that the water accepts the proton. If you want to extend their ideas about acid-base models, you can mention the Brønsted-Lowry model at this time. They would be able to see that water in this case is a Brønsted-Lowry base.

In Step 9, students shift their thinking to model bases and simple dissociation of the bases. The final generic equation is $MOH_{(aq)} \longrightarrow M^+_{(aq)} + OH^-_{(aq)}$. Water is not shown directly in this equation, but it is the vehicle by which the base dissociates.

Students will build an alternate model of bases in Step 10 as they build a model of ammonia. They will use their second water molecule from Step 7 to model the reaction of ammonia and water. During this step, your students build the molecules, manipulate the equation using their models, verbally describe what is happening, and illustrate the process in their science notebooks. Make sure your students participate in each stage of the process.

Step 11 directs them to read a passage to learn about acid and base strength. Having them complete the T-table as they read will help you assess their ongoing understanding of the reading. Figure T5.2 shows a possible completed T-table.

c. Use your models as props to discuss how water and ammonia react.

Be sure to include what happens to produce hydroxide ions, a description of the charges, and the forces that are involved.

d. Draw the 2 resulting ions as the product of this reaction. Be sure to include the charges and write the names of each particle underneath the drawing.

11. Complete the T-table in figure 5.5 in your science notebook as you read *Acid-Base Strength*.

Term	How term relates dissociation and acid-base strength
Hydronium ion	
Dissociation	
Equilibrium position	
Soluble	
Double arrow	
Cation	
Anion	
Force of attraction	

Figure 5.5 T-table for the reading *Acid-Base Strength*. Find the terms in the reading. Then explain in the right-hand column how each term helps relate dissociation and acid-base strength.

READING

Acid-Base Strength

Have you ever worked on a car and accidentally gotten battery acid on your clothing or skin? This acid can be very dangerous. Car battery acid is typically the strong acid, sulfuric acid (H_2SO_4). Bases like drain cleaner and oven cleaner can be harmful to your skin as well. They typically contain a strong base such as sodium hydroxide (NaOH). These acids and bases are strong and can be potentially dangerous if not handled properly. However, you shampoo your hair or wash your hands with bases every day. Are those bases strong or weak? Just because an acid is defined as weak, does that mean it is harmless? What are the fundamental differences at the molecular level between strong and weak acids and bases?

In the reading *Dissociation*, you saw the general acid equation represented with a double arrow. What does that mean? You studied reversible reactions and reactions at equilibrium in chapter 3. The same general equation with the water molecule included in the reaction would look like this:

$$HA_{(aq)} + H_2O_{(l)} \rightleftharpoons H_3O^+_{(aq)} + A^-_{(aq)}$$

238 Unit 1 Interactions Are Interesting

Term	How term relates dissociation and acid-base strength
Hydronium ion	The more hydronium ion there is in solution, the stronger the acid strength.
Dissociation	The greater the amount of dissociation, the stronger the acid strength.
Equilibrium position	The farther to the right an equilibrium is, the more dissociated the substance is and the stronger the acid.
Soluble	For acids to dissociate in water, they must be soluble; high solubility does not automatically produce strong acid solutions.
Double arrow	The double arrow infers reversible reactions at equilibrium; the relative position of equilibrium determines acid-base strength.
Cation	When bases dissociate, they produce cations; generally, the higher the concentration of OH_ produced from dissociation, the stronger the base.
Anion	When acids dissociate, they produce anions; generally, the higher the concentration of H_3O^+ produced from dissociation, the stronger the acid.
Force of attraction	If the acid proton is strongly attracted to the anion, the acid tends not to dissociate very much and is a weak acid.

▲ **Figure T5.2 T-table for the reading, *Acid-Base Strength.*** Use students' responses in this table to assess their understanding of the reading.

Some acids dissociate very readily, and some hardly dissociate at all. We call acids that dissociate completely **strong acids**, and those acids that do not dissociate readily **weak acids**. Acids that are strong, such as hydrochloric acid (HCl), could be written like this:

$$\text{(a) } HCl_{(aq)} + H_2O_{(l)} \longrightarrow H_3O^+_{(aq)} + Cl^-_{(aq)}$$

or

$$\text{(b) } HCl_{(aq)} + H_2O_{(l)} \rightleftharpoons H_3O^+_{(aq)} + Cl^-_{(aq)}$$

Since the HCl molecule dissociates almost completely, there essentially would be no HCl molecules remaining. Equation (a) is usually used to represent this. In this acidic solution, there would only be hydronium ions, chloride ions, and few HCl molecules. The equilibrium position for this reaction lies far to the right, as shown by the arrows. Equation (b) shows a very slight reverse reaction, thus the shorter arrow to the left.

A weak acid such as acetic acid (CH_3COOH), since it dissociates much less, would reach equilibrium and is written as

$$CH_3COOH_{(aq)} + H_2O_{(l)} \rightleftharpoons H_3O^+_{(aq)} + CH_3COO^-_{(aq)}$$

In this weak acidic solution, there would still be molecules of CH_3COOH and water as well as some hydronium ion (H_3O^+) and acetate ion (CH_3COO^-). Only about 0.4 percent of the CH_3COOH molecules are dissociated at any one time in a solution containing 1 mole (mol) of CH_3COOH molecules per liter (L) of solution. The equilibrium position for this process lies far to the left, as shown by the arrows in the equation.

Some basic solutions behave similarly. For the metal hydroxides, it is as simple as knowing if the hydroxide is soluble. If it is soluble, then the hydroxide will dissociate completely in water and, essentially, the dissociation reaction goes to completion. Sodium hydroxide (common household lye) is very soluble in water and would be represented like this:

$$NaOH_{(aq)} \longrightarrow Na^+_{(aq)} + OH^-_{(aq)}$$

Sodium hydroxide is considered a strong base. So are all the other group 1 hydroxides. However, the reaction you modeled in the previous steps represents a reaction of a weak base. Ammonia is a weak base because, even though it produces hydroxide ions in water by removing a hydrogen ion from the water molecule, most of the NH_3 molecules do not react in solution. The reaction of NH_3 and H_2O should be represented using a double arrow.

What is the difference in these two types of acids and bases? What is it about their molecular makeup that makes one strong and dissociate completely and the other weak and only dissociate slightly? You can answer this by considering the competitive forces involved in the chemical reaction.

For the acid to dissociate, the hydrogen ion must be lost from the acid molecule and attach to the water molecule. The force of attraction between the water molecule and the hydrogen ion must be sufficient to remove the hydrogen ion from the anion (A^-). Positive ions are called **cations**, and negative ions are called **anions**. For a strong acid, the H^+ ion is pulled from the anion in the acid molecule by the stronger force of attraction by the water molecule. For weak acids, the acid anion has a stronger attraction for the H^+ than water, so the acid molecule stays intact. For bases, water either acts as the dissolving agent or donates one of its hydrogen ions to produce OH^- ions.

SCILINKS NSTA
Go to: www.scilinks.org
Topic: anions
Code: 2Inquiry239a
Topic: cations
Code: 2Inquiry239b

NOTES:

Answers to Steps 12–15, SE pages 240–241

12a. The electrostatic force of attraction between the positively charged hydrogen and the negatively charged remainder of the atom is the cause of the force.

12b. Water is a polar molecule, and the negative end of the water molecule is attracted to the positive charge of the hydrogen ion.

12c. The strength of the attraction between the water molecule and the hydrogen ion is greater than the strength of the attraction between the hydrogen ion and the other anion.

12d. The force of attraction between the hydrogen ion and the anion is greater than the force of attraction between the hydrogen ion and water. Thus, the acid molecule does not dissociate easily to produce hydronium ions.

13. See the following for answers to Steps 13a–c.

a. $HNO_2 + H_2O \rightleftharpoons H_3O^+ + NO_2^-$

b. $HCN + H_2O \rightleftharpoons H_3O^+ + CN^-$

c. $HI + H_2O \rightleftharpoons H_3O^+ + I^-$ or $HI + H_2O \rightarrow H_3O^+ + I^-$

14. In strong acids such as HI, the H^+ and the anion dissociate to a large extent. For strong acids, water has the greatest attraction for the H^+. In weak acids (nitrous acid (HNO_2) and hydrogen cyanide (HCN)), most of the acid molecules stay together in solution. Therefore, the anions (nitrous ion (NO_2^-) and cyanate ion (CN^-)) have the greatest attraction for the H^+.

15. The pH of vinegar is close to 3 and is close to the far left side of the pH scale. The relatively low pH of this weak acid may surprise your students. They may equate weak acid with acids that have a pH near 7.

In Step 16, students read *A Matter of Concentration* to find out what concentration has to do with pH values.

NOTES:

12. Discuss Questions 12a–d with your partner and record your best answers in your science notebook.
    a. What causes the force between the hydrogen ion and the anion (A^-) in the acid molecule?

Think about the force between the H^+ and the A^- in the HA molecule.

    b. What causes the force between the water molecule and the proton (H^+) once the proton is removed from the acid molecule?
    c. Strong acids readily lose a hydrogen ion (hydrogen nucleus) to water. To which particle is the hydrogen most strongly attracted, water or the anion of the strong acid? Write your answer in terms of relative strengths of attraction. See figure 5.6.
    d. Weak acids *do not* easily lose a hydrogen ion (hydrogen nucleus) to water. To which particle is the hydrogen most strongly attracted, water or the anion of the weak acid? Write your answer in terms of relative strengths of attraction. See figure 5.6.

▲ **Figure 5.6 Strong and weak acids differ because of the amount of dissociation of the acid molecule.** For the molecule to dissociate, which force is stronger?

13. Write the dissociation reaction for the following acids in your science notebook.

Consider if the acid is strong or weak and use your knowledge to represent the equation with the appropriate arrows. Make water part of the chemical reaction.

    a. Nitrous acid (HNO_2) (weak)
    b. Hydrogen cyanide (HCN) (weak)
    c. Hydroiodic acid (HI) (strong)

14. For each of the acids in Step 13, indicate if water or the anion in the acid molecule (A^- in the HA molecule) has the greatest attraction for the hydrogen ion. Justify your answer.
15. Look back to your experiment in Part I of the explore activity, *Gathering Evidence*. Find the pH of vinegar to answer the questions in Steps 15a–b.

Dilute acetic acid is what we commonly call vinegar. Acetic acid is considered a weak acid.

NOTES:

a. Is this value closer to the left side of the pH scale or to the neutral position on the pH scale?

b. Does this surprise you? Why or why not?

16. Read *A Matter of Concentration* to find out what concentration has to do with pH values and acid-base strength.

READING

A Matter of Concentration

You may have noticed that the pH values of some *weak* acids are low, indicating increased acidity. This may seem counterintuitive to you since you might think that weak acids will have pH values near 7, or neutral. What is the reason for this? It all has to do with the strength of the acid *and* the concentration of the acid. We use "strong" and "weak" to indicate the extent to which an acid (or base, for that matter) dissociates when placed in water. The concentration refers to how much of the substance is dissolved in water.

A strong acid or base can be either concentrated or dilute. We can say the same for a weak acid or base. Just keep in mind that "concentrated" and "dilute" refer to the number of particles in the solution and "strong" and "weak" refer to the extent to which these acid or base particles dissociate.

One way that chemists express concentration is in *molarity* (M), or moles of solute per liters of solution. What does it mean to have a 1 M solution of hydrochloric acid? It means that there is 1 mol of HCl dissolved in enough water to make 1 L of solution. The formula for calculating molarity is

$$M = \frac{\text{moles of solute}}{\text{liters of solution}}$$

In this example, HCl is the solute. If you had 0.10 mol HCl in a liter of solution, what would be the concentration of the solution? This solution would have a concentration of 0.10 M and would be expressed as 0.10 M HCl.

The pH scale is based on concentrations such as these. pH stands for "power of hydrogen," and the scale reflects the concentration of the hydrogen ions in solutions. You know that the more hydrogen or hydronium ions in solution, the more acidic the solution. This relationship is extended to basic solutions as well. You will learn more about bases in the next part.

SCI LINKS NSTA
Topic: molarity
Go to: www.scilinks.org
Code: 2Inquiry241

Chapter 5 Forces of Attraction 241

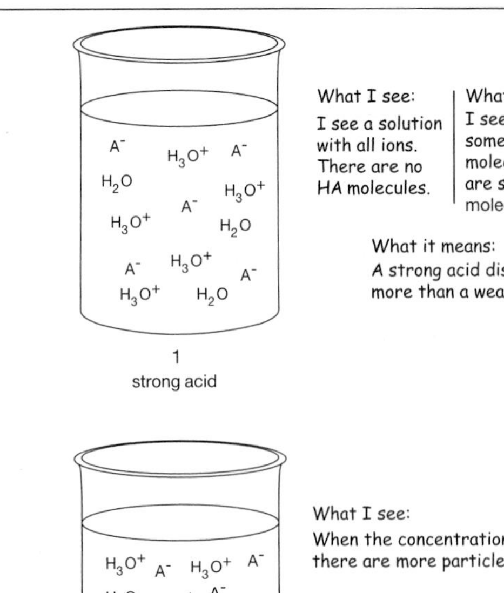

Figure T5.3 Beakers for *Stop and Think* Question 1. Your students should have drawings and highlight comments similar to these.

Answers to Stop and Think, SE page 242

1. Figure T5.3 shows the expected answer to Question 1.

2a. For a strong acid,

- a concentration of H_3O^+ ___=___ 1 M.
- a concentration of HA ___≪___ 1 M. (In words, the acid concentration is much smaller than 1 molar.)
- a concentration of A^- ___=___ 1 M.

2b. For a weak acid,

- a concentration of H_3O^+ ___≪___ 1 M. (The hydronium concentration is very much smaller than 1 molar.)
- a concentration of HA ___<___ 1 M. (The concentration of HA is very close to, but smaller than 1 M.)
- a concentration of A^- ___≪___ 1 M. (The anion concentration is very much smaller than 1 molar.)

Stop & THINK

You have looked at the differences in the pH values on the pH scale and how concentrations determine the pH values. Take a closer look and compare how strong and weak acids are different from concentrated and dilute acids.

1. Acid molecules can be represented generally by using HA. Use this designation as you complete Questions 1a–g.
   a. Draw 4 beakers that will represent different acidic solutions. Use a blank page in your science notebook and allow room for highlight comments outside the beakers and drawings inside the beakers. Label your 4 beakers from "1" to "4."
   b. Title beaker 1 "strong acid" and beaker 2 "weak acid."
   c. Using 5 molecules of acid and 5 molecules of water, illustrate the differences in these 2 acids once they are dissolved in water.

   You can use just general chemical symbols or you can draw atomic representations of each particle. In either case, be sure to label everything clearly.

   d. Title beaker 3 "concentrated strong acid" and beaker 4 "concentrated weak acid."
   e. Using the same method of illustration as you did in Question 1c, represent solutions of concentrated strong and weak acids.

   For easier comparison, change the number of acid particles for each acid by the same amount.

   f. Write highlight comments on your drawings for "What I see" and "What it means."
   g. Share your drawings with another team.

   Consider using the think-share-advise-revise (TSAR) strategy.

2. You learned to use molarity to represent concentrations of solutions. Consider 1 M solutions of a strong acid and a weak acid. Use the relationships =, >, >>, <, and << to answer Questions 2a–b.
   a. For a 1 M strong acid solution,
      - a concentration of H_3O^+ ________ 1 M.
      - a concentration of HA ________ 1 M.
      - a concentration of A^- ________ 1 M.
   b. For a 1 M weak acid solution,
      - a concentration of H_3O^+ ________ 1 M.
      - a concentration of HA ________ 1 M.
      - a concentration of A^- ________ 1 M.

242 | Unit 1 Interactions Are Interesting

Answers to Reflect and Connect, SE pages 243–244

1a. The 1 M solution of HCl will be the stronger electrolyte since the acid is strong and dissociates in water essentially completely. The 1 M solution of CH_3COOH, a weak acid, would not have as many ions in solution since weak acids do not dissociate to a large extent.

1b. The 1 M solution of HNO_3 would be the strongest electrolyte. A 1 M solution would be more concentrated, and since both solutions contain the same acid, the more concentrated solution would have more ions.

1c. The solution of 0.5 M LiOH will be the strongest electrolyte since it is the strongest base and will dissociate completely.

2a. The chemical reaction between a strong acid and a strong base is

$$HA + MOH \rightarrow H_2O + MA.$$

In net ionic form, the reaction would be

$$H^+ + OH^- \rightarrow H_2O.$$

2b. Depending on which version (complete or net ionic) of the reaction your students answer, the highlight comments will vary. Watch for evidence of their understanding of the formation of water from the H^+ from the acid and the OH^- from the base. Also, they should indicate that all the H^+ and the OH^- react to leave a solution of water and a soluble salt.

3. Water is still neutral even though it contains H^+ ions and OH^- ions because the concentration of the ions is equal.

4. A strong base could have the same pH as a solution of a weak base if the weak base was concentrated and the strong base was dilute.

5. The stronger acid is HBr since water has a greater attraction for the H^+ than the bromide ion (Br^-) does. Therefore, water will take the H^+ from the hydrogen bromide HBr molecule and it will dissociate completely, as in

$$HBr + H_2O \rightarrow H_3O^+ + Br^-.$$

The weaker acid is hydrofluoric acid (HF). Since the fluoride ion (F^-) has a greater attraction for the H^+ than water, the molecule will largely stay together in solution.

$$HF + H_2O \rightleftharpoons H_3O + F^-$$

6. The correct balanced chemical equation is

$$Mg_{(s)} + 2HCl_{(aq)} \rightarrow H_{2(g)} + MgCl_{2(aq)}.$$

7a. Since HCl is a strong acid, $[H+] = [HCl]$, the pH range would be from $pH = -\log(0.01) = 2.0$ to $pH = -\log(0.1) = 1.0$. So the range is 1.0 to 2.0.

7b. Taking an antacid would cause a neutralization reaction to take place in the stomach. The antacid would neutralize some of the stomach acid. The resulting gastric juice would still be acidic for several reasons. One reason is that a reaction between a strong acid (present in gastric juice) and a weak base (present in the antacid) would result in a solution that is acidic. This is true if equimolar amounts are mixed. Another reason that the resulting solution would be acidic is because there is much more gastric juice present than antacid.

7c. The most obvious reason is safety. A strong base would be extremely harmful to the body. Students may mention that dissolving fats and oils is a property of bases and since the body has fats and oils, bases would be harmful.

17. Look at the simulation *Determination of the Molarity of an Acid or Base Solution* on the *Student Resource CD (SRCD)*. In it, you will find out how to use acid-base neutralization chemistry to determine the concentration of unknown solutions. This process is called **titration**.

Reflect and Connect

Show your best thinking and write answers to the following questions in your science notebook. After you are done, revise your answers based on discussions with your teammates.

1. You have learned a lot about ions in solution in this activity. You also learned in earlier classes that electrolytes are substances that, when dissolved in water, will produce an electric current. Electric currents will flow through a solution in which ions are present. The more ions present, the more current flows. Choose the example from each pair that would be a stronger electrolyte. (If you think they are equal, then say so.) Consider all amounts to be equal. Justify each selection.
   a. A 1 M solution of HCl or a 1 M solution of CH_3COOH
   b. A 1 M solution of HNO_3 or a 0.5 M solution of HNO_3
   c. A solution of 0.5 M LiOH and a solution of 0.5 M NH_3
2. Use the general form for an acid (HA) and the general form for a base (MOH) to answer Questions 2a–b.
   a. Write a chemical reaction that represents a reaction between a strong acid such as hydrochloric acid and a strong base such as sodium hydroxide.
   b. Write highlight comments for the reactants and products.
3. Water contains both H^+ and OH^- because of its self-ionization. Explain why water is neutral even though it contains these ions.
4. Describe how you could have a solution of a strong base with the same pH as a solution of a weak base. Use the words *strong*, *weak*, *concentrated*, and *dilute* in your answer.
5. Consider the following particles listed in order of decreasing attraction to H^+ ions: $F^- > H_2O > Br^-$. Which is the stronger acid, HF or HBr? Explain your answer. Use chemical equations in your answer.
6. Think about the reaction you observed in Part II of the explore activity. You used a dilute solution of hydrochloric acid (HCl). You put different metals in the acid, and a gas was produced that you identified as hydrogen gas (H_2). Write a chemical equation for this reaction using magnesium as the metal.

EXPLAIN

Redox Reactions

Activity Overview

In this activity, students continue connecting what they experienced in the explore activity to specific chemical reactions. Here students gain direct experience with redox reactions. From their observations and readings, they learn how to balance redox reactions by the half-cell method. Students also learn how to use a table of relative metal activity to predict the relative strengths of oxidizing and reducing agents, as well as to predict whether certain redox reactions will occur. If the reactions do occur, students learn how to predict what the products will be.

Before You Teach

Background Information

Oxidation-reduction reactions are often called redox reactions for short and are reactions that involve the transfer of electrons. Oxidation is the loss of electrons, and reduction is the gain of electrons. Oxidation cannot occur independently of reduction; they must occur together. Another way to look at redox reactions is that a redox reaction is one in which the oxidation state or oxidation number of an element changes. In this chapter, we do not go into oxidation numbers and assigning them in compounds. We take a different approach. However, this information is included here for your background and if you decide to take your students further in the study of redox reactions.

Oxidation states or oxidation numbers provide a way to keep track of electrons in a redox reaction. If the compound is ionic, the charge of the monotonic ion is the same as the oxidation number. In covalent compounds, however, the oxidation number is obtained by a systematic method of assigning electrons to particular atoms. Electrons in covalent compounds are shared and, if the atoms are not identical, then they are not shared equally. In assigning oxidation numbers, the electrons are assigned to the atom in the molecule that has the stronger attraction for the electrons (more electronegative). For example, consider water, where oxygen has a greater attraction for the electrons than do the hydrogen atoms. Therefore, oxygen is assigned the two extra electrons from the two hydrogen atoms and oxygen has a −2 oxidation number. Each of the hydrogen atoms has a +1 oxidation number. There are a set of rules for assigning oxidation numbers. They are summarized as the following:

- The sum of the oxidation states must be zero for an electrically neutral compound. For ions, the sum of the oxidation states must equal the charge of the ion.
- The oxidation state of an atom in an element is 0. (The elements in $Na_{(s)}$, $O_{2(g)}$, $Hg_{(l)}$, and $O_{3(g)}$ all have an oxidation state of 0.)
- The oxidation state of a monatomic ion is the same as its charge ($Na^+ = +1$, $O^{2-} = -2$, etc.).
- Oxygen is assigned an oxidation state of −2 in covalent compounds and polyatomic ions except in peroxides, where it is assigned an oxidation state of −1.
- Hydrogen is assigned an oxidation state of +1 in covalent compounds with nonmetals and −1 with metals.

Answers to Reflect and Connect are on TE page 243.

7. The gastric juice in your stomach has a H^+ concentration between 0.01 and 0.1 M. When a person suffers from acid indigestion, the pH of the gastric juice (a strong acid) drops below the normal range. Often, a dose of antacids (made from a weak base) will alleviate the symptoms of indigestion.
   a. In what pH range is gastric juice, acid or base?
   b. Describe how taking an antacid will help a person suffering from indigestion. Include in your answer what kind of reaction this is, the expected products, and their pH range.
   c. Why would it be inadvisable to use a strong base as an antacid?

EXPLAIN

Redox Reactions

Magnesium burns in air to produce the bright white light in many fireworks. Iron in the body of a car starts to rust where the paint is scratched off. Metabolic processes in our bodies process sugars, fats, and proteins to provide the energy necessary for life. Gold ions react to form a layer of gold atoms on a necklace to give us less expensive gold-plated jewelry. The combustion of the fuel in a rocket propels the rocket into outer space. What do all these chemical processes have in common? These reactions may seem unrelated. But in fact, they are all the same type of chemical process. These reactions represent a category of reactions called oxidation-reduction reactions, or redox reactions.

Historically, oxidation reactions were defined as reactions in which an element combines with oxygen to form an oxide. The rusting of an iron nail to form iron oxide is an example. Reduction was represented as the reverse reaction. Here a chemical process removes the oxygen from the oxide to yield the pure metal. It was called reduction because the pure metal weighs less than the oxide. This reaction is still very important in industry. The removal of oxygen from iron ore in steelmaking is still the first step in the process today.

Topic: oxidation-reduction reactions
Go to: www.scilinks.org
Code: 2Inquiry244

However, now we define these reactions in a more general way. **Oxidation-reduction reactions** or **redox reactions** involve the transfer of electrons. This is similar to the way acids transfer protons. It's similar because both the electron and proton are charged particles. And just like your study of acids and bases, your prior knowledge of forces will help you understand redox reactions. Can you see this transfer take place? No, electrons are much too small to see. But you can see the results of a redox reaction. From the evidence you can see, you infer what happens at the atomic level.

244 | Unit 1 Interactions Are Interesting

- In compounds, fluorine always has an oxidation state of −1.

These numbers are helpful in determining if a chemical reaction is a redox reaction. Notice that there is not a rule for every element. You must use the process of elimination and reasoning to determine the oxidation number of elements not represented by a rule. For example, consider the compound potassium permanganate, $KMnO_4$. You know that the potassium ion in this compound has a charge of +1 in this compound. Therefore, according to the rule, K would have an oxidation number of +1. There is no rule for manganese, so move on to oxygen. Oxygen has an oxidation number of −2 according to our set of rules. Now to determine the oxidation number of manganese, apply the last rule. All the numbers must add to zero in a neutral compound. You must consider both the oxidation number and the number of atoms. To calculate,

$$K = +1$$
$$O = 4(-2) = -8$$

So you have a total of −7, and Mn must have an oxidation number of +7 to bring the total to zero.

Many of the transition metals have multiple oxidation states; manganese has at least 7. It is not uncommon for each oxidation state to produce a compound or solution with a different color. For instance, Cr^{6+} (which occurs as part of a complex ion) gives a solution with an orange color. When the Cr^{6+} ion is reduced to the Cr^{3+} ion (also part of a complex ion), the solution turns green.

Redox reactions are often shown in net ionic form, and to balance these reactions properly, you must consider that the reaction must be balanced not only according to mass but also according to charge. The student book gives the steps in balancing redox reactions using the half-reaction method.

Just like the competitive forces involved in the transfer of hydrogen ions in acid-base chemistry, there is a competition for a charged particle in redox reactions. In the case of redox reactions, the charged particle is not a proton but an electron. This is what drives the redox reaction. It is what makes some reactions spontaneous and some not. Additional background material can be found in the student book and in a college-level general chemistry text.

What would it look like if metal ions such as silver (Ag^+) in a solution were to gain electrons? You will work with a partner and individually to answer this and other questions as you conduct investigations and read about these very important chemical reactions.

Materials

For each team of 2 students

- 2 pairs of safety goggles
- 2 laboratory aprons
- 2 pairs of safety gloves
- 1 petri dish
- 1 dissecting scope or 2 hand lenses
- silver nitrate solution ($AgCl_{(aq)}$)
- 1 dropping pipet
- thin copper wire
- tape
- white paper
- colored pencils

Cautions

Wear safety goggles, safety gloves, and a lab apron during the experiment and do not touch any chemicals or solutions. Silver nitrate is toxic by ingestion and inhalation. It may cause irritation to skin, eyes, and mucous membranes. Use care in handling this chemical. Avoid contact with skin and clothing. Silver nitrate will permanently stain skin, nails, and clothing.

Process and Procedure

What changes can you observe when a redox reaction occurs? Work with your partner as you observe a redox reaction and discover how and where electrons are being transferred.

1. Tape a piece of thin copper wire to the inside of a petri dish. Make sure the wire is flat against the bottom of the dish.
2. Sketch your setup following Steps 2a–f.

Make your sketch large enough to record important detail. Leave room around the sides for comments.

   a. Sketch a top view of your setup. Focus on a small area of the center of your wire.
   b. You will add a few drops of silver nitrate ($AgNO_3$) solution to the center of your wire. But *before* you add it to your wire, draw this "puddle" of $AgNO_3$ solution. Do not add the $AgNO_3$ at this time.
   c. Label your copper wire.
   d. Label the ions in solution on your drawing.

Materials

For each team of 2 students

2 pairs of safety gloves
2 laboratory aprons
2 pairs of safety goggles
1 petri dish
1 dissecting scope or 2 hand lenses
0.1 M silver nitrate ($AgNO_3$) solution
1 dropping pipet
thin copper wire
tape
white paper
colored pencils

Advance Preparation

Prepare the silver nitrate ($AgNO_3$) solution before class. To make a 0.1 M solution of $AgNO_3$, dissolve 1.7 grams (g) $AgNO_3$ in enough distilled water to make 100 mL solution. One hundred mL will be plenty since each team only uses a couple of drops. It is important to use distilled water. The silver nitrate will react with any chlorine in tap water or many ions in drinking water to form a white precipitate. Be careful not to get any silver nitrate crystals or solution on your skin because it will turn the skin and nails dark brown. The brown color will not wash off; it will have to wear off or, in the case of your skin or fingernails, it will have to grow off.

If you can locate dissecting scopes, the visual impact of this reaction is intensified. The experiment will work with hand lenses, too, but try to have at least 1 dissecting scope or a scope that connects to a computer monitor.

Prepare a test tube of silver nitrate solution with a coiled piece of copper wire. Allow the mixture to set overnight. Students will need to observe the blue color of the solution in their procedures. Do not have this sitting out so students can see it beforehand.

If you decide to perform any of the suggested demonstrations of redox reactions, acquire the materials ahead of time and use proper safety equipment.

Educational Technologies

If you have a microscope that connects to a computer or large monitor, use it in addition to the hand lenses.

Cautions

Silver nitrate is toxic by ingestion and inhalation. It may cause irritation to skin, eyes, and mucous membranes. Use care in handling this chemical. Avoid contact with skin and clothing. Silver nitrate will permanently stain skin, nails, and clothing.

As You Teach

Outcomes and Indicators of Success

By the end of this activity, students should

1. understand elementary oxidation-reduction (redox) reactions.

   They will demonstrate their understanding by

   - identifying what is oxidized, what is reduced, what gains electrons, what loses electrons, what the oxidizing agent is, and what the reducing agent is in a redox reaction;
   - balancing simple redox reactions according to mass and charge;
   - relating an activity series for metals and the table of oxidizing and reducing agents to experimental evidence;
   - explaining, based on competitive attractions of electrons, the transfer of electrons in redox reactions;
   - describing reactions and nonreactions based on the reactant's location on a table of reducing and oxidizing agents; and
   - evaluating methods of preventing corrosion for their effectiveness.

2. use logic and evidence to formulate and revise scientific explanations.

   They will demonstrate their use of logic and evidence by

   - deducing how to apply the law of conservation of charge to redox reactions and
   - using the evidence of actual redox reactions to imply which specific changes took place in several redox reactions.

Strategies

Getting Started

There are numerous examples of redox reactions and many can be used to introduce the activity. Consider lighting a sparkler, burning a candle, or lighting a strip of magnesium. Be sure to do these safely and away from combustible items. Students will naturally be curious about the topic if they equate it with fire. Combustion is only one example of redox reactions, and they will see another as they do the first activity.

Reminder of Possible Misconceptions

Common student misconceptions regarding redox reactions follow:

- Oxidation is only the addition of oxygen in a reaction, and

The silver nitrate dissolved to form a solution. Therefore, there are silver ions (Ag^+) and nitrate ions (NO_3^-) in the solution.

e. Use your colored pencils to make your sketch more realistic.
f. Title your drawing "before reaction."

3. Place 2–3 drops of the silver nitrate solution in the center of your petri dish. Make sure that the drops cover the copper wire.

Caution: Don't let silver nitrate touch your skin.

4. Place the dish under a dissecting scope immediately or examine the reaction with the hand lenses. Watch the reaction for several minutes.
5. After the reaction has proceeded for several minutes, compare the results with the color of the "before reaction" solution. Describe any changes you see in your science notebook.

To help you see color changes, carefully lay the dish on a sheet of white paper. You may have to wait a few minutes to notice any change from the colorless solution.

6. Sketch the results of this reaction by following Steps 6a–c.
   a. Draw a picture of your petri dish and the results of this chemical reaction. Use the same view and scale as you did in Step 2. Include the wire, the solution, and the new substance that was formed. Do not label anything yet.
   b. Add color to your drawing with your colored pencils to represent the colors in the reaction.
   c. Title this sketch "after reaction."
7. Discover what these crystals are by working with your partner and following Steps 7a–c.

Remember the law of conservation of matter: atoms are neither created nor destroyed. So the atoms making up the crystals in your petri dish must have been present at the beginning, but in another form.

   a. Write the particles present at the beginning as reactants in a chemical equation.

These were labeled in your "before" sketch. Write them down as reactants in a chemical equation. Don't forget to include charges. Since copper is in its elemental state, it has no charge.

   b. Write your ideas for products to complete your chemical reaction.

Think about the possibilities for the new substances formed as the products of your chemical reaction. Remember, atoms in their elemental state have no ionic charge.

reduction is only the removal of oxygen in a reaction.

Historically, this is how the reactions got their name, but the more modern definitions of these reactions include many more types of reactions.

- Oxidation and reduction can occur independently.

Oxidation and reduction always occur as a pair. If oxidation is the loss of electrons, then there must be a process to take the electrons (reduction). Often, we look at half reactions of the process, but this does not in any way indicate that oxidation takes place separately from reduction.

Cautions

Silver nitrate is toxic by ingestion and inhalation. It may cause irritation to skin, eyes, and mucous membranes. Use care in handling this chemical. Avoid contact with skin and clothing. Silver nitrate will permanently stain skin, nails, and clothing.

Process and Procedure

In Step 1, students work in pairs to prepare a petri dish with a piece of copper wire. Very thin wire will work the best.

In Step 2, students sketch their setup along with the drops of solution they will add. Make sure they do not add the drops and then sketch the setup or the reaction will proceed and they will miss it. They are supposed to sketch the "puddle" of $AgNO_3$ solution *before* they add it to the dish. They should include all the proper labels. Students should not disturb the growing silver crystals in any way, until the reaction is complete.

In Step 3, students place 2–3 drops of the solution on the copper wire. Make sure they are watching either with hand lenses or through a dissecting scope immediately after the addition of the silver nitrate solution. Expect students to be very interested in what is going on in the dish. Do not give away the products of this reaction; students will figure this out on their own.

In Step 5, students carefully move the dish and place it on a piece of white paper. Some may notice a bluish color to the puddle. If students have difficulty seeing this, be sure to set up a "teacher" reaction earlier in the day. Within an hour, the solution becomes blue due to copper nitrate. If the reaction has gone long enough, students should notice a blue tint to the solution. If they need to place a drop of the original silver nitrate solution beside the puddle to compare, allow them to do so. They may have to wait for the reaction to continue to get enough of the copper into the solution to turn it blue. Again, do not give away what is happening chemically. They are to record their observations in their science notebooks.

In Step 6, students sketch an "after" picture of their experiment. They will label their sketch later. Note that some silver crystals will be black due to tarnishing in sunlight.

In Step 7, students start to formulate their ideas about what the products of this chemical reaction might be. They are instructed to think about the particles that were present in the beginning and to write them down as reactants in a chemical reaction. They should already have these written as labels on their before drawing. The reactants are copper metal, the silver I ion, and the nitrate ion ($Cu + Ag^+ + NO_3^-$). Next, students consider the possibilities for the products. The law of conservation

Answers to Steps 9–12 are on TE page 248.

c. Share your ideas with another team and follow the TSAR strategy to formulate and record your best ideas.

8. Share your ideas in a class discussion led by your teacher. Write down any changes or new ideas that you hear in the discussion.
9. In your science notebook, fill in any missing atoms and charges in Steps 9a–b.

Notice that some of the atoms involved in this chemical reaction changed charges.

a. $Cu_{(s)} \longrightarrow \_\_\_\_\__{(aq)}$

b. $Ag^+_{(aq)} \longrightarrow \_\_\_\_\__{(s)}$

10. Determine whether the electric charge is balanced in the equations from Steps 9a–b by following Steps 10a–c.
    a. Determine the total charge on the reactant side of each equation and see if it is the same as the total charge on the product side. Treat each reaction separately.
    b. Write the total charge under each side of each reaction.
    c. Check your answer with another team and modify your science notebook if necessary.
11. What is the charged particle responsible for changes to the metals in these chemical reactions? What charge does the particle have?

Remember, atoms contain electrons (−), protons (+), and neutrons (0).

12. Add the charged particle you identified in Step 11 to balance the total charge for each chemical reaction by following Steps 12a–d.
    a. Remember that mass *and* charge are conserved in chemical reactions. This means the total amount of charge on both sides of a chemical reaction must be the same.
    b. Decide to which side of each equation you must add some of the charged particles selected in Step 11.
    c. Determine the appropriate number of these particles you must add to ensure conservation of charge.
    d. Incorporate these charged particles into each reaction from Step 9 by using coefficients.
13. Apply a reading strategy to *The Redox Exchange* to increase your understanding of the terms half reaction, lose electrons, gain electrons, oxidized, reduced, oxidation, reduction, spectator ion, and oxidation number.

of matter tells us that it has to be from the same atoms as were present in the reactants. They should come up with an idea about what they think are the products. Do not give them the right answer yet, but the products are $Ag_{(s)}$ and Cu^{2+} and NO_3^-. If some students get it correct, do not let them know that they are correct or they will immediately stop thinking or tell the rest of the class. Rather, keep those students engaged in questions that ask them to justify their reasoning. They will be sharing with other teams. You may want to use the think-share-advise-revise (TSAR) strategy to get them to develop their best answers.

In Step 8, lead the class in a discussion and, as before, let the class discuss its ideas; your role is a mediator who keeps students on track. You can use questioning strategies to guide them to the correct answers. You probably should say that the +2 charge is the most common oxidation state of copper, but that copper also exists as a +1 cation, just not in this reaction. By the end of the discussion, the class should have the correct complete chemical equation:

$$Cu_{(s)} + Ag^+_{(aq)} + NO_3^-{}_{(aq)} \rightarrow Ag_{(s)} + Cu^{2+}_{(aq)} + NO_3^-{}_{(aq)}$$

Do not expect students to have the equation balanced yet. They will also learn about spectator ions (NO_3^- in this case) later in the chapter. Take this opportunity to connect the blue tint of the solution after the reaction to the presence of copper ions. Most common copper solutions are blue.

Answers to Steps 9–12, SE page 247

9. The half cell reactions for Step 9 are as follows:

   a. $Cu_{(s)} \rightarrow Cu^{2+}_{(aq)}$

   b. $Ag^+_{(aq)} \rightarrow Ag_{(s)}$

10a. The correct half cell is as follows—this reaction has a 0 charge on the left and a 2+ charge on the right:

$$Cu_{(s)} \rightarrow Cu^{2+}_{(aq)}$$

This reaction has a 1+ charge on the left and a 0 charge on the right:

$$Ag^+_{(aq)} \rightarrow Ag_{(s)}$$

10b. The correct reactions follow.

$$\underset{0}{Cu_{(s)}} \rightarrow \underset{2+}{Cu^{2+}_{(aq)}}$$

$$\underset{1+}{Ag^+_{(aq)}} \rightarrow \underset{0}{Ag_{(s)}}$$

11. Electrons are involved in chemical reactions. Electrons are negatively charged.

12. Mass is conserved in chemical reactions and charge is conserved as well. Look back to the reactions that students completed in Steps 9a–b. They should add the charged particle identified in Step 11 to balance the charge for each chemical reaction. They can add these particles to either side of the equation. They can choose the appropriate side by examining the charge balance. If charge is not conserved, they should balance the charge by adding or changing coefficients.

$$Cu_{(s)} \rightarrow Cu^{2+}_{(aq)} + 2e^-$$

$$Ag^+_{(aq)} + e^- \rightarrow Ag_{(s)}$$

Students may write out the word "electron," but make sure that they include the charge. Show them the shorthand way to write electrons as an e^-. Students may need extra practice in adding these negative charges to get the charge on each side of the arrow to balance.

Students read *The Redox Exchange* in Step 13. Strongly urge them to use a reading strategy that has helped them increase active reading and understanding in the

READING

The Redox Exchange

The reactions you have been working with are called **half reactions**. They represent only half of the chemical reaction taking place. Did you notice that the nitrate ion did not appear in these half reactions? That is because the NO_3^- ion does not change in any way during the chemical reaction. It is a spectator ion. Think back to adding iron to hydrochloric acid in the explore activity. At the beginning of the reaction, these atoms and ions were present:

$$Fe_{(s)} \quad H^+_{(aq)} \quad Cl^-_{(aq)}$$

At the end of the reaction, the following atoms, ions, and molecules were present:

$$Fe^{2+}_{(aq)} \quad H_{2(g)} \quad Cl^-_{(aq)}$$

Note the ion that is unchanged in the chemical reaction. The chloride ion (Cl^-) is the spectator ion in this reaction. The two half reactions for this redox reaction would be

(a) $Fe_{(s)} \longrightarrow Fe^{2+}_{(aq)} + 2e^-$ and
(b) $2H^+ + 2e^- \longrightarrow H_{2(g)}$.

Always check to see that the reactions are balanced according to mass and charge. Notice in reaction (a) how Fe changes from having a charge of zero to a charge of plus 2 (written Fe^{2+}). You can see from the two electrons on the product side that Fe lost two electrons in the process. Atoms or ions that lose electrons are said to be **oxidized**. When something is oxidized, its oxidation number or charge increases. An **oxidation** reaction is a half reaction in which electrons show up on the product side of the arrow. That is, electrons are lost.

Ions have charges. These charges are the same as the ion's oxidation number. All elements have oxidation numbers even if they do not form ionic compounds. These oxidation numbers can be helpful in determining what is oxidized and what is reduced in a redox reaction. Oxidation numbers are given to atoms according to the charge they would have if the electrons are all assigned to the atom with the highest attraction for electrons—the most electronegative atom.

In reaction (b), hydrogen changes from having a charge of 1^+ to zero charge since H_2 is the elemental state of hydrogen. Electrons are gained to make this change. Atoms or ions that gain electrons are said to be **reduced**. The charge is reduced or the charge moves to a more negative direction. A **reduction** reaction is a half reaction in which electrons are gained. One way to remember this is to think of the mnemonic device OIL RIG, which stands for "Oxidized Is Loss and Reduced Is Gain."

There are two equations—two half reactions—for one process. These reactions can be "added" together. First, you must make sure that both reactions are balanced according to mass (the same number and kinds of atoms on both sides). Second, the reaction must be balanced according to charge, adding electrons to either side to balance the reaction. The third step is to see if the same number of electrons is in both reactions. If one substance loses two electrons, then another substance must gain two electrons. If the number of electrons is not the same, use a coefficient to balance the electrons. Remember, if you change the coefficient of one substance in the half reaction, you must change the coefficients of all substances in the

248 Unit 1 Interactions Are Interesting

past. Some may try to avoid demonstrating the use of a specific strategy. In this case, use your knowledge of that particular student's ability to suggest a specific strategy.

Answers to Steps 14, 16, and 17, SE pages 249–250

14a. The half reactions are balanced according to mass.

14b. The correct equations follow.

$$Cu_{(s)} \rightarrow Cu^{2+}_{(aq)} + 2e^-$$
$$Ag^+_{(aq)} + e^- \rightarrow Ag_{(s)}$$

14c. The correct equations follow.

$$Cu_{(s)} \rightarrow Cu^{2+}_{(aq)} + 2e^-$$
$$2Ag^+_{(aq)} + 2e^- \rightarrow 2Ag_{(s)}$$

14d. The correct equations follow.

$$Cu_{(s)} \rightarrow Cu^{2+}_{(aq)} + 2e^-$$
$$2Ag^+_{(aq)} + 2e^- \rightarrow 2Ag_{(s)}$$

$$2Ag^+_{(aq)} + Cu_{(s)} + \cancel{2e^-} \rightarrow 2Ag_{(s)} + Cu^{2+}_{(aq)} + \cancel{2e^-}$$
$$2Ag^+_{(aq)} + Cu_{(s)} \rightarrow 2Ag_{(s)} + Cu^{2+}_{(aq)}$$
$$2 \times (+1) = 2 \qquad 1 \times (+2) = 2$$
$$\text{charge on left} = +2 \qquad \text{charge on right} = +2$$

16a. The correct equation follows.

$$Cu_{(s)} \rightarrow Cu^{2+}_{(aq)} + 2e^-$$
oxidation

16b. The correct equation follows.

$$2Ag^+_{(aq)} + 2e^- \rightarrow 2Ag_{(s)}$$
reduction

16c. Cu is oxidized.

16d. Ag^+ is reduced.

16e. Students should label the crystals silver ($Ag_{(s)}$); the solution contains Cu^{2+} ions and NO_3^- ions.

half cell by the same factor. It is like multiplying everything by the same number—it will still be balanced. The last step is to double-check your combined equation to make sure it is balanced according to mass and charge.

Check the equations to see how to add them together and produce one overall redox equation for the reaction. Start by collecting all the reactants on the left and all the products on the right.

Did you notice that the same number of electrons appear on opposite sides of the equation in the half reactions? That is because if one substance loses electrons, then another must gain those electrons. Oxidation and reduction must come as a pair of reactions; if something is oxidized, then something else must be reduced. The transfer of electrons makes redox reactions occur.

$$Fe_{(s)} \longrightarrow Fe^{2+}_{(aq)} + 2e^-$$
$$2H^+ + 2e^- \longrightarrow H_{2(g)}$$

$$2H^+ + \cancel{2e^-} + Fe_{(s)} \longrightarrow Fe^{2+}_{(aq)} + \cancel{2e^-} + H_{2(g)}$$

(You can cancel anything that appears on both sides.)

$$2H^+ + Fe_{(s)} \longrightarrow Fe^{2+}_{(aq)} + H_{2(g)}$$

14. Reads Steps 14a–e and determine which steps you have already accomplished for the half reactions from Step 10.
    a. Balance each half reaction according to mass.
    b. Balance each half reaction according to charge.
    c. Make the number of electrons gained and lost the same by using coefficients.
    d. Add half reactions together, canceling out electrons.
    e. Double-check the final reaction for balance (both mass and charge).
15. Check your reaction with the reaction of another team or with your teacher for accuracy.
16. Add labels to your equations by following Steps 16a–e.
    a. Label the half reaction that is oxidation.
    b. Label the half reaction that is reduction.
    c. On the combined equation, label the particle that is oxidized.
    d. On the combined equation, label the particle that is reduced.
    e. Go back to the "after" sketch that you did in Step 6. Identify the solution that is now the puddle and the crystals forming on the wire. Label these on your sketch.

NOTES:

NOTES:

17a–b. Ag^+ caused the oxidation and will be labeled the oxidizing agent.

17c–d. Cu caused the reduction and will be labeled the reducing agent.

17e. The particle that is oxidized is the reducing agent—they are the same particle.

17f. The particle that is reduced is the oxidizing agent—they are the same particle.

17. Read the following paragraph and answer the questions in Steps 17a–f in your science notebook.

When a particle loses electrons (is oxidized), another particle is the agent that caused the oxidation. **Oxidizing agent** is the term given to this particle. The same is true for particles that gain electrons (are reduced). There is another particle that is the agent that gives up an electron or electrons in the process. This particle is called a **reducing agent.**

a. What particle *caused* the oxidation in your reaction?

It will be the one that has stolen the electron!

b. On the combined equation from Step 14, label the particle "oxidizing agent."

c. What particle *caused* the reduction in your reaction?

It will be the one that donated the electron!

d. On the combined equation from Step 14, label the particle "reducing agent."

e. What is the relationship between the particle that is oxidized and the reducing agent?

f. What is the relationship between the particle that is reduced and the oxidizing agent?

18. When you studied acid and base reactions, you learned about the role that forces play in determining if an acid or a base is strong or weak. Forces play an essential role in redox reactions as well. Read *Fundamental Forces* to discover the role of forces in redox reactions.

READING

Fundamental Forces

Understanding forces helps you understand the strengths of acids and bases. For example, the competitive forces on an H^+ determine relative acid strength. Understanding forces helps you understand redox reactions as well. That's because redox reactions involve competitive forces on electrons. Electrons move from one atom or ion to another in redox reactions. Because of the electron's charged nature, at least two particles will be competing for the electron. Who will win? The answer lies with how easily the atom gives up electrons.

Look back to your results from Part II of the explore activity where you placed different metals in hydrochloric acid solution (HCl). You have already looked at one of the redox reactions from this activity. This reaction happened when you placed iron in the acid.

NOTES:

Iron readily gave up two electrons to the hydrogen ions to produce hydrogen gas and the iron II ion (Fe^{2+}). How did that reaction compare with the reaction of magnesium and the acid? You noticed that the "fizzing" was much more vigorous with the magnesium metal than with the iron metal. What did that tell you? You said that magnesium was more reactive than the iron. This must mean that magnesium gives up its electrons more readily to hydrogen than iron. The force of attraction of the hydrogen ion for the electron must be greater than the magnesium's force of attraction. Hydrogen wins. The electron is transferred to the hydrogen ion (H^+), and the result is hydrogen gas (H_2).

What happened when you put copper in the HCl? You should have observed no fizzing. What does that mean? There were still H^+ ions that have a force of attraction for electrons, but the copper does not give them up. Did copper or hydrogen win the struggle for the electron? Did copper or hydrogen have the strongest force of attraction for the electron? The copper ion's force of attraction for its electrons is greater than the attractive force that the H^+ has for an electron. So copper keeps its electrons and no reaction occurs.

The table in figure 5.7 shows the relative strengths of reducing and oxidizing agents. The strongest reducing agents (most easily oxidized) are on the top left. Lithium (Li) is the strongest reducing agent. These agents lose electrons very easily and therefore are very reactive. These metals are close to the same order that you found in the explore activity.

The strongest oxidizing agents (most easily reduced) appear on the bottom right of the table. You see that fluorine (F_2) is the strongest oxidizing agent. Strong oxidizing agents have a strong force of attraction for electrons. Recall that fluorine has the highest electronegativity of all elements. This supports the fact that F_2 is the strongest oxidizing agent. The general trend for these agents is shown in figure 5.8.

You can use the information in the table shown in figure 5.7 to predict if a redox reaction will occur. Think back to the reaction you observed at the beginning of this activity. You placed solid copper in a solution that contained silver ions. Look at the placement of copper and the silver ion (Ag^+) in the table in figure 5.7. For a reaction to occur, copper must lose electrons to the silver ions in solution. From the table, you can see that copper is a stronger reducing agent than silver. In other words, copper loses electrons more easily than silver and is more reactive. Elements shown on this table lose electrons to the positively charged ions of any element below them in the series. The more

(Reducing agents: increasing strength ↑ upward; Oxidizing agents: increasing strength ↓ downward)

Reducing agents	Oxidizing agents
Li	Li^+
K	K^+
Ca	Ca^{2+}
Na	Na^+
Mg	Mg^{2+}
Al	Al^{3+}
Zn	Zn^{2+}
Cr	Cr^{3+}
Fe	Fe^{2+}
Ni	Ni^{2+}
Sn	Sn^{2+}
Pb	Pb^{2+}
H_2	H_3O^+
Cu	Cu^{2+}
I^-	I_2
Hg	Hg_2^{2+}
Ag	Ag^+
Br^-	Br_2
Cl^-	Cl_2
F^-	F_2

▲ Figure 5.7 **Relative strengths of oxidizing and reducing agents.** You can use this table to predict redox reactions.

Answers to Reflect and Connect, SE pages 252–254

1. The answers to Questions 1a–c follow.
   a. Cu^{2+}
   b. Cl^-
   c. Cu

2a. There is no reaction because lead is a weaker reducing agent than zinc and cannot displace zinc in a compound.

2b. Students would see copper coating on the chromium (plating out) and the solution would turn less blue. This happens because chromium is a stronger reducing agent than copper and can displace copper from a compound.

2c. Nickel is a stronger reducing agent than hydrogen and so it can displace it in hydrochloric acid. Students would see H_2 gas fizzing from the surface of the nickel.

3. For Cr^{6+} to be reduced to Cr^{3+}, the Cr^{6+} ion must gain 3 electrons. This is a reduction reaction. There must be an oxidation reaction in which another substances loses 3 electrons.

4a. The correct equations follow.

$$Mg \rightarrow Mg^{2+}$$
oxidation

$$H_2O \rightarrow H_2 + OH^-$$
reduction

4b. The correct equations follow.

$$Mg \rightarrow Mg^{2+} + 2e^-$$
$$2H_2O + 2e^- \rightarrow H_2 + 2OH^-$$

$$Mg + 2H_2O + \cancel{2e^-} \rightarrow H_2 + \cancel{2e^-} + Mg^{2+} + 2OH^-$$
$$Mg + 2H_2O \rightarrow H_2 + Mg^{2+} + 2OH^-$$

4c. The solution would be basic since there are OH^- ions produced.

Fundamental Forces, continued

active an element from this table is, the greater its tendency to lose electrons. This makes it the strongest reducing agent.

What if you switched the reaction around and placed solid silver in a solution that contained copper ions? Would a reaction occur? Since silver appears below copper in the table and is a weaker reducing agent, no reaction would occur. Consider the following equation:

$$Cu + 2Ag^+ \longrightarrow Cu^{2+} + 2Ag$$

This pair is reactive. This pair is stable (nonreactive).

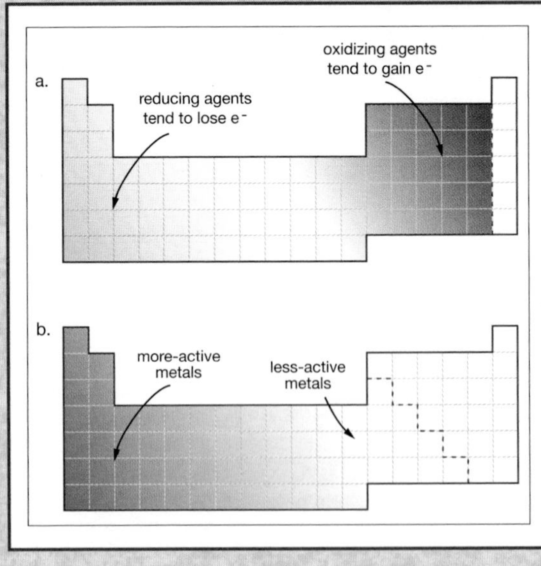

Figure 5.8 Trends in the periodic table. (a) The general trend is that the strongest reducing agents are on the left side of the periodic table and the strongest oxidizing agents are on the right of the table. Noble gases (group 18) are inert and therefore are not oxidized or reduced. (b) This figure shows the general trend for metal activity.

Reflect and Connect

Answer the following questions in your science notebook.

1. Redox reactions are important reactions to your everyday life. A redox reaction involving a biochemical process occurs when cut fruit turns brown on the surface. Colorless compounds are oxidized by the oxygen gas (O_2) in the air to produce a

252 | Unit 1 Interactions Are Interesting

ELABORATE

Electrochemistry

Activity Overview

In this activity, students apply what they have learned about redox reactions to explain how batteries work. In Part I, students read about generating electric current with redox reactions to make a voltaic cell. In Part II, students apply what they experienced in Part I to reverse the redox process in an electrolytic cell. That is, students use electricity from a battery to force redox reactions to progress in the opposite direction they would in a spontaneous voltaic cell.

Before You Teach

Background Information

Students learned in previous chapters that all chemical reactions involve energy changes. They studied endothermic and exothermic reactions in which the exchange of energy was heat energy. The redox reaction that occurs when you place a piece of zinc in a solution of copper sulfate is a spontaneous reaction and will release heat as the reaction progresses—it is exothermic. This reaction involves the transfer of electrons from the zinc that is being oxidized to the copper ions in solution that are being reduced. When you place zinc directly in the solution, this redox reaction and the exchange of electrons happens at the surface of the metal where reacting particles collide. This flow of electrons is an electric current, and this system is an example of the conversion of chemical energy to electrical energy. This is an example of electrochemistry. All electrochemical processes involve redox reactions.

If this flow of electrons is going to be useful, then the reactions must be separated and the electrons made to flow through a conducting wire. The electrons lost by the zinc in the system described above must pass through an external circuit to the copper ions if useful electrical energy is going to be produced.

Electrochemistry is best defined as the interchange of chemical and electrical energy. It is mainly concerned with two processes that involve redox reactions. These processes are the generation of an electric current from a spontaneous chemical reaction and the opposite process, the use of a current to produce a chemical change. If the redox process is not spontaneous as the one described previously, the reaction can be forced to occur by applying an electric current.

Oxidation numbers help in the study of electron transfer reactions. You can recognize a redox reaction because the oxidation number of at least two elements changes. If working with ions and ionic compounds, the oxidation number is the same as the charge. For example, the calcium ion would be given the oxidation number of +2 and chlorine would have a −1 oxidation number. Oxidation numbers are assigned to atoms in these compounds based on how atoms compete for electrons.

Oxygen is the more electronegative element in the compound (3.5 for oxygen compared with 2.1 for hydrogen). Oxygen competes for electrons better than hydrogen. Because of this, electrons are around the oxygen atom more than the hydrogen atom. Since electrons are negative, the oxygen atom is negative, relative to hydrogen. This gives the water molecule its polarity.

When assigning oxidation numbers to oxygen and hydrogen in H_2O, assume that the oxygen atom actually possesses all the bonding electrons. Recall that a neutral

brown pigment on the surface of cut fruit. The skin of the fruit keeps this from happening much the same way paint on a car keeps its body from rusting. Is there any way to keep a fruit salad from turning brown before you eat it? Yes, add lemon juice. The citric acid in lemon juice acts as an antioxidant in this chemical reaction. When the lemon juice (or a commercial additive) is added to your fruit salad, the oxygen in the air reacts to oxidize the citric acid. The citric acid loses electrons to the oxygen more readily than the fruit-browning compounds and, in so doing, it spares the fruit from oxidation and turning brown. The citric acid is a stronger reducing agent than the compounds in the fruit.

Knowing the strength of oxidizing and reducing agents is important in trying to protect substances from unwanted reactions. Which is the stronger oxidizing agent in each of the following pairs? Explain how you arrived at your answer.

a. Cu^{2+} or Fe^{2+}

b. H_2 or Cl^-

c. Pb or Cu

2. Describe the reactions or nonreactions set up for you in Questions 2a–c. If a reaction occurs, describe what you would see. If no reaction occurs, explain why.
   a. A piece of lead (Pb) is placed in a solution of zinc chloride ($ZnCl_2$)
   b. A piece of chromium (Cr) is placed in a solution of copper II nitrate ($Cu(NO_3)_2$)
   c. A piece of nickel (Ni) is placed in a solution of hydrochloric acid (HCl)
3. A Breathalyzer test for roadside alcohol investigations is a redox reaction. The reaction occurs as Cr^{6+} ions are reduced to Cr^{3+} ions. What does that mean? Use the terms *loses*, *gains*, *electrons* (include the number involved), *oxidation*, and *reduction* in your explanation.
4. Magnesium is a reactive metal and can lose electrons readily. It reacts slowly with water. The 2 half reactions depicting the oxidation of magnesium as it reacts with water follow. Complete Questions 4a–c using these reactions.

$$Mg \longrightarrow Mg^{2+}$$
$$H_2O \longrightarrow H_2 + OH^-$$

   a. Which reaction represents oxidation and which represents reduction?

hydrogen atom has one electron. In water, oxygen has formally "taken" the electron from two hydrogen atoms. This gives the oxygen an excess of two electrons, and we assign it an oxidation number of −2. Each hydrogen atom will then have an oxidation number of +1. In an electrically neutral compound, the sum of the oxidation numbers of all the elements in the compound will add to zero. Similarly, for any ion, the sum of all the oxidation numbers should equal the charge of the ion.

The student book supplies the additional background needed for all the activities. If you want deeper coverage of electrochemistry, consult a college-level general chemistry text.

Materials—Part I

For each student

1 pair of safety goggles

Materials—Part II

For each team of 2–3 students

2–3 pairs of safety goggles
1 plastic pipet
1 100-mL beaker or small cup
clear aquarium tubing
1 9-V battery with battery clip
2 small alligator clips
2 pencil leads (Minimum diameter of 7 mm; do not purchase high-polymer leads as they will get very hot and may ignite. Purchase graphite leads.)
copper II chloride solution ($CuCl_2$)

Advance Preparation

For Part I, purchase the fruits that you plan to use in the lab. If the metals you are using are corroded, sand or clean them with steel wool. Locate voltmeters and have enough for each team to have one. Check with the physics department for these and ask for instructions if you are unfamiliar with their use. If your wire does not already have alligator clips attached, take the time to do this before class.

For Part II, make a 0.2 M solution of copper chloride by adding 3.4 g of $CuCl_2$ to make 100 mL of solution.

Educational Technologies

Consider using CBLs and voltage sensors for this lab. These sensors come as part of the standard probe package on most brands of CBLs. The probes have wires and a type of alligator clip already attached.

Cautions

Students should wear safety goggles during both Parts I and II of this activity.

As You Teach

Outcomes and Indicators of Success

By the end of this activity, students should

1. apply their understanding of redox reactions and acid-base chemistry to electrochemistry.

   They will demonstrate their ability by

   - designing and testing a fruit battery using different fruits and electrodes,
   - diagramming a voltaic cell and identifying the redox reactions occurring,
   - imagining a life without batteries and writing a short essay, and

Answers to Reflect and Connect are on TE page 252.

Remember that these 2 processes occur in pairs.

b. Using the process you learned earlier, balance these 2 half reactions and combine them into 1 overall redox reaction.

c. Would the resulting solution be acidic or basic? Explain your answer.

ELABORATE

Electrochemistry

What do an MP3 player, a laptop computer, a cell phone, and your school calculator have in common? They all use the chemistry of redox reactions as a source for the electric current. That current makes these devices work. Often, the source for the electric current is a battery. How do batteries work? Redox reactions within the battery supply electric current. But are these redox reactions occurring even if the battery is still in its package? In *Electrochemistry*, you will apply your understandings of redox reactions and use some of your knowledge about acid-base chemistry to the practical application of these reactions.

Electrons move from reducing agent to oxidizing agent, from metal atoms to metal ions. When you place a metal into a solution of HCl, the electrons move from atom to ion. Energy is lost as heat. What would happen if you separated these oxidation and reduction agents and made the electrons flow through a wire? Could you harness these moving electrons to produce useful work?

You will investigate this possibility in Part I. Then in Part II, you will look at instances where you can force a reaction to take place that would not normally do so. You can do this by adding energy. This will be the focus of Part II.

Part I: Electricity by Chemistry

Materials

For each student

1 pair of safety goggles

Process and Procedure

What would happen if you bit down on aluminum foil and it touched one of your fillings? If you have done this, you may have felt a tiny shock and felt the pain go through your tooth to the nerve hiding beneath your filling. You had just created a battery in your mouth and a tiny amount of electricity was generated when the foil, the silver amalgam filling, and the electrolyte solution provided by your saliva all came into contact with one another. In Part I, you will

- comparing and contrasting voltaic cells and electrolytic cells.

2. apply their understanding of inquiry to recognize and analyze explanations and models of electrochemical cells.

   They will demonstrate their ability to do inquiry by

   - reading about competition for electrons and connecting this information to batteries,
   - reading about competition for electrons and connecting this information to electrolytic cells, and
   - analyzing the similarities and differences between voltaic and electrolytic electrochemical cells.

Strategies

Getting Started

The introduction to Part I of this activity describes the sensation you get if you have dental work and bite down on a piece of aluminum foil. You will know by the looks on their faces which students have experienced this! It feels like a little shock going through the nerve of the tooth. Get students who have had this experience to describe it to the class.

For Part II, consider having the two reactions that are described in the introduction already set up so students can see what is going on. Have one beaker with a solution of zinc sulfate (or nitrate or chloride, it really doesn't matter) and a piece of copper metal immersed in it. No reaction occurs in this beaker. In a second beaker, have a solution of copper sulfate and a piece of zinc immersed in it. This beaker should show a reaction as copper metal forms on the zinc and may even pile up at the bottom of the beaker if left to react long enough. The blue copper sulfate solution will fade to clear, so it might be a good idea to have a beaker of copper sulfate solution for comparison. As the students examine the reactions and the contents, refer them to figure 5.7 in their student books to compare the metals on the chart.

Cautions

Students should wear safety goggles during both Parts I and II of this activity.

Process and Procedure

Part I: Electricity by Chemistry

Materials

For each student

1 pair of safety goggles

In Steps 1 and 2, students construct and complete a reading T-table. This process helps them gain a deeper understanding from the somewhat involved reading titled *A Battery of Cells*. Note the list of keywords to be included in the table; add and subtract terms at your discretion. With lower-level students, you might have to conduct a class debriefing in order to complete the T-table. Be careful not to replace students' active reading with your debriefing lest students learn to wait for the debriefing, thus thinking they do not have to read carefully.

work individually and with a team to investigate what it takes to make a battery and what redox and acid-base chemistry are involved in the process.

In the introduction for this activity, you read about getting something useful out of electric current. This current comes from redox reactions. But when a redox reaction takes place in a beaker, the reaction and the transfer of electrons are instantaneous. You get no useful work from the system. But if you separate the oxidation and reduction parts of the reaction, you can cause the electrons to flow through a wire. Then you can get something useful out of the process. The flow of charge in a particular direction is called an **electric current**. What causes this charge to flow?

1. Make a T-table in your science notebook with the headings "term" and "how term relates to voltaic cells."
2. Complete the T-table as you read *A Battery of Cells*. Use the following terms in the left-hand column: *spontaneous reaction*, *electric current*, *competition for electrons*, *reducing agent*, *oxidizing agent*, *active metal*, *salt bridge*, *anode*, *cathode*, and *useful work*.

READING

A Battery of Cells

The type of electrochemical cell that produces electricity is called a voltaic cell. Another name for this type of electrochemical cell is a galvanic cell. In a **voltaic cell**, a spontaneous chemical reaction generates an electric current. Metals are often used as electrodes. Electrodes are the part of an electrochemical cell where oxidation or reduction often takes place. If you used zinc and copper for electrodes, then an oxidation reaction takes place at the zinc electrode. That happens because zinc is a more active metal than copper.

Reduction takes place at the copper electrode. This happens because the electrons lost by the zinc are diverted to the copper electrode. By conducting this reaction in a beaker, you can see what is going on. If you place a piece of zinc into a solution of copper II sulfate ($CuSO_4$), will a reaction occur? Check the table in figure 5.7 for the answer. Notice that zinc is a more active metal than copper; zinc is a stronger reducing agent, and the reaction will occur. When this reaction occurs, as pictured in figure 5.9, the electrons are transferred instantaneously. Zinc atoms lose electrons and become zinc ions in solution, and copper ions in solution attract these electrons and form copper atoms. These copper atoms form, or plate out, on the zinc strip.

Let's separate these two reactions by using two beakers and two solutions. Put the zinc

NOTES:

A Battery of Cells, continued

metal into a solution that contains zinc ions and put the copper metal into a separate beaker that contains copper ions. Figure 5.10 shows this setup.

Will the electrons lost by the zinc atoms in figure 5.10 be transferred to the copper ions in the other beaker? The electrons have no mechanism in which to get from one beaker to another. What if you connect the two pieces of metal with a piece of conducting wire as in figure 5.11?

Now there is a mechanism in which the electrons can flow from the zinc metal to the copper ions. But will the current flow? It will, but only for an instant. When the current begins to flow, charge builds up in each beaker, causing the flow to stop. Consider the beaker with the zinc metal and the zinc ions in solution. Zinc loses electrons to form zinc ions (Zn^{2+}), and the electrons move through the wire to the other beaker. Here they go into the solution and are quickly taken up by the copper ions to form copper metal. The zinc side develops a buildup of positive charge, and therefore it is harder and harder to lose more electrons. The copper side develops a buildup of negative charge and, because like charges repel, it becomes harder and harder to take on more negative electrons, and the reaction stops. To remedy this, something must be in place to keep the charge balanced or the reaction will not proceed. Look at figure 5.12 to see how a salt bridge is used to balance the charge.

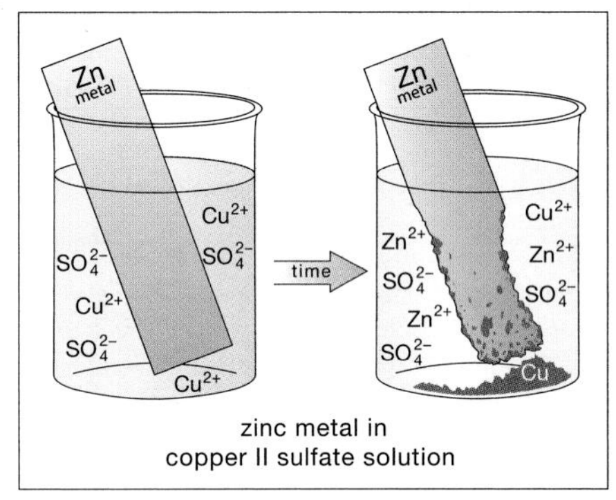

▲ **Figure 5.9 Redox reaction of zinc and copper II sulfate.** In this reaction, the electrons are transferred very quickly. Notice that the zinc strip is "eaten away" as zinc atoms lose electrons and become zinc ions in solution. The blue color of the solution fades in time because the copper II ions that give the solution its color are gaining electrons and becoming copper atoms. These atoms either attach to the zinc metal or fall off into the beaker. Sulfate ions (SO_4^{2-}) are spectator ions.

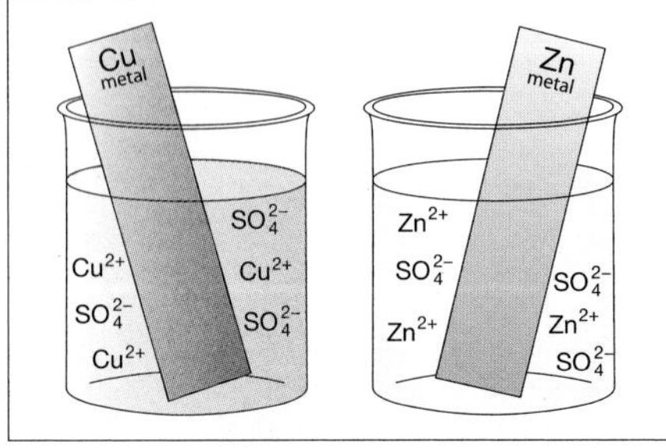

▲ **Figure 5.10 Separate beakers for each half redox reaction.** The reactions are separated in this setup, but will the reaction occur? How will the electrons lost by the zinc be transferred to the copper ions?

NOTES:

The salt bridge can be made from any soluble salt because there will be both positive and negative ions in solution. The salt solution is usually held in place by some type of gel or porous plugs. Notice that the electrodes are labeled "**anode**" and "**cathode**." Oxidation always occurs at the anode, and reduction always occurs at the cathode. You can remember this by remembering that oxidation and anode both start with vowels and reduction and cathode start with consonants. Another important thing to note is that the electrons flow from anode to cathode (from A to C).

In voltaic cells, chemical reactions are used to produce electricity. These chemical reactions occur because of the careful selection of reducing and oxidizing agents that will react. This type of reaction is essential to our way of life, as so many of the devices we use today are powered by batteries. A battery is an application of this type of chemistry. The proper setup of reducing agents and oxidizing agents can convert chemical energy into electrical energy to do useful work.

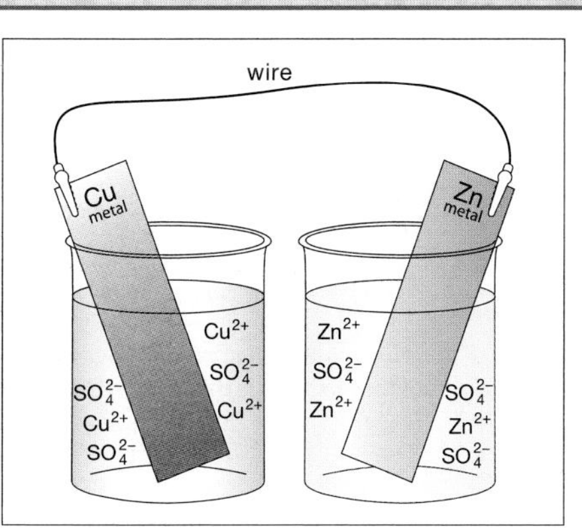

Figure 5.11 Metal strips connected with a wire. The reactions are separated in this setup and connected with a wire. Will the reaction occur now that there is a pathway for the electrons to move?

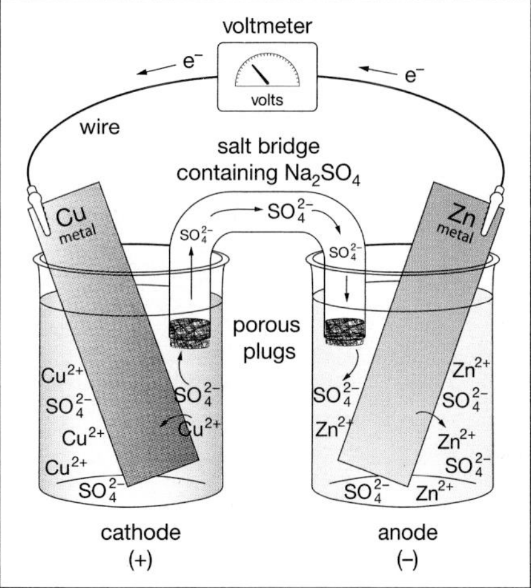

Figure 5.12 Voltaic cell. The reaction will occur in this setup because there is a salt bridge to keep the charge balanced in each beaker.

In Step 3, students continue learning about peer and self-assessment by comparing T-tables. Listen to teams as they read each T-table. You will be able to assess their ongoing understanding of the reading and thus be able to adjust your teaching based on real-time student feedback.

Answers to Stop and Think—Part I, SE pages 258–259

1. Student sketches and answers should be similar to figure T5.4.
2. The solutions must be connected so that ions can flow to keep the net charge in each compartment zero. If the salt bridge or porous boundary were not there, a charge would build up on each side and the current would cease to flow. Either of these devices allows ion flow without extensive mixing of the solutions. The circuit is complete when the ions can flow. A porous boundary would work by allowing the ions in the solution to flow between the 2 solutions without allowing the solutions to mix.
3. No, students should recognize that at some point the zinc or the copper ions would be used up. This is equivalent to a battery that has gone dead.
4. The mass of the zinc electrode would decrease since the oxidation product is soluble. The zinc atoms in the electrode are losing electrons and becoming Zn^{2+} ions in the solution. The mass of the copper electrode gains mass since the copper ions (Cu^{2+}) in solution are being reduced to copper atoms. This reaction happens at the surface of the electrode and the copper atoms adhere to the electrode.

Answers to Stop & Think—Part I are on TE page 258–258b.

NOTES:

3. Compare and contrast your T-table with the T-table of 1 or more classmates. Record any changes you made to your table and the reasons for those changes.

Stop & THINK

PART I

1. Sketch the illustration in figure 5.12 in your science notebook. Complete 1a–c using this drawing.
   a. Write the half reaction that occurs at each half cell.
   b. Label the cell in which oxidation occurs and the cell in which reduction occurs.
   c. Balance both half reactions and add them together to form 1 equation.
2. Sometimes a salt bridge will be replaced by a porous boundary (one that allows particles to move through it) between the 2 solutions (see figure 5.13).
   a. Explain why either a salt bridge or a porous boundary is needed.
   b. Why would a porous boundary work as well as a salt bridge?
3. Would the reaction in the cell depicted in figure 5.13 continue indefinitely? Why or why not?
4. Suppose you took the mass of each of the electrodes before you made this voltaic cell. How would the mass before the reaction compare with the mass after the reaction for each metal? Explain any changes.

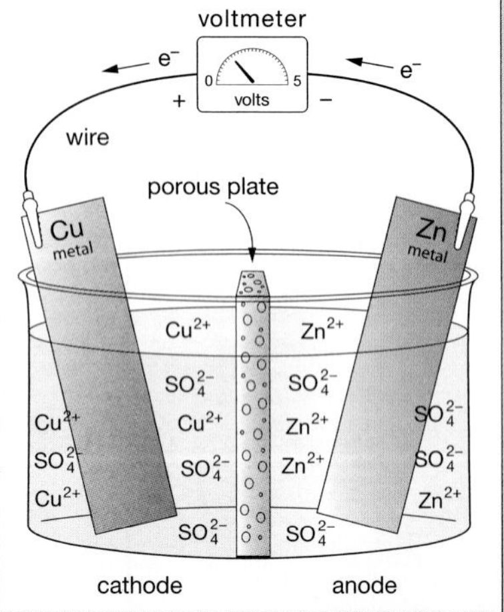

▲ **Figure 5.13 Voltaic cell with porous plate.** Why will the reaction occur in this setup?

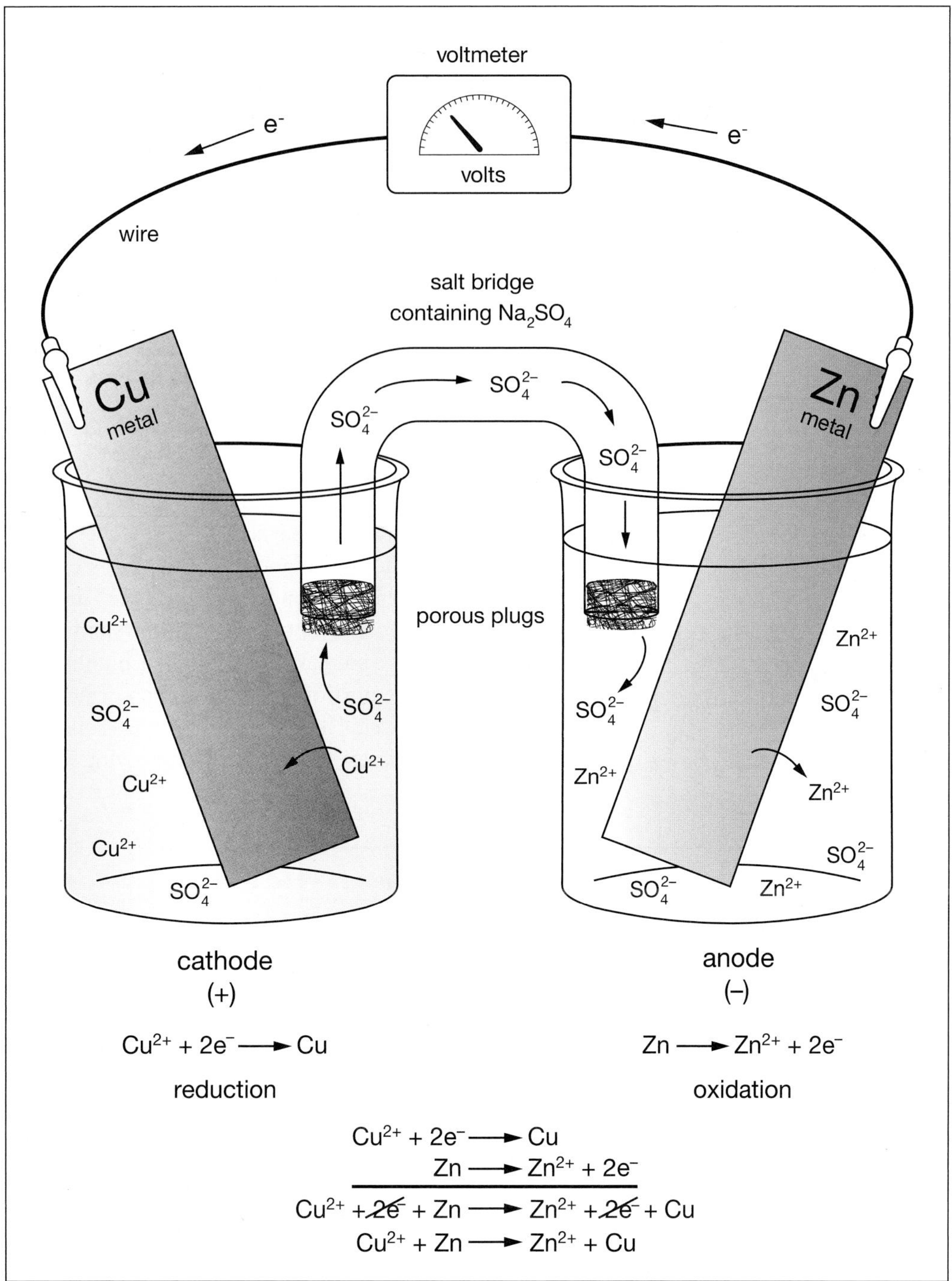

▲ **Figure T5.4 A voltaic cell.** Your students' sketches and answers should be similar to this.

5. Answers will vary, but assess for true engagement in the question.

Process and Procedure

Part II: Batteries Included

Materials

For each team of 2–3 students

2–3 pairs of safety goggles
1 plastic pipet
1 100-mL beaker or small cup
clear aquarium tubing
1 9-V battery with battery clip
2 small alligator clips
2 pencil leads (Minimum diameter of 7 mm; do not purchase high-polymer leads as they will get very hot and may ignite. Purchase graphite leads.)
copper II chloride solution ($CuCl_2$)

In Step 1, students set up their investigations. Double-check their setups as you monitor each team.

In Step 2, students sketch their setups. Remind them to leave room around their sketches to add labels, highlight comments, and captions later.

In Steps 3–5, they continue to add to their sketches with additional observations. In Step 5, students note the odor of the gas that is produced at one of the electrodes. They should be able to smell chlorine gas distinctly. They should recognize the smell as similar to bleach or the water in a swimming pool.

In Step 6, students record what is being produced at the other electrode. The substance should have the brown color of copper. They add this to their sketches.

Students then predict what will happen when they reverse the alligator clips. They should predict that copper will form on the other electrode and that the electrode that has copper on it from before will have bubbles forming. Students will reverse the electrodes and observe what happens.

In Steps 10 and 11, students add highlight comments to their sketches and label all parts of their sketches.

In Step 12, they add the balanced overall redox equation. Make sure students respond to "What I see" and "What it means." Student responses should be similar to figure T5.5. Encourage students to write their highlight comments close to the portion of the sketch associated with the observation. This helps them link words and observations of the material world, thus improving memory connections.

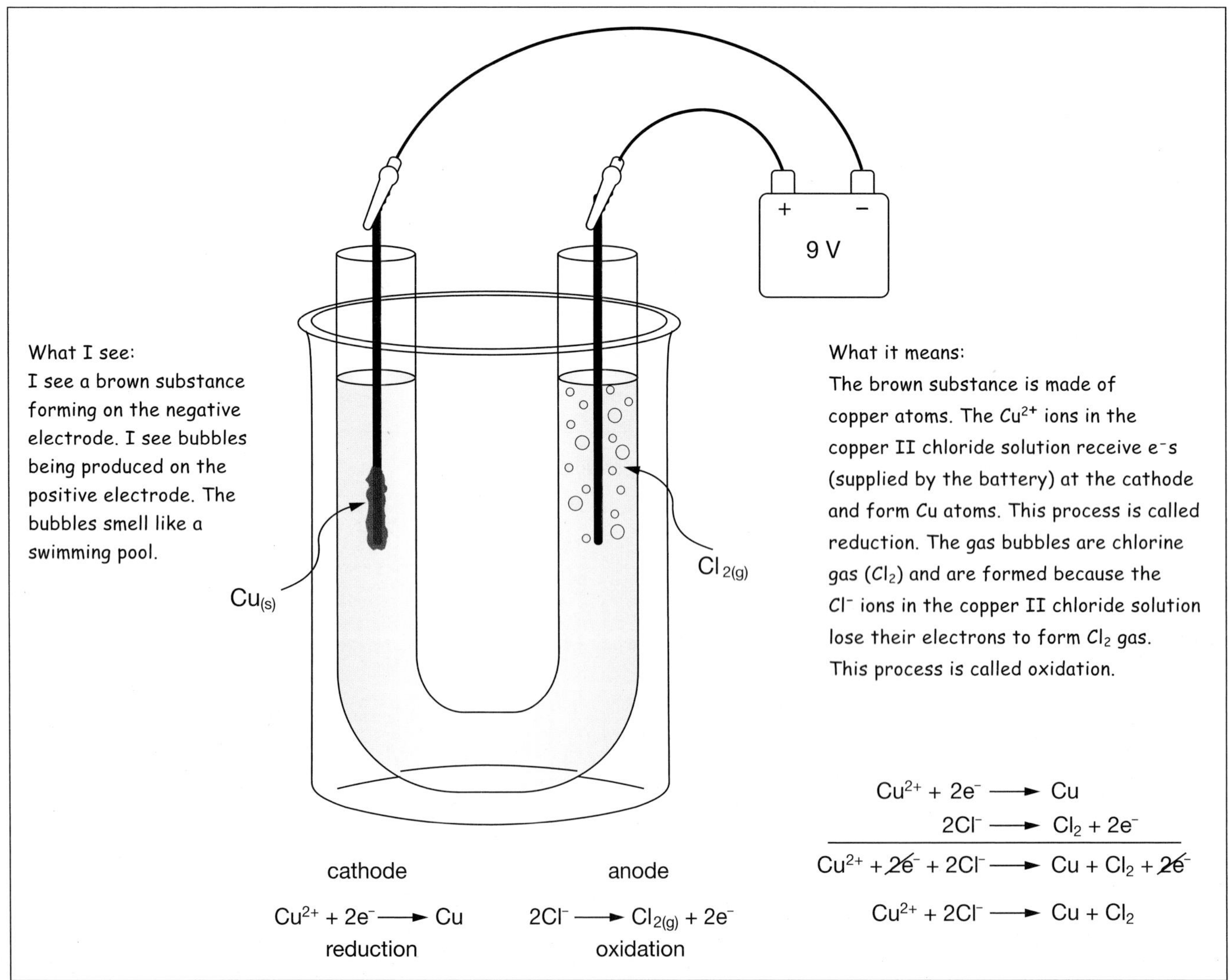

▲ **Figure T5.5 Electrolytic cell.** Your students' sketches and highlight comments should be similar to these.

Look at the animation *Voltaic Cells* on the *SRCD* to see voltaic cells in action.

5 Consider life without batteries. Write a short essay depicting life without batteries. Include how you would feel and how you would have to adapt to this way of life.

Part II: Batteries Included

Materials

For each team of 2–3 students

- 2–3 pairs of safety goggles
- 1 plastic pipet
- 1 100-mL beaker or small cup
- clear aquarium tubing
- 1 9-volt battery with battery clip
- 2 small alligator clips
- 2 pencil leads (minimum diameter of 7 mm)
- copper II chloride solution ($CuCl_2$)

The reactions that occur in voltaic cells convert chemical energy to electrical energy. These reactions are spontaneous. However, many reactions are not spontaneous. You have seen the reaction that occurs when a piece of copper is placed in a solution of silver nitrate. Silver crystals form as the electrons are transferred from the copper metal to the silver ions in the solution. What would you expect to happen if you placed a piece of silver in a solution of copper nitrate? If you look at figure 5.7, you see that silver is a weaker reducing agent than copper, so no reaction will occur. This reaction is not spontaneous. Other reactions are nonspontaneous as well. Consider the decomposition of water:

$$2H_2O \longrightarrow 2H_2 + O_2$$

This does not occur spontaneously, but you can make the reaction happen by applying an electric current to water. See figure 5.14. Note the two half reactions that occur at the electrodes. Water is reduced at the cathode and hydrogen gas is produced. Notice that OH^- ions are also produced. This would make the solution at the cathode basic.

NOTES:

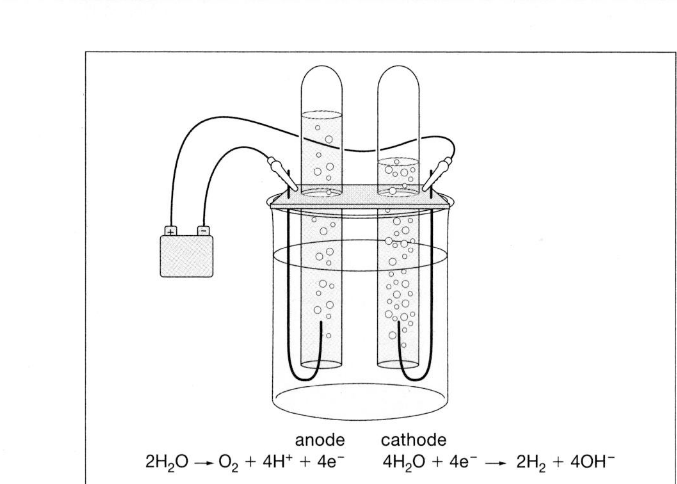

▲ **Figure 5.14 Electrolysis of water.** The electrolysis of water produces hydrogen gas and OH^- ions at the cathode and oxygen gas and H^+ ions at the anode. What do you notice about the volumes of gas produced at each electrode? What is the significance of this ratio?

Water is oxidized at the anode and oxygen gas is produced. Since H^+ ions are produced at the anode, what does this tell you about the pH of the solution near the anode?

Applying an electric potential causes current to flow and can force nonspontaneous reactions to occur. These types of reactions use electrical energy to produce a chemical change. Instead of the reaction proceeding in the same way as in voltaic cells, these reactions *require* a battery (source of electric potential).

Electrolytic cells are cells that include a battery as an energy source. Look at figure 5.15 to see a comparison of these cells.

In Part II, you will work with a team to make an electrolytic cell. As you observe the changes that occur, you will use your understanding of redox reactions to explain the chemistry involved.

Process and Procedure

The nature of metals is characterized by their ability to donate electrons to form ions. Because metals are typically such good reducing agents, most metals are not found in nature in their pure form. They occur as metal ores, and some chemical means must be used to separate

NOTES:

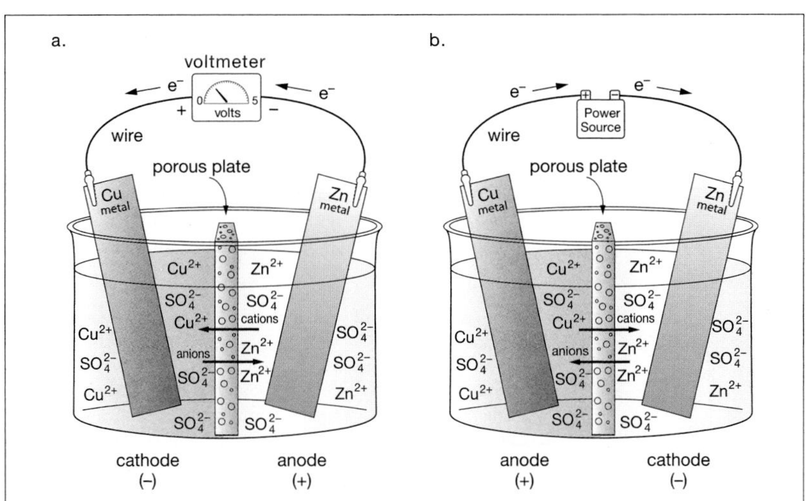

▲ **Figure 5.15 (a) Voltaic cell and (b) electrolytic cell.** Both of these cells involve chemical energy and electrical energy. Notice that the flow of electrons is in the opposite direction (but still from anode to cathode) for an electrolytic cell compared with a voltaic cell.

the metal from other substances in the ore. Suppose you wanted to extract copper metal from a solution of copper II chloride ($CuCl_2$). To do this, the copper ions in the solution (Cu^{2+}) must gain two electrons to become copper metal (Cu). This reaction is not spontaneous, and therefore you must set up an electrolytic cell.

1. Set up your investigation apparatus by following Steps 1a–f.
   a. Place your length of tubing in a U shape in your beaker.
   b. Use your pipet to fill the tube with the copper II chloride ($CuCl_2$) solution to about 5 mm from the top of each end of the tube.
   c. Attach the alligator clips to the wires on the battery clip. The clip should not be on the 9-volt (V) battery at this time.
   d. Carefully attach the alligator clips to 2 pencil leads, 1 on each clip.
   e. Immerse 1 pencil lead into each end of the filled tube.

Be careful with the pencil leads; they break easily.

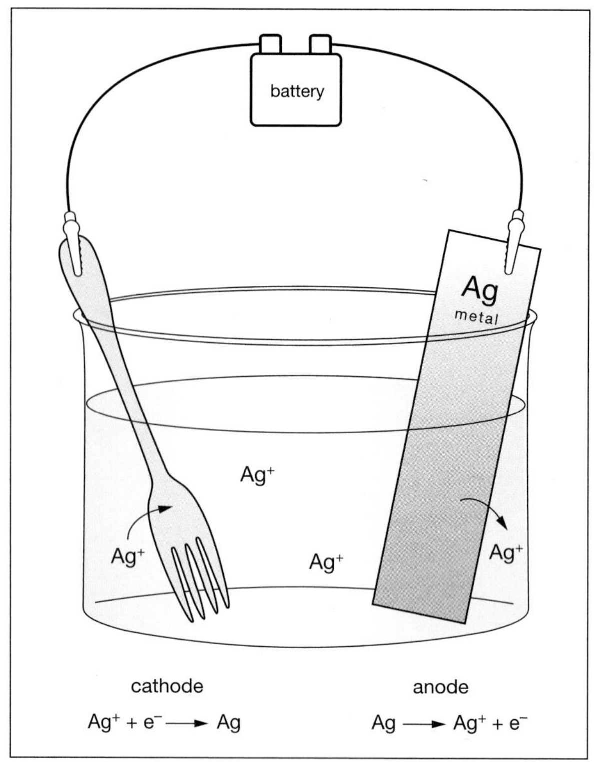

▶ **Figure T5.6 Electrolysis apparatus.** Use this as a guide for student answers for *Reflect and Connect* Question 3.

Answers to Reflect and Connect, SE page 263

1. The reactions do not occur spontaneously and must have a current applied for the reaction to occur.
2. The silver electrode supplies silver ions to the solution as the electrons are removed from the silver. These ions in the solution are reduced and form the silver metal that plates out on the other electrode.
3. Figure T5.6 provides a reasonable answer to Question 3.

f. Attach the battery clip to the 9-V battery. Your setup should look like figure 5.16.

2. As the reaction proceeds, sketch the setup in your science notebook. Make the drawing large enough to add labels, highlight comments, and captions later.
3. After a few minutes, note any changes to the system or observations you make. Add these to your sketch.
4. Note which electrode is connected to the negative terminal of the battery and which electrode is connected to the positive terminal. Add this information to your sketch if you have not already done so.
5. Note the odor of the gas that is produced at one of the electrodes and record your observations in your science notebook.
6. What is being produced at the other electrode? Describe the substance in your science notebook and add it to your sketch.
7. Predict what would happen if you reversed the alligator clips.
8. Check your prediction. Reverse the alligator clips by disconnecting the battery clip from the battery and flipping the connection. You will have to hold the connection in place because it will not snap onto the battery.

Caution: To safely smell odors in the science classroom, gently fan the fumes toward your nose with your hand. Ask your teacher to demonstrate if necessary.

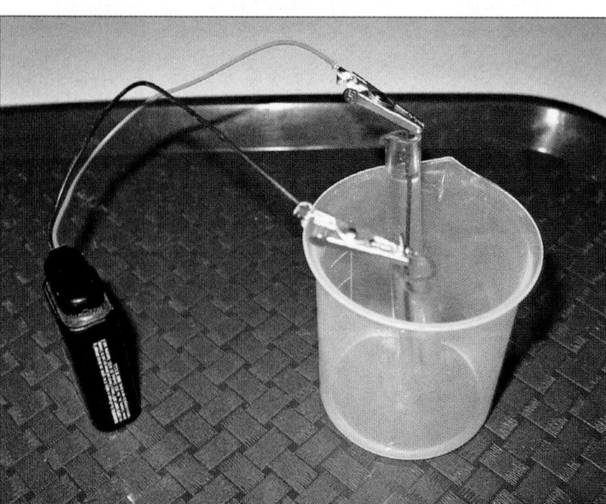

▲ **Figure 5.16 Electrolytic cell setup.** Your lab setup should look like this.

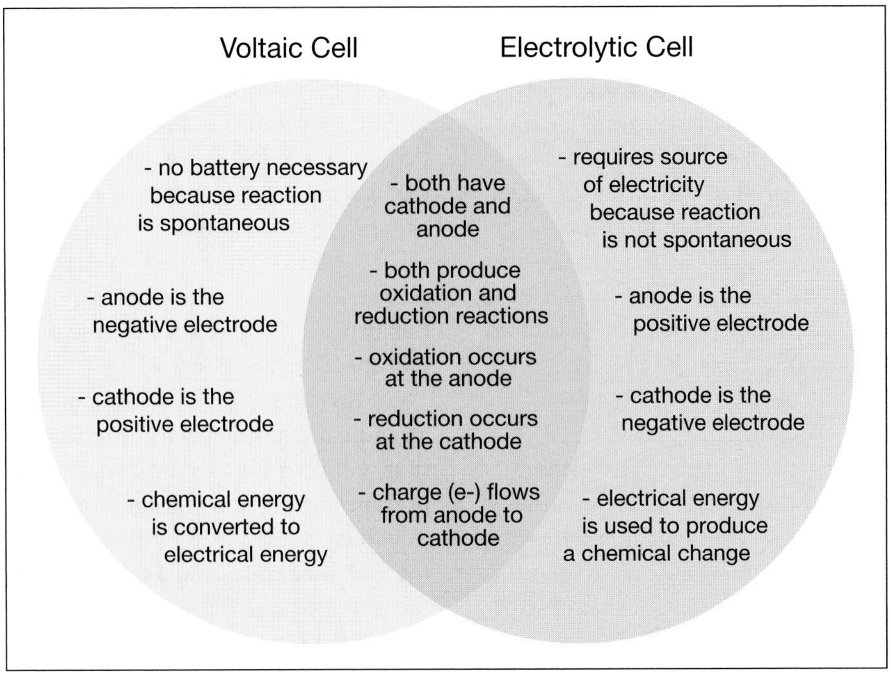

Voltaic Cell	Both	Electrolytic Cell
- no battery necessary because reaction is spontaneous	- both have cathode and anode	- requires source of electricity because reaction is not spontaneous
- anode is the negative electrode	- both produce oxidation and reduction reactions	- anode is the positive electrode
- cathode is the positive electrode	- oxidation occurs at the anode	- cathode is the negative electrode
- chemical energy is converted to electrical energy	- reduction occurs at the cathode	- electrical energy is used to produce a chemical change
	- charge (e-) flows from anode to cathode	

Figure T5.7 Comparison of voltaic and electrolytic cells. Student responses to *Reflect and Connect* Question 5 should be similar to these.

Answers to Reflect and Connect are on TE pages 262–263.

9. Disconnect the battery from the clip and clean up the lab as you teacher directs.
10. Add highlight comments to your sketches by responding to "What I see" and "What it means."
11. Label all parts of the sketch including the balanced half reactions that are taking place at each electrode.
12. Write a balanced overall chemical reaction for the redox reaction that is occurring. Place this on your sketch. Remember that the gas that is produced is diatomic (occurs as X_2).
13. For a short history of the chemistry of the kinds of batteries we use every day, read the sidebar, *Current History*.

Reflect and Connect

1. Electroplating is sometimes used to coat a less expensive metal with a more expensive metal. Sterling silver flatware, or silverware, is made of solid silver and is very expensive. Less expensive silverware can be made by plating silver onto items that are made from less expensive metals. This can be arranged by making an electrolytic cell where a piece of pure silver and an item such as a fork are used as electrodes. These electrodes are placed in a solution containing silver salts and a battery is connected, as shown in figure 5.17.

   Why is it necessary to supply energy to reactions in an electrolytic cell such as the one pictured in figure 5.17?
2. What is the purpose of the solid silver metal as one of the electrodes in figure 5.17?
3. Sketch figure 5.17 in your science notebook and label the cathode and the anode. Include the half reaction that is occurring at each electrode.
4. If copper is placed in a solution of silver ions, then no battery is necessary for silver to plate out on the copper as you saw in a previous activity. Why is a battery not necessary for this process?
5. Use a Venn diagram to compare and contrast voltaic cells and electrolytic cells.

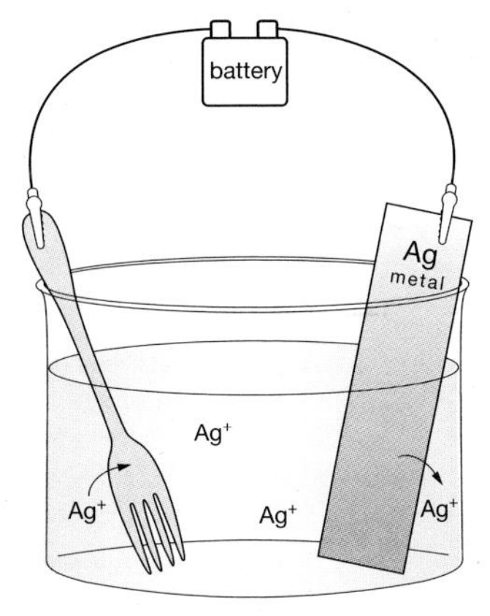

Figure 5.17 Electroplating cell. Electroplating silver onto a less expensive metal can make beautiful silverware and is much less expensive than solid silver utensils.

4. Because copper is a stronger reducing agent than silver, the reaction occurs spontaneously and no battery is needed.
5. Student answers will vary. A sample diagram is shown in figure T5.7.

EVALUATE

Nail It Down

Activity Overview

In this activity, students assemble all they have learned and use it to demonstrate their understanding of acid-base and redox chemical reactions. The context for this demonstration is a role play. Students assume the role of a corrosion engineer. Then they use their expertise to offer analysis and practical suggestions for preventing corrosion in highway bridges.

Before You Teach

Background Information

Some of the background for this activity is included in the previous activities. Additional information on corrosion is included here for your benefit. Corrosion can be viewed as the process of returning metals back to their original state found in nature. Most metals are obtained from their naturally occurring ores. Corrosion involves oxidation of the metal. Since corroded metal often loses its integrity and its attractiveness, this spontaneous process is of great interest and has an enormous economic impact. The oxidation of most metals is spontaneous. Some metals form a protective coating when oxidized. An example of this is tin. The tin oxide coating is very hard and serves to protect the underlying tin from further oxidation. Iron, on the other hand, forms the powdery, orange-red rust with which we are all familiar. This coating crumbles easily and does not provide any sort of protection for iron.

Since steel is the main metal used in construction and a major component of steel is iron, controlling the corrosion of iron is extremely important. Due to physical strains on iron metal or pits in the surface, parts of the iron are more easily oxidized (anodic regions) than other parts (cathodic regions). In the anodic region, each iron atom gives up two electrons to form the Fe^{2+} ion.

$$Fe \rightarrow Fe^{2+} + 2e^-$$

The electrons that are released by the Fe atoms flow through the iron, as they do through a wire of a voltaic cell, to a cathodic region. In this region, the electrons react with oxygen.

$$O_2 + 2H_2O + 4e^- \rightarrow 4OH^-$$

This process is shown in the illustration in figure T5.8.

The Fe^{2+} ions formed in the anodic regions travel to the cathodic regions through the moisture on the surface of the iron. This is similar to the process of ions traveling through a salt bridge in a voltaic cell. You can see the important role water plays in this process. If there is salt present, it will speed up this process.

In this activity, you will include an indicator in the gelatin mixture that will turn blue to indicate the presence of Fe^{2+} ions. Potassium ferricyanide ($K_3Fe(CN)_6$) will react with the Fe^{2+} ions produced as the iron in the nail oxidizes ($Fe_{(s)} \rightarrow Fe^{2+}_{(aq)} + 4e^-$). The reaction of the Fe^{2+} ion and the $KFe(CN)_6$ produces a complex

SIDEBAR

Current History

What do batteries supply that powers electric motors in CD players, the electromagnetic signal in a cell phone, and the screen display of a laptop computer? Batteries provide much of the flow of electrons required to accomplish this and other work important in our daily lives.

But how did batteries come about? How do they produce electric current? Certainly people couldn't always go to a store and buy them. It turns out that the first modern battery can be traced to the work of Alessandro Volta, an Italian scientist. Volta reinterpreted the work that his countryman, Luigi Galvani, had accomplished with electricity. Galvani studied how dissected frog legs twitched when hooked up to metal connectors and lightning occurred. He thought "animal electricity" caused the twitching. But Volta thought the muscle twitches were induced by electric current flowing between two dissimilar metals connected by the moist flesh of the frog's leg. This led Volta to develop the first device that demonstrated the chemical production of electric current. In 1799, Volta arranged a vertical pile of metal disks (zinc with copper or silver). He then separated those disks from each other with paperboard disks that had been soaked in a salt solution. This stack was the first electric battery.

In 1802, William Cruickshank designed the first electric battery capable of being mass produced. He arranged sheets of dissimilar metals (copper and zinc) of equal size in a box. The box was then filled with an electrolyte of dilute acid. This flooded design resisted drying out and provided more energy than Volta's disk arrangement.

In 1836, John Daniell invented the first battery that produced a constant and reliable source of electric current over a long period of time. And in 1866, Georges Leclanché patented a new battery. He assembled his original cell in a porous pot. The positive electrode consisted of crushed

Volta explaining his first battery. What role did dissimilar metals play in Volta's thinking about batteries? Why was moisture important?

manganese dioxide (MnO_2) with a little carbon mixed in. The negative pole was a zinc rod. The zinc rod and the pot were immersed in an ammonium chloride ($AlCl_3$) solution, which served as the electrolyte. Leclanché's battery became the forerunner to the world's first widely used battery, the carbon-zinc cell (see the modern carbon-zinc battery in the figure).

264 Unit 1 Interactions Are Interesting

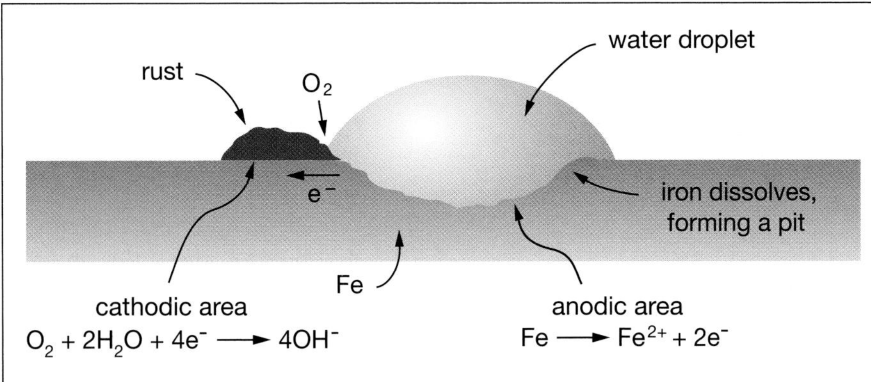

▲ **Figure T5.8 The corrosion of iron.** This diagram illustrates the electrochemical process involved in the corrosion of iron.

ion that is blue in color, according to the reaction

$$Fe^{2+}_{(aq)} + H_2O_{(l)} + K^+_{(aq)} + [Fe(CN)_6]^{3-}_{(aq)} \rightarrow KFe[Fe(CN)_6] \cdot H_2O \text{ (blue)}.$$

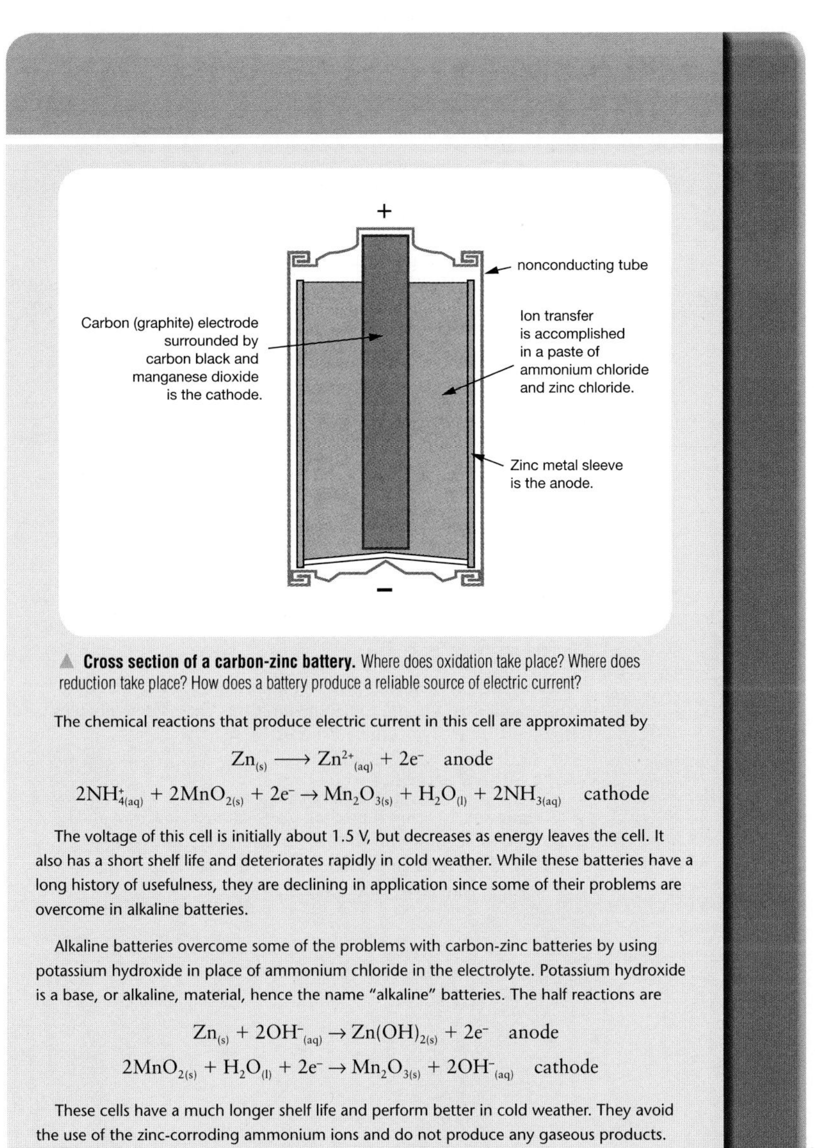

▲ **Cross section of a carbon-zinc battery.** Where does oxidation take place? Where does reduction take place? How does a battery produce a reliable source of electric current?

The chemical reactions that produce electric current in this cell are approximated by

$$Zn_{(s)} \longrightarrow Zn^{2+}_{(aq)} + 2e^- \quad \text{anode}$$

$$2NH^+_{4(aq)} + 2MnO_{2(s)} + 2e^- \rightarrow Mn_2O_{3(s)} + H_2O_{(l)} + 2NH_{3(aq)} \quad \text{cathode}$$

The voltage of this cell is initially about 1.5 V, but decreases as energy leaves the cell. It also has a short shelf life and deteriorates rapidly in cold weather. While these batteries have a long history of usefulness, they are declining in application since some of their problems are overcome in alkaline batteries.

Alkaline batteries overcome some of the problems with carbon-zinc batteries by using potassium hydroxide in place of ammonium chloride in the electrolyte. Potassium hydroxide is a base, or alkaline, material, hence the name "alkaline" batteries. The half reactions are

$$Zn_{(s)} + 2OH^-_{(aq)} \rightarrow Zn(OH)_{2(s)} + 2e^- \quad \text{anode}$$

$$2MnO_{2(s)} + H_2O_{(l)} + 2e^- \rightarrow Mn_2O_{3(s)} + 2OH^-_{(aq)} \quad \text{cathode}$$

These cells have a much longer shelf life and perform better in cold weather. They avoid the use of the zinc-corroding ammonium ions and do not produce any gaseous products.

Phenolphthalein (an acid-base indicator) is also added to the gelatin mixture. Phenolphthalein turns pink at pH 8 and higher. A pink color indicates the reaction process.

$$O_2 + 2H_2O + 4e^- \rightarrow 4OH^-$$

The OH^- ions produced in the reaction will raise the pH, and the solution will turn pink.

This activity explores cathodic protection. In this process, a wire to the iron or steel connects an active metal, such as magnesium. Because the magnesium is a better reducing agent than iron, electrons are furnished by the magnesium rather than by the iron, keeping the iron from being oxidized. As the oxidation occurs, the magnesium anode dissolves and must be replaced periodically. For an advanced peek at what the reactions described in this activity look like, see the schematic diagrams in figure T5.9 (TE page 271).

Materials

For each team of 3 students

3 pairs of safety goggles
3 petri dishes
gelatin solution containing indicators
- gelatin
- phenolphthalein solution
- 0.5 M potassium ferricyanide solution ($K_3Fe(CN)_6$)
- sodium chloride (NaCl)

3 iron nails
6-cm magnesium ribbon
6-cm copper wire
3 copies of copymaster 5.4, *Scoring Rubric for Corrosion Engineering*

Advance Preparation

Prepare the gelatin solution before class and keep it warm so it will not congeal. To prepare enough gelatin for a class of 30, sprinkle 2 packages of gelatin on top of 200 mL cold water and let stand for 2 minutes. Add 200 mL boiling water and stir until the gelatin is dissolved. Add 10 mL 1% phenolphthalein solution and 10 mL 0.5 M potassium ferricyanide solution ($K_3Fe(CN)_6$). To make the 0.5 M $K_3Fe(CN)_6$ solution, dissolve 16.5 g $K_3Fe(CN)_6$ in distilled water to make 100 mL of solution. Add 5 g of sodium chloride to the gelatin solution.

Nails should be iron or steel and free from rust. For best results, use raw nails.

Make enough copies of copymaster 5.4, *Scoring Rubric for Corrosion Engineering* for each student.

TRCD

NOTES:

Educational Technologies

Students may want to use a digital camera to record the results of their experiments. They may want to use these photographs in their reports.

Cautions

Students should wear safety goggles during the laboratory portion of this activity.

As You Teach

Outcomes and Indicators of Success

By the end of this activity, students should

1. demonstrate their understanding of oxidation-reduction (redox) reactions.

   They will demonstrate their understanding by

   - correctly analyzing a simple electrochemical cell and identifying what is oxidized, what is reduced, and what the oxidizing agent, the reducing agent, the anode, and the cathode are;
   - writing balanced half reactions that occur at the anode and the cathode;
   - balancing the complete redox reaction according to mass and charge; and
   - using a table of oxidizing and reducing agents to predict redox reactions.

2. demonstrate their understanding of acid-base reactions.

   They will demonstrate their understanding by

   - analyzing a simple electrochemical cell and recognizing

EVALUATE

Nail It Down

Many very important chemical reactions involve the transfer of charged particles such as protons in acid-base chemistry and electrons in redox chemistry. You have studied many of these reactions in this chapter. You are now prepared to demonstrate your knowledge in this evaluate activity. You will work both individually and with a partner to complete this activity.

Materials

For each team of 3 students

3 pairs of safety goggles

3 petri dishes

gelatin solution containing indicators

3 iron nails

6-cm magnesium ribbon

6-cm copper wire

3 *Corrosion Engineering Scoring Rubric* handouts

Cautions

Be careful with metals; sharp edges can cut you. Handle the gelatin mixture with care. Do not touch the mixture. Wear safety goggles during the laboratory portion of this activity.

Process and Procedure

1. Study the scoring rubric for *Corrosion Engineering* and determine how you will be evaluated on your work.
2. Read the following article and the description of the job for which you have just been hired.

that hydroxide ions (OH^-) are produced at one electrode, causing a change in color of an indicator;
- comparing and contrasting acid and base properties;
- using pH to identify certain solutions and comparing the relative acid-base strength of these solutions;
- explaining acid strength using pH;
- connecting acid strength to equilibrium and the force of attraction for hydrogen ions; and
- connecting base strength to equilibrium, solubility, and the force of attraction for hydroxide ions.

3. demonstrate their ability to formulate and defend scientific explanations based on evidence.

   They will demonstrate their ability by
   - deducing what chemical reactions take place based on indirect evidence such as color changes and
   - writing explanations of the redox reactions they observe such that other students can read and understand the explanations.

Strategies

Getting Started

This activity can be done in teams or as individuals. You can decide what is best for your class. The materials are given for teams of students; increase the amounts if you decide to do this as an individual evaluation. If you have an engineer in your area who specializes in corrosion prevention, consider having him or her as a guest speaker, either before or after your class completes this activity.

If you are pressed for time, consider giving the students the reading the day before. They can take it home and read it before class the next day. Also, you may choose to have students give an oral presentation instead of or in addition to the written report.

Cautions

Students should wear safety goggles during the laboratory portion of this activity.

Cost of Corrosion Study Unveiled

The U.S. Federal Highway Administration (FHWA) released a breakthrough two-year study on the corrosion of metals. The study addressed the direct costs of metallic corrosion in U.S. industry. Example industries include infrastructure, transportation, and manufacturing. Initiated by government and private organizations, the study provides current cost estimates and identifies national strategies to minimize the impact of corrosion.

Results of the study show significant costs. For example, the total annual estimated direct cost of corrosion in the United States is a staggering $276 billion—approximately 3.1 percent of the nation's gross domestic product. The study reveals that although corrosion management has improved, the United States must find more and better ways to encourage, support, and implement improved corrosion control practices.

Corrosion—a Natural but Controllable Process

Corrosion is a naturally occurring phenomenon. It is commonly defined as the deterioration of a substance (usually a metal) or its properties because of a reaction with its environment. Like other natural hazards, corrosion can be dangerous and expensive. Corrosion can damage everything from automobiles, home appliances, and drinking water systems to pipelines, bridges, and public buildings. Over the past 22 years, the United States has suffered 52 major weather-related disasters—including hurricanes, tornadoes, tropical storms, floods, fires, droughts, and freezes. These natural disasters have shown total losses of more than $380 billion (averaging $17 billion annually). According to the current U.S. corrosion study, the direct cost of metallic corrosion is $276 billion *on an annual basis.* Unlike weather-related disasters, corrosion can be controlled, but at a cost.

Corrosion Control Methods

Various time-proven methods for preventing and controlling corrosion depend on several factors. These factors include the specific metal to be protected; environmental concerns such as humidity, exposure to salt water or industrial environments; and the type of product to be processed or transported. The most commonly used methods include protective coatings, corrosion-resistant alloys, plastics, and cathodic protection. Cathodic protection is a technique used on pipelines, underground storage tanks, and offshore structures that creates an electrochemical cell in which the surface to be protected is the cathode and corrosion reactions are lessened.

Originally published in the 2002 *Cost of Corrosion Supplement to Materials Performance* magazine, the membership magazine of NACE International. Reprinted by permission.

Chapter 5 Forces of Attraction 267

NOTES:

Process and Procedure

Materials

For each team of 3 students

3 pairs of safety goggles
3 petri dishes
gelatin solution containing indicators

- gelatin
- phenolphthalein solution
- 0.5 M potassium ferricyanide solution ($K_3Fe(CN)_6$)
- sodium chloride (NaCl)

3 iron nails
6-cm magnesium ribbon
6-cm copper wire
3 copies of copymaster 5.4, *Scoring Rubric for Corrosion Engineering*

In Steps 1 and 2, students need to spend some time reading the scenario and the scoring rubric to understand what you expect of them. They will complete the tasks assigned in the activity either individually or as a team according to your instructions. Use your best judgment and your knowledge of your class to determine the best method for your class.

In Step 3, students read more information about the task and its purpose.

In Step 4, students prepare their petri dishes of testing materials. Best results are obtained by leaving the top of the nails uncovered by the gelatin mixture to allow oxygen to react in the reduction process. The dissolved oxygen in the solution is quickly depleted and, if part of the nail is not exposed, it may be difficult to see the pink color forming. Encourage your students to look for the pink color at and very near the nail's surface. This may appear quickly after the solution is first poured over the nails and may be more difficult to see later. If a student or team of students has pronounced pink color forming on the unwrapped nail, encourage other teams to look at these results. All teams should be able to observe a pink color on the top of the nail's surface initially, but the pink color may be short lived.

You can decide if you want this to be an individual task or a team task. You might also consider having teams prepare these dishes and then ask your students to answer the questions and prepare their reports individually. Consider using digital photography to preserve data.

In Step 5, students draw, label, and color their investigations. If you have a digital camera available or if students bring cameras from home, encourage them to record their data digitally.

The U.S. Federal Highway Administration (FHWA) has just hired you as a corrosion prevention specialist to help with a project to control corrosion in the reinforcing metal rods embedded in the concrete of bridges and overpasses. Your knowledge of redox and acid-base chemistry will be important in helping to solve a major corrosion problem. These reinforcement rods are made of iron, and corrosion is a continuing problem. Because of this recent report, the FHWA is aware of the problem and the costs involved in repairing and maintaining structures affected by corrosion. They want you to advise them on the proper use of cathodic protection for these rods.

3. Read the following information to learn more about your new job.

   To help you give the FHWA the best advice, you will conduct a set of experiments, record observations, and gather data. You will use the evidence from your experiments to write a report that will advise the FHWA of the benefits and problems of using cathodic corrosion control. The financial executives who will be reading your report have a limited background in chemistry, so you will have to include the chemistry background for them to understand your arguments.

   You learned about cathodes earlier in this chapter. Cathodic protection is the prevention of corrosion of a metallic structure by causing it to act as the cathode rather than as the anode of an electrochemical cell. This is done successfully by carefully selecting metals based on their relative reactivities.

   Financial advisers have given you important information. You have money to buy the metals that you need for this type of protection. But they have asked you to consider using copper since they have a source for copper that is inexpensive. You must argue either for or against using copper as part of the protection process for the iron rods. For your argument, you must have evidence. You can use your chemistry knowledge, but you also need experimental proof that this method will or will not work. And, if it doesn't work, you must be ready to supply the advisers with an alternative solution.

4. To help with this assignment, prepare 3 petri dishes with a gelatin solution. The gelatin will set into a semisolid material that will allow the reaction to occur undisturbed.

268 | Unit 1 Interactions Are Interesting

Answers to Steps 6–14, SE pages 269–271

6a. The pH range of the original mixture would be below 8. Students know this because the original mixture is not pink. Phenolphthalein turns pink at pH 8.

6b. This range of pH values is mostly in the acidic region up to slightly basic. This means that the solution contains a [H+] between 1 and 1×10^{-8} M.

6c. The blue color indicates that the iron nail is corroding since the blue color indicates the presence of Fe^{2+} ions.

6d. The correct equation follows.

$$Fe \rightarrow Fe^{2+} + 2e^-$$

6e. This is an example of oxidation since Fe is losing electrons and the charge is going from 0 to +2.

7a. When the solution turned pink in certain areas, this indicated that the pH changed in those areas to a pH of 8 or higher.

7b. Since phenolphthalein changes to pink at pH 8, the range would be from 8 to 14.

NOTES:

Your teacher has mixed 2 chemicals in the gelatin solution that will act as indicators for some of the reactions that take place. The first is an indicator that turns blue when the following process occurs: $Fe \longrightarrow Fe^{2+}$. The other indicator is phenolphthalein and turns pink when a solution reaches pH 8. Your teacher also added salt to the gelatin solution to speed up the corrosion process.

a. Prepare two of the iron nails by wrapping the middle of one nail with a piece of copper and the middle of the other nail with a piece of magnesium. Leave one nail unwrapped.
b. Place one nail in each of your three petri dishes.
c. Pour the liquid gelatin solution over the three nails. Pour enough gelatin solution to almost but not completely cover each nail.
d. Do not disturb the dishes. Allow the gelatin to congeal.

5. As you wait for the gelatin to congeal, make careful observations.

You will want to draw diagrams and add color and detailed labels and captions to your drawings. If you have access to a digital camera, take pictures of the reactions. You will need this evidence when you write your report.

6. Consider the indicators in the gelatin solution as you answer the questions in Steps 6a–e.

You will use your answers when you create your report to your advisers. Remember, they want you to use copper. Is this a good idea? You must support your case *for* or *against* using copper. A table of relative strengths of oxidizing and reducing agents is shown in figure 5.18.

a. What is the pH range of the original gelatin mixture? How do you know?
b. What does this pH indicate?
c. What color indicates that the iron nail is corroding?
d. What is the balanced redox half reaction for this process?
e. Is it an example of oxidation or reduction? How do you know?

7. Answers the questions in Steps 7a–d about how the pH of the solution changed.

a. What is the evidence of a pH change?
b. What is the pH range of this area around the nails?

Reducing agents (increasing strength ↑)	Oxidizing agents (increasing strength ↓)
Li	Li^+
K	K^+
Ca	Ca^{2+}
Na	Na^+
Mg	Mg^{2+}
Al	Al^{3+}
Zn	Zn^{2+}
Cr	Cr^{3+}
Fe	Fe^{2+}
Ni	Ni^{2+}
Sn	Sn^{2+}
Pb	Pb^{2+}
H_2	H_3O^+
Cu	Cu^{2+}
I^-	I_2
Hg	Hg_2^{2+}
Ag	Ag^+
Br^-	Br_2
Cl^-	Cl_2
F^-	F_2

▲ **Figure 5.18 Table of relative strengths of oxidizing and reducing agents.** Use this table to determine the relative strengths of reducing agents.

7c. This range is basic, so that means that $[OH^-] > [H^+]$.

7d. The term concentrated refers to the amount of solute dissolved in the solution. Strength refers to the degree to which an acid or base dissociates in water.

8a. The ion that is produced is OH^-. Students should be able to tell this since the OH^- would make the solution basic and they saw a pink color forming due to the indicator. Also, the equation would not balance with H^+. In addition, if they tried to balance the equation with H^+, they would have to add electrons to the product side of the equation indicating that the reaction is an oxidation reaction. There cannot be 2 oxidation reactions without a reduction reaction.

8b. The following equation answers the question in Step 8b.

$$O_2 + 2H_2O + 4e^- \rightarrow 4OH^-$$

8c. This reaction is reduction since electrons are gained.

9. Fe is the reducing agent and oxygen is the oxidizing agent.

$$2(Fe \rightarrow Fe^{2+} + 2e^-)$$

$$2Fe \rightarrow 2Fe^{2+} + 4e^-$$

$$O_2 + 2H_2O + 4e^- \rightarrow 4OH^-$$

$$O_2 + 2H_2O + \cancel{4e^-} + 2Fe \rightarrow 2Fe^{2+} + \cancel{4e^-} + 4OH^-$$

$$O_2 + 2H_2O + 2Fe \rightarrow 2Fe^{2+} + 4OH^-$$

10a. It is not possible to have one process without the other. Oxidation and reduction always come as a pair of reactions that happen simultaneously. If one particle loses electrons, another substance must gain them.

10b. The process that students cannot see is the oxidation of the magnesium. They cannot see it because an indicator is not included in the solution for this reaction. Also, the magnesium ions are colorless.

NOTES:

c. What does this pH range tell you about the type and concentration of ions present in this part of the solution?

d. What is the difference between a concentrated acid or base and a strong acid or base?

8. Read the information below and answer the questions in Steps 8a–c.

In some parts of the gelatin solution near the nails, the dissolved oxygen in the solution (O_2) and the water (H_2O) together are the reactants of the redox half reaction:

$$O_2 + H_2O \longrightarrow ?$$

Either H^+ ions are produced or OH^- are produced.

a. Describe 2 lines of evidence for the ion that is produced.

b. Balance this redox half reaction according to mass and charge.

c. Is this oxidation or reduction? How do you know?

9. Combine the 2 balanced half reactions from the questions in Steps 6 and 8 to form an overall balanced redox reaction. Label the oxidizing agent and the reducing agent.

10. Read the following information and use it to answer the questions in Steps 10a–b.

In 1 dish, it appears that only 1 process of oxidation-reduction chemistry is occurring because only 1 color is appearing.

a. Is it possible to have only oxidation or reduction? Why or why not?

b. Why can't you see evidence of the other process?

11. Describe what would happen if you used a battery and connected one terminal to the copper wire and the other terminal to the iron nail in the petri dish. What would you see happening? Describe the process.

12. Label your sketches or photographs completely and write captions for each. Your labels should include the following:

a. The anode and the cathode

b. The point where oxidation occurs and the point where reduction occurs

c. Half reactions that are occurring at each anode and cathode

Look back at your diagrams. You will need to redraw them in your report.

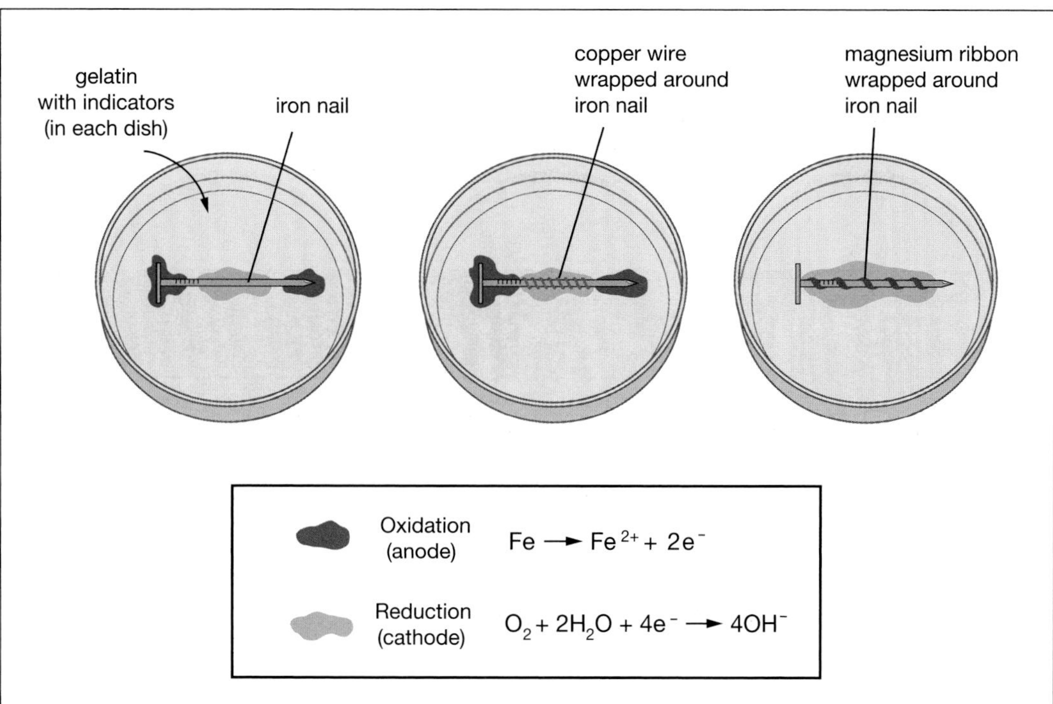

Figure T5.9 Iron nail experiment. Your students' drawings should be labeled similar to these.

13. Make a decision. Is copper the best choice for this process? Is magnesium the best choice for this process? Do you have another metal that you think would be better than either of these? Whichever way you answer, you must justify your decision, provide evidence that it is the best decision, and convey your reasoning in a way that your advisers will understand.
14. Prepare a report. It must contain illustrations, explanations, and justifications for your decision on the best metal to use to prevent the corrosion of the iron support rods.

Read over the scoring rubric again to make sure you understand your teacher's expectations for the report.

11. The copper would not do anything for the iron—the iron would continue to corrode since iron is the stronger reducing agent. If a battery were used and connected to the copper wire and the iron nail, the copper would be forced to give up electrons and be oxidized.
12. The sketch in figure T5.9 represents an answer to Step 12.
13. Students should recognize and state evidence that using copper will not slow the oxidation of the iron. They should indicate that this is because copper is less active (a weaker reducing agent) than iron. The same reactions are visible in the dish both with and without the copper. Students may say that magnesium would be good to use for the cathodic protection or may suggest another metal less active than magnesium but more active than iron.
14. Your students' reports should reflect the expectations outlined in the scoring rubric. Copper is not the best choice—it does not stop the corrosion of the iron. Magnesium or another metal that is a stronger reducing agent than iron would serve as a good metal for this purpose. But for practical reasons, magnesium probably would not be used since it is too reactive with common substances such as water.

UNIT 2

Inside Life

Unit Introduction

Unit Overview

Unit 2, *Inside Life*, addresses concepts related to biological evolution and the molecular basis of heredity. The first chapter in the unit introduces students to evolution and the fossil record. Students will learn that the diversity of life on Earth is the result of billions of years of evolution. They will discover that traits of some organisms make them better adapted for the environment than others and maybe more likely to survive and reproduce. Chapter 7, *Tracking Traits*, focuses on the process of inheritance. Students will learn how traits are passed from parent to offspring. They will learn how meiosis is related to this process and how it contributes to genetic variation. In chapter 8, *Instructions for Life*, the focus shifts from traits and how they are inherited to the molecules that code for the traits—deoxyribonucleic acid (DNA). Students will learn about DNA's structure, how it replicates, and how it codes for the production of proteins. They will see that similarities in DNA show the relatedness of organisms and that changes in DNA can lead to the evolution of species. In chapter 9, *Genetic Engineering*, students will expand on what they learned in chapter 8. They will model how sequences of DNA are isolated and manipulated by scientists. They will learn about different applications of genetic engineering and consider the ethical issues that arise from these applications.

Goals for the Unit

In unit 2, your students will learn about change in living systems. By the time your students finish the unit, they should understand the following:

- Evolution of species occurs through the process of natural selection acting on genetic variation.
- Parents transmit genetic information to offspring through gametes.
- Genetic variation results from cells containing two copies of each gene and from mutation.
- DNA carries the code for the characteristics of all living things.
- DNA serves as the template for proteins, which are substances essential to life.
- Genetic engineering makes it possible to transfer DNA sequences from one organism to another.
- Genetic engineering brings up ethical issues that are influenced by multiple factors.

As your students learn about change in living systems, they will also refine their ability to do science and develop a better understanding of scientific inquiry. They will

- use math and models to gather data,
- develop and revise explanations using evidence, and
- communicate information using a variety of methods.

Names of Chapters

Chapter 6: Exploring Change

Chapter 7: Tracking Traits

Chapter 8: Instructions for Life

Chapter 9: Genetic Engineering

Strategies for the Unit Engage

Use this introductory activity to transition your students from thinking about physical interactions to interactions in living systems. Begin by asking students to give some examples of interactions in living systems. Prompt students for interactions that occur between organisms as well as within an organism. An example of an interaction between organisms is a hummingbird getting nectar from a flower. Interactions within an organism include a plant breaking down sugars to provide energy for the growth of a new leaf and increased muscle activity in a person that causes an increase in heart rate. Encourage students to think of examples at the cellular level. Record students' ideas on a large sheet of paper.

Once you have a diverse list of ideas, ask students how these interactions could cause change in living systems. For example, the hummingbird feeding on nectar from a flower may go to another flower and transfer pollen, which may result in the development of a seed and eventually a new plant. In the other example, muscle activity and increased heart rate may contribute to a more fit individual who has an increased life span or can participate in more physical activities. Record students' ideas on a large sheet of paper. As students go through the chapters, they could add new examples of interactions and the change that may result to the class list. This will give students a gauge of what they are learning.

NOTES:

CHAPTER 6

Exploring Change

Chapter Overview

In chapter 6, *Exploring Change*, students will learn about some of the evidence for evolution and a mechanism for the process of evolution. (Students will learn about molecular evidence for evolution in chapter 7, *Tracking Traits*, and in chapter 8, *Instructions for Life*.) They will begin by sharing their current understanding of the similarities and differences (unity and diversity) in organisms. Students then will explore how rocks and fossils provide evidence for change across time. They will discover that rock layers enable geologists to determine the relative ages of fossils. They also will recognize that some fossils are similar to organisms that exist today and other fossils inform us about organisms that only existed in the past. After reading about radiometric decay and radiometric dating, students will learn how certain isotopes help geologists determine the absolute ages of rocks, fossils, and the age of Earth. Students will apply their understanding of rock layers and radiometric dating to determine the age range for rock layers. Students will continue to explore evidence for change across time as they begin to construct their own explanation of evolution.

Students will begin exploring how change across time might occur by modeling the process of natural selection. They do this through two simulations of different predator-prey relationships. They will explore how variations in characteristics of a population affect the survival of individuals within the population. They will notice that some characteristics are more beneficial than others, depending on the environment or the food source. Students will reflect on how the survival of some individuals over others would affect the fossil record.

Students will learn that evolution explains how species change across time and that natural selection is a mechanism for evolution. Students will reflect on how descent with modification helps explain Earth's history. Students will continue to elaborate on the concept of evolution by creating a timeline for Earth. They will explore the idea of geologic time as they look at events in Earth's history, including the emergence of different kinds of life on Earth. Students will apply their understanding of evolution and natural selection by interpreting a rock sequence containing proboscidean (elephants and their relatives) fossils. Students will use what they have learned to explain how some species of proboscidean might have evolved.

Goals for the Chapter

When students finish chapter 6, they should be able to answer the following questions:

- How do changes to organisms across time support evolution?
- What lines of evidence lead to a theory of evolution?
- What are the underlying biological mechanisms of evolution?

Use these questions to focus your daily lesson plans. One way to do this is to use these questions as a filter through which you pass your lesson plans. That is, write your plans so that they are in some way helping students answer one of these questions *every day*. If you cannot see an obvious and meaningful connection between a task and one of these questions, then seriously consider eliminating that task from your lesson plan. Using these goal questions as a filter helps you generate effective lesson plans that foster long-term achievement gains in students, especially those who struggle with science concepts.

Look at the chapter organizer each day to remind yourself of where students are in the overall sequence of events in the chapter.

Chapter 6 Organizer

EXPLORING CHANGE

Major Concepts

► **Evolution explains the diversity of life on Earth**

- Organisms change across time
- Natural selection explains how species change across time
- Multiple lines of evidence confirm evolution
- Physical properties change

ENGAGE Unity and Diversity ★

Key Idea: • Observing organisms allows us to see unity and diversity.

Activity: Students look at several photographs of organisms and seek the ways these organisms are similar and different.

LINKING QUESTION: How do we know the relative age of rock layers?

EXPLORE Gifts from the Past ★

Key Idea: • The arrangement of rock layers can tell us the relative age of the layers and any fossils found in them.

Activity: Students look at fossils in rock layers to determine the relative age of rock layers and the fossils in those rock layers.

LINKING QUESTION: How are rock layers dated on an absolute scale?

EXPLAIN Clocks in Rocks ★★ to ★★★

Key Idea: • Radioactive isotopes help date rocks on an absolute scale.

Activity: Students simulate the radioactive decay process with coin-flips, which help students understand how to date rocks on an absolute time scale.

LINKING QUESTION: How does competition among organisms affect populations?

EXPLORE Who Will Survive? ★★ to ★★★

Key Idea: • Strategies for survival affect the population of all organisms.

Activity: Students simulate predator-prey interactions to explain how these interactions affect the survival of organisms.

LINKING QUESTION: What is the historical background of evolution?

EXPLAIN Learning about Life: A Great Discovery ★★

Key Idea: • Darwin described the mechanism of evolution—natural selection.

Activity: Students read several passages, which explain key concepts important to biological evolution.

LINKING QUESTION: On what scale did the changes associated with evolution take place?

★ = One Class Period ☆ = ½ Class Period *Note:* Based on a 50-minute class period.

ELABORATE — Twine Time ★★

Key Idea: • The events of evolution have occurred over vast time periods, mostly before the present.
Activity: Students create a physical model of evolutionary time scales.

LINKING QUESTION: Did modern day elephants evolve from ancient ancestors?

EVALUATE — Ancient Elephants ★★

Key Idea: • Evidence for elephant evolution can be pieced together to explain modern day elephants.
Activity: Students demonstrate what they know and understand by explaining how elephant fossils exhibit the main ideas of evolution.

★ = One Class Period ☆ = ½ Class Period *Note:* Based on a 50-minute class period.

Standards Covered by Chapter 6

EXPLORING CHANGE

STANDARD B: Physical Science. As a result of activities in grades 9–12, all students should develop an understanding of

structure of atoms

- Radioactive isotopes are unstable and undergo spontaneous nuclear reactions, emitting particles and/or wavelike radiation. The decay of any one nucleus cannot be predicted, but a large group of identical nuclei decay at a predictable rate. This predictability can be used to estimate the age of materials that contain radioactive isotopes.

STANDARD C: Biological Science. As a result of activities in grades 9–12, all students should develop an understanding of

biological evolution

- Species evolve over time. Evolution is the consequence of the interactions of (1) the potential for a species to increase its numbers, (2) the genetic variability of offspring due to mutation and recombination of genes, (3) a finite supply of the resources required for life, and (4) the ensuing selection by the environment of those offspring that are better able to survive and leave offspring.
- The great diversity of organisms is the result of more than 3.5 billion years of evolution.
- Natural selection and its evolutionary consequences provide a scientific explanation for the fossil record of ancient life forms, as well as for the striking molecular similarities observed among the diverse species of living organisms.
- The millions of different species of plants, animals, and microorganisms that live on Earth today are related by descent from common ancestors.

STANDARD D: Earth and Space Science. As a result of activities in grades 9–12, all students should develop an understanding of

the origin and evolution of the Earth system

- Geologic time can be estimated by observing rock sequences and using fossils to correlate the sequences at various locations. Current methods include using the known decay rates of radioactive isotopes present in rocks to measure the time since the rock was formed.
- Evidence for one-celled forms of life—the bacteria—extends back more than 3.5 billion years. The evolution of life caused dramatic changes in the composition of Earth's atmosphere, which did not originally contain oxygen.

STANDARD E: Science and Technology. As a result of activities in grades 9–12, all students should develop an understanding of

science and technology

- Scientists in different disciplines ask different questions, use different methods of investigation, and accept different types of evidence to support their explanations. Many scientific investigations require the contributions of individuals from different disciplines, including engineering.
- Science often advances with the introduction of new technologies. Solving technological problems often results in new scientific knowledge. New technologies often extend the current levels of scientific understanding and introduce new areas of research.

STANDARD G: History and Nature of Science. As a result of activities in grades 9–12, all students should develop an understanding of

nature of scientific knowledge

- Science distinguishes itself from other ways of knowing and from other bodies of knowledge through the use of empirical standards, logical arguments, and skepticism, as scientists strive for the best possible explanations about the natural world.
- The historical perspective of scientific explanations demonstrates how scientific knowledge changes by evolving over time, almost always building on earlier knowledge.

Prerequisite Knowledge

Students who have had some middle school life science and earth science should have been exposed to basic taxonomy, physiology, and the fossil record. This knowledge in conjunction with some exposure to student-designed activities is helpful, but not essential.

Commonly Held Misconceptions

- Many students think that individual organisms within a population evolve, rather than a population of individuals. For example, if a weight lifter's biceps grew an inch, some students would think that this person evolved. In conjunction with this misconception, many students think that the weight lifter will pass on his or her larger arms to offspring because the extra exercise helped him or her evolve.
- Many students think events in Earth's history do not reach back billions of years.
- Many students think that natural selection only favors the fastest, strongest, and largest animals.

NOTES:

ENGAGE

Unity and Diversity

Activity Overview

In *Unity and Diversity*, students will think about what they know about life on Earth. They will have the opportunity to describe the similarities and differences they see in organisms. Scientists refer to these similarities and differences as the unity and diversity of life.

Before You Teach

Background Information

Throughout this chapter, students will be looking at some examples of evidence that supports the theory of evolution. Evolution is the process through which species (populations of individuals) change across time. One of the more obvious, or at least more easily observable, pieces of evidence is the morphological similarity and differences of organisms. This pattern of organisms sharing similar characteristics while also exhibiting differences is referred to as the unity and diversity of life on Earth.

Students do not need to know what evolution is at this point. They will be building an understanding of the evidence for evolution with each activity. They will be given a clear definition and background on evolution in the explain activity *Learning about Life: A Great Discovery*.

Many students understand and scientists have found that similar organisms such as horses, donkeys, and zebras are related. In many instances, the less organisms look like one another, the less closely related they are. Species look more similar to closely related species because they are descended from a common ancestor through the process of evolution. Scientists classify species into a hierarchy of taxonomic categories based on the degree of similarity between species. Today, scientists often use DNA technology to confirm or dispute classifications established by morphological characteristics. The differences or diversity we observe in organisms are the result of modifications that have occurred across millions of years of evolution. You will find more detailed information in the background for the explain activity *Learning about Life: A Great Discovery*.

Materials

For each student

1 copy of copymaster 6.1, *Unity and Diversity*

Advance Preparation

Display pictures of diverse organisms, including extinct species, about the room.

As You Teach

Outcomes and Indicators of Success

By the end of this activity, students should

1. share their current understanding about the diversity and unity of organisms on Earth.

   They will demonstrate their current understanding by

   - contributing to a list of diverse organisms,
   - taking part in a class discussion of similarities and differences in organisms, and
   - describing what they think is meant by the unity and diversity of life.

2. become engaged by the patterns of unity and diversity of organisms on Earth.

   They will demonstrate their interest by

   - recognizing a variety of ways in which organisms are alike and different,
   - creating an organizing scheme for the organisms on the class list, and
   - asking questions during class discussions that will be answered in the unit over time.

3. become curious about how living systems function in order to demonstrate similarities and differences.

   They will demonstrate their curiosity by

   - generating individual questions about similarities among organisms and
   - pondering the questions their classmates offer.

Strategies

Getting Started

If you have displayed pictures of organisms, direct students to study them. Ask if they have thought about how the organisms on Earth are alike and how they are different. Tell students that scientists describe these similarities and differences as the unity and diversity of life on Earth. Explain that in this chapter they will be looking at the evidence for change across time. The unity and diversity of life on Earth is the result of change across time.

Process and Procedure

In Step 1, divide students into teams of 3 and give each student a copy of copymaster 6.1, *Unity and Diversity*.

Send the teams outside to complete the handout. If you cannot send them outside, have them look out the window or think of some organisms they saw on the way to school.

In Step 2, call on students for examples of the organisms they listed on their handout. Write the organisms on the board. Try to group the organisms as you record them on the board. Make a point not to tell the students how you are grouping the organisms. They will help you do that later.

In Step 3, encourage students to add to the list by naming other organisms than the ones they might have seen outside the classroom. If students only list living organisms, ask them if they have been thinking about all the organisms that have lived on Earth.

As students contribute to the class discussion, ask these probing questions:

- "Can we see all organisms?"
- "Are all the organisms that have lived on Earth alive today?"

In Step 4, ask students to look at the list of organisms and think about how they are similar to one another. This is an opportunity for students to talk about what they know about the unity, or the relatedness, of life. Make a list of the similarities on the board. Then ask students to think about how the organisms are different from one another. Make a list of differences, or the diversity of life. Try to get contributions from every student in the class. Remind students to record the results of the class discussion in their science notebooks.

As students contribute to the class discussion, ask these probing questions. Use these questions to assess students' prior knowledge of organisms.

- "What are some characteristics that organisms share?"
- "Can you think of something that a plant and an animal would have in common?" Students should recognize that both have cells.
- "What are some characteristics that distinguish organisms?"

After you feel that the class list of similarities and differences is sufficient, ask students how they could group the organisms by their similarities and differences. For example, students might suggest the following groups: birds, plants, microorganisms, insects, and mammals. Create a graphic organizer by circling different groups of organisms. The graphic organizer will help show the pattern of unity and diversity among organisms. An example of a possible graphic organizer is pictured in figure T6.1.

To get students thinking about some of the things they will learn later in the chapter, ask the following probing questions:

- "How much or little have organisms changed across time?"

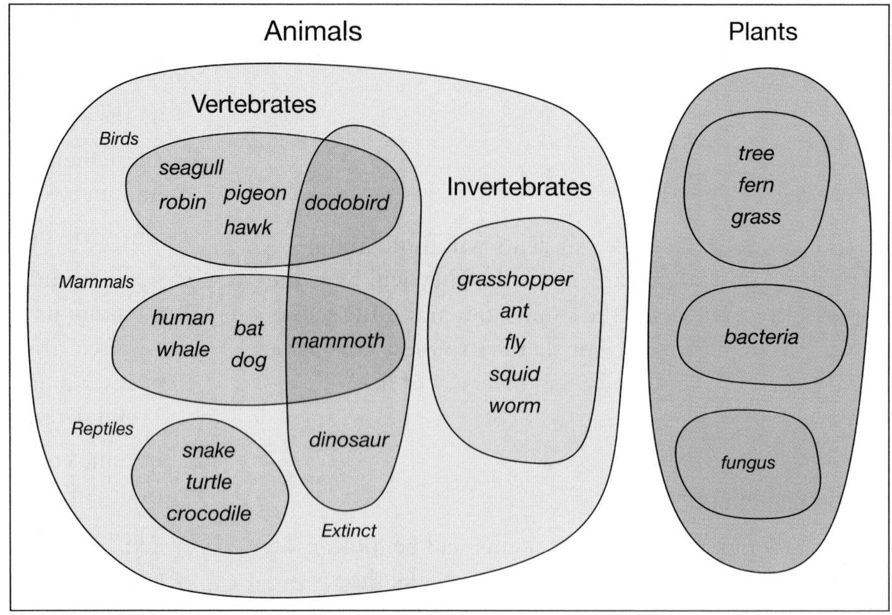

Figure T6.1 Sample graphic organizer. Students will provide the list of organisms. As you record each organism on the board, place different types of organisms on different parts of the board, as shown. After students have discussed the similarities and the differences in these organisms, ask them what groups they see. Circle groups and label them to create a graphic organizer.

ENGAGE

Unity and Diversity

Earth is inhabited by a variety of living things. How much do you know about life on Earth? Have you ever thought about all the types of organisms that live on Earth? Scientists observe and compare different types of organisms to learn more about them. As scientists gather information about each type of organism, they begin to organize their observations and identify patterns. Many scientists have discovered that life on Earth reveals a pattern of unity and diversity. In the activity *Unity and Diversity*, you will work individually and with your class to discover if you see a pattern of unity and diversity in the life on Earth. Begin by looking for a pattern in the organisms pictured in figure 6.2.

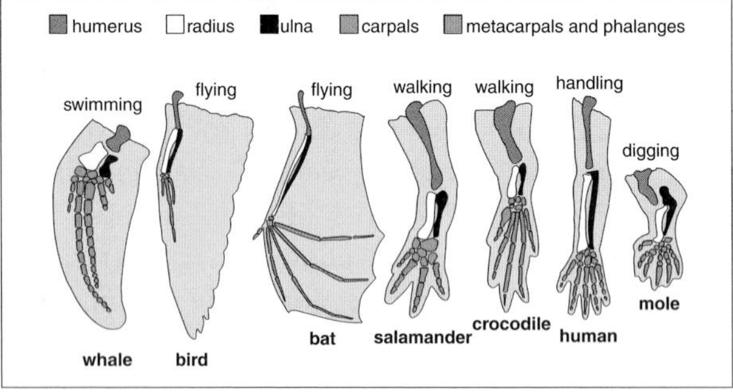

Figure 6.2
Variation in arms. Do you notice any similarities or differences in the arms of different organisms? How do these similarities and differences affect the way an organism survives in its environment?

Materials

For each student

1 *Unity and Diversity* handout

Process and Procedure

1. Work in a team of 3 to complete the *Unity and Diversity* handout provided by your teacher.
2. Compare the 3 organisms you described on the handout with the organisms described by other teams in the class. Are they the same? What do you notice about them?
3. What other kinds of organisms can you think of? Contribute to a class list of organisms, which your teacher will compile on the board.
4. How are the organisms listed on the board similar to one another? How are the organisms different from one another?

- "Why do you think there are so many different organisms on Earth?"

Answers to Reflect and Connect, SE page 283

1. When scientists talk about the unity and diversity of life, they are describing the fact that organisms on Earth share characteristics such as hair or cells, but at the same time they can be very different. They might look different or live in different environments. Students might make references to the similarities and differences discussed as a class.

   Students will learn more about the unity of life in chapters 7 and 8 and the diversity of life in chapter 9.

2. Organisms are similar because many live in similar environments and need similar characteristics to be successful. For example, hair helps keep mammals warm, and wings help many kinds of organisms move from place to place. Organisms are different because they occupy different environments, eat different foods, and have different kinds of movement.

   Some students might explain that organisms are similar because they are related to one another. Later, students will learn that this is true and supports the idea of evolution—descent from a common ancestor.

3a. Students should indicate the thinking process they went through during this activity. They might explain that grouping organisms helped them see patterns in similarities and differences. These patterns reveal the unity and diversity of life on Earth.

3b. Students might discuss how they organize their room or closet with shirts all in one place and shoes in another. Answers can be personal to each student, but must reflect an understanding that things can be organized according to their similarities and differences.

5. Participate in a class discussion of the similarities and differences among the organisms. Record the results of your class discussion in your science notebook.

Reflect and Connect

Work on your own to answer the following questions. Record your best thinking in your science notebook.

1. Describe what you think scientists mean when they talk about the unity and diversity of life on Earth.
2. Why do you think organisms are similar? Why are they different? Explain your reasoning.
3. Consider the similarities and differences in organisms.
   a. You grouped organisms according to their similarities and separated them according to their differences. How did these tasks help you understand the unity and diversity of life on Earth?
   b. When else do you organize things according to their similarities and differences?

Gifts from the Past

EXPLORE

In the activity *Unity and Diversity*, you learned that life on Earth is diverse, yet many organisms share similar characteristics. How do scientists know about organisms that lived on Earth in the past? How do they piece together life on Earth? Scientists continuously discover evidence of how Earth and the life on it have changed across time. Figure 6.3 provides one example of a discovery of past life on Earth.

In *Gifts from the Past*, you will have an opportunity to work individually, with a partner, and with your class. You will use your critical-thinking skills and observational skills to piece together some important ideas about change. Focus your investigation with this question: "What do rock layers tell us about the relative age of organisms?"

▲ **Figure 6.3 Mammoth discovery.** A volunteer from a Denver museum carefully removes dirt from a mammoth tusk uncovered by a construction crew. The tusk was discovered in July 2002 while workers were digging up an area in Denver for a housing development. How often do you think evidence of past life is discovered?

Chapter 6 Exploring Change 283

EXPLORE

Gifts from the Past

Activity Overview

In *Gifts from the Past*, students will begin learning more about past life on Earth. They will look at rock layers and fossils and learn that they provide evidence for the order that events have occurred on Earth. Scientists used these pieces of evidence to form some of the earliest descriptions of Earth's history.

Before You Teach

Background Information

Evidence of evolution extends across disciplines and methods. The following brief descriptions will give you an idea about how fossils support the theory of evolution.

The fossil record shows a succession of forms across geologic time for many groups of organisms (for example, whales and humans). The fossil record shows a vertical succession of forms across geologic time—evidence for descent with modification. There are newly discovered and well-known transitional fossils between dinosaurs and birds (for example, *Sinornithosaurus* and *Archaeopteryx*). These fossils provide evidence for the existence of intermediate forms.

Only a fraction of the species that have lived during past geologic history is preserved in the rock record. An even smaller portion has been discovered and described by scientists. Biologists have described about 1.5 million species that live today out of 10–50 million probable total species. For comparison, paleontologists have only cataloged about 250,000–300,000 fossil species representing over 540 million years of Earth's history.

Soft-bodied organisms are rarely fossilized except under extraordinary conditions. However, entire organisms can become fossilized in hardened tree sap (amber), tar pits, and ice. Destructive processes, such as scavenging by other organisms and weathering, often prevent the preservation of shelled organisms. Not all organisms have been preserved in the fossil record, and many fossils have yet to be discovered. As a result, paleontologists must reconstruct evolutionary relationships from branches of an originally very bushy tree.

Geologists study the history of Earth's surface by studying the layers of rock (stratigraphy). Stratigraphy deals with all the characteristics of layered sedimentary sequences of rocks and includes the study of how these rocks relate to time and past environments. Most fossils are found in sedimentary rocks. Sedimentary rock layers are the result of sediments that have been deposited in horizontal layers and then have been compressed across time as they are buried. Examples of deposits include shells on the ocean floor (limestone), fine mud on a lake bottom (slate), and gravel and sand along a riverbed (conglomerate). The two other types of rock are igneous rocks (formed from deposits of lava, volcanic ash, and other formerly molten rocks) and metamorphic rocks, which are altered by heat or pressure.

Geologists use their understanding of how rocks are deposited to determine the relative age of rock layers. In a vertical sequence of rocks (where rock layers have not become tilted), the oldest rock layers are found in the lowest layers in a column of rock, and the youngest layers, which were deposited more recently, are found near the surface of a column of rock. This is the principle of superposition: a higher rock is younger than a lower rock. Superposition applies to sequences of sedimentary and volcanic rocks.

Each rock layer, or strata, provides a record of past events and past environments. One example of an event might be the first appearance of a fossil of a particular species. The order of these events creates a relative timescale: we learn that event A occurred before event B, which occurred before event C, but we don't know how much time passed between each event. As geologists reconstruct Earth's history using strata, they find that the distribution of fossils is not random. Fossils are more unique than rock types and allow a way of more precisely dividing strata and events within them. Fossils provide important evidence to help determine what happened in Earth's history and when it happened. Scientists have observed that fossils occur in a consistent succession and that there are trends in the morphology of organisms across time. This is referred to as the principle of faunal or floral succession.

Materials

For the teacher

1 100-mL glass graduated cylinder or other cylindrical container

various sediments (at least 3 types such as sand, sugar, and aquarium rocks)

marbles or other objects representing fossils

pictures of fossils (optional)

real samples or models of fossils for the following organisms:

- crinoid
- seed fern or tree fern
- trilobite
- polychaete
- Brachiopods (preferably from the Cambrian or Ordovician)
- coral (preferably from the Ordovician, Devonian, or Mississippian)
- shark tooth (preferably from the Triassic)
- dinosaur bone (preferably from the Jurassic)
- petrified wood or angiosperm leaf (preferably from the Tertiary)

1 transparency of copymaster 6.2, *Fossil Data* (optional)

TRCD

Advance Preparation

Using a 100-milliliter (mL) graduated cylinder, create a sediment column. Make sure you use a glass cylinder or other container that will show the layers. The smaller the diameter of your container, the less sediment you will have to use. Alternatively, pour in layers of sediment such as sand, sugar, and aquarium rocks into the container. Each layer should be several centimeters thick. In a few of the layers, place marbles or other objects to represent fossils. Display pictures or models of rock layers and fossils as students enter the classroom.

Purchase fossil specimens or models. If you can only purchase a few fossils, try to get specimens or models of the first 4 from the materials list (crinoid, seed fern or tree fern, trilobite, and polychaete). These will be the most helpful to students as they try to identify the organisms in Step 6.

You might want to make a transparency of copymaster 6.2, *Fossil Data* to show students information about the fossils they chose in Step 5.

Educational Technologies

Consider conducting a search on the Web for other examples of rock layers in which fossils have been shown for the purpose of teaching. Use keywords such as *rock layer*, *fossil*, and *relative time*. Students can also learn more by taking a look at the *Fossil Deposition Animation* on the *Student Resource CD*.

As You Teach

Outcomes and Indicators of Success

By the end of this activity, students should

1. be able to analyze rock layers.

   They will demonstrate their ability by

   - contributing to a class discussion of a model of a sediment column,
   - sketching rock layers with the oldest on the bottom and youngest on the top,
   - indicating the relative ages of fossils in a rock column with the oldest on the bottom and the youngest on the top, and
   - identifying a good model of strata that indicates that the oldest layers are deposited first and the youngest layers are deposited last.

2. be able to infer from the fossil record that many organisms that existed in the past are not alive today and that organisms that exist today have changed from those in the past.

   They will demonstrate their ability by

   - comparing and contrasting fossils of organisms by observing physical characteristics and
   - describing whether fossil organisms look like organisms alive today.

3. be able to use records of rock layers and fossils as evidence of change across time.

   They will demonstrate their ability by

   - describing how geologists determine a sequence of events by looking at the order in which rock layers were deposited,
   - describing how the environment and organisms at a location have changed by interpreting rock layers and fossils, and
   - describing how fossils provide evidence of change across time because fossils in younger layers differ from fossils in older layers.

4. become aware of the techniques used by scientists to determine the age of fossils.

   They will show their awareness by describing how strata can be used to determine the relative ages of fossils.

5. formulate and revise ideas regarding how fossils help date rock layers.

   They will demonstrate their ability to formulate and revise ideas by

   - answering questions in the procedure,
   - listening to what other students say, and
   - recording any revisions to answers in their notebooks.

Strategies

Getting Started

If you have displayed pictures of rock layers and fossils, initiate a discussion about how the items might be connected. Revisit student ideas from the engage about the unity and diversity of life on Earth. Ask students how we know what organisms have lived in the past. How do we know that those organisms are similar to or different from organisms alive today?

Fossil	Organism	When this organism lived	Interesting facts about this organism
A	Crinoid (marine invertebrate)	360–320 million years ago	Also called sea lilies. Crinoids are the most common invertebrate found in the fossil record from 544 to 245 million years ago. Many limestones from this period are composed of crinoid skeletons. Ancient crinoids lived in shallow coastal habitats. Modern crinoids, such as feather stars, are less abundant and found in deepwater habitats.
B	Seed fern (fernlike plant)	360–286 million years ago	A common coal-swamp plant. Also called pteridosperms, seed ferns are not ferns. They are true seed plants and are one of the earliest plants with seeds. Although they are extinct, seed ferns are the predecessors of gymnosperms, which include the conifers we see today.
C	Trilobite (marine invertebrate)	410–360 million years ago	A group of extinct arthropods that have a distinctive three-lobed, three-segmented form. Trilobites lived in shallow coastal habitats. They are the most diverse group of fossilized organisms. The first fossil records of trilobites are from about 410 million years ago.
D	Polychaete (marine invertebrate)	540–500 million years ago	Polychaetes are marine worms that live in both shallow and deep marine habitats. Many live in tubes buried in sand or mud. Soft-bodied organisms, such as polychaetes, are rarely preserved as fossils. This fossil was found in Burgess Shale, which contains many fossils of soft-bodied organisms as well as those with hard parts. Polychaetes are a common marine invertebrate even today.

▲ Figure T6.2 **Fossil data.** The time periods given in "when this organism lived" refer to the ages of the fossils determined by scientists when they were collected. The time periods given in "interesting facts about this organism" refer to the time period in which this type of organism is believed to have existed on Earth.

Process and Procedure

In Step 1, show students the sediment column. Then ask the following probing questions to determine how much they know about rock layers:

- "Which layer was added first and which layer was added last?"
- "Are the layers closer to the bottom older or younger than the layers closer to the top?"

The older layers were deposited first, so they are closer to the bottom. The layers closer to the surface are progressively younger.

If students understand this concept, move on to Step 2. If this concept is new for many students, spend more time using the sediment column as an analogy for how sediment is deposited. Explain that sediments are deposited in horizontal layers in environments such as lakes and oceans. Layers can also be deposited by lava flows or windblown sand. These sediments eventually become rock.

In Step 2, students work in pairs to sketch and label rock layers from oldest to youngest. Circulate around the room to observe student progress. If students are struggling, ask these probing questions:

- "If you add the daily paper to the recycle bin every day, which papers would be the oldest and which would be the most recent?"
- "Think about how the rock layers were formed. How was the sediment deposited that eventually forms rock layers?"

Answers to Step 2, SE page 284

2. Students should understand that the oldest rock layer is on the bottom because it was deposited first. The layer that is second to the bottom is the second oldest, and so on. The youngest layer, which was deposited last, is the top layer. The students might note that occasionally layers are folded and faulted, making it difficult to determine the bottom layer. In these cases, other evidence helps scientists determine which rock was deposited first. For example, the order of layers of rocks in the surrounding area can offer a clue to the true order. Also, some features in rocks help scientists determine the top of the layer from the bottom of the layer.

In Step 3, students answer questions about rock layers. Circulate among teams and check their progress to see how well they understand the information that rock layers provide. A variety of responses are acceptable because students have not been provided with this information yet. Instruct students to record their best thinking at this time.

Answers to Step 3, SE page 284

3a. Students might explain that rock layers provide a record of events on Earth, such as oceans depositing limestone, lava flowing, or sand dunes blowing around. Because we can determine the order in which the rock layers were deposited, geologists can determine the order of events on Earth. The examples that students provide will vary depending on the knowledge they have with how rocks are formed. Because the specifics of earth science are not discussed in this activity, many students might only describe that rock layers provide a record of the sediments deposited at a location.

3b. Students might recognize that rock layers can provide information about the environment that was present when the sediment

Materials

Fossil Deposition animation on the *Student Resource CD* (*SRCD*)

Process and Procedure

SCILINKS NSTA
Topic: stratigraphy
Go to: www.scilinks.org
Code: 2Inquiry284

1. You might have already studied the rock cycle and how rocks are formed, but you might not know as much about rock layers. Do you know a little or a lot about rock layers? Look at the sediment column your teacher has created. Then participate in a class discussion about stratigraphy, which is the study of rock layers (called strata).
2. With a partner, study the layers of rock in figure 6.4. Then do Steps 2a–c to show what you have learned about rock layers.
   a. Discuss the relative age of each layer.
   b. Sketch the major rock layers in your science notebook and label them from oldest to youngest.
   c. Write a few sentences under your drawing to explain why you labeled the rock layers the way you did.

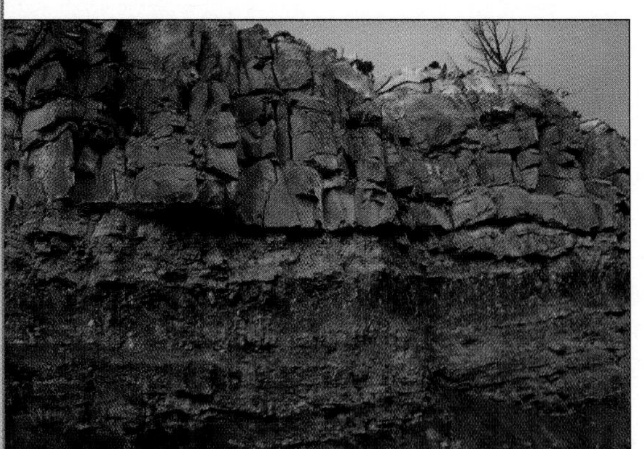

▲ **Figure 6.4**
Rock layers. Erosion often exposes rock layers such as these along Highway 68 in Maryland. Layers of rock, called strata, hold fascinating records of time. Geologists use stratigraphy to help determine the relative age of rock layers by looking at the position of the strata.

3. There are probably many times in your life that you have been on a road that ran along a wall of exposed rock layers. But you might not have thought about what you could learn from the rocks.

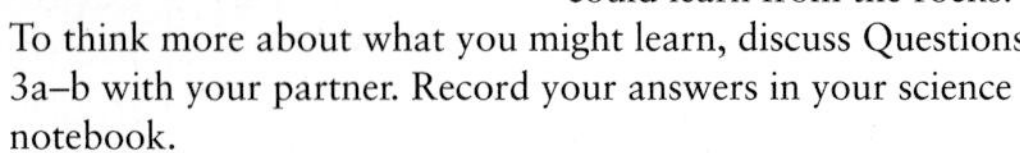

To think more about what you might learn, discuss Questions 3a–b with your partner. Record your answers in your science notebook.
   a. Describe how you think rock layers help geologists determine a sequence of events in Earth's history.
   b. What other kinds of information could you learn from a study of rock layers?
4. Remains of organisms are often found in layers of rock and provide scientists with information about life on Earth. To learn more about this kind of evidence, read the following paragraphs. Then discuss your understanding with your partner.

was formed. Also, fossils in the layers provide information about the types of organisms that lived in the environment.

In Step 4, listen as students discuss the paragraphs on fossils with their partners. Check to see that students know what fossils are and recognize that fossils provide evidence of past life on Earth.

Explain that scientists cannot know exactly what ancient animals looked like because they cannot be observed. Instead, scientists look at the bones and other remains of an animal and compare them with existing animals that are similar. Based on this information, scientists make inferences about what an animal might have looked like. For example, saber-toothed cats are relatives of the big cats, such as mountain lions, tigers, and leopards alive today. Scientists assume saber-toothed cats were covered with hair, which was colored to camouflage them in their environment. Scientists don't know exactly what ancient animals looked like, but they can make inferences based on the information they have.

If students are curious about horseshoe crabs, explain that horseshoe crabs have changed very little in the last 254 million years. Horseshoe crab species have become larger across time, but their basic body plan has changed very little. Scientists refer to such species as "living fossils." Crocodiles are another example of a living fossil.

NOTES:

Evidence from geologists' studies of rock layers reveals some interesting information about organisms. Many types of organisms from the past no longer exist today. In fact, many of the types of organisms that have lived on Earth are now extinct; they no longer exist on Earth. The next time you walk outside, look around you. What types of plants and animals do you see? These organisms are only a small fraction of the life on Earth today and an even smaller fraction of the life that has existed across time. Figures 6.5 and 6.6 provide examples of organisms that lived in the past on Earth.

Take a look at the *Fossil Deposition* animation on the *Student Resource CD (SRCD)* to get an idea of how fossils are dated by the layers of rock they are found in.

SRCD

What evidence do we have in rock layers that extinct organisms once existed? **Fossils** are one example of a type of evidence that scientists discover and study. When the hard parts of organisms (such as bones and teeth) are buried under silt, mud, and sand, a fossil forms across time. Look at figure 6.7 to see an example of how a fossil is formed. Entire organisms can become fossilized when they get trapped in ice (woolly mammoths), tar pits (saber-toothed cats), and tree sap, which becomes amber when hardened (insects). Fossils also can be imprints, such as a footprint or an imprint of a leaf. These remains or traces of organisms provide a geologic record of ancient life. Using fossil evidence as one piece of the puzzle, and the sequence of rock layers as another, scientists can construct a historical account of life.

▲ **Figure 6.5 Extinct dinosaur (*Ornitholestes*).** Many organisms such as the *Ornitholestes* pictured here are extinct. Fossils of *Ornitholestes* aren't found in rock layers younger than 65 million years old. How do you think pictures and exhibits of ancient animals are made? How do we know what the outside of a dinosaur or a prehistoric mammal looked like?

a.

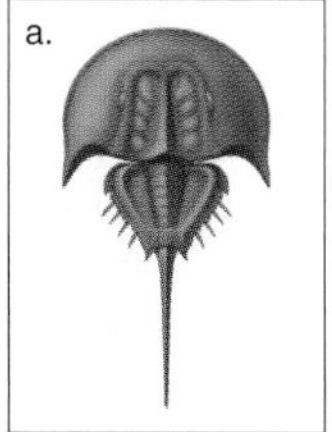

b.

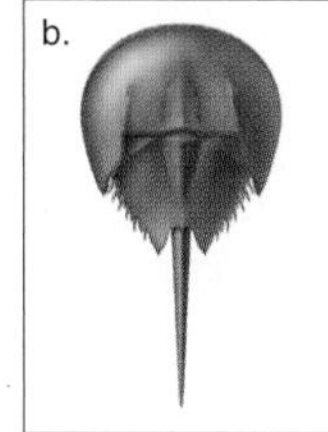

◄ **Figure 6.6 Living fossil.** Many species of horseshoe crab have existed during Earth's history. (a) This species of horseshoe crab (*Paleolimulus avitus*) lived about 250 million years ago. (b) This species of horseshoe crab (*Limulus polyphemus*) is found along the East Coast of the United States. Another three species of horseshoe crabs are found in other parts of the world. What is your evidence that horseshoe crabs have changed a little or a lot across time?

NOTES:

In Step 5, tell students to choose a fossil from figure 6.8 in the student book. Then distribute the fossil specimens or models that match those pictured (crinoid, seed fern or tree fern, trilobite, and polychaete). Encourage students to look closely at the fossils because they will be answering questions about them in the next step. You probably couldn't find a fossil of a polychaete. Explain to students that this fossil is rarer than the other fossils and a specimen was unavailable.

In Step 6, students answer questions about the fossil they have chosen in Step 5. Circulate among students to learn how skilled they are at making observations and how much they know about existing and past life on Earth.

▶ **Figure 6.7 Fossil formation.** (a) Dead organisms or their skeletons may remain intact in underwater sediments through long periods of time. Eventually, minerals circulating in underground water replace the bone of the skeletons, forming fossils. (b) Buried fossils may be brought to the surface by any of the forces that uplift segments of Earth's crust. Once near the surface, the fossil-containing rock layers are exposed to erosion, which can free the fossils from the rock.

5. Fossils provide additional evidence of Earth's history. Choose a fossil from those shown in figure 6.8 and study it closely.
6. Use your observation skills to make some inferences about the fossils in figure 6.8. Identify some distinctive characteristics of the fossils and use this knowledge to answer the following questions in your science notebook.

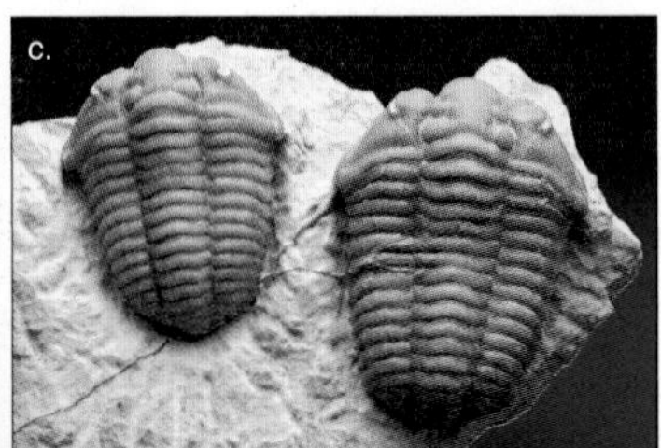

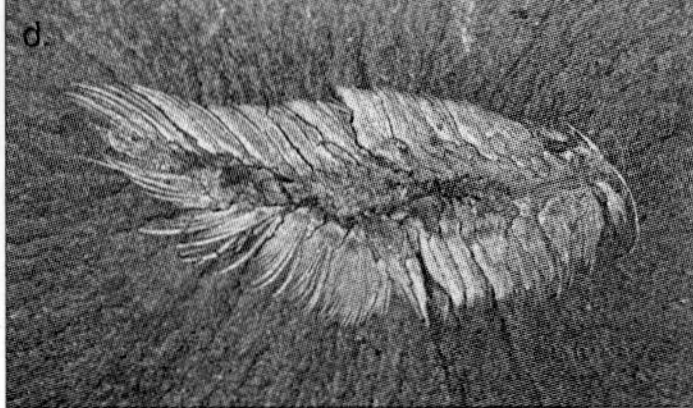

▲ **Figure 6.8 Fossil organisms: (a) crinoid, (b) fern, (c) trilobite, and (d) polychaete.** Do any of these fossils look similar to organisms you have seen before?

NOTES:

a. Describe what you think the organism is. What kind of organism is it? Where might it have lived?

b. Do you think there are similar organisms alive today, or did the organism only exist in the distant past? Explain your reasoning.

c. What other evidence would you want to collect to understand more about this organism?

How could you find out about its environment? How could you know when it lived?

7. Think about what you have learned so far about the rock layers. Fossils often are uncovered during excavation for the construction of new buildings and roads. With your partner, study the rock layers and fossils pictured in figure 6.9.

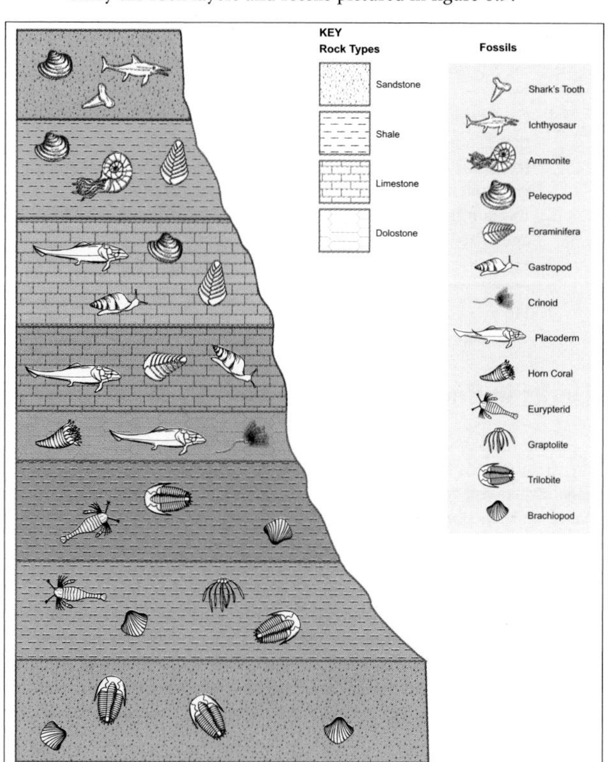

Figure 6.9 Fossils and rock layers correlate. Several fossils have been found in the newly exposed rock. What kind of information can you gather from the fossils and rock layers?

Answers to Step 6, SE page 286–287

6a. Students might think the organism looks like a plant or an animal. They might be more specific and name a particular organism, such as a fern or clam. Based on their knowledge of a similar organism today, students should be able to be more specific and name a possible environment. For example, a fern would inhabit a forest and a clam would inhabit an ocean.

Students should look at the structure of the organism. Does it remind them of an organism alive today?

6b. Some students might recognize the trilobite (c) and know that it is an extinct organism. Others might think the seed fern (b) and polychaete (d) look like plants that are alive today. Accept a variety of answers as long as students have explained their reasoning.

6c. Students might want to collect DNA evidence or make comparisons to life-forms that exist today. They might suggest that finding more fossil evidence would help or that the rock layers in which the fossils were found would provide more evidence.

In Step 8, students use what they have learned about stratigraphy to determine the relative age of two fossils and describe the past environments of the fossil organisms. If students struggle with Question 8b, suggest that they look back at the work they did in Step 3b.

Answers to Step 8, SE page 288

8a. The coral fossil is older than the dinosaur bone because it was located in a lower rock layer than the dinosaur bone. Lower rock layers are older than rock layers closer to the surface.

8b. The brachiopod shell, ammonite shell, coral, and shark tooth would indicate a marine environment. They might have lived deep in the ocean or in shallow seas near the coast. The crocodile fossil might indicate a swamp or river environment. The dinosaur bone would indicate a terrestrial environment. Students might describe a tropical, forested, or swamp environment. The petrified wood or leaf imprint from a tree would indicate a forest environment. The horse fossil would indicate a terrestrial environment. Students are most likely to describe a grassland because that is where they might see a horse today, but they could also describe that the horse might indicate a forest environment. The fish-scale imprint might indicate a marine environment (ocean or shallow sea) or a freshwater lake or river environment.

8c. The environment at this location has changed from a marine environment to a terrestrial environment. The oldest fossils were organisms that probably lived in the ocean. As the fossils were in younger and younger rock layers, these organisms resembled organisms that lived in terrestrial environments.

In Step 9, students participate in another class discussion about the sediment column. Ask if students notice the objects you placed in the column. These objects represent fossils. Then facilitate a discussion about what they can infer about the fossils from the column based on what they have learned in this activity.

Answers to Reflect and Connect, SE page 288

1. One model for rock layers might be a retaining wall with several layers. Another might be the brick layers that make up the school building. The model must have layers of material. Then students must relate ideas about stratigraphy to their model; the oldest layers are on the bottom (or the first ones laid down).
2. If a fossil is found below another one in a series of rock layers, then it is probably older because it was in a layer that was deposited first.
3. Fossils of plants and animals in a series of rocks can show that environments have changed because the types of plants and animals have changed. For example, the environments have changed from desert to ocean. Also, the types of plants and animals might change as the layers get younger. Each of these situations provides evidence for change across time. Acknowledge student ideas about topics that have not been discussed in this chapter. For example, students might recognize that some organisms became extinct in the past,

Answers to Reflect and Connect are on TE pages 288–289.

8. Use figure 6.9 to answer Questions 8a–c in your science notebook.
   a. Which fossil is older, the dinosaur bone or the coral? Explain your reasoning.
   b. Choose 2 fossils and describe the environment that you think they might have lived in.
   c. How have the environment and the organisms that live in it changed at this location?
9. You have been building on your previous understanding of rock layers. To learn how your understanding of rock layers has changed, look at the sediment column from Step 1 again and participate in a class discussion.

Reflect and Connect

Answer the following questions individually in your science notebook.

1. Go explore your environment. Find an object or structure that is a good model of rock layers to help you understand stratigraphy. Describe your model or draw a picture of it in your science notebook. Then explain your analogy.
2. Explain how rock layers are used to help determine the relative age of fossils.
3. How does the fossil record provide evidence for change across time?
4. How exact is relative age? Do you think you could find the exact age for a fossil? How?

EXPLAIN

Clocks in Rocks

Now you know how to determine the relative age of rock layers by their relative positions. You also know that by using the relative age of rock layers, you can infer which fossils are older and which are younger based on their position. You might recognize that you can apply your knowledge to other situations. Think about your locker at school. The papers you threw in there last semester are at the bottom. The book you just put in today is at the top. As you dig through the pile, all your work is correlated to (depends on) how long ago it was put in the locker. Now imagine that one of the papers was a dated memo about class changes from your counselor and another was a school newspaper (see figure 6.10). If you haven't rearranged your locker recently, you can infer the age of the papers between the memo and the school paper.

such as dinosaurs, and that fossils of these organisms would not be found in younger rock layers (layers deposited after the extinction). Similarly, students might recognize that some fossils might be present in one layer and not before or after. Those fossils are called index fossils and are not discussed in this unit.

4. Relative age provides the order that things occurred in, but does not provide a date. It is not precise. Some students might recognize that scientists have techniques to measure a precise age. Although they may not be familiar with the term radiometric dating, they might describe carbon dating or recognize that scientists can measure something in a material to calculate its age.

EXPLAIN

Clocks in Rocks

Activity Overview

In *Clocks in Rocks*, students will read about how scientists determine the age of rocks using radiometric dating techniques. Then they will model radioactive decay as a class to confirm their understanding. By the end of this activity, students will be able to infer the age ranges of rock layers by comparing their positions with dated rock layers.

Before You Teach

Background Information

Obtaining information on the ages of rocks has greatly improved our understanding of Earth's history. Nineteenth-century geologists and paleontologists believed that Earth was quite old, but they had only crude ways of estimating just how old, such as using sedimentation and erosion rates. Lord Kelvin suggested in 1882 that Earth would have needed about 100 million years to solidify. The discovery of radioactivity in the late 1800s made it possible to assign the ages of rocks in thousands, millions, and billions of years.

Minerals that contain naturally occurring radioactive elements are used to calculate the absolute age of a rock in years. Radioactive isotopes decay from parent to daughter isotopes at a constant rate. When only half of the parent is left, one half-life (given in number of years) of the isotope has passed. Scientists determine the age of a rock by measuring how much parent and daughter isotope is present and then calculating how many half-lives have passed since the rock was formed. The dating techniques differ for each radioactive isotope. Although carbon-14 is a radioactive isotope, it is not useful for dating rocks because it is found in organic remains. The half-life of carbon-14 is short (5,730 years). Therefore, radiocarbon dating is very useful for archaeologists or oceanographers studying Earth's recent history but cannot be used to determine the age of Earth. See the student pages for a more complete explanation of radiometric dating.

Scientists often use igneous rocks for radiometric dating because they can contain amounts of multiple radioactive isotopes. When rocks or meteorites contain multiple radioactive isotopes, scientists can calculate the age of the rock using different dating techniques and therefore be more confident in the ages they calculate. Volcanic ash layers are especially useful because these deposits are usually found and correlated on a regional scale.

Rocks aren't stamped with a date, but geologists can determine the age of rocks. What tools do they use? In *Clocks in Rocks*, you will see that geologists use the properties of atoms and nuclei, something you have already studied.

Materials

For each student

1 penny

1 cup

graph paper

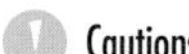

Cautions

Hold your hand firmly over the opening of the cup so that pennies don't fly out and hit anyone.

▲ **Figure 6.10 Papers stacked in a locker.** How old are the papers below the memo? Above the memo?

Process and Procedure

1. Draw a T-table in your notebook with the headings "Key Word" and "Meaning of Key Word." Then read *Radiometric Dating* and complete your T-table as you read.

READING

Radiometric Dating

In the late 19th century, scientists discovered that some minerals in rocks contain radioactive elements. Radioactive elements have different forms. These forms are called **isotopes**. You might remember from Level 1 of BSCS *Science: An Inquiry Approach* that isotopes are atoms of the same element. But they have different numbers of neutrons. For example, all potassium atoms have 19 protons, but different isotopes of potassium have 20, 21, or 22 neutrons. These give atomic masses of 39, 40, and 41. Some isotopes are radioactive. The potassium isotope with 21 neutrons (potassium-40) is radioactive and is commonly used in geologic dating.

The nuclei of radioactive isotopes such as potassium-40 are unstable. They break down spontaneously. When they break down, they form stable isotopes across time. In this process, called **radioactive decay**, an isotope loses particles from its nucleus. The result is an isotope of a new element. The original element, called the **parent element**, decays into the new element, called the **daughter element**. The rate of decay from parent to daughter is reflected in a number called the **half-life**. The half-life of a radioactive isotope is the length of time it takes for exactly one-half of the parent atoms to decay to daughter atoms. Figure 6.11 illustrates the process of radioactive decay.

Each radioactive isotope has a unique half-life. Many radioactive isotopes have rapid rates of decay. They lose their radioactivity

Scientists can use more than 40 different radiometric dating methods (using different isotopes and techniques) and a number of nonradiometric methods, such as electron spin resonance and thermoluminescence. A complete explanation of all these methods would be too lengthy to include.

Materials

For each student

1 penny
1 cup
graph paper

Advance Preparation

Gather pennies and cups for the class.

Educational Technologies

Conduct a Web search for a radiometric dating simulation and you will find a number of sites offering interactive computer visualizations of the process modeled in this activity.

Cautions

Make sure students hold their hands firmly over the openings of the cups so that pennies don't fly out and hit anyone.

As You Teach

Outcomes and Indicators of Success

By the end of this activity, students should

1. be able to describe the process of radioactive decay and how radiometric dating techniques can be used by scientists to date rocks.

   They will demonstrate their ability by explaining that scientists use the isotopes of some elements to determine the age of rocks.

2. be able to apply their knowledge of rock layers.

   They will demonstrate their ability by inferring the age range of rock layers using the ages of volcanic ash layers.

3. be able to describe how radiometric dating techniques help explain change across time.

NOTES:

Radiometric Dating, continued

within a few days or years. Other isotopes decay slowly. A few of these isotopes are useful as geologic "clocks." That's because they tell the amount of time since the rock was formed.

For example, radioactive isotopes of uranium decay into lead. The half-life for one of these isotopes is 704 million years. If uranium-235 was a mineral in a rock, half of it would decay into lead-207 in 704 million years. Therefore, after 704 million years, equal amounts of uranium-235 and its daughter product lead-207 would be present in the mineral. After another 704 million years (a total of 1.4 billion years), only one-quarter of the original uranium isotope would be left. Scientists measure the amount of parent and daughter element in a rock. They use these amounts to calculate how many half-lives have passed.

Geologists must purify and concentrate minerals in rocks that contain radioactive isotopes. When they study the youngest rocks, they see that very little of the parent element may have decayed. When they study the oldest rocks, they find that a substantial amount of the parent element has decayed into a stable element. Geologists can measure the presence of several different isotopes to help them determine the age of rocks. Figure 6.12 shows the half-lives of some elements commonly used in radiometric dating.

Scientists have spent the last 100 years establishing the techniques and developing the technology used in radiometric dating. After the discovery of radioactivity in the late 1800s, physicists began experimenting with how to measure decay rates. By the 1950s, physicists were using mass spectrometers to measure the amount of

SCILINKS NSTA
Topic: radioactive decay
Go to: www.scilinks.org
Code: 2Inquiry290

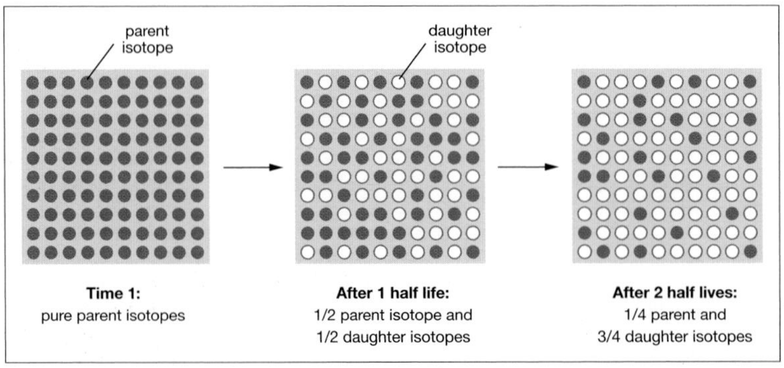

▲ **Figure 6.11** **Radioactive decay.** When an igneous rock forms, some minerals in the igneous rock contain only parent isotopes. After one half-life of the radioactive element has passed, the rock contains one-half parent and one-half daughter isotopes. After two half-lives have passed, the rock contains one-quarter parent isotopes and three-quarters daughter isotopes. How many daughter isotopes will the rock contain after three half-lives have passed?

They will show their ability by describing how rock layers, fossils, and radiometric dating provide evidence that different fossils are found in different rock layers and that these rock layers are different ages.

4. formulate a model for radioactive decay.

   They will demonstrate their ability to formulate a model by

   - collecting data from a simulated radioactive decay process,
   - graphing the data, and
   - translating the graph into what it means about radioactive decay.

Strategies

Getting Started

Ask students what they think about the idea of clocks in rocks. What do they think rocks contain that could provide a measure of time? Tell them that in this activity they will find out what material provides the clock for scientists.

Process and Procedure

In Step 1, students read about radiometric dating, then use a T-table as a literacy strategy. As students read, take this opportunity to listen to their discussions and assess their current understanding of isotopes and radioactive decay.

NOTES:

various isotopes found in rock samples. Now more than 50 years later, geologists use the radiometric dating techniques developed by physicists to determine the absolute ages of rocks. Radiometric dating has helped scientists establish that Earth formed about 4.6 billion years ago (see figure 6.13).

Isotope		Half-life of parent (years)	Useful range (years)
Parent	Daughter		
Carbon-14	Nitrogen-14	5,730	100–50,000
Potassium4-0	Argon-40	1.3 billion	100–0.5 billion
Rubidium-87	Strontium-87	47 billion	10 million–4.6 billion
Uranium-238	Lead-206	4.6 billion	10 million–4.6 billion
Uranium-235	Lead-207	710 million	10 million–4.6 billion

▲ **Figure 6.12 Radioactive elements.** This table shows some of the radioactive elements used in radiometric dating. Some elements such as uranium have more than one radioactive isotope. Notice that the half-life for carbon is much smaller than the half-life for the other elements. Isotopes with long half-lives decay very slowly.

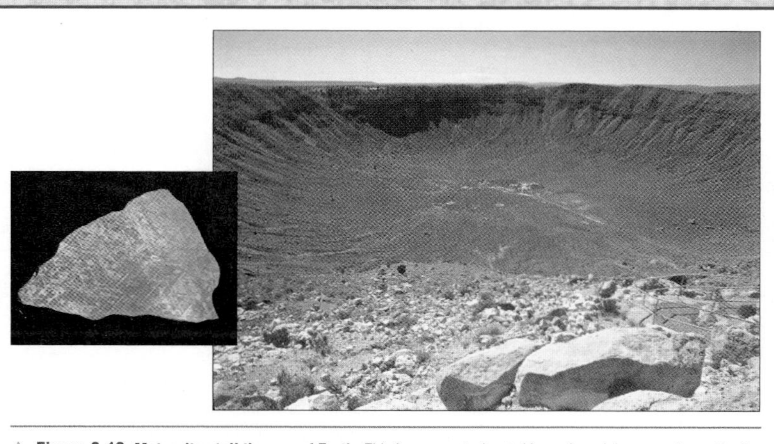

▲ **Figure 6.13 Meteorites tell the age of Earth.** This famous crater located in northern Arizona was formed by the Canyon Diablo meteorite. Meteorites are material left over from the creation of the solar system. Therefore, scientists expect Earth to be the same age as the meteorites. Scientists use radiometric dating techniques on meteorites such as Canyon Diablo to determine the age of the solar system. All data from these techniques suggest that the solar system is about 4.6 billion years old. Therefore, Earth is about 4.6 billion years old.

In Step 2, students use the reading to complete a task.

Answers to Step 2, SE page 292

2. Scientists use the isotopes of elements that are radioactive. These isotopes are unstable and break down into a more stable isotope. This process is called radioactive decay. The rate of decay is described by half-life. The half-life is the amount of time it takes for half the parent element to decay into the daughter element. If scientists know the amount of parent and daughter element in a rock, they can determine how many half-lives have passed.

In Step 3, distribute pennies and cups to the class. Draw a blank table on the board similar to the one shown in figure T6.3 to record the class decay events. You might want to ask students to help you develop the table to gauge how much they have learned about radioactive decay so far.

In Step 4, tell the entire class to stand up. Explain that when the class is standing each student represents a radioactive atom (parent element). Ask the students what you should record for the number of parent atoms for time zero (the number of students standing).

In Step 5, students will determine if they decay. Tell students that they will shake their cups for 10 seconds and then turn their cups over on the desk. Shaking the penny in the cup will represent the time during which their atom might decay. They should notice whether they have heads or tails. If students have heads, they should sit down because their atoms have decayed. The students who are sitting represent daughter atoms. Repeat the shaking step until all students are sitting (decayed). Record the results of each 10-second shaking period on the table on the board. Ask the students to repeat the entire procedure 2 more times for a total of 3 trials. Pooling the trials will give students more data to work with when they plot the graph in the next step. It is likely that pooled data give a "smoother" exponential decay curve than any single trial.

Type of atom	Trial No.	Time in seconds						
		0	10	20	30	40	50	60
No. of parent atoms	Trial 1	24	13	6	5	2	1	0
	Trial 2	24	12	7	6	3	0	0
	Trial 3	24	15	6	2	1	0	0
	Sum	72	40	19	13	6	1	0
No. of daughter atoms	Trial 1	0	11	18	19	22	23	24
	Trial 2	0	12	17	18	21	24	24
	Trial 3	0	9	18	22	23	24	24
	Sum	0	32	53	59	66	71	72

Figure T6.3 Data table for penny activity. This sample data table shows the results that a class of 24 might get after three trials. Students could wait to fill in the number of daughter atoms until after completing the activity. To get this value, simply subtract the number of parent atoms left from the number of initial parent atoms.

Answers to Step 7 are on TE page 293.

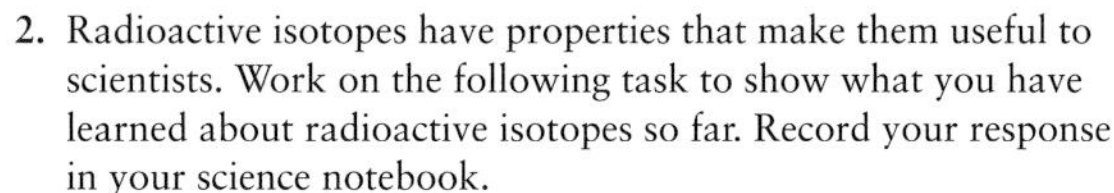

2. Radioactive isotopes have properties that make them useful to scientists. Work on the following task to show what you have learned about radioactive isotopes so far. Record your response in your science notebook.

   Explain how scientists use the isotopes of some elements to determine the age of rocks. Include the following words in your description: *isotope*, *radioactive decay*, *parent*, *daughter*, *half-life*.
3. Sometimes it is easier to understand a complicated process such as radiometric dating after you model it in an activity. Obtain a penny and a cup to model radioactive decay.
4. Begin the activity with the class standing. Each of you represents a radioactive atom.
5. To determine if your atom decays, do Steps 5a–c.
   a. Place the penny in your cup. Hold the cup in one hand while covering it with the other hand.
   b. When your teacher tells you to start, begin shaking the cup. Shake for 10 seconds or until your teacher tells you to stop.
   c. Turn the cup over and look to see if you have heads or tails. If you have heads, sit down. Your atom has decayed.
   d. Your teacher will record the results of the first round on the board.
   e. Repeat these steps until the entire class is sitting (decayed).
   f. To represent more atoms and collect more data, repeat Steps 4 and 5 two more times.

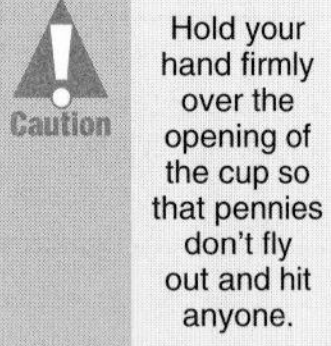

6. Using the numbers in the table recorded by your teacher, plot the data on a graph. Place your graph in your science notebook. Then compare your graph to the graphs showing exponential and linear change in *FYI—Changing Rates of Change*.

Always include highlight comments and a caption for *xy* plots you place in your notebook.

7. Answer the following questions in your science notebook.
   a. Explain how the penny activity modeled radioactive decay.
   b. What was the half-life for your class isotope? Show your calculations.
   c. Describe the curve in the graph you plotted in Step 6. Did the number of decay events stay the same, increase, or decrease with the passage of time (each trial)?
8. Where would you find rocks that contain radioactive isotopes? Learn more about the rocks used in radiometric dating by reading the following paragraph. Discuss your understanding with your partner.

In Step 6, add up the trials and tell students to use these values to plot a graph on graph paper. Time is plotted along the x-axis on a graph. Ask students what should be plotted along the y-axis. Figure T6.4 illustrates a completed graph. Students should keep the graphs in their science notebooks. Once students have drawn their graphs, direct them to answer the questions in Step 7. Use these questions to assess what the students know about radiometric dating after modeling the process.

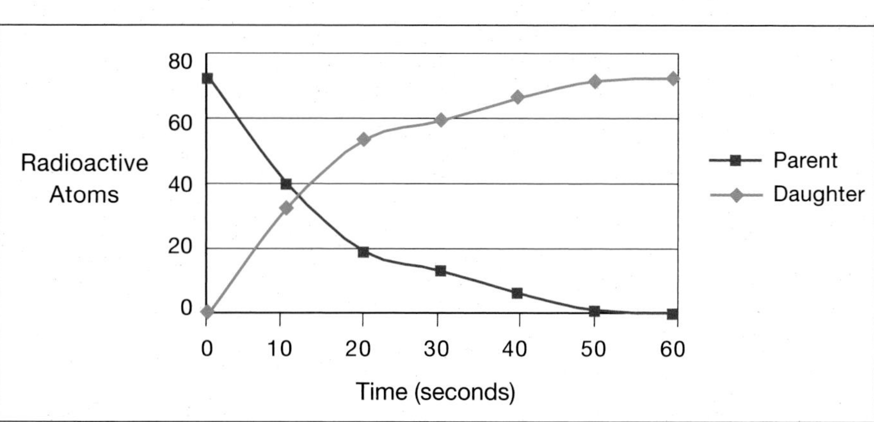

Figure T6.4 Sample graph from penny activity. The data in this sample graph might result from a class of 24 students that averages the data from three trials of the activity. The half-life occurs when exactly half of the parent atoms (36 of the 72) have decayed.

Radioactive isotopes can be found in rocks from volcanoes, such as ash layers and lava flows. A variety of radioactive elements tend to become concentrated in these types of rocks. Radiometric clocks "start" when a rock is formed. Once the rock has solidified, the products of decay can begin to accumulate in the minerals. Radiometric dating measures the amount of time that has passed since the rock was formed. Because volcanic rocks often contain many radioactive elements, scientists can use many radiometric dating techniques and compare the results. Volcanic ash layers can be valuable to scientists because they are deposited worldwide. Scientists can find the same deposit at many locations on Earth.

Reflect and Connect

Discuss the following questions with your partner and record your own answers in your science notebook.

1. Explain how radiometric dating works.

   What are scientists measuring in rocks? How do they use the measurements to determine the age of rocks?

2. Study figure 6.14 and determine the age range of the limestone and sandstone layers. Record your response in your science notebook. Be sure to explain your reasoning.

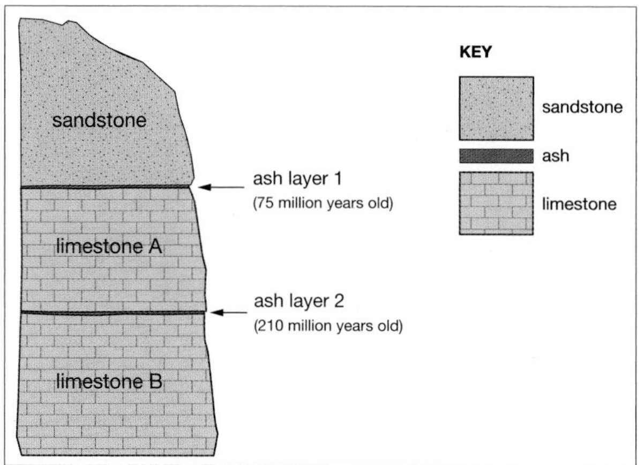

Figure 6.14 Limestone and sandstone layers. This rock column contains three types of rock (limestone, sandstone, and 2 ash deposits). Ash deposit 1 is approximately 75 million years old according to radiometric dating techniques; ash layer 2 is 210 million years old. Use what you know about rock layers and radiometric dating to estimate the age range of both limestone layers and the sandstone layer.

Answers to Step 7, SE page 292

7a. Standing students represented parent atoms. Shaking the penny represented time passing and a chance for each atom (student) to decay. If the penny landed as heads, the student sat down because his or her atom had decayed into a daughter atom.

7b. The half-life of the class should occur when only half of the parent atoms are left. Look at the graph in figure T6.4. In this graph, the half-life was about 12 seconds. You can check students' answers against the graph of the class data.

7c. If you were able to pool the results of several trials, students should describe a curve that was steep initially and then flattened out. The number of decay events decreased with the passage of time.

In Step 8, students read a paragraph and learn that rocks of volcanic origin, especially ash layers, provide a source of isotopes used in radiometric dating techniques.

Answers to Reflect and Connect, SE pages 293-296

1. Radioactive isotopes are unstable and break down into more stable isotopes through a process called radioactive decay. The rate of decay for a particular isotope is a constant and can be expressed as half-life. If scientists measure the amount of parent isotope and daughter isotope in a mineral of a rock, they can calculate how many half-lives have passed. Geologists use isotope systems that let them measure ages of millions or billions of years.
2. The limestone layer is older than 30 million years because it is found below the ash layer dated at 30 million years old. The sandstone layer is between 30 and 14 million years old because it is found above the ash layer dated 30 million years old and below the layer dated 14 million years old.

NOTES:

FYI

Changing Rates of Change

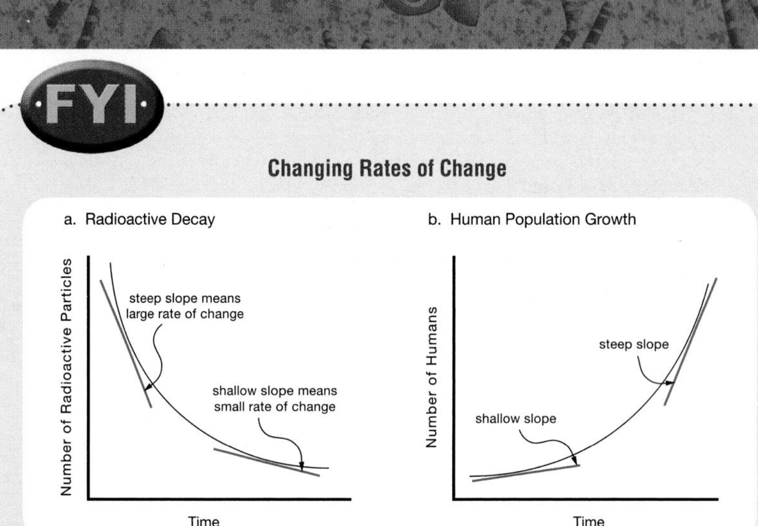

Rates of change can change. (a) Radioactive decay begins quickly and then slows down. How do the slopes show this? (b) Human population increases slowly at the beginning and then increases even more. How do the slopes show this?

Radioactive decay results in changes to the original amount of radioactive isotope. In fact, many phenomena result in changes to the original amount of "stuff." For example, populations of organisms, concentrations of chemical reactants, the position of an accelerating car, and even the value of investments change over time. How these things change has much in common. Scientists seek to understand the common features of change that these phenomena share. Using that knowledge, they can predict what will happen at some future point in time.

Look at the graphs of radioactive decay and human population increase. Note how they are both curved. This suggests they are related mathematically. Though one graph shows decreases and the other shows increases, they both show slow and fast rates of change. You can see the differences in rates of change by looking at the slopes at specific times. A steep slope means a large rate of change, and a shallow slope means a small rate of change.

Now contrast changing rates to nonchanging rates, as shown in the following graphs. Observe the amount of change for equal time periods. Note how curved lines show different amounts of change when compared with lines with no curve. Scientists associate curved lines with **exponential** mathematical relationships. This simply means the equation used to describe the line has an exponent in it. You will see the same curved line anytime something changes by the same percentage in each time period. For example, an inflation rate of 4 percent results in exponential increases in costs.

You have already seen many examples of exponential relationships in this program. Study the following table to refresh your memory. As you continue learning about science, remember to look for curved lines. When you see them, think about the amount of change. It's not always constant. When it's not constant, exponential growth or decay occurs. And exponential changes affect your predictions dramatically.

NOTES:

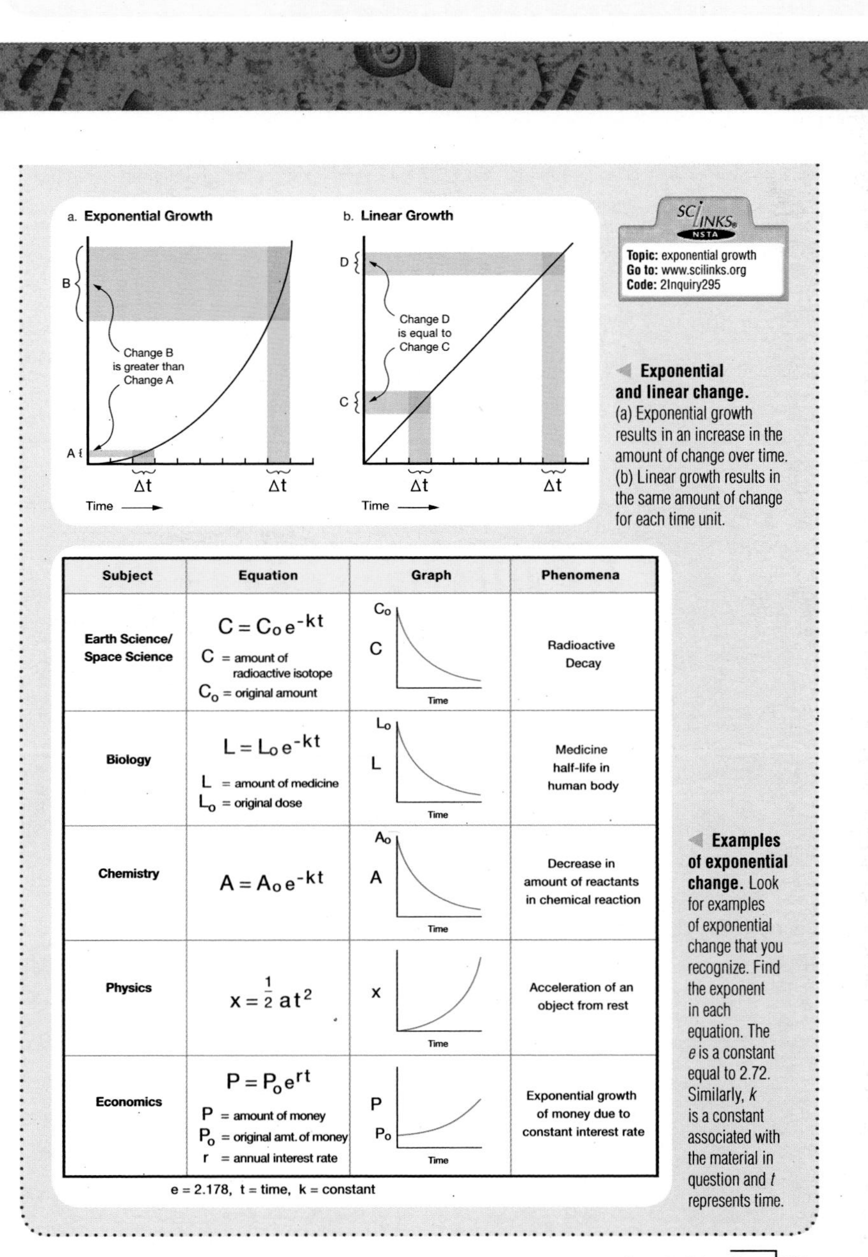

Exponential and linear change. (a) Exponential growth results in an increase in the amount of change over time. (b) Linear growth results in the same amount of change for each time unit.

Subject	Equation	Graph	Phenomena
Earth Science/ Space Science	$C = C_o e^{-kt}$ C = amount of radioactive isotope C_o = original amount	C_o, C, Time	Radioactive Decay
Biology	$L = L_o e^{-kt}$ L = amount of medicine L_o = original dose	L_o, L, Time	Medicine half-life in human body
Chemistry	$A = A_o e^{-kt}$	A_o, A, Time	Decrease in amount of reactants in chemical reaction
Physics	$x = \frac{1}{2} a t^2$	x, Time	Acceleration of an object from rest
Economics	$P = P_o e^{rt}$ P = amount of money P_o = original amt. of money r = annual interest rate	P, P_o, Time	Exponential growth of money due to constant interest rate

e = 2.178, t = time, k = constant

Examples of exponential change. Look for examples of exponential change that you recognize. Find the exponent in each equation. The *e* is a constant equal to 2.72. Similarly, *k* is a constant associated with the material in question and *t* represents time.

Chapter 6 Exploring Change 295

3. Rock layers provide evidence for the order that sediments were laid down. You can determine the relative age of fossils based on what rock layer they are found in. Radiometric dating of rock layers such as ash can give an accurate age for that layer. Then the age range of the surrounding rock layers can be determined. With all 3 pieces of information, we know environments have changed and when those changes occurred.
4. This question gets students thinking about the next activity. They might not know an answer, but they should record their best thinking.

   Most students will recognize that organisms change because they have heard about extinct organisms or are familiar with the evolutionary history of humans or Darwin's finches. Here are some possible pieces of evidence students might provide:

   - Fossils in older rock layers that are similar but slightly different from fossils in younger rock layers
   - Bacteria that survived exposure to an antibiotic and became resistant to it

EXPLORE

Who Will Survive?

Activity Overview

Students have examined multiple lines of evidence for change across time. They can easily see that environments, including the organisms in them, change across time. But students have more difficulty understanding how a species can show gradual changes. In *Who Will Survive?*, students will experience how change in organisms might occur across time. Students will simulate this by playing the role of predators. In Part I, the students are predators of a varied population of prey. In Part II, there is variation in both the predator and the prey population. The simulation helps answer the question, "How might biological change occur and be reinforced over time?"

You might recognize that students are simulating natural selection. This activity is truly an explore exercise for the students. Refrain from providing explanations here and avoid using the term natural selection. Students will be provided with explanations in the explain activity that follows.

Before You Teach

Background Information

Within a population, there is variation in morphological, physiological, biochemical, and behavioral characteristics. In this activity, students will be looking at variations in physical characteristics because these are easily seen and described. They will model how some characteristics are more likely to be passed on than others. You might recognize this as the process of natural selection. Because this is an explore activity, however, students will not be introduced to the term natural selection until the explain activity *Learning about Life: A Great Discovery.*

In Part I, the predator and prey activity models how variation within a population affects the survival of individuals from that population. In this case, individuals within one population are competing with one another not to be eaten by a predator (competition within species). In Part II, the bird beak activity models how variation among species with

3. How do fossils, rock layers, and radiometric dating techniques work together to provide evidence for change across time?
4. Do organisms ever change? What evidence would you look for to support the idea that an organism has different characteristics now than in the past?

EXPLORE

Who Will Survive?

You have been learning about the evidence that supports the idea that things change across time. The fossil record provides one piece of evidence. The type of organisms at a particular location can change across time, for example, from ocean organisms to terrestrial (land) organisms. Because the type of organisms changed, we know that the environment in that location changed. You will consider this idea again in chapter 13, *Time for Change*, for the history of life in Colorado. But the same species of organism also can change across time. What do you think happens across time to cause a species to look different?

▲ **Figure 6.15 Predator and prey.** Will the rabbit survive? What factors influence the answer? What physical changes would result in more successful coyotes?

In *Who Will Survive?*, you will simulate how this change might occur. In each simulation, you will act as the predator. In Part I, you will explore what happens across time to a population of prey that has variations in its characteristics. In Part II, you will explore what happens across time to populations of predators and prey when they both have variations in their characteristics. In both parts, focus your thinking with this question: "What variables affect who will survive?"

Part I: Predator and Prey

In Part I, you and your classmates will represent predators in an environment. Beans will represent the species of organisms that are your prey. The different colors and shapes of the beans will represent variation within the species of prey. After the simulation, you will analyze the selective effects of predation in this simulation. That analysis will help you gain a better understanding of how the average characteristics of a population can change across many generations.

296 Unit 2 Inside Life

different adaptations affects the survival of different species. In the second example, individuals of one species are competing with other species for a limited supply of food resources (competition among species).

Individuals within a population might also have variation in a characteristic that helps them survive a change in their environment. Individuals are faced with the challenge of staying alive in a different environment rather than as a result of competition. A change in the environment is not modeled in this activity, but students are asked to make predictions about how changes in the environment might affect the survival of a species.

The survivors are not a random sample of the population or species. They survived because they possessed characteristics that helped them to survive. To get a more detailed description of natural selection, read *Background Information* for the next activity, *Learning about Life: A Great Discovery*.

In the next chapter, students will begin learning where the variation is "stored" as they learn about genetics. They will learn that there is a considerable amount of genetic variation in natural populations.

Materials—Part I

For each team of 4 students

3 plastic cups or other containers
3 forceps (optional)
25 lentils, 25 split peas, 25 navy beans, and 25 red beans in a bag labeled "starting population"
50 lentils in a bag
*Vary the type of bean according to the environment you use
50 split peas in a bag
50 navy beans in a bag
50 red beans in a bag
1 empty bag
1 meterstick
4 colored pencils similar to the color of the dried beans
2 sheets of graph paper
1 large sheet of wrapping paper
2 copies of copymaster 6.3, *Three Generations*
4 copies of copymaster 6.4, *Predictions across Time*

A species is a group of organisms that reproduces most successfully with individuals of the same type. A population is a group of organisms of the same species that lives in a particular area.

Materials

For each team of 4 students

3 plastic cups or other containers
3 forceps (optional)
25 lentils, 25 split peas, 25 navy beans, and 25 red beans in a bag labeled "starting population"
50 lentils* in a bag
50 split peas* in a bag
50 navy beans* in a bag
50 red beans* in a bag
1 empty bag
1 meterstick
4 colored pencils similar to the color of the dried beans
2 sheets of graph paper
1 large sheet of wrapping paper
2 *Three Generations* handouts
4 *Predictions across Time* handouts

*Vary the type of bean according to the environment you use.

Cautions

Use utensils properly.

Process and Procedure

1. Spread out your wrapping paper in one of the locations provided by your teacher. The wrapping paper will represent a habitat. Crumple the paper to make the habitat more 3-dimensional.
2. Decide on your roles for the activity.

Three members of your team will be predators of beans (the prey). As predators, each of you will hunt the prey in your environment. The fourth member will be the game warden, who will keep track of the hunting.

Materials—Part II

For each team of 4 students

1 forceps
4 cups
1 container (plastic tub or dishpan) filled with water
1 spoon
small marbles in a container (approximately 60)
raisins (approximately 60)
uncooked elbow macaroni (approximately 60)
Styrofoam peanuts (packing material, approximately 60)
1 or 2 toothpicks
1 clothespin (spring type)
1 box top (used to contain prey, especially marbles)
4 plastic sandwich bags

Pliers, screwdrivers, and tweezers can also be used as beaks. For prey, use washers, nuts, bolts, nails, corks, or other household items.

Advance Preparation

For Part I, purchase 4 different colors of dried beans. For example, you could purchase lentils, split peas, navy beans, and red beans. Divide the beans into bags for each team. Each team of 4 students will need 1 set (5 bags) of beans (see *Materials*). Purchase wrapping paper or fabric to represent habitats, 1 meter (m) by 1 m for each team. You will need at least 2 designs of wrapping paper or fabric. Ideally, pick up several different designs of wrapping paper so that each team has a different design. Choose designs that simulate natural habitats and that will camouflage some beans but not others. Look for floral, rain forest, and forest designs. Using 2 or more designs enables the students to demonstrate the evolution of different prey types from the same starting population in different habitats. Students will crumple the wrapping paper to make the habitat more 3-dimensional. Decide where you will have students set up their habitats. If you have a few teams of 5, assign 2 game wardens to the same team.

As an alternative to beans, you might use toothpicks. Use a grassy area outside, a tabletop covered with craft moss, or a shag carpet as the habitat. Select colors according to the habitat you use. For example, if you use grass, you might pick natural, green, red, and blue toothpicks. You can use food dye to color natural toothpicks. Paper dots could be another alternative for beans. Dots can be made with a hole punch and colored paper. Storing dots in film canisters or medicine jars from a pharmacist works well.

For Part II, gather the "foods" (marbles, raisins, macaroni, Styrofoam peanuts) and store them in bags for each team. Approximate the number of pieces of each food for each group (it does not have to be exact). Place the Styrofoam peanuts in a container of water to simulate water bugs. Make sure you use Styrofoam peanuts rather than starch peanuts. Starch peanuts will dissolve if you place them in water. If you have a few teams of 5, you might have a few students alternate between being a predator and watching the activity.

Educational Technologies

Consider allowing some students to use graphing programs.

Cautions

Use utensils properly.

As You Teach

Outcomes and Indicators of Success

By the end of this activity, students should

1. be able to interpret predator-prey relationships from a simulation.

   They will demonstrate their ability by

   - creating a graphic representation of changes in the prey population and
   - predicting the distribution of individuals in future generations.

2. be able to explain that variations in a characteristic of a species influence whether an individual from a population will survive and reproduce.

   They will show their ability by

   - developing their own explanations for the survival of certain types of beans after several rounds of hunting,
   - describing that capturing a particular color of bean affects the color of subsequent generations,
   - predicting that bean colors with fewer individuals in the first three generations will continue to have fewer individuals in the future,
   - predicting that a bird with a beak that can capture a particular food source will survive better than a bird with a beak that cannot capture a particular food source, and
   - explaining that variation affects the survival of an individual in

3. Draw a data table in your science notebook similar to the one in figure 6.16.

Population	Number of individuals			
	Lentils	Split peas	Navy beans	Red beans
First Generation Starting				
First Generation Surviving				
Second Generation Starting				
Second Generation Surviving				
Third Generation Starting				

▲ **Figure 6.16 Data table for Part I.** Adjust the bean types in your data table according to the bean types you will use in your simulation.

4. Examine the beans in the bag labeled "starting population." Record the number of individuals of each color in your table as the first-generation starting population.

The beans (prey population) represent a variation in the color of individuals within a species. The individuals of this species can be 1 of 4 color variations (lentils, split peas, navy beans, or red beans). There should be 25 "individuals" of each color.

5. Set up the simulation as follows.
   a. Predators: Obtain a cup to put your captured prey in. Face away from the selected environment.
   b. Game warden: Spread the beans from the bag labeled "starting population" throughout the selected habitat. Keep the boundaries to about 1 meter (m) by 1 m.

Spread the beans as uniformly as possible so that no beans are sticking together or covering others.

6. Begin the simulation as follows.
   a. Game warden: Direct the predators to face the environment and begin picking up prey.

Tell predators to use a pinching motion with one hand (or forceps) to pick up beans 1 at a time. They must pick up only 1 bean at a time and place it in their cup before taking another bean. Predators should locate the prey using their eyes. Make sure they locate their prey before picking it up.

298 Unit 2 Inside Life

a population and the survival of future generations of a population.

3. be able to describe how variation might lead to change in populations across time.

   They will demonstrate their ability by

   - describing that variations within a species, such as color, might cause individuals in a population with an advantageous characteristic to survive better than individuals without that characteristic and
   - describing that Parts I and II modeled how variations in a characteristic can cause some individuals to survive better than others.

4. be able to apply their knowledge of fossils, rock layers, and the effect of variation on populations.

   They will demonstrate their ability by drawing what fossil birds might be found in rock layers if the food source changed across time.

5. be able to use and interpret models.

   They will demonstrate their ability by

   - simulating predator-prey relationships,
   - describing the simulation in Part I as a sequence of events,
   - drawing a conclusion about data from Part I,
   - predicting the survival of birds with different types of beaks, and
   - describing that aspects of the simulations such as color variations, environments, and beak shapes were simplified.

6. develop the abilities necessary to design an investigation.

   They will practice their skills by

   - using their experience in Part I to help design an investigation in Part II,
   - deciding how to display data from the investigation in a table, and
   - conducting an investigation on how variation in beak type affects the foods captured.

Direct the predators to stop when only 25 percent of the prey remains. For a starting population of 100, 75 will be removed so that 25 remain.

   b. Predators: For a team of 3 predators, each predator should pick up 25 prey.

7. Finish round 1 of predation in your simulation as follows.
   a. Predators: Place the "eaten" prey from your cup into the empty bag. You might need to reuse these later to represent offspring.
   b. Game warden: Collect the remaining (surviving) prey from the environment and sort them by type. Count the number of each color of prey that "survived."

To make them easier to count, arrange the beans in rows.

   c. Game warden and predators: Record in your data table the number of each color of prey that survived as the first-generation surviving population.

8. Prepare for round 2 of predation in your simulation as follows.
   a. Game warden: Simulate reproduction among the surviving prey by adding 3 new beans of the same color for each surviving prey. The number of each type of surviving prey is recorded in your data table (Step 7c).

These beans represent offspring. Obtain them from the bags containing the single colors of beans. If necessary, use the beans that have already been eaten.

   Thoroughly mix the prey that survived with their offspring. You should end up with a total of 100 prey.

   b. Game warden and predators: Record the number of each color of prey in your data table as the second-generation starting population.

9. Repeat Steps 5 through 7 for round 2 of predation. Use the second-generation starting population as your prey. When your simulation is complete and you have recorded your results, sort the colored beans into their respective plastic bags. Then return the bags to the materials area.
10. Suppose each surviving prey after round 2 produced 3 offspring. How many prey of each color would there be? Record this information as the third-generation starting population in your data table.
11. Prepare 2 graphs to show how many of each color prey were in the starting population at the beginning of each generation.

Sometimes it is helpful to describe the results of your investigation in a different way. Graphing your data can represent the information visually from your data table.

Chapter 6 Exploring Change 299

Strategies

Getting Started

Ask students if they can think of some examples of variation in a species. Some examples might be small differences in size, shape, and color of hair, scales, or feathers. Some students might even mention variations in behavior or genes (they will learn about genes in chapter 7). Tell students they will be simulating variations within a species in Part I.

Process and Procedure

Part I: Predator and Prey

Materials

For each team of 4 students

3 plastic cups or other containers
3 forceps (optional)
25 lentils, 25 split peas, 25 navy beans, and 25 red beans in a bag labeled "starting population"
50 split peas in a bag
50 navy beans in a bag
50 red beans in a bag
1 empty bag
1 meterstick
4 colored pencils similar to the color of the dried beans
2 sheets of graph paper
1 large sheet of wrapping paper
2 copies of copymaster 6.3, *Three Generations*
4 copies of copymaster 6.4, *Predictions across Time*

TRCD

For Part I, students will work in teams of 4. The activity uses a jigsaw strategy with half of the teams using one environment and half of the

Population	Number of individuals			
	Lentils	Split peas	Navy beans	Red beans
First Generation Starting				
First Generation Surviving				
Second Generation Starting				
Second Generation Surviving				
Third Generation Starting				

▲ **Figure T6.5 Sample data table for Part I.** Adjust the bean types in your data table according to the bean types you use in your simulation.

	First	Second	Third
lentils	25	20	15
split peas	25	40	55
navy beans	25	25	20
red beans	25	15	10

▲ **Figure T6.6 Sample data for the table in Part I.** These sample data are for three generations of predator and prey relationships.

teams using a different environment. Before the students begin, review the procedure with them. Briefly review the concept of predator-prey relationships.

In Step 1, tell students to gather materials for the activity. Designate an area of your room for each team to place its habitat (wrapping paper). Ask students to spread out the wrapping paper and remind them to crumple the paper. Ask the students to choose one person from their team to be the game warden. The others will be predators.

In Step 3, instruct students to draw a table in their science notebooks similar to the one shown in figure T6.5. Remind the students that the beans are the prey. Students record in the table the number of individuals of each color and label them "first-generation starting population." Explain to students that the prey are individuals of the same species that exhibit color variations.

In Step 5, the predators must turn away from the habitats so that the game wardens can place the prey on the habitat randomly. They can turn around when the game wardens tell them. In Step 6, students begin the simulation. The predators must stop hunting when only 25 percent of the prey remains. For a team of 4, each predator will need to collect 25 prey. If you have more than 4 students in a team, divide the number of prey between the predators so that they collect a total of 75 prey. You might provide forceps for the predators to pick up the prey. Predators should locate the prey with their eyes rather than feeling for them with their hands. This will ensure that the well-camouflaged prey survive better than the other prey. Otherwise, predators might be preferentially "eating" prey based on a variation other than color. Circulate among teams as they conduct the activity and take the opportunity to ask the following probing questions. These questions will help students think about how organisms might change across time.

- "Do some prey survive better than others?"
- "What do you think would cause some prey to survive better than others?"
- "What do you think will happen to the prey population across time?"

In Step 7 at the end of round 1, make sure the game wardens carefully collect all of the beans that remain on the paper and that they sort and count them by color. Students should record the data in the table as the first-generation surviving population.

In Step 8, remind the students that they are simulating reproduction in the surviving population. They must add 3 prey for each surviving prey. Then they can begin round 2 of predation. Make sure students have a total of 100 prey (25 surviving prey and 75 new "baby" prey) for their second-generation starting population in round 2.

In Step 10, students calculate the number of individuals that would be in the third-generation starting population. Instruct all team members to record the 3 starting populations and 2 surviving populations in their data tables. Instruct students to sort and repackage their sets of beans. A sample of a complete data table is shown in figure T6.6.

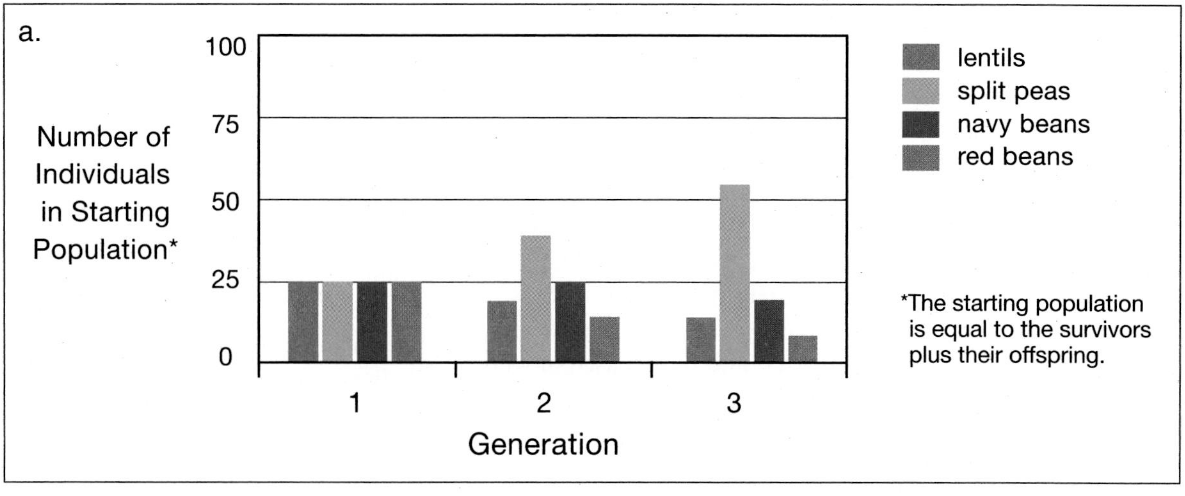

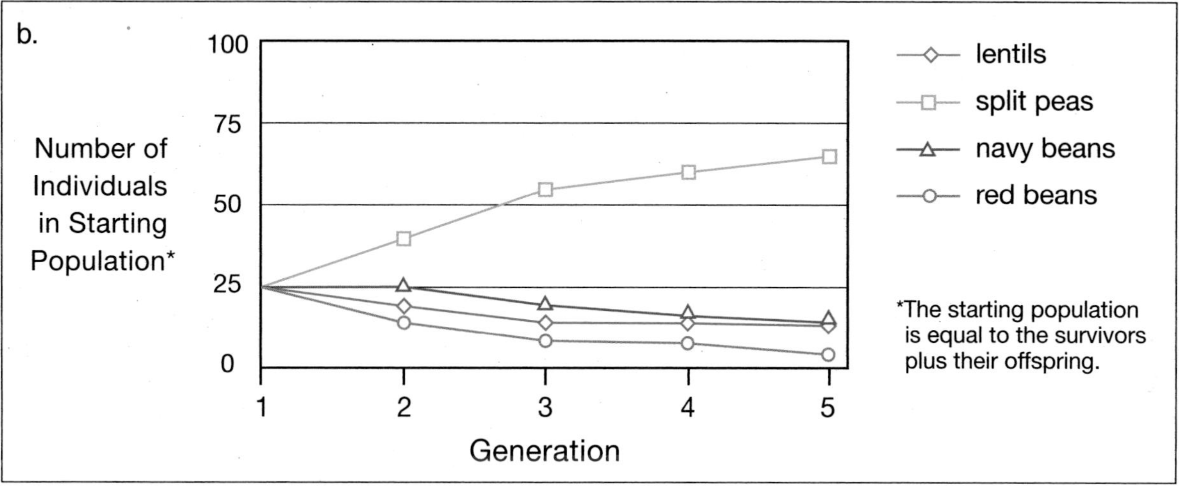

▲ **Figure T6.7 Sample data graphs for the simulation in Part I.** These are sample (a) bar and (b) *x-y* graphs for three generations of predator and prey relationships.

In Step 11, half of each team will prepare graphs. Encourage each student to draw a different kind of graph (bar graph or *x-y* plot, for example). Instruct the remaining team members to go to Step 12 and create a visual representation of what happened during this activity by using their data to color in copymaster 6.3, *Three Generations*. Instruct one student to begin filling in the circles of the first generation while the other fills in the circles of the third generation. Encourage them to work out a way to fill in the circles for the second generation. Remind the students working on Steps 11 and 12 to include on their graph or handout an indication of what the habitat looked like. They could attach a piece of the wrapping paper used or write a description of the habitat. Ask the following probing questions to get students thinking about what they can learn from their graphs:

- "Why do you think prey of one color are decreasing while prey of another color are increasing?"
- "Do you think populations of animals in nature change across time?"
- "What might cause populations in nature to change across time?"

The construction and analysis of the graphs and diagrams in Steps 11 and 12 are a critical but time-consuming part of this activity. The bar graph and the *x-y* plot in figure T6.7 are examples of what you might expect from the students who make the graphs. If you have access to computers and spreadsheet programs, you could use them during this step, but it is also fine to make the graphs with pencil and paper. You might coordinate with the math department to integrate graphing concepts or extend learning in your own class with types of graphs you have already explored.

In Step 13, use the questions to conduct a class discussion. Listen to students' answers to learn how much they understand about the survival of a population with a variation in color.

Answers to Step 13, SE page 300

13a. The starting populations for the second and third generations should include more prey that are of colors similar to the environment and fewer prey of other colors. The change between the first and third generations should be more dramatic than the change between the first and second generations.

13b. Some prey were better camouflaged than others—they blended into the environment. Because they were camouflaged, predators were less likely to see them and eat them.

13c. Once a prey was captured, it could not contribute to the next generation (reproduce). The prey found in future generations consisted only of prey of the color that survived. For example, if more white prey and red prey were captured than the other prey colors, then the future generations had more prey of the other 2 colors (brown and green).

In Step 14, students work in their teams to predict what would happen over the next several generations if the predator remains the same and the environment stays the same. Direct students to record their ideas in their science notebooks. As students continue to discuss their investigation, check their understanding by asking the following probing questions:

- "What physical or behavioral characteristics (besides camouflage) might cause some prey to survive better than others?"

This question will help students generalize from the example of camouflage to other factors that contribute to reproductive success (for example, better night vision, ability to move quickly, ability to survive with little water). Some students might advance to alternative explanations for the unity and diversity of life that are based on other ways of knowing. Acknowledge the wide range of opinions that students might hold, but help them make a distinction between explanations that are derived scientifically (that is, those based on observation and testable hypotheses) and those based in whole or in part on other criteria.

- "Did the prey on your background change color or did the population change across time?"

Students should recognize that the population changed across time. This question will point out to students that individuals don't change, populations do. The sample response for the next question explains this idea further.

- "Did the prey change color from one generation to the next? What did change?"

Students should recognize that the prey didn't change color, the number of prey of a particular color changed. This is because prey with a better camouflaged color were more likely to survive and reproduce. The change in the population results from more individuals being born of a particular color. Students often describe that a characteristic of an individual changes rather than the number of individuals with a particular characteristic changing. This question will give you an opportunity to redirect students away from this misconception.

To make your graphs, follow these directions.

a. Choose 2 team members to prepare graphs. Each team member can make a different kind of graph.

One team member can make a bar graph. The other can make a line graph. Then you can compare them.

b. Both graphs should show the number and color of prey for all 3 generations.

c. Use different-colored pencils that correspond to the 4 colors of the prey.

d. Somewhere on your graph paper indicate what the habitat looked like.

You could paste a sample of the wrapping paper or write a description of the habitat.

12. While 2 team members are making graphs, the remaining team members should do the following.
    a. Get a *Three Generations* handout. On the handout, each generation is represented by 50 circles and each circle represents 2 individuals.
    b. Color each circle to represent members of the starting population of each generation. Use colored pencils that correspond to the colors of prey. For example, if there were 30 split peas in the second-generation starting population, you would color 15 of the circles with a green pencil. You can color only half of a circle if your numbers are not divisible by 2.
    c. Somewhere on your handout indicate what the habitat looked like.

You could paste a sample of the wrapping paper or write a description of the habitat.

13. Compare the completed graphs and handout. Answer Questions 13a–c with your class. Record your own answers in your science notebook.
    a. Which colors of prey survived better than others in the second- and third-generation starting populations?
    b. Predators did not select the surviving prey as much as they did prey of other colors. Why?
    c. What effect did capturing a particular color of prey have on the number of that color in the generations that followed?

300 Unit 2 Inside Life

Answers to Step 14, SE page 301

14a. Prey colors with fewer individuals in the first 3 generations will continue to have fewer individuals in the future. Also, the prey colors that showed an increase in the first 3 generations will continue to increase.

14b. Students might explain that the well-camouflaged prey increased in number and that they also see that pattern in the circles shown on the *Predictions across Time* handout. Some students might say that 2 colors of prey survived equally in the simulation and that this differs from the *Predictions across Time* handout.

After students have completed Step 14, tell them to answer the *Stop and Think* questions in their team and record their answers in their science notebooks.

Answers to Stop and Think—Part I, SE page 301

1. Three predators picked up prey from the first generation. The surviving prey reproduced. The survivors and their offspring were the second generation and were picked over again by predators. The surviving prey reproduced to make the third generation.
2. Students might explain that the graphs and the circle diagrams were more helpful than the data table because the colors helped them see patterns more easily.

   Some students might prefer the graphs because they can easily see numbers and colors, while others may prefer the circle diagrams because they look for a visual pattern without the detail.
3. Students might describe specific conclusions such as which color of prey survived better on their habitat. They might explain that these prey were better camouflaged and were not as easily seen by the predators. Camouflaged prey continued to survive better in future generations.

   Other students might make a general statement explaining that individuals in a population show variation. Some variations are beneficial to individuals and make them more likely to survive. Future generations will have more individuals with beneficial traits than individuals without those traits.

14. You have been thinking about how different factors affected the survival of prey. Now work in your team to predict what might have happened to the prey population across time. Record your ideas in your science notebook.
    a. Predict the starting populations (of all 4 colors) for the next 4 generations. You do not have to predict actual numbers, but describe a trend.
    b. Compare your prediction with the data supplied on the *Predictions across Time* handout. Describe similarities and differences. Explain why you see these patterns. Does your prediction match the predictions on the handout? Explain how you arrived at your prediction.

Stop & THINK

PART I

As a team, study your graphs and the circle diagrams. Consider the following questions and record your team's responses in your science notebook.

1. Describe the simulation as a sequence of events. What was happening to the population of prey at each step in the sequence?
2. Which of the 3 methods of presenting data—the data table, the graphs, or the circle diagrams on the handout—helped you most easily interpret the data? Why?
3. What conclusions can you draw from your data?

Part II: Bird Beaks

In Part I of this investigation, you discovered how predators affect the variation that exists within a population of prey across time. In Part II, you and your team will investigate how **variation** in characteristics of predators affects their survival and their population across time. You will simulate how birds collect their food. The variation within the population of predators is their beaks—they vary in size, shape, and

Part II: Bird Beaks

Materials

For each team of 4 students

1 forceps
4 cups
1 container (plastic tub or dishpan) filled with water
1 spoon
small marbles in a container (approximately 60)
raisins (approximately 60)
uncooked elbow macaroni (approximately 60)
Styrofoam peanuts (packing material, approximately 60)
1 or 2 toothpicks
1 clothespin (spring type)
1 box top (used to contain prey, especially marbles)
4 plastic sandwich bags

For Part II, ask students to name several types of birds. List them on the board. Discuss variations among the birds. Check whether other students in the class know these birds and their beaks. Lead students to a discussion about variations of bird beaks. Ask students why they think birds have different types of beaks. Encourage students to look at the

NOTES:

birds pictured in figure 6.17 in the student book.

In Step 1, tell students to get into teams of 4. Each team member should select a different utensil from the materials table to simulate a beak. Tell students that they are the birds and the forceps, spoon, clothespin, and toothpicks are their beaks. Instruct students to read Step 2 to learn how to use their beaks.

In Step 3, distribute the food to each team. Show students how to float the Styrofoam peanuts in the container of water to simulate water bugs.

In Step 4, students work in teams to design an investigation. Remind them to think about Questions 4a–d to help them decide what to include in the investigation. Circulate among the teams and listen to their discussions. Their discussions will help you learn how much they know about designing an investigation to answer a question.

In Step 5, check the design of each team's investigation. Look for the following:

- All birds should feed at the same time and should feed on the same food. This will allow students to see how variation in beak type affects the amount of food captured.
- There should be a round of feeding for each food type.
- Students should plan how they will keep track of how much food each bird captures.
- Students should develop a data table such as the one in figure T6.8.

function. Figure 6.17 shows examples of birds with different beaks. What happens to birds with a variety of beaks when the food source changes?

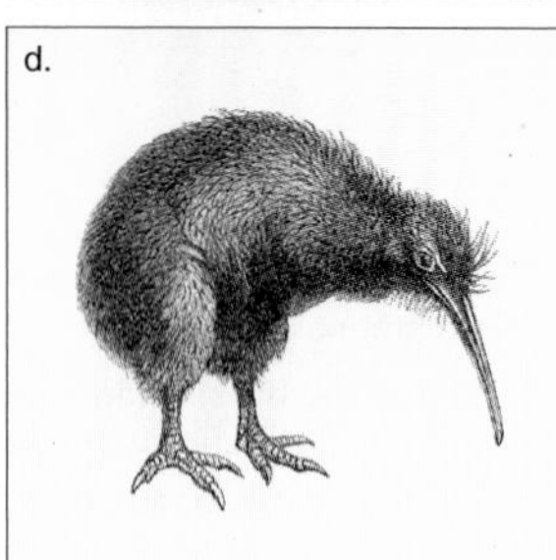

Figure 6.17 Birds have different beaks. Different bird species have different types of beaks. Look at each bird beak: (a) eagle, (b) duck, (c) finch, and (d) kiwi. What influences might have led to the diversity of beak function you see?

Materials

For each team of 4 students

- 1 forceps
- 4 cups
- 1 container (plastic tub or dishpan) filled with water
- 1 spoon
- small marbles in a container (approximately 60)
- raisins (approximately 60)
- uncooked elbow macaroni (approximately 60)
- Styrofoam peanuts (packing material, approximately 60)
- 1 or 2 toothpicks
- 1 clothespin (spring type)
- 1 box top (used to contain prey, especially marbles)
- 4 plastic sandwich bags

	Macaroni worms	Raisin slugs	Marble seeds	Styrofoam water bugs
Clothespin				
Toothpick				
Forceps				
Spoon				

▲ **Figure T6.8 Sample data table for Part II.** Make sure students include a place in their tables for each beak type and food type.

In Step 6, students conduct the investigation they have designed. Suggest that they use the box top to keep the prey in one area, especially when they feed on marble seeds. As students collect data for each of the foods, make sure they are recording the amount of food captured by each bird. In Step 7, tell students to return the materials to the storage area.

In Step 8, ask teams to share their data. Fill in a class data table on the board similar to the one in figure T6.8. Students will have a chance to compare their results with other teams' results.

In Step 9, lead a class discussion of the questions. Adjust the discussion depending on the results of the teams.

NOTES:

Cautions

Use utensils properly.

Process and Procedure

1. Get in your team of 4. Select a utensil (toothpick, clothespin, spoon, or forceps) and a cup from the materials your teacher distributes. Each member of your team must have a different utensil.

The utensils represent types of bird beaks for different species of birds. The cups represent a bird's stomach.

2. You will use the utensil as a bird beak to collect food. Read the following descriptions about how you will collect food with the different bird beaks.
   - Clothespin: Hold the clothespin at the very end so that it opens as wide as possible. Pinch and release with 1 hand.
   - Toothpick: Hold the toothpick in 1 hand and use it to carefully spear the food. Use 1 finger of the opposite hand to push the food off the toothpick into the cup.
   - Forceps: Hold the forceps with 1 hand and squeeze to collect the food.
   - Spoon: Hold the end of the spoon and scoop the food. Use only 1 hand.
3. Obtain bird food from your teacher. You should see that you have marble "seeds," raisin "slugs," macaroni "worms," and Styrofoam "water bugs."
4. Design an investigation to answer this question: "Suppose only 1 food source is available at a time in an environment. Which of the 4 birds living in the environment would be most likely to obtain food and survive?"

   To design the investigation, think about the following things.
   a. How could your experience with the investigation in Part I help you design this investigation?
   b. How many different trials do you need to run?

How many different food sources are you testing?

   c. In a real environment, the 4 birds would be competing for the food source. What does that mean about what the 4 team members will be doing in the investigation?
   d. What would a data table look like for your investigation? Draw one in your science notebook.

Chapter 6 Exploring Change 303

Answers to Step 9, SE page 304

9a. The spoon represented a beak that could capture the greatest variety and highest quantity of foods. The clothespin also captured a wide variety of foods, but lower quantities of each food.

9b. The toothpick beak and the forceps beak are more specialized in the type of food they could capture. Students might have noticed that the toothpick beak was best at capturing raisins and Styrofoam water bugs and the forceps beak was best at capturing macaroni worms and raisins. These two beaks were not successful at capturing marble seeds.

Overall, the spoon beak should have been able to capture all the foods successfully. Predators that feed like this are called generalists. Students might want to answer Question 9b with "spoon beak." Encourage students to focus on which beak was only successful at capturing one or two types of food. Although the spoon beak might have captured more Styrofoam water bugs than the toothpick beak, the toothpick beak was only able to capture Styrofoam water bugs and raisins. Predators that focus on only a few types of food are called specialists. Focusing on those differences might help students understand how the different bird beaks show different adaptations.

In Step 10, instruct students to answer the questions individually in their science notebooks. Answers to Questions 10a–c follow. Students are likely to provide different answers because of differences in their results. Make sure they give answers consistent with the class results.

Answers to Step 10, SE page 304

10a. Generally, the bird with the toothpick beak would have the greatest chance to survive because it is specialized at eating the Styrofoam water bugs. The bird with the spoon beak also would survive because it can eat almost anything.

10b. Generally, the bird with the spoon beak or forceps beak would have the greatest chance to survive because both are successful at collecting seeds. The clothespin-beaked bird might be able to eat a little, but would probably die out eventually. The bird with the toothpick beak would not be able to eat at all and therefore would not survive.

10c. Generally, the bird with the spoon beak would have the greatest chance to survive because it can eat all types of food and would not have to rely on 1 or 2 specific types. The bird with the clothespin beak also might survive because it could eat all types of food even though it might not be able to eat as much as the bird with the spoon beak.

In Step 11, tell students to read the paragraph about the advantages and disadvantages of variation. You might want to take time to facilitate a class discussion of the question, "What was the purpose of the two lab activities?" This will give you an opportunity to hear what the students have learned and help prepare students to answer the *Reflect and Connect* questions. Then instruct students to answer the *Reflect and Connect* questions in their science notebooks.

Answers to Reflect and Connect, SE page 305

1a. Variation causes individuals in a population to have slightly different characteristics. The individuals with beneficial characteristics will be more likely

5. When you have an designed your investigation, check it with your teacher.
6. Conduct your investigation. Record your results in your data table.
7. When you have completed your investigation, return your materials to the storage area.
8. Share your data with the rest of the class as your teacher directs.
9. Compare the results from your team's investigation with other teams' results by discussing the following questions as a class.
   a. Which beak captured the greatest variety of foods?
   b. Which beak was best at capturing an individual food?

Was there a beak that successfully captured only 1 or 2 types of food?

10. In Part I, you simulated 3 generations of a prey population. Now make some predictions about what would happen to the predator population in this simulation after several generations. Answer Questions 10a–c in your science notebook.

    Which bird would have the greatest chance to survive if
   a. there were flooding and only water bugs were left? Why?
   b. there were a drought and only seeds were left? Why?
   c. changes occur so that there is some food but a limited supply of each kind? Why?
11. Read the following paragraph. Then use the TSAR procedure to answer the following questions:
   - How does variation in the predator population affect the foods the organism can eat?
   - How might the variation be an advantage or a disadvantage to the predator?

   Characteristics of a species, such as beak shape, influence what abilities to eat an organism will have. These abilities influence how likely an individual is to survive. A characteristic can change to an advantage or a disadvantage when an organism's environment or its prey changes. Individuals that are better at coping in an environment are more likely to survive and reproduce. When they reproduce, these individuals pass their advantageous characteristics on to their offspring. The result is that, across time, more individuals will have characteristics that help them survive in a particular environment.

304 | Unit 2 Inside Life

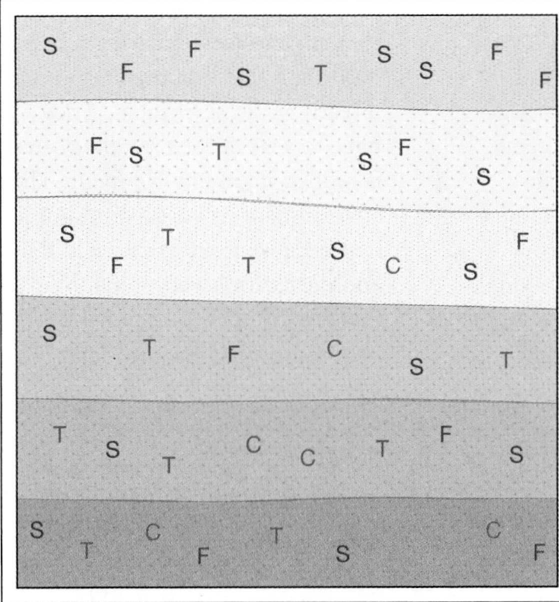

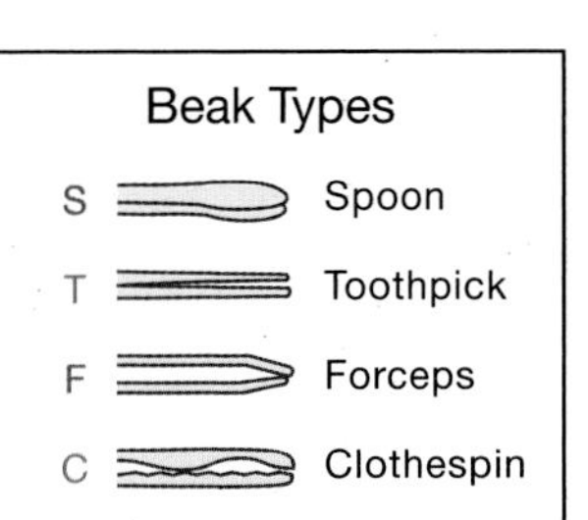

◀ **Figure T6.9 Example drawing for *Reflect and Connect* Question 3.** Make sure students illustrate the trend described in the answer to Question 3. Students can write out the names or draw pictures that represent the fossils. Check that they label their drawings appropriately.

to survive than the individuals without those characteristics.

1b. The survival of an individual with beneficial characteristics gives that individual a chance to reproduce. That individual's offspring will be more likely to have the traits that its parents had that allowed them to survive. The offspring's offspring will then be more likely have the beneficial traits, and so on.

2. Variations within a species, such as color, might cause individuals in a population with an advantageous characteristic to survive better than individuals without that characteristic. Also, variations between species, such as beak shape, might cause some species to be able to capture food better than others. The species that can capture food better would be more likely to survive. Other characteristics that might increase the chance for survival might be the ability to move quickly to get away from predators or having thicker fur to keep warm in a cold climate. Across time, the characteristics that cause some individuals to survive better will result in more of the population having those characteristics.

3. Students might create slightly different drawings of rock layers depending on their results. Figure T6.9 gives one example of a drawing that a student might

Answers to Reflect and Connect are on TE pages 304–307.

Reflect and Connect

Answer the following questions in your science notebook.

1. Think about the concepts of variation and survival as you answer Questions 1a–b in your notebook.
   a. How does variation affect the survival of an individual in a population?
   b. How does the survival of a particular individual affect the makeup of future generations of a population?
2. What might cause a population of organisms within a species to change across time? List at least 3 causes.

Think about variations within a species and between species.

3. The fossil record contains evidence for descent with modification in organisms. What would the fossil record of birds look like in the following scenario?

   Hundreds of thousands of years ago, the 4 birds and 4 food types you investigated in Part II lived in a particular location. Across time, the macaroni worms became the primary food source. This affected the 4 populations of birds.

   Draw a series of rock layers and label the fossils you would find in each.

Think about how the fossils in the rock layers for the years with more macaroni worms would differ from fossils in other layers.

4. Think about simulations and models as you answer Questions 4a–b in your notebook.
   a. In what specific ways do the simulations in Parts I and II model how populations change across time?

For Part I, how is the environment simulated? Through variation? Reproduction? For Part II, how were characteristics modeled?

   b. In what ways do these simulations simplify what actually happens to populations across time? Provide specific examples.

create. The oldest rock layers would have an equal number of fossils of all birds with each type of beak. At some point, younger rock layers would have more fossils of birds that are more successful at eating macaroni worms, such as the birds with spoon or forceps beaks. There also would be fewer fossils of less successful birds, such as those with toothpick or clothespin beaks.

Students might also indicate in their drawing that the rock layers would show a change in fossils of food types. Just below the rock layers that show a change in the birds, the rock layers would show an increase in the number of fossils of macaroni worms compared with the other types of food in the layers.

4a. Parts I and II modeled how variations in a characteristic can cause some individuals to survive better than others. Some characteristics are more advantageous than others. The individuals that survive can reproduce and have higher survival rates of descendants. As more individuals with advantageous characteristics reproduce, more of the population has the advantageous characteristics.

4b. The color variations in Part I were simplified because the colors were dramatically different. Individuals within a species usually have only slight color differences in hair, feathers, scales, and so on. The process of catching prey in both Parts I and II was simplified because predators have to look harder for their food than just looking at an area directly in front of them. They have to search for prey that often is hidden in an environment. The environment in Part I was simplified because it was relatively flat and didn't look very much like a real environment. The bird beaks were simplified because each beak was represented by a different object. Real bird beaks differ in their shape and length, but in many ways look very similar. Some students might recognize that for many species there are months or a year, instead of minutes, between the appearances of each new generation. Some students might also explain that

NOTES:

EXPLAIN

Learning about Life: A Great Discovery

In the previous activities, you have been looking at evidence for change across time. Along the way, you have been developing an understanding of biologic **evolution**—a theory that explains how species change across time. So how did the theory of evolution come about? How long has the theory been around? And who first thought of it? Although many scientists and philosophers contributed ideas, we generally attribute the theory of evolution to Charles Darwin (see figure 6.18). In *Learning about Life*, you will work with a partner to learn about Darwin and the evidence that supports his theory of evolution.

Materials

Natural Selection handout (optional)

Process and Procedure

1. In your notebook, predict which animals should be most alike, ones from the same continent or ones from different continents. Share your prediction with your partner.
2. Read *The Voyage* to learn how Darwin's travels answered the question about similarity among animals.
3. Compare your prediction from Step 1 to what you learned from reading, *The Voyage*.
4. Read *Fossils* to understand the role of buried evidence in Darwin's theory.

Figure 6.18 Charles Darwin (1809–1882). Charles Darwin studied medicine and theology to please his father, but his real interest was in natural history. Eventually, he left medical school to enroll at the University of Cambridge to study natural history, the term then used for biology. His mentor, the Reverend John Henslow, was a famous botanist who later recommended Darwin to the captain of the HMS *Beagle*.

the process of individuals reproducing is much more complicated than adding beans.

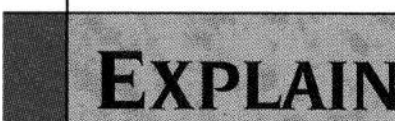

EXPLAIN

Learning about Life: A Great Discovery

Activity Overview

In *Learning about Life: A Great Discovery*, students will work with a partner and read about Charles Darwin's observations and how these observations provided the evidence for him to propose the theory of evolution. Students will learn that the evidence of change across time they have been learning about is similar to the evidence collected by Darwin. They will also learn that they were modeling natural selection in the previous activity, *Who Will Survive?* By the end of this activity, students will have an understanding of natural selection and biological evolution.

Before You Teach

Background Information

Evidence for Evolution

Although not enough discoveries have been made to produce a continuous fossil record, we have a general understanding of large-scale patterns and trends in evolutionary history. Each fossil is the same age as the layer in which it is found, and thus by looking at rock layers we can see a pattern in the species that has been fossilized. The fossil record provides persuasive evidence for evolution and descent with modification. The pattern of appearance of fossil species through geologic time is critical for reconstructing evolutionary relationships.

One common misunderstanding of the fossil record as it relates to evolution is that fossil species form a single line of descent. This view of evolution is called orthogenesis and has been rejected by paleontologists as a model of evolutionary change. The fossil record reveals that the history of life can be understood as a densely branching bush with many short branches (short-lived lineages). Evolution does not occur in a straight line toward a goal; instead, evolution is like a branching bush, with no predetermined goal.

READING

The Voyage

Darwin changed his focus from medicine to theology in college. He was presented with an opportunity of a lifetime at the age of 22. In 1831, he was invited to go on an incredible journey aboard a ship. He was to explore, observe, and map the voyage. Figure 6.19 shows the path of the voyage. It turned out that on this journey Darwin began his study to explain the great diversity of life. Darwin's observations of nature led him to reject many cherished ideas about the natural world. As a result, he developed a different understanding. His study eventually led to new ideas about geologic and biological change across time and to the theory of evolution.

Darwin's 5-year journey began aboard the ship the *Beagle*. The primary mission of the *Beagle* was to chart sections of the coast of South America. While the ship's crew completed that work, Darwin made remarkable observations. Darwin also collected thousands of specimens and took detailed notes on all that he saw.

Darwin noticed that many plants and animals have **adaptations**. Adaptations are characteristics that help an organism survive and reproduce within a particular environment. Specialized body structures such as protective shells or wings are examples of adaptations. Many organisms use the same type of body structure for different functions. Darwin found

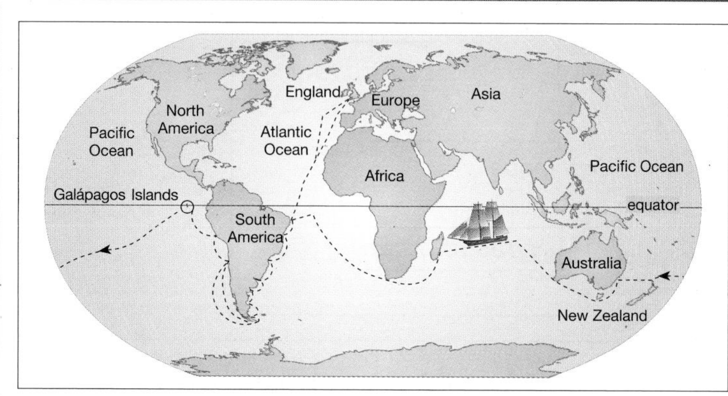

Source: Darwin Museum Down House. Courtesy of the Royal College of Surgeons of England

▲ **Figure 6.19 Voyage of the HMS *Beagle*.** Darwin sailed around the world on the *Beagle*. The route included stops in South America and a stay in the Galápagos Islands. During the trip, Darwin collected evidence that he later used to support the theory of evolution.

NOTES:

The fossil horse series is a good example (see figure T6.10). Horses did not evolve in a straight line. The fossil record indicates that many horse species have been present at the same time. They were adapted to different diets and had various numbers of toes. We often have the impression that evolution occurs in a straight line because only one genus happens to still be alive today. The species we see today are not the "targets" of evolution; instead, they are merely the current surviving representatives, surviving branches of a once sprawling bush.

In the evaluate, students will investigate a series of fossils of elephant-like species.

In addition to the fossil record, other lines of evidence supporting evolution and common descent include similarities in body structure and embryological development, the molecular structure of organisms, and the geographical distribution of organisms (biogeography). The lines of evidence are sometimes called the pillars of evidence for evolution. Read the paragraphs that follow to learn more about the other lines of evidence.

Examples of similar body structures include the bones in the forelimb (see figure 6.2 in the student book) and in the ear and the jaw. Structures that have the same basic parts and are in a similar position but serve a different function are called **homologous** structures. For example, forelimbs are used for very different purposes including writing (humans), flying (bats and birds), and running (many animals). Reptiles have several bones in their lower jaw. All mammals have only one bone in their lower jaw but have several bones in the ear that are homologous to jawbones in reptiles (see figure T6.11). Many organisms also have structures that are only partially functional or not functional at all. These structures are called **vestigial structures** and were functional in an ancestor of the species but now are greatly reduced. Some examples are the human caecal appendix and the eyes in many cave animals.

Diverse species also share similarities in their early developmental stages. Even though vertebrates are very different as adults, the embryos of different vertebrate species look very similar in the early stages of development.

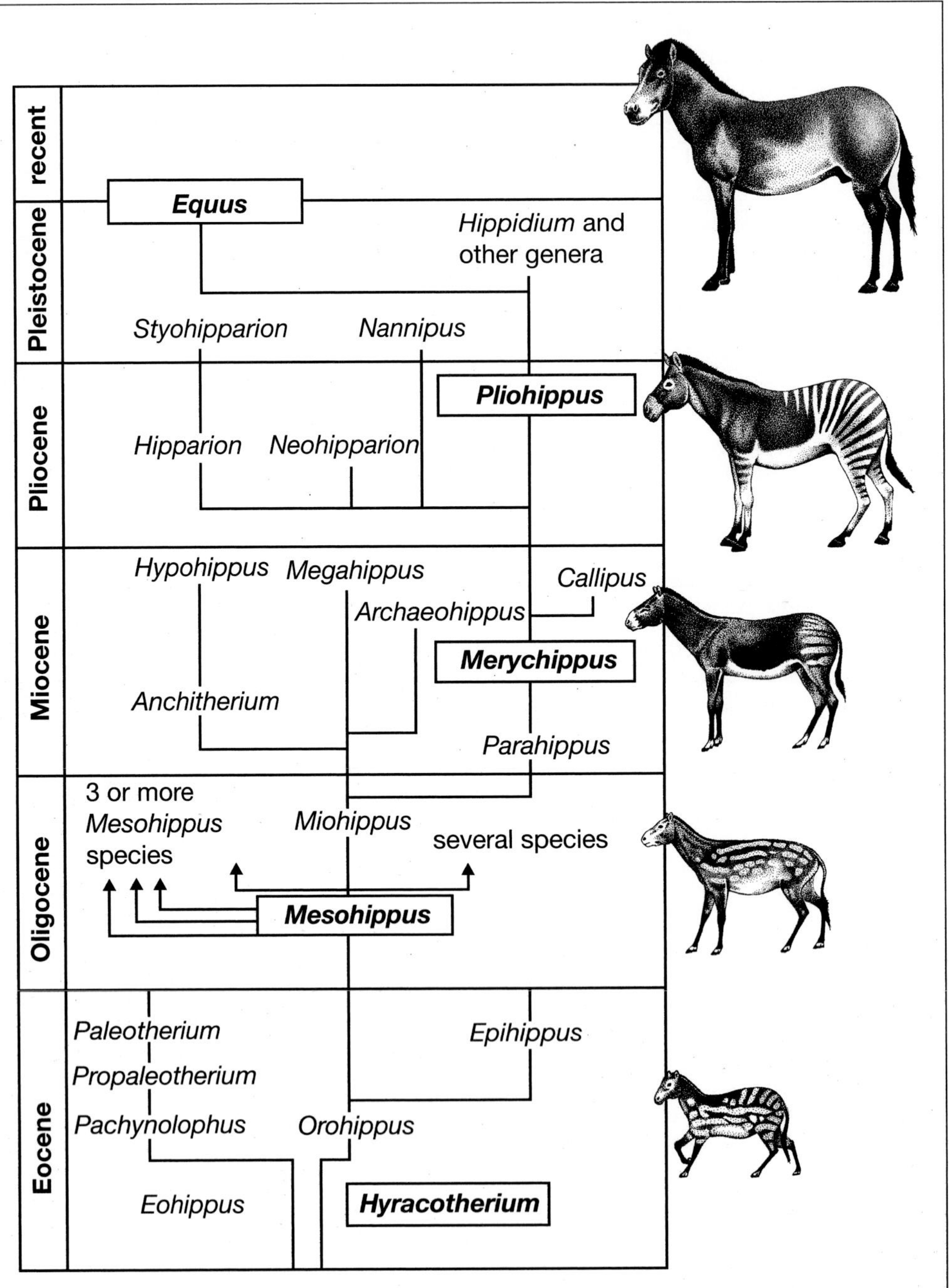

▲ **Figure T6.10 Horse evolution.** Descriptions of the evolution of horses often provide a simplified explanation of how horses evolved. In many cases, four or five ancestral horse species are described and illustrated, which show a progression of four-toed to one-toed horses and an increase in size. Brief explanations do not have the space to include the number of horse species that lived during the same period of time or the small species of horse that existed at the same time that many horse species were larger. These explanations are more linear and leave out the many branches of the evolutionary tree.

Darwin's idea of common descent has been reinforced by discoveries in molecular biology and biochemistry. With new technology, scientists have been able to look at DNA evidence to learn about the evolutionary history of organisms. The molecules that make up genes undergo evolutionary change just as morphological structures undergo change. Students will learn about this evidence in chapter 8.

Biogeography, the study of the geographical distribution of organisms, also has contributed evidence for descent from common ancestors. Biogeography helps explain why the faunas of Europe and North America are relatively similar, whereas the faunas of Africa and South America are so different. If one species has descended from a common ancestor, there must be some geographical continuity from where the common ancestor is found to where the new species is found. The present distribution of organisms is due to the history of their dispersal from their points of origin. The faunas of two continents become more and more different the longer the continents have been isolated from one another. Students may have studied this with Australia. They will see examples with South America in chapter 13.

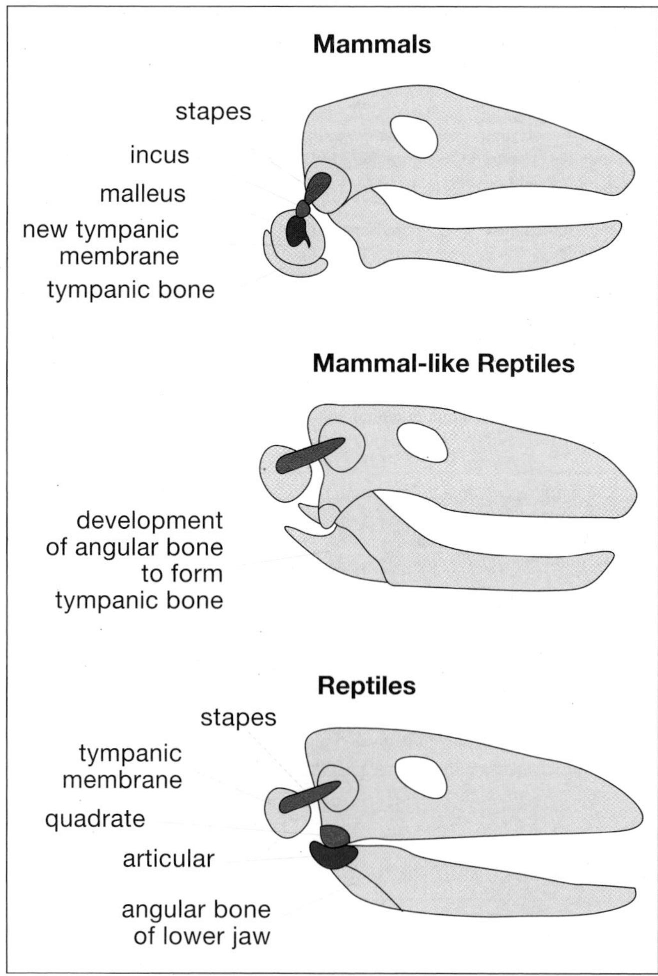

▲ **Figure T6.11 Mammalian and reptilian jawbones.** Parts of the jaw are common to reptiles and mammals.

Natural Selection and Evolution

Darwin observed that within a species there is variation in their characteristics. He was also aware that for centuries plant and animal breeders had bred organisms to emphasize or increase certain prized characteristics. Darwin reasoned that perhaps selection in nature also could bring about change in the characteristics of organisms. Some organisms survive better than others because of the characteristics they possess. Darwin called this process natural selection. Natural selection provides a way to explain how new species could eventually appear from ancestral forms; it is a mechanism for evolution. Alfred Russel Wallace developed a similar explanation around the same time. To learn more about the observations and inferences Darwin used to propose the idea of natural selection, read the sidebar *Natural Selection* in the student book.

Darwin was unable to explain what causes the variation in a species or how it was passed from one generation to another. Inheritance provides the explanation that Darwin was looking for and will be discussed in chapter 7. Students will develop a better understanding of evolution once they understand inheritance and DNA (chapter 8).

Natural selection is a process of elimination. The individuals with characteristics that make them well adapted to an environment survive and reproduce. Sometimes this is described as "survival of the fittest." This phrase was not used in the student book because students are most familiar with fitness in terms of a measure of strength and athletic ability. In the context of natural selection, "to be fit" means that an organism possesses a characteristic that increases its chances of survival relative to other individuals of the species in a population.

Another confusing term is selective pressure or selective force. There is no pressure or force that "pushes" a population to a more adapted state. Evolutionary biologists borrowed this term from the physical sciences. Selective pressure is a metaphor to indicate the severity of selection. Selection favors characteristics that increase an individual's chance of survival. Selection does not cause beneficial characteristics to appear in a population.

Examples of Evolution

Evolution, in the minds of many students, is a prehistoric process that produced the diversity of life around us and then stopped. They may fail to realize that evolution not only continues, but it can be observed and even subjected to experimental manipulation. The following examples show evolution through natural selection.

Darwin's finches. Darwin's finches continue to be studied by Peter and Rosemary Grant on the Galápagos archipelago. Factors including environmental stress, competition, and predation affect finch populations, especially with regard to beak length and sexual selection. Diversity and genetic variation within populations are important to survival. Recent work by the Grants suggests that some genetic variability was derived from interspecies hybridization.

Antibiotic resistance. Mechanisms of natural selection also occur at the molecular level, as in antibiotic resistance. Among bacteria, resistance can be acquired through (1) mutations in the bacterial genome and (2) transferable genetic elements. Resistance genes can even be exchanged with individuals from a different species. Humans create environments, such as hospitals, that promote resistance to antibiotics. Hospitals contain concentrations of various bacteria, use various disinfectants on hospital surfaces, serve patients prone to infection, and administer antibiotics to many of those patients. Animal husbandry also contributes to the spread of antibiotic-resistant genes by using antibiotics on livestock as prophylaxis (treatment to prevent disease) and as growth promoters.

Evolution of the AIDS epidemic. Evolution, as Darwin first pointed out, is continuous and ongoing but typically occurs at rates that are slow in human terms. The AIDS epidemic, in contrast, is very much a story of evolution in a human time frame.

The epidemic and the evolution of its causative agent, the human immunodeficiency virus (HIV), starkly exposes in months and years every element of Darwin's thesis. The entire argument of *On the Origin of Species* is demonstrated in the brief history of this one virus: variation within populations, descent with modification, and adaptation through natural selection. This virus resists efforts to bring it under control by constantly changing and adapting to its environmental conditions.

In this activity, students have the opportunity to read about scientists whose ideas revolutionized our way of thinking about Earth and the life upon it. These ideas did not always match the prevailing thoughts of the day. Scientists had to provide evidence to support their ideas to convince other scientists and society. Students see that the process of science is open to peer scrutiny and depends on the accumulation of confirming evidence rather than on popular opinion or on belief systems.

The *National Science Education Standards* support the use of historical examples to help students understand scientific inquiry, the nature of scientific knowledge, and the interactions between science and society. By learning about the human dimensions of science, students can appreciate how difficult it was for scientific innovators to "think outside the box." Those conclusions that we now take for granted once were cutting-edge science. People greatly distrusted those conclusions until they were supported by a wide variety of confirmations and evidence.

Scientists have always worked within the context of societal, cultural, and personal beliefs and ways of viewing the world. When science is at odds with the prevailing thought, it is essential that it be consistent with experimental and observational evidence about nature. It is through this process of adhering to evidence that important changes in how we look at the world have become commonplace knowledge.

What has distinguished science from other ways of knowing throughout history is that it depends on the use of empirical standards, logical arguments, and skepticism. Rather than being based on myths, personal beliefs, religious values, or superstition (all of which may have a place in

The Voyage, continued

three birds in South America that used their wings for purposes other than flight (penguin, steamer duck, and rhea). Each bird wing showed a different adaptation. Study figure 6.20 and think about what adaptation each bird has.

Darwin had many questions about his observations. One of the most important questions had to do with the geographical distribution of the organisms. Although similar to organisms in Europe, the plants and animals that lived in South America and the southeastern Pacific were distinct. That was not surprising. But what perplexed Darwin was the fact that organisms living in temperate (mild) areas of South America were more similar to organisms living in tropical areas of South America than to organisms living in temperate regions of Europe. Orchids, army ants, marine iguanas, and penguins are species well suited to their environment. Yet each seemed to be related to species living in other parts of that huge continent. How could one account for both the similarities and the differences among species? How could one account for their specific patterns of geographical distribution?

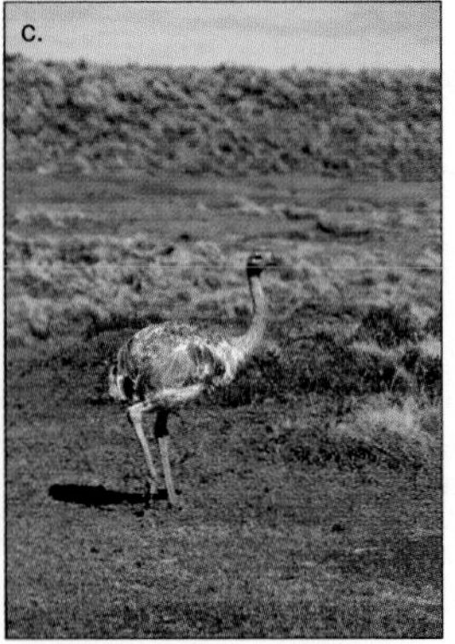

▲ **Figure 6.20 Wing adaptations: (a) South American penguin, (b) steamer duck, and (c) rhea.** For what purpose do you think each bird's wings are adapted?

308 Unit 2 Inside Life

society), science is based on evidence. As such, scientific explanations are subject to change as new evidence becomes available. New explanations are open to criticism and must withstand the review of peers. That the ideas of Charles Darwin and Alfred Russel Wallace and others have stood the test of time is credit to the rigor of their scientific explanations and the validity of the evidence on which they are based.

Materials

For the teacher

posters of Darwin's voyage of the *Beagle* (optional)

1 copy of Darwin's book *On the Origin of Species*

For each student

1 copy of copymaster 6.5, *Natural Selection* (optional)

Advance Preparation

If available, have posters of Darwin's voyage posted around the room and have Darwin's *On the Origin of Species* available for students to look at. If you decide your students would benefit from additional reading about natural selection, make copies of copymaster 6.5, *Natural Selection*.

Answers to Stop and Think Questions 1 and 2 are on TE page 310.

Stop & THINK

QUESTIONS 1–2

Read each question before writing an answer in your notebook. Then compare your answers to a teammate's. Revise your answers based on what you learn.

1. List 3 adaptations from the human body and explain why they are important.
2. What surprised Darwin about the adaptations of animals on the same continent compared to those on different continents?

READING

Fossils

Darwin did not just make observations of living organisms. He also paid careful attention to the fossils he found. He noticed that younger rock layers contained fossils that looked very similar to species that still existed. He also noticed that older rock layers had fewer fossils but they looked like existing species. Two examples of fossils discovered by Darwin are shown in figure 6.21. Remember that younger rock layers are found closer to the surface. Older rock layers are found in the lower layers farther beneath the surface.

The fossils found in rocks of different ages differ because life on Earth has changed. For example, if we begin at the present layer of rock

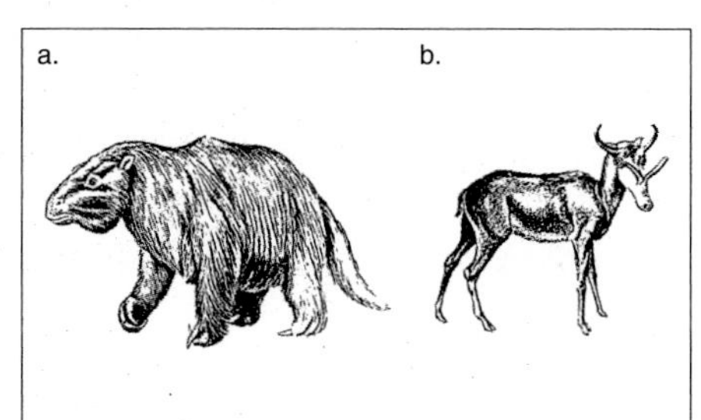

▲ **Figure 6.21 Similar species in the past and present: (a) extinct *Megatherium*, (b) extinct *Syndyoceras*.** Darwin found abundant fossil remains. Many of the remains were similar but not identical to similar existing species. What do these species remind you of? Similar species of both animals live in South America today.

As You Teach

Outcomes and Indicators of Success

By the end of this activity, students should

1. be able to use the idea of natural selection to explain the success of certain members of a species.

   They will demonstrate their ability by

   - describing the details of the mechanism at work in the simulations including variation, reproductive potential, and differential survival;
   - inferring that an antibiotic acts as a selective pressure on a population of bacteria by limiting the survival of bacteria to those that are resistant to the antibiotic; and
   - describing that some species become extinct because they were no longer able to survive in their environment.

2. be able to give examples of evolution within families of plants and animals.

   They will demonstrate their ability by

   - describing that evolution helps explain the diversity of life on Earth because the process of natural selection leads to new species;
   - describing what evolution means using six keywords (adaptation, population, natural selection, selective pressure, variation, species); and
   - describing that the theory of evolution helps explain that across time, different characteristics are selected for that can lead to new species and can change the life on Earth.

3. recognize that evidence is used to support a scientific theory.

   They will demonstrate their recognition by giving examples of the types of evidence Darwin gathered such as fossils, rock layers, adaptations, and similarities in body structures.

4. recognize that scientists often develop similar explanations around the same time.

They will demonstrate their recognition by justifying why they think scientists make similar discoveries or develop similar explanations.

Strategies

Getting Started

Ask students if they have heard of Charles Darwin (most have) and if they know what he did. Listen as they give their ideas about what he did and said. Discuss with them whether they think his ideas were accepted at the time. Explain to them that they are going to read about Darwin, how he observed species around the world, and how he eventually proposed the theory of evolution through natural selection.

Process and Procedure

In Step 1, try to get students to think about how separation distance affects species similarity. Ensure that they have enough time to make predictions in their notebooks.

In Step 2, students read about some of the observations Darwin made during his voyage on the HMS *Beagle*. There are five sections of reading in this activity. Stop and Think questions are at the end of some readings. Students make a T-table during their longest reading.

If you want to engage their thinking about adaptations, consider asking the following probing questions:

- "What are adaptations?"

They should understand that adaptations are advantageous characteristics that help an organism survive and reproduce.

- "Can you think of some examples of adaptations that have not been listed in the chapter?"

Examples include the ability of a chameleon to change the color of its skin, thick fur for animals in a cold climate, or the ability of eagles to see prey at great distances.

Students might want to know what the wings of the birds pictured in figure 6.20 (student book) are adapted for. Penguins use their wings as fins. The steamer duck uses its wings as paddles. Rheas use their wings as sails.

In Step 3, encourage students to compare and contrast their predictions from Step 1 to their understanding from the reading. Then ask them to complete the tasks in *Stop and Think*, Questions 1 and 2.

Answers to Stop and Think—Questions 1 and 2, SE page 309

1. Answers will vary. At this point, consider just about any answer; focus on student justification. Most students will mention physical adaptations such as arm length, skin color, or ability to run fast.
2. Students should recognize that Darwin was surprised about the greater similarity among animals from the same continent versus animals in the same climate. This ultimately led him to think that similar species came from a common ancestor, which was closer in proximity than closer in type of environment.

In Step 4, students read about fossils and evolution. Get students to focus on the last paragraph, which lists 6 important lines of evidence supporting evolution.

Answers to Stop & Think Question 3 are on TE page 311.

Fossils, continued

and examine older and older layers of rock, we eventually will come to a layer where no fossils of humans are present. Farther down through the layers, we will come to layers where no fossils of mammals are present, and so on.

Fossils are not the only piece of evidence for change across time. Scientists have identified six other lines of evidence that support evolution. They are (1) the structural similarities among organisms, (2) the geographical distribution of organisms, (3) the embryological similarities among organisms, (4) the pattern of organism groupings, (5) the molecular similarities among organisms, and (6) the direct observation of evolutionary changes in the laboratory and in the wild.

Stop & THINK

QUESTION 3

3. Use what you have learned so far about Darwin and work with your partner to complete the following tasks. Record your own responses in your science notebook.
   a. Give examples of types of evidence that Darwin gathered to develop the theory of evolution. Record at least 3.
   b. Compare the types of evidence Darwin gathered with the types of evidence you have learned about in this chapter. Think about these things when you respond:
      - Did anything Darwin observed remind you of something you learned about earlier in this chapter?
      - Were any of Darwin's observations new information for you?

5. Make a T-table in your notebook with the headings "Fact or Idea from Reading" and "Question I Have."
6. Complete the T-table you drew in Step 5 as you read *Natural Selection*.
7. Exchange T-tables with your partner and attempt to answer each other's questions. You may want to talk to other students or your teacher as well.
8. Read *Evolution* to discover the role of "descent with modification" in evolution.

310 Unit 2 Inside Life

Answers to Stop and Think—Question 3, SE page 310

3a. Here are some examples of evidence collected by Darwin. Make sure students list at least 3.

- Plants and animals have adaptations.
- Some species have similar body structures that are adapted for different purposes.
- Organisms living in temperate areas of South America were more similar to organisms living in tropical areas of South America than to organisms living in temperate areas of Europe.
- Many fossils look similar to existing species.
- Younger rock layers had more fossils that were similar to existing species than older rock layers.

3b. Students should explain that they investigated rock layers and the fossil record in *Gifts from the Past*. They might explain that they learned about how fossils indicate what the environment was like when the rock formed, but that Darwin noticed differences in the similarity of fossils, depending on the relative age of the rock layer. Students also should recognize that they learned about adaptations when they did Parts I and II of *Who Will Survive?*, but they were called advantageous characteristics in the activity. Students might explain that they were simulating variations instead of observing the adaptations of species in nature. Students might explain that Darwin's observation about the geographical distribution of organisms was new information that they hadn't learned earlier in the chapter. They might also mention specific examples given in the figures such as the different wing adaptations observed by Darwin.

READING

Natural Selection

On the Galápagos Islands, Darwin took particular notice of the incredible variety of plants and animals. He also noticed how these same plants and animals varied from island to island and from habitat to habitat on the same island. When he arrived back in England, he studied the specimens he had collected much more carefully. He began to think about the variety of species and how this variety came to be. He also thought about how these many organisms could coexist and how they were geographically distributed.

Darwin knew that the characteristics of organisms varied, but he did not know what caused those variations or how these characteristics were passed on to the next generation. It turns out that near the same time, two other scientists were working on these very ideas. You will learn about these two scientists in the next two chapters.

Although he could not explain what caused variation in organisms, Darwin observed that the individuals of any species have a lot of variation in their characteristics. Darwin reasoned that variations in a population might result in some individuals being slightly better adapted to a certain environment than others. Because well-adapted organisms tend to survive, they are more likely to produce more offspring. The adaptations that improved their ability to survive then would be passed to their offspring.

Across time, as this pattern continued, future generations would look more and more like the well-adapted organism. The other organisms that were not as well adapted would die out. We now generally refer to this process as **natural selection**. Natural selection is a mechanism for biological evolution. Evolution only occurs when there is variation within a population and when there are mechanisms that affect variation.

You experienced the process of natural selection in the activities you did in this chapter. In a population of one species, well-camouflaged prey (beans) had a better survival rate and produced more offspring than prey that stood out against the background. Let's think about this. The characteristic of blending in with the environment is an advantage to that individual. This helps to be hidden from a predator. In other words, this characteristic was adaptive. It was "selected for" in nature. Predators were the **selective pressure**. They acted as a selective pressure that influenced which prey survived. Across time, organisms that lacked this adaptive characteristic tended to die out. Organisms that were more easily spotted were more often eaten! In this example, natural selection acted on a color variation within a species.

"Selection" can be a confusing term. Selection occurs in a population when an individual possesses a characteristic that increases its chances of survival.

The finches found on the Galápagos Islands are good examples of similar bird species with different beaks. A few million years ago, one species of finch migrated to the Galápagos Islands from Central or South America. The ancestral finch species was a ground dweller and ate seeds. Evidence collected by scientists supports the idea that 13 species of finch have evolved from this single common ancestor. Across time, each species of finch developed

Chapter 6 Exploring Change | 311

In Step 5, make sure students make the T-table before they begin reading. Consider walking around the room to assess if they are filling out the table as they read. This would be some evidence of active reading. Some possible questions are

- "What's the evidence of natural selection?"
- How does natural selection influence evolution?

Students will probably assume that scientists have collected evidence about natural selection, but might not be able to think of any examples. Some examples to share with students are Peter and Rosemary Grant's research of the Galápagos finches since 1973 and research conducted on fruit flies (*Drosophila*).

There are many potential areas of confusion for students while they begin to develop an understanding of evolution and natural selection. A common misunderstanding or preconception is that organisms adapt to their environment. Along the same line, students often think that variation in a population or a new characteristic is acquired in response to the environment: organisms get new adaptations because they "have to" to survive. If you hear students using this type of language, ask the following probing questions to help them begin to develop an accurate understanding of evolution and natural selection:

- "Does there have to be variation in a population for natural selection to take place?"

Students should realize that variation must be present in a population before evolution can occur. Remind students that organisms either survive or don't survive. Whether an organism survives depends on the characteristics that it already possesses. Then after an individual survives, it can pass on its characteristics to the next generation.

- "Why might one individual in a population have a different version of a characteristic than another individual in the same population?"
- "What causes the variation in a population?"

Students should be unsure about what causes variation because they haven't learned about this yet. Explain that changes in organisms can occur by chance and that they will learn what causes the appearance of new characteristics in chapter 8. In this chapter, they will learn that mutations are one cause of increased genetic variation. If a student realizes that mutations might be a cause of genetic change, acknowledge the idea and tell the student that he or she is on the right track. Then, to bring out another common misunderstanding, ask the student when the mutation occurred. Students might think that a mutation occurred in the organism as it struggled to survive in its environment. Explain that a mutation must occur in a germ cell (sperm or egg cell) in order for it to be passed on to the next generation. Tell them they will learn about genetic variation and mutations in chapter 8.

- "Does natural selection lead to 'perfect' species?"

The language used to describe evolution often leads us to think that natural selection and evolution lead to perfection. Phrases such as "evolved into a new species" or "this species was better adapted and survived" can be misleading. Focus the students on the idea of a species being better adapted while pointing out that the species isn't perfectly adapted. Many species have become extinct because they had adaptations that helped them survive in one environment, but when the environment changed, their adaptations were no longer helpful. Emphasize that many species have become extinct across time. Whether there is enough variation in a population to help it survive in a changed environment often is a matter of chance.

Once students have finished reading the second section, tell them to work with a partner to complete the tasks in *Stop and Think*, Question 3.

In Step 7, ask students to exchange T-tables and do their best to answer each other's questions. Listen for teachable moments when you can gently introduce yourself into the conversation to help finalize an answer.

In Step 8, students continue reading facts about evolution.

Natural Selection, continued

distinctive beak sizes and shapes as well as distinctive behaviors that were adaptive to particular environments. The bill of each species of finch is adapted for different purposes such as cracking the shells of seeds, pecking wood, and probing flowers for nectar (figure 6.22).

We saw natural selection acting on variation within a species. Natural selection can also act on variations that exist across species. Variation in beak shape occurs randomly. A variation in beak shape may cause some species of birds to be better adapted to some environments than other species are. Species of birds that are best adapted to an environment survive and produce more offspring than other bird species. Successful individuals within a species will pass along their adaptation to the next generation. In this scenario, natural selection is acting among several species. Competition among species for limited food resources acts as a selective pressure between species.

The fossil record indicates that there has been a consistent change in the plant and animal species in a region from one period in Earth's history to another. New species appear, and other species disappear as they become extinct. Species face changes in their environments across

SCILINKS NSTA
Topic: natural selection
Go to: www.scilinks.org
Code: 2Inquiry312

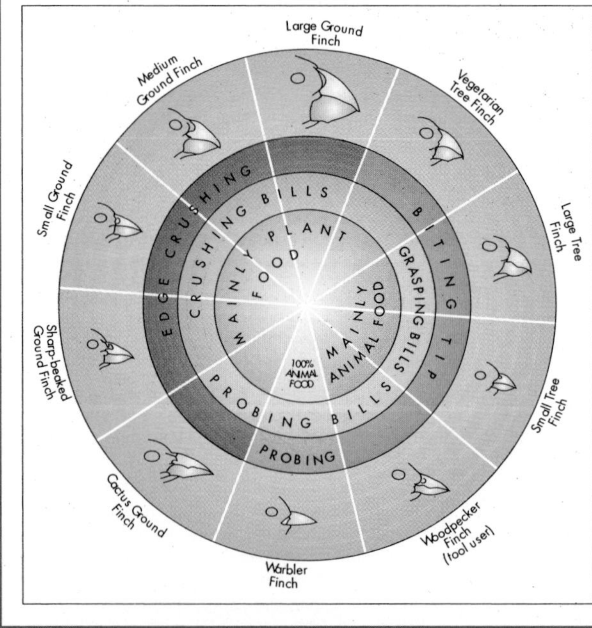

Figure 6.22 Galápagos finches. The Galápagos finches were able to use many different food sources because few species competed with them. The variations in the sizes and shapes of the beaks show how the beak structure of each finch species has adapted to gathering its primary food source.

NOTES:

time. Some species might have adaptations that increase the chances to survive in an environment that has changed. Species that lack those helpful adaptations might become extinct. To learn about some extinct organisms, study figure 6.23.

What determines an organism's ability to survive and reproduce despite various selective pressures? Generally, a mix of characteristics is the answer. It is not only one or two characteristics that help organisms adapt in a particular environment. Organisms, however, do not *acquire* these characteristics to help them survive. These characteristics occur naturally among individuals in a population. This is a result of natural, inherited variation. Selective pressures in the environment act on differences in individuals. These pressures influence which organisms survive to contribute their characteristics to the next generation.

▲ **Figure 6.23 Adaptations.** Not all adaptations help organisms survive if the environment changes. Look at each extinct organism: (a) *Ornitholestes*, (b) dodo bird, (c) Stellar's sea cow, and (d) Tasmanian wolf. Try to decide what adaptation did not help the organism survive.

NOTES:

READING

Evolution

Individual organisms do not evolve. Instead, populations of species evolve. Darwin's theory of evolution by natural selection proposes this idea. Characteristics of a population can sometimes change dramatically because of natural selection. Eventually, scientists recognize the population as a distinct species. This new species is different from the ancestor. Here we return to Darwin's basic idea: descent with modification.

Descent with modification provides a powerful explanation for the similarities we see among closely related forms of life. Descent with modification also explains the similarities we see in all forms of life. Modification, variation, and natural selection provide an explanation for the differences we see among organisms.

Across time, all types of organisms changed and inherited new characteristics from their parents. All species must have descended from a common ancestor. As billions of years passed on Earth, new characteristics appeared in organisms. These characteristics help the organisms survive. Beneficial characteristics pass from generation to generation. Eventually, the differences in this new population are so great that the new population branches off from the ancestral population. Figure 6.24 shows how scientists illustrate the results of evolution as a branching tree or bush.

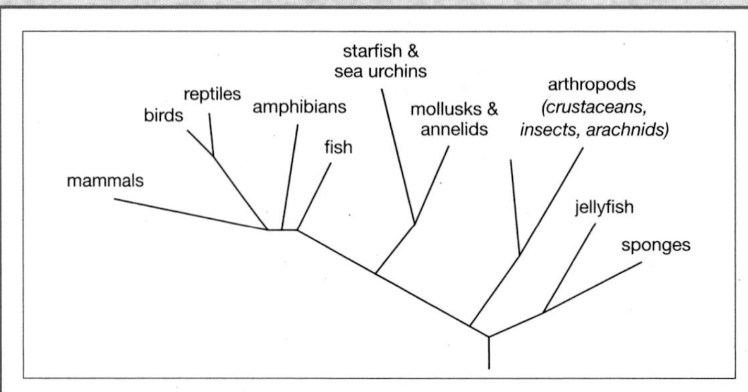

▲ **Figure 6.24 Tree of life.** Different species diverge from a common lineage much like branches of a tree diverge from the trunk.

314 Unit 2 Inside Life

Answers to Stop and Think—Question 4, SE page 315

Students apply what they have learned about natural selection to complete 2 tasks. Listen as students work to learn how much they know about natural selection. Remind students to record their answers in their science notebooks.

4a. In Part I, the variation was within 1 species and predators were the selective pressure. In Part II, the variation was across different species of birds with different beaks and the selective pressure was competition for a limited food supply. Part I simulated natural selection acting on 1 species. The individuals of that species were better camouflaged and thus had a better chance to survive and reproduce. Part II simulated natural selection acting on different species that share a common source of food. A species that was better at capturing that food source had a better chance to survive and reproduce than the other species.

4b. An antibiotic acts as a selective pressure on bacteria because after bacteria are exposed to an antibiotic, most of the bacteria die but some might survive. The bacteria that survive are resistant to the antibiotic. Therefore, the resistant bacteria are selected for in their environment. After students answer this question, you might ask them if they think bacteria evolve.

When discussing examples of change in populations, students might give immunity as an example. Explain to students that immunity to a disease such as the flu virus is an acquired characteristic. Immunity cannot be passed from one generation to another.

4c. Evolution helps explain the diversity of life on Earth because the process of natural selection results in distinct (or new) species. Across time, the characteristics of a population change as more and more individuals pass on a beneficial characteristic. Eventually, the population is so different from the original population that it is considered a different species.

Listen as students read the final section about Darwin. As students work, ask the following probing questions to see how well they understand the idea of a common ancestor. Explain that they will learn more about common ancestors in the next three chapters.

- "Why do you think that Darwin's idea of descent from a common ancestor is important?"

Descent from a common ancestor helps explain why different species are similar and why they share many of the same characteristics. It helps explain the unity of life on Earth.

- Read the following statement and then ask if it describes a scientific theory. Why or why not?

"My friend has a theory that there will be more snow days during this school year."

Often, when we have an idea about something, we describe our explanation as a theory. The theories that we develop, such as the one in the statement above, are tentative. We don't have evidence to support that it is correct. Scientists use the word "theory" in a very different way than we do in everyday life. Scientific theories are explanations that are well accepted by the scientific community because they are supported by a variety of strong evidence. Some

Stop & THINK

QUESTION 4

Read each question and task carefully. Record your own responses in your science notebook and then compare your answers to a classmate's.

4 Work with your partner to complete the following tasks.

a. Explain how Parts I and II in the explore activity *Who Will Survive?* simulated the process of natural selection differently. Think about the following:
   - Was the variation within 1 species or across different species?
   - Were the selective pressures different?

b. Explain how an antibiotic acts as a selective pressure on a population of bacteria.

One characteristic of bacteria is their resistance or lack of resistance to an antibiotic.

c. Explain how you think evolution helps to explain the diversity of life on Earth.

You will learn how evolution helps to explain the unity of life on Earth in the next 2 chapters.

9. Read *Summary* before working with your partner to answer each question in *Reflect and Connect.*

READING

Summary

It took Darwin more than 20 years to come up with his theory. Only then was he confident enough to publish it in 1859. In his book *On the Origin of Species*, Darwin presented his theory of biological evolution and descent with modification. Darwin did not use the word "evolution" in the first edition. Instead, he proposed the concept of descent with modification (figure 6.25). This phrase expressed his view that all organisms on Earth are related through descent from some unknown ancestor that lived long ago. This idea helped

NOTES:

examples of scientific theories are the atomic theory and the cell theory.

- "Why do scientists call Darwin's explanation of descent with modification the *theory* of evolution instead of the *hypothesis* of evolution?"

A hypothesis is a tentative explanation that can be tested. A theory is a hypothesis that has been extensively tested and is supported by a large body of observations and evidence. Darwin's explanation of descent with modification is called the *theory* of evolution because of the enormous amount of evidence that suggests that it is a correct explanation. Students have been learning about this evidence throughout the chapter.

In Step 9, students read a summary of the previous readings. After they are finished reading, instruct students to answer the *Reflect and Connect* questions.

Summary, continued

Darwin explain the diversity of organisms that he encountered on his travels. The phrase also explained the patterns in geographical distribution that he observed.

Darwin theorized that the process of evolution might have been going on for millions of years. His theory predicted that similar species existing today are related and that they descended from a common ancestor. Darwin's ideas provide an explanation for changes in the number and diversity of organisms that we see in the fossil record. The fossil record provides evidence of the extinction of species as well as evidence of the new species that survived changes in the environment. The fossil record also provides evidence of long periods of time with little change. One fossil record is shown in figure 6.26.

Darwin was not the only naturalist to think about the ideas of evolution through natural selection. A biologist named Alfred Russel Wallace developed the same explanation. In his letter to Darwin, Wallace enclosed a draft of a scientific paper that described a theory of evolution. His theory was less detailed than Darwin's theory, but almost identical in its basic outline.

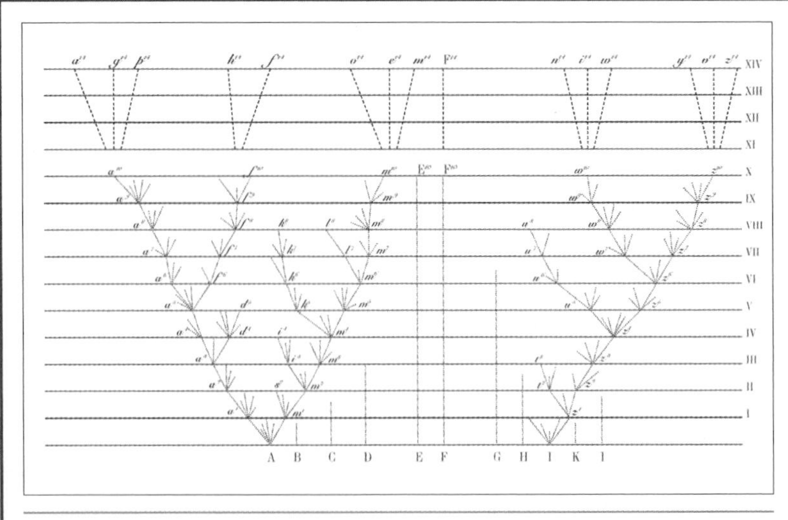

▲ **Figure 6.25 Descent with modification.** Depiction of Darwin's drawing of descent with modification.

NOTES:

Occurrence (in millions of years ago)	Appearance*	Name	Year of Discovery	Description*
55		*Mesonychid*	prior to 1989	• Hyena-like land mammal • 4 long legs • Slender tail
50		*Ambulocetus*	1989	• Land and sea mammal • 4 short legs with feet • No tail fluke but probably swam like an otter
46		*Rodhocetus*	1994	• Whale-like sea mammal • Legs shorter than *Ambulocetus* • May have been able to move awkwardly on land • Strong tail for swimming
40		*Prozeuglodon*	1994	• 15-foot long aquatic mammal • Tiny 6-inch hind legs that could not support weight on land • Tail fluke for swimming

*Based on fossils of skeleton

Source: From C. Zimmer, Back to the Sea, January 1995, *Discover* magazine, pp. 82-84.

NOTES:

SIDEBAR

Unpopular Ideas

Throughout history, people have had many ideas about the natural world. Before the 17th century, people believed that Earth was the center of the universe. This belief was called geocentricism. As more and more evidence supported the idea that the Sun was the center of the solar system (heliocentrism) and Earth was one of many planets that revolved around it, the old idea was rejected. However, the rejection of this idea took time and much scientific evidence.

Each time an idea is expressed, that idea is open to review by the scientific community. Before Darwin published his ideas about natural selection in *On the Origin of Species*, he spent 20 years thinking carefully about his ideas and testing them with new observations and evidence.

Charles Darwin was not the first person to propose a natural explanation for life. More than two dozen naturalists before him developed natural explanations. These explanations had an evolutionary theme. In fact, natural explanations for diversity, unity, and adaptation date back at least 2,600 years. Most of these explanations were based on philosophical reasoning. There was little evidence to support these explanations. In contrast, Darwin had evidence to back up his theory of evolution by natural selection.

Darwin tried to anticipate every possible objection others would have. He used evidence to answer each new objection. This process strengthened his argument. As a result, his ideas withstood scrutiny from the scientific community and the public. This process of skeptical review is an essential part of science.

Skeptical review involves the careful examination of ideas. The examination depends on evidence. It does not depend on emotional judgments or opinions. Skeptical review works to eliminate individual bias and subjectivity. Other people must be able to determine whether an idea is consistent with the evidence. In this way, public scrutiny leads to new observations and the advancement of science.

Many ideas proposed by skillful scientists must be set aside because additional observations and evidence do not support the ideas. Some withstand the test of time and accumulated evidence, increasing our knowledge about the natural world.

Science is a process—growing in some directions, changing in others. Many ideas we consider fundamental to science today were once very unpopular. For example, consider Darwin's idea that all life has a common ancestry. In parlors and tearooms across England in the 1800s, people mocked Darwin for his theory. Biological evolution still disturbs some people today, more than 150 years later.

Darwin was cautious and used the methods of science to slowly and carefully build a body of evidence to support his ideas. The theory of evolution has withstood the test of time and is the foundation upon which modern biology is structured. Today, scientists continue to refine and add to our knowledge about evolution and how it works. Scientists also continue to contribute ideas and support them with evidence.

Darwin was not alone in his time in proposing a new explanation in science.

318 Unit 2 Inside Life

NOTES:

New ideas that went against the popular view of Earth's history were emerging. Many people believed that Earth had existed unchanged since its relatively recent formation. Darwin was influenced by the work of geologists James Hutton and Sir Charles Lyell. They began to gather evidence to indicate that Earth was changing all the time. These changes occurred over millions of years. They saw that Earth's crust had made vertical movements in England. New sediments had formed in freshwater lakes. They found fossils of sea animals in land formations and in rocks thrusting high above the ocean. They found volcanoes erupting to form mountains, such as Mount Etna in Italy. They believed that these geologic processes, on both small and large scales, had been operating throughout the history of Earth, continuously modifying its form.

To justify their observations, geologists found it necessary to create a vast timescale of Earth's history. By doing this, however, they questioned the social and religious views of the day. For this, they were sometimes accused of heresy.

Today, we accept these views and the scale for Earth's history, a doctrine known as uniformitarianism. The idea is, "the present is the key to the past." Processes we see today have taken place on Earth since its formation. Example processes are the carving of canyons by rivers, the deposition of layers of silt in still water, the eruptions of volcanoes, and the blowing of sand into dunes.

Radiometric dating of rocks has shown the age of Earth to be approximately 4.6 billion years old. This dating validates Hutton and Lyell's idea that Earth is much older than people of their time believed. Like Darwin's work, the work of these scientists laid the foundation for our understanding of an important science. That science is geology, or the study of Earth.

Scientists with new models and new theories do not always agree with one another. Darwin's *On the Origin of Species* drew upon Sir Charles Lyell's book *Principles of Geology*. Lyell did not, however, up to that time, share Darwin's belief in evolution, even though both of these scientists' ideas depended on the view that Earth's history was long and ever changing.

After reading Darwin's book, Lyell began a series of studies. He wrote *The Geological Evidences of the Antiquity of Man*. In this book, and in his *Principles of Geology*, Lyell added powerful arguments of his own from the science of geology. These ideas supported Darwin's theory of evolution by natural selection. Darwin clearly understood the pressure Lyell underwent for refuting the popular views of the day. Darwin said, "Considering his age, his former views, and position in society, I think his action [to support the theory of evolution] has been heroic."

It's not easy to propose new ideas, even when there is a chance that you're right. So what do scientists do when faced with criticism about their ideas? They continue to gather evidence to support their ideas until the sheer amount of evidence convinces even those who are skeptical.

Answers to Reflect and Connect, SE page 320

1. Evolution provides an explanation for how species change across time. Evolution only occurs when there are variations in a population and when there are selective pressures acting on those variations. For example, some individuals within a population might have variations in one or more characteristics. Selective pressures cause individuals with beneficial characteristics, also called adaptations, to survive and cause individuals without the adaptations to die off. Across time, more of the individuals with the adaptations survive and reproduce. As more of the population has the adaptation, eventually the population can be recognized as distinct species.
2. Species become extinct when the entire population of individuals is no longer able to survive in its environment. If the environment of a species changes and the species doesn't possess characteristics or adaptations that would help it survive, the species will become extinct.
3. The theory of evolution helps explain how, across time, different characteristics are selected that can lead to new species. Evolution helps explain why the fossil remains of species in younger rock layers look more similar to existing species than the fossil remains in older rock layers. Across time, different adaptations are needed to survive in changing environments.
4. Scientists often focus their research on similar topics or make observations of similar phenomena. Scientists investigating similar subjects often see the same patterns and develop similar explanations because they approach research in the same way. Students should recognize that all scientists use a similar process of going back and forth between making observations, asking questions, and making inferences. Look for answers that reflect the idea that when scientists make observations of similar experiences, they are likely to come to the same conclusions.

For students who need more details and enrichment, there is an optional copymaster 6.5, *Natural Selection.*

Reflect and Connect

Answer the following questions with your partner. Record your final answers in your notebook.

1. Explain what evolution means. Include the following words in your description: *adaptation*, *population*, *natural selection*, *selective pressure*, *variation*, and *species*.
2. Explain why some species become extinct.
3. Describe how you think the theory of evolution helps explain Earth's history.
4. You may have been surprised that Darwin wasn't the only scientist to come up with the theory of evolution. Describe why you think scientists make similar discoveries or develop similar explanations around the same time.

ELABORATE

Twine Time

Now that you have had an opportunity to share some of your ideas about change on Earth, let's put that change in a context. Let's see when in the history of our Earth these changes might have taken place. Some of the events in Earth's history are shown in figure 6.27. We have reliable evidence from radiometric dating that dates Earth back billions of years. During *Twine Time*, you will learn more about that evidence. To get a better sense of Earth's history, you will develop a timeline dating from Earth's formation, approximately 4.6 billion years ago, to the present day. You will work in teams of four for this activity.

Materials

For each team of 4 students

20 m of twine, marked every meter

1 tape measure

tape (multiple colors)

markers

colored pencil

1 set of biological and abiotic event cards

4 *Events in Evolution* handouts

ELABORATE

Twine Time

Activity Overview

Twine Time will allow the students to explore significant biological and geologic events. Students predict the order in which the events occurred and then determine whether or not their predictions are accurate, based on evidence that scientists have collected. This activity should give students an appreciation of the length of geologic time and an understanding that change occurs across time both in the biological and abiological environments.

Before You Teach

Background Information

Earth is about 4.5 billion years old. Most of us will live for less than 100 years, so we have trouble comprehending hundreds, thousands, millions, and billions of years. Geologists have created a geologic timescale to provide a common way of talking about Earth's history. Important biological and geologic events are found throughout Earth's history. However, most of the organisms we see today appeared recently in Earth's history—at the end of the geologic timescale (figure T6.12).

Creating a timeline that depicts the duration of time since Earth was formed will help give students a concrete way to look at time and the biological and geologic events that have occurred. By constructing the timeline and placing events on it, students will look through history to see both the number of events that have occurred and the periods in which they occurred. They will also see that the general trend shows that the diversity of species increases across time.

Materials

For the teacher

1 transparency of copymaster 6.6, *Geologic Clock*

For each team of 4 students

20 m of twine, marked every meter
1 tape measure
tape (multiple colors)
markers
colored pencil
1 copy of copymaster 6.7, *Biological and Abiotic Event Cards*

For each student

1 copy of copymaster 6.8, *Events in Evolution*

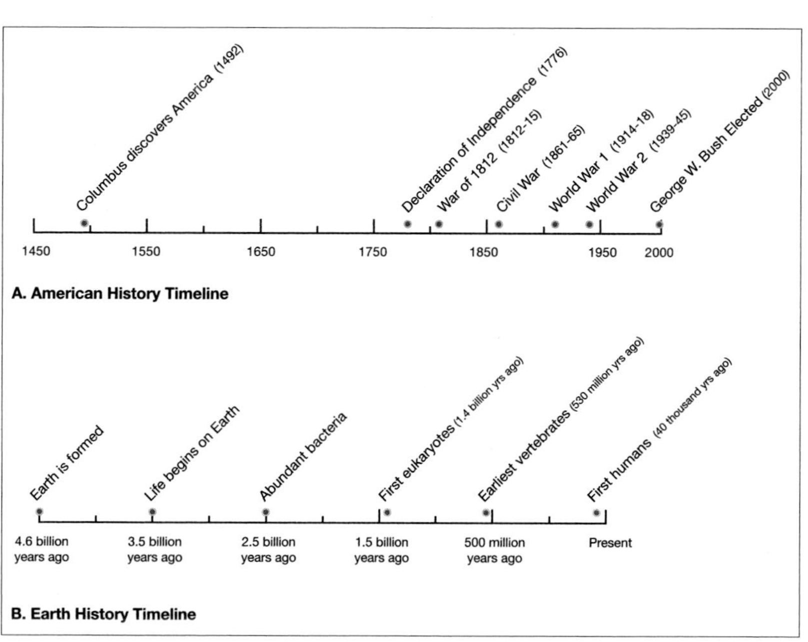

▲ **Figure 6.27 Record of events.** We have clear records about recent history and present-day events. As we look farther into the past, records are less clear or nonexistent.

Process and Procedure

1. Obtain the biological and abiotic event cards.
2. Sort the event cards into 2 piles: biological events and abiotic events. Use a colored pencil to lightly shade the abiotic event cards.

The term abiotic **describes the physical and chemical (nonliving) aspects of an environment. Here we are talking about Earth's environment.**

3. Place the biological event cards on your desk in the order in which you think they occurred. Think about why you placed each card where you did. Be prepared to contribute your ideas in a class discussion.
4. Repeat Step 3, this time using the abiotic event cards.
5. Compare your order of events with the order proposed by other teams.

Chapter 6 Exploring Change 321

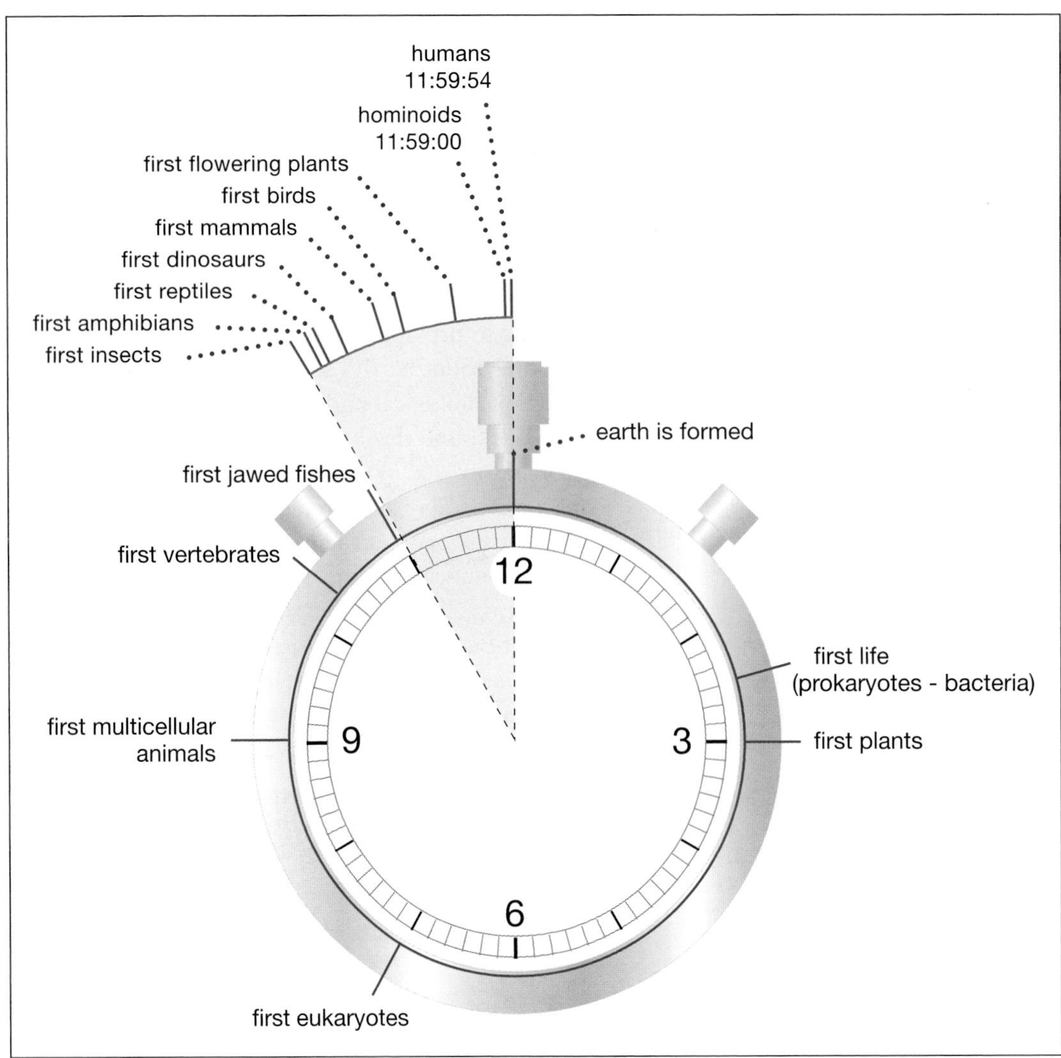

▲ **Figure T6.12 Geologic time clock.** Notice that most organisms on Earth appeared recently in Earth's history. This figure is also available on copymaster 6.6, *Geologic Clock*.

Advance Preparation

Purchase enough twine for each team of 4 or 5 students to have 20 m of twine. You might also need to purchase tape measures and different colors of tape, such as electrical tape. Preferably buy bright-colored tape, such as yellow, for students to label the billion-year marks on their timelines. Use a marker or piece of black tape to mark each meter on the twine.

Make a copy of copymaster 6.7, *Biological and Abiotic Event Cards* for each team. Cut each set of cards apart. Each team will have 35 cards. Make a copy of copymaster 6.8, *Events in Evolution* for each student.

Think about where you would like to have students work on their timelines. Ideally, students would work outside, in a gymnasium, or in a long hallway where they have more room. If a large area won't be available, decide how you will let students work in the classroom. You might want to use 10 m of twine for each team if your space is limited.

As You Teach

Outcomes and Indicators of Success

By the end of this activity, students should

1. appreciate the enormous expanse of time since the formation of Earth, approximately 4.5 billion years ago.

   They will demonstrate their appreciation by

   - building a timeline to scale, including calculating how much time is represented in each meter and centimeter and
   - relating their lifetime to the amount of time Earth has been around.

2. be able to interpret the biological and geologic events in Earth's history.

   They will demonstrate their ability by

   - correctly placing the events on the timeline,
   - comparing and evaluating their predictions by studying the dates when these events occurred,

- describing patterns in the placement of events,
- comparing the location of abiotic events with biological events and describing how they might be related, and
- explaining why one event of their choice is an important part of Earth's history.

3. be able to apply their knowledge that species evolve across time.

   They will demonstrate their ability by

   - placing biological events on their timeline that represent the appearance of species existing at different times in Earth's history and
   - explaining that natural selection and evolution might lead to new species because these processes cause advantageous characteristics to be passed on to more and more individuals in a population.

4. understand how mathematics is essential to scientific inquiry.

   They will demonstrate their understanding by developing the proper mathematical scale for representing the time periods in this activity.

Strategies

Getting Started

Ask students if they have thought about how life on Earth has changed over the last 4.5 billion years. Do they think the same species have always lived on Earth? Has the number of species on Earth increased across time? What about Earth itself—have the physical and chemical environments changed? Tell students that they will learn more about how life and the environments on Earth have changed across time.

Process and Procedure

In Step 1, distribute copymaster 6.7, *Biological and Abiotic Event Cards* to the students. Explain to students that the abiotic events are changes in the physical and chemical environments on Earth. The biological events are changes in Earth's living environment.

In Step 2, tell students to work in their teams to sort the event cards into a pile of biological events and abiotic events. They should lightly shade the abiotic event cards with a colored pencil.

In Step 3, tell students to place the biological event cards in the order they think they occurred. Encourage students to base their predictions on prior knowledge, on relative times to other events, and on discussions with their team. Remind students to think about how they decided to place their cards because they will need to support their predictions in the class discussion in Step 5.

In Step 4, students repeat Step 3 with the abiotic event cards. Circulate among teams as students sort their cards into an order of events. Use this opportunity to learn what students currently understand about events in Earth's history.

In Step 5, facilitate a class discussion of how teams ordered the events. Ask teams to explain why they placed events in the way they did. Listen to their contributions to learn what kinds of evidence students provide. After all teams have contributed, decide on an order of events as a class. Tell students to record the order of the biological and abiotic events in their science notebooks. If students disagree with the placement of an event, suggest that they make a note of this in their science notebook.

In Step 6, instruct teams to predict which biological event and abiotic event occurred closest to the middle of Earth's history. Students should record their predictions in their science notebooks by circling the event in their event list.

In Step 7, teams begin constructing their timelines. Move students to the area where they will be constructing their timelines. Tell students to use labels to indicate the ends that represent the present day and when Earth formed. Encourage students to work from left to right with the formation of Earth on the left. Their timelines will display the oldest to most recent events, similar to a historical timeline.

In Step 7b–c, students should calculate how many years are represented in 1 m and 1 centimeter (cm). The twine is 20 m long and represents 5 billion years, so they will calculate as follows:

$$\frac{5{,}000{,}000{,}000 \text{ years}}{20 \text{ m}} = 250{,}000{,}000 \text{ years/m}$$

$$\frac{250{,}000{,}000 \text{ years}}{100 \text{ cm}} = 2{,}500{,}000 \text{ years/cm}$$

Listen to teams as they work on Step 7. You might need to help students work through the calculations or label the billion-years-ago marks.

Answers to Step 7, SE page 322

7b. 1 m = 250 million years

7c. 1 cm = 2.5 million years

7d. Students should place the 1-billion-year-ago mark 4 m away from the end labeled "present day."

7e. Two billion years ago should be marked 8 m from the end labeled "present day." Three billion years ago should be marked 12 m from the end labeled "present day." Four billion years ago should be marked 16 m from the end labeled "present day."

If the teams used 10 m of twine instead of 20 m, the answers for Questions 7b–e will be half as much.

Students might struggle because the timeline records events that occurred in the past. As the number of years ago increases, the events are farther in the past. This will be counterintuitive for many students because our calendar year gets larger as we progress into the future (2008, 2009, 2010, and so on). Explain to students that they are working with the number of years ago rather than dates.

In Step 8, distribute copymaster 6.8, *Events in Evolution* to the class. Instruct students to study the events and compare the actual order of events with the order of events predicted by the class. They should record how the actual order and the predicted order of events compare in their science notebooks.

Students might have trouble interpreting the timescale used in copymaster 6.6, *Events in Evolution*. The numbers range from 1 to 650 but the scale on the side shows that the numbers are in billions, millions, and thousands. Talk to teams individually or take time as a class to talk about what each number really is. Have students write out what 4.6 billion years looks like with all the zeros (4,600,000,000 years ago). Then do the same for a date from the millions and the thousands columns.

In Step 9, students begin the process of placing the event cards on the timeline. In Step 9a, they should begin by dividing the 35 events among the team so that everyone has events to place. In Step 9b, circulate among teams to see if some students need assistance placing their cards on the timeline. Remind them to use the billion marks, the 1-m marks, and their calculations from Step 7 to help them place the events correctly. Students do not need to calculate the exact position for each card. Focus students' attention on the relative placement of cards and how more events occur later in Earth's history. As students work on their timelines, ask the following probing questions. Listen carefully to their answers to learn how well they apply what they have learned in the chapter.

- "How might scientists have determined how many years ago each of these events occurred?"

Students should know that scientists must have found rock layers that preserved evidence of the events. Then somewhere above and below those rock layers there were rocks that were successfully dated by a geologist. The amount of parent and daughter isotopes in the rocks allowed scientists to determine the age of the rocks using radiometric dating techniques.

- "Do you think the kinds of organisms living on Earth millions of years ago also exist today? If so, do you think they are exactly the same species now as they were in the past?"

a. Listen as each team explains why it placed the cards the way it did.
b. As a class, decide the order of the events for each group, biological and abiotic.
c. Record the order of biological and abiotic events in your science notebook. If you disagree with the placement of an event, make a note of where you would put it and why.

6. Decide which biological event and abiotic event you think occurred closest to the middle point of Earth's history (about 2.3 billion years ago). Record your 2 predictions in your science notebook by circling the events you chose in the lists of biological and abiotic events.

Remember that the events must occur between now and 4.6 billion years ago.

7. As a team, spread out the twine for your timeline and secure it on the floor, the wall, between 2 posts, or on the athletic field. Then do the following tasks.
   a. Label the twine to indicate which end represents the present day and which end represents when Earth formed.
   b. Your twine is 20 m long and represents 5 billion years. Calculate how many years are represented in 1 m. Record your answer in your science notebook.
   c. Calculate how many years are represented in 1 centimeter. Record your answer in your science notebook.
   d. Determine where 1 billion years ago would be found on your timeline. Use colored tape to mark this spot and use a marker to write "1 billion years ago" on the tape.
   e. Repeat Step 7d for 2 billion, 3 billion, and 4 billion years ago.

Your teacher has marked the twine every meter.

8. Study the handout *Events in Evolution* that your teacher gives you. The table shows what scientists have discovered about events in Earth's history. How does the actual order of events compare with the order you recorded in your science notebook?
9. Place the event cards in the correct spot on your timeline. To do this, you will need to do the following.
   a. Divide the event cards among your team members. You will need to do a few calculations to determine where to place them.
   b. Use the values you calculated in Step 7 to help you place each card on the timeline.
   c. Fold your event cards over the twine at the appropriate spot.

Students should recognize that organisms such as bacteria and algae not only lived on Earth over 3 billion years ago but also exist on Earth today. They might recognize that although bacteria and algae exist today, the species alive today probably are different from the bacteria and algae from the distant past because the environment is different today.

- "Do you think many organisms have become extinct during Earth's history? Why do you think this might have happened?"

Students are very familiar with the extinction of dinosaurs and might be able to think of many other organisms that have become extinct. Make sure you ask them why they think these organisms became extinct. This will give them an opportunity to apply their understanding of natural selection.

- "What process would explain the changes in life on Earth?"

Students should understand that biological evolution explains how species change across time and thus why life on Earth has changed.

In Step 10, students examine their timeline and those of other teams and answer a few questions. They should record their answers in their science notebooks. As students work, listen to their discussions and look at their answers to find out how much they have learned about Earth's history.

Answers to Step 10 are on TE pages 323–324.
Answers to Reflect and Connect are on TE page 324.

10. Examine your timeline and those from other teams to answer Questions 10a–d. Record your answers in your science notebook.
    a. What patterns do you see in the placement of events? Find at least 4 patterns.
    b. What surprised you about the timelines?
    c. How close were your predictions of the halfway point in Earth's history that you made in Step 6? What does this tell you?

Give a specific reason why your prediction was accurate or inaccurate. Then explain what the prediction and the real timeline helped you learn.

    d. How does the amount of time you've been alive compare mathematically with the amount of time Earth has been around? Where would your life fall on the timeline? What do you think about this?
11. Look at the timelines and the geologic clock displayed by your teacher. Discuss as a class what you've discovered about the past 4.6 billion years.

Reflect and Connect

Answer the following questions in your science notebook.

1. Compare your timeline and the clock diagram displayed by your teacher in Step 11. Which did you find more helpful as a representation of Earth's history? Why?
2. Look at the events that represented changes in Earth's surface or atmosphere. Compare the location of these events on the timeline with the events showing the appearance of different plant and animal life. How do you think these events are related?
3. Explain how you think the process of natural selection and evolution might lead to the appearance of new species.

Think about the Galápagos finches discovered by Darwin.

Answers to Step 10, SE page 323

10a. Students might notice the following patterns:

- One or more biological events occur after an abiotic event.
- More events occur near the present.
- Very few events are given for the first 3 billion years of Earth's history.
- The biological events tend to be grouped together. For example, between 280 and 210 million years ago, mammal-like reptiles and mammals appeared and palm trees, ferns, and pine trees became abundant.
- Many animal events happened after plant events. For example, plants appeared on land before animals.

10b. Students might be surprised that for more than 1 billion years there was no life on Earth, that modern humans appeared so late in Earth's history, or that flowering plants haven't been on Earth as long as other types of plants. Answers can be personal to each student, but must reflect an event or pattern on the timeline that the student found surprising.

10c. The halfway point in Earth's history is 2.3 billion years ago. The closest abiotic event to 2.3 billion years ago is atmospheric oxygen increasing beyond about 1 percent. The closest biological event is abundant prokaryotic life (bacteria). The students should compare these events with their predicted events from Step 6.

Student predictions are probably much different from the actual "midpoint" events. Students most likely picked a card in the middle after ordering their events.

Students should recognize that before constructing the timeline they didn't realize how much time passed on Earth before many significant events occurred. Students might also recognize that because the predicted order of events wasn't accurate, their predictions for the halfway point were less accurate. Students should explain that looking back at their predictions helped them see how much they learned while constructing the timeline.

This question brings students' attention to their misconceptions about what events occurred and when they occurred in Earth's history.

10d. Students should compare 15 or 16 years with billions of years. Students could make a comparison in several ways. They might explain that the amount of time Earth has been around was represented with 20 m of twine and that their lifetime wouldn't even represent a fraction of a millimeter on the same scale. They should realize their life falls at the end and only makes up a tiny part of the timeline. Students should note the huge difference in time. Some students might even do the math to give an exact number: Earth has been around approximately 306,666,667 times longer than they have (4.6 billion years/15 years).

In Step 11, display copymaster 6.6, *Geologic Clock* as a transparency. Explain that scientists use a variety of ways to show large amounts of time. A geologic clock is another way of representing the information displayed on their timelines. Then facilitate a class discussion about what the class has discovered about the past 4.5 billion years. To help students visualize their timeline as a record of Earth, tell students to compare rock layers in Earth with the timeline they created. Then tell them to imagine the timeline held upright with the formation of Earth at the bottom. Each event on an event card might represent another rock layer. Explain that in the geologic clock example each second mark represents a rock layer.

Answers to Reflect and Connect, SE page 323

1. Students might explain that the timeline representation was more helpful because they worked with their team to create it and learned a lot during that process. They might also explain that because the timeline is larger, they can more easily read all the events. Other students might explain that the clock diagram was more helpful because it is smaller and allowed them to quickly see all the events grouped near the present.
2. If students are struggling with this question, give them a hint. Tell them to look at when oxygen levels increased and how that compares with plant and animal life. Expect that your students will make connections between the rise of oxygen gas and the appearance of plants, for example. In general, the changes in Earth's environment are followed by changes in the types of plants and animals.
3. Natural selection and evolution might lead to the appearance of new species because these processes cause advantageous characteristics to be passed on to more and more individuals in a population. Eventually, a large portion of a population might have an advantageous characteristic that makes these individuals distinct from the original population. These distinct individuals might be considered a new species.

SIDEBAR

Ongoing Research, Ongoing Evolution

Imagine working on one question for more than 30 years. That's exactly what Peter and Rosemary Grant have been doing on several of the Galápagos Islands. What kind of question would require that much work to answer?

Simply put, the Grants' question was, "Does evolution take place in short time frames?" The Grants (and several graduate students) first needed to identify a natural setting that gave them a reasonable chance of collecting data to answer their question. They chose to study a species of finch (small, seed-eating birds) that lives on a small island named Daphne Major, located a few hundred miles west of Ecuador. The finch population remained isolated from outside influence and was small enough for the Grants to identify *every* bird by sight.

The researchers knew they would have to document changes in the finch population over a few years' time. A key measurement was beak depth (depicted above the graph). The Grants determined that shallow-beaked birds cannot open hard seeds, but deep-beaked birds can. During droughts, more hard seeds exist than soft seeds. Thus, deep-beaked birds tend to survive and produce more offspring than do shallow-beaked birds. The result in the next generation of birds is a change in the finch population from shallow-beaked birds to deep-beaked birds.

But the Grants knew one such occurrence of this change was not sufficient to show ongoing evolution. As all researchers do, they needed to reproduce their results. To do so, they continued measuring beak-depth changes in medium ground finches over several cycles of wet and dry years. The results are shown in the graph.

You can see the same thing the Grants saw. During dry years, the population of the medium ground finch changed. More deep-beaked birds survived and reproduced because they could use the hard seeds better than the shallow-beaked birds. This difference in survival rate influenced the distribution of finches, favoring deep-beaked

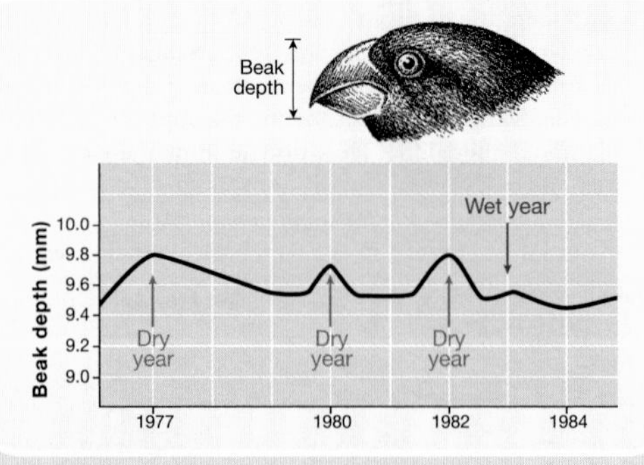

Changes in beak depth over time. The graph shows evolutionary changes in beak depth in medium ground finches on the Galápagos island of Daphne Major under different environmental conditions. How much did average beak depth change between dry years and wet years in the 1970s and 1980s?

324 | Unit 2 Inside Life

Ancient Elephants

Activity Overview

In *Ancient Elephants*, students will demonstrate what they have learned about rock layers, fossils, radiometric dating, natural selection, and evolution. The context of the evaluate is the evolution of elephants. Students will be presented with rock layers and fossils of elephants and their relatives. Each student will work individually to complete a series of tasks and answer questions about the sequence of fossils.

Before You Teach

Background Information

Look at the elephant evolutionary tree in figure T6.13 as you read this background section. Try to find each species of elephant as it is discussed. This evolutionary tree will help you assess student answers to questions posed in the *Process and Procedure*.

Elephants and their relatives are members of the order Proboscidea. The order is named after the most distinguishing feature of this group, the trunk, also called the proboscis. Only two species of this order exist today, the African elephant (*Loxodonta africana*) and the Asian elephant (*Elephas maximus*). They differ physically. Asian elephants have

NOTES:

birds. Thus, the population of deep-beaked birds spiked during dry years.

What would happen to the medium ground finch if dry years continued for thousands of generations? What would happen if many wet years occurred in a row? With no other influences, the population of medium ground finches would show deeper beaks as a result of many dry years. Similarly, many wet years in succession would produce more shallow-beaked birds. In short, the species would evolve in response to changes in the environment.

The Grants' work has shown evidence for ongoing evolution. In conjunction with the fossil record and other lines of evidence, evolution explains the changes we see in species across millions of years *and* in our lifetime.

Ancient Elephants

EVALUATE

Throughout this chapter, you have been learning about change across time. You began by learning about how rock layers, fossils, and radiometric dating are evidence of change across time. Then you learned that Charles Darwin developed an explanation for change across time in life-forms on Earth. You also learned about natural selection, which is the mechanism of evolution or a means through which evolution occurs. In *Ancient Elephants*, you will work individually to demonstrate your understanding of evolution by using your growing knowledge of rock layers, fossils, and change across time to piece together a story about the evolution of elephants.

Materials

For each student

1 *Proboscidean and Rock Layers* handout

1 *Proboscidean Pictures* handout

1 *Ancient Elephants Scoring Rubric* handout

Process and Procedure

1. Imagine that you are part of a research team studying the evolution of elephants. Read the following paragraph to learn about your work.

   Elephants and their closest relatives are called proboscideans. Scientists named them this because of their long trunk, which is also called a proboscis. In your search to learn

smaller ears, are smaller overall, and are primarily grazers rather than browsers, like the African elephant. Elephants are the largest living terrestrial mammals on Earth. They have several unique adaptations including tusks, a trunk, a large size, and a specialized pouch found behind the tongue that allows elephants to store water that can be withdrawn later by the trunk.

The trunk is a combination of a nose and an upper lip. Most of the 352 species and subspecies of proboscideans recognized by paleontologists have trunks. However, the earliest proboscideans such as *Phosphatherium* from about 58 million years ago and *Moeritherium* from about 38 million years ago did not have trunks. Early proboscideans were limited to Africa, but later they were common in North America, South America, and Asia.

The characteristics that all proboscideans share include other anatomical details such as tooth structure (such as tusks and distinctive molars), number of teeth, and bone structure. For example, most proboscideans have pillar-like legs that support their massive weight and enlarged incisors that form tusks. Possible functions of proboscidean tusks include food gathering, defense, offense, and display. Some of the tusks of woolly mammoths preserved in permafrost are worn at the tips, suggesting that they were used for scraping snow to expose edible plants.

The Gomphotheriidae family is considered a long-living ancestral group of proboscideans that first appeared about 24 to 20 million years ago and evolved into many other groups. Descendants of early gomphotheres migrated to all continents except Australia and Antarctica. Gomphotheres arrived in Europe about 18 to 17 million years ago and in North America about 14.5 million years ago.

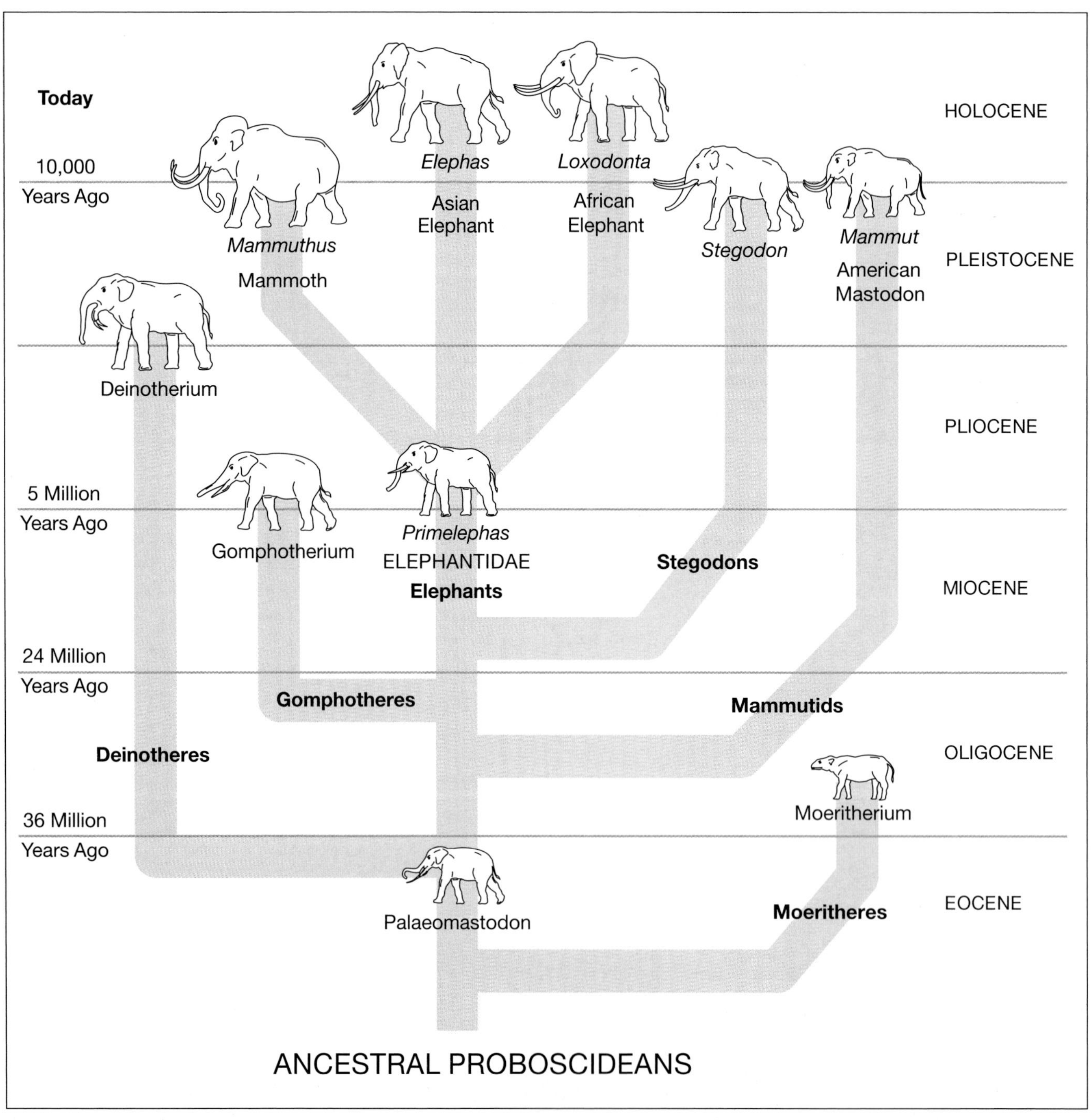

▲ **Figure T6.13 A simplified evolutionary tree of the Proboscidea.** This evolutionary tree shows the ancestry of living elephants. The closest living relatives of elephants are manatees.

Members of the *Gomphotherium* genera had a pair of tusks in both the upper and lower jaws and were nearly as large as an Asian elephant. Scientists also believe that *Gomphotherium* had well-developed trunks, based on the position of the external nasal opening and the short neck. Remains of *Gomphotherium* have been found in Africa, Asia, Europe, and North America. Some of the more recent gomphotheres looked more similar to modern elephants, but with the absence of the lower tusks. *Gomphotherium* were browsers, feeding on the tender shoots, leaves, and twigs of trees and shrubs. Gomphotheres became extinct about 2 million to 10,000 years ago.

The Elephantidae family emerged from the gomphotheriids as early as 6 to 4 million years ago in Africa. A distinctive feature of this group is the reduction and loss of the lower tusks. The loss of lower (mandibular) tusks allowed this group to change their mastication, or chewing, technique. They were able to shear or cut their food rather than grind food with complex rotary movements like earlier proboscideans. The early genera of the subfamily Elephantinae, which includes mammoths and existing elephants, did not appear until about 5 million years ago. The mammoth and elephant genera appeared about 4 to 3 million years ago. Figure T6.14 shows some structural differences in elephant and mammoth teeth.

Mammoths lived from about 4 million years ago and until they became extinct 4,000 years ago, at the end of the most recent ice age. They were distributed throughout Africa, Asia, Europe, and North America. Mammoths migrated to North America about 1.4 million years ago. Woolly mammoths (*Mammuthus primigenius*), found primarily in the arctic regions of Europe, Asia, and North America, evolved 120,000 years ago. They are one of the best-known mammoths. Complete, frozen carcasses have been discovered in Siberia and Alaska. Woolly mammoths were the most specialized of the elephant family. They were small, had dense hair with a thick undercoat, and had an 8-cm thick layer of fat to keep out the cold. They are also distinguished from elephants by their spirally twisted tusks and the wavy pattern of their tooth enamel. They are thought to have eaten grasses and tundra legumes in summer and shrub leaves and bark in winter.

African elephants are the result of more than 50 million years of evolution. African elephants first appeared about 5 million years ago. Scientists speculate that African elephants migrated throughout Africa during prehistoric times but did not leave the continent. In contrast, fossil evidence suggests that Asian elephants evolved in Africa and then migrated to Asia. There are two species of African elephant, the bush African elephant (*Loxodonta africana*) and the forest African elephant (*Loxodonta cyclotis*). African elephants are browsers and feed on tree foliage, bark, and fruit.

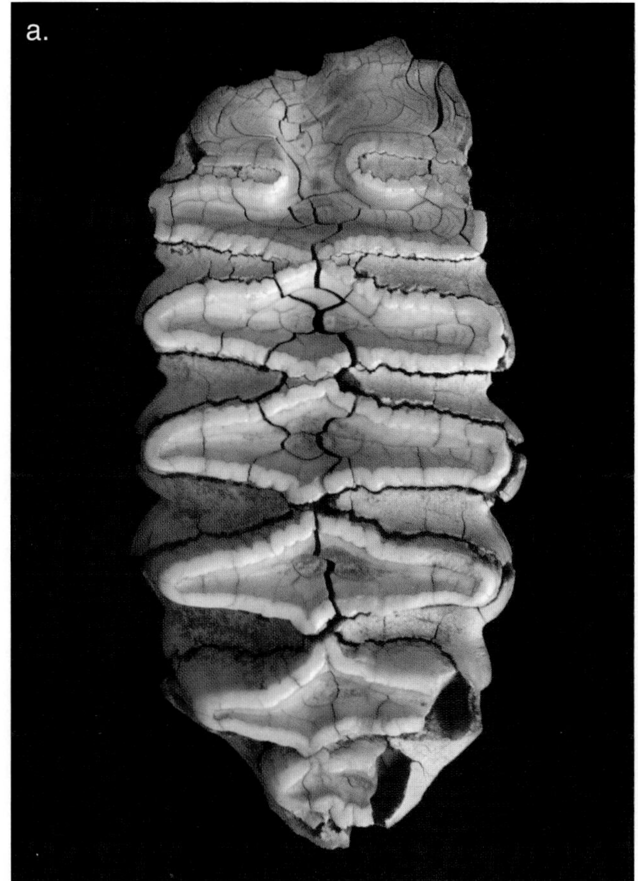

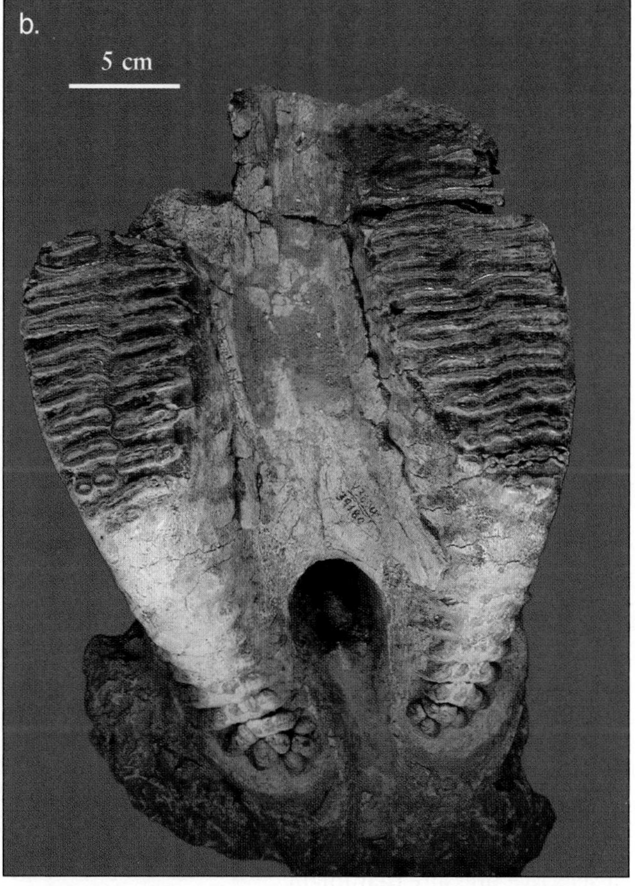

▲ **Figure T6.14 (a) Elephant tooth and (b) mammoth tooth.** The teeth of elephants and mammoths have structural adaptations such as increased height of the molar crown and increased number of the enamel bands. These changes in their teeth are believed to correlate with a shift from woodland browsing to grazing in the grassy habitat that became more and more prevalent from 24 to 5 million years ago.

Materials

For the teacher

1 transparency of copymaster 6.10, *Proboscidean Pictures*

For each student

1 copy of copymaster 6.11, *Scoring Rubric for Ancient Elephants*

1 copy of copymaster 6.9, *Proboscidean and Rock Layers*

Advance Preparation

Make a transparency of copymaster 6.10, *Proboscidean Pictures*. Make copies of copymaster 6.9, *Proboscidean and Rock Layers* for the class.

TRCD

As You Teach

Outcomes and Indicators of Success

By the end of this activity, students should

1. demonstrate their understanding of how rock layers and radiometric dating techniques provide evidence for evolution.

   They will demonstrate their understanding by

   - determining the relative age of the fossil proboscideans;
   - determining the time period in which fossils lived based on the age of ash layers;
   - predicting where an intermediate proboscidean might be found in a series of rock layers; and
   - applying their knowledge of stratigraphy, fossils, and radiometric dating to interpret a series of events that might have led to the sequence of fossil proboscideans.

2. demonstrate their understanding of natural selection and biological evolution.

   They will demonstrate their understanding by

   - interpreting a paragraph about mammoth evolution, suggesting a selective pressure that might have acted on one of the proboscideans, and explaining how this pressure led to the evolution of the woolly mammoth;
   - suggesting how natural selection led to the evolution of *Gomphotherium* into the African elephant and the ancestral mammoth by using six keywords (adaptation, population, natural selection, selective pressure, variation, and species);
   - providing two examples of evidence for change across time and explaining why these examples support the theory of evolution; and
   - analyzing a statement about giraffe evolution and explaining whether it is accurate or inaccurate based on their understanding of natural selection.

3. demonstrate their understanding of the process of radiometric dating.

   They will demonstrate their understanding by explaining the process of radiometric dating, which is used to determine the age of rocks such as ash layers.

4. demonstrate their ability to use the skills of scientific inquiry and their knowledge and understanding of scientific inquiry.

   They will demonstrate their ability by

   - using tools such as the relative dating of rocks and ages

Answers to Steps 3–7 are on TE pages 327–328.

more about proboscideans, you have obtained a picture of a column of rock layers. Some of the rocks consist of an ash layer that scientists have been able to date. Some of the rock layers also contain fossils of proboscideans. Based on the fossilized skeletons, artists have illustrated what the proboscideans and their environment might have looked liked. Your research team must use what you know to piece together what might have happened to proboscideans across time.

2. Look carefully at the rock column and the proboscideans pictured in the handout *Proboscidean and Rock Layers* and in the *Proboscidean Pictures* handout.
3. You learned a lot about the study of rock layers and change across time in this chapter. Using what you have learned, you can make some inferences about the proboscideans from the rock column and the pictures of the environments. To demonstrate your understanding of the concepts in this chapter, answer Questions 3a–c. When you respond to each question, explain how you arrived at your answer.
   a. When did the different proboscidean species live relative to one another? Which species lived most recently and which species lived farther in the past?
   b. Determine the time period in which each of the proboscideans might have lived.

Look at the rock layers where their fossils first appear and last appear.

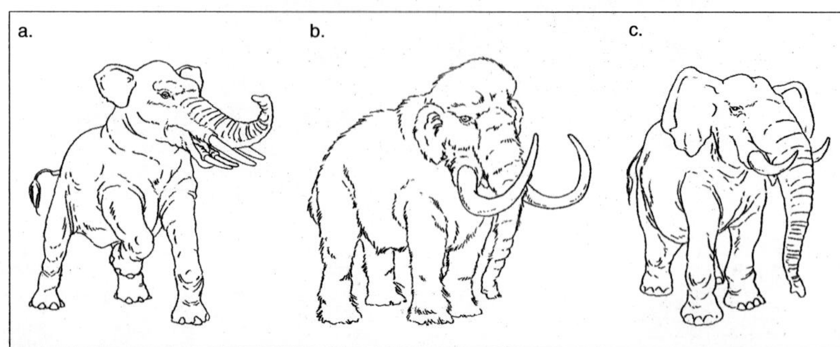

Figure 6.28 Three types of proboscideans (a) Gomphothere, (b) wooly Mammoth, (c) African elephant

acquired from the radiometric dating of rocks and

- developing explanations based on scientific knowledge and evidence.

Strategies

Getting Started

Display the transparency of copymaster 6.10, *Proboscidean Pictures*. Ask students the following questions:

- "Do these species appear to be related?"
- "Why do you think so or why do you think not?"

Remind students that species have characteristics, some of which are selected for because of the environment. Tell them they will be studying the evolution of these elephant-like organisms, which are also called proboscideans. They will have to figure out what might have happened to them across time.

Process and Procedure

In Step 1, tell students to read the paragraph to learn what their task will be. In Step 2, distribute copymaster 6.8, *Proboscidean Pictures* to the class. Instruct students to study the pictures carefully and read the descriptions. Then tell students to complete the remaining steps and record their responses in their science notebooks.

c. Consider a proboscidean that is descended from gomphotheres and is a common ancestor of African elephants and mammoths. In which rock layers would you look for a fossil of this proboscidean? Respond using a clearly labeled drawing or a written description. Briefly explain your answer.

4. Scientists piece together evidence from locations around the world to learn more about proboscideans. In this way, they know more than they can learn from only 1 set of rock layers. To learn what else scientists know about proboscideans, read the following paragraph about mammoths. Then answer Questions 4a–c.

Mammoths migrated out of Africa about 2 million years ago. Several species of mammoth evolved from the ancestral African mammoth. One of these species was the woolly mammoth, which lived from about 350,000 to 10,000 years ago. Scientists have collected the oldest woolly mammoth fossils from Siberia and western Europe. More recent fossils of woolly mammoths have been collected in North America as well as in Asia and Europe. Younger fossils are more abundant near the Arctic Circle. Because scientists have found frozen carcasses of woolly mammoths in Siberia and Alaska, they know the mammoths were covered with a thick coat of hair. Mammoths are extinct in all parts of the world today.

a. Describe a selective pressure that might have caused the woolly mammoth to evolve from the ancestral mammoth. Explain how this selective pressure could lead to the evolution of a woolly mammoth.

b. Explain what has caused some species of proboscideans to become extinct. You might not know the exact reasons, but you can use what you have learned in this chapter to develop a general explanation.

c. Describe how the process of natural selection leads to a diversity of species. Use the evolution of gomphotheres into the African elephant and the ancestral mammoth as an example. Include the following words in your explanation: *adaptation*, *population*, *natural selection*, *selective pressure*, *variation*, and *species*.

Answers to Steps 3–7, SE pages 326–328

3a. African elephants are still alive on Earth today. Gomphotheres lived farthest in the past, before mammoths and African elephants existed on Earth. Students might also suggest that it is possible that all 3 proboscidean species might have lived on Earth about 4 million years ago.

3b. Gomphotheres lived from just before 24–20 million years ago until just after 4 million years ago. African elephants lived from just after 4 million years ago until the present. Mammoths lived from 12,000 to 8,000 years ago depending on geography.

3c. A fossil of a proboscidean that is a descendant of gomphotheres and an ancestor of African elephants and mammoths might be found in rock layers older than 4 million years and younger than 24–20 million years old. Fossils would have to be found in rocks older than 4 million years old because African elephants appear in the fossil record after the ash layer dated 4 million years old. Fossils should be older than 24–20 million years old because gomphotheres only appear in 1 rock layer before the ash layer dated at 24–20 million years old.

4a. One selective pressure might have been a colder climate. As the ancestral mammoth migrated from Africa to Asia and western Europe, it might have had to endure colder winters. Some of the ancestral mammoths might have had more hair than other ancestral mammoths. The ancestral mammoths with more hair would have been more likely to survive colder winters. As more and more ancestral mammoths with the adaptation of more hair survived and reproduced, more of the mammoth population would have this adaptation. Eventually, there were enough mammoths with the hair adaptation to represent a distinct species of woolly mammoth.

4b. Species become extinct when they are no longer able to survive in their environment. Species of proboscidean such as gomphotheres might have become extinct because the species lacked adaptations that helped it survive a change in its environment.

4c. The process of natural selection leads to a diversity of species because species such as gomphotheres have variation in their populations. Individuals in the gomphothere population might have different characteristics such as variations in body size; size, shape, or length of tusks; or the presence or lack of lower tusks. Some of these characteristics might help an individual gomphothere survive. These characteristics are called adaptations. Some gomphotheres might have had the adaptation to be bigger or to not have lower tusks. Bigger size or only having upper tusks might have helped those gomphotheres survive in the African environment.

5. Scientists use radiometric dating to determine the age of rocks. Scientists measure the amount of parent and daughter isotopes. Because scientists know the half-lives of radioactive isotopes, they can calculate how much time has passed since the rock formed. The half-life of a radioactive isotope is the amount of time that has passed after one-half of the parent has decayed into a daughter. Scientists can date rocks that contain multiple radioactive isotopes, such as rock layers containing volcanic ash or other geologic deposits of volcanic origin. Because multiple radioactive isotopes are present in these rocks, scientists can calculate the age of the rocks using several methods. Using multiple methods gives scientists more accurate dates and lets them confirm geologic age.

6. Fossils support the theory of evolution because they show that the species on Earth have changed across time. Many fossils look similar to species that exist today, and the farther you go back in the fossil record (to older fossils), the less the fossils look like species that exist today.

   Radiometric dating supports the theory of evolution because it provides absolute dates for events in Earth's history. Using radiometric dating and relative dating, scientists can determine when different species lived on Earth and know how much time has passed between the appearances of different species. They also know that since Earth is about 4.5 billion years old, there has been a vast amount of time for change to have occurred on Earth.

   The theory of evolution also is supported by the fact that species have variations in their characteristics and that some of these variations help them survive.

7. This statement is inaccurate because species such as giraffes do not develop long necks by stretching them. Some individuals within a species have variations in a characteristic that may help them survive, such as a longer neck to reach higher tree leaves. These individuals would possess this characteristic and then pass the adaptation to their offspring. If the adaptation continued to be beneficial, more of the population would have long necks across time as the adaptation was passed from generation to generation.

5. The rock column pictured on the *Proboscidean and Rock Layers* handout is particularly useful because scientists could date some of the rock layers. How do scientists determine the age of rocks? Think about the following when constructing your answer:
   - Why are some rocks used more often than others?
   - What do scientists measure during this process?
   - Why is knowing the half-life important?
6. It is difficult to watch evolution happen across millions of years, yet scientists are certain of the theory of evolution. That is because they have a lot of evidence of change across time and descent from common ancestors. Give at least 2 examples of evidence for change across time and explain why each supports the theory of evolution.
7. Read the following statement. Use what you have learned about natural selection and evolution to explain why you think the statement is an accurate or inaccurate description of how species change across time.

   "Giraffes developed their long necks and legs because of generation after generation of giraffes stretching to eat leaves high in the trees."

CHAPTER 7

Tracking Traits

Chapter Overview

In chapter 6, *Exploring Change*, students learned that living systems have changed across time. Species alive today share characteristics with their ancestors. In chapter 7, *Tracking Traits*, students will learn how characteristics are passed from one generation to the next through the process of inheritance. Inherited characteristics are called traits.

Students will share their current understanding of inheritance by generating a list of statements about inheritance. Then students will explore inheritance of traits by crossing strains of yeast. They will observe the inheritance of a trait that was not visible in the parent generation. After reading about Mendel's experiments, students will be provided with explanations for the observations they made in their yeast experiment. They will learn about dominant and recessive traits, genes, and alleles. Then students will read about chromosomes and the mechanism of inheritance—meiosis. They will learn that meiosis ensures that gametes have half the number of chromosomes of other body cells. Students will show their ability to illustrate and describe the process of meiosis by modeling meiosis with clay.

Punnett squares and a simulation of the inheritance of traits will give students the opportunity to apply their knowledge of the inheritance of alleles from parents. Then students will learn about three common patterns of inheritance and use them to analyze and create a pedigree. In the evaluate, students will demonstrate their understanding of inheritance by interpreting information about a genetic disorder of a hypothetical family member, using this information to choose the alleles of individuals for the family, and then creating an appropriate pedigree. To show their understanding of meiosis, students will explain how one of the offspring got his or her traits. By learning about inheritance, students will begin to understand how living systems have both changed and remained the same throughout Earth's history.

Goals for the Chapter

The overarching goal for this chapter is for students to understand how traits are passed from one generation to another. By the end of chapter 7, students will understand that

- transmission of genetic information to offspring occurs through gametes that only have one representative from each chromosome pair,
- meiosis results in the formation of gametes that contain half the genetic information of other cells, and
- the variations between generations are explained by the fact that cells contain two copies of each chromosome and therefore two copies of each gene.

Look at the chapter organizer each day to remind yourself of where students are in the overall sequence of events in the chapter.

Chapter 7 Organizer

TRACKING TRAITS

Major Concepts

- **Traits are transmitted from parent to offspring through gametes.**
- **Meiosis results in the formation of gametes that contain half the genetic information of other cells.**
- **Cells contain two copies of each chromosome and therefore two copies of each gene.**
- **Variations in the traits of different generations are explained by the fact that each individual gets two copies of each gene.**

ENGAGE — It Runs in the Family ★

Key Idea: • Family members tend to share some of the same traits.

Activity: Students react to a letter that describes a teenager's worries about an inherited genetic disorder (myotonic muscular dystrophy, or MMD). Students share their current understanding of inheritance.

LINKING QUESTION: How can I investigate if traits are inherited?

EXPLORE — What Shows Up? ★★★★

Key Idea: • Some offspring have the same traits as the parents, but other offspring have different traits from the parents.

Activity: Students work in teams of two to cross two strains of baker's yeast (*Saccharomyces cerevisiae*; one strain is red, the other is cream colored) and look at the resulting first generation.

LINKING QUESTION: How are traits inherited, and how is meiosis part of the process of inheritance?

EXPLAIN — How Do We Get Our Traits? ★★

Key Ideas:
- Genes determine the traits exhibited by an organism.
- Genes for the same trait can exist in different forms called alleles.
- The transfer of genetic information occurs through gametes.
- Meiosis produces gametes that have half the genetic material of other body cells.

Activity: In Part I, students read about Gregor Mendel's experiments and the process of meiosis. In Part II, they simulate meiosis using play dough as chromosomes.

LINKING QUESTION: How can we make predictions about what traits offspring will inherit?

EXPLAIN — All about Alleles ★★

Key Ideas:
- Tools such as Punnett squares help make predictions about the traits of offspring.
- Gametes have one representative from each chromosome pair, allowing offspring to receive different combinations of alleles from their parents.

Activity: In Part I, students use a graphical tool (Punnett square) to show how different combinations of alleles from parents result in different traits of offspring. In Part II, they assume the role of lab technicians who are making a human by uniting a donated sperm and a donated egg cell in the lab. They simulate the random separation of alleles during meiosis and the joining during fertilization to give an offspring its traits.

LINKING QUESTION: Are there patterns in how traits are inherited?

ELABORATE — Inheritance Patterns ★★

Key Ideas:
- Tools such as pedigrees help make predictions about the traits of offspring.
- Traits can be autosomal dominant, autosomal recessive, or sex linked.

Activity: In Part I, students look for patterns in three pedigrees. In Part II, they read a story about a high school student who finds out that he has inherited a genetic trait. They create a pedigree for the student and a Punnett square for his parents.

LINKING QUESTION: How can I use what I have learned to demonstrate my understanding of how traits are inherited and the process of meiosis?

★ = One Class Period ☆ = ½ Class Period *Note:* Based on a 50-minute class period.

EVALUATE Passing Genes—Who Gets What? ★★

Key Ideas:
- Each parent contributes one-half of the genetic makeup of the offspring.
- Meiosis facilitates the transfer of genetic information from one generation to the next through gametes.
- Differences in the traits between generations result from individuals having different alleles of the same gene.
- Traits are inherited through different inheritance patterns.

Activity: Students create and label pedigrees based on known alleles and know affected individuals. Then students answer questions about meiosis.

★ = One Class Period ☆ = ½ Class Period *Note:* Based on a 50-minute class period.

Standards Covered by Chapter 7*

TRACKING TRAITS

STANDARD C: Life Science. As a result of activities in grades 9–12, all students should develop an understanding of

the cell

- Cells have particular structures that underlie their functions. Every cell is surrounded by a membrane that separates it from the outside world. Inside the cell is a concentrated mixture of thousands of different molecules which form a variety of specialized structures that carry out such cell functions as energy production, transport of molecules, waste disposal, synthesis of new molecules, and the storage of genetic material. [See Unifying Concepts and Processes]

the molecular basis of heredity

- Most of the cells in a human contain two copies of each of 22 different chromosomes. In addition, there is a pair of chromosomes that determines sex; a female contains two X chromosomes and a male contains one X and one Y chromosome. Transmission of genetic information to offspring occurs through egg and sperm cells that contain only one representative from each chromosome pair. An egg and a sperm unite to form a new individual. The fact that the human body is formed from cells that contain two copies of each chromosome—and therefore two copies of each gene—explains many features of human heredity, such as how variations that are hidden in one generation can be expressed in the next.

**Note:* Bracketed portions of the standard are addressed elsewhere in the program.

Prerequisite Knowledge

Students should have knowledge about basic cell structure and function. For example, they should know that cells contain genetic information. Students should know that mitosis or cell division results in new cells that are genetically identical to the parent. They will revisit mitosis as they learn about meiosis in this chapter. Students will use their experiences from chapter 1, *Investigations by Design*, when they streak plates with yeast in the activity *What Shows Up?*

Commonly Held Misconceptions

Some misconceptions about inheritance held by students and adults include the following:

- Traits are only inherited from one of the parents.
- Specific traits are inherited from the mother and different traits are inherited from the father.
- The traits of the parents merge in the offspring.
- Only observable traits such as eye color or face shape are inherited.
- Traits influenced by the environment can be inherited.

Many students have difficulty understanding that the probability of the traits, and more specifically the alleles, of offspring can be predicted by observing what traits the parents have.

NOTES:

ENGAGE

It Runs in the Family

Activity Overview

In *It Runs in the Family*, students will read a letter that describes a teenager's worries about myotonic muscular dystrophy (MMD), an inherited genetic disorder. Students will begin to think about how traits are passed from one generation to the next and how knowledge about inherited disorders can both help them and generate questions. They will generate a list of statements about inheritance to show their current understanding.

Before You Teach

Background Information

The fact that parents and children have similar traits is not a new idea for students; they have personal experience with these similarities. Students are less familiar, however, with *how* the similarities occur. This activity engages students in this question and the phenomenon of inheritance.

An important part of the activity is a discussion of a fictional letter written by a teenager who finds out his father has a real disorder: myotonic muscular dystrophy. MMD is the most common adult form of one of the many types of muscular dystrophy. All types of muscular dystrophy are hereditary, progressive, and cause a pattern of muscle wasting and weakness. MMD is a rare genetic disorder mostly affecting the muscular system. MMD is also known as Steinert's disease and dystrophia myotonica.

There is a wide range of symptoms associated with MMD. Symptoms include muscle weakness, involuntary clenching of the hands and jaw, swallowing problems, eye problems, heart disorders, and extreme fatigue. Muscle weakness is accompanied by myotonia, the delayed relaxation of muscles after contraction. This symptom is unique to MMD and is not exhibited by those affected with other types of muscular dystrophy. MMD is multisystemic. It can affect the tissues and organs of many body systems in addition to the voluntary muscle system.

The symptoms usually appear later in life (after age 50), although children can experience symptoms and 50 percent of those with the disorder show signs by age 20. Careful examination sometimes reveals typical abnormalities before symptoms appear. Congenital myotonic muscular dystrophy is rare and is present at birth. Symptoms range from mild to severe. Those with the most severe symptoms usually die by age 50.

The gene involved in MMD is on an autosomal chromosome (not one of the sex chromosomes), so the disorder can affect both males and females. In affected individuals, one gene in a pair of genes on the 19th chromosome does not function correctly and expresses itself more strongly, dominating the other working gene. An affected parent passes either the MMD gene or the other working gene on to his or her offspring. Affected males and females have the same chance of having affected children: there is a 1:2 (50 percent) chance that a child of an affected parent will receive the gene for MMD. The child's symptoms are often more pronounced than the parent's. The effects of MMD seem to be more pronounced as it is passed through each generation.

A variety of genetic testing options are available to people concerned about MMD. DNA can be obtained from a blood sample so that the presence of the MMD gene can be detected.

ENGAGE **It Runs in the Family**

Members of the same family share many traits. Children with tall parents often grow to be tall adults. Grandchildren sometimes look astonishingly like the photographs of their grandparents at a similar age. A mother beams proudly when people mistakenly think she and her daughter are sisters.

Some traits that run in families affect more than how you look (figure 7.1). The biological process that makes offspring look like their parents can also transfer genetic disorders from one generation to the next. How does this all happen? In *It Runs in the Family*, you will begin to think about how traits are inherited. You will explore how our knowledge of inheritance has led to the understanding of genetic disorders.

Materials

none

Process and Procedure

1. Read the "Dear Counselor" letter in figure 7.2 with your class. You will learn some of the questions a teenager has for a genetic counselor when he learns his father has a disorder.
2. Consider the questions and thoughts "Afraid and Wanting to Know More" has about how inheritance works. What are your ideas about inheritance?
   a. Generate 2 statements about inheritance.
   b. Share your statements with the class. Your teacher will record your statements.
   c. Record the class list of statements in your science notebook.
   d. Make a note of whether you think each statement is true or false.
   e. Participate in a class discussion about inheritance.

You might think your statements are true, but you might disagree with some of the other statements. You will have an opportunity to look back at the list later in the chapter when you have learned more about inheritance.

▼ **Figure 7.1 Family.** What physical resemblances among the family members do you see? Do you think you can see all the traits the individuals in a family share?

Materials

For the teacher

large sheet of paper

For each team of 2 students

1 copy of copymaster 7.1, *Inheritance* (optional)

Advance Preparation

Decide whether you will have students generate their own statements in Step 2 or you will provide them with statements.

As You Teach

Outcomes and Indicators of Success

By the end of this activity, students should

1. communicate their prior knowledge about how traits are passed from one generation to the next.

   They will communicate their prior knowledge by

   - discussing that the boy who wrote the letter in the activity thinks he could have MMD because it is a disorder that is inherited from previous generations;
   - generating two statements about inheritance with a partner;
   - comparing traits that are inherited with traits that are acquired; and
   - describing what doctors might observe in blood to inform them about a disorder their patients might have, such as MMD.

2. be able to empathize with the author of a fictional letter.

   They will demonstrate their ability by

   - relating to a teenager who is concerned that he might have inherited a disorder and
   - considering whether they would be tested for MMD if they were in the same position as the teenager writing the "Dear Counselor" letter and whether individuals under age 18 should be allowed to be tested for a genetic disorder.

Strategies

Getting Started

This activity uses examples of disorders to explore inheritance. It is important to stress to students that there are many inherited traits that are not abnormalities. You might ask students to determine if they have any of the following classic Mendelian traits:

- Cleft chin: presence of a dimple in the chin
- Camptodactyly or bent pinky syndrome: the presence of a digit or digits that bend noticeably toward the other fingers
- Mid-digital hair: the presence of hair on the middle section of a finger

It is important to include students who are adopted or otherwise unfamiliar with their biological parents by having them describe acquired traits or speculate what their own offspring might inherit from them. In addition, be aware that the anxiety expressed in the letter from "Afraid and Wanting to Know More" is similar to that of some adopted children when they are faced with unknown ancestry.

Process and Procedure

In Step 1, read the "Dear Counselor" letter together as a class. Call on a few students to read sections aloud to the class. You might take time to ask if students have heard of myotonic muscular dystrophy. Encourage them to think about questions they might have if they were in the same position as "Afraid and Wanting to Know More."

In Step 2, students generate 2 statements about inheritance. There are no right or wrong answers here. This task allows you to gauge how much students know about basic genetic principles and any preconceptions they might have. Resist the urge to verify or acknowledge correct answers because students will have an opportunity to learn the correct answers as they complete the activities in the chapter. Try to get students to generate a variety of statements. Listen to students as they work on the task and use these probing questions to bring out their ideas about inheritance. Answers are provided here for your background information only. Do not provide students with the answers.

- "If you look more like one parent than the other, do you think you are more likely to inherit a trait from the parent you look more similar to?"

No, in most cases the inheritance of one trait is not related to the inheritance of another trait.

- "Does a person have to exhibit a trait to pass it on?"

No, each trait is determined by two alleles. A person might carry a recessive allele but not express the trait.

- "Does a child receive equal amounts of genetic information from both parents?"

Yes, children receive 23 chromosomes from each parent.

- "Do you think all traits are visible?"

Not all traits are visible. For example, the ability to taste sodium benzoate tasting paper is not a visible trait.

- "If a person has dimples, do you think at least one of his or her children will inherit them?"

It is possible that one of the children will inherit the dimples. The probability of inheriting a trait depends on what alleles each parent carries.

- "Are some traits more common in males than females?"

Yes, some traits are passed on the X chromosome. Since males only inherit one X chromosome, they will exhibit each trait on that chromosome, while females will express those traits in half of their cells.

- "Are identical twins always the same sex?"

Yes, because identical twins inherit the same sex chromosomes.

- "Do all organisms have the same number of chromosomes? Do you think humans have more or less than an organism such as a dog?"

The number of chromosomes varies between organisms.

Once teams have generated their statements, call on them to share their statements with the class. Record the statements on a large sheet of paper (the class will refer to this list later in the chapter). Make sure all teams can contribute at least 1 statement. Even if some students do not agree with a team's statement, explain that there are no right or wrong statements. At this point, everyone is sharing current ideas. Accessing students' prior knowledge through this exercise will help you discover where you need to focus time to develop accurate understandings in students during later activities.

Make a class list of 8 to 12 statements or all the statements if you have a way to capture all of them. Try to make sure the list is diverse. If students have very similar statements, look back to the probing questions and encourage the class to come up with some different statements based on those questions. After the list is complete, instruct students to record the class list of statements in their science notebooks. In Step 2d, tell students to make a note of whether they think each statement is true or false. If they disagreed with one of the statements, this is their chance to note that. Suggest that they use red ink, a highlighter, or a sticky note to make their comments stand out in their notebooks. Remind students that they will revisit the list later in the chapter.

After students have completed Step 2, facilitate a class discussion of the *Reflect and Connect* questions. You might choose to have your students record their answers to the *Reflect and Connect* questions. Then students could reexamine their answers later in the chapter to see how much they have learned.

NOTES:

Answers to Reflect and Connect, SE pages 335–336

1. "Afraid and Wanting to Know More" knows that the disorder has been passed from his grandmother to his father, and he understands enough about inheritance to predict that it is possible that his father passed the disorder on to him.
2. Many students will be confused about the difference between acquired and inherited traits at this point. Encourage students to share their ideas about acquired and inherited traits. You might explain that acquired traits are traits that a person gets during his or her lifetime.

   Genetic factors for inherited traits are present at birth, whereas acquired traits arise as the result of accidents or intentional changes that occur after birth. Scars, cosmetic changes in hair or eye color, and accident-induced limps are all examples of acquired traits. Some acquired traits involve environmental factors, including many behaviors and habits modeled by parents (e.g., hair twisting and nail biting). Classifying traits is not always easy, however. Some traits that appear after birth might have an inherited (genetic) component as well. For example, the height of an individual is the result of a combination of genes and diet, an environmental influence. By the end of the chapter, students will understand that acquired traits cannot be passed on.
3. Listen to students' answers to assess their current understanding of the mechanism that underlies inheritance. For example, do students suggest that doctors can observe the cells of the blood and look at the chromosomes within the cells? Do students mention genes or DNA? Students will most likely be familiar with DNA, but they won't know much about it at this point. Assure students that they will understand more after they complete the chapter.
4. Students will express their own opinions and should be able to support their ideas.
5. This question is intended to invite discussion and thoughts about ethics and people's rights to know their fate despite the limited things they can do. The question might invite discussion about people who choose not to have a family if they know there is the possibility of passing on a genetic disorder. Again, students will express their own opinions and should be able to support their ideas.

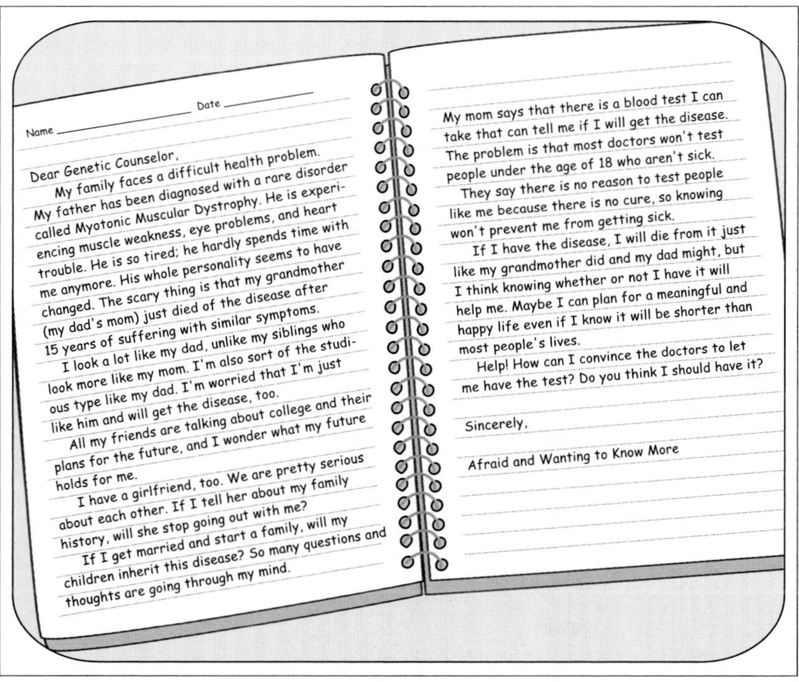

Name ______________ Date ______________

Dear Genetic Counselor,

My family faces a difficult health problem. My father has been diagnosed with a rare disorder called Myotonic Muscular Dystrophy. He is experiencing muscle weakness, eye problems, and heart trouble. He is so tired; he hardly spends time with me anymore. His whole personality seems to have changed. The scary thing is that my grandmother (my dad's mom) just died of the disease after 15 years of suffering with similar symptoms.

I look a lot like my dad, unlike my siblings who look more like my mom. I'm also sort of the studious type like my dad. I'm worried that I'm just like him and will get the disease, too.

All my friends are talking about college and their plans for the future, and I wonder what my future holds for me.

I have a girlfriend, too. We are pretty serious about each other. If I tell her about my family history, will she stop going out with me?

If I get married and start a family, will my children inherit this disease? So many questions and thoughts are going through my mind.

My mom says that there is a blood test I can take that can tell me if I will get the disease. The problem is that most doctors won't test people under the age of 18 who aren't sick. They say there is no reason to test people like me because there is no cure, so knowing won't prevent me from getting sick.

If I have the disease, I will die from it just like my grandmother did and my dad might, but I think knowing whether or not I have it will help me. Maybe I can plan for a meaningful and happy life even if I know it will be shorter than most people's lives.

Help! How can I convince the doctors to let me have the test? Do you think I should have it?

Sincerely,

Afraid and Wanting to Know More

▲ **Figure 7.2 "Dear Counselor" letter.** What questions would you have for a genetic counselor if someone in your family had a genetic disorder?

Reflect and Connect

Answer the following questions individually and then discuss your answers as a class. This is an opportunity to share your ideas and current understanding with your classmates. It is likely that you will also generate more questions.

1. Why does "Afraid and Wanting to Know More" think he could have myotonic muscular dystrophy (MMD)?
2. Suggest some characteristics that people acquire during their lifetimes. What is the difference between acquired characteristics and traits that are inherited? Make a list of acquired characteristics and a list of inherited traits.

Chapter 7 Tracking Traits 335

EXPLORE

What Shows Up?

Activity Overview

In *What Shows Up?*, students will conduct an investigation with yeast to see what traits are passed from one generation to another. They will cross two strains (one is red, the other is cream colored) of baker's yeast (*Saccharomyces cerevisiae*) and look at the resulting first generation.

Before You Teach

Background Information

Yeast are good organisms to use when studying genetics because they go through their entire life cycle in a few days. This investigation is designed to use an inquiry approach to study inheritance. Students will take cream-colored yeast cells and mate them with red-colored yeast cells. The yeast cells they mate contain half the number of their full set of chromosomes (they are haploid cells). The first-generation yeast cells have a complete set of chromosomes (they are diploid cells). It is not important that students understand how this works at this point. They will learn about how cells get half the number of chromosomes later when they learn about meiosis.

When students conduct their cross, they will see that the first-generation cells are all cream colored. Ideally, they will wonder what happened to the red color trait. In this strain of yeast, cream color is dominant to red. The red color trait is still present in the first generation of yeast but is masked by the dominant cream color trait.

If students cross the first-generation yeast with itself, the red-colored yeast would reappear in the second generation. This investigation does not ask students to do this because the first generation of yeast already has a full set of chromosomes, so the cells cannot mate. There are methods that can be used to get the yeast to a haploid stage, but they are beyond the scope of this activity.

Haploid yeast are found as one of two mating types; one is called "a" and the other is called "alpha." Diploid cells only form when two different strains of haploid cells come into contact with each other. In nature, we have found that these haploid strains can switch mating types, ensuring that there will be two mating types and diploid cells can always be formed. Laboratory strains have been genetically modified so that this does not happen. Your haploid strains will reproduce by budding (a form of cell division or asexual reproduction) indefinitely and will never become diploid unless mated with an opposite strain.

The mating process is initiated when the cells of one mating type encounter a chemical (called a peptide pheromone) produced by the cells of the opposite mating type. Haploid cells that are the "a" mating type produce a-factor pheromone, and cells that are alpha produce alpha-factor pheromone. When cells of opposite mating type are close together, the pheromone of one cell type binds to a receptor on the surface of the opposite cell type. A series of reactions occurs within each cell, resulting in the cells growing toward each other, stretching into a pear-shaped cell called a "shmoo." Shmoos are the gametes in yeast. (The name comes from a cartoon character

Answers to Reflect and Connect are on TE page 335.

3. What do you think doctors can observe in the blood that tells them about a disorder that someone might get in the future?
4. If you were the writer of the letter, would you have the test performed? Why or why not?
5. In your opinion, should people under the age of 18 be allowed to be tested for a genetic disorder? Give reasons for your thoughts.

EXPLORE

What Shows Up?

In *It Runs in the Family*, you discussed some of your ideas about inheritance. How do we know that traits are inherited? Scientists have conducted experiments on a wide variety of organisms to learn more about heredity. They choose organisms that are easy to handle, have short life cycles, produce large numbers of offspring, and, most important, have variation among the individuals in the population. Figure 7.3 shows some examples of organisms that have contributed to our understanding of heredity.

In *What Shows Up?*, you will work with a partner to conduct an investigation of your own on one of these organisms: yeast. By making observations of yeast, you will begin thinking about how traits are passed on.

Part I: The First Generation

Materials

For each team of 2 students

2 pairs of safety goggles

access to biohazard bags or buckets with 10% bleach solution

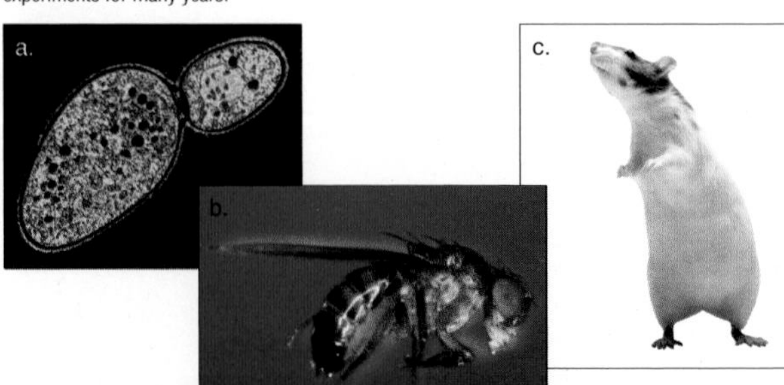

Figure 7.3 Organisms used in genetics experiments. Scientists have used (a) yeast, (b) fruit flies, (c) rats, and (d) corn in genetics experiments for many years.

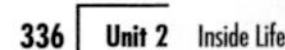

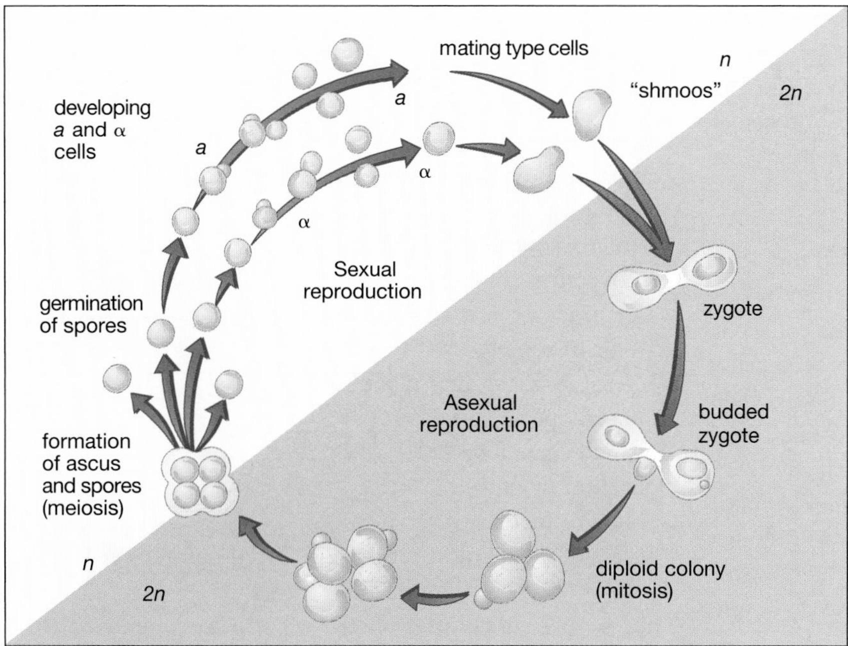

▲ **Figure T7.1 Yeast life cycle.** The yeast life cycle consists of both asexual and sexual reproduction. Yeast cells reproduce asexually during the diploid phase. Sexual reproduction occurs between yeast cells of opposite mating types during the haploid phase.

- 1 microscope slide
- 1 coverslip
- 1 dropper
- 1 pair of forceps
- 1 yeast nutrient agar plate (YED)
- microscope
- 10% bleach solution
- access to incubator set at 30°C
- access to 2 subcultures of strain 2 (red-colored) yeast colonies (a2 and alpha2)
- access to 2 subcultures of strain 3 (cream-colored) yeast colonies (a3 and alpha3)
- access to sterile toothpicks or sterile inoculating loops
- 1 small cup of water
- 1 glass marking pencil or marker

Cautions

The yeast used in this investigation are nonpathogenic laboratory strains. "Nonpathogenic" means the yeast cannot cause disease. However, it is always good practice to disinfect all materials that come in contact with live organisms. Make sure your lab area is clean. Wipe the top surface of your lab area with a 10% bleach solution before and after the investigation. Wear goggles while working with the agar plates and yeast. Pull your hair or loose clothing back if necessary. Wash your hands thoroughly before leaving the laboratory. Dispose of all materials as directed by your teacher.

Process and Procedure

1. Observe the yeast subcultures provided by your teacher. What do you think yeast cells will look like through a microscope? Record your ideas in your science notebook.
2. Get a closer look at yeast cells using a microscope by completing Steps 2a–g.
   a. Obtain a clean microscope slide.
   b. Add a drop of water to the slide.
   c. Put on your safety goggles. Touch a sterile toothpick to a colony of yeast from one of the subcultures provided by your teacher.

Safety Goggles

in the old comic strip *Li'l Abner*.) Eventually, the cell walls of the yeast cells fuse, allowing the cell nuclei to fuse and form a zygote (diploid). The zygotes are peanut- or cloverleaf-shaped cells. The sexual life cycle of yeast is shown in figure T7.1.

The shmoos and zygotes form within three to four hours after the yeast cells have been crossed (mated). They can be seen with a microscope. However, viewing shmoo and zygote cells was omitted from this activity because it is difficult to time viewing them. Within 24 hours, the diploid yeast cells look just like the haploid yeast cells. The easiest way to distinguish diploid from haploid yeast cells is to transfer the yeast to a minimal vitamin medium (MV) agar plate. The haploid strains grow well on nutritionally rich yeast extract–dextrose general growth medium (YED) agar plates but do not grow on nutritionally poor MV plates. Diploid yeast cells can grow on MV plates. Exploring haploid and diploid cells goes beyond what the students need to learn at this point. For this activity, it is most important that students explore what traits "show up" in the crossed yeast.

There are many experiments that can be done with yeast, including investigating the entire sexual life cycle of yeast. If you have a student who is especially interested in this activity, you might suggest that he or she investigate yeast further in a full inquiry.

The yeast strains in this activity come in different colors because of each type's ability to metabolize adenine. Adenine is a small organic compound that can be converted into AMP (adenosine monophosphate). AMP is a precursor to DNA and RNA and to several other molecules needed for energy production. When grown in media containing excess adenine, yeast cells store adenine for later. When normal (wild-type) cells use up their stored adenine, they can make their own AMP through a pathway involving 12 sequential enzymatic steps.

The red-colored yeast cells you are using are labeled as ade⁻ (or adenine-requiring mutants) because they require adenine to be provided in the growth medium. These cells have one or more mutations along the pathway by which AMP is made. If adenine is supplied to these cells, a one-step process allows the adenine to be converted to AMP, and the cells continue normal metabolism.

When the red-colored yeast cells are starved for adenine, the pathway of AMP biosynthesis cannot be completed, and by-products made to this point collect at the enzymatic step where the mutation occurs. The cells you are using in this activity show a colorful result when starved for adenine. The biosynthetic pathway can begin, but is blocked at one of two steps, so an intermediate compound accumulates (like cars at a roadblock). This particular compound takes on a red color in the presence of oxygen. A mutation at an earlier step or at a later step (if there are no other mutations in the pathway) will not show the red color.

Materials

For the teacher

1 pair of safety goggles
1 pair of gloves (optional)
5 biohazard bags or buckets of 10% bleach solution
20 YED plates for growing initial yeast colonies (5 sets of plates, 4 plates of each strain)
5 YED plates for growing mated colonies (optional)
incubator set at 30°C (optional)
packet of bread yeast soaking in sugar water (optional, for *Getting Started*)
slant of yeast strain a2 (HAR), red
slant of yeast strain alpha2 (HBR), red
slant of yeast strain a3 (HAT), cream
slant of yeast strain alpha3 (HBT), cream
sterile, flat toothpicks or inoculating loops

Materials—Part I

For each team of 2 students

2 pairs of safety goggles
2 pairs of gloves (optional)
access to biohazard bags or buckets with 10% bleach solution
1 microscope slide
1 coverslip
1 dropper
1 pair of forceps
1 yeast nutrient agar plate (YED)
microscope
1 small cup of water
parafilm or tape
access to incubator set at 30°C
access to 2 subcultures of strain 2 (red-colored) yeast colonies (a2 and alpha2)
access to 2 subcultures of strain 3 (cream-colored) yeast colonies (a3 and alpha3)
access to sterile toothpicks or sterile inoculating loops
1 glass marking pencil or marker

Materials—Part II

2 pairs of safety goggles
2 pairs of gloves (optional)
access to biohazard bags or buckets with 10% bleach solution
1 agar plate with yeast growth from Part I
access to incubator set at 30°C
1 pair of forceps
parafilm or tape
access to sterile toothpicks or sterile inoculating loops
colored pencils

NOTES:

Advance Preparation

Consider working through the entire investigation several weeks before the students begin so that you understand what is happening and are better prepared for the types of problems or confusions that might arise.

Purchase flat toothpicks and keep them as sterile as possible. Prepare boxes of toothpicks for access by students by cutting a small hole in the corner of an unopened box of flat toothpicks. This will allow students to shake out each toothpick far enough to grasp the pointed end. The flat end is less likely to tear the agar. New toothpicks from the store are sterile, and students should not touch the agar surface with the toothpick end that they handled.

To Prepare YED Plates

Science supply companies carry prepoured, prepared YED plates. Allow 2 weeks for delivery because they only ship live materials at the beginning of the week. The plates can be stored in closed plastic bags at room temperature in a dark cupboard for up to 5 months. Prepared plates often arrive with labels affixed to the bottom of the plate. If there are labels on the bottom of the plates, remove them. Students will be drawing grids on the bottom of the plates. This method of preparation is the easiest.

Alternatively, you can make your own YED plates. Obtain bottles of prepared growth medium (YED). Science supply companies also sell sterile petri dishes. To make the plates, do the following.

1. Work in an area protected from air currents and away from plants, animals, and obvious sources of dust. Wipe countertop surfaces with alcohol. You want to reduce the chances of bacteria growing in the YED plates.
2. Follow the directions for liquefying the agar and keeping it sterile. Open 1 petri dish at a time and pour enough agar to cover the bottom of the plate. Close the plates immediately. Pour the plates in stacks if possible; this technique reduces contamination and condensation.
3. After the agar has solidified, invert the plates to prevent condensation from dripping on the agar.
4. Allow the medium to cure for about 3 days after you pour it so that its surface becomes stronger and easier for students to work with.

Order tube cultures of yeast strains a2 (HAR), alpha2 (HBR), a3 (HAT), and alpha3 (HBT) from your Kendall/Hunt representative or your local science supplier within 3 to 4 weeks of use. The yeast cultures will arrive grown as lawns on slants of yeast extract adenine dextrose (YEAD) growth medium. Each slant is sufficient to prepare 25 plates.

Starting Yeast Subcultures

You will need to grow each strain on YED plates. This is especially important for the a2 and alpha2 strains that only produce red colonies when deprived of adenine. Grow the yeast on 5 sets of plates for a class of 30 students. A set of plates should include 1 plate of each strain (a2, alpha2, a3, and alpha3). Students from 3 teams can share 1 set of plates. Having multiple sets of plates will help you conduct this lab with large groups of students

NOTES:

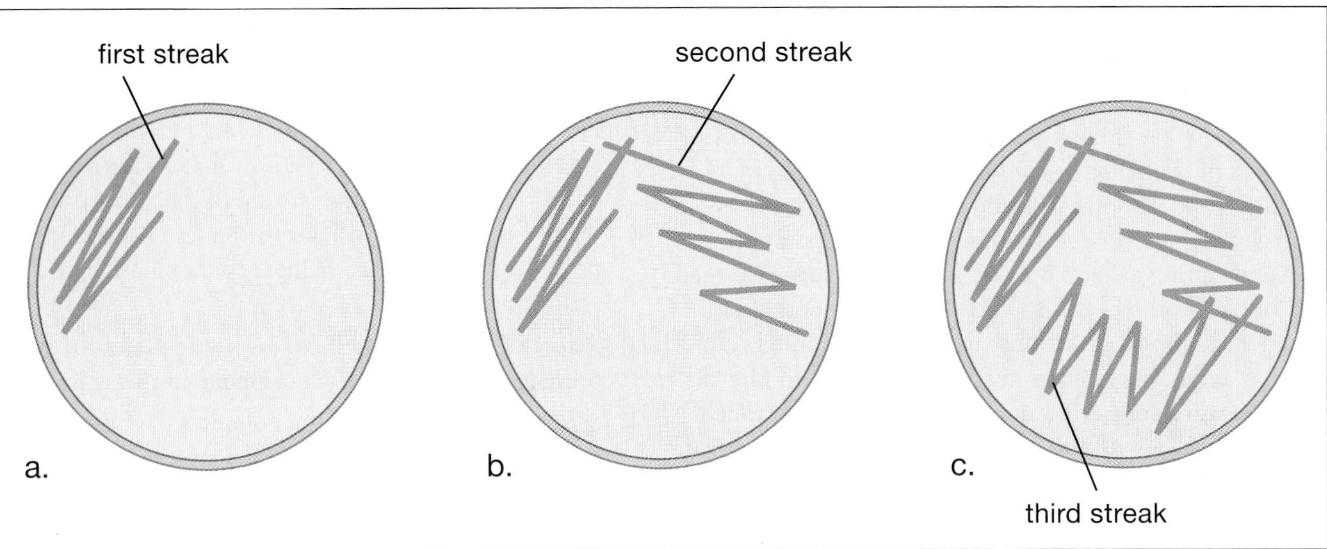

▲ **Figure T7.2 Streaking plates.** (a) Make an initial streak from the slant. (b) (c) Then distribute the cells by streaking the plate with one of the patterns shown. This technique dilutes the cells on the agar in successive overlapping streaks, until individual cells are distributed to form isolated colonies.

and reduce the chance of contamination. To grow yeast on plates, do the following.

1. Obtain a sterile, flat toothpick or inoculating loop to streak the plates. If you want to reach the yeast at the bottom of the slant, you might need to use an inoculating loop. If you use a metal inoculating loop, make sure you sterilize it by putting it in a flame and letting it cool.
2. Remove the cap from the yeast slant culture.
3. Using care not to touch the rim or outside edges of the culture tube, touch the toothpick to the cells on the slant. You do not need to transfer many cells.
4. Remove the toothpick and make a streak of cells on a plate. Make the streak about 2 centimeters (cm) long and about 1 cm away from the edge of the plate. Discard the toothpick in a biohazard bag or bucket with 10% bleach solution.
5. With a fresh toothpick, make another streak that overlaps the first at a slight angle. Make several more parallel streaks with the same toothpick. Repeat with a fresh toothpick several more times until the entire plate has been covered with streaks. This is illustrated in figure T7.2.

d. Touch the end of the toothpick containing yeast to the water on the slide. Stir gently. Dispose of the toothpick according to your teacher's instructions.
e. Place a coverslip over the drop of water.
f. Observe the slide using the high-power objective of the microscope. Look for small, circular yeast cells.
g. (optional) Make a second slide from a yeast colony of the other color using a fresh toothpick and compare the 2 slides.

3. Make a detailed sketch of a few yeast cells in your science notebook.
4. Work with a partner to discuss how you can investigate inheritance using yeast by completing Steps 4a–d. You may not know exactly what inheritance is, but be patient. This activity will help you begin to understand how inheritance occurs. Record your ideas in your science notebook.
   a. Read *Yeast* to learn about the organism and how it reproduces.
   b. Describe how yeast reproduce using a labeled drawing.
   c. What visible trait do baker's yeast exhibit?
   d. Discuss with your partner how you might investigate what traits yeast pass to the next generation through reproduction.

READING

Yeast

Yeast are a type of fungus. Other common fungi include mushrooms, truffles, and molds. Yeast are single-celled microorganisms that are known for their ability to ferment (break down) carbohydrates (see figure 7.4). Yeast are found in a wide variety of natural habitats such as plant leaves, soil, and on the skin surface and in the intestinal tracts of warm-blooded animals. Yeast are also cultivated for commercial use. They are used in the baking industry to expand and raise dough and are used to ferment the sugars of grains to produce alcoholic beverages. In this activity, you will work with the yeast *Saccharomyces cerevisiae*, commonly called baker's or brewer's yeast.

◄ **Figure 7.4 Baker's yeast.** When yeast ferment the sugars in flour, they are converting the sugar into carbon dioxide and ethanol. Yeast are not the only microorganisms found in food products. The next time you are in the store, look at the ingredient list on a container of yogurt. The active cultures are bacteria.

338 | Unit 2 Inside Life

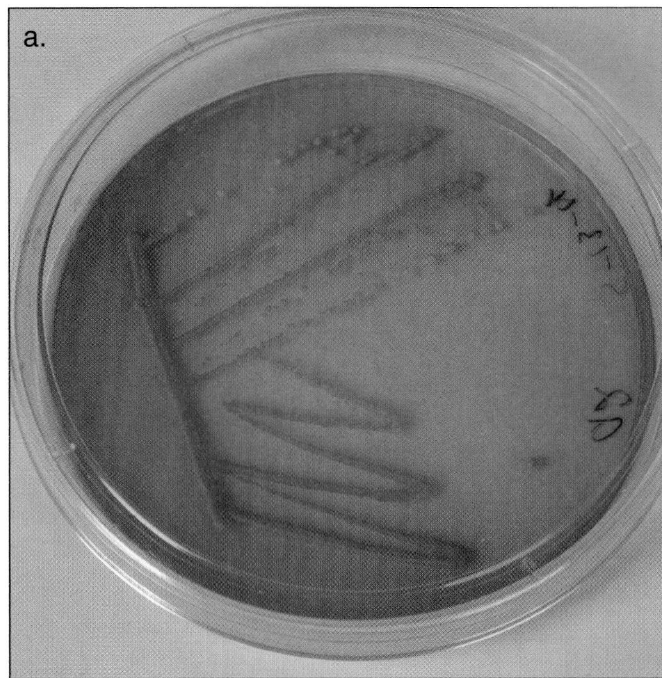

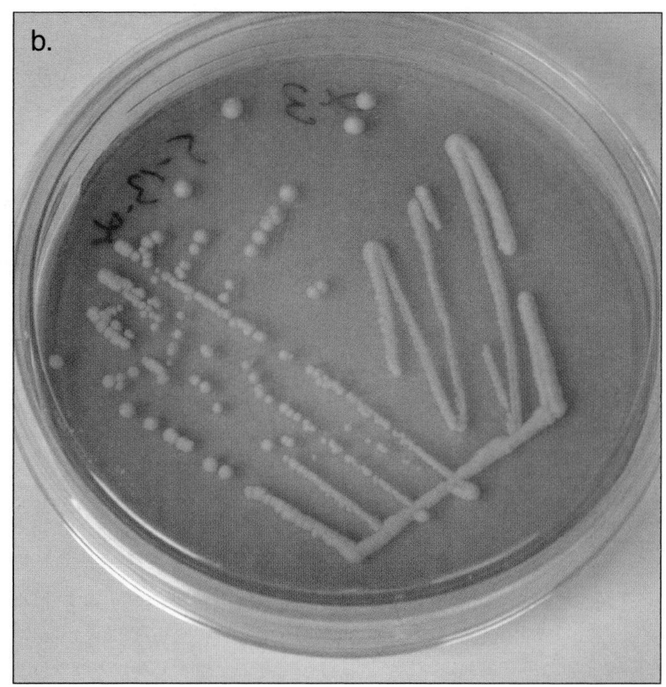

Figure T7.3 Yeast growth on YED plates. You might notice that the plates (a) with red-colored yeast have smaller colonies than the plates (b) with cream-colored yeast. This is because the cream-colored yeast cells grow better than the red-colored yeast cells.

After your experience in chapter 1, *Investigations by Design*, you might be more familiar with a different kind of single-celled organism, bacteria. Bacteria are very different from yeast; they are prokaryotes (organisms without a cell nucleus). Yeast are eukaryotes (organisms with a cell nucleus). Plants, animals, and fungi are all eukaryotes. Many eukaryotic microorganisms, such as yeast, do not have two "sexes" (male and female). Instead, certain types of yeast occur in two mating types: mating type *a* and mating type *alpha*. The mating types are morphologically the same. That is, the mating types look identical. But mating only occurs between yeast cells of the opposite mating type. When cells of opposite mating types (a and alpha) come in contact, they secrete hormonelike substances called **pheromones**. These pheromones cause cells of the opposite mating type to develop into new yeast cells. You can **cross**, or mate, yeast strains of opposite mating types and let them grow to see what the resulting generation looks like. A cross is a deliberate mating to study how traits are passed from parents to offspring.

Yeast can also reproduce asexually by budding and may grow into a visible colony that contains up to 100 million cells. Budding is the development of a new cell from the outgrowth of a parent cell. Buds look like bubbles growing on the side of the yeast cell. The buds separate from the parent yeast cell, forming new yeast cells.

There are many strains of baker's yeast. **Strains** of yeast are the same species but are physiologically distinct, meaning they function differently from one another. The strain of yeast used for baking bread is different from the strains of yeast used in scientific experiments. You will be using two strains of yeast in this activity. They will be identified as strain 2 and strain 3. Strain 2 exhibits a red color trait. Strain 3 exhibits a cream color trait. Now that you know more about yeast, remember to complete the tasks in Step 4.

5. Work with your partner and use the protocol to investigate what color traits are passed on from different strains of yeast. Steps 5a–d will serve as a guide.
   a. Read *Yeast Monohybrid Cross Protocol* to learn a technique for studying the traits passed from one generation of yeast to the next.

A monohybrid cross is a mating of individuals to study 1 trait.

   b. Discuss what yeast strains you should cross to study the color trait in baker's yeast.
   c. Draw a mating grid in your science notebook showing which strains and mating types you will cross.

The mating grid should look like the mating grid you would draw on a petri dish to cross yeast.

   d. Have your teacher approve your mating grid.
6. Follow Part I of *Yeast Monohybrid Cross Protocol* to grow parent colonies. Use your mating grid to guide your work.

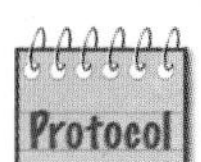

6. Repeat Steps 1–4 for 4 more plates of the same yeast strain. Then repeat this process for the other 3 sets of 5 plates, each set from a different strain of yeast.
7. Invert the plates and place in an incubator so that the yeast cells can grow. Allow the cultures to grow for 1 day in an incubator at 30° Celsius (C) or 2 days at room temperature. You will know you have enough growth when your plates look like those shown in figure T7.3.

This species will grow fastest in a 30°C incubator (optimal temperature for this species of yeast; growth can be inhibited at higher temperatures) and each growth step will take only 1 day. The amount of time needed for growth might vary in different locations. If necessary, you can hold the experiment by placing the yeast in the refrigerator and slowing the growth of the yeast.

Always incubate the plates upside down so that condensation does not drip onto the agar surface. If there is condensation on the lid after refrigeration, keep the plates upside down while you remove the lid and wipe out the condensation with a clean tissue. Alternatively, keep the plates upside down while you remove the lid, and, with a flick of the wrist, whip the water out of the lid.

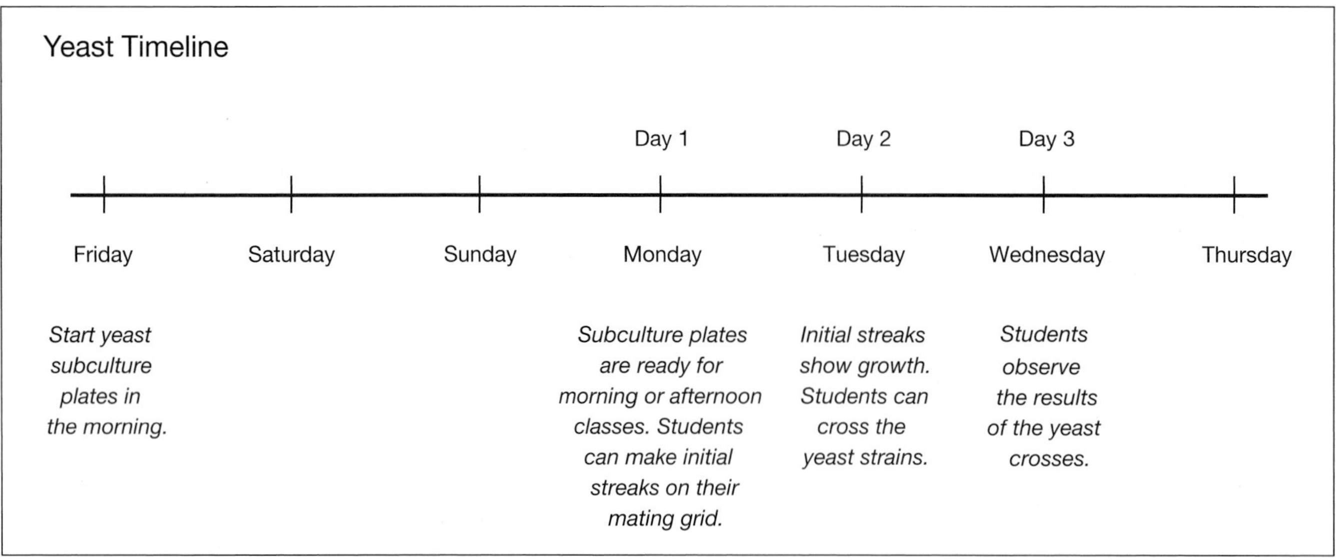

▲ **Figure T7.4 Timeline for yeast investigation.** This timeline shows three full days between starting the subculture plates and students beginning day 1 of the investigation. Three days gives adequate time for the subculture plates to develop colonies. The length of time is especially important for the subcultures of a2 and alpha2, which need to be deprived of adenine for a couple of days before the red color trait will appear. This timeline assumes that the yeast are incubated at 30°C.

The timing of this investigation is challenging because you need at least 1 day to see yeast growth. In an incubator at 30°C, yeast growth is easily seen after 1 day. The investigation takes a minimum of 3 days. However, the same amount of yeast growth occurs over a minimum of 2 days at room temperature. In a cooler room, it might take 3 or 4 days to see enough yeast growth. If you do not have access to an incubator, try to find the warmest part of your lab or classroom to store the plates. Figure T7.4 has been provided to help you plan your class time for this investigation. Remember that you can place the plates in a refrigerator at any time to temporarily "stop" the investigation.

Troubleshooting

The red-colored yeast strain might not look red when it arrives on its slant. This is because the agar slant contains adenine. Once you streak the yeast on the YED (lacking adenine) plates, you will see the red color show up in 2 to 3 days at room temperature.

There are 2 main reasons why your *haploid* cells might not show the red color during the class time you have set aside for this activity.

1. There is a very small amount of adenine in YED medium. If there is even a small amount of

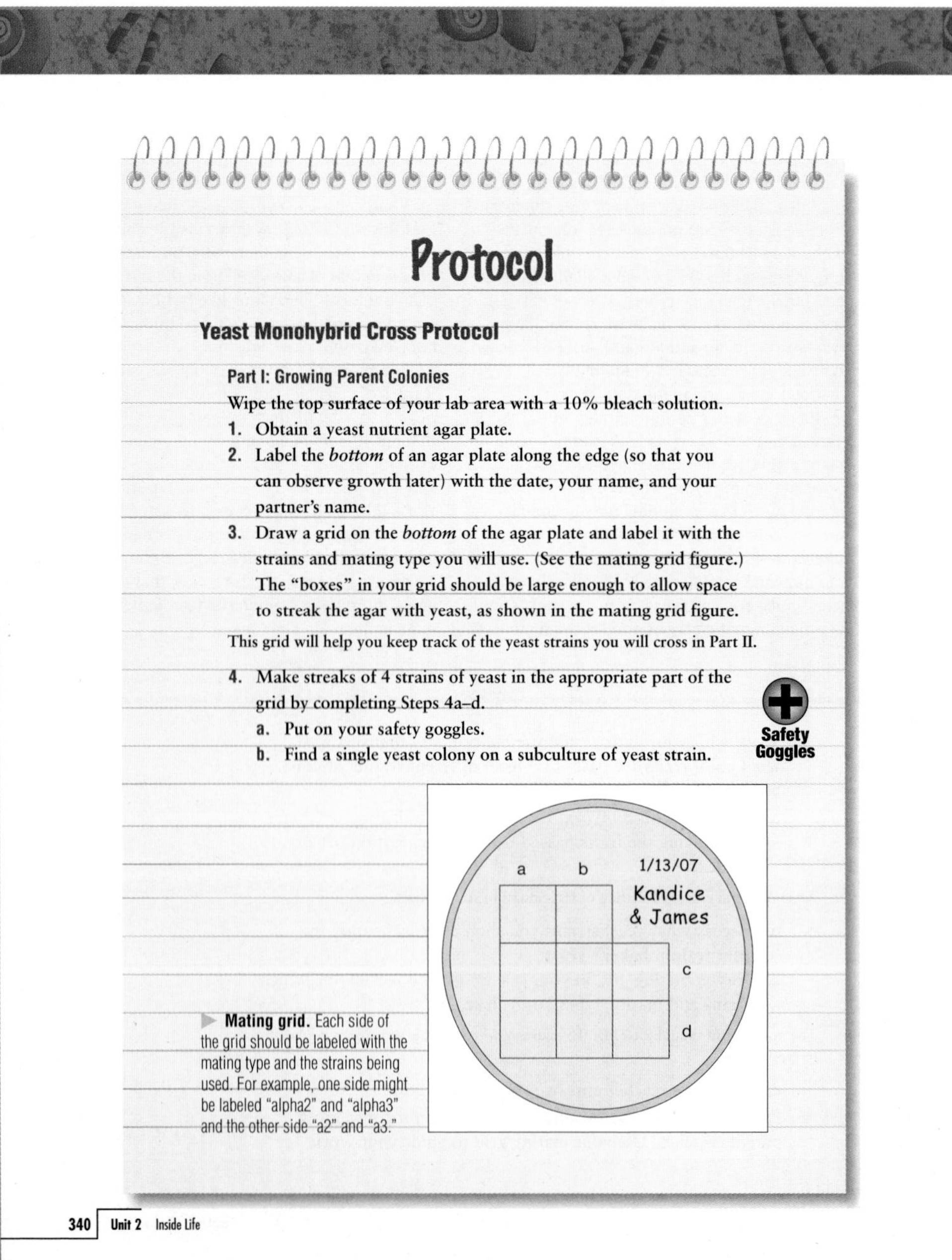

Protocol

Yeast Monohybrid Cross Protocol

Part I: Growing Parent Colonies

Wipe the top surface of your lab area with a 10% bleach solution.

1. Obtain a yeast nutrient agar plate.
2. Label the *bottom* of an agar plate along the edge (so that you can observe growth later) with the date, your name, and your partner's name.
3. Draw a grid on the *bottom* of the agar plate and label it with the strains and mating type you will use. (See the mating grid figure.) The "boxes" in your grid should be large enough to allow space to streak the agar with yeast, as shown in the mating grid figure.

This grid will help you keep track of the yeast strains you will cross in Part II.

4. Make streaks of 4 strains of yeast in the appropriate part of the grid by completing Steps 4a–d.
   a. Put on your safety goggles.
   b. Find a single yeast colony on a subculture of yeast strain.

▶ **Mating grid.** Each side of the grid should be labeled with the mating type and the strains being used. For example, one side might be labeled "alpha2" and "alpha3" and the other side "a2" and "a3."

340 Unit 2 Inside Life

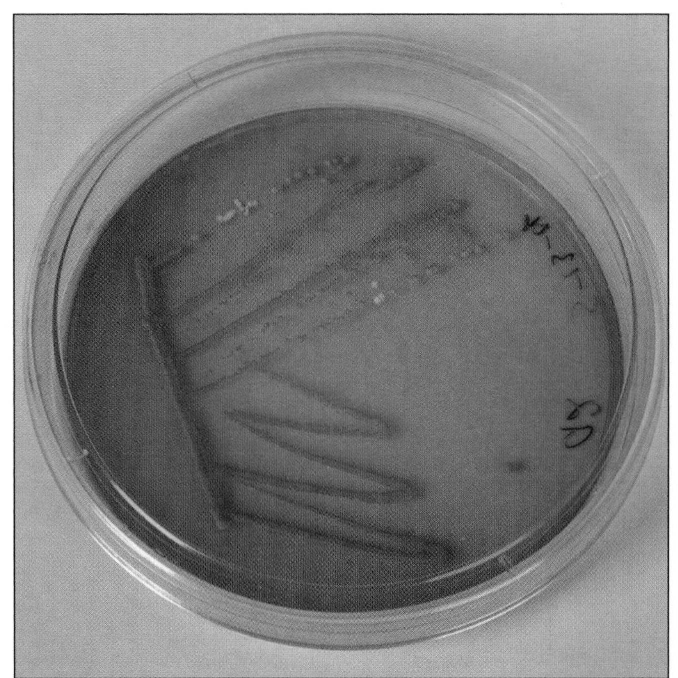

◀ **Figure T7.5 Cream-colored mutants.** Cream-colored mutants are common in colonies of a2 and alpha2 yeast colonies. Make sure students select only yeast cells from a red-colored colony on subcultures of a2 and alpha2 yeast colonies.

adenine in the medium, the cells will use it and will not show a red color. You will notice that the red is more intense where the cells are the most dense (in thick glops), because those cells have exhausted the supply of adenine in that area of the agar. *Solution*: Just wait; the color will develop when the cells use up the adenine.

2. The cells you are using in the lab have acquired a mutation that affects the production of the red color. *Solution*: Prevent this from happening by storing your original shipment of yeast in the refrigerator until you are ready to make the streaks on the YED plates. Your yeast should have been shipped in YEAD. Stored this way, the cells are not stressed metabolically, so there is no selection for other mutants.

Even if you have done your best to properly store the yeast, the red-colored yeast colonies are likely to acquire a mutation. The mutations occur spontaneously during the growth of a colony. The mutant cells will appear as cream-colored spots in red colonies as shown in figure T7.5. You will notice that the cream-colored spots will get larger as time passes. This is because the cream-colored mutants grow better than the original red-colored yeast colonies.

Look for areas of growth that are isolated and have a circular shape. When you compare the growth of the red-colored strains with the cream-colored strains, you might notice that the red-colored strains have less growth (the colonies are smaller). Don't worry about the size of the colony you pick. You will pick up hundreds of yeast cells by touching even the smallest colony.

c. Touch a sterile toothpick to the single yeast colony you have chosen. Using the end of the toothpick with yeast, make a short streak on the agar in the part of the grid that matches the yeast strain and mating type you have. Be careful not to tear the agar.

d. Discard the toothpick in the disposal area provided by your teacher.

Try to keep everything as sterile as possible. Do not touch the end of the toothpick that you are going to use to streak the yeast. Use a different toothpick for each strain of yeast.

e. Select another single yeast colony from the same subculture.

f. Repeat Steps 4c–d, placing a second streak next to the first. This will give you 2 parent colonies of the same strain of yeast from which to choose in Part II.

5. Repeat Steps 4b–f with the 3 remaining yeast strains. Make sure you streak each strain in the correct part of the mating grid. Your plate should look like the one in the figure.

6. Place the lid back on the plate. Seal the plate with parafilm or tape according to your teacher's instructions. Place your plate upside down in an incubator set at 30° Celsius (C). Allow the parent colonies of yeast to grow at least 1 day. You need enough growth so that you can cross the parent colonies in Part II.

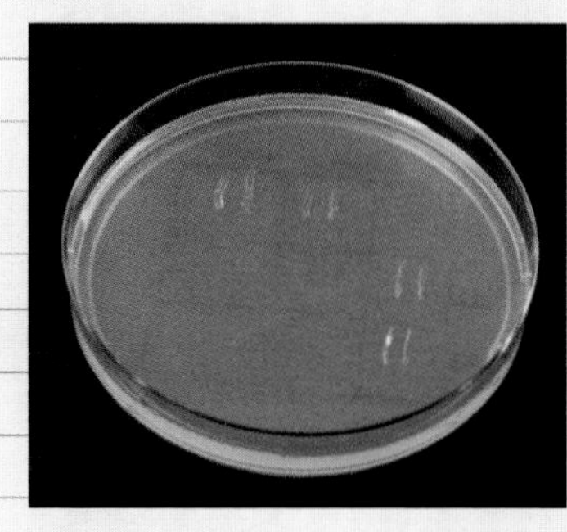

▲ **Streaked plate.** Your plate should have two streaks for each yeast strain and mating type.

Agar plates should be stored upside down with the lid on the bottom. This prevents condensation from forming on the agar. If you don't have an incubator, store your agar plate in the area provided by your teacher.

Chapter 7 Tracking Traits 341

Educational Technologies

For additional information on yeast and experiments with yeast, see the following Web pages:

- "The Gene Project" home page at Kansas State University
- The Research Link 2000 "Yeast" Web page at Kansas State University
- Fred Sherman's Web page, "An Introduction to the Genetics and Molecular Biology of the Yeast *Saccharomyces cerevisiae*"

Cautions

The yeast used in this investigation is *Saccharomyces cerevisiae*, which is a nonpathogenic laboratory strain. However, it is always good practice to disinfect all materials that come in contact with live organisms. Have students seal their plates with parafilm or tape after they have mated their cultures. When students are finished with the investigation, have them remove the parafilm and place their plates in a bucket of 10% bleach solution. If the plates are disposable, discard them after soaking them in the bleach overnight. If the plates are glass and reusable, soak them in bleach or autoclave them, and then discard the agar and bleach solution. An autoclave is a device that uses steam and pressure to sterilize items. Students should discard all used toothpicks in biohazard bags. Biohazard bags should be sealed tightly shut and discarded. If biohazard bags are not available, students should place the toothpicks in a 10% bleach solution. Later, you can remove the toothpicks and dispose of them in any waste container. Students must wash their hands before leaving the lab. Microscope slides can be dipped in a 10% bleach solution and then washed with liquid soap and water if you reuse slides.

NOTES:

As You Teach

Outcomes and Indicators of Success

By the end of this activity, students should

1. be able to use equipment, follow safety precautions, and apply logic to conduct a scientific investigation.

   They will demonstrate their ability by

   - observing yeast cells with a microscope and sketching yeast cells and
   - using the information from a reading to correctly follow the *Yeast Monohybrid Cross Protocol* to cross two strains of yeast.

2. be able to make inferences about the inheritance of traits.

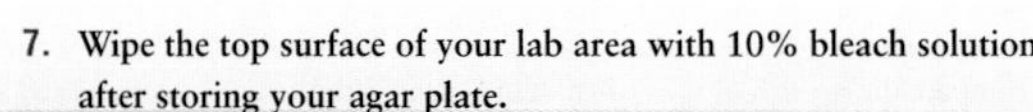

7. Wipe the top surface of your lab area with 10% bleach solution after storing your agar plate.
8. Wash your hands after storing your agar plate.

Part II: Crossing Parent Colonies

1. Wipe the top surface of your lab area with 10% bleach solution.
2. Put on your safety goggles.
3. Use the yeast crosses diagram as a guide to cross yeast in Steps 3a–d.

Safety Goggles

   a. Touch a sterile toothpick to one of the (a) streaks, as shown in the diagram of yeast crosses. Then touch the toothpick to the agar in the box directly below it.

Remember to be careful not to tear the agar.

   b. Discard the toothpick in the disposal area provided by your teacher.
   c. Touch a sterile toothpick to one of the (c) streaks. Then touch it to the agar close to the spot you just made in Step 2a. Discard the toothpick.
   d. Obtain a sterile toothpick and mix the 2 spots of yeast together as shown in the mating yeast figure. Discard the toothpick.

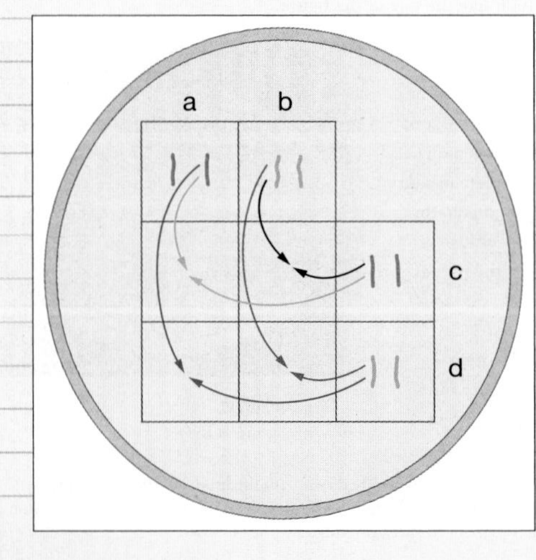

Yeast crosses. Your plate should have four possible crosses: streak (a) with (c), (a) with (d), (b) with (c), and (b) with (d).

342 Unit 2 Inside Life

They will show their ability by

- making a justifiable prediction about the result of their yeast cross,
- reflecting on what previous experiences helped them make a prediction about the results of their cross, and
- describing what a mixed-breed dog might look like based on what its parents look like.

3. be able to analyze the results of an investigation.

   They will demonstrate their ability by studying, describing, and interpreting the results of a genetic cross between two strains of yeast including that some traits are not exhibited in the first generation even when they are present in the parent generation.

Strategies

Getting Started

Just before students come into class, place a packet of bread yeast in a small dish of warm water with a spoonful of sugar. To make sure the yeast becomes activated and students can see a change, check that you have fresh yeast (look at the expiration date) and that the water is not too hot (not over 54°C). You might also want to have some dry yeast available for students to look at. Ask students if they recognize this organism. Although some students might have seen yeast before, they might not have thought of yeast as an organism. Explain that when you buy yeast at the store, it is in a dormant state. Once yeast is placed in warm sugar water, it becomes "activated." It begins growing and starts fermenting the sugar. You can compare this with seeds that do not become growing plants until you plant them in moist soil. Ask students why they think the yeast looks foamy. Listen to a few students' ideas. Then explain that when yeast is used in baking bread, it ferments the sugars in the flour added to the dough. This process gives off carbon dioxide and ethanol. Tiny carbon dioxide bubbles in the dough cause it to rise and expand.

Have the class read the introduction. Explain that the students will be looking at yeast in this investigation. Tell them that yeast can be used for the study of heredity because it goes through its life cycle very quickly.

Cautions

The yeast used in this investigation is *Saccharomyces cerevisiae*, which is a nonpathogenic laboratory strain. However, it is always good practice to disinfect all materials that come in contact with live organisms. Have students seal their plates with parafilm or tape after they have mated their cultures. When students are finished with the investigation, have them remove the parafilm and place their plates in a bucket of 10% bleach solution. If the plates are disposable, discard them after soaking them in the bleach overnight. If the plates are glass and reusable, soak them in bleach or autoclave them, and then discard the agar and bleach water. Students should discard all used toothpicks in biohazard bags. Biohazard bags should be sealed tightly shut and discarded. If biohazard bags are not available, students should place the toothpicks in a bucket with 10% bleach solution. Later, you can remove the toothpicks and dispose of them in any waste container. Students must wash their hands before leaving the lab. Microscope slides can be dipped in a 10% bleach solution and then washed with liquid soap and water if you reuse slides.

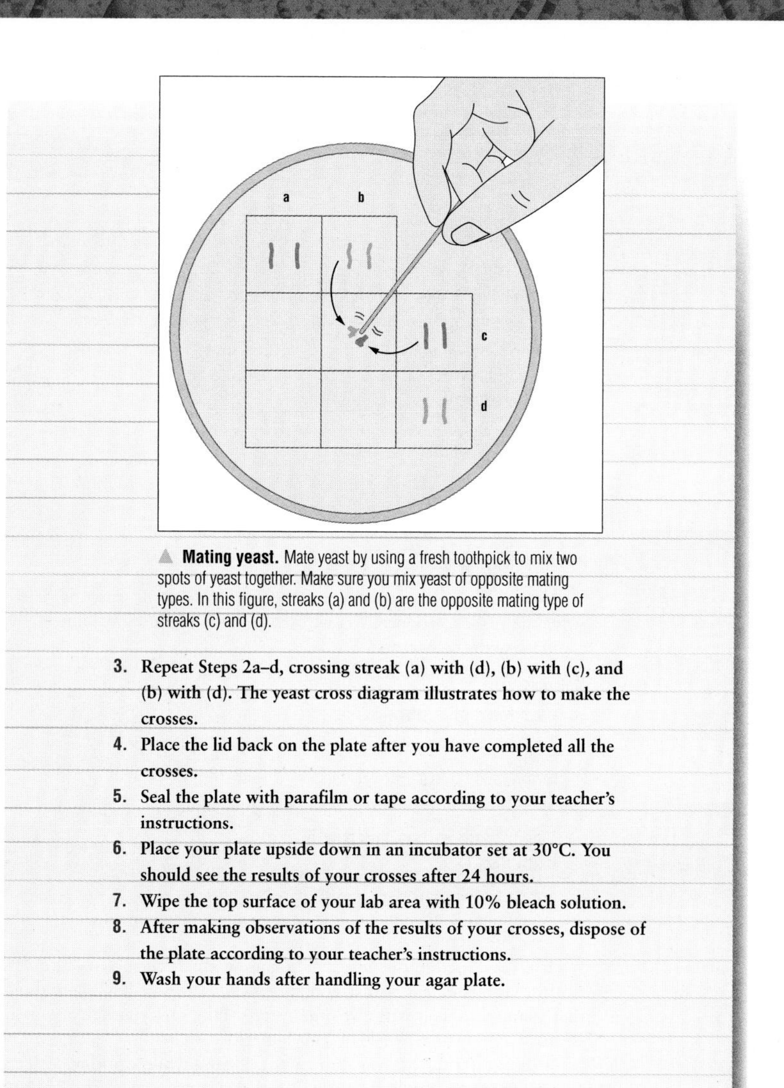

▲ **Mating yeast.** Mate yeast by using a fresh toothpick to mix two spots of yeast together. Make sure you mix yeast of opposite mating types. In this figure, streaks (a) and (b) are the opposite mating type of streaks (c) and (d).

3. Repeat Steps 2a–d, crossing streak (a) with (d), (b) with (c), and (b) with (d). The yeast cross diagram illustrates how to make the crosses.
4. Place the lid back on the plate after you have completed all the crosses.
5. Seal the plate with parafilm or tape according to your teacher's instructions.
6. Place your plate upside down in an incubator set at 30°C. You should see the results of your crosses after 24 hours.
7. Wipe the top surface of your lab area with 10% bleach solution.
8. After making observations of the results of your crosses, dispose of the plate according to your teacher's instructions.
9. Wash your hands after handling your agar plate.

Chapter 7 Tracking Traits 343

Process and Procedure

Part I: The First Generation

Materials

For each team of 2 students

2 pairs of safety goggles
2 pairs of gloves (optional)
access to biohazard bags or buckets with 10% bleach solution
1 microscope slide
1 coverslip
1 dropper
1 pair of forceps
1 yeast nutrient agar plate (YED)
microscope
1 small cup of water
parafilm or tape
access to incubator set at 30°C
access to 2 subcultures of strain 2 (red-colored) yeast colonies (a2 and alpha2)
access to 2 subcultures of strain 3 (cream-colored) yeast colonies (a3 and alpha3)
access to sterile toothpicks or sterile inoculating loops
1 glass marking pencil or marker

In Step 1, allow students to make observations of the yeast subcultures. In Step 2, students look at yeast cells using a microscope and sketch the cells they see. Help students prepare slides from the yeast subcultures. Instructions on how to use a microscope and how to prepare slides are provided in *How to Use a Compound Microscope* in the back of the book. If the yeast cells are moving too much, a drop of clear nail polish added to the slide can slow them down. Figure T7.6 shows an example of what you can expect yeast cells to look like. If you have time, you might encourage students to look at yeast cells from a strain of the opposite color. Or direct half the students to look at one color and the other half to look at the other. Then the students could move to a different microscope to see both colors. Cells from the cream-colored yeast strain are translucent, but the cells from the red-colored yeast strain look darker. You cannot see a distinct red color but you can tell that the red yeast cells are pigmented.

Steps 1–2 could be time-consuming steps depending on how much experience your students have using microscopes. You might need to limit the time students spend looking at the yeast cells to ensure that students have time to streak their YED plates with yeast. It is crucial that the students streak the yeast plates the first day of the activity because the yeast needs time to grow. If you have limited time, looking at yeast in a microscope in Steps 1–2 would be an appropriate step to skip.

In Step 4, students learn more about yeast by reading *Yeast*. Circulate and listen to students' conversations as they answer the questions in Step 4 and discuss how to investigate yeast traits. Make sure they understand how yeast reproduce and that yeast exhibit a red and a cream color trait. In Step 5, students read *Yeast Monohybrid Cross Protocol* and decide how to investigate the inheritance of a trait in yeast. Check to see that students decide to cross yeast as shown in the mating grid in figure T7.7.

In Step 6, place the 5 sets of yeast subcultures (1 plate of each strain in each set) at designated locations that will allow teams of 2 easy access. Teams should follow Part I of *Yeast Monohybrid Cross Protocol.* Make sure students label their plates along

Answers to Stop and Think—Part I are on TE page 345a.

Stop & THINK

PART I

Answer the following questions on your own and record your answers in your science notebook.

1. Did the yeast cells look like you expected them to look after seeing the subcultures of yeast your teacher provided? Explain why or why not.
2. How do you think learning about a microscopic, single-celled organism, such as yeast, can help scientists learn about a large multicellular organism, such as ourselves (humans)?

For example, how can studying other organisms help scientists learn about disorders such as MMD, discussed in the last activity?

Part II: Mating Game

Now that you have grown parent colonies, you will mate the yeast. After the yeast reproduce, you will see how the offspring colonies compare with the parents.

Materials

For each team of 2 students

2 pairs of safety goggles
biohazard bag or bucket with 10% bleach solution
1 agar plate with yeast growth from Part I
access to incubator set at 30°C
1 pair of forceps
parafilm or tape
access to sterile toothpicks
colored pencils

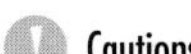

Cautions

The yeast used in this investigation are nonpathogenic laboratory strains. However, it is always good practice to disinfect all materials that come in contact with live organisms. Make sure your lab area is clean. Wipe the top surface of your lab area with a 10% bleach solution before and after the investigation. Wear goggles while working with the agar plates and yeast. Pull your hair or loose clothing back if necessary. Wash your hands thoroughly before leaving the laboratory. Dispose of all materials as directed by your teacher.

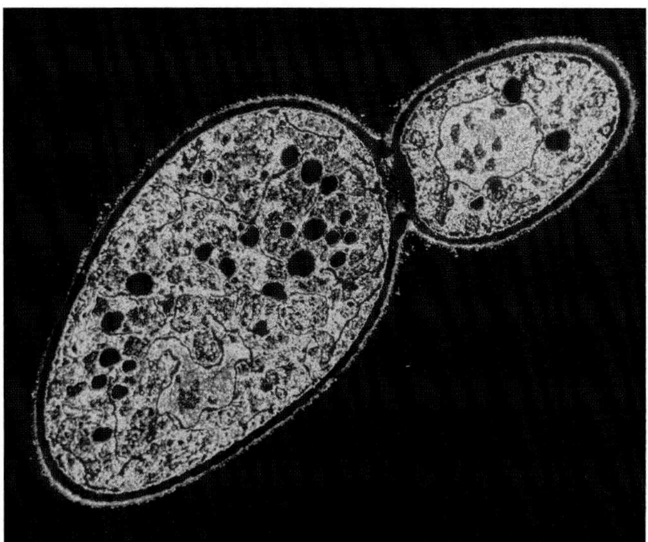

▲ **Figure T7.6 Haploid yeast cells from the a3 strain.** Haploid yeast cells multiply through budding. The smaller shape to the right is a bud.

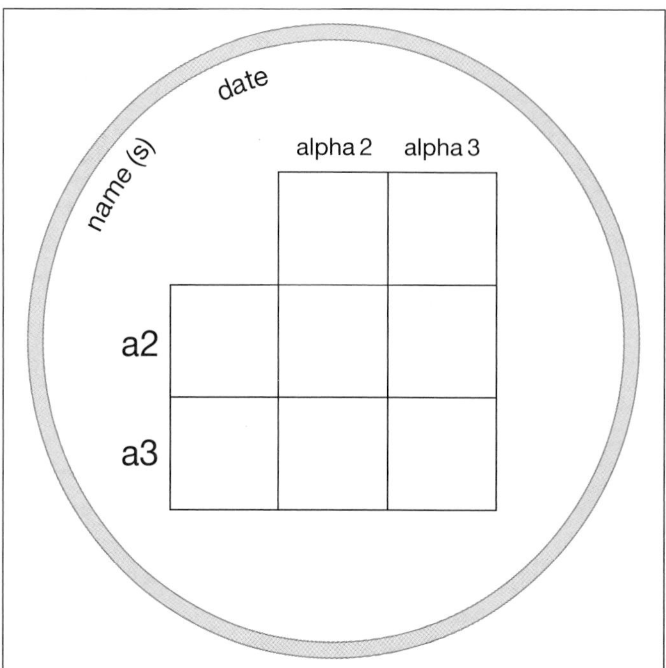

▲ **Figure T7.7 Yeast mating grid.** Students should draw a mating grid similar to this for Step 5. They should cross strain 2 with strain 3, making sure they use opposite mating types as shown. If students are curious why they are using strains 2 and 3 but not strain 1, explain that strain 1 does exist but that this strain was not chosen for this investigation.

Answers to Steps 4–5 are on TE pages 345a–345b.

Process and Procedure

1. Get your agar plate from your teacher.
2. Follow Part II of *Yeast Monohybrid Cross Protocol* to cross your yeast strains.
3. Draw a sketch of your agar plate showing the grid and the location of the yeast. Label the yeast strains and the color of the yeast using colored pencils.
4. Work with your partner to discuss your ideas about the investigation by completing Steps 4a–b. Record your ideas in your science notebook.
   a. Why did you cross specific strains of yeast?
   b. Predict the results of your cross. Record your prediction and justify your prediction for each cross.
5. Discuss the following questions as a class and record your answers in your science notebook.
   a. Why were you able to make a prediction about the results of your cross?

What previous experiences have you had that helped you make your prediction?

   b. When someone tells you he has a Dalmatian, you can predict that this Dalmatian will look like all other Dalmatians even before seeing it. But what if someone tells you she has a mixed-breed dog and she thinks the parents are a beagle and Pomeranian, like those pictured in figure 7.5. What do you think her mixed-breed dog looks like? Why?

All organisms have traits that make them distinct. The yeast you worked with were either red or cream. Dogs are different colors, different sizes, and have different lengths and textures of hair.

   c. Why do you think offspring look something like their parents?
6. Observe the colonies produced when you crossed the parent yeast colonies. The new colonies are called the first generation. Discuss with your partner how the actual results compare with your predictions.
7. Add your results and highlight comments to your drawing from Step 3.

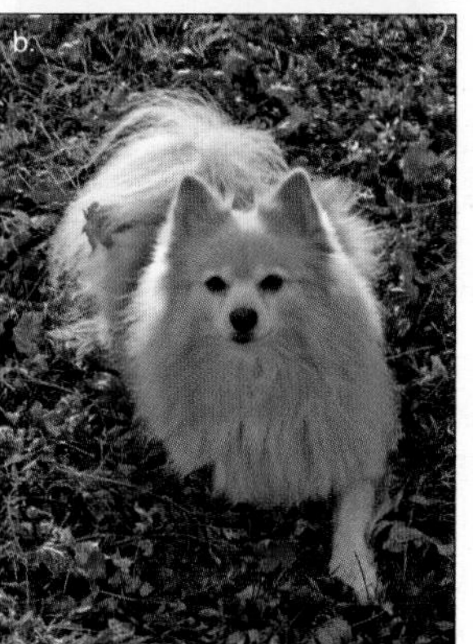

▲ **Figure 7.5 Two dog breeds.** Both (a) beagles and (b) Pomeranians are dogs, but they look very different.

the edge with a glass marking pencil or marker before they begin. Explain that it is important that the label be on the edge so that they can easily see the yeast as it grows. They should draw grids on the bottom of their plates as they decided on in Step 5. Circulate among the teams to make sure they have drawn the mating grids correctly.

Students begin streaking their plates with yeast from the subcultures you prepared. Help students find single colonies on the subcultures. Remind them to look for circular, isolated growth. Once they have found a colony, tell students to gently touch the colony with a sterile toothpick. Emphasize the need for sterile techniques. Help students streak the yeast correctly on their plate. Remind them not to tear the agar. They should make 2 streaks from each subculture in the correct place on the mating grid. The figure of the streaked plates in *Yeast Monohybrid Cross Protocol* in the student book shows them how their plates should look when they are finished. Tell students to place their plates upside down in an incubator or a designated area of the room. You can continue to incubate or refrigerate the subculture plates in case students want to compare their plates with the subcultures in Part II.

Some of the colonies on the a2 and alpha2 subcultures (red strain) might be cream colored. This is likely to confuse students. Explain that the red strain yeast often spontaneously mutate and stop producing the red pigment. Tell them they will learn about mutation in the next chapter. A more detailed explanation is provided in *Background Information*. Tell them to select a red colony from the subculture.

Answers to Stop and Think—Part I, SE page 344

1. Students might have expected the yeast cells to look larger. Alternatively, they might have expected all the cells to be close together, similar to how the yeast colonies were grouped together. Accept a variety of answers as long as students support their ideas.
2. Scientists can experiment with organisms such as yeast to learn which traits are passed on. Students might explain that experiments with unicellular organisms might be easier because they grow quickly and have many offspring. They might also explain that scientists can learn things about multicellular organisms from unicellular organisms because they share characteristics.

Process and Procedure

Part II: Mating Game

Materials

2 pairs of safety goggles
2 pairs of gloves (optional)
access to biohazard bags or buckets with 10% bleach solution
1 agar plate with yeast growth from Part I
access to incubator set at 30°C
1 pair of forceps
parafilm or tape
access to sterile toothpicks or sterile inoculating loops
colored pencils

In Step 1, students will need access to their plates from Part I. In Step 2, students follow Part II of *Yeast Monohybrid Cross Protocol* to cross their yeast. Watch students as they cross their yeast, reminding them to use sterile techniques and to be gentle so that they do not tear the agar. You also need to ensure that they follow the protocol carefully. If students cross the wrong colonies, they will not get the desired results. As students conduct the cross, you might want to ask the following probing questions:

- "Why do you think it is important that you cross *a* with *alpha*?"

Students should remember from the *Yeast* reading that yeast have two mating types, *a* and *alpha*. Mating only occurs between yeast of opposite mating types.

- "Think about the yeast cross you just completed. What process do you think you are modeling?"

Students should recognize that the cross is modeling the process of reproduction. You might ask them how the cross is different from reproduction.

Once students have finished crossing their yeast, they should seal their plates using parafilm or tape. They will not be manipulating their plates after this point. Students should turn their plates upside down and store them in an incubator or designated area of the room. Explain to students that over the next three to four hours the yeast will form pear-shaped cells, called shmoos. The shmoos will mate and form zygotes. Students will learn about the significance of this in the next activity. Refer to *Background Information* to learn about the sexual life cycle of yeast.

In Step 3, instruct students to make a sketch of their plates. The yeast strains and color of each strain should be labeled on their diagrams. Tell students to work with their partners and answer the questions in Step 4.

Answers to Step 4, SE page 345

4a. Specific strains of yeast should be crossed because yeast can only be crossed if the strains are different mating types. Also, the only way to see what traits are inherited is to cross all strains of yeast.

4b. Students might make the following predictions for each cross:

- Cream × cream: Students are likely to predict that the result will be cream-colored yeast because both parent strains are cream colored. Students should be able to support their ideas.
- Red × red: Students are likely to predict that the result will be red-colored yeast because both parent strains are red colored. Students should be able to support their ideas.
- Red × cream: Students might predict that the result will be red-colored yeast because red is darker than cream. Or they might predict that the result will be pink because that would be a mixture of the 2 colors. Students should be able to support their ideas.

Then in Step 5, facilitate a class discussion of the following questions. These questions will give students the opportunity to think about what they might already know about inheritance.

Answers to Step 5, SE page 345

5a. Students should explain that they could make a prediction about the cross because they have seen the results of "matings" before; they know what they look like compared with their parents or what animals look like compared with their parents. Students will express their own opinions depending on the experiences they have had and should be able to support their ideas.

5b. Students are likely to explain that the mixed-breed dog will look like a mixture between a beagle and a Pomeranian because it will get characteristics from both parents. They might describe a dog with the coloration of a beagle and the coat length and texture of a Pomeranian. Students will express their own opinions about what the dog will look like but should understand that both parents will contribute to what the mixed-breed dog looks like.

5c. Students are likely to explain that offspring look like their parents because they share genes or DNA with their parents. They might also say that offspring inherit traits or characteristics from their parents. Students do not need to understand what genes or DNA are at this point and do not need to understand how offspring inherit traits. This question simply gives you the opportunity to asses your students' current understanding.

In Step 6, students need access to the plates they crossed the day before. They should compare the parent yeast colonies with the first-generation colonies resulting from the cross. In Step 7, students should record the results of their crosses and highlight comments on their drawings from Step 3.

Students should have the following results if their crosses were successful:

- Cream (alpha3) × cream (a3) = cream
- Red (alpha2) × cream (a3) = cream
- Cream (alpha3) × red (a2) = cream
- Red (alpha2) × red (a2) = red

Students might find on the edge of the red × cream cross that some red-colored yeast is growing. Explain that the yeast was not thoroughly crossed. Some of the red yeast continued to grow like parent colonies. Explain that if the yeast were grown on a special agar plate (MV plate), the parent colonies would not grow, but the first-generation yeast (the crossed yeast) would grow. A more thorough explanation is provided in *Background Information*.

If students have completely different results than those listed, find another team that has the desired results. Make sure students have the opportunity to see the correct results. Then talk through why they might have gotten the wrong results. Perhaps they used the wrong strains for the parent colonies or crossed the strains incorrectly.

Instruct students to clean up the lab. Students should place the plates in a bucket containing 10% bleach solution. After the dishes are soaked in the bleach, they can be washed and used for other purposes. If they are plastic, they cannot be sterilized. If the dishes are glass, they can be sterilized and used again.

NOTES:

Answers to Reflect and Connect, SE page 346

1. Most students likely predicted that the cream-colored yeast crossed with the red-colored yeast would produce pink yeast, so the results will surprise them. Students might also predict that half the yeast will be red and the other half will be cream. In the next activity, students will learn the cream color is dominant.
2. Students might explain that the cream color trait is "stronger" than the red color trait or they might explain that the cream color trait is dominant to the red color trait. Students should understand that something must be different about the cream color trait because it appeared in the red × cream cross, instead of the red color trait.
3. The yeast experiment helped students learn about heredity because they are able to see which color trait (red or cream) was passed on to the resulting first generation after yeast were crossed.
4. Students might suggest taking the first generation and mixing it with itself to see if the red color trait shows up again. Accept a variety of answers as long as students support their ideas.

EXPLAIN

How Do We Get Our Traits?

Activity Overview

In Part I, students will read about Gregor Mendel's experiments and learn about how traits are inherited. Then they will learn about the process that determines what traits are inherited when they read about meiosis. In Part II of *How Do We Get Our Traits?*, students will model meiosis with play dough and show their understanding of the process.

Before You Teach

Background Information

Johann Mendel was the first person to gain some understanding of the principle of heredity. Mendel became a monk at the St. Thomas monastery in what is now the Czech Republic. The monks in this order were encouraged to become educated and conduct research. Mendel spent 2 years at the University of Vienna in Austria and studied science and mathematics. His experiences there helped him develop an excellent background for designing and analyzing experiments. He also had his first exposure to pea plants and crossbreeding while in Vienna.

Mendel spent 9 years breeding pea plants and keeping excellent records of his experiments. Breeding experiments had been performed by others for centuries, but Mendel was the first to discover the principles of heredity. Because Mendel chose the pea plant, which was easy to grow and had traits found on different chromosomes (transmitted independently), he was able to recognize distinct patterns of inheritance. The student book provides a more detailed explanation of some of Mendel's findings.

Mendel reported his conclusions in 1865, but the significance of his work was not recognized until the early 1900s. Mendel's experiments

Answers to Step 1 are on TE page 351.

Reflect and Connect

Answer the following questions individually in your science notebook. Then compare your answers with a partner's and adjust your answers if you learn something new.

1. Were you surprised at the results of the cross? What was unexpected in your results and why?
2. Why do you think you obtained the results that you did?
3. How did this yeast experiment help you learn more about heredity?
4. What new questions do you have about the yeast strains? What future experiments could you try with your yeast to answer these questions?

EXPLAIN

How Do We Get Our Traits?

You have been thinking about traits that are passed from one generation to the next. You might be surprised to learn that until the 1860s, people did not even realize that organisms inherited their traits from a previous generation. In the 1860s, a man by the name of Gregor Mendel began to change people's thinking about how organisms acquire their traits. Mendel discovered some of the fundamental principles of **genetics**. Genetics is the science of heredity.

In Part I, you will read about Mendel and his work (figure 7.6). Then you will take a look at the process of meiosis, which determines what traits are inherited. In Part II, you will develop your understanding of meiosis by modeling the process with clay.

▲ **Figure 7.6 Gregor Johann Mendel (1822–1884).** Experimenting in his monastery garden, Mendel developed the fundamental principles of heredity that became the foundation of modern genetics.

Part I: Mendel's Discoveries

Materials

none

Process and Procedure

1. Complete an analogy map while you read *Mendel: The Founder of Genetics*. The headings for your analogy map should be "Part of Yeast Investigation," "Part of Mendel's Pea Plant Experiment," "How the Yeast Investigation Is Similar to Mendel's Pea Plant Experiment."

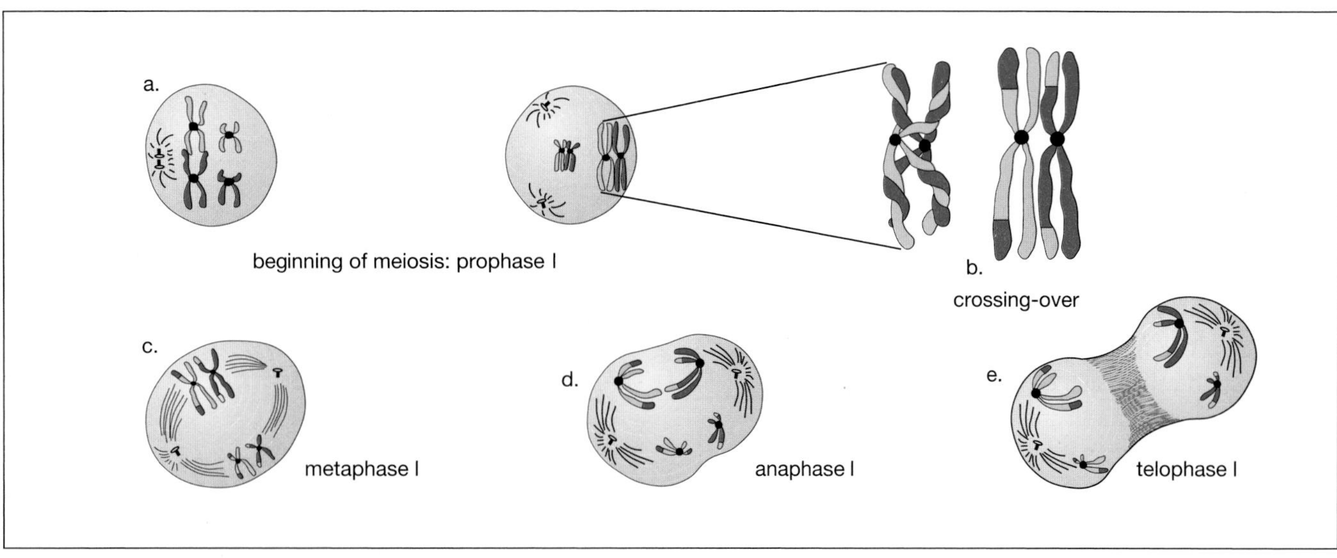

▲ **Figure T7.8 First meiotic division and crossing-over.** (a) When meiosis begins, each chromosome is a double structure made of two sister chromatids. The chromatids are joined at a specialized area called the centromere. (b) During the first meiotic division, matching pairs of homologous chromosomes come close together and may twist around each other. In this position, parts of a chromatid of one chromosome might break off and exchange places with the identical parts of a chromatid of the other matching chromosome. This process is called crossing-over. (c–e) Note that at the end of the first meiotic division, the chromosomes are still in the duplicated state (the sister chromatids have not separated).

established that traits are inherited, and he inferred that genes (he called them factors) existed. However, he did not know that genes were located on chromosomes or about the process of meiosis.

Meiosis is the process in which a diploid cell undergoes duplication of the chromosome pairs followed by two successive cell divisions. The members of a chromosome pair are called homologous chromosomes and are shown in figure T7.8a. Homologous chromosomes are doubled in the nucleus of the diploid cell through one DNA replication cycle. (An explanation of DNA replication is provided in chapter 8, *Instructions for Life*.) The product of chromosome duplication is two exact copies called sister chromatids. In the first cell division, the sister chromatids of homologous chromosomes attach to each other during prophase I. In this position, parts of a chromatid of one chromosome occasionally break off and exchange places with the identical parts of a chromatid of the other matching chromosome. This process is called crossing-over, because the chromatid segments are exchanged between the two chromosomes of a pair, which results in new combinations of genes. The chromosomes that result from crossing-over contain a new combination of genes from the original chromosome pair.

READING

Mendel: The Founder of Genetics

Gregor Mendel grew up as Johann Mendel in a German-speaking region of Austria (now the eastern part of the Czech Republic). Mendel grew up in a peasant farming family. Because his family had very little money, his only way of getting an advanced education was to become a monk. He joined the St. Thomas monastery (figure 7.7) in 1843 and was assigned the name Gregor. This particular order of monks encouraged teaching and research and was a wonderful place for Mendel to further his studies.

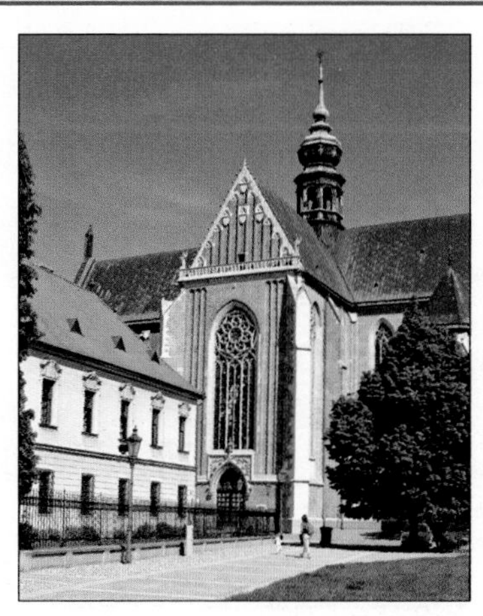

▲ **Figure 7.7 St. Thomas monastery.** The monastery is located in Brünn, which was a large city of 70,000 even in the 1800s. Brünn, now called Brno, had many fine schools and scientific societies.

Mendel was exposed to the ideas of scientists and mathematicians during his first 10 years at the monastery. At one point during his studies, he learned about plant breeding methods. He also learned about a particular plant, the common garden pea (*Pisum sativum*), which was well suited for crossbreeding because of its easily identifiable characteristics. Mendel was particularly interested in the inheritance of animal and plant features—or traits. As a result, he began investigating inheritance patterns in the pea plants he had learned about.

Garden pea flowers contain both male and female reproductive parts, as shown in figure 7.8. Under natural conditions, a pea plant usually self-pollinates. However, plant breeders can collect pollen grains from flowers of one pea plant and transfer them to the flowers of another pea plant. This technique, called cross-pollination, results in seeds (from pea pods) that are the offspring of two pea plants, not just one.

To begin his work, Mendel spent 2 years collecting various strains of garden peas and tested each strain to make sure it was genetically true, or true breeding. True-breeding plants produce offspring, through self-pollination, that are identical to themselves generation after generation. Mendel worked with strains that were true breeding except for one trait. These plants would show one of two different forms of this trait, while all other traits were exactly the same. For example, plants were either tall or short, or produced either green or yellow seeds. By having distinct and contrasting forms of only one trait, Mendel could follow the differences in that trait in the offspring. Figure 7.9 shows the seven traits of pea plants that Mendel investigated in his experiments.

Chapter 7 Tracking Traits 347

Crossing-over is not covered in the student book. However, an optional activity is provided in figure T7.15 after the answers to step 4 in Part II.

After the homologous chromosomes have joined and lined up in prophase I, the homologous chromosomes are separated and the cell divides. The first meiotic division results in two cells. Each cell contains one chromosome (duplicated) from each of the original pairs of homologous chromosomes. The cells contain half the number of chromosomes of the original cell, but each chromosome is still in its duplicated state. Because the amount of genetic information per cell has been reduced by one-half, the first meiotic division often is called *reduction division.* Figure T7.8 illustrates the first meiotic division and crossing-over.

In the second cell division, the chromosomes do not divide. Instead, sister chromatids are separated from each other. Both cells divide. Each of the four resulting cells is haploid and contains one chromosome from each original homologous chromosome pair (see figure T7.9). Figure 7.17 in the student book provides a complete description of each of the stages in meiosis.

Meiosis results in the formation of gametes. Gametes (haploid cells) have half the genetic material of other body cells. Human body cells have 46 chromosomes (23 pairs); human gametes have 23 chromosomes. In sexual reproduction, gametes join and form a zygote. Meiosis is a significant process because (1) meiosis ensures that each generation has the same number of chromosomes, (2) meiosis results in a large number of possible chromosome combinations in gametes, and (3) crossing-over during meiosis generates more variation in the combinations of chromosomes in gametes.

Meiosis, which must occur in organisms that reproduce sexually, is an important source of genetic variation. The new combinations of genes that result from meiosis produce offspring with unique genotypes (the genetic plan of an organism). The genotypes, in turn, result in offspring

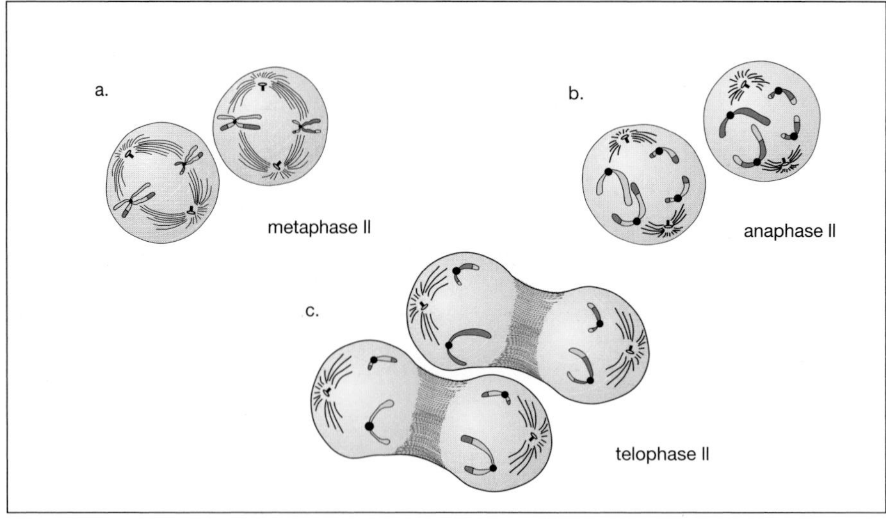

▲ **Figure T7.9 Second meiotic division.** The second meiotic division is very similar to a mitotic division. (a) The chromosomes move to the equator in each of the two cells. This time, however, there are no matching chromosome pairs. (b) The chromosomes line up in single file down the center of each cell, just as in mitosis. (c) The centromeres divide, and the two sister chromatids are separated from each other and are now called chromosomes. A nuclear membrane forms around each set of chromosomes. The result is four haploid cells, each containing *n* single chromosomes.

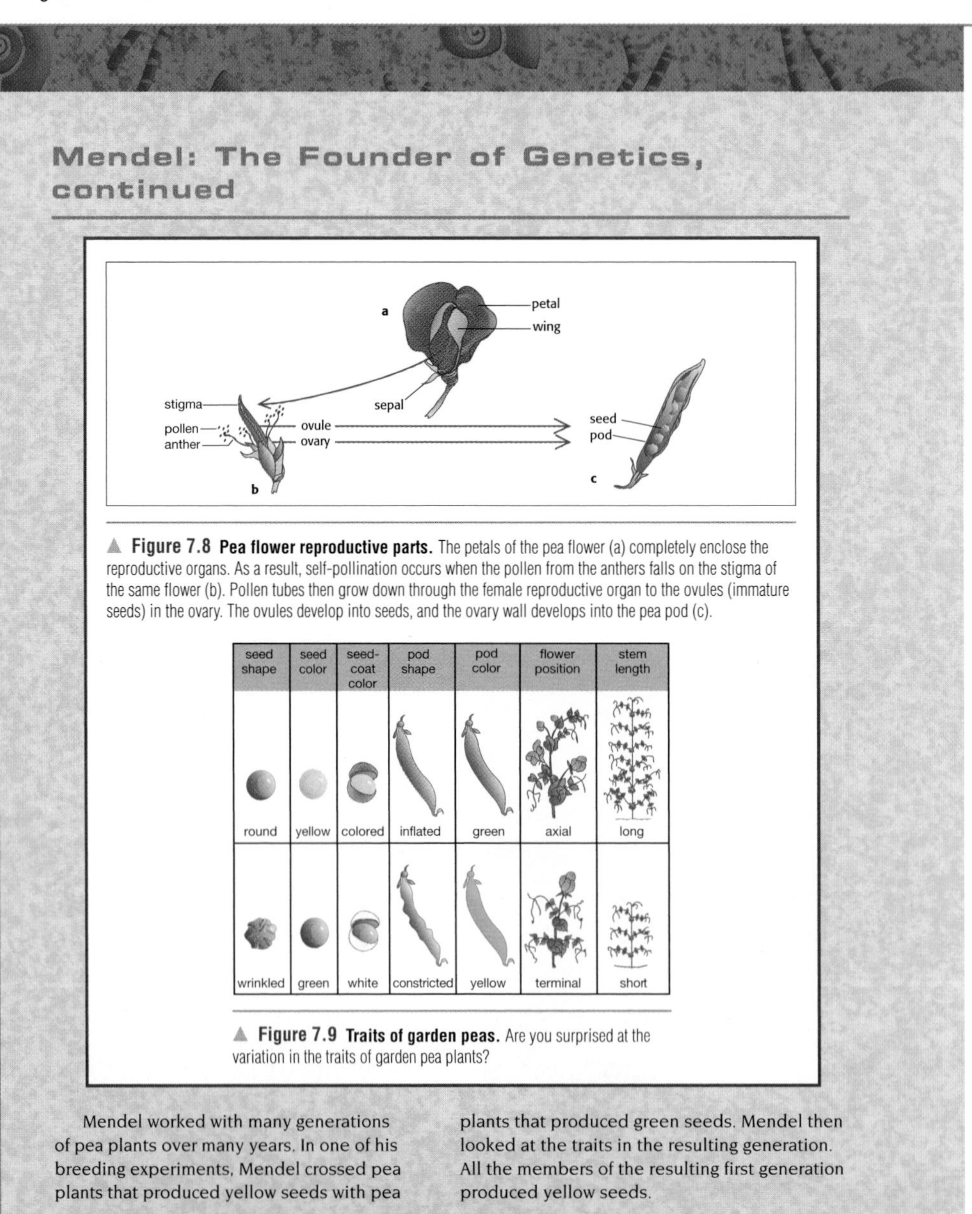

Mendel: The Founder of Genetics, continued

▲ **Figure 7.8 Pea flower reproductive parts.** The petals of the pea flower (a) completely enclose the reproductive organs. As a result, self-pollination occurs when the pollen from the anthers falls on the stigma of the same flower (b). Pollen tubes then grow down through the female reproductive organ to the ovules (immature seeds) in the ovary. The ovules develop into seeds, and the ovary wall develops into the pea pod (c).

seed shape	seed color	seed-coat color	pod shape	pod color	flower position	stem length
round	yellow	colored	inflated	green	axial	long
wrinkled	green	white	constricted	yellow	terminal	short

▲ **Figure 7.9 Traits of garden peas.** Are you surprised at the variation in the traits of garden pea plants?

Mendel worked with many generations of pea plants over many years. In one of his breeding experiments, Mendel crossed pea plants that produced yellow seeds with pea plants that produced green seeds. Mendel then looked at the traits in the resulting generation. All the members of the resulting first generation produced yellow seeds.

348 Unit 2 Inside Life

with unique phenotypes (the observable properties of an organism).

Materials—Part I

For the teacher

pictures of different genetics experiments (optional)

1 copy of copymaster 7.2, *Calculating Probability of a Genotype*

Materials—Part II

For the teacher

ingredients to make homemade play dough (optional; see *Advance Preparation*)

For each team of 2 students

red and blue play dough

1 large sheet of paper

1 small sheet of scratch paper

1 pair of scissors

paper

1 copy of optional activity *Alternate Modeling Meiosis* (on *TRCD*)

Advance Preparation

Before class, display pictures of genetics experiments. If you would like to make your own play dough, use the following recipe. For Part I, make a transparency of copymaster 7.2, *Calculating Probability of a Genotype*.

For Part II, decide whether you will provide the steps for the meiosis simulation by making copies of the optional activity *Alternate Modeling Meiosis* for each team. This activity is available on the *TRCD*.

Play Dough Recipe

1 c flour

½ c salt

1 c water

1 tbsp mineral or vegetable oil

2 tbsp cream of tartar

food coloring

Mix all ingredients. Heat over low heat, stirring constantly, until the mixture thickens and sticks together in a ball. Remove from heat and knead until smooth. This recipe makes about 16 ounces.

Cream of tartar can be purchased in bulk at a food cooperative or warehouse stores to reduce costs. Unsweetened (sugarless) gelatin can also be used to color the play dough. This will give the play dough a nice smell as well as color.

Educational Technologies

To help students visualize the process of meiosis, they can view the video clip of meiosis on the *SRCD*. They can also get practice understanding how genes are distributed to gametes during meiosis with the meiosis activity on the *SRCD*.

As You Teach

Outcomes and Indicators of Success

By the end of this activity, students should

1. be able to explain that an organism's genes determine what traits it has and that traits can be dominant or recessive depending on the alleles found on their genes.

   They will demonstrate their ability by

   - using information from reading about Mendelian genetics to interpret which seed color in Mendel's experiments and which yeast color in the last investigation was dominant and which was recessive;
   - comparing and contrasting genotype and phenotype;
   - describing that genes determine the traits exhibited by an organism;

You probably wondered what happened to the red color trait in your yeast experiment. Mendel, too, wondered what happened to the trait of green seeds in his experiment. Mendel felt that the green pea trait was not lost for good, so he took his experiment one step further. Mendel crossed members of the first generation (called F_1) with themselves (self-pollination) and looked at the resulting generation (called F_2). He found that in the F_2 generation, about 75 percent (3 out of every 4) of the offspring produced yellow seeds and about 25 percent (1 out of every 4) produced green seeds. Figure 7.10 illustrates the crosses and the results.

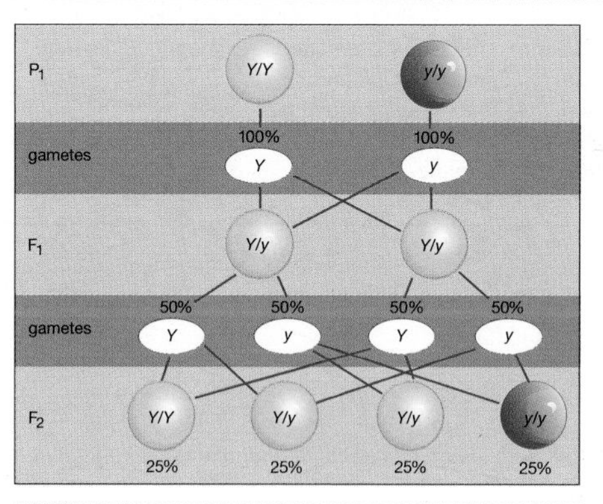

▲ **Figure 7.10 Yellow seed and green seed cross.** Two generations of one of Mendel's crosses using yellow and green seeds. Note that the alleles of a gene segregate, or separate, during gamete formation.

Mendel determined that whether seeds were yellow or green was determined by factors. We now call these factors **genes**. Genes determine the traits expressed by an organism—the traits that an organism has. They are the basic unit of information passed along from generation to generation through inheritance. Between 1854 and 1863, Mendel patiently grew thousands of pea plants, conducting different crosses. He repeated the same two-generation cross, shown in figure 7.10, with the six other traits.

After many years of study, and many plant breeding experiments, Mendel concluded that some expressions of traits were masked by other expressions of the trait. If the trait was the one that showed up in the first generation, he called it the **dominant** trait. If the trait did not appear again until the second generation, he called it the **recessive** trait.

Mendel realized that each trait existed in different forms. For example, the color trait could be yellow or green. The height trait could be tall or short. We now call different forms of the same gene **alleles**. For the gene that controls the height of a pea plant, there are two alleles. One allele results in the production of a tall plant. The other allele results in a short plant. The allele for the dominant form (tall plant) is commonly represented by a capital letter (in this cross, *T* for tall plants). The allele for the recessive form is represented by the same letter in lowercase (*t* for short plants).

Alleles form the genetic plan, or **genotype**, of an organism. The genotype of an individual is responsible for its **phenotype**. Phenotype describes the appearance or observable traits of an individual, such as seed color or petal shape. For instance, garden peas can have the tall plant or the short plant phenotype. Mendel found that both the *TT* and *Tt* genotypes produce the same phenotype exhibiting the dominant trait: tall plants. The *tt* genotype only produces the phenotype exhibiting the recessive trait: short plants.

If the alleles are the same (*TT* or *tt*), they are **homozygous**. An individual can be homozygous dominant or homozygous recessive for a trait.

- describing what the alleles must be for an organism with a recessive phenotype and an organism with a dominant phenotype;
- creating a visual representation of the relationship between chromosomes, genes, alleles, and traits; and
- documenting the allele that each parent must contribute for a particular genotype.

2. understand that most of the cells in a human contain 46 chromosomes: two copies of each of 22 chromosomes and another pair that determines the sex of an individual.

   They will demonstrate their understanding by

   - correctly identifying that humans have 46 chromosomes,
   - correctly identifying that humans have 22 pairs of autosomes and one pair of sex chromosomes, and
   - contrasting autosomes and sex chromosomes.

3. understand that gametes have half the genetic material of other body cells.

   They will demonstrate their understanding by

   - documenting how many chromosomes are present in human cells before and after meiosis,
   - documenting how many chromosomes human diploid and haploid cells have,
   - describing which yeast colonies from the previous investigation contained half the number of chromosomes and predicting what would have to happen before the first-generation yeast colonies could be crossed, and
   - explaining that meiosis accomplishes segregation of alleles by producing gametes that contain only one allele for each trait.

4. be able to explain the role of meiosis in passing genetic information from one generation to the next through gametes (sperm and egg).

   They will demonstrate their ability by

   - describing the major steps in meiosis and how meiosis leads to a reduction in genetic information in gametes,
   - using a flowchart to illustrate the steps of how an individual chromosome behaves during meiosis,
   - using play dough to model the movement of chromosomes through the process of meiosis,
   - illustrating the process of meiosis using cell diagram circles of the play dough model, and
   - describing the genotypes for eye color and wing color they obtained in the play dough model and describing the other genotypes that might be possible.

5. recognize that individuals such as Mendel contribute to the scientific enterprise and that what we know about science is the result of many experiments.

   They will demonstrate their recognition by

   - using the information in a reading about Mendel to infer why he might be called the "Founder of Genetics" and
   - describing that what we know about an area of science is the result of many experiments conducted by many scientists over many years.

6. be able to use the skills of scientific inquiry and their knowledge

Mendel: The Founder of Genetics, continued

The true-breeding plants that Mendel used to start his experiments were either homozygous dominant (*TT*) or homozygous recessive (*tt*). If the alleles are different (*Tt*), they are **heterozygous**. Heterozygous offspring are called **hybrids**.

Phenotype is not determined solely by the genotype, however. Environmental factors play a critical role as well. For example, the average height of Japan's human population increased by several inches during the early and middle 20th century (see figure 7.11). Did the genetic plan for the entire population change? No, the environment for the population changed. Japanese children had more nutritious diets in the early and middle 1900s than did children of earlier generations. Poor diet is an environmental factor. This environmental limitation prevented earlier generations from getting as tall as permitted by their genetic plan. Complex phenotypes involve many genetic and environmental factors.

Mendel's work is the basis for the modern study of heredity and variation. Geneticists now call his work Mendelian genetics. His experiments were unique in four important ways. First, he concentrated on one trait at a time. Second, he used large numbers of organisms to minimize the influence of chance on his data. Third, he combined the results of many identical experiments. Fourth, he used the rules of probability to analyze his results. By using these methods, Mendel was able to recognize distinctive patterns of inheritance.

Mendel's experiments defined the basic unit of inheritance, genes, but he could provide no information about its physical or chemical nature. Unable to see genes in his studies, he inferred their existence from his experiments. The answer to the riddle of what genes are and how they work could not be known until nearly 100 years later. This was when techniques for studying biological molecules were developed.

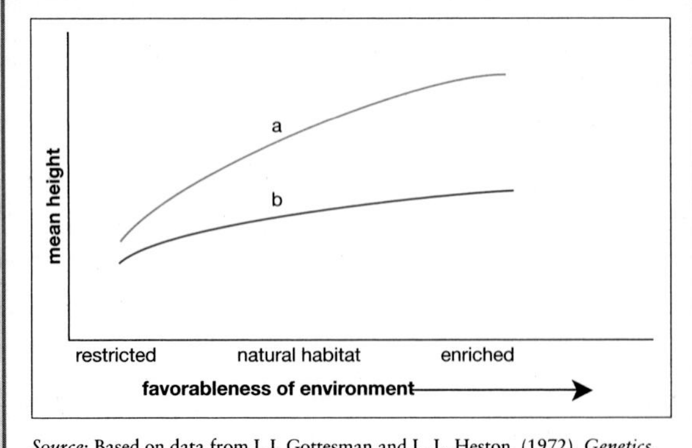

Source: Based on data from I. I. Gottesman and L. L. Heston. (1972). *Genetics, Environment, and Behavior*. Academic Press.

▲ **Figure 7.11 Height in Japanese boys and girls in relation to environmental conditions.** Improved environmental conditions in Japan led to a phenotype for increased height during the early and middle 20th century. Curve A represents 13-year-old girls and curve B represents 15-year-old boys. The units for both mean height and environmental conditions are not to scale.

Part of yeast investigation	Part of Mendel's pea plant experiment	How the yeast investigation is similar to Mendel's pea plant experiment
Red-colored yeast was crossed with cream-colored yeast.	Mendel cross pollinated pea plants with yellow seeds with pea plants with green seeds.	In both investigations, organisms were mated and these organisms had different traits.
The cross resulted in cream-colored yeast.	The cross resulted in all yellow seeds.	One trait was dominant over another for both yeast and pea plants.

▲ **Figure T7.10 Analogy map for yeast investigation and Mendel's experiment.** Students should generate an analogy map like this for Step 1.

about understanding of scientific inquiry.

They will demonstrate their ability by using a model of a cell and chromosomes to develop an explanation of how meiosis occurs.

Strategies

Getting Started

Ask students if they have heard of Gregor Mendel. They might already know that Mendel was a monk who studied pea plants. Ask if they know what he studied or the importance of what he studied. Explain that in Part I of this activity they will learn how Mendel's experiments with pea plants contributed to our understanding of genetics.

Process and Procedure

Part I: Mendel's Discoveries

Answers to Steps 2–3 are on TE pages 351–352.

2. Explain which of the following pairs of traits from Mendel's experiments is dominant and which is recessive and why.

   Write out the possible genotypes for each trait if you are unsure which is dominant and which is recessive.

   a. The yellow or green seeds in Mendel's experiment
   b. The red- or cream-colored yeast in the investigation from the last activity
3. Answer the following questions to show what you learned about Mendel's discoveries.
   a. Describe the difference between genotype and phenotype. Include in your description what determines the traits exhibited by an organism.
   b. Why do you think Mendel is often referred to as the "Founder of Genetics"?
   c. Do you think most of what we know about an area of science is the result of research across many years or the result of a few experiments? Why?
4. Select a technique you have found that helps you understand as you read. Apply your technique to the reading titled *Chromosomes and the Genes They Contain.*

   Some example techniques include T-tables, importance pyramids, and the TSAR process.

READING

Chromosomes and the Genes They Contain

In *Mendel: The Founder of Genetics*, you read about Mendel's experiments with peas and learned that the traits of an organism are determined by its genes. Specifically, the genetic information for an organism is stored in **DNA** (deoxyribonucleic acid) molecules. Genes are small sections of DNA molecules. In humans and other eukaryotes, the DNA molecules are organized into distinct structures called **chromosomes**. Each chromosome contains just a small part of an organism's total genetic information. The DNA in each chromosome, however, contains enough information for many phenotypic traits. For example, the very tip of just one human chromosome contains the piece of genetic information that causes blood to clot.

Humans have 46 chromosomes (23 pairs) in the nucleus of just about every cell of their bodies. The number of chromosomes varies from species to species and does not necessarily have to do with the complexity of the organism. Ants have two chromosomes, dogs have 78, cats have 38, and some species of ferns have 1,000.

Chapter 7 Tracking Traits 351

Materials

For the teacher

pictures of different genetics experiments (optional)

Students will begin by reading about Mendel's experiments with peas. Instruct students to complete an analogy map while they read. The analogy map should compare Mendel's pea plant experiments with the yeast investigation.

Answers to Steps 1–3, SE pages 346 and 351

1. See the analogy map in figure T7.10. The yeast experiment is similar to Mendel's experiments with pea plants because in both experiments organisms with different traits were crossed. Only one of the traits was expressed in the offspring. One of the traits masked the other trait.

2a. The yellow seeds are dominant and the green seeds are recessive. The yellow seeds are dominant because in the first-generation cross all the offspring had yellow seeds. The yellow trait masked the recessive green trait.

2b. The cream-colored yeast was dominant and the red-colored yeast was recessive. This is because only the red color trait was expressed in the cross of red-colored yeast. The cross of cream to cream and cream to red resulted in cream-colored yeast. The cream color trait was masking the red color trait.

3a. Genotype is the genetic plan for an organism. The alleles an organism carries for a trait determine its genotype for that trait. An organism's traits are determined by its genes. Students might also explain that the form or version of the trait is determined by the organism's alleles. The phenotype of an organism describes its observable traits. For example, yellow-colored seeds are a phenotype of pea plants and cream-colored yeast cells are a phenotype of yeast. The phenotype of an organism is the result of both the environment and the organism's genotype.

3b. Mendel is referred to as the Founder of Genetics because he was the first person to recognize that there are factors, called genes, that determine the traits expressed by an organism. His understanding of genes and the patterns the traits pass from generation to generation has provided the foundation for the study of genetics today.

3c. Most of what we know about science is the result of many experiments conducted by many scientists over many years. Because students often hear only about the work of one scientist who made a dramatic discovery, such as Mendel, students think only a few very special scientists contributed to our current understanding. Actually, the daily work of scientists results in incremental advances in our understanding of the natural world.

In Step 4, suggest different literacy strategies that students can use for the reading titled *Chromosomes and the Genes They Contain*. Before students begin reading, ask how many chromosomes students think human cells have. How many students feel they have half the genetic makeup of each parent? Some may think that they have more from one parent than the other because they look or act just like one of them. Explain that despite their appearances or behaviors, they received equal amounts of DNA from each parent. Explain that the reading will help clarify this concept.

Students begin by reading about chromosomes. Then they learn that during sexual reproduction, offspring receive one-half of their genetic information from each parent.

Chromosomes and the Genes They Contain, continued

In humans, the first 22 pairs of chromosomes are called **autosomes**. The 23rd pair is referred to as the **sex chromosomes** because the chromosomes in that pair determine whether a person is male or female. If an individual has two X chromosomes in the 23rd pair, she is female. If an individual has one X and one Y chromosome in the 23rd pair, he is male.

Each of the 46 human chromosomes contains many genes. The largest chromosome contains about 3,000 genes. The smallest one, the Y chromosome, contains only about 230 genes. Figure 7.12 illustrates some of the many genes present on two human chromosomes. Each gene occupies a specific location on the chromosome.

Populations of organisms have more than one form of most genes. You learned about these forms of genes, or alleles, when you read about Mendel's experiments. For example, some individuals in the human population have a blood type gene that specifies type A blood. Others have a version of the same gene that specifies type B blood. Remember that the particular combination of alleles determines the organism's phenotype. To learn what your alleles might be if you have type A blood, see figure 7.13.

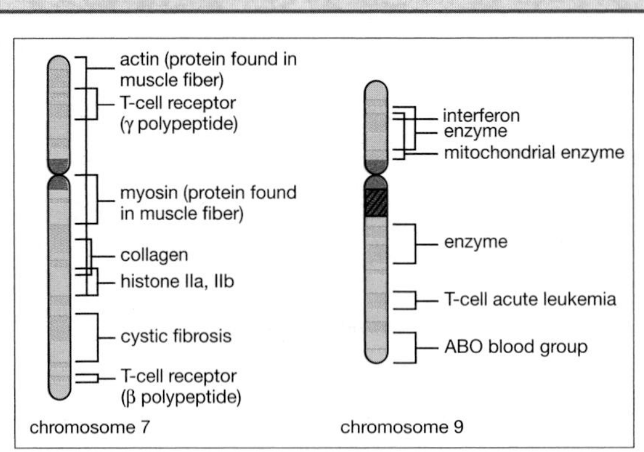

▲ **Figure 7.12 Genes on a chromosome.** Each chromosome carries many genes. This illustration shows a few of the genes that have been mapped to two human chromosomes, chromosome 7 and chromosome 9. Humans have two copies of each of 23 different human chromosomes, which carry an average of 1,000 genes each.

Phenotype	Genotype(s)
O	OO
A	AA, AO
B	BB, BO
AB	AB

▲ **Figure 7.13 Blood types.** Humans can be one of four blood types (O, A, B, or AB). In this table, the alleles are represented by A, B, and O. You have two blood type alleles because you receive one blood type allele from each parent.

SCILINKS NSTA
Topic: chromosomes
Go to: www.scilinks.org
Code: 2Inquiry352

352 Unit 2 Inside Life

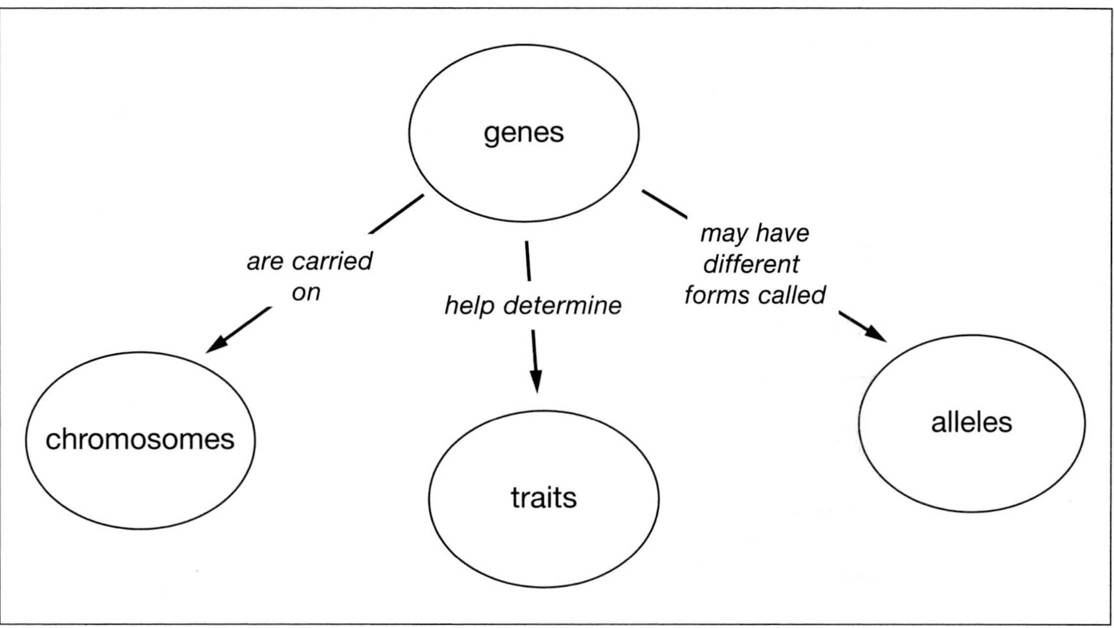

▲ **Figure T7.11 Graphic organizer.** Students' graphic organizers for Step 6 should look similar to this.

Organisms that are the result of sexual reproduction generally receive two alleles for every gene. One allele comes from one parent. Another allele comes from the other parent. For a trait like seed color of peas, an offspring that results from a cross receives one allele from each parent, either *Y* or *y*. Despite the notion that offspring might look more like one parent than the other, an offspring receives exactly one-half of its genetic information from each parent. How does this happen? Think about this as you read in the next section about how sex cells are produced. Read FYI—*Asexual Reproduction* to learn how some organisms reproduce asexually.

5. Answer the following questions to keep track of what you have learned about chromosomes in humans.
   a. How many chromosomes are present in human cells?
   b. How many pairs of autosomes and sex chromosomes do humans have? Describe the difference between autosomes and sex chromosomes.
   c. If 2 human body cells joined, how many chromosomes would be in the newly formed offspring cell? What problems do you think could arise if this happened?
6. Use a visual representation to show the relationship between the following terms: *chromosomes*, *genes*, *alleles*, and *traits*. Label your representation to show how the terms are related. An example is provided in figure 7.14.

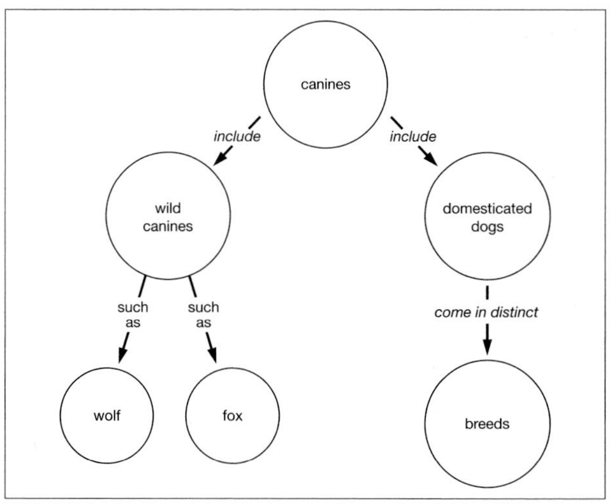

◄ **Figure 7.14 Canid graphic organizer.** Canids are carnivorous members of the dog family. Examples of canids include foxes, wolves, coyotes, jackals, dingoes, and domestic dogs. Notice how phrases are used to connect the major words ("canid," "domesticated dogs," and "breeds").

Answers to Steps 5–6, SE page 353

5a. There are 46 chromosomes (23 pairs) in human cells. There are some exceptions to this. One exception is red blood cells, which do not have a nucleus. It is not important that students know about the exceptions at this time.

5b. Humans have 22 pairs of autosomes and 1 pair of sex chromosomes. Sex chromosomes determine the sex of an individual. The remaining chromosomes are autosomes.

5c. Students should calculate the number of chromosomes as follows: 46 chromosomes + 46 chromosomes = 92 total chromosomes. Students might explain that the joining of 2 human body cells would result in too many chromosomes for a cell to function properly.

6. Students' answers should accurately reflect the relationship of the terms. Make sure students connect the words with phrases such as those shown. See figure T7.11.

NOTES:

Asexual Reproduction

During sexual reproduction, both parents pass genetic information to their offspring. Sexual reproduction increases the amount of genetic variation in a population because sexual reproduction combines genetic information from two different individuals.

Not all organisms reproduce sexually. Many organisms reproduce through **asexual reproduction**. In asexual reproduction, individuals originate from a single parent. Either the parent divides into two (or more) individuals, or new individuals arise as buds from the parent's body. Because new individuals arise from only one parent, asexual reproduction does not increase genetic variation in a population. Instead, new individuals are genetically identical to the parent organism.

Some animals and plants can reproduce both sexually and asexually. For example, the potato is a flowering plant that can use sexual reproduction to produce seed, but it also can reproduce asexually. In plants, this is called vegetative reproduction. The little "eyes" on potatoes are actually buds—groups of cells that can undergo rapid mitosis and develop into new plants. The buds can sprout and begin to grow, as shown in the figure.

The yeast you investigated in *What Shows Up?* reproduced both sexually and asexually. When you crossed the yeast, they reproduced sexually. How do you think yeast reproduced asexually? Yeast reproduce asexually through budding, a type of vegetative cell division, which is similar to potatoes budding. The division of yeast cells begins with an unbudded cell. Then yeast cells bud, and the bud grows to nearly the size of the "parent" cell. The nucleus of the parent cell divides, and the two cells separate. You might have noticed that your yeast colonies grew larger across time. Yeast cells divide rapidly, causing colonies to grow quickly under the right conditions.

Budding potatoes. After a dormant period, some of the eyes or buds on a potato begin to sprout and form shoots. The shoots like you see in this photo can develop into new potato plants.

7. Continue using the technique you selected in Step 4 or switch to a new technique to read *Meiosis: The Mechanism behind Patterns of Inheritance.*

354 Unit 2 Inside Life

NOTES:

READING

Meiosis: The Mechanism behind Patterns of Inheritance

In sexual reproduction, genetic information is passed from generation to generation by cells called **gametes**. Gametes have only *half* the genetic information of other body cells. They have half the chromosomes and thus half the alleles.

How and when does this reduction occur? Most of the solution to this question was discovered just before the beginning of the 20th century. The key is a process called **meiosis**. Meiosis is the special type of cell division that produces gametes (egg and sperm cells) in male and female organisms that reproduce sexually. Meiosis accomplishes three major tasks: (1) It reduces the number of chromosomes in gametes to half of all the chromosomes found in body cells. (2) It forms cells that will allow each parent to contribute equal amounts of genetic information to the offspring. In humans, the gametes have 23 chromosomes in each cell. (3) It creates gene combinations in the offspring that are distinct from the parents.

Following the chromosomes during meiosis provides a way to understand certain patterns of inheritance. In all cells other than gametes, chromosomes occur in matching pairs. This is called the **diploid** condition. For each pair, one chromosome came from the mother's egg cell and one chromosome came from the father's sperm cell. The maternal and paternal chromosomes of each pair contain genes that affect the same traits. As you learned earlier, however, the alleles for each gene may be different.

In contrast, gametes (egg, or ovum, and sperm) contain only *one* chromosome from each matching pair. Gametes are **haploid**: they contain half the number of chromosomes that other body cells such as skin and nerve cells have. In sexual reproduction, a sperm fertilizes the ovum and the nuclei of both cells fuse to form a new cell with the correct number of chromosomes. The single cell that results from the joining of the egg and the sperm is called a **zygote**. The zygote will have matching pairs of chromosomes. Each pair is composed of one chromosome from the egg and one chromosome from the sperm. Thus, fertilization restores the diploid number of chromosomes in the zygote. What would happen if chromosome numbers were not halved during meiosis? The number of chromosomes would double with each generation! Such a condition in humans and other animals would lead to the death of the zygote.

The zygote begins a series of cell divisions, through the process of **mitosis**, to produce an **embryo**. Mitosis forms many new cells, each with 46 chromosomes (23 pairs) if the organism is a human. Those cells eventually specialize into tissues and organs, giving rise to the human body. Each new cell formed has the genetic makeup of the zygote.

Sometimes two sperm fertilize two eggs. When this happens, fraternal twins are produced. Fraternal twins really are no more genetically similar to each other than other siblings are. At other times, one sperm fertilizes one egg and, for reasons that scientists do not completely understand yet, the cell doubles in chromosome number and then splits into separate zygotes. Identical twins are the result of one sperm fertilizing one egg. Identical twins have identical genetic information.

Students continue reading and learn how meiosis occurs. When students get to step 9b, display a

transparency of copymaster 7.2, *Calculating Probability of a Genotype*. Fill out the transparency as a class to help students understand how to predict the genotypes of offspring. Later, students will learn how to use Punnett squares to help them calculate the probability of a genotype.

NOTES:

Meiosis: The Mechanism behind Patterns of Inheritance, continued

Meiosis is similar to the process of mitosis. In meiosis, as in mitosis, the number of chromosomes doubles at the beginning of the process. In mitosis, one cell division follows, restoring the usual diploid number of chromosomes. In meiosis, however, cell division occurs *twice*. The process results in four cells, each with the haploid number of chromosomes. The four cells produced by meiosis each have just one set of chromosomes. In humans, meiosis results in one large egg cell for females and four sperm cells for males (see figure 7.15).

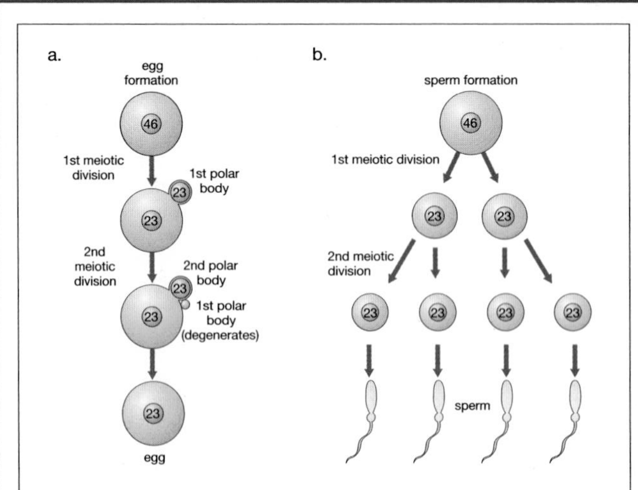

▲ **Figure 7.15 Human gamete formation.** In human males, meiotic division usually results in four equal-sized sperm, each with 23 chromosomes. The formation of an egg is somewhat different. Two unequally sized cells are formed in the first meiotic division. The larger cell of the two again produces a smaller cell in the second meiotic division. The result is one large ovum that can be involved in reproduction and three polar bodies that will not be involved in reproduction. The polar bodies are by-products of meiosis in female animals and will eventually disintegrate. What do you think is the advantage of producing a large egg? Think about what the yolk provides for a developing chick.

NOTES:

Figure 7.16 illustrates what happens to one pair of chromosomes during meiosis. Let's examine the process in more detail. Just before meiosis begins, each chromosome pair doubles. During the first meiotic cell division, the two doubled chromosomes separate into two cells. Each of these cells contains one doubled chromosome. During the second meiotic cell division, the doubled chromosome in each cell separates into two more cells. This second cell division results in a total of four cells. Each cell contains one chromosome from the original pair.

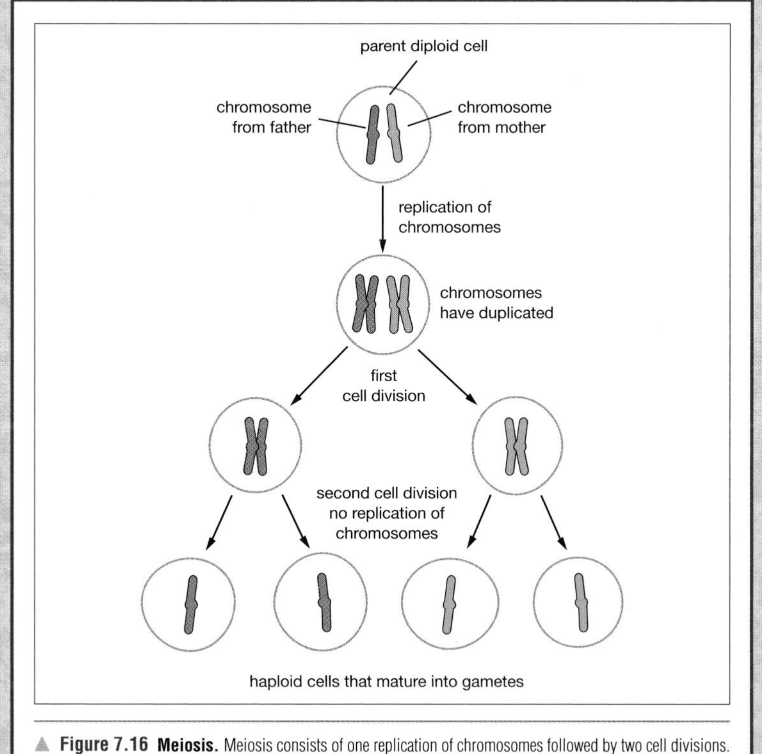

▲ **Figure 7.16 Meiosis.** Meiosis consists of one replication of chromosomes followed by two cell divisions.

NOTES:

Meiosis: The Mechanism behind Patterns of Inheritance, continued

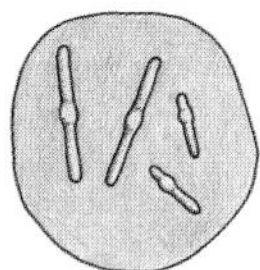

diploid parent cell

a This cell has 2 pairs of chromosomes.

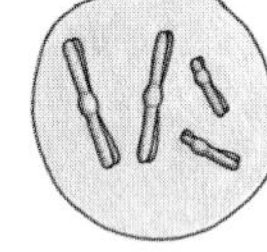

beginning of meiosis prophase 1

b Just before this diploid cell begins meiosis each chromosome is replicated.

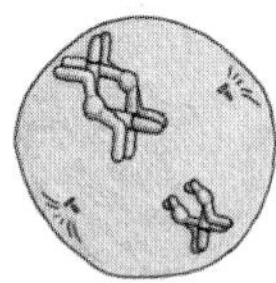

crossing-over

c The pairs of replicated chromosomes become closely aligned and join in several places. At these junctions, equivalent pieces of the chromosome pair might exchange places. This exchange process, called crossing over, results in the switching of alleles. Because the chromosomes involved in the exchange originally came from different parents, a new combination of information now exists.

metaphase 1

d The joined chromosomes line up along the middle of the cell. Cytoplasmic fibers attach to each replicated chromosome.

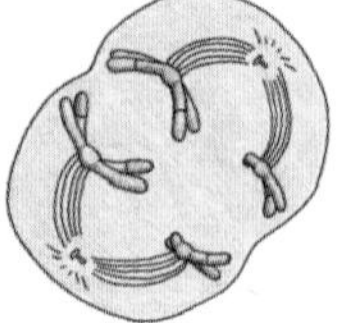

anaphase 1

e The cytoplasmic fibers pull apart each pair of duplicated chromosomes during the first cell division.

▲ **Figure 7.17 The stages of meiosis.** This figure illustrates the events of meiosis for a cell that has two pairs of chromosomes.

358 Unit 2 Inside Life

NOTES:

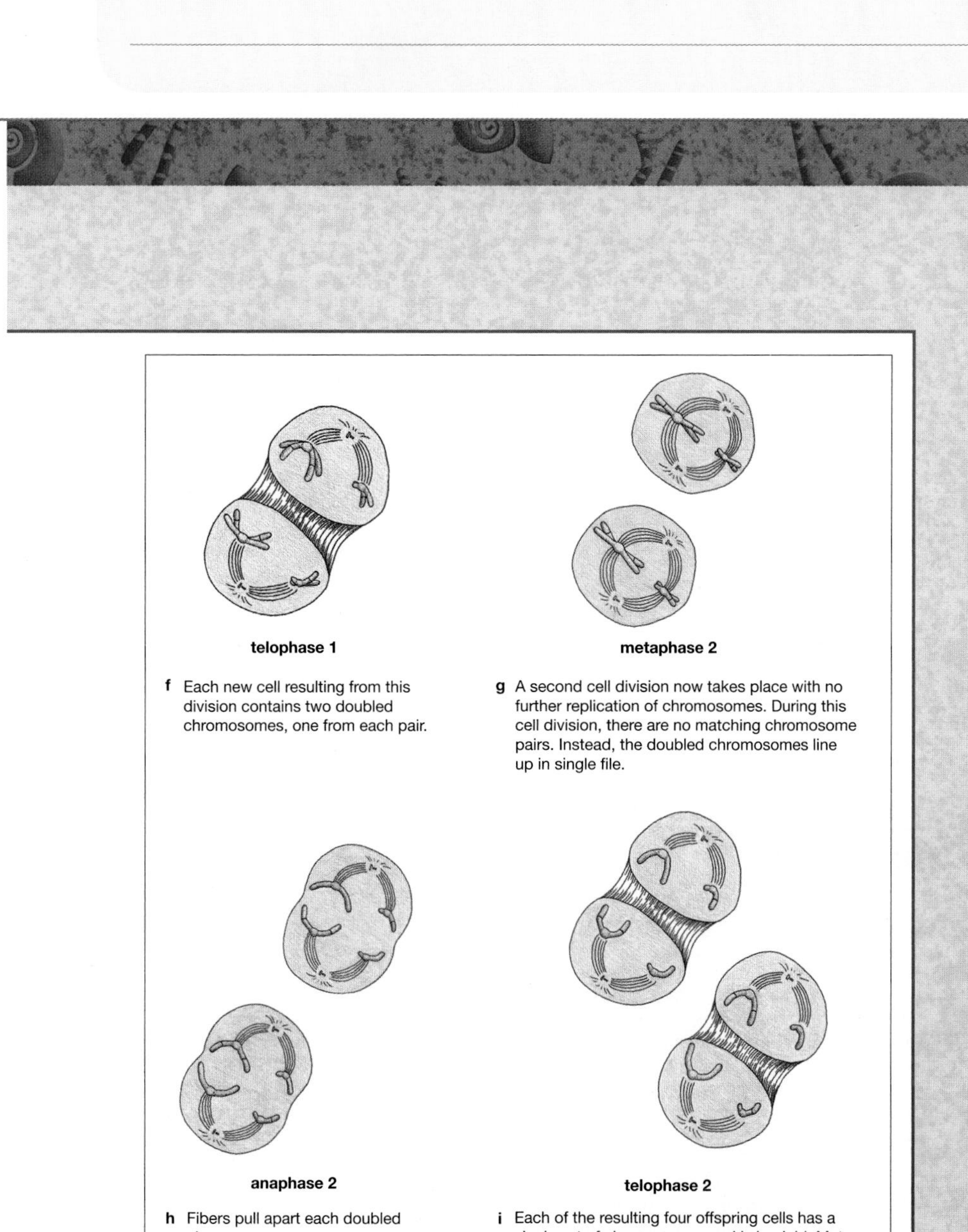

telophase 1

f Each new cell resulting from this division contains two doubled chromosomes, one from each pair.

metaphase 2

g A second cell division now takes place with no further replication of chromosomes. During this cell division, there are no matching chromosome pairs. Instead, the doubled chromosomes line up in single file.

anaphase 2

h Fibers pull apart each doubled chromosome.

telophase 2

i Each of the resulting four offspring cells has a single set of chromosomes and is haploid. Mature human gametes form from the products of meiosis.

Chapter 7 Tracking Traits 359

Answers to Steps 8–9, SE page 360

8a. Humans cells have 46 chromosomes before meiosis.

8b. Human cells have 23 pairs of chromosomes.

8c. Human cells have 23 chromosomes, or half the full set of chromosomes, after meiosis. Some students might explain that human cells with half the chromosome pairs are called gametes. Students should explain that cell division occurs twice, resulting in half the number of chromosomes.

8d. Diploid cells have matching pairs of chromosomes. Haploid cells have only 1 chromosome from a matching pair.

9a. The principle of independent assortment helps explain the variation in species because the genes for different traits are often located on different chromosomes. Individuals will have different combinations of traits depending on which genes they inherit. The principle of segregation helps explain the variation in a species because each offspring receives 1 allele from a given gene from a parent. Individuals have different traits depending on the alleles they get from each parent.

9b. See the completed tables from copymaster 7.2, *Calculating Probability of a Genotype* in figure T7.12.

9c. See figure T7.13.

9d. See figure T7.13.

In the final section of the reading titled *Sorting Genes*, students learn about Mendel's key discoveries of the principle of segregation and the principle of independent assortment and how our understanding of meiosis confirms Mendel's ideas. These principles are covered only briefly in the reading because they are not part of the *National Science Education Standards*. You might choose to spend more time on these concepts if they are part of your state standards.

gametes			
sperm		egg	
probability of g	probability of G	probability of g	probability of G
½	½	½	½

offspring			
genotype of offspring	number of ways to get genotype	total number of fertilization combinations	probability of genotype (fertilization combination)
gg	1	4	¼
Gg	2	4	½
GG	1	4	¼

▲ **Figure T7.12 Completed tables to calculate probability of a genotype.** The class should help fill in the transparency of copymaster 7.2, *Calculating Probability of a Genotype* as shown here.

8. Study figure 7.17, which shows the events of meiosis in a cell with two pairs of chromosomes. Then record your answers to Questions 8a–d in your science notebook.
   a. How many chromosomes do human cells have before meiosis?
   b. How many *pairs* of chromosomes do human cells have?
   c. How many chromosomes do they have after meiosis? Explain why this is so.
   d. Describe the difference between haploid and diploid cells.
9. Read *Sorting Genes* and complete the following tasks to show your understanding of how offspring can have different combinations of alleles from the same parents.
   a. Describe how the principle of independent assortment and the principle of segregation might help explain the variation in a species, such as humans or pea plants.
   b. Copy and complete the table from figure 7.18 in your science notebook. Use the information in the figure to help you fill in the blank spaces.
   c. Determine the number of ways to get each genotype (*gg*, *Gg*, or *GG*) using the information from figure 7.18.
   d. Calculate the probability of each genotype (*gg*, *Gg*, or *GG*). Show your work.

READING

Sorting Genes

Gregor Mendel worked out the principles of simple inheritance decades before the scientists understood how cells carry out meiosis. He accomplished this astounding intellectual achievement by designing creative experiments, making observations, keeping detailed records, and applying mathematical reasoning to his results.

Meiosis explains Mendel's key discoveries. One of Mendel's discoveries was the **principle of independent assortment**. In meiosis, the chromosome pairs separate independently. When Mendel looked at multiple traits of pea plants, such as seed color and seed shape, he found that specific seed colors are not inherited with specific seed shapes. Genes governing those two traits undergo **independent assortment**. Independent assortment occurs because the genes for seed color and seed shape are located on different chromosomes. The movement of one chromosome does not depend on the movement of another chromosome.

Mendel also understood that offspring received alleles from each parent. Mendel called this separation the **principle of segregation**. Remember that (1) genes are located on chromosomes and (2) alleles are versions of a

360 | Unit 2 Inside Life

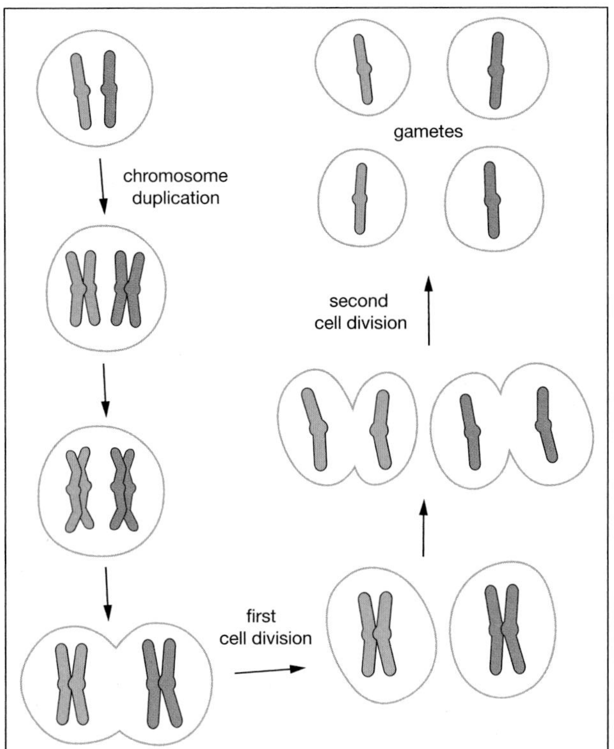

Figure T7.13 Student flowchart of meiosis. This figure is an example of how students might answer *Stop and Think* Question 1b.

gene. Alleles on the two chromosomes in a pair segregate (separate) when the two chromosomes separate during meiosis. Each gamete, therefore, receives only one allele for a given gene. You will model how meiosis explains the principle of segregation in Part II.

Understanding meiosis also allows us to make predictions about the genotypes and phenotypes of offspring. We can predict the frequency of offspring genotypes when parents of a known genotype mate and produce large numbers of offspring. Figure 7.18 presents an example using guinea pigs. Short hair is a dominant trait in guinea pigs. *G* represents the allele for short hair, *g* the allele for long hair. Both parents are heterozygous for short hair (*Gg*). Each parent produces equal numbers of *G* and *g* gametes through meiosis. When fertilizations occur, the gametes join in random combinations. In this case, ½ of the egg and ½ of the sperm contain the *G* allele. We can, therefore, expect that ¼ (½ × ½ = ¼) of the offspring will have the homozygous genotype *GG* of short hair.

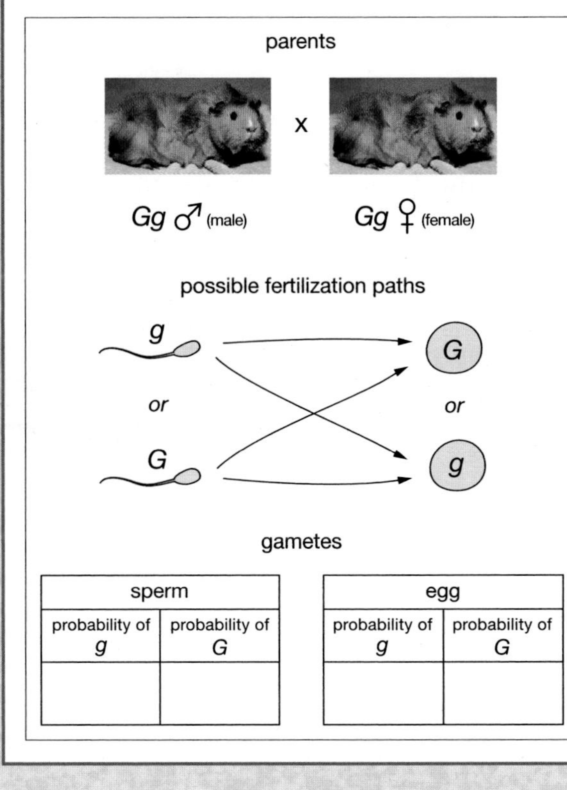

Figure 7.18 Predicting genotype. Allele segregation occurs in a regular pattern that makes it possible to predict offspring. If the genotypes of the parents are known, then the gametes that result can be known as well. If one parent was homozygous for short hair (*GG*), how many offspring would you expect to be genotype *GG*?

NOTES:

Chapter 7 Tracking Traits 361

NOTES:

Sorting Genes, continued

What about the other half of the ova (plural of ovum) and sperm—those that carry the *g* allele? Fertilization of these gametes will probably result in about ¼ of the offspring having the homozygous genotype *gg* of short hair. The rest of the offspring will be heterozygotes. Half of the heterozygotes will come from unions of *G* egg with *g* sperm. The other half will come from unions of *g* egg and *G* sperm. (Both are written *Gg* because biologists record the dominant trait first, regardless of which parent passes it on.) Of the resulting offspring at one mating, ¾ will have short hair (½ *Gg* plus ¼ *GG*) and 1/4 will have long hair (*gg*). Biologists refer to this pattern as a 3:1 phenotypic ratio (¾:¼, reduced to lowest terms).

The laws of inheritance do not allow us to make exact predictions for a specific mating, however. Each fertilization involves the union of a single egg and a single sperm out of *many* possible egg and sperm. We cannot predict with absolute certainty that a particular mating will result in a zygote that is *Gg*, for example. Flipping a coin illustrates this phenomenon. Is it possible to toss four heads in a row with a coin? What about tossing 100 heads in a row? The predicted result of getting heads in a coin toss is 50:50, a prediction that can be verified by observing a large number of tosses. You might not be surprised at tossing four heads in a row, but you would be surprised at tossing 100 heads in a row.

Imagine that the parent guinea pigs in figure 7.18 have a litter of four. Recall that both parents are heterozygous (*Gg*) for the short hair allele. If we examine *many* such litters, we probably would find that ½ of the offspring had the *Gg* genotype, ¼ the *GG* genotype, and ¼ the *gg* genotype. However, it is quite possible that in any given litter, all may have the *GG* genotype or all may have the *gg* genotype. Isn't it possible to toss four heads in a row with a coin? You may have to flip a coin many times to get the same number of heads and tails. Similarly, many matings would have to occur to get the frequencies of genotypes predicted by the parents' alleles.

SCILINKS NSTA
Topic: independent assortment
Go to: www.scilinks.org
Code: 2Inquiry362

Answers to Stop and Think—Part I, SE page 363

1a. It is not necessary that the students explain all the stages of meiosis here. It is sufficient if they simply explain that (1) the chromosomes in the parent cell are duplicated and (2) they undergo 2 meiotic divisions that result in a reduction from the diploid to the haploid number of chromosomes. In the first division, the cell divides into 2 cells, and then in the second division the 2 cells divide again to produce 4 cells, called gametes. Because the cell divides twice, but the chromosomes duplicate once, the resulting gametes only have half the chromosomes.

1b. Make sure students represent the following in their flowcharts: duplication of chromosomes, the first cell division, 2 cells with doubled chromosomes, the second cell division, and 4 cells (gametes) with single chromosomes. Encourage students to label parts of their flowcharts similar to those shown in the example in figure T7.13.

2a. The parent colonies had half the number of chromosomes because each colony represented a separate mating type.

2b. In the yeast investigation, the parent colonies had half the number of chromosomes. The parent colonies must have had half the chromosomes because these colonies were mated (crossed) to produce the first generation. The cells would have to undergo meiosis in order to reduce the number of chromosomes to half.

Process and Procedure

Part II: Modeling Meiosis

Materials

For the teacher

ingredients to make homemade play dough (optional; see *Advance Preparation*)

For each team of 2 students

red and blue play dough
1 large sheet of paper
1 small sheet of scratch paper
1 pair of scissors

Stop & THINK

PART I

Complete the following tasks and questions with a partner and record your answers in your science notebook.

1. Using what you just learned about meiosis, work with your partner to complete the following tasks.
   a. Write a description in your science notebook of how the major events in meiosis lead to a reduced amount of genetic information in gametes. Include in your answer how many gametes are produced by a single parent and explain why the process of meiosis results in this number of gametes. You may want to use sketches as you complete this task.
   b. Create a flowchart to record the steps for how an individual chromosome behaves during the process of meiosis. Provide labels if necessary on your flowchart.
   c. Check your answers with your classmates and then your teacher. You will use this information in Part II.
2. Answer the following questions about the yeast investigation.
   a. Which yeast colonies contained half the number of chromosomes: the parent colonies or the first generation? Explain your answer.
   b. What would have to happen before you could cross the first generation of yeast with itself as Mendel did with his pea plant experiments?

Do you think scientists such as Mendel learn everything there is to know about an area of study?

Part II: Modeling Meiosis

The fruit fly (*Drosophila melanogaster*) is commonly used in genetic experiments. Studies of fruit flies have demonstrated the direct relationship between genes and chromosomes. In this part of the activity, you will follow the chromosomes and genes of a male fruit fly gamete through the process of meiosis.

NOTES:

NOTES:

In Step 1, students use a list of phrases about the meiosis model to help them develop a plan to simulate meiosis with play dough. They use information from figure 7.19 in the student book and their answers from Question 1 of *Stop and Think—Part I*. Students will work in pairs for this activity. In Step 2, use the steps provided in the optional activity *Alternate Modeling Meiosis* on the *TRCD* to check students' plans. If you think your students will struggle with developing their own plans for the meiosis simulation, you can also provide them with this activity.

Distribute large sheets of paper and play dough to each team. As the students draw their circles on the large paper, make sure that they leave enough space for the intermediate circles (which represent the doubling of chromosomes, the first meiotic division, and the second meiotic division). They can draw 4 circles with tails at the bottom of the page to represent maturation of meiotic products to gametes (sperm).

In Step 3, students move their models through the process of meiosis. As the teams use the play dough models and answer the questions in Step 4, circulate among the teams to assess their understanding of the meiotic process.

Materials

For each team of 2 students

red and blue play dough

1 large sheet of paper

1 small sheet of scratch paper

1 pair of scissors

paper

Process and Procedure

1. Develop a plan for simulating meiosis. Your simulation plan should include the following elements. They will help you develop an effective plan on your own. Record your plan in your science notebook.

The simulation will be your own visual representation of the various stages of meiosis. Refer to the reading *Meiosis: The Mechanism behind Patterns of Inheritance* in Part I for details about meiosis. Use your answers from Question 1 of *Stop and Think—Part I* as a guide.

   a. A male fruit fly (a diploid animal) that has 2 pairs of chromosomes
   b. Circles on a large sheet of paper to represent cells at different stages of meiosis
   c. A way to represent *replication* of chromosomes before meiosis begins

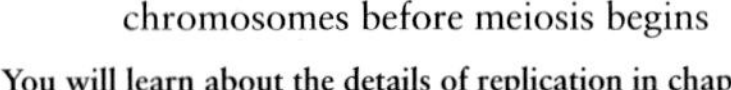
You will learn about the details of replication in chapter 8, *Instructions for Life*.

   d. Play dough to represent 2 different pairs of chromosomes
   e. Different colors of play dough to represent the chromosome of each pair that came from the female parent and the male parent
   f. Labels to represent genes for each chromosome (see figure 7.19)
2. Have your teacher approve your plan.
3. Carry out your plan to simulate meiosis by completing Steps 3a–b.
   a. Using your cell-diagram circles, move your chromosome models through the process of meiosis and into the sperm.

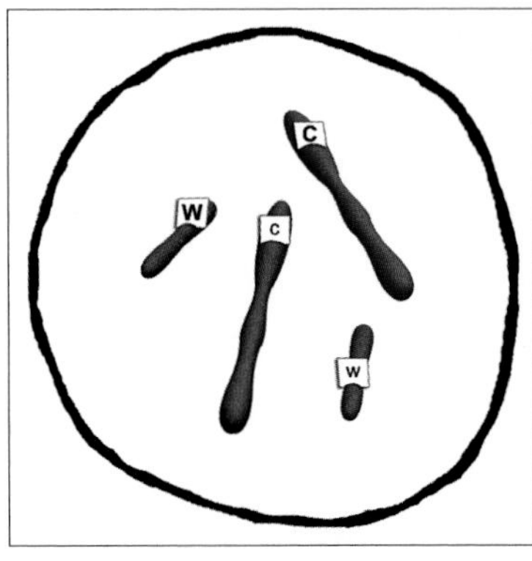

▲ **Figure 7.19 Simulating meiosis.** Clay models and paper labels can represent chromosomes and genes in a diploid animal cell.

364 Unit 2 Inside Life

NOTES:

Answers to Step 4 are on TE page 365a.
Answers to Reflect and Connect are on TE page 365b.

b. Sketch in your science notebook how you line up the chromosome models during each meiotic division.

4. Think about how you just modeled meiosis and answer the following questions with a partner.
   a. In your model, what is the genotype of each sperm for eye color and wing color?
   b. What other genotypes are possible?

Check the results of other teams.

   c. At what points would you change how you positioned your chromosome models to obtain the other possible genotypes?

Reflect and Connect

Work on your own to answer the following questions. Record your answers in your science notebook.

1. What can you say for sure about the alleles for a particular trait in an organism that exhibits a recessive phenotype? A dominant phenotype?
2. Explain how your cell diagrams and the answers to Questions 8a–d from Part I of this activity illustrate how meiosis accomplishes segregation of alleles.
3. If an organism has the genotype *AA*, what can you say about the alleles present in the gametes that gave rise to that organism?
4. Consider how tall you are, how tall you will likely be when you are fully grown, and how tall you might have been if you were raised in a very different situation. How do your genes and the environment interact to determine how tall you will be?

Modify the diagram in figure 7.20 to illustrate your answer. Explain why you modified the diagram.

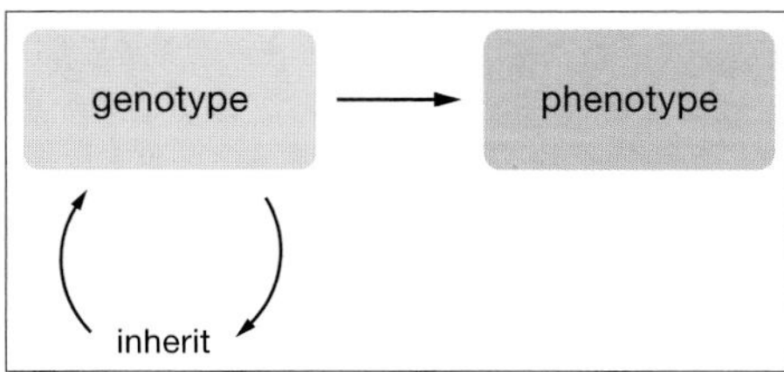

▲ **Figure 7.20 Relationship between genotype and phenotype.** How do genes and the environment interact to determine your phenotype (your traits)?

Answers to Step 4, SE page 365

4a. Depending on how the chromosomes pair up before the first meiotic cell division, 2 different results are possible, as demonstrated in figure T7.14. In solution (a), 2 *CW* gametes and 2 *cw* gametes will form. Solution (b) illustrates how 2 *Cw* gametes and 2 *cW* gametes will form. (Note that this assumes that no recombination occurs between the gene loci and their centromeres.)

4b. See the answer to 4a.

4c. The 2 possible lineups from the first meiotic division are (a) *CC* with *ww* and *cc* with *WW*, and (b) *CC* with *WW* and *cc* with *ww*.

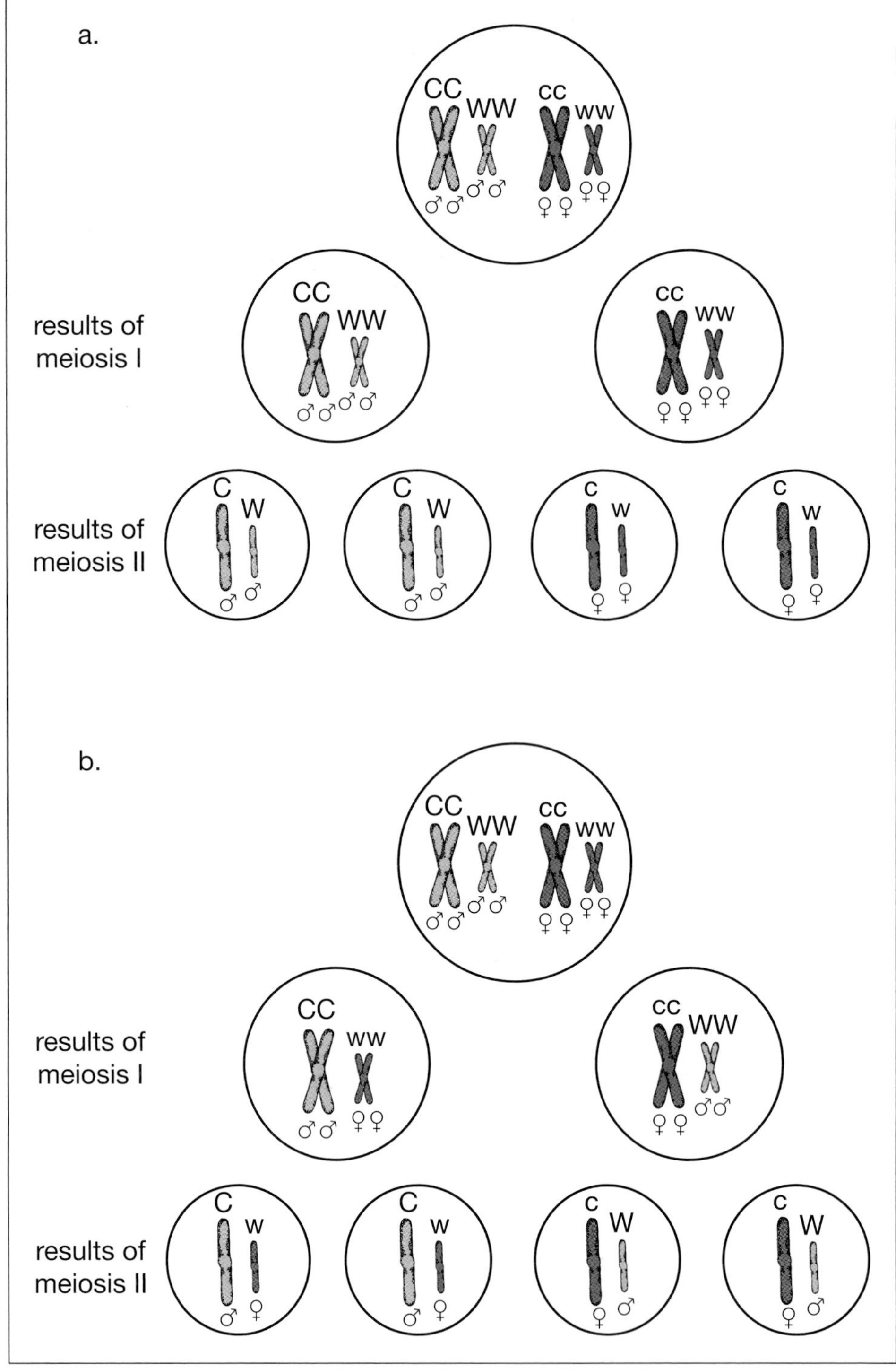

▲ **Figure T7.14 Meiotic products.** Two possible meiotic products for eye color and wing color alleles (a and b).

To challenge your more advanced students, you might have them model the process of meiosis again, this time exchanging parts of one chromosome with the other chromosome in its pair. This process of exchanging identical parts of matching chromosomes is called crossing-over. Figure T7.15 illustrates how you might have students model crossing-over.

Crossing-over is not discussed in this chapter because it is not part of the *National Science Education Standards*. However, crossing-over results in new combinations of genes or recombination. Recombination is any process that results in offspring that have combinations of genes different from those of either parent. Crossing-over and independent assortment of chromosomes during gamete formation are examples of recombination. Refer to *Background Information* for a detailed explanation of crossing-over.

Answers to Reflect and Connect, SE page 365

1. An organism that exhibits a recessive phenotype must have the same 2 recessive alleles. An organism that exhibits a dominant phenotype might have 1 dominant and 1 recessive allele or 2 dominant alleles.
2. By working through the models and sketching meiosis in Part II, students already have demonstrated an understanding of the role of meiosis in segregating alleles. The way students express these points may vary. Some possible responses might include the observation that meiosis leads to gametes that contain only 1 allele for each trait or that only the paternal or maternal allele is represented in a gamete for a given trait, but never both.
3. Both the male and female parental gametes contributed an *A* allele to this organism.
4. The diagram (figure 7.20 from the student book) is included here, with the addition of an "environment" component (see figure T7.16). You will notice that it is an organizer that students may find useful in thinking about genetics. It shows visually the 2 aspects of genetic information: the information gets expressed (to produce traits) and it gets inherited (through reproduction). Students might add another arrow to the diagram leading from the "environment" to the "genotype ⇒ phenotype" arrow.

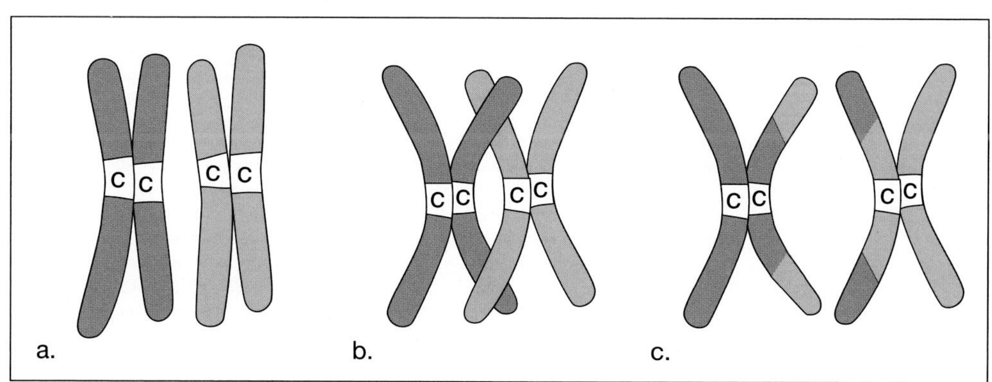

Figure T7.15 How to model crossing-over. (a) At the beginning of prophase I, the duplicated pairs of chromosomes come close together. (b) When the chromosomes are close together, part of one chromosome (blue clay) might break off and (c) exchange places with identical parts of the matching chromosome (red clay).

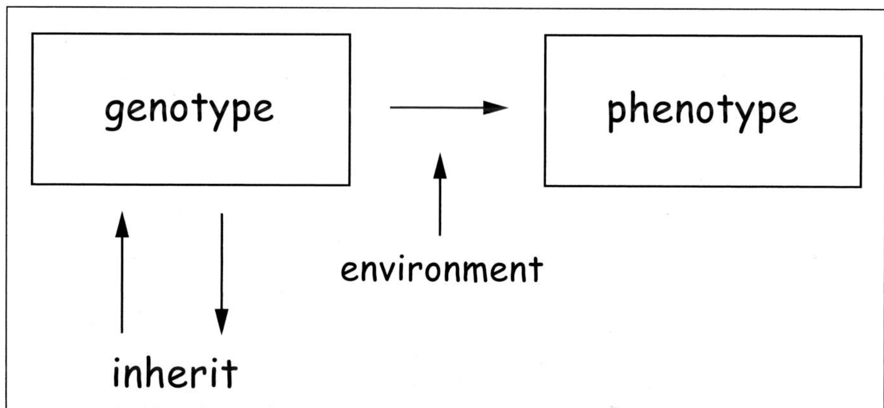

Figure T7.16 Relationship between genotype and phenotype. Students should draw something similar to this figure for *Reflect and Connect* Question 4.

NOTES:

SIDEBAR

When Meiosis Has a Glitch

It is amazing that processes like meiosis and mitosis occur continuously without any significant problems. Cells divide to produce new body cells, and certain cells form gametes. These processes occur like a well-orchestrated symphony. However, sometimes there are mistakes that occur during the processes of meiosis and mitosis.

If a mistake during meiosis is major, a gamete will not form. Many gametes containing an error are not involved in fertilization. Those errors are "lost." We are not aware of their existence. In other instances, the gamete containing the error forms and is involved in the production of a zygote. The effects of the error can be

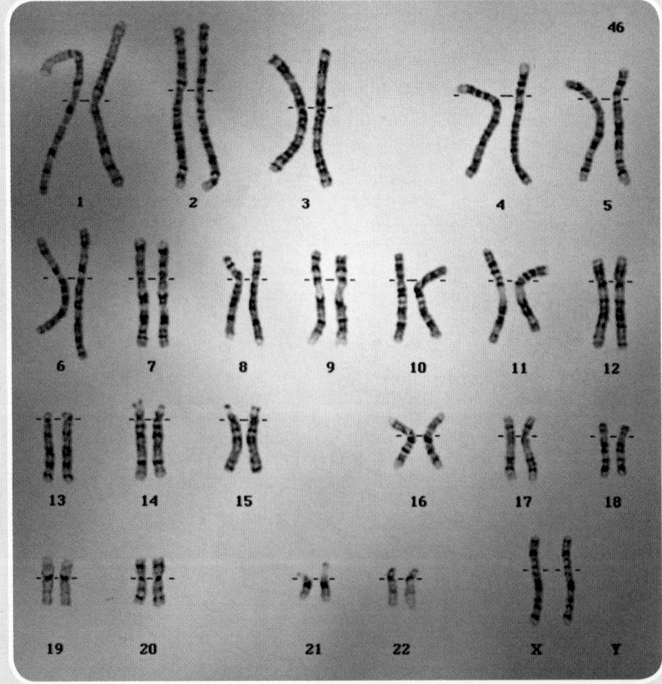

Karyotype of a human. A karyotype is the appearance and characteristics of chromosomes in a cell. The karyotype on the right is prepared by cutting out individual chromosomes from a photograph and matching them, pair by pair. Is this the karyotype of a male or a female?

366 | Unit 2 Inside Life

NOTES:

detrimental and the effects are different depending on which chromosome has the error.

Scientists can actually take cells, stain them, and take a picture of the chromosomes. The appearance and characteristics of chromosomes in a cell is called a **karyotype**. Look at the figure showing a karyotype from a cell of a normal human (image on the left). You will notice that the chromosomes are scattered. This is the way they occur in the nucleus of the cell. The chromosomes have been arranged into pairs in the image on the right. Looking at chromosomes in pairs helps us understand how genetic information is inherited.

Down syndrome, often referred to as trisomy 21, occurs when there is an extra chromosome in the 21st pair (see figure). Down syndrome affects about 1 in every

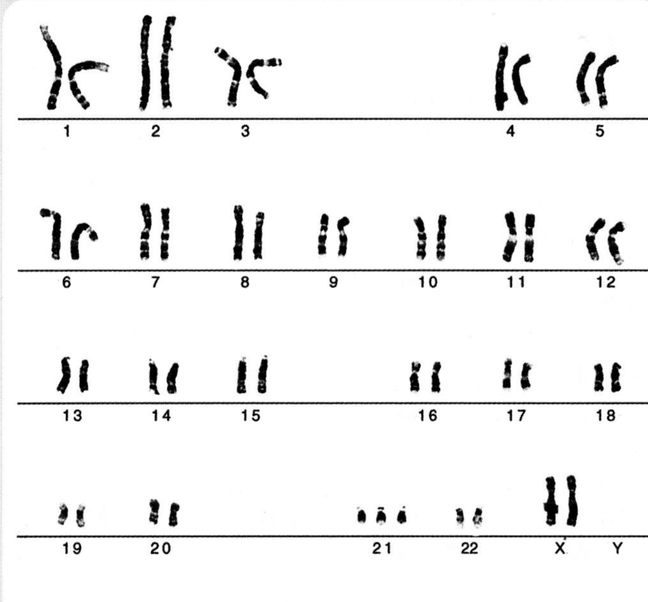

▲ **Karyotype of Down syndrome.** How many chromosomes were present in the gametes that resulted in a cell with 47 chromosomes?

EXPLAIN

All about Alleles

Activity Overview

In Part I, students will learn how to use a Punnett square to predict the traits of offspring. Then in Part II, students will work in pairs to assume the role of lab technicians who are producing a child through in vitro fertilization. Students will work with index cards that represent alleles. They will draw to learn which alleles a mother and a father have for a list of common genetic traits. They then will simulate the traits an offspring would have if a male gamete joined a female gamete to produce the baby. Students then will simulate what happens to the alleles when their in vitro child grows up and mates with another in vitro person from another team. Students experience how alleles randomly separate during meiosis and then join during fertilization to give an offspring its traits.

Before You Teach

Background Information

In Part I, students will learn to use Punnett squares to predict the traits of offspring. A Punnett square is a tool used by geneticists to predict the possible genotypes of an offspring when the alleles of the parents are known. Because all the potential genotypes are calculated, the odds of an offspring having a specific genotype can be calculated. The Punnett square was designed by Reginald C. Punnett (1875–1967), a British geneticist from Cambridge University. See figure T7.17 for an example. The student book provides instructions on how to fill in a Punnett square.

In Part II, students will determine the traits of offspring using their understanding of meiosis. Refer back to the teacher and student materials from the previous activity, *How Do We Get Our Traits?*, for any information you might need.

Materials—Part I

none

Materials—Part II

For the teacher

5 copies of copymaster 7.3, *Trait Cards*

10 bags

For each team of 2 students

access to sodium benzoate tasting paper

index cards (3×5 in white, blank index cards or 5×7 in white, blank index cards cut in half; 2 different colors, optional)

1 marker

access to 9 bags of chromosomes (each for a different trait)

Advance Preparation

For Part II, purchase sodium benzoate tasting paper.

Make 5 copies of copymaster 7.3, *Trait Cards*. This will give you 15 alleles for each of the 9 traits.

Label bags with the 9 traits given in figure 7.23 of the student book. Cut the cards apart and place in the appropriate bag. Have the materials out and available to the students. You might want to have 2 different colors of index cards for the sex chromosomes. Students will label half the index cards as female and the other half of the cards as male. Separate the XX and XY on the cards and make them look similar to the *Trait Cards*. This will ensure that students can easily cut the cards in half. Place the sex chromosome cards in the remaining bag.

When Meiosis Has a Glitch, continued

1,000 births worldwide. Extra genetic material is responsible for the characteristics of Down syndrome. The severity varies from individual to individual. People with Down syndrome have some degree of mental retardation, slow physical development, and organ abnormalities. The most common physical features of those with Down syndrome include short stature, low muscle tone, and altered facial features. Often, males with Down syndrome are sterile but females may be fertile.

Turner's syndrome occurs when chromosomes fail to separate during meiosis. Normally, chromosome pairs separate before cell division. Occasionally, the two X chromosomes do not separate and eggs are produced with either two X chromosomes or no X chromosomes,

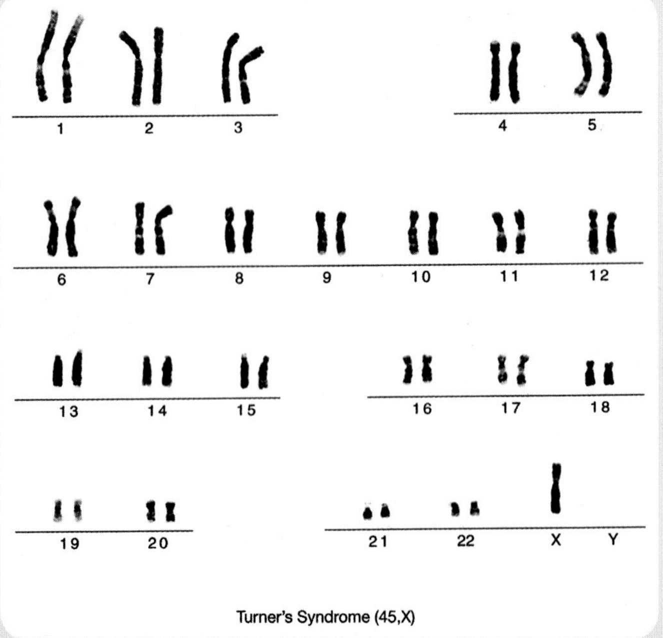

Karyotype of Turner's syndrome. How many chromosomes would be present in a gamete that results in Turner's syndrome?

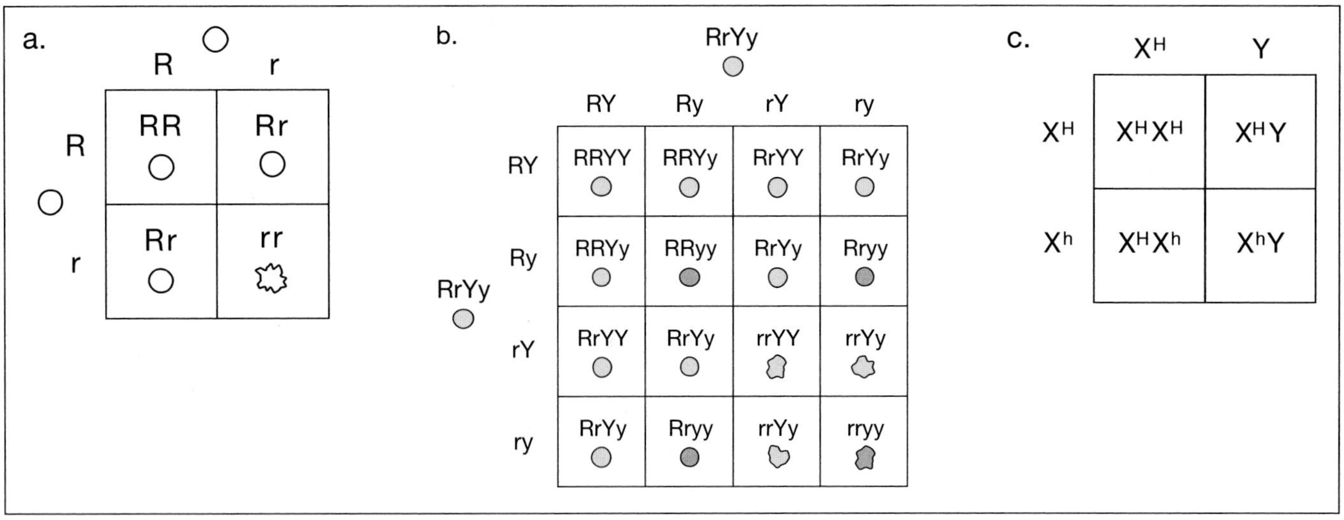

a.

	R	r
R	RR	Rr
r	Rr	rr

b.

RrYy	RY	Ry	rY	ry
RY	RRYY	RRYy	RrYY	RrYy
Ry	RRYy	RRyy	RrYy	Rryy
rY	RrYY	RrYy	rrYY	rrYy
ry	RrYy	Rryy	rrYy	rryy

c.

	X^H	Y
X^H	X^HX^H	X^HY
X^h	X^HX^h	X^hY

Figure T7.17 Examples of Punnett squares. These examples show how Punnett squares can be used to determine the probability of the traits of offspring. (a) When two pea plants with round seeds are crossed, the ratio of round to wrinkled seeds is 3:1. (b) This example shows a dihybrid cross of two pea plants with round, yellow seeds. Both plants are heterozygous for both traits (*RrYy*). In this cross, four phenotypes are possible. The ratio of smooth, yellow to smooth, green to wrinkled, yellow to wrinkled, green seeds is 9:3:3:1. (c) Dihybrid Punnett squares are also used to predict inheritance of sex-linked traits, such as hemophilia. This example shows a male who doesn't have hemophilia (X^HY) and a female who is a carrier for hemophilia (X^HX^h). Daughters of these parents have a 50 percent chance of being a carrier for hemophilia. Sons have a 50 percent chance of having hemophilia.

instead of the normal one X chromosome in an egg. Individuals with Turner's syndrome are born with only one X chromosome, but no second X or Y chromosome.

Turner's syndrome affects approximately 1 out of every 2,500 female live births worldwide. As with Down syndrome, some individuals with Turner's syndrome may have only a few characteristics of the syndrome. Others may have many. Almost all people with Turner's syndrome have short stature and loss of ovarian function, making them sterile, but the severity of these problems varies considerably among individuals. In general, individuals with Turner's syndrome have normal intelligence. This characteristic is different from many other chromosomal syndromes, such as Down syndrome.

You will notice that the chromosomes affected in these instances involve chromosomes that are small. Individuals with too many or too few chromosomes (**aneuploidy**) of the larger pairs likely will not survive. That is because there is a great deal of genetic information in the larger pairs. Many individuals with aneuploidy of the sex chromosomes do not suffer from significant detrimental effects because there is less genetic information on the sex chromosomes than on the others. However, people with aneuploidy of the sex chromosomes are often sterile. If their condition is not severe, people with aneuploidy often lead full and productive lives.

All about Alleles

EXPLAIN

You have learned that an organism's traits are determined by the genes it carries on its chromosomes. You also know how organisms are able to pass their genes from one generation to the next. Even though you have an understanding of how traits are inherited, you still might wonder why some people in a family have a trait while others do not. Much of what we know about human genetics is used to predict what traits we will inherit.

In *All about Alleles*, you will work alone to learn how the traits of offspring can be predicted. Then you will work with a partner to piece together the complicated process of heredity by simulating the inheritance of traits through two generations.

Part I: Punnett Squares

Mendel knew what traits his true-breeding pea plants carried. Do you think he might have been able to predict what traits the offspring from a cross would carry? In this part of the activity, you will learn how predictions can be made.

Cautions

Tasting food items in the lab should not be allowed. However, sodium benzoate tasting paper is designed for use in the lab. The tasting paper should be kept sterile; dispose of the paper in the trash immediately after use.

As You Teach

Outcomes and Indicators of Success

By the end of this activity, students should

1. be able to use a Punnett square to predict the possible outcomes from a cross of parents whose genotype for a trait is known.

   They will demonstrate their ability by

   - creating Punnett squares for a cross of pea plants and a cross of the yeast from the investigation *What Shows Up?*,
   - predicting the possible phenotypes from a cross of pea plants and a cross of the yeast from the *What Shows Up?* investigation, and
   - using their knowledge of possible genotypes based on a known phenotype to create a Punnett square to predict the chance that "Afraid and Wanting to Know More" has MMD.

2. be able to model and describe that transmission of genetic information to offspring occurs through sperm and egg cells that contain only one representative from each chromosome pair.

   They will demonstrate their ability by

   - using a simulation to model how alleles might separate during meiosis, correctly contributing hypothetical alleles to a hypothetical child;
   - applying their knowledge of alleles and phenotypes to determine the traits for a first- and a second-generation child from their simulation; and
   - explaining how the process of meiosis and fertilization was simulated in this activity.

3. understand that a pair of sex chromosomes determines the sex of an individual human. Females have two X chromosomes. Males have an X chromosome and a Y chromosome.

   They will demonstrate their understanding by determining the sex of a hypothetical child in their simulation using a random selection of the X and Y chromosomes.

4. know that there are two alleles for each trait carried in an individual.

   They will demonstrate their knowledge by

   - describing the parent traits and the traits of the first- and second-generation child using two alleles and
   - simulating the formation of an offspring by combining an allele from each parent.

5. be able to use the skills of scientific inquiry and their knowledge about understanding of scientific inquiry.

   They will demonstrate their ability by

   - using tools such as Punnett squares to help make predictions and
   - using a model of alleles to show how they separate during meiosis.

Strategies

Getting Started

Ask students if they think that it is possible to predict whether a trait will appear in the offspring of two organisms. Remind students of Mendel's experiments. When Mendel crossed pea plants with green and yellow seeds, he got plants with all green seeds. Remind students of what happened in the yeast investigation where all the crosses resulted in cream-colored yeast except for red crossed with red. But when Mendel crossed these first-generation plants with green seeds, the result was 75 percent of the plants with green seeds and 25 percent with yellow seeds. By looking at the alleles of the parents, the probability of 75 percent green seeds could be predicted. Tell students that in Part I they will learn how to use a tool that will help them calculate the probability of an offspring's traits.

Process and Procedure

Part I: Punnett Squares

Materials

none

In Step 1, students read about Punnett squares. As students work individually to set up the Punnett square, check to see that they record the alleles correctly. Remind them that the dominant allele for tall plants is represented with a capital letter (*T*) and the recessive allele for short plants is represented with the same letter in lowercase (*t*).

Materials

none

Process and Procedure

1. Read the following paragraph to learn about one of the tools scientists use to make predictions about the traits of offspring.

   Punnett squares are a mathematical tool that provides a way to predict all the possible outcomes for combining alleles from parents in a cross. When you predict something, you make a statement that something will or will not happen with a certain amount of confidence. In the study of heredity, this type of prediction is expressed in terms of **probability**. Probability is an area in mathematics that predicts the chances that a certain event will occur. Geneticists use probability to predict the outcomes of matings.

2. Set up a Punnett square that you can use to predict the results of a cross between a tall heterozygous (hybrid) garden pea plant and a short homozygous recessive garden pea plant. The tall allele is dominant over the short allele. To do this, do the following.
   a. Sketch a Punnett square like the one shown in figure 7.21 in your science notebook.
   b. Determine the alleles of each parent (a tall and a short pea plant) using the information provided about the parent plants.
   c. Write the alleles of one parent across the top of your Punnett square and the alleles of the other parent along the left side of your Punnett square. Make sure you write only 1 allele next to each box.

Only 1 letter goes above or to the left of each box. It does not matter which parent is on the side or the top of the Punnett square.

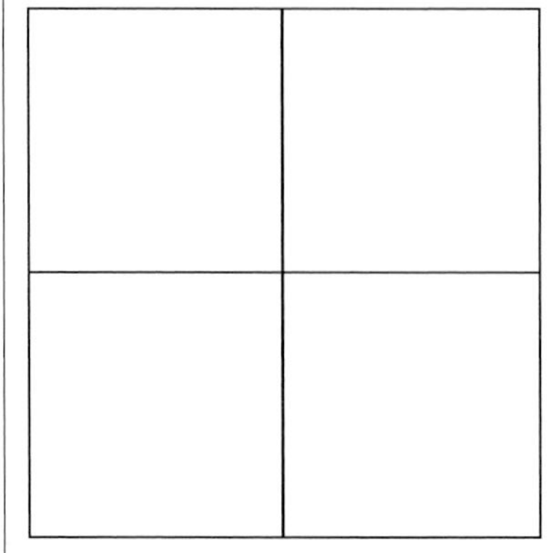

▲ **Figure 7.21 Punnett square.** A Punnett square looks similar to a windowpane.

Answers to Steps 3–4, SE page 371

3. Students' completed Punnett squares from Step 3 should look like the one shown in figure T7.18.

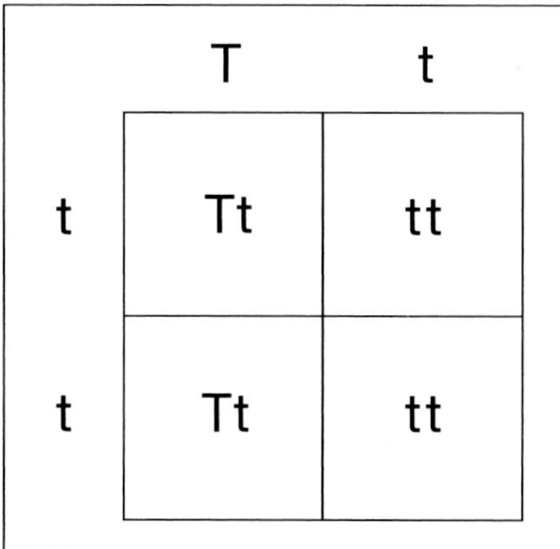

▲ **Figure T7.18 Punnett square of a heterozygous tall pea plant crossed with a homozygous short plant.** Students should draw a Punnett square like this for Step 3.

4a. 3:4, or 75 percent would have the dominant phenotype for height.

4b. 1:4, or 25 percent would have the recessive phenotype for height.

If you think your students might benefit from more experience with Punnett squares, use the optional activity *Can You Sort It Out?* on the *TRCD*.

Answers to Stop and Think—Part I, SE page 371

1. A Punnett square illustrates which alleles are combined. Because the strains represented alleles of the "parents," the alleles of the crossed yeast can be predicted (figure T7.19). Students might also have noticed that the mating grid drawn on the agar plate looked similar to a Punnett square.

	C	c
C	CC	Cc
c	Cc	cc

▲ **Figure T7.19 Punnett square for yeast experiment.** If students struggle with the Punnett square, remind them that the yeast experiment was similar to a cross between heterozygous parents. Students might choose to represent the alleles as shown—*C* for the cream trait because it is dominant and *c* for the red trait because it is recessive. Make sure they have one dominant allele (capital letter) and one recessive (lowercase letter) allele for both parents on the Punnett square.

2. A Punnett square is a useful tool because it allows people to predict what alleles an offspring might have if the alleles of the parents are known. The usefulness of a Punnett square is limited because you have to know what alleles the parents have. Also, if there is more than 1 possible outcome, you don't know which outcome will result from a cross. You can only predict the chance of a particular outcome.

3. Determine the alleles of the offspring by taking each allele from the parent column and combining it with an allele from the parent row in the corresponding square, as shown in figure 7.22. Remember that each parent contributes 1 allele for each trait to the offspring.

The predicted alleles of the offspring are the likely outcome of a cross of a tall and a short pea plant, not the actual outcome.

4. Answer the following questions about your Punnett square for each phenotype.

   What fraction of the offspring would you predict to have each of the following phenotypes? Record your response in your science notebook as a percentage or as a ratio, such as 1:2.

   a. The dominant phenotype for height
   b. The recessive phenotype for height

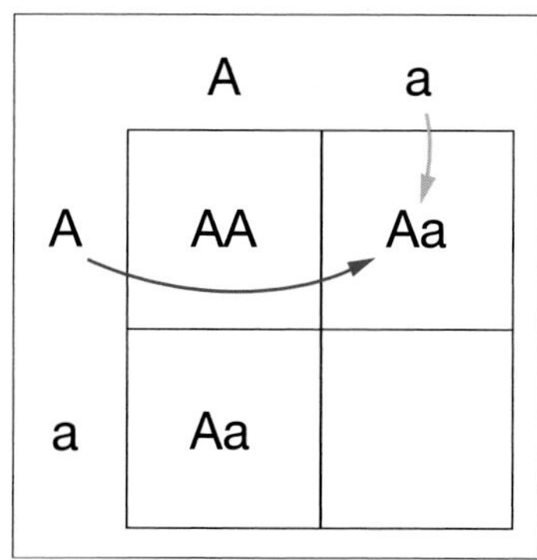

▲ **Figure 7.22 Filling in a Punnett square.** In this example, both parents are heterozygous. They both carry a dominant and a recessive allele (Aa) for a trait. Complete the Punnett square by taking an allele from the top and combining it with an allele from the left. What alleles will the offspring represented by the lower left box have?

Stop & THINK

PART I

Work on the following tasks on your own and record your answers in your science notebook.

1. Think back to the yeast experiment you conducted. How could you have used a Punnett square to predict the outcome of your experiment? Explain your answer and draw a Punnett square to show the predicted outcomes.

   The yeast experiment was similar to a cross between heterozygous parents. Imagine that strain 2 (red color) and strain 3 (cream color) were different alleles of the color trait.

2. Why do you think a Punnett square is a useful predictive tool? Describe in what way you think the usefulness of a Punnett square might be limited.

Process and Procedure

Part II: Making a Human

Materials

For the teacher

5 copies of copymaster 7.3, *Trait Cards*

10 bags

For each team of 2 students

access to sodium benzoate tasting paper

index cards (3×5 in white, blank index cards or 5×7 in white, blank cards cut in half; 2 different colors, optional)

1 marker

access to 9 bags of chromosomes (each for a different trait)

Cautions

Tasting food items in the lab should not be allowed. However, sodium benzoate tasting paper is designed for use in the lab. The tasting paper should be kept sterile; dispose of the paper in the trash immediately after use.

In Step 1, students begin by studying a list of human traits shown in figure 7.23 of the student book. Remind students of Mendel's discoveries about dominant and recessive alleles. Many of them will know about some common human traits. Then in Step 2, students record whether or not they have the dominant or recessive version of the trait and describe anything that surprised them. Provide students with sodium benzoate tasting paper to determine whether they have the dominant or recessive trait for tasting sodium benzoate. Instruct students to dispose of the paper in the trash after they have determined whether they can taste sodium benzoate.

For the students who can taste the paper, the sodium benzoate might taste sweet, salty, or bitter. The paper is tasteless for some individuals.

NOTES:

Part II: Making a Human

Most traits are the result of the interactions of many genes. Geneticists are still working to understand all the interactions. However, there are a few traits or disorders that are better understood because they are the result of different alleles on a single gene, such as the traits of pea plants that Mendel studied. Traits or disorders that are the result of single genes are sometimes called *Mendelian.* Some human traits, such as dimples, also appear to be the result of a single gene and follow dominant or recessive inheritance patterns. To simplify the study of inheritance patterns, you will work with a partner to investigate some human traits that follow these patterns. If the study of genetics interests you, read the sidebar *Careers in Genetics* to learn about the diverse jobs available in the field of genetics.

Materials

For each student

access to sodium benzoate tasting paper

index cards

1 marker

access to 9 bags of chromosomes (each for a different trait)

Cautions

This activity uses sodium benzoate tasting paper. Although food and drink items should not be allowed in the lab, sodium benzoate is designed for use in the lab to test a genetic trait. Use the paper according to your teacher's instructions and then discard it immediately in a trash can.

Process and Procedure

1. Study figure 7.23, which lists 9 common human traits that seem to follow dominant and recessive inheritance patterns.

Human genetics is very complex and often involves more than 2 alleles for a trait. This activity is simplified, but it will give you an idea of how dominant and recessive patterns of inheritance work.

Answers to Step 2, SE page 373

2a. Students should identify the traits they have, and the alleles (provided in figure 7.23 of the student book) should match their traits. Students might have trouble knowing whether they are heterozygous (designated with 1 capital and 1 lowercase letter) for a dominant trait or homozygous dominant (2 capital letters) for that same trait. There really is no way of knowing without further investigation, so tell them to write down both possibilities.

2b. They might find the fact that polydactyly (6 fingers) is a dominant trait rather interesting. You may want to explain that being dominant does not mean that the trait is expressed more often than a recessive trait. Students will gain an understanding of this concept in the next activity. (Let's say a population has 10 people and 1 person has polydactyly and has the alleles *Hh*. Everyone else would be *hh*. The allele frequency would not change in a stable population without some selective pressure.) Acknowledge a variety of answers that are well supported. Students might find other traits surprising such as the presence or lack of mid-digit hair or that not having MMD is a recessive trait.

In Step 3, explain to students that they will simulate making a hypothetical human with some common traits through in vitro fertilization. Let students know that human genetics is quite complex and that there are many gene interactions. The traits they will study follow dominant and recessive inheritance patterns, but the gene functions are more complex than they appear. If students are unfamiliar with in vitro fertilization, take time to explain that it is one of several reproductive technology techniques used to help infertile couples conceive a child. Then tell students to draw a data table in their science notebooks like the one shown in figure 7.24 of the student book. Students will title this table "First Generation." They should decide who will work with the sperm and who will work with the egg.

Trait	Dominant	Recessive
Dimples	Having dimples (DD or Dd)	No dimples (dd)
Ear lobes	Free (EE or Ee)	Attached (ee)
Mid-digit hair	Having mid-digit hair (MM or Mm)	No mid-digit hair (mm)
Freckles	Freckles (FF or Ff)	No freckles (ff)
Number of fingers	6 on each hand (HH or Hh)	5 on each hand (hh)
Chin	Dimple in center cleft (CC or Cc)	No dimple in center (cc)
Taster of Sodium Benzoate	Can taste (TT or Tt)	Cannot taste (tt)
Albinism	Has pigmentation (PP or Pp)	Lacks pigments (pp)
MMD (also called Steinhart's disease)	Having MMD (SS or Ss)	Not having MMD (ss)

▲ **Figure 7.23 Common human traits.** These traits seem to follow dominant and recessive inheritance patterns. What do you notice about the genotypes for dominant traits compared with recessive traits?

2. Answer the following questions about the traits in figure 7.23. Record your answers in your science notebook.
   a. Which of the traits listed in the chart do you have? According to the chart, what are your alleles for each of these traits?

   If you have not already done so, obtain sodium benzoate tasting paper from your teacher. Use the paper according to your teacher's instructions to determine whether you have the dominant or recessive trait for tasting sodium benzoate.

   b. Did any of these traits or dominant and recessive patterns surprise you? Why?
3. Simulate with a partner how alleles might separate during meiosis and randomly recombine during fertilization. Steps 3a–c will help guide your work.
   a. Assume the roles of lab technicians who are making a human by uniting a donated sperm and an egg cell in the lab. When this is done to help infertile couples conceive a child, it is known as in vitro fertilization.
   b. Make a data table that looks like figure 7.24 in your science notebook. Title it "First Generation."
   c. Decide which one of you will work with the sperm cell and which one will work with the egg cell.

This is a simulation involving cards that represent alleles. You will not be working with real cells.

NOTES:

NOTES:

In Step 4, make the materials available to students. Explain to students that they are simulating the production of an offspring by *arbitrarily* choosing parental alleles. The students are not the parents. This can be a touchy subject. Explain that the cards represent a chromosome pair. Students should use index cards to create the sex chromosomes for the hypothetical parents. As students work on this step, ask the following probing questions:

- "What does cutting the sex chromosome card in half represent in the process of meiosis?"
- "What part of meiosis is not being modeled?"

Students should understand that cutting the sex chromosome card in half represents the division of a cell in meiosis and results in cells with the haploid number of chromosomes. The doubling of the chromosomes has not been modeled.

Tell students to choose the chromosomes randomly because this simulates what happens in real life. Once both team members (lab technicians) have determined the sex chromosomes of the child, they should record the sex of the child in their data tables.

Trait	Father's alleles	Father's allele contributed to child	Mother's alleles	Mother's allele contributed to child	Child's alleles	Trait expressed in child
Sex						
Dimples						
Ear lobes						
Mid-digit hair						
Freckles						
Number of fingers						
Chin						
Taster of Sodium Benzoate						
Albinism						
MMD						

▲ **Figure 7.24 First-generation traits.** Use a table similar to this one to record the alleles of the parents and a child.

4. Determine the gender of the new offspring by completing Steps 4a–g.
   a. Use index cards to represent chromosome pairs. Each index card (chromosome pair) carries 2 alleles, 1 for each chromosome.
   b. Obtain an index card to represent each parent.
   c. Label the cards as follows. The technician on your team who works with the female gamete (egg) labels that card with two *X*s for sex chromosomes. The technician on your team who works with the male gamete (sperm) labels one-half of that card with *X* and the other half with *Y*.
   d. Cut the mother's and father's sex chromosomes in half. What does this step represent in the process of meiosis?
   e. Place the sex chromosome cards face down, so that the blank side of the cards faces up.
   f. Shuffle your 2 cards by yourself and randomly choose 1 chromosome without looking. Place it on the table in front of you face down.

Recall from your reading that chromosomes separate randomly during meiosis and might combine during fertilization. In this step, you are simulating how this might happen.

   g. Turn your card and your partner's card over. What sex is the new child? Fill in the information in your data table.

NOTES:

5. Determine the other traits of the child by completing Steps 5a–c. Determining the other traits of the child is a little more difficult because you need to know the alleles of the parent gametes.
   a. Draw a chromosome pair from the teacher's bag of cards to learn what alleles each parent carries for dimples. Each chromosome carries 1 allele.

The technician working with the sperm cell draws the chromosome pair for the father. The technician working with the egg cell draws the chromosome pair for the mother. Each technician keeps his or her own chromosome pair.

   b. Fill in this information for the mother's and father's alleles in your data table.
   c. Repeat Steps 5a–b for the remaining traits.
6. How will you know which alleles are passed on to the child? Recall that humans have pairs of chromosomes and they receive 1 chromosome of each pair from their mother and the other from their father. Complete the following tasks to find out.
   a. Cut the father's and mother's chromosome pairs for dimples in half. What does this step represent in the process of meiosis?
   b. Turn upside down your pair of chromosomes that carries the alleles for dimples, so that you cannot see the alleles. Shuffle them as you did for the sex chromosomes. Randomly choose an allele and place it face down on the table in front of you.
   c. Turn over the cards after both technicians have contributed an allele for dimples. Record the allele for dimples that is contributed from each parent in your data table.
   d. Combine the 2 contributed alleles in the column labeled "Child's Alleles." This step simulates the chromosomes coming together during fertilization.
   e. Begin a stack of cards that represents the child's chromosomes. Place the "unused" alleles in another stack and put them aside.
   f. Repeat Steps 6a–e for the remaining traits. When you are finished, you should have 1 pile of chromosome cards on the desk that represents all the alleles of the offspring.
7. Use the information in figure 7.24 to determine the traits the child expresses based on his or her allele pairs. Record the traits, such as dimples or no dimples, in your data table.

Congratulations! You have made a new human being.

8. Place the chromosomes not used in a stack and put them aside. Keep the chromosomes of the child in a stack. You will follow them into the next generation.

In Step 5, students determine the traits of the parents by drawing from the bags of alleles you have provided. Remind students to fill in their data tables with the traits of the mother and father. Then in Step 6, teams randomly determine which allele will be contributed to the child from each parent. Once they know the child's alleles for all 9 traits, in Step 7, they record the traits expressed, or the phenotype, of the child.

In Step 8, once each team creates its child, help the students find another team with a child of the opposite sex. If there is an unequal male-to-female ratio of in vitro children, you could have students wait until one group is finished. Then you could have students imagine that a parent got a divorce and remarried and has a new mate. Students determine the traits for a second-generation child by "mating" their team's in vitro child with another team's in vitro child. Tell them to create another data table titled "Second Generation" and then fill in the data table following the same process they used for the first-generation child.

Answers to Reflect and Connect, SE page 376

1. Student drawings should show the traits listed in their tables for the second generation. Make sure students label all the traits of the second-generation child.
2. Students simulated meiosis by shuffling their chromosomes and randomly choosing one. In meiosis, the chromosome pairs separate and only 1 of each pair is used in the formation of a gamete. Students simulated fertilization when they tossed the selected chromosomes on the desk and put them in pairs to find out the traits that the new child has. In fertilization, the gametes fuse, giving the new baby a complete set of chromosomes.
3. Students should recognize that their simulation of meiosis is simplified compared with what happens in the human body. They only had to manipulate cards that represented a pair of sex chromosomes and 9 pairs of autosomes. The human body has 46 chromosomes, 22 pairs of autosomes and 1 pair of sex chromosomes. Students might also explain that each autosome only carried the gene for 1 trait, when autosomes actually carry numerous genes.
4. There are actually 2 ways students can answer this question because we do not know which alleles the father has. We know he is not *ss* because he has MMD and MMD is a dominant trait. We do not know, however, if the father is *SS* or *Ss*. Students may come up with different Punnett squares, but figure T7.20 shows how the alleles could be matched up. We know that the mother is *ss* because she does not have MMD.

a.

mother \ father	S	S
s	Ss	Ss
s	Ss	Ss

b.

mother \ father	S	s
s	Ss	ss
s	Ss	ss

▲ **Figure T7.20 MMD Punnett square.** (a) If the father is *SS*, there is a 100 percent chance that "Afraid and Wanting to Know More" has inherited MMD. (b) If the father is *Ss*, there is a 50 percent chance that "Afraid and Wanting to Know More" has MMD.

9. Determine the traits for a second-generation child by doing the following.
   a. Gather the first-generation child's chromosomes and separate them into their chromosome pairs.
   b. Find another team that has a child with the opposite sex of your team's child. Ask your teacher for help if you cannot find a child of the opposite sex.
   c. Pretend the in vitro child has grown up and is married to the other team's child. The two are now going to have a child.
   d. Make another data table in your notebook like figure 7.24. Title it "Second Generation."
   e. You already know the alleles that each parent has for each trait. Record this information in your second-generation data chart.
   f. Starting with the sex chromosomes, and using the chromosomes from each team's children, repeat the procedure you followed for the first in vitro child. With the cards face down, shuffle the chromosome pairs and randomly choose 1 chromosome from each pair. Look at the resulting pair of chromosomes and record them on your data table.
   g. Complete the remainder of your data table to determine the traits of the second-generation child.

Reflect and Connect

Work on your own to answer the following questions in your science notebook. Be prepared to share your understanding with your classmates.

1. Draw a picture of the second-generation child from Part II that shows off his or her traits. Label the traits he or she carries, including those that are not apparent.
2. Outline the steps of the simulation and describe how they simulated the processes of meiosis and fertilization.
3. Compare the simulation with what actually happens during meiosis in humans.

Think about the number of chromosomes (autosomes and sex chromosomes) in the simulation compared with the number of chromosomes in the human body.

4. If the mother of "Afraid and Wanting to Know More" from the engage activity earlier in this chapter does not have MMD, what are the chances that "Afraid and Wanting to Know More" has the disorder? Draw a Punnett square from this investigation that shows how you arrived at your answer.

Refer back to figure 7.23 if you do not remember what the alleles are for a person who has or does not have MMD.

NOTES:

Careers in Genetics

SIDEBAR

Do you find genetics interesting? If you do, many career options exist in a variety of areas such as medicine, pharmaceuticals, law, agriculture, and business. Depending on what career you are interested in you need different kinds of training.

Medical technicians are sometimes involved in the field of genetics. For example, technicians called phlebotomists collect blood samples from patients, which can be used for genetic testing. Technicians generally have an associate's degree from a community college or a certificate from a hospital or technical school. Medical technicians need to have good eyesight, steady hands, and the ability to follow procedures accurately.

Forensic science technicians examine biological evidence from crime scenes to identify individuals. They also provide testimony on laboratory findings for criminal cases. Forensic science technicians generally have either an associate's degree or a bachelor's degree.

Genetics technologists study the morphology or structure of chromosomes and their relationship to disease. A technologist prepares cell samples for analysis. Genetics technologists analyze the samples using microscopes and computer image analysis. An important part of their job is generating reports that outline the results from their analysis. Technologists usually have a bachelor's degree with a major in medical technology or one of the life sciences.

Remember "Afraid and Wanting to Know More" from the first activity? He wrote to a genetic counselor about his concerns regarding a genetic disorder he might have inherited from his father. Genetic counselors try to help people make sense of what scientists know about genetic disorders. They look at an individual's family history, interpret information about a disorder, explain the inheritance patterns (see photo), and review the options for genetic testing. They also help individuals and families cope with changes to their life that may occur after learning test results. Genetic counseling is a good career if you are interested in genetics but would also like to interact with people. In the future, jobs in genetic counseling may become more common as the use of genetic testing increases. Genetic counselors must have a master's degree in genetic counseling.

The business world requires people with an understanding of genetics as well. With a bachelor's degree in a biological science, you can work in a variety of areas such as management, marketing, writing, sales, and public relations. Many agricultural, biotechnology, and pharmaceutical companies need individuals with an understanding of genetics to help them better market and sell their products. For example, agricultural companies might want to sell seeds for a new corn plant that is drought resistant. Some lawyers also need to be familiar with genetics. Ethical and legal issues associated with genetics arise and require the expertise of lawyers. Patent lawyers also are important for determining intellectual property such as new processes or products developed by genetics researchers.

If you would like to conduct research to understand genetic disorders and improve

ELABORATE

Inheritance Patterns

Activity Overview

In *Inheritance Patterns*, students will gain an understanding of a pedigree and how to use pedigrees to study patterns of inheritance. In Part I, students will look for patterns in three pedigrees. After reading short descriptions of the patterns of inheritance, students will determine the pattern of inheritance for each pedigree. In Part II, students then will apply their knowledge of inheritance patterns by making a pedigree based on a description of a trait that runs in a family. This activity pulls together the concepts that the students have learned about genetics thus far, so they can see how inheritance patterns follow through generations.

Before You Teach

Background Information

The principles behind genetic inheritance are quite complex. Once general principles are understood, inheritance patterns are more easily understood. Inheritance patterns are determined by looking at the occurrence of a trait in several individuals within a family, across as many generations as possible. This information can be displayed on a pedigree. Pedigrees are a graphical representation of the family history of a trait. Pedigrees are used to find out how a trait is passed on through a family—what the inheritance pattern is. In pedigrees, a square represents males and a circle represents females. If the square or circle is darkened, that individual is affected—he or she has the trait that we are following. Some individuals are carriers of a trait, meaning they have one of the two alleles that cause the trait. Geneticists often study pedigrees to learn how a trait is inherited or to predict the likelihood of someone inheriting a trait.

Students will investigate three inheritance patterns: autosomal dominant, autosomal recessive, and sex-linked recessive. Autosomal traits are caused by genes on autosomes; sex-linked traits are caused by genes on one of the sex chromosomes. Most inherited diseases are caused by genes on autosomes because there are 22 pairs of autosomes compared with only one pair of sex chromosomes. Of the sex-linked traits, most are X-linked because the X chromosome holds more genes than the Y chromosome. X-linked traits can be dominant or recessive. Students will only be exposed to the X-linked recessive inheritance pattern in this chapter. See copymaster 7.4, *Pedigree* for a detailed list of characteristics for the three inheritance patterns.

Traits can also be inherited through mitochondrial inheritance. DNA is found in mitochondria as well as in the nucleus of a cell. The genes present in mitochondria are only inherited through the egg because sperm do not contribute mitochondria to a zygote. As a result, traits carried on mitochondrial genes can only be inherited from the female. Very few human genetic disorders are caused by mitochondrial genes.

Materials—Part I

For each student

1 copy of copymaster 7.4, *Pedigree*

Advance Preparation

Make 1 copy of copymaster 7.4, *Pedigree* for each student.

Materials—Part II

None

Careers in Genetics, continued

human health, you might be interested in becoming a medical scientist. They work in government, private company, or university laboratories exploring new areas of research. For example, a new field in the drug industry is pharmacogentics. Pharmacogentics is the study of how genes influence an individual's response to drugs. Individuals respond to the same drugs and dosages in different ways because of genetic variations among the human population. Scientists working in this field research how medications can be adjusted based on genetic factors. Medical scientists require a doctor's degree (PhD) in a life science to gain the skills necessary to direct research programs. Often medical scientists have a medical degree as well. A medical degree is necessary if the scientist will interact directly with patients. For example, a medical scientist might need to dispense gene therapy or perform procedures to remove tissue.

Many jobs are available in the field of genetics. The education required to enter this field varies depending on the job. Some require a doctor's degree, but many jobs are available for individuals with an associates or bachelor's degree. No matter what career route you choose, a good background in math and science during high school is important for working in the field of genetics.

SCI LINKS NSTA
Topic: genetic counseling
Go to: www.scilinks.org
Code: 2Inquiry378

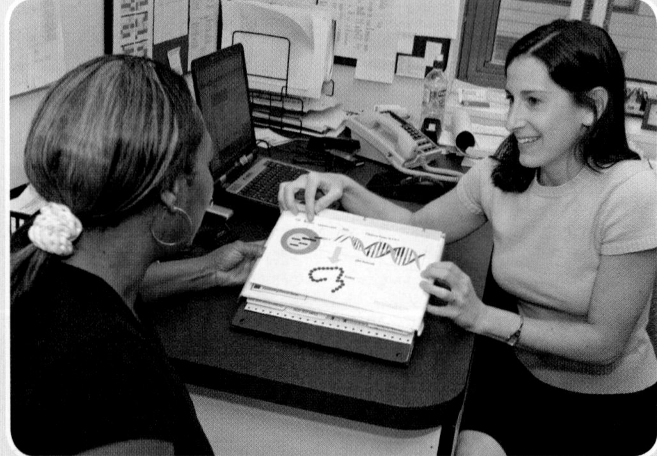

▲ **Genetic counselor.** Genetic counselors describe the genetic disorder and how it is inherited and help an individual decide if he or she wants to be tested for the disorder.

Educational Technologies

To give students practice working with pedigrees and seeing how which traits for one generation are passed to another, they can work with the *Can You Sort It Out?* activity on the *TRCD*.

As You Teach

Outcomes and Indicators of Success

By the end of this activity, students should

1. be able to apply their knowledge of inheritance patterns as they create and interpret a human pedigree.

   They will demonstrate their ability by
   - analyzing generic pedigrees and describing patterns in the way a trait is passed to each generation;
   - labeling the alleles on three pedigrees;
   - using information about three inheritance patterns (autosomal dominant, autosomal recessive, and sex-linked recessive) to infer which inheritance pattern is described in a statement;
   - drawing a pedigree and labeling the alleles of individuals on the pedigree based on a description of members of a family who have the red-green color blindness trait; and
   - explaining how a pedigree is used to illustrate inheritance.
2. be able to distinguish between an autosomal trait and a sex-linked trait.

   They will demonstrate their ability by
   - correctly identifying sex-linked versus autosomal inheritance patterns in pedigrees,
   - contrasting the inheritance pattern of sex-linked traits with the inheritance pattern of autosomal traits, and
   - correctly identifying the pattern of Ben and Chris's family as sex-linked recessive.
3. be able to distinguish between a dominant trait and a recessive trait.

   They will demonstrate their understanding by
   - correctly identifying autosomal dominant and autosomal recessive patterns of inheritance in pedigrees and
   - contrasting dominant trait patterns with recessive trait patterns.
4. be able to apply their knowledge of alleles, genotype, and phenotype and demonstrate that traits are passed from generation to generation.

   They will demonstrate their ability by
   - explaining why a male fruit fly with the genotype X^RY has white eyes,
   - creating pedigrees by correctly combining alleles from parents to show all the possible traits their offspring might carry, and
   - describing that pedigrees are useful tools to illustrate inheritance patterns because they allow us to see how a trait is passed from generation to generation.
5. be able to use the skills of scientific inquiry and their knowledge about understanding of scientific inquiry.

   They will demonstrate their ability by using tools such as pedigree analysis to help make predictions.

Inheritance Patterns

ELABORATE

Observing patterns is an important part of science. By making many observations, scientists have noticed patterns among family members and their ancestors. By continuing to look at these patterns, scientists now have a better understanding of inheritance. In the previous activities, you observed how traits are passed from one generation to the next. You also learned that tools such as Punnett squares are used to make predictions about the traits that will be inherited. Another tool used by geneticists is a pedigree. In this activity, you will work with a partner to use pedigrees to help you identify patterns of inheritance and make predictions based on these patterns.

Part I: Interpreting a Pedigree

In Part I, you will look at a new tool, called a pedigree, and begin to understand how certain traits follow patterns. You will then be able to apply this knowledge to create a pedigree in Part II.

Materials

For each student

1 *Pedigree* handout

Process and Procedure

1. Read the following 2 paragraphs and check your understanding of inheritance and pedigrees with your partner.

   Inheritance is the process through which characteristics of an organism are passed from one generation to the next. "Afraid and Wanting to Know More" from the engage activity was concerned that he had inherited MMD. A disorder is genetically linked, which means that it can be inherited, when the trait can be passed from one generation to the next by a specific gene or set of genes. If a pattern of inheritance is determined for a disorder, this information can be used to predict the risk of future generations inheriting the disorder.

   One way to determine the pattern of inheritance for a disorder is to look at its occurrence within a family across multiple generations. The information is drawn up using a tool called a pedigree. Geneticists use pedigrees to study the inheritance of genes in humans. A **pedigree** is very similar to a family tree, except that a pedigree is a tool that is used to follow a trait through multiple generations of a family. You also might be familiar with the use of pedigrees by dog or horse breeders. Figure 7.25 shows an example of a dog pedigree and a family tree.

NOTES:

Strategies

Getting Started

Ask students if they are aware of particular disorders that are inherited other than MMD. Have them give you examples of disorders. Explain to students that a disorder or a disease is any condition that impairs normal functioning of the body. They might mention asthma, diabetes, heart disease, cystic fibrosis, AIDS, or breast cancer. Discuss how they might go about determining whether a condition was inherited.

Students might know about tracing family lines. Explain that they are now going to apply their knowledge of genetic principles to understand how traits are passed from generation to generation.

Process and Procedure

Part I: Interpreting a Pedigree

Materials

For each student

1 copy of copymaster 7.4, *Pedigree*

Have students work with their partners from Part II of the previous activity. Instruct students to read the paragraphs about pedigrees. In Step 2, students learn how to read pedigrees. Make sure students understand what each of the symbols means. Students might not be familiar with the term *carrier*. Explain that heterozygous individuals, for example, yellow-colored peas with the *Yy* genotype, exhibit the dominant

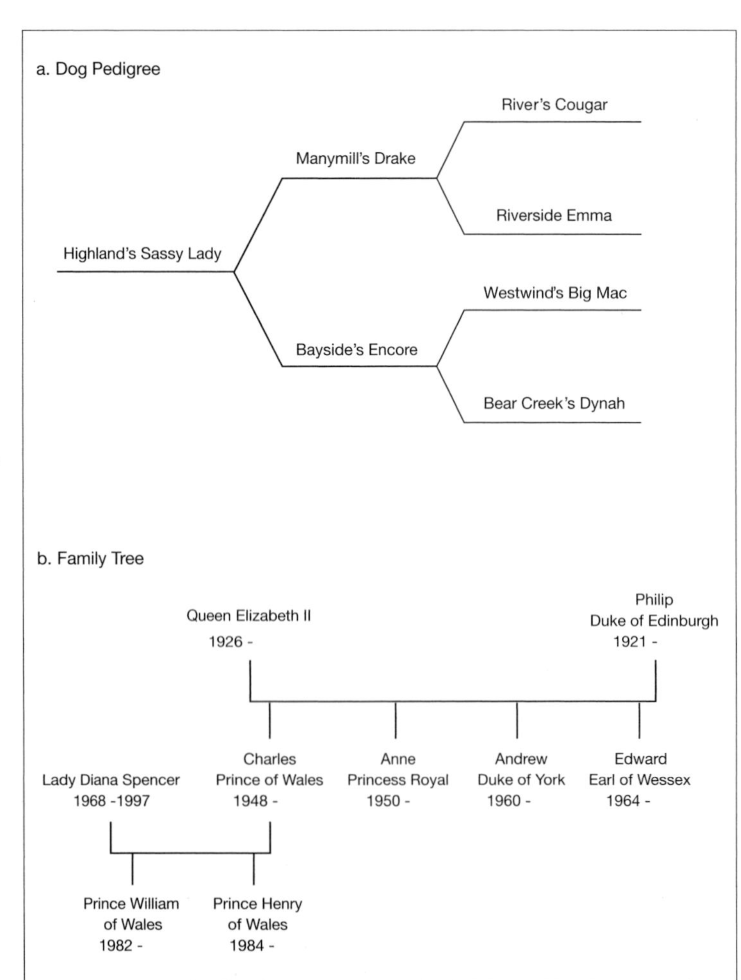

▲ **Figure 7.25 Dog pedigree and family tree.** (a) Dog pedigrees show the male's name on the top part of the branches. Females are shown on the bottom part of the branches. You might notice that dogs are often given unusual names that include the name of the kennel that owns the dog. (b) Family trees, such as this one shown of the British royal family, often show the birth and death dates for each of the individuals on the tree. Notice that the pedigree and the family tree do not have information about genetics.

380 Unit 2 Inside Life

yellow color trait, but also *carry* the recessive green color trait.

Then in Step 3, students describe the patterns they observe in the pedigrees shown in figure 7.27 of the student book. They should record their ideas in their science notebooks.

Answers to Step 3, SE page 381

3. Student answers might vary slightly, but common answers include the following:
   - Pedigree A: The trait is evenly distributed among males and females. There are no carriers.
   - Pedigree B: More females than males have the trait. There are no carriers.
   - Pedigree C: The trait is evenly distributed between males and females. The carriers are also evenly distributed between males and females.

In Step 4, students then read a description of characteristics that describe 3 patterns of inheritance. Encourage students to use what they already know to guide them in understanding the patterns of inheritance. Students should check their understanding with a partner and answer the questions in Step 4.

Answers to Step 4, SE page 381

4a. Pedigree B shows a sex-linked trait.

4b. Pedigree A shows an autosomal dominant trait.

4c. Pedigree C shows an autosomal recessive trait.

NOTES:

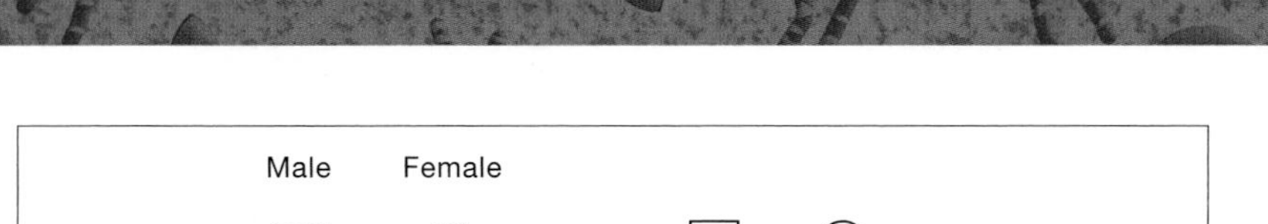

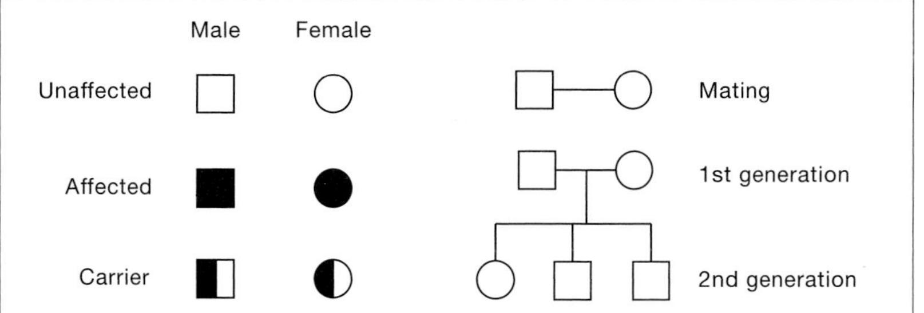

▲ **Figure 7.26 Symbols used in pedigrees.** Pedigrees make it easier to look at the occurrence of a trait within a family. The trait might be a physical characteristic such as eye color, or the trait might be a disease. Unaffected individuals do not express the trait. Affected individuals express the trait. Carriers carry the trait, but do not express the trait. A horizontal line between a circle and a square indicates mating; vertical lines indicate the children from the mating.

2. Study figure 7.26 to learn what each of the symbols used in a pedigree represents. You will use this information to interpret pedigrees in the steps that follow.
3. Study the pedigrees shown in figure 7.27. Do you notice any patterns? Describe patterns that you observe in the way the trait is passed to each generation. Record your ideas in your science notebook.
4. Read the following descriptions and decide which of the pedigrees from figure 7.27 shows the inheritance pattern for the following.
   a. A sex-linked trait
   b. An autosomal dominant trait
   c. An autosomal recessive trait

Use what you know about dominant and recessive traits. Which of the traits in Mendel's experiments skipped a generation: the dominant trait or the recessive trait?

Some traits are **sex linked.** A sex-linked trait is carried on one of the sex chromosomes. A common sex-linked (in this case, X-linked) trait is color blindness. The gene for color blindness is carried on the X chromosome, but not the Y chromosome. Most sex-linked traits are located on the X chromosome. The X chromosome is longer and holds more genes than the Y chromosome. Recall from reading about meiosis that 22 of the 23 pairs of human chromosomes are called autosomes. Autosomal traits are carried on any chromosome other than a sex chromosome. Traits can be **autosomal dominant** or **autosomal recessive.**

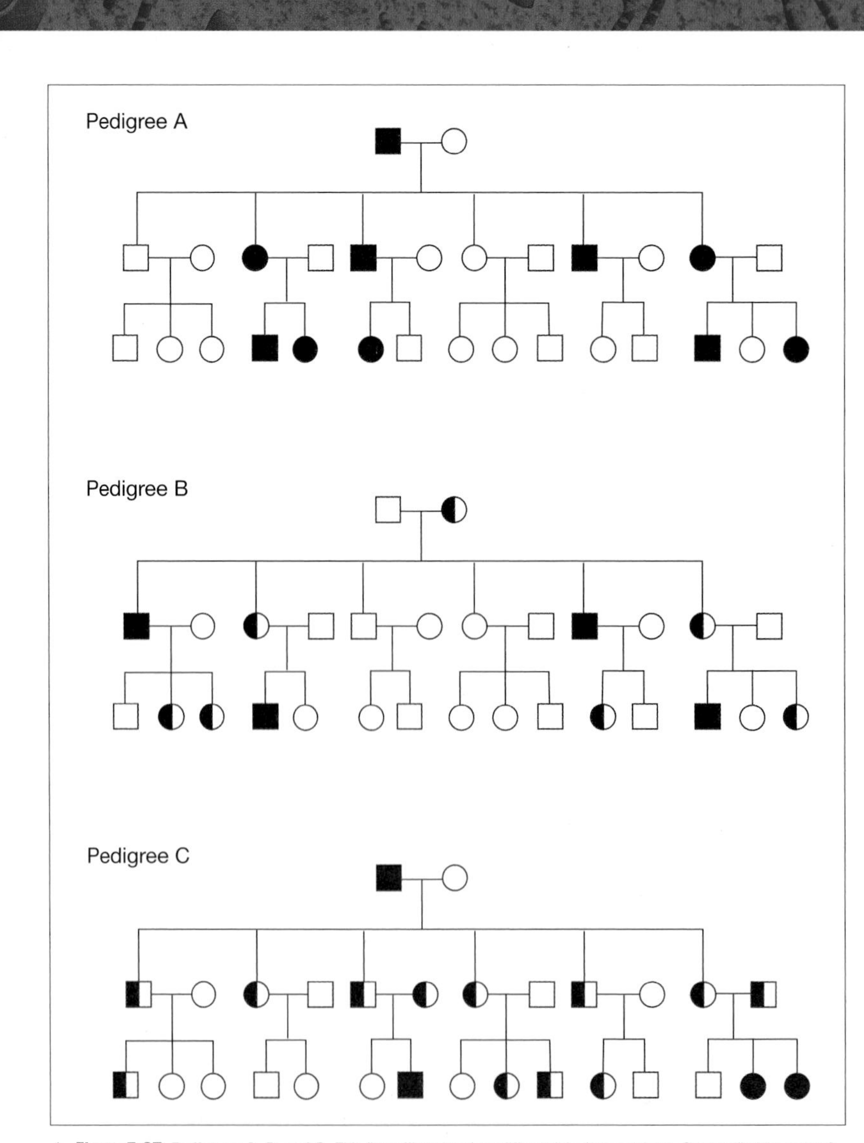

▲ **Figure 7.27 Pedigrees A, B, and C.** This figure illustrates three different inheritance patterns. Can you find the pattern?

NOTES:

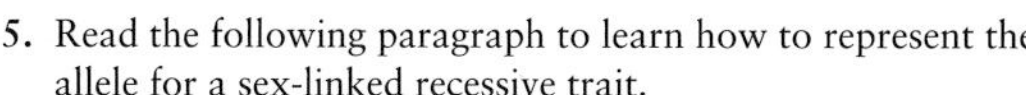

5. Read the following paragraph to learn how to represent the allele for a sex-linked recessive trait.

   You just learned that some traits are carried on one of the sex chromosomes. Most of these traits are **X-linked recessive**, like color blindness discussed in the previous step. One example of a sex-linked trait is fruit fly eye color. The eye color gene for fruit flies is carried on the X chromosome, making it an X-linked trait. The X chromosome carrying a dominant red eye allele is symbolized by X^R. If the X chromosome carries the recessive white eye allele, it is symbolized by X^r. Study figure 7.28 to learn which genotypes have the red eye trait and which genotypes have the white eye trait.

6. Answer the following questions about sex-linked recessive traits.
   a. Why do you think the male fruit fly with the genotype X^rY has white eyes?
   b. What genotype do you think a female fruit fly would have if she had white eyes?
   c. Why do you think eye color in fruit flies is called an X-linked recessive trait?

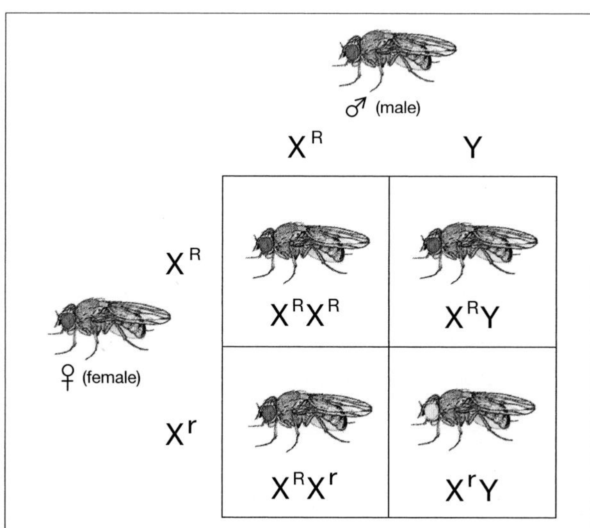

Figure 7.28
Fruit fly Punnett square. Eye color in fruit flies is an X-linked trait. The X chromosome carries the allele for eye color.

In Step 5, students learn how the alleles of sex-linked, specifically X-linked, traits are represented. Then they answer a few questions about sex-linked traits in Step 6.

Answers to Step 6, SE page 383

6a. Males with the genotype X^rY have white eyes because they have an X chromosome with the white eye allele. Because the Y chromosome does not carry a gene for eye color, the white eye color allele is expressed.

6b. Females with the genotype X^rX^r would have white eyes because both X chromosomes have the allele for white eyes.

6c. Eye color in fruit flies is called an X-linked recessive trait because the white eye trait is only expressed if the allele for red eyes is not present. Red eyes are dominant over white eyes.

In Step 7, distribute copymaster 7.4, *Pedigree.* The copymaster includes pedigrees of 3 disorders, 1 for each inheritance pattern. Each pedigree includes a list of the characteristics of its inheritance pattern. Tell students to study the pedigrees carefully and find the characteristics. In Step 8, teams use what they have learned to decide whether statements describe an autosomal dominant, autosomal recessive, or sex-linked pattern of inheritance. As students analyze the pedigrees, observe them applying the rules and general terms associated with inheritance. Look at the patterns of inheritance they choose for each statement and read the reasoning behind their choices.

Answers to Step 8, SE page 384

8a. If brothers and sisters are equally likely to have the trait, it could be autosomal dominant or autosomal recessive.

8b. If all family members from all generations have the trait, it would be autosomal dominant.

8c. If the trait can be inherited from either parent, it could be autosomal dominant or autosomal recessive.

8d. If men in the family are more likely to have the trait, it would be sex-linked recessive.

8e. If the trait might appear in offspring without appearing in their parents, it could be autosomal recessive or sex-linked recessive.

Answers to Stop and Think—Part I, SE page 384

1. Autosomal traits do not depend on gender. Males and females are equally likely to get the trait. Autosomal traits are carried on the autosomes. Sex-linked (X-linked) traits are carried on the sex chromosomes.
2. In the dominant pattern, the trait is expressed in every generation. In the recessive pattern, the trait skips a generation.

3a. Figure T7.21 shows the Punnett square for fruit flies where the parents' genotypes are X^RY and X^rX^r. The possible genotypes are X^rX^R and X^rY.

3b. The phenotype for X^rX^R is red eyes. The phenotype for X^rY is white eyes.

3c. The probability of both genotypes is 1:2 or 50 percent.

4. A person with two dominant alleles cannot be a carrier because they express the trait. For a person to be a carrier, they can only carry one version of an allele.

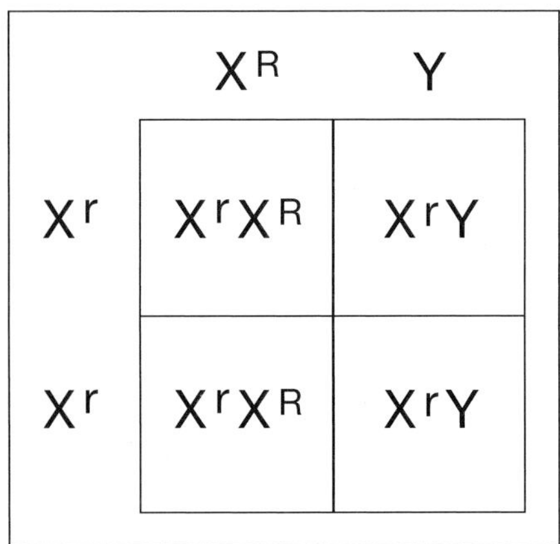

	X^R	Y
X^r	X^rX^R	X^rY
X^r	X^rX^R	X^rY

▲ **Figure T7.21 Punnett square for fruit flies with parents with the genotypes X^RY and X^rX^r.** Students should draw a Punnett square like this for Step 3c.

7. Study the inheritance patterns in the *Pedigree* handout. Use the information provided to do Steps 7a–c.
   a. Find the characteristics described for each inheritance pattern.
   b. Make notes on the handout indicating each characteristic.
   c. Label the alleles of each individual on the pedigree. For simplicity, use *A* and *a* as the alleles.
8. With a partner, use the handout and what you already know about inheritance to decide if each statement describes an autosomal dominant, autosomal recessive, or sex-linked recessive pattern. Some might describe more than 1 pattern. Record your answers in your science notebook.
   a. Brothers and sisters are equally likely to have the trait.
   b. Family members from all generations have the trait.
   c. The trait can be inherited from either parent.
   d. Men in the family are more likely to have the trait.
   e. The trait might appear in offspring without appearing in their parents.

Stop & THINK

PART I

1. What are some differences between the patterns of sex-linked traits and those of autosomal traits?
2. What are some differences between dominant and recessive trait patterns?
3. Create a Punnett square for fruit flies where the parents' genotypes are X^RY and X^rX^r and answer the following questions.
   a. What are the possible genotypes?
   b. What is the phenotype for each genotype?
   c. What is the probability of each genotype occurring?
4. Explain why a person with two dominant alleles cannot be a carrier.

384 Unit 2 Inside Life

NOTES:

Part II: Making a Pedigree

Materials

none

In Step 1, students read a story about Ben, a high school student who finds out that he has inherited a genetic trait. Then in Step 2, students work with their partners to draw Ben's pedigree. In Step 3, students draw a Punnett square for Ben's parents. By reviewing the pedigrees and Punnett squares that they generate, you will determine their understanding of genetic principles as applied to inheritance patterns.

Part II: Making a Pedigree

In Part II of this investigation, you will apply your understanding of alleles and pedigrees to make your own pedigree.

Materials

none

Process and Procedure

1. Read the following story about Ben, a high school student who finds out that he has inherited a genetic disorder.

    During his senior year of high school, Ben started weighing his options for life after graduation. First Ben thought about finding a job. Then he decided to check the possibility of attending college. Ben applied to a variety of colleges throughout the United States. As Ben began receiving acceptance letters in the mail, he was not satisfied with any of his choices.

    Eventually, he decided to take advantage of his excellent grades and pursue a passion for flying. Ben visited and applied to the U.S. Air Force Academy.

    Ben was accepted into the academy but he still needed to pass one more test: a full physical exam. He passed the physical without any problems except for the eye exam. It turned out that Ben's eyesight was fabulous. The problem was his ability to distinguish between colors. What appears red and green to many of us does not appear the same to Ben.

    Ben already had a private flying license and had been flying for 2 years. Ben can still fly airplanes privately, but he cannot enter the Air Force Academy. Ben's mother remembered that Ben's cousin Chris had experienced the same type of disappointment as a young adult. Ben contacted Chris and found that he, too, was accepted to the academy but could not pass the eye exam. Instead, he attended college and became a successful software designer.

    In the end, Ben decided to attend Michigan Tech. Even though it was not his first choice, Ben was excited to move to the dorms and study aeronautical engineering.

    The genetic disorder that both Ben and Chris exhibit is red-green color blindness. The phenotype, or observable trait, of color blindness is the inability to distinguish the colors red and green. People with red-green color blindness also do not see as well at night as those individuals without red-green color blindness.

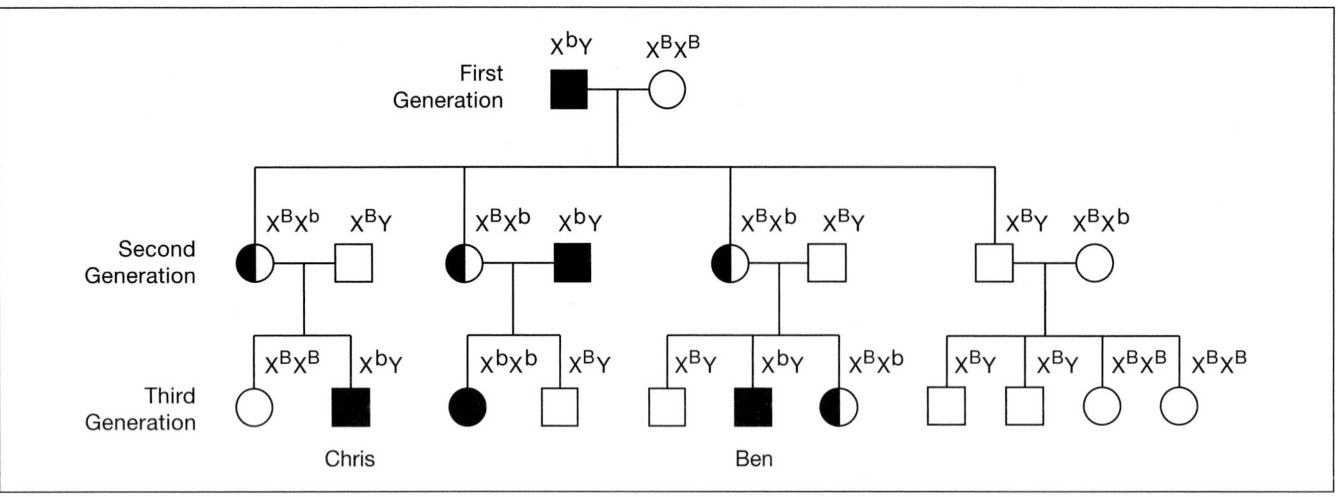

▲ **Figure T7.22 Ben's pedigree.** This is an example of one way students might diagram Ben's pedigree. Student pedigrees will differ depending on the alleles the students choose for the mates. Check that students have given children appropriate alleles based on the alleles of the parents. In this pedigree, *B* represents the dominant allele for color blindness and *b* represents the recessive allele for color blindness. Because color blindness is a recessive trait, make sure that the color-blind males have one recessive allele and that color-blind females have two recessive alleles. Heterozygous females should be diagrammed as carriers.

Answers to Steps 2–3 are on TE pages 386–387.
Answers to Reflect and Connect are on TE page 387.

Answers to Steps 2–3, SE page 386

2. Figure T7.22 provides one example of how students might diagram Ben's pedigree. Students can use whatever letter they choose to represent the color-blind allele. Students can choose the alleles of some of the family members. Encourage students to use a Punnett square if they need help determining what alleles are possible. The following must be present on the pedigree:
   - The first-generation male must be color blind.
   - All of the second-generation females must be carriers.
   - The second-generation male must be normal—he has the dominant allele for color blindness.
   - At least 2 third-generation males must be color blind and in different families (cousins Ben and Chris).

2. Draw Ben's pedigree showing 3 generations. Ben and his cousin Chris will be the third generation and their grandparents will be the first generation. Use the following information (and information from the story) in your diagram.
   - A first-generation male is color blind.
   - There are 3 daughters and 1 son in the second generation; all are married.
   - Two of the second-generation daughters have 2 children (1 girl and 1 boy) and 1 daughter has 3 children (2 boys and 1 girl).
   - The second-generation son has 4 children (2 boys and 2 girls).
   - Ben and Chris, the third generation, are both descendants of daughters in the second generation.
   - Label Ben and Chris on your diagram.
   - Label each person on the pedigree with the alleles that he or she is likely to carry for color blindness.
3. Determine the probably that Ben was going to inherit the color-blindness trait. Assume that his father was not color blind. Draw a Punnett square with Ben's parents and explain how likely his parents were to have a boy with color blindness.

Using a Punnett square when creating a pedigree can help determine all the possible traits offspring might have or carry.

Reflect and Connect

Discuss the following questions with your teammate. Record your answers in your science notebook.

1. Why are pedigrees useful tools to illustrate inheritance patterns?
2. What pattern of inheritance did you draw for Ben and Chris's family? Explain why you say this.
3. From Part II of the explain activity *All about Alleles*, construct a pedigree for your team's in vitro child, following the patterns of inheritance for dimples. Start from the original parents and label the alleles for dimples next to each individual. On that same pedigree, follow the pattern for color blindness. Label the alleles for color blindness next to each individual.

3. Ben's parents had a 50 percent, or 1:2, chance of having a boy with color blindness. Figure T7.23 shows the Punnett square.

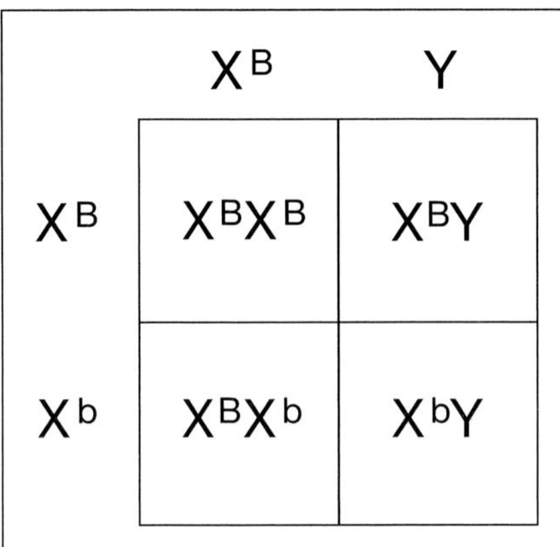

	X^B	Y
X^B	X^BX^B	X^BY
X^b	X^BX^b	X^bY

▲ **Figure T7.23 Punnett square for Ben's parents.** Based on the information provided, students should know that Ben's mother was a carrier (X^BX^b) and Ben's father was not color blind (X^BY).

Answers to Reflect and Connect, SE page 386

1. Pedigrees allow us to observe how a trait is passed from generation to generation and predict how each person may have inherited the trait. We can then conclude which pattern of inheritance the trait follows.
2. The pattern for Ben and Chris's family is X-linked recessive inheritance. The reasons are that more males have the trait, all the daughters of a male with the trait are carriers, and mothers of males who have the trait are either carriers or express the trait.
3. Each team's pedigree will be different. You can look at the data charts for the second generation to see if the pedigree is drawn correctly.

Passing Genes—Who Gets What?

EVALUATE

Throughout this chapter, you have been exploring the inheritance of traits. You observed the traits of two generations of yeast. Then you learned that traits are inherited through the process of meiosis. You modeled meiosis using play dough and the inheritance of alleles for a hypothetical child. You have also used Punnett squares and pedigrees to illustrate how alleles are inherited by family members. All these experiences have contributed to your understanding of inheritance and meiosis. In *Passing Genes—Who Gets What?*, you will work individually and with a partner to demonstrate your understanding of inheritance and meiosis. You will do this by interpreting the inheritance pattern of a genetic disorder and creating a pedigree that shows the inheritance of the disorder.

Materials

For each team of 2 students

current resources

plain paper

access to the "gene pool"

ruler

markers

2 *Passing on Genes—Who Gets What? Scoring Rubric* handouts

Process and Procedure

What if there was a genetic disorder in your family? What inheritance patterns could you figure out if you understood the disorder? In this evaluate activity, you will have the opportunity to demonstrate what you know about inheritance by tracing a specific disorder through several generations.

1. Review the *Passing on Genes Scoring Rubric* handout so that you learn the expectations for this activity.
2. Imagine that you and your partner are siblings. You have just learned that a third sibling has been diagnosed with a genetic disorder.
   a. Select a genetic disorder from the container provided by your teacher to find out which disorder your sibling has.
   b. Do you already know something about the disorder you selected? What are some questions you have about the disorder? Record your ideas in your science notebook.

EVALUATE

Passing Genes—Who Gets What?

Activity Overview

In this evaluate, students will apply their knowledge of inheritance patterns and dominant and recessive alleles to a genetic disorder (figure T7.24). Students will create and label pedigrees based on known alleles and known affected individuals. Then students will answer questions.

Before You Teach

Background Information

The background information you will need can be found in copymaster 7.7, *Disorder Descriptions.* The descriptions of the disorders have been simplified. If students conduct their own research, they are likely to encounter information that is filled with medical jargon and terms that are beyond the scope of this chapter. Try to help students focus on locating information about the inheritance pattern of the disorder. Students will also need information on the expected life span of individuals with the disorder. Be aware that many sources on the Web provide "clues" about the inheritance pattern, such as the chance of offspring inheriting the disorder from one affected parent.

Materials

For the teacher

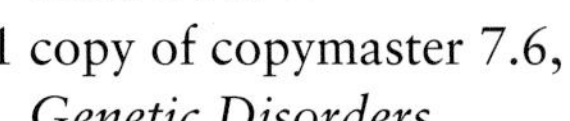

1 copy of copymaster 7.5, *Gene Pool*

1 copy of copymaster 7.6, *Genetic Disorders*

2 copies of copymaster, 7.7, *Disorder Descriptions* (descriptions of 15 disorders, 1 description for each team)

team bowls or hats

cards (optional)

For each team of 2 students

current reference resources

plain paper

access to the "gene pool"

ruler

markers

Autosomal dominant	Autosomal recessive	X-linked recessive
Huntington's disease	Tay-Sachs disease	hemophilia A
achondroplasia	sickle cell anemia	red-green color blindness
Marfan syndrome	albinism	Duchenne muscular dystrophy
osteogenesis imperfecta	cystic fibrosis	Menkes syndrome
	phenylketonuria (PKU)	juvenile retinoschisis
	galactosemia	

▲ **Figure T7.24 Genetic disorders.** Teams of two students will be assigned to one of these disorders. The genetic disorders are inherited through one of three inheritance patterns—autosomal dominant, autosomal recessive, or X-linked recessive.

2 copies of copymaster 7.8, *Scoring Rubric for Passing On Genes—Who Gets What?*

Advance Preparation

Make 1 copy of copymaster 7.5, *Gene Pool* for the class. Then cut apart the cards so that each card has a pair of alleles. Keep the cards for each inheritance pattern separate. Create 3 "gene pools," 1 for autosomal dominant traits, 1 for autosomal recessive traits, and 1 for X-linked recessive traits. Place the gene pools in 3 separate bowls or hats for student pairs to draw from.

Copy and cut apart the 15 disorders on copymaster 7.6, *Genetic Disorders*. Place the names in a bowl or hat for student pairs to draw from. In a class of 30 students, each pair of students will work on a different disorder. If you have smaller classes, remove disorders evenly from each of the inheritance pattern categories. This will assure adequate representation across your class of each type of disorder.

Do not tell students ahead of time what inheritance pattern each disorder represents. They will find out this information when they read over the information provided in copymaster 7.7, *Disorder Descriptions*.

Make 2 copies of copymaster 7.7, *Disorder Descriptions*. Then cut apart the descriptions. If you choose to have students research the disorders, have reference materials available for students. It is helpful for students to have access to the Web.

Organizations with useful Web sites include the following:

- Medline Plus
- National Center for Biotechnology Information (NCB), page on genes and diseases
- Dolan DNA Learning Center, page titled Your Genes, Your Health

Answers to Steps 6, 8, and 9 are on TE pages 389a–389d.

3. Obtain information about the genetic disorder your sibling has from your teacher.
   a. Look for the following information:
      - The cause of the disorder
      - The symptoms, effects, and possible cures
      - The inheritance pattern
   b. Record your findings in your science notebook. Make sure you take notes on your own because you will be using them to complete the next steps.
4. Work with your partner to decide the sex of your sibling. Justify your decision with the information you learned about the genetic disorder in Step 3.

Use what you know about the inheritance pattern of the disorder. For some disorders, the alleles of individuals with the disorder are different depending on gender.

5. Determine the alleles for you and your sibling's mates by doing these things.
   a. Go to your teacher's "gene pool" and draw a pair of alleles. This will be your mate's alleles for the trait. You and your partner will draw for your mates. If necessary, draw a pair of alleles for your sibling's mate.

Your teacher will provide the gene pool. Before drawing a pair of alleles for your sibling, think about the symptoms of your sibling's disorder. Is your sibling expected to survive to a reproductive age? Is drawing for his or her mate appropriate?

   b. Record the alleles of your mate, your partner's mate, and your sibling's mate, if appropriate, in your science notebook. Then return the alleles to the gene pool.
   c. Work with your partner and decide what you and your partner's alleles are. Use what you have learned in the chapter and the information provided about your sibling's disorder to help you decide.

Make sure you have recorded the alleles for you, your siblings, and their mates. You will use this information in the next step.

   d. Record the alleles of you and your partner in your science notebook.
6. Work individually to create a pedigree of your hypothetical family.
   a. Use what you know about your sibling's disorder and the alleles of the rest of the family members to determine how the disorder could be inherited through 3 generations.

388 Unit 2 Inside Life

- National Human Genome Research Institute, page on specific genetic disorders
- National Institute of Neurological Disorders and Stroke
- The Gene Tests Web site, funded by the National Institutes of Health
- National Organization for Rare Disorders
- Genetic Alliance
- National Society of Genetic Counselors
- Foundation Fighting Blindness

As You Teach

Outcomes and Indicators of Success

By the end of this activity, students should

1. demonstrate their understanding of the process of inheritance—how traits are passed from generation to generation.

   They will demonstrate their understanding by

   - interpreting the inheritance pattern of a genetic disorder based on information provided in a copymaster,
   - diagramming a pedigree that shows the inheritance of a genetic disorder,
   - labeling possible alleles of individuals in a pedigree based on affected individuals, and
   - explaining how one of the offspring in the third generation of the pedigree got his or her alleles.

2. demonstrate their understanding that each parent contributes one-half of the genetic makeup of the offspring.

   They will demonstrate their understanding by

   - predicting the traits of offspring given the parental alleles;
   - diagramming a pedigree with the alleles of the individuals labeled; and
   - explaining that an offspring gets chromosomes from his or her parents, who each contribute a gamete with half the chromosomes of other body cells.

3. demonstrate their understanding of meiosis and its role in passing genetic information from one generation to the next through gametes.

   They will demonstrate their understanding by

   - explaining that meiosis results in the formation of gametes that carry half the number of chromosomes found in other body cells and
   - describing that meiosis is important because it allows each parent to contribute equal amounts of genetic information to offspring.

4. demonstrate their understanding that transmission of genetic information occurs through gametes (sperm and egg cells) and that a pair of sex chromosomes determines the sex of a human. Females have two X chromosomes. Males have an X and a Y chromosome.

   They will demonstrate their understanding by

   - applying their knowledge of sex chromosomes and meiosis to determine the sex of their offspring and the offspring of their sibling and
   - explaining that an offspring receives an X chromosome from the mother and the sex of an offspring is determined by whether an X or a Y chromosome is received from the father.

---

b. Include your parents (first generation); you, your mate, your partner and mate, and your affected sibling and mate (second generation); and a third generation based on the couples' alleles.

c. Generate as many offspring from each couple as you choose to.

7. Label the alleles for *all* the individuals on the pedigree after you have all 3 generations drawn for your pedigree. For the sake of consistency, use the letters *A* and *a* to represent the alleles.
8. Write a paragraph that describes how one of the offspring in the third generation got his or her alleles. Include in your description what determines the sex of the offspring and the number of chromosomes (autosomes and sex chromosomes) found in the cells of most humans. Include the following words in your description:
   - *Meiosis*
   - *Gametes*
   - *Chromosomes*
   - *Genes*
   - *Alleles*
9. Briefly describe the importance of meiosis. Include information about the amount of genetic information passed from each parent to the offspring.

Chapter 7 Tracking Traits 389

5. demonstrate their understanding of inheritance patterns (autosomal dominant, autosomal recessive, sex-linked recessive).

   They will demonstrate their understanding by inferring the inheritance pattern of a genetic disorder from information provided in a copymaster and then diagramming a pedigree based on their knowledge of the inheritance pattern.

6. demonstrate their ability to use the skills of scientific inquiry and their knowledge about understanding of scientific inquiry.

   They will demonstrate their ability by

   - using tools such as pedigree analysis and
   - developing an explanation of how a third-generation offspring got his or her traits, based on scientific knowledge of meiosis and inheritance patterns.

Strategies

Getting Started

Before you begin this assignment, go back to the statements the students created in the engage activity and discuss them with students. This serves as a review prior to this activity. If your class used the statements provided in copymaster 7.1, *Inheritance*, then refer to the answers to the statements provided at the end of the copymaster.

Process and Procedure

In Step 2, make the container with genetic disorders available to students. Each team of 2 students should draw a genetic disorder from the gene pool. You might also choose to assign the disorders. In Step 3, students work with their partners to learn about their "sibling's" genetic disorder. Tell them to study the bulleted list in Step 3 carefully. To obtain the information on the list, students need information about the disorder available on copymaster 7.7, *Disorder Descriptions*. Distribute the appropriate description to each pair of students. Make sure each student has a copy of his or her disorder description. You might choose to have students conduct research on their sibling's genetic disorder. This is likely to be a time-consuming step and students will find more information on some disorders than others. Remind students to take their own notes on the condition because they will need this information when they work individually to create pedigrees. If you decide to have teams conduct research on their own, provide resources and access to the Web. They can use their research to supplement what they learn from copymaster 7.7, *Disorder Descriptions* and help them answer the questions in this activity. See the list of organizations that have reliable Web sites in *Advance Preparation*.

In Step 4, students work with their partners and decide on the alleles and sex of their sibling with the disorder. Students with X-linked disorders might assume that their affected sibling must be male. Males are more likely to inherit an X-linked disorder, but it is possible for females to have an X-linked disorder if they are homozygous recessive (*aa*).

In Step 5, make the gene pools available to students. All students should draw a card for the alleles of their mate. Make sure each pair of students draws from the correct gene pool. Before students draw for their sibling's mate, encourage them to think about the symptoms associated with their sibling's disorder. Ask students if they think their affected sibling will have the opportunity to reproduce. Students should only draw a card for the alleles of their sibling's mate if the sibling is expected to live to a reproductive age.

Once students have determined their mate's alleles and possibly their sibling's mate's alleles, tell them to record these alleles in their science notebooks. Students should return the allele cards to the gene pool so that the portion of each genotype will remain the same as each student pair draws. Then tell students to work with their partners to decide what their alleles are. Instruct students to record this information in their science notebooks.

In Step 6, students begin individual work. They should draw a pedigree of a hypothetical family that includes their parents, their siblings, their children, and their siblings' children. In Step 7, students should label the alleles of each family member.

Once they have completed the pedigree, they write a short paragraph in Step 8 that describes how one of the third-generation children got his or her alleles. In Step 9, students describe the importance of meiosis. If you have time, you might give students the opportunity to see each other's pedigrees. They will learn more about genetic disorders by viewing other students' pedigrees.

Answers to Steps 6, 8, and 9, SE pages 388–389

6. Figures T7.25–29 illustrate how students' pedigrees should look for each disorder. Notice that in all the figures the second generation shows all the possible genotypes based on the parent genotypes used. On the student pedigrees, the alleles of the student, the partner, the mates, and the children will vary depending on which alleles were chosen or drawn from the gene pool.

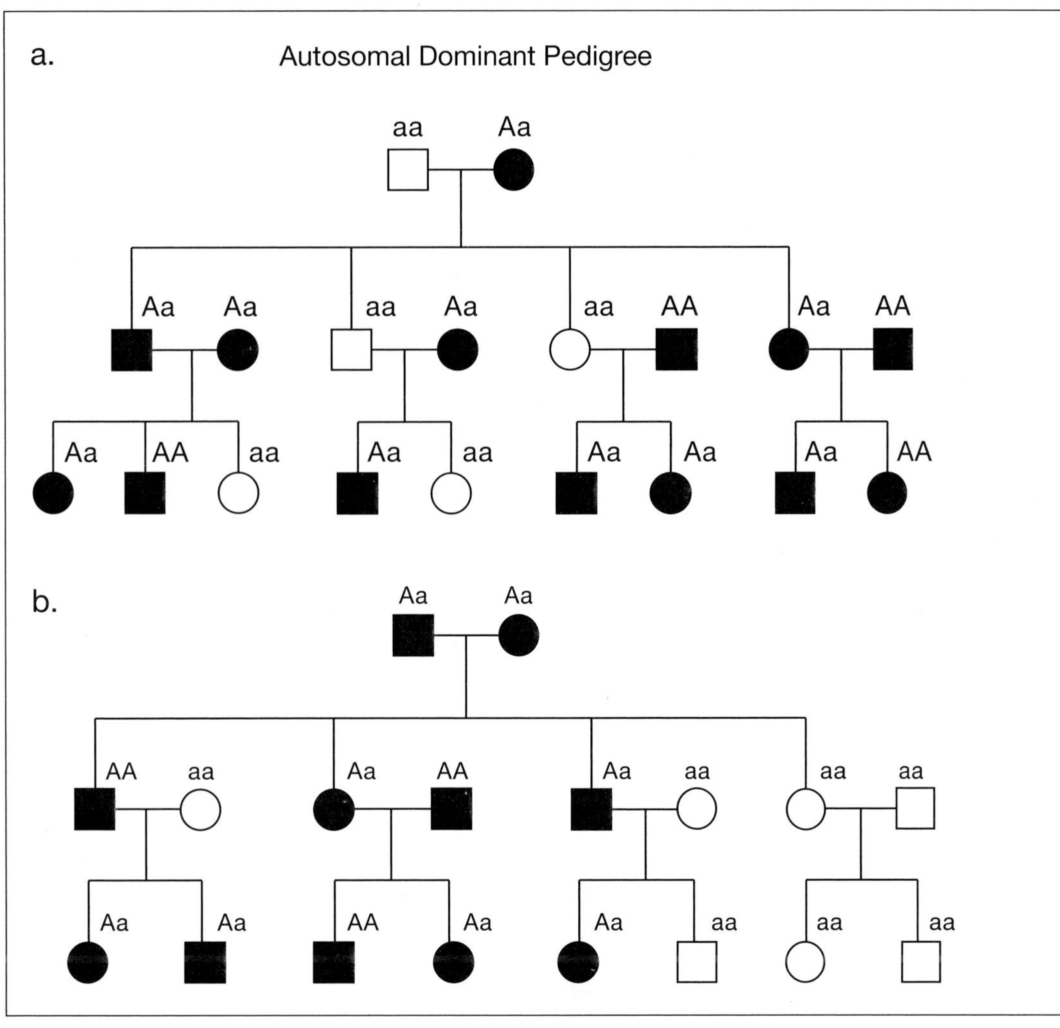

◀ **Figure T7.25 Autosomal dominant pedigrees.** Students should draw pedigrees similar to one of these for the following disorders: Huntington's disease, achondroplasia, Marfan's syndrome, and osteogenesis imperfecta. Students must have one sibling in the second generation with the disorder (*Aa* or *AA*) on their pedigree. The alleles for the parents can be (a) *aa* and *Aa* or (b) *Aa* and *Aa*.

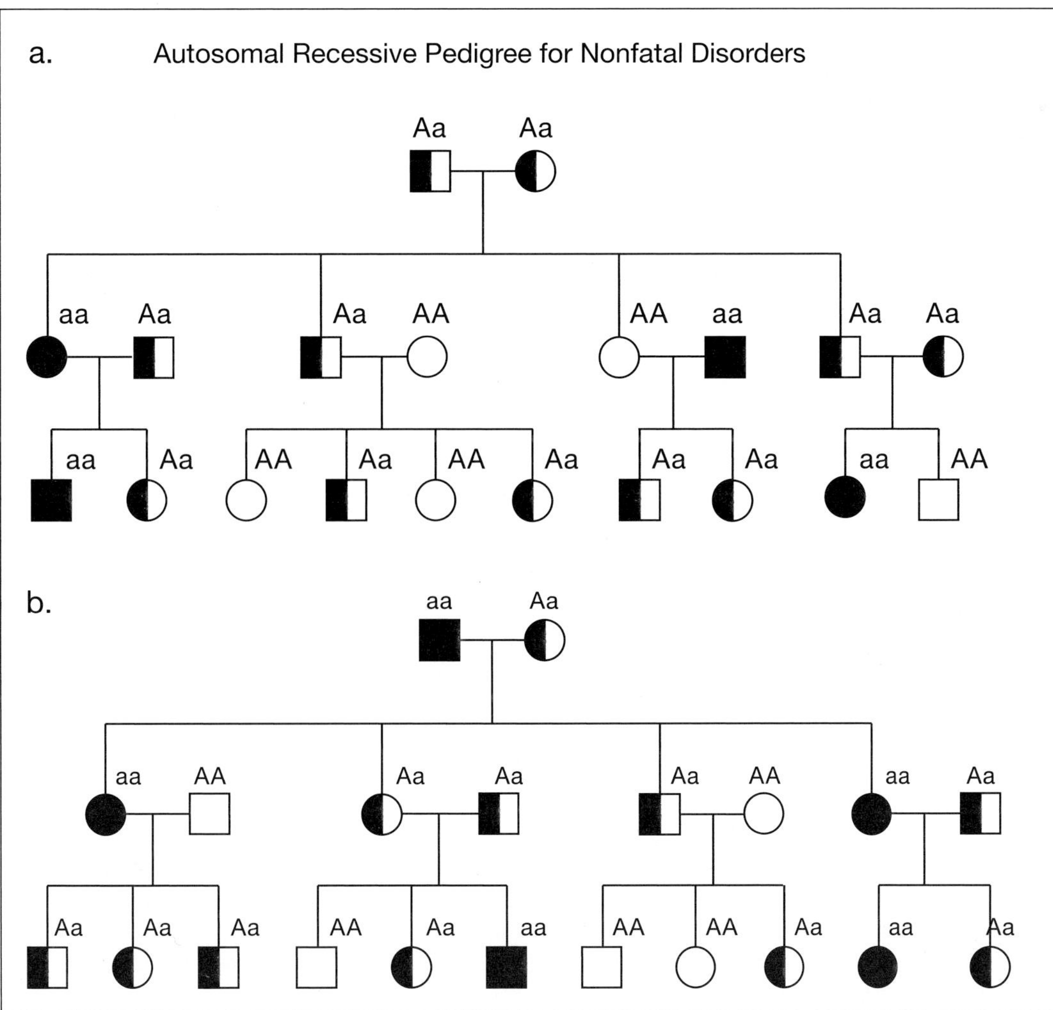

◀ **Figure T7.26 Autosomal recessive pedigrees for nonfatal disorders.** Students should draw pedigrees similar to one of these for the following disorders: sickle-cell anemia, albinism, cystic fibrosis, phenylketonuria (PKU), and galactosemia. Students must have one sibling in the second generation with the disorder (*aa*) on their pedigree. The alleles for the parents can be (a) *Aa* and *Aa* or (b) *aa* and *Aa*.

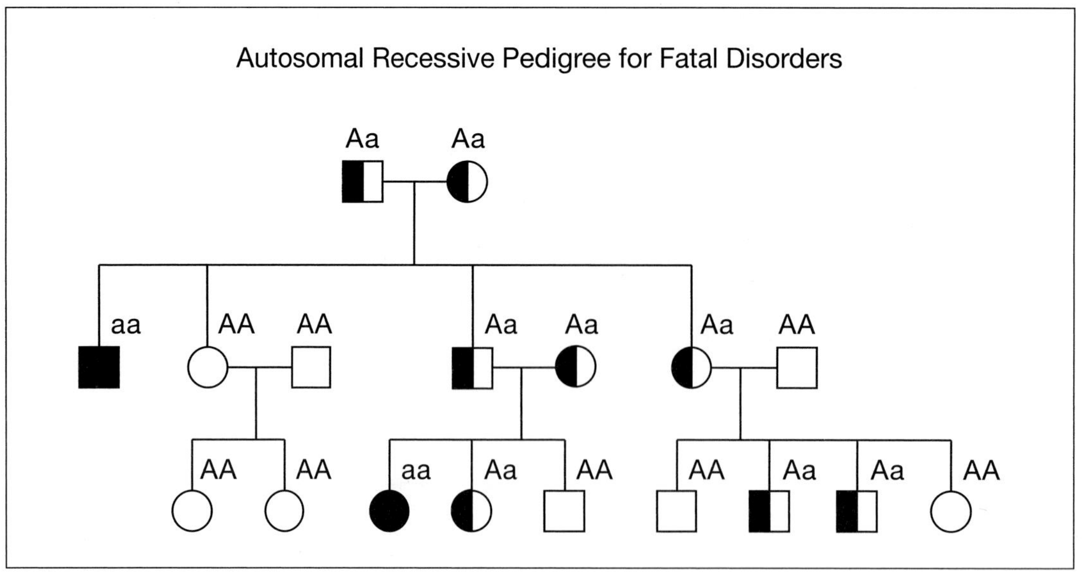

▲ **Figure T7.27 Autosomal recessive pedigree for fatal disorders.** Students should draw a pedigree similar to this for Tay-Sachs disease. Some students might draw a pedigree like this for a male who has cystic fibrosis. Because men with cystic fibrosis are likely to be sterile, students might not draw children for the affected sibling. Students must have one sibling in the second generation with the disorder (*aa*) on their pedigree. Individuals with the disorder should not have children because the disorder is fatal before reproductive age or affects fertility. The alleles for the parents can only be *Aa* and *Aa*.

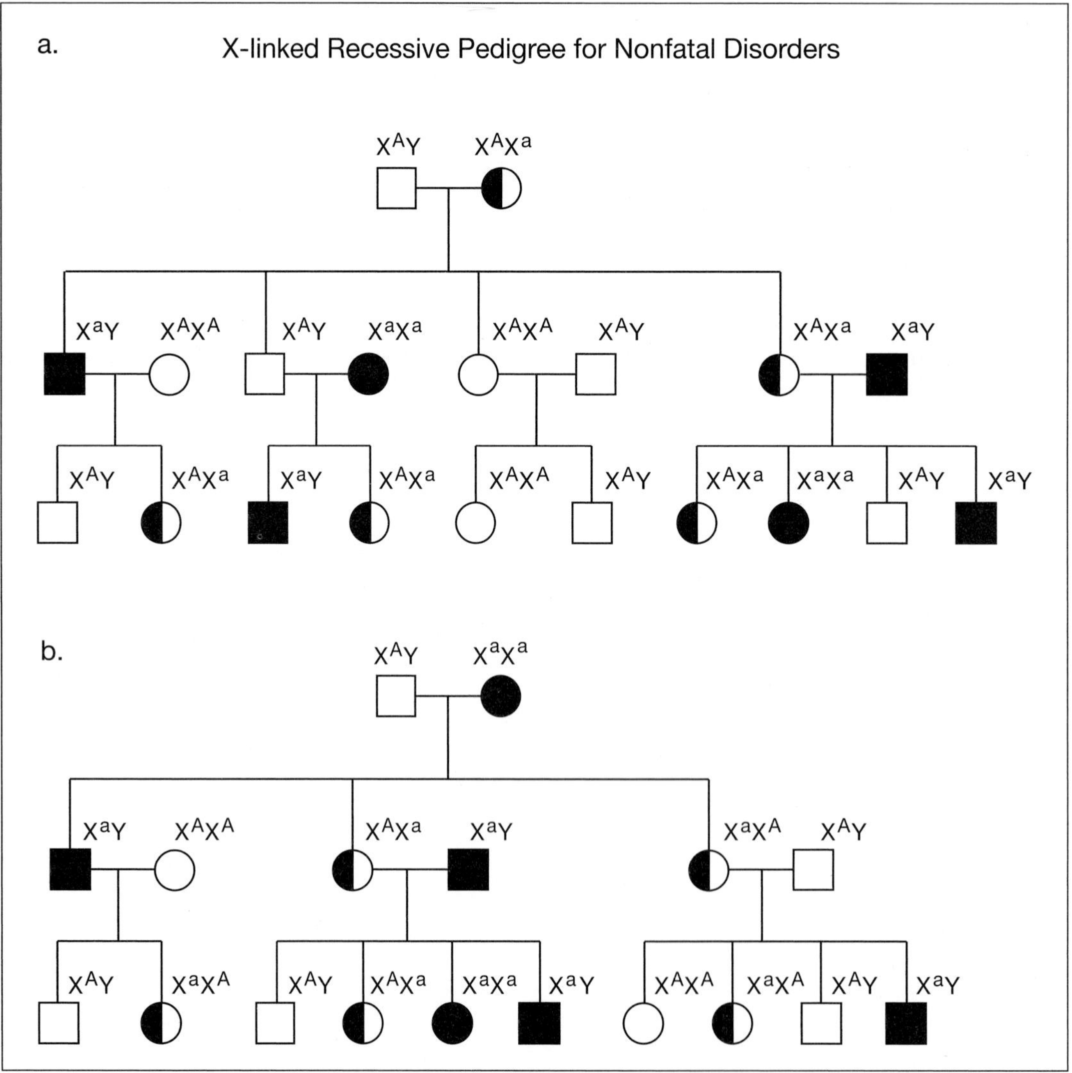

▲ **Figure T7.28 X-linked recessive pedigrees for nonfatal disorders.** Students should draw a pedigree similar to this for the following disorders: hemophilia A, red-green color blindness, Duchenne muscular dystrophy, and juvenile retinoschisis. The pedigree must have one sibling in the second generation with the disorder (X^aY or X^aX^a). Students are more likely to make the affected sibling male because more males have X-linked recessive disorders than females. The alleles for the parents can be (a) X^AY and X^AX^a or (b) X^AY and X^aX^a.

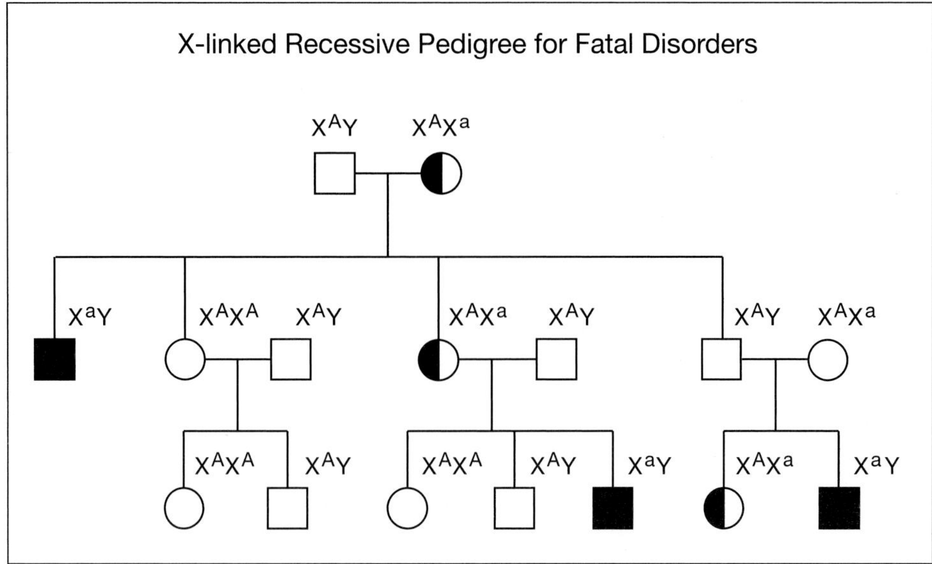

▲ **Figure T7.29 X-linked recessive pedigrees for fatal disorders.** Students should draw a pedigree similar to this for Menkes syndrome. Some students might draw a pedigree like this for individuals with Duchenne muscular dystrophy. Their reasoning would have to be that the individual with the disorder did not reproduce before he reached 25—the average life span for the disorder. The pedigree must have one sibling in the second generation with the disorder (X^aY or X^aX^a). Students are more likely to make the affected sibling male because more males have X-linked recessive disorders than females. Individuals with the disorder should not have children because the disorder is fatal before reproductive age or affects fertility. The alleles for the parents can only be X^AY and X^AX^a.

8. Students should briefly describe the process of meiosis and how alleles are passed to offspring. Look for answers that address the following ideas.

   The second-generation parents' gametes (egg and sperm) combine to form a zygote that develops into a child (third generation). Gametes are formed through the process of meiosis. Humans have 46 chromosomes (23 pairs): 22 pairs of autosomes and 1 pair of sex chromosomes. During the process of meiosis, the number of chromosomes in the cells doubles, and then cell division occurs twice. As a result, the gametes contain half the number of chromosomes of other body cells (23 chromosomes).

   The sex of a third-generation child is determined by whether the male gamete (sperm) carried an X or a Y chromosome. The mother can only contribute an X chromosome to the child.

   The genes of the child are determined by the genes present on the chromosomes in the gametes. Because gametes have half the number of chromosomes, each gamete only has 1 allele for a gene. Therefore, the mother and father each contribute only 1 allele for a gene to their child. An allele is a form or version of a gene. The traits of an individual are determined by the alleles he or she has.

9. Students should understand that meiosis is important because this process ensures that each generation has the same number of chromosomes. The parents each contribute half of their genetic information to the next generation. Without meiosis, offspring would have too many chromosomes. Some students might explain that meiosis also contributes to variation in populations because offspring receive 1 copy of a gene from each parent. As a result, new combinations of alleles might occur, giving the offspring traits different from the parents' traits.

CHAPTER 8

Instructions for Life

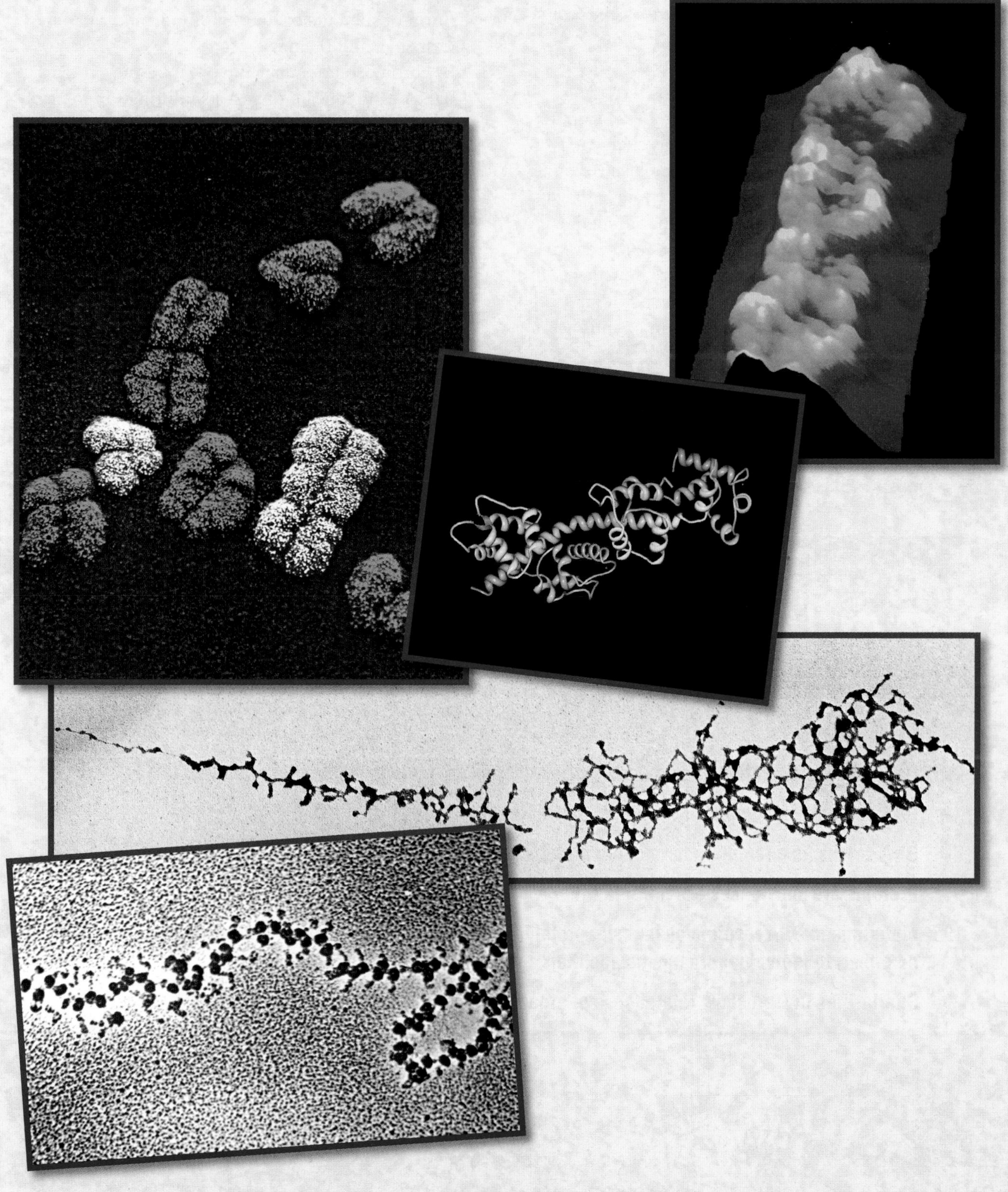

Chapter Overview

In chapter 6, *Exploring Change*, students began to study the diversity of life on a large scale. They began to see how populations of organisms change over vast amounts of time as a result of natural selection. In the next chapter, *Tracking Traits*, students looked at organisms on a smaller scale to see how traits are passed from generation to generation.

In chapter 8, *Instructions for Life*, students will look closer still at the mechanism for heredity—DNA. This chapter serves as a connection between DNA's role in evolution and its role in inheritance. In this chapter, students will look closely at DNA as the molecule that stores genetic information in the form of a code. Students will experience how DNA carries the code for individual traits, as well as how the code in DNA influences entire populations of organisms. Students will see how the DNA structure itself is constant, but small changes within it can alter the genetic code, leading to changes in organisms over time.

Goals for the Chapter

The overarching goal for this chapter is that students will understand how DNA carries the genetic instructions for all living things, including the instructions for making proteins, which are essential for life. By the end of chapter 8, students will understand the following:

- DNA is found in all living things and carries the code for their characteristics. This code is in the form of subunits of four kinds (adenine, guanine, cytosine, and thymine).
- A chromosome is made up of DNA and proteins.
- DNA can replicate to pass its information to newly formed cells.
- DNA serves as a template for making proteins through the processes of transcription and translation.
- Proteins are substances essential to life.
- Mutations in DNA result in changes in proteins that can be advantageous, detrimental, or neutral (have no effect) to individual organisms and their species.
- Similarities in DNA show relatedness of organisms. Changes in DNA lead to the evolution of species, and DNA serves as evidence for evolution.

Look at the chapter organizer each day to remind yourself of where students are in the overall sequence of events in the chapter.

Chapter 8 Organizer

INSTRUCTIONS FOR LIFE

Major Concepts

- **DNA is found in all living things and carries the genetic code for their characteristics.**
- **DNA can replicate to pass its genetic information to newly formed cells.**
- **DNA serves as a template for making proteins.**
- **Proteins are substances essential to life.**
- **Mutations in DNA result in changes in proteins that can be advantageous, detrimental, or neutral (have no effect) to individual organisms and their species.**
- **Similarities in DNA show relatedness of organisms.**

ENGAGE — Just the Fax ★

Key Idea: • Codes can carry a lot of information.

Activity: Students decipher a code to get a message. Each student has a different word in their messages that is associated with proteins. They will need to research their word to prepare for a later activity.

LINKING QUESTION: How can you extract the substance that makes up the chromosomes and carries the code of life?

EXPLORE — What Is This Stuff? ★ ★

Key Idea: • The same substance can be extracted from three different organisms.

Activity: In Part I, students extract a visible substance (DNA) that is common to all of these organisms. In Part II, students relate a teacher demonstration to the DNA extraction from Part I.

LINKING QUESTION: What is DNA made of and how is it inherited?

EXPLAIN — Clips of DNA ★ ★ ★

Key Ideas:

- DNA is a long chain of repeating subunits called nucleotides.
- Copies of DNA are made through DNA replication.
- DNA replication is important in mitosis and meiosis to ensure that new cells get the genetic instructions they need.

Activity: In Part I, students read about DNA and make a model of it using paper clips. In Part II, they read about the process of DNA replication and how it relates to mitosis and meiosis. Then they model the process of DNA replication.

LINKING QUESTION: What is significant about the words from the *Just the Fax* activity and how are they related to DNA?

EXPLAIN — Words to Live By ★ ★

Key Idea: • Proteins are essential for life.

Activity: Students share with the class what they learned about the words from the *Just the Fax* activity. They create a concept map of the words and discover that all of the words are associated with proteins.

LINKING QUESTION: How does DNA store the information that directs protein production?

EXPLAIN — Transcription and Translation—the Road to Making Proteins ★ ★

Key Ideas:

- Protein synthesis occurs through a two part process that involves transcription and translation.
- During transcription, part of a DNA sequence is copied into a complementary sequence of mRNA.
- During translation, the information on mRNA is converted to form a sequence of amino acids that form a long protein chain.

Activity: In Part I, the students are introduced to RNA and they model transcription using paperclips. In Part II, students simulate both transcription and translation through a role-playing activity.

LINKING QUESTION: What happens if a mistake occurs during DNA replication, transcription, or translation?

★ = One Class Period ☆ = ½ Class Period *Note:* Based on a 50-minute class period.

ELABORATE Nobody's Perfect ★★

Key Ideas:
- Mutations can be beneficial, detrimental, or neutral to organisms.
- Mutations lead to variability in populations.

Activity: In Part I, students read about the causes and possible effects of mutation in DNA. In Part II, students explore how the variation within a population of seeds might contribute to the seeds' survival when exposed to different selective pressures.

Linking Question: How do scientists know how similar the genetic code is among different organisms?

ELABORATE DNA and Evolution ★

Key Ideas:
- DNA can be used to determine the relatedness of organisms.
- DNA can be used as evidence to support theories of evolution.

Activity: Students will explore how scientists use DNA sequences to determine the relatedness of organisms and how this information helps scientists piece together the possible evolutionary pattern for different species.

Linking Question: How can I use what I have learned to demonstrate my understanding of DNA and related processes?

EVALUATE Sharing Your Knowledge ★★

Key Ideas:
- DNA is the genetic code for all living things.
- DNA replicates to transmit genetic information to newly formed cells.
- DNA serves as a template for making proteins through the processes of transcription and translation.
- Mutations in DNA result in changes in proteins.

Activity: Students show their understanding of DNA and the processes they have learned about by creating a summary in a format they choose. For example, students might choose to summarize what they know using a concept map, storyboard, flash cards, a game board, a skit, a computer presentation, or a summary essay.

★ = One Class Period ☆ = ½ Class Period *Note:* Based on a 50-minute class period.

Standards Covered by Chapter 8*

INSTRUCTIONS FOR LIFE

STANDARD A: Science as Inquiry. As a result of activities in grades 9–12, all students should develop

abilities necessary to do scientific inquiry

- Formulate and revise scientific explanations and models using logic and evidence. Student inquiries should culminate in formulating an explanation or model. Models should be physical, conceptual, and mathematical. In the process of answering the questions, the students should engage in discussions and arguments that result in the revision of their explanations. These discussions should be based on scientific knowledge, the use of logic, and evidence from their investigation.

STANDARD C: Life Science. As a result of their activities in grades 9–12, all students should develop an understanding of

the cell

- Cells store and use information to guide their functions. The genetic information stored in DNA is used to direct the synthesis of the thousands of proteins that each cell requires.

the molecular basis of heredity

- In all organisms, the instructions for specifying the characteristics of the organisms are carried in DNA, a large polymer formed from subunits of four kinds (A, G, C, and T). The chemical and structural properties of DNA explain how the genetic information that underlies heredity is both encoded in genes (as a string of molecular "letters") and replicated (by a templating mechanism). Each DNA molecule in a cell forms a single chromosome. [See Content Standard B (grades 9–12)]
- Changes in DNA (mutations) occur spontaneously at low rates. Some of these changes make no difference to the organisms, whereas others can change cells and organisms. Only mutations in germ cells can create the variation that changes an organism's offspring.

biological evolution

- Species evolve over time. Evolution is the consequence of the interactions of (1) the potential for a species to increase its numbers, (2) the genetic variability of offspring due to mutation and recombination of genes, (3) a finite supply of the resources required for life, and (4) the ensuing selection by the environment of those offspring better able to survive and leave offspring. [See Unifying Concepts and Processes]

---

* *Note:* Bracketed portions of the standard are addressed elsewhere in the program.

Prerequisite Knowledge

Students need to know about cell structure. For example, DNA is located within the nucleus of eukaryotic cells, and ribosomes are involved in the process of making proteins. Students also need to be familiar with the cellular processes of mitosis and meiosis. Students will learn that DNA replication is an important part of both of these processes. Students are expected to recognize and understand terms from the previous life science chapters such as genes, chromosomes, variation, and natural selection.

Commonly Held Misconceptions

Students have many misconceptions about DNA. Some misconceptions are related to scale. Many students think that you can see DNA's structure in a microscope like parts of a cell. At the same time, students often think that DNA sequences are smaller than they really are. Some of these ideas come from the models that students are exposed to in textbooks. Confusion also results if they conduct labs with viral DNA. Often models only show less than 20 base pairs. Viral genomes that students conduct investigations with may have only several thousand base pairs. These are tiny fragments of DNA compared to the more than 3 billion base pairs in the human genome. Similarly, students sometimes take models of DNA literally. They do not realize that they are representations of DNA and that the actual structure is more complicated.

Many misconceptions are related to students' experiences when studying DNA. For example, students usually are asked to wear goggles when conducting investigations with DNA. This can give some students the impression that DNA is dangerous and should be treated as a potentially toxic chemical rather than a naturally occurring substance. You can address this concern by asking students what is in the nucleus of all cells. They should realize that the nucleus contains DNA. Then ask students if they are consuming cells when they eat an apple. This will help them see that they consume DNA every time they eat. Students also have difficulty understanding the relationship between chromosomes, DNA, and genes. Confusion is sometimes generated because chromosomes and genes are discussed in a chapter covering Mendelian genetics, but DNA is discussed in a separate chapter. We have made an effort to make a connection between chapters 7 and 8 to help reduce confusion.

Students also have misconceptions related to mutation. Many students have the misconception that whole organisms mutate during their lifetimes. This chapter will help them understand that mutations can only be passed to offspring if the mutations affect an organism's gametes.

NOTES:

NOTES:

ENGAGE

Just the Fax

Activity Overview

In *Just the Fax*, students will decipher a code to get a message. The activity introduces students to the efficiency and use of codes. They will see how codes with just two symbols can carry a great deal of information. The students each will have a different word in their messages that is associated with proteins. (In larger classes, there might be some duplication.) They will need to research their word to prepare for a later activity. Later in the chapter, students will report on their words to learn more about the significance of proteins.

Before You Teach

Background Information

This activity gets students thinking about codes because codes work as a bridge to understanding DNA as the code of life. The code that students will be working with is a form of binary code using 0s and 1s. The original fax machines worked this way, but modern ones use much more complex codes. The first fax machines had an optical device that read the reflectivity of light. White has high reflectivity, and black has low reflectivity. In the presence of high reflectivity, from the white part of a document, the code is 0. In the presence of low reflectivity from the black on a document, the code is 1. So words or pictures on a document were coded using 0s and 1s. Early fax machines deciphered the code and replicated the document by printing black for 1s and leaving blank spaces for 0s.

Binary code is an efficient way to store large amounts of information. Binary code only uses two symbols (0s and 1s) and is how much of today's computers store information. Modern computers use the symbols differently from the first fax machines, but the principle of storing information using symbols is the same. DNA is able to store vast amounts of genetic information using four symbols in the form of nucleotides. This activity gets students thinking about how codes can store information. Later in the chapter, they will relate this activity to their study of DNA.

Materials

For each student

1 coded message from copymaster 8.1, *Coded Messages*

TRCD

1–2 sheets of graph paper

1 large sheet of paper

sticky notes

access to reference material (see *Advance Preparation*)

Advance Preparation

Make 1 or 2 copies of copymaster 8.1, *Coded Messages* per class. There are 15 messages on the copymaster, and each student should have his or her own message. Cut out each code to distribute to the students.

Have graph paper available for students if the paper in their science notebooks is not suitable for graphs. Some messages might extend beyond the edge of the graph paper depending on the size of the paper. Have extra graph paper available so students can attach it to their sheets. Use regular graph paper with even grids (not logarithmic).

When students begin to research their word from the code during *Reflect and Connect*, Question 5, be sure that everyone has access to references. Helpful resources to make available are encyclopedias, general biology textbooks, and genetics

---

ENGAGE

Just the Fax

Imagine that you want to send a note to a friend but you don't want anyone else to know what it says. What could you do? One of your options might be to write the note using a code. People use codes quite often for many different reasons. You might be surprised at where we find codes. Figure 8.1 shows some common examples of how people use codes.

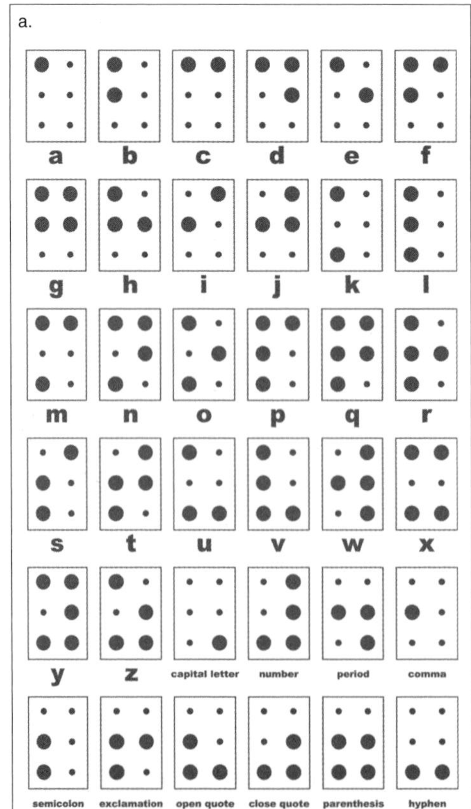

▲ **Figure 8.1 Different types of codes.** (a) Braille alphabet, (b) bar code, (c) alarm keypad. How do people use these codes?

396 | Unit 2 Inside Life

textbooks. Dictionaries will provide a good start for students but will not provide enough detailed information. On-line encyclopedias are an especially good resource for this activity.

As You Teach

Outcomes and Indicators of Success

By the end of this activity, students should

1. be engaged in codes as efficient ways to store information.

   They will become engaged by

   - thinking about common examples of codes,
   - deciphering a code, and
   - discovering that only two symbols can code for a large amount of information.

2. communicate their current understanding of words related to DNA and proteins.

   They will communicate their current understanding by creating a concept map of the words from the coded messages.

Strategies

Getting Started

Introduce this activity by asking students how messages are traditionally relayed. Some student responses might include through talking, writing, or codes. Pose the question, "What if there were fewer than 26 letters in the alphabet? Could you get your message across in some shortened way?" Guide the students into a discussion about codes. How are codes unique? Why do people use codes?

Read the introduction to the activity and elicit additional examples of codes from your students. For example, students might consider the alphabet to be a code. Ask students why they think codes are so useful and effective. Explain to them that they are going to be given a coded message and be asked to decode it.

Avoid talking about DNA at this point. This activity is meant to get students thinking about the value and efficiency of codes.

Process and Procedure

Hand out one coded message to each student. There are 15 messages, so some students might have the same message depending on the size of your class. In Steps 2 and 3, the students are asked to decipher their message without any instructions. Do not hand out graph paper until Step 5 because the graph paper might give a hint.

In Step 3, students think about how to decode the message. Give students a chance to analyze the code, predict how they could read the message, and compare it with their partner's message. When students are ready to decode the message, provide each student with a sheet of graph paper. Allow students to work through the decoding instructions in Step 5. Some students may want to work with their partners to read the symbols to them. If so, have them help each other decipher each of their codes. Circulate around the room to see if they need any help from you. Students will approach deciphering the code differently. Some students may take shortcuts when they begin to see a pattern emerge. This is fine. Let the students approach revealing the message in any manner they are comfortable with.

In Step 6, when the students have revealed their words, have them record the words on a class list posted in the room. If you have space in your classroom, leave the list posted. Your class will be learning more about these words as students research their significance as assigned

In *Just the Fax*, you will experience one code that people use to communicate with one another. Later in the chapter, you will relate your understanding of this code to how a code can direct life's processes.

Materials

For each student

coded message

graph paper

1 large sheet of paper

sticky notes

access to reference material

Process and Procedure

1. Obtain a message from your teacher.
2. Try to determine what your message says. Can you figure it out?
3. Compare your message with a partner's message and discuss the following questions with your partner. Record your ideas in your science notebook.
   a. What is similar and what is different about your message compared to your partner's message? How do you know?
   b. What information do you need before you can read your message?
4. Read the following paragraphs to help you decipher your message.

   Your message was written using digital coding. Digital coding allows us to program computers for many different applications such as games, word processing, and mathematics. Digitally encoded information allows us to take pictures or video and put them on the computer. Television is based on interpreting a digital code. Communication networks also are digitally encoded.

   To get a sense of how a digital code can provide information, think about how the first fax machines worked. Fax machines provide us with the technology to send an exact copy of a document across telephone lines. The information is transmitted using a digital code. Simple fax machines use the numbers 0 and 1 as a code. In fax machines, an optical device looks for bright light. White on a document has high reflectivity (bright light), and the code is 0. Black on a document has low reflectivity, and the code is 1. An image in a document consists

in *Reflect and Connect*, Question 5. All of these words have to do with proteins. In the activity *Words to Live By*, the students report their findings about these words to learn about proteins and their significance.

Copymaster 8.3, *Term Chart Completed* lists the important information about these words. Do not share this information with your students.

Answers to Reflect and Connect, SE page 398–399

1. Some students might say that they could make out a word within the 0s and 1s in the message, but it is unlikely. Without knowing the rules, it is difficult to know where to start to decode the message. There are too many ways to go about it.
2. There are 15 words on the class list even though there are only 2 symbols used. The symbols could code for many more words because there are many more possible arrangements of 0s and 1s. The arrangement of symbols in the code is how the message is stored.

3a. Examples of words whose meaning is altered by the addition of an "e" at the end include stat and state, fat and fate, hat and hate, mat and mate, us and use, war and ware, or alga and algae.

3b. In the same way the placement of a 0 or 1 in a fax code changes the word it represents, the addition of an "e" changes the meaning of a word.

4. This task gets students thinking about how the words might be related. It also gives them practice at creating a concept map, which is one of the ways they can summarize their understanding of DNA in the evaluate activity. Accept all ideas at this stage. They will learn what the words have in common in the activity *Words to Live By*.
5. Remind students that they have the assignment of finding out more about the word. If you have fewer than 15 students, you will have to assign some students 2 words to make sure that each word is covered. The information they need to discover is more than simply a dictionary definition. Suggest to students that they look in encyclopedias, biology textbooks, and the Web. Encourage them to look at common information sources. Students might come across very complex language when researching their terms in science journals or research studies. Suggest that they keep their research simple but thorough. Inform them that later they will explain their terms to their peers.

Decide on a due date and let students know what it is. The assignment needs to be complete before your class starts the activity *Words to Live By*. For your own reference,

the chart in copymaster 8.3, *Term Chart Completed* summarizes the pertinent information that students should find out about their terms.

EXPLORE

What Is This Stuff?

Activity Overview

In Part I of *What Is This Stuff?*, students will investigate a common thread in the diversity of life. They will explore what is inside the cells of three representative organisms—bananas, peas, and chickens. Students extract a visible substance

of many densely packed dots. So a fax machine codes the document as a series of 0s and 1s. It transmits the code and prints black dots or leaves blank spots. When all the code is printed, the document is reproduced exactly like the original. Look at figure 8.2 to see how some fax machines interpret a code.

Document	Optical reading (reflectivity)	Code	Means	Action
White	High	0	Off	Blank
Black	Low	1	On	Dot

▲ **Figure 8.2 Interpreting fax machine code.** Some fax machines use 0s and 1s to transmit a message.

5. Obtain a sheet of graph paper from your teacher. Use it to help you decipher the code following these guidelines.
   a. Starting at the top left corner of your graph paper, match each square on the graph paper to the corresponding number (0 or 1) in the code. Proceed from left to right across one row then start on the next row.
   b. If the code says "1," fill in the box. (This is your "dot.")
   c. If the code shows a "0," leave the box blank. If you run out of room on your graph paper, staple another sheet to it.

You might find it easier to work with a partner to decipher your message. If so, help each other with each of your codes.

6. When you have revealed your message, record your word on the class list as directed by your teacher.
7. Copy the class list into your science notebook.

Reflect and Connect

Work individually to answer these questions. Record your answers in your science notebook.

1. Would you have been able to read the message if guidelines were not provided for you? Explain your answer.
2. Digital coding only uses 2 symbols (0s and 1s). How many different words are on the class list? Could the same code be used to make more words? Explain your answer.
3. The letter "e" is part of many words.
   a. Give 3 examples of how the addition of an "e" at the end of a word alters its meaning.

that is common to all of these organisms. This substance is DNA. Students observe that, despite the fact that these organisms look different, they all have DNA, and the DNA looks similar among the organisms.

In chapter 7, students learned that chromosomes carry genetic information. In Part II of this activity, you will make a model of a cell that includes representative chromosomes. The students watch as you pop open this model to reveal the chromosomes. They relate this model to their DNA extraction in Part I. Part II of this activity shows students how they obtained their DNA and sets the stage for the next activity, where they will learn about DNA at the molecular level.

This activity enables students to actually collect and see DNA. They can then visualize how they got that DNA and how it relates to the chromosomes.

Before You Teach

Background Information

Deoxyribonucleic acid (DNA) is located in the nucleus of eukaryotic organisms (organisms whose cells have a true nucleus and organelles). DNA makes up about 40 percent of the chromosomes. The rest of the components of the chromosomes are proteins. In prokaryotes, the DNA is in the cytoplasm of the cell. Prokaryotes are organisms without a nucleus in their cells, such as bacteria.

DNA can be extracted from most organisms in a school lab by using a series of chemicals. Usually, the first step is to break up, collect, wash, and resuspend tissue in a salt solution. The salt solution allows the cells to be at a neutral pH and the salt ions help weaken the cell membrane. The next step is to disrupt the cell membranes. Just as detergent removes oils and proteins from laundry or dishes, the detergent in the extraction protocol dissolves the components of the lipid (fat) cell membrane along with some of the cellular proteins. The cells "break open," and the contents spill out. In chapter 5, *Forces of Attraction*, students learned that many soaps and detergents are basic and that bases dissolve or break up fats and oils. The meat tenderizer used in the protocol removes proteins that are around the DNA. The enzymes in the meat tenderizer cut the proteins so that the sample of DNA is "cleaner." When cold alcohol (at least 90 percent) is added to the mixture, it is less dense than water, so it stays on top of the mixture. Protein and oils that were separated out will sink to the bottom. Alcohol precipitates DNA quickly and proteins more slowly, so DNA will precipitate and go toward the alcohol layer. The DNA can then be "spooled" or collected from the top of the test tube. This is a simple extraction, but it allows students to actually see DNA and realize it is a real substance in all living things. DNA can be extracted from many organisms using the protocol from this investigation. Bananas, peas, and chicken liver give particularly good results.

b. Explain how the addition of an "e" is like the code for a fax machine or a bar code.

4. What do you think the words in the class list have in common? Show what they have in common by placing all the words in a concept map as directed in 4a–d.
   a. Write each word on a separate sticky note.
   b. Arrange the sticky notes on a large sheet of paper.
   c. Add linking words between the class words to show what they have in common.
   d. Copy the concept map into your science notebook. You will revisit this concept map in the activity *Words to Live By*.

Review the end of chapter 3, *Collisions—Atomic Style*, to remind yourself how to create a concept map with linking words.

5. Gather information about what your word means. Later in the chapter, you will discuss the words from the class list in more detail. Answer Questions 5a–e as you gather information about your term.
   a. What is it?
   b. What is its function?
   c. Where is it found?
   d. What is it made of?
   e. Why is it important?

You will likely have to look in a few sources, such as on-line encyclopedias. Looking at Web sites and textbooks that focus on biology will also help you. A dictionary alone will not give you enough information to complete the assignment.

What Is This Stuff?

EXPLORE

In chapter 7, you learned that chromosomes carry genetic information. In *Just the Fax*, you saw how codes are used for storing information. Could a code on the chromosomes be responsible for giving organisms their unique characteristics? After all, there are millions of species of organisms, all with their own unique characteristics. That is quite a bit of information! A code would be one way to store this information.

If there is such a code, where is it found? What does it look like? Is this code found in all organisms? Does it look the same for all organisms? In *What Is this Stuff?*, you will work with a partner to go inside the cells of some common living things to search for the substance that makes up the chromosomes and carries the code of life.

Materials—Part I

For the teacher

1 pair of safety goggles
1 safety apron
1 500-mL beaker
1 blender
1 strainer
cheesecloth (Recommended for the chicken liver filtrate. The liver is difficult to remove from a strainer.)
100 mL each of DNA source (½ banana, ½ c chicken liver, and 100 mL dried split peas)
⅛ tsp (pinch) salt
200 mL water
bleach solution

For each team of 2 students

2 pairs of safety goggles
2 safety aprons
1 5-mL graduated cylinder
1 10-mL graduated cylinder
1 50-mL glass beaker
1 large test tube
1 test-tube rack
1 wooden splint or metal spatula
1 glass stirring rod (optional)
20 mL filtrate
Woolite liquid detergent in beakers or bottles
meat tenderizer in small containers
cold ethanol
1 clock or timer

Materials—Part II

For the teacher

6 pieces of yarn, each 10 cm long
1 small, resealable, clear plastic bag
1 paper bag

Advance Preparation

For Part I, purchase the necessary materials. You can get meat tenderizer, Woolite, chicken liver, split peas, and bananas at a grocery store. Ethanol can be purchased through a laboratory supply company. Ethanol is also sold under the name of grain alcohol and is available at liquor stores. Denatured ethanol will not work. Check with your school to find out the policy of purchasing and using ethanol in this manner. Rubbing alcohol will not work for this protocol because it is not pure enough alcohol to pull the DNA from the filtrate. Ethanol is recommended because it is close to 100 percent alcohol.

Prepare filtrates from 3 different sources separately. The procedure for preparing all the filtrates is the same. The only factor that changes is the DNA source. To prepare the filtrate, do the following.

1. Place the DNA source (the banana, the peas, or the chicken liver) in a blender with a pinch (⅛ teaspoon) of salt and 200 milliliters (mL) of water.
2. Blend the mixture for 15 seconds on high speed.
3. Strain the mixture through the strainer (cheesecloth works best for chicken liver) into a 500-mL beaker.
4. Put 20 mL of filtrate in 50-mL beakers to distribute to the students.

Use fresh filtrate to distribute to the class. Try to make the filtrate within a few hours of using it. You can prepare it in front of the students so that they see what you are doing, but you must clean out the blender between each batch of filtrate.

Fill small beakers or bottles with the detergent so that students can access it easily.

Fill small containers (film canisters, paper cups, etc.) with meat tenderizer so students can access it easily.

Put a container of ethanol on ice or in a chemical freezer.

For Part II, make a model of a cell by doing the following.

1. Cut up a piece of yarn so that you have an even number of pieces, each about 10 centimeters long.
2. Place the yarn pieces in a resealable, clear plastic bag.
3. Place the bag containing the yarn in a small paper bag.
4. Blow air into the paper bag to expand it. You can do this step just before the demonstration.

Cautions

Many of the materials in this investigation are common household substances, but students need to exercise caution throughout. Students should be careful working with the chicken liver mixture

Part I: Extracting Information

Materials

For each team of 2 students

2 pairs of safety goggles
2 safety aprons
1 5-mL graduated cylinder
1 10-mL graduated cylinder
1 large test tube
1 test-tube rack
1 50-mL beaker containing 20 mL of filtered material (from your teacher)
1 wooden splint or metal spatula
Woolite liquid detergent
meat tenderizer
cold ethanol
1 clock or timer

Cautions

During this investigation, wear safety goggles at all times. Ethanol is very flammable. Make sure there are no open flames or burners turned on nearby. Keep the lids on all of the solutions when not in use. Do not inhale any fumes. Be sure to wash your hands thoroughly after this investigation. Wash your hands thoroughly after handling the filtrate. Wipe counters with a dilute bleach solution if you spill any filtrate.

Process and Procedure

1. Look at the names of the organisms your teacher has written on the board.
   a. Think back to the activity *Unity and Diversity* in chapter 6. What are some things these organisms have in common?
   b. Write down your ideas in your science notebook.

2. Read the protocol *Extracting the Substance of Life* to learn how you can search for the special substance that organisms have in common. You will need to get into the cells of organisms to find it.
3. Gather the materials you need and follow the protocol.

400 Unit 2 Inside Life

because harmful bacteria grow readily on raw chicken. Make sure students wash their hands after working with this mixture and wipe surfaces with a dilute bleach solution. Students should wear safety goggles at all times. Ethanol is highly flammable. Make sure there are no open flames when working with the ethanol. Limit the amount of ethanol in the classroom to 300 mL. Ethanol is a laboratory chemical, and chemicals should never be stored with food. Do not store ethanol in a freezer with food. Tell the students to keep the lids on all the solutions when they are not using them and not to inhale fumes. Remind students to wash their hands after this investigation.

As You Teach

Outcomes and Indicators of Success

By the end of this activity, students should

1. understand that all organisms have DNA in their cells.

   They will demonstrate their understanding by

   - extracting the same substance (DNA) from both plants and animals,
   - describing a way to prove that DNA is found only in living things, and
   - modeling DNA extraction with a paper bag cell.

2. become aware that DNA makes up the chromosomes.

   They will demonstrate their awareness by modeling DNA extraction with a paper bag cell, plastic bag nucleus, yarn chromosomes, and one strand of yarn representing DNA.

3. be able to follow a protocol to extract DNA and relate a model to the extraction.

   They will demonstrate their ability by

   - reading and following the instructions in a protocol to spool DNA successfully and
   - matching each step in the DNA extraction to part of the teacher demonstration.

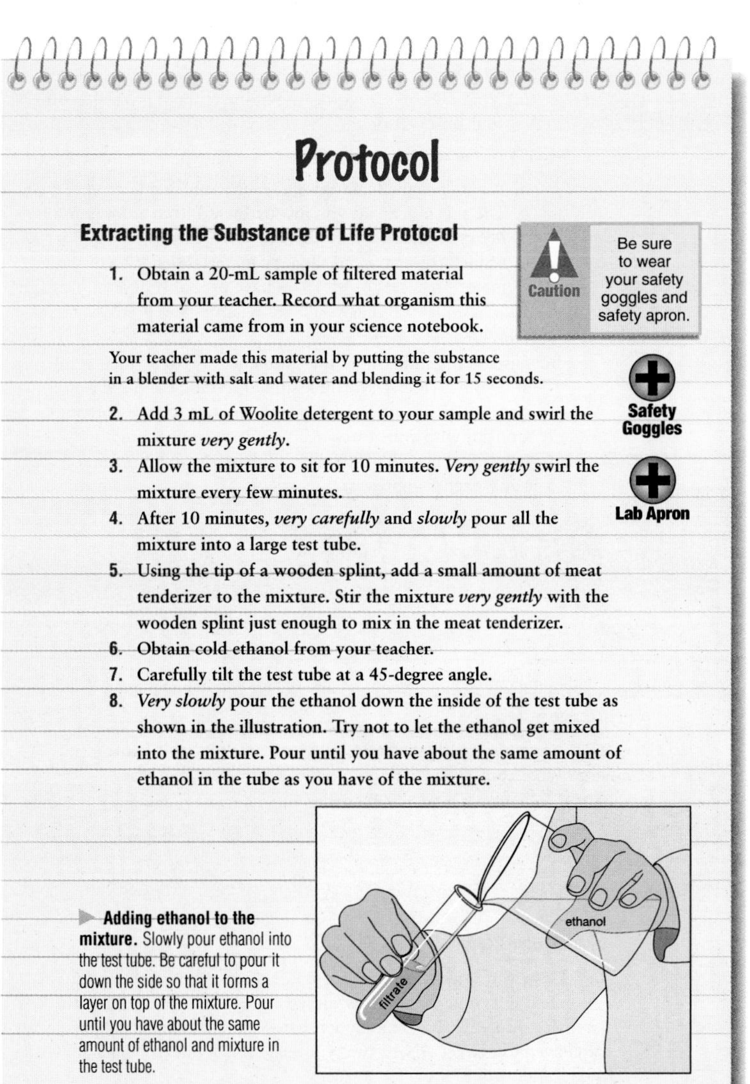

Protocol

Extracting the Substance of Life Protocol

Caution Be sure to wear your safety goggles and safety apron.

Safety Goggles

Lab Apron

1. Obtain a 20-mL sample of filtered material from your teacher. Record what organism this material came from in your science notebook.

Your teacher made this material by putting the substance in a blender with salt and water and blending it for 15 seconds.

2. Add 3 mL of Woolite detergent to your sample and swirl the mixture *very gently*.
3. Allow the mixture to sit for 10 minutes. *Very gently* swirl the mixture every few minutes.
4. After 10 minutes, *very carefully* and *slowly* pour all the mixture into a large test tube.
5. Using the tip of a wooden splint, add a small amount of meat tenderizer to the mixture. Stir the mixture *very gently* with the wooden splint just enough to mix in the meat tenderizer.
6. Obtain cold ethanol from your teacher.
7. Carefully tilt the test tube at a 45-degree angle.
8. *Very slowly* pour the ethanol down the inside of the test tube as shown in the illustration. Try not to let the ethanol get mixed into the mixture. Pour until you have about the same amount of ethanol in the tube as you have of the mixture.

▶ **Adding ethanol to the mixture.** Slowly pour ethanol into the test tube. Be careful to pour it down the side so that it forms a layer on top of the mixture. Pour until you have about the same amount of ethanol and mixture in the test tube.

Chapter 8 Instructions for Life 401

Strategies

Getting Started

Have a student read the introduction out loud to the class. Ask the class if it is aware of any codes in the chromosomes. A student might suggest DNA. If so, use this opportunity to assess students' prior knowledge of DNA. Ask the class if it knows what DNA looks like or how it works. If students have figured out that they are looking for DNA, ask them how they might go about doing that.

Cautions

Many of the materials in this investigation are common household substances, but students need to exercise caution throughout. Students should wear safety goggles at all times. Ethanol is highly flammable. Make sure there are no open flames when working with the ethanol. Limit the amount of ethanol in the classroom to 300 mL. Ethanol is a laboratory chemical, and chemicals should never be stored with food. Do not store ethanol in a freezer with food. Tell the students to keep the lids on all the solutions when they are not using them and not to inhale fumes. Remind students to wash their hands after this investigation.

Process and Procedure

Part I: Extracting Information

Materials

For the teacher

1 pair of safety goggles
1 safety apron

1 500-mL beaker
1 blender
1 strainer
cheesecloth (Recommended for the chicken liver filtrate. The liver is difficult to remove from a strainer.)
100 mL each of DNA sources (½ banana, ½ c chicken liver, and 100 mL dried split peas)
⅛ tsp (pinch) salt
200 mL water

For each team of 2 students

2 pairs of safety goggles
2 safety aprons
1 5-mL graduated cylinder
1 10-mL graduated cylinder
1 50-mL glass beaker
1 large test tube
1 test-tube rack
1 wooden splint or metal spatula
1 glass stirring rod (optional)
20 mL filtrate
Woolite liquid detergent in beakers or bottles
meat tenderizer in small containers
cold ethanol
1 clock or timer

For Step 1, write the terms "chicken," "pea," and "banana" on the board. Ask the class what these three organisms have in common. Students might say that they are all living or once living and that they are all made of cells. Since they just finished chapter 7, they might say that they all have chromosomes. Use this response as a starting point to ask them if they know what chromosomes are made of. Tell the class that it is going to journey into the cells of these organisms to look at the material that makes up the chromosomes.

For Step 2, make sure that the students have read and understand the *Extracting the Substance of Life Protocol.* Tell each team what organism it is investigating. Provide each team with 20 mL of filtrate. Arrange the number of teams so that there are equal numbers of teams working with each filtrate. After the teams have their filtrates, circulate around the room, reminding students to be very gentle stirring the mixture when adding the detergent and meat tenderizer. Emphasize that the protocol uses the words *gently* and *slowly* for a reason. In Step 8 of the protocol, the students will pour ethanol into their test tubes of filtrate. Remind the students to add the cold ethanol very slowly down the side of the tube. Students hold their test tubes at a 45-degree angle; they must not let the layers mix. The alcohol will pull the DNA out of the filtrate as long as the alcohol layer remains above the filtrate layer.

Students should observe the alcohol pulling the strange material (DNA) out of the filtrate. Encourage the students to observe closely what is happening in the test tube as they slowly add the alcohol. The interface between the layers might be more visible by placing a dark-colored sheet of paper behind the test tube.

Remind students to keep a continuous record of their observations in their science notebooks. Circulate around the room and ask probing questions about their observations. For example, ask are following:

- "What do you notice in the ethanol?"
- "What does it look like?"
- "Does it look the same as the other teams'?"
- "What does that tell you about this material?"

The students' answers to the questions in Step 4 might vary slightly depending on the quality and yield of the DNA.

Answers to Step 4 are on TE page 403.
Answers to Stop and Think—Part I are on TE page 404.

4. Answer the following questions in your science notebook as you follow the protocol.
   a. What do you see happening in the ethanol layer? Record your observations.

Recall what you know about solubility.

   b. What does the material in the ethanol layer look like?
   c. The substance that you just extracted from an organism is **deoxyribonucleic acid (DNA)**. DNA carries the code for all of life. You extracted the very material that directs all the major processes of life! You have probably at least heard of DNA. List 3 things you already know about DNA.
5. Observe other teams' results.
6. Discuss the similarities and differences between their results and yours. Does DNA look similar among the organisms your class used? Record your thoughts in your science notebook.
7. Consult with your teacher if you want to perform any further investigations with the DNA. Only perform investigations that your teacher approves.

Stop & THINK

PART I

Work individually to answer these questions. Record your answers in your science notebook.

1. Does DNA appear to be the same for all organisms? What is your evidence? What could you do to be more certain of your answer?
2. How could you show that DNA is found only in living or once-living things?

Part II: What Happened in the Cells?

How were you able to get enough DNA to see it in the test tube? Where did it come from? How did you reach it? In this part of the activity, you will observe a model that explores the protocol you followed to extract DNA. You will relate this model to your DNA extraction from Part I.

Answers to Step 4, SE page 402

4a. Students should observe a substance collecting at the interface between the ethanol and the filtrate. It will look as though the DNA is collecting in a stringy mass. Figure T8.1 shows what this substance should look like.

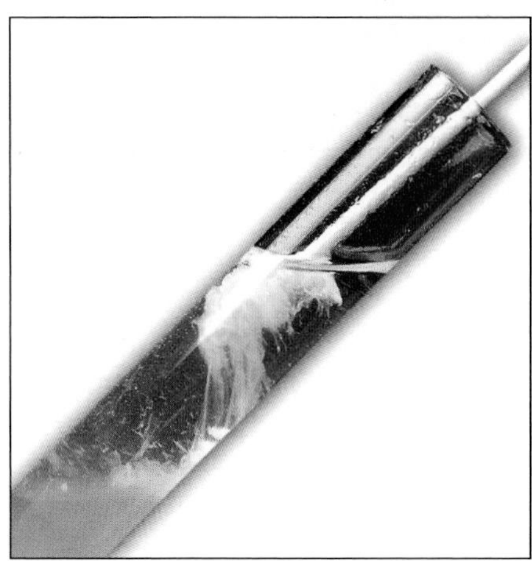

▲ **Figure T8.1 Spooled DNA.** The extracted DNA should look similar to this.

4b. The material in the ethanol is a white, stringy, filamentous mass.

4c. Students probably already have heard of DNA and know something about it. Their answers will vary depending on their prior knowledge, but typical answers might include, "DNA is used to identify people." "DNA is the code of life." "DNA is in cells." "DNA has parts called A, C, T, and G."

Ask probing questions to help prompt their thinking and help you assess their prior knowledge. You might ask the following:

- "What have you heard about DNA?"
- "Do you know what 'DNA' stands for?"
- "What is special about DNA?"

In Step 5, the teams will look at other teams' DNA samples. Have the teams display their samples along with the name of their organism so that other teams can easily observe them. Have them label their test tubes with where the sample came from and place the tubes in a test-tube rack located in an area of the room where students can easily observe it. The DNA can be "spooled" by taking a glass stirring rod, putting it in the DNA sample, and slowly turning the stirring rod. You might explain that their DNA sample is not pure. The stringy mass contains proteins and cell fragments as well as DNA.

Step 7 is an optional challenge for students. Students might want to further purify the DNA by putting it in fresh alcohol. They might want to dry their DNA sample. Some students might want to look at the DNA through a microscope. If you take time for students to do this, realize that they won't be able to see much more than they can with the naked eye. Only allow students to perform investigations that are safe and acceptable classroom practices.

To challenge your students after the class has completed this activity, you might provide them with the opportunity to conduct an inquiry investigation around this protocol. The protocol used for extracting DNA in this activity is a standard protocol for DNA extraction, but many modifications can be made. Students could investigate questions such as, "Does the amount of meat tenderizer affect the results?" and "Do different brands of detergent work as well as Woolite?" (Actually, you do not have to use Woolite. As long as the detergent contains SDS—sodium dodecyl sulfate—it should work [dodecyl = lauryl]. Woolite produces excellent results, so we recommend it in the protocol.) Other inquiries might involve the timing of the steps. The source of DNA could also be an inquiry. "Do kidney beans yield as much DNA as peas per milliliter?"

Materials

none

Process and Procedure

1. Think about the purpose of each step in the protocol. What happened to the filtered material during each step? Discuss your thoughts with your partner. To help prompt your thinking, do the following.
   a. Look at figure 8.3 to refresh your memory of cell parts.
   b. Locate the chromosomes in figure 8.3.
   c. Read through the protocol again including how your teacher made the material to give to you.

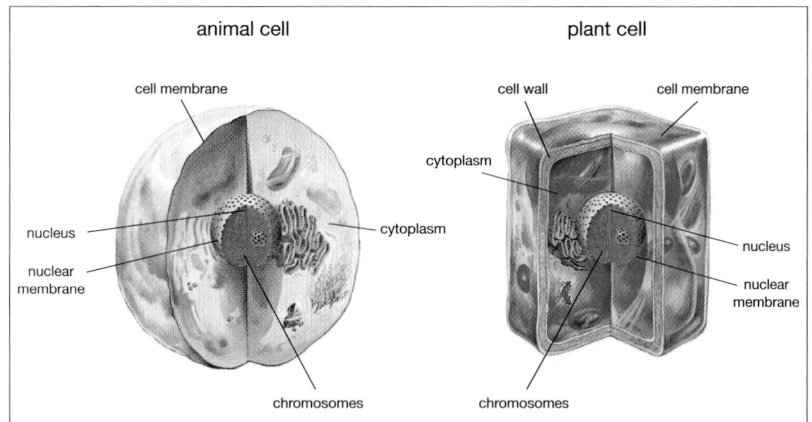

▲ **Figure 8.3 Plant and animal cells.** How did you extract DNA from cells?

2. Look at the model that your teacher has prepared. This model represents 1 cell. Watch as your teacher conducts a demonstration with the model and think about how this demonstration relates to your investigation.

Any additional inquiries should be conducted in your classroom under your supervision and with your approval.

Answers to Stop and Think—Part I, SE page 402

1. Yes, DNA appears to be the same for all organisms. The evidence is that DNA was extracted using the same protocol for each of the 3 organisms. The DNA looked the same for all 3 organisms. Students could have more confidence in their answers if they extracted DNA for other organisms following this protocol.

   This protocol might not always produce the same results. The nature and quantity of the cells removed will vary among organisms. If following this protocol failed to extract DNA, it does not mean that the organism does not have DNA.

2. Students could show that DNA is found only in living things by following this protocol to try to extract DNA from nonliving things such as rocks, fabric, and metal.

Process and Procedure

Part II: What Happened in the Cells?

Materials

For the teacher

6 pieces of yarn, each 10 cm long
1 small, resealable, clear plastic bag
1 paper bag

In Step 1, the students begin to think about how they released DNA from the cells. Remind them of basic cell parts and encourage them to look at figure 8.3 in their student books.

For Step 2, tell the students that you are going to present them with a visual model of extracting DNA from a cell. Ask them to watch carefully and think about how what you are demonstrating relates to cells in nature and to Part I of this activity. Hold up the model of the cell so that all students in the class can see it. Perform the demonstration as follows. Make sure that the entire class can see what you are doing during each step.

1. Pop the paper bag, revealing the plastic bag inside.
2. Rip open the inside bag, allowing the pieces of yarn to spill out.
3. Pick up 1 piece of yarn.
4. Remove 1 strand of thread from 1 piece of yarn and hold it up (see figure T8.2).

In Step 3, have students look at the table in figure 8.4 of their books. Students fill out the table by relating your demonstration to the DNA extraction. See figure T8.3 for a completed table to help you guide the students. The students might not know

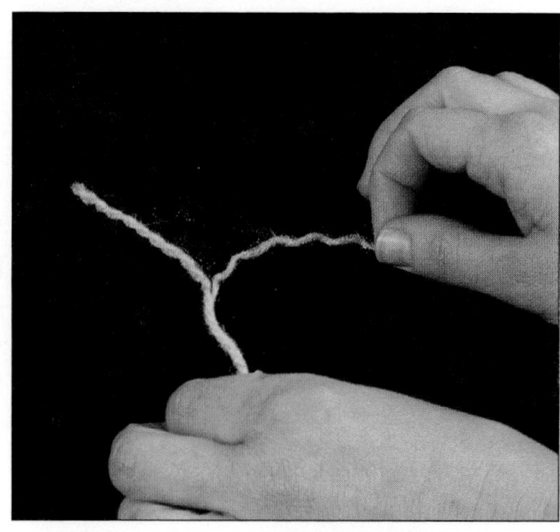

▲ **Figure T8.2 Removing strand from yarn.** Help students recognize that each piece of yarn represents DNA. Each human chromosome consists of one DNA molecule and proteins. As you remove a strand of thread from the yarn, you model separating DNA from the proteins, which are also in chromosomes.

Answers to Reflect and Connect are on TE page 404a.

3. In your science notebook, make a copy of the table shown in figure 8.4. Fill in the table, which relates the DNA extraction process to your teacher's demonstration.

Part in the model	What part of the cell is represented in the model?	What happens to the part in the demonstration?	How did you achieve this step in your DNA extraction?

▲ **Figure 8.4 Comparing DNA extraction with the teacher demonstration.** How did you reach the DNA?

Reflect and Connect

Answer these questions individually. Write your answers in your science notebook.

Describe in your own words what you did at the cellular level to extract DNA from your organism.

1. You probably did not have much success in finding a code in the DNA that you extracted. In fact, scientists didn't find the code in DNA until the 1950s. Why do you think it was so difficult to find the code in DNA?
2. How did observing the teacher demonstration help you understand your DNA extraction process?

EXPLAIN

Clips of DNA

In *What Is This Stuff?*, it might have seemed that you magically made a substance appear out of a blended mess! In reality, however, you have just taken a journey inside the many cells of an organism. At the end of that journey, you isolated DNA—deoxyribonucleic acid. You learned that all organisms have DNA. If all organisms have DNA, then it must be pretty important to life. What is so special about DNA and how does it code for the many traits of so many organisms? In *Clips of DNA*, you will begin to answer these questions as you look closer at DNA to learn about its structure.

Part in the model	What part of the cell is represented in the model?	What happens to the part in the demonstration?	How did you achieve this step in your DNA extraction?
Paper bag	Cell membrane	The teacher pops the paper bag.	The blender separated many cells. The salt acts as a buffer. The Woolite dissolves the cell membrane and the cell wall because they are made up of lipids (fats). It also breaks up proteins.
Plastic bag	Nucleus or nuclear membrane	The teacher pops the plastic bag.	The Woolite breaks up the lipids and proteins in the nuclear membrane.
Yarn	Chromosomes	Several yarn pieces fall out of the plastic bag.	
1 piece of yarn	1 chromosome	The teacher picks up 1 piece of yarn.	
1 strand of yarn	DNA	The teacher pulls 1 strand from 1 piece of yarn.	The meat tenderizer cuts proteins from around the DNA.

▲ **Figure T8.3 Completed table for Step 3.** Students' completed tables should have information similar to what is provided here.

how each step in the protocol worked in the extraction process. Help them by discussing how the chemicals are used in daily life, such as detergents.

Emphasize the part of the model that shows that DNA makes up the chromosomes. This part of the activity leads into the first explain activity, *Clips of DNA*.

Answers to Reflect and Connect, SE page 404

1. It was difficult for scientists to find a code in DNA because DNA is so small and there are large quantities of it in cells. Scientists also lacked the technology to understand DNA's structure at the molecular level.
2. This model helps students visualize the purpose of each step in the DNA extraction investigation. Visualizing helps learners understand processes because the learners can see what is happening in situations when we are unable to observe something directly.

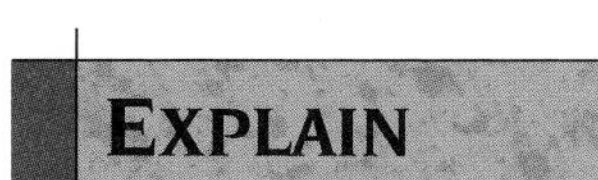

Clips of DNA

Activity Overview

Students will read a short passage introducing them to DNA. They will learn what DNA is made of and they will begin to think of how it plays a role in life. In Part I of *Clips of DNA*, students will read about the DNA molecule and make a model of DNA using paper clips. In Part II, they will read about the process of DNA replication and how it relates to mitosis and meiosis. The students then model the process of DNA replication using paper clips.

Before You Teach

Background Information

Heredity begins at the molecular level with DNA. DNA is the molecule that stores the information for making proteins that are necessary for life. DNA is in all living things. The chromosomes in cells are made up of DNA and proteins.

In 1869, Johann Friedrich Miescher first isolated DNA. He extracted DNA from various organisms and noticed it looked the same from each. He concluded that DNA was an essential component of life but had no idea how essential it was. In 1953, James Watson and Francis Crick proposed a model for the structure of the DNA. Watson and Crick used evidence from studies on DNA to come up with their model. This model explained how the DNA code might work. Watson and Crick stated that DNA was made up of nucleotides arranged in the shape of a double helix. See the sidebar *In Search of DNA* for a detailed discussion on the evidence Watson and Crick used to come up with their model.

DNA molecules consist of a series of nucleotides connected by phosphodiester bonds to form a long strand. There are four different nucleotides in DNA because there are four different nitrogen bases. The four nitrogenous bases are adenine (A), thymine (T), guanine (G), and cytosine (C). DNA is a double-stranded molecule, meaning two long DNA strands are connected through their nitrogenous bases via hydrogen bonds. Adenine can only bond with thymine, and guanine can only bond with cytosine. Because of the specific pairing between bases, the two strands are said to be complementary.

Each strand of DNA is said to run antiparallel, meaning they run in opposite directions. Therefore, DNA strands have two distinctive ends: the 5' (5-prime) and 3' (3-prime) ends. If you count clockwise from the oxygen molecule, 5' is the 5th carbon in the ribose ring; 3' is the 3rd carbon in the ribose ring. The 5' carbon has an attached phosphate group, while the 3' carbon has a hydroxyl group. Since the strands of the helix are antiparallel, the 3' end on one side of the double helix is opposite the 5' end on the other strand (see figure T8.4). DNA replication and transcription always occur in the 5' to 3' direction.

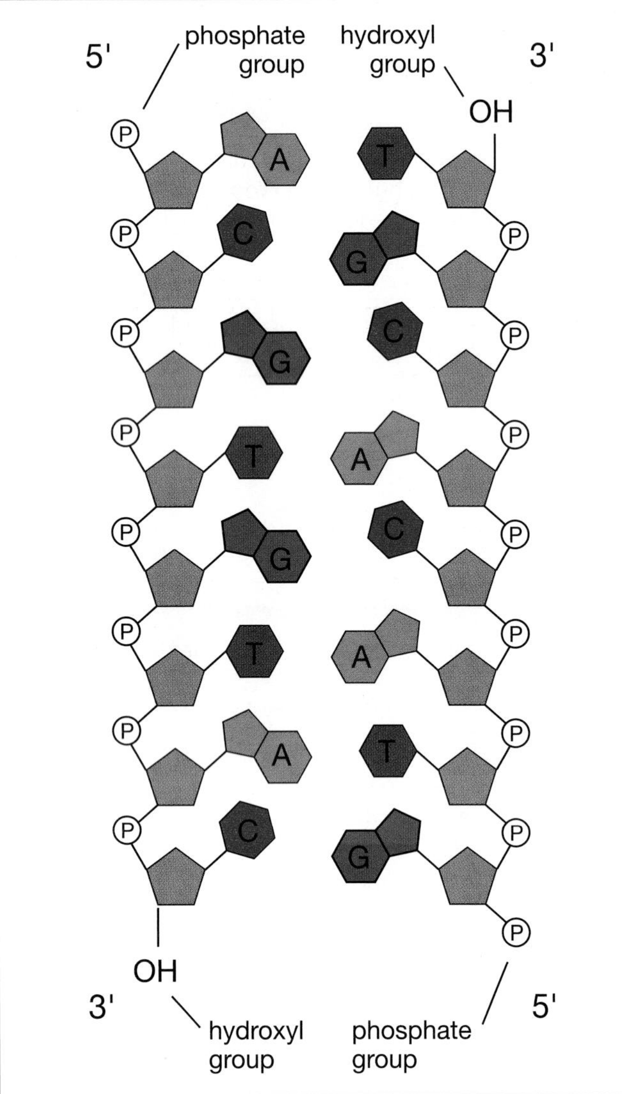

Figure T8.4 **DNA is antiparallel.** The two strands of DNA are arranged antiparallel to each other. The strands have the same chemical structure but run in the opposite direction.

The two complementary strands of DNA intertwine, forming a double helix that winds around a central axis like a twisted ladder that has its sides spiraling. DNA can also twist beyond the helical shape, which allows much important information to be packed into small places. From end to end, there are 6 feet of DNA packed into a single human cell! This would be like packing all the roads and highways in the United States into a single city. The double-stranded structure of DNA is also important in how it is copied, which students will learn about in the next activity.

DNA replication is semiconservative. This means that when the double strands separate, a daughter strand is constructed that is complementary to each original strand. Therefore, after DNA replication, there are two "original" strands of DNA and two complementary "daughter" strands. There are two double helices, each one with one new strand and one old strand.

The sequence of base pairs in DNA ultimately determines a person's genetic makeup and provides the foundation for evolution. The sequence of DNA provides the code to make proteins. The process of protein synthesis will be explored in greater detail in the next investigation.

Materials—Part I

For each team of 2 students

25 red paper clips
25 yellow paper clips
25 green paper clips
25 blue paper clips
tape
cups to hold the paper clips

Materials—Part II

For each team of 2 students

25 red paper clips
25 yellow paper clips
25 green paper clips
25 blue paper clips
tape
cups to hold the paper clips

Advance Preparation

Gather enough colored paper clips for each pair of students. Many office supply stores sell paper clips in individual colors. You can also buy mixed packages and have students sort them.

Educational Technologies

Several Web sites provide helpful animations and activities for students. For example, the PBS Web site has a lot of useful information including an activity titled DNA Workshop. Cold Spring Harbor Laboratory has a Web site called DNA Interactive, which has historical information as well as interesting animations and video clips.

If you have state standards related to developmental and cell differentiation, see the optional reading *Differentiation and Development.*

As You Teach

Outcomes and Indicators of Success

By the end of this activity, students should

1. develop an understanding of the basic structure of DNA.

   They will demonstrate their understanding by

   - building a model of DNA using paper clips showing that DNA is a long chain of repeating subunits called nucleotides;
   - explaining that each colored paper clip represents a different nucleotide (A, C, T, G) in DNA;
   - creating a complementary strand of DNA from an original one; and
   - explaining that it is beneficial for DNA to twist so that it can fit into a cell.

2. better understand the process and purpose of DNA replication.

   They will demonstrate their understanding by

   - correctly making a complementary strand of DNA from an original model strand and

- explaining the significance of DNA being a double-stranded molecule.

3. realize the role of DNA replication in the production of new cells.

   They will demonstrate their realization by

   - describing that the purpose of DNA replication is to make copies of DNA so that copies of the DNA can go into new cells,
   - explaining that the purpose of mitosis is to make new nongerm cells for growth and replacement in organisms,
   - explaining that the purpose of meiosis is to make germ cells for reproduction and those germ cells contain copies of DNA from the original cell, and
   - explaining that DNA replication is important in mitosis and meiosis because DNA carries the instructions that those new cells need.

4. begin to understand the contribution of scientists to the discovery of DNA.

   They will demonstrate their understanding by answering questions about the sidebar *In Search of DNA*.

Answers to Step 1 are on TE page 406.

Part I: The Structure of DNA

DNA makes up part of the chromosomes in cells. The DNA that you extracted in the explore investigation of this chapter sure did not look like pictures you have seen of chromosomes. This is because you extracted such an enormous quantity of DNA from many cells. In order to look at chromosomes, you would have to isolate just one cell and look at it in a way that would not disrupt the chromosomes.

Imagine that DNA is represented by the fiber that your teacher pulled from the yarn at the end of the explore activity. If you have looked at DNA with a microscope, it probably looked stringy or like a blob. If you had the technology and capabilities to look at DNA closer than you can with a microscope, what would you see? What makes up DNA? In Part I, you will work with a partner to begin to learn how DNA relates to chromosomes and what DNA, itself, is made of.

Materials

For each team of 2 students

25 red paper clips
25 yellow paper clips
25 green paper clips
25 blue paper clips
tape
cups to hold the paper clips

Process and Procedure

1. Read *The Code in DNA* to learn about DNA's structure and use Steps 1a–b as a guide. As you are reading, pay close attention to the components of DNA. You will apply your understanding of this reading by making a model of DNA.
   a. Create an analogy map comparing a train with DNA. The headings for your analogy map should be "Part of a Train," "Part of DNA," and "How the Part of the Train Is Similar to a Part of DNA."
   b. Compare your analogy map with another student's map. Revise or add information to your analogy map based on what you learn from your classmate.

Strategies

Getting Started

Remind students about the demonstration in Part II of the activity *What Is This Stuff?* Ask the students if they saw a code in the DNA if they viewed it through a microscope. They will likely say that they did not. Tell the class that it took a long time and elaborate technology to find a code in DNA. Have the class read the introduction. Tell them that they are now going to look at DNA at the molecular level by modeling DNA's structure. Reinforce the concept that a DNA molecule is very small and it took a long time before scientists could understand it at a molecular level.

Process and Procedure

Part I: The Structure of DNA

Materials

For each team of 2 students

25 red paper clips
25 yellow paper clips
25 green paper clips
25 blue paper clips
tape
cups to hold the paper clips

In Step 1, the students read *The Code in DNA*. After the students have read the passage, ask if they have any questions about DNA. Link their understanding from the previous investigation in which they extracted DNA to what they have just read. Remind them that they will apply their understanding of this passage by constructing their own model of DNA. Encourage students to share their understanding with the class or with a partner. They should create an analogy map that looks similar to figure T8.5. Make sure students take time to compare their analogy map to another student's map. They should revise or add information to their map based on what they learn from a classmate.

part of a train	part of DNA	how the part of the train is similar to a part of DNA
type of car	nucleotides	There are four different types of cars and there are four different nucleotides.
box car	cytosine	The box car looks different than the other cars and cytosine is chemically different than the other nucleotides.
oil car	adenine	The oil car looks different than the other cars and adenine is chemically different than the other nucleotides.
coal car	guanine	The coal car looks different than the other cars and guanine is chemically different than the other nucleotides.
lumber car	thymine	The lumber car looks different than the other cars and thymine is chemically different than the other nucleotides.

▲ **Figure T8.5 Analogy map for Step 1.** Students' analogy maps should show how a train is similar to the code in DNA.

Answers to Step 1, SE page 405

1. An example of an analogy map comparing DNA with a train model is shown in figure T8.5.

NOTES:

READING

The Code in DNA

DNA is the genetic material required for the building, maintenance, and regulation of the cells of all living organisms. Recall from chapter 7 that in humans and other eukaryotes DNA molecules are organized into structures called chromosomes. That is, each chromosome consists of one, unbroken DNA molecule and many protein molecules. As figure 8.5 shows, the DNA coils tightly into beadlike clusters.

In *What Is This Stuff?*, you extracted the molecule containing the genetic code, DNA, from three organisms. This code is inherited and carries with it the instructions for all of life. You probably did not see a code in your DNA sample. Even scientists had a difficult time finding the code in DNA. A biologist by the name of Johann Friedrich Miescher first isolated DNA in 1869, but the code was not discovered until the 1950s. This is because DNA is very small. In order to find the code that DNA carries, scientists had to look very deeply into the DNA and examine it at the molecular level. When scientists looked closely at the molecular structure of DNA, they could see DNA's code. Instead of numbers like a digital code,

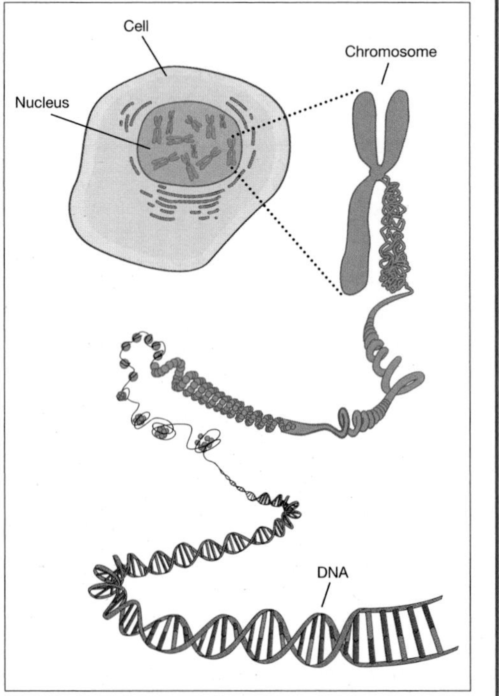

▲ **Figure 8.5 Eukaryotic chromosome structure.** In eukaryotes, chromosomes are found within the nucleus. Each chromosome consists of one molecule of DNA. The molecule is wrapped tightly into beadlike structures. Fully extended, the DNA in one human chromosome would be about 5 centimeters long. What advantage might efficient packing of DNA offer a cell?

NOTES:

DNA's code is made up of a string of molecules. These special molecules are called **nucleotides**. Each nucleotide, in turn, is made up of three components: a sugar molecule, a phosphate group, and a molecule with nitrogen in it, which is called a nitrogen base. To learn more about the discoveries that have contributed to our understanding of DNA, read the sidebar *In Search of* DNA and look at FYI—A DNA *Timeline*.

In DNA, there are four types of nucleotides. Each nucleotide is different because of its nitrogen base. Figure 8.6 shows one type of nucleotide with the nitrogen base: cytosine.

To simplify how DNA is written, scientists label the entire nucleotide with a letter to represent its base. For example, scientists refer to a nucleotide with the cytosine base as "C." The other nitrogen bases in DNA are adenine (A), guanine (G), and thymine (T).

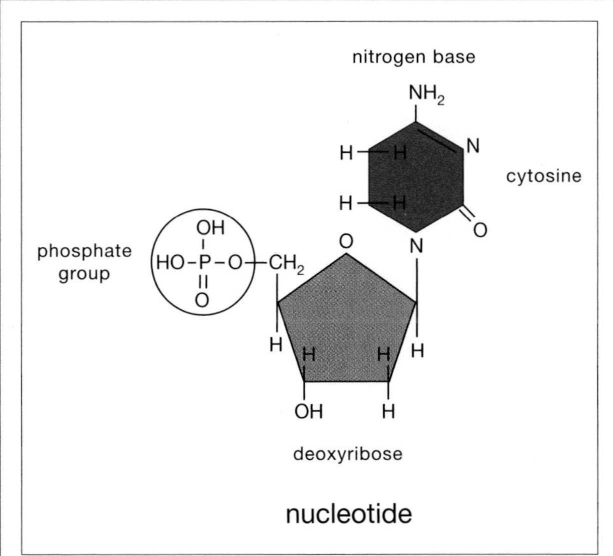

▲ **Figure 8.6 Nucleotide with cytosine as the nitrogen base.** A DNA nucleotide is made up of a phosphate group, a sugar (deoxyribose), and a nitrogen base.

Chapter 8 Instructions for Life 407

NOTES:

The Code in DNA, continued

A DNA strand is a very long strand of nucleotides. These nucleotides are held together by covalent bonds. Figure 8.7 shows a DNA strand of nucleotides.

There are billions of nucleotides in the cells of every organism. You can think of a DNA strand as a very long train with four different designs of railcars. The designs of the cars represent the different types of nucleotides (A, C, T, and G). The arrangement of nucleotides (the order of the railcars) is called the DNA sequence. Figure 8.8 illustrates a segment of DNA using the train analogy. Each of the four types of cars corresponds with one of the four types of nucleotides.

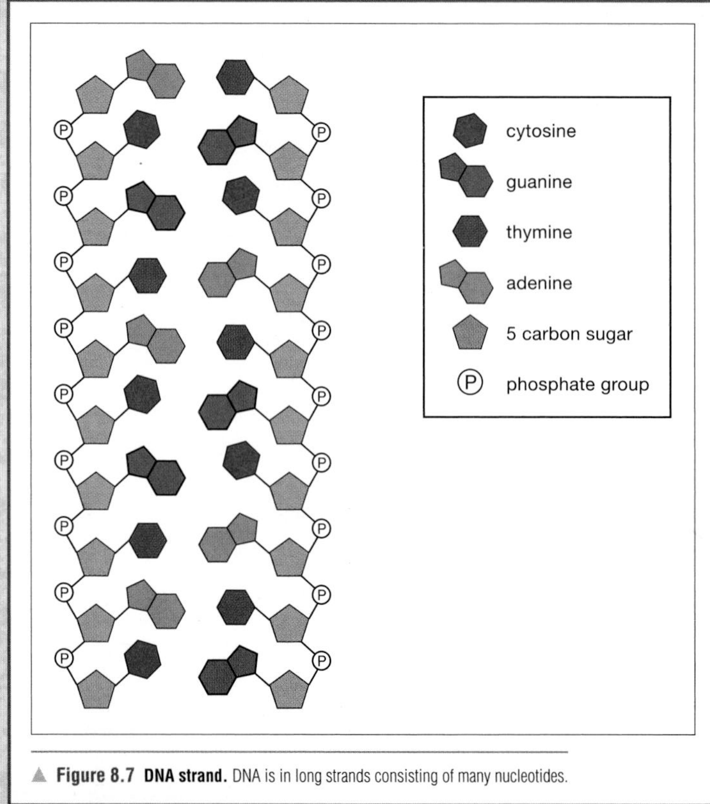

▲ **Figure 8.7 DNA strand.** DNA is in long strands consisting of many nucleotides.

NOTES:

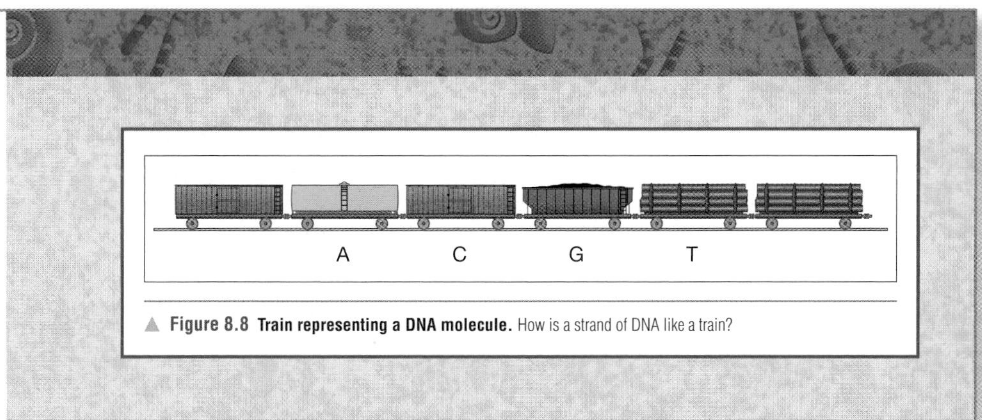

▲ **Figure 8.8 Train representing a DNA molecule.** How is a strand of DNA like a train?

2. Work with a partner and make a model of DNA by completing Steps 2a–c. Often, making a model helps people understand how things work.
   a. Collect 15 paper clips of 4 different colors (red, blue, yellow, and green).
   b. Build a chain of paper clips using different colors. Make the chain 15 paper clips long, in any order. This chain represents a very small section of DNA.

Attach the paper clips end to end to form a long chain.

   c. Label this chain by attaching tape to your starting end.
3. Determine the DNA sequence of your chain by following Steps 3a–c.
   a. Look at the table in figure 8.9 to learn what each colored paper clip represents in your DNA model.
   b. Record the DNA sequence of your chain in your science notebook.
   c. Verify the sequence by comparing the sequence you recorded with that of your partner.

Nucleotide	Color of paper clip
A (adenine)	Green
T (thymine)	Red
G (guanine)	Yellow
C (cytosine)	Blue

▲ **Figure 8.9 Nucleotide key.** In your model, each color of paper clip represents each different nucleotide.

In Step 2, as the students are building their model DNA strands, circulate around the room to see if the students have any questions. At this point, they are constructing a simple, randomly assembled paper clip chain. In Step 3, they will correlate their chain with DNA.

During Step 3, make sure that the students understand how the colors code for the four nucleotides of DNA. Remind the students to label the starting end of their strands with tape. They will use the table in figure 8.9 in the student book as a key so that they can record the sequence of their chains. Check that students are recording their DNA sequence correctly.

NOTES:

In Step 4, the students will answer questions related to their model DNA strands.

Answers to Step 4, SE page 410

4a. Each paper clip represents a nucleotide, which is a subunit of DNA.

4b. The paper clip chain makes a good model of DNA because the different-colored paper clips represent the different nucleotides. Also, paper clips hook together to make a chain much like nucleotides make a strand of DNA. Students could improve this model by making it three dimensional; labeling each component; or breaking down each part of the nucleotide into the sugar, the phosphate, and the nitrogenous base. They could also improve the model by representing the antiparallel nature of DNA. The paper clip model is a simple representation of a complex structure.

4c. When students compare their DNA strands with other groups' strands, they should notice that all strands have the same nucleotides (A, C, T, and G) and all are in a chain. The main difference between each strand is that the sequence (order of the paper clips) is different.

4. Spread your paper clip chain out on your desk and discuss the answers to the following questions with your partner. Record your answers in your science notebook.
   a. What subunit of DNA does each paper clip represent?
   b. Describe what makes this paper clip chain a good model of DNA. What could you do to improve this model? Give reasons for your answer.
   c. Compare your strand of DNA with another team's strand. What are the similarities and differences between the 2 strands?

Recall from the *Just the Fax* activity that all the messages consisted of 0s and 1s. Each message was unique, however, because of how the 0s and 1s were arranged.

5. Read *Double the Code* to learn more about DNA's molecular arrangement. You know about the parts that make up DNA and a little bit about how those parts are arranged in a sequence. However, the parts alone are only one piece of what makes DNA special.

READING

Double the Code

A complete DNA molecule is double stranded. This means that there are two long strands of DNA bonded to each other to form a double helix. The nucleotides play a key role in how the double-stranded molecule is connected. Adenine on one strand always bonds with thymine on the other strand. Similarly, guanine always bonds with the cytosine. Because the nucleotides bond this way, they are said to form complementary base pairs (the base refers to A, T, G, or C). Each nitrogen base only bonds with one other nitrogen base. The two DNA strands are held together by hydrogen bonds between the complementary base pairs. Figure 8.10 shows the **complementary base pairing** between two DNA strands.

So, if two parallel trains moving in opposite directions represent double-stranded DNA, each railcar would represent a nucleotide. The cars would line up so that all of one type of car would pair with a specific type of car from the other train pointed in the opposite direction. This models the complementary base pairing of DNA. A person leaning out of one of the cars and grabbing the hand of a person leaning out of the paired car would represent the hydrogen bonds.

The structure of a DNA molecule is called a double helix. A helix is a spiral form. DNA is a double helix because it has two connecting strands and is twisted in a helical way. Figure 8.11 shows the double helix structure of DNA.

NOTES:

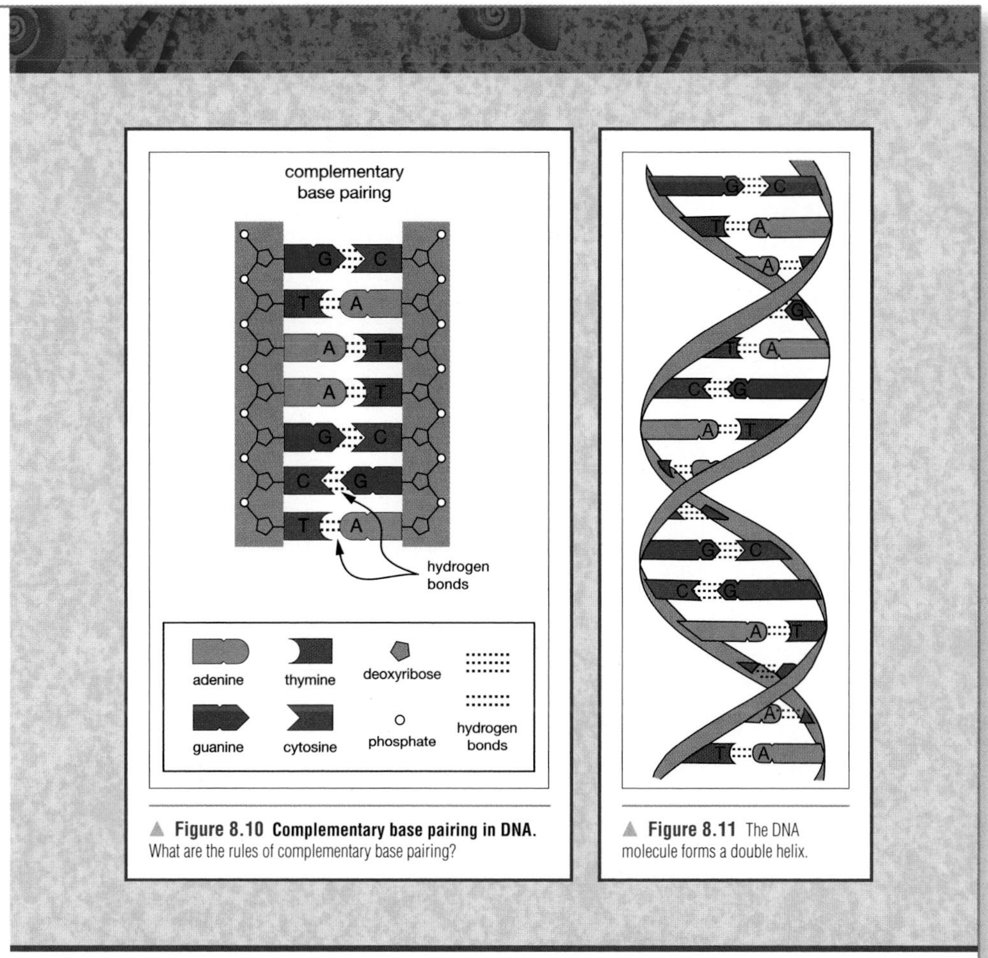

▲ **Figure 8.10 Complementary base pairing in DNA.** What are the rules of complementary base pairing?

▲ **Figure 8.11** The DNA molecule forms a double helix.

In Step 5, students read *Double the Code* to learn that DNA is double stranded and that nitrogen bases in one strand bond with nitrogen bases on the other strand of DNA. In Step 6, students build a strand of DNA complementary to the one they made in Step 2. Check with the groups to see that they are making correct complementary strands.

NOTES:

Answers to Step 6a, SE page 412

6a. Each team's DNA strand is unique, so check to see that the complementary strand is correct when compared with the original strand. (A red paper clip must be opposite a green paper clip and a yellow paper clip must be opposite a blue paper clip.)

In Steps 6b–g, the students put a pencil through the end of their double-stranded DNA and twist it. In Step 6e, remind the students not to twist too tightly. They want to twist it just until it is snug. In Step 6g, remind them to twist the model until they cannot twist it any farther.

Answers to Stop and Think—Part I, SE page 412

1. The code that DNA carries is in the different nitrogen bases. There are 4 nitrogen bases: adenine, guanine, cytosine, and thymine; therefore, there are 4 parts of the code.
2. The sequence of nucleotides on one strand provides a template for the other strand because each nitrogen base only bonds with 1 other nitrogen base. A and T can bond, and C and G can bond. You can determine what the nitrogen bases on one strand will be by looking at the nitrogen bases on the other strand.
3. Students might draw a representation of DNA similar to figure T8.6.

6. Make a model of a DNA double helix and show what you have learned about the structure of DNA by following Steps 6a–g. Record your answers in your science notebook.
   a. Build a new paper clip chain that represents the complementary strand of your original chain. Record the sequence in your science notebook as shown in the following:

      original sequence ______________________

      complementary sequence ______________________
   b. Line up your 2 paper clip chains so that the complementary nucleotides are next to each other (side by side).
   c. Pick up the 2 chains and hold them by one end so that the chains dangle vertically.
   d. Put your pencil tip through the bottom paper clip from each strand.
   e. Turn your pencil so that the 2 chains begin to twist slightly.
   f. Record your observations and sketch the appearance of the chains in your science notebook.
   g. Repeat the twisting process. Continue to turn your pencil until it will not turn anymore. What do you notice the DNA strand doing? Are you surprised at your results? Record your observations in your science notebook.

Stop & THINK

PART I

Discuss these questions with your partner. Record your thoughts in your science notebook.

1. Describe the code that DNA carries. How many parts to the code are there?
2. How does the sequence of nucleotides on one strand provide a template or guide for the sequence of subunits on the other strand?
3. Sketch a representation of a DNA double helix using the train analogy. Include a key with your sketch.

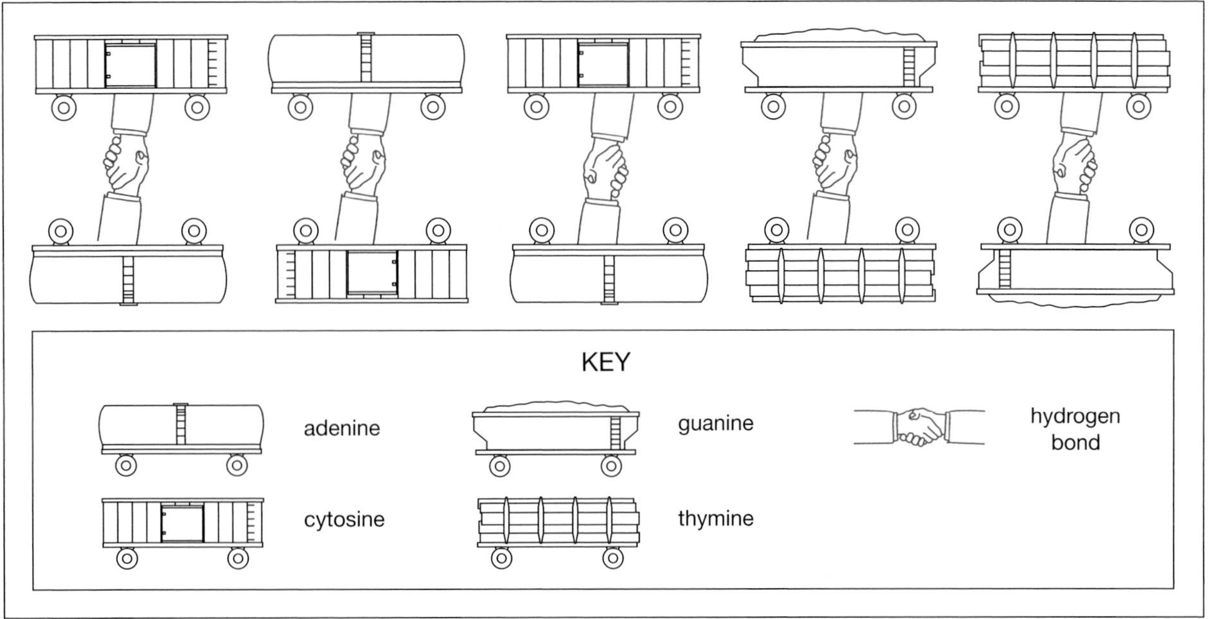

Figure T8.6 Train representing DNA. Students represent DNA as a train for Question 3.

Part II: DNA Replication

So far, you have studied the structure of DNA. But the structure alone does not tell you how DNA is inherited or what information it carries. In Part II, you will see how DNA's form enables it to perform its functions. You will answer the question, "How does the structure of DNA allow it to pass on the genetic information that it carries in its nucleotides?" Later in the chapter, you will experience how this information gives organisms their traits.

Materials

For each team of 2 students

25 red paper clips
25 yellow paper clips
25 green paper clips
25 blue paper clips
cups to hold the paper clips

Process and Procedure

1. Read *Copying DNA* to learn how DNA makes copies of itself. As you read, use the focus question, "How are DNA replication and meiosis related?" to guide your thinking.

READING

Copying DNA

DNA carries the code that gives organisms their traits. In order for DNA to get its code into every cell, DNA must make a copy of itself. This process is called replication and is very important for forming gametes and for making other new cells. Remember from chapter 7 that gametes have half the genetic information of other cells.

The first step in the process of **DNA replication** is the separation of the DNA strands. Special chemicals called **enzymes** cause the DNA molecule to separate. Enzymes are a type of protein that helps reactions occur. **DNA polymerase** is the enzyme involved in DNA replication. The hydrogen bonds between the nitrogen bases of the two strands are weaker than the covalent bonds between nucleotides in a DNA strand. In the train analogy, the hands clasping between trains are weaker than the links between the railcars on each train. Because the bonds between the trains are weaker, the two trains separate just as the DNA polymerase causes the two DNA strands to separate along the hydrogen bonds.

Once the DNA is separated into two strands, each strand can serve as a template to be copied. A template is a pattern or guide. DNA polymerase adds nucleotides one at a time to a new strand that is complementary to the original template. The nucleotides are added according

Process and Procedure

Part II: DNA Replication

Materials

For each team of 2 students

25 red paper clips
25 yellow paper clips
25 green paper clips
25 blue paper clips
cups to hold the paper clips

In Part II, students will use their paper clip models to model the process of DNA replication. Introduce this part of the activity by asking students how they think DNA is transferred from one generation to the next. Remind them that in chapter 7 they learned that copies of the chromosomes are passed through the generations. Ask them if they know how this might happen. How do copies of chromosomes get into the gametes?

In Step 1, students read about the DNA replication process. Encourage them to use the focus question to guide their reading. After they finish reading, they should answers the questions posed in Step 2. Check to see that students are comparing their answers to a classmate's and recording changes in their science notebooks.

NOTES:

Copying DNA, continued

to complementary base pairing (see figure 8.12). Do you remember the rules of complementary base pairing? If the template DNA strand has an A, then a T will be added to the new strand. If a G comes next in the template DNA strand, then a C will be added to the T in the new strand. New strands form along each of the separated strands.

DNA replicates for two reasons: to go into gametes that can result in offspring, and to go into new cells for growth and maintenance. Once DNA has replicated, a copy of the original DNA can go into new cells. Each new cell formed will contain a copy of the original DNA sequence. In chapter 7, you learned how the process of meiosis forms gamete cells. Prior to meiosis, the chromosomes doubled through the process of DNA replication. Recall that eukaryotic chromosomes consist of one DNA molecule. Thus, when DNA replicates, the chromosome doubles. During later stages of meiosis, cell division ensures that the resulting gametes (sperm and egg) have half the number of chromosomes as the original parent cell.

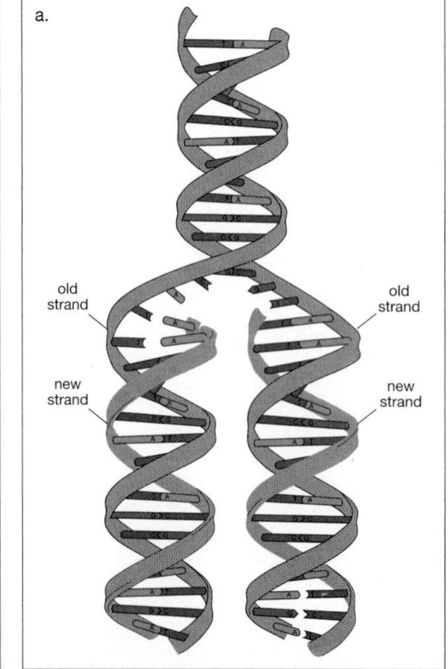

Figure 8.12 DNA replication. (a) During DNA replication, the strands come apart at the bonds between the nucleotides. DNA replicates by adding nucleotides. Eventually, two DNA molecules are produced. Each molecule is exactly alike, and each has one old and one new strand. (b) New nucleotides are added one by one with the original strands serving as templates for the production of new strands. What base would be added next?

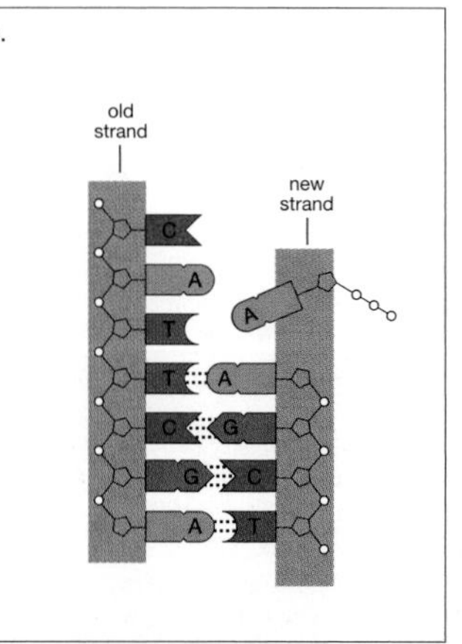

NOTES:

After an egg is fertilized, the zygote (fertilized egg) has one complete set of chromosomes. The zygote cell continues to divide to make more cells. The major process involved in producing these new cells is called mitosis. In mitosis, the DNA replicates and then the cell goes through a series of stages that results in new cells that each contains the same genetic information as the original zygote. The stages that the chromosomes go through during mitosis are similar to those in meiosis except that the cell only divides to the point where each new cell has a complete set of chromosomes. Any cells that divide by mitosis will contain genetic information identical to the original cell. Look at figure 8.13, which shows how cells divide through mitosis.

SCI LINKS NSTA
Topic: mitosis
Go to: www.scilinks.org
Code: 2Inquiry415

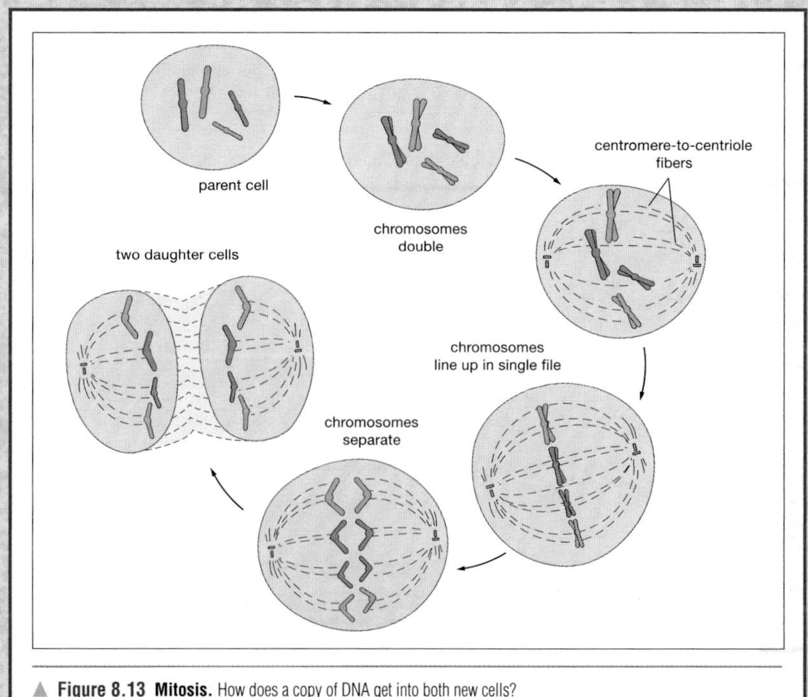

▲ **Figure 8.13 Mitosis.** How does a copy of DNA get into both new cells?

Chapter 8 Instructions for Life 415

Answers to Step 2, SE page 416

2a. Being double stranded helps DNA replicate because each strand provides a template for the new copies.

2b. The chromosomes double during meiosis as a result of DNA replication.

2c. Each new cell contains copies of the original DNA because the DNA was replicated during meiosis.

2d. DNA replication is necessary for an organism to produce new cells for growth and replacement. It is also necessary for an organism to produce gametes for reproduction.

2e. Make sure students take time to compare their answers for 2a–d with a classmate. They should record any additions or revisions they make to their responses including what they changed and why.

In Step 3, students model DNA replication using their paper clip models.

In Step 3a, the students line up their strands of DNA to form a double-stranded molecule. Check that they line up the complementary base pairs correctly.

In Step 3b, students separate their strands of DNA. Circulate around the room to see that they are using their hands to act as a DNA enzyme to separate the 2 strands correctly.

In Step 3c, check with the groups to see that they are correctly adding the complementary bases to their single strands of DNA to form new double strands of DNA. They should have 2 (double-stranded) strands of DNA.

In Step 4, the teams compare DNA strands with another team's.

Answers to Step 4, SE page 416

4a. Students should have 2 double strands of DNA or a total of 4 strands of DNA.

4b. The similarities are that they are both made of paper clips of 4 colors representing nucleotides and both are 15 nucleotides long. The difference is that they have different sequences of nucleotides.

Consider assigning the sidebar *In Search of DNA* as homework. When students come to class the next day, pose the following questions:

- "Why did it take so long for scientists to find the code in DNA?"
- "Did any of the scientists have enough evidence to support the theory that DNA is the substance responsible for inheritance?"
- "How did the sidebar show the nature of science?"

As an optional extension, students could complete the following task. Ask students to imagine that they are scientists working at the same time as Charles Darwin, Gregor Mendel, and Johann Friedrich Miescher. In a short letter to the three scientists, students should describe how their ideas and discoveries are connected to one another. How do their ideas relate to DNA and change across time?

Answers to Reflect and Connect, SE page 417

Students will work with their partners to answer these questions. If students have difficulty with Question 4, stop the class and discuss it.

1. The code in DNA is similar to the fax code because both have only a few parts to the code—0s and 1s for fax code and A, C, T, G for DNA—and these parts can be arranged in different ways to produce different meanings of the code.

---

2. Answer Questions 2a–e to show what you have learned about DNA replication. Record your ideas in your science notebook.
   - **a.** How does being double stranded help DNA replicate?
   - **b.** How did the chromosomes double during meiosis?
   - **c.** Why does each new cell contain copies of the original DNA?
   - **d.** Why is DNA replication necessary to organisms?
   - **e.** Compare your answers with a classmate's. Then add to or revise your answers based on what you learn from his or her responses. Record your changes in your science notebook including what you changed and why.
3. Model DNA replication using your paper clips by following Steps 3a–c.
   - **a.** Reassemble your original 2 paper clip chains so that they lie side by side on your desk.

Make sure the 2 chains line up according to complementary base pairing.

   - **b.** Imagine that your fingers are DNA polymerase. Use your fingers to separate the chains as shown in figure 8.14.
   - **c.** Replicate your DNA by pairing up free paper clips with each chain. Use the extra paper clips you have as your free nucleotides.

Refer to the table in figure 8.9 and to figures 8.14 and 8.15 to guide the replication process in your paper clip model.

4. Answer the following questions about the DNA replication model.
   - **a.** After replicating your original double-stranded DNA, how many strands of DNA do you now have?
   - **b.** Compare your paper clip DNA with another team's strands. How are they the same? How are they different?

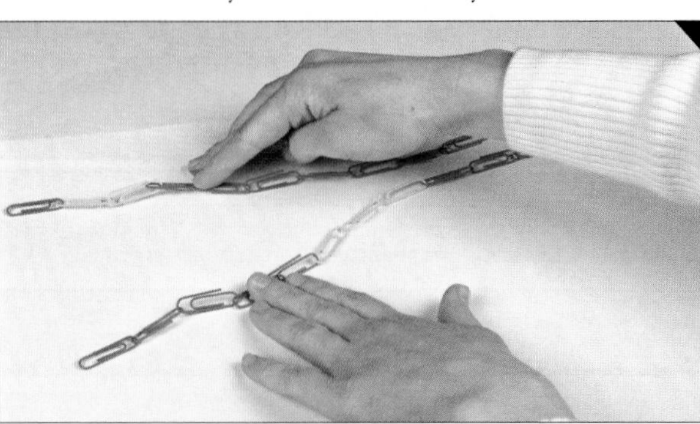

Figure 8.14
Separating strands. How do your fingers represent DNA polymerase?

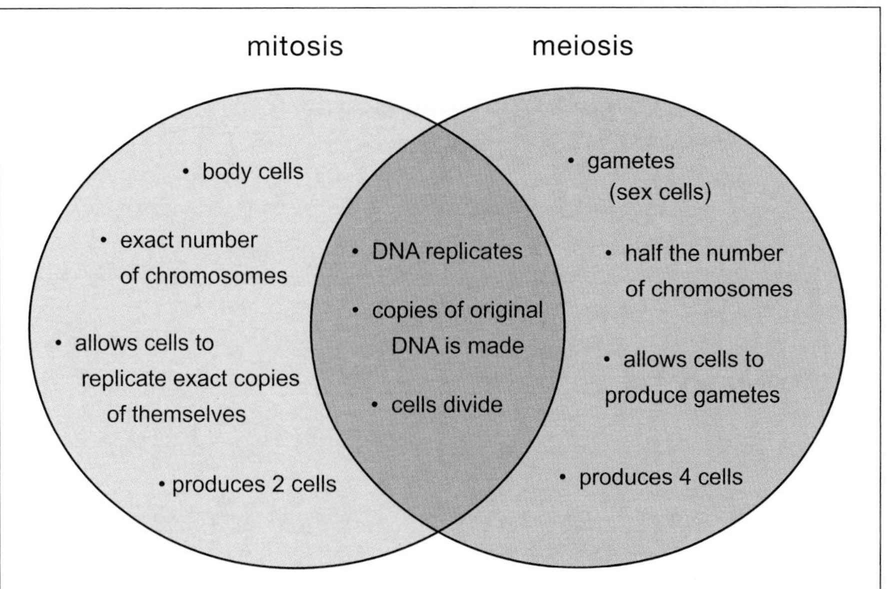

▲ **Figure T8.7 Venn diagram comparing mitosis and meiosis.** Students' Venn diagrams should look like this.

Answers to Reflect and Connect are on TE pages 416–417.

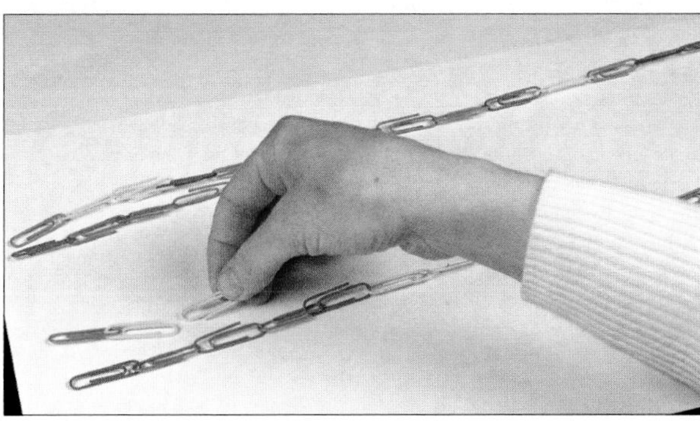

◄ **Figure 8.15 Adding paper clips.** How does adding paper clips to your model show DNA replication?

Reflect and Connect

Discuss the following questions with your partner. Record your best thinking in your science notebook.

1. How is the fax code with 0s and 1s similar to the code in DNA?
2. Study figure 8.13 in *Copying DNA*, which shows the stages of mitosis. Then compare that figure with figure 7.17 in chapter 7, which shows the stages of meiosis. Answer the following questions.
   a. How does the genetic information from a parent get into the gametes?
   b. Why is DNA replication important during mitosis?
   c. If DNA did not replicate accurately, what do you think would happen to new cells?
   d. Generate a Venn diagram comparing the processes of meiosis and mitosis.
3. Why did your DNA model differ from the models of other teams? Do you think this happens with cellular DNA? Explain your reasoning.
4. What is the benefit of the double-stranded characteristic of DNA?
5. How do models like your paper clip model help you understand science concepts?

2a. The genetic information stored in DNA is passed from parent to offspring through the process of meiosis. In meiosis, the chromosomes double through DNA replication. The cells then go through a series of cell divisions until there are 4 new gamete cells, each containing half the number of chromosomes as the original parent cell.

2b. DNA replication is important during mitosis because DNA needs to make a copy of itself so that the copy can go into a new cell.

2c. This question has students think about what might happen if DNA did not replicate properly. Student answers should be reasonable predictions. Their answers might include "New cells would not form." "New cells would not have the correct information." "Cells might be malformed." "There might be too many or too few chromosomes."

2d. A Venn diagram comparing meiosis and mitosis would look like figure T8.7.

3. Students' models of DNA differ from their classmates' models in that the sequence of nucleotides is different. The sequence is different because the students chose their sequence. In real life, DNA does have different sequences.

4. It is beneficial for DNA to be double stranded so that it can separate and have a template for the formation of new DNA. This template ensures that exact copies of DNA go into the new cells.

5. Models like the paper clip model help students understand science concepts because students can visualize what is occurring at the molecular level. Students can also manipulate a physical structure, which helps them understand the structure better.

NOTES:

SIDEBAR

In Search of DNA

In chapter 7, you learned how Gregor Mendel's investigations with pea plants proved that traits are inherited. Scientists' next task was to determine *how* traits are inherited. Scientists quickly began their search for the inherited substance that gives organisms their traits.

The first major breakthrough in the search for this substance came in 1869. A Swiss biologist and medic named Johann Friedrich Miescher wanted to find out what chemicals were in the nuclei of cells. For his search, Miescher collected pus cells from discarded surgical bandages and broke down these cells with chemicals from a pig's stomach. In the cells, Miescher found a white, phosphorous-containing substance that he named nuclein. Miescher conducted similar studies on the heads of salmon sperm cells and found the same substance. What Miescher discovered was DNA. And he believed that DNA was the substance responsible for inheritance. Unfortunately, Miescher did not have enough evidence to support his ideas about DNA. Most scientists of the time ignored Miescher's discovery. They thought the key to inheritance was in the proteins of organisms.

The first hint that DNA was responsible for carrying genetic information came in the 1920s from an experiment conducted by Fred Griffith, an English medical officer. Griffith worked with a type of bacteria that had two forms. One form of the bacteria was deadly and the other form was harmless. Griffith injected mice with living cells of the harmless bacteria together with dead cells from the disease-causing bacteria. The mice died. When Griffith examined the dead mice, he found both types of bacteria living in the mice. Somehow, some substance from the dead cells had been picked up by some of the living harmless bacteria. Griffith called this ability to transfer genetic information transformation.

It was not until 1943 that scientists found direct evidence to support the idea that DNA was responsible for transformation. In that year, three scientists—Oswald Avery, Colin MacLeod, and Maclyn McCarty—focused their studies on finding the substance responsible for transformation. They knew that extracts from transformed cells contained protein, RNA, and DNA. But they did not know which substance carried the information for transformation. The three scientists worked meticulously using the process of elimination. They destroyed each substance one at a time to see what the effect on transformation was. When they destroyed the RNA and the protein, transformation took place as usual. When they destroyed the DNA, transformation did not take place. Their experiment provided evidence that DNA was the substance responsible for transformation and therefore the carrier of genetic information.

Some scientists were still not convinced that DNA was the carrier of genetic information. In 1952, two scientists, Alfred Hershey and Martha Chase, provided visual evidence that DNA was the molecule that carried genetic information. They used a radioactive isotope to follow the DNA for a virus as it infected a host. By following the viral cycle, they saw that the virus injected its host with DNA to provide the information for viral replication. Hershey and Chase proved once and for all that the genetic information was in the DNA, not in the protein coat of the virus.

418 Unit 2 Inside Life

NOTES:

Once scientists were convinced that DNA was the carrier of genetic information, the race was on to understand its structure and how it carried the code for all the variations of life. In the late 1940s and early 1950s, many scientists focused their efforts on understanding the structure of DNA and cracking its code. In 1950, Edwin Chargaff found that certain bases of DNA always occurred at a 1:1 ratio. He discovered that in DNA molecules, there was always as much adenine as there was thymine and as much cytosine as there was guanine. This discovery would later contribute greatly to identifying the molecular structure of DNA.

In 1953, a scientist named Rosalind Franklin took thin strands of DNA, exposed them to an extremely fine beam of X-rays, and examined the resulting patterns. She painstakingly took several photographs from many angles and under many conditions. When she looked at the photographs, she found a specific, now famous, pattern starting to emerge (see figure). Franklin showed her findings to her colleague, Maurice Wilkins. Wilkins then shared Franklin's data with two other scientists, James Watson and Francis Crick. Watson and Crick had also been working on understanding the structure of DNA. When they saw Franklin's photographs, they suggested that DNA was a molecule made up of two chains of nucleotides arranged in a helix. When they learned of Chargaff's findings, they added to their model by pairing adenine with thymine and cytosine with guanine.

Watson and Crick's model explained how DNA could serve as a template for passing genetic information. The model fit the experimental data of the time so well that the scientific community accepted it almost immediately. In 1962, Watson, Crick, and Wilkins won the Nobel Prize in Physiology. Rosalind Franklin died at age 37 in 1958. At that time, the Nobel Prize was awarded only to living recipients. Had she been alive, Rosalind Franklin might have also been awarded the Nobel Prize.

It took almost 90 years from the time DNA was discovered until scientists completely understood its structure and function. Now that scientists have this knowledge, they can help us understand how DNA codes for all of life.

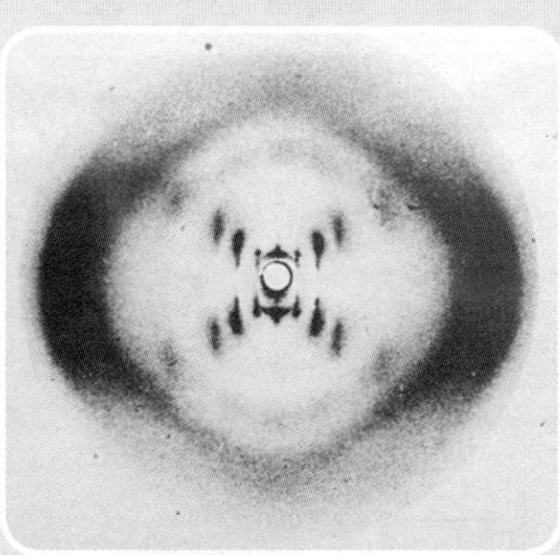

Rosalind Franklin's X-ray diffraction photograph of DNA taken in 1953. This photo showed, for the first time, the double helix shape of DNA.

NOTES:

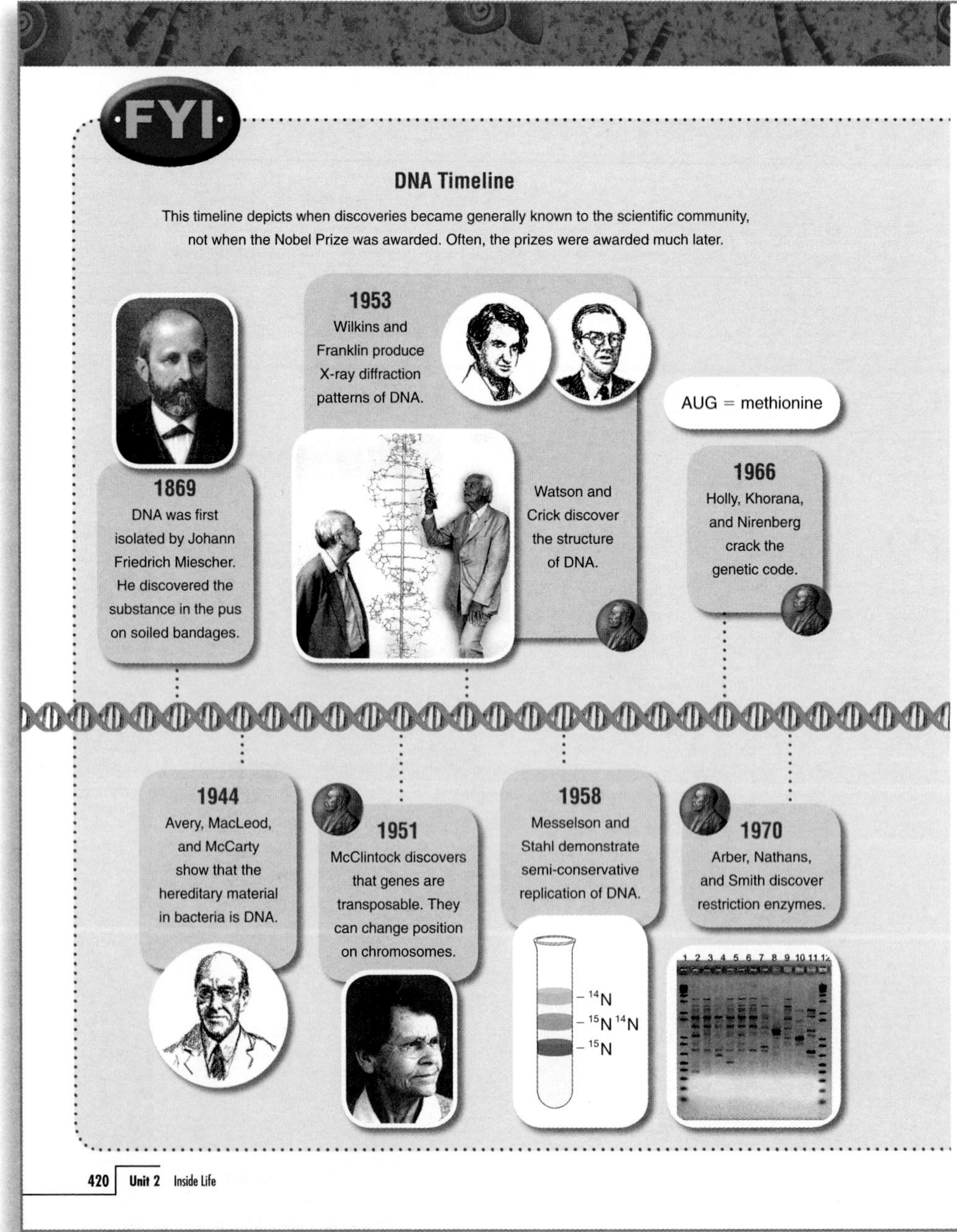
FYI
DNA Timeline
This timeline depicts when discoveries became generally known to the scientific community, not when the Nobel Prize was awarded. Often, the prizes were awarded much later.
1869
DNA was first isolated by Johann Friedrich Miescher. He discovered the substance in the pus on soiled bandages.
1953
Wilkins and Franklin produce X-ray diffraction patterns of DNA.
Watson and Crick discover the structure of DNA.
AUG = methionine
1966
Holly, Khorana, and Nirenberg crack the genetic code.
1944
Avery, MacLeod, and McCarty show that the hereditary material in bacteria is DNA.
1951
McClintock discovers that genes are transposable. They can change position on chromosomes.
1958
Messelson and Stahl demonstrate semi-conservative replication of DNA.
– 14N
– 15N 14N
– 15N
1970
Arber, Nathans, and Smith discover restriction enzymes.
420 Unit 2 Inside Life

NOTES:

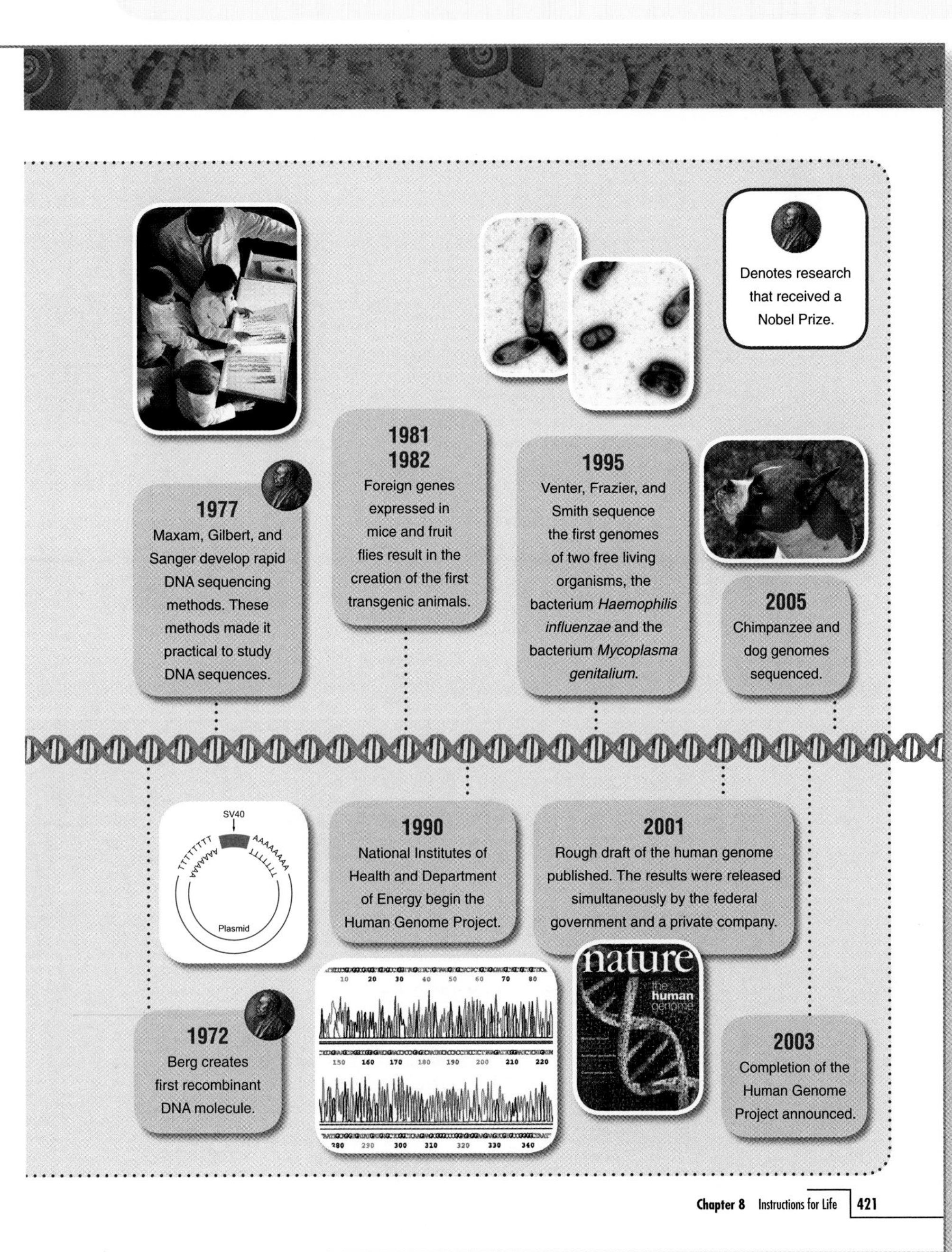

Denotes research that received a Nobel Prize.
1977
Maxam, Gilbert, and Sanger develop rapid DNA sequencing methods. These methods made it practical to study DNA sequences.
1981
1982
Foreign genes expressed in mice and fruit flies result in the creation of the first transgenic animals.
1995
Venter, Frazier, and Smith sequence the first genomes of two free living organisms, the bacterium Haemophilis influenzae and the bacterium Mycoplasma genitalium.
2005
Chimpanzee and dog genomes sequenced.
SV40
Plasmid
1972
Berg creates first recombinant DNA molecule.
1990
National Institutes of Health and Department of Energy begin the Human Genome Project.
2001
Rough draft of the human genome published. The results were released simultaneously by the federal government and a private company.
nature
the human genome
2003
Completion of the Human Genome Project announced.
Chapter 8 Instructions for Life 421

EXPLAIN

Words to Live By

Activity Overview

In *Words to Live By*, students will learn about the significance of proteins. This activity comes before protein synthesis so that students experience the significance of proteins first. In the next activity, they will experience how DNA holds and carries the code for protein synthesis.

In the first activity, *Just the Fax*, the students were assigned a word to research. In this activity, the students will report their findings to the class. The students then will work in teams of two to organize the words based on their meaning and significance. All the words are associated with proteins, and the students should make that connection. The teams will further divide their organization scheme to develop a concept map about proteins. This activity connects DNA's significance with protein synthesis.

Before You Teach

Background Information

Proteins are long chains of amino acids and are the most abundant macromolecules in cells. These chains are held together by covalent bonds. Proteins differ from one another by the sequence and number of amino acids in the chain. There are 20 amino acids commonly found in proteins, but an almost infinite number of combinations and arrangements. The sequence of amino acids determines a protein's function.

Proteins are major structural components in cells and they drive the processes involved in life. There are many types of proteins. Scientists classify proteins slightly differently but, in general, there are structural, nutrient and storage, contractile, defense, regulatory, and other unique proteins. Proteins are responsible for facilitating most of the chemical reactions in organisms. Proteins give organisms their traits. Humans alone have approximately 50,000 different proteins—all with different functions.

Copymaster 8.4, *Protein Summary*, provides more information about proteins.

Materials

For each student

- completed assignment from the *Just the Fax* activity
- 1 5×7 in (or larger) index card
- 1 large piece of construction or butcher paper
- markers
- 1 copy of copymaster 8.2, *Term Chart*
- 1 copy of copymaster 8.3, *Term Chart Completed*
- 1 copy of copymaster 8.4, *Protein Summary* (optional)

TRCD

Advance Preparation

Remind students that they need to have finished researching their word from the *Just the Fax* activity the day before you get to this activity. Have the index cards out and ready for the students to use. If you want students to take notes in a structured manner, make copies of copymaster 8.2, *Term Chart*. Make copies of copymaster 8.4, *Protein Summary* for students who might have trouble organizing their thoughts or for classes that might not have completed their assignment of looking up the words. Cut pieces of butcher paper for the students to use to make their concept maps. Clear off wall space in your classroom where students can post their index cards.

EXPLAIN

Words to Live By

In *Just the Fax*, each member of your class was given the task of finding information about the word you deciphered in your binary code. Now that you have completed the task, it is time to compile the information you gathered. You might be wondering what this assignment has to do with your study of DNA. Surprisingly, these words have a great deal to do with DNA's significance. To connect these words to DNA, however, you first need to understand what is important about these terms. In *Words to Live By*, you will experience the connection between these words and DNA's role in life.

One way to help understand new information is to organize it in a way that makes sense to you. Once you organize information, you can begin to make connections and determine relationships. In this activity, you will work with a partner to organize the words you decoded in the first activity, *Just the Fax*.

Materials

For each student

- completed assignment from the *Just the Fax* activity
- 1 5×7 in index card
- 1 large piece of construction or butcher paper
- markers
- 1 *Term Chart Completed* handout (optional)

Process and Procedure

1. Pair up with someone who researched the same word that you researched. If no one else investigated your word, pair up with any available person.
2. Compare what you learned about the word with your partner by completing Steps 2a–c.
   a. Read the information that your partner gathered about the word.

Remember the 5 questions you were to answer about your word. If you need help remembering, look back at *Reflect and Connect*, Question 5 from the *Just the Fax* activity.

   b. Combine your information to get a thorough description of your word (if you researched the same word as your partner). If you had different words, help each other decide on a thorough description of your terms.
   c. Label an index card with headings that describe the research you conducted on your word.

As You Teach

Outcomes and Indicators of Success

By the end of this activity, students should

1. begin to understand how and why proteins are significant to life's processes.

   They will show their understanding by

   - using examples to report on a protein that is significant to life;
   - describing that proteins are essential for life because they are needed for all of life's processes such as catalyzing reactions, providing support, and maintaining equilibrium;
   - developing an organizational scheme about proteins that shows that all proteins are related; and
   - making a concept map with proteins as the main idea.

2. begin to understand what defines a protein.

   They will demonstrate their understanding by explaining that very different substances are considered to be proteins because they are chains of amino acids.

3. be able to revise an explanation based on new information.

   They will demonstrate their ability by revising the concept map they created in the activity *Just the Fax* after researching information and being presented with new information about the terms in the concept map.

Fill out your index card neatly with the information you gathered about your word. If you did not research the same term as your partner, help each other complete the cards.

3. Present your word aloud to the class when your teacher calls on you.

Read your information using a clear, strong voice. Present the information slowly enough so that your classmates can take notes about important points. Then post your word on the board.

4. Listen carefully as other teams describe their words. Take notes in your science notebook by writing down the important information about each term.
5. Review each of the words posted on the board and decide what they have in common by completing Steps 5a–c. Record your ideas in your science notebook.
   a. In what ways are these words different?
   b. Decide what these words have in common. Justify your answer.

One of the words describes what is common among all the terms.

   c. When you have an idea, check with your teacher. Are you surprised at the commonality of the words? Explain why or why not.

If you are having difficulties making sense of these words, ask your teacher for a copy of the *Protein Summary* handout.

6. Organize the words into a concept map to show the relationship among them using Steps 6a–c as a guide.
   a. Decide on a way to sort these words into categories that make sense to you. Then divide each category further into subcategories. Record your categories and the criteria for your categories in your science notebook.
   b. Revise your concept map from the *Just the Fax* activity to show your organization scheme. Start by rearranging the sticky notes on the large piece of paper.

Remember to add linking words and use verbs to show how these terms relate to one another.

   c. Copy your concept map into your science notebook to create a permanent record of it.
7. Post your concept map as instructed by your teacher. Think about the following questions as you look at other concept maps.
   a. Did other teams organize the terms the same way you did?
   b. Do the other concept maps make sense to you?

Strategies

Getting Started

Tell the students that they are going to leave the topic of DNA for this activity, but that they will be able to relate what they learn to their study of DNA later in the chapter. Ask the students if they had success in finding out information about their words from the first activity. Some of them might have used references that are complex. Remind them that they just need to know the basic information about their words. Explain that in this activity, they are going to learn the significance of these words by making connections among the terms. Have the class read the introduction.

Process and Procedure

In Step 1, help students pair with someone with the same word. Assist those pairs that have trouble combining their information. If you have a smaller class, students may not have a partner to team up with. In that case, students will have to teach one another about their words. Remind the students that they are only combining information if they have the same word. If they have different words, they simply help each other make cards. Circulate around the room to see that students are just recording the basic information about their words. Remind them to write neatly because others will be reading their card. Encourage them to rehearse what they will report to the class.

For Step 3, call on each pair of students to read its information to the class. Encourage each team to speak clearly and loudly enough for the class to hear. Tell the students to listen to each word and take brief notes to help them think about what these words have in common. They can write their notes on

copymaster 8.2, *Term Chart*. Make sure that someone reads the information about the word *protein*. If no one reports on protein, then you will need to read the information about it to the class. Have the students post their cards in the classroom.

In Step 5, the students discuss with their partners what the words have in common. Circulate among the students to see that they are on the right track. If they are having difficulty making the connection that all the terms deal with proteins, ask if the function or definition of their words is consistent among the terms.

The words all have something to do with proteins. Encourage students to review their notes and the index cards. If the students still can't make the connections, provide them with

a copy of copymaster 8.4, *Protein Summary*, which summarizes all the words. Make sure students see that the commonality shared by the words is that they all are associated with proteins.

In Step 6, the student teams organize their words and make concept maps using the terms. If they are having trouble, encourage them to think about the function or significance of the proteins. Each team will approach this task differently, so expect the concept maps to vary.

In Step 7, designate a location for the students to hang their concept maps. Allow the students to view each map. Discourage the students from judging each other's concept maps. Remind them that there are different ways to organize information.

Answers to Reflect and Connect, SE page 424

1. Students should see that life depends on proteins. Proteins regulate processes in organisms in the form of hormones. Insulin is an example of a hormone that regulates body sugar levels. Proteins provide structure. Collagen is an example of a protein that provides structure and support. Proteins provide protection and ways to hunt for food. Snake venom is made from proteins, and organisms can use it to kill prey or protect themselves. Proteins act as catalysts in the form of enzymes to facilitate chemical reactions in organisms. Lactase is an enzyme that helps break down milk into sugars.
2. Many hormones and the components of spider silk are classified as proteins because by definition a protein is a long chain of amino acids. These 2 substances are made up of amino acids so they are both proteins.
3. This question is intended to get students thinking about how they learn. A graphic organizer helps organize concepts, arrange them, and see how they relate to one another. A graphic organizer is a good way to organize and visualize a lot of information. In this case, students defined proteins, identified types of proteins, and described examples of proteins in a relatively short amount of time.

EXPLAIN

Transcription and Translation—the Road to Making Proteins

Activity Overview

So far in this chapter, students have been focusing mostly on DNA. They also learned about proteins in the previous activity. *Transcription and Translation—the Road to Making Proteins* ties the students' knowledge of DNA to proteins because DNA carries the information that codes for protein production.

In Part I of this activity, the students are introduced to RNA. RNA is a very important molecule needed for protein production. Students will use

Reflect and Connect

Answer the following questions individually. Record your answers in your science notebook.

1. Describe why proteins are essential for life. Use specific examples from this activity in your discussion.
2. Why are very different substances such as hormones and the components of spider silk both classified as proteins?
3. How does a graphic organizer help you understand concepts?

EXPLAIN

Transcription and Translation—the Road to Making Proteins

You learned in the activity *Words to Live By* that proteins are very important to life. Life could not happen without proteins. Proteins are what give organisms their traits. How do organisms make the specific proteins they need for all the processes of life? Most genes contain the information required to build proteins. Genes are segments of DNA that code for an organism's traits. Therefore, the path to protein production begins with DNA. In *Transcription and Translation*, you and a partner will crack the code carried in DNA to see how DNA stores the genetic information that directs specific protein production. To learn what scientists know about our genes, read the sidebar *Mapping the Human Genome*.

Part I: Transcription

To understand how DNA relates to protein production, you need to understand a few processes that occur in the cell on the way to protein production. The first step on the road to protein production is the construction of another nucleic acid, **ribonucleic acid (RNA)**. RNA is constructed through a process called **transcription**. Transcription is similar to DNA replication except that transcription copies only part of the nucleotide sequence in DNA. In Part I of this activity, you will learn how transcription occurs.

Materials

For each team of 2 students

- 25 red paper clips
- 25 yellow paper clips
- 25 green paper clips
- 25 blue paper clips
- 25 silver paper clips
- cups to hold the paper clips

their paper clips to model transcription, which is the first process needed for protein synthesis.

In Part II, students will simulate both transcription and translation through a role-playing activity. Students take on the roles of RNA to see how a cell uses the code in DNA to make proteins.

Before You Teach

Background Information

DNA carries information for protein production. It carries this information in its sequence of nucleotides. When DNA strands separate, each strand can serve as a template for replication or a process called *transcription*. Transcription is the copying of one DNA strand to make ribonucleic acid (RNA).

The process of transcription is the first step toward protein production (protein synthesis). Protein synthesis requires the involvement of RNA. RNA is similar to DNA except that the sugar in RNA is *ribose* instead of *deoxyribose* and RNA has the nitrogen base uracil instead of thymine. Often, RNA is single stranded. There are three types of RNA in cells. *Messenger RNA* (mRNA) carries information from the DNA in the cell's nucleus to the cell's cytoplasm, where proteins are made. *Ribosomal RNA* (rRNA) makes up ribosomes along with a number of proteins. *Transfer RNA* (tRNA) carries amino acids to the ribosomes.

There are different functions of RNA in the steps involved in protein synthesis. The first step toward protein production is transcription. In transcription, the template of DNA is transcribed by mRNA. In eukaryotic cells, transcription takes place in the nucleus of the cell. In prokaryotic cells, transcription occurs in the cytoplasm. In transcription, mRNA is formed from the DNA template. mRNA acts as a template for the sections of DNA that code for protein production. These sections are the genes on a chromosome. During DNA transcription, a complementary mRNA strand is constructed from the coding strand of DNA. Either of the DNA's double strands can carry the coding for a particular gene, but different genes are coded on each strand. The direction of the coding is important. On the designated coding strand, if the sequence is read from left to right, then the code is read from left to right. Subsequently, when the mRNA complementary strand is translated, it is read from left to right (see figure 8.16 in the student book).

In translation, tRNA *translates* the code into amino acids by finding complementary anticodon sequences and assembling a chain of amino acids to form a protein. A *codon* is a sequence of three adjacent nucleotides in DNA or messenger RNA that code for an amino acid. An *anticodon* is the three-nucleotide sequence in a tRNA that is complementary to a specific codon in mRNA.

The processes involved in protein synthesis are quite complex, and this activity simplifies them quite a bit. The main understanding that students should attain from this activity is that proteins give us our characteristics and DNA is the message that provides the information for producing proteins. The basic steps for protein synthesis follow.

1. During transcription, a strand of mRNA is formed as covalent bonds are made between RNA subunits. The order is determined by pairing the weak bonding of each new subunit to the DNA template (pattern) that holds the growing chain in place. This occurs in the nucleus of a cell in eukaryotes and in the cytoplasm of prokaryotes.

Process and Procedure

1. Assemble a DNA sequence in preparation for modeling transcription by following Steps 1a–b.
   a. Look in your science notebook to see what your DNA sequence was from the activity *Clips of DNA*.
   b. Reassemble both strands and place them next to each other to represent the double-stranded structure of DNA.

Remember, this strand represents only a very short section of an entire DNA molecule.

2. Read *Making RNA* to learn about RNA and how to model transcription. Refer back to other readings or illustrations if it helps you organize your understanding.

READING

Making RNA

Throughout this chapter, you have been thinking about how DNA carries a code. DNA actually stores information in the form of a code. The code that DNA carries leads to protein production or protein synthesis. Using just four nucleotides, DNA codes for the production of hundreds of thousands of proteins in all organisms. A DNA sequence that codes for a protein is a gene.

Though DNA carries the code, it cannot produce proteins without another molecule called RNA, which is ribonucleic acid. RNA is similar to DNA in that it also is made of nucleotides. Each nucleotide in RNA has a sugar, a phosphate group, and a nitrogen base. But, as you can tell from the name, RNA is a little different from DNA. The sugar molecule in RNA is ribose instead of deoxyribose. There are also two important structural differences between RNA and DNA. In RNA, the nitrogen base thymine (T) is replaced by uracil (U), and RNA is usually single stranded instead of double stranded.

You might remember from your study of cells in earlier science classes that proteins are made in the ribosome of the cell. For proteins to be produced, the code carried in DNA needs to be read. But DNA cannot leave the nucleus of the cell in eukaryotic organisms. If DNA cannot leave the nucleus, how does the information carried on DNA get to the ribosome? There exists a special molecule called **messenger RNA** or mRNA. As the name *messenger* suggests, mRNA carries the message from the DNA sequence. Its only role is to carry a *message* of the DNA sequence to the place in the cell where the sequence can be translated.

The mRNA molecule reads the code on the DNA sequence using a process called transcription. Transcription is the process in which part of a DNA sequence is copied into a complementary sequence of ribonucleic acid (RNA). During transcription, the two strands of DNA separate and a strand of RNA is copied along one strand of the DNA molecule. Figure 8.16 shows you how RNA is formed. Transcription happens in the nucleus of cells in eukaryotic organisms.

Chapter 8 Instructions for Life 425

2. The new strand of mRNA goes to the ribosome. There, the tRNA reads the three nucleotides (a codon) of mRNA. It matches complementary nucleotides (an anticodon). The tRNA with its anticodon encodes for specific amino acids. Each amino acid corresponds to a code word to build a protein (see figure 8.17 in the student book).

If there is a "mistake" (mutation) with the original strand of DNA, then it is possible that the desired protein will not be produced. If these mutations occur in gametes, they can result in a nonviable gamete, cause a genetic disorder, or provide the basis for variability as the foundation of evolution.

Materials—Part I

For each team of 2 students

25 red paper clips
25 yellow paper clips
25 green paper clips
25 blue paper clips
25 silver paper clips
cups to hold the paper clips

Materials—Part II

For the class

1 sign that says "nucleus"
70 labeled 5×7 or 3×5 in index cards (optional)
1 copy of copymaster 8.5, *Anticodon Cards*
1 copy of copymaster 8.6, *DNA Sequences*

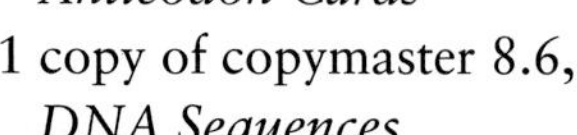

tape
poster paper

Advance Preparation

For Part I, gather colored paper clips.

For Part II, you will need to make the anticodon cards in advance and tape them up around the room with the anticodon side showing. There are quite a few cards to make but once they are made, you can reuse them many times. You might want to laminate them. Make the cards by first printing only the anticodon side

of the cards on copymaster 8.5, *Anticodon Cards*. You might want to use heavier paper such as card stock. Then print or handwrite the corresponding words on the back of each card (see figure T8.8). There are 2 anticodons per page, so you will need to cut the pages in half.

Another option is to make the cards by hand, something a student aide or helper could do. To make the cards, do the following.

1. Purchase 5×7 inch index cards; 3×5 inch cards would work but are not as easy for the students to see.
2. Label the cards as indicated by the table in figure T8.8 by writing the word that the anticodon represents on the back of each card. Write it fairly large. On the front of the card, write the anticodon sequence that corresponds to the word you wrote on the back. Write the anticodon sequence large so that the students can find it when they are looking for it.

Post the cards in the room with the anticodon side facing outward.

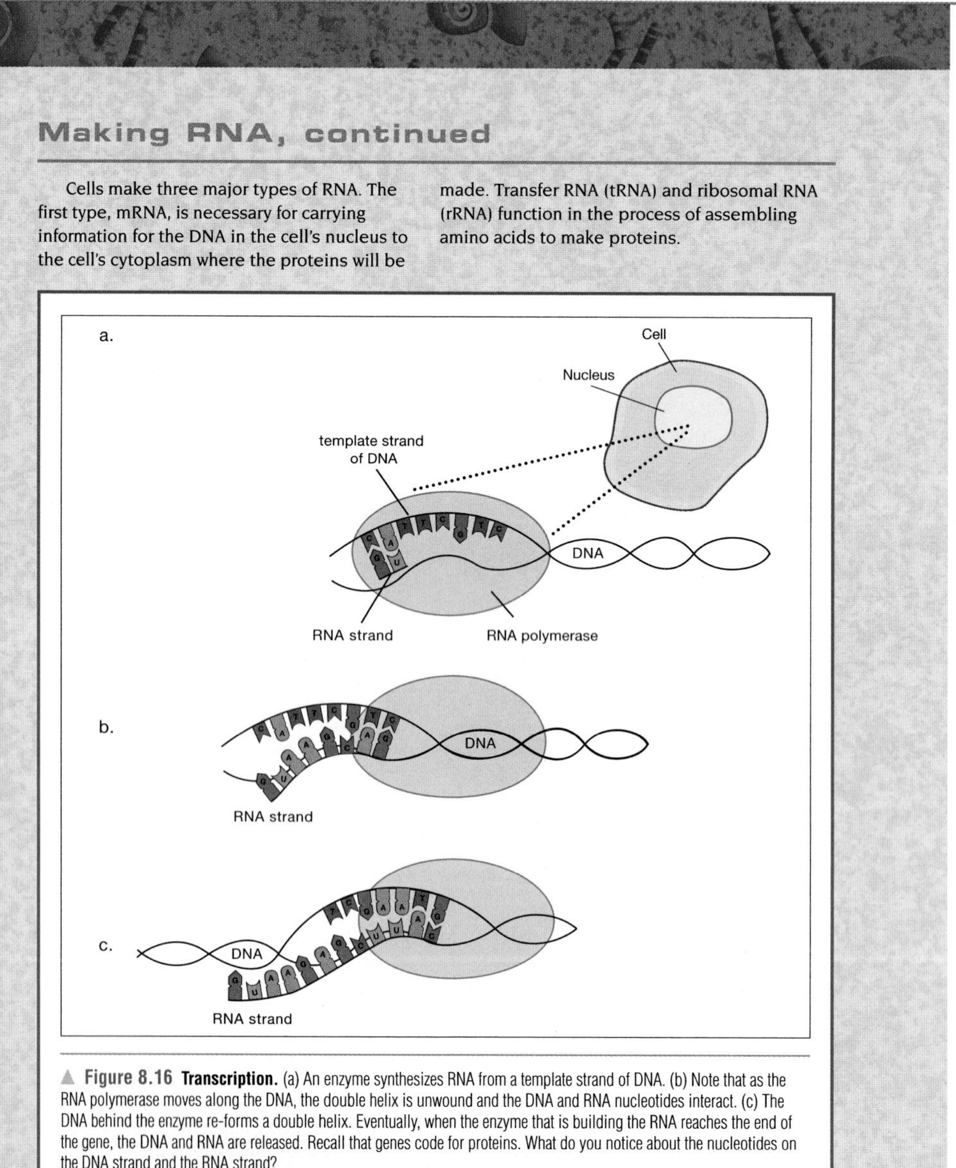

Making RNA, continued

Cells make three major types of RNA. The first type, mRNA, is necessary for carrying information for the DNA in the cell's nucleus to the cell's cytoplasm where the proteins will be made. Transfer RNA (tRNA) and ribosomal RNA (rRNA) function in the process of assembling amino acids to make proteins.

▲ **Figure 8.16 Transcription.** (a) An enzyme synthesizes RNA from a template strand of DNA. (b) Note that as the RNA polymerase moves along the DNA, the double helix is unwound and the DNA and RNA nucleotides interact. (c) The DNA behind the enzyme re-forms a double helix. Eventually, when the enzyme that is building the RNA reaches the end of the gene, the DNA and RNA are released. Recall that genes code for proteins. What do you notice about the nucleotides on the DNA strand and the RNA strand?

426 Unit 2 Inside Life

Make them visible in one general area so that students can find them easily. Taping them up is ideal. Post these before class starts.

Photocopy 1 copy of the list of DNA sequences that mRNA will transcribe from copymaster 8.6, *DNA Sequences* and have it at your desk or at the front counter of the room.

Make a sign that says "nucleus." This sign can be hung above or attached to the area you designate as the nucleus. Students will not be able to leave the nucleus area until they have transcribed the DNA sequence, so ensure that there is room for multiple students to work in the nucleus area.

Educational Technologies

SRCD For extra practice with protein synthesis, students can access the animated activity *DNA to Protein* on the *SRCD*.

Several Web sites provide helpful animations and activities for students. For example, the PBS Web site has a lot of useful information including an activity titled DNA Workshop. Cold Spring Harbor Laboratory has a Web site called DNA Interactive, which has historical information as well as interesting animations and video clips.

UAG = . (period; stop codon)	UUC = production	GAU = due
AUG = start codon	CGC = protein(s)	GUA = , (comma)
AAA = DNA	CGG = drive	GUU = in
AAC = holds	CGU = made	UAU = which
ACG = the	AAU = up	UCG = help
ACA = code(s)	ACU = amino	UGC = maintain
AGU = for	AGG = acids	UUA = therefore
AUC = all	AUA = we	UUU = science
CAC = of	CAA = would	CCG = best
CCA = life	CAU = not	CCU = subject
CUC = sections	CUA = have	CGA = so
GAA = are	CUU = without	AAG = much
GCG = most	GAG = processes	ACC = fun
GGC = genes	GCC = equilibrium	GCA = very
AGA = you	GGA = is	GCU = educational
AGC = learn	GGU = and	GGG = includes
AUU = about	GUG = physics	GUC = earth
CAG = earth	UAC = geology	UAA = some
CCC = chemistry	UCC = answers	UCA = but
CUG = biology	UGA = questions	UCU = to
GAC = also	UGU = around	
UUG = life	UGG = creates	

▲ **Figure T8.8 Words representing anticodons.** Use this chart to make the anticodon cards.

As You Teach

Outcomes and Indicators of Success

By the end of this activity, students should

1. begin to understand the process of transcription.

   They will demonstrate their understanding by

   - modeling transcription using paper clips,
   - explaining the difference between RNA and DNA,
   - explaining the purpose of transcription, and
   - describing what happens during the process of transcription.

2. understand the processes of transcription and translation as they relate to protein synthesis.

   They will demonstrate their understanding by

   - correctly transcribing and translating a DNA strand to form a sentence that represents a protein and
   - describing what happens during the process of translation.

3. understand the sequence of events that leads from original DNA to the formation of proteins.

   They will demonstrate their understanding by

   - correctly portraying their roles as they relate to the formation of proteins and
   - comparing and contrasting this activity with the actual processes involved in protein formation.

4. begin to understand how the sequence of DNA determines an organism's genetic characteristics.

   They will demonstrate their understanding by

   - explaining the significance of the DNA sequence to the formation of the correct protein, which is represented as a sentence in this activity;
   - relating this activity to actual protein synthesis; and
   - describing why an error in the DNA sequence resulted in the malformation of proteins (sentences in this activity).

5. understand the importance of protein synthesis.

   They will demonstrate their understanding by

   - explaining the significance of proteins within the cells of organisms,
   - predicting what might happen if the wrong protein was produced, and
   - predicting what might happen if a required protein was not produced.

6. be able to use a model to help develop their understanding of protein synthesis.

   They will demonstrate their ability by

   - arranging paper clips to represent the process of transcription,
   - following instructions to role-play the process of translation, and
   - creating an analogy map comparing the role-play activity to protein synthesis.

Strategies

Getting Started

Remind the class of the previous activity where students learned about the significance of proteins. Discuss whether life could happen without proteins. Listen to students' responses but make sure they realize that life could not go on without proteins. Ask them where these specialized proteins come from using these probing questions:

- "Where does insulin come from?"
- "Where do proteins come from?"
- "How do spiders produce their silk?"
- "Does silk vary among spiders? Why would it?"

Students should have discovered the answers to these questions through their research into the words from the *Just the Fax* activity. Refer to copymaster 8.4, *Protein Summary*. Explain to the students that in this activity they will experience how proteins necessary for life are made.

Process and Procedure

Part I: Transcription

Materials

For each team of 2 students

25 red paper clips
25 yellow paper clips
25 green paper clips
25 blue paper clips
25 silver paper clips
cups to hold the paper clips

In Step 1, pairs of students reassemble their DNA sequence using paper clips. Remind them to assemble the sequence as they did in the explain activity *Clips of DNA*.

In Step 2, students read *Making RNA* to learn how to model transcription. In Step 3, the students model transcription by making a messenger RNA molecule that is complementary to the original DNA strand. Monitor the students to see that they remember that uracil replaces thymine in RNA. In Step 3c, the students will have a strand of RNA that is complementary to their DNA strand. Check their strand of RNA to see that it is complementary to their DNA strand. In Step 3e, the teams trade original DNA strands to practice transcription and also to recognize that DNA sequences are not always the same. Check that they transcribe the other team's strand correctly.

Answers to Stop and Think—Part I, SE page 427–428

Discuss these questions with your class. Call on individual students to listen to their responses.

1. DNA transcription is like DNA replication in that the original DNA strand separates, leaving a template. In both processes, another complementary strand forms from the template. In DNA replication, the complementary strand is formed from DNA nucleotides. In transcription, the complementary strand is formed from mRNA.

2a. This question gets students thinking about the number of possible combinations that DNA can code for. Because the students' math backgrounds will vary, they might not know how to answer this question. The question shows the students how much information DNA can hold because of all the possible combinations of nucleotides. The answer is 4^{15}, which is equal to 1,073,741,824 or more than 1 billion possible arrangements.

2b. The number of nucleotide combinations in Question 2a is substantially smaller than real DNA because real sequences of DNA are much longer than 15 nucleotides.

3. Transcribing the strands of DNA introduced students to RNA and helped them understand the process of transcription. Repeating the transcription process helped reinforce their understanding of transcription. Also, the students should see that each DNA strand is unique, so the mRNA transcribed also is unique.

3. To model what happens in transcription, work with a partner to carry out Steps 3a–f.
   a. Use your fingers to separate the double-stranded paper clip chain as you did for DNA replication. When DNA separates, it can either replicate or serve as a template for making proteins. Choose one of the strands for transcription.
   b. Use paper clips to transcribe your DNA sequence by making a strand of mRNA that is complementary to your DNA strand.

Remember, RNA has the nucleotide uracil instead of thymine. Use silver paper clips to represent uracil.

   c. Record your original DNA sequence and your mRNA sequence in your science notebook.

      original DNA sequence ______________________

      mRNA sequence ______________________
   d. Trade your original DNA strand with another team's original DNA strand from the previous activity.
   e. Practice transcription by transcribing the other team's strand. Record the original DNA sequence and the mRNA sequence in your science notebook.

      original DNA sequence ______________________

      mRNA sequence ______________________
   f. When you are finished with transcription, double-check your sequences with the other team.

SCILINKS NSTA
Topic: transcription
Go to: www.scilinks.org
Code: 2Inquiry427

Stop & THINK

PART I

Participate in a class discussion of these questions. Record agreed-upon answers in your science notebook.

1. How is DNA transcription like DNA replication? How are the 2 processes different?
2. In this activity, you transcribed 2 different DNA strands. Each one was only 15 nucleotides long. That seems pretty short.
   a. How many different arrangements of nucleotides are possible in a strand of DNA that is 15 nucleotides long?

NOTES:

Process and Procedure

Part II: Translation

Materials

For the class

1 sign that says "nucleus"
70 labeled 5×7 or 3×5 in index cards (optional)
1 copy of copymaster 8.5, *Anticodon Cards*
1 copy of copymaster 8.6, *DNA Sequences*
tape
poster paper

For Step 1, make sure that students are sitting in teams of 3 and that they have placed their desks in a circle representing ribosome. They should label their work area "ribosome."

In Step 2, circulate to see that the students read and understand the guidelines for role-playing protein synthesis. In Step 3, students decide who will play each role.

In Step 4, 1 student from each team will play the role of mRNA. That student will go to the area of the room designated as the nucleus. There, he or she will transcribe the DNA sequence. Assign 1 DNA sequence per team to transcribe. Make sure teams know the number of the sentence they are transcribing. That number will be used later when the class makes a paragraph.

Do not allow the students transcribing the DNA strand to simply write down the DNA sequence. They must transcribe the DNA sequence while they are at the nucleus. Monitor the students at the nucleus very closely to ensure that they are transcribing the sequence while they are there. They should not leave the area of the nucleus until they have a sequence written in the language of RNA.

In Step 5, remind the students that they are looking for *complementary* sections of 3 nucleotides to find their cards. Remind them to return the cards once they have written down the word because other students might need them. Tell the class that in actual protein synthesis, however, the tRNA takes the amino acids and keeps them to form a chain of amino acids. In Step 5g, the students check

Answers to Stop & Think—Part I are on TE page 427.

NOTES:

STOP & THINK, PART I, continued

b. How would the number in Question 2a compare with the number of different arrangements of nucleotides possible in a real strand of DNA?

3 How did transcribing 2 different strands of DNA help you understand the process of transcription?

Part II: Translation

Once the cell has formed a strand of mRNA from the DNA template, that mRNA strand can leave the nucleus and travel through the cytoplasm to the ribosomes. DNA is too large to leave the nucleus, but mRNA is small enough to fit through tiny pores. Proteins are made in the ribosomes. The next process on the road to making proteins is called **translation**. After transcription, the mRNA has information, but still needs to pass on the information for making proteins. Translation is the process of reading the information on mRNA and using that information to make proteins. Up until now, you have modeled the processes of DNA replication and transcription using paper clips. In Part II, you will switch gears a little to simulate both transcription and translation in a role-playing exercise. This simulation will help you get an overview of how proteins are made from start to finish.

Materials

none

Process and Procedure

1. Work in teams of 3 and arrange your desks to form a small circle. Label the area "ribosome." This circle will represent a ribosome in the cytoplasm of a cell. Each person in the team will play a role in protein synthesis.
2. Before you begin the role-playing activity, study the following guidelines:
   - DNA is located only in the nucleus of the cell in eukaryotic organisms. In natural settings, DNA cannot leave the nucleus! (For this activity, your teacher has marked an area that represents the nucleus.)
   - In RNA, uracil replaces thymine.
   - RNA is a single-stranded instead of double-stranded molecule.

with you to see if they have formed a correct sentence. The correct sentences follow.

Round 1

1. DNA holds the code for all of life.
2. Sections of DNA are genes.
3. Most genes code for protein production.
4. Proteins are made up of amino acids.
5. We would not have life without proteins.
6. Proteins drive most of the processes of life.
7. The equilibrium of life is due to proteins.
8. DNA codes for proteins, which help maintain equilibrium.
9. Therefore, DNA holds the code for life processes.

Round 2

10. Science is so much fun.
11. Science is also educational.
12. Science is all around you.
13. We learn about life and the earth.
14. Science includes chemistry and biology.
15. Science includes physics and earth science.
16. Science answers questions about the earth.
17. Science answers some questions but also creates some.
18. Science is fun and educational.

Round 3 (Some of these answers contain intentional errors.)

19. Science is so educational.
20. Science is also fun.
21. Life is all around earth.
22. Science best chemistry biology.
23. Science answers protein about the earth.
24. Subject maintain question about life.
25. Science answers questions about life.
26. We maintain equilibrium and have fun.
27. We would not have life without sections.

If the students' sentences are incorrect, ask them where they think they might have gone wrong.

- Proteins are made from long chains of amino acids.
- Proteins begin forming at a specific RNA sequence called a "start" codon. A **codon** is a sequence of 3 adjacent nucleotides on mRNA. For example, the codon that corresponds to the amino acid tryptophan consists of this sequence of nucleotides: UGG.

3. Decide who in your team will play each of these 3 major roles for the simulation. You will switch roles for the next rounds.

mRNA: This stands for messenger RNA. Messenger RNA transcribes the DNA template and delivers the message from the nucleus to the cytoplasm of a cell.

rRNA: This stands for ribosomal RNA. Ribosomal RNA interprets the transcribed code as sections of 3 nucleotides. These sections are called codons.

tRNA: tRNA stands for transfer RNA. tRNA has a section of 3 nucleotides that is complementary to specific codons on the mRNA. This section on the tRNA is called an anticodon. The tRNA picks up amino acids using the information from its anticodon. It then assembles the amino acids into chains to make proteins at the ribosome. In this simulation, you will facilitate translation by moving the cards that represent tRNA.

4. Role-play transcription in your team of 3 following Steps 4a–d as a guide.
   a. mRNA: Go to the nucleus (the teacher's desk) to get the DNA message.
   b. mRNA: Take a pen and your science notebook to "transcribe" the DNA sequence that your teacher assigns you. You cannot simply write down the DNA sequence. You are mRNA and you must transcribe the sequence in the nucleus.

The mRNA strand is produced by forming a strand of RNA that is complementary to the DNA strand. Remember, uracil replaces thymine.

   c. mRNA: Return to the ribosome with the transcribed message.

This is the last step in transcription. Translation begins when mRNA interacts with the ribosome.

   d. rRNA: Divide the mRNA strand into sections of 3 nucleotides each. Do this by drawing a vertical line between every third nucleotide. These sections of 3 nucleotides represent codons.

5. Role-play translation by following Steps 5a–h.

During translation, the mRNA code is deciphered and the language of RNA is translated into amino acids. Translation is like translating from one language to another language. You are going to take the language from RNA and translate it to make proteins.

NOTES:

Encourage them to retrace their steps so that they begin to understand the entire process.

In Step 5h, call on each team in numerical order (1 going first) to read its sentence out loud. Have each team write its sentence on a piece of poster paper in chronological order so that the class forms a paragraph.

In round 3 (Step 7), some of the sentences intentionally contain errors in the original DNA strand. This might cause the students to think that they did something wrong. Tell them to continue and that they will learn why this happened later in the chapter.

In Step 8, make sure the students read the information about actual protein synthesis as it occurs in cells. Remind them that the proteins they studied in the previous activity were all chains of amino acids.

Answers to Steps 8–9, SE pages 430–432

8b. Students' analogy maps should look similar to figure T8.9.

In this activity, letters on a piece of paper represent DNA. Students play the role of mRNA and transcribe the DNA at the teacher's desk, which represents the nucleus. Students represent tRNA molecules that carry words, which model the amino acids. Student desks are ribosomes.

8c. In this simulation,

- a word represents an amino acid,
- a sentence represents a protein, and
- the paragraph represents a long section of a chromosome.

Note that not all of DNA codes for protein production. Only sections that are transcribed by RNA lead to the formation of proteins.

NOTES:

a. tRNA: Use the codons to find amino acids. Do this by taking the sequence of codons and looking for anticodons listed on the cards placed around the room. The cards actually represent tRNA but you are facilitating the process.

An anticodon is a sequence of 3 nucleotides on a tRNA molecule that are complementary to an mRNA codon.

b. tRNA: Find a card with the correct anticodon. Bring it back to the ribosome and flip it over to reveal the word on the back of the card.

c. mRNA, rRNA, and tRNA: Record the word located by the tRNA in your science notebook.

d. tRNA: Return the card immediately to its original location so that other teams can find it. In the cell, the tRNA would actually take amino acids to assemble the proteins, but you need to return the card back to where you got it from.

e. tRNA: Continue matching the codons from your mRNA to the anticodons on the cards until all of the codons from your mRNA are translated.

f. tRNA: Record the words from the anticodon cards in sequential order. You should end up with a sentence.

g. tRNA: Check with your teacher to see if your sentence is correct. Record the sentence in your science notebook.

h. tRNA: Using the numbers on the sentences, read the sentences aloud in numerical order. Notice that you have now formed a paragraph. Record the paragraph in your science notebook.

6. Switch roles and repeat Steps 3–5.
7. Switch roles one last time and complete Steps 3–5 again.
8. To help you relate this role-playing simulation to what happens during protein synthesis in cells, complete Steps 8a–c.
   a. Read the following paragraph about protein synthesis and study figure 8.17.
   b. Create an analogy map comparing the simulation with protein synthesis. Use the headings "Part of Simulation" and "How It Is Similar to Protein Synthesis."
   c. What do the following analogies from this simulation represent in a real cell?
      - A word
      - A sentence
      - The paragraph

This activity used role playing to simulate the complex processes involved in protein synthesis. In real cells, amino acids are the basic building blocks of proteins and therefore the

Part of simulation	How it is similar to protein synthesis
team arranges desk in a circle	represents ribosome in the cell
teacher's desk	represents nucleus
student goes to teacher's desk to write down complementary nucleotides to a DNA message	a DNA sequence is transcribed into an mRNA strand in the nucleus
student goes to team's desk	mRNA carries mRNA strand to the ribosome
student divides the mRNA strand into sections of 3 nucleotides each representing codons	tRNa translates mRNA strand into amino acids
student finds anticodon card that matches each codon	tRNA translates mRNA strand into amino acids
student records word on back of anticodon card	tRNA translates mRNA strand into amino acids
student sequentially matches remaining codons to anticodon cards and words are recorded	tRNa translates mRNA strand into amino acids
student forms a sentence	amino acid chain is formed
student forms a paragraph	amino acid chains join together to form a protein

▲ **Figure T8.9 Analogy map for protein synthesis.** Students' analogy maps should contain information similar to this for Step 8b.

building blocks of life. The ribosome is like a protein factory: all the components needed for translation gather here to produce a product. Each set of three nucleotides on the tRNA code for amino acids. The tRNA pulls amino acids from the cell one at a time, forming a chain. The amino acid chains make up the specific needed proteins. Figure 8.17 shows how proteins are synthesized in the cell in the process of translation.

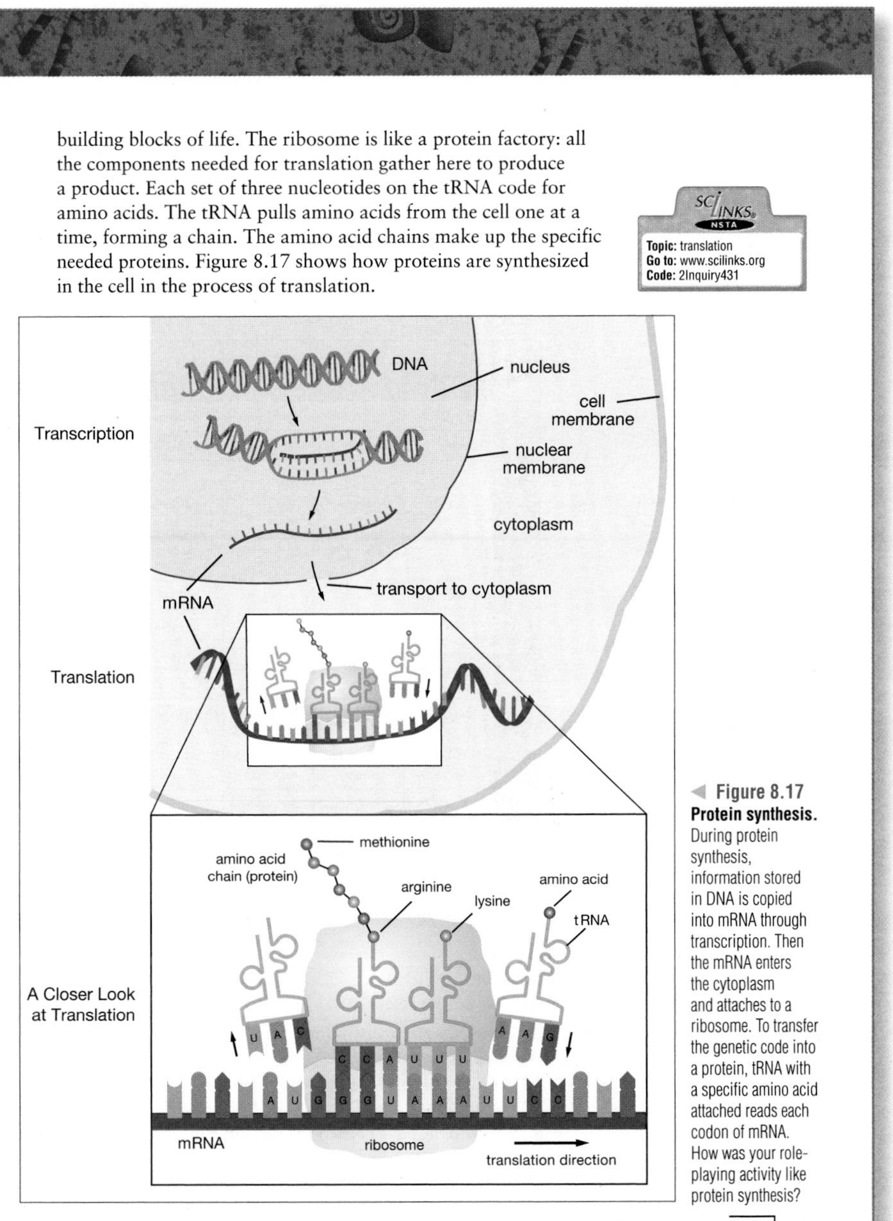

◀ **Figure 8.17 Protein synthesis.** During protein synthesis, information stored in DNA is copied into mRNA through transcription. Then the mRNA enters the cytoplasm and attaches to a ribosome. To transfer the genetic code into a protein, tRNA with a specific amino acid attached reads each codon of mRNA. How was your role-playing activity like protein synthesis?

NOTES:

9a. There are 64 arrangements possible if you took 4 nucleotides in sections of 3 each. Students can figure this out without a formula just by writing down the different possibilities. The easiest way to see this is that it is figured by raising 4 to the third power: $4^3 = 64$ possible arrangements.

9b. Students should see that there are 20 amino acids commonly found in proteins. The answer in Question 9a was 64 possible combinations. There is more than 1 possible combination of sequences for each amino acid.

9c. Students will come up with different answers to this question because there is more than 1 possibility. Answers will include GUU, GUC, GUA, or GUG.

Before directing students to answer the *Reflect and Connect* questions, facilitate a class discussion around the question, "Where do you get the amino acids necessary for the formation of proteins in your cells?" Students might have difficulty realizing that some amino acids are made by their body (nonessential amino acids) and some of the amino acids in their cells come from the foods they eat (essential amino acids). This is a nice opportunity to make that connection. When protein is digested, it breaks into amino acids and the cells use those amino acids to synthesize new proteins. Also, some products such as protein drinks contain high concentrations of amino acids.

Answers to Reflect and Connect, SE pages 432–433

1. In translation, a string of amino acids is formed according to the instructions provided by the mRNA. The mRNA code is translated, amino acids are picked up, and a protein chain is formed. Proteins are very important. They give us our characteristics and drive all of life's processes. Proteins act as enzymes, as structural molecules, and as defense molecules in our immune systems. These are just a few examples of how proteins function and why they are important. Students might share a variety of examples. Verify that their examples are indeed proteins that function in living organisms.

2a. The outcome in Step 7 could have been caused by errors in the DNA sequence, how the DNA sequence was transcribed, or how the RNA was translated into words (amino acids). In this case, it was due to errors in the original DNA sequence.

2b. Accept all answers; this question gets students thinking ahead to the next activity. Students might be familiar with mutations and will say that errors like this do occur in nature. They will learn about mutations in the next activity, *Nobody's Perfect*.

3. An example of a student's written response: "DNA, or deoxyribonucleic acid, is a molecule made up of nucleotides. Nucleotides are molecules composed of a deoxyribose sugar, a phosphate group, and a nitrogen base. There are 4 different nitrogen bases. Nucleotides vary by their nitrogen bases. The arrangement of nucleotides is the DNA sequence. Sections of DNA are genes, and these sections have a particular sequence of nucleotides. Genes provide instructions for protein production, and proteins give organisms their traits. The DNA, which contains genes, is organized into structures called chromosomes. Chromosomes appear in the cells of organisms. In humans, the chromosomes are in the

9. Answer the following questions about nucleotide sequences.
   a. How many arrangements of nucleotides are possible if you take 4 nucleotides, 3 at a time?
   b. Look at figure 8.18. This figure shows the codons for the amino acids in nature. How does your answer from Question 9a compare with the number of amino acids in nature?
   c. What is the corresponding nucleotide sequence for the amino acid valine?

First Base	Second Base: U	C	A	G	Third Base
U	phenylanine	serine	tyrosine	cysteine	U
U	phenylanine	serine	tyrosine	cysteine	C
U	leucine	serine	stop	stop	A
U	leucine	serine	stop	tryptophan	G
C	leucine	proline	histidine	arginine	U
C	leucine	proline	histidine	arginine	C
C	leucine	proline	glutamine	arginine	A
C	leucine	proline	glutamine	arginine	G
A	isoleucine	threonine	asparagine	serine	U
A	isoleucine	threonine	asparagine	serine	C
A	isoleucine	threonine	lysine	arginine	A
A	(start) methionine	threonine	lysine	arginine	G
G	valine	alanine	aspartate	glycine	U
G	valine	alanine	aspartate	glycine	C
G	valine	alanine	glutamate	glycine	A
G	valine	alanine	glutamate	glycine	G

▶ **Figure 8.18 Codons.** The genetic code is written in nucleotide triplets, or codons, in a strand of mRNA. Each codon specifies an amino acid, as shown in the boxes. To use the table, follow a codon's three nucleotides to arrive at the corresponding amino acid. What amino acid does the codon GGA code for?

Reflect and Connect

Work individually to answer these questions. Then compare your answers with a partner's and revise your answers as you learn something new. Keep a record of any revision in your science notebook.

1. Describe what happened during the translation process. Why is this process important?
2. Answer the following questions about round 3 of the simulation (Step 7).
   a. What might have caused the outcome in Step 7 of the activity?
   b. Do you think this happens in nature? Explain your answer.

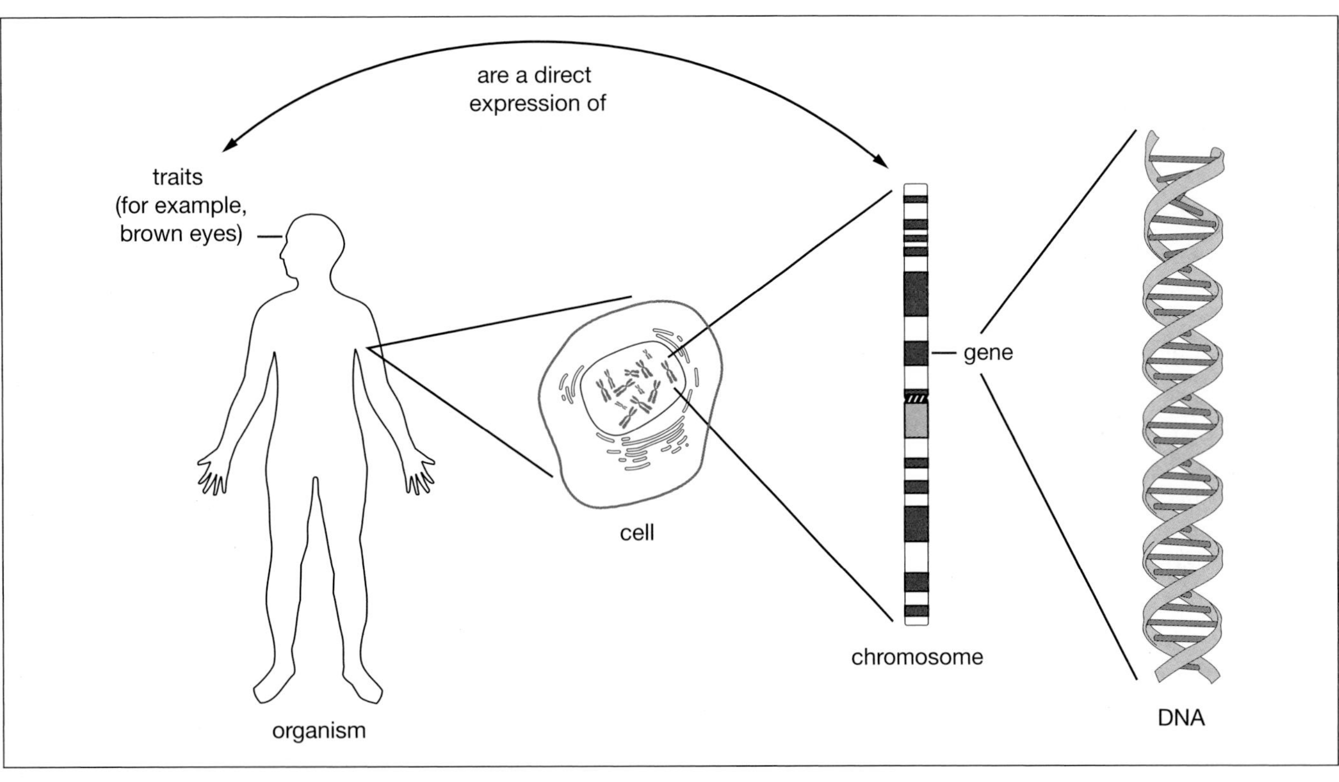

▲ **Figure T8.10 Sample diagram for Question 3.** An example of a student diagram that illustrates the relationship of DNA, genes, chromosomes, cells, and traits.

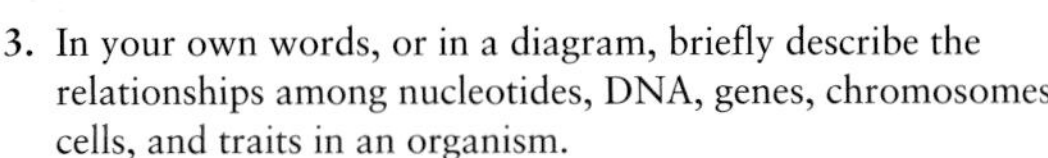

3. In your own words, or in a diagram, briefly describe the relationships among nucleotides, DNA, genes, chromosomes, cells, and traits in an organism.

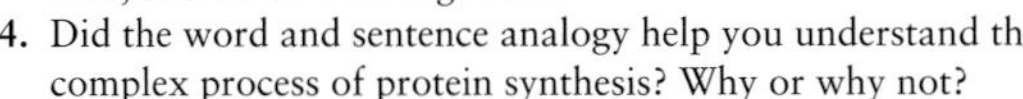

4. Did the word and sentence analogy help you understand the complex process of protein synthesis? Why or why not?

Mapping the Human Genome

SIDEBAR

As technology advances, and our understanding of the mechanism of inheritance increases, we continue to discover more about the human genome. In 2003, scientists finished mapping the entire human genome. The biggest surprise at the completion of the project was that there were fewer genes than scientists had expected.

A **genome** is all of the information coded in the DNA of an organism. It contains the complete set of genetic instructions for making an organism. Human cells that have nuclei (with the exception of egg and sperm cells) normally contain 22 pairs of autosomes (nonsex chromosomes), plus two sex chromosomes (XX or XY). Remember, these chromosomes contain DNA. When the Human Genome Project (HGP) was completed, scientists learned the entire sequence of human DNA and the location of each gene in our chromosomes.

Two major groups worked independently to sequence the human genome. The HGP was the public group, which was funded in the United States primarily by the Department of Energy and the National Institutes of Health. Several other countries were also involved. The other group was a

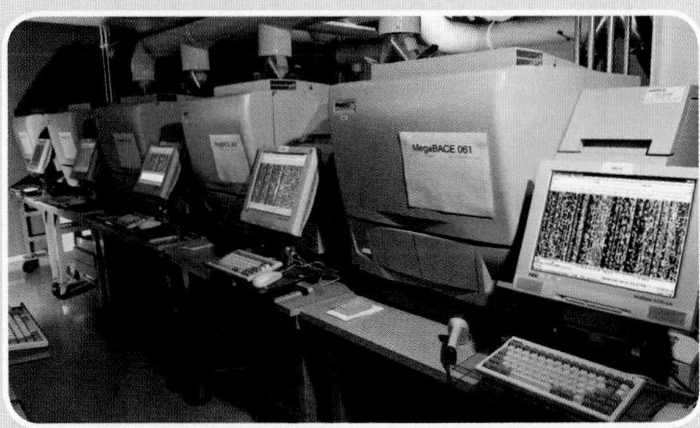

▲ **Automated DNA sequencing.** Scientists use machines to help them sequence multiple samples of DNA. Each of the colors on the screen represents one of the four nitrogen bases.

nucleus of the cell. Organisms are made up of cells." Students might produce a diagram that looks like figure T8.10.

4. This question gets students to think about how they learn. Role playing usually helps those students who like to learn by completing hands-on activities. The students' answers will vary depending on whether or not role playing helps them learn concepts.

After students have completed the activity, you could challenge them by asking them to bring in labels from protein drinks or powders and compare the labels. What are the key ingredients? They should notice that these products contain amino acids. Ask them the reasoning behind how these products are supposed to work. (The more amino acids you have, the more protein you can produce.) Bodybuilders, weight lifters, and other sports figures use these products to build extra muscle protein. Ask the students to investigate the research behind the use of these products. Have them investigate what evidence supports or refutes the practice of consuming large amounts of amino acids.

ELABORATE

Nobody's Perfect

Activity Overview

Students have learned about the structure and function of DNA. They have learned about the processes involved with DNA replication, transcription, and translation. In the last activity, *Transcription and Translation—the Road to Making Proteins*, students experienced the result of a mutation in the DNA while making their sentences. In Part I of *Nobody's Perfect*, the students will learn about the causes and possible effects of mutations in real DNA. Students will begin by testing their own conceptions about mutations. Then they will read a passage about the causes and possible outcomes of mutations.

Mutations in DNA result in variability. In Part II, students will explore the variability within a population of seeds by identifying a particular variation in the population (possibly as a result of a spontaneous mutation). They then will explore how the variation within the population of seeds contributes to the seeds' survival when exposed to different selective pressures. Students will think about how that population might change over time based on the selective pressures it is exposed to. The students will wrap up this activity by readdressing their initial responses to the statements posed in Part I of the activity.

Before You Teach

Background Information

DNA replication and transcription are processes that occur continuously. Massive quantities of DNA are being copied all the time and have been since the beginning of life. Because these processes occur quickly and continuously, mistakes can happen. These mistakes are collectively called mutations. Mutations can occur in a number of ways. Bases might be deleted, added, substituted, or modified chemically. Often, DNA repair enzymes fix the error, but sometimes the error remains in the DNA strand and becomes part of the DNA in an organism. Since DNA serves as a template for the processes of DNA replication and transcription, all new DNA or RNA formed from this template will carry this new sequence. The word *mutation* often has a negative connotation but in reality, mutations in DNA simply mean a slight variation in the DNA sequence. Some mutations have no effect on an organism while others cause very serious problems. Still others can be advantageous to organisms.

If the mutation is in the DNA of a somatic cell (nongerm cell), it can be passed to each new cell that is produced from cell division through the process of mitosis. This is how some cancers grow. The mutation, however, is not passed to the organism's offspring.

If a mutation is in a germ cell (gamete), the mutation can be passed to the next generation. Germ cells are produced from the process of meiosis, so copies of the DNA carrying the mutation might end up in the offspring. Genetically linked disorders are inherited this way. Since each new cell in the offspring contains the mutation, all the DNA in that organism has the mutation.

Mutations in DNA are one cause of the variability that leads to diversity among organisms and populations of organisms. Slight variations in protein production can lead to slight variations in individuals of a population. If a variation is favorable when exposed to selective pressure, the organisms with that variation will

Mapping the Human Genome, continued

private company called Celera Genomics Corporation.

Human DNA contains approximately 3.2 billion base pairs of DNA. So determining the sequence, and finding and mapping the genes was a tremendous task. If the DNA sequence of the human genome was compiled in books, we would need about 200 volumes at 1,000 pages each to hold all this information. Scientists learned that there are approximately 25,000 genes in human DNA.

The major findings of mapping the human genome include the following:

- Scientists were surprised at the small number of genes. It appears that humans have only a few thousand more genes than the roundworm *C. elegans*.
- Humans are 99.99 percent similar to one another in our DNA. It does not appear that there is much variation in the human population.
- Genes appear to be concentrated in random areas along the genome, with vast expanses of noncoding DNA in between.
- Chromosome 1 has the most genes (about 3,000); the Y chromosome has the fewest (about 230).
- Sperm carry twice as many mutations as eggs. This is interesting because mutations are a major source of genetic errors and also lead to variations in a population.
- We do not know the functions for more than half of the genes that were discovered.
- Some genes appear to have come from bacteria that infected our ancestors millions of years ago. This discovery provides additional evidence of evolution.
- Less than 2 percent of the genome codes for proteins.

The human genome map will help in diagnosing, treating, and preventing disease in the future. As genes are isolated, scientists will be able to find small differences in DNA sequences. These variations might be the cause of some genetic disorders in people. Once scientists identify these variations, they may be able to develop treatments and cures for some of the diseases. Eventually, treatments may even be customized to individual genetic profiles. Customizing treatments likely would increase their effectiveness and reduce adverse drug reactions. Some diseases might be cured either by altering the proteins produced or, eventually, by gene therapy (fixing the gene).

As more genes are identified, scientists are finding genetic basis for psychiatric disorders. Identifying such genes will help our understanding of the causes of depression, schizophrenia, and other mental disorders. Once the contributions from those genes are understood, it will be possible to develop better medications.

The process of mapping the human genome has also given rise to new fields of study, such as bioinformatics, proteomics, and pharmacogenics. Bioinformatics uses sophisticated data management systems and computers to identify genes in the DNA sequence data and establish their functions. Proteomics is the study of protein structure, function, and interactions. Pharmacogenics is the study of how genetic variation affects

434 Unit 2 Inside Life

likely survive and reproduce. Since those organisms with the mutation are surviving and reproducing, they are likely to transmit that mutation (coding for the favorable variability) to their offspring. Over long spans of time, mutations lead to the evolution of species.

Mutations are not the only cause of variability in organisms. Actually, mutations only contribute to slight variations in individuals. Sometimes entire sections of DNA are exchanged and recombine during meiosis. Recombination leads to significant variations in populations.

Mutations and recombination eventually provide the foundation for evolution because they cause variability in organisms and eventually, populations of organisms. As students experienced in chapter 6, these slight variations can help organisms within a population survive. Since the organisms survive, they reproduce and pass the favorable trait to the next generation. It is important to remember that the favorable trait is only favorable to the selective pressures that act on it. Selected variations depend on the selective forces.

Materials—Part I

For the class

Large sheet of paper (optional)

Materials—Part II

For each team of 2 students

1 ruler

1 container with 25 seeds of 1 type

graph paper (if the student notebooks are not conducive for making bar graphs)

other materials as needed for measuring variability (for example, a balance, string, small calipers, and a stereomicroscope)

Advance Preparation

For Part I, locate models or charts that show mitosis and meiosis in detail. Have them accessible to the class for the questions in *Stop and Think—Part I.*

For Part II, purchase packages of seeds from the dried bean section of the grocery store. Purchase a variety so that each team of 2 is working with different kinds of seeds. Use seeds that are somewhat large and would not look like they have any variation at first glance. Lima beans, great northern beans, kidney beans, pinto beans, sunflower seeds, and peanuts in the shell work well. Avoid using small seeds such as lentils and split peas. Set up cups that each have 25 of the same seed type.

Decide on the materials students will use for their investigation; have those materials available. These materials will help them investigate variations: a balance for mass, a stereomicroscope for the number of spots, and a string for diameter.

Educational Technologies

Students can learn more about different types of mutations and what affect the mutations have on an organism by going through the activity *Mutations: Changing the Genetic Code* on the *SRCD*. To learn more about advances in molecular genetics and how they relate to Mendelian genetics, students could complete the optional reading activity *Dominance and Recessiveness* on the *TRCD*.

As You Teach

Outcomes and Indicators of Success

By the end of this activity, students should

1. understand that mutations can be both beneficial and detrimental to organisms.

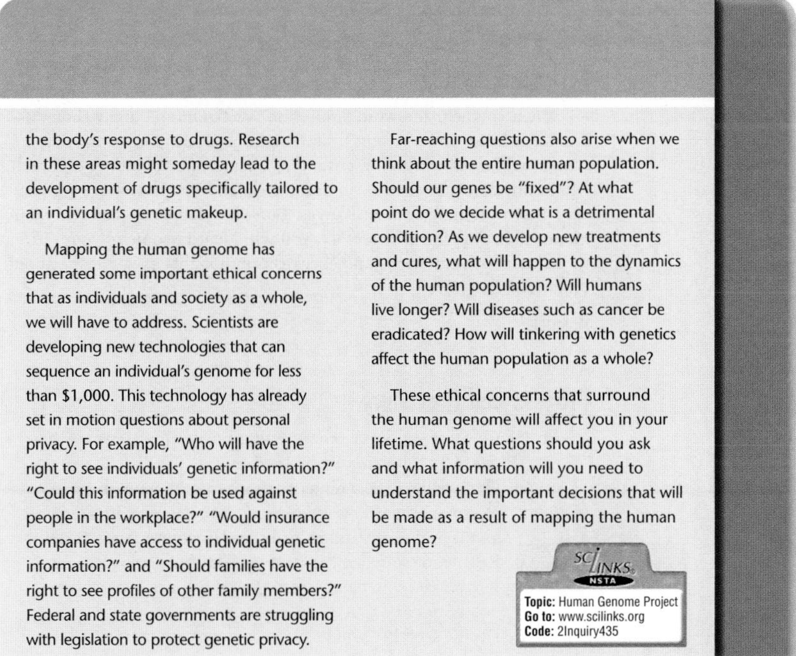

the body's response to drugs. Research in these areas might someday lead to the development of drugs specifically tailored to an individual's genetic makeup.

Mapping the human genome has generated some important ethical concerns that as individuals and society as a whole, we will have to address. Scientists are developing new technologies that can sequence an individual's genome for less than $1,000. This technology has already set in motion questions about personal privacy. For example, "Who will have the right to see individuals' genetic information?" "Could this information be used against people in the workplace?" "Would insurance companies have access to individual genetic information?" and "Should families have the right to see profiles of other family members?" Federal and state governments are struggling with legislation to protect genetic privacy.

Far-reaching questions also arise when we think about the entire human population. Should our genes be "fixed"? At what point do we decide what is a detrimental condition? As we develop new treatments and cures, what will happen to the dynamics of the human population? Will humans live longer? Will diseases such as cancer be eradicated? How will tinkering with genetics affect the human population as a whole?

These ethical concerns that surround the human genome will affect you in your lifetime. What questions should you ask and what information will you need to understand the important decisions that will be made as a result of mapping the human genome?

SCI LINKS NSTA
Topic: Human Genome Project
Go to: www.scilinks.org
Code: 2Inquiry435

Nobody's Perfect

ELABORATE

The processes of DNA replication, transcription, and translation are amazing. These processes are occurring in the cells of all living things, every second of every day. If you take all the DNA from your body cells and place it end to end, your body alone contains more than 3 million miles of DNA! Much of that DNA is either replicating or being used as a template for transcription.

Most of the time, the processes of DNA replication, transcription, and translation occur without any problems. The processes remain constant. However, eventually mistakes do occur. These mistakes are called **mutations**. Mutations lead to changes in DNA sequences. You experienced some consequences of mutations in the activity *Transcription and Translation—the Road to Making Proteins*. In that activity, a mutation affected your sentences. In *Nobody's Perfect*, you will work by yourself and with a partner to apply what you learned in the sentence activity to understand how real mutations affect life.

They will demonstrate their understanding by

- correctly changing their answers to a prequiz to include marking the statement "false" that indicates a population wants to avoid having mutations,
- describing that mutations can be good for a population but sometimes detrimental to individual organisms, and
- predicting how a mutation in color would affect a population of organisms.

2. understand the difference between mutations that occur in germ cells and those that occur at the somatic cell level.

   They will demonstrate their understanding of the distinction by

   - explaining why each new cell carries a mutation from the original cell and
   - describing why only genetically linked mutations get passed from generation to generation.

3. become aware of the consequences of mutations.

   They will demonstrate their awareness by

   - describing possible consequences of mutations, positive, negative, and neutral, and
   - describing how mutations might influence evolution.

4. understand that populations of organisms have variability within them.

   They will demonstrate their understanding by

   - identifying and measuring a variation in a population of seeds and
   - making a bar graph that depicts a variation that the students identified.

5. recognize that mutations lead to variability in populations.

   They will demonstrate their recognition by describing that mutations were the cause of some seeds in a population to fall outside of the average range.

6. be able to investigate a variation in a seed population and record and communicate results from the investigation.

   They will demonstrate their ability by

   - deciding on a characteristic of a seed population to measure,
   - organizing the data they collect in a data table,
   - making a graph of the data including highlight comments and a caption, and
   - analyzing the graph and describing variation in the data.

Strategies

Getting Started

Discuss with the class the results of round 3 of the activity *Transcription and Translation—the Road to Making Proteins*. Ask the following probing questions:

- "What happened in round 3?"
- "Why do you think it happened?"
- "Did the sentences still make sense?"
- "Do you think this happens in real life?"
- "What do you think the consequences might be if there is an error in the DNA sequence or in the processes of transcription and translation?"

Listen as students share their ideas. Explain that in this activity they will learn how mistakes in DNA or in the processes of transcription and translation affect life.

Part I: A Natural Mistake

When you hear the word "mutation" or "mutant," many thoughts and ideas likely come to mind. You might have seen horror movies with a wild mutant running around or alien mutants landing on Earth. Mutations do cause changes in organisms, and the movies are a great way to sensationalize these changes. But what happens when real DNA mutates? In Part I of this activity, you will identify some of your current thoughts about mutations and check those thoughts as you learn about mutations in nature.

Materials

none

Process and Procedure

1. Share what you know about mutations with a classmate and the class by following Steps 1a–d.
   a. Share some ideas you have about mutations with a classmate. Based on your discussion, develop 3 statements about mutations and record them in your science notebook.
   b. Read your statements aloud to contribute to a class list.
   c. Record the statements from the class list in your science notebook.
   d. Decide whether you think each statement is true or false. Explain your reasoning in your science notebook.
2. Read *We All Make Mistakes* to learn about mutations. Use this question to focus your reading: "In what ways do mutations affect organisms?"

SRCD

We All Make Mistakes

What happens when a mutation in DNA occurs? The consequences of a mutation might or might not have an effect on the message the DNA is sending. Imagine a blueprint for a building. The length of a wall might be written on the blueprint as 30 meters (m). What if the architect accidentally spills something on the blueprint? The carpenter begins to measure the boards according to the lengths on the blueprint, but reads 33 m instead of 30 m. The carpenter might notice this mistake and repair it (as some DNA-repairing enzymes do in the cell). If the carpenter does not fix the error, however, it might affect the structural properties of the building.

Process and Procedure

Part I: A Natural Mistake

Materials

large sheet of paper (optional)

In Step 1a, students share their ideas about mutations with a classmate. They should record 3 statements about mutation in their science notebook. Some students might not know what a mutation is at this time. Tell students that the statements will start them thinking about things they will learn in this activity. They will return to the statements throughout the activity.

In Step 1b, ask each pair of students to read its statements. Record the statements on the board or on a large sheet of paper. Students should record these statements in their notebooks as well. In Step 1d, students decide whether each statement is true or false. They should provide a reason for their answers. Even though these statements are difficult to answer with a simple true or false, encourage students to make the best choice possible based on their current understanding.

As an alternative, you could provide students with the following list of statements. Answers to the statements are provided at the end of the activity.

1. Mutations have a negative effect on an organism.
2. Mutations can be fixed.
3. Mutations are passed on to the next generation.
4. Your DNA contains mutations.
5. A population wants to avoid having mutations.
6. Humans would not be alive today without the presence of mutations.

In Step 2, students read about mutation. They should use this focus question to guide their reading: "In what ways do mutations affect organisms?" For Step 3, hold a class discussion about the reading in Step 2. Lead a discussion focused on students' conceptions of mutations. Allow a little discussion around the statements. Ask the class the following questions:

- "What is a mutation?"

A mutation is a change in the DNA sequence.

- "What causes mutations?"

Errors during the normal process of DNA replication can cause mutation. Environmental factors such as ultraviolet radiation and exposure to environmental or chemical toxins can also cause mutations.

- "Are mutations always bad?"

No, most mutations have no effect on an organism.

- "Why does your DNA contain mutations?"

Even if the DNA in your body has not mutated during your lifetime, your body potentially contains mutations that occurred in the gametes of your ancestors.

Answers to Step 3, SE pages 437–438

3a. Mutations can have no effect, a negative effect, or a positive effect on an organism.

3b. **Mutations can occur during DNA replication, transcription, and translation. Mutations also occur as a result of exposure to radiation or toxins.**

Some mutations in DNA happen spontaneously during the normal process of DNA replication. Some mutations happen as a result of natural factors such as radiation. Certain types of radiation such as ultraviolet radiation from the Sun can cause mutations in DNA. Mutations can also be caused by environmental or chemical toxins. Chemicals found in tobacco smoke, charcoal-grilled foods, and toxic waste contain substances that can cause mutations.

The third time you went through the protein synthesis activity, there was a mutation in all of the DNA sequences. You might have noticed, however, that some sentences still made sense. Mutations in DNA do not always have negative effects. Sometimes they have no observable effect on organisms. In other cases, mutations can benefit organisms. In every population, there are many genes coding for traits that exist because of mutations in DNA and new combinations of genes formed during meiosis. How do those mutations stay in a population and how do they help populations? The traits that result from mutations are not always detrimental to the organism. Therefore, the organism thrives and reproduces, passing the trait to its offspring. The traits that result from mutations and recombination lead to variability within populations. You might remember from chapter 6, *Exploring Change*, that variability within a population enables the population to survive through natural selection.

While some mutations might not make a difference to an organism, others might have a great impact on an individual organism. Fortunately, many harmful mutations are fixed before they cause any harm. The cell has repair enzymes that patrol DNA for defects. If a mutation is detected, the damaged nucleotides are cut out and replaced with correct nucleotides. However, the mistakes are not always caught. Just as the carpenter might not detect the mistake in the blueprint, the repair mechanisms in a cell might not always catch or be able to repair mutations. Some inherited mutations are passed to future generations and affect entire populations of organisms. To learn about some examples of how mutations have affected populations, read the sidebar *Mutations and Society*.

When a mutation occurs in any cell other than a gamete (sperm or egg cell), each new cell produced from that cell will carry the mutation. When mutations occur in nongamete (somatic) cells, they only affect the individual. They are not passed to offspring. As the cells carrying the mutation continue to divide, they produce a group of mutated cells within an organism. Cancer is one example of mutated cells growing out of control.

When a mutation is in the DNA of a gamete, it is known as a genetically linked mutation and it can be inherited by the offspring. For example, Huntington's disease and cystic fibrosis are genetically linked conditions that you learned about in chapter 7. In these conditions, and many others like them, certain needed proteins malfunction. If a person does not have these needed proteins, he or she often suffers ill effects and might have a shortened life span. These mutations are passed on through the gametes, sperm and egg, from the parents.

Topic: mutations
Go to: www.scilinks.org
Code: 2Inquiry437

3. Participate in a class discussion of the reading and show your understanding of mutations by answering Questions 3a–c.
   a. Answer the focus question: In what ways do mutations affect organisms?
   b. How can mutations occur?

3c. Mutations in gametes have a different effect because these mutations can potentially be passed on to another generation through reproduction.

In Step 4, give students time to review the statements from Step 1 individually. Do not discuss the answers with them at this time.

As students are working with their partners to answer the *Stop and Think* questions, check that they are looking at diagrams of meiosis and mitosis. The students should be making connections between the two processes and the transmission of mutations. Use these questions as a link back to mitosis and meiosis. If you have charts or diagrams that show mitosis and meiosis, place them in an area of the room where students can easily see them. Remind the students to look closely at these processes.

Answers to Stop and Think—Part I, SE page 438

1. Each new cell carries a mutation from the original cell because DNA replicates as the cell is preparing to divide. In DNA replication, the DNA serves as a template for the formation of new DNA. If the template has a mutation, new DNA formed from that template will carry the mutation. When the DNA replicates, the mutation will be copied. Each new cell will have a copy of the DNA containing the mutation.
2. Genetically linked mutations get passed from generation to generation through the process of meiosis. When the cell prepares to divide, the DNA makes a copy of itself (replication). The cell then divides in half and then each of those cells divides so that there are now 4 new cells. Two of those cells will carry the mutation. Some of those cells might contain a copy of the DNA that has the mutation. Students' diagrams might look like figure T8.11.
3. Usually organisms cannot avoid mutations. Mutations simply happen. Organisms can, however, avoid exposure to substances that produce genetic changes such as radiation or chemicals. Avoiding mutagens would reduce an organism's chances of getting mutations in its DNA.

NOTES:

c. Why can mutations in gametes have a different effect than mutations in nongamete cells?

4. Look back at your responses to the 3 statements you developed in Step 1. Would you change any of your answers? Record your corrected responses in your science notebook.

Stop & THINK

PART I

Work with your partner to answer the following questions. Record your answers in your science notebook.

1. Why does each new cell carry a mutation from the original cell?
2. How are genetically linked mutations passed from generation to generation? Show your understanding by drawing a diagram. Write a caption for your diagram that explains your answer in words.

   Review figure 7.17 in chapter 7 to help you answer this question. Start with a cell containing only 1 pair of chromosomes.
3. Can organisms avoid mutations? Explain your reasoning.

Part II: Mutations Lead to Variation

In *We All Make Mistakes*, you learned that mutations lead to variability in populations and you know that variability helps species survive. Variations are present in all populations of organisms. Some of these variations are not easily observed while others are quite noticeable. We often overlook variability within populations, yet it is an important feature of successful populations.

How does variation in a population help it survive? In Part II, you will work with a partner to observe variability within a population and think about how variability is important to species survival.

Materials

For each team of 2 students

1 ruler

1 container of 25 seeds (all of the same type)

graph paper

access to measuring tools

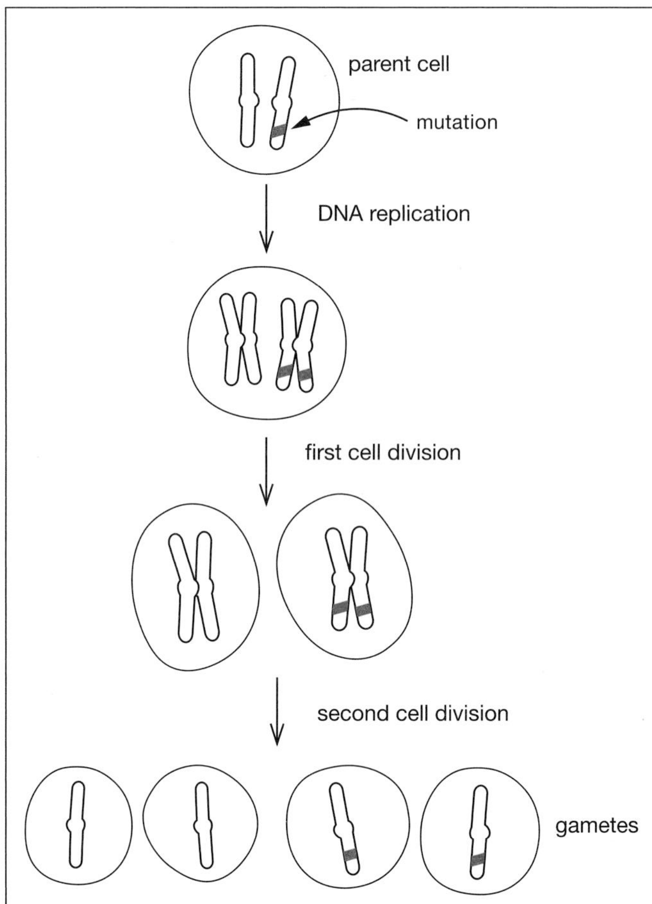

▲ **Figure T8.11 Sample for Question 2.** An example of a student diagram showing a mutation carried to gametes through the process of meiosis.

Process and Procedure

Part II: Mutations Lead to Variation

Materials

For each team of 2 students

1 ruler
1 container with 25 seeds of one type
graph paper (if the student notebooks are not conducive for making bar graphs)
other materials as needed for measuring variability (Some possibilities include a balance, string, small calipers, and a stereomicroscope.)

Distribute seeds for Step 1. Make sure each team of 2 students receives 1 container of one type of seed. Remind the class that these seeds represent organisms in a population.

In Step 2, check that the students are listing in their science notebooks how seeds might vary. In Step 3, encourage students to choose a variation that they can measure. To help students decide, ask these probing questions:

- "What kind of differences could you measure in a population? How could you measure that difference?"
- "What is one thing that might help you tell the difference between two seeds?"
- "How could you group your seeds?"
- "Does this grouping work so that there are some groups with more than one seed in them?"

Guide the students to choose only *one variable* to measure in the seeds. Encourage them to make their data quantifiable since they will be graphing it. Good variations for students to measure in the seeds include length, diameter, color tints (light, medium, dark), and number of spots (pinto beans). Mass can be a good variable to measure, but students' success would depend on the sensitivity of your school's balance. If the seeds are small and the balances are not sensitive, the students will not see any variation. If students choose to measure length, suggest that they measure in millimeters. Measuring in millimeters is more precise than measuring in larger increments such as centimeters. If students choose to measure a variable that is less precise to measure such as color tint, encourage them to group their seeds into categories (light, medium, and dark). If students choose to count the number of spots, they will need to identify a way to group them. One way to group the seeds is by using a range of numbers of spots such as less than 10, between 10 and 15, and greater than 15.

In Step 4, students make a data table to record their data. They might need some assistance with this step. Encourage them to group the seeds. A good data table for length measurements would look like the table in figure T8.12.

Length of seed (mm)	Frequency
6–9	5
10–13	7
14–17	10
18–21	6
22–25	2

▲ **Figure T8.12 Frequency of seed length.** Students should organize their data in a table similar to this if they are recording length and frequency for the seed population.

As students collect their data in Step 5, encourage them to measure accurately and to not measure the same seed twice. In Step 6, discuss making a graph. Ask students these questions to help them remember how to set up a graph:

- "What is the *x*-axis?"
- "What is the *y*-axis?"
- "Why are they set up in this manner?"

In Step 7, students analyze their graphs by answering questions. When most of the class begins to work on Question 7c, allow students a short time to discuss the question with their partners. Then stop the class for a discussion on factors that contribute to variability in populations.

Answers to Step 7, SE page 439

7a. Students will find different degrees of variation in their population. They should notice that variation exists. This might or might not surprise them. They might say that they did not expect any variation and were surprised to find a large range of differences within the seed population.

7b. If the students measured a factor such as length, diameter, or mass, they should have a bar graph that shows the most number of seeds in the middle of the graph. If they measured other variations, the graphs will differ depending on their seeds. The bar graph will help the students visualize how much variation exists in any population.

7c. Stop the class for a short discussion about the causes of variability in populations. Ask the students what responses they recorded for Step 7c. There are several factors that can cause variations in a small sample of a population of seeds. Seeds might vary because of environmental conditions (amount of water, temperature fluctuations, intense UV radiation, etc.). Listen as the students present their ideas. A student is likely to say mutations are the cause of variability. If no one volunteers this response, ask the class if mutations could be the cause of variability in their seed population. You are looking for what ideas students have at this point. Ask the class the following probing questions that can serve as connections between mutations and their role in natural selection:

- "What if mutations caused the variations?"

If mutations caused the variations, then the DNA sequences might differ and cause some genes to express differently than others.

- "How could we find out if the variations were part of the seeds' genetics?"

Scientists could compare the DNA sequence of different seeds.

- "How would mutations affect the population? Think back to chapter 6."

Explain to them that, although other factors besides mutations contribute to differences in individual organisms, mutations contribute to variability within the population as a whole.

In Step 8, remind the students that seeds contain baby plants and seeds are necessary for survival of that plant species. If seeds are not successful in germinating (sprouting), the next generation will not grow and the species might die out.

Step 9 connects variation with species survival through questions. In Question 9c, students are asked to make a prediction about their population based on a change in the climate. Circulate to see what variation the students measured in their seeds. Ask them to think about what environmental factors would select for the factor they measured.

Answers to Step 9, SE page 440

9a. Students' answers to the questions will vary depending on what variable they measured and what seed type they investigated. The explanations here should tie in with why the birds would not eat those particular seeds. Answers include, "The birds would not eat the seeds that were slightly light in color because they could not see them." "They would not eat the small seeds because they could not see them." "They would not eat the seeds with the most spots because those blend in more and the birds will have trouble seeing them."

9b. If the environment became darker, small seeds and seeds with a dark tint would not be easily seen by predators. Those seeds would survive and reproduce. Light seeds and larger seeds would be easily noticed by predators. Those seeds would be eaten and not grow to reproduce their trait. The graph should indicate large or light seeds decreasing in number over time and dark or small seeds increasing in number over time.

9c. If students measured seed size as their variable, they should predict that slightly larger seeds will live because those seeds have more stored food. Since they lived, those seeds can grow and carry on the trait for larger seed production to the next generation. The seeds that are small will not have much stored food and might not survive the long winter. The smaller seeds will die off and that variation will be removed from the population. The graph should reflect this trend. Smaller seeds would be low on the graph and larger seeds would increase. If students measured a variable unrelated to size, they might not see a connection. As you circulate, remind the students that certain traits are selected for at certain times. Sometimes the environment is not acting on a particular trait.

Answers to Reflect and Connect, SE page 440

Have the students work through the *Reflect and Connect* task individually. Then discuss the *Reflect and Connect* questions as a class. Listen to random students' responses to the questions one at a time. Make sure the students see the connections between mutations, variability, natural selection, and evolution.

1. Variability helps the population of seeds survive because selective forces are always acting on populations. Those organisms (seeds, in this case) that have favorable variations for a particular selective pressure will survive and reproduce, passing that variation to at least some of their offspring.
2. Mutations would help the seeds survive because mutations lead to variability. The more variability there is in a population, the greater the chances that some organisms in that population will survive.
3. A mutation resulting in the production of a protein that makes seeds slightly larger could result in

a number of scenarios. The mutation might be favorable to certain influences. If the seeds are larger because they have greater stored food, the seeds might survive through long winters. The variation might be unfavorable depending on the environment. If the winters are not long, those seeds might be noticed and eaten by animals and they would die off.

4. Evolution is defined as the change in organisms over time. Mutations relate to evolution of a species in that mutations lead to variability in populations. Variability enables certain organisms to survive when selective forces act on that population. If the organisms survive despite selective pressures, they will pass the mutation on to their offspring. The populations change over time depending on the selective forces that act on them. One example is a population of seeds in an area that gets colder over time. The seeds with variations that make them larger (possibly caused by mutations) have more stored food so they can survive the winters longer than small seeds. They grow, reproduce, and carry on their traits. Eventually, the population will consist of mostly large seeds.

5. Make sure students provide an explanation of why they did not change a response as well as why they corrected a response. Encourage students to write their corrected responses in a different color so they can see the new information they learned from this activity.

If you used the list of statements provided for Part I, Step 1 (instead of having students generate statements), the answers follow.

1. True and false. Mutations can have a negative effect such as a genetic disorder, but mutations also contribute to the variety of species we see today. Without variety, populations of organisms might die off.
2. Mostly true. Sometimes mutations can be fixed by a repair mechanism within the cell. However, this does not occur all of the time. The goal of some new therapies (gene therapy) is to repair or replace harmful mutations within specific genes.
3. True and false. Mutations, if they are within the DNA of germ cells, can be passed on to the next generation. Mutations in the DNA of nongerm cells are not heritable.
4. True. Your DNA contains mutations. The entire DNA in species today is a result of changes in DNA over vast amounts of time. Each individual also becomes a collection of unique mutations depending on what that individual was exposed to.
5. False. A population does not want to avoid having mutations. The variety within populations is partly due to mutations. The variation allows organisms to survive under selective pressure.
6. True. Humans would not be alive today without the presence of mutations. Without the presence of mutations, there would be no variety within populations. If natural selection worked on a population with a disadvantageous characteristic, the population would die out without reproducing.

Answers to Step 7 are on TE page 438b.

Process and Procedure

1. Obtain a container of 1 type of seeds. These seeds are representatives from their population.
2. Look at the seeds with your partner. Is there much variation among them? Record all the ways in which the seeds might vary from one another in your science notebook.
3. Decide on 1 variation to investigate within this seed population. To help you decide, think about what you could measure as evidence of this variation. Record your decision in your science notebook.
4. Make a data table to record your data in your science notebook.
5. Investigate your chosen variation in your population of seeds. Record your data in your science notebook.
6. Make a graph of your data. Include highlight comments and a caption with the graph.
7. Analyze your graph by completing the following tasks.
   a. Describe the amount of variation you observed in your population of seeds.
   b. Describe the shape of your graph. Where in the graph are most of the seeds found?
   c. What might have caused the variation in your seed population? Describe 2 possible factors.
8. Read the following paragraph, which describes how seeds are adapted for survival. Seeds themselves are specialized in ways to help them survive. Focus your thinking with the question, "How do you think variation might be related to seed survival?"

   Many people do not realize that seeds contain living things. Seeds contain baby plants and seeds are necessary for plant species to survive. Plants produce seeds when their ovules (eggs) are fertilized by pollen. This process is much like the sperm and egg uniting in animals to form a zygote. A seed actually contains a living baby plant (embryo) surrounded by stored food. Look at figure 8.19 to see a diagram of the inside of a seed.

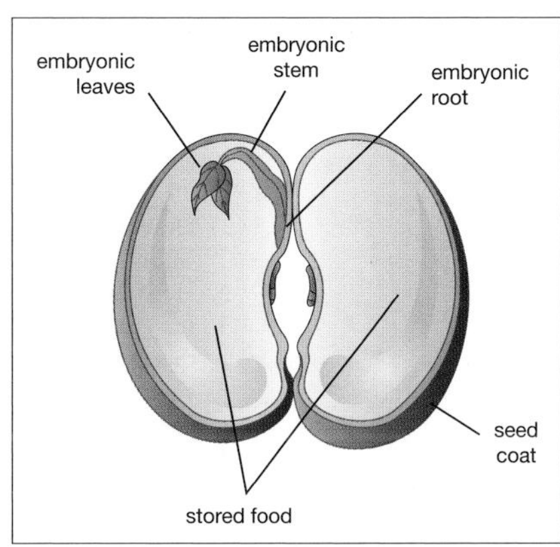

▲ **Figure 8.19 Longitudinal section of a bean seed.** In seeds, the embryo uses the stored food until conditions are right for it to germinate (sprout) and begin growing toward the surface. Seeds depend on the stored food until they can reach the light and begin making their own food through photosynthesis. Sometimes seeds have to wait quite awhile before conditions become favorable for growth. Many animals such as birds, squirrels, and chipmunks eat seeds before they germinate.

ELABORATE

DNA and Evolution

Activity Overview

In *DNA and Evolution*, students will explore how scientists use DNA sequences to determine the relatedness of organisms and how this information helps scientists piece together the possible evolutionary pattern for different species. Students also will see how DNA provides evidence to support the theory of evolution. Students will look at small, representative sequences of DNA from a gorilla, a chimpanzee, and a human. Then they will determine which organisms are closely related to each other. The students will read about two models for the evolution of these three organisms. The students will choose which model is more accurate based on the DNA sequences.

Before You Teach

Background Information

Until recently, scientists relied on physical similarities in organisms to predict how they might be related or how they might have evolved. Now scientists have sophisticated and advanced DNA technologies. New DNA technologies allow scientists

Answers to Step 9 are on TE page 438b.
Answers to Reflect and Connect are on TE pages 438b–439.

9. Answer the following questions using your graph from this activity and the reading in Step 8.
   a. Which group within your population of seeds would most likely not be eaten by birds? Explain your reasoning.
   b. Predict what your bar graph would look like several years from now if the environment slowly changed and became darker. Show your predictions using a dotted line on your graph labeled "d." Explain your reasoning.
   c. What would your bar graph look like several years in the future if the environment slowly changed and the winters became longer? Show your predictions using a dotted line on your graph labeled "w." Explain your reasoning.

Reflect and Connect

Work individually to answer the following questions. Record your answers in your science notebook.

1. How might variability within a population help that population survive?
2. How might mutations help your population of seeds survive?
3. Imagine there is a mutation in the DNA of a few of the seeds that caused the production of a protein that made the seeds slightly larger. How would that affect your population of seeds? Explain your reasoning.
4. How do mutations relate to the evolution of a species? Give examples using your experiences in this unit.

Think back to chapter 6 when you completed the activity *Who Will Survive?* In that activity, you captured seeds that represented different variations within the same species. You determined that influences, such as predators, can make survival of some individuals more likely than others. Differential survival can cause a species to change over time—to evolve.

5. Look back at your initial responses to the statements in Step 1 of Part I. Would you change any of your responses? Why or why not? Write your corrected responses in your science notebook.

to determine DNA sequences from organisms. These DNA sequences give scientists a great deal of information about those organisms. DNA sequences can be used to determine how closely related organisms are. The more base-pair similarities organisms have in a given DNA sequence, the more related two organisms are. If scientists can determine how many base pairs organisms have in common, they can determine ancestral lines.

The entire genome for humans and many other organisms has been sequenced. When they compared the sequences of humans and chimpanzees, scientists found that humans and chimpanzees are very closely related. In fact, chimpanzees and humans have over 95 percent of their DNA in common. Although scientists have finished mapping the human genome, the functions for over half of the discovered genes are unknown. Having the human genome mapped does not give scientists the information to make a human any more than a box of parts allows you to know how to put together a computer.

Before advances in DNA technologies, there was a great deal of debate about how the lines of primates evolved. Based on their data, scientists now theorize that humans and chimps shared a common ancestor until between 5 and 7 million years ago. Then the line split, with humans evolving one way and chimps evolving another. Discussing primate evolution may be an uncomfortable subject for many students. Emphasize that this activity focuses on comparing DNA evidence to show relatedness of organisms.

DNA and Evolution shows students how scientists gather evidence to support their theories about evolution. The sequences in real DNA are quite complex and contain millions of base pairs. This activity is a simplified version of how studying DNA can be used to help scientists formulate theories about evolutionary relationships.

Materials

none

Advance Preparation

Read the 2 theories in Step 4 of the student book about the evolution of primates and become familiar with each one.

SIDEBAR

Mutations and Society

Variability is important for species survival. Humans depend on other organisms. Therefore, the variation in the populations of other organisms can affect our way of life. One example of how variation within a population has affected our society is the Irish potato famine of 1845. The Irish grew potatoes for more than 200 years without any major problems. Most of the potato crops in Ireland were composed of two varieties of potatoes, the *Lumper* and the *Cup*. When a fungus was brought over from North America, it destroyed the entire *Lumper* and *Cup* potato crops. Had there been more varieties of potatoes planted, some might have been resistant to the species of fungus and survived. Because of the lack of variety, nearly the entire food source for the people in Ireland was wiped out.

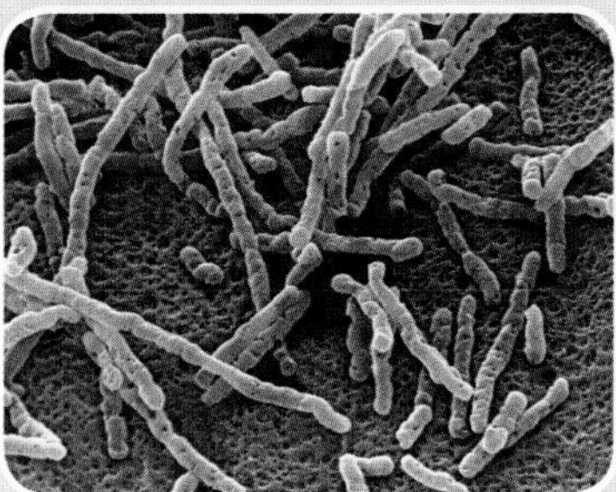

▲ ***Clostridium difficile.*** *Clostridium difficile* is a bacterium that causes diarrhea and occasionally more serious intestinal conditions. Outbreaks of *C. difficile* infections have become more prevalent in hospitals since 2004. Scientists think that a new strain has developed that is more resistant to some types of antibiotics.

Unfortunately, some variations help unwanted organisms to survive. One example is bacteria. Bacteria reproduce quickly. This rapid rate of reproduction increases the chance that mutations will appear in the DNA sequences of a bacteria population. Some species of bacteria have mutated enough to be resistant to antibiotics, and as a result can survive antibiotic treatments. The offspring of these mutated bacteria also are resistant. Eventually, many strains of bacteria will be resistant because these few bacteria had the mutation. It is hard for doctors to treat diseases caused by antibiotic-resistant bacteria.

Sometimes one mutation can affect a population in both positive and negative ways. Sickle-cell disease in humans causes red blood cells to become sickle shaped, which leads to blocked blood vessels. This causes pain and damage to areas that are not receiving an adequate blood supply. People who are carriers for the sickle-cell trait, however, are less likely to suffer from malaria than those without the sickle-cell trait. Malaria kills more than 1 million people each year around the world. Resistance to malaria is a major survival advantage for people who live in areas where malaria is a problem.

Mutations in DNA can be unwelcome, but they are also what enable species to survive. They might cause disease or even death. However, without mutations, we would not have the variation within populations or the diversity of life we have on the planet today.

As You Teach

Outcomes and Indicators of Success

By the end of this activity, students should

1. become aware of how DNA can be used to determine the relatedness of organisms.

   They will demonstrate their awareness by

   - determining that humans are more closely related to chimps than chimps are to gorillas, based on their respective DNA sequences and
   - describing in a *Reflect and Connect* question how DNA is used to determine the relatedness of organisms.

2. realize that DNA can be used as evidence to support theories of evolution.

   They will demonstrate their realization by

   - explaining in a *Reflect and Connect* question that two organisms with similar DNA sequences branched from the common ancestor differently from the organisms with the least similarities in DNA and
   - explaining in a *Reflect and Connect* question that DNA can be used as evidence for evolution because similarities in DNA show relatedness.

3. be able to recognize and analyze alternative explanations and models.

   They will demonstrate their ability by comparing models of primate evolution and deciding which model is most accurate based on the DNA sequence of three primates.

Strategies

Getting Started

The topic of human evolution is somewhat controversial. One reason is that many people have the misconception that scientists theorize that humans evolved from monkeys. Scientists do not theorize that humans evolved from monkeys, but instead that DNA evidence supports that primates and humans evolved from the same common ancestor. Start the class by asking how we could determine if two organisms are closely related. Ask the class these probing questions:

- "How do doctors determine paternity?"
- "How do forensic investigators rule out suspects in crimes?"
- "How might scientists' understanding of DNA provide evidence for evolution?"

Tell the class that it is going to use the same methods scientists use to determine how closely organisms are related and how the theory of evolution can be supported with DNA evidence.

Process and Procedure

In Step 1, some students might take offense because they do not want to think they are related to monkeys or apes at all. Explain that all organisms are related to one another in one way or another. Some are more closely related than others. Ask them to think about how closely related they are to their family compared with one another. Ask the following probing questions:

- "Are you more closely related to your siblings or your cousins? What reasons do you have for your response?"
- "Are you more closely related to your cousin or a stranger in Australia? What reasons do you have for your response?"
- "Which organisms are more closely related? A squirrel and a rat or a squirrel and a lizard? Why do you say this?"
- "Do you think DNA can support your answers to these questions?"

In Step 3, students should see that chimps and humans are more closely related than any other combination. Humans only have 5 differences in DNA when compared with the chimps. The evidence for relatedness lies in the small number of differences in the DNA strands.

In Step 5, students should see that model B is the most logical model because humans and chimps share the most number of base pairs. If model A were correct, all 3 organisms would have the same number of differences in their DNA. The evidence for the degree of relatedness lies in the number of similarities and differences in the DNA strands.

ELABORATE

DNA and Evolution

In *Nobody's Perfect*, you learned that mutation and new combinations of genes formed during meiosis can lead to variation in a population of organisms. But how do scientists know how similar the genetic code is among different organisms? New advances in technology allow scientists to understand more about DNA. Scientists can isolate genes, study their sequence, and determine what proteins they code for. This knowledge can help scientists learn more about how closely organisms are related to one another. Scientists predict how closely related organisms are by looking for similarities in their DNA sequences. Using this information, scientists can determine the common ancestors for organisms and predict how the organisms evolved.

In *DNA and Evolution*, you will work individually to see how scientists use DNA to determine how closely related species are. You will learn how scientists use this evidence to support the theory of evolution.

Materials

none

Process and Procedure

1. Predict which pair of organisms (a, b, or c) you think are the most closely related to each other. Explain your reasoning.
   a. Gorillas and chimpanzees
   b. Humans and gorillas
   c. Humans and chimpanzees
2. Study the 3 DNA sequences in figure 8.20. Scientists use DNA sequences to determine how closely related species are.
3. Compare the DNA sequences. Which 2 organisms appear to be the most closely related? What is your evidence?

Human DNA :	T	C	C	G	T	A	T	T	T	G	G	T	T	G	G	C	T	A	A	T
Gorilla DNA :	T	C	C	G	G	G	G	A	A	G	G	T	T	C	A	T	C	C	G	G
Chimpanzee DNA :	T	C	C	G	G	G	G	A	A	G	G	T	T	G	G	C	T	A	A	T

▲ **Figure 8.20 Sections of DNA sequences from three primates.** Each DNA sequence represents a small section of a gene that codes for the protein hemoglobin and is labeled with the name of the organism it was taken from.

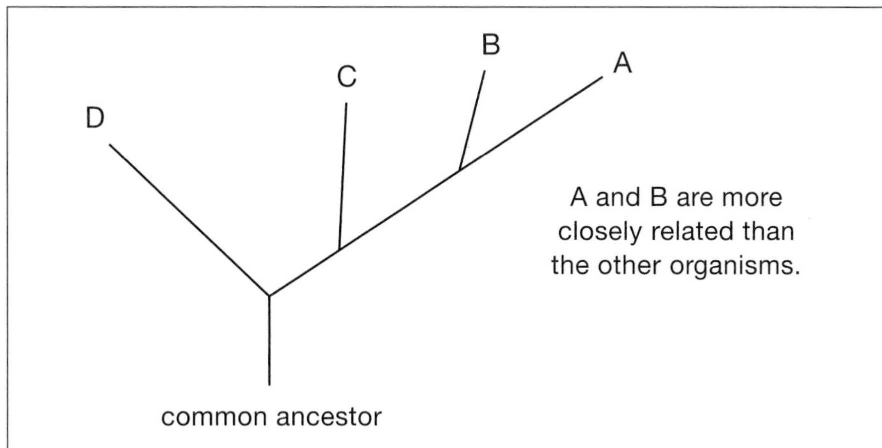

▲ **Figure T8.13 Evolutionary tree for Question 2.** Students' diagrams of possible evolutionary trees may look like this.

Answers to Reflect and Connect, SE pages 443–444

1. DNA is used to determine the relatedness among organisms by identifying the number of nucleotides that they have in common. The greater the number of common nucleotides in a given sequence, the more closely related the organisms are.

2. DNA can be used as evidence to show common ancestry. Two organisms that share many commonalities in their DNA will have branched off at different places from the same evolutionary tree. Figure T8.13 shows what the student diagrams might look like.
3. The nucleotide sequence of DNA from common ancestors would be slightly different than DNA found in organisms today. The farther back you go in the line, the greater the differences in DNA because of mutations or recombination in the DNA. Over the years, the number of mutations and recombination had more time and opportunity to occur. The differences increase the more the DNA is mixed through the generations.
4. DNA evidence can be used to support the theory of evolution by comparing DNA sequences. The more nucleotides that 2 organisms have in common in their DNA, the more related they are. The theory of evolution says that organisms change over time and share common ancestry in their lines of evolution. By mapping sequences, we can see similarities and differences among the nucleotide sequences. By pinpointing these, we can map evolutionary lines.

4. Read the following paragraphs that describe 2 hypotheses of how primates evolved. As you are reading, think about how the 2 theories are similar and how they are different.

   Most scientists agree that humans, gorillas, and chimpanzees shared a common ancestor at one time in evolutionary history. However, one group thinks the fossil record shows that gorillas, chimpanzees, and humans split from one common ancestor at the same time. Their model for this split is shown in figure 8.21a.

   A second group thinks the fossil record shows there were two splits. In the first split, gorillas split from the common ancestor. Humans and chimpanzees then shared another common ancestor for perhaps 2 million years. They then split again and evolved into their present species. The model for this pattern of splitting is shown in figure 8.21b.
5. Use the DNA sequences from Step 2 to investigate this debate. Which model in the evolutionary debate is more accurate based on the DNA evidence? Justify your answer.

Reflect and Connect

Work alone to answer the following questions. Record your answers in your science notebook.

1. How is DNA used to determine relatedness among organisms?
2. How can DNA be used as evidence for common ancestry? Use a diagram like the one in figure 8.21 to support your answer. Include a caption with your diagram to indicate which organisms are more closely related.

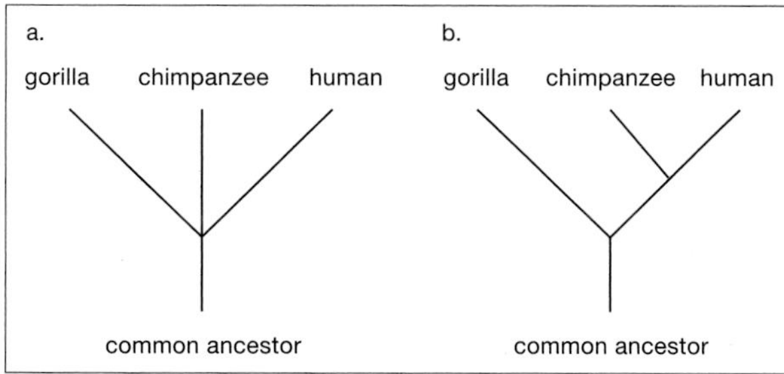

▲ **Figure 8.21 Models of primate evolution.** Diagram (a) shows that gorillas, chimpanzees, and humans share one common ancestor. Diagram (b) shows that chimpanzees and humans have a different common ancestor than gorillas. This also suggests that chimpanzees and humans are more closely related than chimpanzees and gorillas or humans and gorillas.

There have been tremendous advancements in our understanding of DNA and new developments as a result of these advancements. After students have completed this activity, challenge them by having them research a topic about DNA. Examples of research topics include the following:

- The Human Genome Project
- Forensics
- Law (paternity)
- Therapies or treatments
- Cloning
- Evidence of evolution
- Genome research of organisms
- Genetic engineering

Students could produce a brochure, information newsletter, or newspaper article. You might want to structure the assignment with some guidelines. Here are some questions for providing guidance to the students:

- "What is the topic?" (a description of the topic)
- "When was the topic developed?"
- "Where is it being applied?"
- "How is the topic being done? What technology are scientists using? What DNA processes are being used?"
- "Why is the topic important? How could it affect your life?"
- "What should you know to understand the topic?"
- "Why is the topic important to society?"

EVALUATE

Sharing Your Knowledge

Activity Overview

Many new concepts have been introduced in this chapter. To understand fully what the concepts mean, it is important for students to understand the connections and relationships of these concepts to one another. In *Sharing Your Knowledge*, students will show their understanding of DNA and the processes they have learned about so far. They will demonstrate their understanding by creating a summary in a format they choose. For example, students might summarize what they know using a graphic organizer such as a concept map or a story board. They might also choose to create flash cards, a game board, a skit, a computer presentation, or a summary essay.

Before You Teach

Background Information

Background information for this activity is found throughout the chapter.

Materials

For each student

note cards

materials for creating a summary

1 copy of copymaster 8.7, *Example Concept Map* (optional)

1 copy of copymaster 8.8, *Scoring Rubric for Sharing Your Knowledge*

Advance Preparation

TRCD Make 1 copy of copymaster 8.8, *Scoring Rubric for Sharing Your Knowledge* for each student. Have large paper and markers available for students who choose to make a concept map. If you would like to provide students with an example of a concept map, make copies of copymaster 8.7, *Example Concept Map*.

As You Teach

Outcomes and Indicators of Success

By the end of this activity, students should

1. demonstrate their understanding of DNA as the genetic code for all living things.

   They will demonstrate their understanding by

   - describing that chromosomes are made up of one molecule of DNA and proteins,

Answers to Reflect and Connect are on TE page 443.

3. Imagine you could obtain DNA from common ancestors that lived millions of years ago. How would their DNA sequences compare with the species that now exist? Think about how the DNA sequence changes over time to explain your reasoning.
4. How can DNA evidence be used to support the theory of evolution?

EVALUATE

Sharing Your Knowledge

Many people know that DNA is the code of life but most do not understand how it works. In this chapter, you have learned a great deal about DNA. You have learned about its structure and function and why it is so significant to life. In *Sharing Your Knowledge*, you will summarize what you know about DNA to help someone else understand how it functions as the code of life.

Imagine that a new student just transferred to your school. Your teacher has asked you to help bring him up to date on what you have been learning about DNA. But how can you go about condensing the major ideas about DNA for this new student? You decide that the most efficient way to teach him about DNA is to prepare a summary. In this summary, you will address the main concepts you learned in this chapter and show how these concepts are related.

One method you might use to prepare your summary is to create a graphic organizer. Graphic organizers are visual representations of information such as concept maps or story boards. Other ways to prepare a summary include flash cards, game boards, a skit, a summary essay, or a PowerPoint presentation. For this activity, you get to decide which technique you want to use. If you are more comfortable with graphic organizers, then that may be the way you want to go. If you are a good writer and find that writing is a good way to summarize major ideas, then you would probably want to write an essay. The choice is up to you. No matter what summary method you choose, however, you will make a model of DNA to include with your summary.

Materials

For each student

note cards

materials for creating a summary

1 *Example Concept Map* handout (optional)

1 *Sharing Your Knowledge Scoring Rubric* handout

444 Unit 2 Inside Life

- describing that sections of DNA make up genes,
- explaining that similarities in DNA show the relatedness of organisms,
- describing that DNA is composed of four nucleotides (adenine, thymine, guanine, cytosine), and
- explaining that DNA replicates to transmit genetic information to newly formed cells.

2. demonstrate their understanding that DNA serves as a template for making proteins through the processes of transcription and translation.

   They will demonstrate their understanding by relating the processes of transcription and translation to the formation of proteins.

3. demonstrate their understanding that mutations in DNA result in changes in proteins that can be advantageous, detrimental, or neutral to individual organisms and their species.

   They will demonstrate their understanding by relating mutations in the DNA of germ cells to variations in offspring.

4. demonstrate their understanding that changes in DNA lead to the evolution of species and that DNA serves as evidence for evolution.

   They will demonstrate their understanding by showing the relationship between DNA, variation in species, and evolution.

5. demonstrate their understanding of how to use a model to represent the structure of DNA and critiquing the accuracy of their model.

   They will demonstrate their understanding by

   - creating their own model of DNA and
   - describing why the model is accurate and providing at least one weakness of the model.

Strategies

Getting Started

Explain to students that when they study science, it is almost like learning another language. In fact, many scientific terms come from Latin and Greek. Sometimes it can be overwhelming. But tell the students they probably know more than they realize. In this chapter, they have been learning about DNA and how it works. Tell them that in this activity, they are going to put it all together by sharing their knowledge about DNA with someone else.

Process and Procedure

In Step 1, distribute copymaster 8.8, *Scoring Rubric for Sharing Your Knowledge* and give students time to review it and ask questions. In Step 2, the class holds a brainstorming session about the major terms and ideas from this chapter. Listen to students' ideas and write them on the board. Try to focus them on major concepts. Encourage them to look through the chapter and their science notebooks to help them refresh their memory. Examples of questions you can ask to help prompt their thinking follow:

- "What terms come to mind from this chapter?"
- "What words, concepts, or processes do you think of when you think of DNA?"
- "What would someone learning about DNA need to know in order to understand it?"

Process and Procedure

1. Review the *Sharing Your Knowledge Scoring Rubric* to see what your teacher expects of you for this activity.
2. Hold a brainstorming session with your class. Make a list of the terms, processes, and concepts that you learned about in this chapter. Your teacher will record your ideas on the board.

Brainstorming is a process of generating ideas about a specific subject without judging their quality. (You will review the ideas later.) You may want to go back through the chapter and your science notebook to help you identify all the topics, concepts, and terms that relate to DNA.

3. Write the terms and concepts from the class list on the board in your science notebook; include any topics your teacher adds to the list. Place a star next to the terms identified by a star on the class list.
4. List each of these terms on a separate note card.
5. Work with your partner to develop notes that summarize each term. Use the information from your science notebooks and student books. Record your notes in a bulleted list, as sentences that describe each topic, or with labeled diagrams or sketches. Put these notes on the back of the cards.
6. With your partner, decide how the terms are connected and rank the importance of each by following Steps 6a–d.
   a. Arrange your cards in a hierarchy to show the relative importance of each idea about DNA.

A hierarchy is a way of organizing or ranking things.

   b. Arrange the cards on a table according to the hierarchy you assigned in Step 6a.
   c. Rearrange the cards so that those ideas that are connected in some way are placed next to each other.
   d. Sketch the arrangement of the cards in your science notebook. Describe briefly why you arranged the cards as you did.
7. Summarize what you know about DNA by completing Steps 7a–b.
   a. Make a model of DNA. You can use a model similar to the one in this chapter or develop a new model of your own.
   b. Choose your summary method. You can use concept maps, story boards, flash cards, game boards, a skit, a summary essay, or a PowerPoint presentation.

As the students name terms and concepts, write them on the board:

- DNA*
- Nucleotides
- Adenine, thymine, guanine, cytosine (A, T, G, C)*
- Replication*
- Template*
- Gene*
- Chromosome*
- Mitosis
- Meiosis
- RNA*
- Transcription*
- Translation*
- Nucleus
- Ribosome
- Proteins*
- Mutations*
- Variability*
- Genetic disorder
- Evolution*
- Acquire
- Heredity (inherit, inherited)*
- Gametes*
- Nongametes*
- Organism*

If there are terms from the above list that students did not volunteer, add them. Star the terms on the class list that are starred above. The starred terms must be present in the students' products for full credit.

Some of these terms are from chapter 7. This evaluate activity is also designed to see whether students can make conceptual connections between ideas in both chapters.

In Step 3, students copy the class list of terms from the board into their science notebooks and star the terms that you have starred. In Step 4, students write each of the terms from the list on separate note cards. In Step 5, students work with a partner to develop notes for each term on the back of the cards. Suggest that they use their science notebooks and the student book to find information about each term. In Step 6, students continue working with their partners to organize the terms into a hierarchy. They also arrange their cards on a table to show which terms are connected. Consider providing

students with copymaster 8.7, *Example Concept Map*, which illustrates the relationship between words related to evolution. Make sure students sketch the arrangement of their cards in their science notebooks. This exercise should help them organize the terms for their summaries.

In Step 7, students work on their own to develop a plan for their summaries. They must decide what method they will use to summarize what they know about DNA. Students should also make a model of DNA. They can use a model similar to the paper clip model from the chapter or come up with their own model for DNA. In Step 8, students prepare their summaries. In Step 9, students evaluate their own summary using the rubric before turning it in. They also use the checklist in Step 8 to be sure they have met all the requirements and have a complete, polished product. Step 8 spells out the assignment a little more than the rubric alone but correlates with the requirements outlined in the rubric.

In Step 10, students should describe at least 2 ways they could improve their summaries. Make sure they record their ideas in their science notebooks for you to review.

If you choose to design a concept map, you might want to use the hierarchy from Step 6 as a starting point. To complete the assignment successfully, however, you must create a new concept map and follow the guidelines in Step 8.

Whatever method you choose, be sure to show your understanding of the terms and concepts and how they relate to one another. In addition, you must use all of the starred terms (see Step 3).

8. Prepare your summary individually. Your finished product should include the following parts:
   - Title: Describe what your summary is about.
   - Terms and concepts: Use all the terms and concepts generated from the class brainstorming session as well as those your teacher added. Circle all the terms in your summary.
   - Additional terms: You might find that there are some terms that are associated with DNA that did not come up in the brainstorming session. Add these terms and circle them in another color.
   - Relationships and connections: Your summary must show clear connections and relationships between and among the terms and concepts. How are the terms related? What do they have to do with one another? Make the connections clear.
   - Organization: Make sure your summary is neat and easy to follow.
   - DNA model critique: Describe how the model accurately represents DNA; point out at least 1 weakness of the model.
9. Evaluate your summary using the scoring rubric and the requirements listed in Step 8.
10. Describe at least 2 ways you could improve your summary.

CHAPTER 9

Genetic Engineering

Chapter Overview

In the previous chapters, students learned about genetics, heredity, and evolution. In this integrated chapter, students apply their understanding of genetics to learn about ways that genes can be engineered and how genetic engineering applications can include other disciplines, such as environmental science, earth science, and chemistry. Students also learn that, like other technologies, genetic engineering can improve our lives and also create controversy.

Goals for the Chapter

The overarching goal for chapter 9, *Genetic Engineering,* is that students will understand that knowledge of DNA is used to develop technologies, such as genetic engineering, and that these technologies introduce ethical dilemmas. By the end of chapter 9, students should be able to answer the following questions:

- What components of a cell are involved in genetic engineering?
- What laboratory processes are involved in genetic engineering?
- How do scientists apply the processes of genetic engineering to solve everyday problems?
- What is a systematic way of addressing bioethical questions?

Look at the chapter organizer each day to remind yourself of where students are in the overall sequence of events in the chapter.

Chapter 9 Organizer

GENETIC ENGINEERING

Major Concepts

- **Genetic material can be transferred from one organism to another by human intervention.**
- **Only small parts of DNA are required to be transferred from one organism to another in order to effect large changes.**
- **Genetic engineering processes create some organisms with beneficial characteristics and some with damaging characteristics.**
- **Ethical considerations about genetic engineering can be approached systematically, like inquiry.**

ENGAGE Company Policy ★

Key Idea: • Genetically altered food poses many ethical considerations.
Activity: Students examine an advertisement that states a company's policy on genetically altered foods.

LINKING QUESTION: What is one of the key processes of genetic engineering?

EXPLORE Moving Genes—Recombinant DNA Technology ★★

Key Idea: • Cutting, recombining, and transferring DNA fragments follows a specific sequence of procedural steps.
Activity: Students explore recombinant DNA technology by modeling the technique.

LINKING QUESTION: Are all techniques similar and what are some specific applications of the general recombinant DNA process?

EXPLAIN How Can It Be Done? ★★

Key Idea: • Gene therapy, drug therapy, tissue engineering, and gene "bullets" are examples of recombinant DNA processes.
Activity: Students use a jigsaw learning strategy to study different techniques and applications used in genetic engineering.

LINKING QUESTION: What are some technologies dependent on genetic engineering and what ethical issues do these technologies introduce?

ELABORATE Biotechnology and Society ★★★

Key Ideas:
- Many areas of science utilize genetic engineering processes to address important applications.
- Ethical questions can be approached systematically, much like inquiry.

Activity: Students explore different applications of genetic engineering. They suggest novel applications to solve a particular problem. Then students consider ethical issues by applying an ethical decision-making model.

LINKING QUESTION: Will a model ethics problem-solving process help me address current bioethics issues?

EVALUATE Can It Be Done? Should It Be Done? ★★★

Key Idea: • Both scientific knowledge about genetic engineering processes and a systematic approach to solving ethical dilemmas are required to solve modern problems.
Activity: Teams of students assume roles in order to address bioethical questions. Then teams present findings to the class and field questions.

★ = One Class Period ☆ = ½ Class Period *Note:* Based on a 50-minute class period.

Standards Covered by Chapter 9*

GENETIC ENGINEERING

STANDARD A: Science as Inquiry. As a result of activities in grades 9–12, all students should develop

understandings about scientific inquiry

- Scientists rely on technology to enhance the gathering and manipulation of data. New techniques and tools provide new evidence to guide inquiry and new methods to gather data, thereby contributing to the advance of science. The accuracy and precision of the data, and therefore the quality of the exploration, depends on the technology used. [Content Standard E (grades 9–12)]

STANDARD C: Life Science. As a result of their activities in grades 9–12, all students should develop an understanding of

the molecular basis of heredity

- In all organisms, the instructions for specifying the characteristics of the organism are carried in DNA, a large polymer formed from subunits of four kinds (A, G, C, and T). The chemical and structural properties of DNA explain how the genetic information that underlies heredity is both encoded in genes (as a string of molecular "letters") and replicated (by a templating mechanism). Each DNA molecule in a cell forms a single chromosome. [See Content Standard B (grades 9–12)]

STANDARD E: Science and Technology. As a result of activities in grades 9–12, all students should develop

understandings about science and technology

- Science often advances with the introduction of new technologies. Solving technological problems often results in new scientific knowledge. New technologies often extend the current levels of scientific understanding and introduce new areas of research.
- Technological knowledge is often not made public because of patents and the financial potential of the idea or invention. Scientific knowledge is made public through presentations at professional meetings and publications in scientific journals.

STANDARD F: Science in Personal and Social Perspectives. As a result of activities in grades 9–12, all students should develop understanding of

science and technology in local, national, and global challenges

- Science and technology are essential social enterprises, but alone they can only indicate what can happen, not what should happen. The latter involves human decisions about the use of knowledge. [See Content Standard E (grades 9–12)]
- Understanding basic concepts and principles of science and technology should precede active debate about the economics, policies, politics, and ethics of various science- and technology-related challenges. However, understanding science alone will not resolve local, national, or global challenges.
- Individuals and society must decide on proposals involving new research and the introduction of new technologies into society. Decisions involve assessment of alternatives, risks, costs, and benefits and consideration of who benefits and who suffers, who pays and gains, and what the risks are and who bears them. Students should understand the appropriateness and value of basic questions—"What can happen?"—"What are the odds?"—and "How do scientists and engineers know what will happen?"

**Note:* Bracketed portions of the standard are addressed elsewhere in the program.

Prerequisite Knowledge

Students should know what a cell is and its function in a variety of living systems. This knowledge serves as the backdrop for activities in which students simulate changes at the molecular level. Students learn that these molecular changes ultimately result in changes in traits of the entire organism. This reinforces the notion that powerful mechanisms are at work within a cell that lead to differences in the characteristics of the overall organism. Students should know that cells have constituent parts that behave in specific ways and for specific purposes. The primary focus of chapter 9 is DNA. Students should know that changes in a cell's DNA can lead to changes in how the cell functions.

Commonly Held Misconceptions

Review the misconceptions listed in chapters 6–8. Most of them still pertain to the content in chapter 9 about genetic engineering. Because much of what appears in this chapter is an application or extension of the life science content of chapters 6–8, look for lingering misconceptions. In addition, students may harbor the following misconceptions:

- Once genetic material is removed from its original location in the cell, the material is no longer viable.
- Humans cannot form organisms that have never been seen on Earth before.
- Genetic engineering results in totally new, usually bad, organisms.
- If the DNA sequence of an organism is altered in any way, the organism dies or cannot reproduce.
- Ethical decisions are completely a matter of emotions.
- To be ethical, one has to be religious.

ENGAGE

Company Policy

Activity Overview

In *Company Policy*, students will read a magazine advertisement about one company's policy not to use genetically engineered organisms. The advertisement makes bold statements objecting to the use of any genetically engineered products and assures the consumer that the company will never use genetically engineered organisms. Students will develop questions as consumers who have just come across this advertisement and as company executives assessing the adoption of the policy. This reading will get the students thinking about genetic engineering, how it is used, why it is used, and why it may be controversial.

You will be able to gauge students' prior knowledge of genetic engineering by listening to them discuss their questions in their teams, reading their posted questions, and assessing their answers to the *Reflect and Connect* questions.

Before You Teach

Background Information

Biotechnology is the use of a living organism to make a product or drive a process. Biotechnology practices have been around for a long time. Making bread, brewing beer, and even growing trees can be considered biotechnologies. Genetic engineering is a specialized technique of biotechnology in which genes from organisms are removed, added, transferred, or otherwise manipulated. Genetic engineering practices are relatively new and are being developed rapidly. Genetic engineering technology in agriculture was created to improve food production, reduce the use of pesticides and herbicides, and increase agricultural yields. Some people believe that genetic engineering is a natural expansion of existing biotechnologies or even of selective breeding. Others are concerned that genetic engineering sacrifices the nutritional quality of foods and can destroy entire ecosystems.

Materials

For each team of 4 students

2 markers, each a different color

butcher paper or poster paper

Advance Preparation

Prepare butcher paper and gather 2 different colors of markers for each team of 4. Designate an area or areas around the classroom for posting the butcher paper. The butcher paper questions remain posted for the duration of the chapter.

Educational Technologies

You might consider asking students to access Web sites of companies that use or sell genetically engineered organisms. Most companies have feedback capabilities via e-mail. Encourage students to ask the company questions regarding the genetically altered material.

As You Teach

Outcomes and Indicators of Success

By the end of this activity, students should

1. communicate their prior knowledge about genetic engineering applications.

   They will communicate their prior knowledge by

   - developing questions individually concerning a company policy statement about genetic engineering and
   - developing a list of questions about genetic engineering.

ENGAGE

Company Policy

▲ **Figure 9.2 Genetically modified food.** Are these foods safe to eat? What would you need to know to find out?

Genetically engineered food—what is it? Does it affect you? Where does it come from? How is it processed? Is it safe? These are all questions careful consumers ask (figure 9.2). Scientists and engineers also ask these questions as they develop new technologies. With these new technologies come new issues that societies need to address. You will begin thinking about these issues in a systematic way as you work individually and in a team in *Company Policy*.

EDEN FOODS

Eden – GEO-Free Assurance Since 1993

Foreseeing the commercialization of genetically engineered food, Eden established our policy against genetically engineered organisms (GEOs) and their derivatives in food in February 1993. Eden's Purchasing Department, working with our suppliers, has protected our patrons and does everything possible to make sure our food is free of GEOs.

In 1998 the *New York Times* hired a laboratory to test for GEOs in eleven soy and corn based foods, and the only one that tested negative was EDENSOY soymilk.

Eden Foods is doing everything possible to protect our customers from the genetically engineered food experiment.

The EDEN brand is your best assurance of freedom from GEOs. We take every available step to ensure our avoidance of GEOs, including:

- In-house GEO testing of each batch of corn and soybeans.
- Our traditional methods of processing and fermentation, rather than pharmaceutical enzymes.
- Knowing our growers, suppliers, and their families.
- Supporting consumer and environmental organizations working for the mandatory labeling of GE food and ingredients.

13 February 1993

Dear EDEN Patron,

The trend to commercialize genetically engineered food compels Eden Foods to assure you that we will not support or participate in this movement away from natural foods as they are manifest by Nature.

Please let this letter serve as our affidavit and your assurance that Eden Foods will not purchase or sell any food or food ingredient known to be genetically engineered and, that we will act to best ensure our avoidance of such.

You can depend upon Eden Foods to be diligent in avoiding any aspect of the commercialization of genetically engineered food. We object to the introduction of these foods for human consumption in any manner, for any reason. We are fundamentally opposed to these foods for moral, ethical, and practical reasons.

With more than twenty-four years in the natural foods industry, I remain unaware of any other food company that spends a greater percentage of its time or money to be certain of the growing, ingredients, and processing used for foods carrying its brand name.

Very truly yours,
Michael J. Potter
Chairman and President

◀ **Figure 9.3 Company policy.** This company advertises its policy regarding genetically engineered food.

Materials

For each team of 4 students

2 markers, each a different color

butcher paper or poster paper

Process and Procedure

1. Read the magazine advertisement shown in figure 9.3 carefully. As you read the policy, use this focus question to guide your thinking: "What do I need to know about genetically engineered food to form an educated opinion?"
2. Write 5 questions that come to mind after reading the ad. Word your questions as if you were a consumer and title your questions, "Consumer Questions."

2. develop an awareness of issues associated with genetic engineering practices.

They will demonstrate their awareness by

- conducting a brainstorming session about what they would need to know before implementing a company policy concerning genetically engineered organisms and
- describing how consumer avoidance of genetically engineered foods may affect companies and consumers.

Strategies

Getting Started

Set the stage by explaining that the students are leafing through a magazine and find an advertisement that describes a company's policy about genetically engineered products. With the students, read the advertisement in figure 9.3 of the student book.

Process and Procedure

Instruct students to complete Step 2 on their own. Then have students form teams of 4 to complete Steps 3–5. Allow time for students to generate questions in their science notebooks. When students get into their teams, circulate and listen to their discussions. This will give you a sense of their prior knowledge about genetic engineering techniques and any controversies they are aware of.

Consumer questions that students generate in Step 2 will vary but probably will include questions such as the following:

- What does "genetically engineered" mean?
- What is it that consumers object to about genetically engineered organisms?
- Why is there a trend to commercialize genetically engineered food?
- Are genetically engineered foods bad for you?
- What are the moral disadvantages of genetically engineered food?
- What are the moral advantages of genetically engineered food?
- Will it hurt the company to have a policy like this?
- Why would a company establish such a policy?

In Step 4, students' company executive questions will vary, but the information that an executive might need to know includes the following:

- What are genetically engineered foods?
- Will it cost the company money to avoid genetically engineered food?
- Are genetically engineered foods bad? If so, why? How?
- Will this policy help or hurt our sales?

In Step 6, post questions from each team around the room. Periodically revisit the questions as a class as you work through the chapter; cross off questions that students answer.

Answers to Reflect and Connect are on TE pages 453–454.

Always record your thinking in your science notebook. That way, you can go back and track how new information changed your views and helped you learn.

3. Read your questions in a team of 4 students and listen to your team members as they read their questions.

For each question, be sure to ask the questioner why it is important to him or her as a consumer.

4. With your team, write 5 questions that you would ask as the president of this company before you would agree to establish this policy for your company. Title these questions, "Company Executive Questions."
5. Decide as a team how to organize both the consumer and company executive questions on a large sheet of butcher paper so that the entire class can read and understand your questions.
6. Copy your team's list of consumer and company executive questions in your science notebook. Then post your team's list on butcher paper in the classroom.

Reflect and Connect

Answer the following questions in your science notebook;w use complete sentences. Read your answers to your team members and listen to them read their answers. Record any new thoughts that result from hearing your teammates' answers.

1. As a consumer who likes this company's products, how might this policy be a hassle for you?
2. As a consumer, what would you appreciate about this company's policy?
3. As the company's executive, what are some of the advantages and disadvantages to establishing this company policy? How might establishing this policy hurt the company? How might this policy help the company?
4. Speaking for yourself now, would you eat genetically altered food? What information or evidence about genetically altered food do you want to have in order to make your decision?

Answers to Reflect and Connect, SE page 453

1. This policy could be a hassle for a consumer if some foods that were not genetically modified were not available. Nonmodified food could be more costly than genetically modified food. Some foods may be available only at certain times of the year unless they are genetically altered.

2. As consumers, students might appreciate that the company is concerned about their safety and cares about the environment. They might like that this company stands behind its beliefs.
3. As company executives, students may be concerned that the policy may hurt the company because consumers may want genetically engineered food. Also, nongenetically engineered food may cost more. Because of the policy, the company may not be able to offer some foods. On the other hand, the policy may help the company because consumers have questions and concerns about genetically engineered foods and may want to avoid them.
4. Answers will vary, but should include the students' reasons for their opinion. Do not accept a simple yes or no answer. Use their reasons to assess their prior understanding of genetically engineered foods.

EXPLORE

Moving Genes—Recombinant DNA Technology

Activity Overview

In *Moving Genes—Recombinant DNA Technology*, students will learn about recombinant DNA technology, an important technique in genetic engineering. Students will model the technique using paper representations of plasmids and chromosomes. During the investigation, you will have the opportunity to assess student understanding about DNA, including its structure and function. This understanding will become evident as students simulate techniques used in recombinant DNA technology and apply what they learned in previous chapters, including knowledge of DNA replication and translation and complementary base pairing. Assess student understanding by listening in on discussions as students go through the steps and by reviewing their final product, a plasmid containing the human gene for insulin.

This activity simplifies some aspects of manipulating recombinant DNA. For example, the activity models the use of a cloning vector. Cloning vectors allow scientists to make many copies of the DNA sequence of interest in bacteria. A different kind of vector, an expression vector, is needed to actually express the protein in bacterial cells. Expression vectors include specific regulatory sequences necessary for protein expression and they also usually include a label or tag that a scientist can use to purify the protein of interest from other proteins made by bacteria. The principles of working with recombinant DNA apply to cloning and expression vectors.

Before You Teach

Background Information

The term recombinant DNA technology includes important techniques in biotechnology. It literally means to "recombine DNA," usually from different organisms. Recombinant DNA technology is used to isolate and study a plant, human, or other animal gene that has potential use as a therapy. The gene of interest is identified and then isolated using restriction enzymes. Restriction enzymes cut the DNA at a specific sequence. The gene is isolated from the rest of the DNA and put into a vector. A common vector is a plasmid—a small, circular, double-stranded DNA molecule found in bacteria. The plasmid is cut with the same restriction enzyme so that the

EXPLORE

Moving Genes—Recombinant DNA Technology

In *Company Policy*, you might have asked questions like, "What is genetic engineering?" and "How is it done?" In *Moving Genes*, you will begin to understand what is involved in genetic engineering as you explore one technique used in genetic engineering.

In this activity, you will be a genetic engineer! You will use a paper model to simulate recombinant DNA technology. You will work with a partner to simulate standard techniques used in genetic engineering.

Materials

For each team of 2 students

1 pair of scissors

transparent tape

1 highlighter or light-colored marker

1 *Plasmid* handout

1 *Insulin Gene* handout

1 *Restriction Enzymes* handout

Process and Procedure

1. Watch as your teacher demonstrates the first steps in 1 type of recombinant DNA technology.
2. Use an analogy map to record what you learn in a class discussion. Use the headings "Cell Model," "*E. coli* Cell," and "Human Blood Cell."

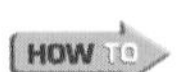

For help in creating an analogy map, see *How to Use and Create Organizing Tables* in the back of the book.

3. Study figure 9.4 and read the following paragraph about the small, circular piece of material that was in the *Escherichia coli* cell model. Add new information to your analogy map as you read.

   Scientists use **plasmids** to transfer fragments of DNA, such as the gene that codes for a particular protein. Plasmids are circular, double-stranded pieces of DNA that occur naturally in some bacteria. Review the picture of a typical bacterial cell (figure 9.4).

4. Collect the materials you need for this activity and the 3 handouts provided by your teacher.

ends of the gene and the ends opened up in the plasmid fit together, like a puzzle. Some restriction sites leave "sticky ends" and some leave "blunt ends" (see figure 9.8a and b in the student book).

The gene is "glued" into the plasmid using an enzyme called ligase. Ligase catalyzes the formation of a phosphodiester bond between the 5' phosphate and the 3' hydroxyl ends in the double-stranded DNA. The newly constructed, or recombined, DNA is then introduced into a bacterial cell. Recombined genes can also be introduced into a yeast or animal cell through different methods than used with bacteria. The gene is then translated and the protein it codes for is induced to express. One result is that the protein is produced in large quantities and can be purified for use.

One of the first genes sequenced and cloned and used for therapeutic treatment of a human condition was the gene for insulin. Insulin is a type of protein hormone. A healthy pancreas produces insulin, whose function is to signal cells, like muscle, liver, and fat cells, to take up glucose (sugar). One type of diabetes is caused by a lack of insulin. People with this kind of diabetes now rely on recombinant DNA technology to produce cloned human insulin as a treatment for diabetes.

Materials

For the teacher

2 paper bags
1 plastic bag (optional)
completed strands of DNA from copymaster 9.1, *Plasmid* and copymaster 9.2, *Insulin Gene*

1 pair of scissors
1 marker
transparent tape
stapler
colored paper for photocopying
1 transparency of student book figure 9.10

For each team of 2 students

1 pair of scissors
transparent tape
1 highlighter or light-colored marker
1 copy of copymaster 9.1, *Plasmid*
1 copy of copymaster 9.2, *Insulin Gene*
1 copy of copymaster 9.3, *Restriction Enzymes*

Advance Preparation

Make copies of copymaster 9.1, *Plasmid*; 9.2, *Insulin Gene*; and 9.3, *Restriction Enzymes*, each on paper of a different color. Make enough copies for each team to have a complete set. Make a few extra copies for you to use in making cell models. Label the scissors "restriction enzyme" and tape dispensers "ligase." Locate the transparency of student book figure 9.10.

Work through the student *Process and Procedure* to familiarize yourself with what the students will be doing. Save your pieces of DNA to use with the cell models.

Make 2 paper bag cell models. You can reuse them for each class if you are careful not to tear the bags. You might want to have extra bags just as a precaution. Consider laminating the paper DNA for repeated use.

- Bag 1: Use a marker and write in large letters on the outside "*E. coli.*" This bag represents a bacterial cell. Inside the bag, place the circular plasmid that you constructed in Step 5 of the *Process and Procedure* in the student book.

If you completed the entire activity for practice, be sure to remove the insulin gene from the plasmid.

5. As a team of 2, you will create the starting material for recombinant DNA technology. To begin, create your own *E. coli* plasmid by following these steps.

Most plasmids that are used in research have been manipulated by scientists to perform a certain function.

   a. Cut out the double-stranded DNA sequence from the *Plasmid* handout (figure 9.5). Be sure to cut along the dotted lines.
   b. Tape the 5 sections together end to end.

You may tape the plasmid strips together in any order.

   c. Tape the ends of the entire strip together so that the plasmid is circular. Make sure to tape the circle where you can see the base pairs on the outside.

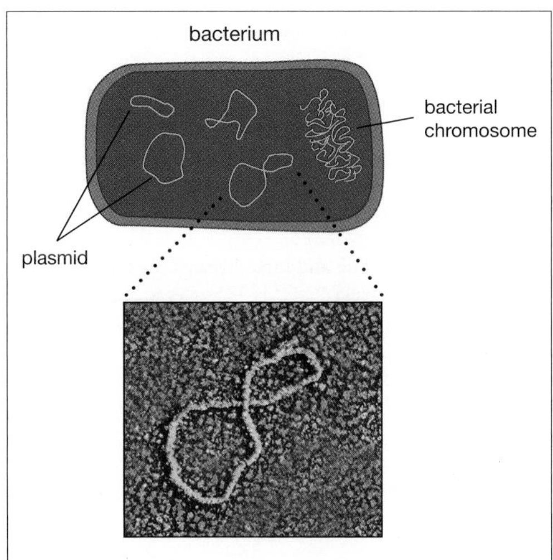

▲ **Figure 9.4 Typical bacteria cell.** This figure shows a typical bacteria cell with DNA and plasmids. A plasmid is a small circular piece of DNA found in some bacteria and other prokaryotic cells. What features of the bacteria cell would have to be changed in order for genetic engineering to occur? Note the figure is not to scale.

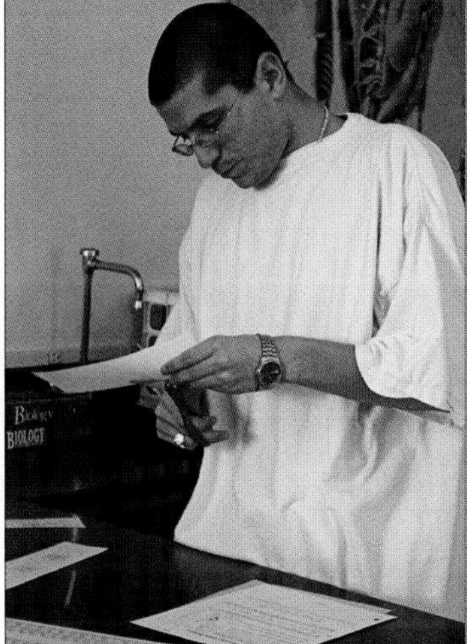

▲ **Figure 9.5 Cutting paper plasmids.** Cut out the double-stranded DNA sequence from the *Plasmid* handout.

Chapter 9 Genetic Engineering 455

Make a large piece of circular DNA by using additional pieces cut from the *Plasmid* copymaster. Include 2 or 3 copies so that the circle is much bigger than students'. This represents the chromosome in the *Escherichia coli* cell. When you finish, you should have a small circle of DNA to represent the plasmid and a larger circle of DNA to represent the *E. coli* chromosome. Place the plasmid and chromosome in the paper bag labeled *E. coli* and staple shut.

An *E. coli* cell is approximately 1 micron long and its chromosome is approximately 1 millimeter long. Therefore, the length of the chromosome is not to scale.

Additionally, the plasmid model that students use in this activity is simplified for use in the classroom. For example, the plasmid that students build represents only a fraction of the actual number of base pairs in a plasmid. Most cloning vectors have about 5,000 base pairs, although there is a good deal of variability in size. Also for simplicity, the classroom model shows only very short sequences for the origin of replication and the antibiotic resistance gene. These short sequences are included as placeholders instead of the approximately 700–1,000 base pairs that make up these sequences in real plasmids.

- Bag 2: Use a marker and write in large letters on the outside "human white blood cell." Inside the bag, place strips of DNA from the *Insulin Gene* copymaster. You should tape them together as instructed in Step 7 from *Process and Procedure* in the student book. This DNA is *not* circular. Highlight the DNA sequence that represents the insulin gene on one of the strands. Consider packing all of the DNA into a plastic bag to represent the nucleus before placing it in the paper bag. If you want to review parts of a cell with your students, use other objects to represent different structures and have students identify them from their function after you pop open the bag in the activity. Place all the contents in the bag and staple shut.

Insulin consists of two protein chains expressed by two different genes. In the body, the A and B chains bond together. In this activity, the DNA sequence for the B chain is included as part of the sequence on the *Insulin Gene* copymaster.

You may want to order a transformation lab kit from a science supply company. This is optional but provides extra practice and a wet lab for the concepts involved in transformation. If you decide to add this optional lab, do it after this Explore activity.

Educational Technologies

If your students need extra practice understanding the techniques of recombinant DNA technology, or if you want them to have a wet lab experience there are several biotechnology kits for *E. coli* transformation available. For more information regarding these kits contact your Kendall/Hunt representative or your local science supply store.

As You Teach

Outcomes and Indicators of Success

By the end of this activity, students should

1. apply their understanding of the structure and function of DNA.

   They will demonstrate their understanding by

6. You have a model of a paper plasmid similar to the one that was in the cell model at the beginning of this activity (figure 9.6). This particular plasmid has a gene that codes for a certain trait. Examine your plasmid and record that trait.

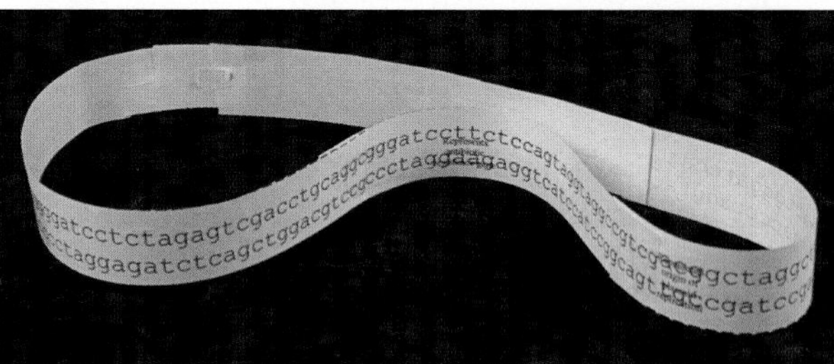

Figure 9.6 Paper plasmid. Your model of a paper plasmid should be similar to this one. The model includes a gene that codes for a particular trait. What is this trait?

7. Now create your second piece of starting material for recombinant DNA technology, a piece of human DNA.
   a. Create a piece of human DNA by cutting out the double-stranded DNA sequence from the *Insulin Gene* handout. This piece of DNA contains the insulin gene that you will manipulate.
   b. Cut along the dotted line and tape the sections together end to end in numerical order.

Be sure to tape the strips representing the human DNA in order as it is in the normal human DNA sequence. In reality, scientists can't specify the order of DNA, so they discover and study it as it naturally exists.

8. To learn what molecular biologists do with these pieces of DNA in genetic engineering, read *Manipulating DNA*.

456 Unit 2 Inside Life

- applying their knowledge about how genetic information is encoded in genes,
- simulating recombinant DNA technology to isolate an insulin gene and insert it into a plasmid, and
- simulating the isolation of plasmid DNA from bacteria.

2. understand how knowledge about biological processes, such as the structure and function of DNA and the replication process, can be used as a technological tool.

   They will demonstrate their understanding by

   - accurately simulating the production of a useful gene, such as insulin;
   - thoughtfully answering *Process and Procedure* and *Reflect and Connect* questions; and
   - articulating the connection between the simulation and practical applications.

3. compare components of recombinant DNA processes with a paper model.

   They will compare these components by

   - thoughtfully comparing each process and structure as they complete the activity and
   - accurately answering *Reflect and Connect* questions about specific comparisons and analogies in the activity.

Strategies

Getting Started

Direct students to read the introduction to *Moving Genes—Recombinant DNA Technology.* Make a list of important terms on the board and discuss them as a class. Terms may include *DNA*, *gene*, *host*, *insulin*, *plasmid*, *recombinant DNA technology*, and *sequence*.

Process and Procedure

In Step 1, you will conduct a demonstration with the 2 paper bag cell models described in *Advance Preparation.* Have students read the instructions in Step 2 and complete their analogy maps as you present the demonstration and lead the discussion. To perform the demonstration, follow these steps.

1. Show the class the paper bag model of the human blood cell, specifically a white blood cell. White blood cells contain DNA, but red blood cells do not. Explain that this is a model of a cell. You might want to review cells with your students by asking the following:
   - "What is in a cell?"
   - "Where is the genetic information stored?"
   - "Is this information the same or different in different types of cells in the same human?"
2. Tell the class that this activity focuses on manipulating the genetic information stored in DNA. Ask the class if it can think of disorders that are passed from parent to offspring through genetics. The discussion should include the example of diabetes. Share the causes of diabetes (see *Background Information*). It is not necessary to share all the details of diabetes—you just want to set the stage for the activity. Students will read about diabetes as part of the procedure.
3. Discuss with your students that they will be modeling a process where scientists remove the insulin gene from human DNA and put it into another cell that will multiply quickly to make insulin. This insulin can be

READING

Manipulating DNA

Through genetic engineering, foreign DNA is introduced into an organism. To do this, scientists need to isolate fragments of DNA. How do scientists isolate and manipulate the genes they are interested in? One method scientists commonly use is called recombinant DNA technology. **Recombinant DNA technology** is the process of cutting DNA at specific locations and putting the pieces back together. The fragments of DNA usually contain part of a gene. This technology allows scientists to isolate specific genes and learn what the genes code for. This technology opens many doors in genetic engineering.

Scientists can put the genes into another organism. For example, if a gene from a cow is put into a bacterium, the bacterium can express the cow protein coded by the added gene.

One of the first genes inserted into another organism was the gene that codes for insulin. Insulin is a protein hormone. A healthy pancreas produces insulin whose function is to signal cells, like muscle, liver, and fat cells, to take up glucose (sugar). One type of diabetes is caused by a lack of insulin. People with diabetes rely on recombinant DNA technology to produce cloned human insulin as a treatment for diabetes (see figure 9.7).

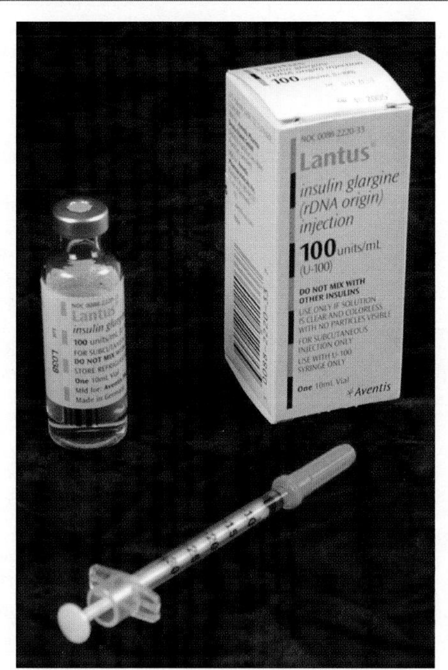

▲ **Figure 9.7 Recombinant human insulin.** At one time, insulin could only be obtained from cattle and hog pancreases. It was in short supply, expensive, and was not effective for some individuals because it was slightly different from human insulin. In 1982, the U.S. Food and Drug Administration approved the recombinant human insulin. Since then, human insulin has been produced inexpensively.

purified and made available to persons with diabetes. Lead the discussion with a question such as, "What would scientists need to do to this cell (the human blood cell) to remove the insulin gene?"

Scientists would have to open the cell, open the nucleus, extract the DNA, and isolate the DNA.

4. Model the process of removing a gene by popping open bag 2 and removing the DNA. Wash away the extra cell material, such as the paper bag representing the cell membrane and the plastic bag representing the nucleus, by pretending to throw it away.

5. Ask students if they can think of an organism that multiplies quickly; lead the discussion to include bacteria. Then show them bag 1, the cell model labeled *E. coli*. Pop open the bag as before and show students the contents. Model washing away the other cell parts by pretending to throw away all of the model except the plasmid. Lead students in a discussion with probing questions such as the following:

- "What are the differences in the contents of this cell and the human blood cell?"

DNA is circular in bacterial cells, and there are small and large circles of DNA. There is no nucleus in the bacterial cell.

- "What are the similarities?"

Both are cells with a membrane and both contain DNA.

- "How might scientists 'pop open' a cell?"

Students might guess that scientists use chemicals, salts, or pressure to pop open a cell. In actuality, scientists use an alkali lysis procedure to break open the cell.

- "How might scientists get rid of the extra cell parts and keep the DNA that they are working with?"

Students' thoughts will vary. They may say that the chromosomal DNA is filtered out. In reality, scientists change the pH of the solution, and most of the "junk" (chromosome, cell membrane, and proteins) precipitates out of the solution. They centrifuge the solution and the junk, which forms a pellet at the bottom of the tube. The plasmid DNA is left in the solution and can be precipitated and cleaned using ethanol.

- "If you wanted to take the insulin gene out of the human DNA and place it in the small circular piece of DNA, what would you have to do first?"

Students will not know the term plasmid yet.

You would have to open up or cut the circular piece, or plasmid. You would also have to cut out the insulin gene.

You might also ask students why a white blood cell was used instead of a red blood cell.

Red blood cells do not have a nucleus so they do not contain DNA.

For Step 2, make sure each team of 2 has the 3 handouts: *Plasmid* (copymaster 9.1), *Insulin Gene* (copymaster 9.2), and *Restriction*

Answers to Step 9 are on TE page 459.
Answers to Step 12 are on TE page 460a.

9. Answer Questions 9a–b about the plasmid and human DNA model in your science notebook. Compare and contrast your answers to your teammate's answers. Adjust your answers based on what you learn from others.
   a. What are the differences between a plasmid and a section of human DNA? What are the similarities?
   b. What would a scientist need to do before he or she could remove a gene from a section of DNA?
10. Read the following paragraph to learn how scientists put a plasmid into a strand of DNA. This process is how scientists use recombinant DNA technology to move genes. As you read, use this question to focus your reading: "How do restriction enzymes work?"

    Restriction enzymes are an important tool that scientists use. Essentially, restriction enzymes work like scissors that cut at specific locations along a DNA strand. There are thousands of restriction enzymes that occur naturally in bacteria. Because restriction enzymes cut DNA at specific locations, scientists can use them as a tool to isolate a specific segment of DNA. Each enzyme cuts at a unique DNA sequence called a **restriction site.**

    Your scissors will be used as restriction enzymes in this activity. On the *Restriction Enzymes* handout, several restriction enzymes are listed next to the DNA sequence at which they cut. But remember that the gene you are interested in must stay intact.
11. Study the DNA sequences where the restriction enzymes cut (restriction site) on the *Restriction Enzymes* handout. Write 1 question you have about how restriction enzymes work in your science notebook.

Read your question to your teammate, and then listen to his or her question. Help each other with the answers.

12. Prepare the *human* DNA strand by following Steps 12a–d.
    a. Locate the restriction sites described on the *Restriction Enzymes* handout.
    b. Label all of the places along the human DNA segment where a specific restriction enzyme would cut.
    c. Mark each site with the name of the restriction enzyme.
    d. Draw a line indicating where the enzyme would cut.

Not every enzyme will cut along this section of DNA.

13. Read the following paragraph, which describes the different ways restriction enzymes work.

458 Unit 2 Inside Life

Enzymes (copymaster 9.3). Each team also should have at least 1 pair of scissors and transparent tape. Students follow the steps to simulate using recombinant DNA technology to put the insulin gene into a plasmid.

Students will add to their analogy maps as they complete the short readings and complete all the steps. Monitor their work to make sure they are adding to their maps as they work.

In Step 5, students create their plasmids using copymaster 9.1, *Plasmid*. They accomplish this by cutting along the dotted lines of the copymaster and taping the strips together. The plasmid can be put together in any order. This allows for variability among the teams. The plasmid is formed into a circle by taping the beginning piece to the end piece after all strips are taped together. Make sure students can see the DNA sequence on the outside of the plasmid.

Step 6 asks student to examine the plasmid DNA. The DNA contains a gene that codes for a particular trait, antibiotic resistance. Your students can see this from the DNA sequence. Remind them of the activities in chapter 1, *Investigations by Design*, where they learned how some bacteria might have this trait. You may want to redirect them to read the sidebar *Antibiotics* to refresh their memory. Students may wonder why all the plasmids they are using have this trait. When scientists have bacteria with recombinant DNA, they need to be able to identify and isolate the bacteria that now have the recombinant DNA from bacteria that do not have the new plasmid. In other words, they want to select a trait they can screen for easily. A recombinant plasmid that has the antibiotic resistance trait as well as the gene of interest allows scientists to do this. When bacteria with an antibiotic resistance gene on the plasmid are grown on an agar plate containing that antibiotic, the bacteria survive. If the bacteria do not have the "engineered" plasmid with the antibiotic resistance gene, the bacteria will die in the presence of that antibiotic. The antibiotic resistance gene is a way to screen for bacteria that have incorporated the plasmid. After all, you can't tell by looking at bacteria which ones took up the plasmid.

During Step 7, students construct part of a human DNA sequence that contains the gene that codes for insulin in human DNA. They accomplish this by cutting along the dotted lines of copymaster 9.2, *Insulin Gene* and taping the strips end to end. The human DNA must be put together in numerical order.

In Step 9, after the teams have created their paper plasmid and human DNA, allow time for them to answer Questions 9a–b.

Answers to Step 9, SE page 458

9a. One difference between a section of human DNA and a plasmid is that the plasmid is circular and the human DNA is linear (a bacterial chromosome is circular, but much larger). Although the paper models are not to scale, students should understand that the plasmid is smaller than the human DNA. They are similar because both the plasmid and the section of human DNA contain DNA.

9b. The scientist needs to locate the gene, determine the starting and ending points, find the appropriate enzyme, and cut it out.

Answers to Step 15 are on TE page 460.

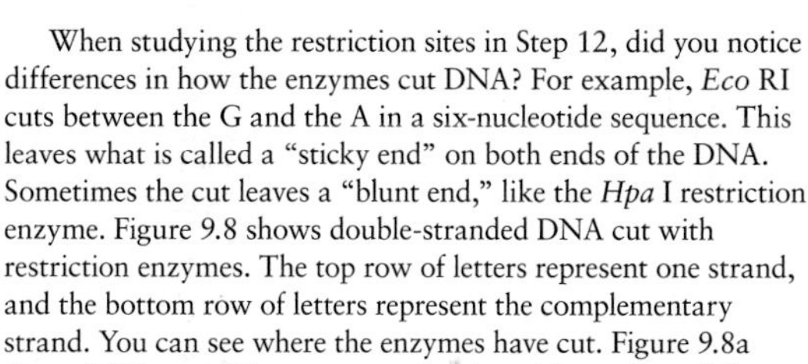

When studying the restriction sites in Step 12, did you notice differences in how the enzymes cut DNA? For example, *Eco* RI cuts between the G and the A in a six-nucleotide sequence. This leaves what is called a "sticky end" on both ends of the DNA. Sometimes the cut leaves a "blunt end," like the *Hpa* I restriction enzyme. Figure 9.8 shows double-stranded DNA cut with restriction enzymes. The top row of letters represent one strand, and the bottom row of letters represent the complementary strand. You can see where the enzymes have cut. Figure 9.8a shows DNA cut with an enzyme, leaving sticky ends, and figure 9.8b shows DNA cut with an enzyme, leaving blunt ends.

14. Think about which restriction enzymes you can use to cut out the insulin gene. Highlight the sites where you can cut out the gene, and record the restriction enzymes you would use. Do not cut out the gene yet.
15. Answer the following questions about restriction enzymes in your science notebook.
    a. Which restriction enzymes would you use to cut out the insulin gene? Why?
    b. What other information might you need before making your final choice?

▲ **Figure 9.8 Restriction enzyme.** The DNA in (a) is cut with a restriction enzyme that leaves sticky ends. The DNA in (b) is cut with an enzyme that leaves blunt ends.

In Step 10, students read the paragraph that introduces the terms restriction enzyme and restriction site. And in Step 11, after looking at copymaster 9.3, *Restriction Enzymes*, both students in each team write a question about the process. Circulate and listen as teammates share their questions and attempt to answer them.

In Step 12, students locate all the restriction sites on the human DNA segment (listed in copymaster 9.3, *Restriction Enzymes*). Check that teams are working to label the sites with the corresponding names of the enzymes (see figure T9.1).

In Step 13, students read the paragraph about restriction enzymes and review figure 9.8.

In Step 14, only 1 restriction enzyme cuts before and after the insulin gene and in the plasmid: *Nde* I. Let students try different combinations and discover the answer on their own.

During Step 15, check student understanding by listening to the teams discuss Questions 14a–b about restriction enzymes.

Answers to Step 15, SE page 459

15a. *Nde* I should be chosen to cut out the insulin gene. This enzyme is the only one that cuts before and after the insulin gene.

15b. Students need to know where the insulin gene fits into the plasmid.

During Step 16, circulate as teams label restriction sites with corresponding names of restriction enzymes on the plasmid DNA and mark where the enzyme would cut (figure T9.2).

In Step 17, students compare the restriction sites of the chromosome and the plasmid and identify the restriction enzyme (*Nde* I) to cut the insulin gene and plasmid DNA. It is the only enzyme that cuts before and after the insulin gene *and* cuts the plasmid. To get the ends of the cut human DNA to match up with the ends of the plasmid DNA, the same enzyme should be used to cut the gene from the human DNA and to open the plasmid.

In Step 18, when students have decided which restriction enzyme to use, make sure they check with you before they actually cut out the gene. Check that they have chosen *Nde* I. This restriction enzyme will successfully cut both the gene and the plasmid.

During Steps 19–21, students remove the insulin gene from the human DNA segment and cut open the plasmid. They then answer Questions 21a–b.

Answers to Step 21, SE page 460

21a. Students retrieve 1 linear piece after cutting the plasmid DNA. The restriction enzyme, *Nde* I, cuts in 1 location, therefore opening up the plasmid. Students cut the human DNA in 2 places, which cuts out the insulin gene. Because the human DNA segment is linear to begin with, there are 3 segments of DNA.

21b. The ends of the plasmid DNA and the ends of the isolated insulin gene complement each other. They fit together like the pieces of a puzzle.

Your goal is to put the insulin gene into the plasmid.

16. Prepare a plasmid by locating restriction sites on the *plasmid* DNA. Use the *Restriction Enzymes* handout as a guide and complete Steps 16a–d.
    a. Locate the restriction sites described on the *Restriction Enzymes* handout.
    b. Label all the places along the plasmid where a restriction enzyme would cut.
    c. Mark each site with the name of the restriction enzyme.
    d. Draw a line indicating where the enzyme would cut.
17. Compare the restriction sites you found on both the human DNA and the plasmid. Identify which restriction enzyme(s) you should use to cut out the insulin gene and to cut the plasmid DNA.

Remember that the insulin gene needs to be placed into the plasmid.

When you cut out the insulin gene, you will need a place to put it for processing. We can use plasmid DNA for this purpose. In fact, plasmids can serve as vectors. Vectors are used to carry a gene to an organism. The gene within the plasmid can then be replicated, transcribed, and translated, all within a host organism, such as the bacteria *E. coli*. Plasmids use the machinery of the host bacteria to do this.

You learned that vectors in physical science are quantities with size and direction.

18. Using the *Restriction Enzymes* handout as a guide, follow these steps.
    a. Decide where to cut the DNA sequence on your human DNA strand.
    b. Compare your decision with another team's. Then have your teacher approve your decision.
    c. Use your scissors as a restriction enzyme to cut the DNA sequence at the sites you have identified.
19. Remove the insulin gene from the human DNA segment. Isolate the gene by removing the rest of the DNA (throw it away).
20. Cut the DNA sequence on your plasmid at the sites you have identified.

You only need to open up the plasmid to insert the insulin gene. You accomplish this by using enzymes.

21. Answer Questions 21a–b about the simulation in your science notebook.
    a. What happens to the plasmid when you cut it?
    b. Compare the ends of the plasmid DNA with the ends of the isolated insulin gene. What do you notice?

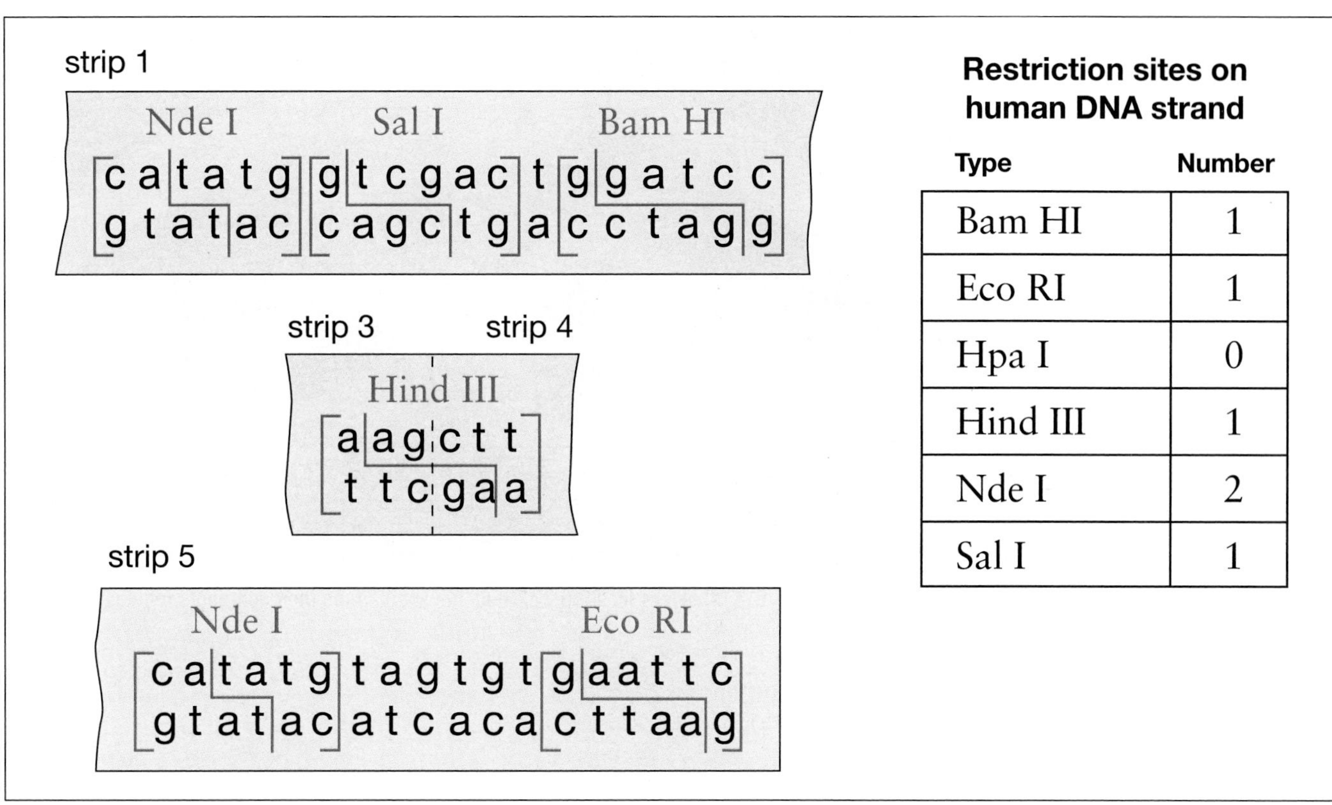

Restriction sites on human DNA strand

Type	Number
Bam HI	1
Eco RI	1
Hpa I	0
Hind III	1
Nde I	2
Sal I	1

▲ **Figure T9.1 Answers for Step 12.** Students should mark their sites as shown in this figure.

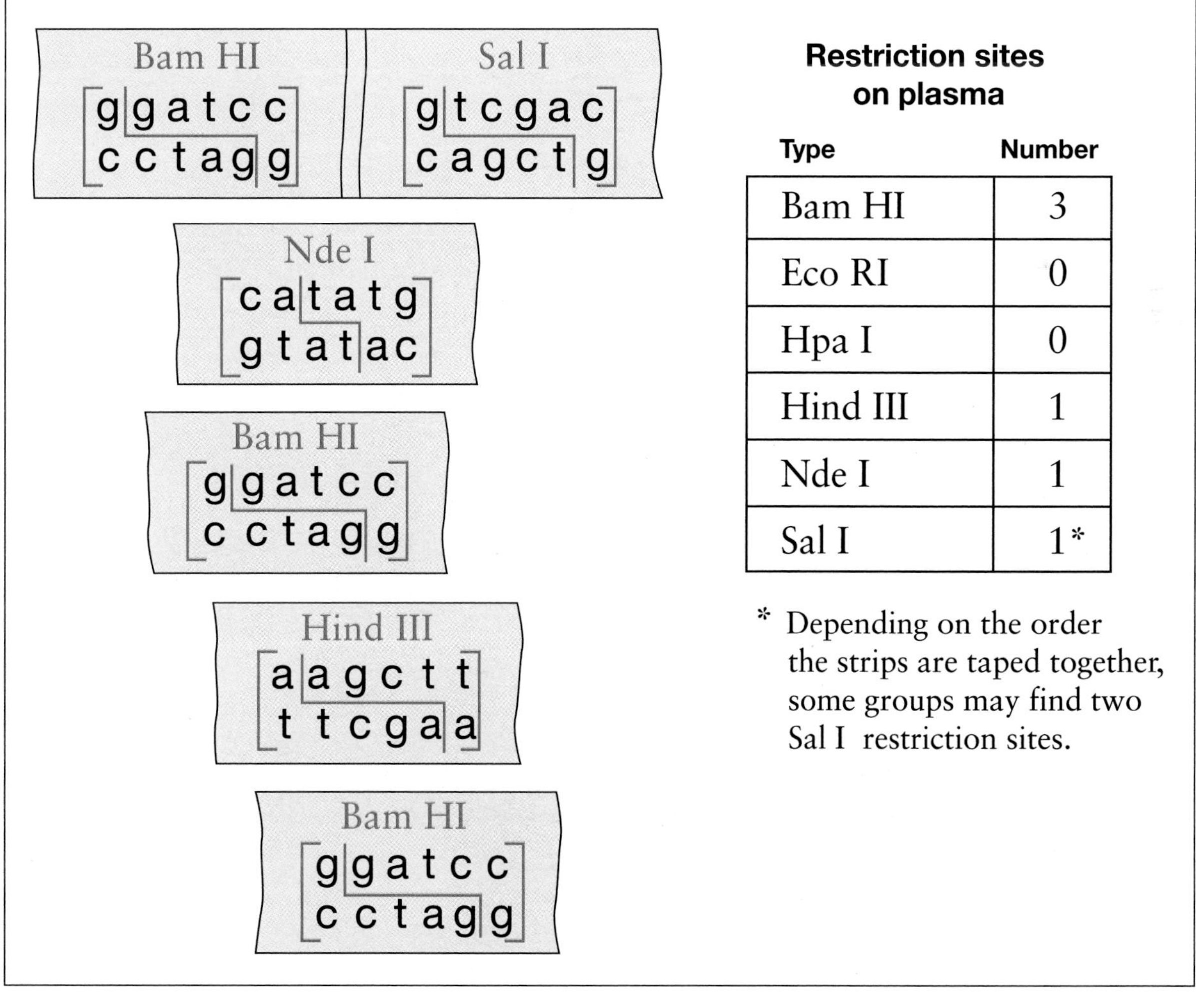

Restriction sites on plasma

Type	Number
Bam HI	3
Eco RI	0
Hpa I	0
Hind III	1
Nde I	1
Sal I	1*

* Depending on the order the strips are taped together, some groups may find two Sal I restriction sites.

▲ **Figure T9.2 Answers for Step 16.** Students should mark where the enzyme would cut as shown in this figure.

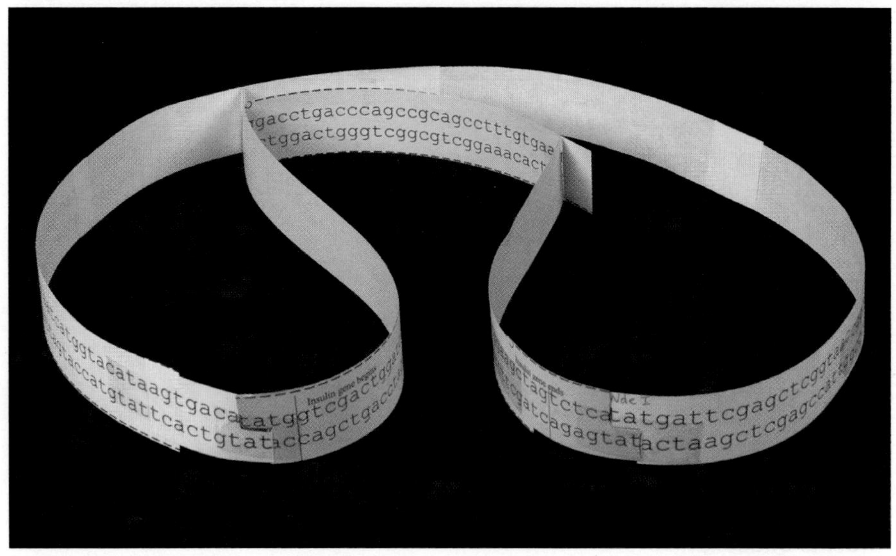

▲ **Figure T9.3 Answers for Step 22.** Students should tape their segments together as shown.

NOTES:

In Step 22, read the information about ligase, put the insulin gene into the plasmid DNA, and tape the ends together. Check that all teams correctly fit the insulin gene into the plasmid (figure T9.3).

To complete the activity, students read the paragraph in Step 23. Display a transparency of student book figure 9.10. This illustration provides an overview of how recombinant insulin is produced. Ask students to identify the parts of the illustration that correspond to the simulation they just completed. Help students understand that the next step in their simulation would be to culture the *E. coli* with the plasmid containing the insulin gene. Each new cell resulting from reproduction is identical to the *E. coli* with the insert and is capable of producing insulin. This description oversimplifies the process, but gives students a general idea of what happens. If your students need extra practice understanding the techniques of recombinant DNA technology, or if you want them to have a wet lab experience there are several biotechnology kits for *E. coli* transformation available. For more information regarding these kits contact your Kendall/Hunt representative or your local science supply store.

Answers to Reflect and Connect, SE page 461

1. The plasmid is the vector used to introduce a gene into a host cell.
2. The gene produces the desired trait or protein. The gene is manipulated and placed in an organism to replicate and produce a large quantity of the gene product.

3a. In the activity, students found the insulin gene on human DNA. It was labeled for them. To remove it, they had to find a restriction enzyme that would cut it close to the beginning and the end without interfering with the gene. They cut it with scissors that represented a restriction enzyme.

3b. Students made a paper plasmid (vector) and cut it open with their scissors (restriction enzyme).

3c. Students took the insulin gene and attached it to the plasmid with tape that represented ligase, an enzyme that forms bonds between molecules.

4. The location of the restriction site is important because the DNA cannot be cut in the middle of the gene of interest or the gene will not express the desired protein. Therefore, restriction sites that would work are located outside the gene of interest in the chromosome. Also, restriction sites must *not* be located within functional sites used in replication or transcription.
5. Students should see that only 1 cell with the desired gene is not enough. The cells must be cultured and allowed to reproduce to make a larger quantity of the insulin. Students may also recognize that the insulin must be purified from the bacterial cells before it is ready for therapeutic use.

22. It is now time to put the insulin in the plasmid. Another enzyme, called **ligase**, assists in the formation of bonds between adjacent, complementary DNA ends. Your tape will play the role of the ligase.
    - a. Insert the insulin gene in the plasmid DNA in the appropriate place.
    - b. Tape the ends together.
    - c. Does it fit?
23. Read the following paragraph about the next steps in recombinant DNA technology.

    How do you get protein from a plasmid? Your goal in this activity was to take the gene for insulin from human DNA and insert it into the plasmid. But the engineering does not stop there. After you have the plasmid with the insulin gene inserted, what comes next? You know that this gene codes for insulin and you want to "manufacture" a lot of insulin. So the plasmid must be put back into the *E. coli* cells. The *E. coli* reproduce rapidly and the new gene is expressed, giving *E. coli* a new trait. Remember from chapter 8 that gene expression results in the production of a particular protein. Many drugs are now made this way. Scientists insert a gene coding for the desired protein into a bacterium, and the desired trait is expressed.

Reflect and Connect

Answer the following questions in your science notebook and then discuss your answers with your partner. Record what you learn from your discussion in your science notebook.

1. What is the role of the plasmid in recombinant DNA technology?
2. What is the role of the gene in recombinant DNA technology?
3. Next to each task in Question 3a–c, explain how you simulated the task in this activity.
    - a. Identify a specific gene and remove it from a chromosome.
    - b. Find a DNA carrier, or vector, to place into living host cells.
    - c. Join the gene to the vector.
4. Why is the location of the restriction site important? Which sites would work and which would not? Why?
5. The technique you modeled in this activity will produce abundant *E. coli* cells that contain the gene that codes for the production of insulin. What would be the next steps to have insulin available for diabetic patients?

NOTES:

SIDEBAR

Agarose Gel Electrophoresis

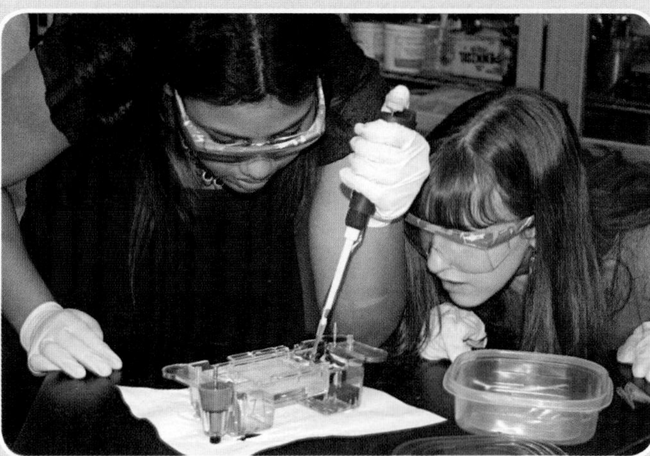

▲ **Electrophoresis.** These students are conducting an investigation using agarose gel electrophoresis. This process separates DNA fragments by size using an electric field. Once separated, the fragments can be identified or compared with a known sample.

In this chapter, you have been learning about how scientists recombine DNA in useful ways. An insulin gene can be put in plasmid DNA so that insulin may be produced in great quantities for use in medicine. A luciferase gene that glows when expressed can transform bacteria to make them glow. (Luciferase comes from fireflies.) These are just two examples of the many ways to use recombinant DNA technology.

How do scientists know when the DNA fragments are recombined correctly? How can they identify and isolate genes? Scientists apply their understanding of physical science by taking advantage of the way DNA molecules behave in an electric field. In a process called **agarose gel electrophoresis**, scientists separate DNA fragments by size and then identify the fragments.

A substance called *agarose* helps separate the DNA fragments. Agarose is extracted from seaweed. Agarose gel has the consistency of gelatin that has very small holes or pores in it and works like a fishnet. A fishnet set in the ocean allows small fish to travel through the net, but slows down or catches the big fish. Agarose gel allows small DNA molecules to pass through quickly, medium-sized DNA molecules to pass through more slowly, and large DNA molecules to pass through slowly, if at all. Agarose gel electrophoresis is a filtering process.

NOTES:

But how does a DNA molecule begin its travels? An agarose gel is set into a container called a "gel box." The gel box contains a solution with positively and negatively charged ions. On one end of the gel box there is a positive electrode, and on the other end there is a negative electrode. When an electric current is applied to this system, it creates an electric field.

It is here that scientists use their understanding of physical science as a tool in biology. They know that opposite charges attract and that like charges repel. DNA is a negatively charged molecule. As an organic acid, negatively charged oxygen atoms branch out from phosphates on the outside of the DNA molecule. Because of this negative charge, DNA travels to the positively charged electrode and is repelled by the negatively charged electrode. The DNA travels horizontally through an agarose gel from the negative electrode to the positive electrode. In fact, the term electrophoresis means "to carry with electricity."

As the DNA travels through the agarose gel, it separates according to size. Scientists have developed DNA molecular-weight markers with DNA fragments of known sizes. These markers are used to "size" the DNA fragments on the agarose gel. Then the DNA is stained with a chemical called ethidium bromide. Ethidium bromide penetrates the DNA, allowing the DNA to be seen under an ultraviolet light.

The fragments, or genes, are filtered using agarose gel electrophoresis. Genes can be identified and isolated using this process. The figure below shows how DNA is separated out using gel electrophoresis.

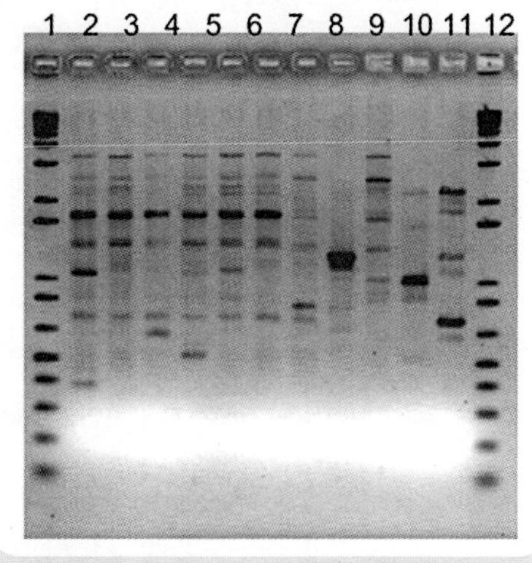

▲ **Electrophoresis result.** What do the positions of the dark spots mean?

SciLINKS NSTA
Topic: electrophoresis
Go to: www.scilinks.org
Code: 2Inquiry463

EXPLAIN

How Can It Be Done?

Activity Overview

In *How Can It Be Done?*, students use a jigsaw learning strategy to study different techniques and applications used in genetic engineering. The activity introduces students to various applications of recombinant DNA technology and a technique used in genetic engineering. This helps them understand the basic processes behind these techniques. As students progress through this investigation, look at their drawings, labeled cards, and science notebooks to see that they understand recombinant DNA technology. Students compare and contrast techniques used in genetic engineering and group and post cards that show their drawings and interpretations. Read students' answers to the *Reflect and Connect* questions to check for understanding.

Before You Teach

Background Information

With recombinant DNA technology, scientists can manipulate DNA (and thus genes) more effectively than ever before. Once genes are isolated, manipulated, and placed in a plasmid, the next question is, "Then what?" Several methods are used to manipulate the genes of an organism. One method includes inserting a plasmid into a bacterium so that it can express a gene. In this case, the plasmid serves as a transport device to carry the gene into the other organism. In another method, scientists insert a gene into a chromosome of a bacterium to change its genome. Sometimes scientists simply insert a gene into an organism. Other times, they remove an unwanted gene. And yet another method calls for scientists to insert plasmids into various cells. Plasmids are generally used to get genes into bacteria. Vectors other than plasmids and different techniques are used to get genes into other kinds of organisms.

Bacteria can be genetically modified to produce a product such as insulin. Prior to recombinant DNA technology, people deficient in certain proteins, such as growth hormone or insulin, were given the protein from human cadavers or produced from animals (e.g., cows). When people were given the protein produced by cows, some people had allergic reactions. The proteins retrieved from cadavers were in short supply. Recombinant DNA technology solves many of these problems and can be used for countless applications. When an organism is genetically altered, the term *transgenic* is used. Transgenic plants, animals, and microorganisms exist due to genetic engineering.

Materials

For each team of 2 students

2 5×7 in index cards

2 copies of 1 of the following copymasters:

TRCD

- copymaster 9.4, *Gene Therapy*
- copymaster 9.5, *Drug Therapy*
- copymaster 9.6, *Tissue Engineering*
- copymaster 9.7, *Gene Bullets*
- copymaster 9.8, *Electroporation*

colored pencils (including red) or thin-line markers

tape

Advance Preparation

Ideally, there are 5 or more teams of 2 students each for this investigation. Each team is assigned a different topic, and so a different copymaster (copymaster 9.4, *Gene Therapy*; copymaster 9.5, *Drug Therapy*;

TRCD

EXPLAIN

How Can It Be Done?

In *Moving Genes—Recombinant DNA Technology*, you explored how genes can be manipulated and recombined so that, when the gene is introduced into bacteria, it produces a desired characteristic. With recombinant DNA technology, we have the ability to change DNA in organisms by adding genes, transferring genes, and stopping the functioning of certain genes. Genetic engineering is the process of changing the genes of an organism. As advancements in this field continue, our understanding of gene function also advances. When new genes, usually from another source, are added to an organism, the organism being changed is called a **transgenic organism**. Transgenic organisms (figure 9.9) are becoming increasingly common.

▲ **Figure 9.9 Genetically engineered organisms.** Can you tell if these organisms are transgenic? How did scientists alter their DNA and why?

copymaster 9.6, *Tissue Engineering*; copymaster 9.7, *Gene Bullets*; or copymaster 9.8, *Electroporation*). Each of the topics is assigned a color:

copymaster 9.4, *Gene Therapy*: orange

copymaster 9.5, *Drug Therapy*: blue

copymaster 9.6, *Tissue Engineering*: green

copymaster 9.7, *Gene Bullets*: yellow

copymaster 9.8, *Electroporation*: red

Make 2 copies of the assigned copymaster for each team. If you have fewer than 5 teams, make sure at least 1 team has each topic. If you have more than 5 teams, assign the topics as evenly as possible (e.g., so that 2 teams work on each topic). At the top of each copymaster, write the assigned color and make enough photocopies for your students.

Gather colored pencils and markers for each team, Make sure there are several red ones available and a variety of other colors for students to use for their diagrams. Designate an area of the room for posting the diagram cards.

Prepare 5 sets of index cards that correspond to the 5 copymasters by drawing a colored stripe along the tops in the following colors: orange, blue, green, yellow, and red. To begin, the 2 students on each team receive the same color card. So you'll need 2 cards for each color per team (2 × number of teams assigned to the color = number of cards in each of the five color sets). If you have a class of 30, you would have 3 teams (of 2 students) for each of the 5 topics and would need to make 6 cards of each color.

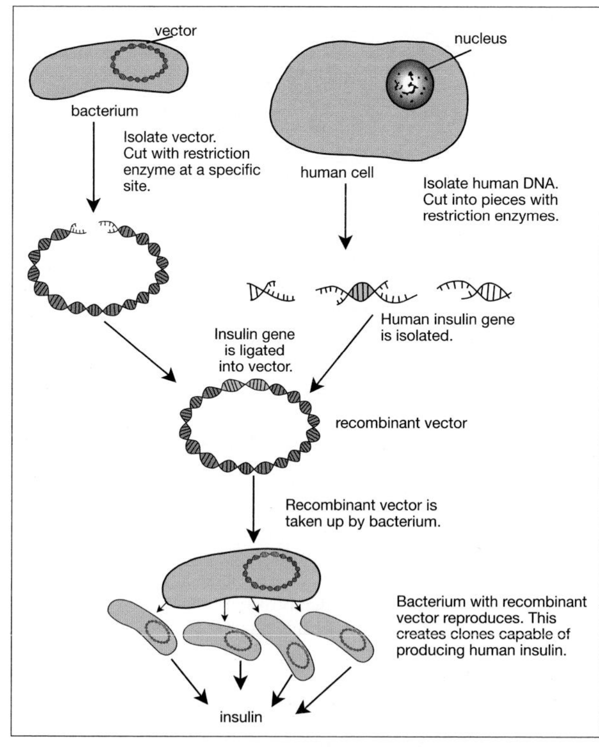

▲ **Figure 9.10 Sequence of recombinant DNA.** How do vectors and fragments combine to make a changed organism?

Review figure 9.10, which summarizes the sequence you followed in the *Moving Genes* activity.

Scientists use many techniques in genetic engineering to obtain a desired result, such as constructing an organism that expresses a new gene. In *How Can It Be Done?*, you will work with a teammate to gain a better understanding of some commonly practiced techniques in genetic engineering and how they might be applied. You will then compare and contrast the techniques. If you would like to learn about careers in the field of genetic engineering and other related fields, read the sidebar *Biomedical Engineering: Making a Good Living.*

Educational Technologies

If time allows, have students do additional research on the Web or in the library.

As You Teach

Outcomes and Indicators of Success

By the end of this activity, students should

1. understand fundamental concepts behind several approaches used to genetically engineer organisms.

   They will demonstrate their understanding by

   - making a labeled drawing of the sequence of steps used in one type of genetic engineering approach and
   - contrasting three approaches used in genetic engineering applications.

2. understand that many genetic engineering techniques have similar fundamental ideas.

   They will demonstrate their understanding by

   - summarizing the major steps common to different approaches in genetic engineering and
   - comparing three approaches used in genetic engineering applications.

3. know common applications for which genetic engineering techniques are used.

   They will demonstrate their knowledge by

   - explaining why some applications were repeated in different genetic engineering procedures and
   - identifying the applications used for each procedure.

Strategies

Getting Started

Instruct students to read the introduction, which defines the terms *genetic engineering* and *transgenic.* Discuss with students whether they think scientists have the ability to insert a gene from a firefly into a plant to make the plant glow. Listen to their thoughts and ideas. Remind them of the activity *Moving Genes—Recombinant DNA Technology.* The investigation showed students how they could insert a plasmid carrying a gene into a bacterium. Have students begin to think about the barriers scientists must face when trying to genetically engineer more complex organisms, such as plants or animals.

Explain to students that the techniques associated with recombinant DNA technology have allowed scientists to become creative with genetic engineering. If people have a need, scientists sometimes can address that need through genetic engineering. Let students know that, in this activity, they will explore some techniques and applications made possible by genetic engineering.

The answer to whether scientists have the ability to insert a gene from a firefly into a plant to make the plant glow is yes. This feat can be accomplished in a number of ways. Scientists can insert a gene directly into the plant's cells or into a vector that can carry the gene to the plant's cells.

Process and Procedure

In Steps 1–5, students work with a teammate on a scenario. Give both students on each team a copy of the same handout. Make sure that at least 1 team is working on each of the 5 scenarios (5 copymasters). Distribute the index cards; each team should receive cards that match the color written on their copymaster.

Allow time for students to complete their diagrams and label the parts in Step 2. They should use red to draw the desired gene in the diagram. Remind students to copy their diagrams into their science notebooks in Step 3; in Step 4, have them write applications for their assigned technique. In Step 5, students switch cards with 2 other teams that have a different color. Instead of having the same color card, the teammates end up with cards that are 2 different colors. Instruct students to answer Questions 6a–b in their science notebook.

Answers to Step 6, SE page 466

6a. Most of the techniques are similar in that they isolate a gene of interest from a host organism. They isolate the gene and put it into a vector. The vector carries the gene into a new organism for expression or to obtain the desired product.

6b. The applications vary because it is not possible to standardize a procedure to work in every situation. Through trial and error, some techniques work better than others, depending on the application.

Materials

For each team of 2 students

2 copies of the handout assigned to your team

2 5×7 in index cards

colored pencils or thin-line markers

Process and Procedure

1. With your teammate, read the sequence of steps described on the handout distributed by your teacher.

Your teacher also will distribute index cards. The color on top of the index card should match the color written at the top of the handout.

2. On your own, draw a labeled diagram on your index card. Your diagram should show the sequence of steps used in the genetic engineering technique you are describing. You may help each other, but you will each make a card.

You will use this card to teach someone else about this technique, so make your diagram clear and label it carefully. You will not be present to describe the process.

The following items must be labeled on your diagram:

a. Desired gene
b. Plasmid
c. Bacteria
d. Donor organism (one that provides the DNA)
e. Recipient organism (one that receives the DNA)
f. Chromosome
g. Vector

Use red to draw the desired gene each time.

3. Copy your diagram into your science notebook.
4. On the back of the card, write the type of applications the technique is used for.
5. When all of the teams have finished their diagrams, trade cards with 2 other teams so that your team has 2 new cards (2 different colors).

If your team drew red cards originally, your team should trade to get 2 new colors. For example, your team could end up with a yellow card and a blue card.

6. Look at the new cards and answer Steps 6a–b in your science notebook.
   a. Compare these 2 new techniques with the one you diagrammed. In what ways are they similar to the technique you drew?
   b. Why do you think the applications vary so much?

In Step 7, post the cards in the room by color. Gather students by the card display and discuss the similarities and differences they observed among the techniques.

Answers to Reflect and Connect, SE page 467

1. All the techniques used in genetic engineering involve isolating a desired gene and placing it into an organism to get the gene to perform a desired function. Even though there are different reasons or applications for these techniques, they all involve manipulating genes. Scientists have discovered that these common steps are the most convenient and effective to use.
2. Yes, the same genetic engineering techniques are repeated in different types of applications. The same basic idea is behind most genetic engineering feats: to find or create a desired gene and then move it to where the gene will fit for an application. There are several variations, but the beginning (locating the gene and using recombination technology) is the same in most cases.
3. Yes, genes in gamete cells (sex cells) can be altered. A gamete, such as an egg, can be removed and its DNA cut using restriction enzymes. A vector containing a desired gene can be introduced. The egg can be fertilized and allowed to develop. Any change in germ cells would result in changing the genetics of future generations.

Use the video, *Understanding Biotechnology*, at the end of this activity as a review or as an additional resource for students that are still struggling with the concepts.

7. Post the diagram cards in your classroom; group cards of the same color together.

Reflect and Connect

Answer the following questions in your science notebook. Use an effective technique to check your answers.

1. Summarize the major steps common to all the techniques used in genetic engineering. Why are they common steps?
2. Were the same genetic engineering techniques repeated in different types of applications? Explain why this would occur.
3. Do you think genes in gamete cells (sex cells) can be altered? Describe how this could happen.

SIDEBAR

Biomedical Engineering: Making a Good Living

What do you need to know to make a good living? Of course, it depends on what you want to do. And that depends on the things you like to do, your talents, and your determination. One career field that combines interesting work, helping others, and great pay is biomedical engineering.

Biomedical engineering is a broad family of career fields. Each branch combines science with technology to enhance the lives of those in need of health care. Look at the graphic organizer with biomedical engineering in the center bubble. Notice how many fascinating career possibilities link to biomedical engineering. No wonder biomedical engineering jobs are projected to grow by more than 31 percent by 2010.

Just imagine being part of the bioinstrumentation team that developed the personal blood-sugar tester, which diabetes patients need to monitor their blood sugar. What would it be like to be the biomedical engineer who made it possible to transplant a pig's heart into a human? Think how it would change lives if you invented the first artificial shoulder? This is the kind of work biomedical engineers do.

Naturally, rewarding careers demand careful preparation. You have to know a lot about living systems, science, and mathematics. In addition, working professionals need to speak and write effectively, especially about science and mathematics concepts. These demands translate to taking as many core classes in high school as possible. Plus, you need to do well in them. It's hard work, but it's also interesting and rewarding. In the end, you not only make a good living, you make living good.

NOTES:

ELABORATE

Biotechnology and Society

Activity Overview

In Part I of *Biotechnology and Society,* students explore applications of genetic engineering beyond the life sciences. They explore ideas about how genetic engineering applications could be used to solve problems. They might share both realistic and unrealistic ideas. This will help you gain an understanding of how much students know about genetic engineering applications. You can use this information to help guide your students to a greater understanding.

With any new technology, ethical issues arise. In Part II of *Biotechnology and Society*, students learn to use an ethical decision-making model and apply it to two ethical dilemmas. You can assess student learning by reviewing the ethical decision-making tables students create in their science notebook and by reading their responses to the *Reflect and Connect* questions.

Before You Teach

Background Information

Part I—Meeting a Need

Genetic engineering of microorganisms has potential use as a solution to many environmental problems, such as getting rid of toxic waste. This is termed *bioremediation.* Some types of toxic waste are pollution, oil spills, and radioactive waste. In many cases, naturally occurring microorganisms are found that "eat up" the toxic waste by degrading it into a stable chemical. These microorganisms are then engineered to enhance their activity, or certain genetic components are used to transform another microorganism to perform a desired function. One example of such an organism is transgenic *Pseudomonas*. This bacterium has been engineered to degrade polyhalogenated compounds (a major class of pollutants) into harmless products. Another example is bacteria that have been developed to convert toxic heavy metal ions, such as mercury, to less toxic elemental forms. These less toxic forms are easier to isolate and remove from the environment.

DNA can be damaged by radiation. When DNA is damaged to a certain degree, the organism usually will not survive. But *Deinococcus radiodurans* is a microorganism that is highly resistant to radioactivity. This bacterium has a means to repair DNA that has been damaged by radiation. Because of the accurate and rapid repair means of *D. radiodurans,* it will withstand exposure to radiation. This microorganism has potential for cleaning up toxic waste sites that contain radioactive isotopes.

There are many examples of organisms used in bioremediation. But genetic engineering also includes production processes that use chemistry applications. One production process that genetic engineering has helped is making beer. Yeasts are genetically engineered to produce great quantities of alcohol during fermentation in the brewing industry.

Genetic engineering has applications that span the sciences. It can be beneficial to the environmental and earth sciences, physical sciences such as chemistry, and life sciences.

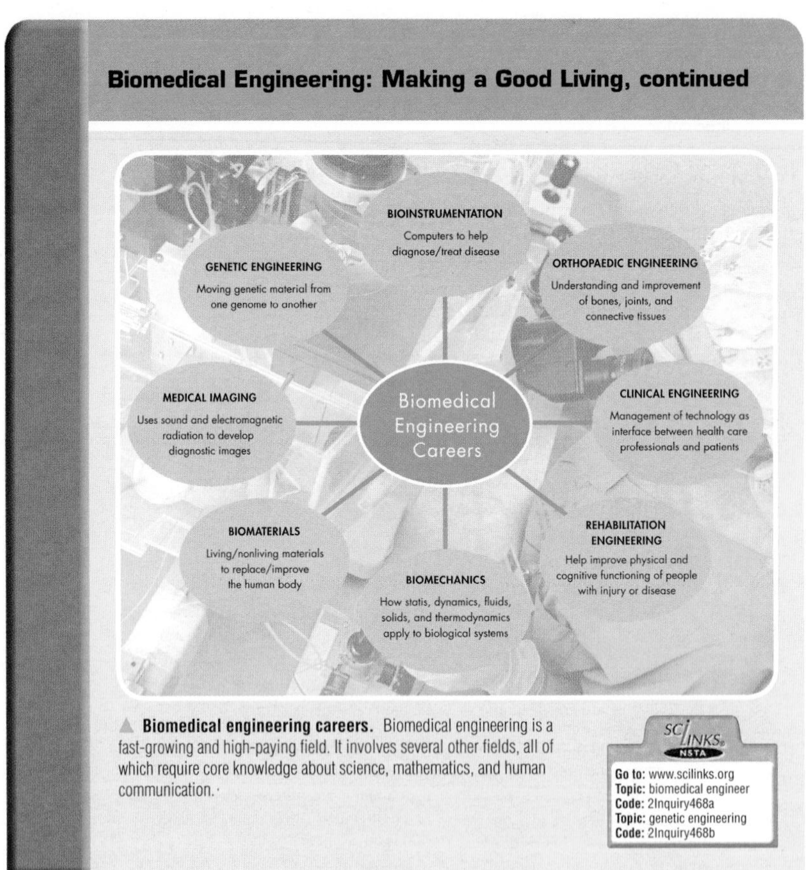
Biomedical Engineering: Making a Good Living, continued

▲ **Biomedical engineering careers.** Biomedical engineering is a fast-growing and high-paying field. It involves several other fields, all of which require core knowledge about science, mathematics, and human communication.

SciLinks NSTA
Go to: www.scilinks.org
Topic: biomedical engineer
Code: 2Inquiry468a
Topic: genetic engineering
Code: 2Inquiry468b

ELABORATE

Biotechnology and Society

When certain needs arise, sometimes we can address those needs through advances in science and technology. Indeed, the need to solve problems is a major incentive for advances in science—and especially in technology. Through technology, humans adapt the natural world to suit themselves and their needs. This is true for both individuals and for societies. Across time, technology leads to changes in our culture.

468 | Unit 2 Inside Life

Part II—Bioethics

Ethics play a major role in science as well as in society. For example, laws, policies, and rules are all based on ethics. *Bioethics* refers to ethics in a biological context. It is not new, but continues to evolve with the advancement of biotechnology. Some people believe we should not tinker with genetics at all; others feel that genetic engineering is simply an expansion of selective breeding that helps our society.

The activity in Part II is designed to help students understand that there are multiple factors to consider when a proposed solution involves ethical issues.

Materials—Part I

For the class

access to the Web
other resources as needed
1 blank overhead transparency (optional)
overhead projector (optional)
Genetic Engineering in California Agriculture video on the *SRCD*

SRCD

Materials—Part II

For each team of 2 students

ruler

Advance Preparation

You may provide extra resources for students to use to research applications of genetic engineering. Internet access is suggested, but students can use alternatives, such as science journals and newspaper articles.

As You Teach

Outcomes and Indicators of Success

By the end of this activity, students should

1. understand different applications of genetic engineering.

   They will demonstrate their understanding by

   - discussing examples of different genetic engineering applications,
   - researching additional examples of genetic engineering applications, and
   - answering questions related to these applications.

2. understand that if there is a need, science tries to solve it.

   They will show their understanding by

   - discussing problems or issues that genetic engineering applications may attempt to address and
   - relating examples of genetic engineering applications to the specific need they address.

3. understand that science is a naturally integrating discipline.

   They will demonstrate their understanding by

   - providing examples of applications addressed by genetic engineering and
   - connecting these examples to different disciplines in science.

4. understand how to use a decision-making model to propose a solution.

   They will demonstrate their understanding by

   - using a decision-making model focused on bioethics,
   - completing a chart of major steps involved in a decision-making model, and
   - proposing a reasonable solution to an ethical question.

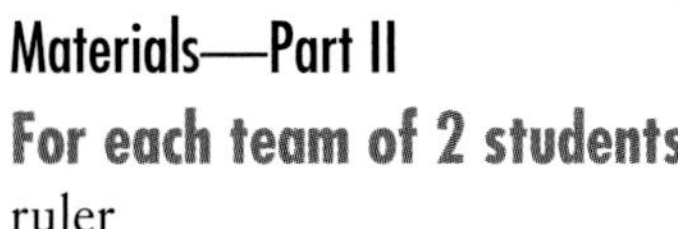

When a solution involves technology *and* living organisms, we call it **biotechnology**. Recombinant DNA technology has created many new forms of biotechnology. Read the sidebar *Biotechnology in the Fields* to learn about one biotechnology that is helping cotton farmers. Because we have the ability to manipulate genes, and genes produce proteins, we can solve many problems.

As you know from your work in chapter 8, proteins are complex molecules found in all living things. As important as DNA and genes are, proteins (figure 9.11) are where the action is. They have many amazing functions, such as breaking down what we eat, moving muscle, and transporting molecules. Proteins keep certain bacteria alive at the depths of the oceans and at the far reaches of the Arctic. Proteins cause some insects to secrete unusual chemicals, give animals their color, and cause fireflies to glow. Enzymes are a type of protein that speeds up chemical reactions in organisms.

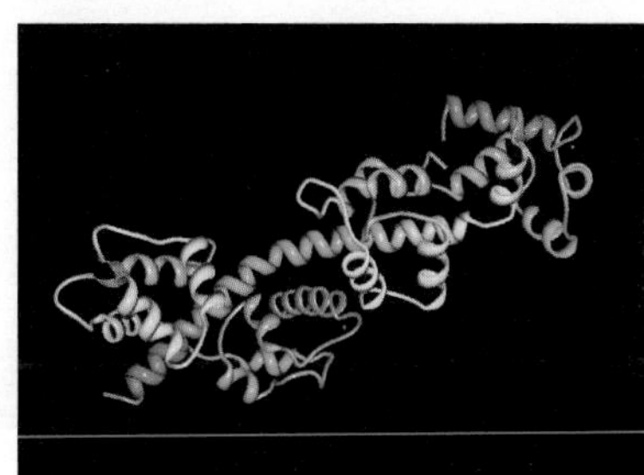

▲ **Figure 9.11 Model of a protein molecule.** Proteins such as this one control many functions of life.

In *Part I—Meeting a Need*, you will learn about some examples of biotechnology. Then, in *Part II—Bioethics*, you will learn about the ethical dilemmas that biotechnology raises.

Part I: Meeting a Need

Earlier in this chapter, you learned that, through recombinant DNA technology, a scientist can incorporate a gene directly into an organism. That gene is expressed so that an organism produces a desired protein. As scientists learned more about how genetic engineering could help us in medicine and agriculture, they began to wonder if genetic engineering could help humans in other ways as well. Could we genetically engineer a bacterium that breaks down oil and withstands

5. Begin to understand the role of ethics in science.

   They will demonstrate their understanding by

   - determining the ethics involved in two scenarios and
   - comparing ethical analysis with scientific analysis.

Strategies

Getting Started

Ask the students to read the opening paragraphs of the activity and of *Part I—Meeting a Need.* Students could also take turns reading the paragraphs aloud.

Process and Procedure

Materials—Part I

For the class

access to the Web

other resources as needed

1 blank overhead transparency (optional)

overhead projector (optional)

Genetic Engineering in California Agriculture video on the *SRCD*

In Step 1, ask the class to generate a list of issues that it thinks individuals, society, and our world face. Record the issues on the board or on an overhead transparency so that the entire class can see them. Issues might include air pollution, ocean pollution, water pollution, energy shortages, global warming, depletion of the ozone layer, shortage of food in some areas, and poverty.

In Step 2, students read about 4 unusual applications of genetic engineering and fill in a table to organize the information. In *No More Toxic Dump Sites*, students read about bioremediation and transgenic organisms. In *Genetically Engineered Blue Jeans*, students read about a gene that codes for an enzyme that converts the nutrient indole into indigo. In *Gold Rush*, students learn that genetic engineering can even be applied to mining. Bacterial strains are being developed to mine minerals for us. *A Cleaner Way* explains how recombinant DNA technology enables researchers to find and use genes that produce enzymes commonly used in detergents.

Step 3 asks students to return to the list of challenges and problems they created in Step 1. Based on their new knowledge from the reading, ask students to revisit the list to find additional problems that could be solved by genetic engineering. Students will draw a rectangle around these issues.

In Step 4, students spend some time researching other applications of genetic engineering. Encourage students to look for examples across the science disciplines. Consider using search words such as *genetic engineering* in a favorite search engine. If your students need help in conducting Web searches, use the How To,

How To Conduct an Effective Web Search at the back of their book. If your classroom does not have Web access, you could print some articles from various Web sites and have them available to students.

Instruct students to describe in their notebooks 2 uses of biotechnology that take advantage of genetic engineering techniques. Then ask them to answer the *Stop and Think* questions in their notebook.

---

salt water? Could we then release this new kind of bacterium to "eat" oil spills? If we could accomplish this, could we go further? Could we genetically engineer organisms to produce detergents? The applications of recombinant DNA technology in genetic engineering are only limited by our current understanding of science and technology and our imagination. What does the future hold?

Materials

For each class

access to the Web

other resources as needed

Process and Procedure

1. As a class, conduct a brainstorming session on some challenges or problems that we face in our lives, in our society, and in our world. Choose one classmate to write down the ideas. Circle the ones you think could be addressed using genetic engineering techniques.
2. Copy the table from figure 9.12 into your science notebook and fill it out as you read about 4 applications of genetic engineering. As you read each example, focus on this question, "How has genetic engineering solved this problem?"

Name of organism(s) involved	Description of problem	How genetic engineering solved problem

▲ **Figure 9.12 Genetic engineering table.** Use this table to organize the information about 4 applications of genetic engineering.

NOTES:

No More Toxic Dump Sites

Every living organism ingests nutrients and produces a waste by-product as a result. Certain bacteria thrive on the chemical components of waste products ("one person's trash is another's treasure"). Their metabolic process converts these hazardous or unwanted materials into less harmful products. The use of microorganisms to degrade waste is called **bioremediation.**

Some examples of bioremediation include organisms that feed on hydrocarbons (oil), methylene chloride (a toxic waste product), detergents, and sulfur. Many of these organisms exist naturally, but new advances in the use of transgenic organisms (those that have been genetically modified) are allowing science to genetically engineer custom-made microbes to perform the duties of digesting unwanted waste. Oil spills may be cleaned up using these microbes.

Transgenic microorganisms have been developed that contain genes for bioluminescence (glowing), coupled with a gene for waste degradation. These microorganisms glow when they are working, and stop glowing when they are done. This indicates when the waste is completely removed. Scientists can monitor the amount of light emitted and determine how much biodegradation is occurring.

Bacteria have been discovered that can live in an environment of very high radiation. *Deinococcus radiodurans* (figure 9.13) has the ability to repair damage within its DNA that is caused by radiation. Scientists are working toward genetically engineering other microorganisms to clean up radioactive waste sites using what they have learned about *Deinococcus radiodurans.*

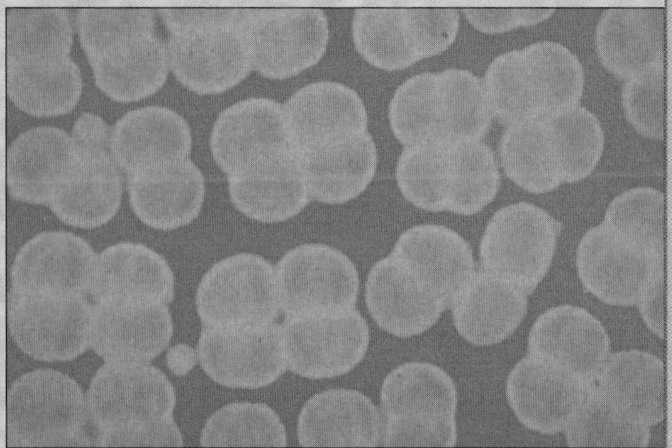

Figure 9.13 *Deinococcus radiodurans.* This bacterium can live in an environment of very high radiation. *D. radiodurans* has the ability to repair damage within its own DNA caused by radiation. Could this trait be genetically engineered to clean up the environment damaged by nuclear wastes?

Chapter 9 Genetic Engineering 471

NOTES:

Genetically Engineered Blue Jeans

Figure 9.14 **Blue jeans.** Could cotton plants be genetically engineered to contain the gene to produce the blue pigment indigo?

A scientist named David Gibson was working with a strain of *E. coli* that could eat hydrocarbons. One day he noticed that the bacterial spots in his petri dishes had turned a brilliant blue. Looking back over his notes, he realized that those were the particular microbes to which he had just added a new gene. The gene he added coded for an enzyme called toluene dioxygenase. He analyzed the blue pigment and reasoned that the color had been produced when the enzyme converted a simple nutrient called indole into indigo. Indigo is the world's largest selling dye and the one that makes blue jeans blue. Presently, indigo is produced chemically, and the process generates toxic by-products. If bacteria could be genetically engineered to produce indigo, the result could be a more environmentally friendly pair of pants (see figure 9.14).

Gold Rush

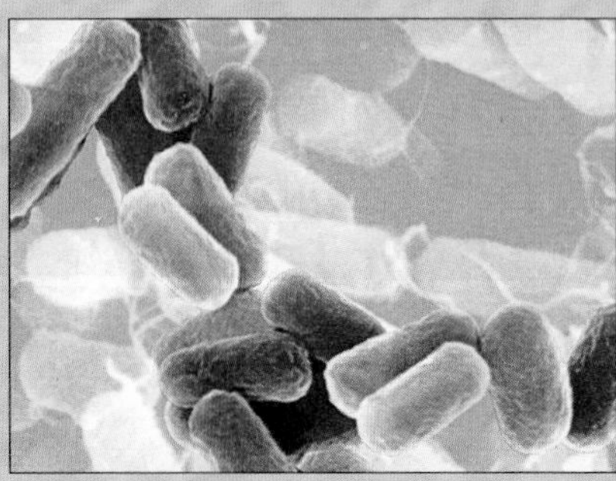

Figure 9.15 **Thiobacillus ferooxidans.** This bacterium can "chew up" copper ore, releasing pure copper that is collected in solution.

Mining is a process that is expensive and time consuming, and it causes a lot of pollution. Efforts are underway to genetically engineer microbes to mine needed minerals. The bacterial strains must be able to withstand heavy metals (such as mercury, cadmium, and arsenic). These microbes must also be able to extract needed minerals from earth. Some naturally occurring bacteria, such as *Thiobacillus ferooxidans* (figure 9.15), "chew up" ore, and copper is released and collected in solution. Scientists are studying how microorganisms can be genetically engineered to withstand heavy metals while leaching out desired minerals.

NOTES:

A Cleaner Way

Most laundry detergents and stain removers contain enzymes (figure 9.16). Enzymes are proteins that help to facilitate processes that occur in organisms. Why are enzymes in laundry detergents? One of the things that enzymes can do is break down proteins. Your digestive system produces many enzymes to break down the food you eat. The enzymes break down the food into basic building blocks that your body uses to build tissue.

Many of the stains that end up on your clothing contain proteins. Some examples of stains that contain proteins are blood, food, grass, and perspiration. The manufacturers of laundry detergents have been using enzymes in their products for many years. These enzymes have traditionally been chemically (synthetically) produced. With recombinant DNA technology, researchers can now find organisms that have genes that naturally produce a desired enzyme. Each gene produces a specific enzyme. One enzyme might break down blood, while another enzyme (possibly from a different organism) breaks down grass stains. These genes can then be spliced into microbes, causing them to produce enzymes that break down a variety of stains. The enzymes can then be added to detergents. Genetic engineering techniques used for producing laundry detergents may be more efficient and environmentally friendly than synthetic detergents.

▲ **Figure 9.16 Stain removers in detergents.** Why are enzymes in laundry detergents?

Chapter 9 Genetic Engineering 473

NOTES:

Answers to Stop and Think—Part I, SE page 474

1. In many cases, making a product synthetically produces toxic by-products or is very expensive. Also, the product (which is usually a protein of some sort) might only be produced in small quantities if made synthetically. Biotechnology allows us to produce a desired protein in large amounts and usually less expensively.
2. Using microorganisms to mine minerals reduces the amount of pollution emitted by standard mining procedures. It might also be less expensive and save time. Using microorganisms to mine minerals would also be less intrusive to the surrounding environment. Disadvantages include that the microorganisms may not be efficient, they have to be kept alive, and they could mutate.
3. Introducing genetically engineered microorganisms to the environment may have unforeseen consequences relating to population (theirs and the population of organisms around them), the evolution of a "new species," or effects on the environment that we cannot predict. Students may come up with other possible consequences or problems for these applications.
4. **Student answers will vary but should include new knowledge from the video.**

3. Look back at your original list from Step 1 of some challenges and problems that humans face. Which items on the list did you think genetic engineering could address? Now that you have read about these unique applications, is there anything new you would like to add to the list? Discuss your ideas and add them to your list. Then draw a rectangle around needs that you *now* think could be addressed by the use of genetic engineering.
4. The genetic engineering applications in these readings are just a few of the ones scientists are working on. The field of biotechnology is growing rapidly. Using the Web, research other applications of biotechnology. In your science notebook, describe 2 uses of biotechnology that take advantage of genetic engineering techniques.

Stop & THINK

PART I

Answer the following questions in your science notebook. Remember to incorporate other classmates' viewpoints into your learning.

1. Why would we want to use biotechnology to make a product instead of making it in a laboratory?
2. What would be some advantages and disadvantages to having microorganisms mine minerals for us?
3. How might these applications of biotechnology, which are being used to solve problems, create new problems? Explain your answer.
4. View the video, *Genetic Engineering in California Agriculture* on the SRCD. Record at least 2 new things you learned about genetic engineering.

NOTES:

Biotechnology in the Fields

SIDEBAR

You have learned that it is possible for scientists to remove genes from one organism and introduce them into an unrelated organism. The new DNA formed through that process is called recombinant DNA. One example of how scientists are using recombinant DNA technology to address a practical problem involves the cotton plant. A pest called a bollworm attacks cotton plants often (see photo). This pest damages cotton crops and costs millions of dollars each year to control. Researchers, however, have known for a long time that a bollworm will die if it eats the common bacterium *Bacillus thuringiensis* (*B.t.* for short). A protein that the bacterium produces is partially digested in the worm's gut and poisons the worm. Because that protein is so effective, for years farmers have sprayed *B.t.* bacteria on their cotton crops to discourage the bollworms from eating them. That protective measure has its drawbacks, though. Sunlight breaks down *B.t.*, and rainfall easily washes it off the plants.

Through genetic engineering, however, researchers have overcome those drawbacks. The figure on the next page shows how scientists can manipulate the DNA of a cotton plant. The new genetically engineered cotton plants (GE cotton) contain recombinant DNA. The GE cotton plants produce a bacterial protein, *B.t.* toxin, in their leaves. In other words, they are engineered to protect themselves from bollworms. When a bollworm begins nibbling on the leaves, it eats the *B.t.* protein and dies. In addition to cotton, food crop plants can be engineered to produce the *B.t.* protein because it is not toxic to humans.

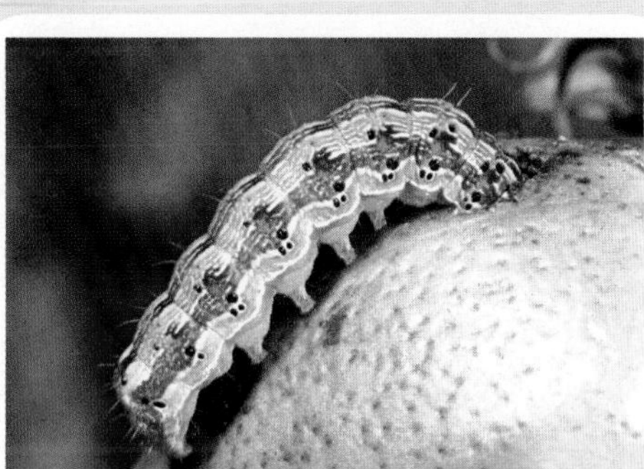

▲ **Bollworm attacking cotton boll.** This pest of cotton plants can be controlled with pesticides or with genetically engineered cotton. What are the advantages and disadvantages to each method?

A benefit of such technology is that farmers can use less insecticide, decreasing the amount of toxic chemicals that enter the water supply and food web. The new technology, however, has not been completely effective. Farmers using the engineered cotton in 1996 reported that many bollworms survived in the new crop. Additional pesticides had to be applied, though the total amount was reduced. The surviving bollworms raise concerns about what prolonged exposure to *B.t.* may do to the bollworm's resistance to the bacterium's toxicity. There also are concerns for the

NOTES:

Biotechnology in the Fields, continued

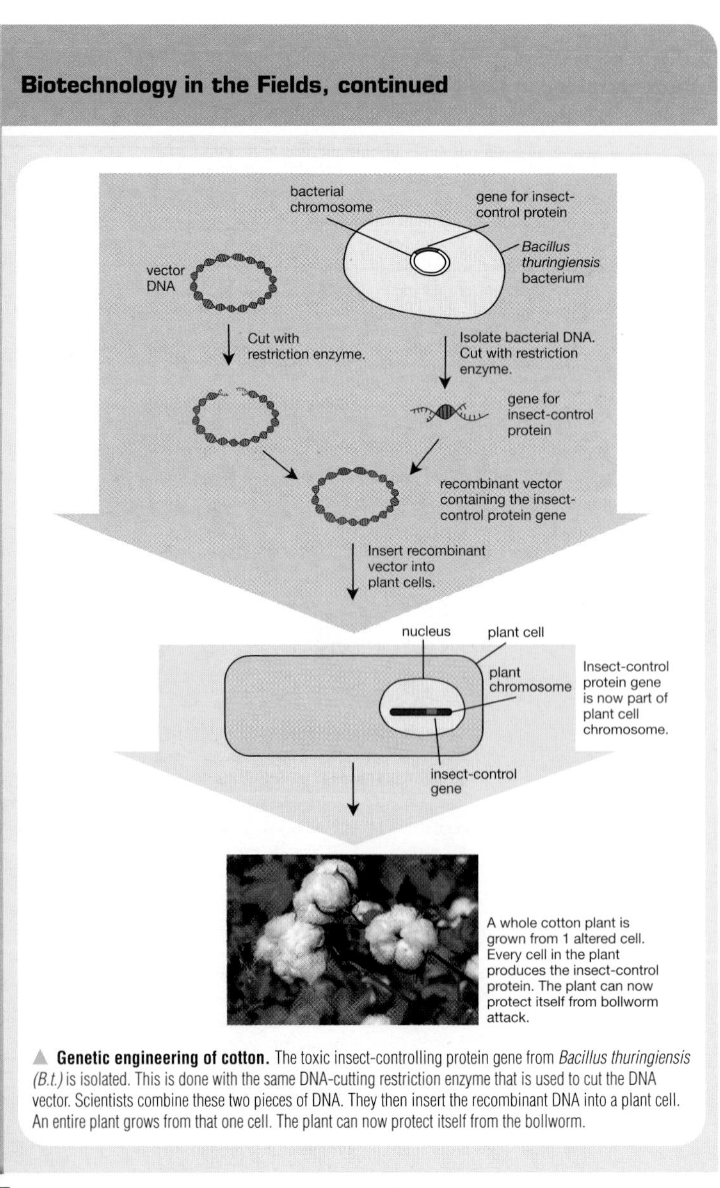

▲ **Genetic engineering of cotton.** The toxic insect-controlling protein gene from *Bacillus thuringiensis (B.t.)* is isolated. This is done with the same DNA-cutting restriction enzyme that is used to cut the DNA vector. Scientists combine these two pieces of DNA. They then insert the recombinant DNA into a plant cell. An entire plant grows from that one cell. The plant can now protect itself from the bollworm.

NOTES:

other organisms that encounter *B.t.* through this technique. Though current tests show that the *B.t.* toxin is nontoxic for most animals, including many beneficial insects, it has the potential to harm endangered and threatened species of moths and butterflies.

GE cotton represents 21 percent of the total cotton planted globally. Since its introduction in 1996, cotton has been one of the lead crops to be genetically engineered, and GE cotton has been one of the most rapidly adopted technologies ever. Varieties of GE cotton with multiple traits are now available. The current varieties that have commercial importance address crop management or agronomic traits that assist with pest management (Bt) or herbicide tolerance (HT). Although insect resistance and herbicide tolerance are the only traits currently available in biotech cottons, a broad range of other traits is under development using modern biotechnology. These may directly affect agronomic performance, stress tolerance, fiber quality, and yield potential.

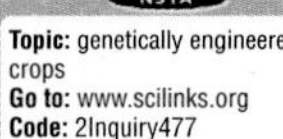

Topic: genetically engineered crops
Go to: www.scilinks.org
Code: 2Inquiry477

Part II: Bioethics

By now, you can see that biotechnology possibly could address many of the world's problems. But, with any new technology comes responsibility. Is there a danger that biotechnology can be used irresponsibly? What about ethics? Should we use biotechnology for every problem possible? **Ethics** refers to the morals of individuals and society. Morals are values and beliefs about what is acceptable behavior. An ethical question asks what "should" or "ought" to be done in a particular situation so that the values of society or the individuals involved are upheld while society and individual needs are met. **Bioethics** is the term we use when the ethical issue is raised by developments in life science technologies, such as new medical technologies.

In *Part II—Bioethics,* you will face an ethical dilemma. You will use a decision-making model to decide on the best solution, while taking into account all viewpoints.

Materials

For each team of 2 students

ruler

Part II—Bioethics

Pose an ethical question to the class such as, "Should people who ride motorcycles be required by law to wear helmets?" Allow students time for discussion. Listen to their responses and point out that there are several opinions. Take a quick class vote. Suggest that students look at the issue using a more structured approach.

Process and Procedure

Materials—Part II

For each team of 2 students

ruler

In Step 1, instruct students to read the introduction to *Part II—Bioethics* and study the description of the Bioethics Decision-Making Model. Discuss the model and its 6 steps with the class.

In Step 2, develop a table similar to figure 9.18 in the student book. Draw the table on the board, chart paper, or transparency. Ask students to construct the same table (with plenty of room to write) in their science notebook.

Students read about a bioethical issue in Step 3. The reading introduces the term *gene therapy*. Step 4 directs students to work with their teammate to discuss bioethical issue 1 and fill in their table. Instruct students to wait to fill out the last column until they have had the class discussion in Step 6.

In Step 5, discuss issue 1 with the class and instruct students to add information to their table based on new ideas posed by the class. Fill out the class table during the discussion. Based on the discussion in Step 6, students fill in the last column of the table.

Students read about bioethical issue 2 in Step 7. In Step 8, they complete the second row of the table for issue 2 individually. Have students then answer the *Reflect and Connect* questions and record their answers in their science notebook.

NOTES:

Process and Procedure

Work with a partner for this activity.

1. Study the following description of a decision-making model and discuss it with your class.

Bioethics Decision-Making Model

1. Define the ethical question being posed.

   Usually an ethical question contains a subjective opinion based on a particular cultural frame of reference. An example of an ethical question might be, "Should there be a law that requires motorcycle riders to wear helmets?" (see figure 9.17).

2. Identify the relevant facts of the case.

   Look at the case from all angles and generate a list of facts.

In the motorcycle helmet example, the facts would center on the numbers of deaths and injuries associated with motorcycle accidents, individual rights, and societal values.

▲ **Figure 9.17 Motorcycle riders and helmets.** Should there be a law that requires motorcycle riders to wear helmets?

3. Identify the stakeholders.

   Stakeholders are individuals, organizations, or other entities that are directly affected by the outcome or decision. Stakeholders sometimes can be difficult to identify because individuals whose opinions cannot be heard (such as infants, animals, and those with minority opinions) may be stakeholders.

In our example, some of the stakeholders are motorcycle riders, insurance companies, and police officers.

4. Address the moral values of society that apply to the case.

   These can include a wide variety of qualities, such as fairness to the various shareholders, privacy, freedom of choice, respect for life or property, religious beliefs, political orientation, and cultural values.

In the motorcycle helmet example, our society's value of human life is weighed against the individual right to choose whether or not to wear a helmet.

5. Consider all of the possible solutions to the dilemma.

   Reflect on possible solutions from multiple perspectives. Consider different points of view—ones contrary to your own.

6. Choose the best possible solution.

   In this final step, a decision is made based on the previous steps. The decision takes into account the facts, the stakeholders, and the moral values of those represented as stakeholders.

NOTES:

2. Draw a table in your notebook that looks like figure 9.18. Make the blank boxes large and leave plenty of room to write under each heading.

	Define the ethical question.	List the relevant facts of the case.	Identify the stakeholders in the case.	Identify the values that play a role in this case.	List several possible solutions to resolve the conflict.	Choose an acceptable solution(s) and justify.
Issue #1						
Issue #2						

▲ **Figure 9.18 Decision-making table for ethical questions.** How can you use this table to organize difficult decisions involving ethics?

3. Read *Bioethical Issue 1*.
4. With your teammate, fill in the table you drew in your notebook for *Bioethical Issue 1* by following the 6 steps of the decision-making model.
5. Participate in a class discussion of ideas for each step of the model and fill in a table for the class as a whole.
6. Following the class discussion, fill in the last column of your table.
7. Read *Bioethical Issue 2*.
8. Fill out the second row of your table individually.

NOTES:

Bioethical Issue 1

Some people do not produce enough growth-hormone (figure 9.19). The deficiency causes them to be significantly shorter than the average person. Doctors used to treat the deficiency with a growth hormone extracted from cadavers shortly after death. This technique worked, but there was a short supply of the growth hormone. Today recombinant DNA techniques enable us to propagate bacteria that produce enough of the growth hormone to supply doctors with the hormone for the individuals who need it. Eventually, we may be able to insert the gene for growth hormone into individuals who have the deficiency, allowing them to produce the growth hormone in their cells. Such a procedure would be a type of **gene therapy**. Gene therapy is the insertion of normal or genetically altered genes into cells as part of the treatment of disorders that have a genetic component. What if other people (without the deficiency), such as athletes who want to be taller, want to use the growth hormone? Should they be allowed to use the hormone therapy?

▲ **Figure 9.19 Growth-hormone deficiency.** Growth-hormone deficiency causes individuals to be shorter than the average person. Recombinant DNA techniques may be able to provide gene therapy for sufferers of this disorder. Should everyone be allowed to use this hormone therapy?

480 Unit 2 Inside Life

NOTES:

BIOETHICAL ISSUE 2

Genetic engineering is used quite extensively in agriculture. Crops can be genetically engineered to be resistant to drought or frost. Plants can even be engineered to produce their own pesticide (figure 9.20). People have a variety of opinions about genetically engineered foods. One concern is that some people might have an allergy to a new protein. If people eat food that has the new protein, they may have an allergic reaction. Some people think that if a crop is only used for livestock consumption, it is acceptable to genetically engineer it. Others feel that allergies happen no matter what and that genetic engineering is no different from what happens in nature. Some people say that all genetically modified foods should be labeled. Still others believe that genetic engineering should not be conducted at all. Some farmers say genetic engineering saves crops and money and that using genetic engineering technology is better than spraying crops with toxic substances. Others feel that, because we can't control genetically engineered crops from crossing with crops that aren't engineered, we shouldn't plant them at all. What do you say?

▲ **Figure 9.20 Cotton field.** Genetically engineered cotton is developed to produce higher yields and reduce the use of pesticides and herbicides.

Chapter 9 Genetic Engineering 481

NOTES:

Answers to Reflect and Connect, SE page 482

1. People have different opinions, religious beliefs, values, and past experiences.
2. Students will answer with a variety of situations. Students may use the motorcycle helmet example. Individuals feel that they have a right to do what they want when they ride a motorcycle, but society wants to keep people safe.
3. Answers will vary. Students might agree that a life-saving procedure is a necessity, whereas a cosmetic improvement is a non-necessity.
4. Both scientific analysis and ethical analysis use a system of checks and balances to defend explanations. Scientific analysis, however, is based on evidence, not opinion. Opinions and beliefs play a large role in ethical analysis.

Reflect and Connect

Answer the following questions in your science notebook. Don't forget how valuable it is to check with your teacher or classmates regarding your answers.

1. Why might different people come up with different biotechnology solutions to the same problem?
2. Give an example of a conflict between an individual's desire and the morals of society.
3. Is there a way to distinguish between which biotechnology solutions are needed and which are not?
4. How is the process of ethical analysis related to scientific analysis? How is it different?

SCLINKS NSTA
Go to: www.scilinks.org
Topic: bioethics
Code: 2Inquiry482a
Topic: gene therapy
Code: 2Inquiry482b

EVALUATE

Can It Be Done? Should It Be Done?

Throughout this chapter, you have explored many aspects of biotechnology. We now have the technology to treat genetic disorders, increase agricultural yields, clean up environmental pollution, and even change the way we obtain valued resources. Because of existing biotechnology, our society also faces many individual, social, ethical, and legal questions.

Imagine a societal problem that biotechnology could solve. Or imagine a unique biotechnology application that you would like to see implemented. The genetic engineering application that you propose could solve a problem or change a current situation.

In *Can It Be Done? Should It Be Done?*, you will work as a team to propose a new biotechnology application. You will have an opportunity to present your idea to the Genetic Engineering Advisory Board (GEAB) for review (figure 9.21). In doing so, you will demonstrate your understanding of the concepts in this chapter. The class will represent the GEAB and hear your presentation, review your proposal, and determine whether or not it should be implemented. The GEAB will vote on whether it can be done and whether it should be done.

Materials

For each team of 4 students

resource materials or access to the Web

poster paper

markers

4 *Can It Be Done? Should It Be Done? Scoring Rubric* handouts

other materials as needed for presentation

EVALUATE

Can It Be Done? Should It Be Done?

Activity Overview

Students form teams of 4, and each student on the team assumes a role in order to address bioethical questions. The teams present their findings to the class, which plays the role of the Genetic Engineering Advisory Board (GEAB), and field questions from the board.

This final activity allows you to assess student understanding of DNA from an evolutionary standpoint all the way to the molecular level. Use copymaster 9.9, *Scoring Rubric for Can It Be Done? Should It Be Done?* to assess student projects for team as well as individual grades. Student presentations will allow you to assess their true understanding of the role of DNA, implications of implementing new technologies, and connections across the disciplines. Listen to the class dialogue, questions, and reasons for voting on certain technologies to help you determine their level of understanding of these major topics.

Before You Teach

Background Information

Can It Be Done? Should It Be Done? is designed to tie together many major concepts. In the previous chapters, students learned about evolution, heredity, and DNA. In this evaluate activity, students will apply that knowledge, along with their newly acquired knowledge of genetic engineering, to propose a new genetic engineering feat that ideally could be used within the physical sciences, earth sciences, or environmental sciences.

Students will also have learned that, with the introduction of new technologies, social and ethical questions arise. In their presentations, students will address potential concerns or propose alternatives. In this assessment, students think about what can be done using genetic engineering and whether it should be done.

Materials

For each team of 4 students

resource materials or access to the Web
poster paper
markers
magazines
scissors
4 copies of copymaster 9.9, *Scoring Rubric for Can It Be Done? Should It Be Done?*

other materials as needed for presentation

Advance Preparation

Gather the materials for each team. In addition to poster paper and markers, supply teams with magazines (to cut pictures from) and scissors. Make 4 copies of copymaster 9.9, *Scoring Rubric for Can It Be Done? Should It Be Done?* for each team. Arrange access to the Web, if possible.

Educational Technologies

Students may want to make a computer presentation. Have appropriate projectors, software, and computer equipment available if you are going to allow this option.

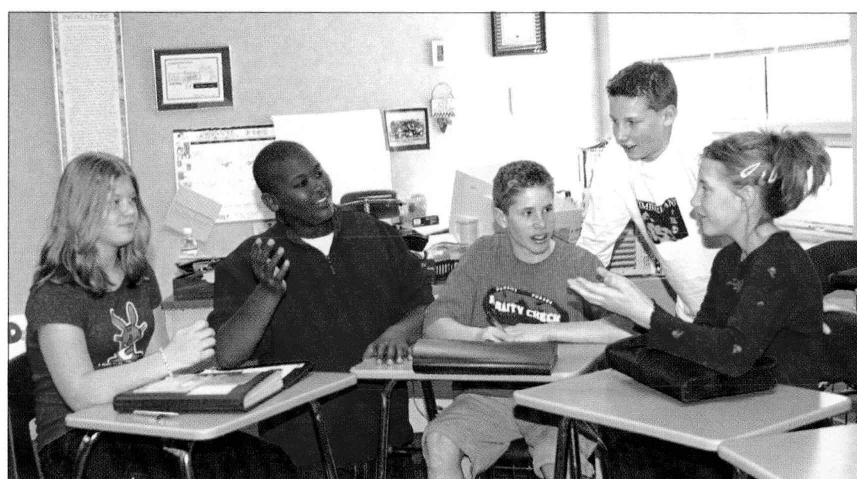

▲ **Figure 9.21 GEAB meeting.** You will have the opportunity to present your ideas for biotechnology to the Genetic Engineering Advisory Board. What do you need to do to prepare for your presentation?

Process and Procedure

1. Read through the entire activity before you begin, and study the scoring rubric your teacher distributes.
2. Form a team of 4 and work through Steps 2a–d.
   a. Discuss some current issues with your team that could someday be addressed using biotechnology. Think about issues that may help individuals or society as a whole or that are just something unique to do.
   b. Imagine you could change anything genetically. What would it be? Could it be done? Should it be done?
   c. Decide on 1 genetic engineering application that addresses a need and that you would like to exist.
   d. Be sure that the application you choose does not already exist. Conduct some research in the library or on the Web to find out.

As You Teach

Outcomes and Indicators of Success

By the end of this activity, students should

1. know that DNA is the basis for heredity.

   They will demonstrate their knowledge by

   - proposing a genetic engineering scenario and
   - describing and justifying a method of transferring genes from one organism to another.

2. understand that science and technology can indicate what can happen but not what should happen.

   They will demonstrate their understanding by

   - proposing a genetic engineering scenario,
   - voting on proposed genetic engineering technologies and justifying their votes, and
   - applying an ethics model to a proposed genetic engineering application.

3. understand that basic concepts and principles of science and technology should precede active debate about the consequences of these technologies.

   They will demonstrate their understanding by

   - presenting a proposed genetic engineering feat to the class and
   - discussing reasons for implementing or choosing not to implement hypothetical genetic engineering feats.

4. become aware that new technologies often extend the current levels of scientific understanding.

   They will demonstrate their awareness by proposing a hypothetical but possibly realistic genetic engineering feat.

5. understand that genetic engineering technologies can be applied to other disciplines.

   They will demonstrate their understanding by

   - describing how genetic engineering spans science disciplines and
   - applying a hypothetical genetic engineering feat to a discipline other than biology.

Strategies

Getting Started

Remind the class that, as it learned in Part I of the activity *Biotechnology and Society*, scientists are using genetic engineering applications in very creative ways. Ask students about the unique applications they discovered when they read about genetic engineering in that activity. Discuss that new discoveries and applications are made daily. They will now get a chance to be creative with genetic engineering. Remind the class of the brainstorming session in *Part I—Meeting a Need* about issues the world faces and how genetic engineering may address some of them. Then ask students to think about individual needs or wants and about some unique situations in which we could use genetic engineering.

Introduce *Can It Be Done? Should It Be Done?* by telling students that they are going to form a company to design a genetic engineering technique that will fill a need in our society. This technology does not exist currently, but possibly could. Encourage students to think of a technology that can be applied outside of the field

3. As a team, discuss Questions 3a–f, and record your best answers in your science notebook.
   a. Is this biotechnology a necessity or only for those with lots of money?
   b. Why would you want this to happen? What is the need that you are addressing?
   c. How could you implement your plan? Include in your plan, what organisms it involves, what techniques it involves, and at what level it takes place (for example, body cell, gamete cell, plasmid, or chromosome).
   d. Who are the stakeholders? Why are they the stakeholders?
   e. Summarize why and how you would implement this technology.
   f. Could this technology have other applications? Describe some of them.
4. Assign each person on your team a role in preparing the presentation to the GEAB. Discuss the following roles and establish who will take which role.
   - *Genetic engineer.* Genetic engineers are the technicians that manipulate the DNA of an organism with tools such as recombinant DNA technology. In this case, the genetic engineer proposes how the technology could be implemented.
   - *Evolutionary biologist.* The evolutionary biologist concentrates efforts on the evolutionary consequences of using this technology.
   - *Marketing or public educator.* The public educator communicates with the GEAB about the risks and benefits to both society and individuals that are associated with the use of the technology.
   - *Ethicist.* The ethicist focuses on the moral and ethical considerations of implementing the technology.
5. Each team member works on his or her own part of the presentation, following Steps 5a–d. Be ready to contribute to the team's presentation.
   a. Genetic engineer
      - Describe the technique that you will use to implement your plan. In your description, include the vectors involved.

of biology, such as in the physical, chemical, or earth sciences. You may even want to require students to gear the assignment toward a more integrated approach.

Process and Procedure

In Step 1, have students get into teams of 4 and read the introduction and assignment. Discuss the assignment with the class and hand out copies of the scoring rubric. If students have trouble understanding any of the items on the rubric, refer them to Steps 3 and 5.

In Step 2, encourage students to refer back to the brainstorm list of issues and to think of new issues that could be addressed with biotechnology. Each team will select 1 issue and a corresponding biotechnology. Allow time and resources for teams to verify that the biotechnology they have chosen does not already exist.

Suggest that students decide what they want to "do" first, and then research an organism that may help them. For example, if a team wants to genetically engineer an organism to break down glass back into sand, they would need to determine if there is a gene out there, who has it, how they will get it, and where they will put it. You should encourage students to be creative but reasonable.

Read Step 3 aloud; make sure the class is clear about the assignment.

Suggest that they research existing genetic engineering applications to help provide ideas for their hypothetical situations. Applications change all the time, so the Web may be the most current source of information.

You may need to help students select their roles (genetic engineer, evolutionary biologist, marketing/public educator, and ethicist) in Step 4. You can let the team members choose their roles or assign students to specific roles. If teams consist of more than 4 students, assign extra roles such as chemist, earth scientist, or environmentalist. Students in these roles could research the physical science behind the technology. For teams of 3, you could eliminate the marketing/public educator role or, if the selected biotechnology does not change major organisms, you could eliminate the evolutionary biologist. The evolutionary biologist has the most difficult task, so you may want to encourage your stronger students to take this role.

In Step 5, students work individually on their part of their team's presentation. The evolutionary biologists may need some extra help. This activity can be modified for students with lesser abilities. Allow them to be more general about how they would go about genetically engineering an organism. Students who relish a challenge could become very involved with researching specific organisms that contain the gene they want. Most microbial genomes are mapped; some plant and animal genomes have also been mapped, and information about them is available on the Web.

- Describe current technology that is similar to your technique. Discuss problems that you would need to overcome in order to get the technology to work. What roadblocks may prevent you from implementing this technology?
- Describe possible side effects to organisms and any problems associated with using the technology. Consider the recipient organism, provider organism, and any other organisms involved in transmission.
- Write a step-by-step sequence of what you will do to implement your plan.
- Draw and label a graphic showing how your team would implement your plan.

b. Evolutionary biologist
   - List all organisms that would specifically be involved. Include their genus and species.
   - Explain how this technology could help an organism adapt to its environment.
   - Predict how overuse of this technology could affect an entire population of organisms. Consider life span, variations, and survival rates.
   - Explain how using this technology could have an effect on natural selection. Provide a scenario by drawing a diagram.
   - Describe how implementing this technology could affect the population of organisms that you are working with. Also, describe how your plan could affect the populations of two other organisms.
   - Describe how using this technology could affect the gene frequency distribution in either the recipient populations of organisms or the vector.

c. Marketing or public educator
   - Describe how this technology will help both the individual and society. Discuss the major benefits of using this technology.
   - Describe the current model of genetic engineering that the technique is most like.
   - Provide other examples of how society is currently using this same type of technology.
   - Describe the successes, drawbacks, and milestones that this type of biotechnology has had in real life.

NOTES:

In Step 6, students work together to prepare their team presentations. Encourage them to be creative. They might want to refer to previous activities for guidance. Ask, "What do you want to accomplish? How will you go about accomplishing it?"

In Step 7, students review the scoring rubric and write down questions in preparation for the team presentations. Each team then presents its genetic engineering feat to the GEAB. Remind teams that they are trying to sell their idea to the board. Encourage the board to ask questions. As each team presents, the board members (other students) complete a rubric for the presentation (Step 8).

Take a board vote following each team's presentation. Board members vote whether or not to approve the company's application. Ask board members why they voted for or against a particular application.

- Describe how using this technology may affect economics or politics.
- Discuss who would favor the use of this technology and why.
- Draw a logo that represents your team's proposed technology.

d. Ethicist
- Would using this technology change life as we know it?
- Describe possible negative consequences of using the technology. Consider the recipient species, transport (vector) species, other species, and the environment.
- Who might object (morally, ethically, religiously) to implementing this technology and why? Consider religions, cultures, human rights groups, animal rights groups, others.
- Discuss some reasonable alternatives to using this technology that may provide a compromise to some people who may object.
- Discuss how money would play a role in the use of this technology. Who would pay for it?
- Prepare a chart that shows both sides of this issue.

6. After team members have completed their assigned parts, get together to prepare your final presentation. Assemble the graphics into an organized format, such as a poster, and prepare your discussion. You are going to present your proposal to the GEAB for their approval.
7. Prepare to give your classmates high-quality feedback on their presentations by following Steps 7a–c.
   a. Read the scoring rubric that your teacher gives you.
   b. Write in your notebook any questions you have about how to use the rubric while your classmates make their presentations.
   c. Ask your questions as part of a class discussion and write your answers in your notebook and hand it in to your teacher.

486 Unit 2 Inside Life

NOTES:

Reflect and Connect

Answer the following questions in your science notebook. Use an effective strategy to check your answers.

1. What criteria did you consider when evaluating a new biotechnology? For each proposal presented, decide whether you would want to see the technology implemented. Support your decision with at least 3 statements.
2. In your opinion, what was the most unique technology presented? Do you think this technology is possible? Explain your answer.
3. Describe how the topic of genetic engineering spans across science disciplines, such as physical science, earth science, and life science.

Answers to Reflect and Connect, SE page 487

1. Answers will vary, but should be specific to what students learned in this chapter and unit. Criteria may include ethics, feasibility, environmental effects, gene pool adjustments, setbacks, money, need, and by-products. For each team's presentation, students need to support their decision with 3 statements.
2. Answers will vary. Students should justify why they think the technology is or is not possible.
3. Genetic engineering spans the sciences in that it can be used to clean up the environment, make fuels, identify pollution, locate needed resources, remove salt from ocean water, break down substances, synthesize substances, make drugs, cure genetic disorders, and so on.

UNIT 3

Moving Matter

Unit Introduction

Unit Overview

In unit 3, *Moving Matter*, students explore how atoms that make up matter on Earth cycle and move among Earth's systems. Sometimes it's easy to see matter moving, such as in the water cycle with water flowing in a river or falling from the sky. At other times, the moving matter is very large, but difficult to visualize. Examples include currents in the oceans or even moving tectonic plates.

In this unit, students will consider moving matter in the water cycle, carbon cycle, ice ages, and plate tectonics. These all involve earth systems that operate on times scales from days to millions of years. The main concepts that apply to many fields are system, scale, and cycles. These are the concepts to ask your students about repeatedly.

Goals for the Unit

By the end of unit 3, students will understand better the following major concepts:

- Matter moves around Earth between reservoirs in geochemical cycles.
- Many kinds of technology help scientists measure moving matter in Earth's cycles.
- Geochemical cycles such as water, carbon, ice ages, and plate tectonics operate over timescales from days to millions of years.
- Geochemical cycles often involve reactions that change the chemical form and properties of the matter.
- Systems on Earth have reservoirs of matter, inputs and outputs, and fluxes of matter between those reservoirs.
- Carbon sinks in the geologic past are now valuable sources of fossil fuels and energy.
- Plate tectonics, mountain building, and erosion have slowly shaped the surface of Earth; many patterns of life on continents and in the oceans are linked to plate tectonics.

Students will see that scientists in all fields study how matter moves around Earth. They will study matter and how it moves around Earth.

Names of Chapters

Chapter 10: The Water System

Chapter 11: Carbon on the Move

Chapter 12: Evidence for the Ice Ages

Chapter 13: Time for Change

Strategies for the Unit Engage

The major concept in unit 3 is geochemical cycles and moving matter around Earth. Sometimes that movement, or cycling, is natural, such as with the water cycle or the rock cycle. At other times, humans can affect the cycling of matter, such as with increasing the content of carbon dioxide in the atmosphere. Students will investigate examples of these in the unit.

Several skills that students will use in the unit are introduced in the unit 3 engage activity, *Planning for the Worst in the West.* These skills include analysis of systems, design and problem solving related to natural resources, scale and change in systems, use and transport of natural resources, and geography. In the activity, students will discuss and debate three possible solutions for delivering more water to Southern California, which is hypothetically in the grips of a prolonged drought. It's a vexing problem, one likely to emerge in the future. This is a brief activity (no more than 45 minutes) designed to help students think about analyzing matter in earth systems.

ENGAGE

Planning for the Worst in the West

Materials

For the teacher

1 color transparency of copymaster 10.14, *Southwest North America*

Process and Procedure

1. Have 1 or 2 student volunteers read *The Worst of Water in the West* from the Teacher Edition. Write the 3 water delivery options on the board. This is the setup for solving the problem.

Use listening strategies for students who are not reading, such as recording information in their science notebooks. For example, ask them to write a sentence stating the "big idea" of the reading. Have them write their preferred solution with reasons before participating in the group discussion. Be open to ideas. Have volunteers use the transparency of copymaster 10.14, *Southwest North America* to point out cities and areas in the reading.

2. Show the transparency of the map of southwest North America. Ask volunteers to outline on the map options 1, 2, and 3 for routing water to Southern California.
3. Have students gather in teams of 3. Tell students that each team will analyze 1 or 2 of the options. The class goal is to recommend to water planners in Southern California which water delivery plan is the most beneficial.

Of course, a "beneficial" plan for Southern California might not be beneficial for other stakeholders. For example, digging a pipeline from Portland, Oregon, to Los Angeles, California, would be a massive engineering project that would cross private properties and take away water from streams in the Pacific Northwest.

4. Have student teams pick 1 or 2 water delivery plans. Make sure that each delivery plan is analyzed by at least 1 group. For each plan, a team should be able to outline the following for the class
   a. Advantages of the plan
   b. Disadvantages of the plan
   c. What else the team needs to know for its evaluation
5. Hold a class discussion about the advantages and disadvantages of each option. What do most teams think?
6. Decide as a class what to propose to water planners in Southern California.

The Worst of Water in the West

It was yet another dry year—the fourth dry year in a row. The drought in the Southwest was getting much worse. In the past, natural events like this had come in cycles. But there was no evidence for a cycle, or for rains in the future, thus far. The Colorado River had dwindled to a fraction of its former size. The snowpack in the Sierra Nevada in California was barely able to quench the thirst of Central California. There was no extra water to send to cities in Southern California, such as Los Angeles or San Diego.

Despite the warnings, planning had been poor. Some hard-hit cities in the desert of the Southwest would be on their own to develop relief plans. These cities included Albuquerque, New Mexico; Tucson and Phoenix, Arizona; and Las Vegas, Nevada. The federal government could do little at this scale. Combined with its rapid growth, Southern California was also in a crisis. From where else could it get water? There just was not enough water to go around. Or was there?

Water planners in Southern California had offered several ideas. Desalination of ocean water was slow, and real estate was too valuable for the large, expensive plants. Conservation measures would reduce use, but could not bring more water to the region. Treating and recycling human wastewater was not popular. That was a last resort.

Still, Southern California did have one advantage over the desert cities. This was its access to the rainy, Pacific Northwest. Could a deal be worked out? Currently, three options were on the table for discussion.

1. Transport glacial ice or icebergs from Alaska, either onboard a ship or by dragging them behind the ship in the water. Consider the following:
   - How fast would the ice melt?
   - How big could the ice be, and what kind of ship could transport it?
   - What would the water planners do with the ice once it arrived at port?
2. Convert oil tankers or train cars to transport water from the Pacific Northwest (Seattle, Washington, and Portland, Oregon) to Southern California. Consider the following:
   - What is the best transportation method—train or boat?
   - What are the trade-offs in energy and gasoline to transport this water?
3. Build an aqueduct from Portland, Oregon, to Southern California. Consider the following:
   - Should the aqueduct be an open canal or a sealed pipeline?
   - Should it be aboveground or below ground?
   - What is the best building material for the aqueduct—metal, concrete, or plastic?
   - Would the need for water justify the costs of construction and pumping?

CHAPTER 10

The Water System

Chapter Overview

In chapter 10, *The Water System*, students will consider water from a new perspective—a *systems perspective*. They probably have already studied the water cycle in middle school, where the cycle was depicted as a series of arrows with water movement at a regional scale through evaporation, precipitation, and runoff. This chapter seeks to give concepts related to the water cycle some substance. The chapter does this by investigating examples of reservoirs containing water on Earth and the fluxes that move water between those reservoirs. The goal is to facilitate a better understanding of how different parts of the earth system relate and interact with one another. This is a major theme of the unit.

Chapter 10 has another key objective. Using a systems perspective to analyze water movement will give students a better set of skills to analyze other kinds of earth systems and cycles. At the same time, they will be strengthening their abilities to analyze comprehensively other sorts of systems in engineering or other sciences, or even in other fields such as economics and business. This includes learning to use box diagrams and flowcharts in their work.

In the engage activity, students will share their current understanding of systems. Then they will explore a familiar system: a fast-food restaurant. Students will analyze the restaurant in terms of some common features of systems. They will identify components and boundaries and consider the flow of matter through systems. They will recognize that the rate of flow of matter can be quantified, thus providing valuable information about the system.

After analyzing the fast-food system, students will turn their focus to another system: their local water system. After exploring this system, students will expand the system boundaries to the continental level and eventually to the global level. With each of these changes in scale, students will focus on the components and boundaries of the system, as well as on the flow of water through the system. They will consider how the system stays the same and how it changes. Students will gain a better understanding of the global water system (hydrosphere) and related subsystems on Earth. They also will look at the interaction of the hydrosphere with other earth systems (geosphere, atmosphere, and biosphere). Students will explore how various features (salinity, surface area) of the system affect how the system functions. Finally, they will apply their increased understanding of water systems as they analyze the Great Salt Lake as a system.

Goals for the Chapter

By the end of chapter 10, students should be able to answer questions like these :

- Where does water exist on Earth?
- How much water do you use?
- What is the global water system?
- How does water move through the global water system?
- What is the earth system and how is the water system part of it?

These questions should help you focus your daily lessons. They might even serve as focus questions that you present to students multiple times in the course of an activity, particularly at the beginning and at the end. You can also use the questions to check that lessons are staying on track. If how you taught an activity does not clearly relate to one of these questions, then you may be straying from the main ideas and concepts. These questions will help you maintain a coherent curriculum.

The chapter organizer is a visual way to represent the conceptual flow or story line of a chapter. Several organizers together show the flow for a unit. It is helpful to post these near the door to your classroom (or some other visible place) to track the class's progress through the chapter or unit. In addition, the organizers center on several key concepts, which may be worded a little differently from the standards for the chapter. The teacher version of the organizer shows estimates for the number of classes for an activity, as well as the main endeavors of an activity (e.g., lab work, reading, research). The teacher organizer helps you see how you will be working with your students and what you'll be helping them to do on a given day.

Chapter 10 Organizer

THE WATER SYSTEM

Major Concepts

- **Water on Earth cycles between several main reservoirs in the hydrosphere, geosphere, atmosphere, and biosphere.**
- **Knowing inputs and outputs lets you determine changes in reservoirs in the water system.**
- **Water helps define the Earth system, and is a vital resource for humans.**
- **Many technologies let scientists monitor different parts of the water system.**

ENGAGE — Entertaining Systems ★

Key Idea: • Systems are part of our world.
Activity: Students identify the parts of an entertainment system.

LINKING QUESTION: How would you describe the parts of a system?

EXPLORE / EXPLAIN — System Structures ★ ★ ★

Part I—A Bathtub System

Key Idea: • Bathtubs have some simple features that help you understand systems.
Activity: Students use a model of a bathtub to analyze systems.

Part II—Systems Syntax

Key Idea: • Several words help you describe systems.
Activity: Students learn several key terms and relationships for describing systems.

Part III—Fast-food Flowchart

Key Idea: • A restaurant is a system with inputs and outputs.
Activity: Students analyze subsystems within a fast-food system.

LINKING QUESTION: Where does your drinking water come from?

EXPLORE — Beyond the Drinking Fountain ★ ★

Key Idea: • Water is vital in your community from initial treatment to waste treatment.
Activity: Students identify the source of their drinking water, and where their wastewater goes.

LINKING QUESTION: How is water distributed on continental North America?

★ = One Class Period ☆ = ½ Class Period *Note:* Based on a 50-minute class period.

EXPLAIN Expanding Boundaries ★★☆

Part I—Where Is the Water?

Key Idea: • Water is transported in North American by evaporation, transpiration, precipitation, and river flow.

Activity: Students study the network of rivers on North America, and link river flow rates to the water cycle.

Part II—The Water We Use

Key Idea: • The U.S. uses many millions of gallons of water per day.

Activity: Students analyze categories of water use in the U.S. compared with flow rates in major rivers on the continent.

LINKING QUESTION: How does water in your community link to the global water cycle?

ELABORATE The Global Water System ★★☆

Part I—Global Reservoirs

Key Idea: • A model can be used to show the sizes of water reservoirs on Earth.

Activity: Students analyze data on global water reservoirs.

Part II—Global Water Movement

Key Idea: • Balancing water fluxes shows how fast water moves in the water cycle.

Activity: Students balance the global fluxes of water between reservoirs.

Part III—Residence Time

Key Idea: • You can estimate the time that water or other matter spends in a reservoir.

Activity: Students use residence time to estimate the average time that matter, such as water, spends in a reservoir before moving to the next part of the system.

LINKING QUESTION: How do ecosystems and communities interact in a water system?

EVALUATE A Salty Situation ★★☆

Key Idea: • Science, technology, dialogue, and clear writing are essential in understanding and solving community challenges, such as those with water resources.

Activity: Students analyze data on water issues at the Great Salt Lake, Utah. They make a written recommendation to balance interests of various stakeholders in that water resource.

★ = One Class Period ☆ = ½ Class Period *Note:* Based on a 50-minute class period.

Standards Covered by Chapter 10*

THE WATER SYSTEM

STANDARD A: Science as Inquiry. As a result of activities in grades 9–12, all students should develop

abilities necessary to do scientific inquiry

- Use technology, mathematics, and models to improve investigations and communications. A variety of technologies, such as hand tools, measuring instruments, and calculators, should be an integral component of scientific investigations. The use of computers for the collection, analysis, and display of data is also a part of this standard. Mathematics plays an essential role in all aspects of an inquiry. For example, measurement is used for posing questions, formulas are used for developing explanations, and charts and graphs are used for communicating results.
- Communicate and defend a scientific argument. Students in school science programs should develop the abilities associated with accurate and effective communication. These include writing and following procedures, expressing concepts, reviewing information, summarizing data, using language appropriately, developing diagrams and charts, explaining statistical analysis, speaking clearly and logically, constructing a reasoned argument, and responding appropriately to critical comments. [See Teaching Standard B in Chapter 3]

understandings about scientific inquiry

- Scientists usually inquire about how physical, living, or designed systems function. Conceptual principles and knowledge guide scientific inquiries. Historical and current scientific knowledge influence the design and interpretation of investigations and the evaluation of proposed explanations made by other scientists.
- Mathematics is essential in scientific inquiry. Mathematical tools and models guide and improve the posing of questions, gathering data, constructing explanations and communicating results.

STANDARD C: Life Science. As a result of their activities in grades 9–12, all students should develop an understanding of

the interdependence of organisms

- The atoms and molecules on the earth cycle among the living and nonliving components of the biosphere.

STANDARD D: Earth and Space Science: As a result of their activities in grades 9–12, all students should develop understanding of

Energy in the Earth system

- Heating of earth's surface and atmosphere by the sun drives convection within the atmosphere and oceans, producing winds and ocean currents.

Geochemical cycles

- The earth is a system containing essentially a fixed amount of each stable chemical atom or element. Each element can exist in several different chemical reservoirs. Each element on earth moves among reservoirs in the solid earth, oceans, atmosphere, and organisms as part of geochemical cycles.
- Movement of matter between reservoirs is driven by the earth's internal and external sources of energy. These movements are often accompanied by a change in the physical and chemical properties of the matter. Carbon, for example, occurs in carbonate rocks such as limestone, in the atmosphere as carbon dioxide gas, in water as dissolved carbon dioxide, and in all organisms as complex molecules that control the chemistry of life.

STANDARD F: Science in Personal and Social Perspectives. As a result of activities in grades 9–12, all students should develop an understanding of

Environmental quality

- Natural ecosystems provide an array of basic processes that affect humans. Those processes include maintenance of the quality of the atmosphere, generation of soils, control of the hydrologic cycle, disposal of wastes, and recycling of nutrients. Humans are changing many of these basic processes, and the changes may be detrimental to humans.
- Many factors influence environmental quality. Factors that students might investigate include population growth, resource use, population distribution, overconsumption, the capacity of technology to solve problems, poverty, the role of economic, political, and religious views, and different ways humans view the earth.

science and technology in local, national, and global challenges

- Science and technology are essential social enterprises, but alone they can only indicate what can happen, not what should happen. The latter involves human decisions about the use of knowledge. [See Content Standard E (grades 9–12)]
- Humans have a major effect on other species. For example, the influence of humans on other organisms occurs through land use—which decreases space available to other species—and pollution—which changes the chemical composition of air, soil, and water.

STANDARD G: History and Nature of Science. As a result of activities in grades 9–12, all students should develop an understanding of

science as a human endeavor

- Individuals and teams have contributed and will continue to contribute to the scientific enterprise. Doing science or engineering can be as simple as an individual conducting field studies or as complex as hundreds of people working on a major scientific question or technological problem. Pursuing science as a career or as a hobby can be both fascinating and intellectually rewarding.
- Scientists have ethical traditions. Scientists value peer review, truthful reporting about the methods and outcomes of investigations, and making public the results of work. Violations of such norms do occur, but scientists responsible for such violations are censured by their peers.
- Scientists are influenced by societal, cultural, and personal beliefs and ways of viewing the world. Science is not separate from society but rather science is a part of society.

**Note:* Bracketed portions of the standard are addressed elsewhere in the program.

Prerequisite Knowledge

By this point in the program, students should be familiar with using notebooks and with how to organize and record information. They should also be able to use strategies such as T-tables, multicolumn tables, and Venn diagrams to organize data. Students should be effective using sketches or diagrams to illustrate concepts.

Students will continue developing and using several quantitative skills in the next four chapters. We expect that students have been getting better at using these skills throughout the program. Exponents continue to be very important, especially due to the large scales involved in length and time. Students will continue their work in canceling units in equations and in converting units (e.g., minutes to years or years to millions of years). Keep stressing to students to show their work—this is the only way that they will find and correct their own errors.

Decide whether you will allow students to use calculators. This is acceptable, but it is essential that students know how to set up the problem accurately. We have observed that this can be a problem, particularly with exponents. If the calculation is not entered properly, the answer will not make sense, but students will not know this. Alternatively, if students cannot use the calculator effectively, their answers still will not make sense. In the end, there will be several possible causes of incorrect answers.

It is helpful if students have been exposed to the water cycle in middle school science and that they are familiar with geography. You may want to have world maps or an atlas available to students.

Commonly Held Misconceptions

There is little research at the high school level on misconceptions relating to the water cycle. You may note students with some incorrect ideas regarding rivers, in that these are a part of the water cycle. Transfers to larger scales can be difficult, so you may note misconceptions such as these:

- Large rivers flow from north to south, or large rivers flow directly to the ocean.

River paths are most often driven by gravity and the tectonic features of the land. This is independent of any north-south directionality used by humans.

An example of north-flowing rivers is the McKenzie River in Canada.

- Floods are always high-energy, catastrophic events.

Floods result in higher water velocities largely in the main channels. Elsewhere on the floodplain and away from the main channel, water velocities are likely to be very slow. Floodwaters on the plains result in a gradual submerging; this covers the ground with a layer of fine-grained silt and sand.

NOTES:

ENGAGE

Entertaining Systems

Activity Overview

Systems are part of our lives. We interact with many systems as we go about our daily lives. These may be systems in our bodies or the larger systems in which we live. Students may have studied systems, perhaps even earth systems, in earlier science classes. In *Entertaining Systems*, students will share their current understanding about systems. They will participate in a brainstorming session to generate a list of systems that relate to the sources of entertainment they encounter every day. Then they will work as a team to consider which characteristics the systems have in common. Their list will be posted in the classroom for future reference.

Before You Teach

Background Information

In this engage activity, students begin thinking about how to characterize properties and features of systems. The activity also provides an opportunity for you to see what your students already know about systems. The activity presages some larger ideas that students will learn by the end of the chapter.

A *system* is any collection of things that interact with one another. Systems have a number of common characteristics:

- Systems have some number of parts (i.e., components) and some amount of material or mass. This could be the number of dollars or apples, gallons of water, or mass of carbon.
- Systems have spatial boundaries or physical limits. Reservoirs contain all or a fraction of the mass within the boundaries of a system. A system can have one or more reservoirs, depending on how its boundaries are defined. Additional mass can be in transit between reservoirs in a system (e.g., water vapor in clouds, water in rivers).
- Systems can be thought of as open or closed. If anything leaves or enters the system (we call this output and input, respectively), we call this an open system. If all matter in the system is preserved and remains within the boundaries, however, we call the system closed.
- Systems can change with time. That is, parts of a system move or change at certain rates. The flux is how much matter is transferred in a given time interval.

Materials

For the teacher

blank transparencies and transparency pen, or oversized paper and markers

For each team of 3 students

1 sheet of oversized paper

2 large markers

sea monkeys or brine shrimp cysts (optional)

3 copies of copymaster 10.1, *Scoring Rubric for A Salty Situation*

Answers to Step 2 are on TE page 498b.
Answers to Step 3 are on TE page 498b.

ENGAGE

Entertaining Systems

Systems make up our world. You are probably already familiar with systems such as the digestive and reproductive systems in your body. Or you probably have used a computer system in your school or at home.

But what first comes to mind when you see the word "system"? What exactly is a system? How big, or how small, is a system? What kinds of systems are shown in figure 10.2? In *Entertaining Systems*, you will work individually and then in a team to explore and share what you already know about systems that you interact with every day—entertainment systems.

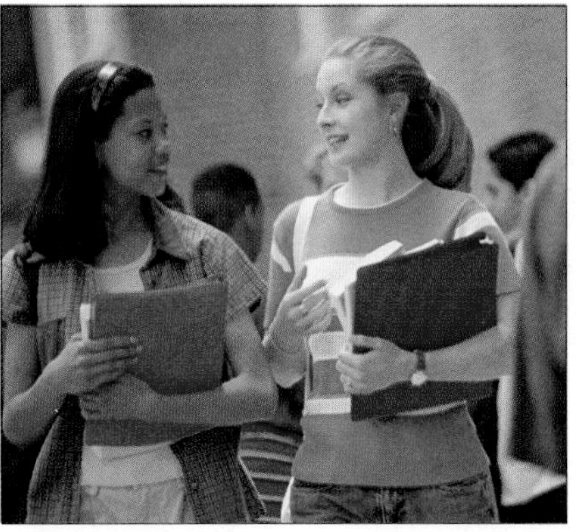

▲ **Figure 10.2**
Systems. Look at the natural and human systems in this photograph. What is similar about these systems? What is different?

Materials

For each team of 3 students

1 sheet of oversized paper

2 large markers

Process and Procedure

1. Work alone to make a list of systems that are related to entertainment. Write down at least 5 systems in your science notebook. Be prepared to share your list with your class.

Think of entertainment as a broad category. What are your favorite forms of entertainment? What sorts of things do you need so that the entertainment system works properly?

2. When you have completed your list, form a team with 2 other students. Answer the following questions in your science notebook.
   a. Do your team members think about an entertainment system as you do?
   b. What are the similarities and differences among the entertainment systems on your 3 lists?
   c. Which systems are you a part of? Carefully explain why you think so.
3. As a team, determine 3 or 4 general characteristics that are shared by all the entertainment systems on the 3 lists. Write these general characteristics on an oversized sheet of paper and post them in the classroom according to your teacher's instructions.

498 Unit 3 Moving Matter

Advance Preparation

Make 1 copy of copymaster 10.1, *Scoring Rubric for A Salty Situation* for each student. Gather oversized paper and markers for student use.

If you decide to purchase a package of sea monkeys, activate them now. Just follow the directions on the package. They provide a nice visual as students work through the chapter to the evaluate. They should be full-grown brine shrimp by the time you reach the evaluate activity.

As You Teach

Outcomes and Indicators of Success

By the end of this activity, students should

1. review and communicate their prior knowledge about systems.

   They will demonstrate their prior knowledge by

   - contributing examples of systems to the class brainstorming session,
   - identifying characteristics common to the many systems generated in the brainstorming session, and
   - applying those characteristics to a system they are familiar with.

2. recognize many systems related to entertainment and their own place within them.

   They will demonstrate their recognition by

   - contributing examples of systems to the class brainstorming session,
   - discussing which systems they are a part of, and
   - explaining their role within a familiar system.

Strategies

Getting Started

If you have not already done so, have the students read the introduction to the chapter. This will provide students with an overview of the chapter and will also introduce students to the evaluate activity, *A Salty Situation.*

Hand out copymaster 10.1, *Scoring Rubric for A Salty Situation.* Tell students that for the evaluate activity they will be analyzing the water system at the Great Salt Lake in Utah. Figure 10.1 in the student book shows an image of the lake. By distributing the rubric ahead of time, you will clarify and reinforce performance expectations for the activity. For example, students always need to show their work for calculations; this is made clear on the rubric. The rubric lets students begin working on abilities and understandings that will help them during the final project, as well as with the rest of the activities in the unit.

Read the short introductory paragraphs of the engage in the student book to your students. Give them five minutes to respond in their science notebooks to the questions posed. (You might also assign this task for homework the night before.) This exercise will give students a chance to organize their thoughts about systems before they begin the engage activity. Read through their answers to assess your students' initial understanding of systems.

Process and Procedure

Materials

For the teacher

blank transparencies and transparency pen, or oversized paper and markers

For each team of 3 students

1 sheet of oversized paper

2 large markers

sea monkeys or brine shrimp cysts (optional)

3 copies of copymaster 10.1, *Scoring Rubric for A Salty Situation*

In Step 1, have students spend five minutes writing in their science notebooks examples of systems related to entertainment. Tell students to think about what objects or devices they use for entertainment. They should list as many systems as possible and be prepared to share examples with the class. Encourage them to identify at least five examples. It is important for them to generate some ideas of their own before joining a team.

Some typical systems for entertainment include a television, VCR, DVD player, CD player, MPEG player, video game system, or computer. Some students might describe an entertainment system that includes several of these smaller systems. For example, a home system might include a TV, DVD player, speakers, and an audio-video receiver. Or students might indicate systems such as movie theaters, amusement parks, gymnasiums, libraries, board games, sporting events, or functions on cell phones.

You can prompt identification of additional examples by asking students to think about a typical day. What interactions do they have with other objects and people related to entertainment? To what systems do these objects and people belong? Encourage students to think of systems related to entertainment that are not found in their homes. Students might think of the stores where they buy CDs or DVDs (retail store systems) or the people involved with producing the products they are interested in (manufacturing systems and the systems associated with the music and movie industries).

You might also suggest that students think about how an entertainment system in their homes is linked to systems outside their homes. What is needed to receive channels on a TV? Without some prompting, students might not think about how their entertainment systems require power provided through batteries or electricity. And the power must be paid for by someone and supplied by another someone. Students are part of a much bigger system than their computers when they use the Internet. Encourage them to think about what systems are involved with surfing the Web and sending e-mail.

Record a class list of examples of systems on a transparency or on oversized paper. This way you will have a permanent record that you can use again in the explore/explain activity *System Structures*. Try to get contributions to the list from every student. Think about the following questions to help you assess how much students already know about systems:

- What examples of systems are students offering?
- How limited is their list of examples?
- How do students view themselves as part of systems?

In Step 2, get students into groups of 3. Questions 2a–c will help students think about what they know about systems and enable them to compare their ideas with other students' ideas. Circulate and listen to their discussions to assess students' current understanding.

Answers to Step 2, SE page 498

2a. Students are likely to think about systems differently. Encourage them to talk about these differences.

2b. The most obvious similarity is that all the systems relate to entertainment. Encourage discussion of other similarities. For example, many of the systems are related to visual or auditory entertainment. Differences might include the size of the system or how the systems work. Students might compare physical systems such as stereos with systems that involve both a variety of people and physical parts (a major-league team, the Internet).

2c. Many students might not think about themselves as being a part of a system. Explain that they can be part of a system without physically being in the system. A computer is a system, but for that system to work, cables have to be plugged in between all the components (computer, monitor, keyboard, mouse, speakers, etc.). The person who connected all those parts has made the computer a system. Without connecting the parts, the computer won't work. Students also become part of bigger systems if they are part of an on-line discussion group or if they post information on the Web.

In Step 3, have each team identify 3 or 4 general characteristics common to all (or many) of the systems listed. Have each team write these characteristics on an oversized sheet of paper. The list of common characteristics generated by a team is a written record of its initial thinking about systems. Use the following questions to help students think about the characteristics of systems:

- "What do many of the systems consist of?"
- "What is it that the systems do that provides entertainment?"
- "What do the systems have in common?"
- "What do the systems use or produce?"

Some teams might seek to identify these properties by developing a definition for a system. Other teams will go beyond a simple definition to the general characteristics that define a system. Gather evidence of student understanding by listening to their contributions in class and their team discussions.

Answers to Step 3, SE page 498

3. Some characteristics of systems include that they contain parts, have parts that interact, have a function, contain stuff, have boundaries, have inputs and outputs, and exhibit change and constancy (balance). It is not important that students identify all these characteristics. Instead, this is an opportunity for them to share what they already know or think they know. To guide your assessment of their understanding, think about the following questions:
   - Can students identify general characteristics or features of systems?
   - Can they generalize about parts of a system, using terms like inputs and outputs rather than specific names like signals, cable, and electricity?
   - Do the students have a fairly sophisticated, or a more simplistic, conception of what a system is?
   - How do their views of a system change after sharing ideas within and among teams? Do their views become more sophisticated?

   Have the students share their lists by posting them in the classroom. Have a few groups volunteer to read their lists. The class will revisit the lists in an upcoming lesson.

In Step 4, students begin to take apart and dissect a system. They represent their system in a drawing and use accurate labels to identify the parts of the system. This will be very important later in the chapter.

Answers to Step 4, SE page 499

4a. Be open to students' ideas at this point on how to develop and label diagrams of systems. They will learn from examples later how to do this.

4b. Let students share ideas about how they fit into systems. The goal is for them to see that they are part of the systems that they will be analyzing.

4c. Check that students can use a phrase or sentence that relates to their system sketch. They will learn how to do this much more carefully later in the chapter.

In Step 5, students share their ideas about what a system is. This is a great time for students to compare how different teams or students used diagrams to represent systems. Have teams offer constructive comments on what features are most effective from the different diagrams and sketches. Students may identify new techniques from the diagrams that they might like to incorporate into their own diagrams.

After students have completed Step 5, tell them to work on the *Reflect and Connect* questions individually. They should record their answers in their science notebooks.

Answers to Reflect and Connect, SE page 499

1. Make sure students write down at least 1 thing they know, 1 thing they think they know, and 1 thing they wonder. This task gives students a chance to organize their thoughts before they begin the next activity. It also gives you another opportunity to assess their current understanding. You might try to address some of the things students wonder about as you go through the chapter.

   You can collect their science notebooks, but it is also good practice to wander the classroom and glean information from looking over students' shoulders at their notebooks.

2. Students likely have not thought about things like VCRs and TVs as systems before. They might explain that discussing these devices as systems helped them to think about the number of things involved in making the systems function.
3. Some typical systems include transportation (bus, train, plane, highway); food service; banking; court; education; military; financial aid; housing; body (e.g., circulatory, reproductive); library; communications; health care; weather; family; and athletics, as well as ecosystems. Students should describe how these systems have the characteristics they listed in Step 3. For example, they might explain that a banking system has parts such as computers, a vault, and employees.

Answers to Step 4 are on TE page 498b.

4. In your team, select 1 entertainment system that includes each of you. Complete Steps 4a–c for that system.
   a. Develop a diagram or sketch that represents that system. Label the parts of the system.
   b. Show how you fit into that system.
   c. Develop a figure caption that describes the main parts of the diagram or sketch.
5. Follow your teacher's instructions to share with the class ideas from your team list and your sketch or diagram. A recorder will list the ideas for everyone to review and compare.

Reflect and Connect

Work on your own to answer the following questions. Record your best thinking in your science notebook.

1. Use a table (or chart) in your science notebook to record your ideas for each of these categories.
   a. What I know about systems
   b. What I think I know about systems
   c. What I wonder about systems
2. Look at the list of entertainment systems you developed as a class. Have you ever thought about these things as systems before? Why do you think it is helpful to think about entertainment as a system?
3. Write the names of 2 other systems (not entertainment) in your science notebook. Describe how these 2 systems have the characteristics of a system that your team determined in Step 3.

Decide whether it might be helpful for you to use a sketch, diagram, or highlight comment.

System Structures

EXPLORE
EXPLAIN

In *Entertaining Systems*, you developed a list of characteristics common to systems. Does material or energy flow through those systems? How do the parts of a system interact? You already started thinking about the kinds of interactions in systems in the unit *Interactions Are Interesting*.

In *System Structures*, Part I, you will work in a team to explore the movement of matter by modeling a bathtub system. Then in Part II, you will work with a partner to learn the terminology used to describe systems. In Part III, you will work with a team and use your understanding of systems to analyze a fast-food restaurant system.

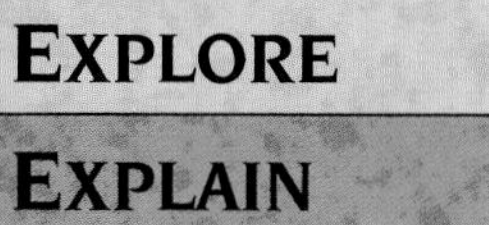

System Structures

Activity Overview

Learning about systems helps students analyze many types of problems. Some examples in *System Structures* will give students a set of tools for analysis to use later in this chapter and book, and in other fields as well.

In Part I, students model a bathtub system and balance matter (water) coming in and going out. They also will see their first example of a box diagram. Then in Part II, students will explore common characteristics of a system and how changes in parts of the system affect the whole system. Students learn to use terms such as *boundaries*, *inputs* and *outputs*, and *open* or *closed systems*. In Part III of the activity, students will use a systems approach to investigate a familiar system—a fast-food restaurant.

Before You Teach

Background Information

Thinking about systems helps students analyze and simplify more complex problems. Students often fail to think of themselves as part of many separate systems, each with a changing network of relationships and interactions. Students are affected by events or decisions made at home, next door, or on the other side of the world. Systems thinking relies on studying interactions at different scales or sizes. It will help you and your students take complicated problems and relationships and distill them into some essential features.

You interact with many systems each day. Some examples in your community include systems for banking, education, transportation, health care, and food distribution. Other examples include the respiratory, reproductive, and circulatory systems of organisms, or even climate patterns on a regional or continental scale.

A *system* is any collection of things that interact with one another. Many systems accomplish a specific set of functions; others are chaotic. Subsystems may exist within a system with their own parts and interactions. Systems share the following common properties: they have boundaries, they have inputs and outputs, they can be open or closed, and they can change with time.

Boundaries are the physical limits of a system. All the interactions between its parts occur within a system's boundaries. The boundary of a river system might be its watershed. Or you might want to define a system of study as where the river enters the ocean. The boundary for a lake might be its shoreline, or thinking in three dimensions, its shoreline, bottom, and surface. For the blood circulation system in an organism, the boundary is the cells of the skin. In contrast, the circulation of large weather patterns can involve large parts of the atmosphere. The atmosphere has a boundary at the top of the stratosphere. Later in the chapter, students will learn that a *reservoir* contains all or some fraction of the matter within the boundaries.

Material entering the system is the *input* and the material leaving the system is the *output*. Both matter and energy flow into and out of an *open system*. In a *closed system*, only energy moves into or out of the system. Matter remains within the boundaries and the total mass does not change. Earth is essentially a closed system because energy enters and exits the system, but matter does not. Matter in the form of meteors does occasionally enter the earth system, but this is negligible compared with the mass of Earth.

Systems can change with time because of changes in the inputs or outputs. If the inputs and the outputs are equal, a system might not change at all, or it might change in a constant, predictable way. The rate at which material, such as water, moves into or out of a system can vary. Overall, some systems maintain a balance, or a *steady state*, if they do not change with time. Or, after they are disturbed, these systems may reestablish a balance at a different set of conditions.

In this chapter, several instructional and practical strategies help to build a clearer understanding of systems. One approach involves designing generalized diagrams or sketches of systems. Systems can also be shown as matter moving through a flowchart. Flowcharts show matter moving from one part of the system to another or the interactions among the parts of a system. These tools are particularly valuable for visual learners.

A second teaching strategy is using generalized variables to represent parameters in the system. For example, a mass of matter moving through a system in a certain amount of time is a *flux*. In Part III, students compare the rates that french fries are bought by a fast-food restaurant, sold to customers, or discarded after spoiling. The fluxes for the inputs and outputs are represented by the variables I_{buy}, O_{sold}, and O_{spoil}. Students will determine values for these variables.

Students will also use schematic diagrams of systems that depict the movement of matter. These diagrams are called box diagrams. Box diagrams help students organize data and observations. An effective feature of box diagrams is the size of the arrows, which can be proportional to the magnitude of the fluxes. The input and output variables of a fast-food restaurant might look like those in figure T10.1. When the net supply of french fries does not change (i.e., fries in the freezer), the input equals the output. In this case, about 95 percent are sold and 5 percent spoil.

Students will create both box diagrams of systems and diagrams of a series of subsystems. The box diagrams should include fluxes. Diagrams of subsystems should show how the subsystems are related.

There are three reasons to have students develop generalized diagrams of systems and fluxes. First, the diagram method will help you check to see that students are correctly identifying parts of a larger system, one that is independent of the values of those parts. By examining a diagram with variables, you can identify student misconceptions about system interrelationships more easily. Second, using variables introduces a common method of nomenclature for describing either dynamic or static (unchanging) systems. This is particularly useful when algebraic manipulations are used in the activity. Third, generalized variables can be integrated with diagrams or flowcharts of systems to represent specific processes (independent of quantities) that are acting in that system.

A key goal in analyzing systems is to determine how they change and evolve with time. Such changes are typically identified by comparing the inputs (I) and outputs (O) of a system, as shown in the following relationship. Note the convention we use in this chapter. We show the inputs and outputs in the balance and then subtract the sum of all outputs (ΣO) from the sum of all inputs (ΣI). In the case of the french fries,

$$\begin{aligned} \pm \text{ change in the system} &= \Sigma I - \Sigma O \\ &= (I_{buy}) - (O_{spoil} + O_{sold}) \\ &= I_{buy} - O_{spoil} - O_{sold}. \end{aligned}$$

If the inputs are greater than the outputs, the change in the system is positive. If the outputs are greater than the inputs, the change in the system is negative. Conversely, if one can measure inputs along with net changes in the system, then you can determine the outputs (the unknown). This convention for analyzing systems is analogous to common practices in accounting and economics.

Note that we have used the convention of subtracting the value, or magnitude, of the sum of the outputs from the sum of the inputs. The outputs and inputs are

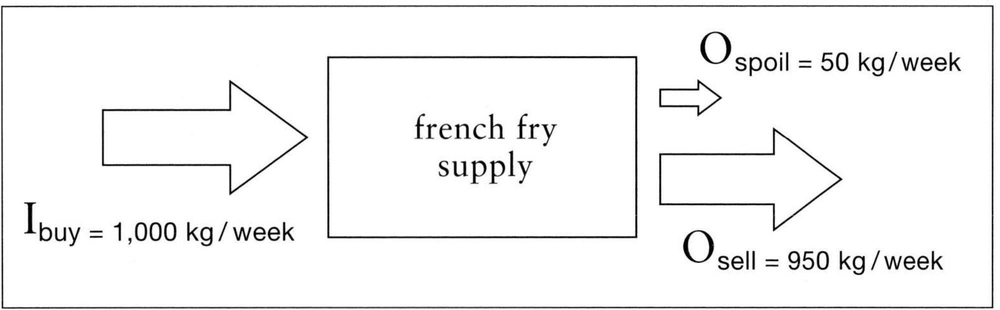

▲ **Figure T10.1 Box diagram for fast-food restaurant.** This diagram shows inputs and outputs for the supply of french fries at a fast-food restaurant. At this time, inputs equal outputs. If one of these parameters were to change, then the supply of french fries would either have to increase or decrease.

all the fluxes of matter in the systems in a given time. There is another approach that gives the same answer but uses a different approach. This approach assigns positive values to inputs (> 0; entering the system or reservoir) and negative values to outputs (< 0; exiting the system). It then sums all inputs and outputs. The equation would not have any minus signs since outputs already are assigned a value less than zero. This is shown algebraically as ± change in the system = $\Sigma I + \Sigma O$.

Materials—Part I

For the teacher

1 permanent marker
1 compass to poke a hole in containers
pictures of systems (optional)

For each team of 3 students

1 1-L plastic bottle or container, preferably clear
1 100-mL graduated cylinder
1 stopwatch

Materials—Part II

none

Materials—Part III

none

Advance Preparation

If available, you might want to display pictures of various systems around the room (ecosystems, businesses, the judicial system, etc.). You might also want to repost the list of systems generated by the class in the engage activity and the team lists of common properties of systems.

Part I of the investigation requires access to sinks. If your faucets have hose connections, you will need to attach hoses to the connections. Otherwise, students might have trouble controlling the rate of the water coming out of the faucet. If you don't have running water in your classroom, consider doing Part I as a demonstration. You could use a pitcher of water, a 1-liter (L) container, and a bucket.

Gather clear, 1-L plastic containers. Clear containers will work best because students can watch the water level easily. Opaque containers such as 1-quart yogurt containers will also work. Make a hole in the bottom of the containers using the point of a compass. Holes should be at least 2 millimeters (mm) in diameter. Using a permanent marker, draw a line on the inside of the container several inches from the bottom. To give teams different experiences, you can make some holes bigger or place the lines at different positions. You might consider having the students do this preparation.

Another option is to see if the chemistry teacher has pneumatic troughs used for water displacement. These will work, however, note that more water is used with the larger drain openings.

As You Teach

Outcomes and Indicators of Success

By the end of this activity, students should

1. begin to understand that matter flows through a system due to interactions.

   They will demonstrate their understanding by

   - identifying inputs and outputs of a bathtub and a fast-food restaurant system and
   - listing some major parts of a fast-food restaurant system.

2. understand that systems have common characteristics.

   They will demonstrate their understanding by defining each system they encounter using the common characteristics of parts, inputs, outputs, and boundaries.

3. be able to use diagrams to represent systems.

   They will demonstrate their ability by

   - creating a drawing and a box diagram of a bathtub system,
   - creating a box diagram of how people get french fries,
   - using mathematical expressions to represent a box diagram,
   - adding other interactions to their box diagrams of the fast-food restaurant system, and
   - adding rates of inputs and outputs to their diagrams.

4. understand that changes in inputs and outputs affect systems.

   They will demonstrate their understanding by

   - changing the input (and maybe the output) in the bathtub system to affect the system,
   - calculating positive and negative change in volume for the bathtub and fast-food systems,
   - estimating how other ways to change inputs and outputs affect the bathtub and fast-food systems,
   - calculating the input and output rates for the fast-food system, and
   - explaining how changes in the inputs and outputs affect the bathtub and fast-food systems.

Strategies

Getting Started

Ask students why they think it might be important to learn about systems. Take a $5.00 bill out of your pocket and ask students how it is part of a system. Use questions such as, "Where does the bill go if you buy a hamburger for $4.83?" "Where do parts of the original $5.00 go (your pocket change)?" "How quickly do parts of the original $5.00 move through the economy?" "Could you trace these now-different parts of the original $5.00?"

Explain that looking at systems is a unique way of looking at the world. By using a systems approach, students can see how things are connected. Instead of thinking about discrete things such as a CD player, for example, students using a systems approach would look at what is involved in producing the CD player and how the CD player is used. Looking at a CD player as a system would help them recognize that changing something about the CD player will affect users and manufacturing companies.

Process and Procedure

Part I: Bathtub System

Materials

For the teacher

1 permanent marker
1 compass to poke a hole in containers
pictures of systems (optional)

For each team of 3 students

1 1-L plastic bottle or container, preferably clear
1 100-mL graduated cylinder
1 stopwatch

In Step 1, direct students to get into teams of 3. Before they begin modeling the bathtub system, remind them to read through all the steps first. Remind students to be careful about wasting water.

In Step 2, students "balance" their bathtub systems by adjusting the flow of water from the faucet to maintain a constant level in their containers. Because the drain hole is small, students will need to turn down the faucets to a steady, slow stream once

Answers to Steps 2–3 are on TE page 501.

Part I: Bathtub System

Materials

For each team of 3 students

1 1-L plastic bottle or container
1 100-mL graduated cylinder
1 stopwatch

Process and Procedure

You will work in a team to model a bathtub system using a small container with a hole and a faucet to provide water. Your team's challenge is to fill your container up to a mark and keep the water level exactly at this mark. Then you will quantify (measure) what is happening in your bathtub system.

1. Get into teams of 3 and go to the area designated by your teacher. Review figure 10.3, which shows a bathtub setup and how you might represent it in your science notebook.

Water is an important resource that shouldn't be wasted. Read all the steps before beginning this activity. Then complete the steps that require water as quickly as possible so that you minimize the water used.

2. Fill your container with water until the water reaches the mark on the container. Then make the necessary adjustments to the flow rate of water to keep the water level exactly at the mark. Record answers to the following in your science notebook.
   a. What adjustments did you make to your system? What did you change?
   b. What could you not change?

Recall that a rate of flow is sort of like a velocity, or rate of motion. It tells the change that occurs in a given amount of time.

3. Several variables indicate the size of the system and how long it takes for the system to change. Measure these and record the results with proper units in your science notebook.
   a. Use a graduated cylinder to measure the flow rate at the faucet. How much water enters the cylinder in a given time period, such as 10 seconds (sec)?

Check that your units for flow rate here make sense. Also confirm that the water is still coming out of the faucet at the same speed that it was in Step 2.

   b. Write in your notebook the flow rate in terms of the mass of water (grams, abbreviated as g). What property of water do you use to determine flow rate as mass?

500 Unit 3 Moving Matter

the water level is reached. Make sure that students do not turn down the water so much that it flows erratically.

In Step 3, students measure the variables for the system. These include the volume to the water level mark, flow rate in, and flow rate out. One way students can measure container volume is to use their finger to cover the hole and let the water drain into a graduated cylinder. They can measure input and output rates by measuring the flow rate of the faucet when the container is at a balance. To do this, have students hold a graduated cylinder under the faucet to measure the volume change in 10 seconds (sec), for example. They can measure the rate flowing out. It would also be valid to use evidence and logic to infer the flow rate out (that equals the flow rate in when the system is balanced).

Answers to Steps 2–3, SE pages 500–501

2a. Students will need to adjust the flow rate of the faucet (input, or flux in) to achieve a balance.

2b. They cannot change the flow rate out because of the size of the hole. They also cannot change the level of the water since it needs to stay at a certain point on the container.

3a. Be open to different ways to measure flow rate. However, it is important that students record how they took their measurements, that they show their work, and that they use units such as milliliters per second (mL/sec).

3b. An example of a flow rate in grams is 8 grams per second (g/sec). This equals 8 mL/sec, using a density for water of 1 gram per milliliter (g/mL).

3c. Check that students show their work and use proper units for a rate, such as mL/sec.

3d. Students should convert the volume (1 L) to mass (1,000 grams, or g) with density:

$$(1\,\cancel{L}) \times \left(\frac{1{,}000\ \cancel{mL}}{1\ \cancel{L}}\right) \times \left(\frac{1\ g}{1\ \cancel{mL}}\right) = 1{,}000\ g$$

In Step 4, students will develop a diagram of their systems. Discuss with them the elements of figure 10.3 that they should use in their diagrams. Also have students compare and contrast their diagrams or sketches against the simple box diagram. The first is an actual diagram; the box diagram is a kind of model or representation. Discuss the difference in answers for the two highlight comments. What they see is water entering and leaving at the same rate. This means that inputs are in balance with outputs, and thus the total mass in the container is not changing (the concept of the conservation of mass).

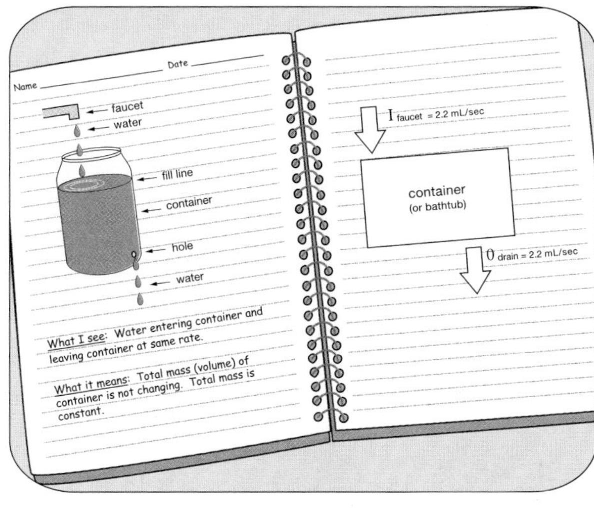

◄ **Figure 10.3 Sketch and box diagram in science notebook.** This diagram shows some elements of science notebooks, such as name, date, labels, and measurement (2.2 mL/sec). The sketch to the left includes simple phrases for "what I see/what it means." The sketch to the right represents the water container as a box with water flowing in and out.

c. Repeat Steps 3a–b for the water flowing out of the container and for the volume of the container.
d. What is the mass of the water in the container at the mark?

4. Develop a simple diagram or sketch for your setup of a bathtub system. Model your diagram like figure 10.3. You should include labels for things like the following in your diagram.
   a. Flow rate into the container (show rates and units for volume change)
   b. Flow rate out of the container (show rates and units for volume change)
   c. Volume of the container (show rates for mass)
   d. Highlight comments or figure caption

Answers to Stop and Think—Part I, SE page 502

1. For a chemical reaction to be balanced, the reaction rate in a forward direction equals the reaction rate in the reverse direction. Students studied this concept in unit 1, *Interactions Are Interesting*. Thus, by considering the reactants or products in the system, the forward and reverse processes can be thought of as flow rates, or inputs and outputs.
2. In a balanced system, the inputs equal the outputs. For example, an input of 2 mL/sec minus an output of 2 mL/sec results in no net change to the system.

3a. If you made the hole bigger, then you would have to increase the flow rate in to maintain the water level. Otherwise, the container would slowly show a net decrease.

3b. If you moved the hole up from the bottom of the container, then the water beneath the hole could not drain. In general, this wouldn't change the flow rate out.

3c. If the mark was moved higher, then the volume of the container to that mark would be larger. You would need to increase the flow rate in to increase the water volume up to that point.

3d. If you increased the flow rate from the faucet, then the water level would go above the mark in the container. Eventually, the water might spill over the top of the container.

Process and Procedure

Part II: Systems Syntax

Materials

none

In Part II, students will read about systems. They will learn the terminology associated with systems including open and closed, boundaries, inputs, outputs, and fluxes. A swimming pool is used as an example in the reading, but feel free to encourage students to think of other examples that show how systems work.

Suggest an appropriate reading strategy for your students. Decide whether to assign part of the reading as a homework assignment. When students have finished the reading, tell them to answer the *Stop and Think* questions.

Stop & THINK

PART I

Work with your team to complete the following tasks. Record your answers in your science notebook.

1. Your bathtub system was balanced when you kept the water at the same level. You also considered chemical reactions that were balanced in chapter 5, *Forces of Attraction*. How are these 2 balanced systems similar?
2. In a balanced system, what is the relationship between the flow rate into and the flow rate out of the system? Use numbers to explain your answer.
3. Describe what would happen to your bathtub system if the following had happened.
   a. You made the hole bigger.
   b. You changed the position of the hole (not the size).
   c. You moved the mark higher in your container.
   d. You increased the flow rate from the faucet.

Part II: Systems Syntax

Materials

none

Process and Procedure

1. Follow your teacher's directions for completing the following reading on systems.

NOTES:

READING

Systems Are Everywhere

By modeling the bathtub system in Part I, you began to define a system. But how do scientists define a system? A **system** is any collection of things that interact with one another. Many systems accomplish a very specific set of functions, while other systems appear chaotic. You were investigating a simple system when you modeled a bathtub system. In science, everything in the physical world is part of a system.

Systems are open or closed depending on how they relate to their surroundings and how the boundaries are defined. **Open systems** exchange both energy and matter with the surrounding environment. **Closed systems** exchange only energy with the surrounding environment. A potted plant is an open system. The plant exchanges oxygen and carbon dioxide with the atmosphere. However, a plant in a sealed, glass terrarium is a closed system. Energy enters the terrarium system daily, but matter is not exchanged. Water circulates only within the terrarium.

Earth is essentially a closed system. Solar energy enters the system, and infrared radiation given off by Earth escapes to space. Matter does not enter or leave Earth. Or does it? Meteors and interstellar dust constantly bombard Earth's atmosphere. Much of this dust vaporizes after entering the atmosphere. Occasionally, a meteorite will reach Earth's surface. But the mass of matter added to Earth is small compared with the mass of Earth.

Every system has **boundaries**, or physical limits. The boundary for a terrarium is the glass container. A container also provided the boundary for the bathtub system you modeled. Expanding the boundaries can increase the number of components and interactions involved in the system.

Within the boundaries, the system contains a particular amount of material. The amount of material entering the system is **input**, and the amount of material leaving the system is **output**. Systems can change with time because the inputs and outputs may be different. If the inputs and the outputs are equal, a system might not appear to change at all. It is in a state of balance. You considered balanced chemical equations earlier in this program.

Even simple systems can have more than one input and one output. For example, trees take in water through their roots, carbon dioxide from the air, and energy through their leaves. Trees expel oxygen and water vapor through their leaves and give off heat as a result of burning stored energy during respiration. The rate that material, such as water, moves into or out of a system, such as a tree, often varies. For example, trees in many parts of North America take in more water in summer when they are growing than in winter when they may be dormant.

How does changing one part of a system affect the whole system? A common saying is "Change is the only constant." An important feature of natural systems is that they are dynamic—they are always changing. Changes in systems are identified by comparing the inputs (I) and the outputs (O). If the inputs are greater than the outputs, the change in the system is positive. If the outputs are greater than the inputs, the change in the system is negative.

NOTES:

Systems Are Everywhere, continued

An outdoor pool is a good example (figure 10.4). The pool receives water from precipitation, and additional water can be added from a faucet. The pool loses water through evaporation. The inputs are water from the faucet and precipitation. The output is evaporation.

When inputs equal output, the volume of water in the pool remains the same. However, if the pool receives more water from precipitation and the output remains the same, the water level in the pool will increase. The change in volume is positive. If more water evaporates and the inputs remain the same, the water level in the pool will decrease. This change in volume is negative. Water circulation in the filtration system does not change the total amount of water. You can show this as

$$\pm \text{ change in pool volume} = \text{inputs} - \text{outputs}$$
$$= (I_{faucet} + I_{rain}) - (O_{evaporation}).$$

Systems can also be characterized by how fast they change mass or volume. You studied rates of change earlier in the year when you saw that velocity was the change in distance over an amount of time, or $v = \frac{\Delta x}{\Delta t}$. With systems, the **flux** tells how fast, or the rate, that matter enters or leaves a system. And just like with inputs and outputs, systems can have fluxes in and fluxes out.

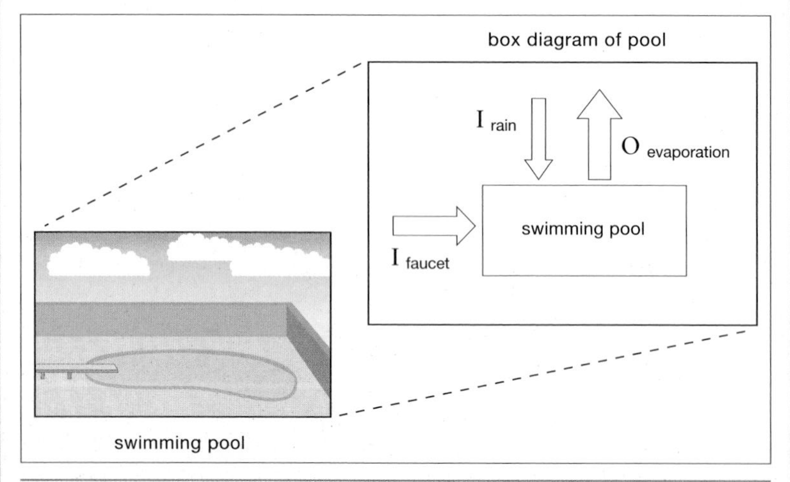

▲ **Figure 10.4 Box diagram of a pool system.** Box diagrams are a way to visually represent systems. The arrows show inputs (I) and outputs (O) of mass to the box. The subscripts show how to label independent inputs and outputs. Arrow sizes represent the amounts of mass (water) entering and leaving the box.

NOTES:

With the pool example, during July the pool might receive water input that changes the level at a rate of 5 centimeters (cm) per month (about 2 inches [in] of summer rain). At the same time, evaporation might equal a net loss at a rate of 15 cm per month. You can see that there is a net decrease in water level of 10 cm per month. This is expressed in an equation as volume (V):

$$\pm \text{ rate of change in pool volume} = \frac{\Delta \text{Volume}}{\Delta \text{time}} = \frac{\Delta V}{\Delta t} \text{ or}$$

$$\frac{\Delta V}{\Delta t} = (\text{flux in} - \text{flux out}).$$

One point is very important. Simple equations like this can be used for any kind of system. But you do need to check that the units match on each side of the equation. Rather than volume per time, each side of the equation could also have units such as mass of carbon per time.

Pool systems tend to change, but a balance can be maintained between the inputs and outputs. You already investigated such balances in chemical systems in *Interactions Are Interesting*. With a pool system, changes in the precipitation or evaporation rates might change the water level of the pool. The manager of a pool would try to maintain the same water level in the pool by adding water from a faucet. In this case, the rate of change is zero and—you guessed it—the flux in has to equal the flux out. This is easy to show.

$$\pm \text{ rate of change in pool volume} = 0 = (\text{flux in} - \text{flux out}) \text{ or}$$

$$\text{flux in} = \text{flux out}$$

The inputs and outputs into natural systems change, but overall they need to maintain a balance. For example, water plays an important role in your body. On average, 55–65 percent of your body consists of water. A healthy body has just the right amount of water inside and outside each cell. When you sweat from hot weather or exercise, your body loses water (figure 10.5). Your body tries to regain balance by sending a message to make you feel thirsty. In response, you drink more water. Your increased water input balances your increased water output.

Your body systems can get out of balance if you don't have access to water. Without water, your body systems will have difficulty functioning properly and their malfunction could lead to death. Inputs and outputs, such as water in our body systems, are an important part of systems. These inputs and outputs change to maintain a balanced system.

▲ **Figure 10.5 Athletes competing.** You can sweat up to 1 liter of water per hour while exercising or competing in sports. You must balance this output with an input—drinking water or a sports drink.

Topic: systems
Go to: www.scilinks.org
Code: 2Inquiry505

Answers to Stop and Think—Part II, SE pages 506–507

1a. Students should realize that their bathtub system was open because matter can enter and leave the system.

1b. The input was the water coming from the faucet. The output was the water exiting the hole in the bottom of the container.

2. Student diagrams should show the basic elements in figure T10.2. Students should be able to to develop accurate box diagrams like this figure throughout the rest of the unit.

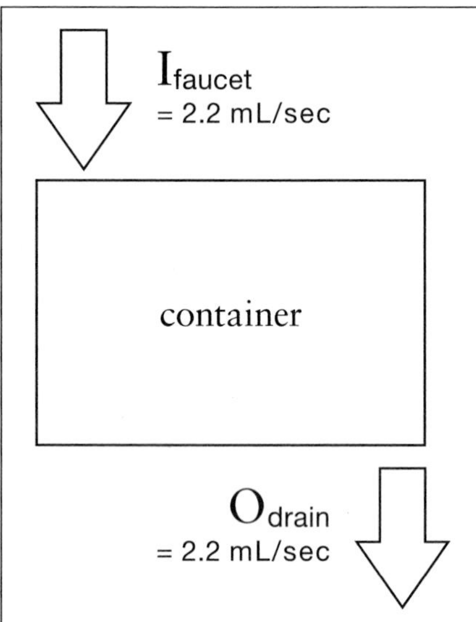

▲ **Figure T10.2 Box diagram for a bathtub.** This diagram shows inputs and outputs for the bathtub simulation.

3. Be open to how students show improvements in their new box diagrams. Depending on the complexity of the diagrams, the improvements can include a T-table that lists inputs and outputs. Other students might include a key for symbols or a scale.

4a. The T-table should show inputs of \$1,600 and outputs totaling \$1,455.

4b. The worker has a net increase of \$145 per month of extra money to support all other expenses, or roughly \$36.25 per week.

4c. If the worker spends money on nothing else, he or she can accrue a maximum of \$1,740 of savings per year.

5. Students should carefully group inputs and outputs to the farm pond. Answer 5e is correct. You might also want to see if students can use simple algebraic manipulation to come up with answer 5c, which is also correct. The other answers do not properly couple inputs and outputs for the farm pond system.

6a. Students need to convert 1.2 L to 1,200 milliliters (mL).

$$(1.2\,\not{L}) \times \left(\frac{1{,}000\ \text{mL}}{1\,\not{L}}\right) = 1{,}200\ \text{mL}$$

6b. It might be easy for students to "see" the answer to this problem right away. Unless they can write out the problem such that units cancel, however, they will have difficulty with more complex problems.

The change in volume to fill the container is 1.2 L. The flux in is 400 milliliters per minute (mL/min), and the flux out is 300 mL/min. This question is analogous to, "How long does one have to drive at 30 kilometers/hour to go a total distance of 60 kilometers?"

Stop & THINK

PART II

Work individually or with one partner to complete the following tasks. Record your answers in your science notebook.

1. Answer the following questions about the bathtub system from Part I.
   - **a.** Was the bathtub system open or closed? Explain your reasoning.
   - **b.** Identify the inputs and outputs.
2. Return to the box diagram in figure 10.3 in Part I. Redraw this diagram in your science notebook using vocabulary and ideas from the reading *Systems Are Everywhere*. Use as a model the diagram in figure 10.4. Assume the system is balanced and use the flow rate you calculated in Step 2 of Part I.

   Include the input and output fluxes on your diagram. You will need to adjust the number and size of the input and output arrows to fit the bathtub subsystem.
3. Look back at the drawing of the bathtub system you created in Part I. Explain how the box diagram you just created in Question 2 is different from the drawing in figure 10.3.
4. Imagine that a full-time worker earning \$10 per hour is paid \$1,600 per month. The worker has monthly expenses for housing (\$700); food (\$350); utilities (water, electricity, heat; \$150); transportation (car insurance, repairs, gas; \$100); car loan payment (\$75); and medical insurance (\$80).
   - **a.** Make a T-table showing inputs and outputs per month to the worker's bank account.
   - **b.** Does the worker have money left each month for other needs, such as clothing, vacations, going out to eat, or buying furniture or recreational items? Explain the net change in the system per month.
   - **c.** How much extra does the worker gain per year? Is it enough to buy a new car?
5. Figure 10.6 shows a farm pond with inputs and outputs. They are from streams (str), rain, evaporation (evap), and a spring. Which expression best shows the net change in water volume in the farm pond? Explain in your science notebook which answer you selected.

$$\frac{\Delta V}{\Delta t} = (\text{flux in} - \text{flux out}) \text{ or, rearranging and using values,}$$

$$1{,}200 \text{ mL} = \left(400\frac{\text{mL}}{\text{min}} - 300\frac{\text{mL}}{\text{min}}\right) \times \Delta t$$

$$= \left(100\frac{\text{mL}}{\text{min}}\right) \times \Delta t, \quad \text{or}$$

$$\Delta t = 1{,}200 \cancel{\text{mL}} \times \left(\frac{1 \text{ min}}{100 \cancel{\text{mL}}}\right) = 12 \text{ min}$$

6c. This is the same as Question 6a, with the change in volume = −1,200 mL and the input going to zero.

$$\pm \text{ change in volume} = (\text{flux in}) - (\text{flux out})$$

$$-1{,}200 \text{ mL} = \left(0\frac{\text{mL}}{\text{min}} - 300\frac{\text{mL}}{\text{min}}\right) \times t$$

$$= \left(-300\frac{\text{mL}}{\text{min}}\right) \times t, \quad \text{or, rearranging,}$$

$$t = -1{,}200 \cancel{\text{mL}} \times \left(\frac{1 \text{ min}}{-300 \cancel{\text{mL}}}\right) = 4 \text{ min}$$

6d. This may seem like a trickier question, but it is easy when students identify the knowns and unknowns in the system. The knowns are change in volume ($\Delta V = +1{,}000$ mL), change in time ($\Delta t = 5$ minutes), and flux out (−300 mL/min). The unknown is the flux in. The general equation in Question 6a is rearranged as

$$\text{flux in} = \frac{\Delta V}{\Delta t} + \text{flux out}$$

$$= \frac{1{,}000 \text{ mL}}{5 \text{ min}} + 300\frac{\text{mL}}{\text{min}}$$

$$= 200\frac{\text{mL}}{\text{min}} + 300\frac{\text{mL}}{\text{min}}$$

$$= 500\frac{\text{mL}}{\text{min}}.$$

Process and Procedure

Part III: Fast-food Flowchart

Materials

none

Use a reading strategy appropriate for your class to read the two paragraphs that introduce this final part of the activity. Explain that they will be thinking about a more complex system—a fast-food restaurant. They will need to think about all the parts and interactions that are possible in this system. Tell them to follow Step 1 and read *Subsystems within Systems* to learn some of the ways larger, more complex systems differ from a simple system such as a bathtub.

In Step 2, tell students to begin answering the questions about fast-food restaurant systems. They should record their answers in their science notebooks. Check their progress as they work on Steps 2 and 3 and provide help as needed.

a. Change in volume = $(I_{str} + I_{spring} + I_{rain}) + (O_{evap} + O_{str})$
b. Change in volume = $(I_{str} + I_{rain}) - (O_{evap} + O_{str} + I_{spring})$
c. Change in volume = $(I_{str} - O_{str}) - O_{evap} + (I_{spring} + I_{rain})$
d. Change in volume = $(O_{evap} + O_{str}) - (I_{str} - I_{spring} + I_{rain})$
e. Change in volume = $(I_{str} + I_{spring} + I_{rain}) - (O_{evap} + O_{str})$

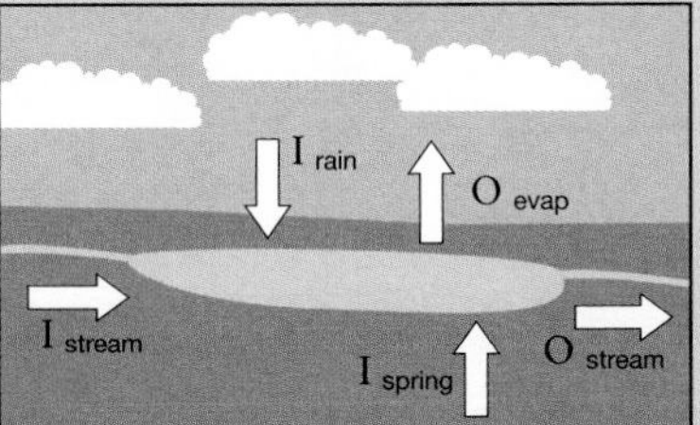

Figure 10.6 Farm pond box diagram. This box diagram for a farm pond has three inputs (stream, rain, spring) and two outputs (evaporation, stream). What balance of these inputs and outputs shows the net change in water level for the farm pond?

6 Recall the container from Part I. It had a hole that let water flow out and a volume of 1.2 liters (L). Imagine that water flows in at a rate of 400 milliliters per minute (400 mL/min), and flows out at 300 mL/min.

a. How many milliliters (mL) does the container hold?
b. How long does it take for the container to fill?
c. If the container is full and water coming in is turned off, how long would you predict for the container to drain to empty?
d. Imagine that the container is empty and it still has a flow rate out the drain of 300 mL/min. What flow rate into the container (input) will give 1.0 L of water in 5 minutes?

Part III: Fast-food Flowchart

Materials

none

Process and Procedure

The bathtub you modeled is a simple system. Other systems you will encounter could be more complicated. They may have multiple inputs and outputs. You will see that natural water systems may be like this. But for now, let's use another example to represent how mass moves through a system. You are probably familiar with this system—a fast-food restaurant.

NOTES:

When did you last have french fries? A lot of people enjoy eating french fries, yet they take for granted that they can buy them ready to eat. What does it take to get an order of french fries into your hands? Where do they come from and how many steps are required before you purchase them? You can answer these questions with a systems approach. In Part III of the activity, you will work in a team to investigate how french fries move through a fast-food restaurant.

1. Large systems often include smaller systems within them. Before diagramming a fast-food restaurant system, read *Systems within Systems*.

READING

Systems within Systems

Large systems may have other systems contained within them. These are called **subsystems**. Subsystems can have their own parts and interactions. For example, a pasture where cattle graze is a system that also includes interactions between grasses and cattle. Each plant also constitutes a subsystem that interacts with the air and soil. An amusement park is another example of a system. Each ride and concession stand is a subsystem within the larger amusement park. The aquarium in figure 10.7 shows another example of subsystems within a larger system.

Figure 10.7
Systems and subsystems. Examine the things in this aquarium. How many subsystems can you find in the photograph?

508 Unit 3 Moving Matter

Answers to Step 2, SE page 509

2a. The major parts of a fast-food restaurant system include equipment, a building, workers, and customers. There is also matter (food) and energy (electricity) flowing into and out of the system.

2b. Inputs are customers, frozen food, carbonation tanks, drinks, napkins, straws, and money, to name a few. Outputs include cooked food, paper products, empty carbonation tanks, and waste.

2c. If students are only thinking about 1 restaurant, the boundaries would be the restaurant itself and perhaps its parking lot. However, they might also think about a chain of restaurants. The boundaries would then include all the restaurants in the chain.

2d. A fast-food restaurant is a subsystem of the fast-food restaurant system and might be a subsystem of a franchise. Because a fast-food restaurant uses energy (electricity) to operate its freezers, cooking areas, and so on, it is a subsystem of the city utilities. Or a fast-food restaurant could be thought of as 1 food source (subsystem) of many food sources (the system) that are used by people. Accept a variety of answers as long as students support their ideas.

2e. Subsystems include the grill area, the refrigeration system, the french fry cooking area, the system needed for employees to get their work done effectively (work schedule for personnel), the parking lot, and the drive-through system. Accept a variety of answers as long as students support their ideas.

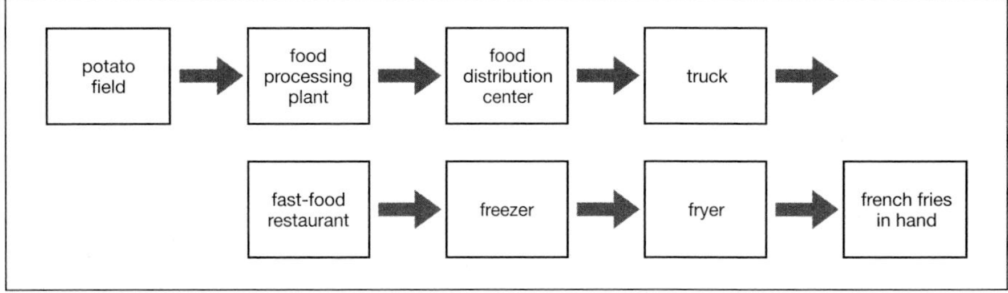

▲ **Figure T10.3 Flowchart of a potato.** This flowchart diagrams the path of a potato from the field to the restaurant to the cooked fries in your hands.

The function of a whole system is different from the function of each of its parts. As a whole, a car is a mode of transportation. The parts of a car are subsystems with functions including gasoline combustion, steering, braking, and lighting. A car would not function properly without each of these smaller subsystems.

Life on Earth is also a web of natural and human-made systems. Your body and life are part of a network of subsystems and larger systems. For example, your body consists of subsystems such as the circulatory, respiratory, reproductive, and muscular systems. These subsystems interact with one another. When you exercise and use your muscles, your heart beats faster and your respiration increases. Oxygen from the air moves into your lungs and is absorbed into the blood. Then the circulatory system increases the flow of oxygen-rich blood to the muscles. You also are a part of larger systems such as a family system, a community, a school system, an ecosystem, and even the solar system.

Here's another example of subsystems—using the World Wide Web. From your Web browser, your computer connects to an Internet service provider (ISP). When connected to the ISP, you become part of its network. The ISP can in turn connect you to a larger network and so on. Each network is its own system. Your personal computer also consists of hardware and software systems including the processor, power supply, keyboard, operating system, and programs.

We are surrounded by systems. We are parts of systems. You are able to investigate and determine the size and properties of these systems.

2. Using what you know about systems, subsystems, and fast-food restaurants, answer the following questions.
   a. What are the major parts of a fast-food restaurant system?
   b. What are some inputs and outputs of a fast-food restaurant system?
   c. What are the boundaries of a fast-food system?
   d. How do you think a fast-food restaurant is a subsystem of a larger system?

For example, money flows into and out of a fast-food restaurant. The flow of money is part of a larger economic system. We can think about a fast-food restaurant as a subsystem of the economic system.

   e. Think of a fast-food restaurant as the larger system. What are 3 or more subsystems of the fast-food restaurant system?
3. Develop a diagram of a series of subsystems showing where the french fries come from and how they get into your hands. Where were the fries before they got into your hands? Where were they before that? And before that?

You may have developed a diagram like figure 10.8 in the activity *Entertaining Systems*.

Chapter 10 The Water System 509

In Step 3, students begin tracing where french fries come from using a diagram of a series of subsystems. Tell students to think about each step required to get a french fry. If students have trouble working backward, suggest they work forward from a potato. They should think about where potatoes come from and the processes necessary to end up with french fries at a fast-food restaurant. Each box in their diagrams should represent a system. You might point out that this diagram is different from the one they created in Part I because they were only diagramming 1 system and its fluxes. This diagram will not include fluxes.

Answers to Step 3, SE pages 509–510

3. Students should draw a diagram similar to figure T10.3.

Once students have drawn diagrams for Step 3, in Step 4 they should think about other systems that the fast-food system interacts with.

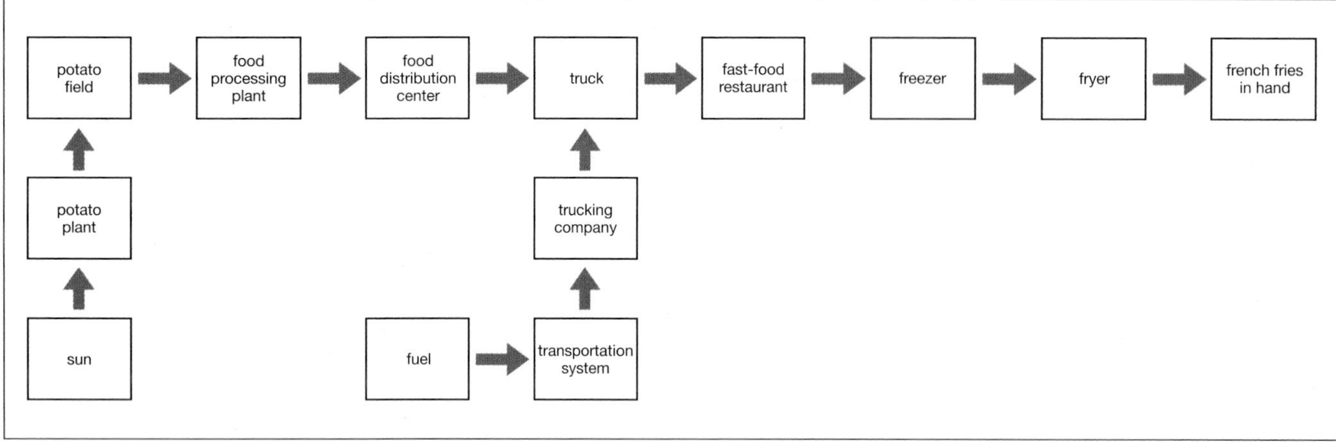

▲ **Figure T10.4 Other subsystems for french fries.** This flowchart elaborates on subsystems that contribute to producing fries at a restaurant.

For example, if students drew a box in their diagrams representing the truck that brings frozen french fries to the restaurant, then this truck is part of a trucking company, which is a system within the transportation system. They should add boxes to their diagrams that represent these systems. Then students should consider how energy flows through these systems. They should add boxes to their diagrams that represent energy. Ask the following probing questions if students are unsure how to include energy in their diagrams:

- "What energy might be required to make a french fry?"
- "What energy might be required for any of the systems in your diagram to function?"

After students have added side chains to their diagrams, in Step 5 they draw a circle around the fast-food restaurant system and 1 other system in their diagrams. The number of systems students add and how well they incorporate energy into their diagrams will help you assess student understanding. A student who uses the systems approach well will have a broad perspective that considers all the possible aspects of a system.

Answers to Steps 4–5, SE pages 510–511

4. Students should draw a diagram similar to figure T10.4, but their boxes might be labeled differently. Make sure they describe the interactions they have diagrammed. Encourage students to include energy in their descriptions.
5. Figure T10.5 shows a possible diagram. In addition to this example, other systems that students might identify include the transportation system, franchise system, agricultural system, or power system. Make sure students circle all the subsystems associated with the system they have chosen.

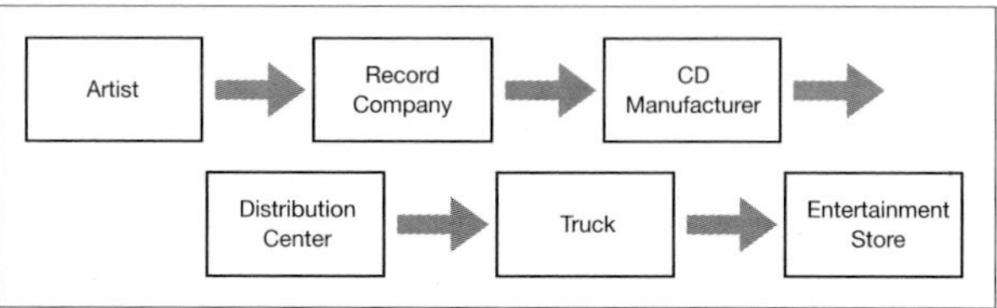

▲ **Figure 10.8 Entertainment system flow diagram.** This flow diagram shows steps to get a CD to a store. Each box is a subsystem. The arrows indicate matter moving through the systems. For example, a CD manufacturer needs music from the record company before it can produce a CD.

4. Pick 1 subsystem (box) in your diagram. Describe and draw any interactions it has with other systems. Consider the movement of both matter and energy in this side chain. Where was the matter and energy before arriving at that system? Where was the matter and energy before that? Share your ideas with your team and use the diagram in figure 10.9 as a model.

For example, you might have labeled the first box before the fries were in hand, "heat lamp." A side chain off of a heat lamp might include the electricity that makes the lamp work. The electricity is supplied by a power plant that may get its power from fossil fuels.

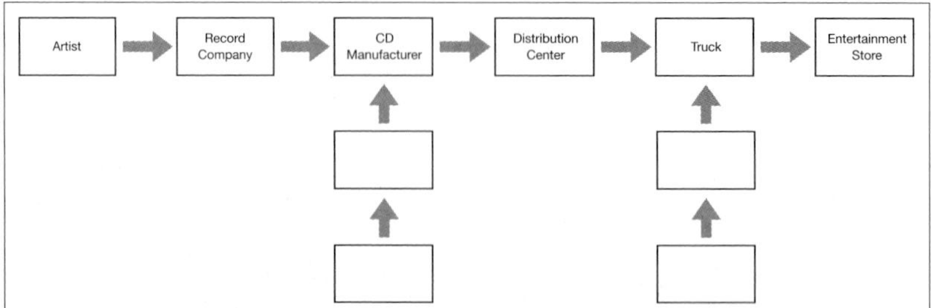

▲ **Figure 10.9 Interactions between subsystems.** Add one or more chains of boxes to your previous diagram. The new chain of boxes (subsystems) represents the flow of matter and energy into one of the subsystems in your diagram. For example, what does the truck need to function?

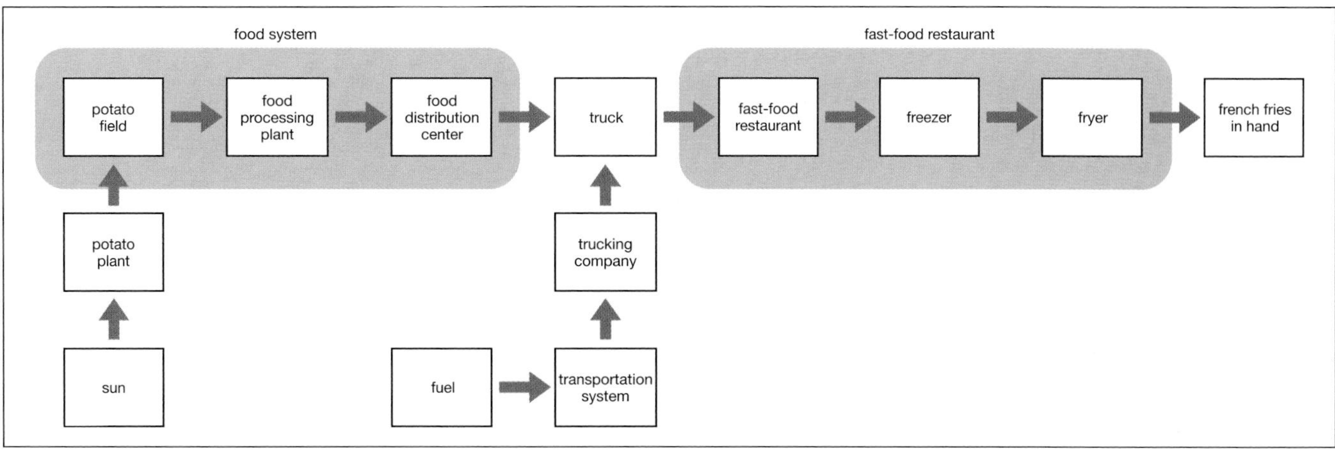

▲ **Figure T10.5 Flowchart with systems circled.** This flowchart distinguishes between the food system and the restaurant system. Each is a part of producing fries for a customer.

In Step 6, students are given data about french fry use. From these data, students should determine the fluxes in and fluxes out for the fast-food restaurant system. In Step 7, students use the fluxes in and the fluxes out that they calculated in Step 6 for a box diagram of the fast-food restaurant system. Remind students that their box diagrams should look similar to student book figure 10.4, the box diagram of a pool system shown in Part II. After students have completed these steps, tell them to answer the *Reflect and Connect* questions individually.

Answers to Reflect and Connect are on TE page 512.

5. Draw circles around the subsystems that are part of the fast-food restaurant system. Circle "fast-food restaurant system." Identify another subsystem in your diagram and draw the boundaries for that subsystem. Label the system you have identified.
6. Use the following data about french fries to calculate the input and output fluxes. Label the inputs and outputs and record the fluxes as kilograms per week (kg/wk) in the diagram.
   - Fry Daze fast-food restaurant receives a delivery of 50 cases of french fries every week.
   - Each case weighs 20 kilograms (kg).
   - Every week, 5 percent of the french fries spoil before they can be sold, with the rest purchased by hungry customers.
7. To check your understanding of fluxes, draw a box diagram of the fast-food restaurant system similar to the one in figure 10.4. Show the fluxes of french fries for the restaurant that you calculated in Step 6. Adjust the size of the input and output arrows to fit the french fry subsystem.

Reflect and Connect

Answer the following questions on your own in your science notebook.

1. What are some of the characteristics of systems? Look at the list of characteristics you developed in *Entertaining Systems*. How do your previous ideas about systems compare with what you learned in this activity? Describe any similarities and differences.

Decide if a strategy such as a T-table or a Venn diagram is useful here.

2. Describe how the following changes would affect the fast-food restaurant system from Part III. The fast-food restaurant sells fewer french fries each day.
   a. Will the number of fries in the restaurant increase or decrease?
   b. How can the owner of the fast-food restaurant adjust the system to maintain the same amount of fries stored in the freezer? Explain your answer.
   c. Imagine that potato crops in Idaho are damaged and the cost of potatoes increases by 5 percent. Estimate how the costs associated with the fluxes in your box diagram from Step 6 in Part III might change.
3. Does a systems approach help you view fast-food restaurants differently? Explain your ideas in your science notebook.

Answers to Steps 6–7, SE page 511

6. French fries coming into the fast-food restaurant is the only input. The two outputs are spoiled french fries and sold french fries. Make sure students include these values in their diagrams in Step 7:
   - Flux in per week (fries bought): I_{buy} = 50 cases/wk × 20 kg/case = 1,000 kg/wk
   - Flux out (fries spoiled): O_{spoil} = 5% × 1,000 kg/wk = 50 kg/wk
   - Flux out (fries purchased): O_{sold} = 1,000 kg/wk − 50 kg/wk = 950 kg/wk
7. Student diagrams should include 1 flux in and 2 fluxes out of fries (figure T10.1). They should include the rates on their diagrams, and the arrows in the diagrams should be scaled to match the rates. Students may come up with different labels for their inputs and outputs. Accept a variety of answers, as long as students have diagrammed the system logically.

Answers to Reflect and Connect, SE page 511

1. Characteristics include subsystems, boundaries, inputs, outputs, and interactions between components. Students also might mention that systems can be open or closed, or be balanced or dynamic. Make sure students compare these answers with their previous ideas. They might recognize that they knew some of the characteristics, but they didn't use systems terminology.

   After students answer this question, it will no longer be necessary to display the characteristic lists from the activity *Entertaining Systems*.

2a. Make sure students give answers that are consistent with the inputs and outputs they diagrammed in Step 7. If the input (fries purchased, or I_{buy}) and the output (fries spoiled, or O_{spoil}) don't change, the fast-food restaurant will have to store more french fries. Or it may have to accept that more will spoil. To remedy the change, the fast-food restaurant will either have to order fewer french fries or let more fries spoil to keep french fries from accumulating. The second option is less cost effective.

2b. The fast-food restaurant owner will have to pay for the same amount of frozen french fries delivered to the restaurant. The owner might either increase the cost of fries sold or try to decrease the amount of french fries lost to spoilage. Look for answers that take into account all the possible changes.

2c. Quantitatively, it will cost the owner 5 percent more to maintain the flux in of french fries. Given that about 5 percent of prepared french fries will spoil and not be purchased, the owner will have to raise the price by a little more than 5 percent in order to offset cost increases and maintain the same profit margin. As an alternative, the owner could leave the price of fries unchanged and raise the price of 2 other products about 2.5 percent to maintain profits. There are numerous permutations on how the restaurant owner might respond to changes in costs for raw products.

3. This is an opportunity for students to think about why a systems approach might be useful. Students might explain that they had never thought about all the processes and equipment necessary to end up with a french fry in a fast-food restaurant. If students have worked at a fast-food restaurant, they might have thought about what happens within the restaurant system but not what happens before the food (french fries) got to the restaurant.

EXPLORE

Beyond the Drinking Fountain

Activity Overview

Now that students have had a chance to expand their understanding of systems using a restaurant system, they will turn their attention to another system. It is one that they rely on each day—their local water system. In *Beyond the Drinking Fountain*, students will work to answer the questions, "Where does the water in your school come from?" and "Where does the water in your school go?" They will research their local water system by accessing data from community resources.

EXPLORE

Beyond the Drinking Fountain

When did you last have a drink of water? You know how important water is. You cannot live without it, yet many people take water for granted. They turn on the faucet, and there it is. They use it to drink, to cook, and to clean. But where does the water in the faucet come from? And where does it go?

In *Beyond the Drinking Fountain*, you will work in a team to explore your local water system in order to answer these and other questions. As you do this activity, be sure to use what you learned from previous work with bathtubs, pools, and restaurants and recall how you diagrammed inputs and outputs. This will help you develop a better understanding of your local water system, both before and after faucets or drinking fountains.

Materials

For each team of 3 students

access to resource materials

Process and Procedure

Every community has important local issues related to water. Perhaps county officials have discovered that a local fishing hole is contaminated. Maybe the city council is trying to decide whether or not to add fluoride to the water. Is there a water shortage? Imagine that because of recent events around a local water issue, your teacher has asked your class to prepare a display for the school hallway that will both interest and inform fellow students about the local water system. You will work in teams to prepare a proposal for the layout of the display. Your proposal will include a diagram and related information about the water system.

You will not actually build the display, so you can propose any type of display you want, even if the materials to make it are hard to find or expensive. The goal is to obtain information and decide on an effective way to present the information.

1. What does your team know about the local water system? Write in your science notebook answers to the following questions.
   a. Where do you think that the water in your school comes from?
   b. Where do you think that the water in your school goes?

   Answer Questions 1a–b with written phrases as well with as diagrams to show your thinking.

Before You Teach

Background Information

Where does your drinking water come from?

Every community needs access to a clean supply of water. In some parts of the country, people drink water that comes from surface water, such as lakes, rivers, and reservoirs. Sometimes these sources are close to the community and sometimes they are located a great distance away. When you think about the source of your drinking water, consider the entire watershed. A watershed is an area of land that catches rain or snow and drains to specific marshes, streams, rivers, lakes, or subsurface regions. Watersheds come in all shapes and sizes and cross all political boundaries.

In some places, people rely on wells for water. These wells tap the groundwater found in aquifers. Aquifers are natural reservoirs under Earth's surface. Aquifers reside in rocks that have cracks or tiny holes, or pores, that hold water much as a sponge does. Because aquifers can span the borders of many states, it is important to remember that activities at a distance might affect the quality of a local source of groundwater.

As you and your students conduct research about your local water system, you may find it helpful to keep in mind the distinction between the water budgets of natural systems and the patterns of water use within those systems. The water budget of a natural system is the amount of water contained within or moving through the system. In contrast, water use refers to how much water is taken and used by households and businesses in a community. Water use is a subsystem of the water budget. It reflects water that is rerouted from the natural system and used by humans.

To illustrate, total water use in the United States in 2000 was just over 400 billion gallons per day (408,000 Mgal/d). Compare this with the budget in a natural system, the Mississippi River: the discharge rate of water from the Mississippi River to the Gulf of Mexico is roughly 420,000 Mgal/d. Thus, the average rate of water use in the entire United States is almost equal to the flow rate of the largest river in continental North America (which is also about the seventh largest water discharge in the world).

You and your students might find that there is more or less information about one of these aspects (water budget, water use) of your water system. Be flexible enough to work with the information you find. As you and your students research your local water system, you are also likely to encounter information about water quality. Although this is an important issue, its consideration is beyond the scope of this activity. Direct your students away from this type of information, unless they want to consider it as a special interest.

Recommendations for how to access information about your local water system are provided in the *Advance Preparation*. Information about some of the common units your students might encounter when accessing water data is provided in *FYI—Units for Water Volumes and Flow Rates* in the student book. This FYI includes analogies to help students visualize the large volumes of water.

Some amounts were estimated for the purpose of these analogies. For instance, the size of a public pool was estimated to be 75 feet (ft; or 25 yards) long by 36 ft wide (6 lanes, each about 6 ft wide). Water depth was estimated at 4 ft deep. This makes the volume of the water in the pool 10,800 ft^3, or 80,784 gallons (gal). Since 1 acre-foot (af) is equal to 43,560 cubic feet (ft^3) or 325,851 gal, the amount of water in 1 af would

2. Research your local water system with your team to answer more specifically Questions 1a–b. Write answers in your science notebook, using both sentences and diagrams with labels. Consider getting information on the following:
   - The boundaries of your local water system
   - The parts or subsystems in the local water system (for example, its use in houses, business, and agriculture)
   - The interactions between parts of the local water system
   - Whether the system is dynamic and changing or the source of water is constant
3. Gather data about the flow of water, or fluxes, in your local water system. Do these amounts change over time? Record your data as a box diagram, with values for inputs and outputs, in the proposal for your display.

As you find information, you might encounter a variety of units used to report water data. Read more about these units in *FYI—Units for Water Volumes and Flow Rates*.

4. As your team does research, note interesting information to display about your local water system. Consider information about local water issues, interesting facts or figures, or creative ways of displaying data.
5. Prepare a design for the layout of your display. The display needs to inform and interest other students in your school about the local water system. The layout should include the following.
   a. A sketch of the hallway display
   b. A description of any visuals you are proposing to use in the display, including the box diagram
   c. Examples of data you have found
   d. A list of all references and sources of information
6. Share your team's display layout with the class.

fill the swimming pool four times (325,851 gal/80,784 gal/pool = 4.0034 pool).

Figure T10.6 provides conversion factors that might be helpful if you or your students pursue analogies of your own.

Materials

For the teacher

recent newspaper clippings, magazine articles, or videos addressing local or regional water issues (optional)

For each team of 3 students

access to resource materials

Advance Preparation

Before you start this activity, decide how much research your students will do, what portion of the research can be assigned as homework, and what resources you will be able to point students toward. Time is a big factor. The amount of time needed to research local water issues varies depending on how accessible the information is and how much information is available.

Obtain some basic information about your local water utilities. Most urban and suburban areas have well-developed utilities with helpful maps and annual publications. Request copies of these. For example, excellent information on the source region, water use, treatment, quality, and so on, is available on the Web for the East Bay Municipal Utility District serving the Oakland and Berkeley areas in Northern California. For areas away from towns and cities, you may have a rural water association or regional water board that helps citizens obtain water. Or a county board may have the responsibility of granting permits to drill new wells.

It can be very effective to have a local water utilities expert visit your class. This would also demonstrate professional possibilities to students. If you do this, have students prepare questions in advance to ask the expert.

Conduct some research of your own on your local water system before you have students begin this investigation. You will need to identify the boundaries of the local water system in order to make students' research manageable. As you think about which boundaries to identify, consider the amount of information available about your local water system. This will vary greatly depending on location.

The following list includes possible resources, accessible at the time of this printing, to obtain information about your local water system. Use the keywords and titles in a search to find the most current Web sites. Also note that the *TRCD* has an example summary of information and data on water resources (procurement, treatment, waste treatment) for the Colorado Springs Utilities (CSU) in Colorado.

- *Local water utilities*
- *American Water Works Association, water utility home pages.* Search by state, then local utilities. This association provides an annual water quality report, including information about water sources, for that utility region. Remember that it is easy for students to be distracted by water quality data, which are not the focus of this activity.
- *United States Geological Survey (USGS) Water Resources of the United States.* Search by state.

Conversion Factors		
Area		
1 acre	=	43,560 square feet (ft^2)
1 acre	=	4,047 square meters (m^2)
Volume (= Area × height)		
1 acre-foot	=	325,851 gallons (gal)
1 acre-foot	=	43,560 cubic feet (ft^3)
1 cubic foot	=	7.48 gallons (gal)
1 cubic foot	=	0.02832 cubic meters (m^3)
1 gallon	=	3.7853 liters (L)
1 million gallons	=	3.07 acre-feet (af)
1 cubic kilometer (km^3)	=	1,000,000,000 cubic meters (m^3)
1 cubic kilometer (km^3)	=	35,320,000,000 cubic feet (ft^3)
1 cubic kilometer (km^3)	=	81,080 acre-feet (af)
Flow Rate		
1 million gallons per day (Mgal/d)	=	1.121 thousand acre-feet per year (×10^3 af/yr)
1 million gallons per day (Mgal/d)	=	0.001380 thousand cubic feet per second (×10^3 ft^3/yr)

▲ **Figure T10.6 Table of conversion factors.** This table shows some useful conversion factors for water volumes and flow rates.

Each state has a home page titled "Water Resources of [State]" with links to information about water data, water studies, publications, projects, news, and related sites. The amount of information can be overwhelming, so help students focus.

- *EPA Surf Your Watershed.* Locate your watershed. A watershed profile is provided that includes information on water specific to a watershed. A map shows the location of the watershed. Information about the rivers, streams, lakes, and aquifers is provided.
- *EnviroMapper for Watersheds.* The EPA's Web site provides interactive geographic information systems (GIS) functionality using environmental spatial data. You can map your watershed with different data layers, including overall watershed characterization. It features multiple mapping features, including the ability to zoom from a zip code region to a watershed to the state.
- *EPA Office of Ground Water and Drinking Water.* Click on your state to access an overview of your state's drinking water. Access your state's water quality report, your local watershed or groundwater source, and other information. This Web site may include information about where your drinking water comes from.
- *Local water conservancy districts.* This resource varies by location. Some sites are quite extensive. Do a Web search of your state's water conservancy districts.
- *National Atlas of the United States.* Use the link to make maps, then generate state maps with layers. Select *Boundaries*, then *State Capitals* and *State Names*; then select *Water*, then *Hydrologic Units (Watersheds)* and *Streams and Waterbodies*; finally, select *Map Reference* then *Cities and Towns*, *Sample Research Summary for Colorado Springs Utilities, Colorado.*

Finding information about your local water system might seem daunting, especially with the large number of information sources. How should you get started? It might help to read about an actual search for water information in Colorado Springs, Colorado, home of BSCS.

Colorado Springs and the outlying areas have a population of about 600,000 people. This large city is located in a semiarid environment. Water is of great importance. Before we began the search, we reminded ourselves of the questions we were trying to answer: "Where does our water come from?" and "Where does our water go?"

Our first step was to go to the water resources department of the local utilities company. There we picked up the small *Fact Book* that describes water resources and information related to water use. It also lists the water sources, water reservoirs, water treatment plants, and how much water each holds. This was a good start, but we were hoping for more information. After some discussion, we were given the name and phone number of an education coordinator who works with teachers and provides additional information through programs and class visits. The education coordinator gave us a brochure called *Water: Colorado Springs Lifeline*. This brochure, distributed by Colorado Springs Utilities water resource department, includes the following information:

- descriptions of where Colorado Springs gets its water and where the water is stored
- descriptions of how water is treated and distributed once it arrives in Colorado Springs
- descriptions of where wastewater goes
- a map of the water system
- a brief description of water use
- the history of bringing water to this semiarid region
- plans for providing water in the future
- conservation plans
- education programs

We recommend that you call the water resources department of your local utilities company before dropping by its offices. A call will ensure that you contact the most appropriate person and will allow staff time to gather multiple copies of the information you need. When you call, ask who you should talk with to answer the two questions. Then ask for brochures with that information. Ideally, the brochure would include a map of where the water comes from and where it goes.

Our next step was to search the Web for a Web site maintained by the local utilities company. We looked for links to water resources and the water system. Part of the Colorado Springs Utilities Web site is devoted to education outreach. The local water system is described in this part of the site. We found that the Web site provides less information than the brochure. The following summary represents some of the types of information that we found.

Colorado Springs gets its water from snow that melts and flows into rivers and reservoirs. Most of the water comes from snow accumulated on the western slope of the Rocky Mountains. All the Colorado Springs water comes from surface water sources. Water is brought to Colorado Springs through a complex system of eight major reservoirs and a series of pipelines and pump stations.

Once water has arrived in Colorado Springs, it enters one of three treatment plants. The treated water is stored in covered reservoirs or tanks and eventually distributed to water customers. Wastewater flows to a wastewater treatment plant for processing until it is safe to return to the environment. Treated wastewater either is reused for irrigation purposes (nonpotable water) or is returned to Fountain Creek. Fountain Creek flows to the Arkansas River, which enters the Mississippi River.

Your local utilities might not provide this much information about water resources. If so, you might need to focus on different questions. How are local water resources used? How much water is used? With this approach, you would look at the water use subsystem within your local water system.

Here is a brief summary of the water use information. In 1999, there were about 375,000 commercial and residential water customers in the Colorado Springs area. Including the watering of lawns and gardens, persons at home used an average of 135 gal of water per person per day. This corresponded to about 77 million gallons per day (Mgal/d) for the water district, or just over 28 billion gal per year. Including water contracts to important customers in the military, commercial, and industrial sectors, the daily rate was 198 Mgal/d.

"What goes in, must come out." This adage holds for the municipal water district as well. In 1999, 47 million gal of wastewater were treated per day for return to the water cycle. This is likely less that the amount consumed, 77 Mgal/d, due to garden and lawn irrigation. About 4 percent of the treated wastewater was reused for landscape irrigation in the city. This is called *nonpotable water*, that is, water not treated to the level of drinking quality.

We felt our search was successful. Hopefully, you will be able to find the information you need by following a similar approach.

As You Teach

Outcomes and Indicators of Success

By the end of this activity, students should

1. explain their local water system.

   They will demonstrate their ability by

   - developing a proposal for a hallway display case about their local water system that informs and interests other high school students;
   - describing the boundaries and components of their local water system;
   - describing the flow of matter (water) through the system (quantitatively, if possible); and
   - identifying current water-related issues in their region.

2. be able to apply the use of technology and mathematics to gather and manipulate data about their local water system.

   They will demonstrate their ability by

   - accessing and analyzing water-related data from appropriate Web sites or print media,
   - using common units of water in the analysis,
   - researching volumes of water and rates of water use in their community and using appropriate units to describe those volumes,
   - converting between units such as acre-feet and millions of gallons, and
   - accurately using a variety of units of water volume and flow rate.

3. use the skills and abilities of inquiry to investigate scientific and technological issues.

   They will use their skills and abilities of inquiry by

   - researching a scientific question about where their water comes from and where it goes,
   - using a sketch to represent a model of a proposed display,
   - synthesizing findings, and
   - using mechanisms such as maps, flowcharts, and tables to represent and summarize data sets.

Strategies

Getting Started

Ask students to recall the last time they took a sip of water at the school's drinking fountain. You might want to have students actually go to the fountain and get a drink of water. Ask your students, "Where did the drinking water come from?" and "Where does the drinking water go?" Facilitate a discussion to see how much the students already know about their local water system. Don't

Units for Water Volumes and Flow Rates

Containers. What units of volume are used for the beverages you drink? What units would you use to describe the volume of water in this reservoir?

When you open the refrigerator for a drink, you might reach for a can of soda or a glass of milk. Containers for these drinks have volume as ounces or gallons (or liters). It is much tougher to visualize the volume of water in lakes or river systems, or the water used in towns or cities, each day or each year. How would you do this? You will see different units for volume when researching water systems.

In water systems, scientists often describe volumes with units of **acre-feet** (**af**). This is the volume of water that covers 1 ac of land with water that is 1 ft deep. A football field is a good analogy. Without the end zones, football fields are 300 ft long and 160 ft wide, for a total area of 48,000 square feet (ft^2). One acre of land is 43,560 ft^2, so a football field is within 10 percent of the area of 1 ac of land. Thus, 1 af of water will cover a football field with 1 ft of water, for about 273 of the 300 feet in length. This is to about the 91 yard line. This may sound like a lot of water. But compared with the volumes of water in natural systems, this is a drop in the bucket.

Public utilities often report water use either in acre-feet or in **millions of gallons** (**Mgal**). How much is 1 million gallons of water? A good way to think about this is to compare 1 Mgal of water with 1 af of water. As indicated earlier, 1 af is 43,560 ft^3. Similarly, 1 cubic foot of water equals 7.48 gallons (1 ft^3 = 7.48 gal). Combining these, making sure that units cancel, shows that 1 Mgal is the same as about 3.07 af. Or 1 Mgal is just 1 ac covered with about 3 ft of water.

$$(1\ \cancel{\text{Mgal}}) \times \left(\frac{10^6\ \cancel{\text{gal}}}{1\ \cancel{\text{Mgal}}}\right) \times \left(\frac{1\ \cancel{\text{ft}^3}}{7.48\ \cancel{\text{gal}}}\right) \times \left(\frac{1\ \text{af}}{43{,}560\ \cancel{\text{ft}^3}}\right) = 3.07\ \text{af}$$

For towns or cities, rates of water use are often recorded as **millions of gallons per day**, (**Mgal/d**). In Colorado Springs, Colorado, for example, water

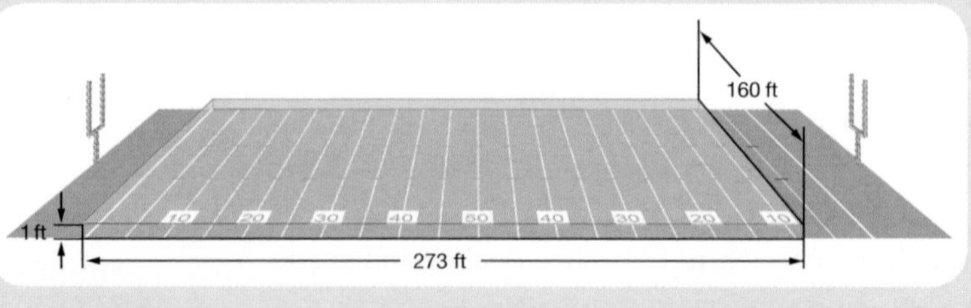

Acre-feet of water. How much water is 1 acre-foot (1 af) of water?

514 Unit 3 Moving Matter

worry about accuracy, just gather information. This can be done as a class or by forming teams of 3 students to address the questions. If you choose to have teams address the questions, be sure to allow time for them to share their thinking. After hearing from students, let them know that they will have an opportunity to check their understanding about their local water system in this activity.

Depending on the level of sophistication of your students, you might be able to keep pressing them in your questioning. For example, see if they can keep answering the question, "Where was the molecule of water before that? And before that? And before that?" If they can, students will effectively be tracing in reverse order steps in a water cycle. You might also press them for ideas of a water molecule after it leaves your community. You could structure this as a three-minute writing or reflection in their science notebooks.

Process and Procedure

Materials

For the teacher

recent newspaper clippings, magazine articles, or videos addressing local or regional water issues (optional)

For each team of 3 students

access to resource materials

Have the students read the first paragraph under *Process and Procedure*. This sets the stage for this investigation. If possible, relate the task to a water issue in your community to make the activity more relevant. Recent newspaper or magazine clippings or video clips from the local news would be valuable.

In Step 1, students discuss their local water system in teams and answer the questions, "Where does the water in your school come from?" and "Where does the water in your school go?" If your *Getting Started* class discussion was rich enough, skip this step.

Students begin research on their local water systems in Step 2. Students focus on learning the parts of their local water system and how those parts interact. Provide some guidelines for the research your students will do. Make it clear what research you have done and what your research expectations are of them. Identify or set the boundaries of the local water system to make the task most manageable. Base this decision on the results of your preliminary search for water information. You might find the most convenient boundaries to be the area served by the local municipal utilities or perhaps the local watershed.

In Step 3, students gather data on flow rates in their local water system. They will use this data to develop a box diagram to represent the system. If possible, they will need to determine the amount of water in each part of the system and the fluxes (volume per time) moving between parts of the system. Students might need help understanding the common units used for reporting water data in the United States. Point them to the *FYI—Units for Water Volumes and Flow Rates*. Notice that values for water volume and flow rates are not reported in metric units. They are reported in acre-feet per year (af/yr), millions of gallons per day (Mgal/d), and cubic feet per second (cfs). Listen and observe as students work in teams to complete the investigation. Your observations will give you information about students' understanding of their local water system and how they go about working in a team to research a topic.

In Step 4, students are encouraged to take note of interesting data that they find. Explain that displays often include visual components such as

use in 1999 for nearly 400,000 customers was at a rate of about 74.3 Mgal/d. How many acre-feet per year (af/yr) is this? It is about 83,000 af/yr. By converting depths of feet to miles, you can show that this would cover a football field in water nearly 16 miles (mi) deep. That's a lot of water!

$$\left(\frac{74.3\ \cancel{\text{Mgal}}}{1\ \cancel{\text{day}}}\right) \times \left(\frac{3.07\ \text{af}}{1\ \cancel{\text{Mgal}}}\right) \times \left(\frac{365.25\ \cancel{\text{day}}}{1\ \text{yr}}\right) = 83{,}314\ \frac{\text{af}}{\text{yr}}$$

$$\left(83{,}314\ \frac{\text{acre}\cdot\cancel{\text{ft}}}{\text{yr}}\right) \times \left(\frac{1\ \text{mile}}{5{,}280\ \cancel{\text{ft}}}\right) = 15.8\ \frac{\text{acre}\cdot\text{mile}}{\text{yr}}$$

Scientists also need to record the rate of water flow in rivers and streams. They do this in units of **cubic feet per second (cfs)**. First, imagine filling a 1-ft cube with water, for a total volume of 1 ft^3. If 1 ft^3 of water passes a point each second, the rate of flow is said to be 1 ft^3 per second, or 1 cfs. While this might not seem like a lot, it is! A flow rate of 1 cfs for one day delivers nearly 2 af of water (1 cfs = 1.983 af/day). Or a flow rate of 1 cfs fills a football field to a depth of 1 ft in just half a day. But this is only for 1 ft^3. A river is many times wider than this.

Water flow rates in cubic feet per second are measured at stream gauges all over North America. Many of these data are available in real time on the World Wide Web from organizations such as the U.S. Geological Survey. When you see rates at thousands of cubic feet per second, this leads to accumulations of millions of acre-feet of water per year—all of which are flowing to the ocean!

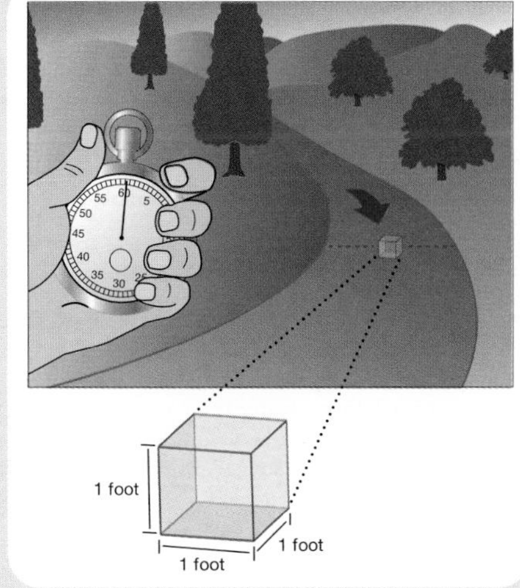

Cubic feet per second of water. How fast does water flow at 1 cubic foot per second (1 cfs)? Is this a large or small amount of water?

interesting facts or figures. Maps, graphs, flowcharts, or box diagrams can be effective for showing the various parts of the water distribution system. Including parts such as the location of the school, major surface water or groundwater features (rivers, lakes, reservoirs, aquifers), water treatment plants, and wastewater treatment plants demonstrates students' knowledge of their local water system. Students should not spend large amounts of time looking for visual components. Instead, as they conduct research, they should note interesting things they find.

In Step 5, students prepare their display layouts for their local water system. The display layouts should have a sketch of what a display of the information they found might look like and a description of any visuals shown in the layout. This display layout will provide written feedback of student understanding of both systems in general and their local water system specifically.

When students have completed their layouts, have them share their findings in Step 6. This will give students a chance to compare what they learned about their local water system with what other teams learned. Decide how much time to spend here. For a single utility, you may only find essentially 1 source of data upon which the entire class must rely. Step 6 is also a good time to probe your students' understanding about volumes of water and flow rates discussed in the *FYI—Units for Water Volumes and Flow Rates*. Ask questions such as, "If there are 3 ac covered with 1 ft of water, what is the total volume of water?" (The answer is 3 af.) Or, "If there is 1 ac covered with 3 ft of water, what is the total volume of water?" (The answer again is 3 af.)

Remind students that they will be undertaking research like this in the evaluate activity, *A Salty Situation*.

Answers to Reflect and Connect, SE page 516

1. Check that student diagrams are consistent with research about their local water system. Students should use a box to show a water molecule in each subsystem as water moves from one part of the local water system to another. The diagram for a water system that is primarily fed by surface water might include the following:

   mountain stream (from snowmelt) → mountain reservoir → water treatment → storage reservoir → school → wastewater treatment → river

   The diagram for a water system that is primarily fed by groundwater might include the following:

   groundwater (aquifer) → storage tank → treatment → school → septic tank → seep area

   These examples show only one possible path of water through the local system. In actuality, there are multiple paths into and out of a system. For instance, some treated water might flow back into local streams, but some could also go to agricultural irrigation. Be open to various opportunities here for students to be both accurate and creative.

2a. See diagrams from Question 1. These should indicate the source of water and the amount of water coming into your community.

2b. Answers might include amount of precipitation (rainfall, snowfall), annual climate and

Answers to Reflect and Connect are on TE pages 516–517a.

Reflect and Connect

Work individually to answer the following questions. Write your responses in your science notebook.

1. Show the path of a water molecule (H_2O) through your local water system by linking a series of subsystems. Each of the subsystems should be a part of your local water system. The first box should show the first subsystem where the water molecule enters your local system at a boundary. The last box should show the subsystem where the water molecule leaves your local water system at the other side of the boundary. Add boxes and arrows as needed. Use figure 10.10 as a model.

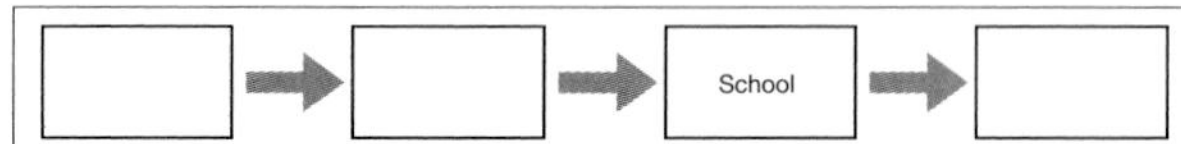

▲ **Figure 10.10 Water through subsystems.** Examine the boxes and arrows in the diagram. Fill in the boxes to show the path of a water molecule through the subsystems of your local water system.

2. Sources of drinking water are typically either surface water or groundwater.
   a. What is the source of water in your community, and how much water does your community use?

   Again, make sure that you use proper units by checking the *FYI—Units for Water Volumes and Flow Rates*.

   b. What factors affect the amount of water available to your community?
   c. Under what circumstances might a community change its primary source of water?
3. Write 2 sentences telling how you are a part of the local water system.
4. Write 2 sentences describing possible impacts of your local water system on a neighboring water system.
5. Write in a short paragraph about how your local water system is like the fast-food restaurant system. Also describe how these 2 systems are different.
6. Imagine that 3 acres (ac) of land are covered with water that is 2 feet (ft) deep.
   a. About how many millions of gallons (Mgal) of water is that?
   b. If people use this much water each day, how many million gallons is this per year?
   c. Use a ratio to compare your answer in Question 6b with the rate of water use in your community.

ambient temperature, distance to accessible aquifer, or pollution. Accessible water might also be limited by water rights.

2c. A community that primarily uses groundwater as its water source might be forced to change if the groundwater becomes contaminated or if the groundwater source is being tapped beyond its ability to recharge, or replenish, its supplies. A community might also choose to change if surface water becomes more readily available or cheaper. A community that primarily uses surface water as its water source might change to groundwater in order to improve quantity (and therefore cost) or quality.

3. Students should write 2 complete sentences. They might mention that by using water, they are taking part in a rerouting of the natural flow of water through their local water system. A small percentage of the water they use is temporarily stored in the reservoir that is their body. In some instances, they might be adding substances to the water that are harmful. If these substances are not removed, perhaps through a water treatment plant, they may be passed on to the next stop (reservoir) in the natural system.

4. Students should write 2 complete sentences. Be open to reasonable ways that your local water system affects neighboring water systems. For example, if multiple communities share an aquifer, a community taking more than its share can deplete the aquifer at a rapid pace. A current example is the Ogallala Aquifer extending from Nebraska to northern Texas. Alternatively, some cities divert large amounts of water from one watershed to another. This can provide additional water for use down some rivers, while depleting waters in the original watershed. Such water is called "non-native" water when it is transported and diverted to another watershed.

5. Because these 2 examples are both systems, they represent components that interact to complete some function. Both have boundaries and both are open systems. They both have matter and energy that flow through the system. The flow of matter can be quantified. The fast-food restaurant system and the water system have both natural and manufactured components.

They are different in that the type of matter is different. The water system deals primarily with water and other matter that may be dissolved or contained in the water. The fast-food restaurant system deals with a greater variety of matter (french fries, people, money, etc.).

6a. Three acres of land covered with 2 ft of water is a total of 6 af of water. Students need to use conversion values from the *FYI—Units for Water Volumes and Flow Rates* to be able to complete the following conversion:

$$(6\ \cancel{\text{af}}) \times \left(\frac{1\ \text{Mgal}}{3.07\ \cancel{\text{af}}}\right) = 2\ \text{Mgal}$$

6b. Feel free to make other simple problems like this to improve students' skills at conversions.

$$\left(\frac{2\ \text{Mgal}}{1\ \cancel{\text{day}}}\right) \times \left(\frac{365\ \cancel{\text{day}}}{1\ \text{yr}}\right) = 730\,\frac{\text{Mgal}}{\text{yr}}$$

Answers to Step 1 are on TE pages 517b–518.

Expanding Boundaries

EXPLAIN

The water that flows out of the drinking fountain is part of the school's water system. In turn, the school's water system is part of your local water system. In the previous investigation, *Beyond the Drinking Fountain*, you explored your local water system. You identified the boundaries of this system. What happens when those boundaries are extended even further? In *Expanding Boundaries*, you will work in teams to expand the boundaries of your local water system and to explore the larger water system of the United States.

Part I: Where Is the Water?

Materials

For each team of 3 students

1 marker or yellow highlighter

3 *North America, Rivers and Streams* handouts

Process and Procedure

Just as french fries are a part of a fast-food restaurant, which is part of the larger fast-food system, your local water system is part of a larger system. Some of this system is shown in figure 10.11. In Part I of this investigation, you will work in teams of three to examine the larger water system of the United States. Your focus will be on the natural flow of water within and around the United States.

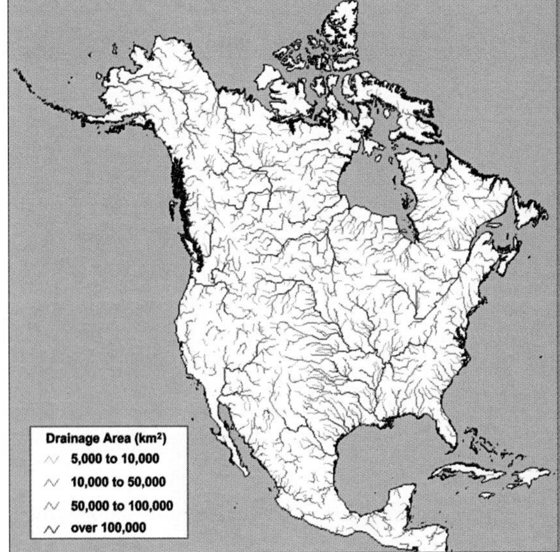

▲ **Figure 10.11 Rivers of North America.** This map shows the network of rivers and streams crossing North America. Where is your community on this map?

1. Answer Questions 1a–c in your team. Show your answers by labeling the map on the handout *North America, Rivers and Streams.*
   a. Mark the boundaries of the water system on the handout. What are the boundaries of the water system?
   b. Where is water stored? Identify and label the major storage areas for water.
   c. Draw and label arrows to reflect processes that move water into and out of the system.

6c. Two million gallons per day from Question 6b is about the amount for a very small community or town. For example, *Sample Research Summary for Colorado Springs Utilities* on the *TRCD* shows that in 1999 Colorado Springs used about 200 million gallons per day (198 Mgal/d). Expressed as a ratio, this amount is a factor of 100 larger than the amount from Question 6b.

EXPLAIN

Expanding Boundaries

Activity Overview

In *Beyond the Drinking Fountain*, students investigated their local water system. In *Expanding Boundaries*, they will expand their view to the continental level, focusing mostly on the United States. They will look at the U.S. water budget and explore how the nation uses water. With this information, they will look back at their local water system to see how the community uses water.

Before You Teach

Background Information

A lot of information is now available characterizing water resource regions in North America. Copymaster 10.2, *North America, Rivers and Streams* shows the network of rivers draining North America at the largest scale. By carefully drawing a line (preferably with a mechanical pencil) between where the tributaries end on this copymaster, you can outline all major watersheds on the continent.

Copymaster 10.3, *Major Water Basins of North America* shows that the continent is sometimes viewed as a series of 10 major river water basins, 9 of which drain to various oceans. Looking a little closer, you will see that the region of the Lower 48 states is divided into 21 major geographic regions. As shown in copymaster 10.4, *Water Resource Regions in the United States*, these water resource regions contain the drainage area of a major river or the combined drainage of a series of rivers. Eighteen of the regions are located within the contiguous United States. The remaining three regions include Alaska, the Hawaiian Islands, and the Caribbean (including Puerto Rico).

The water resource regions are further subdivided into 222 subregions, 352 accounting units, and 2,150 cataloging units. The cataloging units are sometimes called watersheds. A single-sheet hydrologic unit map of the United States (stock number TUS5681) is available from the U.S. Geological Survey.

There is a lot of information about water use in the United States on the Web. The following list includes organizations that provide useful and accurate scientific information:

- USGS water Web site
- USGS water science for schools Web site
- USGS report on water use (Produced every 5 years; chapter 10 includes a summary of information from the 2000 report.)
- Water resource agencies for your state
- EPA Surf Your Watershed (Provides information through the Web.)

Materials—Part I

For the teacher

overhead projector

1 transparency of copymaster 10.4, *Water Resource Regions in the United States*

1 transparency of copymaster 10.3, *Major Water Basins of North America*

1 transparency of copymaster 10.2, *North America, Rivers and Streams*

1 transparency of copymaster 10.5, *Water Use in the United States*

1 transparency of local watershed (from a state agency or the USGS)

For each team of 3 students

1 marker or yellow highlighter

3 copies of copymaster 10.2, *North America, Rivers and Streams*

Materials—Part II

For each team of 3 students

1 set of graduated cylinders (100 mL, 50 mL, 25 mL, 10 mL)

2 water containers (minimum 300 mL each)

8 water containers (minimum 150 mL each)

water

access to food coloring (blue, yellow)

1 calculator

tape for labeling containers

Advance Preparation

For Part I, make 1 copy for each student of copymaster 10.2, *North America, Rivers and Streams*. Decide whether you will use yellow highlighters, markers, or colored pencils for Part I and obtain them. Prepare a transparency of this copymaster as well.

For Part II, obtain a stack of small, clear cups. These work well for allocating between water use categories in Steps 5–8. The maximum volume only needs to be about 136 mL (category A).

Students will need water use data for your local region to answer *Reflect and Connect* Question 3. You may have already come across these data in the explore activity *Beyond the Drinking Fountain*. If not, gather water use data for the local region that you want your students to work with. Data are readily available at the watershed, state, or water resource region level. Review the data and determine how best to help students process the data.

As You Teach

Outcomes and Indicators of Success

By the end of this activity, students should

1. understand that systems contain subsystems and are themselves part of larger systems.

   They will demonstrate their understanding by

   - describing how their local water system fits into larger and larger water systems,
   - analyzing a map showing river systems in North America,
   - comparing the water budget of the United States with patterns of precipitation in the Lower 48 states,
   - measuring river flow in units of cubic feet per second from a diagram,
   - comparing the U.S. water use with the U.S. water budget and the flow rates of major rivers, and
   - comparing water use in their local water system with water use in the United States.

2. understand that systems and their characteristics can be represented through diagrams.

   They will demonstrate their understanding by

   - drawing a systems diagram of the national water budget,
   - constructing a table of surface water and groundwater use in the United States,
   - completing a table showing allocation of water use categories,
   - using containers of water to construct a model of water use categories,
   - analyzing a conversion of water flow rates,
   - showing how to represent on a graph surface water and groundwater use in the United States, and
   - analyzing a diagram of water use in the United States.

3. begin to understand that there is a fixed amount of water on Earth. The water on Earth exists in reservoirs and can move among reservoirs.

   They will demonstrate their growing understanding by

   - identifying the interaction between water sources, uses, and disposition in the United States and
   - analyzing a diagram of water use in the United States.

Strategies

Getting Started

In Part I, the goal is to have students think about how local water systems connect to other larger, regional water systems. In this context, their local system can be thought of as a subsystem of other systems. You can also try this. Have students hold out their hands, with their palms facing up. Place one drop of water in each of their palms. Challenge them to make the water evaporate as quickly as possible. Allow students a few minutes to try the challenge. Students might try spreading the water drop over a greater area or they might try fanning the palm of their hand with a piece of paper.

Next, have them explain as best they can where they think a given molecule of water might have gone. How fast is it moving, and what are all the paths that they can think of for that molecule? For example, it could enter a cloud, be breathed in by someone else in the room, or condense in an air conditioner. There are many creative answers that would show students' understanding of water movement.

Whenever you can in this chapter (such as during whole-class discussion or group work), keep asking students to use vocabulary related to systems approaches. This includes words like input, output, boundaries, and flux. These themes keep coming up in the unit.

Process and Procedure

Part I: Where Is the Water?

Materials

For the teacher

overhead projector

1 transparency of copymaster 10.4, *Water Resource Regions in the United States*

1 transparency of copymaster 10.3, *Major Water Basins of North America*

1 transparency of copymaster 10.2, *North America, Rivers and Streams*

1 transparency of copymaster 10.5, *Water Use in the United States*

1 transparency of local watershed (from a state agency or the USGS)

For each team of 3 students

1 marker or yellow highlighter

3 copies of copymaster 10.2, *North America, Rivers and Streams*

Have students get into teams of 3 for Part I, where they will examine the water system of the United States. They should record the answers to the questions posed in Step 1 by labeling the map of North America on copymaster 10.2, *North America, Rivers and Streams.* This part of the activity is an opportunity for students to share what they already know about water systems.

Answers to Step 1, SE page 517

1a. Look for the following information on the completed maps. Student answers do not need to match exactly the sample answers provided.

Students might draw a line around the shoreline of the United States, defining the boundaries as the region above, on, near, and below the surface of the landmass recognized by political boundaries as the United States. They might express that the political boundaries of the United States are not recognized by water; water is governed by geological boundaries.

1b. Students will likely label rivers, lakes, and oceans, as these are highly visible components. If they think a bit more, they might label the atmosphere and groundwater. Some students might label glaciers. Few students will think to include living things (biosphere) as a water storage place, but a small amount of water would be contained within vegetation.

1c. Water moves into the U.S. water system through precipitation (rain, snow, hail). It moves out of the system as runoff (streams, rivers), evaporation, and transpiration. Water moves within the United States as runoff, seepage into groundwater, and through weather systems. Students should used labeled arrows to reflect these processes.

Your students might already be familiar with the concept of transpiration. If not, you might want to demonstrate that plants give off water. Place a large plastic bag over a healthy broadleaf plant. Gather the bag and loosely tie it shut. Over a period of several days, water drops will appear on the inside surface of the plastic bag.

When students have completed Step 1, ask them if they have any idea how much water is in the U.S. water system and how fast water is moving into, within, and out of the system. Direct them to complete Steps 2 and 3 to answer the questions.

In Step 2, have 1 or 2 students read the paragraph out loud. Ask them what parts of the paragraph are new to them and have them write ideas from the discussion in their science notebooks. It is important that students understand the data here for the next step. Does the area where they live receive more or less than the average 30 inches (in) of rain? How many centimeters (cm) of rain does this equal? (The answer is 30 in × 2.54 cm.)

In Step 3, listen as students work together to analyze the natural water system of the United States by testing their ability to make a systems diagram. Look at individual science notebooks to assess each student's understanding.

Answers to Step 3, SE page 518

3. A sample diagram is shown in figure T10.7. Note the labeled arrows for flux into and out of the system. Students should now be using this type of symbol with units, given the prior activities in the chapter. The rates of transfer are fluxes, whereas an amount that is transferred over a given time is a total input or output.

   Students might also include a box for groundwater and a small arrow showing water movement from surface water to groundwater. This would represent the small percentage of water that seeps into the ground. The flux was not provided for seepage to groundwater, so students might include an arrow representing seepage to groundwater, but they cannot include a value by the arrow.

Have students complete the *Stop and Think* questions in their teams. Remind students that they will need to refer back to the information in Step 2 and the diagram they created in Step 3. Look over student answers to assess their understanding of systems. They should think about all possible parts of the U.S. water system as they think about how changing one part of a system affects another part.

Answers to Stop and Think—Part I are on TE page 519.

2. Read the information in the following paragraph. Check your understanding with your team.

   Each year, the United States receives enough precipitation to cover the entire country to a depth of 30 in. That is approximately 4,200,000 Mgal/d. Scientists call these 30 in of precipitation the U.S. water budget. Of the 30 in of rainfall, 21.5 in (3,010,000 Mgal/d) returns to the atmosphere through **evapotranspiration.** This general process includes both evaporation and transpiration. **Evaporation** occurs when water in the liquid phase passes into the gas phase. **Transpiration** is water loss by plants. (One tree can lose as much as 50 gal of water a day!) Most of the remaining 8.5 in of precipitation (1,190,000 Mgal/d) flows over the land in rivers and returns to the ocean. A small percentage seeps into the ground.

3. Construct a box diagram to summarize the information in the preceding paragraph.
   a. Use 1 or more boxes to represent the storage of water in the United States.
   b. Use arrows to represent the flow of water into and out of the water storage areas.

This is a flux if it is a volume per time.

   c. Label the arrows with symbols that represent the name of the process that is moving water.

Stop & THINK

PART I

Refer to the paragraph in Step 2 and the box diagram you made in Step 3 to discuss the following questions with your team. Write your answers in your science notebook.

1. Why do you suppose the 30 in of precipitation that falls in the United States is called the water budget?
2. The 30 in of precipitation is not evenly distributed. Figure 10.12 shows yearly rainfall in the Lower 48 states. Write answers to the following questions.
   a. What regions have the highest rainfall?
   b. What regions have the lowest rainfall?
   c. What impact does the distribution of rainfall have on the inputs and outputs of the system?

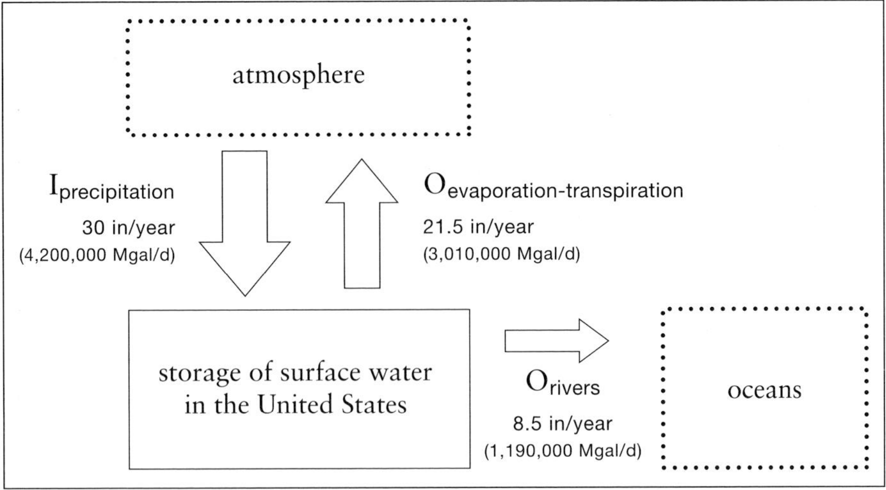

▲ **Figure T10.7 Water box diagram.** This box diagram shows three reservoirs (surface water, atmosphere, ocean) and example fluxes linking these reservoirs.

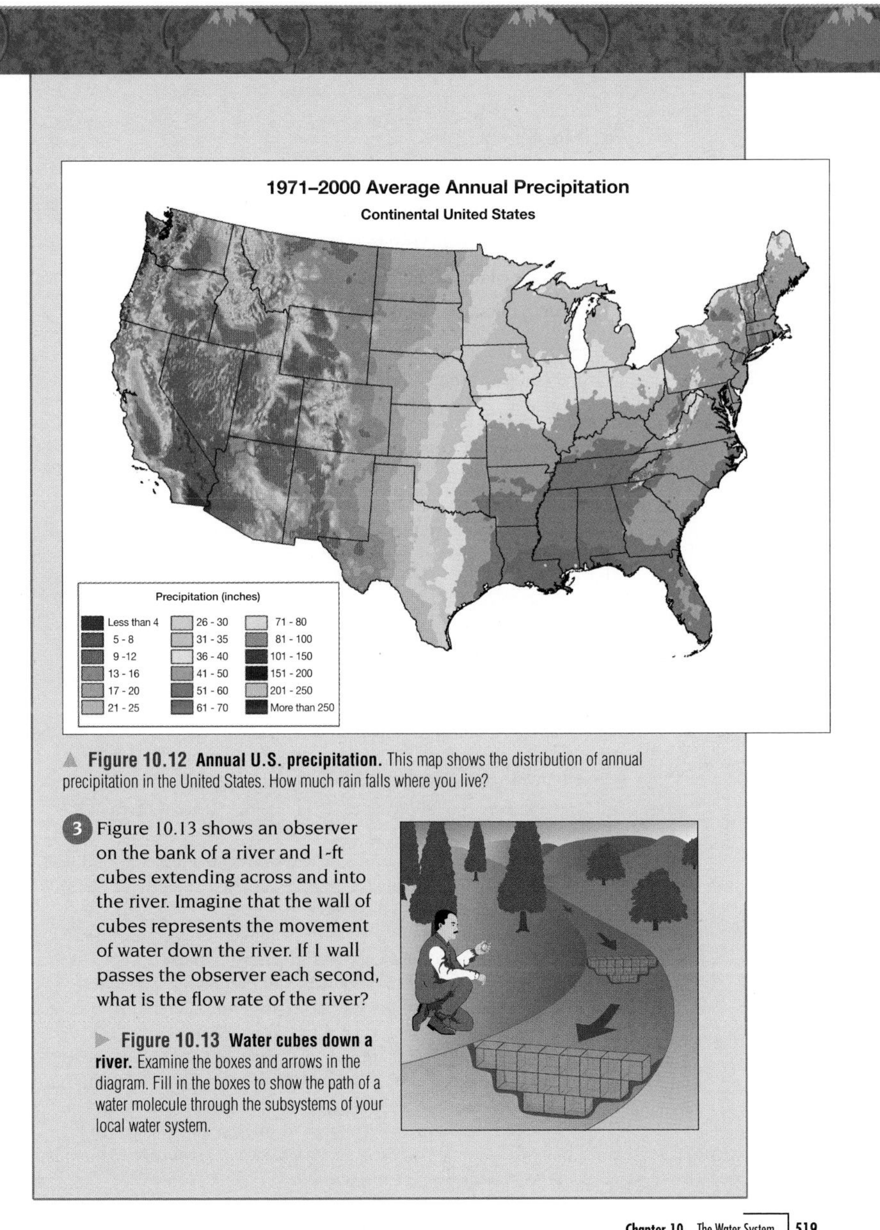

▲ **Figure 10.12 Annual U.S. precipitation.** This map shows the distribution of annual precipitation in the United States. How much rain falls where you live?

3 Figure 10.13 shows an observer on the bank of a river and 1-ft cubes extending across and into the river. Imagine that the wall of cubes represents the movement of water down the river. If 1 wall passes the observer each second, what is the flow rate of the river?

▶ **Figure 10.13 Water cubes down a river.** Examine the boxes and arrows in the diagram. Fill in the boxes to show the path of a water molecule through the subsystems of your local water system.

Chapter 10 The Water System | 519

Answers to Stop and Think—Part I, SE pages 518–519

1. Students might relate this to a money budget in which they have a specific amount of money to be used in a given period of time. The water budget of natural systems refers to the amounts of water contained within or moving through those systems for a specified amount of time. Make sure students support their ideas with data from the activity or chapter.

2a. Precipitation is generally heavier in the eastern half of the map. The Pacific Northwest and selected high elevations in the Rocky Mountains also receive over 30 in of rain. Moisture is also high next to the Gulf of Mexico. Additional very interesting climate and precipitation maps are available on the Web through the Oregon Climate Service.

2b. Other than mountainous regions, most of the West receives relatively little rainfall.

2c. Inputs of rain to the system are concentrated where the rainfall is. Your students may also infer that this leads to the most substantial output on the continent for flow rates along the Mississippi River. They will study this more in a later question.

3. The number of cubes is 17. If a line of all these cubes passes the observer each second, then the flow rate is 17 per second.

Process and Procedure

Part II: The Water We Use

Materials

For each team of 3 students

1 set of graduated cylinders (100 mL, 50 mL, 25 mL, 10 mL)
2 water containers (minimum 300 mL each)
8 water containers (minimum 150 mL each)
water
food coloring (blue, yellow)
1 calculator
tape for labeling containers

Have students work in teams of 3 to complete this activity. This part involves a series of tasks, including answering questions, calculating values of water use, and making a scale model of the water use system of the United States. Check that students use their math skills and understanding of systems to complete these tasks. Remind students to show their work.

To begin, have students read the introductory paragraph. In Step 1, they will think more about where their water comes from.

Answers to Step 1, SE page 520

1a. The estimate is 345,400 Mgal/d. Note that this is somewhat less than the figure of about 400,000 Mgal/d that you might also see quoted. The latter includes use of salt water.

1b. Students should be able to construct a table with 3 headings. The table should show that surface water is about 75.9 percent of the total, and groundwater about 24.1 percent of the total.

1c. These data could be represented as a pie chart or a bar graph. An *xy* plot is not really appropriate since there is only 1 variable, and not an independent (x) and a dependent variable (y).

1d. The total amount of water used per day, 345,400 Mgal/d, is the same as $345{,}400 \times 10^6$ gal. This is divided by 281×10^6 people, the population in 2000. This is about 1,228 gal per person per day. That is a lot of water!

1e. The number should seem high. It does not take into account water uses by agriculture, power, or businesses.

NOTES:

Part II: The Water We Use

Materials

For each team of 3 students

graduated cylinders (100 mL, 50 mL, 25 mL, 10 mL)

2 water containers (minimum 300 mL each)

8 water containers (minimum 150 mL each)

water

food coloring (blue, yellow)

1 calculator

tape for labeling containers

Process and Procedure

Up to now, you have focused on the characteristics of water systems. This includes boundaries, components, interactions, and flow rates. This has helped you understand the source of the water in the drinking fountain at your school. But how else do humans use water? In Part II of this investigation, you will work in teams of three to explore the major ways that water is used in the United States.

In Part I, you diagrammed the U.S. water system. Which part of the system does the water we use come from? In the activity *Beyond the Drinking Fountain*, you learned that the two general sources of drinking water for schools are surface water and groundwater. Next, you will investigate water use in the U.S. water system.

1. Complete the following tasks to explore water sources in the United States.
   a. In 2000, the rate of water withdrawal from the ground was 83,400 Mgal/d. Surface water was used at a rate of 262,000 Mgal/d. Estimate the total water use.
   b. Construct the table with the headings "Source of Water," "Rate of Withdrawal (Mgal/d)," and "Total (%)."
   c. Show in a diagram how you could represent these data graphically. In other words, explain and sketch the types of graphs that you could use to show these data.
   d. On average, estimate how many gallons of water a single person uses per day. In 2000, there were about 281 million people in the United States.
   e. Does this number seem high or low to you? What uncertainties or factors in your estimate from Step 1d might make the estimate inaccurate?

Source	Surface Water (262,000 Mgal/day)			Groundwater (83,400 Mgal/day)			Totals	
Water Use Category	Percent of Surface Water	Rate of Water Use (Mgal/d)	Scaled Volume of Water (mL)	Percent of Ground-water	Rate of Water Use (Mgal/d)	Scaled Volume of Water (mL)	Volume of Water (Mgal/d)	Scaled Volume of Water (mL)
A	52%	136,000	136	0.5%	417	0.4	136,417	136.4
B	32%	83,840	84	71%	59,214	59	143,054	143
C	10%	26,200	26	23.5%	19,600	20	45,800	46
D	6%	15,720	16	5%	4,170	4	19,890	20
Totals	**100%**	**261,760**	**262**	**100%**	**83,400**	**83.4**	**345,160**	**345.4**

Source: Hutson, et. al., 2004, *Estimated use of water in the United States in 2000*: Reston, Va., U.S. Geological Survey Circular 1268.

▲ **Figure T10.8 Surface and groundwater use table.** Categories of use are A, thermoelectric; B, irrigation-livestock; C, domestic-public supply; D, industrial-mining.

In Step 2, students create a scale model to get a better feeling for ground- versus surface water use in the United States. They will have 2 containers, one with 262 mL of water representing surface water, and the other container with 83.4 mL of water representing groundwater withdrawal. The surface water is colored blue, the groundwater yellow. Students will be using both mathematical and measurement skills as they build a scaled-down model of the system they are studying. They should save this model for use in Step 5.

In Step 3, students discuss the categories of water use with their teammates. Circulate among the teams and listen to their discussions. Check that students are writing their ideas regarding which categories shown would use the most water. This is a good point to raise in a whole-class discussion as well.

Students might not be familiar with the thermoelectric category. Most electricity is produced by burning fossil fuels such as coal. But one use of water is in the thermoelectric process, which heats water and produces steam. The steam turns turbines and produces electricity.

Students complete a table in Step 4, showing the allocation of surface water and groundwater to the different use categories in Step 3. Teams then calculate the values to complete the table as shown in figure T10.8.

2. The large volumes of water used in the United States are difficult to imagine. Sometimes it helps to see what you are investigating. Obviously, you cannot measure 262,000 Mgal. Instead, you will create a smaller model of water use. Follow these steps.
   a. Use a scale of 1 mL of water for each 1,000 Mgal/d to measure volumes of water to represent groundwater and surface water.
   b. Place the measured volumes in separate, labeled containers.
   c. Place a few drops of blue food coloring in the container representing surface water.
   d. Place the same number of drops of yellow food coloring in the large container representing groundwater.

Keep your model accessible. You will be modeling the amounts of water used in Steps 5 and 6.

3. Review with your team the 4 main categories of water use for the United States. Which of these categories are used in your town or city? Which category do you think is the biggest water user? Write a reason why in your science notebook.
   a. Domestic—public supply
      - Water for drinking, food preparation, bathing, washing clothes and dishes, flushing toilets, and watering lawns and gardens
      - Water for motels, hotels, restaurants, office buildings, and other commercial facilities and military, educational, and other governmental institutions
   b. Industrial—mining
      - Water for industrial processing, washing, and cooling in facilities that manufacture products
      - Water for the extraction of naturally occurring minerals
   c. Thermoelectric
      - Water for the generation of electric power with fossil fuel, nuclear, or geothermal energy
   d. Irrigation—livestock
      - All water artificially applied to farm and horticultural crops and golf courses
      - Water for livestock, feedlots, dairies, fish farms, and other on-farm needs
4. Now you know the 4 main categories of water use in the United States. But how much of the water used comes from surface water or groundwater? Which category would you guess uses the most water? To answer those questions, follow these steps.

Students make 8 scaled containers of water in Step 5, 2 for each category (A, B, C, D) for surface water and groundwater. The surface waters are blue, and the groundwaters are yellow.

Then in Step 6, students combine surface water and groundwater for each category (A, B, C, D), giving the scaled volumes shown in the far right column of figure T10.8. If students have done the mixing properly, the color scale between blue and yellow (shades of green) would also represent the proportion of surface water to groundwater used per category. This is shown in Step 7. For example, inspection from figure T10.8 shows that virtually all of category A is surface water, leaving the mixture total blue. Category C has the highest proportion of groundwater to surface water (nearly 50:50) and would be green. No mixture is yellow.

Finally, in Step 8, students should guess which water use categories (A, B, C, D) correspond to which of the 4 categories described in Step 3 of the student book. Remind students to record their answers in their science notebooks. Reveal the correct relationships and discuss any categories that surprised students: A: thermoelectric; B: irrigation-livestock; C: domestic-public supply; and D: industrial-mining.

In Step 9, use the color transparency of copymaster 10.5, *Water Use in the United States* to continue the class discussion. Note how some categories with which we are familiar users (domestic, industrial) really are a small part of the total. Students might express surprise that the largest portions of U.S. water use belong to the thermoelectric and irrigation-livestock categories, not domestic and commercial use.

In Step 10, students consider interactions more within water systems. They consider several changes to water systems that would change patterns of use or patterns of water availability.

NOTES:

Source	Surface Water (262,000 Mgal/day)			Groundwater (83,400 Mgal/day)			Totals	
Water Use Category	Percent of Surface Water	Rate of Water Use (Mgal/d)	Scaled Volume of Water (mL)	Percent of Ground-water	Rate of Water Use (Mgal/d)	Scaled Volume of Water (mL)	Volume of Water (Mgal/d)	Scaled Volume of Water (mL)
A	52%	136,000	136	0.5%	417	0.417	136,417	136.4
B	32%			71%				
C	10%			23.5%				
D	6%			5%				
Totals								

Source: Hutson, et. al., 2004, *Estimated use of water in the United States in 2000*: Reston, Va., U.S. Geological Survey Circular 1268.

▲ **Figure 10.14 Water source and use in the United States in 2000.** Percentage values are rounded. For the scale model, 1 mL of water represents 1,000 Mgal/d. Which of the four water use categories do you think uses the most surface water? Groundwater?

a. Review with your team figure 10.14, which shows the percentage of water use per category. The use categories are shown in the left-hand column. Each letter (*A*, *B*, *C*, and *D*) represents 1 category of water use in figure 10.14, but you don't know which one! Write ideas in your science notebook for how you could figure this out.

b. Calculate the missing amounts of water by converting the percentages into actual volumes of surface water or groundwater for the indicated use. Figure 10.14 provides values to do this. Show your work and record your answers in your science notebook.

For example, 52 percent of the withdrawn surface water is used for category A. Since total surface water is 262,000 Mgal/d, 52 percent of this amount is approximately 136,000 Mgal/d.

c. Calculate the scaled, missing amounts of water. Using the scaling in Step 2a, 136,000 Mgal would be represented by 136 mL of water.

5. To help you visualize the water, use the water from the scale model you started in Step 2 to make a model showing water use. The categories in figure 10.14 correspond with the use categories shown in Step 3. Measure the appropriate amounts of surface water (blue) and pour each into a container labeled with "A," "B," "C," or "D." Follow the same procedure to distribute the groundwater (yellow) into the appropriate water use containers.

Answers to Step 10, SE page 523

10a. Abundant rainfall means more surface water and less demand for surface water for the irrigation-livestock category. It means that more surface water would be available for other categories.

10b. Increased population would mean increased domestic use and perhaps increased use in the thermoelectric category due to an increased demand for energy. Since these 2 uses rely heavily on surface water, there would be an increase in surface water withdrawals, assuming that there were additional surface water available. If not, other use categories might experience shortages. On the other hand, increased population might result in all of us needing to be more careful with the amount of water we do use. We might have to ration our water supplies and conserve energy.

10c. Depletion of aquifers would reduce the amount of groundwater available for use. This would most greatly affect irrigation and livestock water use and domestic water use that has primarily groundwater sources. These water users would need to shift to use more surface water as a source, putting a strain on supplies of surface water. If the former groundwater users are far from surface water sources, it might be expensive to bring the surface water to the location where it is needed.

10d. Less demand for water for the purpose of generating power means more surface water available in the system. Very little water in the thermoelectric category comes from groundwater.

After students have completed Step 10, tell students to work in their team on the *Reflect and Connect* tasks. Remind them to record their work in their science notebooks and to show their work for any calculations they make.

Answers to Reflect and Connect, SE pages 523–524

1a. The U.S. water budget is 4,200,000 Mgal/d. Total U.S. water use is 345,400 Mgal/d. The ratio of water budget to water use is about 12:1. This means that the amount of water available is 12 times greater than the amount of water withdrawn per day.

$$\left(\frac{4{,}200{,}000\ \frac{\cancel{\text{Mgal}}}{\cancel{\text{day}}}}{345{,}400\ \frac{\cancel{\text{Mgal}}}{\cancel{\text{day}}}}\right) = 12.2$$

Students might point out that the water budget only refers to surface water, since it is based on precipitation. Only 262,000 Mgal/d of U.S. water use comes from surface water. The ratio of water budget to water use from surface water only is about 16:1. This means that the amount of surface water available is 16 times greater than the amount of surface water withdrawn per day.

Students might also point out that only 1,190,000 Mgal/d of the U.S. water budget is runoff. Using this number with the 262,000 Mgal/d of U.S. water use from surface water gives a ratio of water budget to water use from surface runoff of about 4.5:1. This means that the amount of surface water (runoff) available is only 4.5 times greater than the amount of surface water withdrawn per day.

Answers to Reflect and Connect are on TE pages 523–523b.

6. Fill in the right side of figure 10.14. Do this by summing the water per use category (A, B, C, or D) from the surface water and the groundwater. Your volumes should also be shown in the completed figure 10.14. Check that the measured amount is equal to the calculated amounts.
7. Record observations about the contents of the 4 different water use containers. What do the colors of the waters tell you?
8. Determine which water use categories (A, B, C, and D) correspond to which of the 4 categories described in Step 3. Record your predictions next to the table in your science notebook. Check your answers with your teacher.

Also think about how you would use a pie chart or a bar graph to represent data in these categories.

9. What happens to water after it is used? Discuss this question with your team and represent your ideas in a sketch. Check your thinking with information from a transparency provided by your teacher.
10. Consider interactions between parts of the water system. For the following changes, discuss the likely impact the change would have on the water use system. Record your best thinking in your science notebook and refer to prior diagrams as evidence.
    a. The United States experiences several consecutive years of above-average rainfall.
    b. The U.S. population grows significantly.
    c. Several major groundwater sources (aquifers) are severely depleted by overuse.
    d. Significant advances in solar and wind energy reduce the use of thermoelectric power.

Reflect and Connect

Work with your team to answer the following questions in your science notebook. Always show all work for any calculations.

1. The water use system you explored in Part II is a subsystem of the water budget you worked with in Part I. Answer Questions 1a–d to compare the amount of water in the U.S. water budget with the amount of water used in the United States.
    a. Determine the ratio of the U.S. water budget (in Mgal/d) to the rate of U.S. water use (in Mgal/d). Explain your answer.
    b. Determine how much water it would take to represent the U.S. water budget using the scale 1 mL = 1,000 Mgal/d.

There is not one correct answer to this question. Look for the rationale behind student answers. It may reveal a better understanding of the complexity of the issue.

1b. Using the water budget of 4,200,000 Mgal/d, the conversion is like others. You would need 4.2 L, or about 2 2-L bottles, to represent this at the given scaling.

$$4{,}200{,}000\,\frac{\text{Mgal}}{\text{day}} \times \left(\frac{1\text{ mL}}{1{,}000\,\frac{\text{Mgal}}{\text{day}}}\right)$$

$$= 4{,}200\text{ mL, or } 4.2\text{ L}$$

1c. Estimates for ratios of daily use to average flow rate of rivers are shown in figure T10.9. You will find that the conversion from flow rates in Mgal/d to km^3/yr is not too bad once written out. With the Mississippi River example, start by calculating Mgal per year:

$$420{,}000\,\frac{\text{Mgal}}{\text{day}} \times \frac{365.25\text{ day}}{1\text{ yr}}$$

$$= 153.4 \times 10^6\,\frac{\text{Mgal}}{\text{yr}}$$

Next, use some lengths to convert to volumes:

1 meter (m) = 3.281 ft or

1,000 m = 1 km = 3,281 ft, and cubing each side for volume gives

1 km^3 = 35.32×10^9 ft^3.

Now combine this with the conversion that 7.48 gal equals 1 ft^3:

$$\left(153.4 \times 10^6\,\frac{\text{Mgal}}{\text{yr}}\right) \times \left(\frac{10^6\text{ gal}}{1\text{ Mgal}}\right) \times \left(\frac{1\text{ ft}^3}{7.48\text{ gal}}\right) \times \left(\frac{1\text{ km}^3}{35.32 \times 10^9\text{ ft}^3}\right) = 580.6\,\frac{\text{km}^3}{\text{yr}}$$

1d. The water use system of the United States is a subsystem of the water budget of the United States. The water budget has 12 times the amount of water that is withdrawn (from both surface water and groundwater sources) for human use. The water budget has 16 times the amount of water that is withdrawn (from just surface water sources) for human use.

2. The calculation is incorrect on 2 counts. First, the conversion from liters to milliliters does not accurately let units cancel. Second, students should have a feeling by now that 0.1 L (100 mL) does not equal 1 gallon, and is considerably less. The correct calculation is

$$420{,}000\,\frac{\text{Mgal}}{\text{day}} \times \frac{10^6\text{ gal}}{1\text{ Mgal}} \times \frac{3.79\text{ L}}{1\text{ gal}} \times \frac{1{,}000\text{ mL}}{1\text{ L}} \times \frac{1\text{ g water}}{1\text{ mL}}$$

$$\times \frac{1\text{ kg water}}{10^3\text{ g water}} = 1.6 \times 10^{12}\,\frac{\text{kg water}}{\text{day}}.$$

3. Students will have different answers depending on location. Encourage students to make quantitative comparisons—not just more than or less than, but twice as much as or one-third less than. Local factors will vary, but some common responses include the presence or absence of agriculture, industry, and population and whether or not people need to water their lawns.

Flow Rates of Major River Systems in North America

River System	Annual Flow Rate km^3/yr	Daily Flow Rate Mgal/d	Ratio of river flow rate to water use	River flow rate as a percentage of daily water use
Mississippi	580	420,000	1.23	123%
St. Lawrence	337	244,000	0.72	72%
Mackenzie	304	220,000	0.65	65%
Columbia	250	181,000	0.53	53%
Yukon	195	141,000	0.41	41%
Nelson	110	80,000	0.24	24%
Frazer	100	72,000	0.21	21%
Colorado (1960s)	20	14,500	0.043	5%
Rio Grande (Laredo, TX)	2.4	1,740	0.0051	0.5%

Source: Berner, E. K., & Berner R. A. (1987). The global water cycle: Geochemistry and environment. Englewood Cliffs, NJ: Prentice Hall.

▲ **Figure T10.9 Flow rates of major river systems in North America.** This table compares flow rates (Mgal/d; km^3/yr) of major watersheds in North America with the percentage of river flow as a fraction of daily water use in the United States.

4. Be open to student ideas here. The goal is that students continue making connections at different sizes or scales. The U.S. water system consists of a number of regional water drainage basins. These drainage basins do not stop for political boundaries, but some boundaries follow rivers, such as the parts of the Rio Grande River. Within these basins are a number of local watersheds. These are, for the most part, natural systems that act within natural boundaries. Within these systems are human-made, or human-manipulated, systems of water use. The U.S. water use system is the largest system we have studied, which contains subsystems of state level and local level water use, which in turn contains your school's drinking water system. All these systems are connected with one another.

For Colorado Springs, Colorado, a sample response that includes actual names is the following:

The U.S. water system is composed of a number of regional water drainage basins, including four basins that affect some part of the state of Colorado, including the Missouri Basin, the Rio Grande Basin, the Upper Colorado Basin, and the Arkansas-White-Red Basin. The Colorado Springs area, located in the Arkansas-White-Red Basin, is served by a number of watersheds. The Fountain Watershed (USGS Cataloging Unit 11020003) is the watershed that surrounds the immediate Colorado Springs area. Most residents of Colorado Springs get their water through Colorado Springs Utilities.

ELABORATE

The Global Water System

Activity Overview

In *The Global Water System*, students will expand even further their understanding of water systems to the global scale. In Parts I and II, students will learn about the global reservoirs, compare the volume of water stored in each, and diagram rates of water movement between reservoirs. Part III introduces the concept of residence time. During this part of the investigation, students will calculate the average period of time a water molecule spends in the ocean and in the atmosphere before moving into a different reservoir. Combined with prior activities in this chapter, this investigation will help students move to a new scale in terms of length of observation and interpretation.

Before You Teach

Background Information

The size of water reservoirs varies greatly around the globe, yet water actually moves and circulates quite rapidly among reservoirs. The water fluxes among reservoirs describe how quickly the circulation occurs, such as on a yearly basis. Some volumes and rates for the global water reservoirs are in figure 10.16 in the student book. Note that the rates of evaporation and precipitation over land are much smaller than the rates of evaporation and precipitation over the ocean. This is because the ocean is a large part of the surface area of Earth at equatorial regions, where most evaporation occurs. On average, most water vapor just rains back into the ocean rather than moving over land.

The amount of the time any individual water molecule spends in a given reservoir before moving to the next reservoir in a cycle is the *residence time*. An analogous approach is to assess the duration that a given dollar spends, on average, in a bank (i.e., a money storage facility) before it exits the bank and reenters the economy.

Residence time is easy to calculate and can be expressed in a variety of units (years, days, minutes). Residence time is calculated for systems near a steady state (balanced systems), where the inputs and outputs are close to equal. The residence time of a substance is determined by dividing the mass of that substance in the reservoir by the flux of the substance into (or out of) that reservoir. An equation is in the student book.

Another key assumption in calculating residence time (besides flux in equals flux out) is that the reservoir is well mixed. For example, for precipitation removing rain from the atmosphere, this says that the odds are the same for any molecule that it will be removed from the atmosphere reservoir in a raindrop. Scientists know from other types of data, such as carbon dioxide contents in the atmosphere (see the carbon dioxide curves in chapter 11, *Carbon on the Move*) that the atmosphere does mix rapidly. In contrast, the ocean is layered in temperature and composition, with distinct regions of upwelling and downwelling. The ocean actually does mix fairly well on the time period of years, but it is not always mixed.

Throughout this chapter, students have been discovering how systems interact with one another and how they are part of larger systems. An important part of science education reform has been approaching earth sciences through a systems approach. The earth systems approach recognizes that Earth is composed of four interacting subsystems or spheres (atmosphere, biosphere, hydrosphere, and geosphere). Some people refer to the frozen part of the hydrosphere as the cryosphere. As you will see in chapter 12, *Evidence for the Ice Ages*, however, the mass of the cryosphere varies greatly depending on whether or not the planet is in a glacial or interglacial climate. In this chapter, the cryosphere is considered part of the hydrosphere because they both consist of water. The four subsystems constantly change through natural processes. Because the subsystems interact, any change that occurs in one subsystem affects the other subsystems. The subsystems are not isolated from one another.

Like any systems approach, earth systems science studies Earth as a set of interacting components rather than isolated components. Instead of focusing on processes that occur in one location or time, students can look at processes occurring on a global scale. Looking at earth systems helps students understand the interrelationship between science, technology, and society and the impact that their actions have on Earth.

Materials—Part I

For the teacher

various graduated cylinders (1 L, 50 mL, 10 mL)
6 containers
1 standard glass medicine dropper
overhead projector
blue food coloring
1 transparency of copymaster 10.6, *Global Water Reservoirs*

For each team of 2 students

1 1-L bottle of water
6 smaller containers

Materials—Part II

For each team of 2 students

2 blank pieces of paper
colored pencils (optional)

Materials—Part III

none

Advance Preparation

Gather the materials you will need for Part I. For each team of students, gather a 1-L bottle or beaker filled with water. Also provide 6 containers for each team of students. Make a transparency of copymaster 10.6, *Global Water Reservoirs*.

You also need to prepare the scale model of the global reservoirs. Volumes for the model are provided in figure T10.10. Use graduated cylinders to measure the volumes indicated. You might want to wait to measure the smallest volumes. Adding color to the water will make it easier for students to see the volumes. After measuring the water in the appropriate graduated cylinders, you might want to transfer the water to the same type of containers you provided to students. This will allow students to make comparisons between the scale model you have made with the predictions they make. Make sure the model is hidden from students until they complete the steps in Part I.

As You Teach

Outcomes and Indicators of Success

By the end of this activity, students should

1. understand that there is a fixed amount of water on Earth. The water exists in various reservoirs and can move among reservoirs.

   They will demonstrate their understanding by

   - describing and diagramming how water moves into and out of the global reservoirs;
   - sharing ideas about what a reservoir is;
   - developing scale models for reservoirs of water;
   - calculating fluxes between reservoirs (e.g., ocean and land);
   - considering changes in water reservoirs during different climate conditions; and
   - describing how global water reservoirs are part of a system.

2. understand the global water system.

   They will demonstrate their understanding by

   - discussing their ideas about global water reservoirs and comparing their ideas with the actual reservoirs,
   - solving problems for the movement of water in a global water cycle,

Answers to Reflect and Connect 1c–4 are on TE pages 523a–b.

c. Compare U.S. water use with the amount of water that flows out of a large river system. Calculate the ratio of the flow rate of the Mississippi River to the daily water use of the United States. Repeat the calculation for another one of the river systems shown in figure 10.15.

d. Write in your science notebook a statement comparing water use with the water budget.

2. Flow rates of water (fluxes) are often shown as mass of water per time. Analyze the following calculation for the flux of water in the Mississippi River. If the comparison is not correct, write the correct calculation in your science notebook.

$$420{,}000\frac{\text{Mgal}}{\text{day}} \times \frac{10^6\text{ gal}}{1\text{ Mgal}} \times \frac{0.1\text{ L}}{1\text{ gal}} \times \frac{1\text{ g water}}{1\text{ mL}} \times \frac{1\text{ kg water}}{10^3\text{ g water}} = 8.4 \times 10^8 \frac{\text{kg water}}{\text{day}}$$

Remember that canceling units in the denominator and the numerator is vital. If units do not cancel, that is the first clue that a calculation might not be correct.

3. Obtain information about water use within your local water system. You may have located this information in the activity *Beyond the Drinking Fountain*. Compare water use at your local level with water use in the United States.
   a. How does water use in your local water system compare with water use in the United States?
   b. What local factors might account for any differences?

4. Describe how the following systems are related to one another, using sentences or a diagram. Where possible, identify these systems by name (for example, include the name of your high school and your specific watershed).
   a. U.S. water system
   b. School's drinking water system
   c. Local water use system
   d. Local watershed
   e. Regional water drainage basin
   f. U.S. water use

River System	Flow Rate (Mgal/day)
Mississippi	420,000
St. Lawrence	244,000
Mackenzie	220,000
Columbia	181,000
Yukon	141,000
Nelson	80,000
Frazer	72,000
Colorado (1960s)	14,500
Rio Grande (Laredo, TX)	1,740

Figure 10.15 Flow rates for rivers in North America. This table shows the flow rates for the nine largest rivers in North America where they enter the ocean. What factors do you think control the flow rates?

Source: Berner, E. K., & Berner R. A. (1987). *The global water cycle: Geochemistry and environment.* Englewood Cliffs, NJ: Prentice Hall.

- diagramming the fluxes of water between global water reservoirs,
- comparing depictions of the water cycle with their understanding of the global water system, and
- describing how changes in one flux affect reservoirs and the other fluxes.

3. begin to understand the concept of residence time of matter in a reservoir.

   They will demonstrate their growing understanding by

   - completing a reading on residence time,
   - discussing their ideas of how long a water molecule spends in a reservoir,
   - calculating the residence time for water molecules in the ocean and atmosphere,
   - describing how an increase in the volume of a reservoir affects residence time,
   - calculating residence time for water in an activity earlier in the chapter, and
   - calculating the residence time for a water molecule in the Great Salt Lake.

4. develop further skills in the abilities and understandings of scientific inquiry.

   They will demonstrate their ability and understanding of inquiry by

   - using mathematics to improve their understanding of scientific concepts,
   - revising their diagrams of systems,
   - identifying an unknown variable and solving for the value of the unknown variable in a system,
   - communicating their understanding about systems through mathematics and writing,
   - writing mathematical expressions that show how units cancel in equations, and
   - using different sets of units as appropriate to describe masses of water and fluxes in systems.

Answers to Step 2 are on TE pages 526–526a.

The Global Water System

ELABORATE

In the activity *Beyond the Drinking Fountain*, you looked at water on a local scale. Then you expanded your view to the United States in the investigation *Expanding Boundaries*. In *The Global Water System*, you will expand your view to the water system at a global scale. You will work with a team of 2 students to think of the water cycle as one big system. This accounts for all the water on Earth.

Part I: Global Reservoirs

Materials

For each team of 2 students

1 1-L bottle of water

6 containers

Process and Procedure

More than 70 percent of Earth's surface is covered with water. In Part I of this investigation, you will learn how water is distributed across Earth. Have you ever thought about where all the water on Earth is stored? Discuss the following questions with a partner and record your answers individually in your science notebook.

1. What does the term *reservoir* mean to you? Talk about this term with your partner and prepare to share your ideas with the class.
2. Listen as your teacher describes how scientists study the global water system and use the term reservoir.
   a. Identify global water reservoirs on Earth. Share your ideas with your partner.
   b. Compare your ideas with the actual reservoirs listed on the transparency shown by your teacher. Did you and your partner think of all the reservoirs? Why or why not?
   c. Is all the water from the global reservoirs available for human use? Why or why not?
3. Write ideas in your science notebook about the size of global reservoirs of water.
   a. Which reservoirs do you think hold the most mass of water?
   b. Which reservoirs do you think hold the least mass of water?

Strategies

Getting Started

Remind students that they have been building an understanding of systems throughout this chapter. They might have noticed that they have been looking at larger and larger systems. They started by modeling a simple bathtub system and a fast-food restaurant. Then they looked at the U.S. water system. Explain that all these systems are subsystems of the global water system. The global water system is a subsystem of the earth system. Tell them they will learn about the earth systems (geosphere, hydrosphere, biosphere, and atmosphere) throughout the unit. They will continue to explain and learn how these systems interact. Interactions within and between systems (or subsystems) are a key part of developing better understandings of the physical world.

Process and Procedure

Part I: Global Reservoirs

Materials

For the teacher

various graduated cylinders (1 L, 50 mL, 10 mL)
6 containers
1 standard glass medicine dropper
overhead projector
blue food coloring
1 transparency of copymaster 10.6, *Global Water Reservoirs*

For each team of 2 students

1 1-L bottle of water
6 smaller containers

Have students get into pairs and instruct them to follow Step 1. Listen as students discuss their understanding of a reservoir with a partner and then share ideas with the class. Students are probably used to thinking of a reservoir as a human-made collection of water. But as they will see when discussing carbon in the next chapter, for example, *reservoir* has a much broader meaning in the earth sciences.

As part of Step 2, read the following paragraph describing reservoirs to the class:

In systems thinking, a *reservoir* is any environment in which matter is stored. In a water system, a reservoir is a source or place of residence for water. For example, winter snowpack in the mountains is a distinctive reservoir. The current volume of water contained in, and moving through, the Mississippi River system is another reservoir. However, the Mississippi River can also be thought of as part of a flux between the water content of the atmosphere and the oceans.

Tell students to work with their partners to answer the questions in Step 2. Listen as students identify global water reservoirs. This will give you an opportunity to assess their understanding of reservoirs and their preconceptions of global water reservoirs. Students are not likely to identify all the reservoirs; they only need to discuss some of their ideas.

When students get to Step 2b, show them the global reservoirs listed on the transparency you made from copymaster 10.6, *Global Water Reservoirs*. Make sure at first to cover up all but the list of reservoirs in the left-hand column. Tell them to answer Steps 2b–c and record their answers in their science notebooks.

Answers to Step 2, SE page 525

2a. Any kind of materials that contain water (organisms, ice sheets, minerals) would constitute a reservoir for water. Accept all such answers at this time. For reservoirs suggested by students that really do not contain any water, ask students, "Do you think that this material contains water?" They should be able to demonstrate this in some cases.

2b. In general, large reservoirs of water include oceans, glaciers and polar ice, groundwater, lakes and rivers, the atmosphere, and the biosphere. Students might have easily identified the ocean as a reservoir, but they probably did not think of the biosphere because we rarely think about plants and animals as storage areas for water.

Many students might not be familiar with the term *biosphere*. You might need to take this

Answers to Step 5 are on TE page 526a.
Answers to Stop and Think—Part I are on TE page 526b.

4. Obtain materials to make a scale model of global water reservoirs using 1 L of water and the containers (or beakers) provided by your teacher. Have each container represent a global reservoir. Label your reservoirs and be prepared to share your model with the class.
5. Observe the data your teacher will show you.
   a. Use the volumes given in the table shown on the transparency *Global Water Reservoirs* to calculate the percentage of the global water found in each reservoir. Record your answers in a table in your notebook.
   b. Could you represent these data in a pie chart or a bar graph? Use a sketch to explain how in your science notebook.
   c. Calculate the volume of water (in mL) for each reservoir in a scale model that uses 1 L of water to represent all global water. For example, if lakes and rivers were 10 percent of the total global water, 100 mL (10 percent of 1,000 mL) would represent this reservoir. Record your answers in a table in your science notebook.

Stop & THINK

PART I

Work individually to answer the following questions. Record your answers in your science notebook.

1. A **reservoir** is any environment in which matter is stored. Can you think of systems other than water systems that have reservoirs? For example, a reservoir in a banking system would be a vault. Describe at least 1 reservoir other than a banking system and the system to which it belongs.
2. Describe how you think all the water reservoirs on Earth could be considered part of a system.

opportunity to explain that the biosphere includes all the life on Earth (plants, animals). Just like their own bodies, all organisms consist of a large percentage of water.

2c. Some students might think about the distance to the reservoir. They don't have access to polar ice caps (or the ocean if they don't live on a coast). Other answers might include ideas such as we can't drink water from the ocean because we have to extract the salt first, water from the atmosphere and biosphere accounts for very little of the total water and would be difficult to extract, and polluted groundwater and surface water (lakes and rivers) also wouldn't be available. Recent work for areas without much water *is* focusing on recycling wastewater and developing more advanced desalinization plants.

Tell students to begin Step 3 and think about how much water each of the global reservoirs might hold. Distribute 1-L bottles filled with 1 L of water and 6 beakers or small plastic cups or containers to each team.

In Step 4, tell students that each beaker represents one of the global reservoirs. Instruct students to predict the volume of each global reservoir by pouring water into each beaker (reservoir). Remind them to label their reservoirs. Ask a few teams to show how much water they used to represent one of the reservoirs. They might be interested in what some of the other students predicted.

For Step 5, show students the entire table on the transparency you made from copymaster 10.6, *Global Water Reservoirs*.

Answers to Step 5, SE page 526

5a. Students' models probably had the greatest volume of water in the ocean. However, students might have been surprised to learn the glaciers and polar ice hold a greater volume of water than groundwater and surface water (lakes and rivers) combined. They might be surprised that lakes and rivers contain even less water than the groundwater reservoir. Students probably did not even consider how small the biosphere reservoir would be.

5b. Students should be able to sketch in their science notebooks how they would represent these numbers graphically. These numbers could be shown in a pie chart or a bar graph. (An *xy* plot would not be appropriate since there are no independent and dependent variables.)

5c. Students should use the values in the *Global Water Reservoirs* table to calculate the missing volumes and percentages. To do this, they should first calculate the total volume of all the reservoirs. They can then divide the volume of each reservoir by the total volume and multiply by 100 percent. For the ocean,

$$\left(\frac{1{,}400 \times \cancel{10^6\ \text{km}^3}}{1{,}460 \times \cancel{10^6\ \text{km}^3}}\right) \times 100\% \quad \text{or}$$

$$\left(\frac{1.40 \times \cancel{10^9\ \text{km}^3}}{1.46 \times \cancel{10^9\ \text{km}^3}}\right) \times 100\%$$

$$= \left(\frac{1.40}{1.46}\right) \times 100\% = 96\%.$$

Remind students to record their answers in a table that they construct. Also note that they will need to work with large numbers here. The best way is to write exponents in their notebooks. Some of the large exponents just cancel, however, leaving a relatively simple problem.

The table in figure T10.10 gives the values for total volume and percentage.

After students have calculated the scale model values, show them the scale model you have created. If you have not yet measured the smaller reservoirs, you might wish to demonstrate how difficult it is to measure this small amount, even with drops. Explain that 1 mL of a liquid is approximately equal to 20 drops from a standard medicine dropper. Show them that even one drop is too much water to represent the atmosphere and biosphere reservoirs. The key point here is that by far most of the water is in the ocean and ice caps.

	Volume			
Reservoir	**km³**	**× 10⁶ km³**	**Percent of global water**	**Scale model (1 L)**
Oceans	1,400,000,000	1,400	*95.96*	*960 mL*
Glaciers and polar ice	43,400,000	43.4	*2.97*	*30 mL*
Groundwater	15,400,000	15.4	*1.05*	*10 mL*
Lakes and rivers	127,000	0.127	*0.009*	*0.09 mL (about 2 drops)*
Atmosphere	15,000	0.015	*0.001*	*0.01 mL (about 0.2 drops)*
Biosphere	2,000	0.002	*0.00014*	*0.0014 mL (about 0.03 drops)*
Total	*1,458,944,000*	*1,460*		

▲ **Figure T10.10 Global water reservoirs.** This table shows main reservoirs on Earth for water as volume, percentage of total, and scaled percentage.

Answers to Stop and Think—Part I, SE page 526

1. Students could describe the reservoir of a department store as the warehouse, or the reservoir of the fuel system in a car as the gas tank (or the tank at the gas station). Make sure students support their ideas. Students might have trouble thinking of reservoirs in natural systems other than water systems given the focus thus far in the chapter. Encourage students to think of things that can accumulate in systems. For example, a coal deposit is a reservoir of carbon in the earth system, or reservoirs of metals are needed for aluminum, nickel, gold, silver, and iron.
2. All the water reservoirs on Earth could be considered part of a system because water moves among parts of the system.

Process and Procedure

Part II: Global Water Movement

Materials

For each team of 2 students

2 blank pieces of paper
colored pencils (optional)

As a class, read the introductory paragraphs. Explain that students will be looking at the global water cycle through a systems approach. This will give them the opportunity to look at a natural system and to think about how water moves through this system. Have them begin their work on a blank sheet of paper. You can collect these papers to use for assessment if you cannot interact with each group during its work.

In Step 1, students start to create a box diagram of the global water system. Students should use the information shown in figure 10.16 in the student book to do this. Circulate as students work on their diagrams and provide help through questioning. The key here is to distinguish between a process that moves water (precipitation, evaporation, runoff, atmospheric movement from the ocean to land) and reservoirs that hold water. The movement, or fluxes, of water occur between the reservoirs. Students should note 3 or perhaps 4 reservoirs: ocean, land, atmosphere over the ocean, and atmosphere over the land. It is fine to divide the atmosphere into 2 subsystems since fluxes for evaporation and precipitation are given for the land and the ocean. If the question arises, explain that the groundwater, lakes and rivers, and glacier and polar ice reservoirs can be grouped as 1 reservoir (land).

You can assess students' understanding of the global water system and the interactions between the global water reservoirs by looking at students' box diagrams. Encourage them to redraw ideas, and then see if they are showing arrows proportional in size to the fluxes.

Answers to Step 1, SE page 527

1a. There are 3 reservoirs: ocean, land, atmosphere (over the ocean and over the land).

1b–c. Students should draw a diagram similar to the one in figure T10.11, but their boxes and arrows may be labeled differently. Accept diagrams showing either 1 or 2 boxes for the atmosphere. Some students might recognize that the atmosphere can be divided into one box over land and another box over the ocean because the atmosphere has unique precipitation and

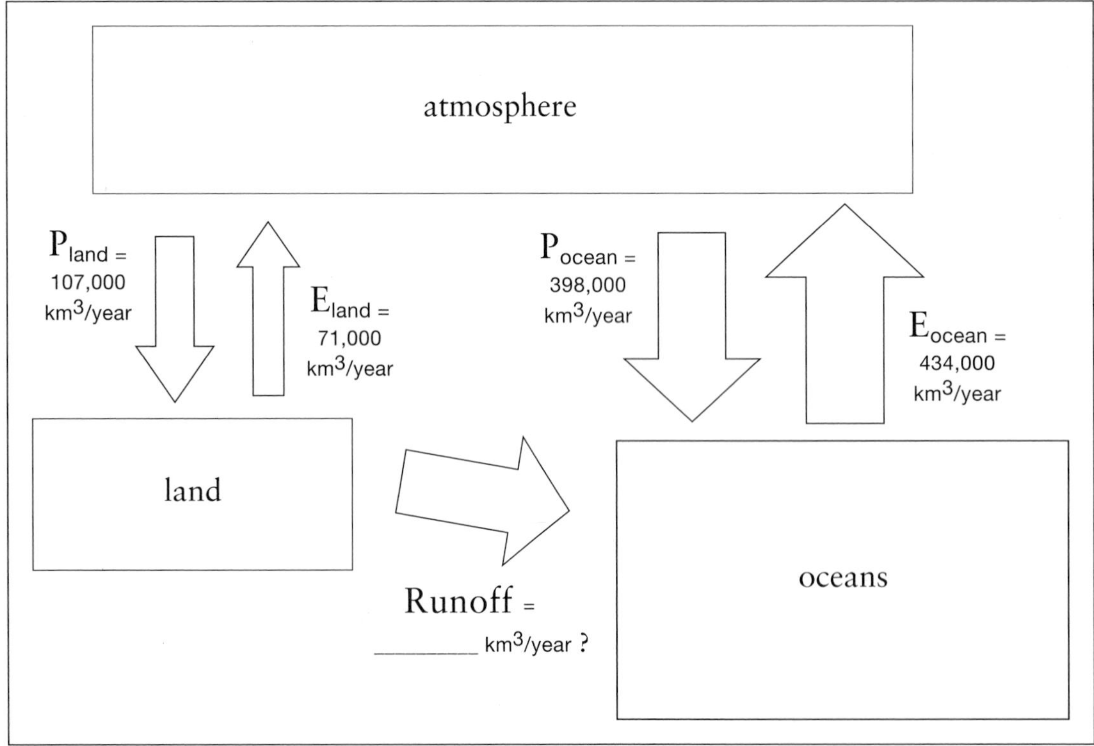

▲ **Figure T10.11 Global water fluxes.** This diagram shows three main reservoirs in the water cycle, and fluxes of water between atmosphere and land, and between atmosphere and oceans. The difference between evaporation and precipitation over land equals the flux of water from land to ocean, or river "runoff." Students show that the runoff flux also must equal the net transport of water vapor from above the oceans to above the continents.

evaporation rates for the land and for the ocean. It is acceptable for students to include all 6 of the global reservoirs on their diagrams:

- E_{land} = Evaporation from land to atmosphere
- E_{ocean} = Evaporation from ocean to atmosphere
- P_{land} = Precipitation from atmosphere to land
- P_{ocean} = Precipitation from atmosphere to ocean
- Runoff = Runoff from land to ocean

1d. These could include groundwater, vegetation, glaciers, ice in permafrost, and lakes.

In Step 2, students determine the flux rates for the missing values in figure 10.16 of the student book. Explain to students that they can assume the system is balanced. (They will see an example in chapter 12, *Evidence for the Ice Ages*, where the ocean swells and shrinks depending on climate cycles between glacial and interglacial periods.) Students should understand that if the system is balanced, the inputs and outputs must be equal for a reservoir, such as the ocean. They did this with their bathtub simulation. Tell them to use this information to help calculate the missing fluxes. Listen as students work on the calculations to assess their understanding of the global water system and the fluxes of water moving through parts of the system.

Students solve the value for runoff from land in Step 2, then the value for water transport from above the ocean to above the land in Step 3. Make sure that they use simple algebra in their solutions. This is a way to demonstrate their results, and it will help them in more complex systems.

Students start by assuming a balance between evaporation, precipitation, and water movement in the atmosphere. In Steps 4 and 5, they begin to consider how the system is affected when one of those parameters changes.

Answers to Step 1 are on TE pages 526b–527.

Part II: Global Water Movement

Materials

For each team of 2 students

2 sheets of blank paper

colored pencils (optional)

Process and Procedure

The flow of water around Earth is the largest scale for water systems. This movement of water is commonly referred to as the water cycle. The water cycle is one of several geochemical systems you will learn about in this unit. A **geochemical cycle** describes the storage and movement of a particular chemical, water in this case, through the earth system. A geochemical cycle could include another element or nutrient, such as carbon phosphorus, calcium, or iron. Geochemical cycles explain how matter moves between reservoirs on Earth.

SCINKS NSTA
Topic: geochemical cycle
Go to: www.scilinks.org
Code: 2Inquiry527

You have diagrammed the inputs and outputs moving through several systems involving humans. Examples are a fast-food restaurant, a swimming pool, and water use in the United States. Now you will learn about and diagram the inputs and outputs for a natural system, the global water system. The inputs and outputs move matter, water in this case, between different reservoirs. Complete the following tasks with a partner and sketch your ideas on a blank sheet of paper.

1. Use the data in figure 10.16 and from Part I to create a simple box diagram of the global water system. Follow these steps.

   Box diagrams of systems help you visualize the parts of a system and how those parts interact.

   a. Identify which reservoirs listed in figure 10.16 contain water. List how many of them are there.
   b. Sketch on the blank sheet of paper the boxes for each reservoir in Step 1a.
   c. Use arrows to show fluxes between and to connect the reservoirs (boxes) given in figure 10.16. Write flux values next to the arrows on your diagram when you know them.

   You may not wish to use the symbols I and O in this diagram. This is because the input for one part of a system might also be the output for another part of the system. For example, rain over the ocean is an input of water for the ocean, but an output relative to the atmosphere.

   d. Consider land to be 1 large reservoir for water. Identify several subsystems within the land that would contain water.

   Recall your findings from Part I.

NOTES:

Answers to Steps 2–5, SE pages 528–529

2a. Evaporation is the only output for the ocean. Precipitation and runoff from the continents are the inputs.

2b. If the mass of the ocean is constant, then it is not shrinking or growing in volume. The net change in volume must be zero. Another way to say this algebraically is

$$\pm \text{ change in ocean volume} = (\text{inputs} - \text{outputs})$$
$$= I_{runoff} + I_{precip} - O_{evap}.$$

2c. The ocean is not, overall, shrinking or growing, so the net change must be zero.

$$I_{runoff} = (O_{evap} - I_{precip}) = \left(434{,}000\frac{\text{km}^3}{\text{yr}} - 398{,}000\frac{\text{km}^3}{\text{yr}}\right)$$

2d. Completing Step 2c indicates a runoff from land of 36,000 km^3 per year to balance evaporation in the ocean:

$$I_{runoff} = 36{,}000\frac{\text{km}^3}{\text{yr}}$$

3a. The inputs to the atmosphere above land are evaporation from land and movement of water vapor from above the ocean to where it resides above

NOTES:

Water transport process	Flux (rate of water movement) km³/year	×10³ km³/year
Evaporation from land to atmosphere	71,000	71
Evaporation from ocean to atmosphere	434,000	434
Precipitation from atmosphere to land	107,000	107
Precipitation from atmosphere to oceans	398,000	398
Runoff from land to oceans	?	?
Water vapor flux from atmosphere over oceans to atmosphere over land	?	?

Source: Berner, E. K., & Berner R. A. (1987). *The global water cycle: Geochemistry and environment.* Englewood Cliffs, NJ: Prentice Hall.

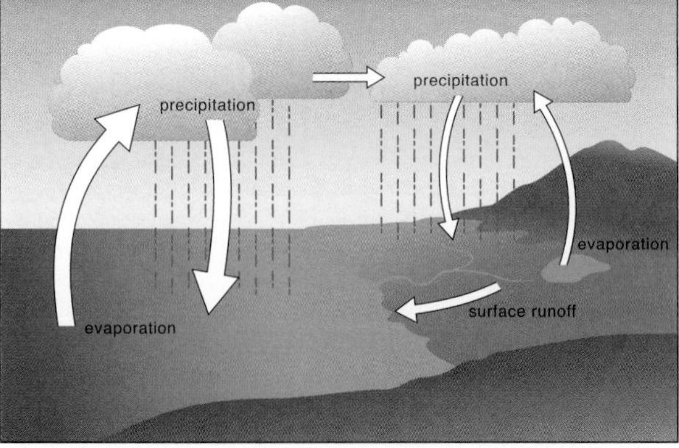

Figure 10.16 Water cycle fluxes. The fluxes of water between reservoirs differ for the land and the ocean (10^3 km³/year = thousands of cubic kilometers per year). These are fluxes because they tell the volume (or mass) per year. How can you determine the flux rate for runoff and water vapor moving between the atmosphere above the ocean and the atmosphere above land?

Topic: water cycle
Go to: www.scilinks.org
Code: 2Inquiry528

2. Use what you know about systems to determine the values of the fluxes missing in figure 10.16. First, consider the ocean as a subsystem of the global water system.
   a. Identify the inputs and outputs for the ocean due to precipitation and evaporation.
   b. Assume that the mass of water in the ocean is constant. What then must be true about the total inputs and outputs of water for the ocean? Explain this both as a sentence and as a mathematical expression.

Recall your system inputs and outputs from Part II of the activity *System Structures.*

the land. This must occur since the rate of precipitation above land is greater than the rate of evaporation from land.

3b. If mass of water vapor above land does not change, the inputs again must equal the outputs. The net change in volume must be zero. Another way to say this algebraically is

$$\pm \text{ change in mass of water above land} = (\text{inputs} - \text{outputs})$$
$$= I_{\text{water from over oceans}} + I_{\text{evap from land}} - O_{\text{precip}}.$$

3c. The unknown is how much water vapor travels from above the ocean to above the land. Rearranging the expression from Step 3b gives

$$I_{\text{water from over oceans}} = (O_{\text{precip}} - I_{\text{evap from land}})$$
$$I_{\text{water from over oceans}} = \left(107{,}000\frac{\text{km}^3}{\text{yr}} - 71{,}000\frac{\text{km}^3}{\text{yr}}\right).$$

3d. Completing Step 2c indicates a runoff from land of 36,000 km^3 per year to balance the amount of rain that occurs over land:

$$I_{\text{water from over oceans}} = 36{,}000\frac{\text{km}^3}{\text{yr}}.$$

c. Use the flux of water from land into the ocean (river runoff) to balance the total inputs and outputs for the ocean. This is easiest to do with a simple equation.

d. Determine the value of water flux for continental runoff in rivers, and thus, a missing value in figure 10.16.

3. Second, consider the atmosphere above land as a subsystem of the global water system.

a. Identify the inputs and outputs for the atmosphere above land.

Divide the atmosphere into 2 boxes if you have not already. One box is the atmosphere over the ocean, and the other is the atmosphere over land.

b. Assume that the mass of water vapor in the atmosphere above land is constant. What must be true about the total inputs and outputs of water for the atmosphere above the land?

c. Use the flux of water vapor from above the ocean to the atmosphere above the land to balance the total inputs and outputs for the atmosphere above land.

d. Determine the value of water flux from the atmosphere above the ocean to the atmosphere above the land, and thus, the other missing value in figure 10.16.

4. The numbers you have been working with are an average across time. Consider what would happen if the system changed. Imagine that during an extreme year, the evaporation rate of the ocean increased because of warmer temperatures near the equator.

a. How would the increase in evaporation rate over the ocean affect the other fluxes?

b. Describe an effect this change would have on a reservoir other than the ocean.

5. Consider a different change in the global water system. What if the global climate becomes colder, and precipitation on the continents falls as snow. If the snow cannot melt away during the summer, then some snowfall is retained from each year on land. This accumulating snow grows into glaciers with yearly layers (figure 10.17).

a. What changes would you predict for the global water cycle?

b. Is the system still in balance for the ocean? In other words, do the inputs equal the outputs?

6. As you finish, listen to directions from your teacher regarding collecting your diagram.

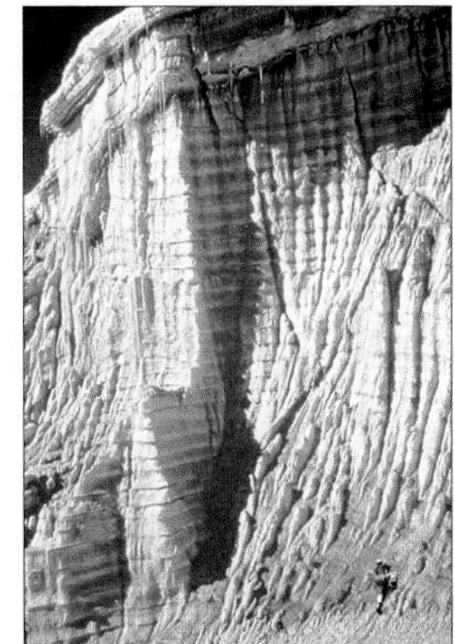

▲ **Figure 10.17** **Annual snow layers.** This photograph shows a cliff of ice where part of a glacier has broken away. The layers show a record of the cycle of yearly snowfall when these layers were on top of the glacier. White layers are winter snowfall. Brown stripes represent dust falling on the snow in summer. What does this tell you about the water cycle?

4a. An increase in evaporation rate puts water into the atmosphere faster. As a result, either the rate of precipitation will increase over the ocean or more water vapor will be transported from the ocean to the land. If the system stays in balance, both of these together must equal the increase in evaporation. Some students might think about how increased evaporation over the ocean might also affect the amount of precipitation over the land. This could also increase precipitation over land and the amount of runoff from land to ocean.

4b. Be open to student ideas here. In general, it is hard to increase the amount of water that can be stored in the atmosphere. Thus, a predicted result would be more rain. In contrast, this case with water is different than the increase in carbon dioxide that is occurring. Because carbon dioxide is a trace gas, it can keep accruing in the atmosphere faster than plants or the ocean can remove it. Students will study this topic more in the next chapter.

5a. Students should see that the global water cycle gets "stuck"; water remains on land as snow. If the snow cannot melt away in the summer, the layers build each year to form a glacier. This leads to reduced runoff, or the annual flux of water returning to the ocean.

5b. As long as evaporation rates stay the same over the ocean, the volume of the ocean would decrease (the sea level would drop) proportional to the mass of snow transferred to the glaciers. The glaciers would be a growing reservoir, with inputs to the land greater than outputs to the ocean.

After students have completed Step 5, decide what pieces of their work you wish to collect for assessment. Have students begin the *Stop and Think* questions.

NOTES:

Answers to Stop and Think—Part II, SE page 530

1. It is important to think about water on Earth because water is an important part of our lives. We cannot live without it. By looking at the global water system, we can learn where all the water is stored and how water moves between those reservoirs. We can also predict the impact of human activities on the system using a systems approach.

2a. Students might explain that a typical water cycle diagram has pictures instead of boxes and doesn't have fluxes like a box diagram. They might also explain that water cycle diagrams often include other parts such as the Sun, both rain and snow, a token animal, and seepage to groundwater. You might explain to students that their box diagrams were simplified because it is difficult to determine fluxes for all the parts. Or if they don't know fluxes for each of the parts, making the diagram begins to be more and more complicated.

2b. The water cycle can be better understood with a systems approach because it helps students think about how each part of the system affects the other. The fluxes also allow students to see how much water is moving through each part of the system. Make sure students support their ideas.

Stop & THINK

PART II

Complete the following questions in your science notebook.

1. Why do you think it is important to think about water on Earth? What can you learn by looking at the global water system?
2. You probably were familiar with the water cycle. Think about how a systems approach has helped you look at the water cycle differently.
   a. Recall a water cycle diagram that you have seen in the past. As best you can, sketch it in your science notebook. How does that diagram compare with the global water system you worked with in this activity?

   Consider using a strategy such as a Venn diagram or a T-table to list similarities and differences.

   b. Describe how you think a systems approach to the global water cycle might help you better understand the water cycle.

   A systems approach focuses on the whole system and how all the parts of the system interact. How would this approach help you make predictions about what might happen if the system changed?

Part III: Residence Time

Materials

none

Process and Procedure

Have you ever thought about the average length of time a library book is on a shelf before it is checked out? Or how long a music CD sits on the store shelf before being sold? On a bigger scale, how long do you think $1 remains in a bank before heading back out into the economy?

In Part III of this investigation, you will learn how to estimate the time that matter, such as water, stays in a reservoir before moving to another reservoir. Discuss the following questions with a partner and record your answers individually in your science notebook.

Process and Procedure

Part III: Residence Time

Materials

none

Instruct students to read the introductory paragraphs. Explain to students that they will begin thinking about how long something is in a system. Ask them their initial thoughts about the questions in the introductory paragraphs. Ask students how they think they could estimate the time that matter stays in a reservoir before moving to another reservoir.

In Step 1, student pairs should make predictions. Hold a class discussion and ask students to share their ideas. They will likely say a water molecule spends less time in the atmosphere than in the ocean before moving on. Be open to their reasons, which may include that wind moves the water molecule to land and then to rain over 1–2 weeks. However, water could also be "stuck" down deep in the ocean for much longer than 1–2 weeks.

For Step 2, students try to answer quantitatively. Remain open to ideas, since students really don't have much of a way to evaluate the question at this point. You could record each prediction to see who comes the closest to the actual amount calculated later.

In Step 3, instruct pairs of students to read about the residence time of matter in a reservoir. Use a reading strategy that is important for your students. Circulate as students read. Make sure that students understand that residence time is most accurate for a balanced system, when the inputs and outputs are equal. Another key assumption with this approach is that the reservoir is well mixed (see *Background Information*), although this assumption may confuse the issue at this point.

1. Do you think that a water molecule spends more time in the ocean or in the atmosphere before moving to the next reservoir? Explain your reasoning.
2. How much time do you think a water molecule spends in the ocean? The atmosphere? Would you guess times of seconds, hours, days, or years? Discuss your best guess with your partner. Be ready to share your ideas and explain your reasoning with the class.
3. Read the following to learn how scientists estimate these values and then study figure 10.18.

Residence time is the average length of time that matter in a system remains in a given reservoir. This value is estimated when there is no long-term change in the system. Residence time is calculated from the mass of material in the reservoir, divided by either the total flux in, or the total flux out, for the reservoir. Remember that flux has units of mass per time. You can also use volume if you remember that mass is related to volume by density.

$$\text{residence time} = \frac{\text{mass of matter (or volume) in reservoir}}{\text{total flux in (or flux out) for reservoir}}$$

A reservoir can have multiple inputs or outputs. In these cases, residence time is estimated from the sum of the inputs or outputs. If you use only one of several inputs, for example, you will underestimate the rate of mass coming into the reservoir and leaving the reservoir. The inputs and outputs can be used interchangeably because the system is balanced. That is, the inputs and outputs are equal.

Here's an example. Assume a bathtub is filled with 24 gal of water and the input of water from the faucet is 3 gallons per minute (gal/min). The residence time for bathwater before it leaves the bathtub through the drain is calculated as 24 gal divided by 3 gal/min. The residence time for bathwater in this system is 8 minutes. So a water molecule entering this bathtub would remain in the bathwater for an average of 8 minutes before leaving through the drain. If the bathtub held 18 gal of water, the residence time would decrease to 6 minutes.

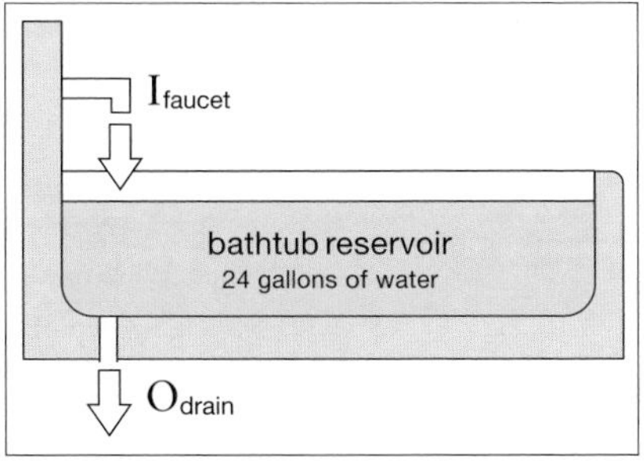

▲ **Figure 10.18 Residing in a bathtub.** If inputs and outputs are equal, they can be used to estimate residence time for a molecule of water in bathwater before it leaves the tub down the drain.

NOTES:

Students estimate some residence times for a water molecule in the ocean and the atmosphere in Steps 4 and 5. Make sure that units cancel properly in the equation. Also, it doesn't matter whether students use units of mass (kg) or volume (km^3) of the matter in the reservoir, as long as they remember that mass and volume are related through density.

Answers to Steps 4–5, SE page 532

4a. A good estimate for the volume of water in the ocean is 1,400,000,000 km^3 = 1.4×10^9 km^3.

4b. Students already determined fluxes (in or out) for the ocean of 343,000 km^3/yr = 3.43×10^5 km^3/yr.

4c. A quantitative answer is better than a qualitative answer (bigger or smaller). For example, "Compared with my guess in Step 2 of 3 years, the residence time I calculated here is about 1,000 times greater." If the residence time seems long, it is because the volume of the ocean is so large.

$$\text{residence time} = \left(\frac{1.4 \times 10^9 \cancel{km^3}}{434{,}000 \frac{\cancel{km^3}}{yr}}\right) \text{ or}$$

$$= \left(1.4 \times 10^9 \cancel{km^3}\right) \times \left(\frac{1 \text{ yr}}{434{,}000 \cancel{km^3}}\right)$$

$$= 3{,}200 \text{ yr}$$

5. The volume of water in the atmosphere is about 15,000 km^3. The total flux of water entering the atmosphere from evaporation is 71,000 km^3/yr + 434,000 km^3/yr = 505,000 km^3/yr. The total flux of water leaving the atmosphere by precipitation is also 505,000 km^3/yr (107,000 km^3/yr + 398,000 km^3/yr).

$$\text{residence time} = \left(\frac{15{,}000 \cancel{km^3}}{505{,}000 \frac{\cancel{km^3}}{yr}}\right)$$

$$= \left(\frac{1.5 \times 10^4 \cancel{km^3}}{5.05 \times 10^5 \frac{\cancel{km^3}}{yr}}\right)$$

$$= 0.0297 \text{ yr}$$

$$= 10.8 \text{ day}$$

Your students should be able to show a conversion to days; the answer is about 10.8 days.

Once students have completed these tasks, tell them to work on the *Reflect and Connect* questions with their partners. They should record their answers in their science notebooks.

Answers to Reflect and Connect—Part III, SE pages 532–533

1. Students' predictions for residence time in the ocean were probably much lower than the actual residence time. They might have been surprised that the residence time was in thousands of years. The reason for this is the large mass of water in the ocean. Look for answers that are consistent with their answers for Step 1.
2. Residence time helps students understand a system because it tells how long something is in a reservoir within a system. The residence time of a CD in a store might help a business predict how often and how many CDs it needs to stock, either by music genre or artist. The rate of sales is a flux out, which the store needs to balance with a flux in, or it will run out of a category of music. Or if it purchases too much (flux in), it will be overstocked.

Answers to Reflect and Connect are on TE pages 532–533.

4. Imagine a water molecule entering the ocean from precipitation or continental runoff. Estimate the residence time for a water molecule in the ocean.
   a. Identify the volume of water in the ocean.
   b. Determine the total flux of water into (or out of) the ocean.
   c. Calculate the residence time. Use a sentence to compare this answer with Step 2.
5. Imagine a water molecule entering the atmosphere. Follow the procedure in Step 3 to estimate the residence time for that water molecule in the atmosphere.

Your answer may make more sense after converting to days. Use a volume of water in the atmosphere of 15,000 km^3.

Reflect and Connect—Part III

Work with your partner to complete these questions.

1. How close was your prediction of how long a water molecule is in the ocean (residence time) to the number you calculated in Step 4c? Were you surprised by the residence time for water in the ocean?
2. Residence time applies to more than just water systems. For example, the residence time for a CD in a department store might be 1 week and the residence time for a calcium atom in the ocean is 850,000 years. How do you think residence time helps you better understand a system? How do you think residence time might help you make predictions about a system?

Calcium enters the ocean from rocks that weather and dissolve on Earth's surface. Calcium is highly soluble in seawater, so it tends to have a long residence time. Calcium can leave seawater when marine organisms use calcium to build their shells. You'll learn more about this in the next chapter.

3. Recall your experiment in Part I of *System Structures* where you maintained the water level at a mark on your container. Estimate the residence time for a water molecule in that system.

Use the procedure in Step 4 to help organize values for this calculation.

4. One group of researchers has estimated that the residence time for a water molecule stored as ice in a glacier and polar ice reservoir is 27,500 years. Assume the system is balanced (the inputs and outputs are equal). Would the residence time increase or decrease if Earth entered an ice age and more water were stored in the polar ice reservoir? Explain your reasoning using the equation for residence time.

The residence time of a calcium atom in the ocean helps scientists predict that calcium cycles between reservoirs across long periods of time.

Another example is stock for a company. A daily parameter reported is the number of shares traded per day (flux in and out), which is then compared with the total number of shares owned by a company.

Students are likely to have difficulty answering this question and might not have answers as sophisticated as those provided here. The primary purpose of this question is to get students to begin thinking about why residence time might be an important piece of information used in systems thinking. Look for answers that indicate students are thinking about systems.

3. Here is an example of the calculation using a volume of 40 mL and a flow rate of 2.2 mL/sec. A water molecule spends about 18 seconds in the container before exiting the hole.

$$\text{residence time} = \left(\frac{40\ \cancel{\text{mL}}}{2.2\ \frac{\cancel{\text{mL}}}{\text{sec}}}\right)$$

$$= 18.2\ \text{sec}$$

4. Students should understand that because the amount of water (volume) in the glacier and polar ice reservoir increases substantially, the residence time of a water molecule in glacier and polar ice would also increase. The flux of water in might not actually change that much. The flux would appear to increase because winter ice is less likely to melt during the summer.

5. It is easy to show that a molecule spends about 4–5 years in the Great Salt Lake before evaporating. This might be longer than students would expect given the lake's "salty" look and appearance of significant evaporation. Indeed, evaporation rates are high at this lake, but they have been occurring at a high rate for many thousands of years.

$$\text{residence time} = \left(\frac{16{,}000{,}000\ \cancel{\text{af}}}{3{,}500{,}000\ \frac{\cancel{\text{af}}}{\text{yr}}}\right)$$

$$= 4.6\ \text{yr}$$

5. In 1993, what was the residence time for a water molecule in the Great Salt Lake? That year, the rate of water entering the Great Salt Lake was nearly equal to the rate of water lost to evaporation. The input and output rates were about 3.5 million af/yr. That year, the volume of water in the Great Salt Lake was about 16 million af.

A Salty Situation

EVALUATE

In *The Global Water System*, you investigated some characteristics of systems, in particular water systems. You have learned that water systems can be described by their boundaries, their components, and the rate that water moves into or out of parts of a system. You also learned about your local water system. This system can be thought of as a subsystem of continental water systems. You might even think of continental water systems as a part of the largest water reservoir on Earth—the hydrosphere.

In *A Salty Situation*, you will first work as a class, then as a team, to investigate a dilemma for a large water system. It is the Great Salt Lake in Utah. Decisions and choices need to be made regarding the uses and management of water in the Great Salt Lake system. What will you recommend?

Part I: The Lake

Materials

For each team of 3 students

3 sets of handouts, consisting of the following:

- *Map of the Great Salt Lake*
- *Water Numbers for the Great Salt Lake*
- *Humans at the Great Salt Lake*

3 *Salty Situation Scoring Rubric* handouts

1 set of 3 handouts, consisting of the following:

- *Shrimp Survival*
- *Minerals: Resources from the Great Salt Lake*
- *A Unique and Evolving Ecosystem*

Students might wonder why there is a question about the Great Salt Lake. This might be a good opportunity to have students read the introduction to the evaluate, *A Salty Situation*. If you are interested in having students do some research on their own, you might consider having students begin working on Part I of the evaluate.

EVALUATE

A Salty Situation

Activity Overview

In *A Salty Situation*, students will show their understanding of water systems by producing a feature article on the Great Salt Lake. In Part I, students will read about different aspects of Great Salt Lake and about how different interest groups connect to the Great Salt Lake. Students will participate in class discussions to share their understanding of the Great Salt Lake system. In Part II, students will work in teams to produce their feature articles focused on the water system and the salt imbalance.

Before You Teach

Background Information

You'll find important background information in the following copymasters and in the sidebar *Why Is the Great Salt Lake So Salty?*

- Copymaster 10.7, *Map of the Great Salt Lake*
- Copymaster 10.8, *Water Numbers for the Great Salt Lake*
- Copymaster 10.9, *Humans at the Great Salt Lake*
- Copymaster 10.10, *Shrimp Survival*
- Copymaster 10.11, *Minerals: Resources from the Great Salt Lake*
- Copymaster 10.12, *A Unique and Evolving Ecosystem*

The summary descriptions of the Great Salt Lake are somewhat simplified. For example, if students conduct their own research, they might find that during flooding in the mid-1980s a bridge was built over a breach in the causeway. The lake elevation in the south part of the lake had risen significantly and was flooding many areas along the shore. The breach helped alleviate flooding and it helped reduce the salt imbalance temporarily. As the lake elevation in the south part declined, the movement of salty water through the breach also declined and virtually stopped. During this time, water was pumped from the north part of the lake west into the Great Salt Lake Desert. This also reduced flooding.

After monitoring salinity levels and brine shrimp populations, local agencies began thinking about ways to manage the Great Salt Lake system and reduce the salt imbalance. The U.S. Geological Survey designed a "water and salt balance" model of the lake. Using this model, the USGS decided that the best way to reduce the salt imbalance was to deepen the breach in the causeway. The breach was deepened in December 2000, causing a 330 percent increase of flow through the breach. For additional information about the Great Salt Lake, see the reference list for this chapter and the *TRCD*.

Details such as these were not shared with students because they make an already complex issue even more complex. Also, if students decide to recommend making an opening in the causeway, you can share with them that they came up with the same solution as professionals who worked on this problem.

Materials—Part I

For the teacher

overhead projector
1 color transparency of figure 10.19
1 large sheet of paper

For each team of 3 students

3 sets of copymasters, consisting of the following:

- copymaster 10.7, *Map of the Great Salt Lake*
- copymaster 10.8, *Water Numbers for the Great Salt Lake*
- copymaster 10.9, *Humans at the Great Salt Lake*
- copymaster 10.1, *Scoring Rubric for A Salty Situation*

1 set of copymasters, consisting of the following:

- copymaster 10.10, *Shrimp Survival*
- copymaster 10.11, *Minerals: Resources from the Great Salt Lake*
- copymaster 10.12, *A Unique and Evolving Ecosystem*

Process and Procedure

It is early in the 21st century, and communities around the Great Salt Lake, Utah, have a dilemma (figure 10.19). Changes in the salinity of the lake have caused a salt imbalance between the northern and southern portions. The salt imbalance is affecting the local ecosystem, the mineral industry, and the brine shrimp industry (figure 10.20). Something needs to be done. Or does it?

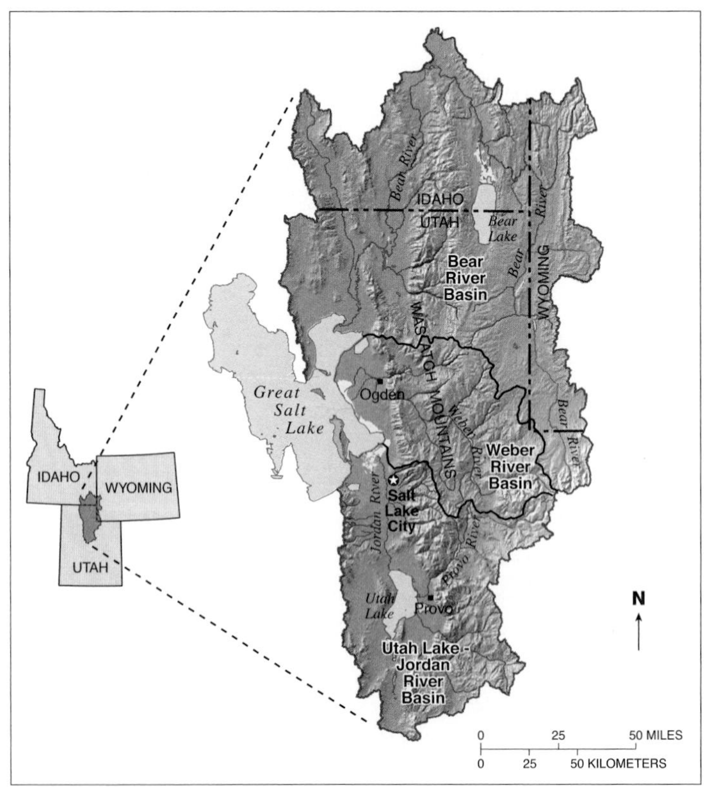

▲ **Figure 10.19 Great Salt Lake map.** This map shows the Great Salt Lake, Utah, and the three major watersheds for rivers draining into the lake. Salt Lake City and the Wasatch Mountains are to the east.

534 Unit 3 Moving Matter

Materials—Part II

copymaster 10.13, *Sample GSL Article to Post*

Advance Preparation

Assign as homework reading the sidebar *Why Is the Great Salt Lake So Salty?* This will help the students understand the setting.

Locate the color transparency for figure 10.19.

Be sure that all students have a copy of copymaster 10.1, *Scoring Rubric for A Salty Situation*. You distributed copies of the rubric during the engage activity, but some copies may have been lost. Make sets of copymasters 10.7–10.12 for the teams as recommended in the materials list. Or you may decide to use only 1 set of all 6 copymasters per team.

Read the sidebar *Why Is the Great Salt Lake So Salty?* and the copymasters to help you guide students in their research.

Obtain a wall map of the world if you plan to talk about other lakes around the world.

Decide which of the informational copymasters and the sidebar you will assign as homework.

Review copymaster 10.13, *Sample GSL Article to Post*. This shows an example of the type of work that you would expect of students. Decide when it might be appropriate to post or share as an example with your class.

In an effort to help the community decision makers understand the issue, your team has been asked to write a feature article for the local newspaper. Your class has been selected because of its ability to analyze the issue from a systems perspective. Here is a chance to apply your understanding of systems to a new situation. Your feature article will include a description of the Great Salt Lake as a system and will provide a recommendation of how to manage the Great Salt Lake system.

Before you begin your work, become familiar with the evaluate *Salty Situation Scoring Rubric* provided by your teacher. Use the rubric to guide your work.

▲ **Figure 10.20**
Brine shrimp. This brine shrimp is about 1 cm long. Brine shrimp are an important part of the ecology of the Great Salt Lake.

1. As a class, make a list of questions about the Great Salt Lake and the salt imbalance dilemma being faced. If you were in the position of making a decision about what to do—or what not to do—what facts and data would you need?
2. Get in your team of 3 and gather information about the Great Salt Lake. Each team member will become an expert in 1 of 3 categories (water, human impacts, or salinity) for the Great Salt Lake system. Information about salinity is in the sidebar *Why Is the Great Salt Lake So Salty?* Carefully complete the reading for your expert group. You might want to conduct further research on your own. Prepare to contribute to a class discussion.

You will have copies of all the handouts. In this step, you are only responsible for reading the handout for your expert group. Keep all the handouts to use as reference in this activity. All team members need to understand the sidebar *Why Is the Great Lake So Salty?*

3. What did you learn about the Great Salt Lake? Participate in a class discussion of the Great Salt Lake as a system. Your teacher will ask you to share what you learned from your handout.

Take notes as you listen to other experts share what they learned. You will need to understand all parts of the Great Salt Lake system to complete this activity.

4. Record in your science notebook who and what depend on the Great Salt Lake. Changes in the Great Salt Lake system affect the local economy and the local ecosystem. In your team of 3, become an expert on 1 of the following special interest groups: the brine shrimp industry, the mineral industry, or the GSL Friends group. You can do further research on your own. Prepare to contribute to a class discussion.

Chapter 10 The Water System 535

As You Teach

Outcomes and Indicators of Success

By the end of this activity, students should

1. understand that a system is a collection of interacting parts that serve a specific function and that a system can be described in terms of its components, boundaries, and inputs and outputs.

   They will demonstrate their understanding by

   - describing the components and boundaries of the Great Salt Lake water system and
   - describing the flow of water through the Great Salt Lake system in both a qualitative and a quantitative manner.

2. understand that there is a fixed amount of water within Earth's systems and that water can exist in various reservoirs and can move among them.

   They will demonstrate their understanding by

   - describing the main reservoirs of water (location, characteristics) found within the Great Salt Lake water system and
   - describing the main inputs and outputs of water in the Great Salt Lake system.

3. understand that there are many kinds of interactions within the earth system and that these interactions can affect other parts of the system.

   They will demonstrate their understanding by describing interactions between the Great Salt Lake water system (representing the hydrosphere) and other earth systems (biosphere, geosphere, atmosphere) that have led to the salt imbalance.

4. begin to understand that human populations need resources from the environment in order to maintain and improve their existence.

   They will demonstrate their understanding by summarizing the impact of the salinity imbalance and the needs of special interest groups (brine shrimp industry, mineral industry, GSL Friends).

5. develop further skills in the abilities and understandings of scientific inquiry.

   They will demonstrate their ability and understanding of inquiry by

   - using key concepts in systems analysis to synthesize information and make a recommendation about the Great Salt Lake;
   - using data in graphs and tables to represent the Great Salt Lake system;
   - investigating and then describing interactions among different parts of the Great Salt Lake system;
   - communicating their understanding and findings in a newspaper feature article;
   - developing a box diagram to represent fluxes in and flux out of the Great Salt Lake system; and
   - strengthening links to other areas of science, such as ecology, solution chemistry, and geography.

Strategies

Getting Started

Students were introduced to the Great Salt Lake early in this chapter. They were given the rubric for this evaluate activity at that time. A question about the residence time of a water molecule in the Great Salt Lake appeared in the *Reflect and Connect* of *The Global Water System*. It's now time to take a close look at the Great Salt Lake. If you started a package of sea monkeys at the beginning of the chapter, point them out to the students. Students likely will become especially interested in the shrimp when they read about them in copymaster 10.10, *Shrimp Survival*.

TRCD

Show students the color transparency of figure 10.19.

Use other maps or images from the transparencies in the explain activity, *Expanding Boundaries* (e.g., watersheds of North America). Ask students how they think the Great Salt Lake fits in with watersheds in North America. How does the watershed for the Great Salt Lake differ from other watersheds? (It does not drain to the ocean.) Do they know anything about this water system?

You might also ask whether students can think of other areas of the world with watersheds that do not drain to the ocean. (Examples are parts of the East African Rift, the Dead Sea, Lake Baikal, the Aral Sea, and the Caspian Sea.) In these areas, evaporation is generally equal to or greater than precipitation. If precipitation exceeds evaporative loss, the lake fills and overflows, forming a river to the ocean. Examples of the latter are the Great Lakes and Lake Okeechobee in Florida.

Process and Procedure

Part I: The Lake

Materials

For the teacher

overhead projector

1 color transparency of figure 10.19

1 large sheet of paper

For each team of 3 students

3 sets of copymasters, consisting of the following:

- copymaster 10.7, *Map of the Great Salt Lake*
- copymaster 10.8, *Water Numbers for the Great Salt Lake*
- copymaster 10.9, *Humans at the Great Salt Lake*
- copymaster 10.1, *Scoring Rubric for A Salty Situation*

GSL Friends is a community group whose mission is to preserve and protect the Great Salt Lake ecosystem. You may come across information from this group on the World Wide Web.

5. How do other systems (such as industries or ecosystems) interact with the Great Salt Lake system? Participate in a class discussion of how the brine shrimp industry, mineral industry, and the ecosystem are affected by the Great Salt Lake system. Share what you know about your special interest group. Provide information that will help answer the following questions.
   a. How would you describe your group? What connection does the group have to the Great Salt Lake?
   b. What does your group bring to the Great Salt Lake region? What value does it have?
   c. How does your group depend on the Great Salt Lake?
   d. How have changes in the Great Salt Lake, such as the salt imbalance, affected your group?

SIDEBAR

Why Is the Great Salt Lake So Salty?

If you live near a river or lake, the water might not be clear. With a magnifying glass, you might see fine particles of silt, organic matter, or microorganisms. This is the **suspended load** in natural waters. The suspended load is all the particles, either floating or suspended, carried by the water.

All natural waters also have a **dissolved load**. These are elements and molecules in an ionic form that are dissolved in the water. This is easy to show by dissolving sugar or table salt (NaCl) in water. In natural waters, the dissolved load often includes cations (Ca^{+2}, Na^{+1}, Mg^{+2}, or K^{+1}), anions (Cl^{-1} or HCO_3^{-1}), and the dissolved gases CO_2 and O_2. **Salinity** refers to the amount of dissolved ions in the water. Dissolved ions are always present in natural waters, even though they cannot be seen. The ions come from rocks and minerals that weather and degrade in rain and snow. This process helps explain why the Great Salt Lake is so salty.

The Great Salt Lake is the largest remaining part of the ancient Lake Bonneville. Lake Bonneville was a huge lake formed by meltwater from glaciers during the last major ice age approximately 30,000 to 20,000 years ago. Over the last 10,000 years, the climate in the region has become drier and warmer. Over this time period, more water evaporated from Lake Bonneville than flowed into it. As water evaporates, it concentrates the ions in the shrinking lake, making it more and more salty. The salts of various types accumulate on the shores of the lake.

Currently, three main rivers drain from the mountains to the Great Salt Lake: the

1 set of copymasters, consisting of the following:

- copymaster 10.10, *Shrimp Survival*
- copymaster 10.11, *Minerals: Resources from the Great Salt Lake*
- copymaster 10.12, *A Unique and Evolving Ecosystem*

After the introductory discussion about the Great Salt Lake, direct the students to the introductory paragraphs of the *Process and Procedure*. Help students complete Step 1 by making a list as a class of questions that students have about the salt imbalance dilemma in the Great Salt Lake. Ask them what they might need to know about the Great Salt Lake. How would the Great Salt Lake function as a system?

Questions might range from specific, like "What is a brine shrimp?" to more general, "What is a salt imbalance and what could cause the salt imbalance?" Tell students to keep these questions in mind as they research and produce their feature article. The questions they have will likely be the same as those of readers of the feature article. Explain that they will have the opportunity to answer many of these questions as they explore the Great Salt Lake and produce their feature article.

In Step 2, get students into groups of 3. You may assign students to groups, allow them to select their own groups, or choose groups randomly. Use the method that seems most appropriate. Groups of 3 will distribute the work but maintain individual accountability.

When students are in their teams, distribute copymasters 10.7, *Map of the Great Salt Lake*; 10.8, *Water Numbers for the Great Salt Lake*; and 10.9, *Humans at the Great Salt Lake*. Students should be familiar with copymaster 10.7, *Map of the Great Salt Lake*. They will need a visual of the lake, including the rivers that feed into the lake. Tell students to take responsibility for specific areas of information within the group. In a team of 3 students, each team member will become an expert on either water, human impacts, or salinity. If students work on this step in class, suggest they gather in expert groups to read and discuss their thoughts. Decide whether you can assign this step as homework.

Use questions like the following to help prepare students for the classroom discussion. Also review the rubric to make sure students are clear on your expectations.

Water expert (copymaster 10.8, *Water Numbers for the Great Salt Lake*)

- "What is so 'great' about the Great Salt Lake?"
- "Where is the lake?" "What does it look like?" "How did it get there?"
- "Why is it salty?"
- "Where is the water?" "How much is there?"
- "Where does the water come from? Go to?"
- "How stable is the water level?" "What affects the water level?"

Human impact expert (Copymaster 10.9, *Humans at the Great Salt Lake*)

- "How have humans changed the Great Salt Lake?"
- "How have these changes affected salinity levels?"

Salinity expert (sidebar, *Why Is the Great Salt Lake So Salty?*)

- "How salty is the water?"
- "What caused the salt imbalance?"
- "What factors influence salinity (flooding, railroad causeway, pumping)?"

▲ **Great Salt Lake.** The shores of the Great Salt Lake, Utah, are very salty. This is due to the evaporation of water and the precipitation of salt compounds at the shoreline.

Bear, Weber, and Jordan rivers (see *Water Numbers for the Great Salt Lake* handout). The region that these rivers cover makes up most of the **watershed** for the Great Salt Lake. A watershed is the area of land that drains into a particular body of water. Within that entire watershed, the streams and rivers slowly weather and dissolve rocks and minerals. While this process is quite slow, the Great Salt Lake watershed is large, about 21,500 square miles. Thus, there is a lot of rock to erode and weather.

These rivers have flowed into the Great Salt Lake for hundreds of thousands of years. Today, they deliver nearly 2 million acre feet of water per year, and perhaps 2 million tons of dissolved salts. Yet the average level of the Great Salt Lake does not change much. This is because the rate of evaporation equals the total flow rates into the lake.

During evaporation, the dissolved ions do not enter the atmosphere as gaseous molecules, so they remain dissolved in the lake. With time, the dissolved ions increase in concentration in the lake water as more ions are added to the lake, and water continues to evaporate. We detect the dissolved ions as a salty taste to the water. This same process of large rivers transporting dissolved ions from the continents to the ocean is what makes the ocean salty as well. The scale of the ocean system is much larger though.

SCILINKS NSTA
Topic: salinity
Go to: www.scilinks.org
Code: 2Inquiry537

Chapter 10 The Water System 537

In Step 3, lead a class discussion on the Great Salt Lake as a system. Call on experts from each group to share some things they learned from their handouts. Make sure every student contributes to the discussion. Explain to students that although they are an expert in only 1 area, they will need information from all the groups to complete the evaluate. Encourage them to take notes from the 2 other expert groups and from the experts within their own group. Students should be able to ask and answer the following types of questions. You might want to use these questions to help guide groups that are having difficulty making progress.

- "Is the Great Salt Lake an open or closed system?" "What are the geographic boundaries of this system?" "Is the Great Salt Lake part of any larger systems?"
- "What are the major water components of the system?" "What other components in the water play a role in the Great Salt Lake?" "How do these components interact to give the Great Salt Lake its unique characteristics?" "What makes the Great Salt Lake different from other water basins?"
- "What is the flow of water through the system?" "What are the inputs and outputs to the water system?" "At what rate is water entering and leaving the system?" "What are the amounts (both quantities and units) of water involved in the system?" "Is the Great Salt Lake water system dynamic or not dynamic? Explain your thinking."

In Step 4, students read about 3 special interest groups that depend on the Great Salt Lake. Give the same teams the second set of copymasters. These handouts provide insight into the impact of the salt imbalance from the point of view of 3 special interest groups (brine shrimp industry, mineral industry, GSL Friends). (GSL Friends has a mission to preserve and protect parts of the Great Salt Lake ecosystem.) Match up interest groups and copymasters as follows:

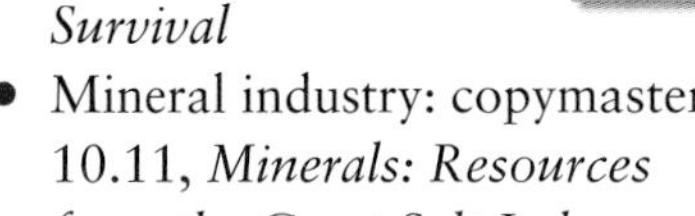

- Brine shrimp industry: copymaster 10.10, *Shrimp Survival*
- Mineral industry: copymaster 10.11, *Minerals: Resources from the Great Salt Lake*
- GSL Friends: copymaster 10.12, *A Unique and Evolving Ecosystem*

Each member of the team should become an expert on 1 of the special interest groups. Students should split up the readings and then discuss in their teams what they have each read. The questions in Step 5 will help guide their reading. Decide whether the readings can be assigned as homework.

In Step 5, lead a class discussion about the special interest groups associated with the Great Salt Lake. Use the questions provided in the student book to guide the discussion. Call on students to share what they know about their special interest group. Get ideas from all students. Remind students that they are expected to understand the perspective of all 3 groups to be able to support the recommendation in their feature articles. Encourage them to take notes about each of the special interest groups.

Consider asking these additional questions to help students with their feature articles and to use a systems approach in problem solving:

Part II: The Article

Materials

none

Process and Procedure

A newspaper in Salt Lake City, Utah, is doing a feature article on Great Salt Lake. In the past, the paper has printed pro and con articles about issues facing the Great Salt Lake. These articles address one specific issue. For the feature article, the paper wants to address a much more complex issue. Changes in the Great Salt Lake since the railroad levee was built have affected the lake and the interests of several special interest groups. Because of your experience with this issue, the paper will hire your team to write the feature article. Your team's work with systems will give the most complete evaluation of the Great Salt Lake and will take into account the special interest groups.

In addition to describing the Great Salt Lake as a system, the paper wants you to include a recommendation in the article. The recommendation will propose how local agencies should manage the lake to meet the needs of all three groups. The Great Salt Lake is managed by three Utah state agencies: the Utah Geological Survey, the Division of Water Resources, and the Division of Wildlife Resources. They monitor salinity levels in the lake and the species inhabiting the lake. These agencies work together to make decisions about how to maintain a balance between using the Great Salt Lake's natural resources and maintaining a healthy lake ecosystem. Your team will have to take into account all parts of the Great Salt Lake system and all special interest groups when writing your recommendation.

1. Work as a team to use what you have learned about the lake and the issue to write a feature article on the Great Salt Lake. Remember, your article must use a systems perspective. It should include the following in the explanation section:
   - A paragraph explanation of the Great Salt Lake system
   - A box diagram with labels showing the boundary of the system, parts of the system, and fluxes (inputs and outputs) of the system
   - Accurate and appropriate systems language
   - Interactions that occur with parts of the Great Salt Lake system (You can develop a diagram for this.)

- "What is causing the salt imbalance?" "What is the relationship between the salinity of the lake and the other components (water level, causeway)?"
- "What is the impact of the salt imbalance on the other components within the system?"
- "How are other related systems affected (lake ecosystem, brine shrimp industry, mineral extraction industry)?"
- "What are some possible solutions to the salt imbalance?" "How could the inputs or outputs of the Great Salt Lake water system be changed to solve the salt imbalance?" "What impact would these solutions have on the lake ecosystem and its related communities?"

Process and Procedure

Part II: The Article

Materials

copymaster 10.13, *Sample GSL Article to Post*

In Part II, students will learn the purpose of their feature articles. Decide an appropriate way to use the example article in copymaster 10.13 in your class. Explain that natural and human-manipulated water systems are often managed. Water levels in lakes with dams are adjusted by changing the amount of water passing through the dam. Natural river systems and lakes are dredged to deepen the system, allowing boats to more easily navigate. Agencies in charge of managing these systems must think about how changes will be a benefit or a detriment to the system itself and to users of the system (special interest groups).

In Step 1, teams begin working on their feature articles. You may choose instead to have students create the feature article on their own. A third option is to let students work in their teams to discuss what the feature article should include. Each student could then put together his or her own feature article as homework or in class the next day. Decide whether group work or individual work will best serve the goals of the activity.

Tell students to review what they have learned about the Great Salt Lake and the special interest groups before they begin work on the feature articles. Emphasize the importance of using a systems perspective. If you have had time to gather examples of similar sorts of issue articles from your local paper (or copymaster 10.13), show students a few recent feature articles on issues that are familiar to them.

In Step 2, students continue to develop their articles. Encourage them to consult the rubric again so that your expectations are clear. Students review criteria for their articles in Step 3 and turn in the article in Step 4. Post several of the articles that are examples of good analysis.

This investigation will generate a variety of responses. Look for evidence of systems thinking. The following suggestions will help you grade students' diagrams for the Great Salt Lake system.

2. The article should also include the following regarding a recommendation by your team for how the Great Salt Lake system should be managed. Use specific evidence from your research to
   - write 2–3 paragraphs that use accurate information of the management of the Great Salt Lake and its salt imbalance,
   - use evidence and data to argue how your proposed solution would change or stabilize salt balance in the Great Salt Lake system, and
   - describe how the management plan either does or does not address the needs of the different interest groups.

In your recommendation, you must consider how changing the system will affect everyone and everything dependent on the Great Salt Lake system. You might think about what costs are involved and who or what will benefit. Use the evidence you have gathered about the Great Salt Lake to decide what you think is most important.

3. Review the overall quality of your article. Is the article
   - neat and easy to read,
   - composed as a feature article that you might find in a newspaper,
   - written in a clear manner with summarizing data and information, and
   - complemented by neat diagrams or maps of the Great Salt Lake?
4. Turn in your article to your teacher.

Students' box diagrams of the Great Salt Lake water system should depict the lake as the main reservoir and should identify several inputs and one output. The diagram should reflect the fact that water only exits the Great Salt Lake (GSL) through evaporation, but that water enters the lake through three main sources. The main inputs and output for the Great Salt Lake system are the following:

- $I_{precipitation}$ (I_{precip}), flux in: inches of water per year as rain into GSL
- I_{rivers} (I_{rvr}), flux in: discharge of water per year from rivers (plus some waste treatment) into GSL
- $I_{groundwater}$ (I_{gw}), flux in: discharge of water per year from groundwater flow into GSL
- $O_{evaporation}$ (O_{evap}), flux out: inches of water per year evaporated from GSL

Students should use the variables and information from the copymasters to make their diagrams. The diagram should show the processes that bring water into and out of the Great Salt Lake system. Values for inputs and outputs are average water fluxes as reported for 1998 in copymaster 10.8, *Water Numbers for the Great Salt Lake*. Students' diagrams might look like the one in figure T10.12.

Students may mention other minor inputs and outputs to the lake, such as communities and businesses discharging water into the lake. Shrimp harvested from the lake removes a small amount of water.

In addition, students might create a diagram that reflects how the Great Salt Lake is part of a larger water system and, in turn, is composed of smaller subsystems. For example, a water molecule that evaporated from the Great Salt Lake might become part of a raindrop five days later in Nebraska. That water molecule, in turn, might flow down the Missouri River into the Mississippi River and on to the Atlantic Ocean. This sequence shows how the Great Salt Lake is part of a larger, continental water system. Students may also point out that the salt dissolved in the water within the lake is an example of a subsystem. Students could demonstrate this understanding by linking multiple systems together in a reasonable fashion.

In students' recommendations, look for descriptions that take into account all parts of the system and consider all special interest groups. Students will focus on different aspects of the Great Salt Lake system depending on what interests them. Make sure they support their ideas.

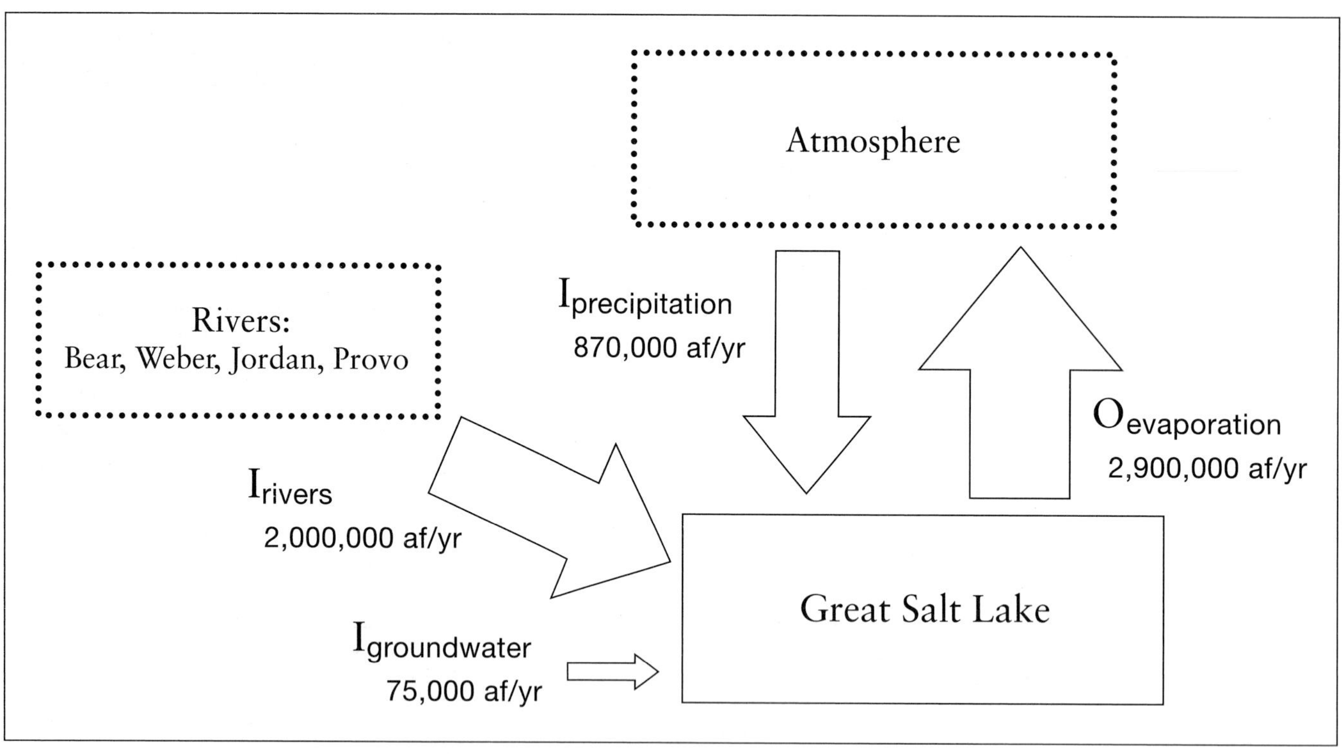

Figure T10.12 Box diagram of the Great Salt Lake. Students may develop a box diagram of the Great Salt Lake with four main fluxes.

CHAPTER 11

Carbon on the Move

Chapter Overview

Carbon. It is a diverse element, and it is vital for life. In a human body, carbon makes up about 50 percent of tissues and about 28 percent of bones. That is a lot. Carbon also makes up roughly half of the various tissues in plants. Students have studied photosynthesis, the process that transfers carbon from the atmosphere to plants or other photosynthesizing organisms. Carbon links to life in many ways.

But carbon's reach does not stop with life. Carbon is also found in nonliving (abiotic) objects such as minerals, like diamond. Carbon is also a part of many types of rocks, such as limestone or rocks with fossil fuels (petroleum, coal, natural gas). Students will learn a good deal about this in chapter 11, *Carbon on the Move.* Yet before arriving on Earth and becoming part of an organism, carbon is manufactured in stars. In other parts of the galaxy, carbon is found as hydrocarbons in massive molecular clouds. Carbon is part of many kinds of systems at many scales.

Goals for the Chapter

How do you think your students would characterize carbon to a friend who is not in your science class? This chapter will give them tools to make distinctions about carbon as a versatile element and as a key part of many substances. The chapter will describe many basic forms of carbon on Earth and their interactions. The chapter is also an elaboration and application of many concepts to which students have been exposed in this program. They will continue to use vocabulary such as *dissolution*, *exsolution*, *solubility*, *acid-base reactions*, *reactants*, *products*, *pH indicator*, *conservation of mass*, and *mole*.

Another goal of this chapter is to help students solidify their understanding of the science of systems. Their analysis of various systems of carbon will include vocabulary such as *simulation*, *model*, *input*, *output*, *flux*, *reservoir*, *residence time*, *source*, *sink*, and *open* or *closed system.* Repeated use of tables and simple calculations will help them develop a quantitative understanding of systems such as the carbon cycle. The chapter seeks to develop a more global view of earth systems and geochemical cycles by not merely showing a typical land-based carbon cycle, but also a carbon cycle with active communication between terrestrial, atmospheric, and oceanic settings.

In chapter 11, students will consider the carbon cycle by addressing questions such as these:

- What are the main reservoirs of carbon on Earth, and how much carbon is in them?
- How is carbon transported among the main carbon reservoirs?
- How do compounds with carbon change form as carbon cycles around Earth?
- How do we analyze simple compounds of carbon?
- What are simple experiments and reactions that simulate the carbon cycle in the natural world?
- What carbon sinks in the geologic past are now valuable sources of fossil fuels and hydrocarbons?

You should notice right away something different about how the concept of geochemical cycles is presented in this chapter. For example, the carbon cycle is typically shown as a figure with many swooping arrows that link in a tidy circle. This figure is then described in several paragraphs for the student. The approach taken here is different. Students investigate a series of experiments that convert and move carbon from reactants to products. Some of these reactions should be familiar to students, while others are new. Students then place the reactions in a global context. The context links the atmosphere, geosphere, biosphere, and hydrosphere. This approach should enable students to construct and build relationships within a global carbon cycle. This also helps them to continue cultivating an understanding of systems and gives them the framework to better understand current issues related to fossil fuels and energy production. Many of these ideas will be addressed further in the next level of the program.

A key feature of this chapter is the simple, safe, hands-on experiments. Most materials are inexpensive and easily obtained at the grocery store. Only two items need to be obtained or ordered ahead of time (bromthymol blue and universal indicator solutions), and they are relatively inexpensive. Keep various materials available in a container, as they are used in multiple activities (indicator solutions, sodium bicarbonate, vinegar). Be sure to phone around well ahead of time to confirm where you can obtain dry ice (solid carbon dioxide) for several of the investigations.

You can begin the chapter by selecting an experiment that you are familiar with that involves carbon. If you choose to engage students this way, try to use effective questioning techniques to get students thinking: "What do you think will happen if . . . ?" "I wonder how this works?" "What do you think?" "Could you share that idea in your science notebook or write it on the board?" This is a good opportunity to assess students' prior knowledge. You'll have another chance in the engage activity, *Characterizing Carbon.*

You could also have students draw what they know about the carbon cycle on a large sheet of paper. Ask them how they think carbon moves from one position to the next. Do they know what things contain carbon in the natural world? This exercise will also allow you to assess what students already know.

The chapter organizer uses graphic design principles and visualization to help students connect one activity to another. It uses reminders of key concepts, linking questions, and the spatial arrangement of activity titles to foster the sense of a conceptual flow, connecting each activity. Explicitly ask students to locate their position within its flow at the beginning of each activity. Use the organizer to review what they have done and where they are going. This action reinforces the connection among the activities, thus enhancing long-term memory.

Chapter 11 Organizer

CARBON ON THE MOVE

Major Concepts

- **Some substances with carbon can be analyzed with simple tests.**
- **Earth has a fixed amount of carbon; that carbon moves among several main reservoirs.**
- **Carbon transfer involves chemical reactions with changes in atomic structures of carbon and in properties of the carbon-bearing material.**
- **Simple reactions simulate carbon cycling in the natural world.**
- **Some carbon sinks in the geologic past are now valuable sources of fossil fuels and energy for society.**

ENGAGE — Characterizing Carbon ★

Key Idea: • Indicator solutions let you monitor carbon movement in simple systems.

Activity: Students use indicator solutions to monitor pH and the movement of CO_2 into (dissolution) and out of (exsolution) water.

LINKING QUESTION: What kinds of reactions move carbon around Earth?

EXPLORE — Carbon Changing Costumes ★ ★ ★

Key Idea: • Simple reactions with carbon-bearing substances at eight stations represent carbon transport between different settings on Earth.

Activity: Students complete reactions with carbon at eight stations. At each station, students identify settings on Earth with a reaction like the one investigated.

LINKING QUESTION: Where do reactions with carbon occur on Earth?

EXPLAIN — The Carbonated Geosphere ★ ★

Key Idea: • Carbon is a key part of terrestrial (land), atmospheric, and oceanic settings. Carbon is stored in these settings as organic and inorganic carbon.

Activity: Students complete readings and questions about carbon in terrestrial, atmospheric, and ocean settings. Students complete carbon reaction and carbon transport tables.

LINKING QUESTION: Are humans part of the carbon cycle?

★ = One Class Period ☆ = ½ Class Period *Note:* Based on a 50-minute class period.

EXPLORE — Fossil Carbon

Part I: Carbonifercous Combustion ★★

Key Idea: • Energy production and fossil fuel combustion make carbon dioxide. The geologic record shows the pattern of humans adding carbon dioxide (CO_2) to the atmosphere.

Activity: A burning candle simulates carbon moving from fossil fuels, to the atmosphere, to the ocean. Students also analyze geologic records of atmospheric CO_2 from Mauna Loa, Hawaii, and Law Dome, Antarctica.

Part II: Showing the Carbon Cycle ★

Key Idea: • A series of reactions with carbon can be linked to represent key parts of the carbon cycle.

Activity: Students arrange sticky notes with carbon reactions and transport processes on large paper to represent carbon movement among reservoirs.

LINKING QUESTION: How fast does a carbon atom move around Earth?

ELABORATE — The Flux Is the Crux ★★

Key Idea: • Carbon cycles at different rates among carbon reservoirs. The carbon flux and reservoir size tell how long on average a carbon atom resides in a reservoir.

Activity: Students complete several short readings on biologic and geologic reservoirs of carbon. They analyze fluxes of carbon between reservoirs to estimate residence time.

LINKING QUESTION: How much do you understand about carbon cycles?

EVALUATE — Carbon Quest ★☆

Key Idea: • You can answer questions and revise your answers about your understanding of the carbon cycle. You learn things better by critically evaluating your own work.

Activity: Students use the *Learn from Mistakes Protocol* to analyze questions about the carbon cycle. They increase their score by explaining the correct answers and reasons for missed questions.

★ = One Class Period ☆ = ½ Class Period *Note:* Based on a 50-minute class period.

Standards Covered by Chapter 11

CARBON ON THE MOVE

STANDARD A: Science as Inquiry. As a result of activities in grades 9–12, all students should develop

abilities necessary to do scientific inquiry

- Design and conduct scientific investigations. Designing and conducting a scientific investigation requires introduction to the major concepts in the area being investigated, proper equipment, safety precautions, assistance with methodological problems, recommendations for use of technologies, clarification of ideas that guide the inquiry, and scientific knowledge obtained from sources other than the actual investigation. The investigation may also require student clarification of the question, method, controls, and variables; student organization and display of data; student revision of methods and explanations; and a public presentation of the results with a critical response from peers. Regardless of the scientific investigation performed, students must use evidence, apply logic, and construct an argument for their proposed explanations.
- Use technology and mathematics to improve investigations and communications. A variety of technologies, such as hand tools, measuring instruments, and calculators, should be an integral component of scientific investigations. The use of computers for the collection, analysis, and display of data is also a part of this standard. Mathematics plays an essential role in all aspects of an inquiry. For example, measurement is used for posing questions, formulas are used for developing explanations, and charts and graphs are used for communicating results.

understandings about scientific inquiry

- Scientists usually inquire about how physical, living, or designed systems function. Conceptual principles and knowledge guide scientific inquiries. Historical and current scientific knowledge influence the design and interpretation of investigations and the evaluation of proposed explanations made by other scientists.
- Mathematics is essential in scientific inquiry. Mathematical tools and models guide and improve the posing of questions, gathering data, constructing explanations and communicating results.

STANDARD B: Physical Science. As a result of activities in grades 9–12, all students should develop an understanding of

structure and properties of matter

- Carbon atoms can bond to one another in chains, rings, and branching networks to form a variety of structures, including synthetic polymers, oils, and the large molecules essential to life.

chemical reactions

- A large number of important reactions involve the transfer of either electrons oxidation/reduction reactions) or hydrogen ions (acid/base reactions) between reacting ions, molecules, or atoms. In other reactions, chemical bonds are broken by heat or light to form very reactive radicals with electrons ready to form new bonds. Radical reactions control many processes such as the presence of ozone and greenhouse gases in the atmosphere, burning and processing of fossil fuels, the formation of polymers, and explosions.

STANDARD C: Life Science. As a result of their activities in grades 9–12, all students should develop understanding of

the interdependence of organisms

- The atoms and molecules on the earth cycle among the living and nonliving components of the biosphere.

STANDARD D: Earth and Space Science. As a result of their activities in grades 9–12, all students should develop an understanding of

geochemical cycles

- The earth is a system containing essentially a fixed amount of each stable chemical atom or element. Each element can exist in several different chemical reservoirs. Each element on earth moves among reservoirs in the solid earth, oceans, atmosphere, and organisms as part of geochemical cycles.
- Movement of matter between reservoirs is driven by the earth's internal and external sources of energy. These movements are often accompanied by a change in the physical and chemical properties of the matter. Carbon, for example, occurs in carbonate rocks such as limestone, in the atmosphere as carbon dioxide gas, in water as dissolved carbon dioxide, and in all organisms as complex molecules that control the chemistry of life.

STANDARD F: Science in Personal and Social Perspectives. As a result of activities in grades 9–12, all students should develop understanding of

natural resources

- Humans use many natural systems as resources. Natural systems have the capacity to reuse waste, but that capacity is limited. Natural systems can change to an extent that exceeds the limits of organisms to adapt naturally or humans to adapt technologically.

Prerequisite Knowledge

Students should demonstrate improving notebook skills by this point in the year. Look for accurate sentences, titles, and dates in their science notebook entries. On diagrams and sketches, look for labels, scale, simple representations, and highlight comments where appropriate.

Students will use concepts from chemistry that they have learned earlier in the year. These include dissolution, exsolution, solubility, acid-base reactions, reactants, products, pH indicator, conservation of mass, and the mole. Several concepts related to systems and models are also part of this chapter, such as simulation, model, input, output, flux, reservoir, residence time, source, sink, and open or closed system. Students should be familiar with these ideas from earlier chapters.

Students should know how to organize data and observations in a table format. In this chapter, T-tables and tables with columns are used to tabulate and calculate results. Students will also complete several qualitative plots, as well as use various quantitative plots (*xy* plots, bar graphs, pie charts). For example, they will show temporal trends in atmospheric concentrations of carbon dioxide (CO_2) at different timescales.

By this point, students should also be proficient at manipulating exponents and decimals. (This has been a good way to link science learning with content and skills from math courses.) A conversion from 3×10^{15} grams (g) carbon to 3 petagrams of carbon (3 Pg C) should be straightforward (10^{15} g = 1 Pg C). It is just like saying that 1,000 g of carbon is the same as 1 kilogram of carbon (1 kg C).

If you feel that your students are weak in any of these areas, use the *How To* activities at the back of the student book to bolster skills with decimals and exponents.

Commonly Held Misconceptions

There is no clear research or classroom observations that address misconceptions about geochemical cycles like the carbon cycle. It is more likely that students' misconceptions in this chapter will result from not having studied global cycles and systems. Please feel free to share with BSCS your observations regarding the following:

- Carbon is a fundamentally "organic" atom, forming complex rings or chain structures as the molecules of life.

Although this is certainly true, carbon also takes many other, simpler forms in different parts of the geosphere and within the carbon cycle. These include forms of carbon such as carbon dioxide (CO_2), the bicarbonate ion $(HCO_3)^{1-}$, and calcium carbonate ($CaCO_3$). Calcium carbonate is common at the surface of Earth, but substantial reserves of carbon likely also reside (as carbonates [$MgCO_3$] or diamond) in Earth's mantle. At the atomic level, the crystalline structure of coal can be considerably different from other live forms of carbon.

- Most carbon on Earth and in the carbon cycle is part of dense tropical jungles, forests, and other areas of dense vegetation.

Terrestrial vegetation and the atmosphere have comparable stores of carbon, but soils harbor about 2–3 times that amount. The bulk of active carbon resides in the ocean, primarily in the middle to deep, cold oceans.

- There is not a lot of carbon in the atmosphere or the ocean.

These are key reservoirs of active carbon. Students' perceptions may relate to the carbon being in forms other than the more common organic carbon. Geologic reserves of carbon—those that we rely on for energy—are substantially larger than the active, biologic exchange of carbon.

- The common material plastic is not a simple carbon compound.

Plastics are everywhere in our lives, but students may not realize that these are carbon compounds and that they are manufactured from hydrocarbons.

NOTES:

ENGAGE

Characterizing Carbon

Activity Overview

In *Characterizing Carbon*, students will complete two simple investigations that transfer carbon into and out of water. In each case, the carbon is in the form of CO_2. Students will also become familiar with using the pH indicator solutions bromthymol blue (BTB) and universal indicator. Students will use these indicators several times in the chapter, where changes in acidity indicate movement of carbon in various systems. The two experiments also represent the exsolution-dissolution sequence in natural waters for CO_2 in the carbon cycle.

Before You Teach

Background Information

The concept of an experimental control is important when using the pH solution indicators. Color changes for some experiments in this chapter can be subtle. The control helps students detect these subtle color changes in the experiment, or in the "treatment" container. It is best to place the control on a piece of plain white paper next to the experiment.

This engage activity raises right away the issue of simple chemical reactions and equilibriums. Students will be analyzing, completing, and writing many reactions. As appropriate, use terminology from unit 1, *Interactions Are Interesting*, such as acid-base reactions, mole, conservation of mass, or stoichiometry. A recurring reaction in the chapter is the formation of carbonic acid with water and carbon dioxide.

Carbonic acid dissociates to hydrogen and bicarbonate ions:

$$CO_{2(aq)} + H_2O_{(aq)} \rightleftharpoons \underset{\text{carbonic acid}}{H_2CO_{3(aq)}} \rightleftharpoons HCO_3{}^{1-}{}_{(aq)} + H^{1+}{}_{(aq)}$$

Bromthymol blue and universal indicator solutions are very useful tools for the investigations in this chapter. Besides their primary use as pH indicators, the change in pH and color also correspond with carbon movement into or out of solutions. Figure T11.1 shows that BTB changes abruptly from blue, to teal, to green, and then to yellow over a narrow pH range from about pH 7.5 to about pH 6.5. Imagine a starting solution buffered to light blue or teal. By quickly adding CO_2 through respiration (blowing through a straw) or with dry ice, you can increase acidity (pH decreases) and change the color from blue to yellow. The reverse is true for making a solution more basic, such as by adding baking soda back to the yellow BTB solution. Making solutions buffered to about pH 7.4 with BTB and distilled water is described below.

Universal indicator is another good qualitative indicator of pH as well as carbon transport. Compared with the "tipping point" behavior of BTB, universal indicator shows changes that are transitional or gradual. In this chapter, for example, you can show that seltzer water starts

ENGAGE

Characterizing Carbon

What color is carbon? You might say that carbon is black like charcoal, coal, or graphite, or clear and sparkly like a diamond. But what about other objects with carbon, such as leaves, gasoline, seashells, plastics, white marble sculptures, or you? What about gases in the atmosphere that contain carbon? How would you characterize carbon in these objects?

After a few minutes, you may realize that this is not a simple question. A description might even be tricky for a system where carbon changes from one substance to another. For example, what about a burning log in a fireplace—where does carbon in the wood go? The more you think about it, the more complex the answer seems.

A good way to start learning about carbon is to consider carbon in small parts. Leave carbon complexity aside for the moment and try to think about carbon in simple ways. In fact, that is a good way to break down and simplify any system. In *Characterizing Carbon*, you will work with a team to explore two interesting processes with carbon. Keep in mind how these investigations might relate to carbon moving around Earth. Color gives a clue here, but the colors you see are not the color of carbon.

Investigation 1

Materials

For each team of 3 students

- 2 plastic bottles or jars with tightly sealing caps
- universal indicator solution
- seltzer water
- 1 ruler
- 1 sheet of plain white paper

Process and Procedure

In this activity, you will do two investigations with carbon and a water system in a team of three students. Listen carefully to your teacher for instructions about materials for the two investigations. For each investigation, keep this focus question in mind: "In what form is the carbon?"

1. Put 1 sample of seltzer water about 2–3 centimeters (cm) deep in each of 2 plastic containers. Quickly add 6 drops of universal indicator to each and close the containers immediately.

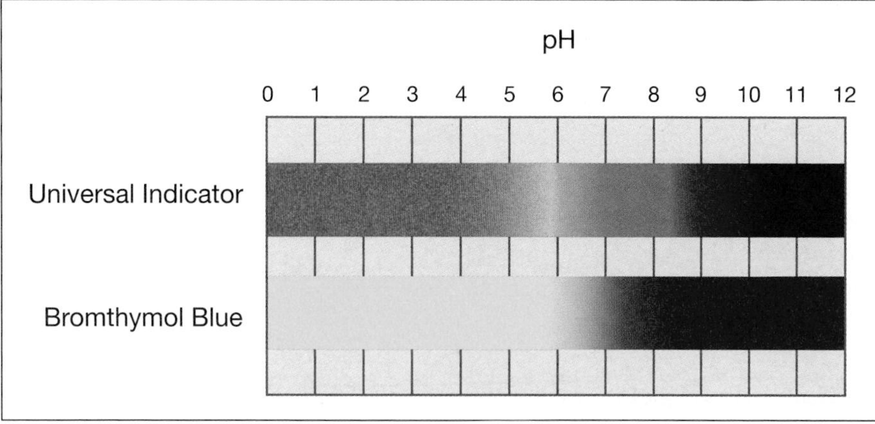

▲ **Figure T11.1 pH-color scale for two indicators.** This diagram shows the relationship between pH and solution color for the two indicators students will use in this chapter. Bromthymol blue shows an abrupt change in color at about pH 7. Universal indicator shows a progression of color changes from about pH 3 to pH 10. In each case, students will use a control to help detect subtle changes in pH and color.

with a pH of about 4 (the universal indicator shows red). Shaking the seltzer water causes CO_2 to leave the seltzer water, or exsolve. This decreases the acidity (increases pH), which leads to a yellow color. The water will change to a neutral color (blue green) after a day as more carbon leaves the seltzer water.

Keep both containers closed very tightly to preserve as much fizz as possible.

2. Complete Steps 2a–c and record your observations in your science notebook.
   a. Select 1 of the water containers as the control. After the universal indicator is added, do not open the control. Place this container on the sheet of white paper and do not move it.
   b. Shake the other container vigorously for 15 seconds (sec). Open the seal on the lid briefly to release the fizz. Close the container.

You can also tilt the container for about 5 sec so that the water comes near the opening. But do not pour out any water!

   c. Repeat Step 2b about 10 times until no more fizz is escaping.
3. During each step, compare the color of the shaken sample with your control. Record in your science notebook all the changes occurring between your sample and the control.
4. Describe in your science notebook the relationship between the amount of fizz and the color.
5. Copy figure 11.1 into your science notebook. Make a qualitative graph showing the amount of fizz relative to the color that you observe.
6. Record in your science notebook your team's ideas about the following questions.
   a. What do you know about seltzer water?
   b. What was happening as you released the fizz?
   c. What process on Earth might this investigation model?
   d. How do you think this investigation involved carbon?

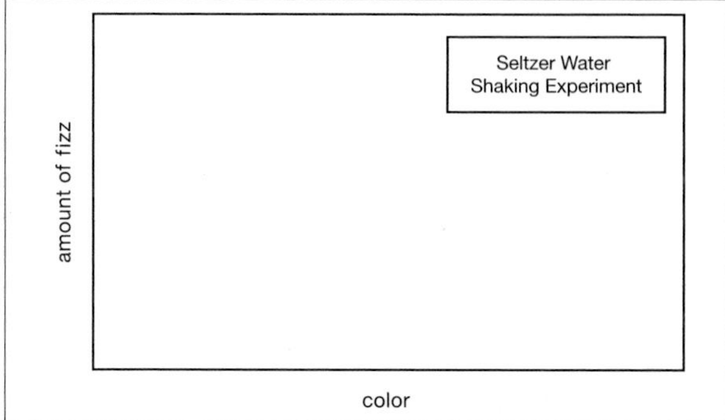

◀ **Figure 11.1 Experiment to shake seltzer water.** Use these axes to plot the amount of fizz versus the color of shaken seltzer water. Copy this diagram into your science notebook and label the axes according to your observations.

It is easy and rather fun to use the BTB and universal indicator solutions. Place about 2–3 centimeters (cm) of water in a glass or beaker and add 4–6 drops of the indicator. Adding more drops to the water will give a more intense color, but can make it harder to detect a change in color. Add small amounts of vinegar (acetic acid, CH_3COOH) or sodium bicarbonate ($NaHCO_3$) to move pH below and above a neutral 7, respectively.

Your local water may be considerably more basic than pH 7.0. This occurs in areas with water that is "hard" or alkaline and that use groundwater or water flowing through limestone ($CaCO_3$). Thus, adding a very small amount of CO_2 to a cobalt blue BTB solution might not be sufficient to decrease acidity below pH 7.5. In this case, use distilled water with BTB and follow the buffering procedure described in *Advance Preparation* to get to a teal or light blue color. This solution should be much more sensitive to the CO_2 addition.

Materials

For the entire class

dropper bottles of bromthymol blue (BTB) solution
dropper bottles of universal indicator solution
2 2-L bottles of seltzer water
aluminum foil
clear tape
distilled water
dry ice (about 1 lb; slightly larger than the size of a baseball)
baking soda
about 1 L of BTB solution in distilled water buffered to sky blue or teal

Materials—Investigation 1

For each team of 3 students

2 plastic bottles or jars with tightly sealing caps (control and treatment)
universal indicator solution
seltzer water
1 ruler
1 sheet of plain white paper

Materials—Investigation 2

For each team of 3 students

3 pairs of safety goggles
1 pair of thick gloves or cloth
2 beakers (at least 350 mL) or tall glass jars (control and treatment) of water solution with bromthymol blue (BTB)
1 10×10 cm square of aluminum foil
1 sheet of white paper
1 ruler
1 small piece of tape
1–2 pieces of dry ice (about 2 cm per side)

Advance Preparation

Find out where to obtain dry ice. Many grocery stores have dry ice (solid CO_2). Store the dry ice overnight in the freezer and in a cooler during the day.

Order the pH indicator solutions or obtain them from a colleague in chemistry. Place the solutions in dropper bottles for students to use throughout the chapter. It is most effective to use fresh, concentrated solutions rather than old, diluted solutions.

Collect tight-sealing small jars or bottles. Rinsed-out plastic soda bottles work well, particularly the 10- or 12-ounce (oz) size. It is best for each group to have a control, but if you can only provide 1 bottle per team, keep the color control at the front of the class.

Depending on your classroom, decide whether you will have all students do each investigation together or whether you want to divide the teams between investigations. It might also be effective to use the stations approach, as described in the next activity.

To help students complete investigation 2, make a container of BTB solution already buffered to just above pH 7. The color will be teal or sky blue. To do this, add about 30 drops of BTB indicator to 0.5 liters (L) of distilled water. Swirl as the solution turns yellow to yellow green. Add the tiniest pinches of baking soda and mix thoroughly. Depending on the color of blue that you start with, the mixture will progress from green, to teal, to sky blue, and then to cobalt blue. Stop adding baking soda when you see teal, light blue, or sky blue. This indicates a pH slightly above 7, and the solution will be sensitive to small additions of CO_2. In the investigation, students will use dry ice to add CO_2, making the solution more acidic. This will change the color back toward yellow.

Cautions

Wear safety goggles for the investigations that involve solutions and glassware. Dry ice can be dangerous if used inappropriately. Handle only with thick gloves such as an oven mitt or a thick folded cloth. Do not expose to skin. Contact with skin for more than a second will freeze cells and can cause injury similar to a burn.

As You Teach

Outcomes and Indicators of Success

By the end of this activity, students should

1. realize that carbon changes form in chemical reactions.

   They will demonstrate their understanding by

   - noting that carbon leaves seltzer water as it loses its fizz by shaking;
   - linking from two investigations that carbon is part of a gas, carbon dioxide (CO_2);
   - sharing ideas about environs on Earth with carbon as CO_2;
   - observing a change in indicator color as CO_2 from dry ice dissolves into water; and

Investigation 2

Materials

For each team of 3 students

3 pairs of safety goggles
1 pair of gloves or cloth
2 beakers (at least 350 mL) or tall glass jars
water solution with bromthymol blue (BTB)
1 10×10 cm square of aluminum foil
1 sheet of white paper
1 ruler
1 small piece of tape
1–2 pieces of dry ice (about 2 cm per side)

Caution: Wear safety goggles. Only handle dry ice with a cloth or gloves.

Process and Procedure

1. Get 2 glass containers. Add the mixture of water and bromthymol blue (BTB) indicator to a depth of 1.5 cm in each container.
2. Place 1 of the containers on a sheet of white paper at least 10 cm from the experiment beaker. Use this container as the control.
3. Squeeze aluminum foil around your thumb to make a holder for 1–2 pieces of dry ice. Use a small piece of tape to attach the foil holder above the water inside one of the jars (figure 11.2).
4. Obtain from your teacher a small piece of dry ice (roughly 2 cm per side). What do you think the dry ice is?
5. Quickly place the dry ice in the foil holder in the open container. Make observations for the next 3–4 minutes (min).
   a. What happens to the dry ice?
   b. What happens to the water?
   c. What happens to the control?

You can place a cover on your container if you have air currents in your classroom.

6. Discuss with your team the sequence of events or changes that must occur for the dry ice to interact with the water. Record this sequence of events as boxes connected by arrows in your science notebook.
7. Discuss with your team where the dry ice goes and how you think it interacts with the water.

- linking changes in carbon forms with concepts from acid-base chemistry.

2. develop further skills in the abilities and understandings of scientific inquiry.

   They will demonstrate their skills in the abilities and understandings of scientific inquiry by

   - conducting and describing investigations with CO_2 and acidity in water;
   - developing graphs of fizz versus indicator color for their inquiries;
   - using control and treatment solutions to gauge the color change;
   - identifying chemical reactions, such as CO_2 and carbonic acid; and
   - using indicator solutions to help develop consistent sets of observations in scientific investigations.

Strategies

Getting Started

You might begin class by asking students what they know about carbonated drinks and dry ice. Do students think that they are more similar or more different? Do they even have anything in common? You can list their ideas on the board if helpful. Ask questions to get the students to share ideas. But don't give any answers at this time, particularly about the carbon in the CO_2 that they will be working with.

Cautions

Wear safety goggles for the investigations that involve solutions and glassware. Dry ice can be dangerous if used inappropriately. Handle only with thick gloves such as an oven mitt or a thick folded cloth. Do not expose to skin. Contact with skin for more than a second will freeze cells and can cause injury similar to a burn.

Process and Procedure

Part I: Investigation 1

Materials

For the entire class

dropper bottles of bromthymol blue (BTB) solution
dropper bottles of universal indicator solution
2 2-L bottles of seltzer water
aluminum foil
clear tape
distilled water
dry ice (about 1 lb; slightly larger than the size of a baseball)
baking soda
about 1 L of BTB solution in distilled water buffered to sky blue or teal

For each team of 3 students

2 plastic bottles or jars with tightly sealing caps (control and treatment)
universal indicator solution
seltzer water
1 ruler
1 sheet of plain white paper

In Step 1, students put 1 sample of seltzer water in each of 2 containers. They quickly add 6 drops of universal indicator to each and seal tightly. Have them agree that each sample is the same color, which should be reddish.

Step 2 involves placing a control container on a sheet of paper. Students shake the other container and release the fizz, and thus, CO_2. As CO_2 exsolves and leaves the seltzer water, it becomes less acidic. The change in color indicates carbon leaving the seltzer water. With several shakes and releases of pent-up CO_2,

Answers to Reflect and Connect are on TE page 549b.

8. Use a strategy such as think-share-advise-revise (TSAR) to explore the character of carbon in this investigation.

If you have time, your team can repeat this experiment by dropping a small piece of dry ice into the water/BTB mixture. Does that test confirm or refute your ideas?

Reflect and Connect

Discuss the following questions with your team and write answers in your science notebook.

1. What gases, liquids, or solids were the parts of each investigation? What is your evidence?
2. For each investigation, revisit the focus question, "In what form is the carbon?"
3. Discuss and record some settings on Earth where you think carbon dioxide (CO_2) goes into liquids.
4. Discuss and record some other settings in the natural world where you think CO_2 leaves or exits fluids.
5. Discuss the following reactions and answer Questions 5a–f.

$$CO_{2(aq)} + H_2O_{(aq)} \rightleftharpoons H_2CO_{3(aq)} \rightleftharpoons HCO_3{}^{1-}{}_{(aq)} + H^{1+}{}_{(aq)}$$

   a. What 2 common molecules combine to make carbonic acid (H_2CO_3)?
   b. When H_2CO_3 dissociates, what are the acid and base components?
   c. Did the water in investigation 1 gain or lose CO_2? What is your evidence?
   d. Did the water in investigation 2 gain or lose CO_2? What is your evidence?
   e. Which direction would the reaction above shift for a system that lost CO_2 by fizzing? Would the system be more or less acidic?
   f. Which direction would the reaction above shift for a system that gained CO_2? Would the system be more or less acidic?

▼ **Figure 11.2 Beaker with dry ice holder.** Gently tape the aluminum foil holder inside the beaker to suspend the dry ice above the water. Place a cover on the beaker if you have strong air currents in your area of the classroom. How does the dry ice interact with the water? What happens to the water?

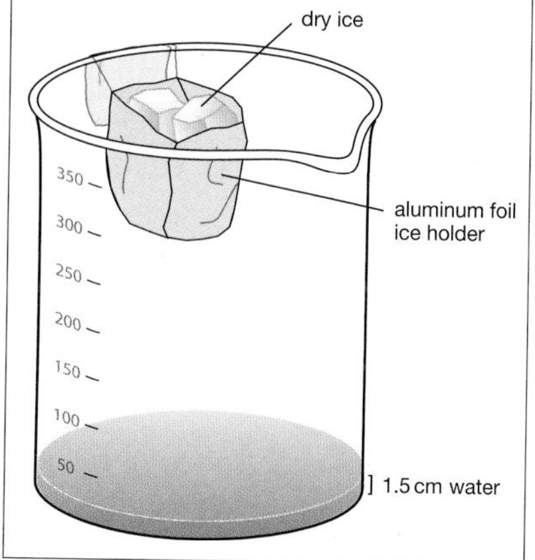

the solution should turn yellow. Students will note this in Step 3 and record their results in Step 4.

In Step 5, students develop a qualitative graph showing the amount of fizz as a function of color (or pH). Their graphs should look similar to figure T11.2. Changes to green are not likely to occur until the following morning when more CO_2 has escaped overnight.

In Step 6, students think more critically as a team about the investigation they just completed. They might even suggest that the investigation relates to CO_2 leaving a solution.

After shaking, the seltzer water will be yellow to yellow green. You can let students leave the solution out for 1 to 2 days; the color will evolve toward neutral and a blue green or blue.

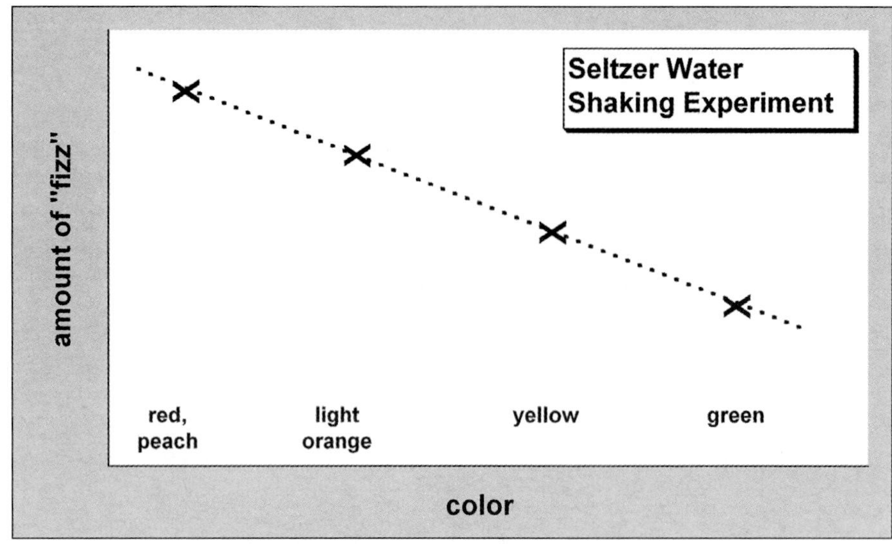

▲ **Figure T11.2 Amount of fizz versus water color.** This plot shows the amount of fizz as a function of seltzer water color with universal indicator. Students should be able to change the color from red to yellow by shaking during investigation 1. The change from yellow to green occurs overnight by leaving the cap off the container.

Process and Procedure

Investigation 2

Materials

For each team of 3 students

3 pairs of safety goggles
1 pair of thick gloves or cloth
2 beakers (at least 350 mL) or tall glass jars (control and treatment)
water solution with bromthymol blue (BTB)
1 10×10 cm square of aluminum foil
1 sheet of white paper
1 ruler
1 small piece of tape
1–2 pieces of dry ice (about 2 cm per side)

In Step 1, students get 2 glass containers and add the premade mixture of buffered BTB water to a depth of 1.5 cm in each. Beakers are preferable, but other widemouthed glass containers will work. Step 2 involves setting up control and treatment beakers. Students then construct a foil support in Step 3 to suspend the dry ice above the solution. The key here is that, because the CO_2 is much denser than air, it will flow into the volume of the beaker above the water and begin diffusing into the water.

Students begin the investigation in Step 4 by obtaining dry ice. Make sure that they handle the dry ice with a thick cloth or gloves. In Step 5, students make careful observations of the changes to the dry ice, water, and the control. In the treatment beaker, students should see a color change from blue to green to yellow as CO_2 dissolves into the water. This creates carbonic acid and lowers pH.

Check in Step 6 that students are seeing several transitions and links in the chain of reactions. They should note that the dry ice is changing to a misty gas that flows onto the water. The water next to the misty gas then changes color. Students should be familiar with CO_2 sublimation. The sequence would be as follows:

$$CO_{2(s)} \longrightarrow CO_{2(g)} \text{ during sublimation}$$

$$CO_{2(g)} \longrightarrow CO_{2(aq)} \text{ during dissolution}$$

$$CO_{2(aq)} + H_2O_{(aq)} \rightleftarrows \underset{\text{carbonic acid}}{H_2CO_{3(aq)}} \rightleftarrows HCO_3{}^{1-}{}_{(aq)} + H^{1+}{}_{(aq)}$$

In Step 7, students should note the movement of carbon into solution and that this is reflected in the color change. It is OK if they do not know the reason at this time; this issue will be raised again in the *Reflect and Connect* questions. Students use a strategy such as think-share-advise-revise (TSAR) in Step 8 to further discuss the character of carbon in this experiment.

Answers to Reflect and Connect, SE page 549

1. For investigation 1, the liquid was water and the gas was carbon dioxide, CO_2. For investigation 2, the liquid was water, the gas was CO_2, and the solid was CO_2.
2. Students may have figured out that dry ice is a solid of carbon dioxide. You can tell them now if they have not yet figured this out. The carbon is a molecule of CO_2 in the dry ice and gas. The carbon is in carbonic acid or the bicarbonate ion in the solution $(HCO_3)^{1-}$.
3. Students may indicate that CO_2 enters the ocean. The goal is to get them thinking about how gases dissolve into fluids, which is not always easy. Other activities in the chapter will reinforce this concept.
4. Students may recognize that CO_2 leaves the ocean. If they consider the atmosphere a fluid, they may suggest photosynthesis, which removes CO_2 from the atmosphere. Students may also suggest volcanic degassing, which releases CO_2 from magma (liquid rock) into the atmosphere.
5. Teams review the following reactions, then answer the 6 questions.

$$CO_{2(aq)} + H_2O_{(aq)} \rightleftharpoons H_2CO_{3(aq)} \rightleftharpoons HCO_3{}^{1-}{}_{(aq)} + H^{1+}{}_{(aq)}$$

5a. The 2 common molecules that combine to make carbonic acid are H_2O and CO_2.

5b. The acid and base components are $(HCO_3)^{1-}$ for base and H^{1+} for acid.

5c. The water in investigation 1 lost CO_2. The evidence was the decrease in fizz and change in color of the universal indicator that changed from reds to yellows.

5d. The water in investigation 2 gained CO_2. Two lines of evidence showed this: the gas from CO_2 was flowing down, onto the water, and the change in color of the BTB indicator to a lower pH.

5e. The reaction shifts to the left with exsolution of CO_2 from water to air. The system has less carbonic acid and H^+, which would give the color change toward blues with the universal indicator.

5f. The reaction shifts to the right with dissolution of CO_2 into water. The system has more carbonic acid and H^+, which would give a color change toward reds with the universal indicator. The change for BTB is from blue to yellow.

NOTES:

EXPLORE

Carbon Changing Costumes

Activity Overview

In *Carbon Changing Costumes*, the class will do one station together and teams of students will complete seven stations where they simulate reactions with carbon. These stations should be completed in 3 to 4 days. The stations will give students the tools and experiences to construct a model of the carbon cycle later in the chapter.

Before You Teach

Background Information

This activity helps students develop the building blocks for understanding the carbon cycle. The carbon cycle is one of several key geochemical cycles. These investigations use a much different approach for learning about geochemical cycles than the typical diagrams that show these cycles, accompanied by brief descriptions in the text.

Here students complete a series of investigations with chemical reactions that convert carbon from reactants to products. Some of these reactions are familiar to students, while others are new. The investigations also use skills that they have been developing through the year in chemistry and physics. The activities build on the two investigations from the engage activity.

Next, students think about carbon transport, such as by rivers or atmospheric mixing. Later in the chapter, students place the reactions in a global context. The goal is to give students the tools and experiences to construct their own representation of the carbon cycle. Figure T11.3 is shown here to help you guide students toward developing similar diagrams.

For each of the stations, students will receive an information summary *after* they complete the stations (copymasters 11.1, *Carbon Chemical Reaction Table,* and 11.2, *Carbon Transport Table*).

Do not tell them at this stage that they will be receiving a summary table of all the investigations. It is important that they take notes at this point on their work at the stations and not rely on a handout that they will get later.

Station 4 considers a reaction for the decomposition of calcium carbonate with heat. Processes analogous to this occur where rocks like limestone are pushed deep into the earth. This process happens at zones of collision between tectonic plates. The regions where rocks are actually pushed down, or subducted, into the earth are called subduction zones. Rocks in such regions may be baked for millions of years at several hundred degrees centigrade (C). This process is called metamorphism, resulting in the family of rocks called metamorphic rocks. Due to the high temperatures of metamorphism (a range of 350°C–600°C), students use a simple analogue material for metamorphism of carbonate rocks—sodium bicarbonate, $NaHCO_3$. Heating both baking soda and rocks gives off carbon as carbon dioxide. More information about subduction zones or metamorphism is available on the Web or in introductory geology texts.

Materials

See the table in figure T11.4 for materials for 2 teams working per station.

EXPLORE

Carbon Changing Costumes

In the engage activity, *Characterizing Carbon*, you experienced carbon on the move. You saw a form of carbon move into and out of water. The color changes in the solution indicated that a chemical reaction was taking place.

On a bigger scale, carbon can participate in many chemical reactions as it moves through natural systems. Photosynthesis is an example of this that you have already studied in Level 1 of this program. Here the carbon changes from a simple molecule to a complex one. During photosynthesis, carbon in CO_2 is converted to organic compounds. Examples of these compounds are starch and cellulose.

In *Carbon Changing Costumes*, you will explore eight simple reactions with carbon. These reactions simulate a series of real carbon pathways. As you carry out the reactions, think about how they relate to the world around you. Also think with your team about how some of the reactions might relate or link together. This helps you understand the pathways of carbon movement around Earth.

Station	Materials per team of 3
2	2 500-mL beakers or jars 1 stirring spoon or rod 1 funnel 1-cup measuring cup 1 filter paper or coffee filter soil, or bag of potting soil or rotting vegetation tap water
3	2 test tubes 2 antacid tablets with calcium carbonate ($CaCO_3$) 2 test tubes vinegar (5% acetic acid, CH_3COOH) tap water 1 calculator
4	3 pairs of safety goggles 2 test tubes 1 test-tube holder Bunsen burner or other heat source 1 scale or weighing station sodium bicarbonate ($NaHCO_3$) 1 dropper bottle of universal indicator solution tap water 1 3×3 cm aluminum foil square matches or flame source
5	2 beakers, at least 300 mL 2 spoons for stirring sodium bicarbonate ($NaHCO_3$) calcium chloride ($CaCl_2$) 1 dropper bottle of universal indicator solution tap water
8	1 test tube or small beaker 1 dropper bottle of distilled water with BTB indicator tap water 1–2 straws

Note: Materials for stations 1, 6, and 7 are at those stations.

▲ **Figure 11.3 Table of materials.** Refer to this table for a summary of materials needed at each station by each team.

Materials

For each team of 3 students

See figure 11.3 for materials for the stations.

Cautions

Wear safety goggles for investigations with chemical reactions and open flames.

550 Unit 3 Moving Matter

Advance Preparation

Obtain the materials you will need for each station (figure T11.4) and decide where in your classroom you will locate the 8 stations. The materials list accommodates 2 teams (i.e., for 1 test tube used per team, the station would have a minimum of 2 test tubes). Most solutions can be discarded down the drain, but check with your school regarding specific rules for disposing of solutions with pH indicator.

You will start this activity by completing station 1, the solubility station, as a class on day 1. We suggest you do this first for 3 reasons. One, this station follows on the ideas of CO_2 movement from the engage activity. Two, it allows the class to become familiar with the format for the 8 stations. Three, the class discussion of Steps 8 and 9 will model what students will be asked to do to wrap up each of the other 7 stations. This also provides a good opportunity for students to continue using some important terms, such as *exsolution*, *dissolution*, *solubility*, and *temperature-dependence*.

For station 1, you will need to warm 2 small bottles of seltzer to about 70–80° Fahrenheit (F), just a bit above room temperature. *Do not place them in a microwave.* Chill 2 more small bottles of seltzer water in a bucket of ice water. Do not let students see where you have these stored, however, or that some of the bottles are chilled. If they do, you can always swap the order of bottles right before the investigation begins. Label the bottles from 1 to 4. Use only clear plastic containers for the seltzer water; do not use glass or colored containers.

For station 2, design an easy way to use soils to filter solutions. You can simply prop a funnel on top of a jar or large beaker, for example.

For station 4, decide on a setup for open flames and a decarbonation reaction in a test tube. You can use Pyrex or other more expensive test tubes or beakers for this experiment, but the reaction may pit and alter the inside of the test tubes. Simple disposable glass works best. Students will need access to a nearby scale or weighing station.

For station 6, obtain a simple potted plant or terrarium. This will act as a visual prompt to accompany the instructions and questions. Also obtain some decaying vegetation for station 7.

For station 8, check whether your local tap water retains a blue color with BTB. If it is green or yellow (i.e., slightly acidic), prepare a batch of premade blue BTB water to have available at station 8. Do this by adding a pinch of baking soda to a container (e.g., 2-L plastic container) with 1 L of water and 50 drops BTB.

Process and Procedure

In the next two class periods, you will explore reactions with carbon at eight stations. At each station, record your answers in your science notebook. Pay particular attention to the chemical reaction that moves carbon from reactants to products. The class will complete station 8 together.

1. Copy the large diagram in figure 11.4 onto a full page in your science notebook. Title it "Carbon Environs." At the end of the activity, your diagram should show the locations of all stations. Feel free to be creative. Add color, shading, or other enhancements to improve your diagram. At each station, you will
   - identify with your team in which natural environment you think the reaction occurs and
   - write the station number on the diagram in the appropriate environment.
2. Listen to your teacher for suggestions or instructions about the stations. Complete all the stations, but not necessarily in numeric order.

Station 1

What does it mean for a gas to dissolve, or be "soluble," in a liquid? How does this relate to gas escaping or leaving a liquid? You will think about these questions in this investigation.

1. Look at the 4 bottles of seltzer water labeled from 1 to 4. Sketch the setup in your science notebook and add the appropriate labels.
2. What variable could be different between the bottles?

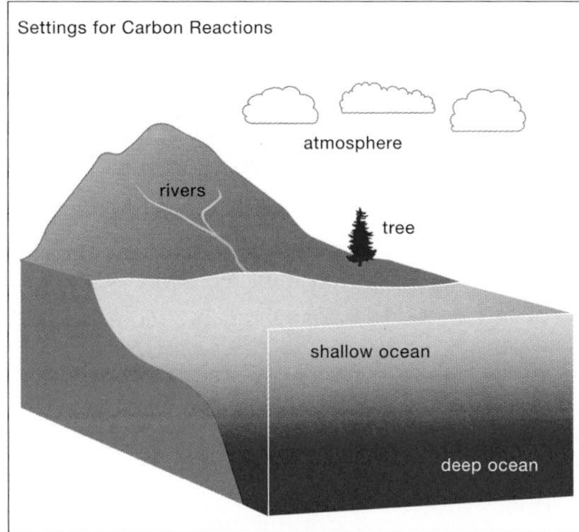

▲ **Figure 11.4 Carbon environs.** This diagram shows natural settings for carbon reactions on land and in the ocean and the atmosphere. Where on the diagram do you think carbon reactions for the eight stations occur? Copy this diagram onto a full page in your science notebook. You will add the number of each station to show where you expect its reaction to occur.

Cautions

Use safety goggles when working with solutions. Students should be careful not to suck BTB into their mouth. Use caution with open flames (station 4).

As You Teach

Outcomes and Indicators of Success

By the end of this activity, students should

1. be able to demonstrate that carbon changes form in chemical reactions.

   They will demonstrate their understanding by
   - completing chemical reactions in stations where carbon changes form and
   - using foundational concepts in chemistry from prior chapters.

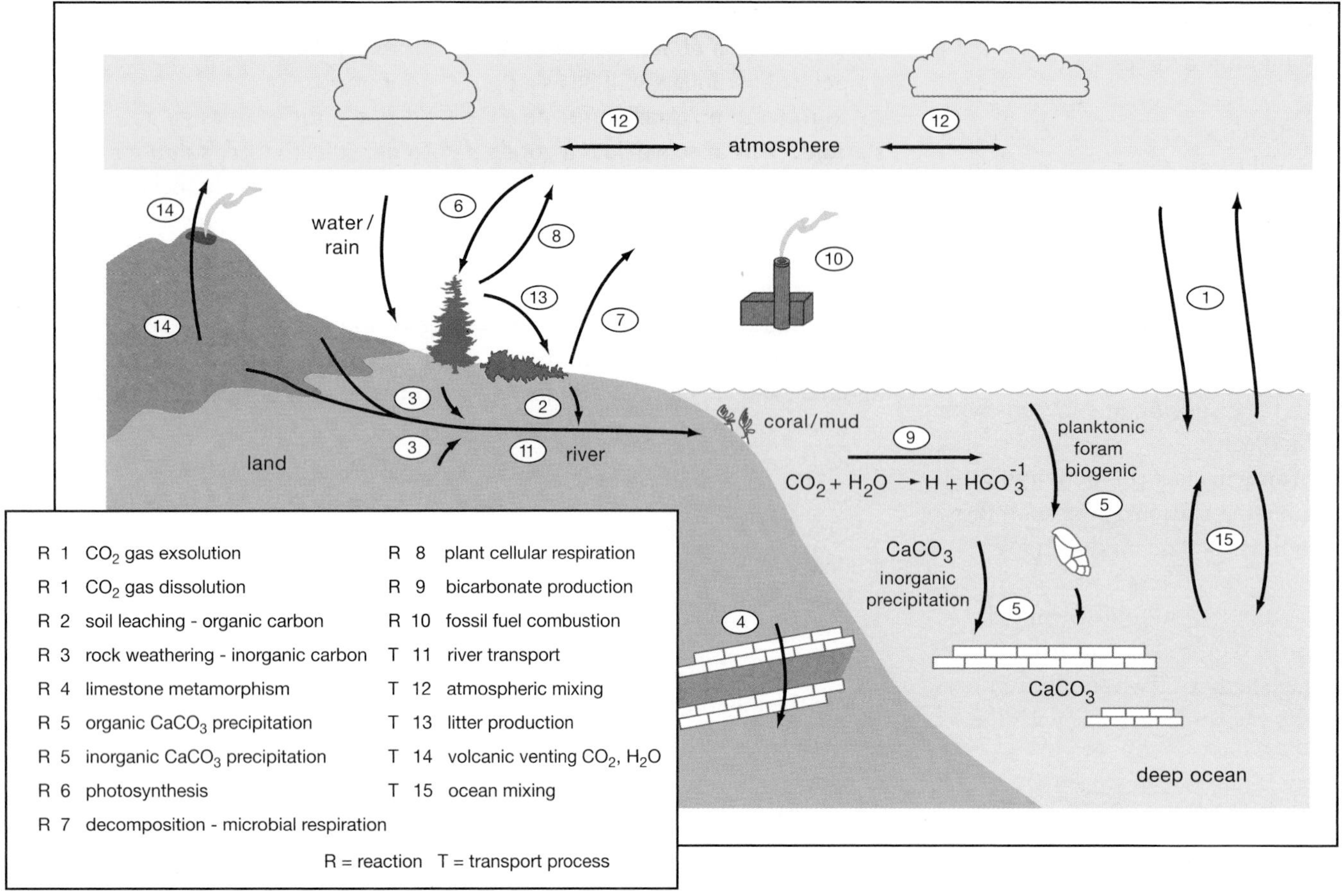

▲ **Figure T11.3 Global carbon cycle.** This figure shows key reaction (R) and transport (T) processes in the global carbon cycle. The numbers link with process numbers on copymasters 11.1, *Carbon Chemical Reaction Table*, and 11.2, *Carbon Transport Table.* After completing initial sets of investigations in the activity, *Carbon Changing Costumes*, students work later in the chapter to construct a diagram like this for the carbon cycle.

2. conduct several types of reactions involving carbon.

   They will demonstrate their understanding by

   - completing acid-base reactions with carbonate,
   - completing and using synthesis and decomposition reactions involving glucose,
   - balancing a decarbonation reaction with $CaCO_3$ and $NaHCO_3$,
   - using the dissociation reaction with carbonic acid,
   - balancing chemical reactions,
   - inferring reactants and products, and
   - working with the dissolution and exsolution of carbon dioxide.

3. be more familiar with quantitative scientific skills.

   They will demonstrate their better use of quantitative skills by

   - determining molar balances in chemical reactions,
   - inferring missing reactants or products in chemical equations,
   - measuring the mass of a test tube and $NaHCO_3$,
   - comparing molar ratios of CO_2 produced by microbial respiration through several reaction pathways, and
   - calculating the mass of $CaCO_3$ lost by heating for decomposition reaction.

4. develop further skills in the abilities and understandings of scientific inquiry.

   They will demonstrate their skills by

   - conducting investigations and recording observations at eight investigation stations;
   - measuring the mass for reactants and products at several stations;
   - using accurate analogies for experiments when the actual materials may be too complicated or dangerous to work with;
   - relying on prior use of pH indicator solutions as evidence for the identification of a powder (NaOH) from a reaction;
   - balancing moles of reactants and products for numerous chemical reactions at each of 8 stations;
   - beginning to link the carbon reaction at 8 stations with the movement of carbon among the atmosphere, geosphere, biosphere, and hydrosphere; and
   - using simple technologies to make scientific observations.

Strategies

Getting Started

Continue probing students about what they know and think they know about forms of carbon. Where is carbon found on Earth? Is there a lot of carbon in the ocean? What forms might carbon take there? How about carbon in the atmosphere? How could carbon move between the atmosphere and the ocean? Between land and the ocean?

Station	Materials (accommodates 2 teams of 3 students per station)	Teacher setup
1	4 bottles of carbonated water, 2 of which are warm, 2 of which are cold	Obtain 4 bottles of seltzer water in clear plastic containers; do not use glass containers. Prepare them at different temperatures (one in ice water, one at 80°F).
2	4 500-mL beakers or jars 2 stirring spoons or rods 2 funnels ½-c measuring cup 2 filter papers or coffee filters soil, organic-rich soil, potting soil, or rotting vegetation tap water	Give clear directions to students regarding where to discard soils and leached solution. Obtain soil, organic-rich soil, potting soil, or rotting vegetation with an even texture and particles so that it can be easily mixed with water.
3	4 test tubes or small beakers 4 antacid tablets with calcium carbonate ($CaCO_3$) vinegar (5% acetic acid, CH_3COOH) tap water 1 calculator	Give clear directions to students regarding where to discard experimental solutions.
4	6 pairs of safety goggles 4 small test tubes 1 test-tube holder 2 Bunsen burners or other heat source 1–2 scales or weighing stations baking soda (sodium bicarbonate, $NaHCO_3$) 1 dropper bottle of universal indicator solution tap water 3×3 cm squares of aluminum foil matches or flame source	Give clear directions to students regarding how to heat 1.5–2 g of $NaHCO_3$, and how to complete measurements of mass on a scale. Do not plunge the hot test tube into water.
5	4 beakers, at least 300 mL 4 spoons for stirring baking soda (sodium bicarbonate, $NaHCO_3$) calcium chloride ($CaCl_2$) 1 dropper bottle of universal indicator solution tap water	Obtain materials.
6	1 plant or terrarium with photosynthesizing organisms	Obtain a photosynthesizing organism or system.
7	decaying vegetation	Obtain vegetation in an advanced state of decay.
8	2 test tubes (preferable) or small beakers 1 dropper with BTB indicator tap water set of straws for the class water disposal container (1–2 L, sink)	Give clear directions to students regarding where to discard water and used straws.

▲ **Figure T11.4 Table of materials and station setup.** This table shows station numbers for the activity *Carbon Changing Costumes,* a materials list per station, and suggestions for setting up each station. The list should accommodate 2 teams per station.

Begin with station 1 as a class. This will familiarize students with the format of the other stations.

Cautions

Use safety goggles when working with solutions. Students should be careful not to suck BTB into their mouth. Use caution with open flames (station 4).

Process and Procedure

The experimental steps and answers to questions are given here in station order, starting with station 1.

Station 1: CO_2 Solubility

Ask for a volunteer to read the station introduction. Have students sketch the setup, using appropriate labels. Ask whether they think all the bottles are similar or different. If they say that the bottles are hot or cold, inquire why there are 4 bottles and not just 2. How could they tell which is hot or which is cold? This is for reproducibility purposes and to confirm hot versus cold behavior. Students will likely guess in Step 2 that the variable is temperature.

In Step 3, students copy a data table into their science notebooks. You will then open all bottles very quickly on the count of 3 in Step 4. Have students describe any differences they observe. They should see rapid exsolution of CO_2 from the warm bottles and much slower exsolution of CO_2 from the cold ones. Have students fill out the observations table in their notebooks. More rapid exsolution means that the CO_2 is leaving much faster. This means that CO_2 has a lower solubility in the warm water (i.e., it is less soluble, so the CO_2 needs to escape). Conversely, CO_2 solubility is higher in the cold water. To summarize, CO_2 is more soluble in cold water than in warm water. The equations for exsolution and dissolution are as follows:

exsolution: $CO_{2(aq)} \longrightarrow CO_{2(g)}$

dissolution: $CO_{2(g)} \longrightarrow CO_{2(aq)}$

Answers to Station 1 Steps 4–8, SE page 552

4. The class should note rapid fizzing and exsolution from the warm seltzer and slower exsolution from the cold seltzer. Thus, CO_2 has a higher solubility in the cold water than in the warm water. (It's easier for CO_2 to dissolve in cold water than in warm water.)

5a. The warm bottles lost CO_2 the fastest.

5b. Substances with high solubility in liquid tend to stay in the liquid.

5c. The two equations are as follows:

exsolution: $CO_{2(aq)} \longrightarrow CO_{2(g)}$

dissolution: $CO_{2(g)} \longrightarrow CO_{2(aq)}$

5d. The CO_2 would have a low solubility in the liquid.

5e. This will reflect the number on the containers that are cold.

6. The solubility of CO_2 in water increases with decreases in temperature.

7a. Students should be able to develop a qualitative graph showing CO_2 solubility as a function of temperature. Their completed graphs should look similar to figure T11.5.

7b. The graph in figure T11.5 shows an inverse relationship.

8. "This experiment shows that carbon in CO_2 moves more rapidly to the atmosphere from hot water than from cold water. This means that carbon dioxide is more soluble in cold water than in hot water."

3. Copy the table in figure 11.5 into your science notebook. Record your observations for the experiment in this data table.
4. On the count of 3, your teacher will quickly open all 4 bottles. What do you observe? Discuss as a class whether the bottles behave similarly or differently.
5. You have been learning that gases like CO_2 either escape from fluids or dissolve into fluids. Use figure 11.5 to record your ideas and observations for Questions 5a–c.
   a. Discuss as a class which of the bottles lost CO_2 the fastest.
   b. You have learned that the **solubility** of a substance indicates how much will dissolve in a liquid. If CO_2 has a high solubility in a liquid, does the CO_2 tend to leave the liquid or remain in the liquid?
   c. Write a chemical equation showing the escape of CO_2 gas from water. Write another equation showing that CO_2 dissolves in water.
   d. If CO_2 escapes quickly from a liquid, does this mean that CO_2 has a low solubility or a high solubility in that liquid?
   e. In which of the bottles (1–4) is CO_2 solubility the highest? That is, which bottle has the least fizzing?
6. Discuss as a class what variable differs between the bottles. Write how CO_2 solubility relates to that variable.
7. Draw in your science notebook axes for a simple graph showing how CO_2 solubility (on the *y*-axis) changes with the variable in Step 6 (on the *x*-axis).
   a. Use your observations to draw a line on that graph.
   b. Does the line in the plot show a direct or an indirect relationship?
8. Write the following sentence in your science notebook and fill in the blanks:

   "This experiment shows that carbon in CO_2 moves more rapidly to the atmosphere from ________ water than from ________ water. This means that carbon dioxide is more soluble in ________ water than in ________ water."

Bottle number	Observations when opened	Rate of CO_2 escape (fast/slow)	CO_2 solubility (high/low)
1			
2			
3			
4			

▶ **Figure 11.5 CO_2 solubility table.** Make a data table like this in your science notebook to record observations of the 4 bottles of seltzer.

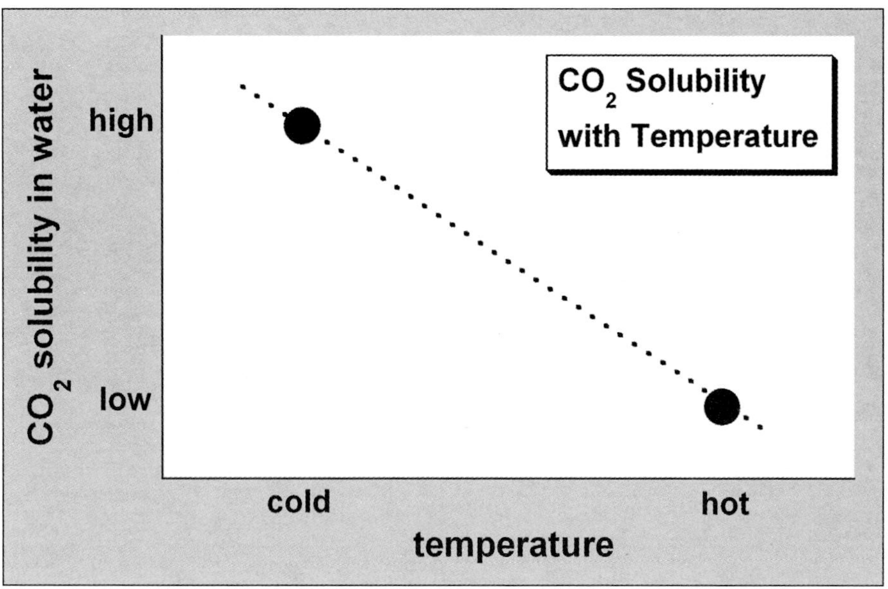

◀ **Figure T11.5 CO_2 solubility with temperature.** This graph shows qualitatively the inverse relationship between CO_2 solubility in water and water temperature. Later, students will use this knowledge to infer more rapid dissolution of CO_2 into cold polar waters than into warm equatorial waters. The difference in temperature in the investigation is comparable to the difference in temperature between polar and equatorial regions.

Answers to Station 3 Steps 4–7 are on TE pages 554–555.

9. Add the station number to your carbon environs diagram in your science notebook.

Station 2

What happens as rainwater percolates through organic **soils**? Do this investigation to explore how natural waters interact with soil.

1. Add 2 cups (c) of water to a beaker.
2. Add ½ c of soil or rotten vegetation to the beaker. Stir thoroughly with a stirring rod or spoon for 1–2 min. Write about the mixture and draw a diagram of it in your science notebook.
3. Prepare a filter assembly with a clean beaker beneath it. Transfer the mixture into the funnel and collect the fluid that drains.
4. What does the filtered solution look like? Explain.
5. Write your ideas for what forms you think carbon takes in the soil. What forms do you think carbon takes in the filtered solution?
6. Write the following sentence in your science notebook and fill in the blanks:

   "Compared with processes in nature, this experiment represents movement of carbon from __________ to __________."
7. Add the station number to your carbon environs diagram in your science notebook.

Station 3

Here is a different type of investigation with carbon. Some antacid tablets are mostly calcium carbonate ($CaCO_3$), and thus contain carbon.

1. Imagine that the antacid tablets represent a carbonate rock. For the 0.5 grams (g) of $CaCO_3$ in a tablet, what percentage of it is carbon?

Use the gram atomic weights for the 3 elements in $CaCO_3$ to estimate. Sum the weights and determine the proportion of carbon.

2. Obtain 2 test tubes. Place 3 inches (in) of acetic acid (CH_3COOH) in one test tube, and 3 in of water in another test tube.
3. Add 1 antacid tablet to each test tube. What happens in each tube?
4. Balance the following reaction with your team. Check that it is charge and mass balanced.

$$CaCO_3 + 2CH_3COOH \longrightarrow Ca^{2+}_{(aq)} + \underline{?}CH_3COO^{1-}_{(aq)} + \underline{?}H_2O + \underline{\qquad}$$

Station 2: Soil Leaching

In Step 1, students add 2 cups (c) of water to a beaker. They then add ½ c of evenly textured soil in Step 2, and stir thoroughly. They should record their observations in their science notebooks. Students transfer the mixture to a filter assembly and collect the filtered water in Step 3.

Students describe the filtered solution in Step 4. Students will need to think a little harder in Step 5 about the forms of carbon in the soil and the form of carbon in the filtered solution. It is OK if they do not know the answer. Soils are a significant source of carbon, yet the types of soils and carbon-bearing compounds vary widely. The important point for students is to realize that the vegetation is not pristine cellulose or other plant matter, but is instead matter that is degrading to some degree. This makes the carbon more accessible to natural processes like leaching.

Answers to Station 2 Steps 4 and 6, SE page 553

4. The filtered soil slurry might have an amber or brownish discoloration. This is likely very fine particulates of dissolved organic carbon (DOC) in solution. The water is getting a new component from the soil. Students will learn more about this in the next activity.
6. "Compared with processes in nature, this experiment represents movement of carbon from soils to rivers or lakes (water)."

Station 3: Rock Weathering

In Step 1, students calculate the percentage of a 0.5 g $CaCO_3$ tablet that is carbon. They sum the atomic masses [40 + 12 + 3(16) = 100 grams per mole] and see that carbon is 12 percent of the mass of $CaCO_3$.

Steps 2 and 3 simulate rock weathering by dissolving an antacid tablet with vinegar and water. This is basically what happens in natural settings, yet over much longer durations of time. The beaker with water is used as a control for nonacidic conditions.

Students balance the reaction in Step 4 for dissolving the tablet in vinegar. The bubbles are CO_2 produced in the reaction. In Step 5, students note fizzing from CO_2.

In Step 6, students work with a more realistic reaction for what happens during rock weathering. This is converting CO_2 to carbonic acid in rainwater, which then weathers rocks. This process *consumes* CO_2 from the atmosphere, thus removing CO_2 from the atmosphere. This is the opposite of reactions from the beginning of the station that give off CO_2. Thus, this station attempts to address directly the misconception that rock weathering moves carbon to the atmosphere. Students complete statements in Step 7 about carbon reactions modeled at this station.

Answers to Station 3 Steps 4–7, SE pages 553–554

4. The reaction product on the far right is 1 mole (mol) of CO_2.

$$CaCO_3 + 2CH_3COOH \longrightarrow Ca^{2+}{}_{(aq)} + \underline{2}CH_3COO^{1-}{}_{(aq)} + \underline{1}H_2O + \underline{1CO_2}$$

5. The evidence for the production of CO_2 would be fizzing in the water and creation of, presumably, CO_2 bubbles. The other 3 reaction products would be soluble and not visible.

6a. Students should be getting comfortable with this reaction by now

$$CO_{2(aq)} + H_2O_{(aq)} \rightleftharpoons H_2CO_{3(aq)} \text{ carbonic acid}$$

6b. Students should note the production of 2 mol of bicarbonate ion per 1 mol of calcium carbonate. Students may try to force the reaction to produce CO_2, just as they saw in the prior experiment. Another key point here is that in this more realistic reaction, CO_2 is consumed during the dissolution (i.e., rock weathering) of calcium carbonate. Thus, carbon in CO_2 is drawn out of the atmosphere and converted to carbon in a bicarbonate ion.

$$CaCO_3 + H_2CO_3 \longrightarrow \underline{1}Ca^{2+}{}_{(aq)} + \underline{2}HCO_3{}^{1-}{}_{(aq)}$$

5. Did you see evidence for the reaction product in the far right side of the equation in Step 4? What was the evidence?
6. In nature, a better model of rock weathering is the reaction between calcium carbonate and carbonic acid, H_2CO_3. Weak carbonic acid forms in rainwater as CO_2 dissolves in raindrops.
   a. Write the reaction to make carbonic acid (H_2CO_3) from rainwater and CO_2.
   b. Complete the following reaction in your science notebook. Be sure to check with your team for charge and mass balance.

   $$CaCO_3 + H_2CO_3 \longrightarrow \underline{?}Ca^{2+}{}_{(aq)} + \underline{?}HCO_3{}^{1-}{}_{(aq)}$$

   c. In the reaction in Step 6b, does the chemical reaction remove CO_2 from the atmosphere or add CO_2 to the atmosphere? Agree on an answer with your team and write your evidence in your science notebook.
   d. How does the reaction in Step 4 with acetic acid compare with the reaction between carbonic acid and $CaCO_3$? In particular, did the reaction of calcium carbonate with acetic acid consume or produce CO_2?
7. Write the following sentence in your science notebook and fill in the blanks:

   "Compared with processes in nature, this experiment represents movement of carbon from the __________ to __________."
8. Add the station number to your carbon environs diagram in your science notebook.

Station 4

Limestone is a rock that contains a lot of carbon. The carbon is in calcium carbonate, $CaCO_3$ (figure 11.6). Often, rocks like limestone get pushed deep into the earth, where it is very hot. What do you think happens to the rock? You can simulate a heated carbonate rock with a similar material, sodium bicarbonate, $NaHCO_3$. This is just baking soda.

1. What do you think will happen if you heat sodium bicarbonate ($NaHCO_3$)? Complete the following chemical reaction. Use the reaction to write a prediction in your science notebook. The reaction shows 1 reaction product.

$$NaHCO_3 + \text{heat} \longrightarrow NaOH_{(s)} + \_\_\_\_$$

6c. See the answer for Step 6b. The best evidence is the reaction where CO_2 and H_2O combine for carbonic acid, which is then consumed in the weathering reaction. Students may find this a little counterintuitive since the antacid tablet experiment gave off CO_2. It might help to rewrite the rock weathering reaction as

$$CaCO_3 + H_2O + CO_2 \longrightarrow \underline{1}Ca^{2+}{}_{(aq)} + \underline{2}HCO_3{}^{1-}{}_{(aq)}.$$

6d. The reaction with vinegar (acetic acid) produced CO_2, while the reaction with a dilute carbonic acid consumes CO_2 from the atmosphere. This experiment does not work well with seltzer water, which contains carbonic acid. The problem is that the tablet is a nucleation site for the formation of CO_2 bubbles, and it "looks" like the tablet is giving off CO_2 (even though it actually is consuming CO_2, but at a slower rate than the exsolution).

7. "Compared with processes in nature, this experiment represents movement of carbon from the geosphere or land to rivers or the ocean (water)."

It is OK to be wrong about a prediction. Scientists use predictions to see how well they understand systems. The key is thinking carefully about why you didn't get the correct answer. This will help you make a better prediction the next time.

2. Complete Steps 2a–f to heat and weigh sodium bicarbonate ($NaHCO_3$).
   a. Measure the mass of a small test tube.
   b. Weigh 1.5–2 g $NaHCO_3$ onto foil or weighing paper. Carefully transfer the powder to the bottom of the test tube.
   c. Heat the test tube for about 3 min. Obtain a dull red glow for the glass and powder. Record all changes that you observe for the $NaHCO_3$.
   d. After heating, gently cover the test tube with a small piece of foil. This keeps the sample from absorbing water vapor.
   e. Let the test tube cool for at least 1 min. If needed, cool the test tube further by immersing it in several inches of water.

Do not get water inside the test tube or around the foil on the top of the test tube.

   f. When the test tube is at room temperature, completely dry the exterior, remove the foil cover, and weigh the test tube plus the powdery substance.
3. Summarize the masses of the reactants and the products.
   a. Write the masses of sodium bicarbonate and product 1 (NaOH):

      mass of reactant $NaHCO_3$ = ________

      mass of product 1 NaOH = ________
   b. How would you determine the mass of product 2? Explain this in your science notebook and write the mass in the form shown.

      mass of product 2 ________ = ________
   c. What percentage of the initial reactant mass is product 2?
4. Chemical reactions are important predictive tools. For example, the completed reaction for Step 1 shows that 48 percent by mass of reaction products should be $NaOH_{(s)}$. Use this data about the reaction to answer Questions 4a–d.
   a. For your initial mass of $NaHCO_3$, predict the mass of NaOH from your experiment.
   b. Explain how similar or different your answers are for measured and predicted masses in Steps 3 and 4. If your answers are different, list sources of error that you think might account for this.
   c. What percentage of the initial mass of reactant do you infer for product 2? Show in your science notebook 2 different ways to calculate this.

Chapter 11 Carbon on the Move 555

Station 4: Limestone Metamorphism

In Step 1, students predict what will happen if you heat $NaHCO_3$. They should complete the reaction (see below) and predict that the reaction will produce CO_2. Make sure that they write their predictions in their science notebooks. Writing an answer forces students to think a little more critically and helps them to understand the correct answer. They may also suggest that the sample will melt, fizz, catch fire, evaporate, or vaporize. Accept all ideas at this point.

$$NaHCO_3 + \text{heat} \longrightarrow \underline{NaOH_{(s)}} + \underline{CO_2}$$

In Step 2, students weigh 1.5–2.0 g of $NaHCO_3$, heat the sample, and weigh the remainder. Make sure they cover the beaker during cooling to keep the NaOH powder in the beaker from absorbing water and increasing its mass. Check that students carefully record the masses in Step 3 and that the percentage of mass loss is determined accurately. Confirm that students can convert to percentages.

In Step 4, students will need to compare their measurement for the percentage of mass loss (due to CO_2) with the theoretical value of 52 percent from the balanced equation. There could be several sources of error that render values less than 52 percent, such as incomplete heating, water absorption, or moisture on the exterior of the beaker due to cooling. Students should infer the loss of CO_2 as reaction product 2.

Step 5 leads students to confirm independently that the product NaOH is indeed different from the initial $NaHCO_3$. The dissolved NaOH is much more basic than an analogous dissolved $NaHCO_3$, even though they both look like a white powder. Students will see this from the dark purple color when they add the universal indicator to NaOH (pH 10), as compared with the sky blue with the $NaHCO_3$ (about pH 8).

In Step 6, students should be able to complete the reaction shown and infer that the unknown reaction product is CO_2. It would not be unreasonable for a student to suggest

2 reaction products of C (carbon) and O_2 (oxygen) based on the reactants. Using conventions, however, they couldn't really place these 2 distinct reaction products on 1 small line in the equation. Thus, the complete reaction is

$$CaCO_3 + \text{energy} \longrightarrow \underline{CaO_{(s)}} + \underline{1CO_2}.$$

The question might arise as to what happens to the CaO that remains inside Earth. That CaO doesn't just sit there. It combines with other minerals to make those minerals enriched in calcium. For example, silicate minerals combined with the calcium make calcium-bearing silicate minerals like pyroxene or plagioclase (i.e., plagioclase feldspar).

Answers to Station 4 Steps 5–7, SE page 556

5d. The test tube with NaOH is a much stronger base than the test tube with baking soda. Students' evidence is the purple, higher pH solution than with the $NaHCO_3$.

6. Students should see that the reaction product is 1 mol of CO_2.

7. "Compared with processes in nature, this experiment represents movement of carbon from inside Earth to the atmosphere."

Station 5: Making Limestone

In Step 1, teams think of ways that carbon can sink from the surface waters of the ocean. They may suggest that animals die and sink, or that currents carry carbon downward. Be open to their ideas at this time. They will see at this station how calcium carbonate ($CaCO_3$) sinks and carries carbon from surface to deeper waters.

In Step 2, students make a solution of sodium bicarbonate ($NaHCO_3$) that is nearly saturated. Then in Step 3, they make a solution of calcium chloride ($CaCl_2$) that is also nearly saturated. In Step 4, students complete the disassociation of each solution. The reactions would be as follows:

$$2NaHCO_{3(s)} \longrightarrow 2Na^{1+}{}_{(aq)} + \underline{2HCO_3{}^{1-}}{}_{(aq)}$$

$$CaCl_{t6g32(s)} \longrightarrow \underline{1}Ca^{2+}{}_{(aq)} + \underline{2}Cl^{1-}{}_{(aq)}$$

In Step 5, students use the reactions from Step 4 to recombine the reaction products in solution (Na, Ca, $HCO_3{}^{1-}$, Cl^{1-}) to predict the precipitation of calcium carbonate, $CaCO_3$.

Students add pH indicators to solutions in Step 6 and then mix the solutions in Step 7. They then describe the mixed solution, which produces several surprises. One is the production of CO_2. This makes the solution more acidic, which changes the color of the indicator. Students will note a solid (precipitate) forming that looks like curdled milk. This is $CaCO_3$. They will be asked to write a chemical reaction for this in Step 8.

▲ **Figure 11.6**
Fossiliferous limestone. This limestone has fossils of shells. The shells consist of calcium carbonate, $CaCO_3$. How much carbon is this?

d. What is product 2? Explain your evidence in your science notebook.

5. Show that the reaction product NaOH differs from reactant $NaHCO_3$.
   a. Dissolve the remaining NaOH in the test tube with 20–30 milliliters (mL) of water.
   b. Dissolve a similar amount of $NaHCO_3$ in 20–30 mL of water in a test tube.
   c. Add 5 drops of universal indicator to each.
   d. Which test tube has a stronger base? Does this correlate with NaOH or with $NaHCO_3$? Explain your evidence.
6. Return to the limestone ($CaCO_3$) analogy, rather than the sodium bicarbonate ($NaHCO_3$) analogy. Complete the following reaction and use it to predict what happens when the $CaCO_3$ in limestone is heated in the earth.

$$CaCO_3 + \text{energy} \longrightarrow CaO_{(s)} + \_\_\_\_$$

7. Write the following sentence into your science notebook and fill in the blanks:
   "Compared with processes in nature, this experiment represents movement of carbon from ________ to the ________."
8. Add the station number to your carbon environs diagram in your science notebook.

Station 5

What do you think the seafloor looks like at a depth of 1–2 kilometers (km)? Yes, it is dark with many unfamiliar forms of life. Complete this investigation to simulate carbon changing forms in the ocean.

1. Think of different ways for carbon to move from the shallow ocean to greater depths. Explain these ideas as best you can in your science notebook.
2. Obtain 2 glass beakers, at least 300 mL in volume. In the first, add 150 mL of water. Add a spoonful of baking soda ($NaHCO_3$) and stir until the solution is clear.
3. In the other beaker, add 150 mL of water. Add 1 large spoonful of calcium chloride ($CaCl_2$) and stir until the solution is completely clear.

556 Unit 3 Moving Matter

Answers to Station 5 Steps 5, 7–9, SE page 557

5a. The reactants for the new reaction would be

$$Ca^{2+}_{(aq)} + 2Cl^{1-}_{(aq)} + 2HCO_3{}^{1-}_{(aq)} + 2Na^{1+}_{(aq)}.$$

5b. The complete reaction for the formation of a $CaCO_3$ precipitate in the beaker follows. Students might get part or all of the reaction at this point. Use this opportunity to guide them toward a prediction and the correct reaction. The calcium carbonate precipitate will look like curdled milk forming in the beaker when they mix the solutions in Step 7. An important piece of evidence is the fizzing of the beakers as the precipitate is forming.

With time, the $CaCO_3$ precipitate gathers as clumps and settles to the bottom of the beaker. This simulates the formation of a layer of limestone in the ocean, especially if you allow a beaker to sit overnight. This must be a new compound because it is so different from either of the initial solids when they were mixed into the solution ($NaHCO_3$ powder or $CaCl_2$ crystals).

$$Ca^{2+}_{(aq)} + 2Cl^{1-}_{(aq)} + 2HCO_3{}^{1-} + 2Na^{1+}_{(aq)} \longrightarrow 2Na^{1+}_{(aq)} + 2Cl^{1-}_{(aq)} + CaCO_3 + H_2O + CO_2$$

5c. Depending on their predictions, ask students questions that test their understanding of the system. Is the reaction balanced? Did they show the Na^{1+} and Cl^{1-} remaining in the solution?

7a. During the mixing of solutions, the color should change to slightly more acidic, as shown by the universal indicator turning toward yellow or red.

7b. Evidence for 2 products is visible. A white precipitate will look like curdled milk throughout the mixed solution. It will be suspended initially, then sink to the bottom, forming a layer of "limestone." There will also be fizzing at this time, indicating the reaction product

Answers to Station 5 Steps 5, 7–9 are on TE pages 557–558.

Have different team members prepare the 2 solutions. If you cannot entirely dissolve either of the powders, add another 50 mL of water and stir.

4. Dissolving $NaHCO_3$ and $CaCl_2$ in water are 2 disassociation reactions. Complete the following reactions and write them in your science notebook.

$$2NaHCO_{3(s)} \longrightarrow 2Na^{1+}_{(aq)} + \_\_\_\__{(aq)}$$

$$CaCl_{2(s)} \longrightarrow \underline{?}Ca^{2+}_{(aq)} + \underline{?}Cl^{1-}_{(aq)}$$

5. What do you think will happen if you mix these 2 solutions? Make a prediction with a chemical reaction by completing Steps 5a–c.
   a. Take the reaction products in Step 4 and rearrange them as reactants. You will mix the 2 solutions in Step 7.
   b. Predict the reaction products from mixing the solutions. Write this prediction in your science notebook.

Note that sodium (Na^{1+}) and chlorine (Cl^{1-}) are very soluble and remain dissolved in a solution.

   c. Show your prediction to your teacher before you begin Step 6.
6. Add 8 drops of universal indicator solution to each beaker. Record the color.
7. Pour the contents of the beakers together. Describe carefully what you see.
   a. What color is the mixture? What does that tell you about the pH of the mixture?
   b. How many reaction products form in the mixture? Describe these very carefully. What happens to the mixture after 20–30 sec?
   c. Make a sketch of the beaker with the mixture; add appropriate labels that show your main observations.

This is a good place to use the labeling strategies "What I see" and "What it means."

8. Evaluate your prediction strategy from Step 5. Consider what you saw and the reactants in this experiment. What is your evidence for the solid? Write a complete chemical reaction.
9. Write the following sentence in your science notebook and fill in the blanks:

   "Compared with processes in nature, this experiment represents movement of carbon from ________ to the ________."

10. Add the station number to your carbon environs diagram in your science notebook.

NOTES:

CO_2. Half of the carbon goes to make the $CaCO_3$, while the other half is evolved as CO_2. The CO_2 in solution will make the mixture slightly more basic than it was, especially compared with the beaker of $NaHCO_3$ that had been blue (basic).

7c. Check that students have accurate sketches of the experiment. Colored pencils could effectively depict the solutions.

8. Students should be working to identify the complete reaction by now, with the solid being calcium carbonate. This is shown in the following:

$$Ca^{2+}_{(aq)} + 2Cl^{1-}_{(aq)} + 2HCO_3^{1-} + 2Na^{1+}_{(aq)} \longrightarrow$$
$$2Na^{1+}_{(aq)} + 2Cl^{1-}_{(aq)} + CaCO_3 + H_2O + CO_2$$

9. "Compared with processes in nature, this experiment represents movement of carbon from ocean water to the seafloor."

Station 6: Photosynthesis

Students should be familiar with photosynthesis from prior science courses. The process is highly generalized in this chapter, as the purpose is to link the photosynthesis reaction within the series of reactions defining the carbon cycle.

In Step 1, students sketch in their science notebooks the plant, terrarium, or other photosynthesizing organism at the station. This is a chance for them to keep cultivating skills of sketching and labeling. The plant may seem silly, but it is an important visual cue to help students keep making links to the real world for the cycling of carbon. Students complete a generalized photosynthesis reaction in Step 2.

Step 3 focuses on the reactants and products for photosynthesis, which may be a review for students. Step 4 has students consider again where those reactions might occur.

Answers to Station 6 Steps 2–4, SE page 558

2. The balanced reaction is

$$\underline{6H_2O} + \underline{6CO_2} + \text{energy} \longrightarrow C_6H_{12}O_6 + 6O_2.$$

3. Carbon is in the form of carbon dioxide as a reactant and glucose as a product. Again, the glucose represents the many more complex types of carbon compounds that the plant synthesizes, such as cellulose or starches.

4. "Compared with processes in nature, this experiment represents movement of carbon from the atmosphere to vegetation or plants."

Station 6

You've studied photosynthesis in this program in several contexts. You know that plants use this process to make the food and tissues that they need. Review the chemical reaction for photosynthesis at this station.

1. Observe and sketch the plant at this station. The plant is growing and needs carbon to grow leaves, branches, roots, and a thicker trunk. Draw a sketch of the plant that shows labels and a scale.
2. Balance the following photosynthesis reaction. Recall that reaction products are glucose ($C_6H_{12}O_6$) and 6 molecules of oxygen gas (O_2). Glucose is one of many thousands of kinds of carbon molecules (figure 11.7).

$$\_\_\_\_ + \_\_\_\_ + \text{energy} \longrightarrow C_6H_{12}O_6 + 6O_2$$

The reaction product is represented here as glucose. A prior step (not shown) builds a 3-carbon sugar that plants convert to glucose.

3. What forms does carbon appear in for the reactants and the products?
4. Write the following sentence in your science notebook and fill in the blanks:

"Compared with processes in nature, this experiment represents movement of carbon from the ________ to ________."

5. Add the station number to your carbon environs diagram in your science notebook.

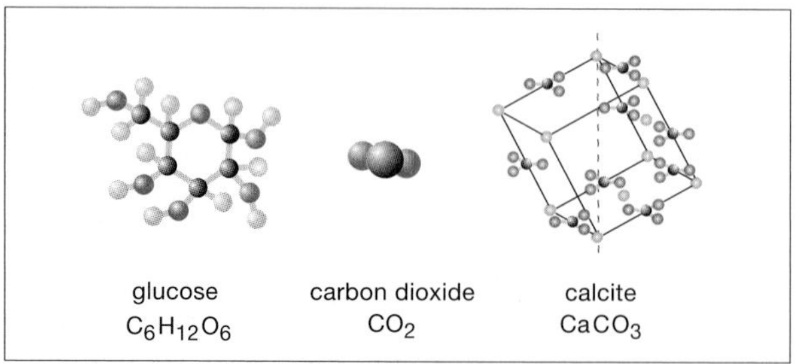

▲ **Figure 11.7 Molecular diagrams with carbon.** The carbon atom is highly versatile and forms hundreds of thousands of kinds of molecules. These 3 diagrams show the atomic structure of carbon in glucose, carbon dioxide, and the mineral calcite ($CaCO_3$).

Station 7: Microbial Respiration

In Step 1, students view, touch, smell, and explore some decaying vegetation and read a paragraph on aerobic respiration. This short reading helps remind students of the role of respiring microbes in soils. In Step 2, students balance a cellular respiration reaction that is aerobic, or with oxygen. This is part of the decay process for dead vegetation, which is represented by glucose.

Answers to Station 7 Step 2, SE page 559

2a. The mass- and charge-balanced reaction is

$$C_6H_{12}O_6 + \underline{6}O_2 \longrightarrow \underline{6CO_2} + \underline{6}H_2O + \text{energy.}$$

2b. The reaction product on the line is 6 mol of CO_2.

In Steps 3 and 4, students see 2 other representations for microbial respiration. Both are anaerobic respiration, and thus don't use oxygen (i.e., oxygen is not a reactant). The important goal is that students will compare the moles of CO_2 given off by aerobic and anaerobic reactions in *Reflect and Connect* Step 4.

Answers to Station 7 Steps 3–5, SE pages 559–560

3b. The completed reaction for anaerobic respiration, such as fermentation, is

$$C_6H_{12}O_6 \longrightarrow 2C_2H_5OH + \underline{2CO_2} + \text{energy.}$$

3c. The reaction generates 2 mol of ethanol and 2 mol of CO_2. This is one-third the CO_2 production of aerobic respiration (with oxygen) for 1 mol of glucose.

4. The completed reaction follows. Note that the reaction generates 3 mol of CO_2 for each mole of glucose. This is one-half the CO_2 production of aerobic respiration (with oxygen).

$$C_6H_{12}O_6 \longrightarrow \underline{3}CH_4 + \underline{3}CO_2 + \text{energy}$$

5. "Compared with processes in nature, this experiment represents movement of carbon from soils to the atmosphere."

Station 7

What might you see if you dug into soils on a forest floor? Mostly, you would see a lot of leaves and branches in a state of decay. But where does the carbon go that is in that vegetation? You explored one such carbon pathway in soils in station 2. See another pathway at this station.

1. View, touch, and smell the decaying vegetation at this station. Have a member of your team read the following paragraph about decaying vegetation.

   In Level 1 of this program, you learned about cellular respiration. During cellular respiration, the cells in your tissues use oxygen and sugars to produce energy for your body. Because this kind of respiration uses or consumes oxygen, it is called **aerobic respiration**. In soils, small organisms called **microbes** "eat" and use fallen vegetation as a source of energy. Some of these are single-celled organisms. Thus, microbial respiration leads to the decay that you see.

2. Use glucose ($C_6H_{12}O_6$) as a product of photosynthesis. Glucose is not quite cellulose, or the parts of plants with leaves, wood, roots, or bark. Still, it is a good molecule to model the decay of vegetation in soils.

   a. Complete the following reaction for microbial respiration with oxygen. Assume that microbes consume glucose. Make sure that the reaction is charge and mass balanced.

   $$C_6H_{12}O_6 + \underline{?}O_2 \longrightarrow \_\_\_\_ + \underline{?}H_2O + \text{energy}$$

   b. What must be the reaction product on the blank line in Step 2a?

3. Follow Steps 3a–c to learn about another kind of cellular respiration.

   a. Use a reading strategy with your team to read the following paragraph.

   Many microbes live deep in soils, the ocean, or even the intestines of animals. In those settings, the microbes do not have oxygen for respiration. Yet they still consume glucoselike molecules to produce energy and stay alive. This energy-generating process is still called respiration. But without oxygen, it is called **anaerobic respiration**. These microbes are sometimes called **anaerobes**. You have already studied anaerobic fungi—yeast. They consume sugar and produce ethanol (C_2H_5OH). Yeast do this without oxygen.

NOTES:

Station 8: Respiration Station

In Step 1, students review a simple representation of cellular respiration and balance the equation. The carbon-bearing reaction product is CO_2.

Answers to Station 8 Step 1, SE page 560

1. The balanced chemical reaction for cellular respiration in a plant or animal is

$$C_6H_{12}O_6 + \underline{6}O_2 \longrightarrow \underline{6CO_2} + \underline{6}H_2O + \text{energy.}$$

In Step 2, students add water and BTB to a test tube, making a blue solution. Students exhale through a straw into the BTB solution in Step 3 and observe a rapid change in color from green to yellow. In Step 4, students reconsider the reaction products, hopefully using the equation that they completed in Step 1. They also consider the link between the color change and pH again, as they have done previously in the chapter and with acid-base reactions.

Answers to Station 8 Steps 3–4 and 6, SE pages 560–561

3. The solution should start blue and rapidly turn from green to yellow. This reflects an increase in acidity due to carbonic acid. The color change corresponds with a change in pH from about 7.5 to 6. (See also figure T11.1.)
4. The reaction products are H_2O and CO_2. Students probably first learned about respiration in a grade nine science course or in middle school. Students' evidence would be that adding CO_2 to water by respiration makes carbonic acid. The carbonic acid causes the BTB color change from blue to yellow, as they learned in the engage activity. This is a shift to the right for the following chemical reaction:

$$CO_{2(aq)} + H_2O_{(aq)} \rightleftharpoons \underset{\text{carbonic acid}}{H_2CO_{3(aq)}} \rightleftharpoons HCO_3{}^{1-}{}_{(aq)} + H^{1+}{}_{(aq)}$$

Students rinse their test tubes in Step 5 and complete the sentence about carbon reactions in Step 6.

6. "The process of cellular respiration moves carbon from food to the atmosphere."

Answers to Station 7 Steps 3c–5 are on TE page 559.

b. Complete the following reaction for anaerobic respiration by microbes.

$$C_6H_{12}O_6 \longrightarrow 2C_2H_5OH + \_\_\_\_ + \text{energy}$$

Is your reaction charge and mass balanced? You might recall that this process is called fermentation.

c. How many moles (mol) of reaction products are made from 1 mol of $C_6H_{12}O_6$?

4. Balance the reaction for the anaerobic production of methane (CH_4). Other anaerobes produce methane from glucose in swamps and from the intestines of animals.

$$C_6H_{12}O_6 \longrightarrow \underline{?}CH_4 + \underline{?}CO_2 + \text{energy}$$

5. Write the following sentence in your science notebook and fill in the blanks:

"Compared with processes in nature, this experiment represents movement of carbon from ________ to the ________."

6. Add the station number to your carbon environs diagram in your science notebook.

Station 8

Complete the following steps to investigate cellular respiration further. Recall that you have already studied cellular respiration in Level 1 of this program.

1. For a molecule of glucose ($C_6H_{12}O_6$), complete and balance the following chemical reaction. This represents cellular respiration for a plant or an animal.

$$C_6H_{12}O_6 + \underline{?}O_2 \longrightarrow \_\_\_\_ + \underline{?}H_2O + \text{energy}$$

2. Fill a test tube with 10 mL of water. Add 5 drops of BTB solution from a dropper bottle. Swirl gently until the solution is a uniform color.
3. Obtain a straw and blow gently into the blue solution. What color does the solution turn? What does the change in color tell you about the acidity of the solution?

It may help you to refer to the reaction in Question 5 of the *Reflect and Connect* from the engage activity. Yellow means more acidic, blue more basic.

Cautions

Do not draw water up the straw. Only blow out through the straw.

560 | Unit 3 Moving Matter

Answers to Reflect and Connect, SE pages 561–562

1. This is the same CO_2 dissolution reaction again, but this time it explicitly refers to the bicarbonate ion in the reaction. Following is one sequence of steps to bicarbonate:

$$CO_{2(g)} \longrightarrow CO_{2(aq)}$$

$$CO_{2(aq)} + H_2O_{(aq)} \longrightarrow \underset{\text{carbonic acid}}{H_2CO_{3(aq)}}$$

$$H_2CO_{3(aq)} \longrightarrow HCO_3{}^{1-}{}_{(aq)} + H^{1+}{}_{(aq)}$$

2. The fluid produced is just water after the HCl has reacted with the $CaCO_3$. With a drop of acid solution on a rock, the $CaCO_3$ is in excess and the acid is rapidly neutralized.

$$CaCO_3 + 2HCl \longrightarrow \underline{Ca^{2+}} + \underline{2Cl^{1-}} + \underline{H_2O} + \underline{1}CO_{2(g)}$$

3a. A dissociation reaction for 2 mol of $NaHCO_3$ is

$$2NaHCO_{3(s)} \longrightarrow 2Na^{1+}{}_{(aq)} + 2HCO_3{}^{1-}{}_{(aq)}.$$

3b. A dissociation reaction for 1 mol of $Ca(OH)_2$ is

$$Ca(OH)_{2(s)} \longrightarrow Ca^{2+}{}_{(aq)} + 2OH^{1-}{}_{(aq)}.$$

3c. Here are the reactants in solution:

$$Ca^{2+}{}_{(aq)} + 2Cl^{1-}{}_{(aq)} + 2HCO_3{}^{1-} + 2Na^{1+}{}_{(aq)}$$

3d. A solution saturated in $Ca(OH)_2$ is sometimes called limewater. When it is combined with the saturated sodium bicarbonate, $CaCO_3$ forms as a precipitate.

$$Ca^{2+}{}_{(aq)} + 2Cl^{1-}{}_{(aq)} + 2HCO_3{}^{1-}{}_{(aq)} + 2Na^{1+}{}_{(aq)} \longrightarrow 2Na^{1+}{}_{(aq)} + 2Cl^{1-}{}_{(aq)} + CaCO_{3(s)} + H_2O + CO_{2(g)}$$

There is an important inference from this reaction. For every 2 mol of carbon in $HCO_3{}^{1-}$, one mole goes to form solid $CaCO_3$ and the other mole of carbon is converted to CO_2 gas. Thus, carbon from $HCO_3{}^{1-}$ actually goes to 2 different reservoirs. You'll see later that the formation of $CaCO_3$ in the ocean actually liberates CO_2 back to the atmosphere.

Answers to Reflect and Connect are on TE pages 561–562.

4. What are the reaction products of cellular respiration? How did the color change serve as evidence for the reaction products?
5. Rinse the solution out of the test tube when you are finished.
6. Write the following sentence in your science notebook and fill in the blanks:

   "The process of cellular respiration moves carbon from ________ to the ________."
7. Add the station number to your carbon environs diagram in your science notebook.

Reflect and Connect

Discuss the following questions with your team and write answers in your science notebook. For all chemical equations, confirm that they are charge and mass balanced.

1. At station 5, you used baking soda ($NaHCO_3$) to make a solution with a high concentration of bicarbonate $(HCO_3)^{1-}$. If $CO_{2(g)}$ dissolves in the ocean or a lake, write a reaction with water (H_2O) to show one way to make a bicarbonate ion $(HCO_3)^{1-}$.

It will help you to recall the acid-base reactions in the engage activity.

2. Geologists test whether a rock is limestone by looking for a "fizz" when they put a drop of hydrochloric acid (HCl) on it. Assuming that the fizz is a release of CO_2, balance the following reaction to represent this handy field test for limestone.

$$CaCO_3 + 2HCl \longrightarrow \underline{?}^{2+} + \underline{?}^{1-} + \underline{\quad\quad} + \underline{?}CO_{2(g)}$$

3. A solution in a beaker is nearly saturated in $NaHCO_3$. Another beaker contains limewater, a solution nearly saturated in calcium hydroxide $Ca(OH)_2$. Predict what happens when the 2 solutions are mixed.
   a. Write a dissociation reaction for 2 mol of $NaHCO_3$.
   b. Write another dissociation reaction for 1 mol of $Ca(OH)_2$.
   c. List the reaction products from the steps above. Imagine that these are reactants when one of the beakers is poured into the other to make a mixture.
   d. Use your results at station 5 to predict the reaction products for Question 3c. Check your equation for charge and mass balance.

Recall that sodium (Na^{1+}) and the hydroxide ion (OH^{1-}) are very soluble and stay in solution.

4a. The reactions follow. They are aerobic respiration and then 2 types of anaerobic respiration. The first is fermentation, and the second a methane-generating reaction (methanogenesis).

$$C_6H_{12}O_6 + 6O_2 \longrightarrow 6CO_2 + 6H_2O + \text{energy}$$

$$C_6H_{12}O_6 \longrightarrow 2C_2H_5OH + 2CO_2 + \text{energy}$$

$$C_6H_{12}O_6 \longrightarrow 3CH_4 + 3CO_2 + \text{energy}$$

4b. Aerobic respiration generates the most moles of CO_2 per mole of glucose.

4c. Fermentation produces the least because much of the carbon from the glucose is used in making ethanol, and so not much CO_2 can be generated.

4d. The molar ratios are 6:3:2 for the production of CO_2 in the 3 respiration equations.

5. Carbon dioxide is more soluble in cold polar waters than in warm equatorial waters. Cold, high-latitude waters are net sinks for CO_2 from the atmosphere. The diagrams of carbon flux in the elaborate activity, *The Flux Is the Crux*, do not distinguish between rates of dissolution in cold and warm ocean waters.

6. Photosynthesis is the basis of the food chain, as shown in station 6. One example is the photosynthesis that occurs in grasses, which form food for herbivores and grazers and seeds for rodents. Another example is photosynthesizing organisms in shallow waters, which provide a food source for animals higher up on the food chain. Also, photosynthesis in algae and corals is a basis of converting sunlight into matter in coral reef ecosystems. Herbivorous fish rely on these photosynthesizing organisms.

EXPLAIN

The Carbonated Geosphere

Activity Overview

In *The Carbonated Geosphere*, students will complete readings about three regions of Earth that have significant stores of carbon. These carbon reservoirs are found in terrestrial, atmospheric, and oceanic settings. As such, they compose a geosphere, the upper or surface layers of Earth. This construct is a little different than distinctions that might be drawn between the geosphere, biosphere, atmosphere, hydrosphere, and cryosphere. Students also will use two tables (copymasters 11.1, *Carbon*

4. Review station 7 with the 3 respiration reactions from glucose ($C_6H_{12}O_6$).
   a. Write each of these reactions together in your science notebook and label them.
   b. Starting with 1 mol of glucose, which of the 3 respiration reactions generates the most CO_2?
   c. Which of the 3 reactions generates the least CO_2?
   d. What are the molar ratios of CO_2 produced in each of the 3 respiration reactions?
5. CO_2 dissolves into the ocean in both polar and equatorial areas. Would CO_2 dissolve more readily into cold polar oceans or warm equatorial oceans? Use your data from station 1 to explain your answer.
6. Which station or stations represent a reaction that is the basis for food chains in ecosystems? Use 2 examples to explain your answer.

EXPLAIN

The Carbonated Geosphere

In the explore activity, *Carbon Changing Costumes*, you saw carbon change costume through chemical reactions. Carbon can move between substances in the liquid, solid, or gas state. You probably even noted that some stations had reactions that were the reverse of other stations.

Indeed, carbon takes many forms. This is because its bond structure is so versatile, as you have been learning in science. But to change settings on Earth and participate in different reactions, carbon has to move around. You have probably traced the flow of water (H_2O) between different reservoirs. The movement of water between reservoirs is the water cycle.

What about carbon? How does carbon move around between different geologic and biologic settings? In *The Carbonated Geosphere*, you and your team will analyze carbon transport on Earth.

Materials

For each team of 3 students

3 *Carbon Chemical Reaction Table* handouts

3 *Carbon Transport Table* handouts

Process and Procedure

Begin by observing as a class 2 containers with water and substances with carbon.

Chemical Reaction Table and 11.2, *Carbon Transport Table*) as important organizational tools. Such organizational tools are important to facilitate science standards linked to abilities of inquiry. The tables will help students with the reading and in constructing their own carbon cycle later in the chapter.

Before You Teach

Background Information

Much of the scientific background for this activity is presented in the student explain readings. A key point is that much of the CO_2 that dissolves into the ocean is used in photosynthesis by phytoplankton. The HCO_3^{1-} from rivers is eventually used for calcium carbonate shells (to simplify a complex process).

The containers of water used in Steps 1 and 2 are important visuals to help students understand and learn about types of carbon. The containers represent the two common forms of carbon found in rivers, lakes, and the ocean (of course, in a highly simplified way).

One container will have its carbon in the form of organic matter (i.e., biogenic), giving it a murky appearance. Students are probably familiar with this form of carbon. It can be termed *dissolved organic carbon*, or *DOC* (even though it may include a component of particulate organic matter). The other container will also have carbon, but in the form of the bicarbonate ion, HCO_3^{1-}. This form of carbon probably is not too familiar to students. Because it is not of plant or animal origin (i.e., organic), it is called inorganic carbon. In the water, it is termed *dissolved inorganic carbon*, or *DIC*. The amount of carbon and the proportions of DOC and DIC depend on the source regions for rivers (e.g., the Amazon basin generates a lot of DOC) and the amount of rock weathering in the source region. Students learned at station 3 in the explore activity, *Carbon Changing Costumes*, that rock weathering generates considerable DIC.

You may also need to clarify for students that dark river waters contain both silt and mud particles along with the DOC. Silt and mud consist largely of fine, weathered fragments of rocks. These probably do not have an organic component. This differs from the soluble HCO_3^{1-} generated by rock weathering.

The second container activity simulates a process that may be very hard for students to envision. You will do this as a *Stop and Think* task to break up the reading. This is the process by which massive amounts of carbon are transported from the shallow ocean to the deep ocean by the downwelling of ocean water. In the simulation, small cells or volumes of water that are relatively enriched in carbon from dry ice can actually be seen moving to deeper portions of the container. The convection of water can be enhanced by adding a little heat to the bottom of the tall container. Continue to refer back to these demonstrations throughout the rest of the chapter.

1. Look at the containers of water your teacher has set up. Are they similar or different? Can you tell which one has dissolved $NaHCO_3$? Discuss these containers as a class and answer Questions 1a–c in your science notebook.
   a. Discuss what forms of carbon you think might be in the 2 containers of water. What is your evidence, and how might you test your ideas?
   b. What do you think will happen if the 2 are mixed? Write a prediction.
   c. What ideas do you have about the geologic or biologic setting that the mixture might represent?
2. Obtain the *Carbon Chemical Reaction Table* and the *Carbon Transport Table* handouts. Refer to these tables with your team as you complete the following reading. The tables are an important tool to help you map pathways of carbon on Earth.
3. Use a reading strategy with your team to complete the following reading, *Carbon Transport across the Globe*. This will help you learn more about how carbon moves around Earth.

READING

Carbon Transport across the Globe

Terrestrial Carbon and Fall Colors

What is it like in the woods, the mountains, or a city park on a brisk fall day? What indicates the changing seasons to you? Maybe you note that the Sun is at a lower angle in the sky, or that not only are leaves changing colors, but many are fluttering to the ground. The leaves fall amidst limbs or trees that have fallen, as well as the remains of other leaves that fell to the forest floor last fall.

Each year, this process repeats itself in forests. Vegetation that grew in the spring and summer is transferred to forest floors in the fall. The buildup of leaves and limbs on the forest floors is called **litter** (figure 11.8). This process moves carbon from trees to the forest floor. As litter, the carbon in that organic material can enter a new series of decay pathways.

When litter starts to decay, it is sometimes called **humus**. In the explore activity, you saw several possible fates for carbon in the humus of the forest floor. Do you remember what these were? One was microbes that consume humus. For the microbes, this is a stage of cellular respiration. Much of the carbon is converted to CO_2.

Another fate for carbon in the humus occurs from the rinsing or leaching of the humus by rainwater. As the rainwater then drains to rivers, the carbon may remain in particles of organic

Materials

For the teacher

Step 1, *Process and Procedure*

1 clear container of dissolved $NaHCO_3$

1 clear container of murky water filtered from a leach of soil

Step 1, *Stop and Think*

1–2 tall plastic containers of water that close tightly

1 dropper bottle of BTB

several small pieces of dry ice

1 aluminum thumb boat (per water bottle)

1 small square of clear tape

gentle source of heat

For each team of 3 students

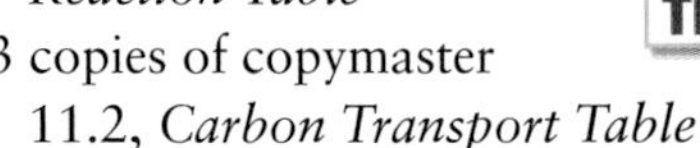

3 copies of copymaster 11.1, *Carbon Chemical Reaction Table*

3 copies of copymaster 11.2, *Carbon Transport Table*

Advance Preparation

Identify a useful reading strategy for your students in class. Decide if you can assign a portion of the reading or figures as homework.

Prepare the 2 solutions that go with Step 1 of *Process and Procedure.* For 1 of the bottles of water, do a quick filter of some potting or garden soil, even with coffee grounds mixed in. The goal is to have a clear container of brownish water containing dissolved organic carbon. The containers with DIC and DOC are important visuals to help students remember the dominant types of carbon in rivers and the ocean. They will likely state that the DOC bottle has carbon. It is important to emphasize to students, using the demonstration and probing questions, that the carbon in DIC is present, but not readily visible.

The second visual comes at Step 1 of the *Stop and Think* task. It is described as a demonstration, but your students may be able to do it themselves. Widemouthed, 32-oz sports drink containers work well. (Use widemouthed containers so that you can get the aluminum boat into the container.) As the dry ice sublimes, the buildup of pressure is useful to help force CO_2 into the water. But the pressure must be relieved every 30 seconds or so to avoid an explosive rupture. Relieve the pressure without letting the water mix or stir. *Do not use glass containers.* A source of mild heat will aid convective turnover in the container, *but do not melt the bottom of the container while at high pressures.*

Make copies of copymasters 11.1, *Carbon Chemical Reaction Table* and 11.2, *Carbon Transport Table* for each student.

Cautions

Use a folded cloth or thick gloves when handling dry ice. Contact with skin for more than 1 second will freeze cells and can cause injury similar to a burn. Do not let the pressure build up inside a closed container with dry ice inside. This could cause a dangerous explosion when the plastic container ruptures.

As You Teach

Outcomes and Indicators of Success

By the end of this activity, students should

1. understand more about carbon reactions and carbon transport processes in terrestrial, oceanic, and atmosphere settings of the geosphere.

   They will demonstrate their understanding by
   - relating parts of readings to their own experiences and interests,
   - aligning reactions and transport in the tables with their experiences at the eight stations in the explore activity,
   - indicating the forms of carbon in different settings of the geosphere,
   - making analogies between 2 containers of water and DIC and DOC, and
   - making analogies between visible carbon transport in tall containers of water and ocean downwelling.
2. develop further skills in the abilities and understandings of scientific inquiry.

Carbon Transport across the Globe, continued

▲ **Figure 11.8 Fall leaves.** These trees are losing their leaves in the fall. Carbon in leaves, limbs, and trunks fall to the forest floor to become litter.

matter. This is often called **dissolved organic carbon**, or **DOC** for short. Rivers carry DOC to the ocean—that's where rivers go (figure 11.9).

But carbon also takes another form in rivers. This is the carbon from rock weathering, such as the weathering of limestone ($CaCO_3$). Do you recall the reaction that makes the bicarbonate ion HCO_3^{1-} from rock weathering? Rivers also carry a lot of this carbon. Since $CaCO_3$ is not organic carbon ($CaCO_3$ doesn't "grow on trees," so to speak), it is called **dissolved inorganic carbon**, or **DIC** for short.

Maybe you have heard the word **terrestrial**. This refers to something found on land. The processes above describe terrestrial carbon—that is, the carbon in forests, rocks, rivers, and lakes. There are two other key parts of Earth with a lot of carbon. You can probably guess what those are.

Atmospheric Carbon

Think back to one of your first activities with seltzer water. Your team noted a very common reaction product that carried carbon straight into the atmosphere. What was it? That's right—it was carbon dioxide, CO_2. The atmosphere doesn't have a huge concentration of carbon as CO_2, but it is enough to support processes like photosynthesis. **Atmospheric mixing** is a key process to help transport and move that carbon around. Rivers are one way to move carbon from the land to the ocean. But atmospheric mixing is a faster way to move carbon around Earth.

With atmospheric mixing, for example, the movement of carbon from the land to the ocean occurs in two steps. Wind moves the atmosphere from the land over the ocean. Then CO_2 dissolves from the atmosphere into the ocean. You have seen in several activities how CO_2 dissolves into water. This also happens with the ocean.

How else does carbon get to the atmosphere? Look at your tables. Another key transport process is **volcanic degassing**. This moves carbon in CO_2 from inside Earth to the atmosphere. But how did the carbon get into the earth? If you study more geology, you will learn how rocks like limestone get pushed deep into the earth. Recall station 4, where $CaCO_3$ decomposes under heat and pressure, releasing CO_2 gas. This is what happens to limestone when it is pushed into the earth.

564 Unit 3 Moving Matter

They will demonstrate their skills by

- completing a reading about key carbon cycle concepts and by answering questions,
- beginning to consider oceanic organisms that incorporate carbon by several processes,
- using simple demonstrations as simple models of water mixing and key parts of global systems,
- using a table summarizing reactions and transport processes as a tool to contribute to better understanding, and
- answering specific questions about how living systems with carbon function as part of the carbon cycle.

Strategies

Getting Started

Use Step 1 as a good visual to help you start class. Work with students to decide on a reading strategy for the three sections. Parts of the reading could also be assigned for homework.

Cautions

Use a folded cloth or thick gloves when handling dry ice. Contact with skin for more than 1 second will freeze cells and can cause injury similar to a burn. Do not let the pressure build up inside a closed container with dry ice inside. This could cause a dangerous explosion when the plastic container ruptures.

Process and Procedure

Materials

For the teacher

Step 1, *Process and Procedure*

1 clear container of dissolved $NaHCO_3$

1 clear container of murky water filtered from a leach of soil

Step 1, *Stop and Think*

1–2 tall plastic containers of water that close tightly

1 dropper bottle of BTB

several small pieces of dry ice

1 aluminum thumb boat (per water bottle)

1 small square of clear tape

gentle source of heat

For each team of 3 students

3 copies of copymaster 11.1, *Carbon Chemical Reaction Table*

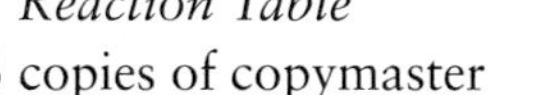

3 copies of copymaster 11.2, *Carbon Transport Table*

Use Step 1 to engage the students and begin discussion about what the containers might represent. Encourage students to think on a global scale, as they are able. The containers represent DOC and DIC in rivers, lakes, and the ocean. These are different types of carbon in natural waters.

Give each team copies of copymasters 11.1, *Carbon Chemical Reaction Table* and 11.2, *Carbon Transport Table* for Step 2. Students should refer to the handouts and complete them as they work through the reading. They should see that each reaction is represented in its setting in the reading (terrestrial, atmospheric, oceanic).

In Step 3, review with the class any specific instructions about reading strategies that you wish to use.

Use the *Stop and Think* questions to break up the reading and do the second demonstration. Guide students to see that the color change of different volumes of the container represents the actual movement of CO_2 into the fluid column. They should also be able to explain that this relates back to an increase in carbonic acid from CO_2 dissolution

Answers to Stop and Think are on TE page 566.

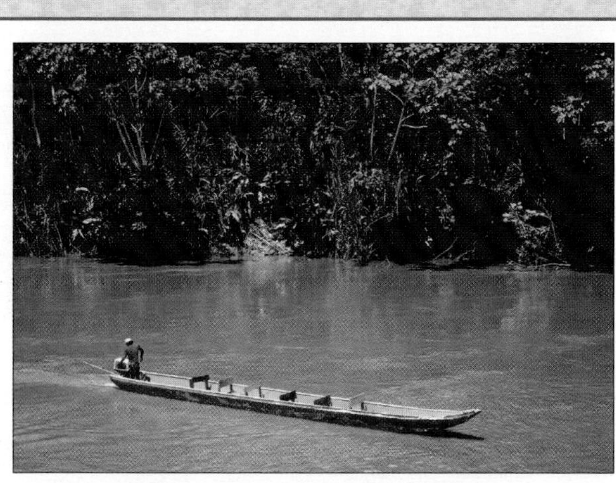

Figure 11.9 River transport. This lowland river has dark water, in part due to the high content of dissolved organic carbon. Even though you cannot see it, the river also carries a lot of dissolved inorganic carbon.

Stop & THINK

Gather around the 1–2 new containers of water at the front of the class. Listen to directions from your teacher for what to do to the containers.

1. Record the following in your science notebook.
   a. What are the components of the setup? You should be answering questions such as, "What do you see?" "How big are the containers?"
   b. Make a sketch with labels of one of the containers. Review what the BTB indicator detects and what it is evidence of.
   c. Watch carefully what happens as your teacher starts the experiment. Write your observations in your notebook.
2. Answer Questions 2a–b about the role of carbon in the experiment.
   a. What compounds of carbon would you predict in the experiment?
   b. What does the experiment tell you about the movement of carbon? In what types of settings on Earth might such movement of carbon occur?
3. Use a reading strategy for your team to continue the reading.

NOTES:

into the water. Check that students have developed accurate sketches of the setup.

Answers to Stop and Think, SE page 565

1a. Students should note characteristics such as container size, drops of pH indicator, type and purpose of indicator, dry ice predictions, and aluminum boat.

1b. Check that students make a sketch with appropriate labels for the experimental setup.

1c. Check that students record comments made during class discussions. It is easy to comment on an investigation but forget to record observations. Students will have to look closely to see the change in color in the different volumes of water.

2a. Students should predict carbon that begins as CO_2. They should be able to describe dissolution into the water and conversion to bicarbonate, HCO_3^{1-}.

2b. The experiment shows the transfer of carbon into water and then the vertical movement of carbon in a water column. This is analogous to processes that occur in all natural waters, including lakes, rivers, or the ocean. The model is particularly good for representing mixing processes in the ocean.

Carbon Transport across the Globe, continued

Oceanic Carbon

Envision carbon moving in terrestrial settings. These settings have a lot of vegetation, and we are familiar with these environments. The transport occurs by processes such as respiration, making forest litter, and carrying DIC and DOC in rivers. Blowing trees, flags, or kites are evidence of CO_2 in the atmosphere being mixed up. But what about the ocean? Is there much carbon that moves around the ocean? What forms would this carbon take?

Indeed, the ocean transports massive amounts of carbon around the globe. In fact, the ocean is the largest reservoir of "active," or mobile carbon on Earth. When ocean waters mix, a massive flux of carbon results. You have used the word "flux" for the mass of matter that is moved in a given amount of time.

You learned that the ocean covers about 70 percent of Earth, making it the largest reservoir of water. The ocean ranges from vast, shallow banks teeming with life, to deep, cold, dark trenches over 11 km deep. These waters are deeper than Mount Everest, the tallest mountain on Earth. How could you visualize the transport and mixing of carbon from shallow ocean waters to deep ocean waters? Actually, you've already done a simulation of this process.

Think back to the tall bottle in the *Stop and Think* demonstration. Your teacher forced CO_2 into water. The BTB indicator recorded changes in acidity, which were a response to adding CO_2 to the water. Depending on the setup, you might have even seen yellow volumes, or patches, of relatively carbon-rich water moving to the bottom of the container. Did you also see blue cells of water moving to the surface? This also happens in the ocean. Upwelling and downwelling transport vast amounts of carbon.

But what chemical forms does carbon take in the ocean? You know this as well. In the ocean, it is just DIC and DOC from rivers, or CO_2 that dissolves in the ocean from the atmosphere.

DOC enters the ocean from rivers. (Recall that DOC comes from the leaching of soils and vegetation.) In the ocean, DOC is eaten by microorganisms and converted to CO_2. This CO_2 can either escape to the atmosphere, be used for photosynthesis, or be converted to HCO_3^{1-}. The latter, the bicarbonate ion, is inorganic carbon (DIC). Another source of DIC into the ocean comes from rivers due to rock weathering. Inorganic carbon is then available to marine animals to make their shells.

So several processes add carbon to the ocean—DIC and DOC from rivers, and CO_2 from the atmosphere. You saw that CO_2 solubility was higher in cold water than in warm water. Cold waters in polar regions (the Arctic and the Antarctic) are much better at absorbing CO_2 from the atmosphere than are warm waters at the equator. Remember the simple experiment you did with several bottles of seltzer water? The CO_2 was more soluble in cold water than in warm water.

How else is carbon transported in the ocean? Another way is by marine animals. These animals consist largely of carbon, and they range in mass from phytoplankton to whales (figure 11.10). **Phytoplankton** are microorganisms at the ocean's surface that use dissolved CO_2 in photosynthesis. Phytoplankton are primary **producers**. They are the foundation of the marine food web, just as plants are the primary producers on land.

Many marine organisms also build houses or shells out of calcium carbonate, $CaCO_3$. At some point, these organisms are either eaten, which moves their carbon up the food chains, or they die. When they die, their carbon sinks to the bottom of the ocean.

566 Unit 3 Moving Matter

Answers to Reflect and Connect, SE pages 567–568

1a. Student teams should be able to fill in the table with the reactant and product from each carbon chemical reaction. These are shown on each side of the chemical equilibrium.

1b. Students should turn in their science notebooks to each prior station. They should add the name of the process that matches their activities and observations at each station.

2a. Check that students are working with these 2 tables as they complete the readings. Both are important tools for constructing the carbon cycle later in the chapter.

2b. Check that students can distinguish between the process where the carbon is part of a reaction and processes that only move or transport carbon.

3a. The second experiment simulated mixing in the ocean.

3b. The first experiment simulated DOC and DIC components of carbon in rivers.

4. Be open to all ideas at this point, as students might not have much knowledge of ocean ecology or trophic levels. In general, the surface waters of the ocean are teeming with microscopic, photosynthesizing organisms called *phytoplankton*. Phytoplankton are primary producers in the ocean (autotrophs) because they convert solar radiation into tissues. Food chains for all animals at higher trophic levels rely on the photosynthesis of phytoplankton. Other photosynthesizing marine organisms include algae and parts of the organisms that make coral.

Other organisms also take carbon from water, but not through photosynthesis. Examples are any organisms that construct a shell or support structure of calcium carbonate, $CaCO_3$. This includes any snails, clams (bivalves), echinoderms, and foraminifera.

5. The activity title *Carbon Changing Costumes* refers to carbon changing its chemical substance or kinds of material as it moves through the carbon cycle. An example would be changes from CO_2 to carbon in chains in plant matter.

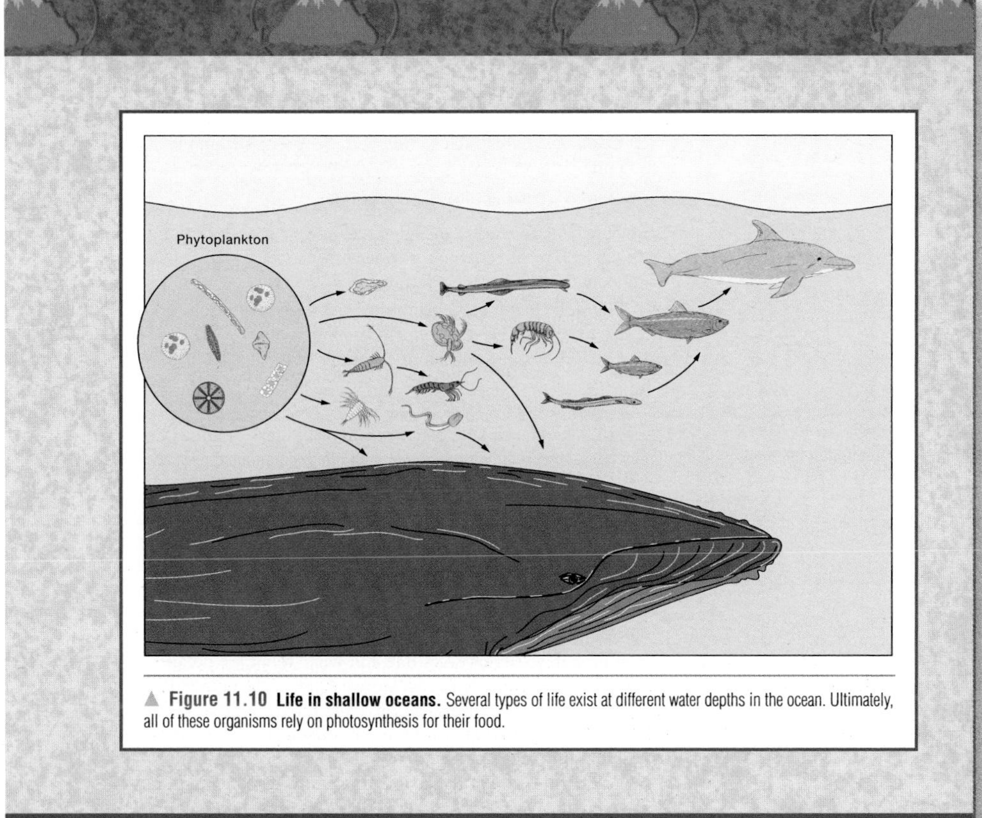

▲ **Figure 11.10 Life in shallow oceans.** Several types of life exist at different water depths in the ocean. Ultimately, all of these organisms rely on photosynthesis for their food.

Reflect and Connect

After completing the reading with your team, discuss and answer the following questions. Your team should prepare to share its ideas with the class.

1. Review the handout *Carbon Chemical Reaction Table*. Review the reactions with carbon.
   a. Fill in the blank columns to the right with examples of carbon-bearing reactants and products.

Review your carbon environs diagram to see whether the reactions occur in the ocean, the atmosphere, or terrestrial settings.

EXPLORE

Fossil Carbon

Activity Overview

So far, students have only considered "natural" parts of the carbon cycle—the reactions and transport of carbon among terrestrial, atmospheric, and oceanic settings independent of humans. But how do humans affect the carbon cycle? Can scientists measure an impact from humans on the carbon cycle?

The effects are rather clear in Part I. First, students will use a candle to model the hydrocarbon combustion of any fossil fuel. This shows that the combustion of hydrocarbons generates carbon dioxide (CO_2). Such reactions are a key to the energy that we rely on every day. Second, students will investigate and analyze the record of humans adding CO_2 to the atmosphere with two geologic records of atmospheric CO_2 concentrations over the past 2,000 years. These data are from Mauna Loa, Hawaii, and Law Dome, Antarctica.

In Part II, students work as teams to construct their understanding of the carbon cycle. Their "maps" or large diagrams of the carbon cycle, *which they create*, will represent the 10 carbon reactions and 5 transport processes from the chapter. Student depictions may differ, but they will need to check for consistency between the setting and whether the reactions and transport processes link in a reasonable way. The sticky notes allow students to shift and adjust the location to where they represent parts of the carbon cycle.

You will note that the student book does not have a figure that represents the carbon cycle. This is because the diagrams that students will construct themselves should be as good or better than typical diagrams of the carbon cycle in other programs.

Before You Teach

Background Information

Much of the pertinent background for this activity is in the answers to the students' investigations. Chapter 11 shows that the use of fossil fuels by humans has been increasing the concentration of CO_2 in the atmosphere. This is important because CO_2 is a greenhouse gas that insulates Earth, leading to an increase in the temperature of the atmosphere and the ocean. Strong evidence shows a correlation between CO_2 concentration and atmospheric warming, currently as well as in the geologic record. The main scientific question is trying to determine the degree to which this temperature increase is caused by humans and how it will affect humans and ecosystems in the future.

Part I of the activity is called *Carboniferous Combustion*. Significant reserves of coal on the eastern half of North America developed in the Carboniferous period, about 290–340 million years ago. Note, however, that many other substantial reserves of coal, petroleum, and natural gas on the western half of the continent or fringing the Gulf of Mexico (including Texas and Oklahoma) were deposited much more recently. Many of these deposits range in age from about 25–100 million years old.

The key point of Part I is for students to simulate the transport of carbon by the combustion of fossil fuels to CO_2. This is analogous to generating energy for society with hydrocarbons. Students may have

Answers to Reflect and Connect are on TE page 567.

b. Go back in your notes to the stations in *Carbon Changing Costumes*. Label each station with the process from the table.

It may help to use a different-colored pen or pencil.

2. Review with your team the handout *Carbon Transport Table*. Review how carbon is transported between terrestrial, atmospheric, and oceanic settings.
   a. Fill in the blank columns to the right with the settings or environments between which carbon is transported.
   b. Go back in your notes to the stations in *Carbon Changing Costumes*. Label each station with a carbon transport process from the table.
3. Recall the water mixing demonstrations at the beginning of this activity. Discuss as a group and write in your science notebook how the mixing experiments can help you remember the chemical forms of DIC and DOC in carbon cycling.
   a. Which experiment models the transport and mixing of carbon in the ocean? Explain why.
   b. Which experiment models carbon in rivers? What is the evidence?
4. Trees and vegetation store carbon in terrestrial environments. You probably see this every day. But what about the ocean? What organisms do you think store carbon in the ocean? For example, what organisms can carry out photosynthesis beneath the ocean's surface? Figure 11.10 provides a clue. Does much carbon reside there?
5. What does the title of the activity *Carbon Changing Costumes* mean to you?

EXPLORE

Fossil Carbon

You have explored carbon transport around the globe that is independent of human actions. But how do we fit into the picture? Humans rely on carbon in many ways. It is a key part of our bodies, our environment, and our economy. In this manner, we are also a part of carbon pathways around Earth.

Do humans affect carbon movement around Earth? The answer is pretty simple. We do. Every time we turn on a light, use the grill, or drive our cars, we are converting carbon from one form to another. In Part I of *Fossil Carbon*, you and your team will investigate how human needs for energy have become part of carbon cycling. Then in Part II, you will use your learning to construct a model of the carbon cycle.

HOW TO some difficulty at first balancing combustion equations. Feel free to review with them the background provided in the *How To* section for balancing chemical reactions.

For hydrocarbons, a simple three-step process will help you. First, equate the number of carbon atoms in CO_2 on the right (product) with the hydrocarbon on the left (reactant). Second, equate exponents for hydrogen in water on the right with the hydrocarbon on the left. Third, sum the oxygen atoms in CO_2 and H_2O on the right. Divide these by two, and then place the result as the molar coefficient for oxygen needed in the combustion. A general formula for the complete combustion in oxygen of hydrocarbons, $C_nH_{(2n+2)}$, is

$$C_nH_{2n+2} + \left(\frac{3n+1}{2}\right) O_2 \longrightarrow nCO_2 + (n+1)H_2O + \text{energy}.$$

You can use this as a check, but students should balance the reactants and products, not just plug into a formula like this. This equation also shows that the molar ratio of CO_2 to H_2O for complete combustion in oxygen is $(^{n}/_{n+1})$. Indeed, recent scientific work shows that as humans generate CO_2 by using fossil fuels, the levels of O_2 are also decreasing proportionally.

Students might not be convinced that a candle represents the family of hydrocarbons, the stuff that they add as gasoline to car tanks. Depending on your time, you can set up a density station with water, oil, or isopropyl alcohol to investigate this. Students will see that paraffin is less dense than water and perhaps also compare it with other liquids like isopropyl alcohol or vegetable oil. Density tends to reflect the atomic weight of elements, so hydrocarbons generally are less dense than water (hydrogen and oxygen).

The *Stop and Think* questions have students analyze several key records of the change in atmospheric CO_2 concentration. The monthly measurements from Mauna Loa are particularly sensitive, showing annual cycles of CO_2 concentration in the atmosphere. The pattern shows increasing CO_2 levels until about April or May each year, when the onset of photosynthesis in the Northern Hemisphere begins to remove CO_2 from the atmosphere. Concentrations of CO_2 decrease, or are drawn down, as photosynthesis occurs in the Northern Hemisphere. The drawdown of CO_2 concentrations stops in the fall as photosynthesis stops for the fall and winter. The increase after the fall shows the CO_2 production by decomposition of organic matter by bacteria in soils.

The main point is that the Mauna Loa CO_2 curve shows 2 important features. The first is the steady average increase in atmospheric CO_2 concentration. The second is the annual effect of photosynthesis during spring and summer in the Northern Hemisphere. This results in a clear, annual drawdown of atmospheric CO_2. Another inference is that CO_2 appears able to mix quite rapidly on a global scale over a time period of weeks to a month. The evidence is the correlation between the drawdown of atmospheric CO_2 and what we see in the generally rapid growth of vegetation in the Northern Hemisphere with the onset of spring each year.

Atmospheric concentrations of CO_2 can also be derived for longer periods of time from glaciers and ice sheets. Students examine a record of atmospheric concentrations of CO_2 from air bubbles trapped in ice. The record extends nearly 2,000 years and gives, in the form of little bubbles, samples of the atmosphere. This record shows that

Part I: Carboniferous Combustion

Materials

For each team of 3 students

1 metal spoon

paper towels

1 ice cube

1 ruler

1 candle

matches

1 *Atmospheric CO_2 Records* handout

Process and Procedure

Gather with your team to complete the following steps. Keep in mind how the investigation relates to fossil fuels as a source of energy.

1. Place a metal spoon on a paper towel, and put a cube of ice on the metal spoon. Over 5–10 min, the ice should conform to the shape of the spoon. The spoon will get very cold.
2. Use a reading strategy with your team for the following paragraph on fossil fuels and hydrocarbons.

   Fossil fuels include many carbon-bearing substances. Humans rely on these substances every day for transportation, electricity, and warmth in our homes. We call them **fossil fuels**, or **hydrocarbons**, for a simple reason. Fossil fuels consist of hydrogen and carbon compounds from geologic deposits of organic carbon. Of course, these hydrocarbons began as organic molecules that were cellulose, wood, bark, or starches in plants, or were even animal remains. Fossil fuels formed many millions of years ago. You have probably heard of fossil fuels such as coal, petroleum, or natural gas. Combusting these fuels provides valuable energy for society. As such, this combustion is an exothermic reaction.
3. Complete these steps to investigate a burning candle. A burning candle is a simple example of combusting hydrocarbons.
   a. Candles may consist of several kinds of wax, or paraffin. A general formula for wax is $C_nH_{(2n+2)}$, where n can vary from about 20 to 30. Write the formula for paraffin with a value of $n = 20$.
   b. Make a T-table showing values of n from 20 to 25 and the corresponding formula for paraffin.
   c. Is a burning candle a source of energy? Explain why.
4. How would you write a chemical reaction for the combustion of fossil fuels? Start with the chemical reaction for burning a candle (figure 11.11). Use these steps to determine the 2 reactants.

Figure 11.11 Burning candle. What are the reaction products of a burning candle?

Go to: www.scilinks.org
Topic: fossil fuels
Code: 2Inquiry569a
Topic: hydrocarbons
Code: 2Inquiry569b

a clear increase in atmospheric CO_2 begins about 1800, the beginning of industrialization in Europe. By the late 1800s, industrialization was well under way in North America as well, which correlates with the CO_2 curve.

Materials—Part I

For the entire class

glass container with glass cover (like a casserole dish)
glass pan without cover (open to atmosphere)
3–4 short, wide votive or tea candles
500 mL distilled water with BTB buffered with baking soda to light blue
matches
2 sheets of white paper

For each team of 3 students

1 metal spoon
paper towels
1 piece of ice
1 ruler
1 candle
matches
3 copies of copymaster 11.3, *Atmospheric CO_2 Records*

Materials—Part II

For each team of 3 students

15–20 sticky notes
1 pair of scissors
1 pencil and eraser
3 pieces of clear tape
1 sheet of 11×17 in paper (optional)
colored pencils (optional)
3 copies of copymaster 11.4, *Terrestrial, Atmospheric, and Oceanic Carbon Cycling*

Advance Preparation

Decide whether teams can do the experiment condensing water on the bottom of a cold, dry spoon. This is the best way to have them show that water is a reaction product of candle burning.

Make copies of copymasters 11.3, *Atmospheric CO_2 Records* and 11.4, *Terrestrial, Atmospheric, and Oceanic Carbon Cycling* for each student.

See figure T11.7 for the setup for the model of fossil fuel combustion. Decide whether you have enough glass containers for students to do this or whether students or you will lead a demonstration. If you do a demonstration, be sure to use effective questioning techniques to encourage students to make the connections necessary for the simulation. This is a great activity for them to actually do, but you can also run it very effectively with enthusiasm and effective questioning of students. You can ask questions such as, "What are you seeing?" "What forms are carbon?" and "How does this relate to carbon movement by humans?"

In Part II, teams may wish to use pieces of paper larger than the approximately 11×17 in pieces that are taped together from copymaster 11.4, *Terrestrial, Atmospheric, and Oceanic Carbon Cycling*. If so, obtain larger sheets of paper. Colored pencils are very nice for adding highlights to completed carbon cycles. This gives them more real estate to construct their understanding of the carbon cycle. Earlier parts of the chapter and the tables (copymasters 11.1, *Carbon Chemical Reaction Table* and 11.2, *Carbon Transport Table*) will help them do that.

Copy and view *Cycle of Carl Carbon Atom* (copymaster 11.5) for *Reflect and Connect* Question 3 in the elaborate activity.

Cautions

Use caution with the open flames on the candle. Do not allow the candle flames to get too close to the glass lid or cover on the container. Do not have open flames near any flammable items or fluids, such as the oils or isopropyl alcohol.

As You Teach

Outcomes and Indicators of Success

By the end of this activity, students should

1. understand more about important hydrocarbons such as petroleum, natural gas, and coal as sources of energy for society.

   They will demonstrate their understanding by

   - writing formulas for hydrocarbons of the $C_nH_{(2n+2)}$ family;
   - linking the paraffin or wax in candles with their sources of hydrocarbons;
   - performing experiments converting $C_{20}H_{42}$ to CO_2 and H_2O;
   - feeling the heat released from a burning candle;
   - balancing chemical equations for the combustion of hydrocarbons, such as natural gas (methane, ethane) and butane;
   - comparing exothermic and endothermic combustion reactions with carbon-containing compounds (paraffin, $CaCO_3$); and
   - balancing a chemical equation for the combustion of propane.

2. be able to interpret and analyze geologic records, such as those recorded for concentrations of atmospheric CO_2.

   They will demonstrate their ability by

   - interpreting the annual patterns in atmospheric CO_2 concentration from Mauna Loa,
   - relating patterns of photosynthesis in the Northern Hemisphere to the atmospheric record of CO_2 concentrations at Mauna Loa,
   - interpreting patterns in atmospheric CO_2 concentration indicating an increase over the last 2,000 years, and
   - comparing decadal with millennial records of carbon concentration in the atmosphere from records of atmosphere bubbles in ice sheets.

3. construct a diagram showing how carbon moves from terrestrial, to atmospheric, to oceanic settings.

They will demonstrate their ability by

- constructing a carbon cycle showing carbon reactions among terrestrial, oceanic, and atmospheric environs;
- constructing a carbon cycle including carbon transport among terrestrial, oceanic, and atmospheric environs; and
- constructing a carbon cycle showing relations among key reservoirs of carbon.

4. continue using and developing their quantitative skills.

   They will continue to use and develop their quantitative skills in

   - balancing chemical reactions,
   - reading graphs of atmospheric CO_2 concentration at several different scales,
   - linking graphs at different scales with boxes,
   - measuring slopes for rate of CO_2 increase at different periods of time,
   - projecting a growth pattern into the future, and
   - reading how to estimate the mass of CO_2 generated from the combustion of one tank of gasoline.

5. develop further skills in the abilities and understandings of scientific inquiry.

   They will demonstrate their skills by

   - completing an investigation linking combustion of fossil fuel analogies (candle) with increased CO_2 concentrations in the atmosphere,
   - investigating transport of carbon from paraffin to CO_2 to water,
   - using pH indicators to detect movement and dissolution of CO_2,
   - analyzing graphs of geologic records of CO_2 emissions,
   - constructing with sticky notes a viable cycle for carbon movement through the geosphere, and
   - communicating ideas and observations to classmates regarding investigations with candles and constructing carbon movement in the geosphere.

Strategies

Getting Started

This activity focuses on the burning of hydrocarbons. See what sources of hydrocarbons you have that could be ignited safely in front of the class, such as oils with safe wicks or butane lighters. The objective is to have students represent this as a chemical reaction. In addition, they need to relate the combustion to the generation of energy.

A good visual is a flame from a butane (C_4H_{10}) lighter. Write the reactants and products for combustion on the board. See how far students can get with inferring reactants and products. Let them write several possibilities on the board. Encourage all ideas. Students need to be able to do this by the end of the activity.

Write this on the board:

$$C_4H_{10} + \underline{?}O_2 \longrightarrow \underline{?}CO_2 + \underline{?}H_2O + \text{energy}$$

butane combustion

The mass-balanced reaction is as follows:

$$C_4H_{10} + \underline{\left(\frac{13}{2}\right)}O_2 \longrightarrow \underline{4}CO_2 + \underline{5}H_2O + \text{energy} \quad \text{or}$$

$$\underline{2}C_4H_{10} + \underline{13}O_2 \longrightarrow \underline{8}CO_2 + \underline{10}H_2O + \text{energy}$$

Cautions

Use caution with the open flames on the candle. Do not allow the candle flames to get too close to the glass lid or cover on the container. Do not have open flames near any flammable items or fluids, such as the oils or isopropyl alcohol.

Process and Procedure

Part I: Carboniferous Combustion

Materials

For the entire class

glass container (like a casserole dish) with glass cover
glass pan without cover (open to atmosphere)
3–4 short, wide votive or tea candles
500 mL distilled water with BTB buffered with baking soda to light blue
matches
2 sheets of white paper

For each team of 3 students

1 metal spoon
paper towels
1 piece of ice
1 ruler
1 candle
matches
3 copies of copymaster 11.3, *Atmospheric CO_2 Records*

In Step 1, students set up a spoon to chill. The spoon will be used as a source of condensation of water. Students then read a paragraph about hydrocarbons in Step 2. These are a key source of energy for society. They produce energy and heat, and are therefore an exothermic reaction.

Step 3 involves more specific thinking about hydrocarbons. A formula is shown for paraffin, $C_{20}H_{42}$, as well as a table for values from n = 20–25 (figure T11.6).

n	Hydrocarbon Formula ($C_nH_{(2n+2)}$)
20	$C_{20}H_{42}$
21	$C_{21}H_{44}$
22	$C_{22}H_{46}$
23	$C_{23}H_{48}$
24	$C_{24}H_{50}$
25	$C_{25}H_{52}$

Figure T11.6 Hydrocarbon T-table for n and $C_nH_{(2n+2)}$. Students should develop a T-table of formulas for paraffin like this one. The actual composition of paraffin can vary depending on the distillation process used.

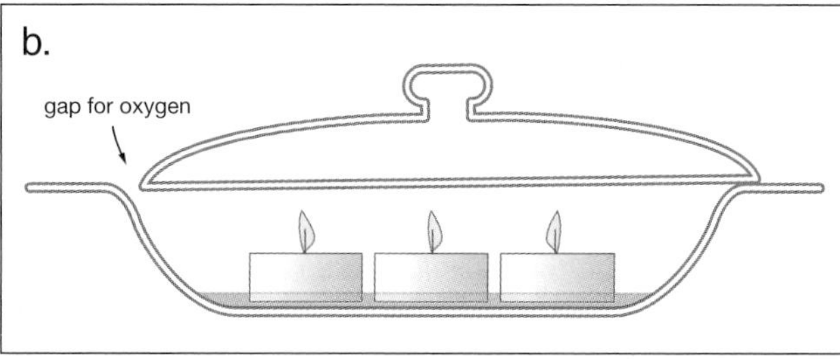

Figure T11.7 Candle in glass container with BTB water. (a) Photograph and (b) cross section diagram for a burning candle in a closed glass container. A glass plate without candles can serve as a control for the color of water with BTB. Place white paper beneath each to help detect subtle changes in water color.

In Step 4, students begin determining reactants and products for the combustion of paraffin. For a value of n = 20, one reactant is $C_{20}H_{42}$. The gas needed for combustion in the reaction is oxygen, O_2. If you need a visual prompt for students at this point, the reaction would look something like the following (they have not yet investigated reaction products):

$$C_{20}H_{42} + \underline{?}O_2 \longrightarrow \underline{\quad ? \quad}$$

Students work to figure out one of the reaction products in Step 5. It is not intuitive that one product is water, H_2O. Students demonstrate this in Step 5 by condensing water on the bottom of a metal spoon. The bottom of the spoon must be completely dry to see the water droplets forming. If the spoon is wet, the water condenses directly onto the water and it will be hard to tell that water is being generated from the reaction.

In Step 5d, be open to students' ideas for how to test whether the condensing liquid is water. The best answers include placing a drop in oil to test for solubility and polarity, which would be one line of evidence. Other tests would be measuring boiling or freezing point, viewing the frozen material to see if it looks like ice, smelling it, or measuring its density. Be open to other ideas, which might even include designing a still (which students did in Level 1 of this program). Elements of a still include a chamber with burning candles, an oxygen inlet, a cold finger, and a track or tube for the distilled water to run to a storage volume.

Students identify a second reaction product in Step 6 as carbon dioxide. The setup with a control pan of water is shown in figure T11.7. The CO_2 from the candle moves into the water, creating a very dilute carbonic acid. This is just enough to tip the pH balance to lower values. The lower values are indicated by changes in the color of the BTB solution. Use very shallow water (no more than 1 cm deep) and use distilled water with

Answers to Steps 8–9 are on TE pages 571–572.

a. Use paraffin with a value of n = 20 as 1 reactant.
b. What gas needs to be present for a combustion reaction? This is your second reactant.

5. Determine 1 of the reaction products using the cold spoon and a lit candle.
   a. Check that your metal spoon is very cold. The ice should be melted into the shape of the spoon.
   b. Draw away all the water around the ice with a paper towel. Completely dry the bottom of the spoon with a dry paper towel. The spoon should be very cold and completely dry on the bottom.

Your teacher may have dry ice to use on the spoon. This will make the spoon much colder than ice, and it will not melt.

   c. Hold the cold, dry spoon about 1 cm above the tip of the candle flame. What do you see happening on the bottom of the spoon?
   d. What is the substance on the bottom of the spoon? How could you test what the substance is? Describe a test in your science notebook for that substance. Show it to your teacher—if it's a good test, you may be allowed to try it.
6. Candle combustion has a second reaction product. Follow these steps and your teacher's directions to determine this product.
   a. Get from your teacher water with BTB indicator that is sky blue. Add this to a depth of 0.5 cm in each of 2 flat glass dishes. Place each on a white sheet of paper.
   b. Place 3 or 4 very short (or cut) candles in the water. Light them.
   c. Place a glass lid on top of 1 of the containers, but do not let the candles extinguish. As the candle flames dim, slide the lid sideways to let in more oxygen.
   d. What do you observe happening to the color of the water in the 2 containers?
   e. What molecule could be causing this effect? Explain several lines of evidence.

7. Write a third reaction product of combusting fossil fuel. This is the whole reason that we use fossil fuels.
8. Write the complete chemical reaction for candle combustion in these steps. Use a candle formula of $C_{20}H_{42}$.
   a. Make a T-table with reactants in the left column and products in the right. Label the columns.
   b. Reconfigure reactants and products around an arrow, as in a chemical reaction.
   c. Work with your team to balance the equation.

BTB buffered to a teal or light blue color with flecks of baking soda. The color change may be subtle, so set up a control with the same solution on a sheet of white paper next to the covered container (see figure T11.7). If the water is too deep, the mass of CO_2 from the candle may be insufficient to note a change of acidity by the BTB. Similarly, the BTB reaction may be slow if the volume of the container is too large (students can use a few more candles).

You might ask students how they could test whether just the candles in the BTB solution were making the color change, and not the CO_2 dissolution. They could test this by placing some unlit candles in solution and compare them with a control with no candles. In Step 7, students shouldn't forget that the third product is energy.

Answers to Steps 8 and 9, SE pages 570–571

8a. The T-table of reactants and products should look like figure T11.8.

8b. Students' reconfigured reactants should look like the following chemical reaction:

$$C_{20}H_{42} + ?O_2 \longrightarrow ?CO_2 + ?H_2O + \text{energy}$$

8c. There are a few ways to balance the equation. The hint indicates the best way to balance the equation: start by equating the number of carbons on the left with the number on the right. Then move to balance the hydrogen. Finally, equate the oxygen. Either of the following equations is correct, depending on whether a team multiplies through by a factor of two.

$$C_{20}H_{42} + \frac{61}{2}O_2 \longrightarrow 20CO_2 + 21H_2O + \text{energy} \quad \text{or}$$

$$2C_{20}H_{42} + 61O_2 \longrightarrow 40CO_2 + 42H_2O + \text{energy}$$

Answers to Stop and Think—Part I are on TE pages 572–575.

To balance the equation, start by equating the number of carbons on the left with the number on the right. Then balance the hydrogen. Balance the oxygen last.

d. Return to the *Carbon Chemical Reaction Table* from the explain activity, *The Carbonated Geosphere*. Add the reaction from Step 8c to line 10 on the handout. Write in the process "fossil fuel combustion."

9. Complete the following 2 sentences in your science notebook.

a. "Two settings or locations where hydrocarbons are combusted to make energy are __________ and __________."

b. "This experiment simulates the movement of carbon from __________ to the __________ to the __________."

Stop & THINK

PART I

After completing the reading in Step 2 with your team, discuss and answer the following questions.

1. Fossil shells have carbon in calcium carbonate, $CaCO_3$. Could you combust shells, a source of fossil carbon, to use as fuel? Use evidence from this chapter in your answer.

It may help you to use the terms endothermic and exothermic.

2. Propane (C_3H_8) is a hydrocarbon used for energy. Balance the following reaction for combusting propane.

$$C_3H_8 + ?O_2 \longrightarrow ?CO_2 + ?H_2O + \text{energy}$$

3. Natural gas is an important source of energy. It is close to a mixture of about 50 percent methane (CH_4) and 50 percent ethane (C_2H_6). Balance the following reaction for combusting natural gas.

$$CH_4 + C_2H_6 + ?O_2 \longrightarrow ?CO_2 + ?H_2O + \text{energy}$$

4. Figure 11.12 shows concentrations of CO_2 in the atmosphere measured each month in Hawaii from 1958 to 2002. Tick marks on the year axis represent January 1.

a. Draw a best-fit line through the center of the squiggle pattern. What is the slope of the line you drew? Be sure to include units on the slope.

Recall that slope is change in y (Δy) divided by change in x (Δx). You may also know this as "rise over run."

8d. Make sure that students return to copymaster 11.1, *Carbon Chemical Reaction Table* to write in the reaction from Step 8c and the process "fossil fuel combustion." This will help them construct the carbon cycle in Part II of this activity.

9a. There are many possible settings or locations where hydrocarbons or fossil fuels are combusted. These could include barbeque grills, coal-burning power plants, automobiles, diesel engines, ships, or gas-powered lawn mowers.

9b. "This experiment simulates the movement of carbon from hydrocarbons or fossil fuels to the atmosphere to the ocean."

Seeing this pathway is important in several regards. First, the students will need to make these links as they construct their own carbon cycle. Second, climate scientists and ecologists note that both vegetation and the ocean

Reactants	Products
$C_{20}H_{42}$	CO_2
O_2 (oxygen)	H_2O
	energy

▲ **Figure T11.8 Reactants-products T-table for candle combustion.** Students should develop a table of reactants and products for combustion of paraffin that looks like this.

remove approximately comparable masses of carbon from the atmosphere. Still, the ocean and vegetation appear to be removing carbon at only about one-half the rate at which fossil fuels are adding CO_2 to the atmosphere. Thus, the concentration of CO_2 in the atmosphere keeps increasing. This is also shown in the following *Stop and Think* questions.

Answers to Stop and Think—Part I, SE pages 571–574

1. No, combusting shells for fuel would not work well. The decomposition reaction for $CaCO_3$ required an input of energy (endothermic) to proceed. For something to be a fuel source, it must give off energy (exothermic).
2. The following reaction is balanced for propane combustion:

$$C_3H_8 + \underline{5}O_2 \longrightarrow \underline{3}CO_2 + \underline{4}H_2O + \text{energy}$$

3. The following reaction is balanced for combusting natural gas:

$$CH_4 + C_2H_6 + \underline{\left(\frac{11}{2}\right)}O_2 \longrightarrow \underline{3}CO_2 + \underline{5}H_2O + \text{energy}$$

The (11/2) is due to the 6 oxygen in the CO_2 and the 5 oxygen in the H_2O. The (11/2) in front of the O_2 gives 11 oxygen atoms total. If the coefficient in front of the O_2 was just 11, this would be 22 oxygen, twice the total on the right-hand side.

4a. Students should be able to show that the slope is an increase of about 1.34 parts per million (ppm) of CO_2 per year. The value will vary depending on where they position their line, but the slope should be around 1.3 ppm per year. One example is

$$\frac{\Delta y}{\Delta x} = \frac{(371 - 315)\ \text{ppm}}{(2001 - 1958)\ \text{yrs}} = \frac{56\ \text{ppm } CO_2}{43\ \text{yrs}} = 1.3\frac{\text{ppm } CO_2}{\text{yr}}$$

NOTES:

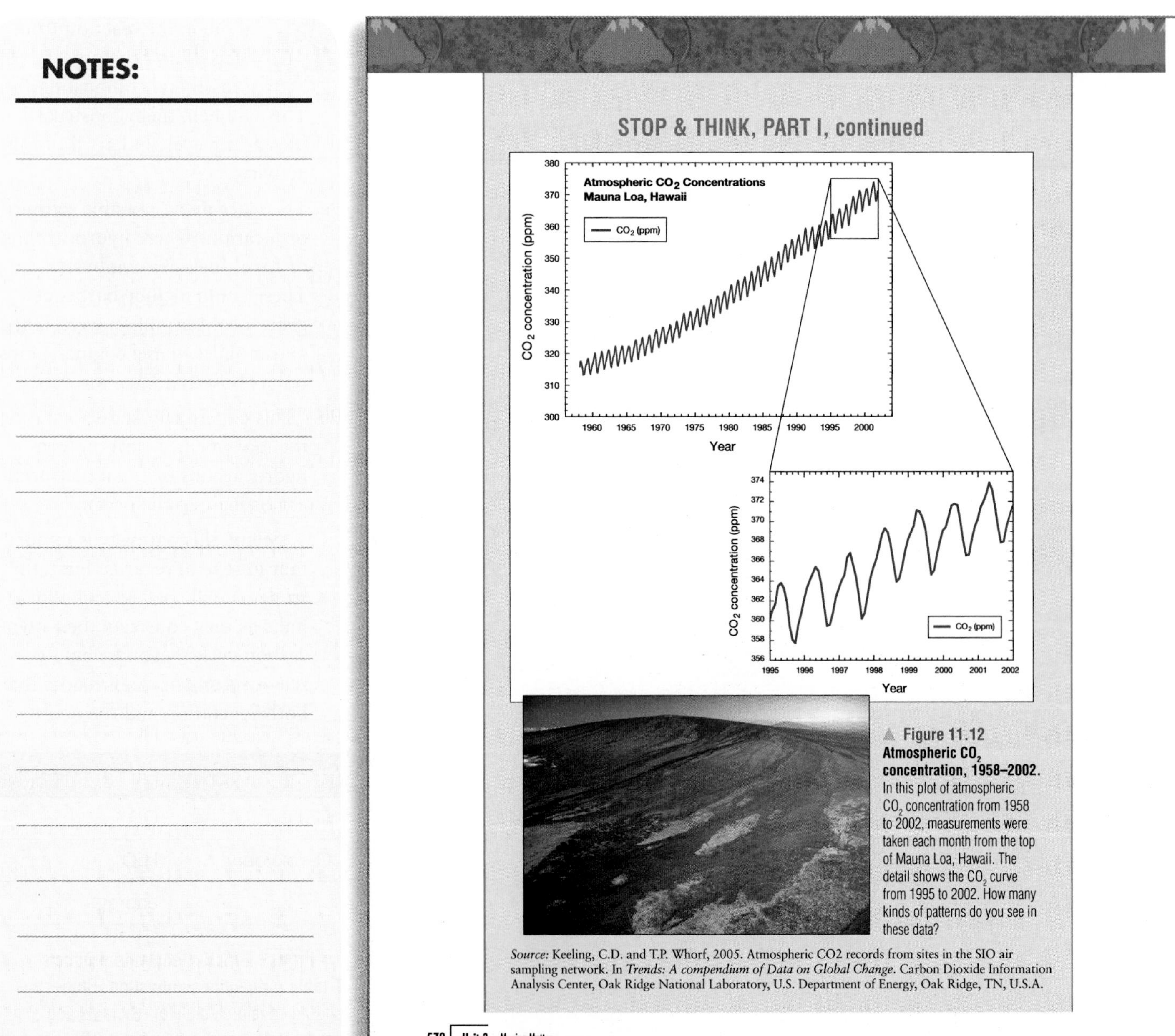

Figure 11.12 Atmospheric CO_2 concentration, 1958–2002. In this plot of atmospheric CO_2 concentration from 1958 to 2002, measurements were taken each month from the top of Mauna Loa, Hawaii. The detail shows the CO_2 curve from 1995 to 2002. How many kinds of patterns do you see in these data?

Source: Keeling, C.D. and T.P. Whorf, 2005. Atmospheric CO2 records from sites in the SIO air sampling network. In *Trends: A compendium of Data on Global Change*. Carbon Dioxide Information Analysis Center, Oak Ridge National Laboratory, U.S. Department of Energy, Oak Ridge, TN, U.S.A.

4b. On the annual basis, the detail of figure 11.12 in the student book shows that CO_2 increases from mid-September through early May. The increase is about 7.5 ppm CO_2.

4c. The concentration of CO_2 decreases from early May through mid-September. The decrease is about 6 ppm CO_2. Note that the difference between 7.5 and 6 is about 1.5, or similar to the overall slope of the curve.

4d. The concentration of CO_2 is the highest in early May.

4e. Photosynthesis accelerates each year in early May across the Northern Hemisphere. This removes CO_2 from the atmosphere. Photosynthesis continues removing CO_2 each year until around mid-September, when plants begin to go dormant for the winter. The concentrations start to rise until photosynthesis kicks in again the following May.

Looking at a global map, there are relatively few really large forested areas at high, southern latitudes. Equatorial jungles (Amazon and Congo river basins, Indonesia, southern Asia) have large biomass, but less of a seasonal photosynthesis signal compared with high-latitude northern forests that turn on and off relatively abruptly each year.

4f. Photosynthesis explains the annual pattern.

NOTES:

b. What months of the year does CO_2 increase in concentration? How much does CO_2 concentration typically increase?

c. What months of the year does CO_2 decrease in concentration? How much does CO_2 concentration typically decrease?

d. What month in each year is CO_2 the highest?

e. Think about the month you identified in Step 4d. What happens each year during that month that would affect the concentration of CO_2 in the atmosphere?

Not counting equatorial forests, the Northern Hemisphere has much more vegetation than the Southern Hemisphere.

f. What process in plants can explain the annual pattern in figure 11.12?

5 Figure 11.13 shows a record of CO_2 concentrations in the atmosphere over the past 1,000 years. The CO_2 is recovered from air bubbles in ice cores from Antarctica (see figure 11.14). The ice cores were recovered at a location called Law Dome.

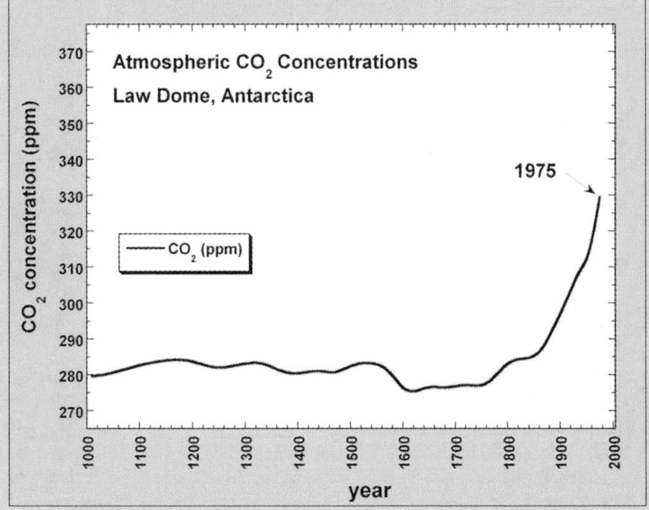

Source: Etheridge, et.al., 1998. Historical CO2 records from the Law Dome DE08, DE08-2, and DSS ice cores. In *Trends: A compendium of Data on Global Change*. Carbon Dioxide Information Analysis Center, Oak Ridge National Laboratory, U.S. Department of Energy, Oak Ridge, TN, U.S.A.

▲ **Figure 11.13 Atmospheric CO_2 concentrations, 1000–1975.** These data were measured from air bubbles preserved in a glacier at Law Dome, Antarctica. What overall pattern do you note here?

▶ **Figure T11.9 Law Dome CO_2 plus Mauna Loa box.** This diagram shows student answers for Steps 5e and 5f. The box shows the limits and position of the more detailed Mauna Loa data from 1958–2002. The *X* indicates the estimated current position, as requested in Step 5f.

Source: Law Dome: D.M. Etheridge, L.P. Steele, R.L. Langenfelds, R.J. Francey, J.M. Barnola and V.I. Morgan. 1998. Historical CO_2 records from the Law Dome DE08, DE08-2, and DSS ice cores. In *Trends: A Compendium of Data on Global Change*. Carbon Dioxide Information Analysis Center, Oak Ridge National Laboratory, U.S. Department of Energy, Oak Ridge, Tenn., U.S.A. // Mauna Loa: Keeling, C.D. and T.P. Whorf, 2005. Atmospheric CO_2 records from sites in the SIO air sampling network. In *Trends: A Compendium of Data on Global Change*. Carbon Dioxide Information Analysis Center, Oak Ridge National Laboratory, U.S. Department of Energy, Oak Ridge, Tenn., U.S.A.

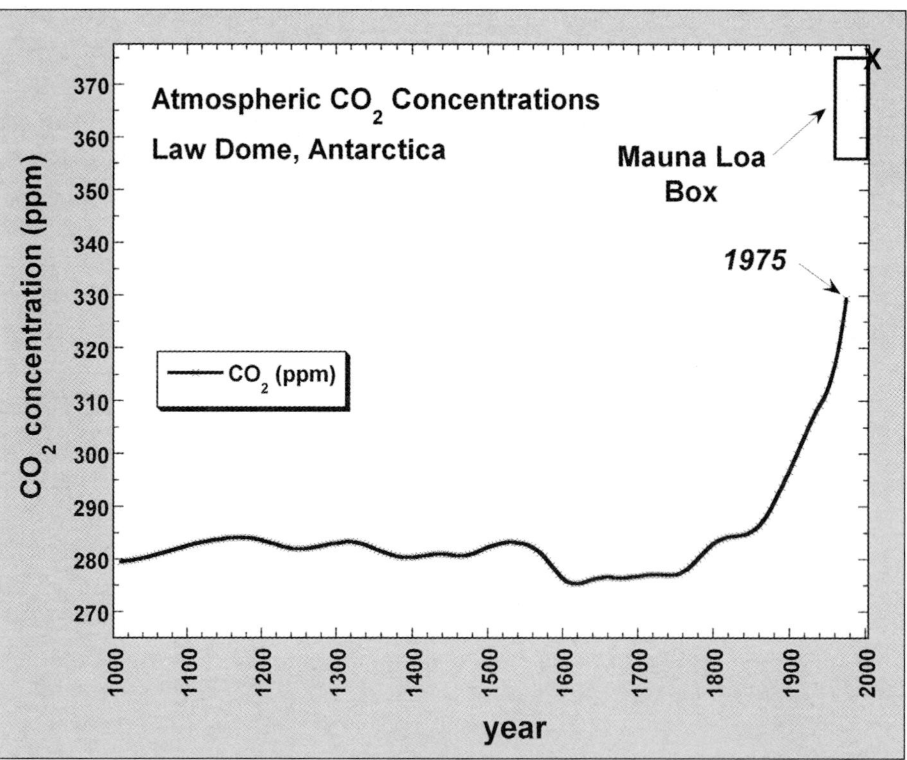

5a. The pattern of CO_2 concentration in the atmosphere from 1000 to 1750 is relatively stable, at about 280 ppm of CO_2.

5b. At about 1750, the CO_2 concentration started increasing, growing about 280 ppm CO_2.

5c. The increase in slope is from about 296 ppm in 1900 to 330 ppm in 1975. This is an increase of about 34 ppm in 75 years, or a slope of about 0.45 ppm CO_2 per year. This is about one-third the current rate of about 1.3 ppm per year from Step 4a.

5d. Much more industry started about the late 1700s in Europe. Coal and trains to transport coal to industrial areas were used more widely in England at that time, particularly after the recognition of geologic stratigraphy and geologic maps by William Smith. Increased growth in CO_2 from the late 1800s probably indicates further industrial development across Europe and North America. Interestingly, a brief respite in the rate of growth correlates with the beginning of World War II, with the growth rate picking up again in the mid-1950s.

5e. See figure T11.9.

STOP & THINK, PART I, continued

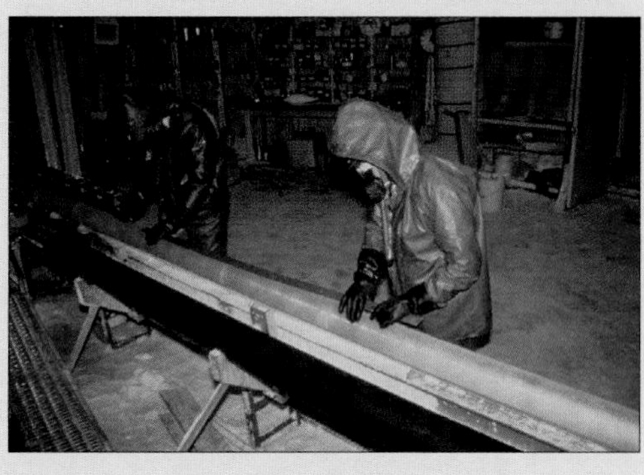

▶ **Figure 11.14 Working with an ice core sample.** Small bubbles in this ice core preserve a record of past CO_2 contents in the atmosphere.

a. Describe the pattern of CO_2 concentration in the atmosphere from 1000 to 1750.
b. Compare the pattern from Step 5a with the pattern from 1750 to 2000.
c. Estimate the slope of the line from about 1900 to 1975. How does this compare with the slope you estimated from Step 4a?
d. Discuss with your team some possible explanations for this change. Write those reasons in your science notebook.
e. Refer back to the data from Mauna Loa in figure 11.12. On your handout, neatly draw a box showing the limits of figure 11.12 from 1958 to 2002.
f. Write an X on the graph for Law Dome to show CO_2 concentrations in 2002.
g. What does this tell you about changes in CO_2 concentrations in the atmosphere?

6 Use FYI—*Fill 'er Up!—What's in Your Tank?* to answer the following questions about CO_2. Assume complete combustion of octane (C_8H_{18}).

a. A typical gas tank is 15 gallons (gal). How much CO_2 does that produce for the atmosphere?
b. On average, each person in the United States uses 461 gallons of gasoline per year. How many kilograms (kg) of CO_2 does this add to the atmosphere?
c. The United States has a population of about 290 million people. Estimate how many kilograms of CO_2 the United States adds to the atmosphere each year.

5f. See figure T11.9. The concentration appears to be increasing at a faster rate.

5g. The rate of increase seems to be greater, which was also inferred from Step 5c.

6a. A 15-gallon (gal) tank gives off roughly 271 pounds (lb) of CO_2. Cars and trucks with larger tanks and lower fuel efficiency give off much more CO_2 per tank. This is easy to estimate for given mileages and fuel efficiencies in miles per gallon.

$$(15\ \cancel{gal}) \times \left(\frac{8.2\text{ kg }CO_2}{1\ \cancel{gal}}\right) = 123\text{ kg }CO_2$$

$$(123\ \cancel{kg\ CO_2}) \times \left(\frac{2.2\text{ lb }CO_2}{1\ \cancel{kg\ CO_2}}\right) = 271\text{ lb }CO_2$$

6b. This is about 3,780 kg CO_2, or about 8,316 lb of CO_2 to the atmosphere per person. This is roughly 4 tons of CO_2 per person each year.

$$\left(\frac{8.2\text{ kg }CO_2}{1\ \cancel{gal}}\right) \times \left(\frac{461\ \cancel{gal}}{1\text{ yr}}\right) = \frac{3{,}780\text{ kg }CO_2}{\text{per person per yr}}$$

6c. Multiplying the result from Step 6b by the population gives us about 1 trillion kg of CO_2, or 1×10^{12} kg of CO_2, or about 2.2×10^{12} lb of CO_2. Remember that these numbers are for the complete combustion of octane. Actual gasoline is not pure octane, and combustion is not complete; it gives off other products. While the "other products" don't contribute to CO_2 increase, they are parts of smog.

$$\left(\frac{3{,}780\text{ kg }CO_2}{\text{per }\cancel{person}\text{ yr}}\right) \times 290 \times 10^6\ \cancel{persons} = 1 \times 10^{12}\,\frac{\text{kg }CO_2}{\text{yr}}$$

Fill 'er Up!—What's in Your Tank?

When were you last in a car or bus? Did you ride in one of those to school today? Did you use a car or bus to go shopping last weekend? You know that a transportation system won't work without a source of energy. That energy usually comes from a fossil fuel, particularly gasoline. Scientists are concerned that the amount of gasoline humans use might be affecting Earth's climate.

Gasoline is made by distilling and refining crude oil that is extracted from the ground. The final chemistry depends on the kind of crude oil, the refining process, and the additives. Still, most of gasoline is a hydrocarbon that can represented with $C_nH_{(2n+2)}$. While n for gasoline may vary from 7 to 11, a good example is octane, with $n = 8$. The formula for octane is C_8H_{18}.

What happens to gasoline after it is combusted in a car's engine? What are the reaction products, and how much of each is produced? Let's take a look by starting with 1 gal of octane that is fully combusted in a car's engine.

Topic: hydrocarbon
Go to: www.scilinks.org
Code: 2Inquiry575

Step 1 is to write a balanced reaction of octane plus oxygen to produce water, carbon dioxide, and energy. The following reaction shows that 1 mol of octane needs 12.5 mol of O_2 ($^{25}/_2$) to produce 8 mol of CO_2 and 9 mol of H_2O and energy:

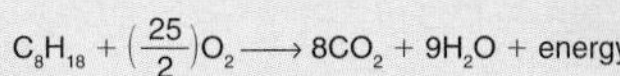

$$C_8H_{18} + \left(\frac{25}{2}\right)O_2 \longrightarrow 8CO_2 + 9H_2O + \text{energy}$$

Step 2 is to determine how many moles of octane are in 1 gallon. We will use the following conversion factors:

- 3.786 liters (L) = 1 gal
- density of octane = 702.5 grams per liter (g/L)
- gram atomic weight of octane = 114 grams per mole (g/mol)

$$\left(1\ \cancel{\text{gal octane}}\right) \times \left(\frac{3.786\ \cancel{\text{L oct}}}{1\ \cancel{\text{gal oct}}}\right) \times \left(\frac{702.5\ \cancel{\text{g oct}}}{1\ \cancel{\text{L oct}}}\right) = 2{,}659.7\text{ g octane}$$

$$\left(2{,}659.7\ \cancel{\text{g octane}}\right) \times \left(\frac{1\ \cancel{\text{mol oct}}}{114\ \cancel{\text{g oct}}}\right) = 23.3\text{ mol octane}$$

Step 3 is to calculate the moles of the reaction products and convert them to mass. We'll start with CO_2:

$$\left(23.3\ \cancel{\text{mol octane}}\right) \times \left(\frac{8\ \cancel{\text{mol }CO_2}}{1\ \cancel{\text{mol octane}}}\right) = 186.4\text{ mol }CO_2$$

$$\left(186.4\ \cancel{\text{mol }CO_2}\right) \times \left(\frac{44\ \cancel{\text{g }CO_2}}{1\ \cancel{\text{mol }CO_2}}\right) \times \left(\frac{1\ \cancel{\text{kg }CO_2}}{10^3\ \cancel{\text{g }CO_2}}\right) = 8.2\text{ kg }CO_2$$

So, 1 gal of octane gasoline produces about 8.2 kg of CO_2, or about 18 pounds (lb) of CO_2. Because about 27 percent of a CO_2 molecule is carbon, this is the same as adding about 5 lb of carbon to the atmosphere (18×0.27).

NOTES:

Chapter 11 Carbon on the Move 575

NOTES:

Process and Procedure

Part II: Showing the Carbon Cycle

Materials

For each team of 3 students

15–20 sticky notes
1 pair of scissors
1 pencil and eraser
3 pieces of clear tape
1 sheet of 11×17 in paper (optional)
colored pencils (optional)
3 copies of copymaster 11.4, *Terrestrial, Atmospheric, and Oceanic Carbon Cycling*

This is a very important activity where students work as teams to construct their understanding of the carbon cycle. The maps or large diagrams that they create of the carbon cycle need to represent the 10 carbon reactions and five transport processes from the chapter. Student depictions should differ, but teams will need to check for consistency between the setting and whether the reactions and transport processes link up in a reasonable way.

Some students will excel at using their creativity to show their understanding of the carbon cycle with this activity. Others may have more difficulty trying to represent and link reactions in a visual way. But this is a valuable skill to develop, and an important part of communicating ideas in any field of work or study. Encourage students to keep the diagrams simple.

Fill 'er Up!—What's in Your Tank?, continued

The same approach shows how much water is produced. Start with the octane:

$$\left(23.3\ \cancel{\text{mol octane}}\right) \times \left(\frac{9\ \cancel{\text{mol H}_2\text{O}}}{1\ \cancel{\text{mol octane}}}\right) \times \left(\frac{18\ \cancel{\text{g H}_2\text{O}}}{1\ \cancel{\text{mol H}_2\text{O}}}\right) \times \left(\frac{1\ \text{kg H}_2\text{O}}{10^3\ \cancel{\text{g H}_2\text{O}}}\right) = 3.78\ \text{kg H}_2\text{O}$$

The sum of the reaction products, water and carbon dioxide, is 11.99 kg (3.78 kg H_2O + 8.21 kg CO_2). But how do you get about 12 kg of reaction products from only 2.66 kg of octane? Does that make sense? Don't forget the other reactant—oxygen. Here's the mass of oxygen used in the combustion:

$$\left(23.3\ \cancel{\text{mol octane}}\right) \times \left(\frac{12.5\ \cancel{\text{mol O}_2}}{1\ \cancel{\text{mol octane}}}\right) \times \left(\frac{32\ \cancel{\text{g O}_2}}{1\ \cancel{\text{mol O}_2}}\right) \times \left(\frac{1\ \text{kg O}_2}{10^3\ \cancel{\text{g O}_2}}\right) = 9.33\ \text{kg O}_2$$

Now you see that the total mass of the reactants is also 11.99 kg (9.33 kg O_2 + 2.66 kg octane).

Pumping gas. Humans rely on petroleum products like gasoline as an inexpensive source of energy, especially for transportation. How many gallons of gas does a car tank hold?

This equals the mass of the products. Does this relationship between reactants and products sound familiar? It should—the law is the **conservation of mass**.

But real cars don't completely combust gasoline made of pure octane. Rather, their incomplete combustion makes smog, particularly in cities. That smog contains nitrogen oxides, the poisonous gas carbon monoxide (CO), and unburned hydrocarbons (soot).

Why should humans be concerned about adding CO_2 to the atmosphere? First, CO_2 in the atmosphere is a greenhouse gas. This means that it traps and retains heat from the Sun inside Earth's atmosphere. Many scientists are concerned that increasing global temperatures could affect the balance of animals in food webs in ecosystems. Climate change also is linked to sea level change, and perhaps to patterns of food production for humans.

Second, besides photosynthesis, CO_2 is also removed from the atmosphere by dissolving into the ocean. You have seen that adding CO_2 to water makes water more acidic. Many scientists are seeing evidence for the impact of increased acidity (decreasing pH) on the ability of marine organisms such as corals and clams to form shells and protective structures of calcium carbonate.

576 | Unit 3 Moving Matter

The goal is that student diagrams look something like figure T11.3. Check that students include or represent the 10 carbon reactions and 5 transport processes in figure T11.3. Student diagrams need not look exactly like this so long as they include reactions and transport processes in a linking manner. Rather than writing the equations on a diagram, however, students will move around sticky notes with the equations written on them.

In Step 1, students tape together the 2 halves of copymaster 11.4, *Terrestrial, Atmospheric, and Oceanic Carbon Cycling.* Students can also use 1 copy of copymaster 11.4 to create a bigger diagram on larger sheets of paper. In Step 2, students write each carbon reaction on its own sticky note. (They write the reaction, not the number of the reaction, from copymasters 11.1, *Carbon Chemical Reaction Table* and 11.2, *Carbon Transport Table.*) Then students write each of the 5 carbon transport processes on its own sticky note. Students can trim the notes so that they can be moved around the diagram more easily.

Students discuss positioning and then place the sticky notes in Step 3. Once students have decided the placement, they link the carbon reactions or carbon processes in Step 4. Students can include additional embellishments in Step 5.

NOTES:

Part II: Showing the Carbon Cycle

Materials

For each team of 3 students

15 sticky notes

1 pair of scissors

1 pencil and eraser

3 pieces of clear tape

1 sheet of 11×17 in paper (optional)

colored pencils (optional)

1 *Terrestrial, Atmospheric, and Oceanic Carbon Cycling* handout

You have explored a lot of carbon reactions so far. You have also been thinking about how carbon moves around. Now it's time for your team to map out a way that these processes join together in the carbon cycle. You'll focus on Earth of course, even though the carbon cycle would be very different on other planets or moons (see sidebar, *Titanic Carbon*).

Process and Procedure

Gather in a team of three for the following steps. Be prepared to share, describe, and answer questions about your carbon cycle in a class discussion.

1. Obtain a copy of the handout *Terrestrial, Atmospheric, and Oceanic Carbon Cycling.* Tape the backs together to make a single sheet about 11×17 in.

Your teacher may also provide large sheets of paper to use as a background. Model the background environmental setting from the handout.

2. Use your completed *Carbon Chemical Reaction Table* and *Carbon Transport Table* to write each of the 10 carbon reactions on a different sticky note. Then write each of the 5 transport processes on a separate sticky note.

Use the main reaction path for microbial respiration.

3. Attach each sticky note to the background in a position where the reaction or transport process might occur. Discuss your reasons for the placement of each sticky note.

During your discussion, you may adjust or move any sticky note.

4. Use your pencil to draw lines and link the different carbon reactions and transport processes.

NOTES:

Answers to Reflect and Connect, SE page 578

1. This is a good way to have teams check for consistency in their carbon paths. You could also have students compare this path on their diagrams with the same path depicted on another team's diagram. Get students to discuss how the paths are similar or different. All settings mentioned in the question need to be included and be linked by reactions and transport.
2. Again, you could have 2–3 groups compare this same path on several of the diagrams. Are they all internally consistent? Does tracing the path help a team identify errors or adjust the positions of their sticky notes? All settings mentioned in the question need to be included and be linked by reactions and transport.

5. Decide on any other visual props or diagrams that you can add to your map of the carbon cycle. For example, what might you add to help visually represent reaction 10?

Reflect and Connect

Discuss and answer the following questions based on your diagram of the carbon cycle. These questions make sure that your team is seeing the links and connections in the carbon system.

1. Complete this check on possible carbon paths. You should be able to follow a carbon atom in a continuous path from arrow to arrow from a power plant, to the atmosphere, into phytoplankton in the shallow ocean, to the deep ocean, and then to sediments. Does your diagram represent this path of carbon?
2. Complete this check on possible carbon paths. You should be able to follow carbon with arrows from the atmosphere, to forests, to litter, to rivers, to the ocean, and into organisms like corals. Does your diagram represent this path of carbon?

SIDEBAR

Titanic Carbon

From all signs, the mission was going well. The capsule plummeted into the thick, orange haze surrounding Titan—Saturn's largest moon. Still, other missions like this had ended in disaster. In the past decade, several spacecraft to Mars had "gone silent" during descent. They had probably crashed directly onto the planet's surface. But those were the risks. Such missions were the only way to study the chemistry of other parts of the solar system.

The descending capsule was the Huygens probe, launched only 3 weeks before (December 2004) from the *Cassini* spacecraft. The *Cassini* spacecraft had spent the past 7 years traveling to Saturn and its 31 moons. *Cassini* had been able to image the outer parts of Titan's atmosphere (see figure). Now it would be up to the Huygens probe to penetrate the upper layers of Titan's atmosphere and to explore the dense, lower atmosphere and Titan's surface.

All evidence was that Titan would have carbon in several forms. But what would they be? Was there evidence for a carbon cycle or even life on Titan? What might that carbon cycle look like?

The carbon cycle on Earth involves gases in the atmosphere, liquids in the hydrosphere, and solids in the geosphere and biosphere. Interactions among these four parts of Earth make up the carbon cycle as the carbon changes forms by chemical reactions. A cycle on Titan would also need to include evidence for transport of

NOTES:

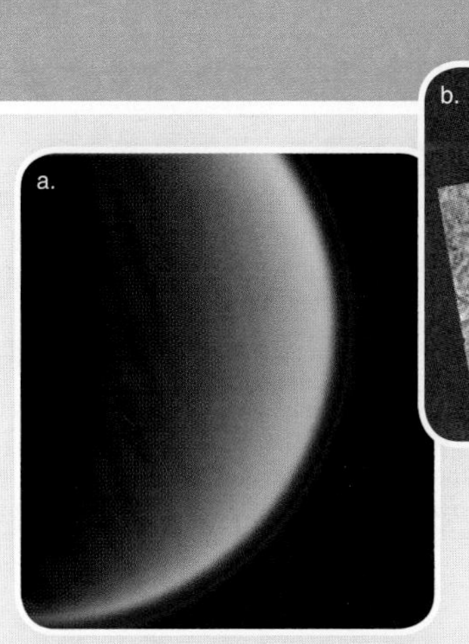

Three views of hydrocarbons on Titan. (a) The first image, taken by the *Cassini* spacecraft, shows layering of gases, mostly N_2 and CH_4, in Titan's atmosphere. (b) This image was taken by the Huygens probe in January 2005 during its descent to the surface. It shows river channels that join and drain a liquid, probably liquid CH_4, from left to right. (c) The last image shows blocks of "dirty ice" and CH_4 on the surface of Titan.

carbon-bearing substances and chemical reactions. The evidence wasn't hard to see.

The mission controllers waited anxiously as the Huygens probe plummeted into the orange haze and toward Titan's surface. Soon, features became clear, showing shapes that resembled river channels and a coastline (see figure). Given temperatures of nearly −300° Fahrenheit at Titan's surface, the liquid could not be H_2O. The liquid likely came from "rains" of liquid methane (CH_4) or ethane (C_2H_6).

Amazingly, after a safe landing, the probe operated for about 2 hours. It sent back a close-up view of Titan's surface (see figure) and detected hydrocarbon gases in the lower atmosphere. Scientists believe that these images show pieces of solid ice (H_2O) or methane (CH_4) blocks. Then the Huygens probe went silent.

Since January 2005, scientists have learned much more about Titan's atmosphere. Like Earth, Titan's atmosphere is about 80–90 percent nitrogen (N_2). Titan's atmosphere also has carbon compounds, particularly CH_4. Dissociation of N_2 and CH_4 by ultraviolet radiation from the Sun results in other hydrocarbons and nitrogen compounds. These include C_2H_6 (ethane), C_3H_8 (propane), C_2H_2 (acetylene), C_2H_4 (ethylene), C_3H_4 (methylacetylene), HCN (hydrogen cyanide), HC_3N (cyanoacetylene), C_2N_2 (cyanogen), and H_2 (hydrogen). There is also evidence for CO_2 (carbon dioxide) and CO (carbon monoxide), just like on Earth, but no free oxygen (O_2).

So, it would appear that Titan has a carbon cycle, of sorts. Combined with the absence of O_2, Titan may be similar to Earth before life formed, but perhaps somewhat colder. Studying carbon pathways on Titan helps us understand our planet and the prospects for life elsewhere in the universe.

Chapter 11 Carbon on the Move 579

ELABORATE

The Flux Is the Crux

Activity Overview

In *The Flux Is the Crux*, students will identify the main reservoirs of carbon on Earth. They will look at the masses in these reservoirs in petagrams of carbon. Sizes of carbon reservoirs are then compared with the fluxes of carbon entering or leaving the reservoirs. This lets students estimate residence time, the average time that an atom spends in a reservoir before moving along through the carbon cycle to the next reservoir.

Some reservoirs are active, containing mobile carbon that exchanges on a daily, monthly, to yearly timescale. Other reservoirs may be largely sequestered in the earth, and thus consist of immobile or inactive stores of carbon. Several processes can transfer carbon from the inactive to active ranks, and vice versa. These are discussed in *Background Information*.

This activity also is an important chance for students to show some developing skills in math with exponents and simple calculations. "Back of the envelope" calculations such as these help students better understand the magnitude or size of things in the physical world, such as reservoirs of carbon.

Before You Teach

Background Information

Part of the background for this activity relates to simple terms for analyzing systems. These include concepts such as *simulation*, *model*, *input*, *output*, *flux*, *reservoir*, *residence time*, *source*, *sink*, and *open* or *closed systems*. Using tables and simple calculations will help students develop a quantitative understanding of systems such as the carbon cycle. The chapter develops a more global view of geochemical systems by showing more than a typical, land-based carbon cycle.

Some reservoirs of carbon, such as the atmosphere and the ocean, actively exchange massive amounts of carbon on a daily basis. Reservoirs that exchange carbon on a daily or monthly to yearly timescale are termed active, or mobile, carbon reservoirs. Their carbon is mobile. Sometimes this part of the carbon cycle is called the biologic carbon cycle. A big surprise to students will be that over 90 percent of active carbon lies in the middle and deep oceans, not in forests. Even soils have more carbon than the world's forests and jungles.

In contrast, other reservoirs of carbon harbor substantial stores, much more than in the biologic carbon cycle, yet they are not at Earth's surface. These reservoirs can sequester carbon for tens of millions of years or more. That carbon is not accessible to the active part of the carbon cycle. Sometimes this is called immobile carbon, or the geologic carbon cycle. This carbon is still very important to society since it contains a valuable store of fossil fuel. Other inactive geologic carbon is sequestered in carbonate rocks such as limestone.

Processes such as geologic deposition and the burying of sediments sequester, or store, carbon in the earth. This carbon then becomes part of the geologic carbon cycle. Subduction of tectonic plates is another process that moves carbon into Earth. Another group of natural processes transfers carbon from the geologic to the biologic carbon cycle. These processes include the use and burning of fossil fuels, the weathering of coal or limestone rocks at Earth's surface, and the emissions of volcanic gases.

ELABORATE

The Flux Is the Crux

Have you seen photographs of the Amazon River basin in South America? It is a vast area of massive trees and dense jungles (figure 11.9). The Amazon basin is almost as big as the United States. Surely the Amazon basin stores massive amounts of carbon. Could anything on Earth have *more* carbon than dense tropical jungles?

You have learned that reservoirs store matter, be it water or carbon. You could even think of a bank as a reservoir—banks store dollars. You also learned that fluxes tell the rate that matter moves into and out of reservoirs. In *The Flux Is the Crux*, you and your team will apply these concepts to carbon in the geosphere. You will be able to figure out the main reservoirs of carbon on Earth. This is a key part of our being able to live on Earth.

Materials

1 calculator

Process and Procedure

Gather with your team and record all information and ideas in your science notebook. This activity will help you to be successful in the evaluate activity, *Carbon Quest*.

1. Discuss with your team whether you think there is more carbon in Earth's atmosphere or in all the vegetation on Earth. Write your reasons or evidence in your science notebook.

Scientists often refer to the biosphere as the living part of the planet. This can include all plants, animals, and soils, plus analogous parts of the ocean.

2. Use a reading strategy with your team for the following paragraphs about rates of carbon transport in the carbon cycle.

   Dissolved carbon flows down a river to the ocean. Maybe the carbon is in a bicarbonate ion used by a clam to build its shell. Or imagine carbon entering a plant by photosynthesis and then leaving the plant by respiration after a week. Or what about carbon in the atmosphere, dissolving into the ocean, and then quickly entering phytoplankton by photosynthesis?

   In each of these cases, carbon is mobile. That carbon moves quickly between carbon reservoirs on Earth. In some cases, the carbon might even cycle back and forth, such as in the photosynthesis-respiration path. Such interactions occur over days, weeks, or perhaps a few years. For this reason, this carbon might be called **active** or **mobile carbon**. Sometimes this quickly moving carbon is referred to as the **biologic carbon cycle**.

Materials

For each team of 3 students

1 calculator

Advance Preparation

Decide whether you can assign parts of the activity as homework, particularly the short readings. Ask students to think of several examples from their lives where matter has a measurable flow or flux. Examples are the amount of food they eat per day and the numbers of students in and out of their school per day. What units are used for those fluxes?

Decide whether you need to review the conversion from grams to petagrams for students. This is quite easy, although it may seem awkward at first. Using the factor 10^{15} greatly simplifies work with carbon reservoirs. For example, it is easy to see that 23 Pg C plus 0.5 Pg C equals 23.5 Pg C. It is less easy to see that (2.3×10^{16} Pg C) plus (5×10^{14} Pg C) equals 23.5×10^{15} Pg C. Once students make the conversions, errors due to exponents cannot occur.

Strategies

Getting Started

You might start class with board work. Have students write in their science notebooks an answer and sketch related to this question: "What do you think is the difference between the biologic and the geologic carbon cycle?" Check some student responses in a quick discussion. Ask students where they think the most carbon resides.

Hopefully, students saw in the last activity the linkages and rapid exchange between organic and inorganic carbon at Earth's surface. The factor that hasn't really been addressed is the very different timescales over which exchange and the rate of transport can vary. Rapid exchange of carbon will eventually tie in quickly with organic or inorganic carbon at Earth's surface (i.e., biologic carbon cycle). Slower exchange also occurs over millions of years as carbon is sequestered in geologic reserves inside Earth.

Answers to Steps 3–5 are on TE pages 581–583.

In contrast, other parts of Earth have large amounts of carbon that interact much more slowly in the ocean, land surface, or atmosphere. This carbon is mostly beneath Earth's surface. It is stored in geologic deposits of limestone or hydrocarbons such as coal, petroleum, or natural gas. These geologic reservoirs of carbon are viewed as **inactive carbon** because they were not part of rapid carbon cycling at Earth's surface. Some geologists call this the **geologic carbon cycle.** This is because such carbon reservoirs require millions of years to develop, mature, and cycle.

3. Recall your carbon reactions and transport processes from earlier in this chapter. Answer the following 2 questions.
   a. Discuss with your team 2 paths or processes where carbon in the geologic carbon cycle is transferred to become active, biologic carbon.
   b. Discuss with your team 2 paths or processes where carbon in the biologic carbon cycle is transferred to become inactive, geologic carbon.

It may be helpful to use a sketch with labels to illustrate your answers.

4. Copy figure 11.15 into your science notebook (including the blank columns) and complete the following steps. The table shows the main active reservoirs of carbon on Earth and their masses.
   a. Rewrite the mass of carbon (g C) from column 2 as the mass of carbon with the exponent of 10^{15} in column 3. Remember how to move decimals and change the exponent.

If you were changing 1,000 g to kilograms, you would use these steps:

$$1{,}000 \text{ g} = 1.0 \times 10^3 \text{ g} = 1 \text{ kg}$$

   After you have done this, do a visual check with your team to make sure that the values make sense.
   b. In column 4, show the mass of carbon as petagrams of carbon (Pg C). Use the conversion where 1 petagram of carbon equals 10^{15} grams of carbon (1 Pg C = 10^{15} g C).
   c. At the bottom of column 4, sum the carbon in Pg C for all the reservoirs.
   d. In column 5, calculate the percentage of active carbon in each reservoir.
   e. Make a T-table in your science notebook. List the reservoirs from largest to smallest in the left column and include their percentages in the right column.
   f. Sketch in your science notebook how you would represent the result from Step 4d as a bar graph and a pie chart.

Process and Procedure

Teams discuss in Step 1 whether they think that there is more carbon in the atmosphere or in all the surface vegetation of Earth. They will see later, and perhaps be a bit surprised, that these reservoirs are pretty similar in mass of carbon. Students then read a few paragraphs with their team in Step 2. The reading distinguishes between the biologic and geologic carbon cycles. In Step 3, students need to consider transfer of carbon between inactive, geologic reservoirs and active, biologic reservoirs. They also do the opposite, considering transfer from active to inactive carbon reservoirs.

Students in Step 4 convert the masses of carbon in 6 main active reservoirs to petagrams. They rank the reservoirs by mass and show how to represent those results as a pie chart and a bar graph. Step 4b will probably be the most difficult, because they have to adjust decimal places to get all the masses in a format with exponents of 10^{15}. But after they do this, using petagrams of carbon is easy. Students then answer some questions about the results in their table in Step 5.

Answers to Steps 3–5, SE pages 581–582

3a. Combustion of gasoline, coal, natural gas, methane, or any fossil fuel transfers carbon to the atmosphere. Weathering of coal layers where they are exposed at

Carbon reservoir	Mass of carbon (g C)	Mass of carbon (g C with × 10^{15} notation)	Mass of carbon (Pg C)	Percent of active carbon (% total carbon)
Soils	1.66×10^{18}	1660×10^{15}	1,660	4
Marine life	3.0×10^{15}	3×10^{15}	3	0.007
Shallow oceans	9.0×10^{17}	900×10^{15}	900	2.2
Middle, deep oceans	3.71×10^{19}	37100×10^{15}	37,100	91
Atmosphere	5.9×10^{17}	590×10^{15}	590	1.4
Vegetation	6.4×10^{17}	640×10^{15}	640	1.6
		Total Pg C	40,893	

Source: Sarmiento, J. L., & Gruber, N. (2002). Sinks for anthropogenic carbon. *Physics Today*, *55*(8) 30–36, and Intergovernmental Panel on Climate Exchange, (2001). *Climate change 2001: The scientific basis*. Chapter 3: The carbon cycle and atmospheric carbon dioxide. Retrieved June 13, 2006, from http://www.grida.no/climate/ipcc_tar/wg1/095.htm

▲ **Figure T11.10 Active carbon reservoirs and petagram conversion table.** Students use a data table like this one to organize data from the 6 main reservoirs of mobile carbon. The answers are shown.

Earth's surface transfers coal to rivers, where they might break down. Weathering of carbonate rocks such as limestone at Earth's surface transfers inorganic carbon from rocks to bicarbonate in rivers. Volcanic release of CO_2 also moves carbon from inside Earth to the atmosphere.

3b. There are several ways to do this. For example, marine life at the ocean's surface dies, carrying carbon to the seafloor, which becomes part of the sediments. Burying carbon in sediments removes that carbon from the biologic carbon cycle. Also, carbon in vegetation is buried by rapid sedimentation on continents to become part of a future coal seam or petroleum field. Carbon incorporated into the shell of a clam, snail, or coral becomes part of a thick limestone layer; while in the earth, that carbon is not available to be part of the biologic carbon cycle.

4a. See the table in figure T11.10 for answers.

4b. See the table in figure T11.10 for answers.

4c. The sum is about 40,893 Pg C.

4d. See the table in figure T11.10 for answers.

Answers to Step 6 are on TE page 584.

Carbon reservoir	Mass of carbon (g C)	Mass of carbon (g C with × 10^{15} notation)	Mass of carbon (Pg C)	Percentage of active carbon (% total carbon)
Soils	1.66×10^{18}			
Marine life	3.0×10^{15}			
Shallow ocean	9.0×10^{17}			
Middle, deep ocean	3.71×10^{19}			
Atmosphere	5.9×10^{17}			
Vegetation	6.4×10^{17}			
		Total Pg C		

Source: Sarmiento, J.L. & Gruber, N. 2002. Sinks for anthropogenic carbon. *Physics Today*, 55(8) 30-36, and Intergovernmental Panel on Climate Exchange, 2001. Climate change 2001: The scientific basis. Chapter 3: The carbon cycle and atmospheric carbon dioxide.

▲ **Figure 11.15 Carbon reservoir table.** Use a table like this one to help you organize the data from the 6 main reservoirs of mobile carbon. Fill in the columns for petagrams of carbon (Pg C), total carbon, and the percentage of active carbon.

5. Answer the following questions based on your completed table from figure 11.15. Use petagrams of carbon to compare reservoir sizes (for example, 50 is 2 times larger than 25).
   a. What are the first- and second-largest reservoirs of active carbon on Earth? Are these the reservoirs that you expected?
   b. Reevaluate your team's response to Step 1. (Is there more carbon in Earth's atmosphere or in all the vegetation on Earth?)
   c. Soils are a key player in the active carbon cycle. How many times larger is the amount of carbon in soils than in the atmosphere? In vegetation?
   d. Notice that land animals are not included in figure 11.15. Why do you think they are not included?
6. Estimate how much carbon is in the inactive, or geologic, carbon cycle by following Steps 6a–d.
   a. Geologists think that sediments and muds beneath the ocean have about 1.5×10^{22} g C. Show how you move decimals to express this number in Pg C.
   b. Geologists estimate that sediments on continents hold about 7.6×10^{22} g C. Express this as Pg C.
   c. How many Pg C from Steps 6a–b?
   d. How many times larger are estimates for carbon in all geologic sediments (Step 6c) compared with carbon in the active (biologic) carbon cycle?

Many of the estimates that you have made in the last 2 questions are sometimes called "back of the envelope" calculations. You can do them on a small piece of paper to make a quick approximation or comparison. But do these in your science notebook.

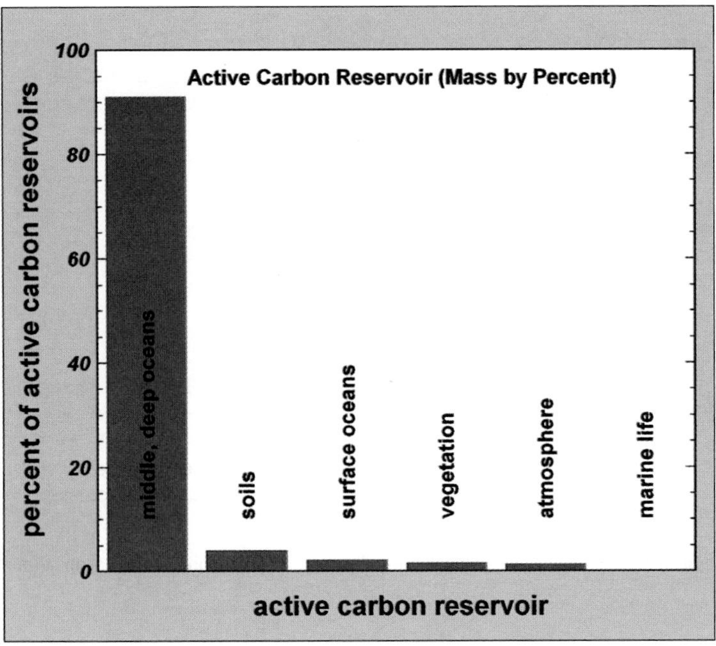

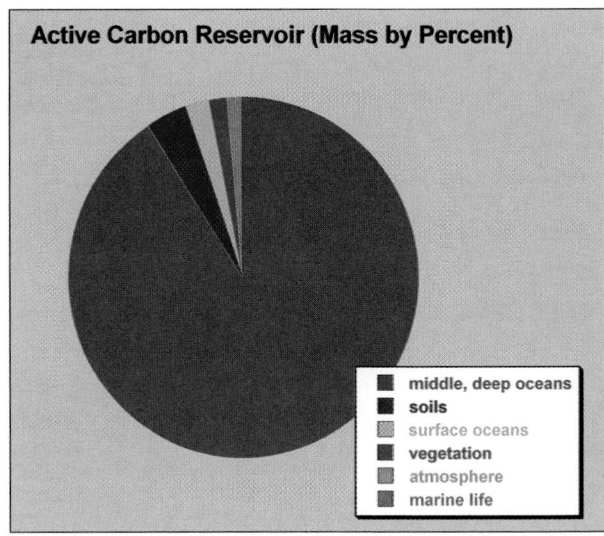

▲ **Figure T11.11 Percentage of active carbon reservoirs.** Pie charts and bar graphs of the percentage of carbon in 6 active carbon reservoirs should look like these.

Source: Sarmiento, J. L., & Gruber, N. (2002). Sinks for anthropogenic carbon. *Physics Today, 55*(8) 30–36, and Intergovernmental Panel on Climate Exchange, (2001). *Climate change 2001: The scientific basis*. Chapter 3: The carbon cycle and atmospheric carbon dioxide. Retrieved June 13, 2006, from http://www.grida.no/climate/ipcc_tar/wg1/095.htm

7. Use a reading strategy with your team for the following reading, *Carbon Taking Up Residence*. Do you remember from chapter 10 how flux was used for french fries and water? This is the same, but with carbon.

READING

Carbon Taking Up Residence

The word **flux** indicates the amount of matter that moves into, or out of, a reservoir in a given time. Reservoirs that interact and exchange matter are a **system**. In this chapter, the matter has been carbon. When there are several inputs (or outputs), all the inputs (or outputs) need to be added together for the reservoir.

For example, figure 11.16 shows fluxes of carbon (Pg C) per year between reservoirs of carbon on Earth. Four arrows point to the

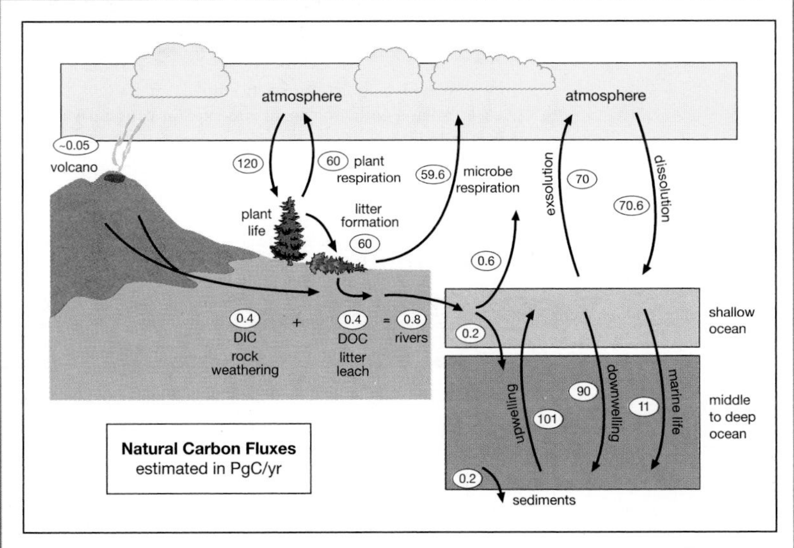

▲ **Figure 11.16 Natural carbon flux.** This diagram shows fluxes of natural carbon between major reservoirs of carbon in the geosphere. Units are petagrams of carbon (10^{15} g C) per year. Where are the largest fluxes of carbon?

4e. Reservoirs from largest to smallest are middle and deep oceans, soils, the surface ocean, vegetation, the atmosphere, and marine life. Note that terrestrial life (land animals) doesn't even make the list.

4f. Check that students know how to represent these data as a pie chart and a bar graph. Examples are shown in figure T11.11.

5a. Middle and deep oceans and soils are the first- and second-largest reservoirs of active carbon on Earth. These are likely not the reservoirs students expected.

5b. These active reservoirs are comparable in size.

5c. Soils are more than twice the size of atmosphere and vegetation (nearly 3 times).

5d. The upper limit would be the about 3 Pg C for the marine life. Still, marine life is much more extensive than terrestrial animals, so the carbon in land animals would be a drop in the bucket compared with the amounts of carbon in this table.

In Step 6, students compare the mass of carbon estimated to reside in geologic reservoirs (inactive) with the biologic (active) carbon. Students see that geologic reservoirs of carbon are much larger than the available, active carbon stores.

Answers to Step 6, SE page 582

6a. Moving the decimal 7 places to the right gives 15 million Pg C, or

$$1.5 \times 10^{22}\text{ g carbon} = 15{,}000{,}000 \times 10^{15}\text{ g carbon} = 15{,}000{,}000\text{ Pg C.}$$

6b. Moving the decimal 7 places to the right gives 76 million Pg C, or

$$7.6 \times 10^{22}\text{ g carbon} = 76{,}000{,}000 \times 10^{15}\text{ g carbon} = 76{,}000{,}000\text{ Pg C.}$$

6c. There are about 91 million Pg C, or 91,000,000 Pg C, from Steps 6a and 6b.

6d. Dividing 91 million Pg C by 40,839 Pg C shows that geologic reserves of carbon are estimated to be over 2,000 times larger than the amount of carbon in the active, biologic carbon cycle.

$$\left(\frac{91{,}000{,}000\text{ Pg C}}{40{,}893\text{ Pg C}}\right) = 2{,}225$$

Students complete a reading about carbon fluxes and residence times in Step 7. The important point here is that residence time is the estimated, average time that an atom spends in a reservoir until moving on to the next reservoir. Residence time reflects how quickly carbon cycles in and out of a carbon reservoir.

Students use a table to determine residence times in Step 8. Then in Step 9, they answer questions about residence times and rates of carbon movement between reservoirs.

Answers to Steps 8 and 9, SE pages 584–585

8a. They would be considered a *source* of carbon. Geologic stores of carbon are "losing" carbon (net loss of carbon) as humans use fossil fuels to generate energy. Using fossil fuels transfers carbon from the geologic to the biologic carbon cycle.

8b. These estimates are shown in figure T11.12.

8c. Total fluxes from figure 11.16 in the student book are shown in column 4 of figure T11.12. Individual inputs (or output for marine life) are shown in column 3. The key is that for a given

Carbon reservoir	Mass of carbon (Pg C)	Individual carbon flux per year (Pg C/yr)	Total carbon flux per year (Pg C/yr)	Average residence time (yr)
Soils	*1,660*	*60*	*60*	*27.7*
Marine life	*3*	*11*	*11*	*0.3*
Shallow ocean	*900*	*0.8 + 70.6 + 101*	*172.4*	*5.2*
Middle, deep ocean	*37,100*	*90 + 11 + 0.2*	*101.2*	*366.6*
Atmosphere	*590*	*60 + 59.6 + 0.6 + 70*	*190.2*	*3.1*
Vegetation	*640*	*120*	*120*	*5.3*

▲ **Figure T11.12 Table for mass, flux, and residence time of carbon.** Students work with this table. Answers are shown.

Answers to Steps 8–9 are on TE pages 584–585.

Carbon Taking Up Residence, continued

atmosphere. Thus, the atmosphere receives carbon from respiration by vegetation (60.0), microbes in the soils (59.6), river carbon moving to the atmosphere (0.6), and CO_2 leaving the shallow ocean (70.0). The total flux to the atmosphere is about 190.2 Pg C per year (60 + 59.6 + 0.6 + 70 = 190.2 Pg C/yr). With humans, emissions of carbon from fossil fuels increase the flux to the atmosphere by about 5–6 Pg C/yr. This is about 2–3 percent of the total.

If a reservoir is accumulating carbon over time, it is a carbon **sink**. The reservoir has inputs of carbon greater than outputs. An example is seafloor sediments. Carbon accumulates there, making geologic sediments. On the other hand, if a reservoir of carbon is losing carbon over time to other reservoirs, it is a carbon **source**. The reservoir has outputs of carbon greater than inputs. Examples of carbon sources are volcanic eruptions and rock weathering. These provide new carbon for the active carbon cycle.

Residence time tells, on average, the amount of time that matter is in a reservoir. For carbon, short residence times mean that carbon cycles quickly to a neighboring reservoir. Long residence times indicate that carbon stays in the reservoir for much longer times. Only then does the carbon move to the next reservoir in a cycle. Here is a key point: residence time comes from dividing the mass in a reservoir by the total flux into (or total flux out of) the reservoir.

8. Copy figure 11.17 into your science notebook. Discuss Questions 8a–d with your team and explain your answers in your notebook.
   a. Consider using fossil fuels to make energy. Are fossil fuels a source or a sink of carbon to the ocean? Explain your evidence and reasons.
   b. Enter estimates for mass of carbon per reservoir in column 2 of figure 11.17. Refer to your work in Step 4 (figure 11.15).

Carbon reservoir	Mass of carbon (Pg C)	Individual carbon flux per year (Pg C/yr)	Total carbon flux per year (Pg C/yr)	Average residence time (yr)
Soils				
Marine life				
Shallow ocean				
Middle, deep ocean				
Atmosphere				
Vegetation				

▶ **Figure 11.17 Carbon mass, flux, and residence time.** Copy this table into your science notebook. Use it to record fluxes for the 6 major carbon reservoirs on Earth. Estimate residence times of carbon in those systems.

584 | Unit 3 Moving Matter

reservoir, students sum fluxes for arrows going in. Arrows going out are similar.

8d. Residence time is shown in column 5 in figure T11.12. This is the mass of carbon in the reservoir divided by the total flux into, or out of, a reservoir. Smaller values for residence time (marine life) indicate that an atom of carbon does not spend much time in the reservoir before transport to the next part of the carbon cycle. Larger values for residence time (middle and deep oceans) indicate that an atom of carbon spends relatively more time in the reservoir before transport to the next part of the carbon cycle.

9a. Carbon resides for the longest period in middle and deep oceans. Ocean circulation occurs over decades, so this makes sense.

9b. Carbon resides for the shortest period in marine life in the shallow ocean. This value is probably dominated by the massive biomass of microorganisms (phytoplankton) that photosynthesize at the surface of the ocean. These organisms are the foundation of the food chain. Many are eaten by larger organisms (zooplankton, small fishes, other filter feeders). The fecal matter of the latter sinks to the deep ocean, or large organisms die and sink to the bottom of the ocean.

Answers to Reflect and Connect are on TE pages 585–587.

c. Examine figure 11.17 with your team. Enter the total flux from inputs or outputs per reservoir into column 3 of your table.

Remember, if a reservoir has several inputs or outputs, they must be summed together for the total flux for that reservoir. Tally the individual fluxes listed in column 3 for the total in column 4.

d. Calculate residence time in years and enter the number in column 5.

9. Complete Questions 9a–c about residence times of carbon in different reservoirs on Earth.
   a. Where does carbon reside for the longest period of time? Explain whether this makes sense to your team, and why or why not.
   b. Where does carbon reside for the shortest period of time? Explain whether this makes sense to your team, and why or why not.
   c. How much longer or shorter are the residence times for carbon in soils compared with vegetation (forests)? Explain whether this makes sense to you.

Reflect and Connect

After creating a carbon cycle with your team, discuss and answer the following questions.

1. What is the residence time for a given dollar in a bank? Use the fictional Bank of the Lower 48, with total holdings of $10 billion. Transfer rates per business day average $7.5 million. How long on average does a dollar stay in the bank before moving out again into the economy?
2. See figure 11.16, which shows estimates for fluxes of natural carbon into and out of the atmosphere. Note that the units are petagrams of carbon per year (Pg C/yr).
   a. In your science notebook, make a T-table with values for inputs and outputs of carbon for the atmosphere.
   b. Show total fluxes for the atmosphere at the bottom of each column. How similar or different are these?
   c. Given these estimates, is the atmosphere gaining or losing carbon?
   d. Fossil fuels are adding carbon to the atmosphere at a rate of 5–6 Pg C/yr. What percentage of the total flux into or out of the atmosphere is this?
   e. Scientists estimate that the ocean and vegetation absorb about 1.5–2.0 Pg C/yr. What percentage of the 5–6 Pg C from humans is this?

9c. On average, a carbon atom stays in soils about 5.2 times longer than in vegetation.

Answers to Reflect and Connect, SE pages 585–586

1. Dividing the total holdings (the size of the reservoir) by the rate of movement of dollars (flux), a dollar remains in the bank about 1,333 days. This is about 3.5 years before a dollar leaves the bank to enter the economy again. For banks with smaller holdings but a similar flux, dollars don't remain in the bank as long.
2. Note that this query is an explicit preparation for a question on the evaluate activity, *Carbon Quest*, where students do a simple flux balance of carbon in the shallow ocean.

2a. Inputs of carbon to the atmosphere are from plant respiration (+60), microbe respiration in soils (+59.6), CO_2 exsolution from the ocean (+70), and a small source related to rivers (+0.6). The total is about 190.2 Pg C. Emissions of CO_2 from volcanism are not included at this scale. Outputs from the atmosphere are due to photosynthesis (120) and dissolution into the ocean (70.6), or about the same amount, 190.6 Pg C.

2b. See the table shown in figure T11.13. This shows that the total fluxes are very similar.

2c. The total in figure T11.13 shows a small net movement of carbon out of the atmosphere. This would not likely be a long-term pattern, however, or else the atmosphere would slowly be depleted of carbon. The net carbon flux leaving the atmosphere is likely within error for the values of flux used. In other words, the integrated flux might just be zero.

Students will see later that this small net flux is offset heavily by inputs into the atmosphere by humans from the combustion of fossil fuels (about 5–6 Pg C/yr, which is about 10 times this net flux).

2d. The human input is about 3 percent of the total flux (190.6/5.5).

2e. This indicates that the ocean and vegetation can absorb about 32 percent of the carbon generated by humans into the atmosphere. Because these reservoirs cannot absorb all the CO_2 created by humans, the CO_2 concentration in the atmosphere is increasing.

3. Students should develop a schematic showing time on the *x*-axis and an indication of carbon reservoirs on the *y*-axis. The following example is reproduced on copymaster 11.5, *Cycle of Carl Carbon Atom.* This example shows a possible route of Carl Carbon between geologic and biologic parts of the carbon cycle. It would be useful for students to critically analyze an overhead of this possible answer. It is valuable if they can identify chemical reactions that move Carl Carbon from stage to stage.

Carl Carbon dissolved in the ocean as part of a HCO_3^{1-} molecule. Carl then entered the shell of a clam at 480 million years ago, becoming $CaCO_3$. When the clam died, the shell was buried by sediments and became part of a limestone. It was underground for hundreds of millions of years (geologic carbon reservoir), until finally exposed to rock weathering as a peak in the Himalaya in, say, 1975. Carl Carbon's elevation is now over 28,000 feet.

From Mount Everest (where that carbon atom is $CaCO_3$), the carbon was transferred to HCO_3^{1-} and traveled back downriver to enter the Indian Ocean. The carbon entered the ocean, where it traveled, say, to the Atlantic Ocean. From there, several options are possible, as shown on copymaster 11.5, *Cycle of Carl Carbon Atom.* In one model, the HCO_3^{1-} becomes part of a phytoplankton. A shrimp eats the plankton. The shrimp is caught and is shipped to a store. A student then eats the shrimp.

Carbon inputs for atmosphere (Pg C/yr)		Carbon outputs for atmosphere (Pg C/yr)	
Plant respiration	60.0	Dissolution into the ocean	70.6
Microbe respiration	59.6	Photosynthesis	120.0
Exsolution from the ocean	70.0		
River component to atmosphere	0.6		
Total =	**190.2**	**Total =**	**190.6**

Source: Sarmiento, J. L., & Gruber, N. (2002). Sinks for anthropogenic carbon. *Physics Today, 55*(8) 30–36, and Intergovernmental Panel on Climate Exchange, (2001). *Climate change 2001: The scientific basis.* Chapter 3: The carbon cycle and atmospheric carbon dioxide. Retrieved June 13, 2006, from http://www.grida.no/climate/ipcc_tar/wg1/095.htm

▲ **Figure T11.13 Table for carbon inputs and outputs for atmosphere.** This completed table shows individual inputs and outputs from figure 11.15 in the student book. The totals at the bottom *for these values* show a small net movement of carbon leaving the atmosphere.

As an alternative, if 2 HCO_3^{1-} combined to make $CaCO_3$ and CO_2, Carl Carbon could end up in the CO_2. The CO_2 could exsolve from the ocean and travel the world to become part of a lettuce leaf in California by photosynthesis. A student might

◀ **Figure 11.18 Mount Everest.** This photograph shows Mount Everest and the buff-colored limestone band near the peak. Limestone consists of organisms such as clams. Clams remove carbon from the ocean to build shells of calcium carbonate ($CaCO_3$).

3. Imagine that you are an atom of carbon, Carl Carbon, in the elbow of 1 of your teammates. At a time in the past, you were in a clam in a limestone that was slowly dissolving and weathering near the top of Mount Everest (figure 11.18). The clam in the limestone formed 480 million years ago in a shallow ocean on the southern part of continental Asia.

   Develop with your team a sequence showing a possible history for Carl Carbon. Begin before the atom became part of the limestone and ended up in your teammate. For a carbon atom weathered from Mount Everest, what series of reactions and transport could move the atom to a human in the United States? Be prepared to share your ideas with the class. Use the *x*-axis to represent time; add labels to show the location or setting of the carbon above.

   You can check a map to see river basins and drainage patterns from Mount Everest.

EVALUATE

Carbon Quest

Indeed, carbon is on the move. You see this all around through processes like photosynthesis, the decay of vegetation in soils, or the use of fossil fuels. You have even worked with some other types of carbon reactions that in nature move carbon from one reservoir to another.

You have also seen how carbon is stored in reservoirs in limestone or coal layers. These range from carbon stored in the deepest, coldest oceans, to carbon stored atop Mount Everest, the highest mountain on Earth.

In *Carbon Quest*, you will complete a short assessment on key features of the carbon cycle. Then you will use the *Learn from Mistakes (LFM) Protocol* from Chapter 4, to analyze, discuss, and explain your answers. This gives you the chance to revise incorrect answers and improve your grade.

then eat the lettuce in a salad or a BLT sandwich.

Scenarios such as these may sound far fetched. However, they actually represent quite accurately how carbon moves around Earth. By integrating residence times, we can see how rapidly and frequently carbon does cycle around the globe.

EVALUATE

Carbon Quest

Activity Overview

In *Carbon Quest*, students will complete a short test about the carbon cycle. They will use the *Learn from Mistakes* (*LFM*) *Protocol* to analyze their answers. You will mark the correct answers immediately and record the number that are correct in red ink. Then you will lead a brief discussion of the concepts in the questions. Students will then have the opportunity to substantially enhance their grades by explaining why they missed questions on the initial test and providing the correct answer and reason why. Students should be familiar with the *LFM Protocol* from evaluate activities in earlier chapters.

Before You Teach

Background Information

The background information for the test is the content and skills developed in this chapter. The answer key is copymaster 11.7, *Carbon Quest Answer Key*, where answers to the questions are also explained. These answers will help guide your brief discussion of the initial test. Students then analyze and correct their answers, explain their reasons, and improve their grades.

Materials

For the teacher

1 hammer

1 piece of wood

1 awl or large nail

1 copy of copymaster 11.7, *Carbon Quest Answer Key*

For each student

1 pencil

1 calculator

1 copy of copymaster 11.6, *Carbon Quest*

Advance Preparation

Make copies of copymaster 11.6, *Carbon Quest*, for your class. The answer sheet for students is the first page of the test. Copymaster 11.7, *Carbon Quest Answer Key*, shows the correct letter answers and provides an explanation. The most reasonable answers for each question appear on the copymaster as well.

As You Teach

Outcomes and Indicators of Success

By the end of this activity, students should

1. know the major reservoirs of carbon on Earth.

   They will demonstrate their knowledge by

   - identifying objects in a list that have and do not have carbon,
   - identifying objects in a list that do and do not consist of $CaCO_3$,
   - answering how carbon moves from the atmosphere to vegetation,
   - indicating the largest reservoir of carbon on Earth, and
   - converting moles of carbon to petagrams of carbon in the atmosphere.

Materials

For each student

1 *Carbon Quest* handout

1 pencil

1 calculator

Process and Procedure

1. Review as a class the *LFM Protocol* (on page 155). To summarize, you will
   - take a short test on the carbon cycle,
   - participate in a discussion about questions that you or your classmates might have missed, and
   - write an explanation for why one of your wrong answers was not correct and what the correct answer would be.
2. Get from your teacher the handout *Carbon Quest*. Take about 15 min to complete the multiple-choice questions on the handout. All answers must be given on the attached answer sheet.
3. Turn in the answer sheet to your teacher.
4. Participate in a class discussion about questions where you or your classmates had incorrect answers. Note that your teacher will not necessarily give you the correct answer. By analyzing the wrong answers, however, you should be able to explain the reason why another answer is the correct one.

It is OK to ask questions during this session. You should also keep notes on questions you missed.

5. For each of the questions you missed on the test, do Steps 5a–e with a small group of 2–3 students. You can earn 50 percent of the original credit for each question you missed (that is, you can raise a score of 60 percent to a score of 80 percent).
   a. Write your raw score as a percentage in the upper right corner of your answer sheet.
   b. List under your score the number of the questions that you missed.
   c. Represent the original question in a different way than it was presented on the test. For example, if the question was mostly words, represent it now with a labeled sketch. Or try representing a sketch with words or phrases. Do not copy questions word for word.
   d. Work with a small group (no more than 3 students) to identify and explain the mistakes that you each made on

2. be able to write the key chemical reactions transferring carbon between major carbon sources and sinks.

   They will demonstrate their ability by

   - analyzing a chemical reaction (calcium carbonate precipitation) to check for mass balance and charge balance,
   - identifying photosynthesis as a key process that transfers carbon from the atmosphere to the biosphere,
   - analyzing a simple box model of carbon fluxes into and out of the shallow ocean, and
   - describing how marine life removes carbon from solution in the shallow parts of the ocean.

3. be able to estimate quantitatively the transfer of carbon between key reservoirs on Earth.

   They will demonstrate their ability by

   - converting moles of carbon to mass of carbon in grams and petagrams of carbon,
   - using inputs and outputs of carbon in the shallow ocean to determine a net annual flux of carbon to the shallow ocean (0.4 Pg C),
   - showing that residence time is the average amount of time an atom spends in a reservoir, and
   - using net annual fluxes of carbon to estimate the increase over 2 years of about 0.8 Pg C.

4. develop further skills in the abilities and understandings of scientific inquiry.

   They will demonstrate their skills by

   - using the *Learn from Mistakes Protocol* to analyze responses in the investigation;
   - analyzing, revising, and correcting missed questions;
   - using mathematics to calculate answers; and
   - identifying net fluxes of carbon in a system.

Strategies

Getting Started

Give clear instructions for the activity and make sure that students understand the *Learn from Mistakes* (*LFM*) *Protocol*. Emphasize that they can substantially improve their grades by explaining their wrong answers. They will get to develop correct answers and explanations in teams.

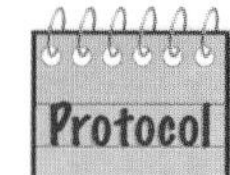

Process and Procedure

In Step 1, review the *LFM Protocol*. Administer the test in Step 2. Collect the exams and answer sheets in Step 3. Separate the answer sheets from the tests and align the sheets with the answer key on the top. Punch the correct answers with a nail or awl through the entire pile. Record the number of correct answers at the top of each sheet in red ink.

In Step 4, return the questions and conduct a discussion about the concepts and questions students missed. Feel free to explain or have them explain why a particular answer is wrong. You can also discuss why a revised answer would be correct, but don't give students the correct answer. They need to discuss and figure this out as a team. Students must explain their conceptual misunderstandings in writing to receive a better score.

Students work in teams in Step 5 to analyze their incorrect questions. They can start developing their revised answers at that time. Tell students in Step 6 when their corrected answers are due.

the test. Be sure to explain conceptual misunderstandings that you might have had. A correct answer with no clear explanation does not receive additional credit.

Explanations like "I read the problem wrong" or "I pushed the wrong button on the calculator" will receive no credit.

e. Show the correct answer or solution. As you can, provide any governing equations with symbolic form, followed by numeric values. Correct answers must include labels on sketches and units for values.

6. Listen to instructions from your teacher about when your corrected explanations are due. This may be at the end of the class period or at the beginning of the next class. For credit, you must include your original answer sheet with your explanations and sketches.

CHAPTER 12

Evidence for the Ice Ages

Chapter Overview

In unit 3, *Moving Matter*, students have been using a systems perspective to understand how matter moves in geochemical cycles. These cycles relate to how matter moves around different parts of the earth system. Students began in chapter 10, *The Water System*, by building on their knowledge of the water cycle and studying different parts of the water system at very different scales. In chapter 11, *Carbon on the Move*, they analyzed the biologic and abiotic parts of the carbon cycle and how chemical reactions facilitate movement of carbon through earth systems. Chapter 12, *Evidence for the Ice Ages*, retains a focus on geochemical cycles but on much longer timescales—thousands of years. A goal of the chapter is to investigate how past climates on Earth can affect geochemical cycles and to learn how to interpret evidence for such events.

This chapter has another objective. Using a systems perspective to analyze patterns of climate on Earth continues to improve students' skills to analyze other systems and cycles. This will help them in other fields in the sciences or even other professional areas such as in business or economics. Using a systems approach also allows students to consider interactions that occur within parts of a system. Naturally, some of the interactions will involve thinking about how humans enter the equation of the earth system. A systems approach also gives teachers some flexibility in deciding how much rigor is appropriate for their students and the degree to which they emphasize natural and human interactions within a system.

This chapter focuses on the movement of oxygen among reservoirs. Students will use evidence largely from oxygen to determine the history of the ice ages. This study of past climates on Earth is called *paleoclimatology*. Students will start by considering four separate observations: large, displaced boulders; mysterious scratches in bedrock; unusual ridges; and mammoth fossils found by a fisherman. After recognizing the role of the ice ages and glaciers in the unusual happenings, students will explore what they already know about ice ages in general and how changes in past climate affect the global water system.

Students next will turn their focus to the cycling of oxygen in the earth system. They will analyze data that reveal changes in the isotopes of oxygen and relate those data to climate patterns on Earth. Then students will examine the astronomical theory as one possible explanation for the pattern of past ice ages. In the final activity, students will apply their understanding of oxygen cycling to analyze additional scientific data. They then will use these data as evidence to answer three questions pertaining to global climate patterns, the astronomical theory of the ice ages, and their work as young scientists.

Goals for the Chapter

From the activities described above, students should be able to answer questions like these by the end of chapter 12:

- What is the evidence that Earth's climate has changed between periods of overall cold climate (glacials) and overall warm climate (interglacials)?
- What causes patterns of ice ages on Earth?
- What kind of geologic evidence is used to learn about ancient ecosystems?
- How are water, oxygen, and carbon part of the record of Earth's past climate patterns?
- Is there any evidence for ice ages in tropical, equatorial oceans?

These questions should help you focus your daily lessons. For example, they could serve as focus questions that you present to students multiple times in the course of an activity, particularly at the beginning and end. You can also use the questions as a check that lessons are staying on track and that students are receiving a more coherent curriculum.

Continue to use the chapter organizers with students to show the conceptual flow of a chapter. It is helpful to post these near the door to your classroom (or some other visible place) to track as a class progresses through the chapter or unit. Moreover, the organizers help focus the chapter on key concepts that relate to standards. Remember that the teacher organizer helps you see how you will be working with your students and what you will be helping them do on a given day.

On day 1 of the chapter, hand out the scoring rubric for the evaluate activity, *More Than Forams*. Tell students that they will show their understanding of evidence for ice ages by working as scientific teams and then answering three questions individually. Being successful with the three questions will rely on using evidence in their written answers that they will examine in the chapter. By handing out the rubric ahead of time, you are being clear to students and their parents about performance expectations. The rubric lets students begin working on skills and knowledge that will help them during the final project.

Chapter 12 Organizer

EVIDENCE FOR THE ICE AGES

Major Concepts

- **Earth's climate changes between overall cold (glacials) and warm (interglacials) cycles; patterns of oxygen isotopes in foram shells ($CaCO_3$) from the seafloor are one way to study these climate cycles.**
- **Climate is the average weather pattern over many years. Weather is the atmospheric condition at a given time.**
- **Many technologies are used to measure cycles of climate change on Earth.**
- **Geologic evidence (forams, dust, pollen, CO_2) are used to test models for the cause of the Ice Ages.**

ENGAGE — How Did They Get There? ☆

Key Idea: • Discoveries in geology lead to new explanations about Earth's climate.
Activity: Students try to explain strange geologic discoveries.

Linking Question: Does an Ice Age affect the water cycle or sea level?

EXPLORE — Ice Blocks: Growing, Shrinking

Part I—Miniglaciers ★

Key Idea: • Ice melts at a rate that depends on the amount of heat.
Activity: Students race to melt an ice cube.

Part II—Glaciers Melting ★ ☆

Key Idea: • Changes in solar radiation play a key role in Earth's climate patterns.
Activity: Students consider the links between solar radiation, climate, glacial periods, and changes in sea level.

Part III—Glacier Melting Rates ★ ☆

Key Idea: • Sea level changes as glaciers and ice sheets grow during glacials, and melt during interglacials.
Activity: Students estimate melting rates for glaciers, and compare with an ice cube.

Linking Question: Do ocean sediments record evidence of Ice Ages?

★ = One Class Period ☆ = ½ Class Period *Note:* Based on a 50-minute class period.

EXPLORE / EXPLAIN — The Core of the Matter

Part I—Heavy Water, Light Water ★

Key Idea: • Water molecules with the heavy isotope of oxygen ($H_2{}^{18}O$) behave slightly differently than "lighter" water ($H_2{}^{16}O$) in the water cycle.

Activity: Students do activity to simulate evaporation of water molecules of different atomic mass.

Part II—The Oxygen Connection ★★

Key Idea: • Foram shells in ocean sediments record a "fingerprint" of oxygen isotopes in seawater.

Activity: Students complete readings to learn about oxygen isotopes in foram shells.

Part III—Analyzing Foram Data ★☆

Key Idea: • Oxygen isotope records from foram shells reveal past cycles of glacial and interglacial periods.

Activity: Students analyze records of oxygen in foram shells over the past 650,000 years.

LINKING QUESTION: What caused the Ice Ages?

ELABORATE — The Astronomical Theory ★★☆

Key Idea: • The solar radiation reaching Earth varies in a regular way due to changes in the shape of Earth's orbital path around the Sun.

Activity: Students do a 3-way jigsaw on the 3 factors in the Milankovitch theory of climate change (tilt, wobble, orbit shape).

LINKING QUESTION: What other kinds of geologic data are used to understand climate cycles on Earth?

EVALUATE — More Than Forams ★★

Key Idea: • Geologic evidence from pollen and dust is another way to test models for the cause of the Ice Ages.

Activity: Students study foram, dust, and pollen records, and then write answers to 3 questions.

★ = One Class Period ☆ = ½ Class Period *Note:* Based on a 50-minute class period.

Standards Covered by Chapter 12

EVIDENCE FOR THE ICE AGES

STANDARD B: Physical Science. As a result of activities in grades 9–12, all students should develop an understanding of

structure of atoms

- The atom's nucleus is composed of protons and neutrons, which are much more massive than electrons. When an element has atoms that differ in the number of neutrons, these atoms are called different isotopes of the element.

STANDARD C: Life Science. As a result of their activities in grades 9–12, all students should develop understanding of

the interdependence of organisms

- The atoms and molecules on the earth cycle among the living and nonliving components of the biosphere.

STANDARD D: Earth and Space Science. As a result of activities in grades 9–12, all students should develop an understanding of

energy in the earth system

- Heating of earth's surface and atmosphere by the sun drives convection within the atmosphere and oceans, producing winds and ocean currents.
- Global climate is determined by energy transfer from the sun at and near the earth's surface. This energy transfer is influenced by dynamic processes such as cloud cover and the earth's rotation, and static conditions such as the position of mountain ranges and oceans.

geochemical cycles

- The earth is a system containing essentially a fixed amount of each stable chemical atom or element. Each element can exist in several different chemical reservoirs. Each element on earth moves among reservoirs in the solid earth, oceans, atmosphere, and organisms as part of geochemical cycles.
- Movement of matter between reservoirs is driven by the earth's internal and external sources of energy. These movements are often accompanied by a change in the physical and chemical properties of the matter. Carbon, for example, occurs in carbonate rocks such as limestone, in the atmosphere as carbon dioxide gas, in water as dissolved carbon dioxide, and in all organisms as complex molecules that control the chemistry of life.

the origin and evolution of the earth system

- Geologic time can be estimated by observing rock sequences and using fossils to correlate the sequences at various locations. Current methods include using the known decay rates of radioactive isotopes present in rocks to measure the time since the rock was formed.

STANDARD E: Science and Technology. As a result of activities in grades 9–12, all students should develop

understandings about science and technology

- Science often advances with the introduction of new technologies. Solving technological problems often results in new scientific knowledge. New technologies often extend the current levels of scientific understanding and introduce new areas of research.

STANDARD G: History and Nature of Science. As a result of activities in grades 9–12, all students should develop an understanding of

science as a human endeavor

- Individuals and teams have contributed and will continue to contribute to the scientific enterprise. Doing science or engineering can be as simple as an individual conducting field studies or as complex as hundreds of people working on a major scientific question or technological problem. Pursing science as a career or as a hobby can be both fascinating and intellectually rewarding.

Prerequisite Knowledge

By this point in the program, students should be familiar with using science notebooks and with including titles, labels, and other methods to record information or data. They should also be able to use strategies to organize data (T-tables, multicolumn tables, Venn diagrams) and complete effective sketches or diagrams. If students are not organized, it is less likely that they will be able to make sense of topics of study. They should be able to analyze *xy* plots, and this chapter will certainly strengthen those skills.

They will continue using quantitative skills that they have been developing through the program. Exponents are still useful for large scales used in length, mass (volume), or time. Canceling and converting units remains important. Students still need to show all their work all the time.

In the first two chapters of the unit, students analyzed the global water system and carbon cycles. The water cycle moves matter over years, while carbon atoms in the carbon cycle move around the globe (the "mobile" carbon component) on the order of years to thousands of years. The geologic timescales in this chapter are extended back further to hundreds of thousands of years. Several of the data sets extend to 650,000 years ago (650 kya). We can think of this as being just over half the way back to 1 million years (Myr), or about 1 percent of the way back to the extinction of the dinosaurs at 65 Myr. The main point is that scientists have recovered an astoundingly rich set of data on a global scale from the period of time from today back to about 650 kya.

This chapter does not require a background in geography, but it does use maps of the ocean and the continents to help students learn about other parts of the world. Combined with topics in this chapter relating to Earth's orbit around the Sun, the use of maps will help foster visual learning and spatial relations. It may be helpful to post a map of the world or have a globe handy when referring to locations discussed in this and the following chapter.

Commonly Held Misconceptions

There is little research at the high school level on misconceptions relating to the history or climate of the ice ages. You may note students with some incorrect ideas about glaciers or rivers, in that these are a part of the water cycle. Transfers to larger scales can be difficult, so you may see some of the following misconceptions:

- Weather and climate are pretty much the same thing.

Weather is what happens on a daily or perhaps weekly basis. For example, summer sunshine and summer rainstorms are part of patterns of weather. Climate reflects patterns that occur seasonally or for longer durations of time.

- Glaciers do not exist at the equator because current glaciers make up polar ice caps.

Glaciers develop when the amount of snow that accumulates during the winter exceeds the amount of

snow that can be melted during the summer. Thus, several locales at low latitudes or nearly at the equator have been characterized by growing glaciers. For example, some are located in the Andes of South America and Mount Kilimanjaro in Tanzania. The rapid shrinkage of some of these glaciers in recent decades has fueled concern about global warming.

- Earth experiences changing levels of solar radiation because the elliptical shape of Earth's orbit changes the distance between Earth and the Sun. This relates to the cause of the seasons.

Earth has an elliptical orbit, but it is still very nearly a circular shape. Thus, the amount of solar radiation does not really change that much. The elliptical shape of the orbit is usually highly exaggerated in diagrams. The seasons are caused by variations in radiation due to the tilt of Earth's axis of rotation.

- Earth experienced but a single "Ice Age."

Students see evidence that Earth has experienced cycles of glacials and interglacials. Recently, these have occurred about every 100,000 years (100 kyr). The evidence for this is found in sediment records. Other records of glaciation in the geologic record are clear in the late Paleozoic and latest Precambrian.

- Melting ice sheets cause the sea level to rise.

This is true, but melting ice sheets are not the only factor that increases sea level. As surface waters in the ocean become warmer, they expand slightly, which raises the sea level. For the current increases in sea level, the split is thought to be roughly 50:50 between meltwater from glaciers and sea level rise due to thermal expansion.

ENGAGE

How Did They Get There?

Activity Overview

The strategy in this activity is to get students to think about multiple types of observations and evidence that might not appear related, but upon further investigation, are related. In this activity, students read headlines about four strange discoveries. Each of these headlines is based on evidence that leads scientists to the discovery that many ice ages occurred during Earth's history. Although students come up with a variety of explanations for each of the headlines, when they look at the headlines collectively, only one thing can explain all of them—large sheets of ice and an ice age. This is very similar to the work that scientists must do. Scientists seek multiple lines of evidence before being compelled to accept an explanation.

Before You Teach

Background Information

This information is provided for your use. It is intended to help you understand evidence for the ice ages a little better and give you some background so that you can ask better questions of students in class.

Early Evidence of Ice Ages

During the early- to mid-1800s, one of the most perplexing and unexplained scientific observations was that vast areas of central and northern Europe were covered with thick heaps of mixed-up dirt, sand, stones, and large boulders the size of trucks. Over wide regions, these geologic deposits were tens to hundreds of meters thick, yet they appeared to have little relation to deposits known to have been laid down by nearby rivers. But ancient seas covering the land could not have laid the deposits because the deposits did not contain marine fossils such as the shells or shark teeth so common to other marine rocks.

The mixed-up geologic deposits were very strange indeed. Explaining their origins was compounded by the intriguing discovery that similar heaps of mixed-up rock and dirt also covered much of the northern parts of North America. Again, these deposits did not have the characteristics common to river deposits and were definitely not marine, either. They were also generally very young deposits, sitting atop all other rocks and strata. Thus, any possible explanations based on local or regional evidence in Europe would also have to pass comparable tests on the other side of the globe in North America.

In trying to explain the strange geologic deposits, the plot thickened when it was noted at several locations that the piles of soil and rock also contained the fossil remains of giant elephant-like animals with long, shaggy fur (figure 12.1 in the student book). Today, we know these creatures as the woolly mammoths, and we associate them with northern latitudes and very cold climates. Another animal that lived with the mammoths was the woolly rhinoceros (*Coelodonta antiquitatis*), a massive rhino also with a long fur coat and a horn up to 1 meter (m) long. This species of rhino only existed in Europe, but clear paintings on cave walls and skeletal records are evidence of their coexistence with early humans there. You can look up images of these or other amazing ice age animals on the Web.

These exciting animal discoveries lent more mystery to the origins of the strange geologic deposits. How could they have been formed? What was the significance of fossilized remains for animal species specially adapted to very cold climates?

Observations such as those described here and in the student book (erratics, striations, and drumlins) were eventually linked to glaciers and ice sheets up to 2 kilometers (km) thick on the continents. There are two types of glaciers, alpine glaciers and continental glaciers. *Alpine glaciers* flow down valleys in high mountain settings. They move like molasses, or large, stiff rivers of ice. In contrast, *continental glaciers* are sheets of ice that cover large parts of entire continents. These are also called ice sheets. These are currently restricted to high latitudes, such as Antarctica and Greenland. When the term *glacier* is used in the student book, it refers to both types of glaciers.

Scientists also use the term *ice cap* when describing the large masses of ice at each of Earth's poles. The Antarctic ice cap is a continental glacier, as it covers the continent of Antarctica. The Arctic ice cap, however, is generally not referred to as a continental glacier, because it lies over water. Ice caps are also visible on Mars.

Recent Evidence for Ice Ages

At certain periods in the geologic past, northern parts of the European and North American continents were covered with thick blankets of ice up to several kilometers thick. The ice sheets persisted for thousands of years. Such cold periods are sometimes referred to as ice ages, glacial periods, or glacials. In contrast, glacials alternate with overall warm periods called interglacials (that is, "inter," or "between," glacials). At these times, continental glaciers have melted substantially, with ice largely restricted to ice sheets at polar areas, as well as minor perennial ice patches on only the tallest, coldest mountain ranges (e.g., the Alps, northern parts of the Rocky Mountains). The ice does not totally melt, but becomes much reduced in size.

It was not until the 1960s, however, that geologic ages and a time frame for those glacial epochs were measured. This was done initially by radiocarbon age dating. Also at that time, scientists realized that not just a single massive ice sheet had covered much of the continents. Rather, glacial epochs had come and gone at regular, periodic intervals many times. A variety of distinctive types of geologic deposits preserved that unique and global record of glacial and interglacial periods. The back-and-forth alternation between warm and cold climates is termed *glacial* and *interglacial cycles*.

The evidence of past ice ages is one aspect of the field of paleoclimatology. The root of this word is not too obscure. The word *climate* describes the expected or predicted ranges of weather in a geographic region in a certain season. In much of the northern United States, for example, we expect a cold climate during the winter months. In southern or western parts of the United States, such as Florida or California, climates might be warm to hot all year.

The word *paleoclimatology* has a slightly different meaning from the word climate. Since the prefix "paleo" indicates "ancient" or "old," paleoclimatology is the study of past climates on Earth. Finding clues about the past climates involves looking carefully at geologic evidence at a series of times. You and your students will see that this evidence for past climates comes from many types of field sites, both on land and from the deep sea. A key is seeking and finding plants and animals in geologic deposits, such as the deposits described earlier, that are found throughout much of Europe and North America. These hold vital clues.

Answers to Steps 1–4 are on TE page 594b.

ENGAGE

How Did They Get There?

A key part of science is observing. Simple observations often lead to puzzling questions for scientists. In *How Did They Get There?*, you will work in a team of three to read about some strange discoveries. Then your team will propose an explanation for each discovery.

Materials

For each team of 3 students

1 *Mysterious Headlines* handout

Process and Procedure

Sometimes newspaper headlines are difficult to believe. The headlines in this investigation might seem unreal, but they are based on actual discoveries and observations. How can you explain these strange occurrences?

1. Look carefully at figure 12.1. Have you ever seen a creature like this?
   a. Read the newspaper passage in the figure and discuss it with your group.
   b. What might have caused this strange event? Come up with a list of 2–3 possible explanations. Record these in your science notebook.

▼ Figure 12.1 Mammoth headlines. This front-page article describes the find of a woolly mammoth.

Mammoth Tooth Discovered by Fisherman

A fossil tooth of a woolly mammoth was recently discovered by a fisherman. He found it while fishing along the Atlantic Coast near New Jersey. Scientists used radiocarbon (C-14) dating to measure its age at about 20,000 years old. Other woolly mammoth fossils have been found in the midwestern United States, Europe, and Siberia. Scientists are now searching the area for *continued on A12*

Artist's rendering of a woolly mammoth.

Materials

For the teacher

map of the world or a globe (optional)

For each team of 3 students

1 copy of copymaster 12.1, *More Than Forams Scoring Rubric*
1 copy of copymaster 12.2, *Mysterious Headlines*
1 copy of copymaster 12.3, *Unidentified Data* (optional)

Advance Preparation

Make copies of copymaster 12.1, *More Than Forams Scoring Rubric*. This helps students see your expectations at the end of the chapter.

Make single-sided copies of copymaster 12.2, *Mysterious Headlines*, 1 per team. Cut out the headlines so that you can give them to students one at a time. If you think your students might struggle with the idea that ice ages are the common cause of all the headlines, you might want to check out several remarkable glacier and ice sheet galleries on-line. Students can view many photographs from around the world. For example, try a search using "swisseduc glaciers world."

Obtain a map of the world to place on the classroom wall. This will be useful in this and the following chapters. A globe would also be handy if a map is not available.

As You Teach

Outcomes and Indicators of Success

By the end of this activity, students should

1. express their current understanding of the process of proposing and revising scientific explanations based on evidence and logic.

   They will demonstrate their current understanding by

   - discussing with their partners possible logical explanations for four individual newspaper headlines,
   - participating in a class discussion about the common explanation for all the headlines (evidence for an ice age), and
   - discussing that scientists are open to making modifications in their explanations when they encounter evidence that does not fit their current explanation.

2. recognize that an ice age occurred in Earth's past and reveal their current understanding of ice ages.

   They will demonstrate their current understanding by

   - contributing to a class discussion that confirms that the common explanation for all the headlines is an ice age in Earth's past,
   - participating in a class discussion of what they know and what questions they have about ice ages, and
   - recording two statements about what they know and two questions they have about ice ages.

3. develop further skills in the abilities and understandings of scientific inquiry.

   They will demonstrate their skills by

   - formulating and revising explanations for four news summaries,
   - evaluating alternative explanations for news headlines, and
   - communicating and defending explanations for news items.

Strategies

Getting Started

Ask your students to look at the photographs in the chapter opener and answer questions such as, "What do you think these are?" "How do you think they might relate to past climates on Earth?" You may wish to have a volunteer record ideas on the board. The round-shaped shells (disks) with holes are a silica-bearing shell from organisms called diatoms. About 8–10 complete diatom shells are shown. The other shells are from organisms called foraminifera, or forams, for short. Students will learn much more about forams in this chapter.

Select a strategy to complete the chapter introduction. Then ask students if they ever read the newspaper and notice unusual headlines. Tell students they will be reading some headlines that are based on discoveries made by scientists in the past. In fact, scientists at different locations throughout the world have made similar discoveries. The students will have to figure out the cause of the observations and discoveries.

Pass out copymaster 12.1, *More Than Forams Scoring Rubric*. This helps students see your expectations at the end of the chapter, where they will be observing and interpreting evidence on their own.

Materials

For the teacher

map of the world or a globe (optional)

For each team of 3 students

1 copy of copymaster 12.1, *More Than Forams Scoring Rubric*
1 copy of copymaster 12.2, *Mysterious Headlines*
1 copy of copymaster 12.3, *Unidentified Data* (optional)

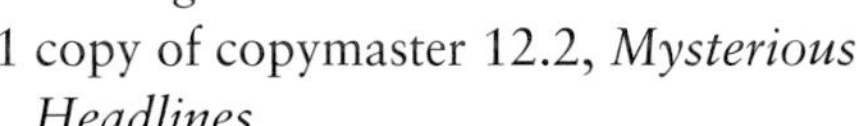

Process and Procedure

In Step 1, students examine figure 12.1 and answer some questions. Remind them to write down their explanations in their science notebooks. Then give each team of students a copy of *Headline A* for Step 2 (large boulder). Make sure students finish recording their explanations for *Headline A* before giving them the next headline. Repeat this process for *Headlines B* (scratches) and C (striations) in Step 3. Circulate around the classroom as teams are discussing the headlines. As you listen to their conversations, you can assess their current thinking about the evidence they are reviewing.

Answers to Steps 1–4, SE pages 594–595

Although it is unlikely that students will guess the actual explanations for each of the headlines, we provide them here for your information. It is not important that student explanations be correct at this time. Look for responses that show thought and are reasonable.

1. Figure 12.1 is about a woolly mammoth tooth. Woolly mammoths had thick, hairy coats and lived in cold tundra environments. They were about the size of modern Asian elephants (3 m tall at the shoulders). Mammoths were larger than mastodons. They became extinct about 10 kya. Isolated teeth are found more often than skeletons. Most woolly mammoth fossils are found in areas covered by savannas, grasslands, or tundra during the last ice age. During that time, sea level was lower and the land extended farther than it does currently, providing a wider range of habitat for these large land animals. This explains why a fisherman could find a woolly mammoth fossil offshore.
2. *Headline A* is about a large boulder in the Swiss Alps. Glaciers carry a variety of sediment sizes, from pebbles to boulders. Glaciers slowly carry sediment over distances of 1 km up to 800 km. As a glacier retreats (melts), it leaves sediment behind. These rocks and boulders are called *erratics*. Because the rocks have been transported long distances, they are often different from the local geology, but the same as the bedrock up the glacial valleys.
3. *Headline B* refers to scratches in rocks. These scratches are called *striations*. Striations are caused by rocks trapped at the bottom of a glacier. The weight of the ice above causes these rocks to gouge the bedrock as the ice flows over it.

   The ridges in *Headline C* are called *drumlins*. The word drumlin is derived from the Irish Gaelic word *druim*, meaning "rounded hill or mound." Drumlins are small, elongated hills deposited by glaciers. They are usually found in clusters. The slope is steep on the side where the glacier advanced and gentle on the side where it retreated. Bunker Hill in Boston Harbor is an example of a drumlin.
4. After reading the woolly mammoth headline, many teams might realize that all the headlines would be explained by the occurrence of an ice age. However, not all students will recognize that the common cause is ice ages. Look for responses that are well thought out.

In Step 5, use the class discussion to see what ideas teams came up with for Steps 1–4. Ask some teams to share their explanations. If no teams propose the ice age explanation on their own, you might want to have the class work together to see the relationship between the 4 headlines (pieces of evidence). A way to do this visually is with 4 ovals overlapping in the center like a Venn diagram (figure T12.1). Each oval could represent explanations for a discovery, with the overlapping center representing a common explanation.

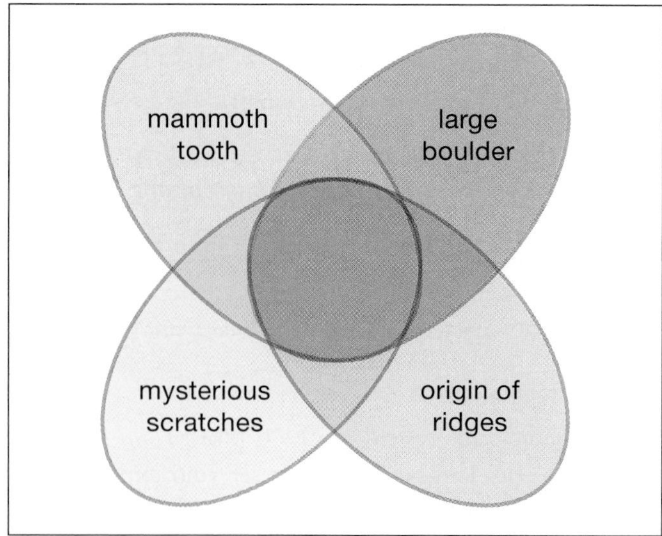

▲ **Figure T12.1 Glacial evidence Venn diagram.** This diagram is one way to represent that different lines of evidence for glaciations have an overlapping, common cause.

You might ask questions like these about the woolly mammoth: "Where did they live and what type of environment did they live in?" "Why would the tooth of a land mammal be found in the ocean?" Students should recognize that woolly mammoths are associated with ice ages. Write "ice ages" in the center of the overlapping ovals.

You can ask other kinds of questions to help focus students' ideas in the class discussion.

- "Where and how much water is stored in cold environments?"

During ice ages, large volumes of water are stored in glaciers and ice caps. About 6 percent of global water is tied up in glaciers and ice caps during ice ages compared with about 3 percent during interglacials. Students might be interested to know that about 30 percent of Earth's land area was covered by ice 20 kya compared with 10 percent ice cover today.

- "How do glaciers move rocks? What evidence do we have of this movement?"

As glaciers move, they pick up and carry debris. Some of the debris is very large—the size of large boulders. Some of the debris at the bottom of a glacier scratches the underlying bedrock. When glaciers melt, they leave their debris behind in characteristic formations.

Many students might have trouble visualizing what a glacier looks like. If students have trouble grasping the idea of glaciers moving rocks, show them transparencies of the images in copymaster 12.3, *Unidentified Data*.

Once students have identified ice ages as a common explanation for the four pieces of evidence, ask them what they already know about ice ages and what questions they have about them. Record their ideas on chart paper or a blank transparency. Listen to students as they participate in the class discussion. This will give you the opportunity to learn what students already know about ice ages. Students will record some of these ideas in their science notebooks in answer to *Reflect and Connect* Question 1.

Answers to Step 5, SE page 595

5. Student answers will vary depending on their current understanding of ice ages. Sample statements about what they know include the following:
   - "Earth is covered with more glaciers during an ice age than during a non–ice age."
   - "The woolly mammoth lived during an ice age."
   - "As glaciers move down valleys, they carry dirt and rocks with them. The dirt and rocks are left behind when the glaciers melt."

   Sample questions about ice ages include the following:
   - "What actually causes an ice age to occur?"
   - "How many ice ages are there?"
   - "How often do ice ages occur?

Have students answer the *Reflect and Connect* questions individually in their science notebooks. Reading their answers will allow you to assess individual student understanding of ice ages and how scientists accommodate conflicting evidence in their explanations.

Answers to Reflect and Connect, SE page 595

1. Student answers will vary depending on their current understanding of ice ages. They should make 2 statements and propose 2 questions about ice ages. See *Answers to Step 5* for sample responses.
2. Students should start to recognize the global nature of ice ages. For all these places to be affected by an ice age, the global climate on Earth would have to have been different.
3. Look for student responses that indicate that scientists keep investigating. They keep looking for additional observations or alternative explanations that they can test. If the evidence does not support their explanation, they either reevaluate the evidence or change their explanation to accommodate the evidence. There is no right or wrong answer here. Instead, the purpose of this question is to get students to think about the work that scientists do.
4. Mammoths are a relatively recent form of elephant. This corresponds with evidence that students will learn that the most recent period of ice ages on Earth is really very young.

c. Decide as a team which explanation seems most reasonable and place a check by it.

2. Obtain the *Mysterious Headlines* handout from your teacher with *Headline A*. Repeat Step 1 for this handout.
3. After finishing *Headline A*, repeat Step 1 for the handouts with *Headline B* and then *Headline C*.
4. You might be surprised to learn that the same process caused all of the strange occurrences you read about. What was that process? Discuss your ideas with your team and record them in your science notebook. Be prepared to share your ideas.
5. Participate in a class discussion about the cause of these strange occurrences. Share what you already know about this process and the questions you have about it.

Reflect and Connect

Answer the following questions individually in your science notebook.

1. Identify 2 things you already know about the process that caused the strange occurrences in the headlines. Then identify 2 questions you still have about the process.
2. How do you think it is possible that the same process affected such different regions of Earth (Swiss Alps, New York, Illinois, Wisconsin, and Ireland)?
3. What do scientists do when they find evidence that does not make sense or does not fit their current understanding?
4. You considered elephant evolution in chapter 6, *Exploring Change*. Where were mammoths in the line of descent?

Ice Blocks: Growing, Shrinking

EXPLORE

In the engage activity, *How Did They Get There?*, you investigated strange occurrences linked by a common explanation—an ice age. You might recognize an ice age as a time when large parts of Earth had thick ice and a cold climate. What might cause an ice age? Why is there less ice now? How much ice counts as an ice age?

In *Ice Blocks: Growing, Shrinking*, you will explore questions like these and learn more about Earth's climate. You will also look at how an ice age affects the water cycle. You will work alone and in a team of three students in this investigation.

EXPLORE

Ice Blocks: Growing, Shrinking

Activity Overview

Students might recognize an ice age as a time when Earth was cooler, but they might not have thought about how an ice age would affect the water cycle. In this investigation, students will explore how an ice age would affect the global water cycle.

During Part I, students will melt an ice cube as fast as possible and calculate the rate of melting. In Parts II and III of the investigation, students will relate their experience to the actual melting of glaciers. In Part II, they will think about what causes ice to melt. They will read about variations in solar radiation that are determined by the location on Earth and its tilt. Then they will begin thinking about how climate changes would affect the global water reservoirs, including sea level. In Part III, students will calculate the melting of glaciers from sea level data and compare this with the melting rate of their ice cube.

Before You Teach

Background Information

Much of the background information presented for the engage activity, *How Did They Get There?* applies to this activity. Review that information as needed. The summary below makes comparisons between the ice ages and the water cycle.

The transport of water through the global water cycle helps scientists compare paleoclimate records between land and sea. The global water cycle can be viewed as the line of communication between the ocean, atmosphere, and continents. Geologic findings show us that those lines of communication via the water cycle have been open for millions of years.

Climate changes on Earth are marked by the slow increases and decreases in the size of massive sheets of ice on continents. Melting may be substantial, but large sheets of ice have been part of Earth's geology for much of the last 25–30 Myr. This process must be driven by an exchange of energy as water converts to snow and glacial ice, and then as glacial ice melts to water. The source of that energy is the Sun. Both current and past climates are, in part, a response to changes in the distribution of solar energy, or solar radiation, as a function of latitude. Energy output from the Sun itself changes very little over time.

But how could the distribution of solar energy change as a function of time? Students already learned one great example of this—seasons. Variations in the distribution of both solar radiation and climate occur on an annual basis to give us the seasons. This yearly climate cycle is caused by the tilt of Earth's rotation axis. In the Northern Hemisphere, the concentration of solar radiation increases when Earth is tilted toward the Sun, providing the Northern Hemisphere with summer. Solar radiation decreases for us when the axis is pointed away, and the amount of radiation per square meter decreases. This leads to the colder temperatures of winter.

Students will read about causes for periods of glaciation later in the chapter. These are caused, in part, by changes in Earth's orbit around the Sun.

Materials—Part I

For the teacher

model of Earth and its rotation axis (optional)
1 stopwatch or clock with second hand

For each team of 3 students

1 25-mL graduated cylinder
access to an electronic balance
1 ice cube
1 small, resealable, sturdy plastic bag
1 calculator (optional)

Materials—Part II

none

Materials—Part III

For each team of 3 students

1 calculator (optional)

Advance Preparation

Gather materials for Part I. Each team of 3 students needs an ice cube in a resealable bag. The ice cubes should be the size made in a standard ice cube tray. A typical ice cube might be about $5 \times 3 \times 3$ centimeters (cm). If the ice cubes are too small, they will melt too quickly. Use sturdy plastic bags to prevent leaks.

It can be very handy to have a model available with a sphere representing Earth and a stick representing the rotation axis. This will be valuable in showing relationships between tilt and solar radiation hitting Earth.

As You Teach

Outcomes and Indicators of Success

By the end of this activity, students should

1. be able to use their understanding of the water cycle as they explore ice ages.

   They will demonstrate their ability by

   - recalling that energy drives the water cycle;
   - comparing the movement of water during glacial periods with interglacial periods;
   - describing that the storage of water shifts from more water in the ocean reservoir during interglacial periods to more water in ice reservoirs during glacial periods; and
   - describing that the increase in the amount of water stored in global ice reservoirs results in a decrease in sea level, and vice versa.

2. be able to relate global climate differences on Earth to differences in the amount of solar radiation received by different regions of Earth due to the tilt of Earth's axis.

   They will demonstrate their ability by

   - acknowledging the role that energy plays in the melting of ice cubes and glaciers;
   - noting that most glaciers tend to be located near Earth's poles;
   - expressing that the reduction of solar radiation at the poles is due, in part, to Earth's tilted axis; and
   - distinguishing climate from weather.

3. be able to use math to further their understanding of the cycling of water on Earth.

   They will demonstrate their ability by

   - calculating rates of melting for ice cubes and glaciers,
   - retrieving data from a graph of change in sea level across time and using it to calculate melting rates for glaciers, and
   - comparing rates of melting for ice cubes and glaciers with appreciable differences in scale.

4. develop further skills in the abilities and understandings of scientific inquiry.

   They will demonstrate their skills by

   - measuring and calculating the percentage of change and rates for melting ice blocks and glaciers,
   - examining the concept of melting ice and melting glaciers with solar radiation,
   - working with colleagues to complete an ice melting experiment,
   - using mathematics to compare melting rates for glaciers with the ice blocks,
   - using and analyzing proxy measurements for systems, and
   - reevaluating solar radiation for a point on Earth given a tilt of 50 degrees (°) for Earth's rotation axis.

Strategies

Getting Started

Begin by asking students the following question about global water reservoirs: "What percentage of the global water is stored as ice during an ice age?" They should be able to return to chapter 10 where they saw that about 3 percent of Earth's water is stored in ice sheets and glaciers. During the last ice age, scientists estimate that there was at least two times as much water stored in global ice reservoirs as there is today.

Process and Procedure

Part I: Miniglaciers

Materials

For the teacher

model of Earth and its rotation axis (optional)
1 stopwatch or clock with second hand

For each team of 3 students

1 25-mL graduated cylinder
access to an electronic balance
1 ice cube
1 small, resealable, sturdy plastic bag
1 calculator (optional)

After discussing the *Getting Started* question, have students read the 2 short paragraphs that introduce Part I. Then have students read through Steps 1–5. It is important that they know in advance what they are going to do. To win, students must be able to calculate the melting rate, as well as the percentage of change in the ice cube. Make sure students understand what they are expected to do. Then allow students to break into their teams and start with Step 1. Monitor teams as they progress through Steps 1–5. This will give you the opportunity to assess their lab and math skills (using a balance and graduated cylinder, calculating melting rates).

NOTES:

Distribute an ice cube to each team for Step 2. Allow time for students to quickly estimate the volume of their ice cubes using a balance. Remind them to record their data.

For Step 3, supervise the 2-minute (min) time period for melting. You might want to start and end all the teams at the same time. Ideally, the teams should not be able to melt the entire ice cube. When time is called, students should measure the volume of the ice that melted according to the instructions in Step 4 and record this in their science notebooks. They can calculate their melting rate and percentage of ice melted in Step 5.

Answers to Steps 2, 5, SE page 596

2. An ice cube's mass might be 28 grams (g). Mass is converted to volume using the density (D) for water of $D = 1.0$ grams per cubic centimeter (g/cm^3). This is an easy calculation on the surface, but make sure that students can demonstrate how to cancel units in the conversion. This is vital in harder problems.

$$\text{volume} = \frac{\text{mass}}{\text{density}} \times \left(\frac{28\text{g}}{1\frac{\text{g}}{\text{cm}^3}} \right)$$

$$= 28.0\, \not{g} \times \left(1\frac{\text{cm}^3}{\not{g}} \right) = 28 \text{ cm}^3$$

5. For 2 min, a team might generate about 8.0 milliliters (mL) (= 8 cm^3) of water. This is a melting rate of 4 cubic centimeters per minute (cm^3/min). From an initial volume of 28 cm^3 (28 g), the percentage melted is about 28.6 percent, or $(8/28) \times 100$.

After teams have completed Step 5, facilitate a class discussion around the questions in Step 6. This is a good time to be sure that students see that for water, 1 g = 1 cubic centimeter (cm^3) = 1 mL, and that they can convert between these.

Have teams complete Steps 7, 8, and 9 as directed. Listen to teams as they discuss the slightly different ice cube melting race. This is an opportunity to see how your students can transfer their ice cube experience to a slightly different setting. Also be sure that they can calculate the percentage of change during melting.

NOTES:

Part I: Miniglaciers

Materials

For each team of 3 students

1 25-mL graduated cylinder

access to an electronic balance

1 small, resealable bag containing an ice cube

1 calculator (optional)

Process and Procedure

In the engage activity, discoveries in headlines suggested large amounts of ice on Earth. You related these discoveries to evidence for ice ages. At present, those areas do not have a lot of ice. This suggests that we are not experiencing an ice age.

But why does the climate of Earth enter or exit an ice age? To begin to answer this question, we will first explore ice on a small scale.

1. Your team will get an ice cube in a resealable bag. Your challenge will be to melt as much of the ice cube as possible in 2 minutes (min). Decide on a strategy for your team. How can you melt the ice faster than other teams?

   There are some rules you must follow:
   - You cannot win unless you calculate accurately the percentage of change in volume.
   - You may not remove the ice cube from the bag.
   - You may not have access to any materials other than those on the materials list.
2. Obtain the ice cube from your teacher.
   a. Quickly measure the mass of your ice cube.
   b. Decide with your team how to convert the mass of ice (grams, or g) to volume of ice (cubic centimeters, or cm^3).
   c. Carefully show these steps in your science notebook.
3. Begin the melting process when your teacher tells you to start.
4. After your 2 min are up, measure how much of the ice cube you melted by pouring the water into a 25-mL graduated cylinder.
5. In order to win, you must make the calculations in Steps 5a–b.
   a. Calculate the melting rate of your ice cube. What volume melted in 2 min?

   Recall that a rate tells how fast something changes per amount of time.

   b. Determine the percentage of change in your ice cube during melting. Write the steps in your science notebook.

Answers to Steps 7–9, SE page 597

7. Students should realize that lamp B with the foil should melt the ice cube faster because more radiation is directed toward the ice cube. Students may also recall how radiation spreads out from a source, such as a star, roughly proportional to $1/d^2$ relationship (i.e., the inverse square relationship, where *d* is distance). The foil focuses toward the light radiation that might otherwise "miss" the ice.
8. Be open to student ideas here for experiment design. Ask questions to encourage students to think critically about what they would measure in the experiments. For example, they might propose (and sketch) to place thin pieces of metal painted black at the same distance from the light with thermometers taped to the metal. The thermometers would record temperature change with time on the metal and how much (or whether) the foil was directing significantly more radiation.

   Or students might suggest an experiment comparing evaporation rates for 2 identical pans with a small amount of water (0.5 cm) in the bottom of each. They might propose to test whether the amount of radiation affects the evaporation rate.
9. The melting rate for heat lamp A is 0.8 cm^3/min (4/5) and for heat lamp B is 1.2 cm^3/min (6/5). However, students should be able to see from the table that the first ratio is a little less than 1, and the second ratio is a little greater than 1. Thus, heat lamp B indeed melts faster.

   This is another good example where students can quickly get the answer by inspection, without needing to plug values into a calculator. They should be able to see that 1/7 for lamp A is smaller than 1/5 for B. Specifically, the proportion melted is (4/28), or just 1/7 (14 percent), for lamp A, and (6/30), or just 1/5 (20 percent), for lamp B. This result is consistent with faster melting for lamp B.

6. Which team melted the most of its ice cube? How did the team do it? As a class, discuss the various methods that teams used. What made some methods more successful than others? Did teams document their melting rate and percentage of change properly?
7. Imagine a slightly different melting race with ice cubes. The setup is shown in figure 12.2. Which ice cube do you think will melt faster: the one in front of heat lamp A or the one in front of heat lamp B? Write your reasons in your science notebook.

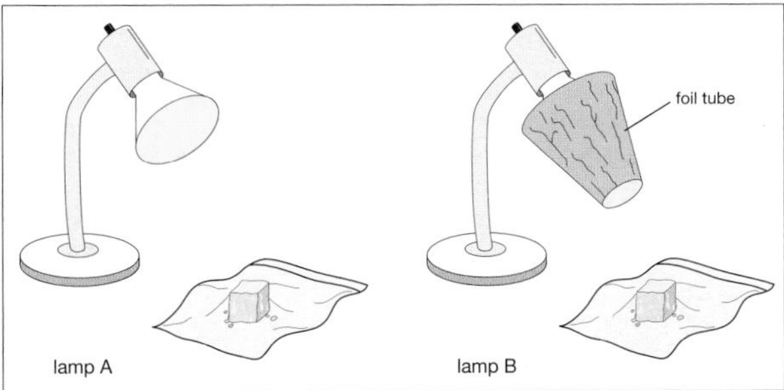

◄ **Figure 12.2 Two lamps, one with foil.** Which ice cube will melt faster? Both heat lamps are 20 centimeters (cm) from the ice cube. Lamp B has been wrapped in foil to direct the light.

8. Look at figure 12.2 again. Discuss with your team how you would design an experiment to measure the relative difference in heat between lamps A and B.
9. A team of students used the setup in figure 12.2 to heat 2 ice cubes for 5 min. The data from their science notebooks are in figure 12.3. Copy their data into your science notebook and complete the cells that are empty.

	Heat Lamp A	Heat Lamp B
Initial volume of ice cube	28 cm^3	30 cm^3
Volume of water melted	4 cm^3	6 cm^3
Melting rate (cm^3/min)		
Percent of cube melted		

▲ **Figure 12.3 Ice melting table.** Copy this table of experiment results into your science notebook. Fill in the cells without answers.

NOTES:

When teams have completed Steps 7–9, have them discuss the *Stop and Think* questions. Students should record their answers in their science notebooks. Listen to the teams discuss the questions and read through individual answers to assess student understanding of the role of energy in the melting process as well as their ability to use math to make predictions.

Answers to Stop and Think—Part I, SE pages 598–599

1. Students should indicate the strategy they used to melt the ice cube. Many teams will have used body heat to melt the ice cube. Given access to other materials or equipment, students will often suggest using other sources of heat—a candle, a lighter, a hot plate, or a Bunsen burner. Some teams might suggest breaking the ice cube into smaller pieces to increase the surface area and speed up the melting process.
2. Student predictions will vary. Students should base their predictions for the length of time to melt an entire ice cube on the melting rate they calculated in Step 4. For instance, if the melting rate is 5 cm^3/min and the volume of the ice cube is 28 cm^3, they should estimate that the entire ice cube would melt in 5–6 min.
3. Students should realize that it takes a source of energy (heat) to melt the ice. They probably discussed several possible sources. Melting glaciers will depend on radiation from the Sun (solar radiation). Thus, similarities are that heat is required for melting. Be open to ideas for differences. For example, glaciers undergo melting largely in the summer, but there could be the addition of a layer of snow in a summer snowstorm. This is common at high elevations, such as in the western United States.

   Similarly, glaciers such as the Antarctic and Greenland ice sheets (figure 12.4 in the student book) may undergo overall melting in the summers, but they will have large additions of snow in the winter. The key factor in whether they grow or shrink is whether more snow is added in winter than can melt in the summer.
4. Students should show a river of sorts either draining off an ice sheet as a waterfall, or perhaps even entering the ice sheet as a river. Eventually, the water would flow to the Atlantic Ocean.

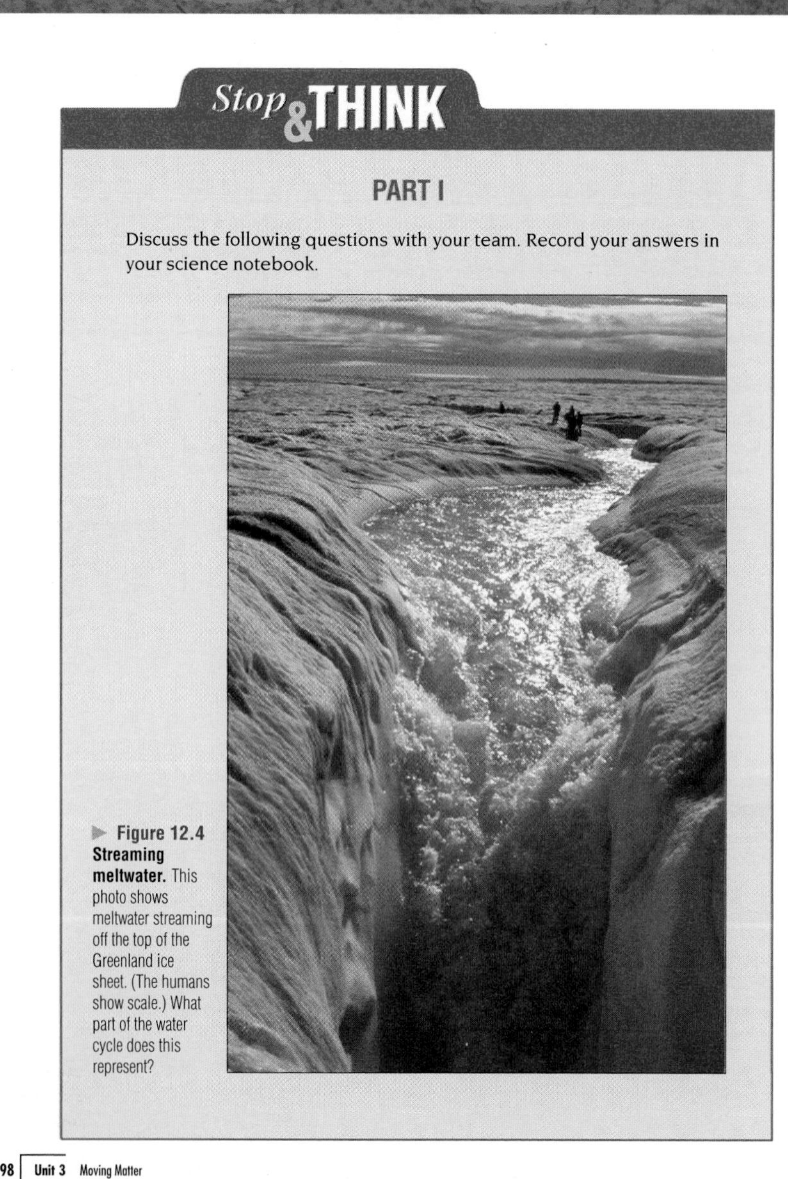

▶ **Figure 12.4 Streaming meltwater.** This photo shows meltwater streaming off the top of the Greenland ice sheet. (The humans show scale.) What part of the water cycle does this represent?

Process and Procedure

Part II: Glaciers Melting

Materials

none

Read the introduction to this part of the investigation with your students. Tell them that they will be focusing on "the real thing"—the melting of glaciers. Explain that glaciers can be relatively small, such as the glaciers found in mountain valleys, or large, such as the ice sheets that cover large parts of continents. The term glacier as used in this chapter refers to both types of glaciers. If you can, project some of the fabulous images available on the Web for your class.

Students will be working on Steps 1–7 in teams. These steps will take them through several short readings, as well as discussion with their team. Decide if you need to use a particular reading strategy with your students or whether you can assign some of the reading as homework.

As teams work through the investigation, listen to their discussions to assess their current understanding of the cause of melting glaciers. Also listen for evidence that students understand the difference between the following pairs of terms: climate and weather, glacials and interglacials.

Answers to Steps 1, 3–5, 7, SE pages 599–602

1. Students might not be sure of the answer to this question, although they may say that it has to do with colder temperatures or darker winters. At this point, just encourage their best thinking. Glaciers tend to be located near the poles because cooler climates allow for the accumulation of snow in the winter that does not entirely melt in the summer.

1. Recall the strategy you used to melt the ice in Step 3. What other strategies might you have used if you had access to other materials or equipment?
2. Predict how long it would take to melt an entire ice cube using the same strategy your team used in Step 3. Use examples of data in your answer.
3. How does the small-scale melting of an ice cube relate to the larger-scale melting of glaciers on Earth? What is similar and what is different?
4. Examine figure 12.4. It shows meltwater flowing off the top of the Greenland continental ice sheet. Think back to your work with the water cycle. Where do you think this water is going? What part of the water cycle is this? Draw a diagram or sketch to show your ideas.

Part II: Glaciers Melting

Materials

none

Process and Procedure

In Part I, you explored how fast an ice cube melts. You also noted that it takes energy to melt an ice cube. In the *Stop and Think* questions, you began to examine how your experience with ice cubes relates to glaciers. But what does it really take for a glacier to melt? Work with your team to think more about that question in Part II.

1. Why do most glaciers tend to be located near the poles? Record the best thinking of your team for this question in your science notebook.

It is useful for you and your team to diagram ideas about glaciers in your science notebooks. If you draw a map, ask yourselves, "Where do glaciers occur on Earth?"

2. You know it takes energy to melt an ice cube. It also takes energy to melt the ice of glaciers. Where does the energy come from? Read the following paragraphs to learn more about that energy.

   The source of energy coming to Earth's surface is the Sun. That energy arrives here as **solar radiation**. Most of the solar radiation coming to Earth is in the form of visible light. You studied this in Level 1 of *BSCS Science: An Inquiry Approach*. Overall, the solar radiation that Earth receives is relatively constant. However, different parts of Earth have different

SCILINKS NSTA
Topic: solar radiation
Go to: www.scilinks.org
Code: 2Inquiry599

NOTES:

NOTES:

3. The diagram would look similar to figure 12.5 in the student book, but with the axis of the Northern Hemisphere tilted 23.5° away from the Sun, rather than toward the Sun.
4. This diagram combines Steps 2 and 3. It should show Earth's orbit around the Sun with the axis or rotation tilted in the same direction on each side of the Sun. Where the axis of Earth tilts toward the Sun (Northern Hemisphere), students should write the label "summer." At the other side of the orbit, where the axis tilts away from the Sun, students should write the label "winter." The transition from summer to winter in orbit is labeled "fall." The label "spring" is opposite fall.

intensities of solar radiation. It all depends on which parts of Earth are most directly "facing" the Sun.

In Part I of this activity, you noticed a difference in how the ice cubes melted between the more and less concentrated outputs from two lamps. Solar radiation coming to Earth varies in a similar way. At low latitudes near the equator, solar radiation affects Earth most directly. At higher latitudes, the intensity of radiation decreases due to the curvature of Earth. This is because the same amount of radiation must be spread over a larger surface area. At the North and South poles, solar radiation has the lowest intensities because the Sun's rays are at such a low angle to Earth's surface. This is shown in figure 12.5.

Still, the poles get solar radiation during their "summers" due to the tilt of Earth's axis of rotation. **Tilt** is the angle between the Earth's rotation axis and incoming solar radiation. The tilt of Earth's rotation axis is toward the Sun (with north facing up) in figure 12.5. Central and North America receive direct radiation from the Sun. Solar radiation falls upon the North Pole, but not the South Pole. This is when it is summer for continents in the Northern Hemisphere (North America, Europe, Asia). The Southern Hemisphere receives less solar radiation at this time. This is their winter (Australia, South America). You probably know that tilt and radiation tell the seasons. You will learn more about variations in solar radiation in the elaborate activity, *The Astronomical Theory*, later in this chapter.

3. Figure 12.5 shows solar radiation striking Earth during summer for the Northern Hemisphere. Draw in your science notebook a diagram showing solar radiation during winter for the Northern Hemisphere.
4. Summer and winter are the extremes in climate for North America. Draw in your science notebook a diagram of Earth orbiting the Sun. For a tilt of 23.5 degrees (°), show 4 positions for fall, winter, spring, and summer for the Northern Hemisphere.
5. The seasonal changes in solar radiation described in Step 2 take place in annual cycles. These changes in radiation affect Earth's climate.

▼ **Figure 12.5 Solar radiation and Earth.** The amount of solar radiation varies with the curvature of Earth and the tilt of the rotation axis. What season is shown for the South Pole?

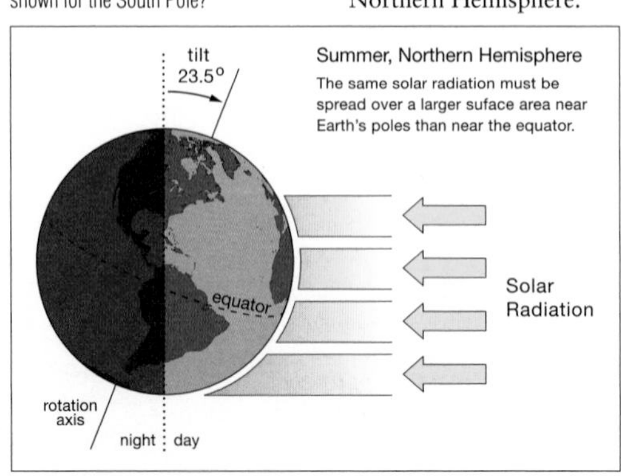

600 Unit 3 Moving Matter

NOTES:

Climate versus Weather

"How's the weather?" "What is the weather like where you live?" All you would have to do to answer these questions is to walk outside. Is it hot or cold, wet or dry, sunny or cloudy, windy or calm? **Weather** includes the conditions we experience in relatively short periods of time, like hours or days. Weather can be the passing of an afternoon thunderstorm, a cold front, or a persistent heat wave. Weather is a snapshot of the atmosphere at a particular time and place.

Climate is different from weather. **Climate** is the average weather in a region over longer periods of time—a year, a decade, a century, or even longer. Descriptions of climates often include average weather conditions (usually averaged over 30 years) as well as statistics of weather extremes. The daily weather report often includes average temperature highs and lows and precipitation rates. These data reflect local climate. The term climate can also be used to describe regions. A region that has consistently high temperatures and rainfall can be described as having a hot, wet, or tropical climate.

Climate refers to the general weather conditions over a long period of time. For instance, in Colorado, the summers tend to be warm and the winters tend to be cold. This is very different from areas around the equator, where temperatures are warm all year.

SCI LINKS NSTA
Topic: climate
Go to: www.scilinks.org
Code: 2Inquiry601

a. Read *FYI—Climate versus Weather.*

b. How would you describe the climate where you live?

Do not confuse climate with weather. If you are not sure what the difference is, refer to *FYI—Climate versus Weather.*

c. The strange discoveries you read about in the engage activity are evidence of the most recent ice age. What do you think Earth's climate was like during the last ice age?

6. Read the following paragraphs to learn more about ice ages and their link to climate. Check your understanding with your team.

The overall climate on Earth is cold during an ice age. The climate is so much colder that glaciers can cover much of the continents. These massive continental glaciers are called **ice sheets**. These blankets of ice can be several kilometers (km) thick. Ice ages have occurred many times in the past. In fact, in recent geologic history, Earth has switched back and forth between warm and cold periods. The cold periods are referred to as ice ages, or **glacials**. Periods of warm overall climate, such as now, are called **interglacials**.

The most recent glacial period is called the **Last Glacial Maximum (LGM)**. This peak was at 21,000 years ago (21 kya).

To save time and space, you can abbreviate thousands of years ago as "kya."

5b. Students should describe the typical seasonal climate for their community. Check that they do not describe weather events that may occur on the scale of days.

5c. The climate was likely colder during the most recent ice age. Evidence includes animals with long fur and the growth and migration south of ice sheets. Students probably would not be aware of the substantial growth of alpine glaciers during the ice ages that occurred at lower latitudes (Rockies, Sierra Nevada, European Alps).

Students might suggest more snow during a glacial. You might ask them whether they actually mean more snow or more precipitation in the water cycle. For the latter, you can ask how they would distinguish between greater amounts of precipitation during an interglacial, if the rain just returned to the ocean in rivers (versus snow being stored in ice caps).

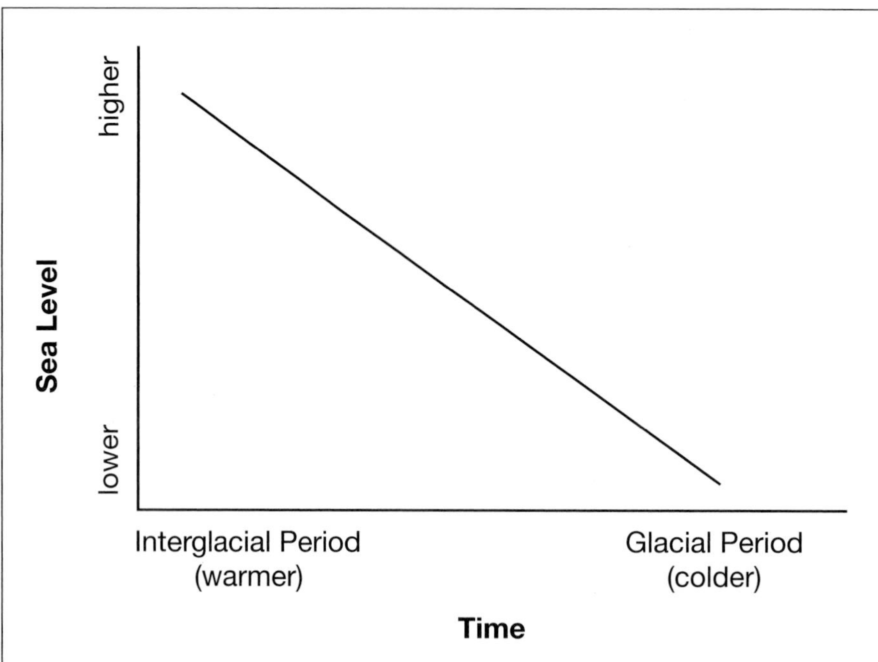

▶ **Figure T12.2 Sea level during glacials and interglacials.** This graph shows a high sea level during warm periods, such as the present, and a low sea level during the LGM. During the LGM, the global climate was cold, and several percent of all water on Earth was stored on the continents as large ice sheets.

7a. Students should realize that the volume of water stored in the global ice reservoir is larger during glacial periods than during interglacial periods. They do not need to memorize values, but water in ice sheets varies from about 3 percent to 6 percent between glacials and interglacials.

7b. Students should realize that sea level would have to be lower during the Last Glacial Maximum (LGM) because more water is stored on the continents in the global ice reservoir. This decreases the water in the global ocean reservoir (figure T12.2).

7c. Students should draw a line on the graph sloping from upper left (interglacial) to lower right (glacial). Higher sea level corresponds to less ice on continents. Lower sea level corresponds to more ice in oceans.

When teams have completed Step 7, have students answer the *Stop and Think—Part II* questions individually. These questions are suitable for homework. If students struggle with the questions, allow discussion of the answers.

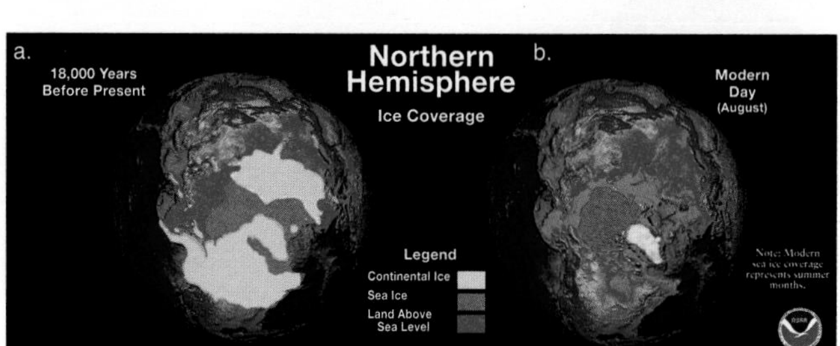

▲ **Figure 12.6 Earth today versus Earth during the Last Glacial Maximum (LGM).** (a) During the LGM, about 6 percent of the world's water was stored in the global ice reservoir. Glaciers covered as much as 30 percent of Earth's land area. (b) Today, only about 3 percent of Earth's water is trapped in the form of ice, covering about 10 percent of Earth's land area.

As shown in figure 12.6a, glaciers covered a large portion of Europe and the North American continent during this period. We are currently experiencing an interglacial period on Earth. This is shown in figure 12.6b. During an interglacial, the climate is warmer overall and ice sheets are restricted to polar regions.

7. Use your understanding of the global water system to discuss Questions 7a–c with your team. Write your answers in your science notebook.
   a. How does the volume of water in different global reservoirs change from glacial periods to interglacial periods? Explain your reasoning.
   b. How do you think sea level has varied from the LGM (21 kya) to today?
   c. Copy the graph in figure 12.7 into your science notebook. Draw a line in your sketch to show the relationship you would predict.

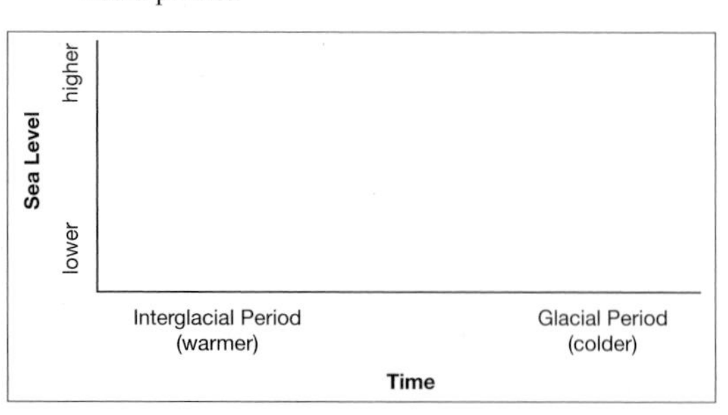

▶ **Figure 12.7 Sea level graph.** These axes show sea level as a function of whether Earth was in a glacial or interglacial period. What will your line look like on this graph?

602 Unit 3 Moving Matter

Answers to Stop and Think—Part II, SE page 603

1a. Some meteorologists say that "climate is what you expect but weather is what you get."

1b. According to one student, "climate tells you what clothes to buy, but weather tells you what clothes to wear."

1c. Students should know that tree rings record 1 year of growth for a tree. They may know (or be able to infer) that features of the tree rings indicate overall climate in a given year. The climate affects the growth record. For example, a single rainstorm may not affect rings too much, but a prolonged series of storms (i.e., a wet summer climate) might result in a thicker growth ring.

2. The climate would need to be warmer for glaciers to melt. Glaciers shrink when the mass of snow that melts on average in the summer is greater than the mass of snow that falls in the winter. This transition to shrinking glaciers can happen with several factors, such as patterns of increased solar radiation at high latitudes. The opposite (decreased solar radiation at high latitudes, and snow accumulation greater than snow melting) can cause glaciers and ice sheets to grow.
3. At this point, students might think colder winters are more likely to cause glacial periods because they associate colder winters with more snow and ice. Later, in the elaborate activity, *The Astronomical Theory*, students will learn that colder summers are more conducive to forming glaciers (characteristic of glacial periods) because there is less melting of snow and ice and therefore more overall accumulation of snow and ice. Students do not need to know the correct answer at this time. Instead, the purpose of this question is to get students thinking about this idea.
4. This is a good question to assess whether students understand the cause of the seasons. Without a tilt of Earth's axis, the amount of radiation per spot on Earth would not vary in a seasonal way. For example, each of the poles would be equally cold and near dark for each day of the year due to the persistent low angle of light. Conversely, the Sun at the equator would always pass directly overhead each day of the year. Locations at midlatitudes would have the same length of day all year, as a function of latitude, and there would be no seasons.

Stop & THINK

PART II

Answer the following questions individually in your science notebook.

1. Do you understand the difference between the terms *climate* and *weather*? Show this by filling in each blank in the following sentences.
   - **a.** Some meteorologists say that "__________ is what you expect but __________ is what you get."
   - **b.** According to one student, "__________ tells you what clothes to buy, but __________ tells you what clothes to wear."
   - **c.** Have you heard of tree rings? Do you think that a series of tree rings tells you about weather or climate? Use a sketch with labels to explain your answer.
2. Describe the conditions that would be necessary for glaciers to melt or to advance.
3. Which do you think would be more likely to cause a glacial period—colder winters or colder summers? Why?
4. Imagine that the rotation axis for Earth had zero tilt. What would this imply for the climate during the year in your community?

   It is best to use sketches to help understand the question and to show your answer.

Part III: Glacier Melting Rates

Materials

For each team of 3 students

1 calculator (optional)

Process and Procedure

In Part I, you melted an ice cube and calculated its melting rate. In Part II, you began to think about how really large chunks of ice—glaciers and ice sheets—can melt. You also looked at some of the factors that increased melting and the advance of glaciers.

In this part, you will investigate the melting rate for glaciers and ice sheets since the most recent ice age. This is the LGM. Work in your team to complete this part of the investigation.

Chapter 12 Evidence for the Ice Ages 603

Process and Procedure

Part III: Glacier Melting Rates

Materials

For each team of 3 students

1 calculator (optional)

Read the introduction to Part III with your students. This part of the explore actually involves a series of discussions, readings, and calculations. Steps 4 and 5 require some mathematical manipulations that include reading graphs and doing unit conversions. Depending on your students' skill level, you might need to review necessary math skills or provide additional support along the way. Some concepts should be relatively straightforward (e.g., volume = area × height), so work with students to apply these concepts to new settings.

Have students work in teams to complete Steps 1–7. Circulate through the room, listening to team interactions, observing calculations, and asking students to share their progress. These interactions will provide opportunities to assess student understanding of glacier melting rates and their relationship to sea level. Interactions and learning within the team are very important.

It is vital that students see that the sea level changes in this section are not a "flood" per se, but a very slow process of submerging the edge of continents. During this slow submerging of the edges of the continents, the total change in sea level was only about 125–135 m. Sea level only *rose* to current levels, but did not cover the continents any further.

In Step 1, students make guesses about the rate of ice melting as the global climate moves from a glacial period to an interglacial period (i.e., LGM to present). Students also offer ideas about how scientists would measure rates of sea level change at a time well before modern instruments.

Steps 2–5 help students make connections between sea level, the melting of glaciers, and determining geologic ages for changes in sea level. For the latter, the method that is discussed is radiometric dating of shallow marine corals.

3a. Sea level rose from about 20–6 kya. The change is about 125 m in about 14 kyr, or about 1 m per 112 years, or roughly 1 m per century. This is also necessarily the "slope" in figure 12.9. The slope has a brief steep section between 14 and 15 kya. This is likely a little meltwater surge to the ocean that increases sea level by about 25 m over 1 kyr, or about 1 m per 40 years.

3b. The rise in sea level effectively ended by 5–6 kya.

3c. Student statements should reflect that sea level rose gradually during the period of time from about 20 kya to about 6 kya, when it reached current levels.

3d. Students should notice that much more land area is exposed in the global map from the LGM. Vast areas currently under the ocean are exposed. For example, Australia is connected to all of Indonesia, the Persian Gulf is dry, and Georges Bank, a prime cod fishing ground off New England, is dry land. The Bahamas appears as several large islands rather than the current scattering of small islands.

Answers to Steps 1, 3–5, 7, SE pages 604–608

1a. Students should make a prediction about glacial ice melting rates. Check that their predictions are actual rates with units of change in volume across time. Be open to ideas at this time.

1b. Students will likely have difficulty coming up with a reasonable guess about how scientists would measure glacial ice melting rates. The point of this question is to get them thinking, as well as to provide a segue to the reading in Step 2.

1. The LGM ended around 21 kya. Since then, large amounts of ice have melted, reducing the size of glaciers on Earth. Discuss the following questions with your team and record ideas in your science notebook.
   a. How fast do you think the ice melted?
   b. How do you think scientists figure out how fast the ice melted?
2. Geologists cannot measure directly how much ice was on Earth during the LGM. Instead, they rely on the water cycle to relate changes in sea level to the melting of ice. Read the following paragraphs to learn more about how sea level links to the amount of ice on Earth.

   Water from the sea travels through the atmosphere and falls as precipitation on the continents. Some of the precipitation is winter snow. If all of that winter snow does not melt in the next summer, the snow will accumulate. Year after year of compacted, piled snow develops into glaciers and ice sheets. This frozen water remains on continents; it cannot return to the ocean. Thus, sea level goes down. A lot of ice must accumulate for a small drop in sea level. Scientists estimate that it takes about 350,000–400,000 cubic kilometers (km^3) of ice for a 1-meter (m) drop in sea level. Of course, there are a number of variables for this estimate. But a value in this range is a good starting point.

   How do scientists measure past changes in sea level? One method is to study coral reefs. The flat tops for some coral species correspond to sea level at low tide when the coral was living. Some types of coral grow at very specific depths in the ocean (figure 12.8). Scientists search for dead corals and measure their height above or below the current sea level. Then they date the corals using radiometric age dating. You learned about age dating in chapter 6. These data tell how long it has been since the sea level was at a given height. Figure 12.9 shows the changes in sea level in meters since the last ice age at about 21 kya.
3. Use Step 2 and figure 12.9 to answer Questions 3a–d about sea level change.
   a. When was the rate of melting the fastest?
   b. When did the glaciers effectively stop melting?
   c. Write a single statement that summarizes the main point of figure 12.9.
   d. Figure 12.10 shows a map of Earth at the LGM. How does this map differ from a current map of Earth?

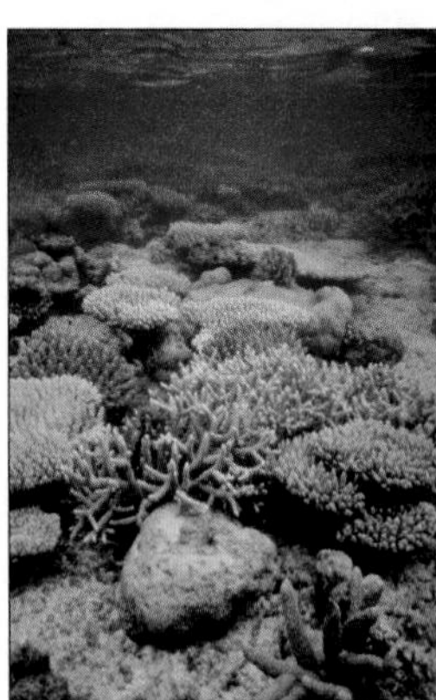

▲ **Figure 12.8 Reef ecosystem near sea level.** Some species of coral in reefs grow at specific depths. These coral are about 1–2 m beneath the surface of the ocean.

604 | Unit 3 Moving Matter

NOTES:

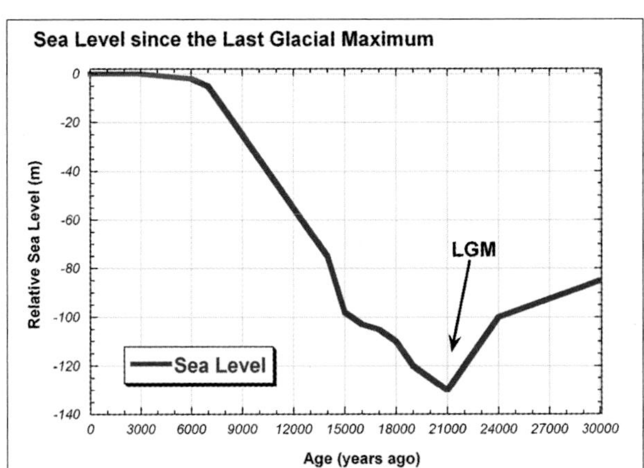

Source: Quinn, T. M. (2000). Shallow water science and ocean drilling face challenges. *Eos, Transactions of the American Geophysical Union*, *81*, 397-404. and Cutler, et al. (2003). Rapid sea-level fall and deep-ocean temperature change since the last interglacial period. Earth and Planetary Science Letters, 206, 253–271.

▲ **Figure 12.9 Sea level from the LGM to today.** Negative numbers indicate lower sea levels in the past relative to today. Today, sea level is at 0 m.

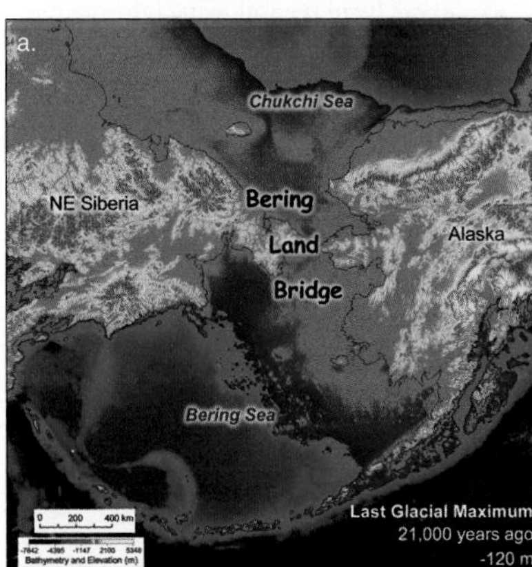

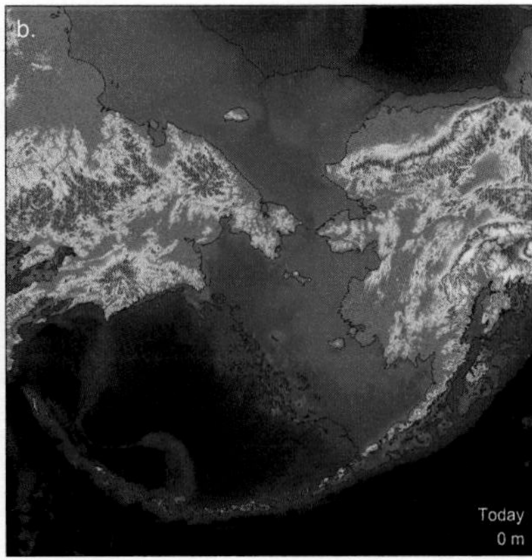

▲ **Figure 12.10 Two maps: Bering Land Bridge at the LGM, and today.** The first map shows the Bering Land Bridge during the LGM about 21 kya. Sea level is about 120 m lower than the current sea level, shown in the second map (today). The map in figure 12.6 shows the locations of continental ice sheets in northeast Siberia and Alaska during the LGM.

Chapter 12 Evidence for the Ice Ages 605

4a. Answers will vary, depending on the data points teams select. For example, 1 pair of points could correspond with the answer for Step 3a. As *xy* coordinates, the points are (20,000, 125) and (6,000, 0). Students could also select points from 12,000 to 9,000: (12,000, −55) and (9,000, −25). This example is used in the next answer, but you should get roughly the same answer for different points on the same line.

4b. Sea level rises from −55 m to −25 m, or a net increase of 30 m.

4c. Using height as 30 m (0.03 km) and area as 3.62×10^8 square kilometers (km^2), the volume added to oceans is about 10 million cubic kilometers (km^3) of water.

$$\begin{aligned} \text{volume} &= \text{area} \times \text{height} \\ &= \left(3.62 \times 10^8\ \text{km}^2\right) \times (0.03\ \text{km}) \\ &= 10.86 \times 10^6\ \text{km}^3 \end{aligned}$$

4d. The time for a sea level increase of 30 m is 3 kyr.

4e. Using volume from Step 4c and time from Step 4d, the melting rate is about 3.620 cubic kilometers per year (km^3/yr). By this point in the program, your students should be able to do this division problem with 2 simple exponents. The steps and equivalent answers follow.

$$\text{change in volume per time} = \frac{10.86 \times 10^6\ \text{km}^3}{3{,}000\ \text{yr}} = \frac{10.86 \times 10^6\ \text{km}^3}{3 \times 10^3\ \text{yr}}$$

$$= \frac{10.86}{3} \times 10^6 \times 10^{-3}\ \frac{\text{km}^3}{\text{yr}} = 3.62 \times 10^{(6-3)}\ \frac{\text{km}^3}{\text{yr}}$$

$$= 3.62 \times 10^3\ \frac{\text{km}^3}{\text{yr}} = 3{,}620\ \frac{\text{km}^3}{\text{yr}}$$

Another way to do the problems gives the same answer. For any 2 points on the curve, the slope is about a 1-m change per 100 years. Using an area of $3.62 \times 10^8\ km^2$ for the ocean and height for a 1-m rise in sea level (0.001 km = 10^{-3} km), the volume is just

$$(3.62 \times 10^8\ \text{km}^2)(10^{-3}\ \text{km}) = 3.62 \times 10^{(8-3)}\ \text{km}^3 = 3.62 \times 10^5\ \text{km}^3.$$

The rate of change per 100 years is just this volume divided by 100 years, or $3.62 \times 10^3\ km^3/yr$, the same as above.

4. Use Step 2 and figure 12.9 to estimate the melting rate of glaciers and ice sheets since the LGM. Follow the method in Steps 4a–c to estimate the volume melted per time, just as you did with the ice cube.
   a. Select 2 points on the curve in figure 12.9 between 6 kya and the LGM.
   b. Write in your science notebook the change in sea level for those 2 points.
   c. Use this change in height of sea level to estimate the volume of water added to the ocean by melting glaciers. Show your answer (and all your work) in units of km^3.

   Volume = area × height

The surface area of the ocean is about 362 million square kilometers (km^2). Can you show this numerically?

   d. Return to the 2 points in Step 4a with figure 12.9. Write the amount of time between the points.
   e. Calculate the melting rate for the 2 points on figure 12.9. Check that you have units of cubic kilometers per year (km^3/yr).

Recall that a rate tells a change in something, such as sea level, per unit time. The melting rate is the slope ($\Delta y/\Delta x$, or rise over run) of the sea level curve.

5. How does the melting rate for glaciers in Step 4 compare with the melting rate for ice cubes? Read the following information and do the steps to make the comparison.

   In Part I, you measured the melting rate of an ice cube in cubic centimeters per minute (cm^3/min). Then you estimated the melting rate of glaciers in units of km^3/yr. To compare these two rates, you will need to use the same units. Which unit should you use? Because an ice cube melts in a few minutes, it would not make sense to use years as the time factor. So it is easiest to convert the melting rates of glaciers to cm^3/min.
   a. Take your answer from Step 4a in units of km^3/yr and first convert it to cubic kilometers per minute (km^3/min). You need to fill in the "?" in the following conversion for this first step.

$$\left(\frac{?\ \text{km}^3}{1\ \text{yr}}\right) \times \left(\frac{1\ \text{yr}}{?\ \text{days}}\right) \times \left(\frac{1\ \text{day}}{?\ \text{hr}}\right) \times \left(\frac{1\ \text{hr}}{?\ \text{min}}\right) = ?\ \frac{\text{km}^3}{\text{min}}$$

Be sure to draw a slash through units that cancel.

5a. You will see that converting cubic kilometers per year down to cubic kilometers per minute should reduce the volume by a factor of 525,960 ($365.25 \times 24 \times 60$):

$$\left(\frac{3{,}620\ \text{km}^3}{1\ \cancel{\text{yr}}}\right) \times \left(\frac{1\ \cancel{\text{yr}}}{365.25\ \cancel{\text{days}}}\right) \times \left(\frac{1\ \cancel{\text{day}}}{24\ \cancel{\text{hr}}}\right) \times \left(\frac{1\ \cancel{\text{hr}}}{60\ \text{min}}\right) = 0.0069\ \frac{\text{km}^3}{\text{min}}$$

5b. The conversion from cubic kilometers per minute to cubic centimeters per minute gives units that can be compared directly with the experiments in your class. Write out the conversions again.

$$0.0069 \frac{\cancel{\text{km}^3}}{\text{min}} \times \left(\frac{10^{15}\ \text{cm}^3}{\cancel{\text{km}^3}}\right) = 0.0069 \times 10^{15} \frac{\text{cm}^3}{\text{min}}$$

$$= 6.9 \times 10^{-3} \times 10^{15} \frac{\text{cm}^3}{\text{min}} = 6.9 \times 10^{(15-3)} \frac{\text{cm}^3}{\text{min}}$$

$$= 6.9 \times 10^{12} \frac{\text{cm}^3}{\text{min}}$$

5c. In class, melting rates might have been about 5 cm^3/min. Melting rates for glaciers are a minimum of 6.9×10^{12} cm^3/min (this is a minimum for several reasons). Thus, these rates differ by a factor of about 1,000 billion (10^{12}), or 1 trillion. Glaciers absorb much more energy from the Sun and their environment than an ice cube does. Moreover, as students will see later, once glaciers become unstable, they tend to collapse and melt very rapidly.

Finally, in Steps 6 and 7, students read about *proxy data*, with tree rings as an example of proxy data. They also consider why the sea level record is a proxy record. This is important for when they consider sea core data in the next activity. The goal is to show that proxy data are not exact measurements, yet proxy data can preserve very detailed information about the history of the planet.

b. Convert your answer from Step 5a from units of km^3/min to cm^3/min. Use the conversion that 1 km^3 equals 10^{15} cm^3.

If you cannot cleanly cancel units on the top and bottom here, then the conversion may not be set up properly.

c. Now you should have 2 melting rates, both in units of cm^3/min. One melting rate is for your ice cube, and the other is for glaciers and ice sheets after the LGM. How do the rates compare? Are they what you expected? What might explain the difference in melting rates? Explain with complete sentences in your science notebook.

6. Read the following paragraphs to learn about **proxy data**.

Paleoclimatology is the study of past climates. Records of past climates from satellites and other human measurements (thermometers, rain gauges) only go back about 100–150 years. This range of time is too small to record the full variation in climates. For example, you have been considering glacial and climate change occurring over thousands of years.

To learn about ancient climates, paleoclimatologists cannot rely on direct measurements. Instead, they rely on indirect measurements, or proxy data, to infer the history of past climates. A **proxy** is something that stands in for something else. It is an indirect measure.

You are probably familiar with one type of proxy data: tree rings. Look at the section of a tree trunk in figure 12.11. The cross section shows the number of rings and their thickness.

◀ **Figure 12.11 Tree rings.** Tree rings give proxy data on the growth history of a tree. Those data often include information about patterns of climate.

Chapter 12 Evidence for the Ice Ages 607

7a. Sea level records are proxy data because they are not measured directly by instruments in time (versus, for example, using a thermometer to measure air temperature). Individual points must be measured, such as a coral of a given age, which indicates when the sea level was at a certain position. The proxy record for sea level history is then constructed from these coral data points.

7b. Be open to other ideas your students have about proxy records for past climate. They may talk about ice cores, sedimentary records, tree rings, pollen, fossils, or mud from the sea. The latter is the topic of the rest of the chapter. In the next activity, students will learn about proxy records from cores in sediments where forams give chemical evidence about past climates. This is an indirect or proxy record because the $\delta^{18}O$ in a foram shell reflects the oxygen isotopes in ocean water at some point in the past. As you will see, the oxygen isotopes indicate the amount of water being stored on continents in glaciers.

7c. If scientists can find multiple, independent lines of evidence to support a particular theory, then they have more confidence in their ideas. Because so many different pieces of data all point to the repeating patterns of glacial and interglacial periods, scientists feel confident that they actually occurred. An example is certain organic materials that have been radiometrically dated both by carbon-14 (^{14}C) as well as uranium-based methods. The agreement between dates for 2 completely independent methods gives confidence in the results.

After *Process and Procedure*, have students work in teams to answer the *Reflect and Connect* questions. Reading student responses to these questions will give you an idea of their current level of understanding of the evidence (changes in sea level) that provides clues to Earth's past climates.

Answers to Reflect and Connect, SE page 608

1. Students should realize that Earth's climate is cooler during glacial periods and warmer during interglacial periods. They might also point out that glaciers are limited to the mountains and the poles during interglacials, and that glaciers covered large portions of Europe and northern North America during the LGM. Animals were likely different and had to adjust where they lived based on different environments. Be open to what students are learning at this point.
2. Students should recognize that during a glacial period, water is added to the global ice reservoir. Less melting in the summer reduces the amount of water returning to the ocean. During an interglacial period, water moves more readily between evaporation and runoff back to the ocean. Moreover, runoff increases by the contribution from melting ice sheets. There is less water stored as ice during an interglacial period. Check that students reflect this in their diagrams.

This is a good time to point out that it is actually the colder summers that reduce the amount of melting, and the accumulation of snow and ice. Snow and ice accumulate during winters during

Answers to Reflect and Connect are on TE pages 608–609.

The total number of rings tells the age of the tree. The thickness of the rings gives information about moisture and temperature conditions during a given year. Thicker rings often mean high rainfall. Thinner rings also can tell of past drought. Scientists do not have to cut a tree down to study its rings. They can simply remove a horizontal core from the tree. They can then analyze the cores for the number and thickness of rings. This gives proxy data about past climates. Some of these climate records extend up to 8,000 years.

7. Answer Questions 7a–c to show your understanding of proxy data.
   a. Explain why sea level data are considered proxy data.
   b. Describe another type of proxy data used to gather information about past climates.
   c. Why do scientists need different kinds of data to test the idea that Earth has had ice ages in the past?

Reflect and Connect

Work in your team to answer the following questions. Record your answers in your science notebook.

1. What are some characteristics of glacial and of interglacial periods on Earth? Think in terms of sea level, climate, or animals.
2. Compare the water cycle during glacial periods with the water cycle during interglacial periods. Address both the storage of water in global reservoirs and the movement of water between global reservoirs.

It may be most useful to use a diagram or sketch here with a written explanation.

3. What factors influence the advance and retreat of glaciers?
4. What do you think would happen to the climate of the Northern Hemisphere if Earth tilted 50° instead of the current 23.5°? Illustrate your answer with a simple sketch. Explain the effect on seasons and climates in your community.
5. How does your past experience with ice and ice cubes help you understand glaciers and ice ages?

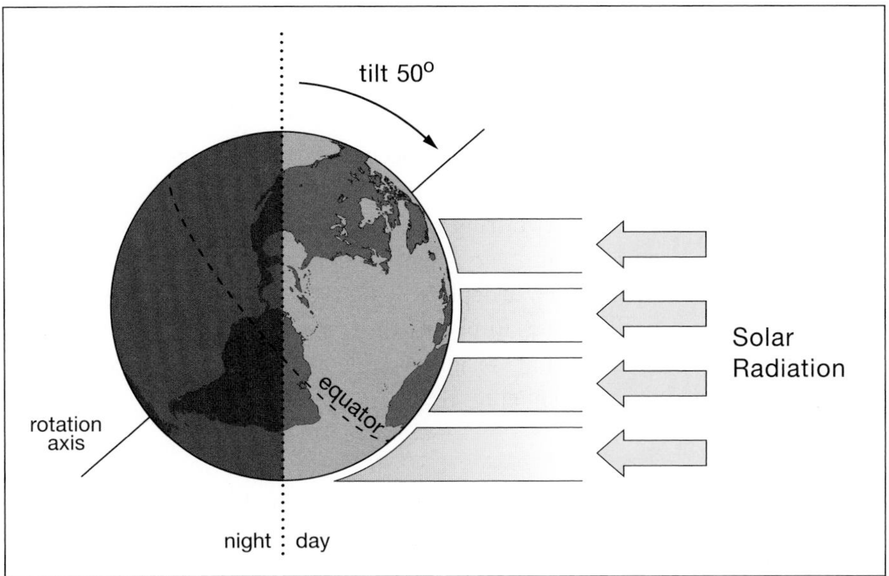

▲ **Figure T12.3 Summer for Earth with a 50° tilt.** The diagram shows the 50° tilt of the Northern Hemisphere toward the Sun, or the season of summer. Shading shows night and day. Rotating North America on a daily basis shows that a location at a latitude of about 40° would have 24 hours of sunlight in the summer, as well as complete darkness for several weeks in the winter.

EXPLORE
EXPLAIN

The Core of the Matter

In the engage activity, you analyzed evidence for past ice ages. In the explore activity, *Ice Blocks: Growing, Shrinking*, you learned about ice in the form of glaciers. You explored why and how fast these huge reservoirs of ice melt. You also learned about the link between these global ice reservoirs and sea level.

But how exactly would the ocean tell you about an ice age? How do oceans at the equator reflect the formation of ice sheets at the North and South poles? In *The Core of the Matter*, you will work alone and in teams to make the connection between the ocean and another key piece of evidence of past ice ages.

Part I: Heavy Water, Light Water

Materials

For each team of 6 students

- 1 shallow plastic box
- 10 light objects (white Styrofoam balls)
- 10 heavy objects (black Styrofoam balls)
- 1 large sheet (plastic drop cloth, bedsheet, or blanket)
- 1 stopwatch
- 1 calculator

Process and Procedure

In the explore activity, you looked at some characteristics of ice ages. You explored the melting of ice to form water and related this to changes in sea level. In particular, you used the water cycle to explore how water moved from one reservoir to another during glacial and interglacial periods. As you saw in chapter 10, *The Water System*, the water cycle is one example of a geochemical cycle. (Remember, a geochemical cycle describes the storage and movement of a particular element in the earth system.) In Part I of this investigation, you will take a closer look at the water cycle.

1. Ice melting and changing the sea level is one way water moves from reservoir to reservoir in the earth system. How does water move out of the ocean reservoir? Observe your teacher's demonstration of the most common process. Write the name of this process in your science notebook.
2. What would happen in a model if some balls that represent water molecules were heavier than other balls that represent water molecules? Work in a team of 6 students to explore this model.

Chapter 12 Evidence for the Ice Ages 609

both glacial and interglacial periods. However, during glacial periods, summers are often colder, which reduces the amount of melting.

3. Students should realize that solar radiation and temperatures are the primary factors affecting the advance and retreat of glaciers. Students might already know that under the weight of the overlying ice and snow, the bottom of glaciers flows like a very slow river of molasses. We would never know this from an ice cube, but that is what helps give the appearance of "ice rivers" in alpine glaciers.
4. Students will encounter a version of this concept in a later activity (the elaborate activity). Answers could be modeled on figure 12.5 in the student book by dropping the rotation axis farther down toward the Sun to a tilt of 50°. By doing this, students can show that even at a latitude of about 40° (roughly in line with San Francisco, Denver, Chicago, and New York), summer would have light for 24 hours per day. The downside is that during the winter, there would be several weeks of darkness (figure T12.3).
5. Student answers will vary. Look for responses that make a connection between students' personal experiences and what they are learning about glaciers and ice ages. Encourage them to organize their thoughts or ideas in a format such as a T-table.

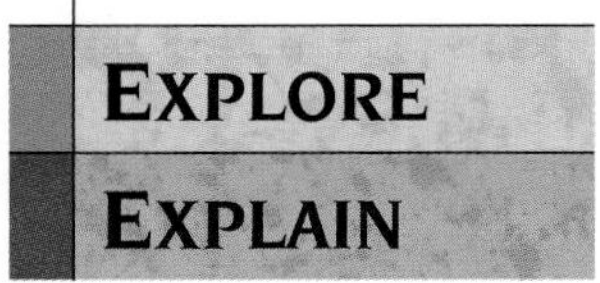

The Core of the Matter

Activity Overview

In the engage activity, students raised some questions about past ice ages. In the explore activity, *Ice Blocks: Growing, Shrinking*, they learned about ice, and about why and how fast glaciers melt. Students also explored the relationship between these ice reservoirs and sea level, and made connections back to their work with the water cycle in chapter 10. In *The Core of the Matter*, students will explore additional evidence of past ice ages and interpret some actual data themselves.

In Part I, students will take a closer look at the water cycle by exploring a model of evaporation of water. In addition, they will take a closer look at water itself by considering the question, "Is all water the same?" They will learn about the isotopes of oxygen in water molecules and that the lighter molecules preferentially evaporate from oceans. In Part II, they will focus on the record of oxygen in the water cycle. The variations in this geochemical cycle contribute to our understanding of paleoclimate. Students will discover the connection between the oxygen from water in the ocean and the oxygen in the shells of forams. In Part III, students will apply their understanding of geochemical cycles to interpret data from sea cores. This is where they can demonstrate with additional data that the evidence for the ice ages and climate change is a global signal.

Before You Teach

Background Information

Much of the background information that is helpful for this activity is in the student book and in the following *Process and Procedure*. You will find information on oxygen isotopes, oxygen reservoirs, foraminifera, and deep-sea cores. Some additional points follow.

Isotope Fractionation (Part I)

Isotopes are atoms with the same atomic number (number of protons) but different atomic masses. The different atomic masses lead to different physical properties. Oxygen has three isotopes: ^{16}O, ^{17}O, and ^{18}O. In this activity, we focus on the lighter ^{16}O isotope and the heavier ^{18}O isotope. These are the two most common oxygen isotopes.

Water molecules that contain the lighter oxygen isotopes ($H_2{}^{16}O$) evaporate more readily than do water molecules that contain the heavier oxygen isotopes ($H_2{}^{18}O$). A process that favors the transfer of one isotope of an element over another is called *fractionation*.

The preferential evaporation of light water ($H_2{}^{16}O$) over heavy water ($H_2{}^{18}O$) results in an increase in the ratio of ^{18}O to ^{16}O in ocean water. Scientists say the ocean is enriched in ^{18}O. It follows that atmospheric water, and the glaciers fed by this water, would be enriched in ^{16}O.

During glacial periods, the ocean is enriched in ^{18}O and there is a large amount of ^{16}O stored in glaciers on the continents. During interglacial periods, the ^{16}O is returned to the ocean, resulting in a lower ^{18}O:^{16}O ratio. Your students will explore this relationship (the ice-volume effect).

Fractionation due to evaporation is also affected by the energy available. Fractionation is more pronounced when the available energy is lower, and it is less pronounced when the available energy is higher. This temperature effect for fractionation (a temperature dependence) is significant in the study of oxygen isotopes in foram shells, but it is not developed for students in this investigation. The ultimate source of energy for the evaporation process is incoming solar radiation.

Fractionation can occur in other settings and for other elements. In carbon, for example, a fractionation effect also occurs during photosynthesis, where plants preferentially (and very slightly) incorporate $^{12}CO_2$ over $^{13}CO_2$. When the ^{13}C-depleted CO_2 ($^{12}CO_2$ enriched) is used to make tissues in plants, those tissues then have an isotopic makeup that is slightly depleted in ^{13}C relative to CO_2 in the atmosphere.

More about Forams (Part II)

The reading *Foram Forum* provides students with basic background information about foraminifera, or forams. These organisms are neither plants nor animals. They are in the kingdom Protoctista. The two types of forams are benthic (seafloor dwelling) and planktonic (ocean-surface dwelling). Of the 4,000 species alive today, only about 1 percent are planktonic.

Forams build their shells from calcium ions (Ca^{2+}) and bicarbonate ions $(HCO_3)^{-1}$. Students studied this reaction in chapter 11. Bicarbonate and calcium ions come from the weathering of rocks and minerals on continents and are carried to the ocean by rivers. For a calcium carbonate ($CaCO_3$) rock such as limestone, recall from chapter 11 that the weathering reaction can be represented by

$$CaCO_3 + H_2CO_3 \longrightarrow Ca^{2+}{}_{(aq)} + 2HCO_3{}^{-1}{}_{(aq)}.$$

Once the bicarbonate ions are in the ocean, an oxygen atom, either ^{18}O or ^{16}O, can move back and forth between bicarbonate, carbonic acid (H_2CO_3), carbon dioxide, and water. This equilibrium reaction keeps the oxygen in bicarbonate in constant isotopic "communication."

$$\underset{\text{carbon dioxide}}{CO_{2(aq)}} + \underset{\text{ocean water}}{H_2O_{(aq)}} \rightleftarrows \underset{\text{carbonic acid}}{H_2CO_{3(aq)}}$$

$$\rightleftarrows \underset{\text{bicarbonate}}{HCO_3{}^{1-}{}_{(aq)}} + \underset{\text{hydrogen ion}}{H^{1+}{}_{(aq)}}$$

As forams build their calcium carbonate shells, they incorporate oxygen from the bicarbonate ions, which has ^{18}O or ^{16}O from the ocean water. This reaction is shown in *Foram Forum* and is essentially the reverse of the limestone weathering reaction. As the oxygen content of the ocean water varies, the oxygen content of foram shells varies. When the ocean contains a higher-than-average amount of heavy oxygen (^{18}O), the forams incorporate this heavy oxygen into their shells. This is detected using mass spectrometry, as described in *δ ^{18}O—a Measure of Heavy and Light Oxygen* in the student book.

In this investigation, we use data from benthic forams. Benthic forams tend to have $\delta^{18}O$ values in the range of +3 to +5 ‰ (parts per thousand, or per mil). Planktonic forams typically have values ranging from 0 to −2 ‰. The variation in the values is related to the water temperature that the forams live in. The fractionation effect is larger in colder water. During the evaluate activity, some of your teams will examine data from both benthic and planktonic forams.

Ocean Drilling Program

Sea cores used in the chapter were completed under the Ocean Drilling Program (ODP). Thus, many refer to ODP site 722, for example. The current program has been reorganized under the Integrated Ocean Drilling Program (IODP). Data sets and current information are found at the IODP Web site, as well as at a number of other repositories for sea and paleoclimatology data.

Materials—Part I

For the teacher

1 shallow plastic box
10 light objects (2-in white Styrofoam balls)

For each team of 6 students

1 shallow plastic box
10 light objects (2-in white Styrofoam balls)
10 heavy objects (2-in black Styrofoam balls, each containing 3 1.5-in finishing nails; see *Advance Preparation*)
1 large sheet (plastic drop cloth, bedsheet, or blanket)
1 stopwatch
1 calculator

Materials—Part II

For the teacher

samples containing oxygen from different earth systems (See figure T12.7 for samples.)
mud samples with forams (and hand lens or microscope for viewing; see *Advance Preparation*)
sieve set (with at least 125-μm and 350-μm screens)
image of forams
1 seafloor model (either the play dough or the sand model):

- play dough model:
  - 4 containers of play dough, each a different color
  - 1 sharp blade (razor blade or craft knife; optional)
- sand model:
  - 1 large coffee can, 39-oz size
  - 1–1.5 qts fine-grained sand
  - white sand and food coloring or different colors of sand
  - water

For each team of 3 students

foram sample, if available
access to seafloor model
1 clear plastic straw
1 sheet of white paper

Materials—Part III

For the teacher

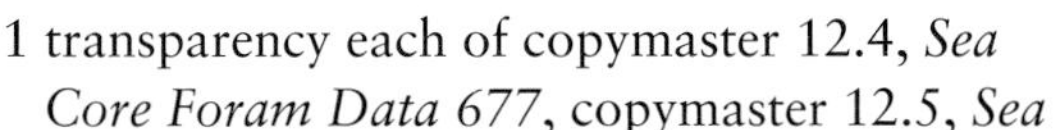
1 transparency of copymaster 12.3, *Unidentified Data*

1 transparency each of copymaster 12.4, *Sea Core Foram Data 677*, copymaster 12.5, *Sea*
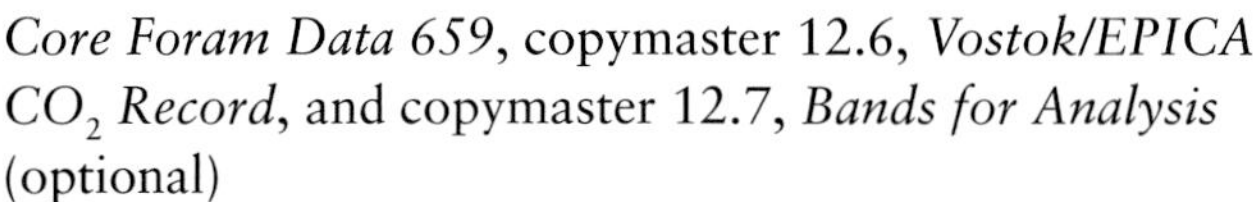
Core Foram Data 659, copymaster 12.6, *Vostok/EPICA CO_2 Record*, and copymaster 12.7, *Bands for Analysis* (optional)

For each team of 3 students

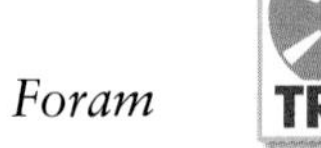
3 copies of copymaster 12.4, *Sea Core Foram Data 677*
3 copies of copymaster 12.5, *Sea Core Foram Data 659*
1 copy of copymaster 12.7, *Bands for Analysis*

Advance Preparation

For Part I, gather the materials needed for Steps 1 and 2. For Step 1, place 10 "light" Styrofoam balls in a shallow plastic box for your demonstration. These can be the same materials you use for the next step. For Step 2, it is important to use the materials as indicated. Use medium-sized plastic boxes that are shallow. Ideally, the heavy and light objects should fit in 1 layer at the bottom of the box, with a little extra room to spare. These boxes are available at most discount stores.

In developing this activity as written with 10 light objects and 10 heavy objects, we used a plastic box measuring 13×8×3 inches (in). This box is easy to hold with one hand and tap firmly with the other. We also had success with a larger box (15×10×5.5 in) and more objects (15 light and 15 heavy). The larger box might give slightly better reproducibility, but it is more difficult to handle. If you find a larger box with the appropriate length and width, you can cut down the height with a pair of scissors.

Use 2-in diameter white Styrofoam balls for the light objects and 2-in black Styrofoam balls for the heavy objects. Poke 3 1.5-in nails into each of the black balls to provide extra mass. Use finishing nails (no heads) and insert them far enough into the balls that students cannot see them. If you cannot find black balls, use all white balls and mark the heavy balls with marker or paint. These represent water containing the heavy isotope of oxygen, ^{18}O, or $H_2{}^{18}O$.

If you have to substitute materials for this part of the activity, be sure to try them out before having your students do the activity. One possible substitution is to use golf balls as the heavy objects and plastic, hollow practice golf balls as the light objects. It is important that the heavy and light objects be the same size. A box lid, like the type used to deliver copy paper, can be substituted for the plastic box.

You can replace the plastic sheet with a cloth sheet. Its only purpose is to keep the balls from going all over the place. If you do not have either type of sheet handy, omit it and gather the balls appropriately. Because the activity requires a lot of space, you might consider having students conduct this step outdoors or in a larger space than a classroom. You could also have one group of students conduct the model as a demonstration.

A clock or a student's wristwatch can be substituted for the stopwatch.

For Part II, gather actual samples of the various compounds that oxygen is found in on Earth. See figure T12.7 on TE page 614a for ideas.

Decide which of the 3 readings you can assign as homework.

Try to obtain sample foraminifera for your students. You need to do this weeks ahead of time. You can request them by filling out a short form at the IODP Web site. Request samples from equatorial regions, as they tend to have the most foram species, possibly up to 25–40 species. A small sieve set can be used to wash muds and other organics from the core. The set should have mesh sizes of at least about 125 μm and 350 μm, which will catch different species of forams. A simple sieve set with 4–6 meshes costs about $60–100 (e.g., Ward's Natural Science, Ben Meadows). Many images of foram shells, also called "tests," are also available at scientific Web sites.

Sea mud samples received from IODP may be fresh (moist and soft) or quite old (dry and hard). Either way, they can be successfully washed and sieved. The goal is that samples must be able to fall apart with very gentle swirling at most. Do not physically break apart any samples. This will crush and fragment the delicate foram tests. Follow these steps.

1. Place a sample in a 250-mL beaker.
2. Add enough water to cover the sample. Add ½ teaspoon of detergent such as Calgon if the sample is dry and hard. Let stand overnight. The next morning, gently swirl the sample. Most samples will be disaggregated by now. If not, swirl gently and let soak for another day.
3. Over a sink, slowly pour the disaggregated sample through the sieve set. Make sure that the set includes a 125–150 μm screen. Fine particles will wash down the drain, while the large particles (foraminifera and radiolaria) will remain on the sieve. Use as much water as necessary to rinse all the fine particles through the sieve, leaving only the larger particles. If the sieve clogs, clear it by gently tapping its side with your hand.

   Continue washing until the water coming out the bottom of the sieve appears clear. To check, pick up a drop of water from the under side of the sieve using your index finger. Place your thumb on the index finger and slowly stretch the drop, holding it up to the light. If the drop appears clear, you are finished.
4. At this point, do 1 of 2 things:
   - set the sieve aside to dry or
   - rinse the forams to one side of the sieve and (using as little water as possible) rinse the forams into a clean beaker by pouring water backward through the sieve. Set the beaker aside to evaporate and dry. You can use gentle heat in a drying oven as well.
5. When dry, use a small funnel (made out of paper if necessary) to pour the forams into small clear glass vials or other closed containers suitable for viewing under a binocular microscope. A good magnification is 25×. View the sample without opening the container to prevent spilling the forams.

You also need to prepare a model of seafloor sediment layers. Two possible models are described here. Select one of them and gather the appropriate materials.

- Play dough model: For this model, you need 4 containers of play dough, preferably each a different color. Remove the cylinder of play dough and use a knife to cut it into layers. Make the layers different sizes, somewhere between 0.5 and 2 cm. Stack the layers, alternating colors. Keep the stack under 5–6 cm. Place the stack back in the play dough container and replace the lid. This will keep students from seeing the layers before they take their core sample. Keep the lid on until you are ready to use the play dough. This model has several advantages. It is possible to cut the core sample in half, just like on a scientific cruise. In addition, it is possible to reuse the model simply by separating the clay, reforming the cylinders, and starting over. The clay layers do get somewhat distorted in size as the clay rubs against the plastic straw. Actual deep-sea cores are sometimes distorted in the same way for the same reasons.
- Sand model: For this model, you need fine-grained sand. You can get this from a scientific supply company or a local craft or home improvement store. Be sure to try this ahead of time. Dampen the sand so that it sticks together when you pick it up. If you need to color the sand, split it into 2 or 3 different bowls. Add a different color of food coloring to the sand in each bowl and mix well. (It is much easier to just buy colored sand.) Layer the sand into the coffee can, making 4–6 layers. Vary the thickness of the layers, but keep them less than 1-in thick. Make a record of the actual layers you use. This model is messier than the play dough model and does not lend itself to cutting open the core sample.

For Part III, make a transparency of copymaster 12.4, *Sea Core Foram Data 677*. It is also very useful to have transparencies of copymaster 12.5, *Sea Core Foram Data 659* and copymaster 12.6, *Vostok/EPICA CO_2 Record* for projecting during class discussion. It is very effective to move and match peaks, which cannot be done with the figures in the student book. A transparency of copymaster 12.7, *Bands for Analysis* is also useful to enable students to explore the concept that climate patterns are global.

As You Teach

Outcomes and Indicators of Success

By the end of this activity, students should

1. be able to use a model for geochemical cycling to describe oxygen cycling on Earth.

They will demonstrate their ability by

- recalling that the water cycle is one example of a geochemical cycle;
- recognizing that when water cycles, the elements that make up water (hydrogen and oxygen) also cycle;
- identifying and describing reservoirs of oxygen in the earth system and the various forms of oxygen (isotopes, elemental compounds) found within the reservoirs;
- acknowledging that there is a fixed amount of oxygen on Earth; and
- describing that oxygen moves from one reservoir to another, often changing from one form to another and occasionally moving among both living and nonliving components of the earth system.

2. understand how scientists use their knowledge of geochemical cycling to learn about past climates.

   They will demonstrate their understanding by

   - acknowledging that not all water is the same (that isotopes of oxygen cause slight difference in water molecules);
   - recognizing that water containing lighter oxygen isotopes evaporates at a different rate than water containing heavier oxygen isotopes, thereby providing clues to past global climates;
   - explaining that the oxygen isotopes found in the shells of forams serve as indirect evidence of the ratio of heavy to light water in past oceans and that this ratio provides evidence of past climate changes; and
   - making sense of foram data found in sea cores by noting patterns in the data and associating those patterns with glacial and interglacial periods.

3. be able to use mathematical tools and models to guide and improve their understanding of science concepts.

   They will demonstrate their ability by

   - using and revising a model of heavy and light objects to enhance their understanding of how oxygen isotopes can provide evidence of past climate changes and
   - using their understanding of the mathematics of ratios to calculate the ratio of heavy to light water molecules and to interpret related data ($\delta^{18}O$) based on ratios.

4. understand that scientists rely on technology to enhance the gathering and manipulation of data.

   They will demonstrate their understanding by

   - identifying the technologies used to obtain and process deep-sea cores and
   - describing that the use of technologies enhances the gathering and manipulation of data, which contributes to the advancement of science.

5. develop further skills in the abilities and understandings of scientific inquiry.

   They will demonstrate their skills by

   - simulating and measuring the fractionation of heavy and light water during evaporation,
   - using Styrofoam balls as a physical model of evaporation,
   - using a parameter ($\delta^{18}O$) to represent physical aspects of a system,
   - integrating content from the physical sciences on isotopes of elements such as oxygen,
   - using a box model of glacials and interglacials,
   - analyzing and interpreting graphs of $\delta^{18}O$ for forams,
   - identifying patterns in $\delta^{18}O$ for forams on a global scale,
   - comparing $\delta^{18}O$ for forams with carbon dioxide patterns for the atmosphere for the past several hundred thousand years, and
   - learning about the use of technology on ships to obtain cores from sea sediments.

Strategies

Getting Started

Ask students to read the introductory paragraph to Part I. Then read Step 1 to your students. Have students write an answer to the embedded question in their notebooks. Most students will recognize evaporation as the process by which water leaves the ocean. Show students the Styrofoam balls for the activity and continue with the *Process and procedure*.

Process and Procedure

Part I: Heavy Water, Light Water

Materials—Part I

For the teacher

1 shallow plastic box
10 light objects (2-in white Styrofoam balls)

For each team of 6 students

1 shallow plastic box
10 light objects (2-in white Styrofoam balls)
10 heavy objects (2-in black Styrofoam balls, each containing 3 1.5-in finishing nails; see *Advance Preparation*)
1 large sheet (plastic drop cloth, bedsheet, or blanket)
1 stopwatch
1 calculator

In Step 1 students consider in detail the process of evaporation. Demonstrate the evaporation of water using a shallow plastic box and 10 light objects. Tell students that the 10 light objects represent water molecules in the liquid phase and the plastic box represents the ocean. Show them how the water molecules can move around freely. Then tap the side of the plastic box firmly with the palm of your hand. Some of the objects will come out of the box, representing water molecules leaving the liquid phase and entering the gas phase. This models evaporation.

In Step 2, review the model for the experiment as a class, but do not give out balls yet. This time there will be 10 heavy and 10 light balls. Discuss with the class what it predicts might happen when the box is shaken. It is very important for students to design an appropriate table in Step 2b to record data in their science notebooks. An example is shown in figure T12.4. Note that the table also needs a column where students fill in ratios of heavy to light. Two samples are shown in figure T12.4 with actual classroom trials for Styrofoam balls and real and plastic golf balls.

Ratios are simply a way of looking at 2 values relative to each other. A ratio is calculated by dividing the second value into the first value. Units might cancel out when using ratios, so there might not be units. For this investigation, ratios for heavy and light objects can be expressed as

$$\text{ratio of heavy to light} = \left(\frac{\text{number of heavy objects}}{\text{number of light objects}}\right).$$

Students obtain materials and do the trials in Step 2c. If no balls are coming out of the box, they are tapping too gently, but if all are coming out, they are tapping too vigorously. Emphasize that they need to tap on the side of the box to simulate molecular collisions, not the bottom.

As students work through Step 2, circulate among the teams, listening in on team conversations, checking data and calculations, and asking probing questions to be sure students understand what they are doing.

For Step 3, facilitate the sharing of data between the different teams. Have teams share the average values for the ratio of heavy to light objects before and after shaking as well as the percentage of difference. You might find it helpful to use a class data table. A sample is shown in figure T12.5. Sharing data with the class provides a great opportunity for students to look at data critically. Point out the value of having multiple teams experience the model and contribute to the class data. Use the class discussion to check student understanding of the evaporation model they have been working with.

Continue with Steps 4–7 as a class discussion. It is very important that students understand, in general, that if you evaporate a mass of H_2O, the remaining water is enriched slightly in $H_2{}^{18}O$. The evaporated water is slightly enriched in water with the light oxygen isotope, ^{16}O. You will build on this idea in Step 8 where the evaporation process from the ocean is linked with glacial and interglacial periods.

NOTES:

Effect of tapping on heavy and light objects—using Styrofoam balls						
Trial	Before shaking			After shaking		
	number of heavy objects (in box)	number of light objects (in box)	ratio of heavy to light objects	number of heavy objects (in box)	number of light objects (in box)	ratio of heavy to light objects
1	*10*	*10*	*1*	*8*	*6*	*1.3*
2	*10*	*10*	*1*	*8*	*4*	*2*
3	*10*	*10*	*1*	*9*	*6*	*1.5*
		Average:	*1*		Average:	*1.6*
Note: These sample data were generated using a 13″×8″×3″ plastic box, 10 white, 2-inch Styrofoam balls, and 10 black, 2-inch Styrofoam balls each containing 3 finishing nails.						

Effect of tapping on heavy and light objects—using golf balls						
Trial	Before shaking			After shaking		
	number of heavy objects (in box)	number of light objects (in box)	ratio of heavy to light objects	number of heavy objects (in box)	number of light objects (in box)	ratio of heavy to light objects
1	*10*	*10*	*1*	*6*	*3*	*2.0*
2	*10*	*10*	*1*	*9*	*2*	*4.5*
3	*10*	*10*	*1*	*10*	*4*	*2.5*
		Average:	*1*		Average:	*3*
Note: These sample data were generated using a 18″×11½″×3″ cardboard box lid, 10 practice (hollow) golf balls, and 10 regular golf balls.						

▲ **Figure T12.4 Example tables for What's Shaking? model.** The 2 tables show results of simulations for the What's Shaking? model that use Styrofoam balls and 2 kinds of golf balls. Students should use tables like these to record their data. A column needs to show the ratios of heavy to light objects after the shaking.

Team	Average ratio (H/L) before tapping	Average ratio (H/L) after tapping
1	*1*	*1.6*
2	*1*	*1.8*
3	*1*	*1.5*
4	*1*	*2.0*
5	*1*	*1.7*
Class average	*1*	*1.7*

▲ **Figure T12.5 Example of class data.** A summary of data for 5 teams in a class shows an average heavy-to-light ratio (H:L) of 1.7.

Answers to Steps 4–5, SE pages 610–611

4a. The plastic box represents the ocean.

4b. The heavy objects represent heavy water ($H_2{}^{18}O$), and the light objects are light water ($H_2{}^{16}O$).

4c. The tapping represents solar energy imparted to get the water molecules to evaporate.

4d. With only a moderate amount of energy being transferred in the model, the light balls are more likely to leave the box. Because of their greater mass, the heavier balls require more energy to leave the box. The ratio of heavy to light balls remaining in the box increases after tapping.

4e. The water that evaporates moves into the atmosphere and continues as part of the water cycle. Some of it will fall as precipitation, as rain or snow. Some of the water will end up back in the ocean, and some will fall on land near or far. During glacial periods, significant amounts of water are stored in glaciers.

5. In Step 5, students need to modify the What's Shaking? model to reflect a change from an interglacial to a glacial period or vice versa. Listen to students' ideas for adaptations of the model. One possible method is to assume that the model as is represents interglacial periods because students return the water molecules (balls) to the ocean (plastic box) between each trial. To change the model to reflect a glacial period, students might try storing some of the evaporated water molecules, just as water is stored in the global ice reservoir during a glacial period. For example, between each trial, students might set aside 1 ball that has left the plastic box. Sample data for this model are provided in figure T12.6.

Light water molecules are more likely to evaporate than heavy water molecules. During glacial periods, some of the evaporated water molecules (mostly light) are stored in glaciers and ice caps. Because the light water molecules do not return to the ocean, the ocean becomes enriched in heavy water. The ratio of heavy to light water in the ocean becomes larger (more positive) during glacial periods. This is shown in the sample data when you look at the ratio of heavy to light objects before shaking.

Your students might find that their adaptation of the simple model does not produce a clear pattern in the data, particularly in the "after shaking" data. You might need to draw their attention to the "before shaking" data. These data should clearly show a steady increase in the ratio of heavy to light water as evaporated molecules are stored in the ice reservoir. Point out that this simple model does not adequately reflect the complexity of the actual evaporation of water from the ocean. As your students will learn later, the ratio of heavy to light water molecules is nowhere near 1:1.

Student teams complete a reading about oxygen isotopes in water in Step 6. This reinforces ideas they have been studying about water at the atomic level with different isotopes of oxygen. In Step 7, they complete some questions about

a. Read the steps described in figure 12.12 for the What's Shaking? model. Ask for clarification if you do not understand what you will be doing.
b. Based on what you think might happen, develop a table with your team to record your data. Your table needs to include a column expressing the number of heavy objects to light objects as a ratio.
c. Have 1 person from the team pick up the materials from your teacher. Work together to follow the protocol.
d. Analyze your data by calculating the initial and final ratios of heavy to light objects in the box. Be prepared to share these data with your class.

3. Share your results with your class.
4. This model represents water evaporation from the ocean. As a class, discuss what conclusions you could draw about water evaporation based on this model. Record your answers to Questions 4a–e in your science notebook.

▲ **Figure 12.12 What's Shaking? model.** Use these steps to model water evaporation. What is the difference between the heavy and light water?

(1) Place 10 heavy and 10 light objects in a shallow plastic box. These objects should be the same shape and size.
(2) Open a sheet and place it below the plastic box. Have 4 students hold 1 corner of the sheet.
(3) Have 1 student firmly rap the side of the plastic box with his hand for 15 seconds (sec). Some objects should come out of the box and fall onto the large sheet.
(4) Count and record the number of heavy and light objects remaining in the box.
(5) Return all of the objects to the box. Mix up the objects so that the different types are spread evenly throughout.
(6) Repeat Steps 3–5 twice.

Effect of tapping on heavy and light objects—using Styrofoam balls						
Trial	Before shaking			After shaking		
	number of heavy objects (in box)	number of light objects (in box)	ratio of heavy to light objects	number of heavy objects (in box)	number of light objects (in box)	ratio of heavy to light objects
1	*10*	*10*	*1*	*5*	*3*	*1.7*
Note: One evaporated object was not returned to the plastic box for trial 2.						
2	*10*	*9*	*1.1*	*6*	*2*	*3*
Note: One evaporated object was not returned to the plastic box for trial 3.						
3	*10*	*8*	*1.25*	*8*	*3*	*2.7*
Note: These sample data were generated using a 13″×8″×3″ plastic box, 10 white, 2-inch Styrofoam balls, and 10 black, 2-inch Styrofoam balls each containing 3 finishing nails.						

Figure T12.6 Evaporation during a glacial. Removing a light ball from the box before each trial could represent evaporation and movement of water from the ocean to an ice sheet during a glacial. The ratios are more highly skewed than prior experiments.

Answers to Steps 4–5 are on TE page 610.
Answers to Step 7 are on TE page 612.

a. In this water evaporation model, what does the plastic box represent?
b. What do you think the heavy objects represent? The light objects?
c. What does the tapping represent?
d. In this model, which water molecules (heavy or light) are more likely to evaporate? Why?
e. What happens to the water that evaporates? Where does it end up?

5. What will happen to the ratio of heavy to light water molecules in the ocean during a glacial period? How would you modify the model from Step 2 and gather additional data? Be prepared to share your answer to this question with your class.

Recall that a major difference between glacial and interglacial periods is where water is stored. During a glacial period, more water is stored in ice sheets on continents. This reduces the runoff to the ocean significantly. How could you alter your model to reflect this change?

6. By now you might be wondering what all this talk is about heavy and light water. Isn't all water the same? Read with your team *Water: Is It All the Same?*
7. To get an idea of the relative amounts of oxygen's isotopes, imagine that you have 10,000 oxygen atoms in a container. Work with your team to answer Questions 7a–e.
   a. From the reading, make a T-table showing the 3 oxygen isotopes and their abundance.
   b. How many of these atoms would be ^{16}O atoms? How many would be ^{17}O atoms? How many would be ^{18}O atoms? Show your work.
   c. Which of the 3 oxygen isotopes is the heaviest? The lightest?
   d. Which of the 2 water molecules in figure 12.13 is the heaviest? The lightest? Give the masses.
   e. Given this information, how does the ratio of heavy to light objects in the model from Step 2 compare with the actual ratio of isotopes of heavy to light oxygen atoms found in nature? Explain your answer and clearly use measurements as evidence.
8. Participate in a class discussion of how the model you used relates to what happens with water during glacial and interglacial periods.

oxygen isotopes. Step 8 provides you and your students the opportunity to address how the What's Shaking? model relates to what happens with water during glacial and interglacial periods. This discussion should prepare students to complete the *Stop and Think—Part I* task. Some possible probing questions include the following:

- "According to your model, which water molecule (heavy or light) evaporates more readily? What evidence do you have to support your answer?"
- "What happens to the ratio of heavy to light water molecules in the container after shaking (evaporation)?"
- "What happens to the ratio of heavy to light water molecules in the container when some of the molecules are not returned to the container?"

When you have completed Step 8, have students complete the task in *Stop and Think—Part I* individually. This would make an appropriate homework assignment and will provide you the opportunity to check their current understanding of the process of evaporation of heavy and light water molecules during glacial and interglacial periods.

Answers to Step 7, SE page 611

7a. Students should show a T-table with abundance.

7b. Students should calculate that there would be 9,976 molecules of ^{16}O, 4 molecules of ^{17}O, and 20 molecules of ^{18}O. Be sure that students show multiplication by the percentage of isotope by 10,000.

99.76 percent of 10,000 molecules = $0.9976 \times 10,000 =$ 9,976 molecules of ^{16}O

0.04 percent of 10,000 molecules = $0.0004 \times 10,000 = 4$ molecules of ^{17}O

0.20 percent of 10,000 molecules = $0.0020 \times 10,000 = 20$ molecules of ^{18}O

7c. ^{18}O is the heaviest, and ^{16}O is the lightest. (Students might need to be reminded that the mass of an atom comes primarily from the particles in its nucleus. Each proton and neutron has a relative mass of 1.)

7d. Molecule B ($H_2{}^{18}O$) is heavier than molecule A ($H_2{}^{16}O$). The respective masses for these are 20 and 18 mass units.

7e. The ratio of heavy to light objects used in the model does not represent the actual ratio of isotopes of heavy to light oxygen atoms found in nature. In the model, the ratio of heavy to light objects is 1:1. In the natural world, there are only 20 atoms of ^{18}O for every 9,976 atoms of ^{16}O. This ratio is difficult to reproduce in a student activity.

Answers to Stop and Think—Part I, SE page 612

1. Student answers will vary. Look for the following big ideas:
   - Light water is more likely to evaporate than heavy water. This leaves the ocean slightly enriched in heavy water. In this case, the ratio of heavy to light water in the ocean is greater than normal. Sample data from the What's Shaking? model show an increase from a ratio of 1 (before shaking) to a ratio of 1.6 (after shaking).
   - Light water is more likely to evaporate than heavy water during both glacial and interglacial periods. However, during a glacial period, the light water is stored in glaciers and ice caps. As a result, the ratio of heavy to light water in the ocean increases. During an interglacial period, glaciers and ice caps are melting, returning light water to the ocean. This means that the ratio of heavy to light water is smaller during an interglacial period. Sample data from the adaptation of the What's Shaking? model show an increase in the before shaking data from a ratio of 1 (trial 1—before shaking) to a ratio of 1.25 (trial 3—before shaking). This model also shows a general increase in the after shaking data from a ratio of 1.7 to a ratio of 2.7.

Stop & THINK

PART I

Complete the following task individually in your science notebook.

1. Write a short summary of what you learned from your experiences with the What's Shaking? model. Your summary should
   - explain how the model relates to water evaporating from the ocean during glacial and interglacial periods,
   - explain what happens to the ratio of heavy to light water in the ocean during glacial and interglacial periods,
   - include a diagram or sketch showing the relationship to the water cycle, and
   - use evidence from your investigation to support points in your summary.

READING

Water: Is It All the Same?

A water molecule consists of two hydrogen atoms and one oxygen atom. It does not matter where the water comes from; if it has two hydrogen atoms and one oxygen atom, it is H_2O. In this sense, all water molecules are the same. However, there are natural variations within each of the atoms that make up water. Look closely at the two water molecules in figure 12.13. What makes each molecule different?

Look more closely at the molecules in figure 12.13. Note that each contains two hydrogen atoms and one oxygen atom. Each hydrogen atom has one proton and one electron. Both oxygen atoms also have the same number of protons and electrons, but they each have a different number of neutrons. One oxygen atom has eight neutrons and the other has 10 neutrons. The two atoms are **isotopes** of oxygen. You might recall that isotopes are atoms of the same element that have different numbers of neutrons.

Both hydrogen and oxygen have naturally occurring isotopes. For the purpose of this investigation, we will look just at isotopes of oxygen. Oxygen has three naturally occurring isotopes that are found in different proportions, or percentages, in nature. These are oxygen-16 (^{16}O, 99.76 percent), oxygen-17 (^{17}O, 0.04 percent), and oxygen-18 (^{18}O, 0.20 percent). These isotopes of oxygen are stable. This means they do not degrade or change mass by radioactive decay or any other process in the nucleus.

Process and Procedure

Part II: The Oxygen Connection

Materials

For the teacher

samples containing oxygen from different earth systems (See figure T12.7 for samples.)

mud samples with forams (and hand lens or microscope for viewing; see *Advance Preparation*)

sieve set (with at least 125-μm and 350-μm screens)

image of forams

1 seafloor model (either the play dough or the sand model):

- play dough model:
  - 4 containers of play dough, each a different color
  - 1 sharp blade (razor blade or craft knife; optional)
- sand model:
  - 1 large coffee can, 39-oz size
  - 1–1.5 qts fine-grained sand
  - white sand and food coloring or different colors of sand
  - water

For each team of 3 students

foram sample, if available

access to seafloor model

1 clear plastic straw

1 sheet of white paper

Read the introductory paragraph with your students. It allows them to see where they have been and where they are going. Then read Step 1 and discuss the question as a class. Students may look ahead and see the word *foram*, and answer "forams" to Step 1. If they do this, gently press them to explain their answer and what they mean. This way you can tell whether they really understand the concepts, or whether they are just focusing on the correct answer.

Answers to Step 1, SE page 613

1. This question gets students thinking about how difficult it is to locate a sample or record of ancient ocean water. Students should realize that the ocean water from long ago has since been cycled through the water reservoirs of the earth system many, many times. You cannot just go out and locate a sample. Some students might suggest looking deep in glaciers. This is a reasonable suggestion, but the glaciers are not really ocean water. There are scientists who study ice cores for clues to past climates, and students will see some of these data in the activity. In addition, scientists who study ice cores are generally only able to gather data for the last 650 kyr. Where would they look for actual ocean water that is even older?

For Step 2, see the table in figure T12.7 for examples of oxygen in earth systems. Listen to team discussions in Step 3. Students should be showing their understanding that oxygen from water enters the calcium carbonate of the foram shell (tests) through the bicarbonate ion. They studied this reaction in chapter 11.

Let your students know that although they might feel they already know the answers to some of these questions, it will be important for them to listen carefully and make notes of any information that is new to them. The answers contain information that is important both to this activity and to the final activity in this chapter. If you notice gaps in students' understanding of oxygen's many forms and reservoirs, you should share additional information with the class.

Answers to Step 2 are on TE pages 614–614a.

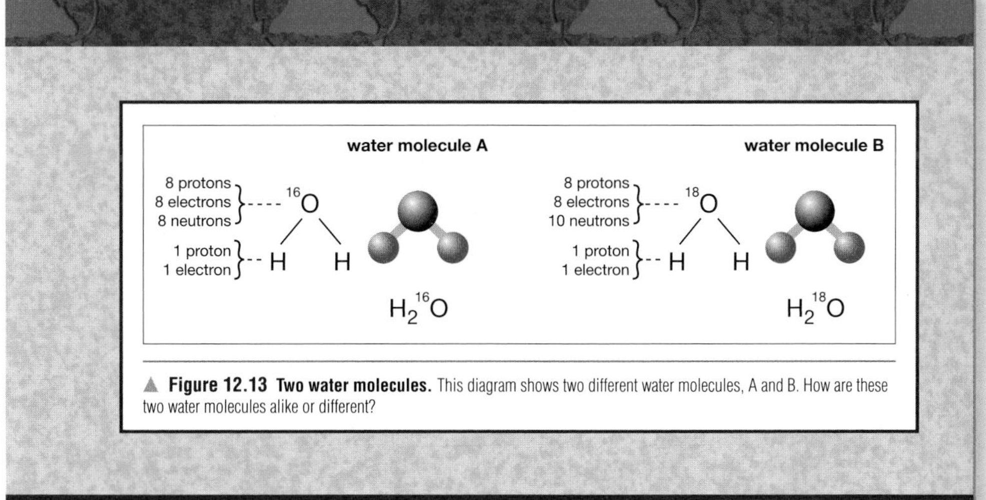

▲ **Figure 12.13 Two water molecules.** This diagram shows two different water molecules, A and B. How are these two water molecules alike or different?

Part II: The Oxygen Connection

Materials

For each team of 3 students

foram sample, if available

access to seafloor model

1 clear plastic straw

1 sheet of white paper

Process and Procedure

In Part I, you learned that not all water is the same. You investigated a simple model that showed how heavy and light water molecules are separated during evaporation. When light water ($H_2{}^{16}O$) evaporates and is stored in ice sheets on continents, the ocean is left enriched in heavy water ($H_2{}^{18}O$). If scientists could measure how the ratio of heavy to light water in the ocean has varied in the past, they would have additional evidence of glacial periods. But how can this be done? You will work in teams to answer this question.

1. Where would a scientist go to find a sample of ancient ocean water? Discuss this question with your class.
2. Scientists needed a way to measure the amount of heavy and light water that was present in the ocean at different times in Earth's history. To address this need, they turned to their understanding of geochemical cycles. Because oxygen isotopes are what cause water molecules to be heavy or light, scientists suspected that the element oxygen held the key to their search. Discuss Questions 2a–c with your team.

Answers to Step 2, SE pages 613–614

2a. Answers will vary. You might need to remind students of the different earth systems: biosphere, atmosphere, geosphere, and hydrosphere (includes the cryosphere).

2b. Oxygen is one of the most abundant elements on Earth. It is essential for life. We need the most common form of elemental oxygen (O_2) as a gas in order to breathe. This form of oxygen is also essential for the combustion of fuels that provide most of the energy for industry and heating. The oxygen that these processes consume is constantly replenished by photosynthesis.

Ozone (O_3) is a less abundant form of elemental oxygen. Ozone is very reactive and is considered harmful in lower regions of the atmosphere. However, ozone in the upper layers of Earth's atmosphere is beneficial because it shields us from the Sun's ultraviolet radiation.

Oxygen combines with many other elements, producing numerous compounds. Some examples of common compounds found within the various earth subsystems are shown in figure T12.7. Virtually everything in your classroom has oxygen. Gather some objects and check for forms of oxygen.

2c. Students should recognize that the amount of a particular element on Earth remains relatively constant. The law of conservation of matter states that matter is neither created nor destroyed. However, matter can change form. An element such as oxygen can reside in different reservoirs and can move, or cycle, among the different reservoirs. As the element changes its form, it will likely exhibit differences in physical and chemical properties.

3. Students should describe to one another that the oxygen from ocean water can react with carbon dioxide and form a bicarbonate ion. That ion combines with calcium ions in the ocean water to form the calcium carbonate shells of forams. They should be able to follow the pathway of oxygen in the chemical equations within the reading.

NOTES:

a. Take a few minutes to review what you already know about oxygen in the earth system.

b. Where on Earth is the element oxygen found? What forms does it take? What properties does it have?

Think about the different reservoirs in the earth system that you learned about in chapters 10 and 11. Where is oxygen in each of these subsystems? Is it found as an atom, an elemental molecule, or in compounds?

c. Does the amount of oxygen on Earth change across time?

3. Scientists realized that what they needed was to find a reservoir that stored the oxygen from ocean water for long periods of time. Read *Foram Forum* to learn about the reservoir they discovered. Check your understanding with your team by describing to one another how the oxygen atom from a molecule of ocean water becomes part of the shells of foraminifera.

"Foram" is short for "foraminifera." If available, look at the foram shells your teacher has on display.

READING

Foram Forum

Foraminifera are tiny, single-celled organisms that live in the ocean (figure 12.14). Often, these are called **forams**, for short. These organisms are abundant and widespread.

a.

b.

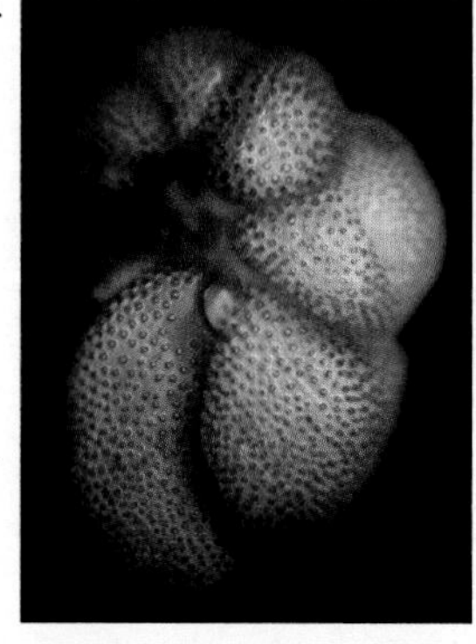

▲ **Figure 12.14 Foraminifera.** Forams are single-celled organisms in the ocean. They consist of an inner shell with many strands of tissue that protrude from the animal into the water (a). When they die, their shells sink to the seafloor (b). The tiny holes show where the strands exited the shell into the water.

614 Unit 3 Moving Matter

Oxygen in the Earth system		
Earth subsystem	**Oxygen form/reservoir**	**Chemical formula**
Biosphere	living organisms contain: water carbohydrates proteins sea shells	 $H_2O_{(l)}$ $C_6H_{12}O_6$ (glucose) molecules containing C, H, O, N $CaCO_{3(s)}$ (calcium carbonate)
Atmosphere	air contains: oxygen ozone water vapor precipitation carbon dioxide carbon monoxide nitrogen oxides sulfur oxides	 $O_{2\,(g)}$ $O_{3\,(g)}$ $H_2O_{(g)}$ $H_2O_{(l)}$, $H_2O_{(s)}$ (rain, snow) $CO_{2(g)}$ $CO_{(g)}$ $NO_{x(g)}$ $SO_{x(g)}$
Geosphere	earth materials made up of: quartz feldspar hematite magnetite limestone, marble, chalk, or calcite gypsum	 $SiO_{2(s)}$ (silicon dioxide) $KAlSi_3O_8$ $Fe_2O_{3(s)}$ (ferric oxide) $Fe_3O_{4(s)}$ $CaCO_{3(s)}$ (calcium carbonate) $CaSO_4{\cdot}2H_2O_{(s)}$ (calcium sulfate dihydrate)
Hydrosphere	water and ice water and ice also contain: dissolved ions and molecules	$H_2O_{(l)}$ and $H_2O_{(s)}$ SO_4^{-2} (sulfates) HCO_3^{-1} (hydrogen carbonate or bicarbonate) NO_3^{-1} (nitrates) $O_{2(g)}$ $CO_{2(g)}$

▲ **Figure T12.7 Oxygen in the Earth system.** Examples of where oxygen is found on Earth.

NOTES:

NOTES:

NOTES:

A cubic centimeter of ocean sediment contains many living individuals, and even more empty fossil shells. Forams are found in all marine environments, from salt marshes to the deep ocean. They are found from the equator to the poles. Different species are found in different environments, reflecting their preferences for different temperature and nutrient conditions. Of the more than 4,000 species alive today, most live near the ocean bottom. Less than 1 percent of forams, about 40 species, live in the upper regions of the ocean.

As they live, forams build internal shells. These shells are tiny, typically ranging from 0.1 millimeters (mm) to 1 mm. Most are about the size of a pinhead. A foram's shell contains at least one, and often many, openings. The name, foraminifera, is actually a composite of Latin words that mean "bearing pores or openings." The single-celled foram itself is similar to an amoeba. The cell forms long, threadlike strands that stream through the openings in the shell. The strands move out in all directions (figure 12.14). Forams use these strands to catch other organisms they feed on. They can ensnare organisms both smaller and much larger than they are. Some forams also use the strands for locomotion. When forams die, their shells retain the holes (figure 12.14).

Most forams make their shells of calcium carbonate ($CaCO_3$), the same compound that forms larger seashells. Forams build their calcium carbonate shells from calcium ions $(Ca)^{2+}$ and bicarbonate ions $(HCO_3)^{1-}$ in ocean water. In chapter 11, *Carbon on the Move*, you studied how the bicarbonate and calcium ions enter the sea from rivers. These ions come from the chemical weathering of rocks and minerals on continents. These and other ions are carried by rivers to the ocean. The red oxygen in the following reaction indicates the transfer of oxygen from reactant to product:

$$Ca^{2+}_{(aq)} + 2HCO_3{}^{1-}_{(aq)} \longrightarrow CaCO_3 + H_2O + CO_2$$

Note that the oxygen atoms in the bicarbonate ions are some of the same oxygen atoms used in the foram shells. The bicarbonate first comes to the ocean from rivers. But then how does the bicarbonate reflect the oxygen isotopes of the ocean? That is, how can a foram shell preserve information about oxygen isotopes in the ocean water? It can because the bicarbonate is in a chemical equilibrium with the ocean's H_2O. The reaction is continuous, so the bicarbonate always has oxygen isotopes related to the ocean water. You also studied this reaction in chapter 11:

$$\underset{\text{carbon dioxide}}{CO_{2(aq)}} + \underset{\text{ocean water}}{H_2O_{(aq)}} \rightleftharpoons \underset{\text{carbonic acid}}{H_2CO_{3(aq)}}$$

$$\underset{\text{carbonic acid}}{H_2CO_{3(aq)}} \rightleftharpoons \underset{\text{bicarbonate}}{HCO_3{}^{1-}_{(aq)}} + \underset{\text{hydrogen ion}}{H^{1+}_{(aq)}}$$

When forams die, they fall to the ocean floor. The soft tissue of their cells decomposes, leaving the hard shell behind. These shells join other sediments on the seafloor. In time, the sediments build up, layer after layer. The layers of sediment with foram shells capture a record of past oxygen in ocean waters.

With this discovery, scientists found one piece of evidence of past climate changes in the shells of forams scattered in seafloor sediments. The oxygen atoms in the calcium carbonate of foram shells hold a record of the ratio of heavy to light oxygen in ocean water at the time the shell was formed. This record is a vital fingerprint for distinguishing between glacial and interglacial periods.

In Step 4, students retrieve a sample core of layered sediment from the model you prepared. If using the play dough setup, you can cut the straw lengthwise down the middle to see the layering of colors. This is how scientists retrieve sediment samples from cores. But you can still see the layering through the clear straw.

Answers to Step 4, SE page 616

4d. Students should indicate that the layers are different colors and have different thicknesses. They should recognize that layers on the bottom of the core sample were laid down first. They might infer that the varying thickness of the layers represents times when more or less sediment was deposited.

Students then learn about how real cores of seafloor sediments are gathered in the reading *The Integrated Ocean Drilling Program* for Step 5. They should compare as best they can their model core in class with real samples. Finally, teams read in Step 6 about $\delta^{18}O$ values for forams. They will see how these values vary between glacials and interglacials in the next activity.

If you have obtained a real core sample from the IODP, take it out now. Before class, you will have washed samples in the sieve and found the tiny white specks. You can wash them very gently into a small petri dish to view under a binocular microscope. Do not try to touch them with your finger. The tests are very fragile. Students will also enjoy cleaning the foram tests if there is the opportunity.

Answers to Step 5, SE page 616

5a. Students should mention that they are similar because both use a tube to retrieve the sample, but the tube for the model is very different from the tube used by scientists. The model only took 1 person, while the actual process used by the IODP requires more people, a very large ship, and equipment that is quite sophisticated.

5b. Students should point out that they are similar because both have sediments in layers, but they are different in that the sediments and the time factor are both quite different. The model is made of play dough (or sand), while real sea sediments are composed of a variety of materials (sand, clay, remains of organisms). The model does not reflect any real timescale, although the lower layers were laid down first. Actual sea cores reflect formation over thousands to millions of years.

Once teams have completed Step 6, have students do the tasks in *Stop and Think—Part II* individually. If you can, read student responses to provide a snapshot of their current level of understanding of the cycling of oxygen in the earth system.

Answers to Step 6 are on TE page 617.

4. In *Foram Forum*, you learned that forams fall to the bottom of the ocean when they die. They mix with other sediments, forming layer upon layer, year after year. How do geologists actually get the samples of forams? They remove samples from the ocean floor. Your teacher has prepared a model that represents a section of sediments on the ocean floor for you to sample.
   a. Use a clear plastic straw to obtain a core sample. Orient the straw vertically and gently push it into the sediment. Twist the straw and then seal it by placing your thumb over the top of the straw. Pull the straw out of the sediment.
   b. Lay the core down on a sheet of white paper. Do not try to remove the sample from the straw. You can view the contents through the clear plastic.
   c. Make a sketch of the sample in your science notebook.
   d. What do you notice about the layers in the sample? What can you infer about this sample?
5. To obtain your core sample, all you needed was a plastic straw, your hand, and access to a sediment sample. Read the information in the sidebar *The Integrated Ocean Drilling Program* to see how scientists in the field gather deep-sea core samples. Write answers to Questions 5a–b in your science notebook.
   a. How was the process of obtaining a model deep-sea core (in the classroom) similar to, and different from, the procedure that actually takes place on an IODP expedition?
   b. How was the model core you obtained similar to, and different from, the actual cores that come from the ocean floor?
6. Once scientists have the core sample, they need to analyze it. Read the information in *$\delta^{18}O$—a Measure of Heavy and Light Oxygen* to find out how scientists analyze the foram samples. Check your understanding with your team. Then answer Questions 6a–b in your science notebook.

The symbol is pronounced "delta oxygen 18" or "dell-oh-18." It is just a chemical indicator. For example, another chemical indicator might be salinity, which indicates concentrations of dissolved salts. Or pH is a chemical indicator that tells the concentration of the H^+ ion in a solution.

   a. How does the information in *$\delta^{18}O$—a Measure of Heavy and Light Oxygen* compare with your experiences with the evaporation model in Part I?

Think about the calculations you did in Part I. How are they like the calculations scientists use to analyze the oxygen in foram shells?

   b. Summarize the relationship between $\delta^{18}O$ values in the ocean and glacial and interglacial periods.

Answers to Step 6, SE page 616

6a. Students should mention that both focused on the differences in evaporation between heavy and light objects, such as water molecules. Students should discuss parallels between the mathematical handling of the 2 types of data. Both use ratios of heavy to light. The $\delta^{18}O$ calculation involves an additional step—calculating a difference between 2 values. This could be done for the classroom experiment, say, by using the initial condition as the "standard" value.

6b. $\delta^{18}O$ values reflect the relative amounts of ^{18}O and ^{16}O in ocean water. The $\delta^{18}O$ values are measured from foram shells. Forams incorporate the oxygen from ocean water into the calcium carbonate of their shells. During glacial periods, light water evaporates and some is stored in glaciers. During this time, the ocean water contains a higher ratio of ^{18}O to ^{16}O. This higher ratio is recorded in the foram shells, which have higher $\delta^{18}O$ values during glacial periods. During interglacial periods, light water from melted glaciers and ice caps returns to the ocean. This results in a lower ratio of ^{18}O to ^{16}O in the ocean water and in the foram shells. This means that foram $\delta^{18}O$ values are smaller during interglacial periods.

NOTES:

SIDEBAR

The Integrated Ocean Drilling Program

How do you get a sea core from the bottom of the ocean? For the answer, look at the Integrated Ocean Drilling Program (IODP). This program has recovered over 160,000 m (almost 100 miles) of deep-sea cores since 1985. IODP uses an oil-drilling ship equipped with state-of-the-art laboratories. For years, the IODP drilling ship, *JOIDES Resolution*, has made about six expeditions per year to recover deep-sea cores for climate researchers. Each expedition lasts about 2 months. During these expeditions, the ship is home to over 100 people, including 50 scientists, engineers, and technicians from around the world. These are examples of professions needed to obtain and study sea cores.

▲ ***JOIDES Resolution.*** This specialized scientific ship, the *JOIDES Resolution*, has been used by climate scientists and oceanographers since about 1985 to recover cores from sediments on the seafloor.

How are the deep-sea cores collected? A hydraulic core sampler is lowered through the drill pipe and driven into sediments on the seafloor. The core is hoisted from the water and taken to shipboard laboratories, where it is carefully opened and studied. An individual core might be up to 9.5 m long and about 10 cm in diameter. Each core is sliced lengthwise. One-half is left intact to provide a permanent record, while scientists sample the other half.

Each core is only one of many from the same hole. As the first core is raised to the surface, the drill penetrates the length of the core just taken. The coring process is repeated many times, thus recovering continuous sections of seafloor sediment. Samples range from hundreds of meters to several kilometers into the seafloor. Scientists study these cores in sequence to construct very long histories of changes in Earth's environment over time.

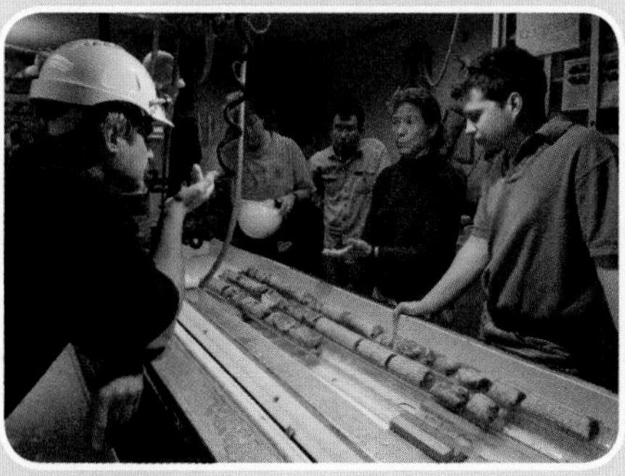

▲ **Core samples.** Scientists slice in half core samples of sediments from the seafloor. The different sections of a core might add up to thousands of meters in total length.

NOTES:

READING

$\delta^{18}O$—a Measure of Heavy and Light Oxygen

A key piece of evidence of Earth's past climate is recorded in the shells of forams. How do scientists determine and report the ratio of oxygen isotopes in foram shells?

Scientists obtain a sample from deep-sea sediment. They wash the sample in a sieve to remove the finer mud and silt. Then forams are handpicked from the sieve using a small paintbrush with a moistened tip. Only a few shells are needed for the oxygen analysis. These calcium carbonate shells are dissolved in phosphoric acid in a small chamber. One of the reaction products is CO_2 gas. You studied this reaction in chapter 11. The CO_2 gas contains the oxygen atoms that were in the foram shell. Remember, these oxygen atoms initially came from ocean water.

$$3CaCO_3 + \underset{\text{phosphoric acid}}{2H_3PO_4} \longrightarrow 3Ca^{2+}_{(aq)} + 2PO_4^{3-} + 3H_2O + 3CO_2$$

The scientists put the carbon dioxide into a mass spectrometer. This instrument can detect and measure small differences in atomic mass between the ^{16}O and ^{18}O isotopes in the CO_2 (figure 12.15). This gives a ratio of ^{18}O to ^{16}O in the sample.

Between measuring samples, the geologists make measurements of a carbonate standard.

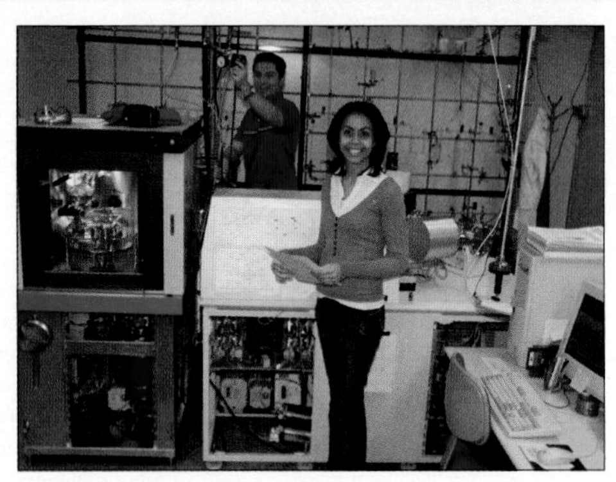

▲ **Figure 12.15 Analyzing CO_2.** Geologists analyze CO_2 from forams in a mass spectrometer. This instrument measures the isotopes of oxygen, ^{18}O and ^{16}O, in CO_2 from the forams.

The standard is the same in all laboratories so that data can be compared. The measured value is multiplied by 1,000. This magnifies the small variations in an already small ratio, making the numbers more workable. The calculated values are called "delta oxygen 18" values (or "dell-oh-18," for short). Their symbol is $\delta^{18}O$ and they are reported in parts per thousand (‰). This is also called per mil (as in per thousand).

$$\delta^{18}O_{\text{foram}} = \left(\frac{\left(\frac{^{18}O}{^{16}O}\right)_{\text{foram}} - \left(\frac{^{18}O}{^{16}O}\right)_{\text{standard}}}{\left(\frac{^{18}O}{^{16}O}\right)_{\text{standard}}} \right) \times 1{,}000$$

NOTES:

If a sample has a $\delta^{18}O$ greater than 0, it means that there is more ^{18}O relative to ^{16}O in the sample than there is in the standard. Samples with a lot of ^{18}O are even more positive. They are said to be ^{18}O enriched.

How does the variation in $\delta^{18}O$ values relate to glacial and interglacial periods? Recall the What's Shaking? model from Part I. You learned that $H_2{}^{16}O$ is more likely to evaporate than $H_2{}^{18}O$. During a glacial period, evaporated water enriched in $H_2{}^{16}O$ is stored in glaciers. This is represented in figure 12.16. This increases the relative amount of $H_2{}^{18}O$ remaining in the ocean. There is still $H_2{}^{16}O$ in the ocean during glacials, but the proportion of $H_2{}^{18}O$ has increased, as do values for $\delta^{18}O$.

During an interglacial period (figure 12.16), evaporation over the ocean still occurs. However, during interglacials, rain returns to the ocean by rivers. Moreover, melting ice sheets return the $H_2{}^{16}O$ to the ocean that was stored on continents during the glacial. This decreases the $\delta^{18}O$ values of the ocean during interglacials. The absolute values of $\delta^{18}O$ are an important detail for geologists. Remember, though, that the best way to tell glacials from interglacials is to analyze the pattern of $\delta^{18}O$ in a sediment core.

Forams incorporate the oxygen from ocean water into the calcium carbonate of their shells. If the surrounding ocean water contains a higher ratio of ^{18}O, the foram shells contain a higher ratio of ^{18}O. This means that $\delta^{18}O$ values for forams become larger (more positive) during glacial periods and smaller (less positive) during interglacial periods.

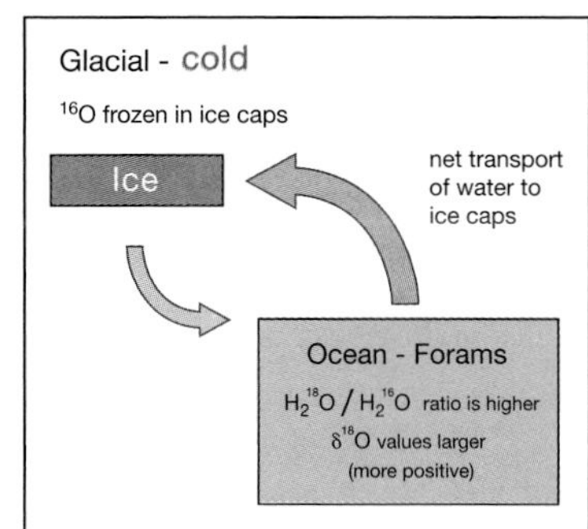

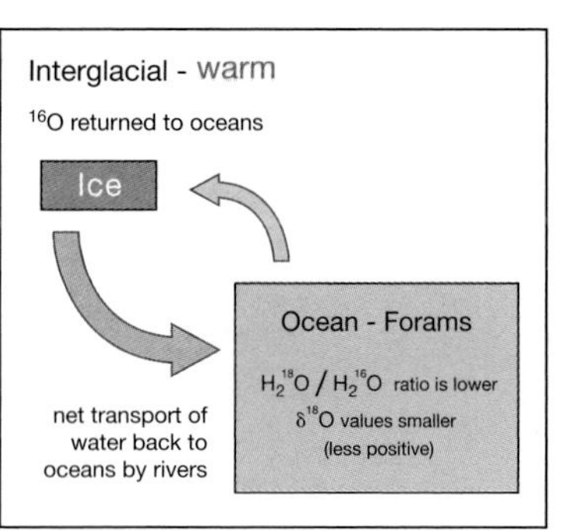

▲ **Figure 12.16 Model for glacials, interglacials.** This simple model shows the net movement of water to continental ice sheets during glacial periods, and to the ocean during interglacial periods. Note the effect on changing sea level shown in each blue box. The blue boxes represent the ocean and show that $\delta^{18}O$ values for the ocean and forams increase during glacials as light water ($H_2{}^{16}O$) is frozen in continental ice sheets. The $\delta^{18}O$ values of foram shells decrease during interglacials as $H_2{}^{16}O$ is returned to the ocean.

Chapter 12 Evidence for the Ice Ages 619

Answers to Stop and Think—Part II, SE page 620

1. Answers will vary. Check that the diagram shows examples of oxygen or its compounds in each of the earth subsystems (biosphere, atmosphere, geosphere, hydrosphere). See figure T12.7 for examples of oxygen reservoirs.
2. Students may use any format to describe the journey of oxygen from ancient ocean water to foram, to carbon dioxide measured in a mass spectrometer. Student answers should make the connection between ocean water, the calcium carbonate of foram shells, and the carbon dioxide.

   Oxygen found in water molecules is incorporated into the shells of forams. In this part of the cycle, the oxygen moves from the water molecule in the liquid phase to a calcium carbonate molecule in the solid phase. The foram shells become part of the ocean sediment, preserving a record of the oxygen ratio of ocean water at that time. Many years later, scientists remove deep-sea cores from the ocean floor. The deep-sea cores contain the foram shells. These foram shells are isolated from the other sediments, and the calcium carbonate of the shells is converted to carbon dioxide. In this part of the cycle, the oxygen moves from the calcium carbonate molecules in the solid phase to the carbon dioxide in the gas phase. Scientists use the mass spectrometer to measure the relative amounts of the different isotopes of oxygen in the carbon dioxide.

Process and Procedure

Part III: Analyzing Foram Data

Materials

For the teacher

1 transparency of copymaster 12.3, *Unidentified Data*

1 transparency each of copymaster 12.4, *Sea Core Foram Data 677*, copymaster 12.5, *Sea Core Foram Data 659*, copymaster 12.6, *Vostok/EPICA CO_2 Record*, and copymaster 12.7, *Bands for Analysis* (optional)

For each team of 3 students

3 copies of copymaster 12.4, *Sea Core Foram Data 677*

3 copies of copymaster 12.5, *Sea Core Foram Data 659*

1 copy of copymaster 12.7, *Bands for Analysis*

Before beginning this part of the investigation, show students the

transparency of copymaster 12.3, *Unidentified Data*. Ask students to note and observe all patterns in these data. What features do they see? How many patterns are there? Students may still be at a stage where they are offering guesses about what the data are. Responses might be an EKG or a seismograph. After hearing several possibilities, tell them that it is actually evidence of past climate changes. Let them know that they will take a closer look at these data in Part III of this investigation. Have students read the introductory paragraphs for Part III.

Distribute the copies of copymaster 12.4, *Sea Core Foram Data 677*. Have students work in teams of 3 to complete Steps 1–4. Monitor their progress, providing assistance as necessary. This part of the activity provides an opportunity to assess your students' abilities to analyze data and recognize patterns. When they reach Step 4, they will need a copy of copymaster 12.7, *Bands for Analysis*.

Stop & THINK

PART II

Complete the following tasks individually. Write your responses in your science notebook.

1. Draw a simple diagram that shows examples of reservoirs where oxygen is stored in the earth system. Include examples of reservoirs in each of the earth subsystems (biosphere, atmosphere, geosphere, hydrosphere, cryosphere). Describe a form of oxygen present in each particular reservoir.
2. Describe how the cycling of oxygen connects ancient ocean water to the $\delta^{18}O$ values scientists obtain from the readings of a mass spectrometer. Highlight the journey of oxygen from ancient ocean water to the carbon dioxide (CO_2) analyzed by a modern mass spectrometer.

   Use whatever format you please to complete this task. You may draw a diagram, write a story, or produce a series of journal entries. If you are unsure if your selected format is acceptable, check with your teacher.

Part III: Analyzing Foram Data

Materials

For each team of 3 students

3 *Sea Core Foram Data 677* handouts

3 *Sea Core Foram Data 659* handouts

1 *Bands for Analysis* handout

Process and Procedure

In Part II, you learned that the oxygen isotopes in forams tell glacial periods from interglacial periods. These periods also link with water being transferred back and forth between the ocean and ice sheets. Studying these patterns enables geologists to determine the history of climate on Earth.

But what is the actual evidence from forams? What do the data look like? In this part of the investigation, you will analyze oxygen

---

For Step 5, distribute copies of copymaster 12.5, *Sea Core Foram Data 659.* As you can, check students' use of the bands and comparison of this equatorial record (site 659) with graph 1 at the Galápagos Islands (site 677).

Answers to Steps 1–5, SE pages 621–624

1. The title of the graph identifies that these data are a record of the oxygen isotopes in foram shells from an ODP core site near the Galápagos Islands. The x-axis begins at 0 kya, which is the present time, and moves back in time. This is probably very different from common experiences students have had with time graphs. The timescale is large. It covers hundreds of thousands of years, from the present back to 650 kya.

   The y-axis displays $\delta^{18}O$ values, with maximum values of about 5.25 ‰, and minimum values of about 3.5. If students have trouble understanding the significance of these values, first refer them back to the reading *$\delta^{18}O$—a Measure of Heavy and Light Oxygen.* If they need additional assistance, refer them to their team members. This is a difficult and important concept, so help them make sense of the information. Remember that the $\delta^{18}O$ values are not oxygen ratios, but indicators of ratios (they are proportional) relative to the isotope ratio of some standard.

2a. Students should note a general cycle, moving up, then down, then up again. It might be helpful for students to make a large dot when the graph crosses a midpoint (perhaps the y-value of 4 on graph 1) and see if any pattern appears. Some students might see a wavelike nature to the pattern and might talk about peaks and troughs, amplitude, frequency, periods, and other terms associated with waves. This is a good way to relate climate cycles to the same concepts of waveforms and cycles in physics.

2b. There are about 6 large glacials, depending on whether you count peaks such as at 540–550 kya. The dominant cycle seems to repeat roughly every 100 kyr. This is just an approximation. Encourage students to come up with actual values and to record how they came up with their values. Check that a T-table organizing these data shows about 6–8 peaks and 6–8 valleys.

2c. Students' fingers should move in a roughly up-and-down (sinusoidal) pattern across the graph.

2d. Students should mention that the top of the sea core relates to the top of the graph, when viewed in a portrait orientation. Successively lower layers are older and deeper, just as the data on the graph represent older periods.

data that scientists collect from foram shells. Work in teams of three for this part of the investigation. Feel free to mark on your handouts. (Use pencil to mark on your graph, just in case you change your mind about something.)

1. Look at the graph in figure 12.17. This is also the handout *Sea Core Foram Data 677*. The core was obtained near the Galápagos Islands in the equatorial Pacific Ocean (see location in figure 12.24). This graph shows data obtained by geologists. Your team should consider questions like these when analyzing a graph:
   - What are the x- and y-axes?
   - What are the maximum and minimum values shown for the x- and y-axes of the graph?
   - How is the grid organized, and how is it set up?
   - What other information is provided?

Look at the title of the graph and the titles of the x- and y-axes. Read the axis labels below the graph. Notice the range of values for each of the axes. For the x-axis, determine where the present and past are located.

2. Now focus on the actual data, the wiggly line. What patterns do you notice in the data? Discuss and record general patterns, but also notice specific details about the patterns. Include numbers in your descriptions of the patterns. Try the following tasks to help you focus on the patterns.
   a. Use your finger to trace over the data. Is there a pattern to the movement of your finger?
   b. Look at the highs and lows on the graph. How much time passes from one major peak to another, or from one major valley to another? Is the time between peaks (or valleys) consistent? How many peaks (or valleys) appear in the 650,000-year time span?

One way to organize your observations is to make a T-table in your science notebook with headings of "peaks" and "valleys" and list the ages down the columns. Feel free to mark in pencil on your handout of figure 12.17 your ideas for any of these questions.

   c. Try tracing the graph with your finger again, but this time begin at the far right side of the graph. Imagine that you are there, 650 kya. Trace the graph as you move toward the left side of it. Is the movement of your finger consistent or does it change?
   d. You have probably been looking at your graph in a landscape orientation. Turn it to a portrait orientation with the y-axis on top and the x-axis on the left side. How is this

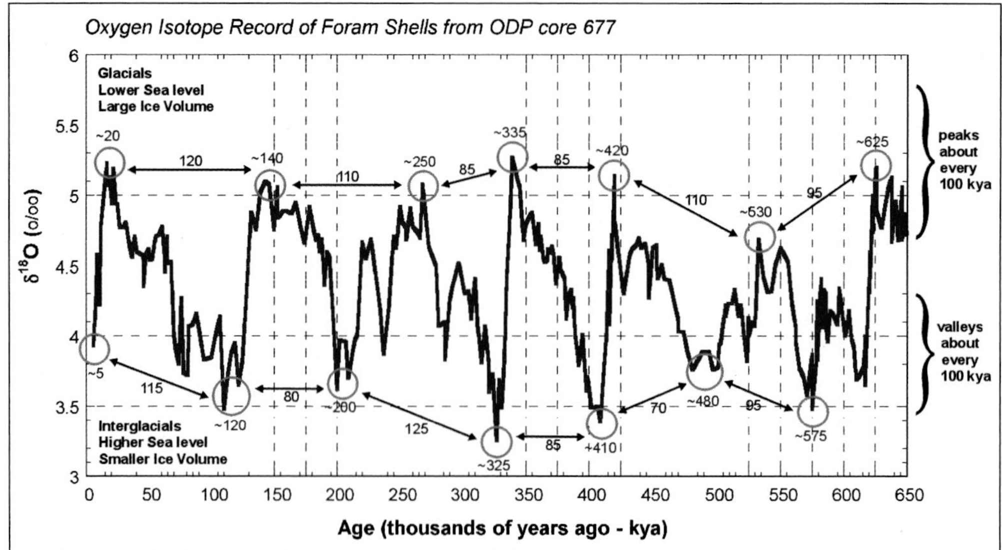

▶ **Figure T12.8 Patterns in sea core ODP 677.** Glacial and interglacial periods and their characteristics are identified. Evidence of quantitative analysis appears on the graph. Check that student graphs include some of these features.

Source: Shackleton, N. J., Berger, A., & Peltier, W. R. (1990). An alternative astronomical calibration of the lower Pleistocene timescale based on ODP site 677. Transactions of the Royal Society of Edinburgh: *Earth Sciences*, *81*, 251-261.

3a. We are currently at the left side of the graph, at 0 kya. Given our current interglacial, students could predict a value of at least 4 ‰, or perhaps a little less. It looks like the very top of the core does not have values reported there. This is because the topmost layer of sediment is sometimes not usable from the rather vigorous coring process. Some of the relationships in Step 3 are shown in figure T12.8.

3b. The LGM shows as a glacial peak from about 20–25 kya (figure T12.8).

3c. The $\delta^{18}O$ values for forams at the LGM are about 5.25 ‰ (figure T12.8).

3d. There are about 6 large glacials, depending on how you count peaks such as at 540–550 kya. The dominant cycle seems to repeat roughly every 100 kya. This is just an approximation. Encourage students to come up with actual values and to record how they came up with their values. The $\delta^{18}O$ values of interglacials span about 4.75–5.25 ‰. Students should list ages for specific peaks on the graph.

Students might also see that glacial periods tend to build slowly, while interglacials seem to

orientation like a sea core? Imagine that the graph represents different layers of sediments. Where are the older, deeper layers? Where are the younger layers?

3. Label glacial and interglacial periods on your handout of figure 12.17. Questions 3a–f will help your team do this.
   a. Where are we now on the graph? What do you predict for current $\delta^{18}O$ values in forams?
   b. What is the age from the graph of the LGM?
   c. What are the $\delta^{18}O$ values for forams at the LGM?
   d. How many glacials do you see in the section? What are typical $\delta^{18}O$ values for glacials? Explain your answer by referring to specific points on the graph.
   e. How many interglacials do you see? What are typical $\delta^{18}O$ values for interglacials? Explain your answer by referring to specific points in figure 12.17.
   f. Label on your graph those areas that represent sea level (high or low), relative size of ice sheets (large or small), $\delta^{18}O$ value (high or low), and global climate cycle (glacial or interglacial).

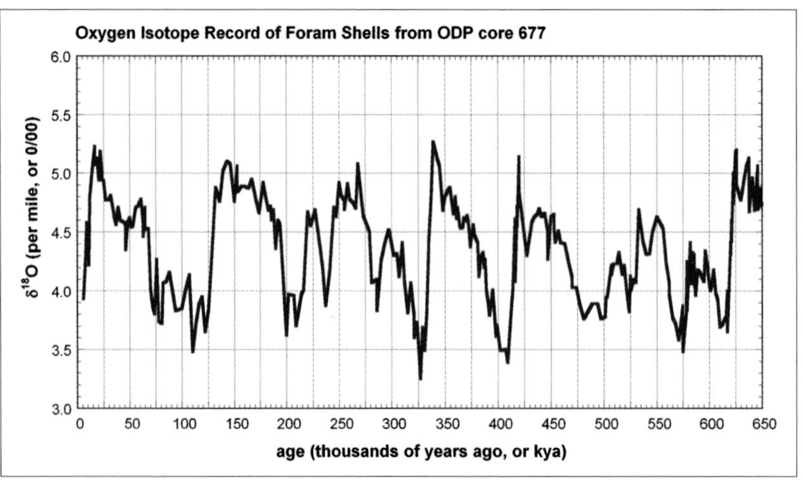

Source: Shackleton, et. al., (1990). An alternative astronomical calibration of the lower Pleistocene timescale based on ODP site 677. Transactions of the Royal Society of Edinburgh: *Earth Sciences*, *81*, 251-261.

▲ **Figure 12.17 ODP site 677.** These data are from site 677 near the Galápagos Islands, Ecuador (see location in figure 12.24). Follow the text to learn what these data tell you about the record of ancient climates on Earth. How do the peaks and valleys relate to glacial periods on Earth?

622 Unit 3 Moving Matter

happen quickly. There is typically a saw-toothed pattern to the graph. For example, look at the intervals 410 to 340 kya. The ice sheets build up over 60 kyr, then collapse and melt in about 10 kyr.

3e. There are about 6–9 large interglacials, depending on how you count valleys such as at 200 and 240 kya. Again, the dominant cycle seems to repeat every 100 kyr. This is just an approximation. Encourage students to come up with actual values and to record how they came up with their values. The $\delta^{18}O$ values of interglacials span about 3.5–3.75 ‰. Students should list ages for specific peaks on the graph or in their T-tables.

3f. Students should be establishing relationships between glacials, overall cool global climate, high $\delta^{18}O$ values, larger ice sheet size, and low sea level. In contrast, interglacials on their graphs correspond to overall warmer global climate, lower $\delta^{18}O$ values, smaller ice sheet size, and high sea level. Some of the relationships in Step 3 are shown in figure T12.8.

4a. The light gray bands represent interglacial periods and the white bands represent glacial periods. Students might point out that Earth, at the present time, is in an interglacial period. The band that appears at age = 0 kya is light gray. They might also point out that the light gray bands align with valleys and the white bands align with peaks.

4b. In general, interglacial periods tend to be longer than glacial periods. This relates to the slow buildup toward glacial periods as opposed to the relatively quick melt-offs experienced during interglacials.

4c. Students should note that the patterns are consistent.

5a. Students should obtain a copy of copymaster 12.5, *Sea Core Foram Data 659* graph and analyze it in the same fashion as the data from ODP 677.

5b. The location is the eastern equatorial Atlantic Ocean. It is offshore of continental Africa and not near the poles.

5c. Students should note that the record of peaks and valleys is very similar to ODP 677, and therefore might represent glacial-interglacial cycles. Actual evidence is the similar range in $\delta^{18}O$ values with a difference of about 2 between the glacials and interglacials (see figure T12.8). About 7 glacials are recorded.

5d. Students again should list evidence that foram data from sites 677 and 659 are very similar. Not only are large cycles timed similarly, but some of the smaller (high-frequency) peaks may line up. Explore these ideas by overlaying copymasters 12.4, *Sea Core Foram Data 677* and 12.5, *Sea Core Foram Data 659* and holding them to a light source (light or overhead projector). The transparencies are also very useful for class discussion and comparison. The similarities in the records suggest a global pattern.

4. Geologists have analyzed data from many other deep-sea cores to identify interglacials and glacials. Get from your teacher a copy of the handout *Bands for Analysis*. Place this sheet behind the graph on the handout *Sea Core Foram Data 677*. Hold the 2 papers up to a light source.
   a. Identify which bands (white or light gray) are glacials and interglacials. Explain your reasoning.
   b. In your team, discuss how interglacial periods compare with glacial periods on the graph.
   c. How does the banding pattern on the *Bands for Analysis* handout compare with the patterns you noticed in Steps 2 and 3?
5. A key question for geologists studying past climates is, "Do sea cores with $\delta^{18}O$ values for forams tell of global patterns in the ocean?" That is, are glacial periods recorded by forams in other oceans in the world? Use figure 12.18 to answer this question.
   a. Look at the graph in figure 12.18. This is also the handout *Sea Core Foram Data 659*.

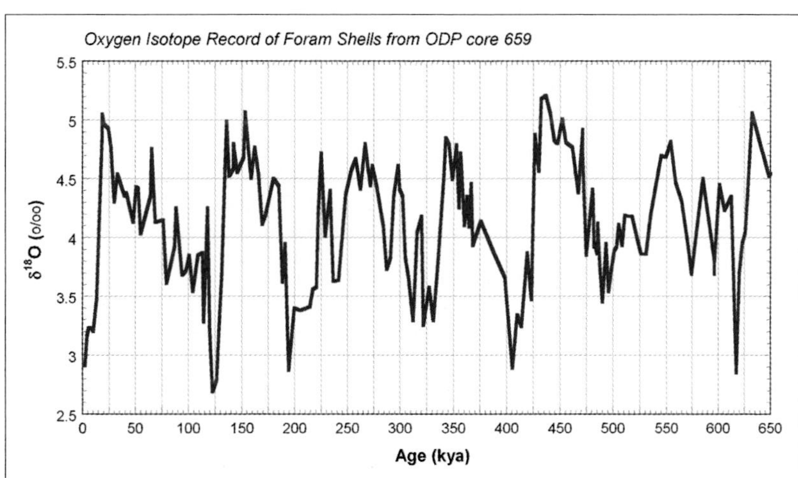

Source: Tiedemann, et. al. (1994). Astronomical timescale for the Pliocene Atlantic delta18-O and dust flux records of Ocean Drilling Program site 659. *Paleoceanography*, 9, 619-638.

▲ **Figure 12.18 ODP site 659.** These data are from ODP site 659 from the ocean offshore of northwestern Africa (see location in figure 12.24). Do you think that this sea core tells the same history of past climates as site 677?

Chapter 12 Evidence for the Ice Ages | 623

Have teams continue with the *Reflect and Connect* questions. It very important that they are seeing the ways that evidence for the history of global climate is recorded by more than one way in cores (seafloor, ice). The elaborate activity will introduce ideas regarding the cause, and then students will need to interpret a new data set in the evaluate.

Answers to Reflect and Connect, SE pages 624–625

1. Data from deep-sea cores are considered proxy data because they are an indirect indicator of global climate. The $\delta^{18}O$ data from deep-sea cores are based on measurements of oxygen isotopes in foram shells. This is a reflection of the oxygen isotopes found in ocean water at some point in the past. That, in turn, is a reflection of how much water is stored in ice sheets at that point in time.
2. Oxygen is present in a wide variety of forms. It is found as an element and in many compounds, and it cycles around Earth in these compounds (e.g., H_2O, O_2, CO_2). It is found in reservoirs within all the earth subsystems. Oxygen moves from one reservoir to another by physical or chemical means. The amount of oxygen, including the relative amounts of each of its isotopes, remains essentially constant across time.

   The water cycle, for example, reflects transport of a substance, and isotopes can be used as a "fingerprint" of the water cycle. Students may also mention oxygen cycling in the context of photosynthesis and respiration. This is a good link. Knowing how oxygen isotopes behave during evaporation at the surface of the ocean lets scientists reconstruct a history of ice ages on Earth. The chapter only looks at the last 650 kyr of that climate record, but the record extends back millions of years.
3. The chapter has demonstrated many types of technology. These range from drilling technologies, to mass spectrometry to measure oxygen isotopes, to radiometric dating of corals. Students may also mention the use of math, computers, and global-scale mapping. As improvements in technologies are made, the ability to gather data improves, as does the accuracy and precision of the data. These improvements contribute to the advancement of science.
4. No. We can obtain a complete record of glacial periods by analyzing sea cores from the equator. This is because both sea level change and oxygen isotopes in forams are a global response to climate change. Students may have thought that records of glacial periods would be restricted to polar regions.

5a. Students should note peaks and valleys in the graphs, and might even write approximate values at this time (see also Step 5b).

5b. Peaks of CO_2 concentration at interglacials are at about 0, 125, 240, 325, 415, 500, 575, and 620 kya. The interglacials occur about every 100 kyr. There are about 5 peaks.

5c. The ages of valleys at glacials are about 20, 170, 260, 350, 445, 520, 590, and 640 kya. Glacials occur about every 100 kyr. There are about 8 valleys.

Answers to Step 5 are on TE page 623.
Answers to Reflect and Connect are on TE pages 624–625.

b. The location of sea core 659 is shown in figure 12.24. Where is the location? Describe whether it is near the poles or near the equator.

c. Are glacial and interglacial periods recorded in figure 12.18? What is your evidence? For example, how many glacials are recorded? When were they?

d. How does figure 12.18 compare with figure 12.17? Do these look similar or different? Do they appear to record a global or a local pattern? List your evidence.

Reflect and Connect

Discuss the following questions with your team. Record your best thinking about these questions in your science notebook.

1. In the explore activity, you learned about proxy data. Explain why data from deep-sea cores are proxy data. Use evidence from your exercises.
2. Describe what you have learned so far about how oxygen cycles in the earth system. How has an understanding of the oxygen cycle helped scientists learn about Earth's past climates?
3. How does technology help scientists understand past climates? In your response, use specific examples of technology you have encountered in this activity.
4. Do you need to look at sea core samples from the poles to understand the history of the ice ages? Explain with evidence from this activity.
5. In chapter 11, you investigated records of CO_2 in the atmosphere in the carbon cycle. Those records went back about 1,000 years. Figure 12.19 shows a record of CO_2 concentrations in the atmosphere that goes back much further. This record was obtained from bubbles in the Antarctic ice sheet (see location in figure 12.24).
   a. Analyze patterns on the graph. Where do peaks and valleys occur on this graph? How often do they occur? How many years back does the record extend?
   b. Carbon dioxide contents correlate with warm periods, or interglacials. How many interglacials do you see? How often do they occur?

5d. The records correspond closely. Note that the polarity is switched here because increasing CO_2 relates to warmer climate. This is easy to show by reversing a transparency on an overhead (i.e., flipping it upside down) and lining it up again with the foram data.

5e. Similarities are values of CO_2 contents the last 1 kyr during our current interglacial at about 280 parts per million (ppm) CO_2. The overall pattern is very different, since 1 kyr is not enough to see glacial and interglacial cycles. Moreover, figure 11.12 shows a dramatic increase in CO_2 since about 1800. Current levels are considerably higher than any values in the past 650 kyr.

5f. Current values (about 380 ppm) are much higher than values recorded in glacial and interglacial cycles the past 650 kyr.

ELABORATE

The Astronomical Theory

Activity Overview

Up to this point in the chapter, the students' focus has been on analyzing data for glacial and interglacial periods in the past 650 kyr. They have considered evidence from fossils, changes in sea level, forams in sea cores, and CO_2 from bubbles in ice cores.

In the foram sea core and CO_2 ice core data, students found patterns suggesting a cycle of change between glacial and interglacial periods. That change reflects warm and cold climate patterns. It also reflects the cycling of water into, and out of, two key water reservoirs on Earth—the ice reservoirs (glaciers and polar ice caps) and the ocean. Thus, oxygen gives one key geochemical fingerprint of change happening on a global scale.

In *The Astronomical Theory*, students will consider the "why" behind the patterns. They will learn about the astronomical theory, which relates the movement of Earth in space to the cycling of glacial and interglacial periods.

c. What are the ages of glacials? How often do they occur?
d. How does this record of CO_2 in the atmosphere correlate with foram records in sea cores?
e. Compare periods of CO_2 highs in figure 12.19 over the last 650,000 years with the last 1,000 years in figure 11.12. Explain any similarities and differences in the patterns.
f. Are current CO_2 concentrations (figure 11.12) higher or lower than variations between recent glacials and interglacials (figure 12.19)?

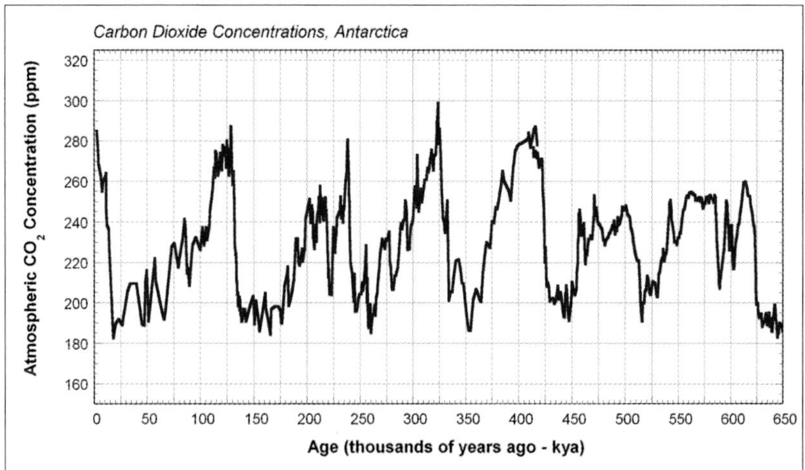

Source: Jouzel, et al. (1993). Extending the Vostok ice-core record of paleoclimate to the penultimate glacial period. *Nature*, *364*, 407–412. and Siegenthaler, et. al. (2005, November 25). Stable carbon cycle-climate relationship during the late Pleistocene. *Science*, *310*, 1313–1317.

▲ **Figure 12.19 Carbon dioxide concentrations, Antarctica.** These data show CO_2 concentrations in the atmosphere from air bubbles in the Antarctic ice sheet. How does the pattern of CO_2 concentrations compare with $\delta^{18}O$ values of forams?

Before You Teach

Background Information

The Astronomical Theory

Useful background information is also included in the student book. If you are interested in an excellent summary of this theory, consider reading *Ice Ages: Solving the Mystery* by John Imbrie and Katherine Palmer Imbrie. This book tells the tale of the scientists engaged in the quest to solve the mystery of why ice ages occur. It highlights the historical development of the astronomical theory from its inception through periods of rejection to its current acceptance as a viable theory for the reoccurring pattern of ice ages.

Beyond the Astronomical Theory

This activity highlights the astronomical theory as one probable cause of the recurring pattern of ice ages. The main cause likely relates to (but is not necessarily "directly proportional to") changes in variations in solar radiation from the Sun hitting Earth. These variations occur on the order of tens of thousands of years. This is not the only theory being discussed, although it does seem to offer the best explanation for the alternation between glacial and interglacial periods. The following list identifies some of the other ideas that scientists are exploring. Some of these effects may enhance or mitigate effects of solar radiation on Earth's climate.

This list is not meant to be exhaustive; rather, it provides a brief overview of the ideas for your consideration.

- *Continental drift:* The continents gradually moved to positions where they obstructed the general transport of heat in the ocean from the equator to the polar regions. Similarly, at very long timescales, tectonics could affect that transport of cold, dense polar water back to the equator. Some workers talk about a "conveyor" pattern for oceanic currents.
- *Carbon dioxide:* A reduction in the amount of carbon dioxide in the atmosphere correlates with the ice ages. Because carbon dioxide is an important greenhouse gas, a decrease in atmospheric CO_2 would correspond to lower temperatures. In contrast, increased levels of carbon dioxide would correlate with global warming. Current findings indicate that the Antarctic warmed first, followed a few hundred years later by increased atmospheric CO_2. This increased CO_2 sets up a positive feedback cycle in which the increased CO_2 leads to further warming. This occurs because CO_2 is a greenhouse gas.

Materials

For each team of 3 students

1 set of copymasters 12.8, consisting of *Graph A*, *Graph B*, *Graph C*, and *Graph D*

1 copy of copymaster 12.9, *Graph E Composite to Foram Scale* (optional)

For each expert group: tilt

1 large Styrofoam ball with a wooden skewer through the center

1 protractor

1 straw cut in half

For each expert group: orbit

1 piece of cardboard

2 pushpins

1 piece of string tied into a circle

1 piece of oversized paper

1 sharp pencil

1 ruler

For each expert group: wobble

1 spinning toy top

Cautions

Some of the materials (skewer, pencil) have sharp points. Students need to be careful not to poke themselves or other students.

Advance Preparation

Make copies of the handouts you will need. These include copymaster 12.8, *Graphs A, B, C, D*. You will only need 1 set of these handouts per team of 3 students. Also make copies of copymaster 12.9, *Graph E Composite to Foram Scale*.

Think about how you will group students for the jigsaw activity described in Step 4. A class of 30 would have 10 learning teams of 3 students each. Each learning team should have 1 expert each in the tilt, orbit, and wobble groups. This means you would have 10 tilt experts, 10 orbit experts, and 10 wobble experts. When students form expert groups (Step 4b), direct them to form expert groups of 3–4 students. Determine the expert group size based on the materials you have and your students' effectiveness in groups.

Gather materials for each expert group station and place the stations around the room. Ideally, there would be room to work at each station. The orbit expert group will need the most space. If you do not have room to set up stations, make the materials available to the expert groups when they need them.

ELABORATE

The Astronomical Theory

Up to this point, you have focused on analyzing patterns in data. This evidence helps you see a history of climate change on Earth between glacial and interglacial periods. You began the chapter by discussing early evidence of ice ages: huge boulders, scratched rocks, and fossils in unusual locations. Next, you analyzed changes in sea level over thousands of years. This is evidence for a large shift in the water cycle from one reservoir to another. You examined the example of moving water from ice sheets to oceans, and back.

In the explore-explain activity, *The Core of the Matter*, you looked to data from deep-sea cores for evidence of past climate changes. You learned that the oxygen locked in the shells of forams provides a proxy record of glacial and interglacial climates from the past. You noted regular patterns in the oxygen isotopes of foram shells. These patterns suggest cycles of climate change in Earth's past. The patterns are global in scale.

But what is the reason for the cycles of climate change? Do the patterns continue back in time before 650 kya? Scientists who study paleoclimatology have wondered that same thing. In *The Astronomical Theory*, you will learn about one theory that scientists have been testing as the cause of the cycling of glacial and interglacial periods.

Materials

For each team of 3 students

1 set of *Graphs A, B, C, D* handout

For each expert group: tilt

1 large Styrofoam ball with a wooden skewer through the center

1 protractor

1 straw cut in half

For each expert group: orbit

1 piece of cardboard

2 pushpins

1 piece of string tied into a circle

oversized paper

1 sharp pencil

1 ruler

For each expert group: wobble

1 spinning top

As You Teach

Outcomes and Indicators of Success

By the end of this activity, students should

1. relate Earth's motions relative to the Sun (tilt, orbit, and wobble) to variations in global climate and describe how these motions relate to the solar radiation at Earth's surface.

   They will demonstrate their ability by

   - revealing (through a diagram) and revising what they already know about the movement of Earth around the Sun;
   - becoming an "expert" on how one of the key factors (tilt, orbit, and wobble) of Earth's movement varies and the impact of that variation on global climate;
   - teaching other team members about their key factor and learning about the two other key factors from their team members; and
   - synthesizing an explanation that combines all three motions to describe that glaciers grow when the incoming solar radiation decreases and retreat when incoming solar radiation increases.

2. be able to use mathematical tools and models to guide and improve their understanding of science concepts.

   They will demonstrate their understanding by

   - using a graphical model to combine data and analyze the resulting patterns,
   - comparing the graphs they used with key variations in Earth's movement in space and with patterns in the sea core data they have analyzed in previous investigations, and
   - recognizing that the combination of the key factors can account for the cycling of glacial and interglacial periods.

3. understand how scientists use coral dating to anchor glacial and interglacial periods to specific times in Earth's geologic history.

   They will demonstrate their understanding by describing that dead coral reefs are an indicator of past sea levels and the dating of these corals allows scientists to assign a geologic time to that sea level. Changes in sea level can, in turn, be linked to changes in global climate.

4. understand that scientific explanations must be logically consistent, abide by the rules of evidence, be open to questions and possible modifications, and be based on historical and current scientific knowledge.

   They will demonstrate their understanding by

   - discussing as a class the validity of the astronomical theory and
   - recognizing that there are other theories that attempt to explain the cycles of glacials and interglacials in Earth's past.

5. develop further skills in the abilities and understandings of scientific inquiry.

   They will demonstrate their skills by

   - using models to understand variations in solar radiation with tilt, wobble, and orbit shape (eccentricity);

Answers to Steps 1, 3–4 are on TE pages 629–630.

Process and Procedure

Why does Earth have glacial and interglacial periods? This is a simple question, but the answer has several parts. One way to look at this question is to break it into smaller pieces.

1. Discuss these questions with your team and write your ideas in your notebook.
   a. What conditions favor the growth of glaciers?
   b. What conditions favor the melting of glaciers?
2. Read the following paragraph and discuss your understanding with your team.

   What causes the climate to cycle between glacial and interglacial periods? Scientists have been trying to answer this for over 150 years. In the mid-1800s, scientists first proposed an astronomical theory of climate change. This theory proposes that the orbit of Earth around the Sun causes ice ages. Milutin Milankovitch, a Serbian mathematician, did a lot of work in the 1920s that supported this idea. He calculated how changes in Earth's orbit caused changes in the intensity of solar radiation across time. Milankovitch proposed that variations in solar radiation caused glacial and interglacial patterns. Because of his contributions, scientists sometimes call the astronomical theory of climate change the Milankovitch theory.
3. Make a drawing that reflects what you already know about Earth's orbit around the Sun. Discuss with your team how to include these things with your diagram.
   a. Label the Sun and Earth.
   b. Show the orientation and path of Earth through space.
   c. Include information you know about distance and time.
4. The astronomical theory focuses on 3 factors in the orbital motion of Earth: the tilt of Earth's axis, the changing shape of Earth's orbit around the Sun, and the wobble of the rotation axis. Your team will study these factors, looking at 1 factor at a time.
   a. This activity has 3 reading passages, 1 for each factor. Each team member will focus on 1 of the key factors. For example, one person will become the team expert on tilt, one on wobble, and so on.
   b. Gather with students from other groups who are experts on the same factor. Read the appropriate handout and discuss the information and the diagrams. Complete the *Try This* section of your reading. Be prepared to explain the information to the other students in your team.

- using mathematics to read a graph, organize data, and develop a composite graph to represent tilt, wobble, and orbit shape (eccentricity); and
- communicating with their team their understandings from working in an expert group.

Strategies

Getting Started

Steps 1 and 2 of *Process and Procedure* provide a good introduction to the lesson and, at the same time, elicit some of the students' prior knowledge about the concepts being addressed in the lesson. You might want to facilitate a discussion of these two steps as a way to get started.

Cautions

Some of the materials (skewer, pencil) have sharp points. Students need to be careful not to poke themselves or other students.

Materials

For each team of 3 students

1 set of copymasters 12.8, consisting of *Graph A*, *Graph B*, *Graph C*, and *Graph D*

1 copy of copymaster 12.9, *Graph E Composite to Foram Scale* (optional)

For each expert group: tilt

1 large Styrofoam ball with a wooden skewer through the center
1 protractor
1 straw cut in half

For each expert group: orbit

1 piece of cardboard
2 pushpins
1 piece of string tied into a circle
1 piece of oversized paper
1 sharp pencil
1 ruler

For each expert group: wobble

1 spinning toy top

Process and Procedure

It might be helpful in Step 1 to remind students to think back to the explore activity. In that investigation, they explored ice ages in general and focused on the melting of ice and its relationship to sea level. Then they considered the role energy played in the advance and retreat of glaciers.

In Step 2, students are given some information to introduce the idea that one cause of glacial and interglacial cycles relates to the motion of Earth around the Sun. In Step 3, students are asked to make a drawing. This drawing will show students' current understanding of the movement of Earth around the Sun.

In Step 4, students participate in a jigsaw activity. They will form groups of 3 to 4 students focusing on a feature of Earth's orbit (see *Advance Preparation*). If your students have not done a jigsaw activity before, they might need help grouping and regrouping. Within each 3-person team, each student will become an expert on 1 of the 3 key factors of Earth's movement in space: the tilt of Earth's axis, the changing shape of Earth's orbit around the Sun, and the wobble of the spinning Earth. Each reading includes a section called *Try This*. Answers to these sections follow. You will want to circulate through the room and listen as students work in their expert groups and learning teams for Step 4. Students return to their original 3-person team and share ideas in Step 5. This is an opportunity to assess their growing understanding of the factors that are key to the astronomical theory.

Students try in Step 6 to explain again the causes for the ice ages. They compare the 3 factors (tilt, orbit, wobble) and consider which might have the largest effect, although they really cannot have a way to know at this point. They see how factors can combine in Step 7.

READING

Reading 1: Tilt

Earth's axis is tilted about 23.5° from its plane of travel around the Sun. You saw this in figure 12.5. You probably know that this tilt causes the seasons. During summer, the Northern Hemisphere is pointed toward the Sun. In this position, the Northern Hemisphere receives the maximum amount of solar radiation. During winter, the Northern Hemisphere is pointed away from the Sun, and thus receives a minimum amount of solar radiation. If Earth's axis were not tilted, there would be no seasons. This is because every point on Earth would receive the same amount of solar radiation each day of the year.

But did you know that the tilt of the rotation axis changes in time? The tilt varies between 21.5° and 24.5°. The variation occurs on a cycle of about 41 kyr (figure 12.20). If Earth's axis is tilted more, the seasons become more severe. Summers are warmer and winters are colder. If the amount of tilt is less, the seasons become milder. Summers are cooler and winters are warmer.

The cool summers are thought to contribute to glacial advances. During a cool summer, the snow that accumulated during the previous winter cannot quite melt away. Thus, snow and ice can continue to pile up in the far north, eventually building massive ice sheets. As the snow and ice accumulate, they also initiate a positive feedback mechanism. Regions covered with more snow reflect more of the Sun's energy, causing even more cooling.

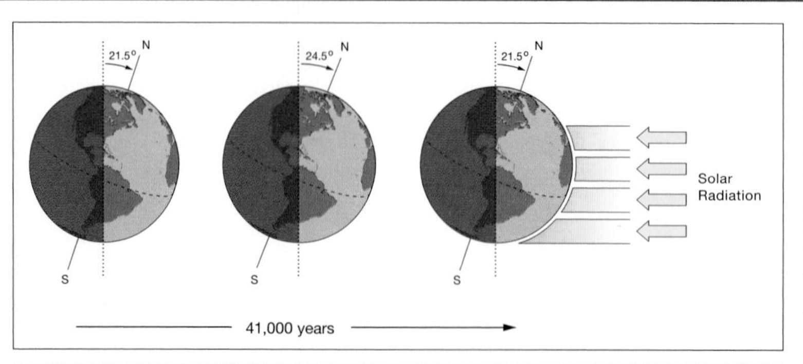

▲ **Figure 12.20 Variation in Earth's tilt.** The tilt of Earth s rotation axis varies from 21.5° to 24.5° and back to 21.5° every 41 kyr. Currently, the tilt is about 23.5°.

628 Unit 3 Moving Matter

In Step 7, students continue in their team of 3 for a graphing activity to learn that each factor can contribute to a total, or composite, curve. In this part of the investigation, they will be adding the curves of three graphs (A, B, C) to make a fourth graph (D). You will need to distribute 1 set of 4 handouts to each team. Do not distribute copymaster 12.9, *Graph E Composite to Foram Scale* at this time.

For Step 7, decide if you can give students just the graphs, and then have them construct a data table in their notebooks to record xy values. This is the best way to have them work through a data table and be responsible for reporting their values to their team.

You will also see that each team will need to select and use the same size steps for the x-axis (i.e., resolution, or Δx). If teams don't do this, they will not be able to add values for the composite graph for y per x. It is OK if different teams use different values of Δx, as this will show different ranges of resolution.

If, however, your students are not as advanced with graphing and organizing data, you can give them copymaster 12.9, *Graph E Composite to Foram Scale*, where graphs A, B, C, and D already have the data tables, and $\Delta x = 5$. We do not recommend this though. It is a very important skill for students to be able to record data in an organized fashion in a table to share with a team, compared with just filling out a table. Students might be able to use a graphing calculator with these data, but only allow this if students are first able to plot by hand with pencil and paper. Students might recognize that these graphs resemble sine or cosine waves. This is how they were generated.

In Step 8, students compare their simulated data with actual data, and in Step 9, they read about the combination of cycles from a scientist's perspective.

Gather the class together to discuss Step 10. Listening to students' responses during the discussion will help you assess their understanding of theories in general and the astronomical theory specifically. You may need to fill in with additional information, as needed.

Answers to Reading 1 Try This are on TE page 630.

Try This

1. Look at the Styrofoam ball or a globe of Earth. The wooden skewer represents the rotational axis of Earth. The straw represents a line that is perpendicular to the plane of Earth's orbit around the Sun. Orient the ball so that it looks like Earth in the diagram in figure 12.20. Notice that the Northern Hemisphere is tilted toward the Sun. Is the Northern Hemisphere receiving more or less incoming solar radiation in this position than the Southern Hemisphere?
2. Change the tilt of Earth by removing the straw and repositioning it so that the angle between the skewer and the straw is larger. (Although the actual variation is only a degree or two in either direction, it might help you see the difference if you exaggerate the change in angle.) Does the Northern Hemisphere receive more or less incoming solar radiation than it did before?
3. Repeat Step 2, but this time make the angle between the skewer and the straw smaller than before. Does the Northern Hemisphere receive more or less incoming solar radiation than it did before?

READING

Reading 2: Eccentricity of Orbit

Earth revolves around the Sun in an elliptical path. The shape of this path changes with time. Sometimes it is nearly circular, other times it is slightly more elliptical. This is shown in figure 12.21. The cycle of this change is about 100 kyr. Currently, Earth's orbit is slightly elliptical.

The change in elliptical shape of Earth's orbit means that Earth's distance to the Sun changes only a very small amount. As Earth's orbit changes shape, the amount of solar radiation Earth receives also varies only a small amount. When the orbit is nearly circular, the distance between Earth and the Sun is nearly equal throughout the year. The total solar radiation received by Earth is nearly equal throughout the year. However, when the orbit is slightly elliptical, the distance between Earth and the Sun varies. But these changes in solar radiation due to distance are very, very small. They would have almost no direct effect on patterns of climate change.

These observations relate to current scientific questions in understanding past climates on Earth. From the discussion above, you would predict that the eccentricity of orbit would have little effect on past climate. You would not expect climate change to relate to 100-kyr cycles. However, data that you investigated also show a strong variation between glacials and interglacials about every 100 kyr. While scientists now understand many parts of past climate cycles, they are still working to solve important details.

Try This

1. Place a blank sheet of paper on top of a piece of cardboard. Place 2 pushpins about 5 cm apart near the center of the paper. Tie the ends of a 30-cm-long piece of string together. Place the string around the pushpins. Place a sharp pencil

Answers to Steps 1, 3–4, 6–10, SE pages 627–634

1. Student answers will vary. This is a chance for students to recall and share what they have learned about glaciers in earlier activities. Students should recognize that in order for ice sheets to grow and accumulate, the global temperature probably has to be cooler overall. In order for glaciers to retreat, global temperature probably has to be warmer overall. Students might also speculate that changes in the intensity of seasons would either encourage or discourage the growth of glaciers. For instance, they might propose that colder winters or colder summers would encourage the advance of glaciers. Students will address this question again, in a *Reflect and Connect* question at the end of this activity.

3. Student answers will vary. Students should draw Earth moving around the Sun in an elliptical path. They might indicate that it takes 1 year to complete the cycle. They also might show that the axis of Earth is tilted 23.5° from the plane of its travel around the Sun.

4. As students read the passages, they are introduced to 3 different factors, each of which changes in a regular cycle. The passages introduce an approximate length of the cycle. You might find slightly different values used in other resources because the length of the cycle is statistically derived from a given set of data. If a data set is of poorer resolution, the researcher might not be able to detect some components of the total signal.

4b. Answers follow for *Reading 1: Tilt, Try This*:

1. The Northern Hemisphere receives more incoming solar radiation in this position than the Southern Hemisphere.
2. The Northern Hemisphere, especially the North Pole, receives more incoming solar radiation than it did before.
3. The Northern Hemisphere receives less incoming solar radiation than it did before.

Answers follow for *Reading 2: Eccentricity of Orbit, Try This*:

3. If you remove a pushpin, the orbit is a circle.
4. The ellipse with the pushpins 10 cm apart was more elliptical than the ellipse formed using the pushpins 5 cm apart. The figure made with only 1 pushpin is actually a circle.
5. One of the pushpins represents the Sun. The Sun is at one of the 2 foci of the ellipse. The other pushpin does not represent an object in space. Earth is represented by the pencil tip and its orbit is represented by the ellipse.

NOTES:

Reading 2: Eccentricity of Orbit, continued

inside the string and pull the string tight. Keeping the string tight at all times, draw an ellipse by moving the pencil around the pushpins.

The pushpins represent the foci of the ellipse of Earth's orbit. In a real orbit, the Sun would lie at one of these foci. In reality, however, Earth's orbit is nearly a circle.

2. Repeat Step 1, but this time place the pushpins 10 cm apart.
3. Predict what would happen if you removed 1 of the pushpins. Try it.
4. Which ellipse was more elliptical, the one with pushpins 5 cm apart, 10 cm apart, or with only 1 pushpin?
5. In this model, where is the Sun? Earth? Earth's orbit?

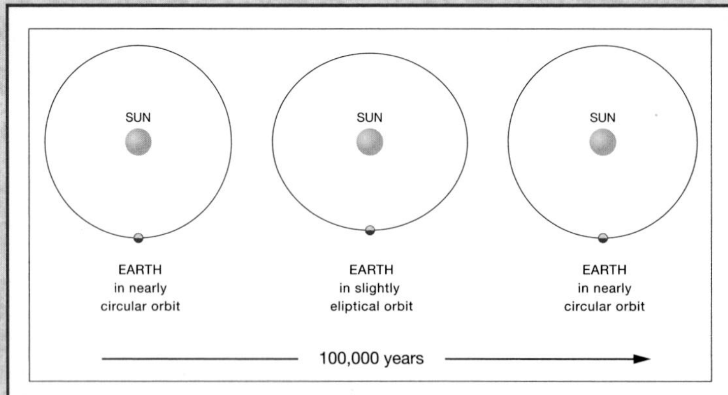

▲ **Figure 12.21 Variation in orbit eccentricity.** The shape of Earth's orbit changes from nearly circular, to slightly elliptical, and back to almost circular. This cycle occurs over about 100 kyr.

NOTES:

READING

Reading 3: Wobble (Precession)

Earth's axis of rotation wobbles like a spinning top (figure 12.22). Of course, Earth spins around the axis with one revolution per day. But then the orientation of the axis itself wobbles in space, making a near circle. A top might complete one cycle of wobble every second or so. In contrast, the Earth takes about 21 kyr to complete a full "wobble." This wobble is known as the precession cycle because of how Earth's axis moves, or precesses, through space.

How does the wobble affect climate on Earth? The wobble affects the axis and the orbit of Earth. Because of the wobble, Earth's axis points in different directions through time. Right

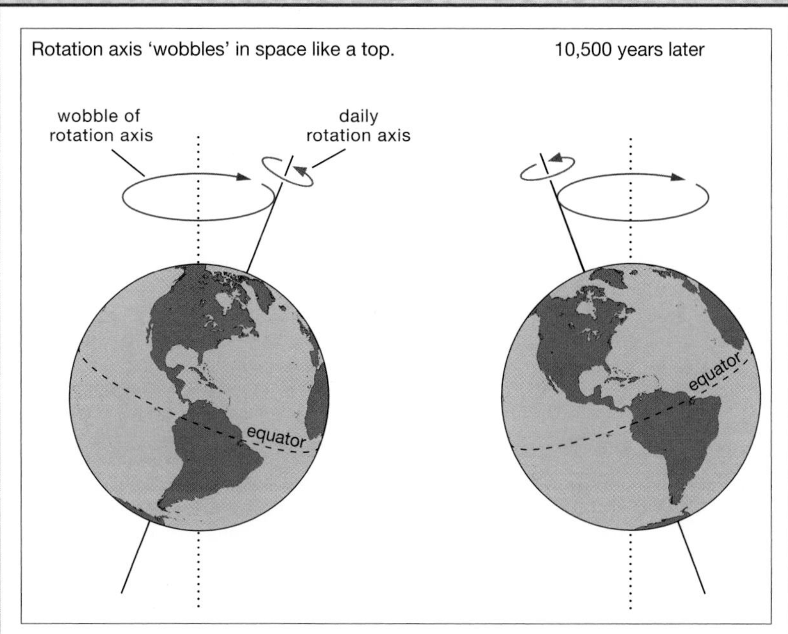

▲ **Figure 12.22 Wobble of rotation axis.** The rotation axis of Earth wobbles much like the motion of a spinning top. The axis moves through space and describes a circle each 21 kyr.

Answers follow to *Reading 3: Wobble (Precession), Try This*:

1. Students should observe that the top spins around its rotational axis, but as it does so, it wobbles around that axis.

6a. Student answers will vary. It is not important that students come up with the same answer, or even the correct answer. It is most important that their rationale be sound. Because the advance and retreat of glaciers depends on changes in incoming solar radiation, they might indicate that the wobble or tilt alone would appear to have the greatest impact. They should see that the changes in the orbit, from nearly circular to slightly elliptical, seem to cause only small changes in incoming solar radiation and might have the least impact.

6b. Student answers will vary. Hopefully, students will find that they have a better understanding of the complexity of Earth's movement through space.

7b. Answers for graph D, the composite curve, are shown in figure T12.9.

7d. Students should notice that the pattern in graph D is much more complex than the individual patterns. They might point out that some of the original cycles are more apparent than others. (The cycle from graph A seems more apparent than the cycle from graph C.) They should also notice that the amplitude of the graph has changed. The *y*-axis now ranges from +4 to −4. These values are higher than any values for the individual graphs.

NOTES:

Reading 3: Wobble (Precession), continued

now, Earth's axis is pointed toward the North Star, Polaris. At other times, the axis has pointed elsewhere in the sky.

What does this mean in the long term? Currently, Earth is closest to the Sun during winter in the Northern Hemisphere. Because Earth is closest to the Sun at this point in its orbit, it receives slightly more solar radiation than it would if it were farther away. But because the axis is pointing away, the Northern Hemisphere still experiences winter.

Summers currently occur in the Northern Hemisphere when Earth is at its maximum distance from the Sun. In about 10,500 years, Earth will experience winters when it is farthest from the Sun and summers when it is closest. Another way to think of this is that the shortest day of the year will keep moving. In 10,500 years, the shortest day will be June 21. At that time, the middle of summer and the longest day of the year will be December 21. In another 10,500 years, radiation conditions will have precessed back to where we are today.

Try This

1. Observe a spinning top. Look carefully at the motion of the top around its central axis. Notice how the top spins around this central axis, but also notice how the axis itself seems to wobble, forming a circle in space. Each time the wobble completes a circuit, it equals a precession cycle.

5. Return to your original team to share what you have learned in your expert group.
6. After you have discussed all 3 key factors, answer Questions 6a–b with your team.
   a. Which factor do you think would have the greatest impact on past climate changes? Which one would have the least impact? Explain your reasoning.
   b. How does what you now know about Earth's movements in space compare with what you included in your response to Step 3?
7. The astronomical theory regards the history of climate change as being due to interactions between the 3 key cycles. No single cycle can completely explain the geologic evidence, such as forams or records of CO_2 concentrations in the atmosphere. Complete Steps 7a–d to see the patterns that emerge when different factors are combined.
   a. Get from your teacher a set of 4 handouts. Three of the handouts contain a completed graph. Each team member needs to take responsibility for 1 of these graphs (A, B, or C). The fourth handout contains a table and a grid for graphing.
   b. What do you think the first 3 graphs represent?

8a. Graph A has a cycle around 100 kyr. This would correspond to the change in shape of Earth's orbit. Graph B has a cycle around 41 kyr, such as tilt of Earth's axis. Graph C has a cycle around 21 kyr, as in Earth's wobble.

Student responses are not likely to use the symbol "kyr." However, you might introduce them to this symbol as a space- and time-saving device. Caution them not to confuse kyr (thousands of years) with kya (thousands of years ago).

8b. Student answers will vary. They are likely to point out that the simulated data are not as complex as the real data. The simulated data are regular, and the pattern is very clear. The real data exhibit fluctuations. For instance, the real data are more jagged in appearance. Students should point out that important peaks in the real data correspond with simulated peaks at about 82, 105, 125, and 200 kya in copymaster 12.9, *Graph E Composite to Foram Scale*. Students might also point out that the patterns seem to match more toward the left side of the graph than toward the right side.

NOTES:

Answers to Steps 7–8 are on TE pages 632–633a.

c. Your task, as a team, is to combine the 3 graphs together to produce a fourth graph (D). The following sequence provides one strategy for doing this:
   - Decide on the spacing that your team will use between *x* values. Think about a trade-off so that you do not have too many, or too few, *x* values.
   - Use the curve in the graph to determine the *y* value for each *x* value.
   - Record all *xy* pairs neatly in a T-table or similar format. Note that your team could also record all the data in a single table with several columns.
   - Add together the *y* value for individual *x* values in the 3 graphs.
   - Make a new table (or set of columns) for the *x* value and the sum of the 3 *y* values.
   - Take turns plotting the *x* and *y* values for graph D.

d. Compare graph D with graphs A, B, and C from the *Graphs A, B, C, D* handout. What similarities and differences do you notice?

8. The data you used in Step 7 simulate the solar radiation that reaches Earth. Although they are not actual data, they are based on the physics of Earth's orbit around the Sun. They can be compared with other evidence.

   a. Imagine that the *x*-axis on each of graphs A, B, and C represents age in thousands of years. How long is 1 cycle on each of these graphs? Which of the astronomical cycles could each graph represent?

To save time and space, you can abbreviate thousands of years as "kyr." However, be careful not to confuse kyr (thousands of years) with kya (thousands of years ago).

   b. Compare graph D with one or all of the graphs you worked with in the explore-explain activity (figures 12.17, 12.18, 12.19). What similarities and differences do you notice?

As you compare graph D with ice or sea core data, note the different *x*-axis scales. You can still compare them by just looking from 0 to 150 kya. Another option is to obtain graph E from your teacher. This graph is an extension of graph D out to 650 kya. (Remember, kya stands for thousands of years ago.)

9. The graphs you worked with in Step 7 actually simulate the work done by Milankovitch and other scientists. Learn more about their thoughts on these cycles and how they interact by completing the following tasks.

   a. Read the following paragraphs to see what Milankovitch and other scientists thought about the role of the 3 factors

X	Y $Y_w + Y_{tilt} + Y_{ecc}$
0	3.4
5	1.6
10	0.5
15	1.5
20	2.1
25	0.7
30	0.0
35	1.3
40	1.9
45	−0.2
50	−2.8
55	−2.9
60	−1.8
65	−2.1
70	−2.8
75	−1.3
80	1.1
85	1.2
90	−0.7
95	−0.8
100	1.1
105	2.1
110	1.4
115	1.5
120	3.2
125	3.4
130	0.8
135	−1.5
140	−1.2
145	−0.4
150	−1.4

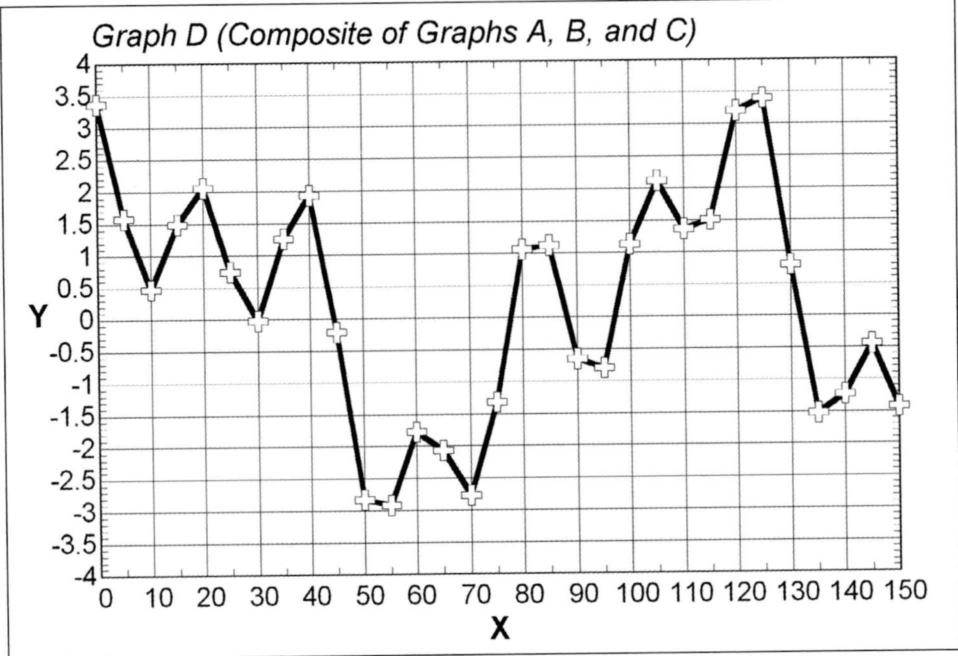

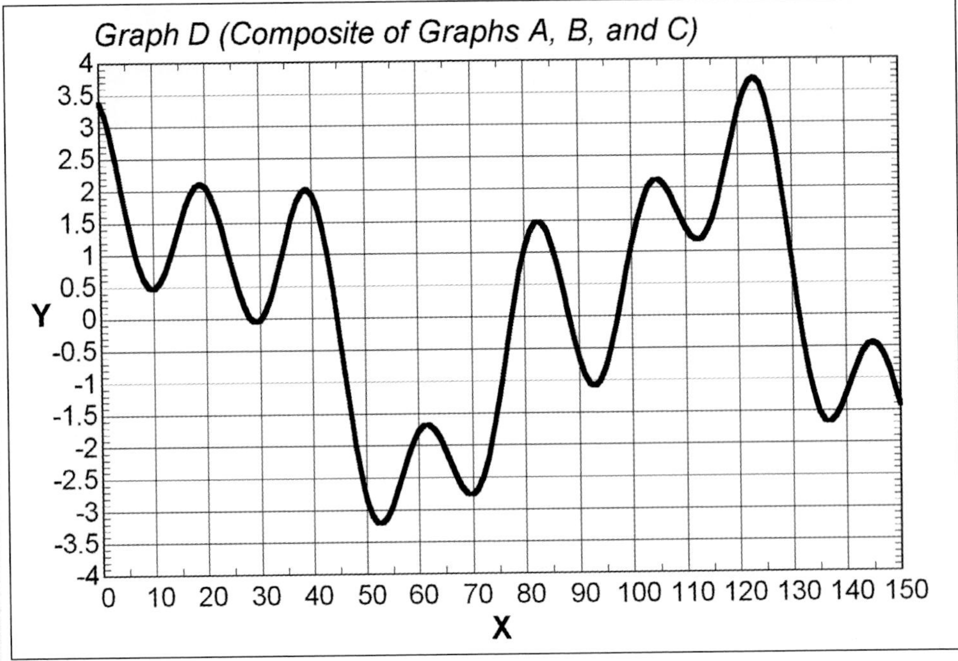

▲ **Figure T12.9 Composite data and curve.** The data table shows the sums for wobble, tilt, and eccentricity represented by graphs A, B, and C. The graphed answer for the resolution of $\Delta x = 5$ is shown by plus marks, as well as a smooth curve for $\Delta x = 1$. Note that a resolution of 5 picks up all main features of the smooth curve.

NOTES:

9b. The 100-kyr cycle dominates.

9c. This passage infers that the 2 shorter cycles (41 kyr and 21 kyr) should dominate and be most strongly influenced by solar radiation. The actual data such as from forams or ice core CO_2 show the longer cycle (100 kyr) dominating. This is actually a current and very important scientific question, and a lot of research is trying to resolve it.

10a. The astronomical theory is a theory and not just a hypothesis because it is supported by a wide variety of data and observations in numerous fields in the sciences. Not only is the theory supported by the theoretical calculations first proposed by Milutin Milankovitch, but it is supported by much actual data. It is also supported by numerical models of radiation to Earth. Scientists have the sea core data from the sites that the students studied as well as a large number of other sites from around the world that provide supporting evidence. The evidence is not limited to oxygen isotope records in forams. Scientists have data from other isotopes in forams, and from dust and pollen in sea cores. They also have supporting data from ice cores, lake cores, corals, and speleothems (stalactites and stalagmites). Because there is such a strong correlation between the theoretical calculations, physical models, and the actual data, this theory has moved well beyond the hypothesis stage. The theory will be strengthened if current burning questions are answered, such as the dominance of the 100-kyr cycle, rather than the predicted 41- or 21-kyr cycles.

10b. As students noticed in Step 6, the astronomical theory predicts a dominance of the 2 shorter cycles (tilt that cycles in 41 kyr and wobble that cycles in 21 kyr). These 2 cycles correspond closely to changes in summer solar radiation. This dominance is found in records that date from 0.95 million years ago (950 kya) to 2.75 million years ago (Mya).

However, the 100-kyr cycle dominates the time period from the present to 0.95 Myr (950 kya), which happens to include the time period that students are studying. This is one of the challenges of the astronomical theory. Scientists are not yet sure why this 100 kyr cycle is so prevalent. This cycle in radiation only changes input at a given latitude by about 0.1 percent over time compared with tilt and precession. The latter 2 factors change the incoming radiation by about 10–12 percent over time at a latitude. This is an exciting area of current research.

It is important to make the point with students that ambiguity exists in our understanding of nature; it is why science exists.

After the class discussion, have students complete the reading in Step 11. Then have them answer the *Reflect and Connect* questions individually. Read through student responses to assess student understanding of the astronomical theory and how it relates to patterns in foram data.

in modifying Earth's climate. Milankovitch proposed that changes in global climate are due to changes in 3 key factors:

i. The tilt of Earth's axis (41-kyr)
ii. The wobble of the spinning Earth (21-kyr cycle)
iii. The changing shape of Earth's orbit around the Sun (100-kyr cycle)

Milankovitch proposed that climate change was greatest when all three cycles reinforced one another. At times, all the cycles work either to minimize or to maximize the solar radiation on Earth. Milankovitch believed that the tilt and wobble cycles would dominate over the orbit cycle. According to his theory, the combination of cycles affects the relative intensity of solar radiation in summer. This, in turn, controls the growth and retreat of glaciers. Cool summers in the Northern Hemisphere, where most of Earth's landmass is located, would allow snow and ice to persist to the next winter. This allows large glaciers to develop over tens of thousands of years. This links with the movement of water from oceans to continents. In contrast, warmer summers melt all snow from the previous winter, plus a little more. This reduces the mass of glaciers and ice sheets.

Computer models and historical evidence suggest that the Milankovitch cycles exert their greatest cooling and warming influences when the peaks and troughs of all three cycles coincide with one another. This probably accounts for the previous major interglacial at 125 kya.

b. Return to figures 12.17, 12.18, and 12.19. Which of the 3 cycles appears to dominate in those data?
c. From the passage in Step 9a, what cycles did Milankovitch predict would dominate? Is this consistent with your answer in Step 9b? Write an explanation in your science notebook.

10. In this investigation, you have learned about the astronomical theory, which is important to studying past climates. As a class, discuss Questions 10a–c.
    a. What makes the astronomical theory a theory and not just a hypothesis?
    b. What features of the astronomical theory might we still be trying to understand?
    c. Are there any other ideas or theories that attempt to explain the cycles of glacials and interglacials in Earth's past? How would you test those ideas?
11. Read *Coral Dating* to find out how corals are used to anchor the astronomical theory in real geologic time.

NOTES:

READING

Coral Dating

The idea that the shape of Earth's orbit around the Sun changed in a regular and predictable manner has been around for a while. In the 1860s, James Croll first argued for a link between Earth's orbit and changes between glacial and interglacial cycles. His work was the first version of an astronomical theory for the history of climate change. The problem was that in the past there was no good way to determine the age when the glacials and interglacials actually occurred. Some other data were needed that would anchor the theory in real time. This was also true of early work with the fossil record. The ability to anchor these geologic records in time did not emerge for another 100 years.

In the late 1950s, scientists turned to coral reefs to measure ages for periods of high sea levels. They expected that high sea levels and coral ages would correspond with interglacial periods. Elkhorn coral (*Acropora palmata*) provided that key piece of information. These coral tend to grow near the surface of the water. They grow upward, then stop growing right at the level of low tide. This gives them a flat-topped appearance (figure 12.23). If the sea level rises,

▲ **Figure 12.23 Elkhorn coral.** Elkhorn coral (*Acropora palmata*) grows upward in shallow seas. It stops growing at the level of low tide. This gives a flat-topped appearance from the side. When geologists measure ages for fossil elkhorn coral, they can determine the sea level at a time in the geologic past.

Chapter 12 Evidence for the Ice Ages 635

Factor	Cycle	Description
Tilt	41,000 years	The tilt of Earth's axis varies from 21.5° to 24.5°. When Earth is tilted more, the seasons are more severe. This is due to changes in the amount of solar radiation that Earth receives.
Wobble	21,000 years	Earth spins like a top. As it does, it wobbles. This wobbling causes changes in the direction that Earth points and shifts its orbit. Both of these impact the amount of solar radiation that Earth receives.
Orbit	100,000 years	Earth's orbit varies from nearly circular to slightly elliptical. When Earth's orbit is more elliptical, the distance between it and the Sun varies from point to point. This change in distance results in only a very, very small change in the amount of solar radiation that Earth receives.

▲ **Figure T12.10 Milankovitch cycle factors.** This chart summarizes the 3 key factors that affect Earth's climate. Signals with these frequencies appear in several of the students' data sets, including the evaluate activity.

Answers to Reflect and Connect, SE pages 636–637

1. Student answers will vary. A sample is provided in figure T12.10. Check that students have made the connection between changes in the key factors and changes in the amount of solar radiation received by Earth.
2. Each of the factors affects the amount of solar radiation received by Earth, with tilt and wobble having the greatest impact. When the factors reinforce one another, resulting in more radiation or less radiation, Earth experiences more extreme seasons. Cool summers in the Northern Hemisphere, where most of Earth's landmass is located, would allow snow and ice to persist to the next winter. This allows large glaciers to grow larger over tens of thousands of years (i.e., net gain per year). In contrast, warmer summers shrink glaciers by melting all snow from the previous winter, plus a little more (i.e., net loss per year).

   Earlier scientists (and perhaps your students) proposed that the extra snow and harsher winter conditions contributed to the growth and retreat of glaciers. Repeated cold winters would encourage glacier growth, while repeated warm winters would encourage glacial retreats. Current understanding supports the idea that it is really summer conditions that contribute to the growth and retreat of glaciers. Years of mild summers leave more snow and ice intact (unmelted), leading to the growth of glaciers, while years of more intense summers lead to an overall loss of glacial mass.

3. Student answers should make the following points:
   - There is a repeating cycle of around 100 kyr in the sea core

Answers to Reflect and Connect are on TE pages 636–637.

Coral Dating, continued

elkhorn coral are "drowned" in water too deep for them. If the sea level falls, or the land is pushed upward, they are stranded in air.

To see changes in sea level in the geologic past, a geologist first must find a dead elkhorn coral still attached at its base. This is where detailed fieldwork is vital. The base of that elkhorn coral was probably about 2 m below sea level at low tide when it was alive. Next, the geologist measures a radiometric age for when the coral was alive. This tells the position of sea level at the time of the coral age.

Spectacular examples of fossil elkhorn reefs have been dated in locations such as Florida, the Bahamas, the Hawaiian Islands, Australia, Barbados, and New Guinea. Such research is used for constructing the sea level curve, such as the one you used in the explore activity. This research has also been used to date high sea levels during the last two interglacial periods. For example, much of the perimeter of Florida is composed of a giant reef that grew approximately 125 kya. At that time, there was even less ice on Earth than today and the sea level was several meters higher. This high sea level at 125 kya is clear in figures 12.17 and 12.18.

Once scientists realized the link between the coral reefs, ancient climate, and sea level, they used radiometric dating for other coral reefs. Work with coral age dating in the 1960s indicated that sea levels were high at time periods such as 82 kya, 105 kya, 125 kya, and 200 kya. Improved laboratory methods in the mid-1980s confirmed these results.

The ages of the coral terraces indicate periods of high sea level and correspond closely to the interglacials predicted by the astronomical theory. You can see these interglacial periods as individual peaks on the deep-sea cores you studied in the explore-explain activity. Take another look at the handout *Sea Core Foram Data* 677. Can you pick out these peaks? This correlation provides compelling evidence for a link between the astronomical theory and the history of glacial and interglacial cycles on Earth.

Dating coral reefs was an important way to test a scientific idea. These data also show that a detailed record of glaciations and climate history is found at the equator in coral reefs.

SCILINKS NSTA
Topic: coral dating
Go to: www.scilinks.org
Code: 2Inquiry636

Reflect and Connect

Work individually to complete the following tasks.

1. Make a chart that summarizes what you understand about each of the 3 key astronomical factors that influence Earth's climate.
2. Describe how the combination of the 3 key factors can lead to more extreme seasons (colder winters, hotter summers). Then describe how the severity of seasons can lead to glacial or interglacial periods.
3. Use what you understand about the astronomical theory to explain the patterns in the sea core data you analyzed in the explore-explain activity.

data. This corresponds to the cycle of change associated with the changing orbit of Earth around the Sun. However, this cycle has very little impact on incoming radiation. Scientists are still trying to figure out why this cycle is so prevalent. (One possibility is that the 100-kyr orbit cycle causes the amplitude of precession to change with a 100-kyr cycle.)

- The 100-kyr cycle is not smooth, as there are smaller peaks and valleys. Some of them occur in smaller intervals. These appear to correspond to the other astronomical cycles for tilt and wobble.
- The highs and lows on the sea core graphs represent changes in the oxygen isotope content of forams. These fluctuations correspond to changes in the $\delta^{18}O$ content of ocean water, which varies from glacial to interglacial periods. The cycling from glacial to interglacial periods is related to changes in incoming solar radiation and seems to be related to changes on the astronomical level.

4. The age and height above or below sea level of elkhorn coral is a direct measure of sea level in Earth's past. This, in turn, can be used as an indirect measure of the amount of water stored in the global ice reservoir or of Earth's climate.
5. Theories are widely accepted when they can explain a wide range of data and can be used to make accurate predictions. The astronomical theory can explain data from many different sources, including the foram and ice core data presented thus far in this activity. Scientists would reject the astronomical theory if and when a dramatically different theory was developed that explained a larger fraction of the data in a fundamentally different way that did not rely on Earth's orbit. Even when the 100-kyr cycle is understood better, however, current bets are that it will strengthen the current understanding of the astronomical theory. It would not be a fundamentally different theory.

4. Describe how corals can provide both direct and indirect data that relate to the study of past climates.
5. What makes the astronomical theory widely accepted by scientists today? What types of observations might be required for scientists to reject this theory?

More Than Forams

EVALUATE

In the explore-explain activity, you used data from cores from the seafloor. You also examined a core of ice from Antarctica. These data told about patterns of climate change on Earth. In *More Than Forams*, you will look again at core data from seafloors. But this time, you will have to use what you know to interpret some new kinds of data from new locations.

Part of the data you will study is forams, but another part of the data set is quite different. You and a partner will act as two scientists interpreting data. You will share your findings with another pair of scientists. The final part of the activity consists of using that evidence to write answers to three questions. Look at the questions ahead of time with your partner. Keep them in mind as you analyze the new data. You should even practice writing answers to these questions ahead of time with your partner. This will show how well you understand the ideas in the chapter.

Part I: Probing for Patterns

Materials

For each team of 2 students

1 *Arabian Sea Data (ODP 722)* handout or 1 *Pacific Ocean Data (ODP 1020)* handout

pencils

1 colored pencil

2 *More Than Forams Scoring Rubric* handouts

Process and Procedure

You and your partner are geologists who study the history of climates on Earth. You will receive some sea core data from one of two locations. Use the expertise you have acquired to interpret these data.

EVALUATE

More Than Forams

Activity Overview

In the explore-explain activity, *The Core of the Matter*, and the elaborate activity, students worked with data from deep-sea cores and an ice core. Then students learned about how these data support the astronomical theory.

In *More Than Forams*, students will investigate new data from deep-sea cores. In addition to looking at oxygen isotope records from forams, students will interpret data from either dust or pollen. The varied data from sea cores allow students to link marine records (forams) with records of climate on continents (dust or pollen).

In Part I, students will work in pairs and take on the role of scientists by making observations about the data and taking notes. Each scientific team will share its observations with another scientific team. Then in Part II, students will demonstrate their understanding by writing answers to three questions individually. The rubric for the

activity (copymaster 12.1, *More Than Forams Scoring Rubric*) shows a substantial weighting toward productive teamwork and using evidence in support of an answer, and not merely in "getting the correct answer."

Before You Teach

Background Information

Students have already seen data from two sea cores. These are ODP 677 (1.1° north, 83.4° west) and ODP 659 (18° north, 21° west). Here is a summary of two additional cores with dust and pollen data.

Dust Data

In the Arabian Sea, the particulates that are carried by wind and deposited in the Arabian Sea are tiny fragments of rock dust from deserts in eastern Africa, the Middle East, and central Asia. Some of that dust is carried even farther south to the Indian Ocean. Measurements from the Arabian Sea core site (ODP site 722; 16.4° north, 59.5° east) show the amount of dust blown to the Arabian Sea varies as a function of depth in the core (that is, with the geologic age of the mud). How do scientists reconstruct past climates on the continents by looking at the amount of desert dust in seafloor sediments? The connection between past climates and dust deposits is straightforward.

Times of relatively high moisture and rain in eastern Africa, the Arabian Peninsula, and the Middle East enable some plants to grow in desert regions. With plants covering more of the continents, less rock and soil are exposed to the forces of wind, and less dust is carried to the Arabian Sea. With lower dust fluxes from continents to the sea, the same amount of mud at the seafloor has fewer windblown fragments.

In contrast, low moisture in eastern Africa, the Arabian Peninsula, and the Middle East decreases vegetation cover, and much more rock and soil are exposed to the wind. More dust is then carried to the Arabian Sea, and mud at the seafloor contains more windblown fragments. Thus, dust fluxes are much higher during more arid conditions.

Note that this is counterintuitive, since we think of this part of the world as currently being very dusty and arid. The geologic record, however, argues that vegetation cover was even less during glacials.

At about 9 kya, much of the Arabian Peninsula was covered in grass.

To measure the amount of dust, scientists weigh it in grams per amount of mud gathered at a spot on the seafloor in 1 kyr. The area of that spot on the seafloor is 1 square centimeter, or 1 cm^2. So dust flux to the Arabian Sea has units of grams of desert dust per 1 cm^2 for every 1 kyr. This is shown on a graph in copymaster 12.10, *Arabian Sea Data (ODP 722)* as units of g/cm^2/kyr. The amount of desert dust in ODP core 722 is a good proxy record for vegetation cover and aridity on the continents surrounding the Arabian Sea.

Pollen Data

Off the shore of Northern California in the Pacific Ocean, many wind-borne particulates are pollen grains produced by plants in western North America. Many people detect such particulates each year and react with stuffed noses and seasonal allergies. If scientists look at the pollen carried by wind today, they see that the types correspond with those of plants growing in a nearby region. Similarly, pollen in seafloor muds from the Pacific Ocean ODP site 1020 (41° north, 126° west) indicate the types of plants growing in western North America at that time.

In the Pacific Northwest, the collection of plants and animals living together defines parts of that ecosystem. Plants and animals in ecosystems can change with factors such as temperature or rain. How do scientists use plant pollen from a sea core to reconstruct past types of plants living together, and thus to reconstruct past climates? The connection is quite revealing.

Interglacial periods such as today are characterized by moderate-to-warm temperatures and higher average rainfall. In the Pacific Northwest, there are specific plants that grow during relatively warm, rainy periods. Examples of trees include dense forests of redwoods (*Sequoia*), alders along creeks, and oaks on ridgetops and sunny hill slopes. When these plants are abundant, the wind carries much of their pollen throughout the region.

In contrast, glacial epochs are generally characterized by colder temperatures and somewhat less rainfall in the Pacific Northwest. These cooler conditions might be like areas of tundra and spruce in northern Canada today. Or the pollen suggests that it could also resemble parts of the Great Basin deserts today (Nevada, Utah, Wyoming) dominated by sage and grasses. In such cold ecosystems, plants such as redwoods, alders, and oaks often cannot survive. Consequently, the pollen carried by wind in past glacial periods would not be expected to contain much, if any, pollen from these trees.

Students will interpret changes in past climates by examining the amount of redwood and alder pollen in a specified amount of core sample. The amount of these particular pollens is a good proxy record for past climates in the Pacific Northwest. In contrast, sagebrush (*Artemisia*) has pollen peaks during glacials.

Materials—Part I

For the teacher

world map (optional)

For each team of 2 students

1 copy of copymaster 12.10, *Arabian Sea Data (ODP 722)* or 1 copy of copymaster 12.11, *Pacific Ocean Data (ODP 1020)*

1 colored pencil

2 copies of copymaster 12.1, *More Than Forams Scoring Rubric*

Materials—Part II

For each student

1 copy of copymaster 12.1, *More Than Forams Scoring Rubric*

access to data for all graphs in chapter

Advance Preparation

Students should still have copymaster 12.1, *More Than Forams Scoring Rubric* from the engage activity.

For Part I, make 1 copy of copymaster 12.10, *Arabian Sea Data (ODP 722)* (4 pages) for each team of students assigned to the Arabian Sea (ODP site 722). Make 1 copy of copymaster 12.11, *Pacific Ocean Data (ODP 1020)* (5 pages), for each team of students assigned to the Pacific Ocean (ODP site 1020). Each pair of students will be working with 3–4 graphs. If you feel this is too much information for your students, consider providing only 2 graphs per pair of students, but they probably will get the hang of it. For the Pacific Ocean team, you can omit the sagebrush record (*Artemisia*). For the Arabian Sea team, omit the planktonic (surface-dwelling) foram data. These records do reinforce patterns from other records, so omitting them is not necessarily better.

Decide the format in which you will have students write the answers to the questions. Obtain sheets of paper or data sets to which they can have access during the assessment.

As You Teach

Outcomes and Indicators of Success

By the end of this activity, students should

1. understand how scientists use their knowledge of oxygen's geochemical cycles to gather and interpret data that provide evidence of past climates on Earth.

   They will demonstrate their understanding by

   - describing the methods scientists use to gather and analyze sea core data and
   - describing that variations in the ratios of oxygen isotopes in the ocean at a given time are recorded in the shells of forams and that those variations reflect global changes associated with glacial and interglacial periods.

2. understand that sea core data (forams, pollen, dust) provide evidence for the astronomical theory.

   They will demonstrate their understanding by describing how the patterns of oxygen isotopes, dust, and pollen records in deep-sea cores are similar to one another and to the cycles predicted by the astronomical theory.

3. have improved their abilities to do inquiry and have achieved a deeper understanding about scientific inquiry.

   They will demonstrate their abilities and understanding by

   - using skills developed in this chapter to analyze oxygen isotope records for patterns in the data and transferring these skills to interpret a new type of data (dust or pollen),
   - making inferences about what might cause changes in dust or pollen levels between glacial and interglacial periods,
   - using patterns in data to support or refute the astronomical theory, and
   - comparing their work in this activity with the work that scientists do.

4. develop further skills in the abilities and understandings of scientific inquiry.

   They will demonstrate their skills by

   - compiling evidence from multiple global sites to show that evidence for the ice ages is globally coherent;
   - using mathematics to analyze the frequency of signals from other types of sea core data (dust, pollen);
   - transferring understanding to the investigation of new sea core data from other parts of Earth;
   - communicating ideas in writing on three key questions (Part II);
   - developing better understanding of relations between the earth and life sciences by studying geologic evidence for the history of ecosystems, as revealed by dust and pollen patterns; and
   - seeing more in depth how scientists use the geologic record of climate histories to better understand current issues such as global warming.

Strategies

Getting Started

Review the scoring rubric (copymaster 12.1) with students. Be sure that students understand the high weighting placed on constructive and engaged teamwork in this activity. The other key piece of the activity is students using evidence in their answers in Part II. This is an individual writing piece.

Remind students that they were introduced to different pieces of evidence for ice ages in the engage activity. Ask them to recall what that evidence was (erratics, striations, drumlins, and mammoth tooth). Then remind them that they worked with another piece of evidence in the explore activity and yet more evidence in the explore-explain activity. Again, ask them to describe that evidence (changing sea level, changes in $\delta^{18}O$ values in foram shells). Tell students that they will work with two additional pieces of evidence for climate history in this activity. They will need to use the skills and understanding they have developed in this chapter to make sense of these new data.

Process and Procedure

Part I: Probing for Patterns

Materials

world map (optional)

For each team of 2 students

1 copy of copymaster 12.10, *Arabian Sea Data (ODP 722)* or 1 copy of copymaster 12.11, *Pacific Ocean Data (ODP 1020)*

1 colored pencil

2 copies of copymaster 12.1, *More Than Forams Scoring Rubric*

Students will work in pairs for this activity. So that they can take on their roles as scientists in Part I, provide students with data from one of two deep-sea core locations. The data from one location in the Arabian Sea focus on dust. The data from the other location, in the Pacific Ocean, focus on pollen. Both cores include foram data for reference. Students act as scientists by interpreting one data set and (later) making comparisons with the other data set. If possible, show students where the two core sites are located on a world map.

In Step 1, check that students understand the 3 climate questions that they will have to answer in Part II. Have them read the questions. Show them how the scoring rubric (copymaster 12.1) relates to the questions. Make sure that your expectations are clear regarding their performance on the activity and how you will assess them.

Give half the teams a copy of copymaster 12.10, *Arabian Sea Data (ODP 722)* and the other half a copy of copymaster 12.11, *Pacific Ocean Data (ODP 1020)*. The Arabian Sea teams should have a 1-page description of the dust data, 1 dust graph, and 2 foram graphs. The Pacific Ocean teams should have a 1-page description of the pollen data, 3 pollen graphs, and 1 foram graph.

Students analyze dust or pollen data in Step 2. They should confirm that they know the location. Walk around the classroom, asking students questions to make sure that they understand the difference in the *y*-axes for the dust and pollen data. Step 3 guides students to make some basic observations. Students then compare the data with the astronomical theory in Step 4. They should write specific pieces of evidence in their science notebooks. This will help reinforce learning for the written, individual part of the assignment (Part II).

As teams analyze pollen, dust, and foram data, ask them probing questions like these. This will help them gather data to use in answering the climate questions in Part II.

- "What are the important patterns in each of the sea core data sets?"
- "How do your dust or pollen data agree, or disagree, with the foram data?"
- "How do the data (foram and dust or pollen) provide evidence of past climates on Earth?"
- "What role do geochemical cycles play in your understanding of the data?"
- "What have you learned about past climates from your data?"
- "Do the sea core data you studied support or refute the astronomical theory?"

In Step 5, students consider how their record relates to conditions on the nearby continents. They should begin thinking about concepts related to vegetation coverage or cooler versus warmer climates.

Students meet with a team that examined a different core in Step 6. They take turns sharing information and interpretations about their core using the list of questions in Step 6. They should be able to have a comprehensive discussion about one core, and then about the other core. They should be able to see that, while some details may differ, the cores have similar overall signals or patterns. The groups should compare these data with sea cores from earlier in the chapter as well (ODP 677, 659). They should see that these data

Answers to Steps 2–8 are on TE pages 639–640.

The two deep-sea cores are from different parts of the globe (figure 12.24). One site is from the Arabian Sea (ODP site 722; 16.4° north, 59.5° east). The second site is from the Pacific Ocean about 170 km west of Northern California (ODP site 1020; 41° north, 126° west). As you look at the data for evidence of past climate changes, also consider the data and handouts from your work with prior cores from seafloors. Do you see any similarities and differences? Can you identify patterns?

The Pacific Ocean teams will look at pollen records. The Arabian Sea teams will look at dust records. You will discuss how these data relate to the foram data you receive from the same location. Later, you will share your findings with another pair of student scientists.

1. You have learned a lot about past climates and the ice ages. You will write about what you have learned by answering the 3 questions in Part II of this activity. Review these questions with your partner before beginning the activity. Also review again the *More Than Forams Scoring Rubric* for this final chapter activity.
2. Obtain data for the dust or pollen sample from your teacher. Examine the deep-sea core data from that location. Read the 1-page description in your handout to learn how scientists get dust and pollen records from sea sediments. Feel free to

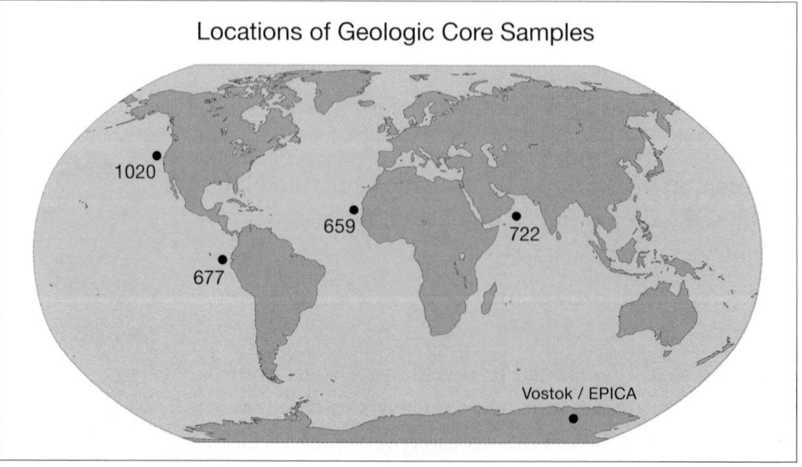

▲ **Figure 12.24 Locations of sea and ice cores.** This map shows the locations of cores discussed in the text. Marine cores are ODP 677, 659, 722, and 1020. The locations of the Vostok and EPICA ice cores are represented on the Antarctic ice sheet. Do the data suggest that paleoclimate patterns are global in nature?

corroborate an interpretation of a global signal for climate history over the past 650 kyr.

Finally, the groups should return to the questions posed in Part II. They should be able to list lines of evidence from sea cores in support of their explanations.

Answers to Steps 2–8, SE pages 638–640

2. Students should be able to recount how deep-sea cores are obtained, and describe how dust or pollen data are obtained from the core itself, based on the 1-page description. Arabian Sea teams should mention that scientists weigh the dust (rock particulates) after all the other components are removed. Pacific Ocean teams should mention that scientists isolate the pollen from the other sediments and mount it on microscope slides. Then they use a microscope to identify and count the pollen grains and report the relative and absolute abundance of pollen in the sample.

   Students should mark where the glacials and interglacials occur. It might help some students to "fill in" the peaks with a colored pencil. This might help them see how the amount of dust or pollen is changing. Encourage them to make marks with pencil. You might even suggest that they wait until Step 3c to compare their data sets with the foram data. This will give students a chance to check their thinking and make any adjustments if necessary. Let students know if you will provide an additional copy of the dust or pollen graphs for each team.

   All graphs are the same size. Students can mix and match records from different parts of the globe by aligning and holding the graphs up to a light or a window. Your students can test whether the signals in the sea core data are global in nature by comparing any evaluate data directly with the data from the rest of the chapter.

3a. Students should note that peaks for the dust occur at glacials. Peaks for sequoia and alder data occur at interglacials, while the sagebrush increases during glacials.

3b. Students should label peaks on their graphs relative to glacial or interglacial periods. The amount of dust changes as land is covered with more or less vegetation. This occurs during interglacials, such as modern times for continents around the Arabian Sea. In the Pacific Northwest, sequoia and alder increase during interglacials, when the climate is relatively warm and moist. During interglacials in this region, *Artemisia* decreases in abundance, suggesting that it moves back to desert areas away from the coast. Relatively more sagebrush is near the coast during glacial periods, with sequoia and alder decreasing in abundance.

3c. Foram data using a chemical ratio are fundamentally different from the dust or pollen, which indicate an amount. However, the pollen data do show patterns of increases and decreases that correspond with the timing of changes in foram data. While the foram data record changes in global ice volume, the dust or pollen record concomitant changes in vegetation on continents.

4. Students from both the Arabian Sea and Pacific Ocean teams should recognize that their data support the astronomical theory.

---

review any other materials from this chapter. Check your understanding with your partner.

3. Your handout also includes 3 graphs for you to analyze. As you work through Steps 3a–c, record your ideas in your science notebook. Take good notes because you will need them later as you share your findings with another team.
   a. What patterns do you notice in the graphs of dust or pollen data? Label your graphs with the major patterns you see. You might want to use a pencil in case you need to make changes.

Begin by identifying the present time period on the graph and thinking about the climate associated with it.

   b. Explain the patterns you see in the dust or pollen data. Why do you think the amount of dust or pollen moving into the seas has changed during Earth's history?
   c. Now look at the foram graphs. Are the patterns in the dust or pollen graphs similar to or different from the patterns you see in the foram data? Note any patterns you see.

Select 1 foram graph and 1 dust or pollen graph. Trace over the lines on the graphs for both cores beginning at the "bottom" of the core (the oldest data). Do the lines move up and down at the same places on the timescale? You might want to review your notes from earlier investigations in this chapter.

4. Consider the patterns you noted in the foram and dust or pollen data. Explain how these data seem to support or refute the astronomical theory. Discuss your thoughts with your partner and record your ideas in your science notebook.
5. Consider the following bullets, depending on your data set:
   - For the dust record for the Arabian Sea, what sort of conditions on the land do you think relate to more or less dust? What does this tell you about changes in the ecosystems of land near the Arabian Sea (figure 12.25)?
   - For the sequoia and alder record, what sort of conditions on the land favor more of these types of plants to grow? Warm interglacials or cold glacials? Use data from the cores to support your answer (figure 12.26).
6. Get together with another team of scientists that has a different core from you. Each team should take about 5–10 minutes sharing information about its core.
   a. What cores did you examine? Where are they from?
   b. What patterns do you see in the data? Do different data sets from the same core show the similar types of patterns?
   c. How do you interpret the patterns? What do the patterns mean in terms of past climates on Earth?

The 100-kyr cycle is dominant, with smaller signals from the 41- and 21-kyr signals mixed in. The patterns in the oxygen isotope data and the dust or pollen data indicate glacials or interglacials during the same times predicted by the astronomical theory. Moreover, foram data from the sites are consistent with the prior 2 sites analyzed in the chapter (677, 659). Students might even mention the similarity with the Vostok data for CO_2 concentration in the atmosphere.

5. For students with Arabian Sea data, more dust relates to less vegetation cover. This occurs during glacials. Less dust relates to more vegetation cover during glacials. This pattern of glacials and interglacials correlates well with foram data in the same muds. For students with Pacific Northwest data, more sequoia and alder pollen (less *Artemisia*) correlates with interglacials. Less sequoia and alder pollen (more *Artemisia*) correlates with glacials. This pattern of glacials and interglacials also correlates well with foram data in the same muds.
6. Students should share with another team their observations of patterns in dust, pollen, and forams, with the global record for the past 650 kyr of glacial and interglacial periods.
7. The 2 teams of 4 students should compare their data from the evaluate with other data in the chapter, such as ODP 677, 659, or the Vostok CO_2 record. They should be listing evidence from each site that the data (foram, pollen, dust) record a consistent record of global climate change over the past 650 kyr.
8. The teams of students should again review the questions in Part II. They will need to use their lines of evidence from cores, perhaps 5 cores, plus other indications of glacials to answer the questions in Part II.

Process and Procedure

Part II: Climate Questions

Materials

For each team of 2 students

1 copy of copymaster 12.1, *More Than Forams Scoring Rubric*

access to data for all graphs in chapter

Decide the format in which you will have students answer the 3 questions and how you will have them record their answers. Answers require students to refer to cores as evidence in support of their answers. Thus, the best way is to give them fresh handouts so that they can refer specifically to peaks and valleys in those data. They can do this by writing on a blank sheet of paper.

A requirement of the assignment is the use of clearly written sentences to indicate data sets in support of students' conclusions.

You could also structure the assignment by having students write answers neatly in their science notebooks. Collect the notebooks and evaluate answers directly from the notebooks where students also have their data. Another possibility is to let them use data in their notebooks, but write on a blank sheet of paper.

d. Do the pollen and dust records tell an overall similar or different story?
e. How do these data relate to other data in the chapter? List specific evidence.

7. Review as a group how these data relate to the sea core data you studied (677 and 659) or even the ice core data.
8. Review as a group any new ideas for answering the 3 questions in Part II.

Part II: Climate Questions

Materials

For each student

1 *More Than Forams Scoring Rubric* handout

access to all graphs in chapter

▲ **Figure 12.25 Dust storm over the Arabian Sea.** This satellite photograph shows dust being blown into the Arabian Sea. Do you think that more dust enters the Arabian Sea during glacial or interglacial periods? How would you test your answer?

Answers to Steps 1–3, SE page 641

1. All evidence in comparing cores for forams, pollen, dust, or CO_2 concentrations indicates that the cores preserve evidence from a global system. Cycling of water, along with the transport of dust and pollen from continents to the ocean, indicates that the patterns also relate to global geochemical cycles. Students should site specific lines of evidence in any of the 5 cores to argue that signals are global.
2. Students should argue that these data are consistent with the astronomical theory, just as the data from sites 677, 659, and Vostok are. The dominant cycle is a 100-kyr cycle, yet scientists do not understand why this effect controls the signals so closely. Other variations in the curves relate to 41- and 21-kyr cycles. Students should give explicit examples that they discussed with their teams.
3. The process that students used was like a scientist's in several regards:
   - Scientists use big concepts, such as change in global climate patterns, to guide their investigations.
   - Scientists design and conduct investigations to collect specific data, such as sea cores.
   - Scientists use technology and math to understand patterns in data.
   - Scientists formulate explanations and use models.
   - Scientists communicate their findings and debate their explanations.
   - Scientists study how physical and living systems function.
   - Scientists study problems in their world, with the intent of providing explanations and solutions.
   - Scientists use an accepted process of investigating, testing, and reporting their results.

Additional information about ODP 722 follows:

- Peaks in the amount of dust reflect glacial periods. During glacial periods, there is less vegetation, allowing greater erosion and transport of dust to the seas.
- Significant peaks do appear at 100-kyr cycles (60, 160, 270, 360, 450, and 650 kya). There might be other, smaller cycles of 20 and 40 kyr. For instance, there are a number of double or triple peaks where the difference between the peaks is 20 or 40 kyr.

Both the bottom-dwelling and surface-dwelling foram records from ODP 722 reveal the following patterns:

- The peaks in the $\delta^{18}O$ values correspond to glacial periods. These peaks occur because the ocean became enriched in ^{18}O during a glacial period due to preferential evaporation of water containing the lighter ^{16}O. The higher ratio of ^{18}O is incorporated into carbonate ions and ultimately into the shells of forams. When the forams die, their shells fall to the seafloor, preserving a record of the climate at that time.
- During glacial periods, the volume of ice on Earth is greater and the sea level drops.

Answers to Steps 1–3 are on TE pages 641–642.

Process and Procedure

Listen to directions from your teacher to answer the questions in Steps 1–3 on your own. You will have about 15–20 min to write your answers on a sheet of paper. You must use clear sentences and references to data to answer these questions.

1. Are the cores that you have studied part of a global system? Are they part of a global cycle? Revisit the locations in figure 12.24. Use at least 2 pieces of evidence or examples from these sites to explain, in writing, why or why not. Feel free to use what you have learned in chapters 10 and 11.
2. Are the data from sites 1020 (pollen) and 722 (dust) consistent with astronomical theory? You have studied the astronomical theory of climate history using data from forams in sea cores. Now use data from sites 1020 and 722 to explain why, or why not.
3. How was the process that you and your partner used to analyze new data from sea cores similar to the work that a scientist does?

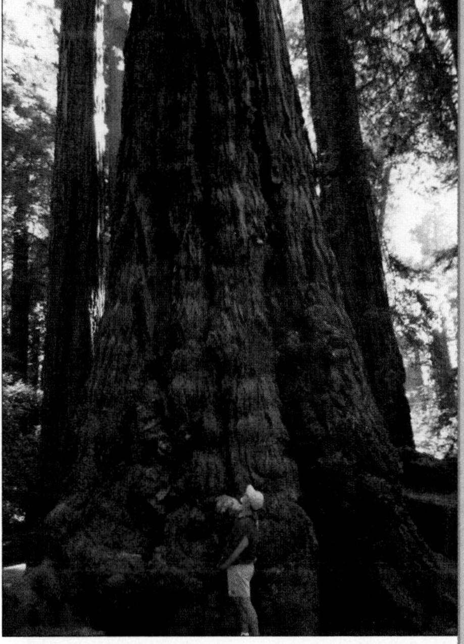

▲ **Figure 12.26 Redwood forest.** Massive redwood trees (*Sequoia*) like this live in Northern California. This tree is about 7.6 m in diameter at the base. Redwoods form a moist, coastal rain forest with about 50–80 inches (about 130–200 cm) of rain per year. How much pollen do you think a redwood forest produces?

- Peaks occur at somewhat regular intervals, including a 100-kyr cycle (60, 160, 250, 350, 450, 540, and 640 kya) and smaller 20- and 40-kyr cycles.
- There is a saw-toothed pattern to the peaks. Moving from right to left, the trend is a gradual increase in $\delta^{18}O$ values followed by a sharp drop. These values reflect a gradual transition into glacial periods, followed by a much more rapid transition into an interglacial period.

The greatest similarities among the three data sets are between the two foram records. These two data sets share a similar jigsaw pattern shape, and many of the peaks correspond to the same points in time. However, there also are similarities between the foram records and the dust record. The majority of the peaks in the dust record correlate to peaks in the foram records. However, as noted on the graphs, there are some differences. The dust record does not have a jigsaw pattern and contains peaks that do not match up with the foram records. The height of the peaks in the dust record varies quite a bit, with higher values for more recent ages.

A summary of ODP 722 follows:

- The foram and dust data provide evidence that Earth's climate has changed through time, varying from glacial to interglacial periods. Earth is currently experiencing an interglacial period. The foram data provide evidence that the amount of ^{18}O in the ocean has changed across time. This change, in turn, reflects $H_2{}^{16}O$ evaporating from the ocean and being trapped as ice. A higher $\delta^{18}O$ in the ocean correlates to a greater volume of ice—a glacial period. A lower $\delta^{18}O$ in the ocean correlates to a smaller volume of ice—an interglacial period. The dust data provide evidence that the amount of dust being blown to the ocean has changed across time, with more dust being associated with glacial periods. The dust data correlate well with the foram data.

Additional information about ODP 1020 follows. The pollen records from the deep-sea core of ODP site 1020 reveal the following patterns:

- Peaks in the amount of sequoia and alder pollen reflect interglacial periods. During interglacial periods, there is more vegetation, particularly more sequoias and alders. These trees do not flourish during glacial periods. Therefore, the percentage of pollen grains drops significantly during a glacial period. This shows up on the graphs as a relatively flat baseline punctuated with peaks that rise and fall sharply.
- In the sequoia data, significant peaks appear at 100-kyr cycles (120, 200, 330, 415, and 500 kya). There might be other, smaller cycles of 20 and 40 kyr. For instance, there are a few double or triple peaks where the difference between the peaks is 20 or 40 kyr (100 and 120 kya, 200 and 240 kya).
- In the alder data, significant peaks also appear at 100-kyr cycles (125, 210, 335, 425, and 520 kya). There might be other, smaller cycles of 20 and 40 kyr. For instance, there are a few double or triple peaks where the difference between the peaks is 20 or 40 kyr (240, 260, and 280 kya).
- Sagebrush data (*Artemisia*) have peaks corresponding with glacial periods. These alternate with sequoia and alder abundance.

The foram record from the deep-sea core of ODP site 1020 reveals the following patterns:

- The peaks in the $\delta^{18}O$ values correspond to glacial periods. These peaks occur because the ocean became enriched in ^{18}O during a glacial period due to preferential evaporation of water containing the lighter ^{16}O. During glacial periods, the volume of ice on Earth is greater and the sea level drops.
- Peaks occur at somewhat regular intervals, including a 100-kyr cycle (18, 130, 225, 340, 430, and 545 kya) and smaller 20- and 40-kyr cycles.
- There is a saw-toothed pattern to the peaks. Moving from right to left, the trend is a gradual increase in $\delta^{18}O$ values followed by a sharp drop. These values reflect a gradual transition into glacial periods, followed by a much more rapid transition into an interglacial period.

The greatest similarities among the data sets are between the two pollen records. These two data sets share similar pattern shape, and many of the peaks correspond to the same points in time. However, there also are similarities between the foram records and the pollen record. The majority of the peaks in the pollen record correlate to valleys in the foram records. However, as noted on the graphs, there are some differences. The pollen record does not have a jigsaw pattern. This correlates with the observation that interglacial periods tend to be smaller time periods than glacial periods.

A summary of ODP 1020 follows:

The foram and pollen data provide evidence that Earth's climate has changed through time, varying from glacial to interglacial periods. Earth is currently experiencing an interglacial period. The last glacial period was about 21 kyr. The foram data provide evidence that the amount of ^{18}O in the ocean has changed across time. This change, in turn, reflects that ^{16}O is evaporating out of the ocean faster and consequently being trapped for a period of time in the form of ice. A higher $\delta^{18}O$ in the ocean correlates to a greater volume of ice—a glacial period. A lower $\delta^{18}O$ in the ocean correlates to a smaller volume of ice—an interglacial period. The pollen data provide evidence that the amount and type of pollen being blown to the ocean has changed across time, with more sequoia and alder pollen being associated with an interglacial. The pollen data correlate well with the foram data.

CHAPTER 13

Time for Change

Chapter Overview

Change. Your students probably see it all around. It occurs in school, in families, and in communities. Change might be construction in your community. And your students will certainly note the changes that are occurring naturally in their bodies. Change is a part of their lives.

But what exactly is a change? How much time needs to pass before we can see a change? Beyond your town, would students be able to see changes that occur in ecosystems or on Earth?

Depending on the perspectives of your students, change may be fairly easy to define. For example, they learned in earlier chapters that a change in distance for a given time defines velocity. This is discrete. They measured velocities in several settings. Another example they saw is how reactants changed to make products in a chemical reaction. Over longer periods of time, they saw how changes in the fossil record defined the history of life on Earth.

A key concept in this chapter is how plate tectonics change geologic and biological systems. Yet this is likely not what students will think of regarding tectonics on a day-to-day basis. Most likely, they are familiar with the latest volcanic eruption or earthquake. Those are the day-to-day manifestations of tectonics. It's a good way to raise the issue with students, especially when such events have been in the news. But remember that it takes many, many such events to create geologically significant results, such as making a chain of mountains.

For example, the tsunami on December 26, 2004, which moved across the Indian Ocean, was a powerful reminder of tectonic adjustments on Earth. The Andaman-Sumatra earthquake that caused it was the largest ever recorded on modern seismometers. This tectonic adjustment occurred where the Indian-Australian Plate is being thrust beneath Indonesia and south Asia. Portions of the earth beneath the ocean were rapidly uplifted 5 meters (m). The displacement of water from the uplifted regions caused a tsunami that spread to the north, northwest, and west. Some areas of seafloor also lurched northward 15–20 m. The fault surface actually ruptured over a distance of about 1,200 kilometers (km) in about an hour.

As stunning as this event was, the salient point is that a single event like the Andaman-Sumatra quake cannot make mountain ranges like the Himalaya to the north. It takes many thousands of such events to make mountains, or more likely, many tens to hundreds of thousands of smaller events.

This chapter seeks to distinguish single events from the broader trends, patterns, and changes that accrue over geologic periods of time. When patterns of change occur again, they can be said to make a geologic cycle.

Plate tectonic movements are a kind of geologic cycle. This chapter also shows how tectonic cycles relate to the record of life.

So if students can identify change, does that mean it is easy to tell if something is constant? What does it mean for something to be constant? Is there anything in your classroom that is constant? You will explore such ideas in chapter 13, *Time for Change*. As you and your students will see, the key consideration is the notion of time. Geologic time adds another dimension to such queries.

Goals for the Chapter

This chapter focuses again on the earth system. In that setting, a key question is, How can you tell when something is constant or is changing? By better understanding ideas with constancy and change, students will be able to better articulate the interactions that occur between the geologic and biological systems. This gives students a more complete framework to understand different types of geochemical cycles in these systems.

By the end of chapter 13, students will be able to answer questions such as

- How fast do tectonic plates move across Earth, and how do they interact?
- What are the driving forces for plate tectonics?
- How are the patterns and cycles of life on Earth related to plate tectonics?
- What is the difference between continental drift and plate tectonics?
- How does plate tectonics relate to the record of life on Earth (the fossil record)?

The chapter organizer uses graphic design principles to help students link one activity to the next. It uses reminders of key concepts, linking questions, and the spatial arrangement of activities to foster a sense of conceptual flow in a chapter. Explicitly ask students to locate their position in the organizer at the beginning of each activity. This will reinforce the connections among activities, coherence in the curriculum, and longer-term retention of key concepts.

Chapter 13 Organizer

TIME FOR CHANGE

Major Concepts

- **Different parts of Earth systems, such as continents, oceans, or ecosystems, change at different rates.**
- **Plate tectonics, mountain building, and erosion have shaped the surface of Earth.**
- **Tectonic plates interact by crashing together, pulling apart, or grinding past one another.**
- **Some tectonic events such as earthquakes are rapid, but it takes many such events over long periods of time to build or erode mountains.**
- **Many patterns of life on continents and in the oceans are linked to patterns of plate tectonics.**

ENGAGE — Mile High Time Machine ★

Key Idea: • Evidence of change between a Colorado ecosystem today, and the same location during the age of the dinosaurs, is found by observing plants, animals, and features of the land.

Activity: Students compare images of animals, plants, and the land for a Colorado location shown today, and in the Cretaceous (70–100 million years ago).

LINKING QUESTION: How do many small changes add up to one large, geologic change?

EXPLORE — Scaling Up to Mountainous Change

Key Idea: • Given enough time, small movements add up to large, geologic changes.

Part I—Paper Plates ★

Key Idea: • Moving paper plates helps show the velocity that tectonic plates move on Earth.

Activity: Students change velocities with paper plates to "scale-up" to tectonic plates moving across Earth.

Part II—Ups and Downs of Mountains ★ ★

Key Idea: • Tectonic uplift makes mountains, and other forces tear mountains down.

Activity: Students measure uplift rates for coral terraces, and estimate erosion with the half-life concept.

LINKING QUESTION: How do tectonic plates interact and change the surface of Earth?

EXPLAIN — Rates of Plates ★ ★ ☆

Key Idea: • Tectonic plates interact by crashing together, splitting apart, or grinding past one another.

Activity: Students read about the 3 general types of plate tectonic boundaries (convergent, divergent, transform), and infer plate motions in several plate reconstructions and settings.

LINKING QUESTION: Why do tectonic plates move?

★ = One Class Period ☆ = ½ Class Period *Note:* Based on a 50-minute class period.

EXPLORE — Sinking Slabs and Convection Connections ★★

Key Idea: • Mantle convection moves heat out of Earth's interior, yet a key force in plate tectonics is the downward "pull" on sinking plates at subduction zones.

Activity: Students sketch classroom simulations of mantle convection and slab pull, and then combine the sketches in a single diagram to show the forces driving tectonic motions at Earth's surface.

LINKING QUESTION: Does plate tectonics affect things like the fossil record of animals on continents?

ELABORATE — Building Bridges ★

Key Idea: • Connecting continents allows animal migration between continents; this alters the animal families preserved in the fossil record.

Activity: Students use 2 paleogeography maps (10–12 Mya; today) and fossil records in 6 geologic sections to infer the age of the land bridge (Central America) connecting North and South America.

LINKING QUESTION: Can geologists predict changes in Earth that occur due to plate tectonics?

EVALUATE — Falling into the Ocean ★★

Key Idea: • Vectors of plate velocities give evidence about where a plate has been, and are used to predict where a plate is going.

Activity: Students use the velocity vector of the Pacific Plate relative to North America, along with ecosystem and rainfall data, to reconstruct the geologic past of Baja and the Gulf of California, and to predict the positions and ecosystems for Baja and the Gulf of California in 20 million years.

★ = One Class Period ☆ = ½ Class Period *Note:* Based on a 50-minute class period.

Standards Covered by Chapter 13*

TIME FOR CHANGE

STANDARD A: Science as Inquiry. As a result of activities in grades 9–12, all students should develop

abilities necessary to do scientific inquiry

- Identify questions and concepts that guide scientific investigations. Students should formulate a testable hypothesis and demonstrate the logical connections between the scientific concepts guiding a hypothesis and the design of an experiment. They should demonstrate appropriate procedures, a knowledge base, and conceptual understanding of scientific investigations.
- Design and conduct scientific investigations. Designing and conducting a scientific investigation requires introduction to the major concepts in the area being investigated, proper equipment, safety precautions, assistance with methodological problems, recommendations for use of technologies, clarification of ideas that guide the inquiry, and scientific knowledge obtained from sources other than the actual investigation. The investigation may also require student clarification of the question, method, controls, and variables; student organization and display of data; student revision of methods and explanations; and a public presentation of the results with a critical response from peers.

Regardless of the scientific investigation performed, students must use evidence, apply logic, and construct an argument for their proposed explanations.

- Use technology and mathematics to improve investigations and communications. A variety of technologies, such as hand tools, measuring instruments, and calculators, should be an integral component of scientific investigations. The use of computers for the collection, analysis, and display of data is also a part of this standard. Mathematics plays an essential role in all aspects of an inquiry. For example, measurement is used for posing questions, formulas are used for developing explanations, and charts and graphs are used for communicating results.
- Formulate and revise scientific explanations and models using logic and evidence. Student inquiries should culminate in formulating an explanation or model. Models should be physical, conceptual, and mathematical. In the process of answering the questions, the students should engage in discussions and arguments that result in the revision of their explanations. These discussions should be based on scientific knowledge, the use of logic, and evidence from their investigation.
- Recognize and analyze alternative explanations and models. This aspect of the standard emphasizes the critical abilities of analyzing an argument by reviewing current scientific understanding, weighing the evidence, and examining the logic so as to decide which explanations and models are best. In other words, although there may be several plausible explanations, they do not all have equal weight. Students should be able to use scientific criteria to find the preferred explanations.
- Communicate and defend a scientific argument. Students in school science programs should develop the abilities associated with accurate and effective communication. These include writing and following procedures, expressing concepts, reviewing information, summarizing data, using language appropriately, developing diagrams and charts, explaining statistical analysis, speaking clearly and logically, constructing a reasoned argument, and responding appropriately to critical comments. [See Teaching Standard B in Chapter 3]

understandings about scientific inquiry

- Scientists usually inquire about how physical, living, or designed systems function. Conceptual principles and knowledge guide scientific inquiries. Historical and current scientific knowledge influence the design and interpretation of investigations and the evaluation of proposed explanations made by other scientists. [See Unifying Concepts and Processes]
- Scientists conduct investigations for a wide variety of reasons. For example, they may wish to discover new aspects of the natural world, explain recently observed phenomena, or test the conclusions of prior investigations or the prediction of current theories.
- Scientists rely on technology to enhance the gathering and manipulation of data. New techniques and tools provide new evidence to guide inquiry and new methods to gather data, thereby contributing to the advance of science. The accuracy and precision of the data, and therefore the quality of the exploration, depends on the technology used. [Content Standard E (grades 9–12)]
- Mathematics is essential in scientific inquiry. Mathematical tools and models guide and improve the posing of questions, gathering data, constructing explanations and communicating results. [See Program Standard C]
- Scientific explanations must adhere to criteria such as: a proposed explanation must be logically consistent; it must abide by the rules of evidence; it must be open to questions and possible modification; and it must be based on historical and current scientific knowledge.
- Results of scientific inquiry—new knowledge and methods—emerge from different types of investigations and public communication among scientists. In communicating and defending the results of scientific inquiry, arguments must be logical and demonstrate connections between natural phenomena, investigations, and the historical body of scientific knowledge. In addition, the methods and procedures that scientists used to obtain evidence must be clearly reported to enhance opportunities for further investigation.

STANDARD B: Physical Science. As a result of activities in grades 9–12, all students should develop an understanding of

motions and forces

- Objects change their motion only when a net force is applied. Laws of motion are used to calculate precisely the effects of forces on the motion of objects. The magnitude of the change in motion can be calculated using the relationship $F = ma$, which is independent of the nature of the force. Whenever one object exerts force on another, a force equal in magnitude and opposite in direction is exerted on the first object.

Standard D: Earth and Space Science. As a result of their activities in grades 9–12, all students should develop an understanding of

energy in the earth system

- The outward transfer of earth's internal heat drives convection circulation in the mantle that propels the plates comprising earth's surface across the face of the globe. [See content Standard B (grades 9–12)]

geochemical cycles

- The earth is a system containing essentially a fixed amount of each stable chemical atom or element. Each element can exist in several different chemical reservoirs. Each element on earth moves among reservoirs in the solid earth, oceans, atmosphere, and organisms as part of geochemical cycles.

the origin and evolution of the earth system

- Geologic time can be estimated by observing rock sequences and using fossils to correlate the sequences at various locations. Current methods include using the known decay rates of radioactive isotopes present in rocks to measure the time since the rock was formed.
- Interactions among the solid earth, the oceans, the atmosphere, and organisms have resulted in the ongoing evolution of the earth system. We can observe some changes such as earthquakes and volcanic eruptions on a human time scale, but many processes such as mountain building and plate movements take place over hundreds of millions of years.

Standard E: Science and Technology. As a result of activities in grades 9–12, all students should develop

understandings about science and technology

- Scientists in different disciplines ask different questions, use different methods of investigation, and accept different types of evidence to support their explanations. Many scientific investigations require the contributions of individuals from different disciplines, including engineering. New disciplines of science, such as geophysics and biochemistry often emerge at the interface of two older disciplines.

Standard G: History and Nature of Science. As a result of activities in grades 9–12, all students should develop understanding of

nature of scientific knowledge

- Science distinguishes itself from other ways of knowing and from other bodies of knowledge through the use of empirical standards, logical arguments, and skepticism, as scientists strive for the best possible explanations about the natural world.

---

* *Note:* Bracketed portions of the standard are addressed elsewhere in the program.

Prerequisite Knowledge

Students should show improving notebook skills by this point in the year. If you have a chance to collect science notebooks, look for abilities such as writing accurate sentences, titles, and dates and using simple organizational features. On diagrams and sketches, look for select labels, scale, simple representations, and adjacent highlight comments where appropriate. These are important strategies to help students organize information—if they cannot organize it, they will likely have trouble understanding it. It is also useful for them to add, in their own words, their ideas and reflections.

Students will use concepts from prior chapters in force and motion. A first priority is observing velocity and determining how long it takes for objects to move a distance at a given velocity. The key is being able to scale up from years to millions of years, and from millimeters to kilometers. These are equivalent, however, with the factors of 10^6 canceling out. Check that students can demonstrate this. If your students check that units are canceling in the numerator and the denominator, then the conversions are pretty straightforward. If they cannot do this, they might have difficulty making transitions from things they see and think of today to the longer timescales needed to understand the past or to predict the future. Scaling up in distance involves trying to think of distances in a global context.

Students also should be developing skills regarding organizing data and observations in a table format. For example, T-tables and tables with columns are used for tabulating and calculating results for the distances and times that plates move. Students need to be able to use *xy* plots to determine the slope and rate of processes. This is rise over run, or $\Delta y / \Delta x$. Examples are determining the northward tectonic velocity of India and the velocity of North America as it slowly migrates over the Yellowstone hot spot. Coax them to think through that if they arrange the time variable on the *x*-axis with a distance on the *y*-axis, the slope will be a velocity.

This chapter uses many maps and much geography. This helps to foster students' understanding of parts of Earth and to develop a more global perspective. Another objective of using maps is to continue to cultivate spatial and visual abilities in students as they study topics in science. Combining maps and cross sections uses three-dimensional skills. These skills are also used when students examine maps or images from different geologic times.

Another skill is being able to convert the length of a scale in a map to distances on the surface of Earth. The Teacher Edition contains one explicit example that determines the velocity of India.

If you feel that your students have weaknesses in any of these areas, check resources on the *Teacher Resource CD* (*TRCD*) and in the *How To* section *Toolbox* activities. These resources have worksheets, short readings, and activities to bolster skills with decimals and exponents.

Commonly Held Misconceptions

No comprehensive research or classroom observations have been published for learning about plate tectonics and related fields in geology. The information that follows is from the experiences of teachers and field-testing of this chapter. Some of the content relates to concepts of biological evolution, which, in this chapter, links with plate tectonics. Please share with BSCS your observations.

- Earthquakes and volcanoes are key indicators of tectonic and geologic activity.

It is true that earthquakes and volcanoes indicate tectonic activity. At the same time, these events tend to occur on timescales of hours to years. Tens of thousands of such earthquakes and volcanoes, however, are required to add up to a geologic history. That history might be recorded in the uplift of mountain chains, the erosion of mountains, the migration of plates across Earth, and the biological evolution on plates or within ecosystems. So volcanoes and earthquakes are important, but they are only a small part of the big picture.

- The idea of continental drift and the jigsaw fit of the continents is essentially the same as the theory of plate tectonics.

Continental drift was proposed long before geologists knew about structures and their ages on the seafloor. Thus, the jigsaw fit of the continents is but a small part of the theory of plate tectonics. This theory shows that plates consist of both continental crust and attached oceanic crust that move slowly (on the order of several centimeters per year) across the surface of Earth. Tectonic plates are produced at spreading centers (oceanic ridges) and consumed in subduction zones.

The idea of continental drift is an important historical idea and a part of plate tectonics. Modern methods that look at plate boundaries beyond continents, as well as at the penetration of plates into the mantle at subduction zones, form the much broader theory of plate tectonics.

- The direction in which volcanoes get younger shows the direction of movement of the hot spot.

Student reasoning is correct with this observation, but mechanically, the plates move, not the hot spot. For example, even after studying the motion of the Pacific Plate, students may still infer a southeast motion of the Hawaiian hot spot. The Hawaiian hot spot is instead relatively still (at present), while the plate moves to the northwest over the hot spot. A similar example in this chapter is the southwest motion of North America over the Yellowstone hot spot.

- Tsunamis, or tidal waves, are related to tides.

Tides are usually caused when a bulge in water several feet deep moves past a point. They occur twice a day. Tides are dominated by the gravitational attraction between Earth and the Moon. Tsunamis have nothing to do with tides. Tsunamis are caused by the rapid, forced displacement of water. The displacement can result from rapid changes in the elevation of the seafloor by earthquakes or by debris slides. The sudden displacement of water generates a large wave that expands through the ocean like a ripple on a pond. This is easy to demonstrate in a tub of water.

- Mantle convection is the driving force for plate tectonics, and plates are passively "propelled" atop the convecting mantle.

In general, mantle convection results from the transport of heat from the core-mantle boundary to Earth's surface. However, tectonic plates probably do not ride passively atop the convecting mantle. Similarly, plates certainly are not propelled by convection (which is mistakenly stated in the *National Science Education Standards*). Specific lines of evidence against this idea are described in *Background Information* in the explore activity, *Sinking Slabs and Convection Connections*.

Rigid plates form due to cooling within the uppermost layers of the mantle and in Earth's crust. This is about the outer 120–150 km of the planet. The forces for movement in the crust are thought to be driven largely by the sinking of slabs at subduction zones. This "slab pull" is thought to be a key factor in the patterns and movements that we observe in plate tectonics. Students do an activity to more closely link concepts of mantle convection and sinking slabs.

- Rocks that are layered are sedimentary rocks.

Sedimentary rocks typically are layered at some scale. But not all layered rocks are sedimentary. For example, many key volcanic rocks form layered strata, many of which give key ages for geomagnetic events or fossils. Metamorphic rocks can also be layered. This layering can be due to modification by heat and pressure.

- Volcanic eruptions can be simulated by the chemical reaction between baking soda and vinegar.

This is a bad analogy in several respects. The "fizzing" in the simulation results from a chemical reaction producing carbon dioxide (CO_2). Volcanoes do release CO_2, but from a different process. Carbon dioxide leaves magma due to decreased pressure and temperature, and to crystallization of minerals. The CO_2 is already in the magma and is not generated during the eruption. The reaction doesn't include an appreciable change in temperature or pressure.

Thus, to simulate a volcanic eruption, it is better to open a container of seltzer water. A sudden release of pressure, as in an explosion, is also a more accurate simulation. Flowing wax is a good way to explore the transitions from liquid to solid as magma leaves the earth in less explosive volcanoes.

NOTES:

ENGAGE

Mile High Time Machine

Activity Overview

In *Mile High Time Machine*, students look at the same part of continental North America at two very different times to note what changes have occurred. One scene is the current setting just west of Denver, Colorado, with snowcapped peaks, a rushing stream, spruce and pine, and a lot of large mammals. These might include elk, moose, deer, bighorn sheep, beaver, and mountain lions.

The other scene is Denver about 100–70 million years ago (Mya). ("Mya" stands for "mega anos," where "mega" stands for million, or 10^6, and *anos* is Latin for "years.") Things have definitely changed since then. Fossil evidence clearly shows this scene to have had dinosaurs, sandy beaches at the edge of a continental sea, and marine estuaries bordered by palms, cypresses, and mangroves. The goal is to engage the students in seeing how many ways the flora and fauna (plants and animals) are similar or different and to consider the changes between the two scenes.

Before You Teach

Background Information

Colorado is certainly well known for many significant dinosaur finds. Perhaps the best known are from the Jurassic-period Morrison Formation (found at several locations in the state), in which extensive work in these rocks was conducted in the 1880s. Colorado also boasts many fossils finds in rocks of Late Cretaceous age, about 75–65 Mya. Discoveries from rocks of this age help to define the plants and animals (flora and fauna) and what the ecosystem was like.

Numerous lines of evidence show that Colorado in the Late Cretaceous was near sea level. The ecosystem was generally a shoreline (or near a shoreline), next to an extensive inland sea. This sea submerged the central part of the continent and is called the Cretaceous Interior Seaway (figure T13.1). The climate in Colorado was warm and subtropical, as shown by fossils of palms, cypresses, and mangroves. Meandering rivers indicate low elevations on a floodplain. The ecosystem and some plants might have been like those in the Gulf Coast (e.g., Louisiana) today.

The animals were very different though. Dinosaurs might have included hadrosaurs, tyrannosaurs, and triceratops. By going east and entering the sea, we see fossil evidence that indicates 30-foot (ft) fish (not little trout in streams), giant sea turtles 8 ft across, pleisiosaurs and mosasaurs, ammonites, and giant sharks. Pteranodons soared overhead.

There are two excellent Web sites depicting these environments and inhabitants. If you can, project images from these Web sites for your class. Some images are fantastic. The first is the Denver Basin Project (Ancient Denvers) hosted by the Denver Museum of Nature and Science. The second, Oceans of Kansas, focuses on shallow marine settings in Kansas. Eastern Colorado has many marine fossil finds similar to the classic sites in Kansas.

Materials

projection equipment (optional)

For each team of 3 students

3 copies of copymaster 13.1, *Scoring Rubric for Falling into the Ocean*

access to the Web

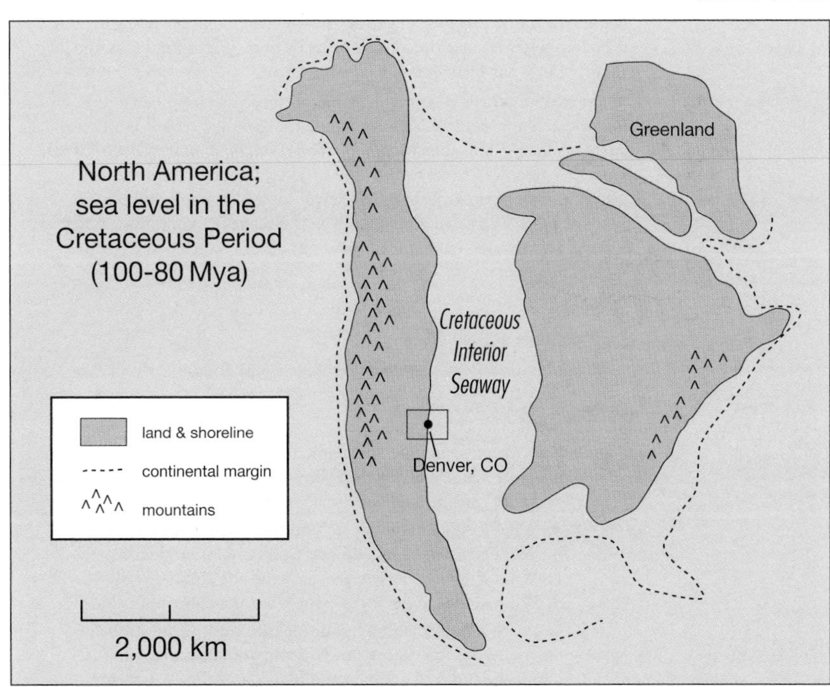

▲ **Figure T13.1 Cretaceous Interior Seaway.** This map shows the Cretaceous Interior Seaway with its shoreline in the region of Denver, Colorado. At this time, western Colorado is mostly a lowland consisting of streams and dense forests, while eastern Colorado is submerged (not "flooded") beneath a shallow sea.

Advance Preparation

Obtain a large map of the world to have available as a resource during this chapter. A large array of geographic features is referred to in the chapter. It's really fun to learn geography in the context of geology.

Hand out and discuss with students the rubric for the evaluate activity, *Falling into the Ocean*, (copymaster 13.1). They will be expected to interpret simple maps of southwestern North America and calculate simple tectonic movements. Their calculations will include reconstructions (back in time) and tectonic predictions (forward in time).

Decide whether to show additional images from the Web sites listed in *Background Information*. The idea at this point is to pique students' interest in changes in Earth between the Cretaceous and the present.

As You Teach

Outcomes and Indicators of Success

By the end of this activity, students should

1. identify lines of evidence that demonstrate that parts of Earth such as Denver, Colorado, have undergone substantial changes over geologic time.

   They will demonstrate their understanding by

   - identifying differences in animals at two different times,
   - identifying differences in plants at two different times,
   - identifying differences in elevation and climate at two different times,
   - answering a question about how they think mountains form, and
   - starting to share their ideas about geologic time.

2. share ideas about different families of animals that lived at different times and places.

   They will demonstrate their understanding by

   - comparing an ecosystem that has dinosaurs with one that has large mammals,
   - developing their own questions about an ecosystem, and
   - working with a partner to study and identify animals in two sets of photographs and diagrams.

3. develop further skills in the abilities and understandings of scientific inquiry.

   They will demonstrate their skills by

   - developing their own questions about a system,
   - making observations and collecting evidence about two systems, and
   - comparing and contrasting two systems.

Strategies

Getting Started

Have any geologic events related to plate tectonics been in the news lately? Has there recently been an earthquake or a volcanic eruption somewhere in the world? Have students heard of plate tectonics, and how might the recent geologic event relate to tectonics?

You might ask students what they know about dinosaurs. Where have famous fossils been found? (Most recently, famous finds are in the western United States and China.) You might also ask what they know about geologic history, such as how mountains are made. What mountains have they visited? Where are these mountains on a map of the world?

Process and Procedure

Materials

projection equipment (optional)

For each team of 3 students

3 copies of copymaster 13.1, *Scoring Rubric for Falling into the Ocean*

access to the Web

In Step 1, students work individually to observe a modern scene from central Colorado. They make some observations before sharing their ideas with a partner (Step 2). They should note the conifers (pines, spruces), trees able to live in cold environs. They should see mammals and high elevations of peaks in the photographs. Rushing streams would be running down those mountains.

ENGAGE

Mile High Time Machine

Time machines. They are a favorite of science fiction thrillers. They can propel you into the future with space travel through wormholes, as you eat nourishing meals of orange-flavored capsules. Time machines in science fiction can also send you back in time. They can propel you back to the American Revolution, the signing of the Declaration of Independence, or the building of the pyramids in Egypt. But imagine that you can dial your time machine back still further in time.

Let's take a part of North America today—the state of Colorado—in the center of the continent. Denver is a large city near the center of Colorado, with the Rocky Mountains lying directly to the west (figure 13.1). Because its official elevation is 5,280 feet (ft), Denver is called the "Mile High City." But has Denver always been like that? What would it be like to travel in a time machine to Denver 70 million years ago (Mya)? How has Denver changed since then?

In real life, there is something that acts just like a time machine. It is the geologic record. You've studied the geologic record in other parts of this program. In *Mile High Time Machine*, you will work with a partner to compare scenes around Denver, Colorado, at two very different time periods. What did Denver look like many millions of years of ago? What can you infer from the scenes? Examining scenes around Denver will help you think about other changes on Earth that take a long time.

Materials

For each team of 3 students

3 *Falling into the Ocean Scoring Rubric* handouts

Process and Procedure

1. By yourself, examine and think about the scene from Colorado in figure 13.1. Answer the following questions about the scene and list your ideas in your science notebook.
   a. What kinds of animals do you think are living there?
   b. What types of plants do you think are living there?
   c. What evidence do you see for what the climate is like?
   d. What evidence do you see for what the elevation is like?
2. Get with a partner. Share your ideas about the questions in Step 1. What inferences can you and your teammate make about the types of animals and plants and the ecosystem?

Snow is evidence for a cold climate at least part of the year.

Students observe a very different setting in Step 3 from the same area, but 70 Mya. Be open to ideas and evidence that they can find in the images at this point. Students try to further articulate those similarities and differences in Step 4.

Students share ideas about how mountains are formed in Step 5. Once again, probe their possible ideas about tectonics by evaluating their answers about how mountains form. Continue to be open to their ideas at this point. It is possible that students might also answer "plate tectonics" at this point. They may have studied this in the past. That is all right at this point, as they will investigate the topic much more in the following activities.

Answers to Reflect and Connect, SE page 650

1. Be open to student ideas for the amount of time that separates the images. They likely will have little way to estimate this, other than prior knowledge (e.g., "millions of years") or by referring back to chapter 6, *Exploring Change*.
2. Let students suggest ideas here. The level of sophistication in their answers may depend on prior life science classes or their understandings of chapter 6. Keep them thinking about differences between animals and patterns of change on Earth.

   Dinosaurs are a reptile with an upright stance due to the position of their legs underneath the pelvis. They lived on Earth mostly in the Jurassic and Cretaceous periods. Mammals extend back to the earliest Jurassic, but flourished largely after the dinosaurs became extinct. Be open to what students know at this point about the similarities and differences between reptiles and mammals.

3a. Keep students thinking about climate, topography, or elevation. Teams should record their question in their science notebooks.

3b. Teams should answer their question as best they can. They will return to Question 3a later in the chapter.

4. The concept of relative age dating for fossils and events is an important idea in earth science. This is the idea that certain fossils lived before others. A similar idea holds for the 2 scenes. Students should note no mountains in the Cretaceous scene and large mountains in the current scene. Thus, the mountains had to have formed *after* the Cretaceous, and *before* today.

▲ **Figure 13.1 Rocky Mountain ecosystem today.** This scene is just west of Denver, Colorado. How does it compare with scenes of the same area from the geologic past?

3. Look at the chapter opener image. It is another scene from central Colorado during the age of the dinosaurs. Pteranodons soar above the shoreline of a continental sea, while dinosaurs like iguanodon amble along warm, palm- and mangrove-lined beaches. With your partner, answer the questions in Step 1 for the scene in the chapter opener.
4. Work as a team to compare the 2 scenes from Colorado, figure 13.1 and the chapter opener.
   a. What things are similar between the 2 scenes?
   b. What things have changed between the 2 scenes?

It will help you to organize your observations in columns of similarities and differences.

5. One of the Colorado images shows mountains. Write in your science notebook all the ideas that you and your partner have for how mountains form.

EXPLORE

Scaling Up to Mountainous Change

Activity Overview

In *Scaling Up to Mountainous Change*, students make analogies for movements across the surface of Earth and for up and down movements of land. They use the lateral motions of a paper plate, and then the vertical motions of uplifted coral terraces. The latter mark proceeds at a rate very similar to the rates of tectonic uplift. The goal is to help students scale up length and time measurement. This ability helps them go from short periods of time to geologic timescales, and from short distances to global distances. The ability to do each of these is a key part of understanding plate tectonics and the history of life on Earth.

Before You Teach

Background Information

There are several fundamental concepts in this activity. One is that tectonic plates move across the surface of Earth at velocities of about 5–10 centimeters per year (cm/yr). This rate is similar to how fast fingernails grow. Scaling up isn't too hard to understand, so the tricky part comes when scaling up to millions of years. How far do plates go in millions of years?

The student book uses two methods to show that units of millimeters per year (mm/yr) transfer directly to kilometers per millions of years (km/Myr). The first method is a table where distances and time increase sequentially by factors of 10. The second method is canceling units in multiplication, as shown in *FYI—Going to Great Lengths.* Thus, 10 cm/yr equals 100 mm/yr, which also equals 100 km/Myr. The latter unit makes it easy to see that a plate can move 300 km in about 3 million years (Myr). Students must understand this so they can make reconstructions and predictions at the global scale in several activities, including the evaluate. Using a factor of 10^3, 100 mm/yr is the same as 100 meters per thousand years (m/kyr).

Part II focuses on how fast mountains grow by uplift, and how fast they are torn down by erosion. First, students estimate uplift rates from coral terraces in two tectonically active areas, Papua New Guinea and Barbados. The uplift rates for Papua New Guinea (2.5 mm/yr) are typical of tectonically active regions, with typical uplift rates of 2–10 mm/yr. Uplift in Barbados is a bit slower, at about 0.4 mm/yr over the past 300,000 years or so (300 kyr). Some of the fastest uplift rates in the world are for areas such as western Himalaya, New Zealand, and Taiwan.

You will note that the ages of coral terraces correlate with the interglacial periods in the last chapter. During interglacial periods, colonization and development of reef ecosystems are prevalent on tropical islands. Coral terraces formed at high sea level are more readily preserved by uplift than terraces formed when the sea level is changing between high and low. More important, the interglacial sea level gives a common frame of reference relative to modern sea level to determine uplift. Recall that we are currently in an interglacial period.

Another key idea that relates to mountain formation and rates of tectonics is included in Part II. This is the idea that the elevations of mountains never quite grow at the rate of uplift. Weathering and erosion wear down mountains as they are being pushed up. Once the tectonic uplift and growth stop, elevations continue to decrease as weathering and erosion continue to act. Students should be able to infer this since mountains don't just keep growing and growing. The evidence in the activity for erosion is the high density of rivers draining from the high Himalaya, shown in figure 13.7 in the student book.

Erosion of mountains is also presented through the concept of erosion half-lives. Erosion half-lives are just like radioactive decay half-lives that students investigated in chapter 6, except they concern elevations in mountains. An *erosion half-life* is the time for the mean elevation of a mountain to decrease by half. Using this concept, we see that the rate of erosion slows down somewhat as the mountains wear down. Similarly,

Answers to Reflect and Connect are on TE page 649.

Reflect and Connect

Discuss the following questions with your partner and write answers in your science notebook.

1. With your partner, estimate how many years ago the scene in the chapter opener occurred. Perhaps you have studied the age of the dinosaurs in other science classes.

Be as specific as you can. It may help you to refer back to chapter 6, *Exploring Change*. You can modify your answer as you learn more.

2. One image you studied had mammals, and the other had reptiles. What are your current ideas about the differences between mammals and reptiles, such as dinosaurs? Write your ideas in your science notebook. You might consider differences and similarities such as food, habitat, or body features.
3. Discuss with your partner questions you may have about the topography, elevation, or climate for the 2 scenes from the Denver area.
   a. Decide on the most interesting question you and your partner have and write it in your science notebook.
   b. Can you answer part of the question at this time? Write a possible answer to that question.

Feel free to draw a labeled sketch as well. This is a good way to represent ideas that you are developing in science.

4. Review the 2 scenes of the Denver area. When do you think the Rocky Mountains formed? Use the words *before* and *after* to explain your evidence.

You can also draw a sequence of 2 to 3 sketches or diagrams showing this change from coastal plain to sharp-peaked mountains.

EXPLORE

Scaling Up to Mountainous Change

Denver, Colorado, sure has changed a lot. If you went to Denver in the geologic past, it might have had dinosaurs and sandy beaches at the edge of a continental sea. Plants would have included palms, cypresses, and mangroves—plants typical of warm, tropical climates. Today, the Rocky Mountains at Denver are not at all like this. There are rivers, cold-water fish such as trout in rushing mountain streams, lizards and snakes, and many types of large mammals. The plants and animals—the flora and fauna—have changed rather dramatically.

But how can you explain the changes that occur over long periods of time? For example, how does land change in elevation from sea level

650 Unit 3 Moving Matter

mountains never really quite erode down to sea level (to generalize), but instead wear down to form the more mature, flat parts of continents. Examples are the flatter parts of Australia, north-central Canada, Africa, or central South America (Brazil) today.

Of course, tectonically active mountains are likely both eroding and being uplifted. In such cases, relative rates of uplift or erosion will determine whether they are decreasing or increasing overall in elevation.

An analogy may be helpful. Think of a tub of water where the rate of water going in is greater than the rate of water going out through a small drain. The level of water in the tub continues to rise, but not quite as fast as if the drain were closed. Moreover, the maximum height is a limit, in this case the volume of the tub, after which the water flows over the sides. Mountains are similar. Erosion of growing mountains is particularly rapid in glaciated regions or areas with high rainfall. At some point, mountains (on Earth) get so high that they start crumbling apart.

Finally, students use their prior work with vectors. The vectors show magnitude (velocity in this chapter) and direction.

At the end of the activity, you will use the set of transparencies in the *TRCD* to bring together ideas about patterns of earthquakes (related to uplift), volcanoes, and other features. Refer to these transparencies throughout the chapter.

Materials—Part I

For each team of 3 students

1 timer or stopwatch
1 paper plate
1 small plastic animal
1 pair of scissors
1 length of masking tape (15 cm)
1 meterstick
1 calculator
1 red pen
1 copy of copymaster 13.2, *Lower 48 States Map*

Materials—Part II

For the teacher

5 transparencies of *Global Tectonic Features* (*TRCD*)
1 copy of copymaster 13.4, *Erosion Half-Life Key*

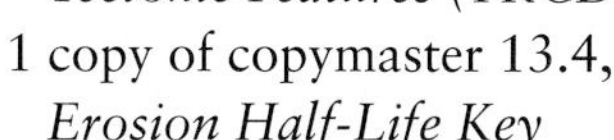

For each team of 3 students

1 ruler
1 calculator
colored pencils
3 copies of copymaster 13.3, *Mountain Profiles* handouts

Advance Preparation

Prepare 1 copy of copymaster 13.2, *Lower 48 States Map* per team (Part I) and 3 copies of copymaster 13.3, *Mountain Profiles* per team (Part II). Obtain materials for the activities, and decide whether you will estimate distances to locations in your school with or without your students.

As You Teach

Outcomes and Indicators of Success

By the end of this activity, students should

1. be able to manipulate and calculate histories by moving a paper plate.

   They will demonstrate their ability by determining the time it takes to move a plate across a work surface, to other parts of school, and to state capitals at a velocity of 2 centimeters per second (cm/sec).

---

to towering, snowcapped peaks? How long does this take? What sorts of movements affect Earth's surface and how the surface looks?

In *Scaling Up to Mountainous Change*, you and two teammates will learn how to scale up from small movements to really large ones. The large movements are truly geologic in scale. You will use simple paper plates to simulate Earth movements.

Part I: Paper Plates

Materials

For each team of 3 students

- 1 timer or stopwatch
- 1 paper plate
- 1 small plastic animal
- 1 pair of scissors
- 1 length of masking tape (15 cm)
- 1 meterstick
- 1 calculator
- 1 red pen
- 1 *Lower 48 States Map* handout

Process and Procedure

1. Obtain 1 paper plate for your team. Cut the plate in the shape of your favorite continent and attach a plastic animal to the plate. Cut or tear the masking tape into 10–15 small pieces.
2. Clear a path across the surface of your team's work surface (your desk, a large table, or a lab counter). Place a piece of tape as a marker every 10 centimeters (cm). Do this across the length of the table.
3. Move your paper plate with your hand from one end of the work surface to the other at a constant rate of 10 centimeters per 5 seconds (10 cm/5 sec).

   It may help to designate one teammate as timer and one as recorder.

4. How long does it take for your paper plate to move from one end of your work surface to the other end? Show your answer in seconds and in minutes. Explain in your science notebook 2 different ways that you could determine the time.
5. Return the plate to its initial spot. You and your teammates will scale up the movement of the paper plate. You will calculate how long it would take for the paper plate to move to 2 other locations in your school at 2 cm/sec.

   Your teacher may write an estimate of distance on the board. Or your class might use other locations if you know their distances.

2. be able to demonstrate abilities to convert between velocities using several units.

They will demonstrate their ability by

- converting 2 cm/sec to units of cm/min, cm/yr, m/yr, and km/yr;
- determining velocity ($\Delta x/\Delta y$) as a rate of change from a graph;
- comparing their plate's velocity with a tectonic velocity of 3 cm/yr;
- determining a velocity for uplift of a coral terrace in units of m/kyr; and
- comparing lurches of earthquakes with the more steady record of geologic change in environments.

3. be able to distinguish between uplift and erosion processes in mountain belts.

They will demonstrate their ability by

- reading about a key indicator of uplift, coral terraces;
- analyzing and comparing two coral terraces to determine from a graph uplift rates of about 2.5 m/kyr for Papua New Guinea and 0.4 m/kyr for Barbados;
- using two methods to convert units of uplift;
- comparing uplift and erosion in the Himalaya;
- reading a comparison of uplift, erosion, and erosion half-lives; and
- thinking qualitatively about a mountain chain like one in Papua New Guinea with rapid rates of uplift and erosion occurring together.

4. develop further skills in the abilities and understandings of scientific inquiry.

They will demonstrate their skills by

- using manipulatives and models in scientific investigations,
- using math in scientific investigations,
- communicating and recording calculations,
- developing a sentence to compare calculations,
- considering interactions between uplift and erosion in making mountains,
- investigating the history of a pattern or the same type of measurement, and
- using logic and reason to consider why mountains don't continue to grow.

Strategies

Getting Started

You can use a quick introductory activity to assess how well your students convert units. There are some simple techniques to make sure that they always do it correctly. You may wish to coordinate with a math teacher. It may also be helpful to have simple examples on hand for a quick review on the board. For example, ask:

- "How many cents in $3?"
- "How many hours in 130 minutes?"
- "How many dozens for 31 eggs?"
- "How many centimeters in 3 m?"
- "How many kilometers in 3 m?"

To get full credit, students will have to show their work, such as in the evaluate activity. Showing work

Answers to Step 6 are on TE page 654.

Figure 13.2 will help you organize your calculations. Record all your work in your science notebook.

a. Rewrite your plate's velocity from Step 3 as seconds per centimeter (sec/cm).
b. Convert this rate to units of seconds per meter (sec/m).
c. What is this rate in units of minutes per meter (min/m)?

Location	Distance (meter, or m)	Time (minute, or min)	Time (hour, or hr)
Cafeteria			
Principal's office			
Gymnasium			

▲ **Figure 13.2 Timetable for recording the distances of the paper plate.** Use a table like this to help organize the distances and times for a paper plate to move to areas like these at a rate of 2 cm/sec. Under the table, show all work and the units canceled.

6. For a paper plate with a velocity of 10 cm/5 sec (or 2 cm/sec), use Steps 6a–f to show how far the plate moves in 1 year. Show all work in your science notebook.
   a. Write the velocity in units of centimeters per 1 second (cm/sec).
   b. Convert the velocity to units of centimeters per minute (cm/min).
   c. Convert the velocity to units of centimeters per year (cm/yr).
   d. Scale up by converting the velocity to units of meters per year (m/yr).
   e. Scale up again to units of kilometers per year (km/yr).
   f. Check your conversion for Step 6e again with your team. When your team thinks you have it, run it by your teacher.

A vital skill that will help you is canceling the units in the numerator and the denominator. Check that you and your teammates understand how to do this.

7. How many years would it take to move your plate to a farther location using the same velocity (km/yr) from Step 6e? Follow Steps 7a–d to find out.
   a. Obtain for your team 1 copy of the handout *Lower 48 States Map*. Place a red star at the location of your school.

Figure 13.3 is a map of the Lower 48 states with a line from San Francisco, California, to Chicago, Illinois. Be sure that you and your teammates can use the scale on the map to show that the line is about 2,900 kilometers (km) long.

is vital, especially where some of the conversions are a little abstract:

$$31\ \cancel{eggs} \times \left(\frac{1\ \text{dozen}\ \cancel{eggs}}{12\ \cancel{eggs}}\right)$$
$$= 2.58\ \text{dozen}\ \cancel{eggs}$$

Ask students about how fast they walk. Let them select units. Next, ask how long it would take to walk around the corner, 400 m, to the store. If they can do an opening activity like this, then they will be on good footing to begin the activity. If not, this is a good opportunity to review a few key concepts before they start the activity.

For Part II, the key is to consider the processes that push the land up and the processes that wear the land down. These processes are tectonic uplift and erosion. Interactions between these processes control the shape of the earth (above sea level) and the localization of regional climates and ecosystems.

Process and Procedure

Part I: Paper Plates

Materials

For each team of 3 students

1 timer or stopwatch
1 paper plate
1 small plastic animal
1 pair of scissors
1 length of masking tape (15 cm)
1 meterstick
1 calculator
1 red pen
1 copy of copymaster 13.2, *Lower 48 States Map*

Answers to Step 8 are on TE page 654.

In Step 1, students get a paper plate, cut it into the shape of a continent, and attach a small animal. The step helps them make a connection between tectonic plates and animals on them moving. Evolution occurring on tectonic plates is a key idea in biological evolution. Students cut masking tape into pieces to use as markers. They then clear an area in Step 2 for sliding their plates and make a scale on this work surface. The velocity is given in Step 3.

In Step 4, students determine how long it takes for paper plates to go a given distance. They should give answers in seconds and minutes for the distance used. One way to do this is to measure empirically with a stopwatch. Another way is to measure the distance and then divide by velocity for time.

Students use the same approach in Step 5. With the much larger distances, however, it is more efficient to divide distance by time than to actually time the event. Similar extensions using math are needed as students scale up to tectonic plates. Before this, students will have to convert velocity to units of seconds per meter, and then minutes per meter. This lets them get an answer in units of minutes. Dividing by 60 (60 minutes per hour) gives an answer in hours.

Step 6 also changes units and scales up magnitude. The goal is to scale up from centimeters per second (cm/sec) to kilometers per year (km/yr). Students show that 2 cm/sec is the same as 631 km/yr. With units of kilometers per year, students can calculate in Step 7 the number of years to move their paper plates to 4 state capitals.

b. Select any 4 states from the map and note the location of their capitals. Draw a line from each capital to your school.

c. Use the scale on the map to determine the distance in kilometers from your school to each capital.

Each teammate should make a table like figure 13.2 in his or her science notebook to organize these data. What table headings will you use? Use Steps 7a–d to decide.

d. Calculate how many years it would take to slide your paper plate to another capital. Use your distances and plate velocity to determine this for each capital.

You may slide your plate to other parts of the globe, such as a vacation destination. But you also need to obtain a map showing the United States and that location, along with the distance in kilometers.

8. Return to the question in Step 4. How long would it take for your paper plate to move from one end of your work surface to the other end at a rate of 3 cm/yr? This is a typical rate for tectonic plates, which you will learn about in this chapter.

There are several ways to determine the answer. Show clearly in your science notebook how your team got the answer.

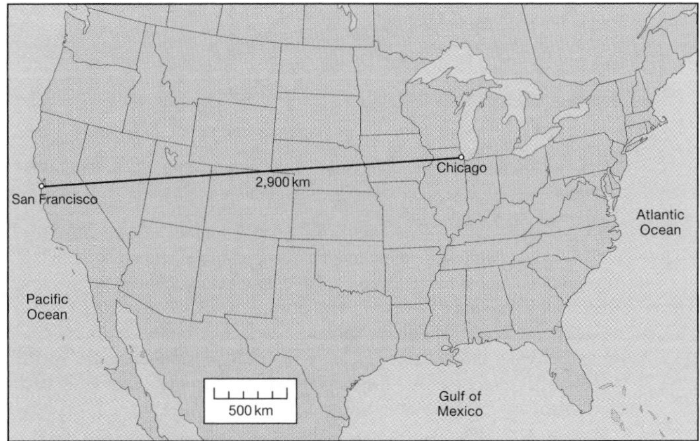

▲ **Figure 13.3 Map of the Lower 48 states.** The line on this map connects San Francisco and Chicago. Be sure that you can use the scale bar (500 km) to show that the length of the San Francisco–Chicago line is about 2,900 km.

Answers to Step 6, SE page 652

6. Correct calculations are as follows.

a. 2 cm/sec

b. $\left(\frac{2\text{ cm}}{1\text{ sec}}\right) \times \left(\frac{60\text{ sec}}{1\text{ min}}\right) = \left(\frac{120\text{ cm}}{1\text{ min}}\right) = 120\frac{\text{cm}}{\text{min}}$

c. $\left(\frac{120\text{ cm}}{1\text{ min}}\right) \times \left(\frac{60\text{ min}}{1\text{ hr}}\right) \times \left(\frac{24\text{ hr}}{1\text{ day}}\right) \times \left(\frac{365.25\text{ day}}{1\text{ yr}}\right) = \frac{63{,}115{,}200\text{ cm}}{1\text{ yr}}$

$= 63.1 \times 10^6\frac{\text{cm}}{\text{yr}} = 631 \times 10^5\frac{\text{cm}}{\text{yr}}$

d. $\left(631 \times 10^5\frac{\text{cm}}{\text{yr}}\right) \times \left(\frac{1\text{ m}}{100\text{ cm}}\right) = 631 \times 10^3\frac{\text{m}}{\text{yr}} = 631{,}000\frac{\text{m}}{\text{yr}}$

e. $\left(631 \times 10^3\frac{\text{m}}{\text{yr}}\right) \times \left(\frac{1\text{ km}}{1{,}000\text{ m}}\right) = 631\frac{\text{km}}{\text{yr}}$

In Step 8, students recalculate the times for their paper plates to move the same distances at plate tectonic rates. For example, they should be able to show that for a 1.5-m-long table, it will take 50 years at 3 cm/yr.

$$1.5\text{ m} \times \left(\frac{100\text{ cm}}{1\text{ m}}\right) \times \left(\frac{1\text{ yr}}{3\text{ cm}}\right) = 50\text{ yr}$$

Answers to Step 8, SE page 653

8. As described above,

$$1.5\text{ m} \times \left(\frac{100\text{ cm}}{1\text{ m}}\right) \times \left(\frac{1\text{ yr}}{3\text{ cm}}\right) = 50\text{ yr.}$$

Answers to Stop and Think—Part I, SE page 654

1a. It is easiest to compare plate tectonic rates of centimeters per year with the answer to Step 6c, 631×10^5 cm/yr, or 63 million cm/yr.

1b. The paper plates are much slower—about 21 million times slower—than real rock tectonic plates.

$$\frac{\left(631 \times 10^5\frac{\text{cm}}{\text{yr}}\right)}{\left(3\frac{\text{cm}}{\text{yr}}\right)} = 21 \times 10^6$$

Process and Procedure

Part II: Ups and Downs of Mountains

Materials

For the teacher

5 transparencies of *Global Tectonic Features* (TRCD)

1 copy of copymaster 13.4, *Erosion Half-Life Key*

For each team of 3 students

1 ruler

1 calculator

colored pencils

3 copies of copymaster 13.3, *Mountain Profiles*

In Step 1, students read a short paragraph about coral terraces. These terraces are key indicators of tectonic uplift rate when we measure age and

Stop & THINK

PART I

Answer the following question about paper plates with your team.

1. Compare the velocity of your paper plate in Step 6 with the movements of continents over the surface of Earth. Except for Australia, continents move about 3 cm/yr.
   a. What step from Step 6 has units that are easiest to compare with a velocity of 3 cm/yr? Explain why.
   b. Is the paper plate's or a continent's velocity faster? How different are the 2 velocities?

Recall that this type of question is best answered with a ratio. A ratio tells you how many times bigger or faster one number is than the other.

Part II: Ups and Downs of Mountains

Materials

For each team of 3 students

1 ruler

1 calculator

colored pencils

3 *Mountain Profiles* handouts

Process and Procedure

In Part I, your paper plate moved in a horizontal direction. The plate moved across surfaces and around your school. You even imagined it moving to other states. Because the paper plate had a velocity, you could determine how far it would go in an amount of time. But what other directions do things move besides back and forth? In unit 1, *Interactions Are Interesting*, you studied objects moving back and forth, as well as up and down.

How about mountains? You saw that tectonic plates move across Earth at rates of roughly 3 cm/yr. How does this compare with how fast mountains can be pushed up? Work with your team to do the following activity. It will help you understand how fast mountains grow and how fast they can change Earth's surface.

NOTES:

1. With your team, view the flat-topped coral terrace in figure 13.4. Then read the following paragraph.

   You learned in the last chapter that the sea level has changed between glacial and interglacial periods. When the sea level drops, a reef ecosystem will be stranded above sea level and will die. The stranded, flat-topped part of the coral reef is called a **terrace**. You learned that radiometric dating of corals can measure when the sea level last covered the terrace with 1–2 meters (m) of water. The terrace in figure 13.4a formed during a sea level high about 125,000 years ago (125 kya). (Remember, kya means thousands of years ago.) The sea level then was about 5 m above the current sea level.
2. Imagine you've just returned from exciting geological fieldwork in Papua New Guinea. Papua New Guinea is an area of active mountain formation located just north of Australia. Your work and diagrams show coral terraces on a hillside (figure 13.5.) Complete Steps 2a–f to determine the geologic history of the coral deposits.
   a. Write down the relationship you observe between the age of the corals and the elevation on the hillside.

Note that all these terraces formed during sea level highs, or interglacials. How do the ages of the terraces compare with the climate patterns in chapter 12, *Evidence for the Ice Ages*?

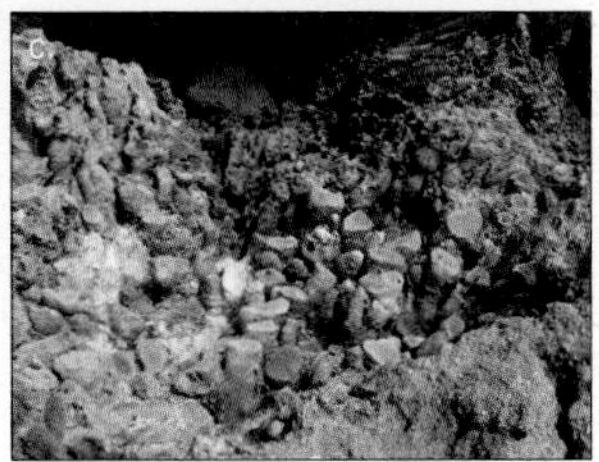

▲ **Figure 13.4 Exposed coral reef, Bahamas.** (a) This flat-topped, exposed coral terrace is at San Salvador, Bahamas. The top of this coral terrace is about 5 m above the current sea level. The close-ups (b and c) show fossil corals in the terrace.

meters of uplift. Students view images of a historically famous coral terrace at San Salvador, Bahamas. The reef has not been tectonically uplifted. However, it is stranded about 5 m above current sea level because sea level during the last interglacial, when it formed, was about 5 m higher than our current interglacial.

Students analyze geologic diagrams of uplifted coral terraces in Papua New Guinea and Barbados in Steps 2 and 3. They should note that older coral terraces are located higher on the hillside. Ages shown are thousands of years. Next, they plot elevation (y-axis) as a function of age (x-axis) for each terrace. The result gives the uplift rate. Students use an appropriate method to determine slope, being sure to include units as meters per thousand years. Highlight comments help students start to make sense of the tectonic uplift rates.

Answers to Steps 2 and 3, SE pages 655–656

2a. Coral elevation correlates with older ages moving up the hillside.

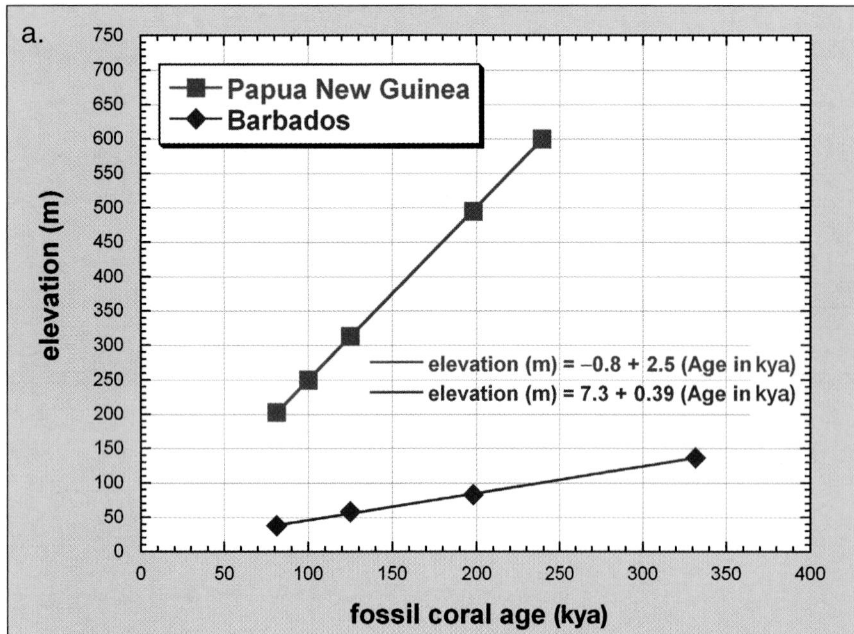

b.

Age (kya)	Barbados (m)	Papua New Guinea (m)
81	38	203
100		250
125	58	313
198	83	495
239		600
332	137	

▲ **Figure T13.2 Data about coral terraces.** These data in (a) graph and (b) table format show elevation and age relationships for coral terraces at Papua New Guinea and Barbados. Kya stands for thousands of years ago. The best-fit lines are shown in a form $y = mx + b$, where the slope, m, equals the uplift rate. For example, Papua is being uplifted at a rate of about 2.5 meters per thousand years (2.5 m/kyr).

2b. The elevation-age relationship suggests that the coral has been moving upward, away from sea level.

2c. Students should organize measurements of age and elevation in their science notebooks. Useful ways to do this are with a T-table or a list of *xy* coordinates. An example is shown in figure T13.2b.

2d. A completed graph for the Papua New Guinea and Barbados terraces is shown in figure T13.2a.

2e. Best-fit lines are shown in figure T13.2a.

2f. Highlight comments on the graph should indicate that older coral terraces are at higher elevations. Thus, uplift is moving the reef ecosystem above sea level and stranding it on hillsides.

3. Answers for Step 3 are included in the answers for Question 2.

Students synthesize their findings further in Step 4 by developing a sentence to compare uplift rates on Papua New Guinea and Barbados. They read a general description of tectonic uplift in Step 5. Then in Step 6, they make connections between uplift rates given in units of millimeters per year, meters per thousand years, and kilometers per million years. They use a table to show that these are all the same.

b. Explain the relationship you identified in Step 2a. That is, what does this relationship tell you about the geologic history of this hillside over the past 350,000 years (350 kyr)? (Remember, kyr means thousands of years.)

Make a quick sketch of figure 13.5 in your science notebook and complete the phrases "What I see" and "What it means."

c. Use a strategy to organize your observations of elevation (in meters) as a function of coral age (in thousands of years). Do this in your science notebook.

d. Make a graph to determine a rate of change shown by these data.

Recall that rates show a change in something per amount of time. Extend time on your graph out to 400 kya.

e. Draw a best-fit line through these data with a pencil and determine the value of the slope. Be sure to check the units for your slope. This is the uplift rate.

HOW TO

It may help your team to review the *How To* section on determining slopes: *How to Use Graphs, Measure Slopes, and Estimate Uncertainty* located in the back of your book.

f. Use highlight comments on your graph ("What I see," "What it means") to explain what the slope on the graph indicates about this region of Papua New Guinea.

3. Complete Steps 2a–f for figure 13.5b for a colleague's diagram. She has just returned from mapping coral terraces on the island of Barbados, an area of active mountain formation in the Caribbean Sea. Add these data for Barbados to the graph you did in Step 2 for Papua New Guinea.

You can use a different symbol or color for these data.

4. Develop a sentence with your team comparing the Papua New Guinea and the Barbados data in your graph.

5. How does the upward movement of coral terraces relate to the making of mountains? Read the following paragraph to learn more about the rates at which mountains are made.

World maps show continents, oceans, or countries. But it can be hard to tell from maps where mountains are growing. In active mountains, such changes are happening all the time. Maybe the evidence is an occasional earthquake or a volcanic eruption. Pushing the land up to form mountains is called **uplift**. Examples of active uplift include the Andes mountains, the islands of New Zealand, the Himalaya mountains, and

656 Unit 3 Moving Matter

NOTES:

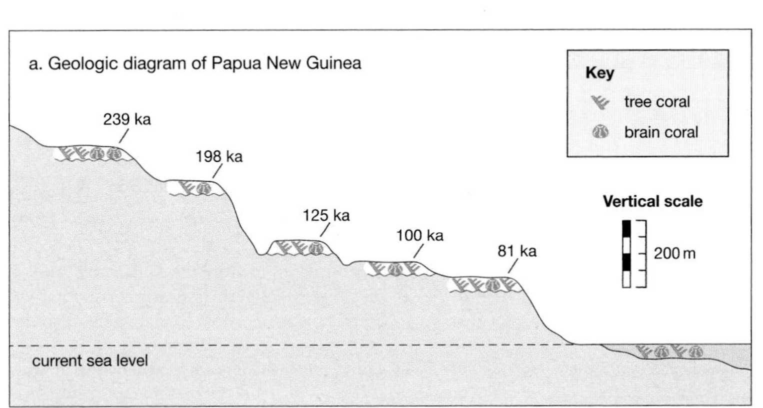

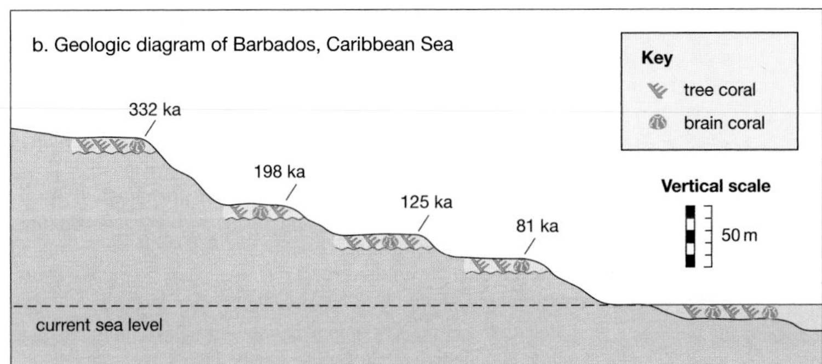

▲ **Figure 13.5 Coral terraces in (a) Papua New Guinea and (b) Barbados.** The geologic diagrams show coral terraces cut into hillsides on Papua New Guinea and Barbados. Radiometric dating tells the age when the corals were living at sea level (as thousands of years ago, or kya). Examples of fossilized tree and brain coral appear in figure 13.4. Living examples are in chapter 12.

parts of the Middle East and western North America. In these areas, uplift rates can be as high as +10 millimeters per year (mm/yr). That may not sound like a lot, but with a lot of time, this uplift can make massive mountains.

6. Uplift over geologic lengths of time is harder to envision than small uplifts each year. Work through Steps 6a–d to estimate how many kilometers can be uplifted in 1 million years (Myr).

Answers to Steps 4 and 6, SE pages 656–658

4. Students' sentences should indicate that uplift is more rapid in Papua New Guinea than in Barbados. The rate is a little over 5 times faster.

6b. Figure T13.3 shows a completed table for changing the units for uplift rates.

6c. The table shows that rows 4 or 5 could correlate with 1 kyr.

6d. Students should see that these are all the same rate. It's best if they can demonstrate this with conversions.

In Step 7, students read about the difference between weathering and erosion in *FYI—Weather to Erode.* Then in Step 8, students compare predicted elevations of the Himalaya at a constant uplift rate with actual elevations of Earth's highest peak, Mount Everest. Predicted elevations at constant uplift are much higher than actual elevations. Patterns of river drainage (figure 13.7 in the student book) are a clue that the discrepancy relates to erosion.

Answers to Step 8, SE pages 658–660

8b. Uplift is 2.5 km in 1 Myr.

$$\left(\frac{2.5 \text{ mm}}{1 \not{\text{yr}}}\right) \times 1 \times 10^{6} \not{\text{yr}}$$

$$= 2.5 \times 10^{6} \text{ mm} = 2.5 \text{ km}$$

8c. Uplift is 25 km in 10 Myr.

8d. There are several ways to make this comparison. Uplift over 30 Myr at the rates in Steps 8b–c would give 75 km of uplift. This is much less than elevations of nearly 9 km. Either the uplift has been much less in the geologic past, or another process mitigates or lessens the net uplift.

8e. Erosion is the culprit. Erosion is always countering the tectonic uplift of mountains, especially in regions of high rainfall.

8f. The maps show a network of rivers carving and constantly eroding the high peaks of the Himalaya. The evidence is the many rivers in this region. Students may also be familiar with the monsoons in this region, which deliver some of the most substantial rainfalls on Earth.

Time (yr)	Distance	Units for distance
1	2.5	mm
10	25	mm
100	250	mm
1,000	2,500	mm
1,000	2.5	m
10,000	25	m
100,000	250	m
1,000,000	2,500	m
1,000,000	2.5	km
1 million = 1×10^{6}	2.5	km

▲ **Figure T13.3 Completed rates for scaling up tectonic uplift.** Tectonic uplift in mountains is a slow process. Uplift occurs over millions of years. This table illustrates how using factors of 10 for uplift rates in millimeters per year translates to meters per thousands of years and kilometers per millions of years.

Time (yr)	Distance	Units for distance
1	2.5	mm
10		mm
100		mm
1,000		mm
1,000		m
10,000		m
100,000		m
1,000,000		m
1,000,000		km
1 million = 1×10^{6}		km

▲ **Figure 13.6 Rates for scaling up tectonic uplift.** Tectonic uplift in mountains is a slow process. Uplift occurs over millions of years. Complete this table for an uplift rate of 2.5 mm/yr. This will help you estimate how much uplift can occur in 1 Myr.

a. Study figure 13.6 with your partner. Copy it into your science notebook.

b. Fill in all the blank cells in the "distance" column so that they correspond with the "time" column.

Note that distance must also correspond with the units in the right-hand column.

c. Identify the row or rows in figure 13.6 that correspond to 1 kyr. Explain why in your science notebook.

d. Compare the following uplift rates. Explain your answer in your science notebook.

i. 2.5 millimeters per year (mm/yr)

ii. 2.5 meters per thousand years (m/kyr)

iii. 2.5 kilometers per million years (km/Myr)

7. Read *FYI—Weather to Erode.* This will help you learn about 2 processes that describe how mountains wear down: weathering and erosion. Refer to this FYI in Steps 8 and 9.

8. You just looked at uplifted coral terraces. Now do Steps 8a–f to start thinking about how chains of mountains form.

a. Locate the Himalaya on a map. The Himalaya mountains have the highest elevations on Earth. They have been forming for 30–40 Myr. The limestone at Mount Everest (the highest peak on Earth) shows that those rocks were near sea level in the past (figure 13.7).

b. Determine how much uplift occurs in 1 Myr when there is an uplift rate of 2.5 mm/yr.

Use your work in Step 6 and figure 13.6 to help with this conversion.

c. Determine how high a mountain such as Mount Everest would grow in 10 Myr with an uplift rate of 2.5 mm/yr.

d. Geologic evidence shows that Mount Everest has grown to about 8,850 m (29,035 ft) in about 30 Myr. Compare this with your result in Step 8b.

A good way to make comparisons is to use words like "greater than" and "less than" or to estimate how many times slower or faster something is.

NOTES:

Weather to Erode

You certainly have experienced things wearing out. Perhaps it's your shoes, your car's tires, a soccer ball, or a pencil eraser. An object loses mass as small bits or fragments of material are taken away.

But by "wear out," you also could mean a chemical change. Maybe wear out refers to the chemical reaction in batteries as they lose their "juice." Or perhaps the change is the deterioration of lawn furniture exposed to rain and solar radiation. What about a hammer left out in the rain? It gets a rust coating that can be wiped off with your finger.

Mountains wear out, too. And just like car tires and outdoor lawn furniture, they do it by chemical and physical processes. Think about a rock outside, on a mountain, or even on a building's facade. As the rock is exposed to the weather, minerals in the rock begin subtle chemical changes. A good analogy is the hammer—iron metal turns to iron oxide, or rust. The process of the natural chemical alteration of minerals is called **weathering**. Water is often part of a weathering change.

Chemical changes by themselves, however, do not decrease the mass of the rock. Another process must move matter away. This is how mountains can wear down. **Erosion** is the process where weathered rock fragments and soils are transported and moved downward due to gravity. Erosion of mountains occurs along steep slopes and river valleys. Erosion by flowing rivers moves sand and silt away from mountains and closer to oceans. Some parts of rocks, such as carbonate or salt deposits, will even dissolve right into rivers and be carried away to the ocean.

How long does it take for mountains to weather and erode? How would you tell this? Effects that you might notice are a decrease in elevation or a gentle rounding of mountain peaks. An easy way to estimate the decrease in elevation is with the concept of half-lives. You already used half-lives in chapter 6 with radioactive elements. For mountains, the **erosion half-life** is the time needed for the elevations of a profile to decrease by about half.

Consider mountains made of hard granite that have an average elevation of 12,000 ft and an erosion half-life of 10 Myr (see the graph). After about 10 Myr (one half-life), the elevation would have been reduced by about 6,000 ft to an elevation of about 6,000 ft. After a total of 20 Myr (two half-lives), the elevation would have decreased by about 9,000 ft, to an elevation of about 3,000 ft.

This is a simple way to quantify how Earth's surface wears out. Of course, Earth is much more complex than radioactive isotopes in decay. Still, it's nice to have a good rule of thumb to help learn about rates of erosion and weathering.

SCI LINKS NSTA
Go to: www.scilinks.org
Topic: weathering
Code: 2Inquiry659a
Topic: erosion
Code: 2Inquiry659b

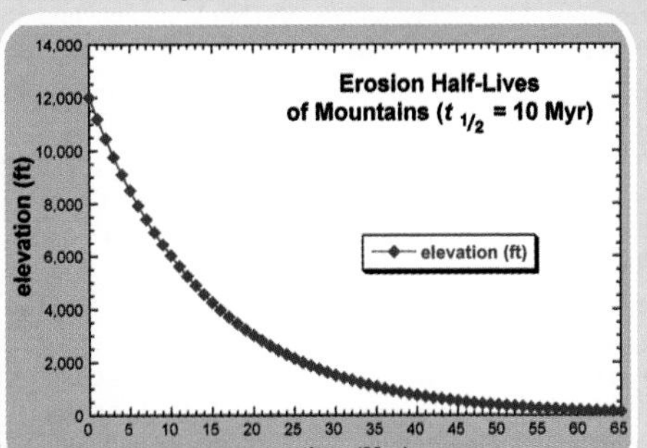

Graph showing erosional half-lives of mountains. This graph shows the average elevation of mountains with time due to erosion. The average elevation decreases by half every 10 Myr. How tall will the mountains be in about 40 Myr?

Chapter 13 Time for Change 659

Students use a copymaster in Step 9 to make predictions about elevations in mountains with an erosion half-life of 5 Myr. In Step 10, they consider further the interplay of tectonic uplift at Papua New Guinea with the rapid erosion that occurs concomitantly in that climate.

Answers to Steps 9 and 10, SE pages 660–662

9a. Students should label the elevations of peaks and valleys.

9b. Given an erosion half-life of 5 Myr, students should show each point at half of its elevation after 5 Myr. They should connect the points to represent the topography. A sample answer is shown on copymaster 13.4, *Erosion Half-Life Key* for 5 and 10 Myr of erosion.

9c. Students should draw another profile of topography at 75 percent of the original elevation.

9d. To predict elevations 5 Myr before the profile (today), students should explain that they should double all elevations in the profile.

9e. Students might list several possible limitations. One is that uplift has actually ceased and that erosion is the only factor acting on topography. Another is that this model suggests that within 50 years, all mountains have decreased in elevation to about 0.1 percent of their elevation. However, mountains such as the Appalachians still have elevations greater than this. They formed about 300 Mya. So some process makes the erosion process slower than would be suggested by rivers alone. This is an area of active research.

10a. The uplift rate was about 2.5 mm/yr for Papua New Guinea and 0.4 mm/yr for Barbados.

10b. Uplift raises rocks and elevation, while erosion decreases elevation. Students should be thinking that if these processes are acting together, the faster process will dominate. For example, early in the history of mountains, uplift creates elevation, and is typically faster than the rate of erosion. Later, especially when uplift has subsided or stopped, erosion takes over and reduces elevation.

10c. These erosion half-lives are 5 times faster than those cited earlier.

10d. When the rate of erosion equals the rate of uplift, the elevation of the mountains does not change overall.

Answers to Reflect and Connect, SE page 662

1. The goal of this question and discussion is to get students thinking at a global scale before the next activity. Start by showing students the transparency of earthquakes, then overlay the recent volcanic eruptions. They should see a close correspondence. To those, add the transparency of hot spot volcanoes. Ask questions and help students to see the evidence that these types of volcanoes don't really match. These high-volume volcanoes originate from deep in the mantle—perhaps from the core-mantle boundary—and don't really link with plate tectonic boundaries (or with earthquakes). In contrast, regions of volcanoes, earthquakes, and plate tectonic boundaries do correlate closely. Students should also note that boundaries of continents do not necessarily equate with plate tectonic boundaries.

   Add the next transparency. Students will see that the locations of volcanoes, earthquakes, or hot spots don't really correspond with the locations of the edges of continents. They do correlate in a few cases, but generally not.

2. Be open to students' ideas here. The objective is to keep in mind the relationship between tectonics and ecology. Generally, an event

Answers to Step 8 are on TE page 658.

e. Discuss with your teammates the factors or processes on Earth that can help explain the comparison in Step 8d.

What factors or processes can you think of that make mountains appear to be growing more slowly than the actual uplift rate? What would you expect in the areas between mountain peaks in the Himalaya?

f. Examine figure 13.7 with your teammates. What evidence in the figures supports the idea that the peaks may not grow at 2.5 mm/yr, even when they are being pushed up that fast?

9. Obtain 3 copies of the *Mountain Profiles* handout. Then follow Steps 9a–e to see how a mountain chain such as the Appalachians changes when it is not being uplifted.
   a. With your teammates, trace your fingers over the profile of elevation in the handout. Label the elevations of the peaks and valleys on your handout.
   b. The profile mimics a mountain chain like the Appalachians, which has an erosion half-life of about 5 Myr. On your diagram, draw a prediction for the elevations of the peaks and valleys in about 5 Myr.

Connect points with lines to make a full profile. Use colored lines or labels to help indicate the future profile of elevation.

   c. Use the concept of erosion half-life again to predict the elevations of the peaks and valleys after another 5 Myr (10 Myr total). Draw your prediction on your diagram.

What color will you use for this line? How will you organize your different profiles in a legend?

   d. Explain how you can predict the elevation profile 5 Myr before the initial profile on the handout.
   e. The erosion half-life model is a good tool for making predictions. List in your science notebook possible limitations to this tool.

10. In Step 2, you investigated a region of current tectonic uplift in Papua New Guinea.
    a. Look up the tectonic uplift rate you determined in Step 2.
    b. With your team, list how erosion and uplift affect mountains. Write in your science notebook what you think would happen if these processes were occurring at the same time.
    c. Predict how the erosion half-lives for mountains like the Appalachians in Step 9 might compare with the erosion half-lives in other areas. Geologists have shown that conditions at Papua New Guinea give an erosion half-life of about 1 Myr. Rocks there are loose volcanic rocks on steep slopes that get heavy tropical rains.

660 Unit 3 Moving Matter

such as an earthquake wouldn't faze animals, besides perhaps provoking mild agitation. A volcanic event could change the ecology of a region. Help students understand that tectonic changes occur on much longer timescales. When those events start affecting elevation and patterns of precipitation, then there will be an effect on animals over long periods of time.

3. Help students start to distinguish between single tectonic events such as earthquakes and how they relate to larger changes to Earth's surface. An earthquake doesn't really change Earth's surface substantially. This problem shows that lurches of 2 m might only occur every 100–150 years. That is not very often. With many such movements, however, kilometers of movement can accrue over millions of years. That can be enough to make new chains of mountains.

$$2 \not{m} \times \left(\frac{1{,}000 \not{mm}}{1 \not{m}}\right) \times \left(\frac{1 \text{ yr}}{15 \not{mm}}\right) = 133.3 \text{ yr}$$

EXPLAIN

Rates of Plates

Activity Overview

In *Rates of Plates*, students will read about the structure of Earth and the three main types of plate tectonic interactions. In these interactions,

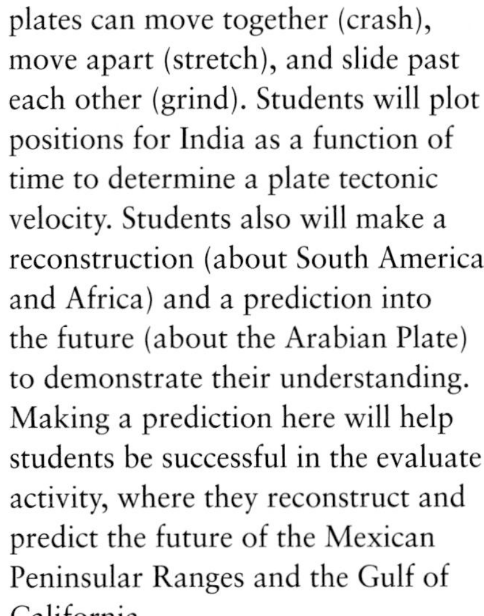

plates can move together (crash), move apart (stretch), and slide past each other (grind). Students will plot positions for India as a function of time to determine a plate tectonic velocity. Students also will make a reconstruction (about South America and Africa) and a prediction into the future (about the Arabian Plate) to demonstrate their understanding. Making a prediction here will help students be successful in the evaluate activity, where they reconstruct and predict the future of the Mexican Peninsular Ranges and the Gulf of California.

Before You Teach

Background Information

The main content is presented in the student reading titled *Crash, Stretch, and Grind*. The reading describes the three main ways that tectonic plates interact—collisions (crash), rifts (stretch), and zones of sliding (grind). These interactions can also be presented as three types of tectonic boundaries or settings. They are convergent boundaries, divergent boundaries, and transform boundaries. Often, maps show these boundaries with discrete symbols or lines. In reality, however, many plate boundaries can be diffuse, with many small subparallel faults. Wide mountain ranges are some of the most obvious evidence for broad zones of rock deformation at plate tectonic boundaries.

It might be unclear how much students know about plate tectonics. If they are familiar with the content, this activity should provide a good summary and build on what they've done in middle school. This chapter integrates some big ideas in life science that are not typically combined with plate tectonics. If students feel the content is familiar, they should be able to understand other key concepts presented later in the chapter, like those in the explore activity *Sinking Slabs and Convection Connections*, where they investigate the driving forces for plate tectonics.

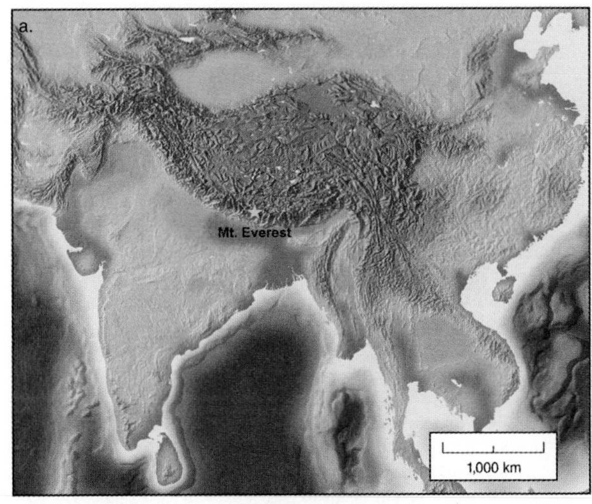

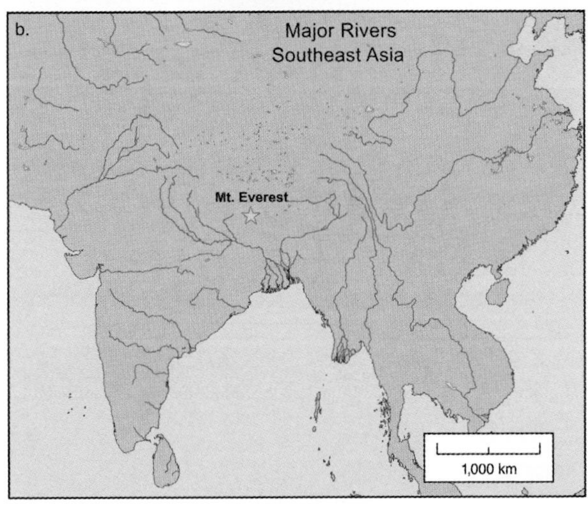

Figure 13.7 Two views of the high Himalaya. (a) The map extends from Iran to China and is centered on the high Himalaya. The star marks Mount Everest. (b) The diagram shows the same region with the land tan, the ocean blue, and major rivers superposed.

Chapter 13 Time for Change 661

You may come across the term lithosphere, although it is not used in this chapter. The *lithosphere* is the mechanically rigid outer layer of Earth. Sometimes the term *lithospheric plates* is used interchangeably with tectonic plates. The lithosphere consists of crust, oceanic or continental, plus the uppermost parts of the mantle. Thus, plates are more than the crust moving atop the mantle, although sometimes plates are presented this way.

In contrast with the lithosphere, the underlying material of the mantle flows slowly like molasses or honey. This is called the *asthenosphere*. The slow convection of ductile mantle minerals contrasts with the more rigid plates of the lithosphere. Thus, the boundary between the lithosphere and the asthenosphere is mechanical. The boundary between the crust and the mantle is compositional. Typically, the two boundaries do not overlap.

Materials

For the teacher

equipment to display Web sites (optional)

For each team of 3 students

1 ruler

1 calculator

3 copies of copymaster 13.5, *Tectonic Boundaries, Hot Spots, and Plate Velocities*

1 copy of copymaster 13.6, *Northward Tectonic Movement of India*

3 copies of copymaster 13.7, *Arabian Plate Velocity*

3 copies of copymaster 13.8, *South America and Africa Map* (optional)

Advance Preparation

The best way to prepare is to be familiar with the content in the student readings. Review the conversions in *FYI—Going to Great Lengths*. Make 3 copies per team of copymaster 13.5, *Tectonic Boundaries, Hot Spots, and Plate Velocities*.

For students to be successful in the evaluate activity, they need to be able to do tectonic reconstructions and make predictions. Review student work for the India reconstruction and the Arabian Plate prediction problems. The South America–Africa problem is an optional challenge opportunity that has historic significance and will help students in the evaluate activity. Decide whether you need this copymaster for teams.

Decide whether you want extra copies of figures 13.12 and 13.17 from the student book (the northward tectonic movement of India and the Arabian Plate's velocity). The figures are reproduced on copymasters 13.6, *Northward Tectonic Movement of India* and 13.7, *Arabian Plate Velocity*.

As You Teach

Outcomes and Indicators of Success

By the end of this activity, students should

1. be able to identify the three main types of plate tectonic interactions.

   They will demonstrate their understanding by

   - using a T-table to group plates according to whether they consist of oceanic and continental crust or oceanic crust only,
   - investigating the collision between the Pacific and Philippines plates at the Mariana Trench,

Answers to Step 10d are on TE page 660.
Answers to Reflect and Connect are on TE pages 660–661.

d. What is the change in elevation for mountains when the rate of erosion equals the rate of uplift? Write your ideas in your science notebook.

Reflect and Connect

Discuss the following questions with your teammates. Write your answers in your science notebook.

1. View the 5 overhead transparencies of patterns around Earth that your teacher will show you. Share with the class the patterns you see about where earthquakes, volcanoes, continents, and several other geologic features occur.
2. How do you think animals might respond to tectonic movements of several centimeters per year? Consider a tectonically active region like California or the Pacific Northwest. Do you think an earthquake could change ecosystems? Explain your reasoning.
3. Consider rates of plate movement of 15 mm/yr. Sometimes these movements don't occur at a steady pace of 15 mm/yr, but rather happen in sudden lurches. Consider an earthquake that gives a sudden movement of 2 m. How often would events with 2 m of displacement occur to give a net rate of 15 mm/yr?

EXPLAIN

Rates of Plates

You have probably heard that rates can be used to indicate change. Rates tell how fast something happens. For example, velocity tells how distance changes in a given time, as you saw in earlier chapters. Maybe the rate is for a paper plate moving in your classroom. Or maybe you're investigating slow, steady velocities in the up-down direction, such as with the uplift of mountains.

But what sorts of patterns would these movements make on the surface of Earth? How do geologic movements relate to paper plates? How could movements across a surface lead to uplift?

Materials

For each team of 3 students

1 ruler

1 calculator

3 *South America and Africa* handouts

Process and Procedure

Complete the following reading with two teammates to learn more about tectonic plates on Earth. Follow your teacher's instructions about using a strategy to better understand and share ideas from the reading.

- indicating that continental rifts fill with sediment, and
- investigating the jigsaw fit of South America and Africa.

2. use plate positions and velocities in tectonic reconstructions and predictions.

   They will demonstrate their understanding by

   - determining the velocity of India for five positions at five times,
   - reconstructing the opening of the Atlantic Ocean (and the shrinking of the Pacific Ocean), and
   - predicting the opening of the Red Sea with further rifting.

3. use analytical and organizational skills to understand and interpret data.

   They will demonstrate their skills by

   - interpreting a map of positions of India and completing a table of position and time,
   - estimating slopes of distance versus time for India,
   - sketching the evolution and the opening of the Red Sea, and
   - using math skills to convert plate velocities from millimeters per year to kilometers per millions of years.

Strategies

Getting Started

Again, a recent earthquake or volcanic eruption is a good way to begin. Daily maps and reports that show earthquakes or volcanism are available from the Web. Web sites for volcanic observatories show volcanic activity. Web sites such as the National Earthquake Information Center (NEIC) show earthquakes and seismicity around the globe each day. Earthquake locations are usually aligned with tectonic boundaries in tectonically active regions. The Web sites would be interesting to share with your class if you are able to project them.

Decide on a reading strategy that is appropriate for your class. Perhaps you can assign one or more of the sections as homework. Another possibility is to use a jigsaw construct for the reading: assign one tectonic interaction to each member of a team of three. The interactions are collisions (crash), rifting (stretch), and sliding (grind).

Process and Procedure

Materials

For the teacher

equipment to display Web sites (optional)

For each team of 3 students

1 ruler

1 calculator

3 copies of copymaster 13.5, *Tectonic Boundaries, Hot Spots, and Plate Velocities*

1 copy of copymaster 13.6, *Northward Tectonic Movement of India*

3 copies of copymaster 13.7, *Arabian Plate Velocity*

3 copies of copymaster 13.8, *South America and Africa Map* (optional)

Students read *Crash, Stretch, and Grind*, which begins with a section on the structure of Earth. They then continue reading about three examples of plate tectonic collisions. Students learn that the mantle resides beneath the crust of Earth, and that most of Earth is mantle—about 80 percent by volume. The *Stop and Think* tasks focus on concepts related to the ideas of collisions that occur between the plates and their pieces of oceanic and continental crust.

READING

Crash, Stretch, and Grind

It's a major scientific discovery of the past 50 years. It's a unifying theory for understanding the surface of Earth. It helps explain the continents, the location of mountains and oceans, natural resources, climate patterns, biological evolution, and many other phenomena. Have you heard of it? It's the **theory of plate tectonics**. You likely studied plate tectonics in middle school. This theory explains the formation of some of the largest features and structures on Earth.

The plate tectonics theory holds that 12 or so rigid **plates** move slowly over Earth. They travel atop the Earth's **mantle**. These plates interact in a number of ways and affect virtually everything in the earth system. Continents ride above sea level and are important parts of several tectonic plates. These parts of plates consist of **continental crust**, the basic rock material of the continents. But there is more to tectonic plates than continents. The other main part is denser than continents and lies beneath the ocean. Rocks in this part of the plate make up what is called **oceanic crust** (figure 13.8).

In many cases, the same plate includes both continental and ocean crust. An example is the eastern margin of the North American Plate. There, continental crust meets oceanic crust at the Atlantic shore (figure 13.9). The South American and African plates are also much larger than their continents alone. In contrast, one of Earth's largest plates, the Pacific Plate, is made up almost entirely of oceanic crust. The Pacific Plate does not have any continents, but only fragments of continental crust in some areas. You'll learn more about this later in the chapter.

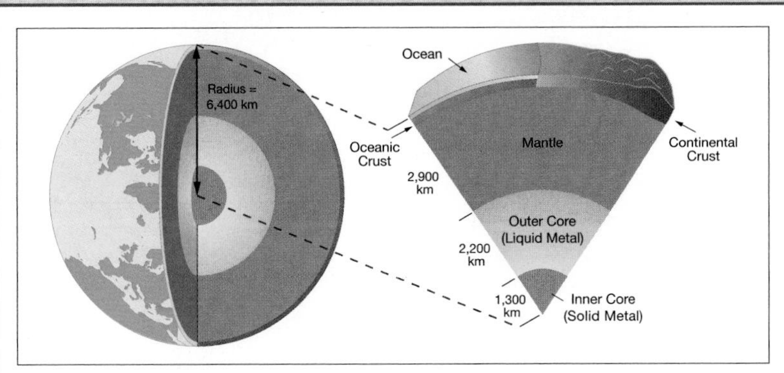

▲ **Figure 13.8 Internal structure of Earth.** Earth consists of several layers arranged like the layers of an onion. Tectonic plates of oceanic crust or continental crust move slowly atop the mantle of Earth.

NOTES:

Crash, Stretch, and Grind, continued

Another important idea led to the theory of plate tectonics. This was **continental drift**, the idea that continents drift slowly across Earth's surface. This idea has proven correct. But, you can also now see that tectonic plates consist of much more than drifting continents. All ocean floors are also part of moving plates.

To better understand tectonic plates, you must look at their interactions. What happens where plates come together? What about where they split apart? Do these interactions affect humans? Where plates meet, they can interact in three general ways. They can either crash, stretch and split apart, or grind past each other. A way to describe these interactions is as three main tectonic settings. To help you answer those earlier questions, read on to learn more about these interactions.

Tectonic Setting 1: Crash—Colossal Collisions

Collisions are dangerous, especially when you are in a car. In a car collision, a car and an object come together too fast. The area where they meet has several characteristic shapes. Some of those shapes are shown in figure 13.10. What evidence do you see to indicate a collision?

Tectonic collisions are similar to car collisions. Of course, a tectonic collision is much slower. But still, zones of collision can be thousands of kilometers long. These collision zones form long chains of mountains. They are distinct areas of uplift, just like the area on the car hood in figure 13.10.

Sometimes the collision zones occur when regions of continental crust crash together

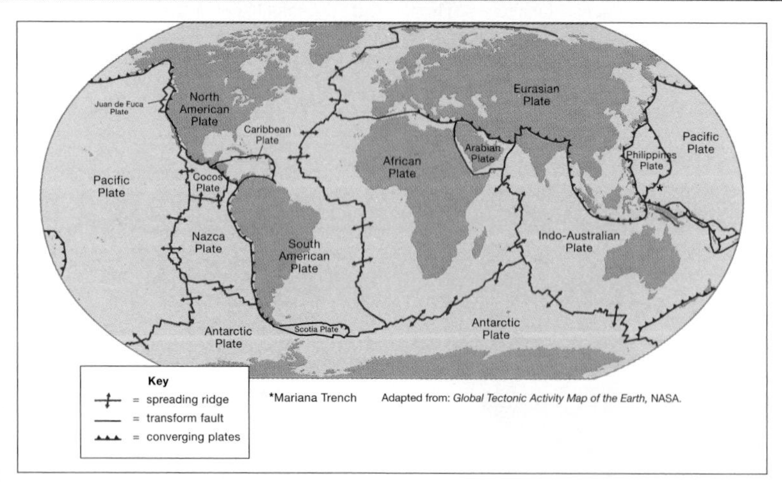

▲ **Figure 13.9 Tectonic plates of Earth.** This map shows the 12 main tectonic plates on Earth. Note that plates can consist of continents as well as large areas of ocean and oceanic crust. Tectonic plates are more than just continents.

NOTES:

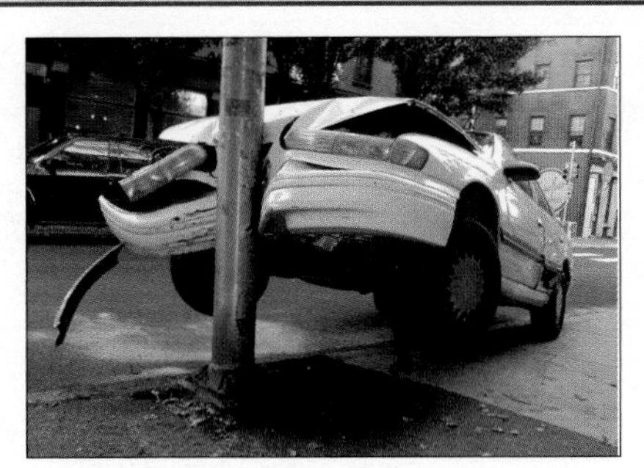

▲ **Figure 13.10 Car collision.** This car has collided with a pole. What evidence do you see to indicate the collision?

(figure 13.11). Because the crust comes together, or converges, at the edges of plates, such areas are called **convergent zones**. Examples include the Himalaya, the Alps, and the Appalachian mountains.

At other times, the parts of tectonic plates made of oceanic crust collide with continents. These are also convergent zones since plates are crashing together. Because the oceanic crust is more dense than continental crust, it is thrust downward, or **subducted**, beneath the continent (figure 13.11). This dense oceanic crust then sinks into the mantle.

Several large tectonic features form where oceanic crust sinks into the mantle. The down-going crust forms **subduction zones**. Deep **trenches** on the ocean floor indicate where ocean crust is being subducted. The subducted oceanic crust is sometimes called a slab. Lines of volcanoes above subduction zones are called **volcanic arcs**. For example, a deep trench and line of volcanoes are found as the Juan de Fuca Plate is subducted beneath North America in the Pacific Northwest (figure 13.11). They are called volcanic arcs because of their broad, curved shape. Examples are the Indonesian and Caribbean volcanic arcs in figure 13.9 and the spectacular Aleutian and Japan arcs.

Go to: www.scilinks.org
Topic: theory of plate tectonics
Code: 2Inquiry665a
Topic: subduction zones
Code: 2Inquiry665b
Topic: volcanic arcs
Code: 2Inquiry665c

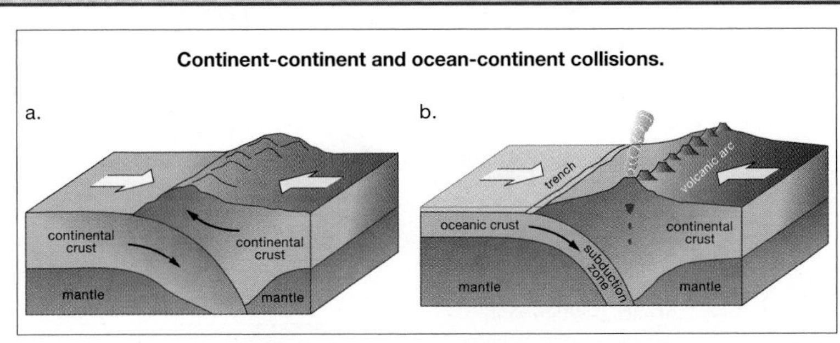

▲ **Figure 13.11 Two tectonic collisions.** Collisions between (a) continents and (b) oceanic crust and continental crust result in chains of mountains. Regions where oceanic crust is pushed beneath continental crust are called subduction zones.

Answers to Stop and Think, SE pages 666–667

1. Plates with oceanic crust, or those with oceanic and continental crust, are shown in figure T13.4.
2. The Mariana Trench marks a subduction zone where the Pacific Plate is sinking or being subducted beneath the Philippines Plate. The Mariana volcanic arc lies above the subduction zone. A largely volcanic island at the south end of the arc, Guam, was taken over for a period by the Japanese in World War II. About half of the island has been an American military base since the end of World War II.

3b. Example distances in centimeters are shown in column 2 in figure T13.5.

3c. A completed table is shown in figure T13.5 for the scale shown in figure 13.13 in the student book. Actual map positions in centimeters will vary depending on the magnification of the figure; the scaled distance in kilometers will not. Note that actual distances will have to be adjusted to the scale bar if the figure changes dimension.

3d. See figure T13.6.

3e. Note that the slope of students' best-fit lines may vary within 10–20 percent of the line shown.

Plates consisting of continental and oceanic crust	Plates consisting only of oceanic crust
North American	Cocos
Caribbean	Juan de Fuca
South American	Nazca
Antarctic	Philippines
African	Pacific
Eurasian	Scotia
Arabian	
Indian-Australian	

Figure T13.4 A sample T-table showing plates and crust types. This T-table divides tectonic plates into those consisting of continental and oceanic crust and those consisting almost entirely of oceanic crust.

A best-fit regression has a slope of 69 mm/yr. This corresponds well with the Australian part of the plate, where it is unimpinged by a continent. Points for the last 30–40 Myr have a lower slope, which corresponds well with rates since India collided with the Eurasian continent.

Students may note that the slope changes with time. From about 70 to 40 Myr, the velocity for India is pretty rapid (figure T13.6). Since about 40 Mya, India has slowed considerably, as shown by a shallower slope for the 3 left points in the figure. Estimates for different velocities follow. Again, a likely explanation is slower velocities with collisions with Eurasia.

71 to 38 Mya:

$$\left(\frac{\Delta x}{\Delta t}\right) = \left(\frac{5{,}714 - 1{,}679 \text{ km}}{71 - 38 \text{ Myr}}\right) = \frac{4{,}035 \text{ km}}{33 \text{ Myr}} = 122\frac{\text{km}}{\text{Myr}} = 122\frac{\text{mm}}{\text{yr}}$$

38 Mya to today:

$$\left(\frac{\Delta x}{\Delta t}\right) = \left(\frac{1{,}679 - 0 \text{ km}}{38 - 0 \text{ Myr}}\right) = \frac{1{,}679 \text{ km}}{38 \text{ Myr}} = 44\frac{\text{km}}{\text{Myr}} = 44\frac{\text{mm}}{\text{yr}}$$

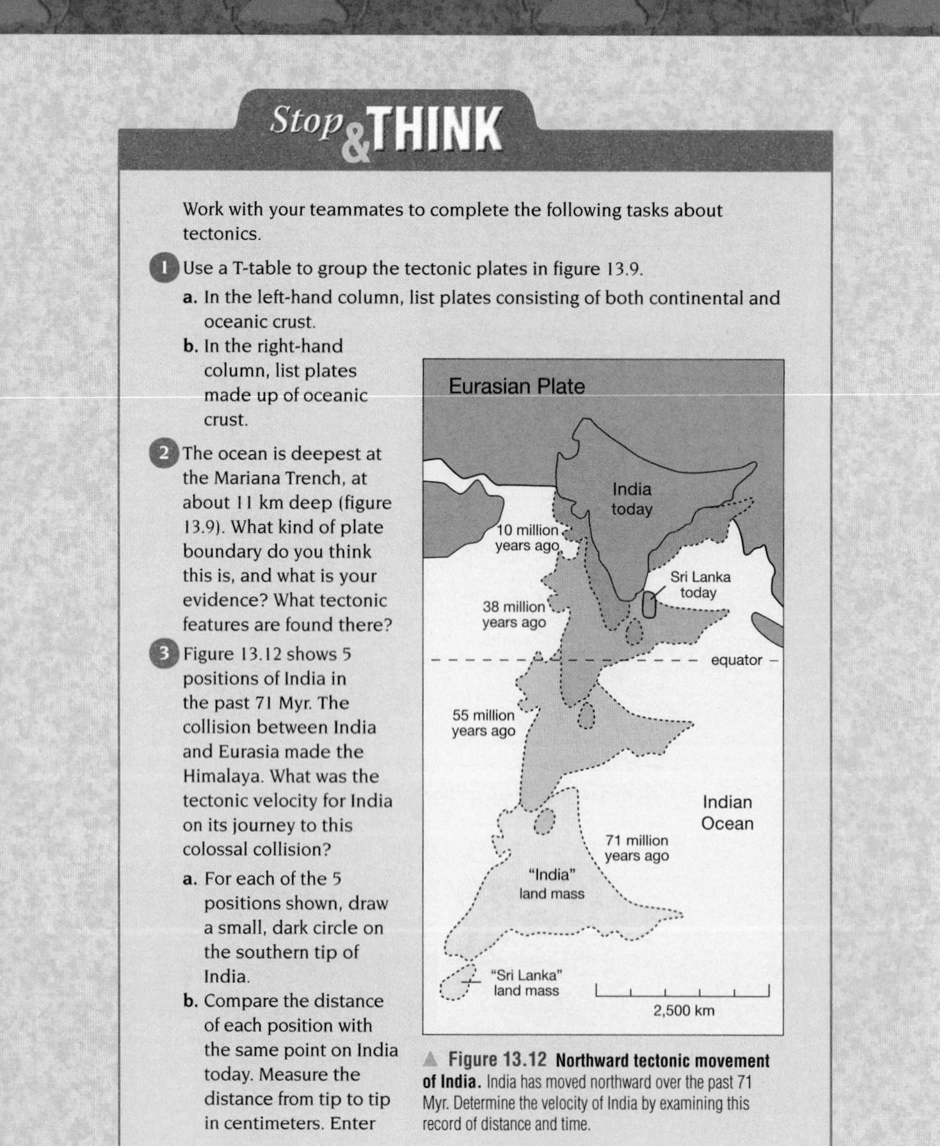

Time (Myr)	Distance (cm)	Distance (km)
0	0	0
10	0.65	464
38	2.35	1,679
55	4.75	3,393
71	8.00	5,714

Figure T13.5 Completed table showing scaled positions for India's tectonics. This table shows positions for India at given times. Positions are first measured from the map in centimeters, then converted to kilometers using the map's scale. Note that the map scale will vary depending on figure enlargements, but scaled distances should still be about the same (column 3).

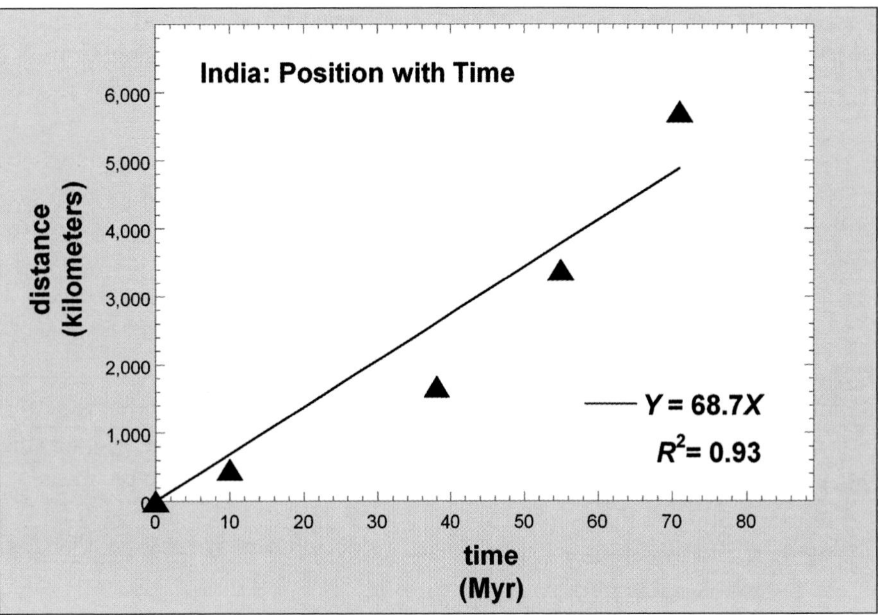

Figure T13.6 Graph of distance (km) with time (Mya) for India. The line shown is a linear regression, which may be different from students' slopes. Another approach is to display the changing slopes, or velocities, at different time periods. For example, this type of graph may show a velocity decrease for the past 40 Myr. This is probably when India collided with Eurasia.

these measurements in your science notebook in a table like figure 13.13.

c. Use the map scale to convert the centimeters that you measured to kilometers.

d. Plot 5 points on a graph of distance (in kilometers on the *y*-axis) as a function of time (in millions of years on the *x*-axis).

e. Use a pencil and ruler to draw a best-fit line through the points. What are the units for the slope of the line on your graph? What does the slope of the line tell you? Explain your answer.

Check that the line goes through zero. It's OK if the line does not connect all points. This is how you get a quick estimate.

Time (Myr)	Distance (cm)	Distance (km)
0	0	
10		
38		
55		
71		

Figure 13.13 Table for recording India's tectonics. Use a table like this to record distances for India at the times given in figure 13.12. Use the scale at the bottom of the map to convert centimeters on the map to kilometers on the ground.

4 Consider again your measurements for India. What if you connect data on your graph from point to point? What inferences can you make about the velocity of India? How might you explain the "low" point on your graph at about 40 Myr?

Crash, Stretch, and Grind, continued

Tectonic Setting 2: Stretch—Breaking Up Is Hard to Do

It's not too hard to imagine tectonic plates crashing together. They've been doing that for millions of years! One possible result is that plates collide to form mountains chains. Another result is one plate can be pushed into a subduction zone beneath the other. But what about the opposite? What happens when plates move in opposite directions? What happens when plates are stretched to the limit?

Just as with stretching chewing gum or rubber bands, plates will eventually break and begin to rip apart. Geologists can observe this process happening at many places today on Earth. The point where plates have broken is called a **rift**. Rifts often form long valleys, or **rift valleys**. These can be many thousands of feet deep. Examples of rifts on continents are the Rio Grande Rift, extending from northern Mexico to Colorado in the United States. A famous rift is the East African Rift. There, a large fragment of continental Africa is being torn away to the east. The floor of the rift valley provides a rich, unique ecosystem for many species. This rift valley also records the

NOTES:

Answers to Reflect and Connect, SE pages 670–672

1. The rift valleys never appear as deep as the actual breaks in the continental crust associated with the rift. This is because erosion fills continental rifts with gravel and sediments. The implication is that mountains next to the rifts are weathering and eroding, filling in the rift valley. These mountains may be volcanoes or may contain many other rock types.
2. The figure 13.16b is the best representation of the vectors. This figure in the student book shows spots with discrete jumps or changes in vector length at active segments of the fault. Figure 13.16b shows slip at 3 positions in a zone of faulting. Figure 13.16a is too simple, and there is no evidence for a single zone of slip between the Pacific and North American plates. Figure 13.16c shows a bending and "twisting" (or shearing) of the land next to a single fault. Figure 13.16 does not show a gradual change in vectors, but relatively consistent vectors within slivers between zones of slip.

3a. The answer assumes that the velocity does not change over this time period. An example in the last activity showed that India slowed down when it collided with Eurasia.

$$\left(\frac{20\text{ mm}}{1\text{ yr}}\right) \times 10\text{ Myr} =$$

$$\left(\frac{20\text{ km}}{1\text{ }\cancel{\text{Myr}}}\right) \times 10\text{ }\cancel{\text{Myr}} = 200\text{ km}$$

3b. Rifting would continue between the Arabian and African plates. This is the active zone of rifting. Collision would occur where the Arabian Plate is colliding with the Eurasian Plate. This is to the northeast of the Persian Gulf in Iran.

3c. The Red Sea will get wider, and the Persian Gulf will shrink. Students might predict that with more uplift next to the Persian Gulf, the marine water would "drain" or part of it might become a landlocked, saltwater sea. (The Persian Gulf is much shallower than the Red Sea.)

3d. Students' diagrams should show the Red Sea about 200 km wider, and perhaps mountains where the current Persian Gulf is located.

NOTES:

Crash, Stretch, and Grind, continued

history of hominids (the family and ancestors of humans) in many famous fossil finds.

Continental rifts can grow wider and wider with more stretching. They also can get deeper, leaving the land surface below sea level. When these rift valleys meet the ocean, marine waters can move in to submerge the floor of the rift valley. Modern examples of this are the Red Sea and the Gulf of California.

Rifts are not only found on continents. In fact, the largest system of rifts on Earth is found beneath the ocean where tectonic plates are moving apart, or diverging. Rift zones are sometimes called **divergent zones**. These rifts form wide ridges of high topography, even though they are underwater. The areas of rifting are sometimes called **mid-oceanic ridges** due to their historic link with the ridge down the center of the Atlantic Ocean. This long oceanic ridge is also a divergent boundary (figure 13.9) between spreading plates. Figure 13.9 also shows that not all oceanic ridges are in the centers of oceans.

Tectonic Setting 3: Grind—Living on the Edge

How do tectonic plates interact when they are not crashing together or pulling apart? Parking lots offer a clue. Have you ever seen a car try to squeeze through a space that is too small? The result could be a dramatic screeching and grinding as one car scrapes past the other.

Tectonic plates do the same thing. The surface where the two plates grind past each other is called a **transform fault**. Perhaps the best-known transform fault between two plates is on the southwest part of North America.

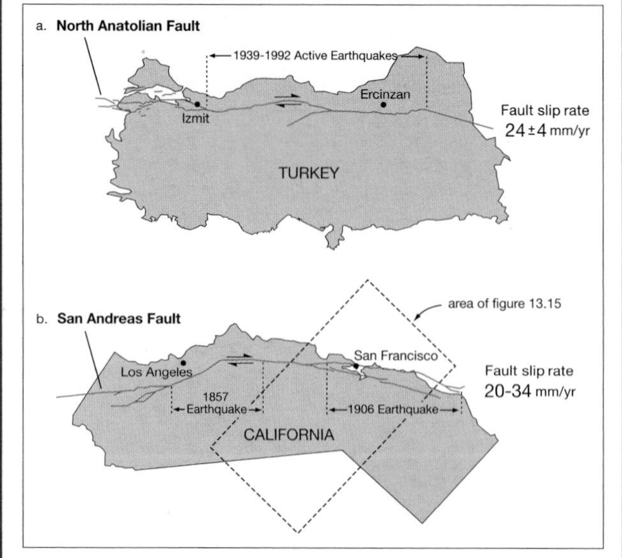

▲ **Figure 13.14 North Anatolian and San Andreas faults.** These maps show two transform faults: (a) the North Anatolian Fault and (b) the San Andreas Fault. Each fault has ruptured in massive earthquakes during the past 100–200 years. The net movement along each fault is several centimeters per year, about the growth rate of your fingernails.

668 Unit 3 Moving Matter

3e. Elephants would most easily walk around the Red Sea and the Persian Gulf. Similarly, it is not unheard of for animals to swim across a body of water to reach the other side. This question starts students thinking about animal migrations between continents, which they will investigate later in the chapter.

4a. The range in distance at different latitudes is 5,000–6,000 km across the southern Atlantic. Some areas appear closer, while others are farther. This suggests differences for measurements at current sea level.

4b. Average distances might be around 5,500 km.

4c. Students estimate a velocity of South America relative to Africa by dividing the distance by time. An example is

$$\left(\frac{5{,}500\text{ km}}{120\text{ Myr}}\right) = 45.8\,\frac{\text{km}}{\text{Myr}} = 45.8\,\frac{\text{mm}}{\text{yr}}$$
$$= 4.6\,\frac{\text{cm}}{\text{yr}}.$$

4d. If the Atlantic Ocean is opening, students might infer that the Pacific Ocean is getting smaller between North and South America and Eurasia. The geologic evidence is entirely consistent with a slowly "shrinking" Pacific Ocean. This process is continuing today.

4e. Students' sketches should show the jigsaw fit of South America and Africa. Another good way to visualize this is to cut out the continents and join them together. Students will do something like that in the evaluate activity.

5. Students can make very similar inferences about the opening of the Atlantic Ocean between North America and Africa and Europe. The best and most consistent evidence is found in the pattern of topography on the ocean floor. Geologic evidence also supports that inference (although it also shows that the North Atlantic started opening a bit before the South Atlantic).

There, the San Andreas Fault marks where the Pacific Plate is grinding its way northwest along the edge of the North American Plate. A massive lurch along the San Andreas Fault was the cause of the massive 1906 earthquake in San Francisco. This earthquake and the fires that resulted destroyed three-quarters of San Francisco and killed more than 3,000 people. Other devastating earthquakes have struck along the San Andreas Fault since 1906. A massive earthquake in October 1989 hit the San Francisco Bay area in the middle of the World Series between the San Francisco Giants and the Oakland Athletics. The death toll was 65, with thousands injured and an estimated $8 billion of damage.

Another example of a transform fault on a continent is the North Anatolian Fault in Turkey (figure 13.14). It also has a dangerous history of sudden movements, violent earthquakes, and significant damage and deaths.

Geologists used to think that transform faults were sharp zones of slip between rigid blocks. But modern technology shows that this is only part of the story. For example, geology clearly shows a history of movement exactly on the San Andreas Fault. At the same time, sensors show that the total slip at the boundary is spread over a zone about 200 km wide. The increasing total slip is shown by longer and longer velocity vectors as one moves from Nevada to the ocean near San Francisco (figure 13.15). The same is true in Southern California, where the fault slip is spread across a wide region.

So boundaries between tectonic plates may be shown on maps as distinct faults. In reality, transform faults can be broad zones of broken rock that are tens to hundreds of kilometers wide. Large earthquakes will likely occur within these zones. Similarly, wide zones of mountains show that collisions between plates do not form only a single fault. The boundaries are broad and dynamic.

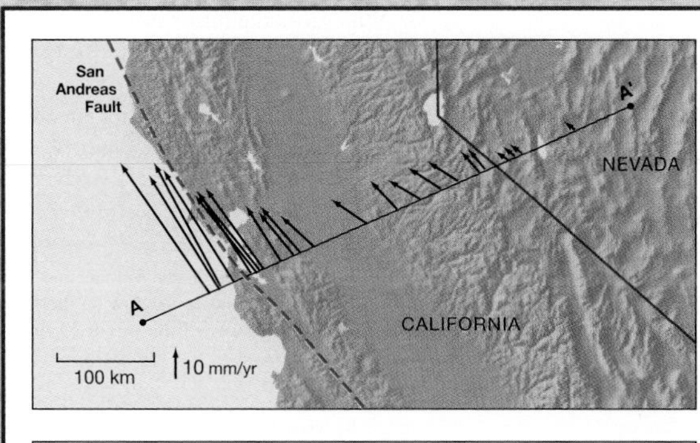

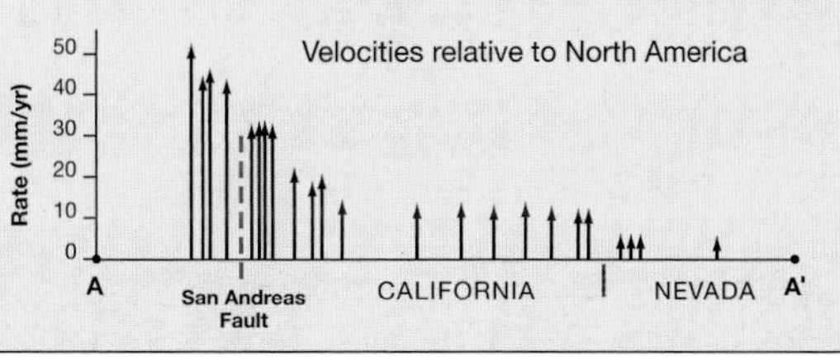

▲ **Figure 13.15 San Andreas Fault slip.** Vectors indicate the slip in an east-west cross section of California. The slip relates to deformation centered on the San Andreas Fault. Arrows show velocity of points relative to stable parts of North America (for example, Missouri).

NOTES:

EXPLORE

Sinking Slabs and Convection Connections

Activity Overview

In *Sinking Slabs and Convection Connections*, students will investigate one of the more vexing questions in earth science—what makes tectonic plates move? Or, what is the driving force for the processes that we see on Earth's surface? These questions have generated spirited debate for several decades. Modern technologies have helped to give clearer evidence, and perhaps some better answers.

This activity begins with two demonstrations. The first demonstrates convection. It simulates how heat leaving Earth's core moves upward in convection cells or plumes through the mantle. The second demonstration shows how the downward force from a dropping (or sinking) weight is transferred to lateral motion in a plate. The combination of these two demonstrations gives a more accurate account of the driving forces for tectonics than the standard model of plates riding and shifting passively on convection cells in the mantle.

Before You Teach

Background Information

What makes tectonic plates move? This question is often the impetus for activities involving convection, the transfer of energy out of Earth. And typically, the activity consists of observing convection in a container of fluid, such as a beaker, with dye added to water. But this typical demonstration, which is demonstration 1 in this activity, is only part of the story. While slow convection moves heat from Earth's core through the mantle to its surface, the process does not explain the majority of plate tectonic processes or patterns that we see at Earth's surface.

What humans experience at Earth's surface is not simple convection. If this were the case, it would imply that the convecting mantle simply drags around plates at the surface of Earth. Even the *National Science Education Standards* are inaccurate in this regard, by stating that mantle convection "propels the plates comprising earth's surface across the face of the globe" (NRC, 1996). If this were the case, we would expect plate motions to be moving away from areas of active upwelling, such as hot spots and deep-seated mantle plumes. The data don't bear this out. Several lines of evidence indicate that the downward pull of subducted slabs is a key force in moving plates and making the tectonic patterns that we see at Earth's surface. Students will explore some of this evidence in this activity.

First, plates move in several directions. They do not move only away from plumes or hot spots that upwell from deep in the mantle. In fact, a few clear cases show plates moving toward and over hot spots.

Second, if plates were driven by upwelling at divergent ridges, we might expect a correlation between the amount or length of a ridge and a plate's velocity. This correlation is weak or doesn't even exist. Rather, the correlation is much stronger between plate velocities and the length of a trench. This correlation is proportional to the amount of subducted slab, which indicates that the pull of sinking slabs is an impor-

Answers to Reflect and Connect are on TE pages 668–669.

Reflect and Connect

1. Basins in rifts on continents, like the Rio Grande Rift, can be over 10 km deep. Why do you think they appear as broad valleys instead of deep troughs that are 10 km deep? What processes can you infer are occurring in the land or mountains on the flanks of the rifts?

Think back to the last activity. What factor makes mountain peaks never really grow at the rate of tectonic uplift?

2. Models are a key part of science. In geology, simple block models can show how tectonic plates move past each other. Compare the blocks in figure 13.16 with the velocity vectors in figure 13.15. Which block model do you think most accurately shows slip between the Pacific and North American plates? Use sketches of block models in your answer to explain.
3. What does the future hold for the geology of the Middle East? Predict the tectonic changes and evolution of the Middle East in the next 10 Myr.
   a. The Arabian Plate is moving away from Africa with a velocity of 20 mm/yr (figure 13.17). How far will the Arabian Plate move in 10 Myr?
   b. Where do you predict zones of rifting? Where do you predict zones of collision?

Remember that velocities for the Arabian and Eurasian plates are relative to Africa. This is as if you were standing on the African Plate and noting the Arabian Plate moving away from you at 20 mm/yr, while the Eurasian Plate got closer by 10 mm/yr.

   c. What do you predict will happen to the Red Sea? To the Persian Gulf?
   d. Develop a sketch of the geography of the Middle East in 10 Myr.

For example, what will be the width of the Red Sea? Use the scale to diagram the future Red Sea.

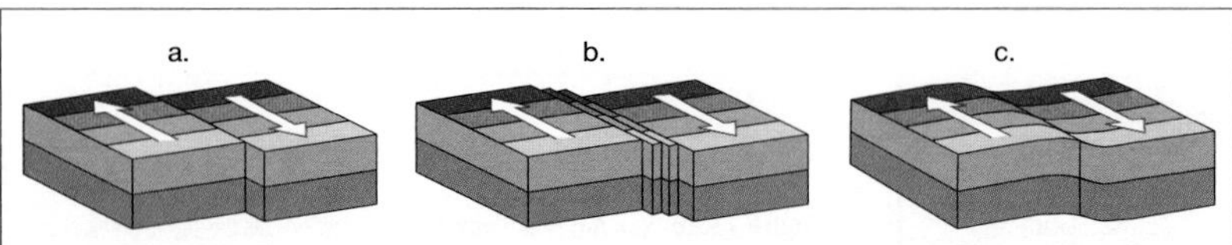

▲ **Figure 13.16 Block models of slip at faults.** The 3 models illustrate how plates deform as they slide past each other. Which model do you think most closely relates to the data—the current velocity vectors—along the San Andreas Fault (figure 13.15)? Note the style of faulting, not the direction of the arrows.

tant driving force for plate tectonic patterns.

Third, mathematical models by geophysicists suggest that substantial forces will be transferred to plates at the surface of Earth, while dense, subducted slabs sink into the mantle. The models also suggest that convection plumes that develop in the lower mantle can be modified somewhat in the upper mantle with dramatic decreases in pressure and temperature. They probably do not retain their plumelike structure all the way through the upper mantle.

In your reading, you may see references to another force on plates—a ridge push. A ridge push is a force on a plate from gravitational potential energy due to the difference in elevation between spreading ridges and trenches at subduction zones. We do not really address this force in chapter 13 because it is rather difficult for students to envision and geologists' current thinking is that ridge push is not as significant a force as slab pull.

The objective of this activity is to move beyond simple conceptions and models of plate tectonics as being driven strictly by convection, where a convecting mantle propels plates around the surface of Earth. Rather, students observe a convection demonstration (demonstration 1) and couple it with a second demonstration (demonstration 2).

In the second demonstration, a weight on a string hanging off the edge of a table pulls a piece of wood laterally along the table. This represents sinking oceanic crust (and upper mantle) at a subduction zone. That ocean crust and upper mantle is relatively cold, and therefore, more dense than the underlying mantle. This is why slabs begin to sink into the mantle. (Imagine taking a hot-air balloon and filling it with a cold, dense gas like CO_2; the balloon would drop straight to the ground.) Combining convection with sinking slabs gives a more complete view of how plate tectonics works.

The goal with the sliding block in demonstration 2 is to move the block at a constant velocity. This means there is no acceleration, and thus no net forces, and the force is equal to and opposite the pulling weight. That force is a viscous resistance to the flow of the corn syrup on the bottom of the block. In other words, the fluid has a viscosity that resists flow. This is similar in a macroscopic way to a frictional resistance, but the latter is reserved for solids moving past each other.

The students will also see a three-dimensional image in a transparency of a subducting slab. The path of the subducting slab from the trench into the mantle is reflected in deeper and deeper earthquakes within the downward slab. The earthquake record is a snapshot of the subducted Pacific Plate penetrating beneath Japan at least 500–700 km into the mantle.

The Yellowstone hot spot problem frees students to use what they've been learning about mapping the rates of plates (slopes on *xy* plots). It also introduces the idea of frame of reference. For example, the Yellowstone hot spot in figure 13.19 in the student book can be viewed as moving to the northeast under North America, which at first appears reasonable since the volcanism gets younger in that direction. Overall, however, other data show that North America is moving to the southwest over a mostly stationary Yellowstone hot spot. Beware of the very common student misinterpretations in this problem and with other hot spots. In general, hot spots tend not to move much relative to each other, and much less than plates.

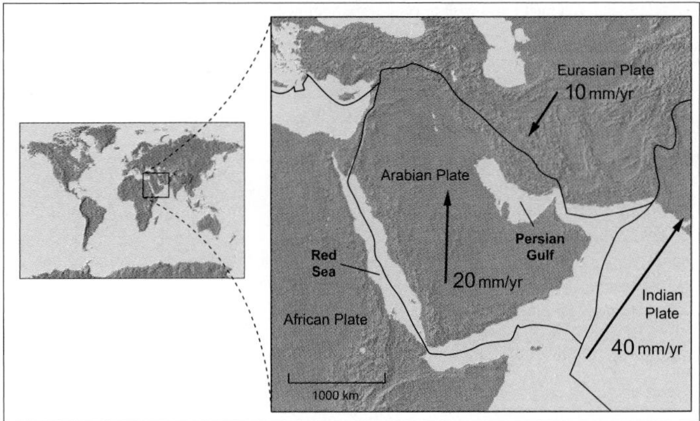

▲ **Figure 13.17 The Arabian Plate's velocity.** The map shows the Arabian Plate and its boundaries. The plate's velocity vector shows its projected movement relative to Africa. What might the Red Sea and the Persian Gulf look like in 5 Myr?

e. Consider an African elephant that wishes to visit its cousin, an Asian elephant, in India. What migration routes could the African elephant take to get to India? Show this with a colored pen or pencil. Describe the migration options.

Challenge Opportunity

4. Early evidence for plate tectonics was the jigsaw fit of South America and Africa. Use the handout *South America and Africa* from your teacher to reconstruct the Atlantic Ocean between these 2 continents. Show your work in your science notebook.
   a. Measure the distance in kilometers (in the east-west direction) between the coasts of South America and Africa. How similar or different are the measurements at different latitudes?
   b. Calculate the average of your distances in Question 4a.
   c. Assume that South America and Africa started rifting apart at 120 Mya. Estimate the velocity of South America relative to Africa.
   d. Consider your calculations for the Atlantic Ocean. What can you infer about changes in the size of the Pacific Ocean over that same time period?
   e. Draw a sketch of what Africa and South America might have looked like with no Atlantic Ocean between them. Draw this in your science notebook or on a sheet of paper.

Materials

For the teacher

Demonstration 1

1 clear Pyrex glass container (at least 1 L)
1 long (6-in) plastic transfer pipet, or 1 long, disposable glass Pasteur pipette and rubber bulb
1 hot plate
cold water
red and blue food coloring
paper towels
1 white sheet of paper for a background

Demonstration 2

1 wooden block, 21×21 cm (about 8×8 in)
1 cup hook to attach to the block
1 1-m string
1 cookie sheet or completely flat surface for sliding the block on
corn syrup

Hot Spot Demonstration

1 small candle and matches
aluminum foil
1 60-cc (mL) syringe
low-melting-temperature red wax, or 1 tube of red toothpaste

For the entire class

1 color transparency of copymaster 13.10, *A–A′ Japan Cross Section Map View*

For each student

1 blank sheet of paper
1 pencil
1 ruler
1 copymaster 13.5, *Tectonic Boundaries, Hot Spots, and Plate Velocities*
1 copymaster 13.9, *Yellowstone Hot Spot Track*

Advance Preparation

Decide whether you will do the 2 demonstrations, or whether your students can manipulate both demonstrations.

Decide whether you want extra copies of figure 13.19 in the student book. This is reproduced on copymaster 13.9, *Yellowstone Hot Spot Track*. Decide on animations

from the *Student Resource CD (SRCD)* or Web sites that you can project to the class. Try a Web search on "mantle plumes."

You may also wish to set up 2–3 stations for observation so that the students can see better. Have a large glass container for each station.

Try each demonstration ahead of time, if possible. This will help you become familiar with how the demonstration runs and what questions to ask students. The goal of demonstration 2 is to balance the size of the weight with the resistance of the corn syrup on the bottom of the block so that the block keeps a constant velocity as it moves across the table. For example, you could have the weight pull down an incline, like a real subduction zone (although some subduction zones appear to be near vertical).

Another way to accurately demonstrate the physics of subduction is to have a plastic bag containing very cold water (4° Celsius) or salt water sink in a bucket of warm water. The cold or salt water is a few percentage points more dense that the warm water, and therefore sinks into the warm water. This is the process at subduction zones where a dense slab sinks into the mantle.

You may decide not to use the corn syrup under the block, as it can be sticky and hard to clean up if you

Answers to Reflect and Connect Question 5 are on TE page 669.

You might also wish to cut out the continents and glue them together on another piece of paper. Refer as needed to *FYI—Going to Great Lengths*.

5. Consider what you noted for South America and Africa in Question 4. What inference can you make about the history of the North Atlantic? What is your evidence?

Going to Great Lengths

Some simple conversions will make it easy for you to do quick calculations. These are called back-of-the-envelope calculations because you can do them on a small piece of paper. For example, if something is only moving at 12 mm/yr, how could you tell how far it would travel in 2 Myr?

This is easier than it sounds. In fact, you already did this when you completed figure 13.6 by scaling up with factors of 10. You showed that 2.5 mm/yr equals 2.5 km/Myr. You also need to be able to show this by canceling units.

For example, how would you convert 12 cm/yr to kilometers per million years? First, change the 12 cm to millimeters (mm). Then include two factors: one factor of 10^6 from millimeters to kilometers, and then another factor of 10^6 from years to millions of years. These steps are easier to see:

$$\left(\frac{12\ \text{cm}}{1\ \text{yr}}\right) \times \left(\frac{10\ \text{mm}}{1\ \text{cm}}\right) = \left(\frac{120\ \text{mm}}{1\ \text{yr}}\right) = 120\ \frac{\text{mm}}{\text{yr}}$$

Second, complete the conversion to kilometer per million years either in separate steps or all together. They are the same thing. The separate steps are

$$\left(\frac{120\ \text{mm}}{1\ \text{yr}}\right) \times \left(\frac{10^6\ \text{yr}}{1\ \text{Myr}}\right) = \frac{120 \times 10^6\ \text{mm}}{\text{Myr}}, \text{ and then}$$

$$\left(\frac{120 \times 10^6\ \text{mm}}{\text{Myr}}\right) \times \left(\frac{1\ \text{km}}{10^6\ \text{mm}}\right) = 120\ \frac{\text{km}}{\text{Myr}}.$$

You should also be able to show a single step with all units canceling:

$$\left(\frac{120\ \text{mm}}{1\ \text{yr}}\right) \times \left(\frac{10^6\ \text{yr}}{1\ \text{Myr}}\right) \times \left(\frac{1\ \text{km}}{10^6\ \text{mm}}\right) = \frac{120\ \text{km}}{\text{Myr}}$$

So the rule of thumb is that units of millimeters per year transfer directly to kilometers per million years. A plate moving 12 cm/yr moves 120 km in a million years. You can also show that it would move 240 km in 2 Myr, or 1,200 km in 10 Myr. This is handy to remember for quick calculations. Now you should be able to prove it, too!

EXPLORE

Sinking Slabs and Convection Connections

Tectonic plates are always changing, but why do they move? What causes large pieces of crust to move about the surface of Earth? How do plate interactions relate to the oceans, continents, mountain chains, or natural resources? Is there a simple way to explain these changes on Earth's surface?

Indeed, this has been one of the more vexing questions in science: What makes tectonic plates move? Because of several modern technologies, geologists are better able to answer this question now

don't have a sink nearby. However, it is an excellent visual clue to represent a rigid block or tectonic plate (lithosphere) moving atop a ductile slowly flowing mantle (asthenosphere) with viscous resistance underneath. Practice a time or two. Keep the string out of the corn syrup. It gets sticky and difficult to manipulate.

Review how to determine plate velocity from a plot of distance (km on the *y*-axis) versus time (Mya on the *x*-axis). The slope, in units of km/Myr, converts directly to units of mm/yr.

Procedure for Demonstration 1

Steps 1–7 can be done prior to class.

1. Fill a glass container with cold water. Place it on the counter next to the hot plate and let it sit about 1 minute (min) until there is no turbulence in the water and all bubbles have risen.
2. Place about 1–2 mL of red food coloring in the Pyrex glass container.
3. Slowly draw the food coloring into the long, thin pipet.

Do not draw any air bubbles into the food coloring.

4. Wipe the tip and have the food coloring exactly even with the tip.
5. Submerge the tip smoothly until it reaches the bottom of the container.
6. Slowly expel the food coloring from the pipet so that it forms a layer across the bottom of the glass container; stop when a bubble is ready to come out of the pipet tip.

The goal, which is easy to do (once you get the hang of it), is to have an entirely clear container of water with a thin (approximately 1 millimeter [mm]), bright red layer on the bottom of the beaker. This demonstration works because the glycerol in the food coloring is a bit denser than the cold water.

7. Place the white sheet of paper behind the hot plate as a background, and check that the lighting is good.
8. Move the container from the counter to the hot plate without any swirling.
9. Watch carefully as plumes of slightly lower-density water and food coloring move upward and through the cold water.

This is similar to how heat and matter migrate upward from the core-mantle boundary into the overlying mantle. The convection cells or plumes will begin in 10–20 seconds (sec) after being placed on the hot plate.

10. After the red food coloring has mixed fairly well, use a long pipet to add a similar dose of blue food coloring to the bottom of the container.

With the convection cycling fairly well by now, the darker color will help you see the convection cells.

11. Ask questions such as the following during the demonstration to emphasize the use of inquiry:
   - "How many upward moving structures do you see?"
   - "How many downward moving structures do you see?"
   - "What are other examples of buoyant things moving up?"

A hot-air balloon and a helium-filled balloon are examples.

   - "What are other examples of dense things flowing down?"

A cold-air balloon, a CO_2-filled balloon, and cold salt water in the oceans are examples.

---

than when plate tectonics was first proposed in the early 1960s. *Sinking Slabs and Convection Connections* will help you better understand why tectonic plates change position on Earth. You will gather as a class to observe and diagram two demonstrations that your teacher will show you.

Materials

For each student

1 blank sheet of paper

1 pencil

1 ruler

Process and Procedure

1. As a class, discuss the first setup. Do Steps 1a–d during the demonstration.
   a. Draw a clear sketch of the setup.

Remember that when you do scientific sketches, it is helpful to include a title, data, appropriate labels, a scale, and the orientation.

   b. Identify the source of energy for the system. Clearly label it on your diagram.
   c. How does the system respond to that source of energy? Use arrows in your diagram to show any movement in the system.
   d. Explain how you think the system relates to plate tectonics.

Be prepared to share your ideas and questions in a class discussion.

2. Read the following paragraph. Record in your science notebook any words that you are not familiar with.

Many people have learned that the mantle is a key layer in the structure of Earth. But did you know that about 80 percent of the volume of Earth consists of mantle (figure 13.8)? Most of the rest of Earth is a metal core consisting mostly of iron and nickel. Some heat escaping Earth's core travels up through the mantle in plumes. These plumes of upwelling through the mantle create hot spots when they reach Earth's surface. Hot spots are characterized by outpourings of molten rock (lava) at volcanoes. Examples of hot spots are the Hawaiian volcanoes, the island of Iceland, the Galápagos Islands, and the Yellowstone hot spot. Do you know of others? After upwelling toward the crust, other parts of the mantle must also go back down into the earth. The slow movement of the mantle due to upwelling and sinking is called mantle convection.

You might also find that squeezing toothpaste upward through holes in a moving paper plate covered with foil works well, too. To do this, cover the paper plate in foil and poke holes every 3 cm. Then move the plate over an upright tube of toothpaste. This analogy will help students with several steps in the activity. Seeing the foil (i.e., plate) move across the candle will help them with the misconception that the continent is stationary when the hot spot (i.e., candle) moves in the opposite direction. Ask students questions about which of the wax or toothpaste structures were created first relative to the direction of the plate's motion.

As You Teach

Outcomes and Indicators of Success

By the end of this activity, students should

1. use simple models to simulate the forces acting on tectonic plates.

   They will demonstrate their abilities by

   - drawing a diagram of convection that is demonstrated through food coloring in water,
   - using appropriate labels in a scientific sketch,
   - drawing and labeling a simple sketch of a weight pulling a board, and
   - combining sketches of convection and the weight pulling a board into a single model.

2. analyze data regarding the forces that act on tectonic plates and plate motions.

   They will analyze their data by

   - participating in class experiments that use heat as a force driving convection of water;
   - participating in class experiments that use a falling weight as a force driving the movement of a block across a surface;
   - comparing directions of plate motions with locations of hot spots, spreading ridges, and trenches;
   - determining the velocity of the North American Plate relative to the Yellowstone hot spot; and
   - examining the depth-distance relationship for earthquakes in a subduction zone.

3. develop further skills in the abilities and understandings of scientific inquiry.

   They will demonstrate their skills by

   - conducting, as a class, a simulation of convection and the forces from slab pull;
   - revising and developing models for how convection and slab pull are complementary;
   - comparing two species of bison in the fossil record, *Bison bison* and *B. latifrons*;
   - using data on locations of hot spots, spreading ridges, and trenches to evaluate the relationship to direction of plate motion; and
   - analyzing locations of earthquake foci that help define subduction zones.

Strategies

Getting Started

Decide if you can have more than one station so that students can do the demonstrations. Obtain the appropriate materials for the number of stations. Think of probing questions to ask during demonstrations 1 and 2

Answers to Questions 6 and 7 are on TE page 675b.

3. As a class, develop a list of words from the paragraph in Step 2 that you do not know. Discuss these words and link them to features in the setup from Step 1. Record your best thinking in your science notebook.
   a. What might have represented mantle in the demonstration?
   b. Did you observe upwelling, downwelling, or a hot spot?
   c. Did convection move the piece of wood? What might the wood represent?
4. Your teacher will show a second setup to your class. Listen carefully for instructions on observing that system.
   a. Sketch the setup. What do you predict will happen when your teacher lets go of the weight?
   b. What forces act on the system and move the block? Use arrows to show these forces in your diagram.
   c. Does the velocity of the weight or block change? Explain whether there is a net force on the system.
   d. If there are no net forces, what force is resisting the motion on the block? Identify what is keeping the weight from accelerating.

Recall from chapter 2, *Collision Course*, where you dropped the coffee filter in the elaborate activity, *With and Without a Net*.

   e. Write in your science notebook how this setup may relate to plate tectonics. What plate tectonic setting might this represent?
5. You have seen 2 setups: a sliding block and a falling weight. Combine these into a single, simple diagram to represent elements of plate tectonics. Steps 5a–c may help.
   a. Obtain a blank sheet of paper from your teacher.
   b. Sketch the setup from Step 1 near the middle of the paper.
   c. Use arrows to show the direction of motion in the system.
   d. Add a sketch of the setup from Step 4.

Your diagram should include the container, convection, the string, the weight, the block, and arrows for the direction of motion.

   e. How many areas of convection do you have? If helpful, add 1 block-and-weight combination per convection cell.
6. Complete the following sentences to help you better understand why plates move.
   a. "If plate motion is only driven by mantle convection and upwelling, then plates should be moving __________ hot spots."

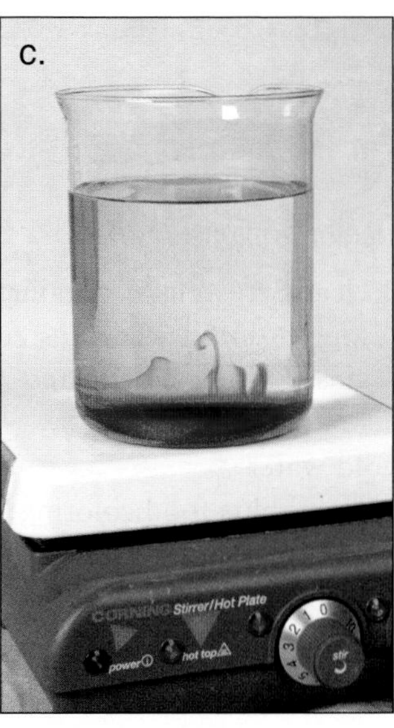

▲ **Figure T13.7 Water convection.** (a) This photo shows the experimental setup for convection in demonstration 1. (b) The layer of red food coloring is deposited on the bottom of the beaker with a long pipet. Because it is slightly denser than water, the food coloring will remain on the bottom. Be careful not to swirl, mix, or blow out bubbles from the pipet. (c) Upwelling plumes develop near the hot plate and then deteriorate as they move upward through the colder water column.

b. "If plate motion is only driven by plates being pulled, then plates should be moving ______ subduction zones."

7. Get with a partner at your work area. Use evidence and examples from figures 13.9 and 13.18 to complete Steps 7a–c.
   a. Review your answers for Step 6. Then read the caption for figure 13.18 together.
   b. Write in your science notebook how many hot spots you see.
   c. Describe the directions that plates move, in general, relative to the positions of hot spots. Use specific examples to explain.

In other words, do plates move away from the upwelling at hot spots?

   d. Describe the directions that plates move, in general, relative to subduction zones. Use specific examples to explain.
   e. Discuss with your partner what these movements tell you about the forces that drive plate tectonic motions across Earth's surface.

It may help to relate this question to the demonstrations that you saw.

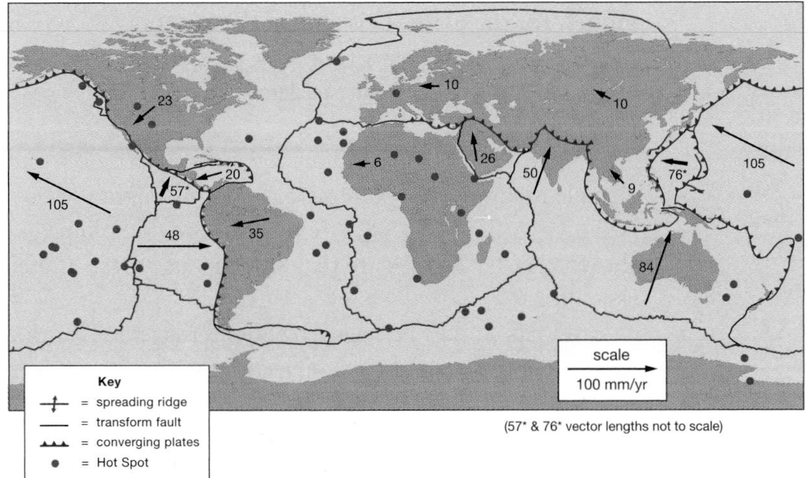

▲ **Figure 13.18 Tectonic boundaries, hot spots, and plate velocities.** This map shows the 12 main tectonic plates on Earth, locations of ridges and trenches, and hot spots. Estimates for velocity vectors are also shown. Use this map to evaluate whether plates move away from hot spots, toward trenches, or some combination.

that will help students analyze the system for upward convection (figure T13.7) and slowly falling weight.

You can start with the hot spot demonstration. Move a piece of aluminum foil slowly over a candle. This will leave a sooty, dark hot spot track on the bottom of the foil. The track will help students envision the tracks of hot spots recorded on plates. Or, poke a line of holes in the foil and allow the flames to progress along the holes. This will help students visualize the hot spot track in the "foil" plate.

This demonstration will help students understand the record of volcanism as a plate moves over a hot spot. Hold a 60-cc (mL) syringe with hot red wax in a vertical position. Slowly move the aluminum foil over the syringe, periodically poking through the foil so that a small flow of wax forms next to the rupture. This is a good analogy for the volcanism at Hawaii and the record of the Hawaiian-Emperor hot spot track (to about 43 Mya). The wax will dry in a progression from one end to the other. See the instructions in Advance Preparation for substituting toothpaste for the wax. Students do a problem with the Yellowstone hot spot.

Process and Procedure

Materials

For the teacher

Demonstration 1

1 clear Pyrex glass container (at least 1 L)
1 long (6-in) plastic transfer pipet, or 1 long, disposable glass Pasteur pipette and rubber bulb
1 hot plate
cold water
red and blue food coloring
paper towels
1 white sheet of paper for a background

Demonstration 2

1 wooden block, 21×21 cm (about 8×8 in)
1 cup hook to attach to the block
1 1-m string
1 cookie sheet or completely flat surface for sliding the block on
corn syrup

Hot Spot Demonstration

1 small candle and matches
aluminum foil
1 60-cc (mL) syringe
low-melting-temperature red wax, or 1 tube of red toothpaste

For the entire class

1 color transparency of copymaster 13.10, *A–A′ Japan Cross Section Map View*

For each student

1 blank sheet of paper
1 pencil
1 ruler
1 copymaster 13.5, *Tectonic Boundaries, Hot Spots, and Plate Velocities*
1 copymaster 13.9, *Yellowstone Hot Spot Track*

In Step 1, start by having students sketch the demonstration 1 setup. Did they remember to add a title and a scale? Ask students to explain what they think will happen when heat is added under the dish. Will the water boil and froth? What do they predict? If they offer ideas about convection, press them to try to explain their ideas and why the convection occurs. Then do the experiment. Ask students what they are thinking after the demonstration.

The source of energy is the hot plate, and the system responds by developing upward-moving plumes of warmed water. This part of the system is shown in figure T13.7. Be open to ideas that relate this system to tectonics. Students may suggest that the system relates to the motion of the mantle with plates moving on top.

The reading in Step 2 introduces several new ideas and vocabulary terms. Students will need to identify those words that they are not familiar with. You will then use those terms in Step 3. Students have just read about the mantle. They might ask about words such as plumes, upwelling, hot spots, or convection.

- *Plumes* occur in the mantle where hot material moves upward from the lower mantle, in some cases, to erupt at Earth's surface. (It is sort of like a hot-air balloon.)
- *Upwelling* refers to the upward motion of material in plumes through the mantle.
- *Hot spots* are the surface representation of plumes as they erupt at Earth's surface. Earth has a variety of types of hot spots (figure 13.18 in the student book), such as those in Hawaii, the Galápagos Islands, Iceland, and Yellowstone National Park.
- *Convection* is the circular motion of a fluid as it transports hot material and heat upward, and then transports cooled material downward. This appears to occur in the mantle as part of plate tectonics. The hot material is lower in density, while the colder material is higher in density and sinks.

In Step 4, students investigate a system with a different set of forces. This system consists of a weight pulled downward by gravity, and a board pulled across a surface over a viscous fluid (corn syrup). Students see that a downward force can be transferred to a lateral motion on the block of wood.

While students are making their sketches, ask whether they think the weight will accelerate or have a constant velocity. Based on information in earlier chapters, do they recall the significance of this? Ask them what forces they think are acting in this investigation. If velocity is not changing (i.e., no net forces), what is countering the falling weight so that it has no net force? This would be the force on the bottom of the board—the stickiness of the corn syrup. This force is a viscous resistance to horizontal motion. What might the viscous liquid represent? It would represent a slowly flowing mantle.

With regard to subduction zones, students should note that a downward force clearly transfers to a lateral motion for the plate. This part of the system is shown in the upper left of figure T13.8. Ask probing questions that allow students to see that the demonstration relates to processes in subduction zones.

In Step 5, students combine the 2 demonstrations into a single diagram. An example of how this might look is shown in figure T13.8. Are upward-moving plumes shown clearly? Make sure that students use these in their sketches.

Students should be seeing by Step 6 that plate motions cannot be driven solely by convection, with plates passively riding around the top. If this were the case, students would suggest that most plates would be moving away from hot spots. But students can see this is not the case when they look at the tectonic map of Earth (figure 13.18 in the student book or copymaster 13.5). In Step 7, students connect their observations to actual tectonic features.

Answers to Questions 6 and 7, SE pages 674–675

6a. "If plate motion is only driven by mantle convection and upwelling, then plates should be moving away from hot spots."

6b. "If plate motion is only driven by plates being pulled, then plates should be moving toward subduction zones."

7b. About 53 hot spots are shown.

7c. In general, plates pass over hot spots. There is little, if any, correlation between hot spots and plate direction. For a relatively small number of hot spots on spreading ridges, the plate moves away from the hot spots (e.g., Iceland, Galápagos, or Afar at the base of the Red Sea). Many more are distributed beneath oceanic plates or continents. Geologic evidence indicates that those hot spots are generally relatively stationary for tens of millions of years (although detailed recent work shows that they can at times drift or migrate through the mantle).

7d. Plates move toward subduction zones. For example, the Pacific Plate has a rapid velocity to the northwest toward the Japan and Aleutian trenches. Also, the Australian-Indian Plate is being subducted at the Java Trench, which led to the Andaman-Sumatra earthquake and tsunami in December 2004. Closer to home, the Juan de Fuca Plate is being subducted beneath the Cascadian volcanic arc.

7e. From a strict correlation point of view, plate motions do not correlate well with the location of hot spots. Hot spots indicate upwelling and convection in the mantle. This suggests that convection by itself is not a sufficient explanation for plate tectonic motions and the development of landforms that we see. Thus, the "pull" of oceanic crust entering subduction zones correlates much better with the directions of plate motions and the tectonic patterns and landforms on Earth's surface.

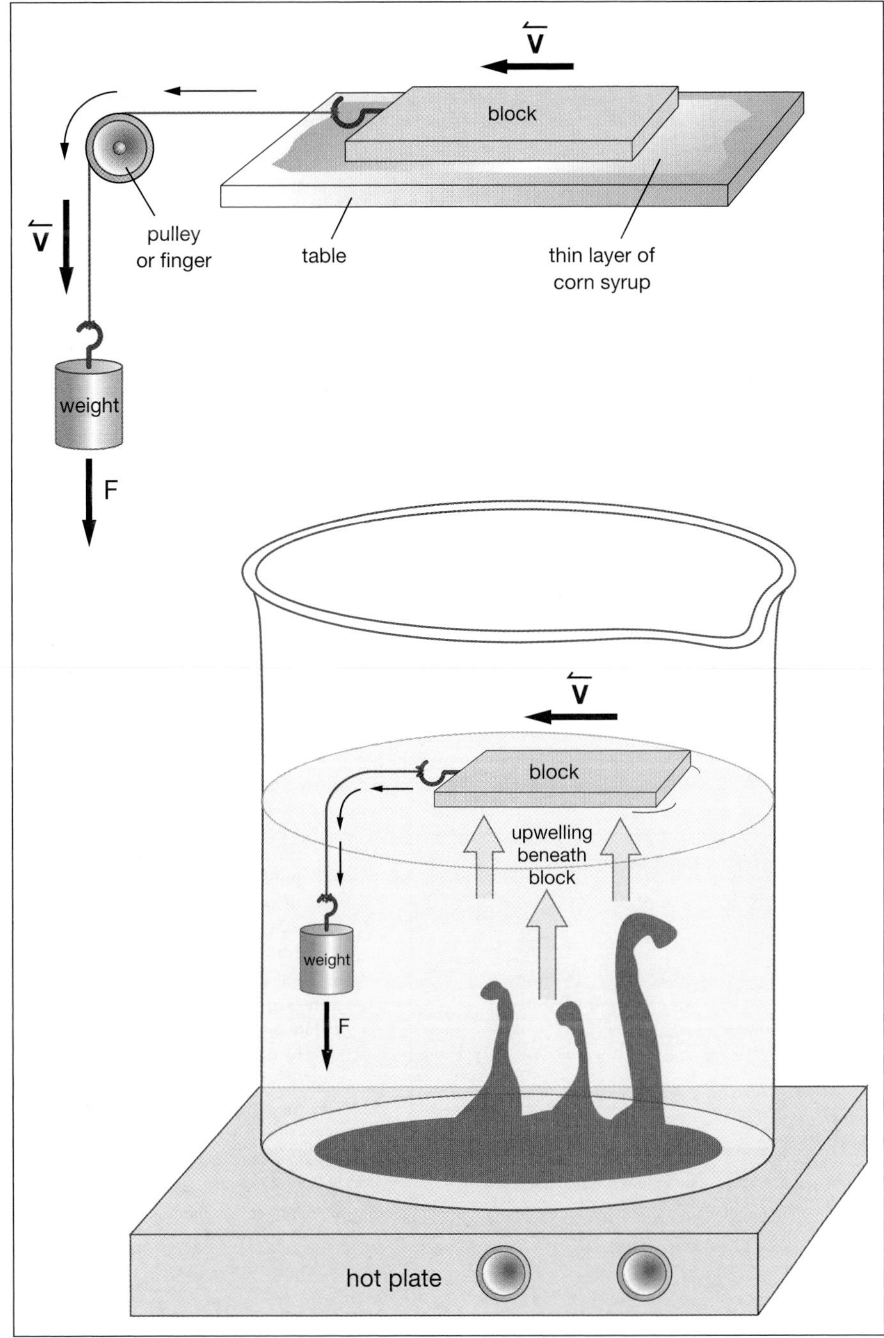

◀ **Figure T13.8 Convection and slab system.** This diagram shows the convection system (lower right) and slab system (upper left). They are combined in the lower diagram, which shows how a slab system and a convection system might be combined as a model. The plate is being pulled across the area of upwelling, as happens at many hot spots on Earth.

Answers to Reflect and Connect, SE pages 676–678

1a. Have a contest using maps (e.g., copymaster 13.5, *Tectonic Boundaries, Hot Spots, and Plate Velocities*) to figure out what part of the world is shown in the color transparency of *A–A′ Japan Cross Section Map View* (copymaster 13.10). How can students confirm their ideas? Who is correct? You might steer students toward the coastline for clues. When students ask about the circles (earthquakes), tell them the circles are another clue that the map appears to encompass a tectonic boundary.

1b. Correlating the shoreline with a map shows that this is the boundary between the Pacific and Eurasian plates in northern Japan. This boundary is characterized by subduction of the Pacific Plate beneath the Eurasian Plate.

1c. There is a pattern for earthquakes as a function of depth. Earthquakes occur at greater depths moving to the northwest from the trench. Some additional shallow quakes are shown at the northwest end of the cross section.

1d. The deeper and deeper earthquakes record seismic events within a subducting slab of the Pacific Plate. Subduction occurs at a collisional or a convergent tectonic boundary.

1e. Students should develop a sketch along line A–A′. This cross section shows distances from A′ (or A) where bands of certain colors are centered. The scale (which is the same as the horizontal scale) shows the depth for clusters of events. Figure T13.9 shows that the events increase in depth and that the slab is sinking at about a 45-degree (°) angle to the northwest. Some additional shallow events are plotted near A, but these are not part of the subduction zone's seismicity.

Be sure to return to what students saw in demonstration 2, the slab pull activity. Ask them how they might modify that experiment given these data.

2b. Velocity tells the distance a plate moves during a given amount of time.

2c. Students should use the Yellowstone data to plot their results, just as they did with the problem about the velocity o India. First, they should be able to organize measurements in a table, and then plot those measurements as a graph. Examples are shown in figure T13.10.

All data suggest a velocity of 46 km/Myr, or 46 mm/yr (slope on the first graph). This is also about 4.6 cm/yr. The fit is a little better for the last 10 Myr, which suggests a slightly slower velocity of about 2.7 cm/yr (slope on the second graph). The latter value is supported by current measurements.

3. An ancestral species is a species in the past from which a subsequent species evolved (the descendant). *B. bison* is a descendant of *B. latifrons*. Extinct 3-toed horses are ancestral to modern 1-toed horses. These concepts are a common part of understanding the fossil record and the biological evolution of animal families.

Reflect and Connect

Complete the following steps.

1. Your teacher will show you an overhead transparency. Each circle represents an earthquake, and the color indicates how deep underground (in kilometers) the earthquake occurred.
   a. What part of the world is shown? How can you figure this out?
   b. What tectonic plates are included in the figure?
   c. Look at the pattern of earthquakes. Write in your science notebook the relationship between earthquakes and depth.
   d. What kind of tectonic setting do you think is shown by the pattern of earthquakes?
   e. A line is labeled "A–A′." Sketch in your science notebook where earthquakes occur along this line. What does the depth of the earthquakes indicate?
2. Figure 13.19 shows the history of volcanic eruptions (in millions of years ago) for the Yellowstone hot spot beneath North America.
   a. Determine a vector for the velocity of North America relative to the Yellowstone hot spot and sketch it in your science notebook. Keep these points in mind:
      - View this hot spot as stationary, with North America moving over the hot spot.
      - The "0.6" symbol shows the most recent volcanic eruption at Yellowstone Park about 0.6 Mya.
      - The shapes with numbers give the ages of volcanic rocks in millions of years. This line of volcanic eruptions records when the Yellowstone hot spot was beneath those positions.
   b. What does "velocity" mean in regard to a tectonic plate?
   c. How would you represent the velocity of North America in a graph from these data?

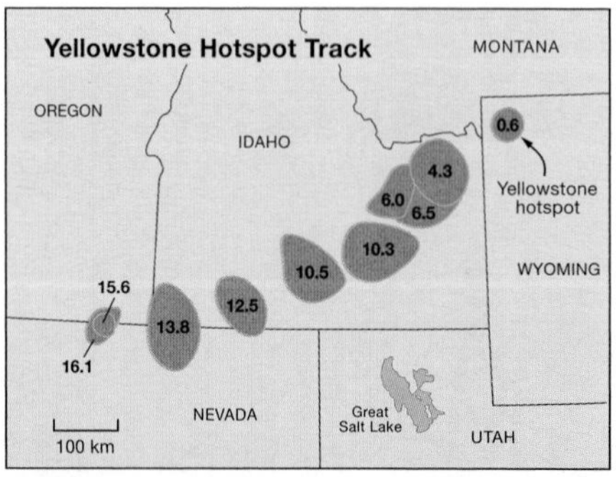

▲ **Figure 13.19 Yellowstone hot spot track.** The Yellowstone hot spot has a history of volcanic eruptions that crosses several states. The age of eruptions are shown as millions of years ago. How fast is North America moving over the Yellowstone hot spot?

Watch the demonstration your teacher does with aluminum foil, a candle, wax, and a syringe.

Remember how you determined the velocity of India in figure 13.12 in the explain activity, *Rates of Plates*.

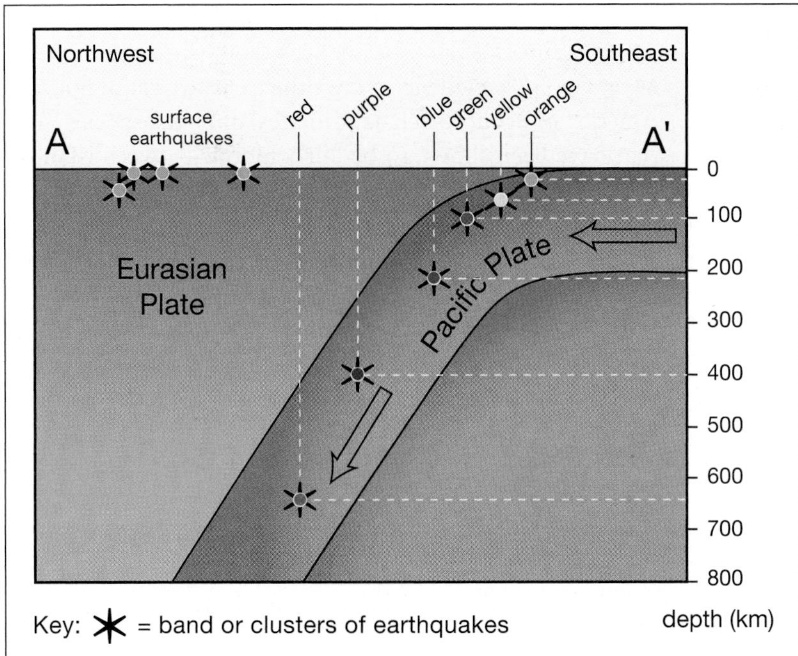

◀ **Figure T13.9 A-A′ Japan's seismicity in cross section.** This sketch along A–A′ from a color transparency and copymaster 13.10, *A–A′ Japan Cross Section Map View*, shows the increase in earthquake depth as the Pacific Plate is pushed to the northwest beneath the Eurasian Plate. Earthquake clusters are represented by asterisks. Dashed lines show the approximate distance along A–A′ for earthquakes at a given depth. Dashed lines connect to depth on the right axis. The vertical scale on the cross section is the same as the horizontal scale on the map. This gives an accurate representation of the angle of the subduction zone at about 45°.

a.

Distance (km)	Age (Myr)
0	0.6
117	4.3
149	6.5
182	6.0
269	10.3
474	12.5
575	13.8
669	15.6
669	16.1

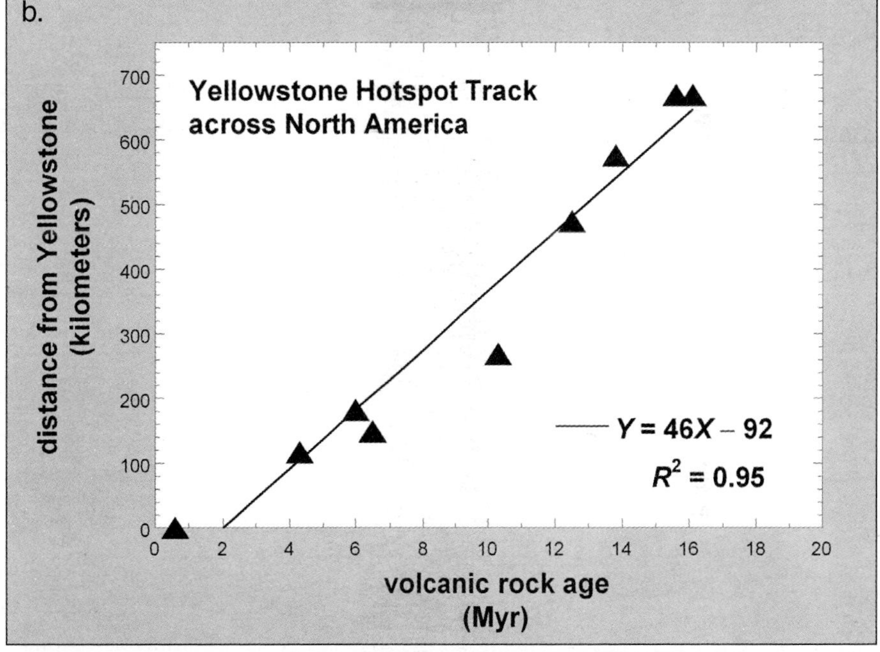

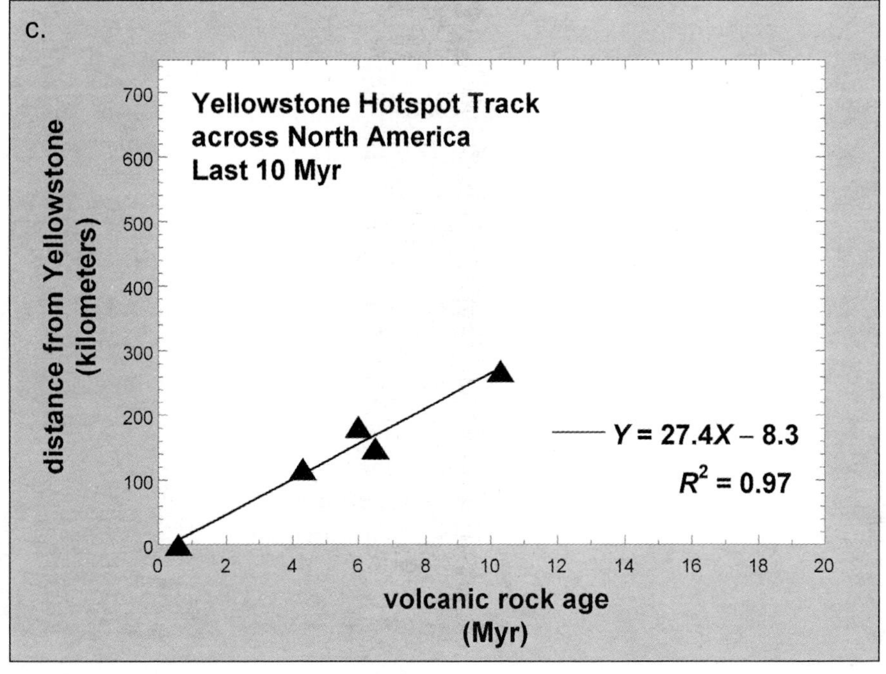

▲ **Figure T13.10 Yellowstone hot spot table and graphs.** The table (a) contains estimates of distance and age for volcanic rocks relative to current hot spot positions at Yellowstone National Park. The graph in (b) includes all points in a best-fit. The graph in (c) only calculates velocity for the last 10 Myr. This graph gives a slower velocity for North America that is actually within error of current, measured values.

ELABORATE

Building Bridges

Activity Overview

In *Building Bridges*, students combine in a real way what they have learned about plate tectonics and the geologic record with biological evolution. They will discover from analyzing maps and geologic records of sediments and fossils how the land bridges between continents strongly affect the fossil record, as well as the current distribution of animals. The goal is to interweave key concepts in tectonics, the fossil record, and biological evolution with real data and a real "story." In a nutshell, geographic isolation can be a driver for biological evolution, and plate tectonics can be shown to control geographic isolations.

Before You Teach

Background Information

Most biology textbooks discuss the geographic isolation of Australia and the evolution of marsupials on that continent in a general way. In contrast, this activity uses an analogous set of data with animals that are a little closer to home.

Starting about 55 Mya, a land bridge between South America and Antarctica broke as South America drifted northwestward into isolation in the Pacific Ocean. It was largely an island continent for the next approximately 50 Myr. Starting with the initial stock on the continent—the endemic groups of animals—biological evolution occurred over this time period. While evolving groups also include birds, reptiles, and plants, the mammals provide a stark contrast with animals that we know today. The formation of the Central American land bridge between the continents at about 4 Mya then led to what is called the *Great American Interchange*. This was the migration and immigration between continents of many types of animals.

A key taxonomic order representing evolution on the island continent of South America is the *edentates* (*Edentata*). The name means "toothless," although it is a bit of a misnomer since only the anteaters truly lack teeth. Examples include the armadillos, sloths, glyptodonts, and anteaters. Opossums are descendants of marsupials that evolved on South America. Another unique group is the rodents that evolved on South America, represented by the capybara and the guinea pig. They are very different from the rodents such as the mice, voles, gophers, rats, and lemmings found in North America. An example of one of the key predators that evolved in South America and migrated to North America is *Titanis*. One look at a reconstruction of the giant, flightless bird *Titanis* leaves little doubt that it ate what it wanted. You can search the Web for an image of this predator.

Not all groups were entirely isolated on South America until the land bridge was established around 4 Mya. Geologic evidence shows the early arrival in South America of groups such as primates and bats, species that have been shown to be fairly mobile between islands or continents through rafting or flight. Primates likely originated in Africa about 40–30 Mya.

Regarding the formation of the Central American land bridge, the geologic record can be used not only for terrestrial deposits (limited to land), but also for focusing on familiar mammals. Before the land bridge, however, evidence indicates a large reef ecosystem extended from the Caribbean, between the continents, and into the Pacific. The tectonic uplift of the land bridge isolated species into the Caribbean and the Pacific reef ecosystems. These have been evolving independently since then. An additional event starting 7–6 Mya was the formation of the Gulf of California. This new habitat effectively expanded the range of the Pacific reef system on the west side of the land bridge.

Virtually all textbooks discuss key evidence for the formation of the land bridge at about 2.5 Mya, during the Great American Interchange. The date was based largely on geologic records from the United States, such as in California (e.g., Anza-Borrego), southern Arizona (111 Ranch), New Mexico (Rio Grande Rift), and Florida. Complementary evidence in South America has been studied from Colombia and Argentina. Recent work in Mexico seems to tell a slightly more involved story than is typically presented.

Several lines of evidence indicate that some animals such as sloths, glyptodonts, and capybaras were in southern Mexico by 3.5 Mya. This suggests that some individuals or groups crossed a nascent land bridge by that time. However, there is currently no evidence from the U.S. data that individuals had migrated north of the border by that time. A pronounced exchange between the continents does not occur until about 2.7 Mya. Groups moving south include horses, dogs, cats, camels, bears, squirrels, gophers, and mastodons. There is little evidence thus far in South America for a strong influx of these groups before about 2 Mya. Examples of animals moving into North America at that time include sloths, glyptodonts, armadillos, *Titanis*, capybaras, and porcupines. Students will determine the above animals by analyzing sample geologic records from strata at various locations on the two continents.

The Great American Interchange is widely written about as an example of land bridge development and the movement of animals. As discussed above for Mexico, the fossil record does show evidence of several fossils that moved between continents at 9–7 Mya. These are all species with current descendants known to swim. Similarly, some groups such as primates, sloths, and rodents show limited radiation from South America onto the Antilles island chain in the Caribbean Sea by 9–7 Mya, somewhat before the land bridge at 4 Myr. These data demonstrate that these groups are certainly able to island-hop without the development of a full land bridge.

Note that the stratigraphic records also reflect two other significant geologic datums. One is that no species of rhinoceros is found in North America after about 4.8 Mya. Rhinos are closely related to horses, two families that originated in North America. The last rhino datum at 4.8 Mya represents an extinction event. The other key datum is a mammoth at about 1.8 Mya in New Mexico. This datum represents the actual find in New Mexico of the first recorded mammoth immigrant arriving from Eurasia in North America across the Bering land bridge.

We still see some of the ramifications of the Great American Interchange in current animal groups. For example, while we think of jaguars and some other cats as denizens of the Central and South American jungles, this family (Felidae) evolved in North America long before heading to jungles. Similarly, camels are an ancient North American family, but the only surviving representatives in the Americas are llamas, vicuñas, and alpacas in South America. In effect, these are simply modern mountain camels, an evolved variant of the many types of plains camels that used to roam and inhabit North America. Another group of camels that migrated to Eurasia across the Bering land bridge are the dromedary and Bactrian camels of the Old World.

Note also that the diagrams and text refer to groups. This is because few individual species persist over the 10 Myr of the geologic sections. With the cat family, for example, several representative species occur in North America and then across the Americas after the interchange. The crux of the issue is that cats show up relatively abruptly in South America. Many sloth species are found in North America, however, once they arrived on the continent. More research or reading about the Great American Interchange will provide more information on many animals that we know.

Materials

For each team of 2 students

colored highlighters (optional)

access to reference materials such as atlases and maps

2 copies of copymaster 13.11, *Six NAM SAM Strat Sections*

Advance Preparation

If you can, project images from the Web sites for students. There are numerous sites with impressive reconstructions of *Titanis* and the mammals participating in the Great American Interchange. Images of glyptodonts (which look like a mammalian turtle with a bike helmet) are a favorite because students never expect that these can be the size of a Volkswagen Beetle. Giant ground sloths (*Megatherium*) and saber-toothed cats are also very popular.

Colored highlighters are a good way to mark occurrences of given fossils in geologic strata. Make them available for student use.

As You Teach

Outcomes and Indicators of Success

By the end of this activity, students should

1. use real data to construct links between the processes of plate tectonics and the records of biological evolution.

   They will demonstrate their ability to construct links by

   - listing animals at six paleontologic sites,
   - determining mammal groups endemic to North and South America based on paleontologic evidence,

SIDEBAR

Shakin' Like Jell-O

Have you ever eaten molded gelatin for dessert or a snack? It's funny how it shakes and quivers. But during a massive earthquake, wiggling back and forth isn't merely funny—it is a good thing for a building with people in it to do. Being rigid and stiff can lead to the collapse of buildings or bridges, especially for those constructed of brick, stone, or cinder blocks. Collapsed buildings have killed tens of thousands of people. It is the job of seismic and civil engineers to ensure that buildings can move during earthquakes. This saves human lives.

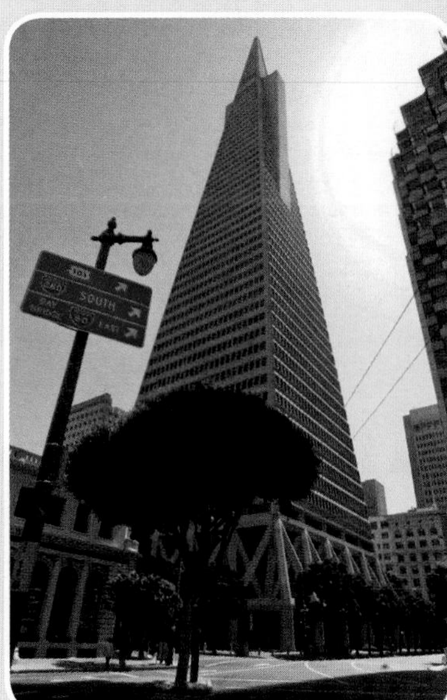

Transamerica Pyramid Building.

So what do seismic or civil engineers do? In areas prone to earthquakes, they have several vital tasks. One is to design buildings that shake like Jell-O! Take the Loma Prieta earthquake in the San Francisco Bay area in 1989. The Transamerica Pyramid Building swayed back and forth several feet. This is exactly what earthquake engineers had hoped it would do.

Another vital task is analyzing existing buildings. Engineers decide how to strengthen them to withstand earthquakes. This is called seismic retrofitting. It is a very important job in cities prone to large earthquakes, such as San Francisco, California; Seattle, Washington; Tokyo, Japan; and Istanbul, Turkey. Seismic retrofitting can save thousands of lives when the next big earthquake hits. Sadly, it's hard to know when that will be.

SRCD

Seismic and civil engineers are also very involved in planning. Their roles include planning for structures such as bridges, stadiums, subways, roadways, and public utilities. These are areas where humans would be at risk during a large earthquake.

So, remember next time you eat gelatin: shakin' like Jell-O during an earthquake is a good thing. Professions of seismic and civil engineers ensure that things keep shakin'.

- reasoning that the sites probably are not at mountaintops because the sediments with the fossils would erode and wear away, and
- using paleontologic data to constrain the formation of the land bridge.

2. analyze the plate tectonic setting and evolution of North, Central, and South America during the past 15 Myr.

   They will demonstrate their ability by

   - comparing maps of the North and South American regions at 12–10 Mya and today,
   - identifying the construction of the Central American land bridge after 12–10 Mya,
   - noting the formation of the Mexican Peninsular Ranges and the Gulf of California, and
   - arguing that the land bridge formed at a convergent plate tectonic boundary between the Cocos and Caribbean plates.

3. use data to better learn key concepts in biological evolution.

   They will demonstrate their ability by

   - studying a prime example of a cause of geographic isolation and endemism,
   - identifying the location and timescales for the construction of a continental land bridge in Central America,
   - studying an example of geographic isolation of a marine reef ecosystem into Pacific and Caribbean parts,
   - looking at evidence in the geologic record for immigration of mammoths to new continents from South America and Siberia,
   - discerning evidence in the geologic record on a continent for an extinction event of the rhinoceros family, and
   - answering questions about the relationship between immigration and plate tectonic events.

4. develop further skills in the abilities and understandings of scientific inquiry.

   They will demonstrate their skills by

   - critically evaluating a question that they designed in the first activity of the chapter,
   - analyzing a data set containing dimensions of space and time and making inferences from those data,
   - using data to develop a model for a past ecosystem and evaluating changes in that ecosystem and its inhabitants across time,
   - using fossil data to establish constraints and temporal limits for a system with interdependencies, and
   - developing alternative and valid explanations for data that do not directly relate to the formation of a land bridge (rhinoceros, mammoth).

Strategies

Getting Started

You might start by asking the class to list some ways that earth processes like tectonics affect animals. What do fossil plants and animals tell you about a location in the past? Can students identify any mammals that used to live in North America but do not live here today? How did animals get to continents after the age of the dinosaurs?

Continue by reading the introduction as a class. Follow up on questions that the students have that

Answers to Reflect and Connect Question 3 are on TE page 676.

3. Yellowstone National Park is famous for many things. One is large mammals. At Yellowstone, visitors can see bison grazing in the park. But during the last volcanic eruption of the Yellowstone hot spot about 0.6 Mya, a much larger bison was present on the Great Plains—*Bison latifrons*. Evidence shows that this species is ancestral to the modern bison, *Bison bison*. What does it mean for *B. latifrons* to be **ancestral** to the current bison, *B. bison*, in Yellowstone?

ELABORATE

Building Bridges

Have you ever seen an armadillo or an opossum? They may seem like typical North American mammals. But what does the geologic record say about animals like armadillos and opossums in North America? Can we trace records of other animal families in the geologic record? What might the geologic record say about animals on other continents, such as zebras in Africa or kangaroos in Australia? Can plate tectonics explain the occurrences of different families of animals on different continents?

In *Building Bridges*, you will investigate real evidence for why certain mammal families are found on certain continents. You and your partner will analyze how plate tectonics affects ecosystems and how it plays a key role in the geologic record and evolution of mammals. This might even include some animals that are now common pets. Work with a partner to investigate geologic evidence for the history of mammals on North and South America.

Materials

For each team of 2 students

colored highlighters

access to reference materials such as atlases and maps

2 *Six Strata from North and South America* handouts

Process and Procedure

1. Study the 2 maps in figure 13.20. Use a T-table to list how they are similar and different. You may wish to use an atlas to identify geographic features that you do not know.
2. Review your T-table and the major differences between the maps. Explain the differences.

appear to interest them. Then have them join with a partner to begin *Process and Procedure.*

Process and Procedure

Materials

For each team of 2 students

colored highlighters (optional)

access to reference materials such as atlases and maps

2 copies of copymaster 13.11, *Six NAM SAM Strat Sections*

In Step 1, student pairs study the maps in figure 13.20 in the student book and list similarities and differences. They explain the differences between the maps in Step 2. They should note main features such as the formation of the Central American land bridge, rifting of the Mexican Peninsular Ranges away from Mexico, the formation of the Great Lakes (after the most recent ice age), and the change in the drainage pattern of the paleo–Amazon River. At 15–10 Mya, rivers in northern South America drained north to a submerged part of the continent. There was no Amazon River at that time. Be open to students' ideas about what the differences might mean.

In Step 3, student pairs consider where reef ecosystems similar to those of the Caribbean might be found. Geologic evidence shows that the reef ecosystem would have been continuous between North and South America at 12–10 Mya. Students can predict that it would have been segmented sometime before today. The goal here is to get students thinking about how marine ecosystems, and not just the terrestrial ecosystems, are affected by tectonics.

Student teams analyze geologic strata in Step 4 from 4 locations in North America and 2 locations in South America. They list and tally the number of animals recorded as fossils at 1 of those sites in Step 5. In Step 6, they continue analyzing the fossil evidence to determine groups of animals that are endemic to North America and to South America. This analysis continues in Step 7. Encourage students to use a strategy of tables to help organize their analysis.

Answers to Steps 4–7, SE pages 679–681

4. A key concept and "rule" in earth science is that for sedimentary and volcanic rocks, the older rocks are found on the bottom of a section of strata. The layers get younger moving up, with the youngest at the top. This is called the principle of superposition. In rare cases, sequences can be broken or end up out of order because of fault movements, but the change must have happened after the layers were deposited.
5. Students can tally animal groups per site with a 7-column table showing animals down the first column, then totals in columns 2–7. They can then identify those sites with the most and the fewest representative groups. The Florida site is rich in fauna, with 11 representatives shown. (In reality, the total number of distinct fossils is much greater, likely on the order of several hundred for the period 0–12 Myr.)

Answers to Steps 4–7 are on TE pages 679–680.

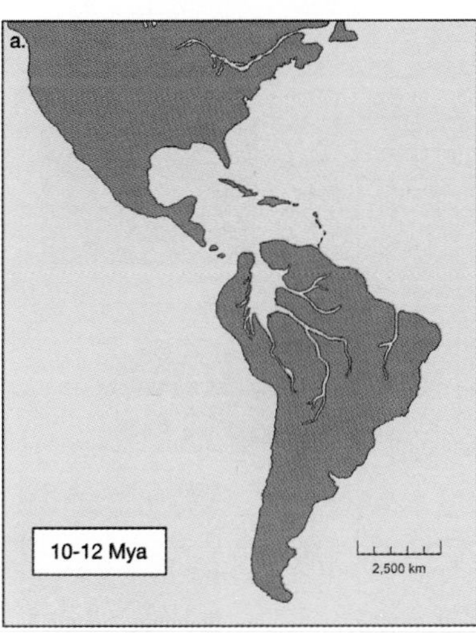

▲ **Figure 13.20 North and South America at 2 geologic times.** The maps show the outlines of North America and South America at (a) 12–10 Mya and (b) today. What changes do you see in the landforms over approximately 10 Myr?

3. The Caribbean region has hosted a coral reef ecosystem for at least 20–30 Myr. Use the maps in figure 13.20 to explain where else you think the reef ecosystem might be found during that time.

   Would the organisms in that reef ecosystem have been isolated in the Caribbean during that time period?

4. Figure 13.21 shows geologic sections (rock layers, or strata) with fossil finds at 6 sites in North and South America. Obtain a copy of this figure from your teacher. The strata span from today back to 10 Mya. At a given site, are older rocks found at a deeper or shallower position? Explain how you know.

   The singular form of strata is stratum.

5. Pick a site in figure 13.21 and make a list of all the mammals recorded at that site. Which sites have the most mammals? Which have the fewest?

   Making a table that shows mammals per site may help you here. Also check that you can locate the states and countries where each stratum is found on figure 13.20.

6a. Endemics would only be found in a certain region. Students could determine this by grouping the sites by continent and by a certain time period, such as 6–8 Myr. They would then investigate patterns of occurrence, which would show animals like opossums, glyptodonts, sloths, capybaras, and porcupines restricted (endemic) to South America.

6b. Students should pick Colombia and Argentina to study for South America endemics. They would search the bottom part of the strata, as groups from North America appear to be part of the fauna in the tops of the strata. This makes it a little harder to see the purely South American endemics. The other 4 sites are part of North America.

6c. South American endemics include armadillos, porcupines, glyptodonts, opossums, capybaras, and sloths. North American endemics might include cats, camels, dogs, and horses. Because of the animals' positions and sudden change in status (the disappearance of the rhino; the appearance of the mammoth), students would need additional information to evaluate mammoth and rhinoceros families.

6d. Step 6c said "might" because at this point we don't have any information about whether North America was isolated as an "island continent" in the same way that South America was. We cannot see the top of North America in figure 13.20 in the student book. In fact, North America is connected to Siberia by the Bering land bridge. This enabled immigrant animals to "show up" in the rocks of North America, such as mammoths at 1.8–1.6 Mya.

7a. South American animals are first recorded in Arizona, Florida, and New Mexico about 2.7–2.5 Mya. In a sense, the geologic sections in figure 13.21 in the student book are just like a table or list of when each fossil was recorded, as a function of depth. Some evidence suggests sloths and glyptodonts arrived in Mexico by 3.5 Mya.

7b. One explanation is migration through Central America after Central America had formed. Evidence for this is the movement of animal groups on 2 continents in opposite directions at the same time. The land bridge was a 2-way street.

7c. North American animals are first recorded in Colombia and Argentina about 2.7–2.5 Mya. The geologic strata in figure 13.21 in the student book shows where and when each animal is recorded, effectively forming a table with "columns" of data at different depths. (Indeed, some geologic strata are called geologic columns.) An interesting scientific question is to revisit some of these sites to see if evidence was missed for a trickle of early arrivals from North America to South America by 3.5 Mya. This is the time for evidence of a trickle into Mexico.

7d. One explanation is migration through Central America after it had formed. Evidence for this would be the movement of animal groups in 2 directions at the same time.

In Steps 8 and 9, students consider a different record of evidence from 2 other groups. For the rhinoceros family, the sudden disappearance at about 4.8 Mya indicates geologic evidence of an extinction event. The rhinoceros family is unknown in South America, and no rocks in North America younger than 4.8 Mya have ever produced a rhinoceros. In contrast, the sudden

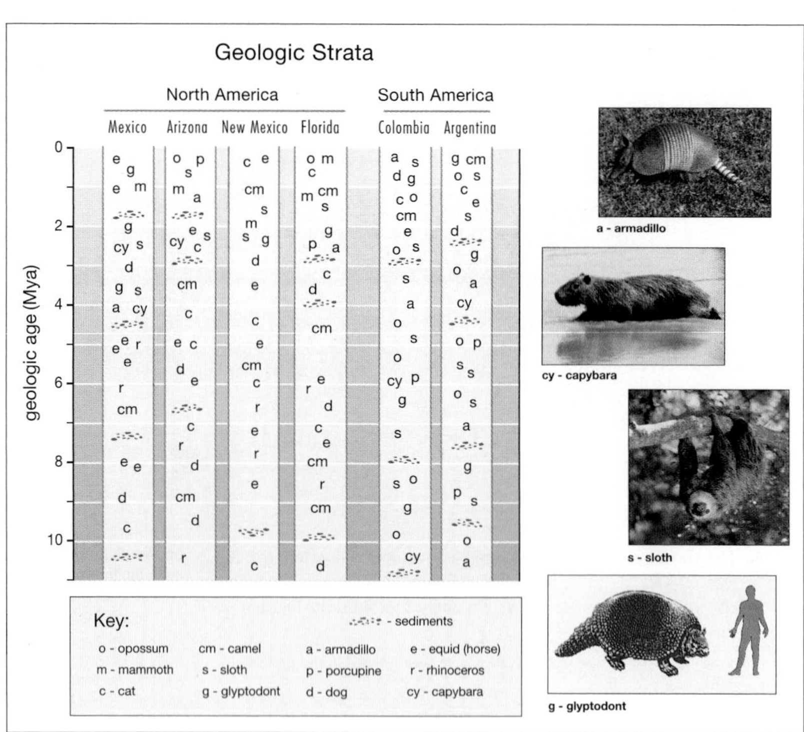

▲ **Figure 13.21 Six geologic strata from North and South America.** The fossil finds from 6 locations (across top) are a function of geologic age (left). The key lists 12 representatives of animal families from North and South America. Current examples (right) are the sloth, the capybara (a large rodent), and the armadillo. Glyptodonts are extinct.

6. Animals or plants that are restricted to a specific region are called **endemic**. Follow Steps 6a–d to evaluate what animals were endemic to South America 12–10 Mya.
   a. Determine with your partner how to tell whether an animal is endemic to a continent based on the geologic record. Explain this strategy in your science notebook from the geologic strata.
   b. Explain which sites you would study in order to list the mammals that were endemic to South America. Would you search the tops or bottoms of those strata? Write your best response in your science notebook.

680 | Unit 3 Moving Matter

appearance of mammoths in North America at 1.8–1.6 Mya (well after the Great American Interchange), must relate to a distinct event of migration to North America. Indeed, mammoths are found in the Eurasian record both before and after 1.8–1.6 Mya, arguing that mammoths crossed a Bering land bridge to North America at about 1.8 Mya.

Answers to Steps 8–9, SE page 681

8. The rhinoceros family shows a different pattern of abruptly terminating in the fossil record. This is evidence for an extinction event on the continent. The fossil record has many other extinction examples at many other times. Indeed, even though rhinos evolved on North America, there is no evidence for a single rhino fossil after about 4.8 Mya. Students can then draw the reasonable inference that some members of the rhino family had migrated to Eurasia before the extinction event in North America.
9. Rather than abruptly disappearing, mammoths abruptly appear. They could not have come from South America, as there is no evidence for mammoths in South America before 2 Mya. Rather, mammoths came from somewhere else. Students can infer this as a possibility, but they will not know that mammoths arrived in North America over the Bering land bridge. As mentioned earlier, mammoths are found in Eurasia both before, during, and after their arrival in North America 1.8–1.6 Mya.

c. Make a T-table showing animals that were endemic to South America and animals that might be endemic to North America.

d. Explain why you think Step 6c said animals that "might" be endemic to North America.

7. Answer Questions 7a–d for the animal groups endemic to South America 12–10 Mya.
   a. When do South American animals arrive in North America? List specific evidence from fossils in the strata in figure 13.21.
   b. How can you explain the arrival of South American endemics in North America?
   c. When do North American animals arrive in South America?
   d. How can you explain the arrival of North American animals in South America?
8. Examine the geologic record of the rhinoceros family in figure 13.21. What is the time period of when they are found? What inferences can you make about the history of the rhinoceros family?

It is helpful to highlight all fossil finds of rhinos. A relative of the rhinoceros family is the horse.

9. Based on figure 13.21, make some inferences about the mammoth family. What is the earliest evidence of its appearance in the fossil record?

It is helpful to highlight mammoths in another color.

10. Discuss with your partner the concept of a **land bridge**. Consider Questions 10a–f related to land bridges and write specific examples from figures in the activity.
    a. What do you think is the land bridge between North America and South America?
    b. When do you think the land bridge formed? What is your evidence?
    c. Which animals did or did not use a land bridge?
    d. Which tectonic plates were involved in the land bridge? Use a map to describe the tectonic setting of the land bridge between North and South America.

Consult figure 13.9 and draw a simple sketch of the plates involved.

    e. Which of the 3 main types of tectonic settings best applies to the Central American land bridge?
    f. What process resulted in the Central American land bridge? Is this consistent with the tectonic setting? Base your answers on your responses to Questions 10a–e.

Chapter 13 Time for Change 681

Student pairs explore and consider more explicitly the concept of a land bridge in Step 10.

Answers to Step 10, SE page 681

10a. Students can now link the actual bridge that they have been inferring and studying with a real location. It is the region of Central America (Costa Rica, Panama).

10b. From the maps, the bridge had to have formed after 12–10 Mya and before today. From the geologic strata, fossil evidence indicates an interchange by 2.7 Mya, so a continuous bridge is inferred by that time. Some evidence from Mexico indicates periods of land connection or animals swimming occurring by 3.5 Mya. This is a current topic of research and scientific discussion.

10c. There is geologic evidence that all animals in the figure except the rhino used the Central American land bridge when it formed. For example, each South American endemic is represented in the top of the fossil record in North America, and vice versa. Rhinos could not have used the bridge, as they were extinct in North America before the land bridge was formed.

10d. The Central American land bridge resides in a zone of convergence or collision extending between North and South America. Evidence of convergence is the pushed up mountain chain between the 2 continents. From a tectonic map (e.g., copymaster 13.5, *Tectonic Boundaries, Hot Spots, and Plate Velocities*, or figure 13.9 in the student book), convergence is expected between the Caribbean and Cocos plates.

10e. A zone of tectonic convergence best applies, not a zone of divergence or transform motion.

10f. Students should infer uplift within a zone of collision. This is consistent with the tectonic setting and collision between the Caribbean and Cocos plates.

Answers to Reflect and Connect, SE page 682

1. Give students the chance to critically evaluate their questions from the engage activity, *Mile High Time Machine*. They should now have a better basis with which to try to answer the question. Moreover, returning to a question is part of the scientific process. It is typical to return to a question when more evidence or data are obtained and revise earlier ideas in light of those new data. It is also possible that students still won't be able to answer the question. Ask the teams what more information they think they need to be able to answer the question.
2. The geologic strata show animals recorded from a sampling of the rock layers at a site. This typically is only a fraction of all the animals that lived in an ecosystem. Moreover, we might expect sampling to favor animals that were large and easy to find as fossils or that were common in the ecosystem. In North America, for example, horse remains are much more typical than carnivore remains, like those of a cat. This is probably because horses are common herbivores that move in herds in lowlands where geologic deposits occur. As carnivores are at higher trophic levels, cats are much rarer, and some species are relatively solitary for much of their lives. Organisms at the top of the food chain are less abundant than organisms such as grazers, which are at the bottom of the food chain. Similarly, it might be difficult to find small, fragile remains of animals such as shrews, moles, and mice or other rodents.
3. Rocks at the tops of mountains are subject to constant erosion. This means that material is constantly being stripped away. In contrast, the geologic strata in figure 13.21 in the student book have a continuous record of rock. There is no evidence for erosion, such as occurs at the tops of mountains.
4. The Bering Sea has an extensive region with water depths less than 100–150 m that lies between Siberia and Alaska. Thus, changes in sea level are sufficient either to have a bridge (Last Glacial Maximum) or not to have a bridge, such as during our current interglacial. A lowering of sea level by only 100 m is sufficient to expose the bridge. No tectonic uplift is needed.
5. Students have investigated a number of locations on Earth during this chapter. By making a list, they learn a little geography in this chapter, as well as earth science. Examples include the Rocky Mountains in Colorado, the Lower 48 states, the Bahamas, Papua New Guinea, Barbados, New Zealand, the Himalaya, the Middle East, the Appalachians, the Alps, the East African Rift, the San Andreas Fault, and Africa, as well as many others.

EVALUATE

Falling into the Ocean

Activity Overview

The scenario of a massive earthquake in Southern California is used to evaluate whether the old cliché holds true—that California is ready to "fall into the ocean." Like many clichés, people say it, but does it really make any sense? Could a massive chunk of land cleave and sink, in one fell swoop? It is easy

Reflect and Connect

Work individually on the following tasks. Write ideas and evidence in your science notebook. Be prepared to contribute your ideas to a class discussion.

1. In the engage activity, *Mile High Time Machine*, you developed a question about climate, elevation, or topography related to figures 13.1 and the chapter opener. These show the Denver area at different geologic times. Write in your science notebook how you would answer that question now.

Some questions aren't always easy to answer, or they take a while to figure out. Even a little progress, though, moves you toward a better understanding.

2. Consider figure 13.21 again. Do you think each site indicates all the animals that were living at that site at a geologic time? Explain why or why not.
3. Recall the geologic strata in figure 13.21. Would you expect the sites to be near the tops of mountains? Write why or why not in your science notebook.
4. Refer to the image of the Bering land bridge in chapter 12 (figure 12.10). Compare the causes of that land bridge with the development of the Central America land bridge discussed in this activity.
5. Make a list of all the geographic areas that you have studied in this chapter. Decide whether to list them by city, country, continent, or tectonic plate.

EVALUATE

Falling into the Ocean

"This just in from our affiliate station in Los Angeles. A massive earthquake has just struck Southern California. Initial geologic reports are a magnitude of 8.6 and an epicenter in the rugged mountains 15 miles east of San Diego. Reports of damage are coming in from Los Angeles, San Diego, and south to Ensenada, Mexico. It's too early to tell about human casualties. This earthquake is sure to rekindle fears, once again, that California is going to fall into the ocean."

You've probably heard that California is going to "fall into the ocean." Could this really happen with a massive earthquake, even if it was "the Big One"? What sort of changes might there be? Could earthquakes affect the many types of habitats and ecosystems in coastal California? While the short-term effects could be catastrophic, what does the future—the geologic future—hold for the Golden State?

to dismiss this and say of course it couldn't. Using geologic evidence to analyze why such eventualities would not happen is a skill that students have been developing in this program. The goal now is to use evidence to say exactly why.

Students will use concepts in plate tectonics to critically evaluate the question, "In a massive earthquake, could the state of California break off and fall into the ocean?" They will make a more astute prediction for what happens during earthquakes along the West Coast. The context for this is analyzing the 6–8-Myr history of rifting in the Gulf of California and the formation of the Mexican Peninsular Ranges.

The rift in the center of the Gulf of California changes to a strike-slip tectonic boundary to the north, in California along the San Andreas Fault. Students' predictions will let them develop a rather different view of California; the predicted location of Los Angeles, California; and the widening of the Gulf of California over the next 20 Myr. Moreover, they will be able to predict changes in ecosystems that would be predicted from the northward movement of the deserts of the Mexican Peninsular Ranges. This process will help them understand how past changes have brought us to our current distribution of ecosystems on the continent.

Answers to Step 4 are on TE pages 686–686b.

In *Falling into the Ocean*, you will work with your teammates to address questions like those. You will become a geology team making real predictions about tectonic and ecological changes in California and northwestern Mexico. You'll have the data and evidence to argue whether or not California is really poised to fall into the ocean.

Materials

For each team of 3 students

3 pairs of scissors

colored pencils

clear tape

several sheets of blank white paper

1 calculator

1 ruler

6 *Tectonic Map of PAC and NAM* handouts

3 *Falling into the Ocean Scoring Rubric* handouts

Process and Procedure

1. Review the *Falling into the Ocean Scoring Rubric* before you begin the activity. This will help you understand your teacher's expectations for your work. You will do this as a class.
2. Work with your teammates to critically evaluate this question: "In a massive earthquake, could the state of California break off and fall into the ocean?"
   a. Discuss each teammate's answer to the question.
   b. Write on a blank sheet of paper whether you think that California could fall into the ocean. If you think it could, record the reasons why and describe what California would look like afterward. If you think it couldn't, make a list of reasons why not.

Another strategy is to make a T-table on the blank sheet of paper outlining "reasons for" and "reasons against."

   c. Turn in this paper to your teacher.
3. Work with your teammates to complete the following reading. It gives some information to help you analyze whether California might fall into the ocean.
4. Work with your teammates to determine how the Mexican Peninsular Ranges and the Gulf of California formed. Follow Steps 4a–d in your reconstruction.
   a. Consider the movements of the Pacific and North American plates. Use a vector to demonstrate how the movements could form the Gulf of California.

Before You Teach

Background Information

The Mexican Peninsular Ranges are not part of the United States, yet they are one of the major geographic features of the continent. This feature is a peninsula nearly twice the length of Florida. The Mexican Peninsular Ranges and the Gulf of California are also linked closely with many geologic features that extend into California. Terrestrial ecosystems on the peninsula are largely desert. The adjacent marine ecosystems in the Gulf of California and the Pacific Ocean host rich, tropical marine ecosystems. Many ancestral species in this coral reef ecosystem were isolated from similar species in the Caribbean Ocean by the tectonic uplift of the Central American land bridge at about 2.7–2.5 Mya.

You may have heard the Mexican Peninsular Ranges also referred to as Baja California, or Baja. However, this is considered a derogatory term, so the activity refers to the mountain range, the Peninsular Ranges, that extend from the tip of the peninsula into the coastal mountains of Southern California.

The Gulf of California is dominated by a system of linked spreading ridges and transform faults. This system is typical of divergent tectonic boundaries. These tectonic features accommodate the northward movement of the Pacific Plate relative to the North American Plate of about 50 mm/yr. At about the Salton Sea east of San Diego, California, this system of ridges and transform faults changes to a big transform fault (or more accurately, a transform fault system) between the Pacific and North American plates. Running much of the length of California is the *San Andreas Fault.* The fault is the main seismic, or earthquake, hazard on the continent. Los Angeles is actually on the Pacific Plate (west side of the fault), whereas cities like San Francisco and Oakland, California, are on the North American Plate (east side of the fault), if only by a few hundred meters in some areas.

This part of North America also shows striking changes in important ecosystems. While some differences in rainfall are due to elevation, the main changes relate to increases in rainfall. These latitudinal changes are pronounced going from south to north, from the Mexican Peninsular Ranges, to central California, and then to northern California. Figure 13.23 in the student book shows the progression of ecosystems moving from the deserts of the Peninsular Ranges to the moist, temperate, coniferous rain forests of northern California.

The student analysis is based on the assumption that the slip between the Pacific and North American plates will remain localized approximately on the San Andreas Fault. But it is not clear that this pattern of tectonic deformation will continue for 20 Myr. For example, recent evidence shows some localization of slip on the east side of the Sierra Nevada. If all the slip of the San Andreas Fault localized there, would the Gulf of California penetrate northward along the California-Nevada border? That could happen, but not for a very long time.

Materials

For each team of 3 students

3 pairs of scissors
colored pencils
clear tape
several sheets of blank white paper
1 calculator
1 ruler
3 copies of copymaster 13.1, *Scoring Rubric for Falling into the Ocean*
6 copies of copymaster 13.12, *Tectonic Map of PAC and NAM*

Advance Preparation

Gather materials that will help students complete their reconstructions. Make 3 copies of copymaster 13.1, *Scoring Rubric for Falling into the Ocean* and 6 copies of copymaster 13.12, *Tectonic Map of PAC and NAM* for each team.

Review the rubric's expectations for reconstructing the plate boundaries and the progression of ecosystems as the Peninsular Ranges slide north. A key part of the rubric is that students must show their work for all calculations. The rubric can also be shared with parents to show your expectations for the chapter.

As You Teach

Outcomes and Indicators of Success

By the end of this activity, students should

1. demonstrate the use of basic elements of plate tectonics.

   They will demonstrate their ability by

   - comparing the relationship between continental-scale geographic features and tectonic features,
   - using simple vector analysis of the tectonic boundary between the Pacific and North American plates,
   - completing predictions for the evolution of a boundary with rift and strike-slip components of motion, and
   - showing a future location of Los Angeles in a redwood forest north of San Francisco.

2. be able to show the interdependence between plate tectonics and some ecosystems.

   They will demonstrate their ability by

   - explaining whether they think earthquakes have an impact on ecosystems,
   - showing with a simple calculation that the Gulf of California and its reef ecosystem had not begun to form by 20 Mya,

READING

Tectonic Changes in the Southwest

It is a striking feature of our North American continent. It's shaped like Florida, yet nearly twice as long. And it's part of Mexico. Do you know what it is? It's a long spit of land surrounded by water—a **peninsula**—called the Mexican Peninsular Ranges (figure 13.22). Some maps show this peninsula as Baja California.

But the Peninsular Ranges are more than just a long spit of land. They host a unique desert ecosystem that extends from sea level to jagged peaks. The peninsula is bound by the warm waters of the Pacific Ocean to the west and the Gulf of California to the east. The Gulf of California harbors a rich reef ecosystem. The gulf is also a valuable breeding and wintering ground for many larger fish, sharks, seabirds, and mammals.

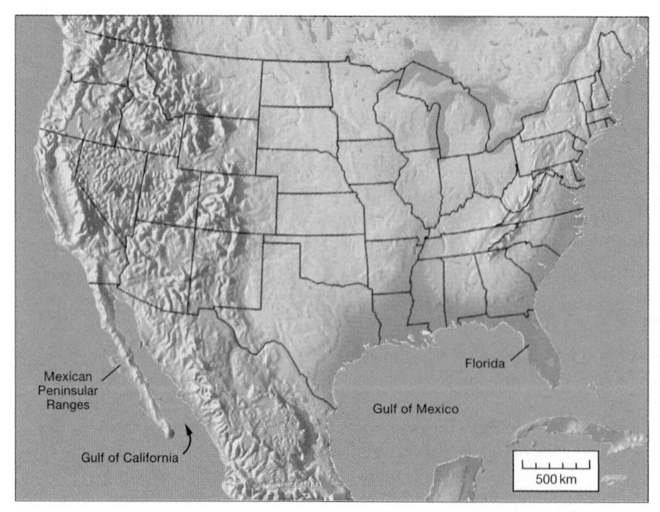

▲ **Figure 13.22 North America with Mexico's Peninsular Ranges.** This map of the southern part of North America shows the location and scale of the Mexican Peninsular Ranges and the Gulf of California. This peninsula is nearly twice the size of Florida, one of the United States's largest states.

684 | Unit 3 Moving Matter

- showing with a simple calculation that the Gulf of California and its reef ecosystem will be at least 1,000 km wider in another 30 Myr,
- representing the succession of terrestrial ecosystems from arid to chaparral and mixed coniferous forests (higher elevations) as the Peninsular Ranges move to higher latitudes along the San Andreas Fault, and
- showing the Coast Ranges of Southern California being replaced by moist Pacific Northwest rain forest.

3. develop further skills in the abilities and understandings of scientific inquiry.

They will demonstrate their skills by

- comparing common ideas in lore (e.g., the Big One, falling into the ocean) with concepts in science;
- using logic, skepticism, and common sense to evaluate whether California could fall into the ocean;
- using scientific data and evidence to evaluate whether California could fall into the ocean;
- using additional evidence to revise a scientific explanation;
- comparing a model of falling into the ocean with other models based on plate tectonics;
- communicating and discussing contrasting models using evidence and observations;
- using mathematics to construct and explain a tectonic model; and
- drawing sketches to depict ideas and tectonic models for the past (10 Mya) and future (30 Myr from now) for the Mexican Peninsular Ranges.

The rugged desert mountains of the Peninsular Ranges go farther north than the Gulf of California. They form a long chain of mountains that connects with the Coast Ranges east of San Diego and Los Angeles, California. In fact, rugged, tectonically active mountains extend along the entire West Coast to Canada.

Moving north from the tip of the peninsula, the mountains pass through a sequence of ecosystems (figure 13.23). This is due to increasing precipitation (rainfall) as one moves north (see the key in figure 13.23). For example, upon going from Mexico to Southern California, the desert ecosystem gives way to chaparral at low elevations and mixed chaparral and coniferous forests at higher elevations.

Farther north, the Coast Ranges undergo another ecosystem change. Central California is largely mixed chaparral, oaks, and grasslands. Then from central California north, chaparral and mixed coniferous forests give way to a much more humid, coniferous rain forest. This transition occurs in central California (figure 13.23). This rain forest is dense, hosting plants such as ferns, Douglas fir, and coast redwood (*Sequoia sempervirens*). You learned about pollen from redwoods in the last chapter.

This region hosts an active tectonic boundary. Figure 13.24 shows that the boundary lies between the Pacific Plate and the North American Plate. It is localized in the center of the Gulf of California as a rifting or opening gulf. Farther north, the rift zone changes to the renowned San Andreas Fault. This fault trends northward to the east of San Diego and Los Angeles, extending through the San Francisco Bay area. The San Andreas Fault then enters the Pacific Ocean in northern California. It also passes through a region where tens of millions of people live.

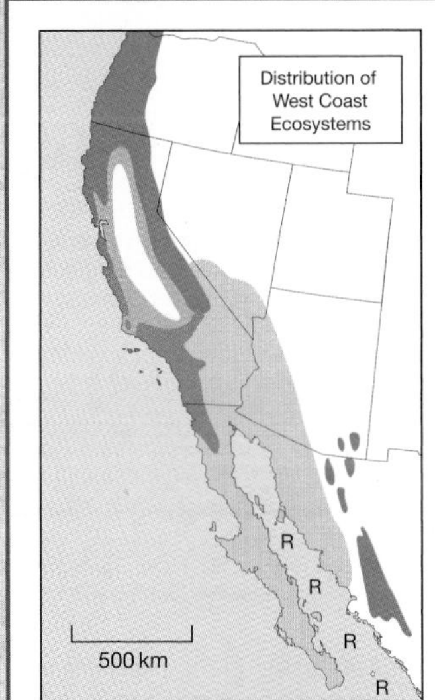

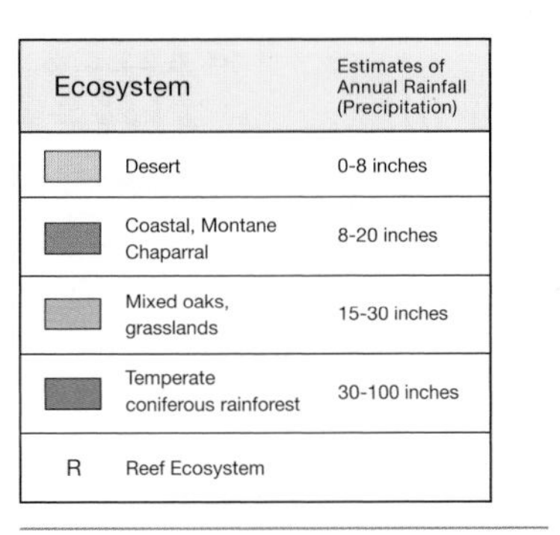

Ecosystem	Estimates of Annual Rainfall (Precipitation)
Desert	0-8 inches
Coastal, Montane Chaparral	8-20 inches
Mixed oaks, grasslands	15-30 inches
Temperate coniferous rainforest	30-100 inches
R Reef Ecosystem	

▲ **Figure 13.23 Ecosystems of southwestern North America.** This map shows the major ecosystems of southwestern North America from the Mexican Peninsular Ranges to northern California. The key matches ecosystems with estimates for annual rainfall.

Chapter 13 Time for Change 685

Strategies

Getting Started

Getting started involves two steps. First, have a volunteer read the introduction to the activity, which is a television announcer's report. Ask the class what it thinks of the scenario. Is it realistic? Why or why not? It is fine for students to disagree at this point, but in the activity they will be challenged to give geologic evidence of why it isn't realistic. This task is the essence of science, as well as tectonic reconstruction and prediction. It demonstrates that the students have an understanding of how a system is changing and is predicted to change with time.

Students might not be familiar with the Mexican Peninsular Ranges or the Gulf of California. These are major geographic features of our continent. Locate them on a map.

Process and Procedure

Materials

For each team of 3 students

3 pairs of scissors
colored pencils
clear tape
several sheets of blank white paper
1 calculator
1 ruler
3 copies of copymaster 13.1, *Scoring Rubric for Falling into the Ocean*
6 copies of copymaster 13.12, *Tectonic Map of PAC and NAM*

TRCD

In Step 1, review copymaster 13.1, *Scoring Rubric for Falling into the Ocean*, so that students are clear about your expectations. They will then be better prepared to complete the activity.

Students evaluate and write ideas in Step 2 about the prospects of California breaking off and falling into the ocean. They do this with 2 teammates. Teams record ideas and reasons on a sheet of paper and hand it in. They will critically evaluate their preliminary ideas in Step 7.

In Step 3, students and their teammates complete a reading on the Peninsular Ranges and the Gulf of California. This reading discusses valuable, rich marine ecosystems in the Gulf of California, ecosystems from south to north along the West Coast, and the tectonic setting of this region. It is important that students note the latitudinal changes in ecosystem from the southern tip of the Mexican Peninsular Ranges to northern California. These are from desert; to coastal and mountain chaparral; to mixed chaparral, oak, and grasslands; to moist, temperate coniferous forests. The latter extend from the San Francisco Bay Area north.

Step 4 involves reconstructing the Mexican Peninsular Ranges. Students turn in their reconstructions, which show that the Gulf of California first started forming after 10 Mya. There are a few ways to demonstrate this. Two possible views are shown at 5 and 10 Mya ago in figure T13.11. As the gulf opened, new shallow marine waters formed, establishing new reef ecosystems that extended from the Caribbean region. Students learned in the elaborate activity, *Building Bridges*, that there was no Central American land bridge until about 2.5 Mya. They might postulate that reef communities moved into the Gulf of California after 10 Mya.

Answers to Step 4, SE pages 683–687

4a. The representation of vectors should show a movement of the Peninsular Ranges to the northwest, away from where it had been "docking" against Mexico (figure T13.11). This outer fringe of Mexico was actually ripped from the Sierra Madre Occidental, the western mountain belt of Mexico.

4b. Students will use the current plate velocity of the Pacific Plate to project where the Peninsular Ranges were 5 and 10 Mya. A possible representation is shown in figure T13.11 for 5 and 10 Mya. The gulf would not yet have been opening at 10 Mya.

4d. The astute student geologist will predict no. From the simple reconstruction, there is no evidence that the Gulf of California had begun rifting and opening by 10 Mya. Similarly, for research geologists, there also is no evidence.

Students make predictions about tectonic movements in Step 5. This includes predicting how far to the northwest the Pacific Plate will move in 20 Myr. Figure T13.12 shows predicted positions for 10 and 20 Myr for a Pacific Plate velocity of 50 mm/yr. Students demonstrate that the Gulf of California will move north as the Peninsular Ranges continue rifting away from Mexico. In 20 Myr, Los Angeles (with or without *Homo sapiens*!) will reside north of San Francisco.

Tectonic Changes in the Southwest, continued

Due to a history of big earthquakes, the San Andreas Fault is watched closely. Current work shows that the Pacific Plate is sliding to the northwest at about 50 mm/yr. This is not fast if the sliding is steady. The risk for massive earthquakes arises when the fault locks up. The result can be sudden, massive lurches along the fault every 100–200 years. Events like this probably caused the great 1906 San Francisco earthquake and even many other large earthquakes along the fault in the past 20–25 Myr.

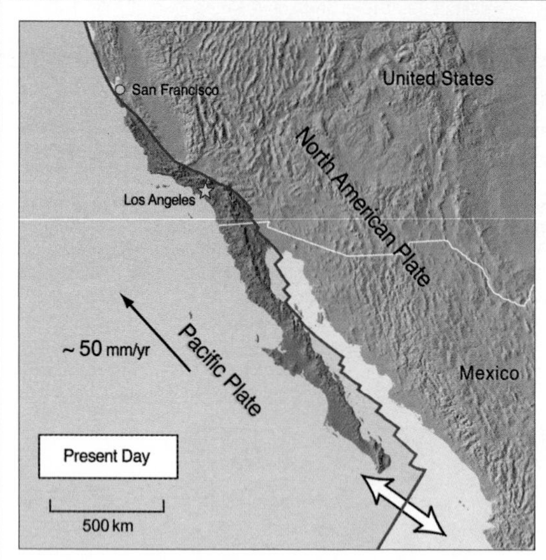

▲ **Figure 13.24 Tectonic map of the Pacific and North American plates.** The region shown extends from the tip of the Mexican Peninsular Ranges to northern California. Rifting in the Gulf of California changes to the north and slips along the San Andreas Fault. The vector shows the magnitude and direction of the Pacific Plate (in millimeters per year) relative to North America. Northward movement of the Pacific Plate causes a spreading ridge (red) in bottom left.

Recall the steps in the explain activity that reversed the motion for North and South America and closed the Atlantic Ocean. This was like "playing the movie backward" with the Atlantic Ocean.

b. Use your handout *Tectonic Map of PAC and NAM* to sketch the coastline of the Mexican Peninsular Ranges at intervals of about 5 and 10 Mya.

686 Unit 3 Moving Matter

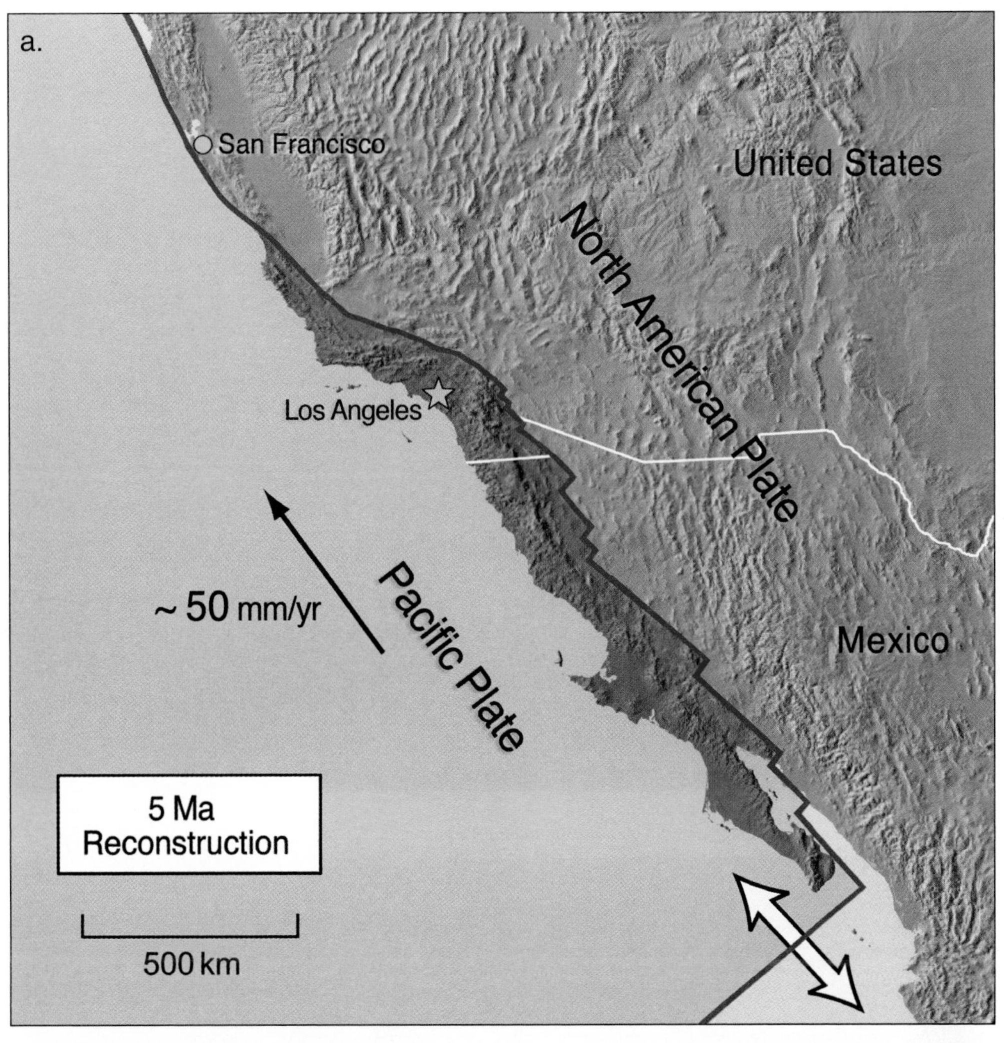

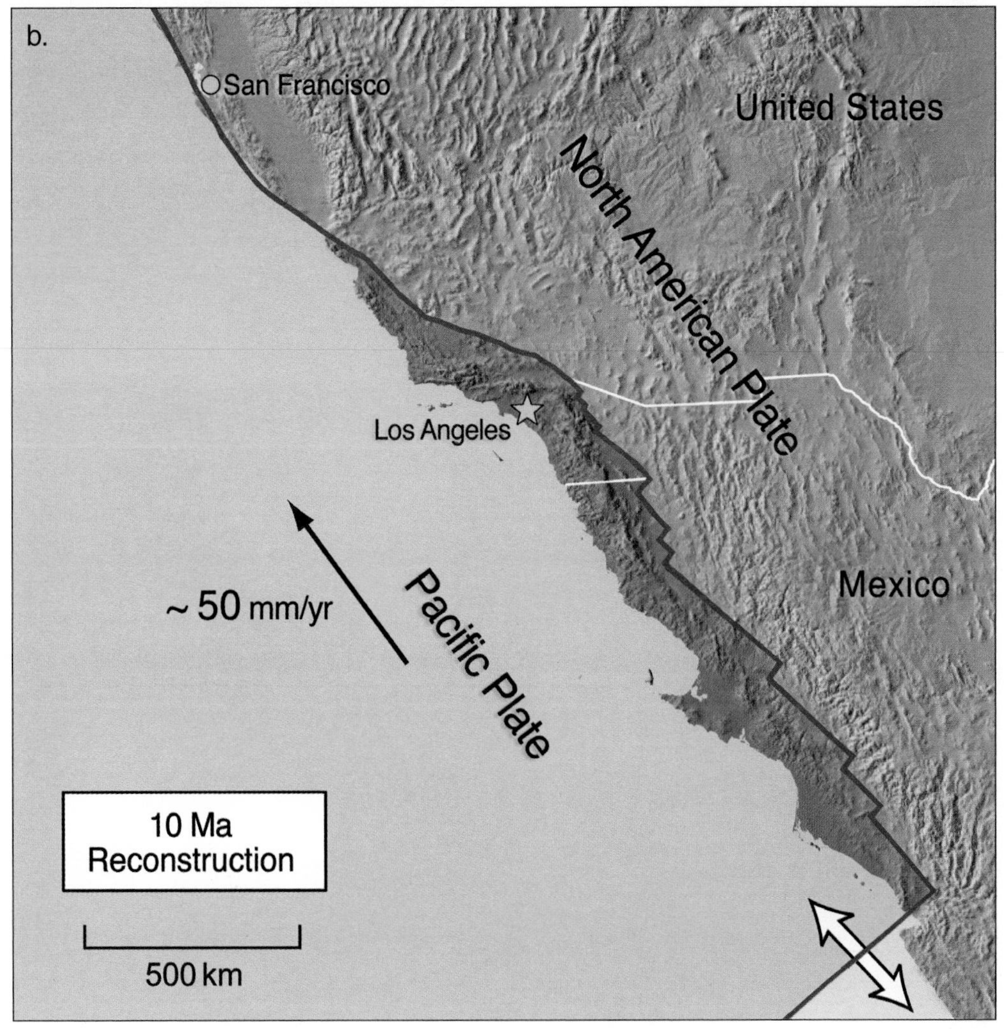

◀ **Figure T13.11 The Peninsular Ranges at 5 and 10 Mya.** The reconstructions show what the Peninsular Ranges and the Gulf of California might have looked like (a) 5 Mya and (b) 10 Mya. Note the much smaller size of the Gulf of California at 5 Mya and that it did not exist at 10 Mya. Note that at 10 Mya, some areas for what became Los Angeles reside south of the current United States–Mexico border.

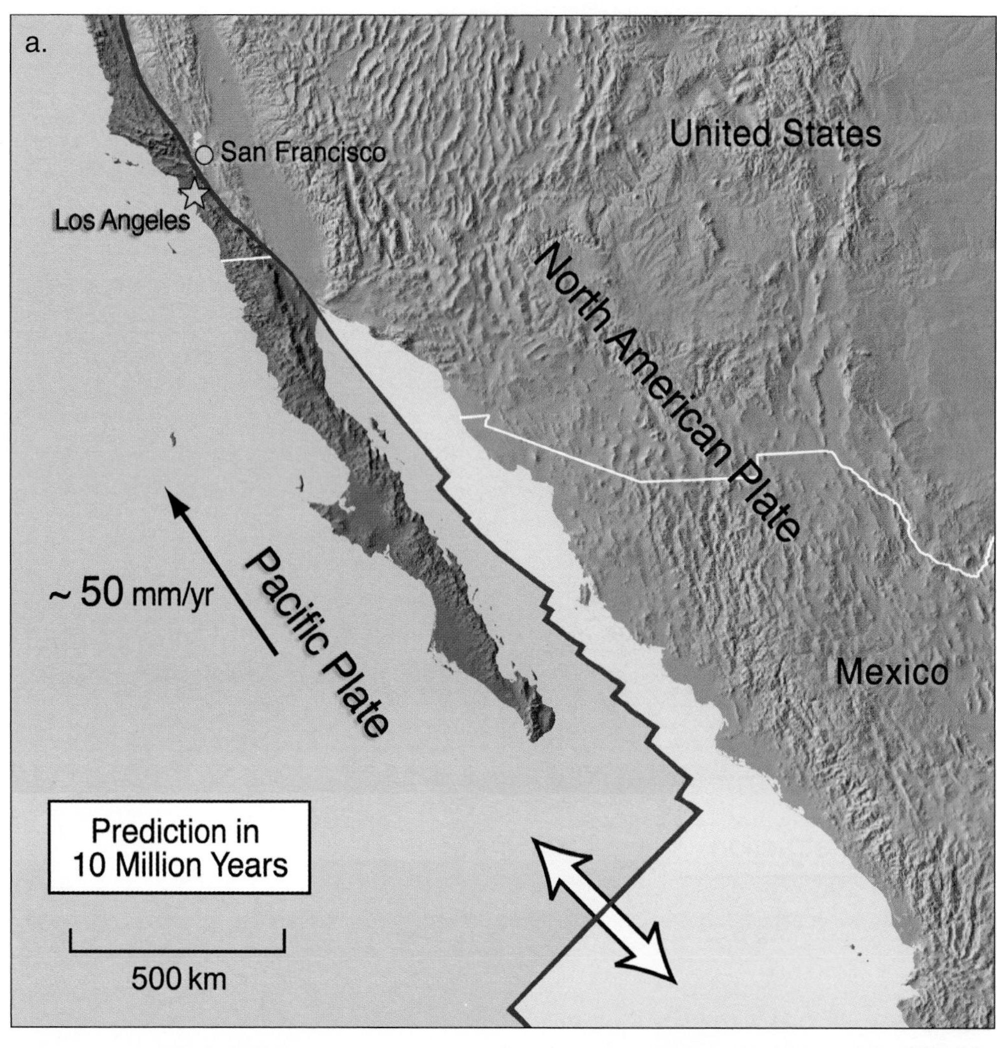

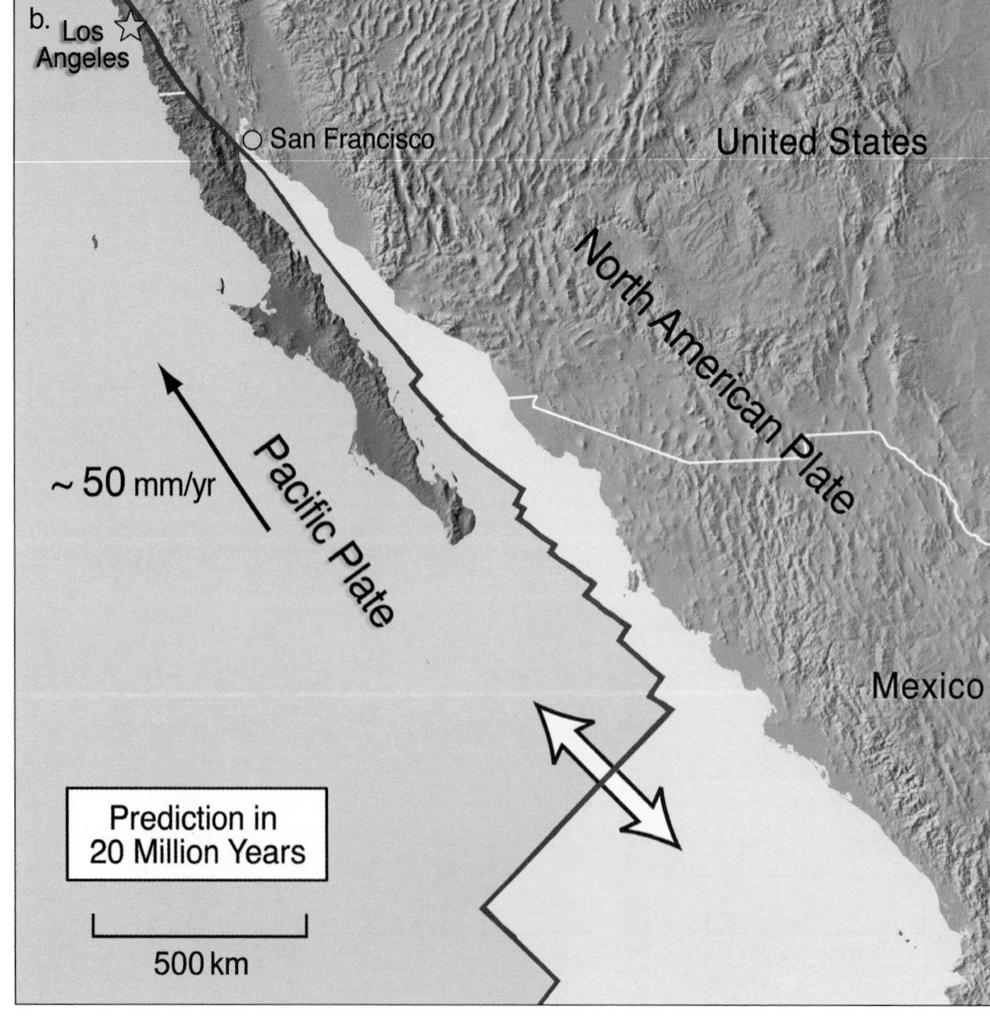

▶ **Figure T13.12 Peninsular Ranges at 10 and 20 Myr in the future.** These diagrams show the predicted positions of the Peninsular Ranges at (a) 10 Myr and (b) 20 Myr in the future. Key features of the diagrams are the northward movement of Los Angeles on the Pacific Plate and the significant widening of the Gulf of California. Assuming that plate velocities do not change, Los Angeles will lie north of San Francisco in 20 Myr.

Answers to Step 5, SE page 687

5a. The Pacific Plate will move about 1,000 km, assuming that the velocity does not change and the slip remains localized along the current San Andreas Fault. After converting 50 mm/yr to 50 km/Myr, the math shows

$$\left(\frac{50\text{ km}}{1\text{ }\cancel{\text{Myr}}}\right) \times 20\text{ }\cancel{\text{Myr}} = 1{,}000\text{ km}.$$

In reality, the slip probably wouldn't stay localized on a single fault for this duration. For example, some evidence indicates that strain between the Pacific and North American plates is transferring to the zone immediately east of the Sierra Nevada range. Thus, while the problem focuses on slip continuing to be centered on the San Andreas Fault, faulting could cause a rupture to the north toward Death Valley and the California-Nevada border.

5b. The direction is to the northwest, basically parallel to the San Andreas Fault.

5c. A possible solution is shown in figure T13.12. Be open to how students use scissors, tape, and colored pencils in their reconstructions. The key is to cut along the fault line (the boundary between the Pacific and North American plates) in order to slide the Pacific Plate northward.

5d. All evidence indicates that the Gulf of California will continue to increase in size and to shift north. Evidence includes past reconstructions, as well as current motions of the Pacific Plate. In contrast, there is no way that the gulf could close given the current information.

5e. The future location of Los Angeles is shown in figure T13.12.

In Step 6, students infer changes in ecosystems that would occur as the Peninsular Ranges progressively slide north. Due to latitude, most of the Mexican Peninsular Ranges is a desert ecosystem. Figure 13.23 in the student book shows the current progression of ecosystems along the West Coast of North America moving from lower to higher latitudes. It is difficult to know exactly how ecosystems will change, yet it is reasonable for students to use these data to make predictions for much more moist and temperate conditions as the Mexican Peninsular Ranges slide north. An example solution is shown in figure T13.13.

Answers to Step 4 are on TE pages 686–686b.
Answers to Step 6 are on TE page 688.

It may help to indicate the coastline with colored pencils. For example, use orange for 5 Mya and red for 10 Mya.

c. Organize your data in a T-table that lists millions of years ago and distance (in kilometers).
d. Imagine you are a geologist. Would there have been a rich reef ecosystem extending up into the Gulf of California 10 Mya? Explain your answer.

5. Predict the geologic future for the Mexican Peninsular Ranges, the Gulf of California, and the state of California in 20 Myr. What might the geography of the shoreline look like?
   a. Use the *magnitude* of the Pacific Plate vector to determine how far it will travel relative to North America in 20 Myr (20×10^6 years).

For full credit, you must show all your work. You might also add this row to your T-table from Step 4c.

   b. Use the *direction* of the Pacific Plate vector to show how far it will go along the San Andreas Fault in 20 Myr.

Before you do this step, try sketching the progress of the Mexican Peninsular Ranges 10 Myr into the future.

   c. Identify the part of the Pacific Plate that moves north. Use a pair of scissors to cut it out of your *Tectonic Map of PAC and NAM* handout. Place small pieces of tape to show the parts of the Pacific Plate in their future positions. Use the scale on the map to determine the size of each piece of tape.
   d. Predict what will happen to the size of the Gulf of California. List evidence to support your ideas.
   e. Draw a star on your diagram to show the position of Los Angeles in 20 Myr.

If you wish, draw stars in increments of 5 Myr.

6. Predict the types of ecosystem in different sections of the Mexican Peninsular Ranges in about 20 Myr. Refer to the succession of ecosystems up the Pacific coast in figure 13.23.

It is OK to predict, but only use data from the activity as evidence to support your speculation.

   a. Add neat labels to your diagram from Step 5c to indicate the type of ecosystems.

Colored pencils and a key will best illustrate your predicted distribution of ecosystems along the west coast in 20 Myr.

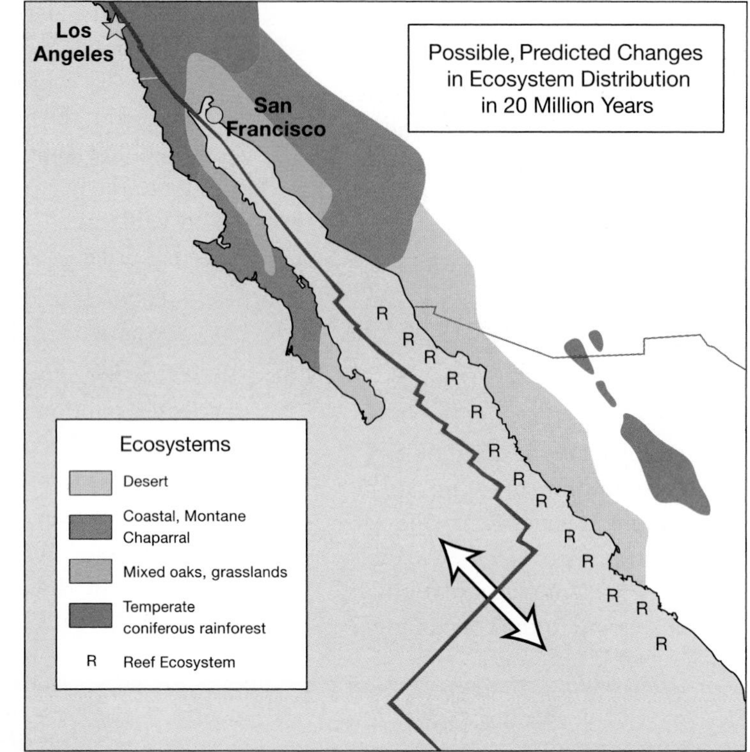

Figure T13.13 West Coast ecosystems in 20 Myr. This diagram shows a possible representation of ecosystems along the West Coast 20 Myr from now. The goal is for students to use the ecosystem distribution in figure 13.23 in the student book to project ecosystems after the Peninsular Ranges have slid north about 1,000 km. For example, ecosystems in the central and southern Peninsular Ranges have changed from desert to mixed desert and chaparral. Chaparral ecosystems around Los Angeles have changed to temperate coniferous forests similar to those in modern northern California.

Answers to Step 6, SE pages 687–688

6a. Figure T13.13 shows a possible progression of ecosystems that might be part of the change from desert to more heavy vegetation as the Peninsular Ranges move north. The succession of ecosystems is from desert; to coastal and mountain chaparral; to mixed chaparral, oak, and grassland; to temperate coniferous forest.

6b. If the Pacific Plate is inching northward along the West Coast, something must be happening to the plate at the other side. Indeed, the Pacific Plate is being subducted beneath the Japan and Aleutian volcanic arcs. Students have global maps of tectonics and prior activities from which they should be able to infer this.

In Step 7, students critically evaluate their initial predictions from Step 2 about whether California will fall into the ocean. This step is key to the nature of science—being able to revise and improve predictions and explanations when given additional evidence and data.

Students turn in a summary of sketches and their notes in Step 8.

b. Go to the farthest, northwestern edge of the Pacific Plate in figure 13.9. This is in Siberia and Japan. What geologic process is occurring there to allow 20 Myr of slip along the San Andreas Fault?

7. Obtain from your teacher your team's response to Step 2 about whether California will sink into the ocean during the Big One. With your teammates, critically evaluate the answers that you gave for Step 2.

Critically evaluating an issue means to give real evidence and documentation for your position. If your position is the same, you review this position, giving any new supporting evidence. If your position has changed, you outline the new position, giving evidence for your revisions.

8. Turn in all of the following to your teacher:
   - Initial ideas and evidence (Step 2b)
   - The sketch and answers for Steps 4b–d
   - The sketch and notes from Steps 5 and 6
   - The critical evaluation from Step 7

Conducting Your Own Inquiry

Overview

This section of *BSCS Science: An Inquiry Approach* serves as an opportunity for students to consider what they have learned so far during this program and to apply their improved habits of mind and inquiry skills to an investigation of their choice. The students consider the key features of scientific inquiry, select a question that interests them, and then conduct a full inquiry.

Goals

By the end of this section, students should successfully design and conduct their own inquiry. Their full inquiry should include asking a testable question, developing a hypothesis, designing an experiment, gathering information, conducting an experiment, analyzing data, drawing conclusions, communicating results, and modifying an explanation based on feedback.

Before You Teach

Background Information

In a successful investigation, students propose, design, carry out, analyze, and communicate the results of a scientific inquiry. The opportunity to conduct a full inquiry provides a comprehensive way for students to apply and evaluate their critical-thinking and scientific-process skills. Students have had a chance during the first three units to develop all the skills required to complete this process. A full inquiry also represents an authentic performance assessment of the students at this point in the year. This activity should have an independent feeling for the students, and we anticipate that the majority of the work will be conducted outside of class hours.

In *Conducting Your Own Inquiry*, students are required to work more independently than at other times. They will need to take full responsibility for all parts of a scientific inquiry. While they may use the protocols included elsewhere in the curriculum, these useful tools are not included here, so that this activity emphasizes the *thinking* steps of a laboratory exercise. These thinking steps include posing a testable question, which then is restated as a hypothesis; designing an experiment with adequate controls; analyzing data and using those data to draw logical conclusions; planning how best to communicate results to an outside observer; and using feedback to modify an explanation and redesign an investigation.

The techniques and processes promoted in this activity are similar to those required by many science fairs. If you usually ask students to complete science fair projects, this activity could serve as a template for meeting that goal, and it does so in the context of a complete curriculum.

Scientific inquiry is not a rigid series of steps, but rather a process and a set of characteristics that distinguish science from other ways of knowing. Anyone can use the habits of mind that characterize scientific inquiry to think scientifically about any issue. Features such as requiring evidence and natural explanations, blending logic and imagination, explaining outcomes, predicting future results, and identifying and avoiding bias typify a scientific inquiry or study.

Conducting Your Own Inquiry

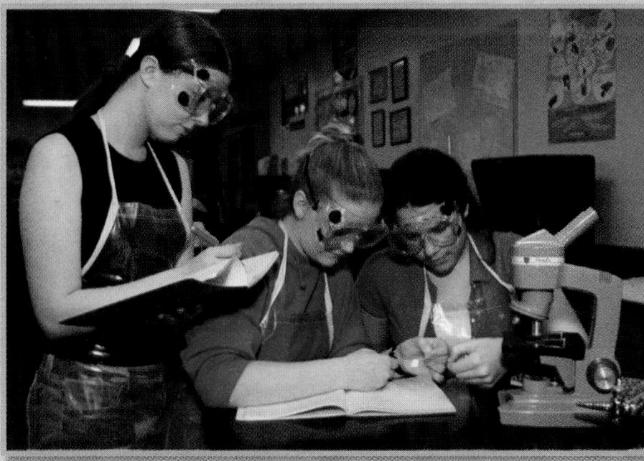

As you have been learning, science is a way of knowing the world around you, whether it becomes your career or you use it to make informed decisions. In *Conducting Your Own Inquiry*, you will use your understanding and skills of inquiry to conduct an interdisciplinary investigation that interests you. By now, you should have enough experience to realize that thinking scientifically is a valuable way of answering many questions.

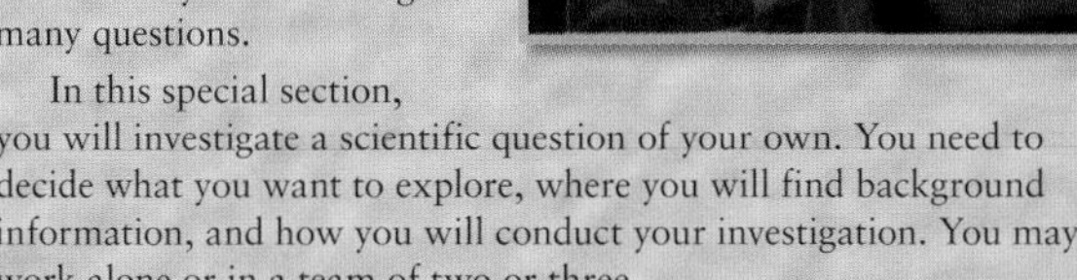

In this special section, you will investigate a scientific question of your own. You need to decide what you want to explore, where you will find background information, and how you will conduct your investigation. You may work alone or in a team of two or three.

The goal is for you to conceive, design, and conduct a scientific investigation of your choice about the natural or human-made world—one that integrates concepts from more than one discipline of science. If you used Level 1 of this program, you may have conducted an inquiry that left you with additional questions to explore. Consider following up on one of those questions.

One reason to study science is to learn how to use the methods of science as you study the natural world around you. Another reason is to understand the events that influence your life. As you design and conduct your own inquiry, remember that each of the *thinking* steps, such as asking a good question, deciding how to test it, and analyzing the meaning of the data, is just as important as the hands-on steps of *doing* an investigation. Your performance in this activity will demonstrate your understanding of the following:

- science concepts that you investigate,
- your understanding of the nature of science,
- your ability to think scientifically, and
- your ability to use scientific processes.

Part III involves the actual work of conducting an investigation. Students should complete most of this work outside of regular class time, but they should always work under direct adult supervision.

Materials

For the teacher

1 copy of copymaster FI.1, *Scoring Rubric for Conducting Your Own Inquiry*

1 transparency or 1 handout for each student of copymaster 1.2, *Process of Inquiry* (optional)

For each student

1 copy of copymaster FI.1, *Scoring Rubric for Conducting Your Own Inquiry*

Materials will vary from project to project. You must approve materials before they are collected.

Advance Preparation

Your students may need access to a wide variety of materials for the investigations they design and conduct. Allow 4–6 weeks for students to complete this activity.

Part of planning a reasonable investigation involves being realistic about materials. You may want to limit the expense of materials acquired outside of class, and you may find it useful to supply students with a list of available or appropriate materials with which to work. You will need to monitor their choice of materials for safety, following the guidelines described in the caution section that follows.

Assign this activity with sufficient time for students to complete the process before the end of the school year. Each student's project will vary in the type and amount of advance preparation necessary. As you approve each investigation, keep in mind the variations of the experiments so that you are not caught short of supplies or space. If you want students to display their project results, arrange for the necessary display area. You also should build in time for students to present to each other in class.

Make each student 1 copy of copymaster FI.1, *Scoring Rubric for Conducting Your Own Inquiry*. Prepare a transparency or 1 handout for each student of copymaster 1.2, *Process of Inquiry* if you decide to use it in Part I.

Cautions

One of the central features of this activity is for students to develop their own procedures. For this reason, it is impossible to provide specific safety notes or precautions as in other activities in this program. It is essential, therefore, for each student to submit a *written* experimental design that shows comprehension of the concepts involved, a complete procedural plan, and a safety plan. You might refer the students to *How to Write a Lab Report* in the *How To* section at the back of the student book. The safety plan should demonstrate a student's awareness of the hazards inherent in the procedures and the precautions necessary to prevent harm.

It is your responsibility to review each student's plan carefully, discuss any necessary changes, and approve the revised plan before a student begins work. Be sure that the students show in their written plans that they are familiar with and understand the hazards and precautions of each chemical and all the equipment with which they plan to work. Similarly, be sure the students demonstrate that they are familiar with any

Materials

For each student

Materials will depend on the investigation you design. You will need your teacher's approval before you assemble materials.

1 *Conducting Your Own Investigation Scoring Rubric* handout

Cautions

Depending on what you choose to investigate, you may be working with harmful chemicals.

Process and Procedure

Part I: Preparation

1. Study figure 1.10 in chapter 1, *Investigations by Design*, as you discuss the following questions with a partner. Record your best ideas in your science notebook.
   a. How has your understanding of the ideas represented in figure 1.10 changed since the beginning of the year?
   b. Identify 4–5 specific times during this program when you have used these processes.

Looking through your science notebook may help you answer this question.

2. Obtain a copy of the *Conducting Your Own Investigation Scoring Rubric* handout from your teacher. Examine the tasks and the criteria your teacher will use to score your investigation.

Part II: Asking the Question

You will begin your inquiry with a question. As you proceed, you will record all your work in your science notebook.

1. Choose a problem or topic in the natural or human-made world that interests you. Think of problems or topics that involve an integrated science perspective. In other words, the problem you select should include more than 1 discipline of science, such as life science and physical science or physical science and earth and space science.

biohazards that may be associated with biomaterials they use and that they honor the necessary precautions. Hazards include, but are not limited to, electrical shock, sharp edges, recently bent or fire-polished hot glass tubing, other hot surfaces (such as hot plates), blending equipment, bright lights, and loud noises. Be sure that students identify any such hazards and plan for the appropriate precautions. Have students review the information in *Laboratory Safety* in the back of the student book before they begin any independent work.

The hazards and precautions of chemicals that may be used in each independent inquiry are summarized on their container labels and are described in more detail in the Material Safety Data Sheet (MSDS) for each chemical. Do not allow a chemical to be used without knowledge of the hazard and precautionary information. Also, *never* send laboratory chemicals home with students. If you do not have an MSDS for a chemical, do not use the chemical or a mixture of chemicals until you have obtained the information. (Obtain Material Safety Data Sheets from your supplier; all suppliers of hazardous chemicals are required by law to provide this information to their customers.) MSDS information can be found on the Web at the MSDS/Hazard Communication Library at http://www.setonresourcecenter.com/MSDS/index.htm.

Because of the independent nature of this investigation, do not approve experiments that involve dangerous chemicals or procedures.

As You Teach

Outcomes and Indicators of Success

The following outcomes and indicators allow you to assess the students' understanding of inquiry and their related performance at this point in the year.

By the end of this activity, students should

1. demonstrate their ability to conduct a full scientific inquiry.

   They will demonstrate their skills by

   - asking a testable question of their own choosing;
   - designing a controlled experiment and gathering data;
   - analyzing data;
   - drawing conclusions;
   - making connections among their work, a major concept in science, technology, and perhaps history;
   - communicating the results of their full inquiry; and
   - reflecting on the feedback from others and considering how to incorporate these new ideas in a modification to an explanation or a design.
2. be able to communicate scientific ideas to others.

   They will show their ability by

   - using evidence to support their statements,
   - describing the scientific concepts related to their work,
   - describing their experimental procedures, and
   - displaying their work in a clear and creative manner.

Strategies

Process and Procedure

Encourage the students to make the most of this experience. What they get out of it will depend on what they put into it.

Part I: Preparation

Part I allows students to focus on planning their experiment. If you know that your students' planning skills are weak, schedule time to help them with these steps.

If you are having difficulty thinking of an area or a problem, consider looking through your science notebook. Review the investigations, readings, and activities that most interested you. You also might want to do some Web or library research about a topic that interests you. This new information will provide useful background and may give you an idea for a testable question.

2. Consider some focused and testable questions that you might want to investigate related to this area or problem. Record 2 or 3 good questions in your science notebook and discuss them with a partner.
   a. Select 1 question to investigate.

   Consider which question interests you the most and which one best meets the criteria of a testable question.

   b. Explain why your question is significant and how it is testable.

   Write several sentences describing what is already known about the topic that you wish to investigate. Be sure to explain why your question meets the criteria of a testable question.

   c. Restate your question as a hypothesis that can be tested.
   d. Record the major concepts in the sciences that relate to your question and hypothesis. Then explain how those concepts represent an integrated science perspective.
3. Show your question to your teacher for approval before you proceed.

Conducting Your Own Inquiry 691

In Step 1, allow students time to reflect on what they have learned about the process of inquiry by reviewing figure 1.10 from the student book. They should look for investigations in the previous units and reflect on these with a partner. You may wish to use a transparency or handout of this figure (copymaster 1.2, *Process of Inquiry*) so that it is easy to review with the entire class.

In Step 2, allow students time to thoroughly discuss each area of *Scoring Rubric for Conducting Your Own Inquiry* (copymaster FI.1). Then call on students randomly to piece together a description of an outstanding investigation and presentation. Use your own ideas to elaborate on these student descriptions. Students should clearly understand your expectations for successfully completing this inquiry. Have the students record in their science notebooks important deadlines along the 4–6-week period.

Part II: Asking the Question

In Step 1, consider providing a list of starters if your students struggle greatly to come up with ideas. An alternative is to discuss the areas in science that most interest them and help them select problems or topics that integrate the sciences.

In Step 2, students consider several questions that they might want to pursue and then select one. Some students may need to restate their questions as testable hypotheses and explain their significance. For many students, the classic if-then construction is a useful tool for constructing hypotheses. For example, suppose a student asks, "What difference does the wavelength of light have on a flower's ability to bloom?" The question could be restated as, "If a flower is exposed to shorter wavelengths of light, then it will bloom earlier than other similar flowers exposed to longer wavelengths." This example also illustrates a significant question. For example, because plants require light for life, there is good reason to think that certain wavelengths of light might have better or worse effects on plant growth and development. Students often have a hard time distinguishing between meaningful questions and trivial questions. Your guidance at this step can help set them in the direction of a rich and rewarding experience.

Identifying the major concepts across the sciences that relate to the hypothesis will help the students place their inquiry in a broader context. Although most of this step can be completed outside of class, you will want to check their progress in class.

During your review in Step 3, look for testable ideas, safe ideas, and integration across the sciences. This will be your last opportunity to identify insignificant or untestable questions that are not appropriate for this full inquiry.

Part III: Gathering Information and Conducting Your Investigation

In Step 1, encourage students to be creative and diverse in locating sources of information. Discourage the use of encyclopedias as the sole source of information. There are likely some valuable sites on the Web. Students might also talk with other students, scientists, and teachers. Science magazines, journals, and topic-specific science textbooks offer different types of information.

In Step 2, students write descriptions of their experimental design and their detailed procedure. In doing so, they should model the type of procedural text they have experienced in this program. Emphasize the need for a controlled experiment and one that consciously attends to safety issues.

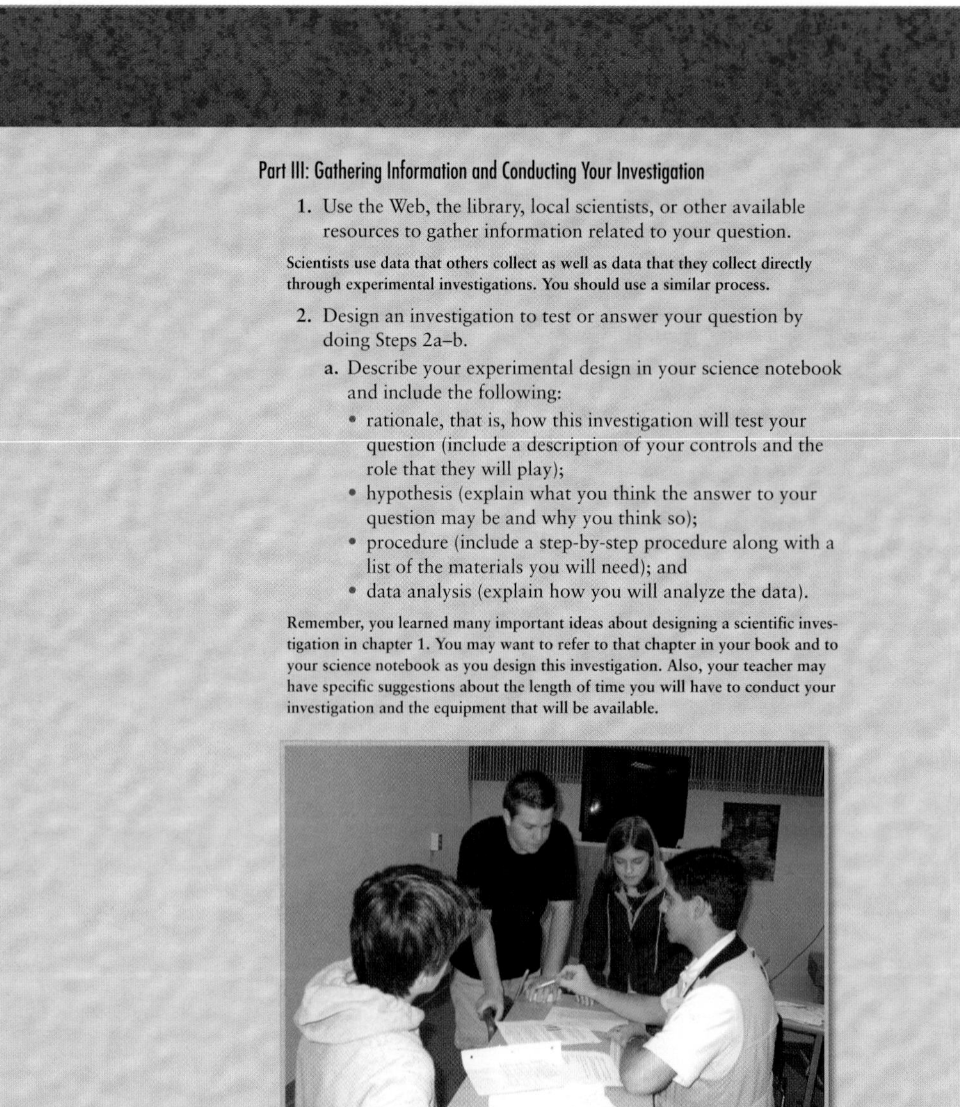

Part III: Gathering Information and Conducting Your Investigation

1. Use the Web, the library, local scientists, or other available resources to gather information related to your question.

Scientists use data that others collect as well as data that they collect directly through experimental investigations. You should use a similar process.

2. Design an investigation to test or answer your question by doing Steps 2a–b.
   a. Describe your experimental design in your science notebook and include the following:
      - rationale, that is, how this investigation will test your question (include a description of your controls and the role that they will play);
      - hypothesis (explain what you think the answer to your question may be and why you think so);
      - procedure (include a step-by-step procedure along with a list of the materials you will need); and
      - data analysis (explain how you will analyze the data).

Remember, you learned many important ideas about designing a scientific investigation in chapter 1. You may want to refer to that chapter in your book and to your science notebook as you design this investigation. Also, your teacher may have specific suggestions about the length of time you will have to conduct your investigation and the equipment that will be available.

692 Conducting Your Own Inquiry

Depending on materials, space, and the nature of your students, you should clarify whether they should work alone, with a partner, or in a larger team.

In Step 4, monitor students' work to ensure safety as they conduct their experiments. Remind the students to use their science notebooks to record data. You also may want to review the many methods for recording data: photographing; videotaping; sketching; or recording readings such as temperature, time, and growth.

Part IV: Analyzing Your Data

In Steps 1–2, you may want to provide class time for students to analyze their data. If so, have them work in pairs to review each other's analysis. This process will increase the quality of the presentations later. This intermediate critique of the analysis also provides an opportunity for students to repeat parts of their experiment that may have been problematic. Encourage students to revise their procedure to accommodate suggestions for improving the experiments.

Part V: Drawing Conclusions

In Steps 1–2, encourage the students to do more than just restate their results. Results summarize data that have been gathered, whereas conclusions tie the results back to the hypothesis. The students should state whether their hypothesis was supported or disproved and suggest how future experiments might reveal an even better understanding of the process or phenomenon being investigated. Look for evidence of thoughtful analysis and an effort to connect the inquiry with the larger conceptual picture of integrated science.

Part VI: Communicating Your Results

For Step 1, make the parameters for this section clear to students. Some possibilities for the presentations include the following:

- Private presentations such as verbal or written reports that are presented to the teacher
- Public displays in a hallway, showcase, or the classroom
- Posters and oral presentations to their peers
- A science fair after school in the gymnasium or other large area

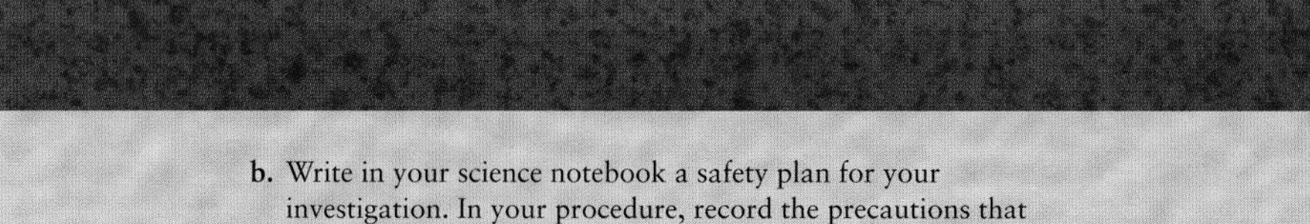

b. Write in your science notebook a safety plan for your investigation. In your procedure, record the precautions that you will follow when you
- use chemicals,
- handle equipment, and
- handle biological hazards such as bacteria or yeast.

Ask your teacher to explain any hazards that you do not understand and to help you identify the precautions necessary to prevent harm from an accident.

Cautions

Review *Laboratory Safety* in the back of your student book and be sure that you understand all the safety considerations involved in your experimental design. Make sure that you have read and understood the hazards and precautions described on the labels and Material Safety Data Sheets for all the chemicals you plan to use in your experiment. Report all accidents, no matter how small, to your teacher.

3. Discuss your library research and experimental design with your teacher and have your teacher approve your safety plan before you continue. If your plans are reasonable and safe, your teacher will approve further work.
4. When you have your teacher's approval, carry out the investigation you have designed to test your hypothesis.

Remember, use the proper controls to make it a valid test and record data in your science notebook in a way that will be most useful.

Part IV: Analyzing Your Data

1. Reorganize your data in a way that makes it easier to see patterns or understand what the data show you.

Consider the many ways you have represented data in other investigations in this program: graphs, tables, diagrams, formulas, and words, for example. Which ways will best show the important information about your results? Also, remember to keep your original data.

2. Decide what your data tell you and record these ideas in your science notebook.
   a. How confident are you that your results will help you answer your question?

In Step 2, the students identify ways in which their investigation related to integrated science, technology, society, or the history of science. For example, recall the earlier project about the dependence of plant growth on particular wavelengths of visible light. This project would integrate life science and physical science and rely on technology that enables the isolation of specific wavelengths of light. The students also discuss the ways in which this experience deepened their understanding of the relevant concepts. This phase of the inquiry offers another opportunity for students to discuss the generation of new hypotheses and predictions about the direction of subsequent related investigations.

In order to close the inquiry in a manner that relates their work to the larger context of the program, encourage the students to put a lot of thought into Step 2. Making the connections to the integrated context, and to technology, society, or history, relates directly to the program goals for *BSCS Science: An Inquiry Approach*. This program focuses on the relevance of integrated science and the importance of science in society. In addition, activities that reflect on the characteristic nature of scientific approaches to knowing the world help students distinguish

NOTES:

science from other ways of knowing the world.

In Step 3, it is important for students to practice the formal communication of results from their investigation. If you have the time to do presentations, this should be a significant advantage for the students. It is also important for students to develop better analytical skills as they listen to other presentations.

For Step 4, we suggest that you assign 2 or 3 students to give written feedback for each presentation. You will need to make these assignments before the presentations begin. Those students providing written feedback can use the scoring rubric for this activity, or you may want to develop a slightly different tool for them to use.

If you have the time for Step 5, you may want the students to meet briefly with the teams they reviewed.

Step 6 is an important opportunity to draw out what the students gained from this experience and how their understandings and abilities of scientific inquiry are improving and deepening.

b. Do you think your experimental design could be improved to help you get results that would better answer your question?

c. Did you have any unexpected results? Explain your answer.

The strategies "What I see" and "What it means" might be useful as you complete this step.

Part V: Drawing Conclusions

1. Use the evidence that you have collected to develop an explanation and preliminary conclusions for your investigation.

What can you say based on the evidence you have?

2. Explain what your conclusions mean at this point. Do your conclusions help you answer your question? Why or why not?
3. Describe how your results
   a. connect to the major concepts in the sciences that you selected,
   b. deepen your understanding of these concepts, and
   c. represent an integrated science perspective.

Part VI: Communicating Your Results

1. Develop a presentation of your inquiry that makes it possible for someone else to understand what you did, why you did it, and what you found out.

HOW TO

Your teacher will provide you with guidelines for your presentation. You might also want to refer to *How to Write a Lab Report* in the back of your book for some additional guidance. Also, consider the many different ways you have presented and communicated information to your classmates and your teacher during the year.

2. Identify the connections between your investigation and any of the following that are relevant:
   - How the investigation represents an integrated science perspective
   - How the investigation deepened your understanding of specific concepts in the sciences that you have been studying this year
   - The processes of inquiry that are featured in figure 1.10 in chapter 1

NOTES:

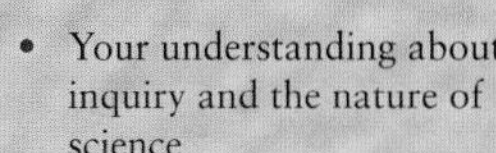

- Your understanding about inquiry and the nature of science
- Additional questions that your findings generate
- Society and technology
- The history of science

3. Present your work as your teacher directs.
4. Your teacher may assign you several of your classmates' presentations to pay particular attention to. Record your ideas about these presentations using the scoring rubric or other device your teacher provides. Justify the ideas you record using examples from the presentations.
   a. What evidence or examples illustrate that they used a scientific approach to answer their question?
   b. Can you suggest other ways to improve their designs?
   c. Did the presenters use evidence and logic to communicate their findings?
   d. Was their means of presenting their findings effective?
   e. How do their findings lead to other questions?
5. According to your teacher's instructions, share your ideas about the presentations with the teams that gave them.
6. Participate in a class discussion of important ideas that arise during this special investigation.

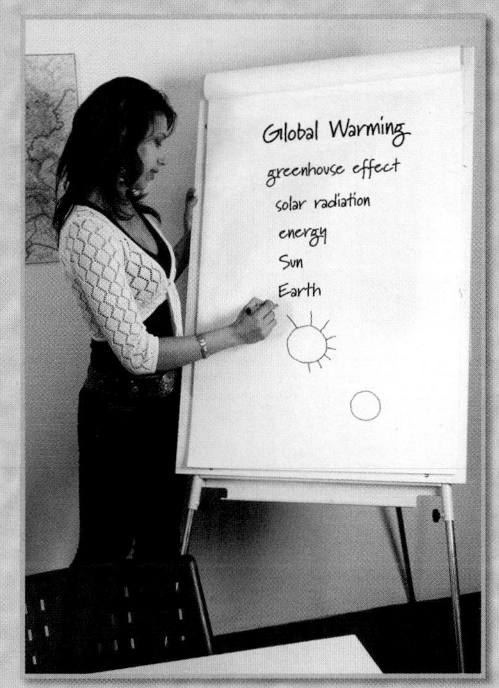

Conducting Your Own Inquiry 695

UNIT 4

Sustaining Earth Systems

Unit Introduction

Unit Overview

In unit 4, *Sustaining Earth Systems*, students will make connections between what they have learned about the physical and living worlds during this program. Students have learned what systems are and how interactions can change systems. Now they will look into how interactions between the physical and living world influence ecosystems. The processes that occur in ecosystems are not only important for maintaining the systems, but also for providing resources that humans depend on.

The unit begins by looking at populations and what influences population sizes. Interactions between populations and the abiotic environment make up ecosystems. Students will learn that important processes such as the cycling of matter and the flow of energy occur in ecosystems. Then students will discover that human populations are influenced by the same factors as other organisms, as we face the challenge of maintaining the supply of resources we need to survive. Finally, students will think about how human activities alter processes in ecosystems and how this might affect environmental quality.

Goals for the Unit

The overarching goals for unit 4 are for students to understand that populations grow, ecosystems provide important functions for life on Earth, human populations depend on the resources ecosystems provide, and human activities alter natural processes in ecosystems and affect environmental quality.

As students learn to meet these goals, they will also refine their abilities and understandings of scientific inquiry, such as designing investigations, creating and analyzing tables and graphs, formulating explanations, and understanding that scientists are influenced by current and historical scientific knowledge.

Names of Chapters

Chapter 14: Population Interactions

Chapter 15: Earth's Capacity

Chapter 16: Sustaining Earth's Environmental Quality

Strategies for the Unit Engage

Use this activity to transition your students from geochemical cycles and interactions in earth systems to how these interactions influence ecosystems and affect the functions they provide. Begin by recording the names of the four chapters of unit 3, *Moving Matter*, on four separate large sheets of paper. Then ask students what geochemical cycles they learned about in each of the chapters. Record their ideas on the sheets of paper. Students should recall that they learned about matter moving in the water cycle, in the carbon cycle, during ice ages, and in relation to plate tectonics. Then ask students to think of examples of how human and nonhuman populations are related to the movement of matter. For example, you could have students use two sheets of paper to fill out a table in their science notebooks similar to figure T14.1. Explain to students that in unit 4, they will learn about how organisms depend on ecosystems on Earth and how humans can affect those ecosystems.

Chapter	What matter is moving?	Are living organisms involved in the movement of matter? Explain why or why not.	How does this movement of matter affect nonhuman populations?	How does this movement affect human populations?	Can humans have an effect on this movement? Explain why or why not.
Chapter 10, *The Water System*	Water	Yes. Plants contribute to the water cycle through transpiration. Organisms also contribute small amounts to the water cycle through respiration and decay.	All living organisms need water to survive. Some organisms need water for habitat as well.	Humans need water for their bodies to function, but also use water for transportation, manufacturing, and recreation.	Yes. Humans can affect the water cycle by using large amounts of water, by transporting water to cities, and by polluting water.
Chapter 11, *Carbon on the Move*	Carbon	Yes. Plants contribute to the carbon cycle by making carbon compounds during photosynthesis. Animals contribute to the carbon cycle through respiration and decay.	Plants need carbon from the atmosphere to make their own food in the form of carbon compounds. Carbon molecules are the building blocks for all living organisms.	Humans rely on carbon for their bodies to function, for many products they use, and for fuel.	Yes. Humans can affect the carbon cycle by burning fossil fuels.
Chapter 12, *Evidence for the Ice Ages*	Oxygen isotopes and water	No. The record of oxygen isotopes is stored in forams, but organisms are not responsible for the movement of oxygen isotopes. The amount of solar radiation entering the earth system determines the ratio of heavy to light oxygen isotopes.	Different organisms live during periods of glacials or interglacials because the climate is different.	During an ice age, humans would have to survive in a different climate with different organisms.	No. Glacial and interglacial cycles occur over thousands of years and result from changes in the amount of incoming solar radiation. Scientists are investigating whether humans are influencing the cycles today.
Chapter 13, *Time for Change*	Tectonic plates	No. Tectonic plates move as a result of mantle convection.	When tectonic plates shift, land bridges sometimes form that can allow animals to migrate to new regions.	When earthquakes or other events occur along the edges of tectonic plates, structures created by humans may be destroyed.	No. Humans cannot affect tectonic plate movement because it is the result of mantle convection.

▲ **Figure T14.1 Table to connect what students know about the movement of matter to populations of organisms.** Use questions like these to prompt students to think about how living organisms are connected to the movement of matter.

CHAPTER 14

Population Interactions

Chapter Overview

Chapter 14, *Population Interactions*, addresses many of the concepts typically included in a traditional ecology chapter. Students will learn about characteristics of populations and ecosystems. For example, they learn about factors that influence population size, including what limits population growth. They will learn that populations of organisms together with the nonliving environment make up ecosystems. Processes that occur on a microscopic scale (i.e., photosynthesis and cellular respiration) and on a global scale (e.g., geochemical cycles discussed in unit 3) are connected to the functions of ecosystems. Specifically, students will learn the role of ecosystems in the movement of matter and energy on a regional scale. Students also connect the process of natural selection to interactions in ecosystems.

Goals for the Chapter

The overarching goals for this chapter are that students will understand that populations grow and decline, ecosystems are composed of biotic and abiotic components, matter and energy move through ecosystems through the interrelationships between organisms and the abiotic environment, and interactions between organisms contribute to the diversity of organisms on Earth through the process of natural selection. By the end of chapter 14, students will understand the following:

- Populations grow or decline through the combined effects of births, deaths, immigration, and emigration.
- There are limits to population growth and a maximum number of individuals an environment can support.
- Ecosystems are made up of the biotic and abiotic environments.
- Organisms both cooperate and compete in an ecosystem.
- Natural selection involves interactions among populations and the environment and contributes to the diversity of organisms.

The chapter organizer uses graphic design principles to help students connect one activity to another. It uses reminders of key concepts, linking questions, and the spatial arrangement of activity titles to foster the sense of a conceptual flow, connecting each activity. Explicitly ask students to locate their position within its flow at the beginning of each activity. This action reinforces the connection among the activities, thus enhancing long-term memory.

Chapter 14 Organizer

POPULATION INTERACTIONS

Major Concepts

- **Populations grow and decline.**
- **There are limits to population growth.**
- **Ecosystems are made up of the biotic and abiotic environments.**
- **Organisms both cooperate and compete in an ecosystem.**
- **Interactions among populations can lead to natural selection and contribute to the diversity of organisms on Earth.**

ENGAGE — What Do You Know about Populations? ★

Key Idea: • Different kinds of interactions occur in ecosystems.

Activity: Students justify their true or false responses to a series of statements. Their answers indicate what their current ideas are about populations and ecosystems.

LINKING QUESTION: How can I build on what I know about populations to determine what factors affect population size?

EXPLORE — Changing Populations ★ ★ ★

Key Idea: • The size of a population is affected by environmental factors and interactions with other organisms.

Activity: Students design an investigation to test the effects of different environmental conditions on a yeast population. They also look at data from Isle Royale and make inferences about populations that inhabit the island.

LINKING QUESTION: How are populations and ecosystems related?

EXPLAIN — Systems in Balance ★ ★

Key Ideas:

- Population growth is limited by limiting factors that can be abiotic or biotic.
- Interactions occur between organisms and between organisms and the abiotic environment.
- Ecosystems are important for the flow of energy and the cycling of matter.

Activity: Students graph exponential and logistic growth and read about limiting factors. Then they read about the abiotic and biotic components of ecosystems and how they interact and are related to the flow of energy and the cycling of matter. They identify the components and interactions in the ecosystems they have been studying and diagram the flow of energy in a grassland ecosystem.

LINKING QUESTION: How are competitive interactions related to natural selection?

ELABORATE — Finding Your Niche ★ or ★ ★

Key Idea: • Interactions among organisms are part of the process of natural selection and can lead to diverse species on Earth.

Activity: Students identify the niches for six species of shorebirds and think about how competition could lead to diverse species of shorebirds.

LINKING QUESTION: How can I use what I have learned to demonstrate my understanding of populations and ecosystems?

EVALUATE — Interpret the Interactions ★ or ★ ★

Key Ideas:

- Population growth is affected by many factors.
- The interactions between the biotic and abiotic parts of an ecosystem result in the transfer of energy and the cycling of matter.
- Interactions can lead to natural selection.

Activity: Students revisit their responses from the engage activity *What Do You Know about Populations?* and discuss their answers in class. Then students take an open-ended test that involves interpreting data from scientific research.

★ = One Class Period ☆ = ½ Class Period *Note:* Based on a 50-minute class period.

Standards Covered by Chapter 14

POPULATION INTERACTIONS

STANDARD C: Life Science. As a result of their activities in grades 9–12, all students should develop understanding of

abilities necessary to do scientific inquiry

- Identify questions and concepts that guide scientific investigations. Students should formulate a testable hypothesis and demonstrate the logical connections between the scientific concepts guiding a hypothesis and the design of an experiment. They should demonstrate appropriate procedures.
- Design and conduct scientific investigations. Designing and conducting a scientific investigation requires introduction to the major concepts in the area being investigated, proper equipment, safety precautions, assistance with methodological problems, recommendations for use of technologies, clarification of ideas that guide the inquiry, and scientific knowledge obtained from sources other than the actual investigation. The investigation may also require student clarification of the question, method, controls, and variables; student organization and display of data; student revision of methods and explanations; and a public presentation of the results with a critical response from peers. Regardless of the scientific investigation performed, students must use evidence, apply logic, and construct an argument for their proposed explanations.

biological evolution

- The great diversity of organisms is the result of more than 3.5 billion years of evolution that has filled every available niche with life forms.

the interdependence of organisms

- The atoms and molecules on the earth cycle among the living and nonliving components of the biosphere.
- Energy flows through ecosystems in one direction, from photosynthetic organisms to herbivores to carnivores and decomposers.
- Organisms both cooperate and compete in ecosystems. The interrelationships and interdependencies of these organisms may generate ecosystems that are stable for hundreds or thousands of years.
- Living organisms have the capacity to produce populations of infinite size, but environments and resources are finite. This fundamental tension has profound effects on the interactions between organisms.

STANDARD F: Science in Personal and Social Perspectives. As a result of activities in grades 9–12, all students should develop an understanding of

population growth

- Populations grow or decline through the combined effects of births and deaths, and through emigration and immigration. Populations can increase through linear or exponential growth, with effects on resource use and environmental pollution.
- Populations can reach limits to growth. Carrying capacity is the maximum number of individuals that can be supported in a given environment. The limitation is not the availability of space, but the number of people in relation to resources and the capacity of earth systems to support human beings. Changes in technology can cause significant changes, either positive or negative, in carrying capacity.

Prerequisite Knowledge

Students should be familiar with photosynthesis, cellular respiration, and biological evolution through natural selection. If time allows, spend a few minutes reviewing photosynthesis and cellular respiration before Part II in the explain activity, *Systems in Balance*. Students are expected to understand the role of these processes in the transfer of energy and the movement of organic matter. Use the elaborate activity, *Finding Your Niche*, to reinforce what students know about natural selection and biological evolution. Experience using a microscope will also be necessary for the explore activity, *Changing Populations*, where students count yeast cells.

Commonly Held Misconceptions

Some common misconceptions about populations and ecosystems include the following:

- Populations will increase indefinitely due to limitless resources.

Students often fail to understand that populations are constrained by resources.

- Populations only depend on the organisms that they prey on.

Populations depend on abiotic factors as well as the organisms they prey on.

- Ecosystems are simpler than they really are.

Ecosystems are complex systems with many interactions between biotic and abiotic components.

- Populations exist in states of either constant decline or constant growth depending on their position in the food chain.
- Varying the population of an organism will only affect the others that are directly connected through a food chain.

Changes in a population of organisms affects those directly in the food chain as well as organisms indirectly affected. For example, competing populations affect each other.

- Only large animals are important in ecosystems, not smaller organisms such as nematodes.

Ecosystems consist of microorganisms as well as plants and large animals.

- The role of abiotic aspects of the environment is often discounted.

Organisms are dependent on abiotic aspects of the environment such as light, temperature, and water.

NOTES:

NOTES:

ENGAGE

What Do You Know about Populations?

Activity Overview

What Do You Know about Populations? provides you and your students an opportunity to consider what they already know about populations and ecosystems. To show their current understanding, students identify statements as true or false and answer a few questions about populations. Students revisit their answers in the evaluate activity, *Interpret the Interactions*, and revise them based on what they learned.

Before You Teach

Background Information

This activity gives you an opportunity to see what ideas students have about populations and ecosystems. Review *Commonly Held Misconceptions* and compare this list with what you hear your students saying. As students go through the chapter, you can focus your efforts on the areas where they have misconceptions or struggle with the concepts.

Materials

none

As You Teach

Outcomes and Indicators of Success

By the end of this activity, students should communicate their prior knowledge of populations and ecosystems.

They will demonstrate their prior knowledge by

- identifying a series of statements as true or false and explaining why they answered the way they did,
- describing things that might increase or decrease a population of plants, and
- applying what they know about the carbon cycle to describe how organisms contribute to the cycling of carbon.

Strategies

Getting Started

Read the introduction to the activity as a class and facilitate a brief discussion about the kinds of interactions students have and how those compare with the interactions other organisms have.

Process and Procedure

Instruct students to work alone to identify each of the statements in Step 1 as true or false. For each statement, they should provide an explanation for their answer. The purpose of this activity is to have students share their current conceptions about populations and ecosystems. Students may not recognize some of the terms in the statements, such as abiotic. You can give them a definition for these terms, but avoid explaining the statements. It is OK for students to struggle at this stage. Don't expect students to have the correct answers now; they will develop the understandings they need as they complete the activities. Although the correct answers are provided here, wait to grade their responses until the evaluate activity, when students revise their answers.

In Step 2, students should provide examples to support their explanations. Then in Step 3, they compare their examples and explanations with those of a classmate. Depending on how much time you want to spend on this activity, you may want students to compare only 1 or 2 of their explanations. In Step 4, students should record why their explanations are valid or not. This forces students to think about what they have written and whether it makes sense.

This activity simply introduces the chapter. If you spend only part of a class period on these statements, you will have time to introduce the next activity, *Changing Populations*, the same day. This will give students time to begin planning their investigations one day and set up their investigations the next day.

Answers to Step 1, SE page 706

1a. False. Populations are limited by resources and environmental conditions.

1b. False. Food and water are 2 resources essential to organisms. But other factors also limit the continual growth of populations within a system. For example, populations are limited by space because waste can build up and affect living conditions. In addition, the spread of disease increases when organisms are in close contact, and the stress due to the lack of space can decrease reproduction rates.

1c. False. Each population has its own set of limiting factors. The population size of the same species in different locations also varies because environmental conditions are unique.

1d. True. All organisms both cooperate and compete with other organisms.

1e. True. The abiotic environment in an ecosystem consists of light, water, temperature, nutrients, physical space, and other factors.

1f. True. Most species can only survive in a certain range of temperatures. If the temperature is outside that range, organisms are likely to die.

1g. False. Each trophic level supports fewer organisms than the trophic level below because energy is lost between trophic levels. See the answer for 1h.

1h. False. Organisms use much of the energy they get from their food for metabolism and movement.

Answers to Reflect and Connect, SE page 707

1. Accept all answers that provide some explanation. In this instance, you are just looking for what students know at this point. Some examples that students might come up with include the following:
   - Larger amounts of water and higher temperatures might increase a population of plants because plants tend to thrive in wet and warm areas.
   - Cold temperatures and low light might decrease a population of plants because fewer plants survive in cold and dark areas. Students might also mention that herbivores, animals that eat plants, might cause a population of plants to decrease.
2. See how much students remember from chapter 11, *Carbon on the Move*. Students might mention plants as an important part of converting atmospheric carbon to organic matter through photosynthesis. Organisms also shift organic matter in the food they eat to atmospheric carbon through cellular respiration. The remains of organisms also collect in environments such as forests and the ocean, forming large carbon reservoirs.

EXPLORE

Changing Populations

Activity Overview

In Part I of this investigation, students will obtain firsthand experience with population dynamics and further develop their scientific inquiry skills. This part of the activity will take place across seven class periods: one class period to set up and make the initial counts, and thereafter, approximately 15 minutes (min) each day to make the counts. On the seventh day, students will make their final counts and spend a full class period graphing their data and analyzing their results. In Part II, students will investigate populations by looking at data from a long-term study on Isle Royale National Park. They will interpret how moose, wolf, and balsam fir populations interact on Isle Royale.

Before You Teach

Background Information

Yeast are good organisms to use when studying populations because they reproduce quickly and population estimates can easily be made in the classroom. This investigation is designed to use an inquiry approach to study populations. In this activity, baker's yeast is grown in a nutrient medium made from common ingredients. Because yeast have few requirements for survival, it is relatively simple to vary the environmental conditions for yeast populations. For example, students can vary the temperature or the amount of food.

Materials—Part I

For the teacher

1 16×150-mm test tube with screw cap with 10 mL nutrient medium
1 package active dry yeast
100 mL molasses
900 mL water
20 fresh or frozen peas
blender

Answers to Step 1 are on TE page 705.

ENGAGE — What Do You Know about Populations?

Every day populations of organisms surround you. For example, all the students in your school system make up a population (figure 14.1). Many things influence the size of the student population and how the students in the school system interact. Your school population shares some characteristics with biological populations.Do you ever think about the interactions between organisms in other systems? In *What Do You Know about Populations?*, you will share your current ideas about populations and natural systems.

▲ **Figure 14.1 Student population.** Does your school population change? What might limit the size of the population at your school?

Materials

none

Process and Procedure

1. Record in your science notebook whether you think each of the following statements is true or false. Provide a 1 or 2 sentence explanation for each of your answers.
   a. Populations can grow indefinitely. (T or F)
   b. You have a population of fruit flies in a large building. If you gave the population all the food and water it needs, the population would continue to increase in size. (T or F)
   c. All of the species in an environment have the same maximum population size. (T or F)
   d. A species of fish can cooperate with one organism and can compete with another. (T or F)
   e. Light, water, and nutrients are abiotic parts of an ecosystem. (T or F)
   f. Temperature can influence the size of a population. (T or F)
   g. A forest contains as many woodpeckers that eat insects as there are insects. (T or F)
   h. When one organism eats another, all the energy stored as food is passed to the consumer. (T or F)
2. Add a specific example to support each of your explanations in Step 1.
3. Compare your examples and explanations from Steps 1 and 2 to those of a classmate.
4. Record in your science notebook why each explanation is or is not valid for each statement.

You will revisit your explanations in the evaluate activity, *Interpret the Interactions*.

For each team of 3 students

3 pairs of safety goggles
2 16×150-mm test tubes with screw caps, each with 10 mL yeast suspension
2 18×150-mm test tubes
1 dropping pipet
microscope slides
coverslips
1 compound microscope
1 test-tube rack
density indicator strips (optional)
Spec 20 (optional)
methylene blue (optional)
1-mL graduated pipet (optional)
water (optional)
paper towel
1 glass-marking pencil
1 transparent metric ruler
4 sheets of graph paper
1 tally counter

Materials—Part II

none

Advance Preparation

Make your own nutrient medium by using a blender to combine 100 mL molasses, 900 mL water, and 20 peas. Pour 10 mL of the excess nutrient medium into a screw-cap test tube. Use it as a control to watch for the growth of contaminants such as bacteria.

Make the yeast suspension by combining half a package of dry yeast with 600 mL nutrient medium. Stir well before pouring 10 mL yeast suspension into screw-cap test tubes for students.

Make the nutrient medium the day before the activity and make the yeast suspension the day of the activity. Keep the yeast suspension chilled in an ice bucket or refrigerator until used to reduce the amount of growth before students begin the investigation. You should have enough yeast suspension for 4 or 5 classes of 30 students if each team uses 10 mL for a treatment and 10 mL for a control.

As an alternative, you can purchase freeze-dried yeast and sterile Sabouraud dextrose broth from Ward's Natural Science; allow 1 week for delivery. Fill screw-cap test tubes with 10 mL sterile broth medium and, when students are ready, transfer 0.1 mL yeast stock culture to the test tubes before students begin the investigation.

Gather screw-cap test tubes. It is best to begin the experiment on a Monday. If you use freeze-dried yeast, rehydrate it on Friday of the week before or on the day before the investigation, according to the instructions in the package.

Consider purchasing density indicator strips so that students can determine turbidity in addition to making direct cell counts each day. The strips come with instructions for use. If you have a Spec 20, you could use it to estimate population size as well. A greater absorbance of light passing through the medium will indicate a larger number of yeast cells. If you use either of these techniques, do not make your own nutrient medium with molasses because the dark color will interfere with the measurements.

Educational Technologies

If your students need practice with microscope techniques, consider having them go through the activity *How to Use a Compound Microscope* in the *How To* section in the back of the student book.

Answers to Reflect and Connect are on TE page 706.

Reflect and Connect

Record your ideas to the following questions in your science notebook.

1. List 2 factors that you think might increase a population of plants. Then list 2 factors that might decrease the same population. For each factor, explain why it would cause an increase or a decrease.
2. Recall what you learned about cycles in chapter 11, *Carbon on the Move*. Use what you learned in unit 3 to describe how you think organisms contribute to the cycling of carbon. For example, how would a pine tree contribute to the cycling of carbon?

Changing Populations

EXPLORE

A group of individuals of the same species that lives in a particular area and interbreeds is called a **population**. Each population has certain characteristics, such as size, density, and distribution. In *Changing Populations*, you will investigate how the size of populations changes across time. In Part I, you will discover how different environments result in yeast populations of different sizes. In Part II, you will review almost 50 years of data to learn how populations of wolves, moose, and balsam fir interact on an island.

Part I: Yeast Population Explosion

Changes in the population size of organisms are difficult to investigate in the classroom. The changes occur over long periods of time. For example, scientists monitor changes in animal populations across years. Even changes in the size of insect and plant populations take weeks to occur. Can you think of any populations that change size in a shorter time frame? Scientists use different techniques to estimate population size, depending on the organism they are investigating (see figure 14.2).

Microorganisms are small, reproduce rapidly, and have short life spans, so they are good to study in the classroom. Bacteria and yeast are examples of microorganisms. If you have had food poisoning, you have experienced a bacterium population rapidly growing and causing illness.

In this investigation, you will use common baker's yeast (*Saccharomyces cerevisiae*) to observe a population of yeast cells. The cells are growing in a test tube in a liquid called a broth medium. This population is a closed population. A closed population lets you estimate the rate of population growth more easily than an open system. In nature, open populations increase or decrease in size as organisms enter or leave them. Matter can cycle through the open population.

Cautions

Students should wear safety goggles when working with any liquid. Culture test tubes should be inverted gently to avoid foaming, which would result in inaccurate counts. Caps on culture tubes should be loosened slightly before storage to prevent gas buildup. Avoid contact with methylene blue because it will dye skin and clothes. Methylene blue is harmful if ingested. Remind students to wash their hands each day before leaving the classroom.

As You Teach

Outcomes and Indicators of Success

By the end of this activity, students should

1. begin to understand how the size of populations changes across time.

   They will demonstrate their understanding by

   - recording the change in a yeast population,
   - interpreting the graphs of the yeast population and describing what the data show about the population, and
   - describing what contributed to the growth of the yeast population.

2. be able to design and conduct an investigation to determine how a yeast population responds to different environmental conditions.

   They will demonstrate their ability by

   - deciding how different conditions could be created for a yeast population,
   - developing two or three hypotheses that predict how a yeast population will respond to different environmental conditions,
   - designing an investigation to test how different environmental conditions affect a yeast population, and
   - following the procedure they designed to collect data.

3. be able to record and analyze data.

   They will demonstrate their ability by

   - creating a data table and filling it in with the data they collect,
   - creating graphs from the data, and
   - providing evidence of whether their hypotheses were supported or not.

4. begin to understand factors that limit populations.

   They will demonstrate their understanding by

   - explaining factors that might cause moose and wolf populations to increase or decrease,
   - describing a factor that might change a balsam fir population, and
   - drawing a graph to show how a yeast population might respond to the presence of another organism.

5. begin to understand how populations interact.

   They will demonstrate their understanding by

   - describing how moose and wolf populations change in relation to each other;
   - drawing a food web showing the relationship between moose, wolf, and balsam fir; and
   - diagramming the relationship between moose and balsam fir.

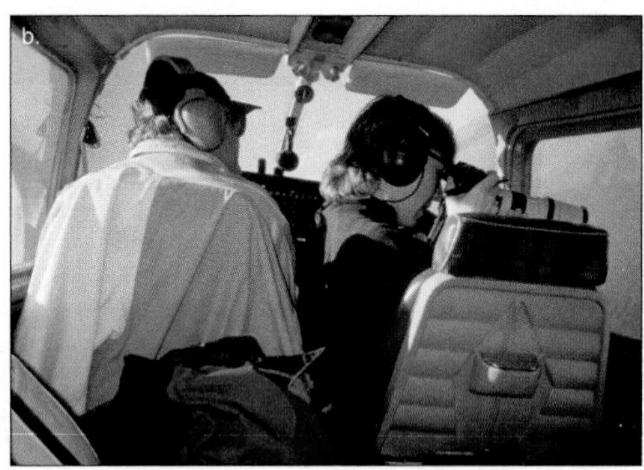

▲ **Figure 14.2 Determining population size.** Scientists estimate population size in different ways, depending on the organism they are studying. (a) In the laboratory, scientists can use microscopes to estimate the population size of microorganisms such as bacteria or yeast. (b) In nature, scientists use techniques such as aerial surveys to sample populations of larger organisms. During aerial surveys, scientists count animals such as birds, elk, or whales from a plane or helicopter. Why might it be valuable to know the population size of different organisms?

Materials

For each team of 3 students

- 3 pairs of safety goggles
- 2 16×150-mm test tubes with screw caps, each with 10 mL yeast suspension
- 2 18×150-mm test tubes
- 1 dropping pipet
- microscope slides
- coverslips
- 1 compound microscope
- 1 test-tube rack
- methylene blue (optional)
- 1-mL graduated pipet (optional)
- water (optional)
- paper towel
- 1 glass-marking pencil
- 1 transparent metric ruler
- 4 sheets of graph paper
- 1 tally counter

Cautions

Wear safety goggles when working with any liquid. Culture test tubes should be inverted gently to avoid foaming, which would result in inaccurate counts. Caps on culture tubes should be loosened slightly before storage to prevent gas buildup. Avoid contact with methylene blue because it will dye your skin and clothes. Methylene blue is harmful if ingested. Wash your hands thoroughly before leaving the classroom.

708 | Unit 4 Sustaining Earth Systems

Strategies

Getting Started

Ask students what they know about yeast. They might mention that yeast are a fungus and are used in baking. Then read the introduction and Step 1 together as a class. If not mentioned by a student, point out that yeast is also used in alcohol fermentation.

Cautions

Students should wear safety goggles when working with any liquid. Culture test tubes should be inverted gently to avoid foaming, which would result in inaccurate counts. Caps on culture tubes should be loosened slightly before storage to prevent gas buildup. Avoid contact with methylene blue because it will dye skin and clothes. Methylene blue is harmful if ingested. Remind students to wash their hands each day before leaving the classroom.

Process and Procedure

Part I: Yeast Population Explosion

Materials

For the teacher

1 16×150-mm test tube with screw cap with 10 mL nutrient medium
1 package active dry yeast
100 mL molasses
900 mL water
20 fresh or frozen peas
blender

For each team of 3 students

3 pairs of safety goggles
2 16×150-mm test tubes with screw caps, each with 10 mL yeast suspension
2 18×150-mm test tubes
1 dropping pipet
microscope slides
coverslips
1 compound microscope
1 test-tube rack
density indicator strips (optional)
Spec 20 (optional)
methylene blue (optional)
1-mL graduated pipet (optional)
water (optional)
paper towel
1 glass-marking pencil
1 transparent metric ruler
4 sheets of graph paper
1 tally counter

After familiarizing students with the organism they will be investigating, divide students into teams of 3 in Step 1. Then in Step 2, ask teams to think about what environmental conditions might affect the growth of a yeast population. After giving teams time to come up with some ideas, facilitate a class discussion and call on each team to share its ideas. Some possible suggestions are light, temperature, pH, amount of food available, and the presence or absence of oxygen. Direct students to think about whether each of these factors would increase or decrease the yeast population. Also, ask students to think about how the carbon dioxide and ethanol given off by yeast during anaerobic respiration might affect the yeast population.

In Step 3, tell teams to develop 2 or 3 hypotheses to predict how different environmental conditions might affect a yeast population. Each team member should record the hypotheses in his or her science notebook. In Step 4, teams discuss how they could test their hypotheses. Emphasize that the purpose of collecting the data is to evaluate these hypotheses. Then ask teams to share their hypotheses and investigation designs with the class. Facilitate a discussion to determine how teams could test their hypotheses. Make sure students mention a control for

Process and Procedure

1. Read the following 2 paragraphs about yeast. Use this question to focus your reading: "What do yeast need to survive?"

   Yeast are fungi that grow as single cells. They can reproduce asexually by budding, or they can reproduce sexually. They reproduce rapidly in moist environments that have a supply of nutrients such as sugars and amino acids.

   Like all organisms, yeast undergo cellular respiration. Cellular respiration produces the energy needed for growth and reproduction. Recall that you investigated cellular respiration in decaying vegetation in chapter 11. Yeast undergo cellular respiration with oxygen present (aerobic respiration) and without oxygen (anaerobic respiration). Anaerobic respiration is also called fermentation. When yeast respire anaerobically, they break down sugars into carbon dioxide and ethanol. These two reaction products alter the environment and affect the yeast's growth and reproduction.
2. Participate in a class discussion about different conditions you could create for a yeast population. Use Questions 2a–c to guide your discussion.
   a. What conditions do you think affect a yeast population?
   b. What conditions might increase reproduction?
   c. What conditions might decrease reproduction?
3. As a team, develop 2 or 3 hypotheses that might explain how different conditions will affect the size of a yeast population. Record these in your science notebook.

A hypothesis is a statement that suggests an explanation of an observation or an answer to a scientific problem.

4. Discuss with your team how you could design an investigation to study yeast population growth under different conditions. Be prepared to share your ideas with the class.

Focus on how to create different environments. In Step 7, you will read a protocol describing how to measure yeast population growth. Remember that a control may help you understand variables, which in this case are the different environments.

5. Participate in a class discussion to decide how to design investigations to study yeast population growth in different environments. Consider how each team could test different conditions.
6. Decide on 1 design for your team and record it in your science notebook. Have your teacher approve your design.

the investigation. They can use one of the test tubes you filled as a control and the other as a treatment.

In Step 6, teams finish their designs and record them in their science notebooks. Approve the designs before they begin the investigation. Direct teams to read *Measuring Population Growth in Yeast Protocol* for Step 7. Circulate as teams review the protocol and check that students understand how they will determine the yeast population size. You might need to spend some time reviewing how to use a compound microscope.

In Step 8, teams begin their investigations. First, they examine a slide of their yeast mixture and determine which magnification is best for viewing cells. Adding stain to the slide will make it easier to see the yeast cells. Tell students to use only 1 drop of yeast mixture and 1 drop of stain when preparing their slides. This will make the counts more consistent among teams. Students count the number of yeast cells in their field of view. As the yeast multiply, there will be more in the sample and it may be impossible to count all of them in a field of view without diluting the sample first. Instructions for making dilutions are provided in the protocol. Students make population counts for 7 class periods. The first day of making counts will take an entire class period. On subsequent days, instruct students to begin Part II after making the population count.

Check in with teams to answer questions and guide their work. Students may require help with the yeast counting techniques. A common source of error is the uneven distribution of yeast cells in the broth culture medium (yeast cells tend to settle to the bottom of a tube). Instruct students to invert the test tubes several times before making counts or readings and to transfer the yeast to the slides quickly. It is not necessary to use sterile techniques when counting. Make sure they count individual cells and not clumps of cells (three or more cells together), air bubbles, or extraneous materials.

Students should get a count as the number of yeast cells per milliliter for each field of view. A general rule of thumb is that 10 drops equals 1 milliliter (mL). Therefore, tell students to assume that 1 drop is 0.1 mL. Although this is not an exact measurement, making this assumption will allow students to focus on estimating the number of yeast cells in each field of view. To get the count for the dilutions, students must multiply by 10 for the first dilution and by 100 for the second dilution. They should get multiple counts by moving the slide to different positions without changing the magnification of the microscope. If you have time, you might also have students make another slide and make more counts, because yeast are not uniformly

Answers to Stop and Think—Part I are on TE page 711.

7. Read *Measuring Population Growth in Yeast Protocol.* Then decide how to create a data table for your investigation. Use an entire sheet of paper for the data table.

Make sure you include space in your table to record the yeast population for different environmental conditions.

8. Collect the materials you need and begin your investigation.

This investigation will continue for 7 class periods. Make population counts each day, then continue with other activities as your teacher directs.

9. Once you have finished collecting data, graph the change in the yeast population size. Include a caption and highlight comments on the graph.

Stop & THINK

PART I

Participate in a class discussion of the following questions. Record your answers in your science notebook.

1. Is there a general trend in how the population size changed? Is the trend the same for all teams? Describe the trend in your own words.
2. Review the hypotheses you developed in Step 3. Are any of them supported by the data the class gathered? Are any of them not supported by these data? Explain.

   A hypothesis is supported when it is consistent with the data collected. For example, consider this hypothesis: "A yeast population will grow faster in an environment where 5 grams (g) of sugar is added than in an environment where no sugar is added." Next, study your graphed data. Does the yeast with the sugar have a steeper slope than the yeast without sugar? If so, the data are consistent with the hypothesis, and thus support it.
3. What factors contributed to population growth? What factors contributed to a decline in population growth? What evidence do you have?

distributed in the nutrient medium. Once students have finished making their counts, they should calculate the average number of yeast cells per field of view.

Students should note whether anything grows in the control test tubes. Bacteria or fungi (not yeast) are common contaminants. If bacteria are introduced, they will quickly overgrow the yeast culture. Should a culture become contaminated, discuss the situation as another example of a limiting factor in population growth. Impress on the students the scientific necessity for uniformity of procedure.

If students measure turbidity using density indicator strips or a Spec 20 measurement, they can compare the measure of turbidity to their cell counts. For example, students might use the turbidity strips or a Spec 20 measurement each day to estimate the growth of the populations and make sample counts on days 0, 1, 4, and 7 (to help them relate the turbidity to the actual number of organisms). Sample counts will be used in calculating estimated population size from the turbidity data. Stress the importance of inverting the tube gently a few times before using either of these techniques.

Have teams record their data each day on a class master table on the board. From the pooled data, students can compare the results from the different environmental conditions they created. They will need their individual data to construct growth-curve graphs.

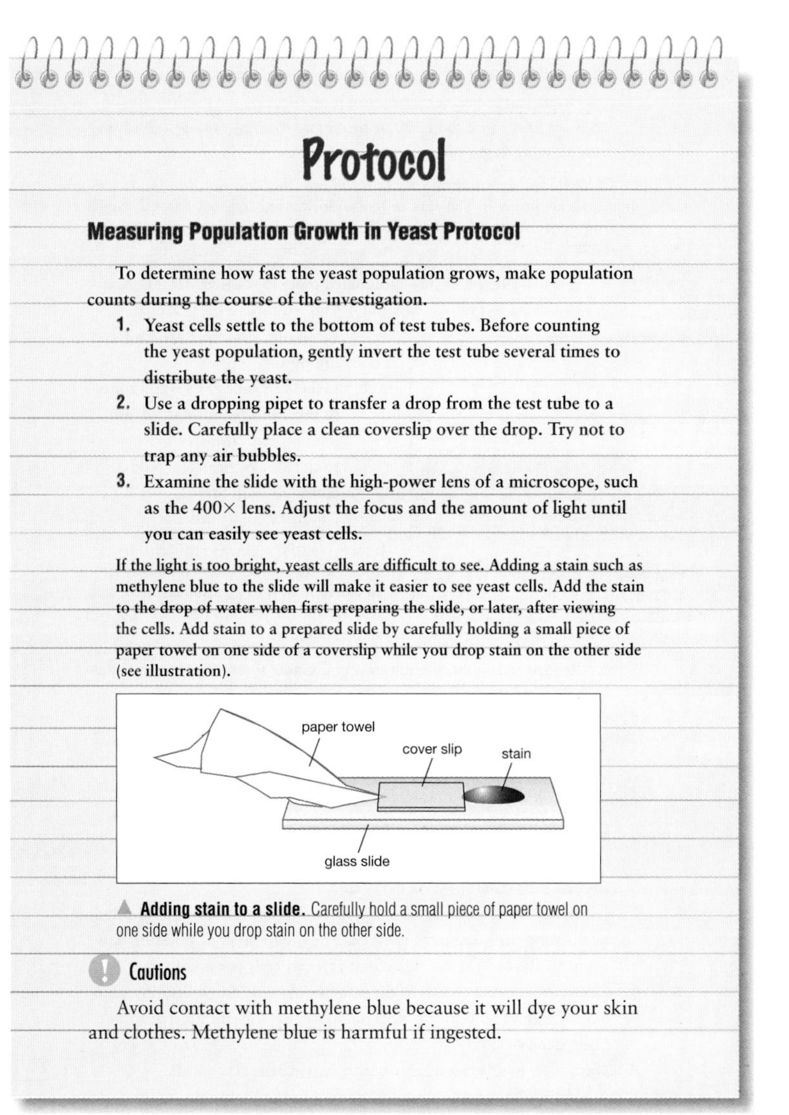

Protocol

Measuring Population Growth in Yeast Protocol

To determine how fast the yeast population grows, make population counts during the course of the investigation.

1. Yeast cells settle to the bottom of test tubes. Before counting the yeast population, gently invert the test tube several times to distribute the yeast.
2. Use a dropping pipet to transfer a drop from the test tube to a slide. Carefully place a clean coverslip over the drop. Try not to trap any air bubbles.
3. Examine the slide with the high-power lens of a microscope, such as the 400× lens. Adjust the focus and the amount of light until you can easily see yeast cells.

If the light is too bright, yeast cells are difficult to see. Adding a stain such as methylene blue to the slide will make it easier to see yeast cells. Add the stain to the drop of water when first preparing the slide, or later, after viewing the cells. Add stain to a prepared slide by carefully holding a small piece of paper towel on one side of a coverslip while you drop stain on the other side (see illustration).

Adding stain to a slide. Carefully hold a small piece of paper towel on one side while you drop stain on the other side.

Cautions

Avoid contact with methylene blue because it will dye your skin and clothes. Methylene blue is harmful if ingested.

Answers to Stop and Think—Part I, SE page 710

1. The general trend should be an increase in the population across time. Some students might see little or no population growth if the conditions they created were inhospitable for the yeast.
2. Check if students understand what it means to have data that support a hypothesis, and spend time clarifying this issue if necessary. The hint below the question in the student book provides some guidance.

   Answers will vary depending on the students' hypotheses and the data they collected. Look for answers that provide evidence from the investigation.
3. Students should have seen faster population growth with more food (sugar) or higher temperatures. Population growth should have been less for yeast populations in a more acidic environment or in an environment with more alcohol. As the population reached higher numbers, the students should also have seen a decline in population growth.

NOTES:

4. Count all the yeast cells in your field of view. Your field of view is the circular area you see when you look through the microscope. If your count is more than 300 or too many to count, make a dilution by following Steps 4a–c.

Make certain you are counting yeast cells and not other material. Buds also count as individual yeast cells. The yeast cells often stick together. Don't count clumps of 3 or more cells as one cell. Refer to the following figure to see the appearance of yeast cells.

   a. Use the 1-milliliter (mL) graduated pipet to transfer 0.9 mL water to a clean test tube. Then add 0.1 mL culture to the test tube. Label this test tube "D1" for first dilution.
   b. Invert test tube D1 several times to mix, and then use the dropping pipet to transfer 1 drop to the grid of the slide. Add a coverslip as in Step 2.
   c. Count the yeast cells.

If there are still too many yeast cells to count, make another dilution by transferring 0.1 mL of D1 to a clean test tube with 0.9 mL water. Label this test tube "D2" for second dilution.

▲ **Yeast cells you might see in your light microscope.** Note the buds that are still attached to the yeast cells. These buds will become new individuals.

   d. Record the count, the dilution you made, if any, and the magnification of the lens you are using in your science notebook.

5. Record the count as the number of yeast cells per milliliter in the data table. Assume that the drop you placed on the slide is 0.1 mL.

What additional calculations must you make if you made the first dilution? The second dilution?

6. Make multiple counts. Do this by moving the slide to different positions without changing the magnification of the microscope. Record each count in your data table.
7. Calculate the average number of yeast cells per field of view. Do this by dividing the number of yeast cells by the number of fields of view counted. Record the average count as yeast cells per milliliter.
8. Continue to make counts of the number of yeast cells in culture each day for 7 days (except for weekends). Repeat the counting procedure from Steps 4–7.
9. Wash your hands thoroughly before leaving the classroom.

Process and Procedure

Part II: Interacting Populations

Materials

none

In Part II, students will interpret data from and read about moose, wolf, and balsam fir populations on Isle Royale. You can have students work on this part of the activity when they make their counts for Part I. Sample answers for questions about the graphs and readings are provided here.

Answers to Steps 1–4, and 6, SE pages 713–719

1a–b. Students should sketch the graphs in their science notebook and capture the following ideas in their highlight comments.

During most years since 1959, the moose population has fluctuated between 500 and 1,500 individuals. There was a spike in the number of moose to almost 2,500 in 1995, but the population declined dramatically in the next 2 years to 500 individuals, and since the late 1990s has fluctuated between 500 and 1,000.

The wolf population has fluctuated between 10 and 50 individuals. The population was largest between 1975 and 1980 at around 50, but dropped to 10 by 1982.

1c. Students should also note that after the moose population decreased in 1995, the wolf population also started decreasing. The wolf population appears to depend on the moose population for food, because the wolf population decreased in response to the decrease in the moose population.

Part II: Interacting Populations

There is another way to investigate populations from your classroom. You can look at data that scientists have already gathered about populations in nature. How does population growth in a natural environment compare with yeast growing in a lab? The conditions you grew the yeast in varied, just as conditions in nature vary. But populations in nature interact with one another. A yeast population in nature would interact with other populations, such as bacteria.

In Part II, you and a partner will analyze scientists' data from Isle Royale National Park. You will learn how the interactions of three populations affect their size. Isle Royale is the largest island in Lake Superior (see figure 14.3). Its isolation gives scientists a unique opportunity to study the interactions of mammal populations. It is a closed system because mammals cannot regularly enter or leave the island. Scientists have learned valuable information about population interactions from this system.

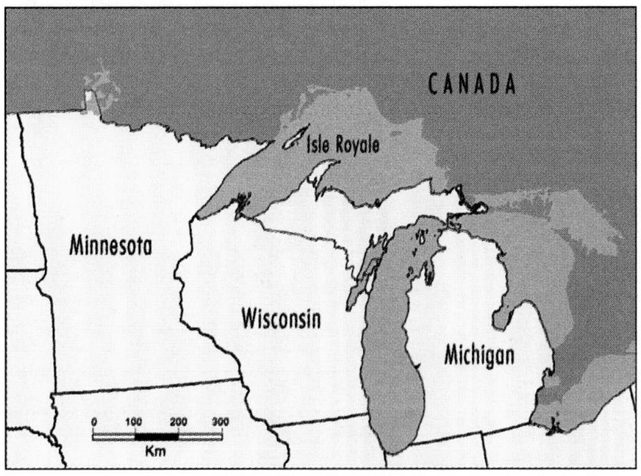

Figure 14.3 Map of Lake Superior and surrounding region. Isle Royale is located off the northern coast of Lake Superior. The island is about 72 kilometers (km) long and 14 km wide at its widest point. It was designated as a national park in 1931.

Materials

none

Process and Procedure

1. Study the graphs in figure 14.4.
   a. Sketch the essential features of the graphs in your science notebook.
   b. Write highlight comments and a caption for each figure.

Focus on any changes you observe.

   c. Look at the change in the moose population between 1995 and 1998. Then look at the wolf population between 1995 and 1998. What do you notice? Describe the changes in the moose and wolf populations. How do you think the moose and wolf populations might be related?

NOTES:

NOTES:

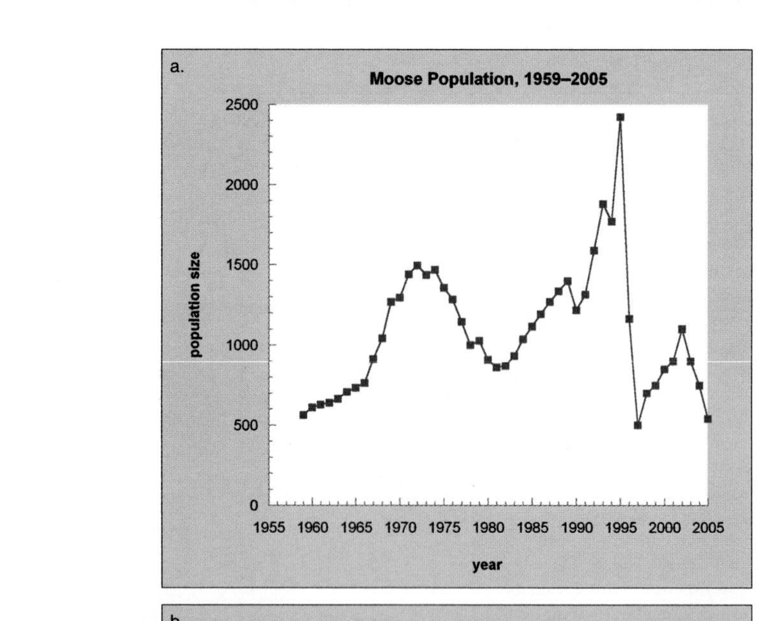

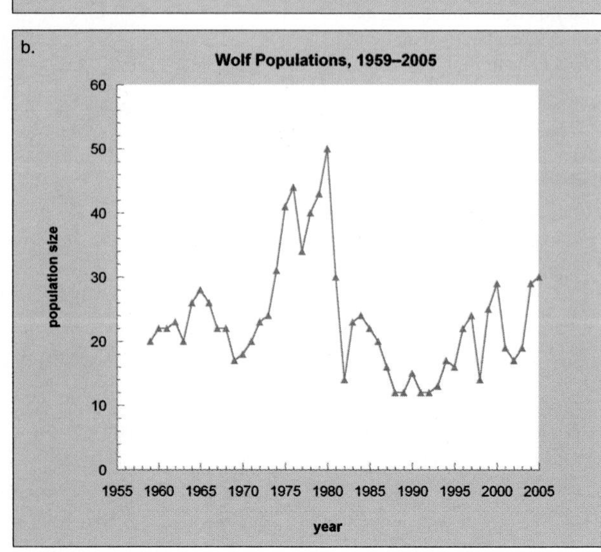

▶ **Figure 14.4 Moose and wolf populations on Isle Royale.** Biologists estimated the (a) moose and (b) wolf populations on Isle Royale from 1959 to 2005. What changes do you notice in the moose and wolf populations?

714 Unit 4 Sustaining Earth Systems

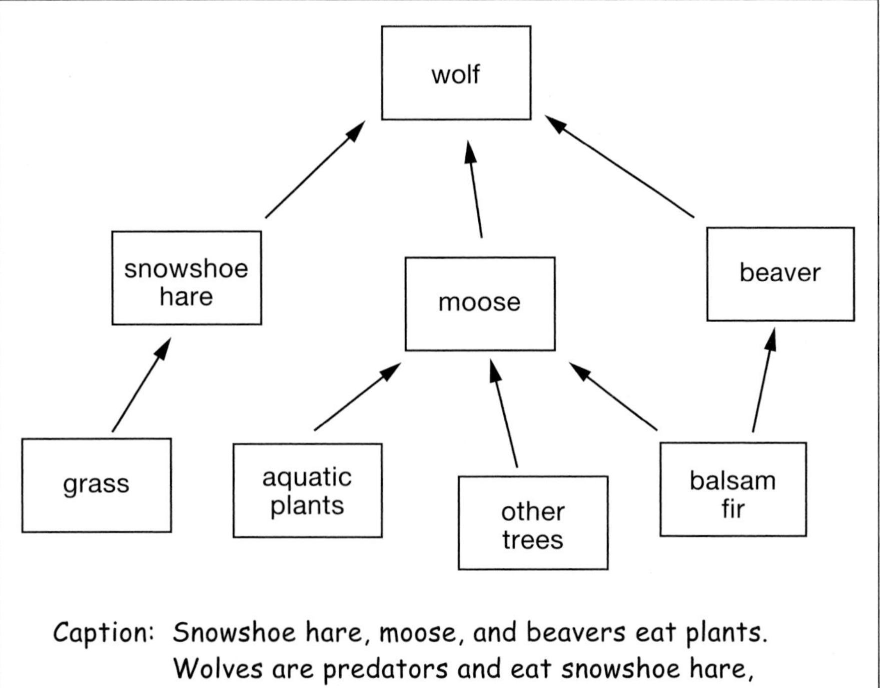

Figure T14.2 Example of a food web for Step 2. Food webs should include more than the relationship between moose, wolf, and balsam fir.

d. Read to a partner your highlight comments, captions, and description of how the moose and wolf populations are related. Modify what you have written if necessary.

2. Read *Moose and Wolves on Isle Royale* to learn what scientists know about these populations.
   a. As you read, draw a food web in your science notebook that shows the relationship between the organisms described. Include a caption with your drawing.
   b. Read your caption aloud to a partner. Then adjust your caption based on feedback from your partner.

READING

Moose and Wolves on Isle Royale

The research on Isle Royale constitutes one of the world's longest, continuous studies of either wolves or moose. Moose arrived on the island around 1900. They either swam or crossed an ice bridge, which rarely forms, from the mainland (see figure 14.5). Wolves crossed an ice bridge around 1950. The monitoring of the moose and wolf populations began in 1959 and has continued since. Isle Royale is essentially a single prey–single predator system. The simplicity of this system is not typical but makes it well suited for research. Scientists hope that studying this simple system will help them better understand more complex systems.

Figure 14.5 Isle Royale in the winter. Isle Royale is separated from the mainland by more than 24 km of water. Very few species have colonized the island. What might bring more organisms to the island?

1d. Give students time to read to a partner their highlight comments, captions, and description of how moose and wolf are related. Make sure they modify what they have written as well.

2. See figure T14.2.

NOTES:

Moose and Wolves on Isle Royale, continued

Moose (*Alces alces*) are the only large herbivores on Isle Royale (figure 14.6). Moose feed on aquatic vegetation in the summer and woody vegetation in the winter. They prefer to feed on balsam fir (*Abies balsamea*) seedlings over other tree species. In 2005, the moose population consisted predominantly of old moose, those that were more than 10 years old. These moose survived a large die-off in their population in 1996, which was caused by a severe winter and delayed spring. Mild winters can also be difficult for moose because of the increased number of winter ticks. A high number of ticks in moose can lead to anemia and reduced feeding. Older moose and moose weakened by winter ticks are more vulnerable to wolf attacks.

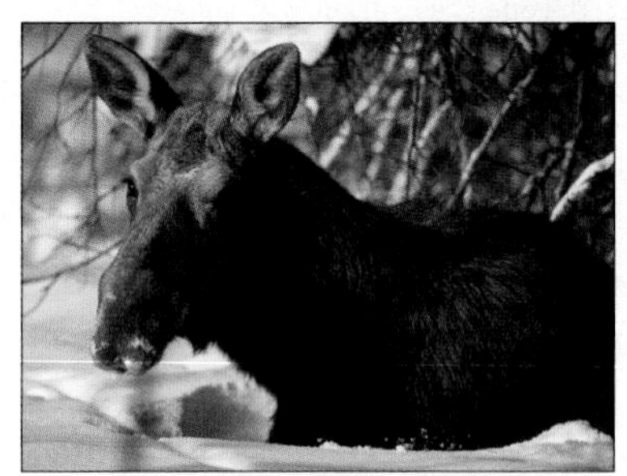

▲ **Figure 14.6 Moose in the winter.** Moose have difficulty moving and finding food in deep snow.

▲ **Figure 14.7 Wolf pack.** Wolves work together in packs to catch their prey. How do you think deep snow affects the likelihood of a wolf pack attacking a moose?

716 Unit 4 Sustaining Earth Systems

3a. Factors that might increase the moose population include smaller populations of wolves reduce predation. More aquatic vegetation provides more food for more moose. A mild winter allows more moose to survive. An increase in reproduction would increase the size of the moose population. An increase in the number of hares, or beavers might divert the food source for the wolf from the moose to the hare or beaver.

Factors that might decrease a moose population include a mild winter that might cause moose to die because moose have more ticks during mild winters. This makes them vulnerable to wolves. An increase in the wolf population might result in more moose being killed by wolves. A decrease in hares or beavers would lead to increase feeding on moose. A decrease in plants would result in fewer moose.

3b. Factors that might increase the wolf population include larger moose populations that would provide more food for wolves, allowing more wolves to survive. Larger beaver or snowshoe hare populations might also allow more wolves to survive.

Factors that might decrease a wolf population include a smaller moose population that would provide less food for wolves. A decrease in genetic diversity might reduce the number of wolves by affecting their ability to survive. Fewer hares or beavers also might decrease the wolf population.

4a. The number of tagged trees has steadily decreased since 1988.

4b. The abundance of balsam fir trees is going to decline. Mature trees will continue to die, and there will be fewer saplings because there are not as many trees producing seeds.

6a–b. See figure T14.3.

Hunting of moose and wolves on the island is prohibited. Gray wolves (*Canis lupus*) are the only predators of the moose on the island (figure 14.7). Moose make up 90 percent of the wolves' diet. The other 10 percent of the diet consists of beavers (*Castor canadensis*) and snowshoe hares (*Lepus americanus*). Beavers eat balsam fir, and hares eat grass. The wolf population responds to fluctuations in its prey population (moose), but it is also influenced by other factors. In the early 1980s, many wolves died from canine parvovirus accidentally introduced by humans or their pet dogs. A decline in genetic diversity might also have the potential to affect the wolf population. Some species inbreeding makes populations more vulnerable to fitness loss. (Inbreeding is breeding between closely related individuals. Fitness is the ability of an organism to survive and reproduce in its environment.) For example, inbreeding might increase the likelihood that individuals in the wolf population will have a genetic disorder. Scientists have gathered evidence of vertebrae abnormalities in the Isle Royale wolf population. But so far, there is no evidence that the survival rate of wolves with the abnormality has changed.

3. Now that you know a little more about moose and wolves on Isle Royale, complete the tasks in Steps 3a–b.
   a. List at least 2 factors that you think might cause the moose population to *increase*. Then list at least 2 factors that might cause the moose population to *decrease*. Explain why for each factor.
   b. Repeat Step 3a for the wolf population.
4. Study the graph in figure 14.8. Then answer Questions 4a–b about the balsam fir population.

Look for and try to explain any changes you see. This is one of many effective ways to study graphs and charts.

   a. Describe the trend for tagged balsam fir trees.

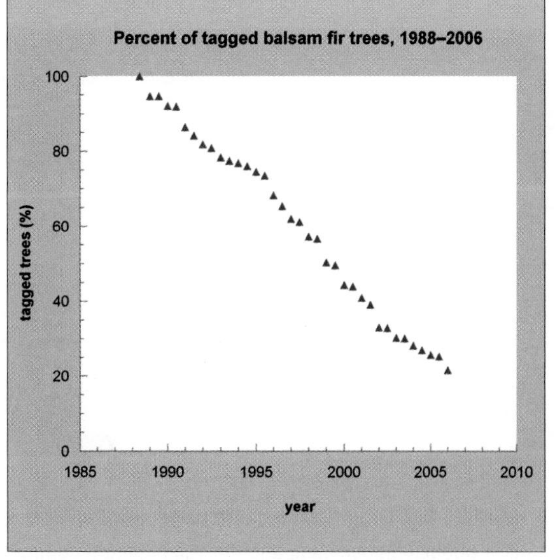

▲ **Figure 14.8 Percentage of tagged balsam fir trees.** Scientists tagged a portion of the balsam fir trees on Isle Royale in 1988. All of the trees were mature, meaning they were able to produce seeds. Since 1988, the number of tagged trees has declined. What has happened to the number of mature fir trees since 1988? What might have caused this change?

NOTES:

a.

N
W E
S

Caption: The west side of the island has mostly mature trees because moose are eating the young trees. The east side of the island has mostly young trees because fire burned many of the mature trees.

What I see: Mostly mature balsam fir trees on the west side of the island. Mostly young balsam fir trees on the east side of the island.

What it means: Moose are eating young trees on the west side. Fire burned many of the mature trees on the east side.

b.

Caption: 10 years later, the west side of the island has fewer trees because many mature trees have died. The east side of the island now has a mix of young and mature trees because many young trees have matured.

What I see: On the west side of the island, many mature trees are dead and a few new young trees are growing. The east side of the island has both mature and young trees.

What it means: After 10 years, many mature trees have died because of old age on the west side of the island. Some young trees have matured in the last 10 years.

▲ **Figure T14.3 Sample student sketches for Steps 6a–b.** (a) For Step 6a, students should show more mature trees on the left and more saplings on the right. (b) For Step 6b, students should show that mature trees have died on the left and that many saplings have matured on the right.

Answers to Reflect and Connect, SE pages 719–720

1. Moose are distributed where balsam fir are more abundant, on the east side of the island.

2a–b. See figure T14.4.

3a–b. See figure T14.5. Look for graphs that show the populations fluctuating but staying within the historic range. If students show dramatic increases or decreases in the populations, they should explain why in their highlight comments.

4. Students might mention temperature and precipitation (snowfall) or disease.

5. This question gets students to think about how competition might affect a population. See figure T14.6 for a sample graph students might create. Any graph is acceptable as long as students provide their reasoning for the change in the populations.

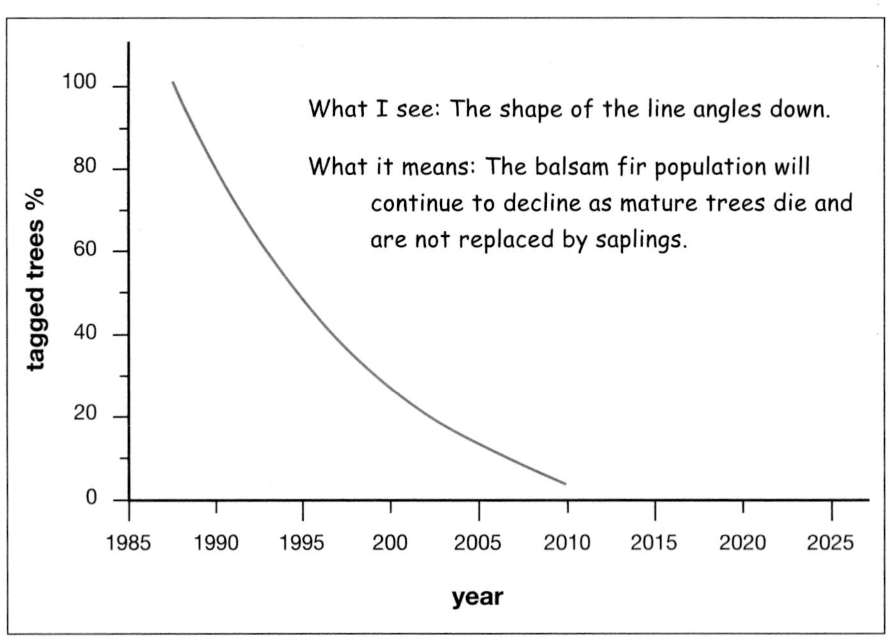

▲ **Figure T14.4 Graph of a balsam fir population for Question 2.** Students should show the balsam fir population declining and include highlight comments similar to those shown.

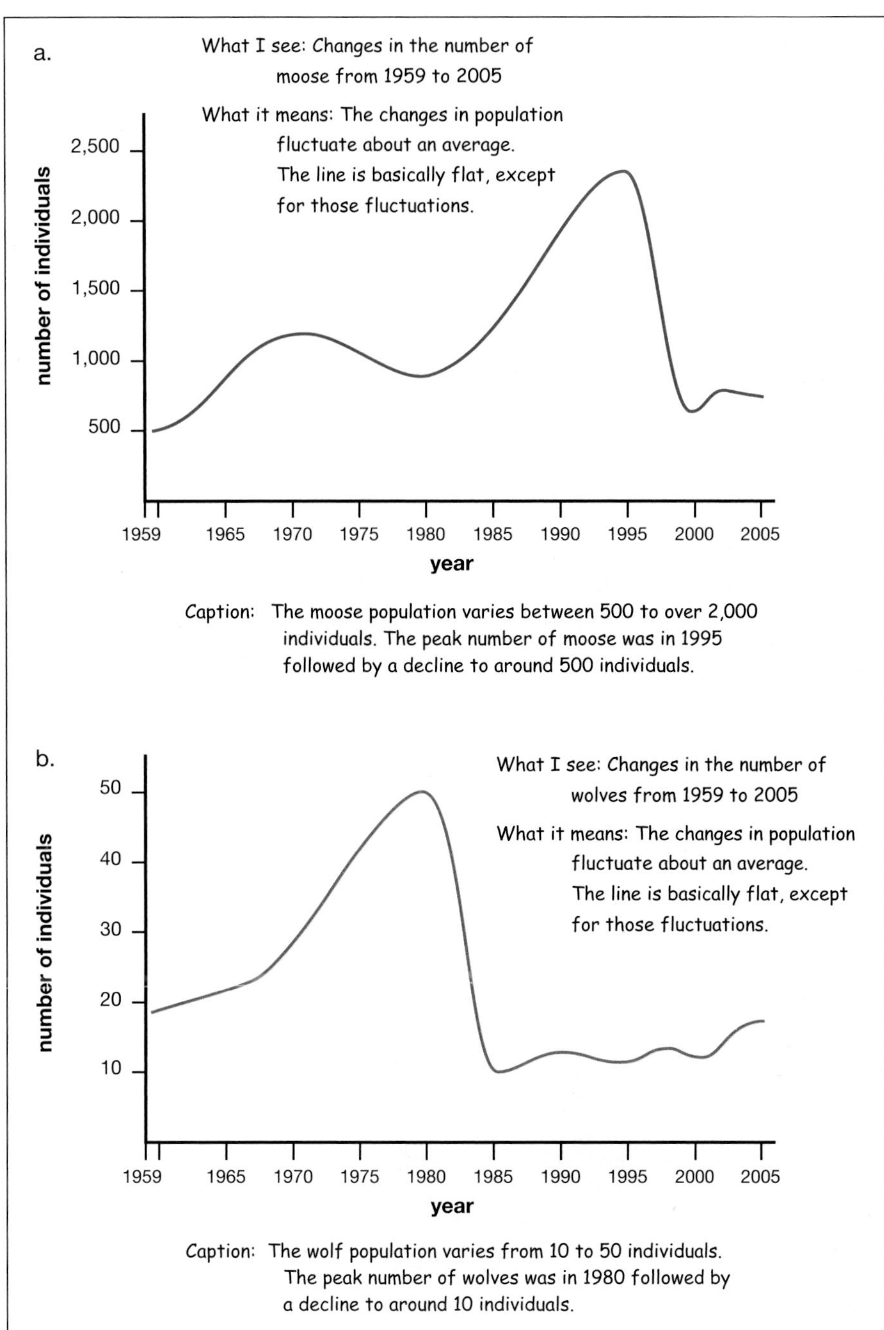

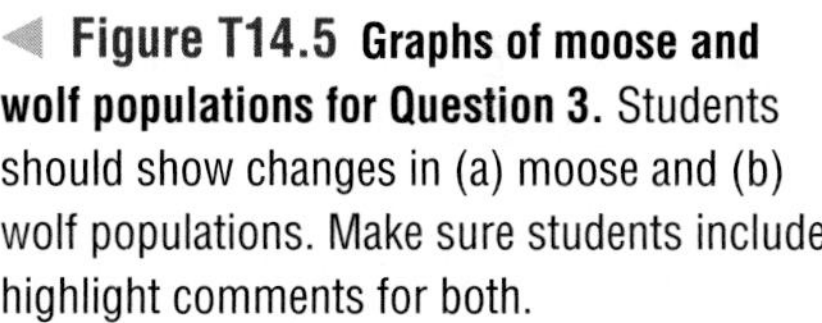

◀ **Figure T14.5 Graphs of moose and wolf populations for Question 3.** Students should show changes in (a) moose and (b) wolf populations. Make sure students include highlight comments for both.

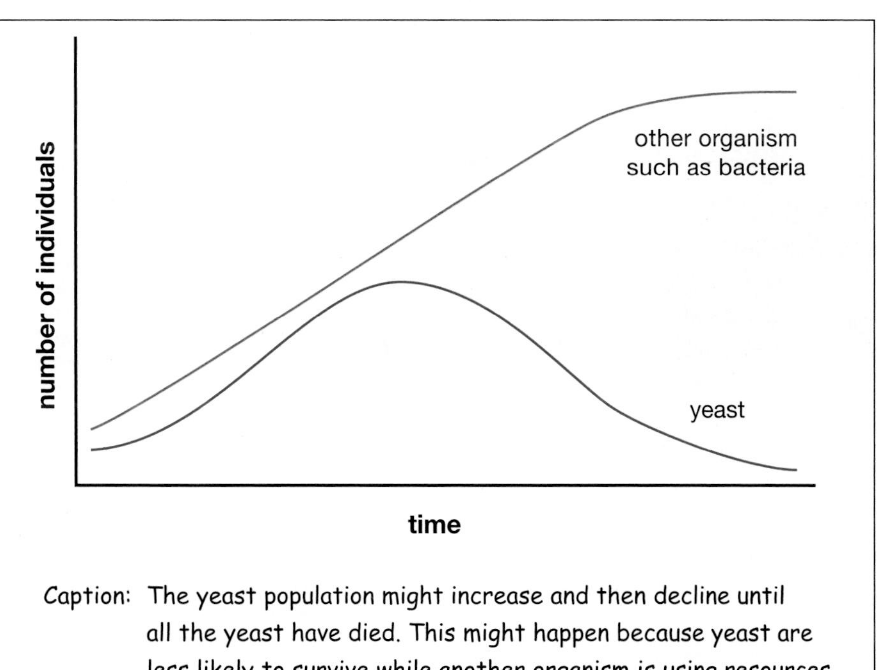

◀ **Figure T14.6 Sample student graphs for Question 5.** Students should show yeast and another population on their graphs. The graphs of the yeast population should look slightly different from the graphs that students created in the yeast investigation.

EXPLAIN

Systems in Balance

Activity Overview

In Part I, students will learn what causes populations to grow and how limiting factors affect populations. In Part II, students will read about interactions between the biotic and abiotic environments in ecosystems.

Before You Teach

Background Information

Limiting Factors

A variety of factors can limit the distribution, abundance, or growth of organisms. These factors, called limiting factors, may affect organisms by being too scarce, too abundant, or too unfavorable.

Some limiting factors are abiotic. Abiotic factors affect the distribution and abundance of organisms in an ecosystem because organisms can live and reproduce only within a specific range of environmental conditions. That is, each species has a range of tolerance for each abiotic factor. A species cannot survive outside this range and, even within this range, it does best within a narrow zone of optimal conditions. As an environmental condition approaches the upper or lower limit of a species' tolerance range, the condition exerts a limiting influence on the species' distribution and abundance by affecting survival, reproduction, or both. The tolerance ranges of species vary. Some species tolerate a broad range of conditions, whereas others have narrower requirements. In general, species with wide tolerances to many factors tend to be more widely distributed in the environment than species with narrow tolerances.

Other limiting factors are biotic. For example, the eastern oyster in the Chesapeake Bay tolerates salinities from 7 to 30 parts per thousand (ppt), but it is most abundant in water with moderate salinities (10–18 ppt). Its abundance in these waters reflects the fact that a number of oyster predators and parasites live in higher-salinity waters. The presence of these predators and parasites limits the abundance of the oysters in these waters, even though the salinity itself is not limiting.

Understanding the factors that limit populations helps to explain why particular species grow in some areas and not in others. It also helps to explain why changes in an ecosystem can trigger changes in the distribution and abundance of the organisms that live in it.

Energy Flow

When one organism eats another organism, energy is transferred from one to the other. In fact, the arrows in a food web indicate how energy flows through an ecosystem because of such transfers. Examining this flow of energy is one way to understand the interactions that occur among organisms in an ecosystem.

Energy enters an ecosystem through the producers, the organisms that occupy the first feeding, or trophic, level of the food web. Producers make their own energy-rich molecules through processes such as photosynthesis. The major producers in the world's terrestrial ecosystems are green plants. In the world's aquatic ecosystems, the major producers are phytoplankton, which consist primarily of algae.

The rate at which producers convert the light energy from the Sun

Answers to Steps 4b–6 are on TE pages 717–717a.

b. The data in figure 14.8 show the percentage of tagged mature fir trees that remain each year since 1988. Mature trees produce seeds. These trees are necessary for saplings (young trees) to become established and contribute new growth in the forest. How do you think the change in the abundance of mature balsam fir trees will affect the overall abundance of balsam fir trees?

Think about a factor that should increase the population.

▲ **Figure 14.9 The effect of moose on balsam fir.** (a) Balsam fir growth is hindered where moose feed intensely. Moose can feed in this forest, where there is an open canopy and very few mature balsam fir. (b) An exclosure is an area fenced off to keep organisms out. This 50-year-old exclosure shows that where moose are excluded, balsam fir are abundant and healthy. This forest is protected from moose and contains mature balsam firs and a dense canopy.

5. Read the following paragraph about the forest vegetation on Isle Royale. Use the following questions to focus your reading:
   - "How does the age and number of trees on the east end of the island compare with the trees on the west end of the island?"
   - "What factors contribute to the differences?"

   Forests on the east end of the island have more young balsam fir trees than forests on the west end of the island. After a wildfire burned many trees on the east end, the number of new balsam fir trees there has been gradually increasing. On the west end of the island, the growth of new balsam firs is very low. As moose feed on balsam fir saplings, they prevent the saplings from growing (see figure 14.9). Most of the trees on the west end are old and produce fewer seeds. Many of the older trees are expected to die in the next 10 years.
6. Complete Steps 6a–d to show what you have learned about the abundance of balsam fir trees and how the abundance might change in the future.

into energy-rich molecules is called gross primary productivity. Producers use about half the energy they produce to carry out the day-to-day processes of life; they use the remaining energy to build new body tissue (biomass). The rate at which producers build biomass through growth and reproduction is called *net primary productivity*. Net primary productivity usually is measured by the amount of energy (in kilocalories, or kcal) that is stored in body tissue per square meter per year. It is also measured by the mass of the tissue (in grams) that is produced per square meter per year.

Ecosystems vary greatly in their productivity. As you might expect, a variety of factors influence ecosystem productivity, including temperature and the availability of sunlight, water, and nutrients. Tropical rain forests, coral reefs, and estuaries are among the most productive ecosystems in the world. Deserts, tundra, and the open ocean are among the least.

The energy that producers store as biomass is available to consumers, organisms that eat other organisms. Thus, herbivores obtain their energy by eating plant material, and carnivores obtain their energy by eating herbivores or other carnivores. Figure 14.20 in the student book illustrates the one-way flow of energy from the Sun to producers and then to consumers.

The total amount of energy decreases as energy is passed from one trophic level to another in an ecosystem. This reduction occurs because only a small amount of the energy that is taken in as food by one organism is actually converted into biomass that can be consumed by the next organism in the food chain. The rest of the energy is used to power activities such as growth, repair of tissues, and movement; stored in an indigestible form that is not available to the next consumer; converted into heat; or lost to decomposition.

The decrease in total available energy (kcal) at higher trophic levels in an ecosystem is reflected in the total number of organisms occupying each level. Typically, a particular ecosystem has many more producers than primary consumers, more primary consumers than secondary consumers, and so on. For example, a small valley may contain a million producers such as grasses, a hundred thousand primary consumers such as mice and grasshoppers, one or two thousand secondary consumers such as snakes, and a hundred or so top-level consumers such as foxes and predatory birds. Likewise, the total biomass of the producers typically far exceeds that of the primary consumers, and so on, up the food chain.

The large energy loss that occurs as energy is transferred from one trophic level to the next in a food chain explains why food chains usually have no more than four or five consecutive links. The amount of energy available at the highest trophic level (for example, the amount of energy available in a few foxes) is simply not sufficient to support another level (for example, animals that might prey on foxes). The energy relationships in ecosystems also explain why ecosystems typically have so few top-level consumers such as tigers, eagles, and sharks, and why these organisms can die off when the ecosystems that support them are disturbed.

Answers to Step 6 are on TE pages 717–717a.
Answers to Reflect and Connect are on TE pages 717a–b.

a. Represent in a sketch what you read about the current abundance of firs. Consider making a map of the island that uses simple drawings to represent the abundance of balsam firs. (A map of Isle Royale is shown in figure 14.10.) Include highlight comments and a caption with your sketch.
b. Create another labeled sketch that represents the abundance of firs on Isle Royale in 10 years.
c. Use an effective strategy to get feedback on your sketch.
d. Record the results of your feedback in your science notebook.

SCILINKS NSTA
Go to: www.scilinks.org
Topic: moose population
Code: 2Inquiry719a
Topic: wolf population
Code: 2Inquiry719b

Reflect and Connect

Work alone to answer the following questions in your science notebook.

1. Study figure 14.10. Explain why moose are distributed unevenly across Isle Royale during the winter of 2002.

Review the paragraph from Step 5 to help you answer the question.

2. Copy figure 14.8 into your science notebook and extend the *x*-axis to 2055.
   a. Predict how the balsam fir population will change over the next 50 years.

Extending the line will help you make your prediction.

   b. Add highlight comments to the graph to explain why you think those changes will occur.
3. Copy figure 14.4 into your science notebook. Extend the *x*-axis to 2055.
   a. Predict how the moose and wolf populations will change over the next 50 years.

Extending the line for both populations will help you make your predictions.

Figure 14.10 Moose distribution on Isle Royale during winter 2002. Moose are more common on one end of the island. What might cause this distribution?

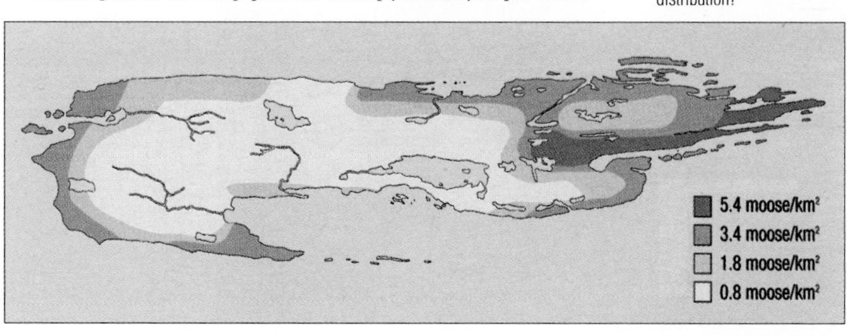

Materials—Part I
For each student

1 calculator
graph paper
graphs of the yeast population from the activity *Changing Populations*

Materials—Part II

none

Advance Preparation

Gather calculators and graph paper for Part I.

As You Teach

Outcomes and Indicators of Success

By the end of this activity, students should

1. be able to explain how populations grow and that populations have limits to growth.

   They will demonstrate their ability by

   - graphing bacterium and paramecium populations and describing the growth curve;
   - drawing a line on their graphs of the yeast and paramecium populations that represents the carrying capacity for those populations;
   - describing what might influence the carrying capacity of the yeast population;
   - writing an equation showing how population size is related to births, deaths, immigration, and emigration; and
   - identifying possible limiting factors for yeast populations and for the moose population on Isle Royale.

2. understand that interactions occur between populations in ecosystems and between the abiotic and biotic environments in ecosystems.

   They will demonstrate their understanding by

   - describing how a predator-prey relationship affects the population size of both organisms;
   - describing how a yeast population would be affected by the presence of another population;
   - identifying the relationships between organisms as predator-prey, competition, or symbiosis; and
   - explaining how abiotic factors affect biotic factors in ecosystems.

3. understand that ecosystems are important for the flow of energy and the cycling of matter.

   They will demonstrate their understanding by

   - explaining that ecosystems can support more primary consumers than secondary consumers because energy is lost between each trophic level,
   - representing the relative amount of biomass in different trophic levels in a diagram,
   - diagramming the energy flowing through a grassland ecosystem, and
   - explaining why energy flows in one direction through ecosystems and why chemicals cycle through an ecosystem.

4. be able to analyze and create graphs.

   They will demonstrate their ability by

   - describing changes in the moose and wolf population graphs across time and
   - extending the lines on graphs to predict how populations will change in the future.

Answers to Reflect and Connect 3b–5 are on TE pages 717a–b.

b. Add highlight comments to the graph to explain why you think those changes will occur.

4. In Part I, you investigated different environmental conditions for a population of yeast. What environmental conditions do you think might affect the populations on Isle Royale? List at least 2 conditions.
5. Suppose you could add an organism that feeds on yeast to the yeast culture. Explain how you think the yeast population would be affected. Give your answer as a graph that shows the resulting yeast population and the population of another organism across time. Include a caption with your graph.

EXPLAIN

Systems in Balance

Natural processes are important to the maintenance of systems. Chemical reactions are one type of natural process. You learned in unit 1 that many chemical reactions are reversible under the right conditions. A chemical system is at equilibrium when the rate of the forward reaction equals the rate of the reverse reaction. These reactions are an important part of processes in living systems. In unit 3, you learned that fluxes into and out of a system maintain the system. In the global carbon cycle, many of the carbon fluxes depend on processes that involve chemical reactions. (Remember, a carbon flux is the movement of carbon between reservoirs.)

In *Systems in Balance*, you will learn how natural processes maintain ecosystems from year to year (figure 14.11). Changes in populations are part of these natural processes. For example, fluxes into and out of a population eventually cause a population to reach equilibrium. Interactions between populations, just like interactions between molecules, influence a system. In this case, the system is an ecosystem. In Part I, you will learn what influences populations. Then in Part II, you will learn what shapes ecosystems, including how the interactions of populations shape ecosystems.

Figure 14.11 Oak-grassland ecosystem. Oak-grassland ecosystems consist of a mixture of oak forest, meadows, and grasslands. What natural process might help maintain this ecosystem?

720 | Unit 4 Sustaining Earth Systems

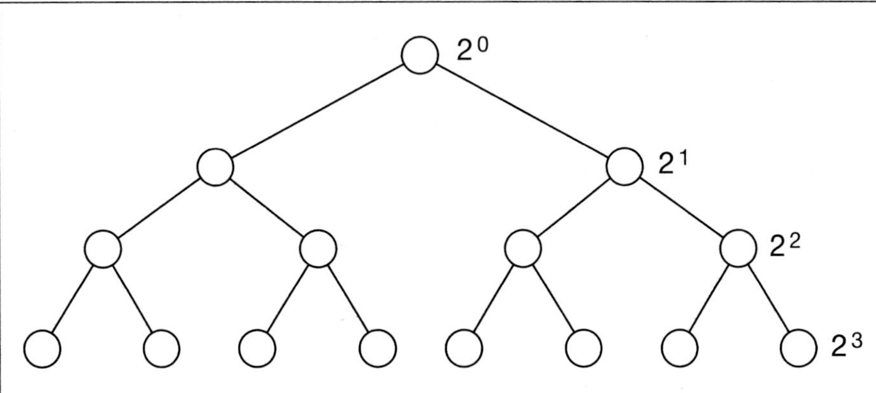

▲ **Figure T14.7 Exponential growth.** A diagram like this might help students see the pattern of growth. They should see that each new row represents the cells dividing.

Strategies

Getting Started

In preparation for learning about limiting factors, ask students what conditions or other factors might limit the size of populations in nature.

Process and Procedure

Part I: Population Dynamics

Materials

For each student

1 calculator
graph paper
graphs of the yeast population from the activity *Changing Populations*

Students may struggle with Step 1. Plan to spend time helping students calculate the bacterium population size across time and then determine the mathematical representation for this change. Begin by helping students see the pattern in the increase in the bacterium population. They should see that the population doubles during each time period. Then help them see the mathematical relationship by writing out the equations $1 = 2^n$, $2 = 2^n$, and $4 = 2^n$. Consider drawing a diagram like figure T14.7 on the board to help students see the pattern. They should recognize that n for the second and the third equation is 1 and 2, respectively. They should begin to see a sequential pattern developing for n. This pattern matches the time period in the first column. For example, 0 hours (hr) is time period 0, 0.5 hr is time period 1, and 1 hr is time period 2. See the answers to Step 1.

Answers to Step 1 are on TE pages 721a–b.

Part I: Population Dynamics

Materials

For each student

1 calculator

graph paper

graphs of the yeast population from the activity *Changing Populations*

Process and Procedure

You have investigated several populations. Did these populations stay the same or change across time? What makes a population change? Given enough space and **resources**, a population can potentially continue to grow indefinitely. In Part I, you will work alone or with a partner to learn what characterizes populations and what limits population growth.

1. Imagine a single bacterium cell in a large container of nutrient medium. If the cell and its descendants divide every 30 minutes (min), how many cells would you expect to find in the container in 24 hours (hr)? Model the population growth of bacteria through calculations and graphing. Steps 1a–e will help you.
   a. Copy the table in figure 14.12 into your science notebook. Add enough rows so that you can calculate for 24 hr in Step 1d. You will calculate the increase in the number of bacterium cells in 3 hr. Perform the calculations and complete the column titled "number of bacterium cells."
   b. Identify the mathematical relationship in the right-hand column. First, read down the middle columns. How much does the number of bacterium cells increase by? Now read down the right-hand column. Calculate what n is by using the amount of increase.

For example, if $2 = 2^n$, then n must be 1 for the second row.

Time (hours)	Number of cell divisions	Number of bacterium cells	Mathematical representation
0.0	0	1	$= 2^n$
0.5	1	2	$= 2^n$
1.0	2	4	$= 2^n$
1.5	3	8	$= 2^n$
2.0	4		$= 2^n$
2.5	5		$= 2^n$
3.0	6		$= 2^n$

◄ **Figure 14.12 Modeling bacterium population growth.** How does the number of bacterium cells change every 30 min?

Time (hours)	Number of cell divisions	Number of bacterium cells	Mathematical representation
0.0	0	1	$= 2^0$
0.5	1	2	$= 2^1$
1.0	2	4	$= 2^2$
1.5	3	8	$= 2^3$
2.0	4	*16*	$= 2^4$
2.5	5	*32*	$= 2^5$
3.0	6	*64*	$= 2^6$

Figure T14.8 Completed table for Steps 1a–b. Answers for the number of bacterium cells (Step 1a) and *n* (Step 1b) are shown in italics.

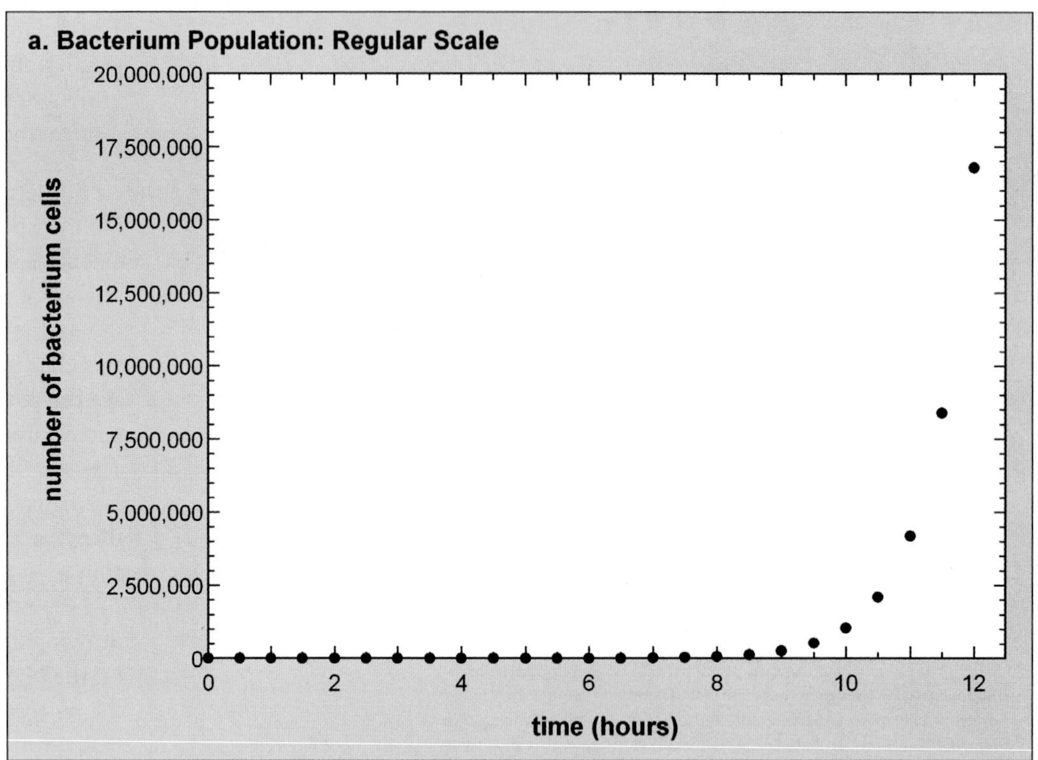

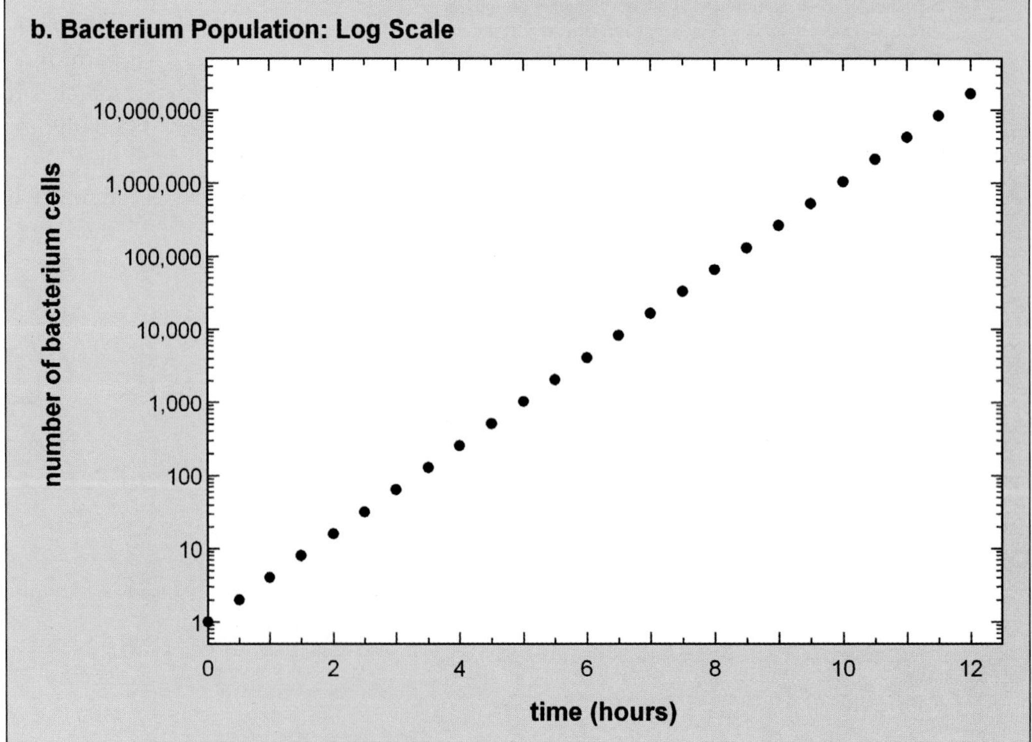

Figure T14.9 Graphs of bacterium population for Step 1e. (a) The students' graphs should show a J-shaped curve for exponential growth on a regular scale, or (b) a constant slope on the log scale.

Answers to Step 1, SE pages 721–722

1a–b. See figure T14.8. Answers are shown in brackets.

1c. The 2 represents the cells doubling every 30 min. The n represents the number of times the cells have doubled (divided).

1d. Since the population doubles every half hour, n is 48 for a 24-hr period. The bacterium population after 24 hr would be $2^{48} = 281{,}474{,}976{,}710{,}656$ or 2.8×10^{14}.

1e. Consider having students plot the population for the number of bacterium cells using a regular scale (figure T14.9a) and a log scale (figure T14.9b). If students need experience with log scales or scientific notation, they can go through the *How to Use Graphs, Measure Slopes, and Estimate Uncertainty*, and *How to Use Very Large and Very Small Numbers* in the *How To* section in the back of the student book.

In Step 2, students read about exponential growth and learn that the bacterium population graph they just created shows exponential growth. Then in Step 3, they create a graph showing the relationship between population growth and population density. They also graph data from a paramecium population. In Step 4, they learn that the paramecium graph shows logistic growth, and they draw the carrying capacity for the population on their graphs.

Answers to Steps 2–4, SE pages 722–723

2. Students should calculate the total for the savings account as follows:

$$\$100 \text{ a month} = \$100 \times 12 \text{ months} = \$1{,}200$$

$$\$1 \text{ that doubles every month} = 2^{12} = \$4{,}096$$

3b. See figure T14.10.

3c. The paramecium graph is similar to the bacterium graph because both populations rapidly increased in size initially. The paramecium graph is different from the bacterium graph because after more time passed, the paramecium population stayed the same size, but the bacterium population kept increasing.

4. See figure T14.10.

Encourage students to choose a literacy strategy for the reading *Population Growth* in Step 5. They should also use the focus question to help guide their reading. They should apply what they learned from the reading to help them complete Step 6 and answer the *Stop and Think* questions.

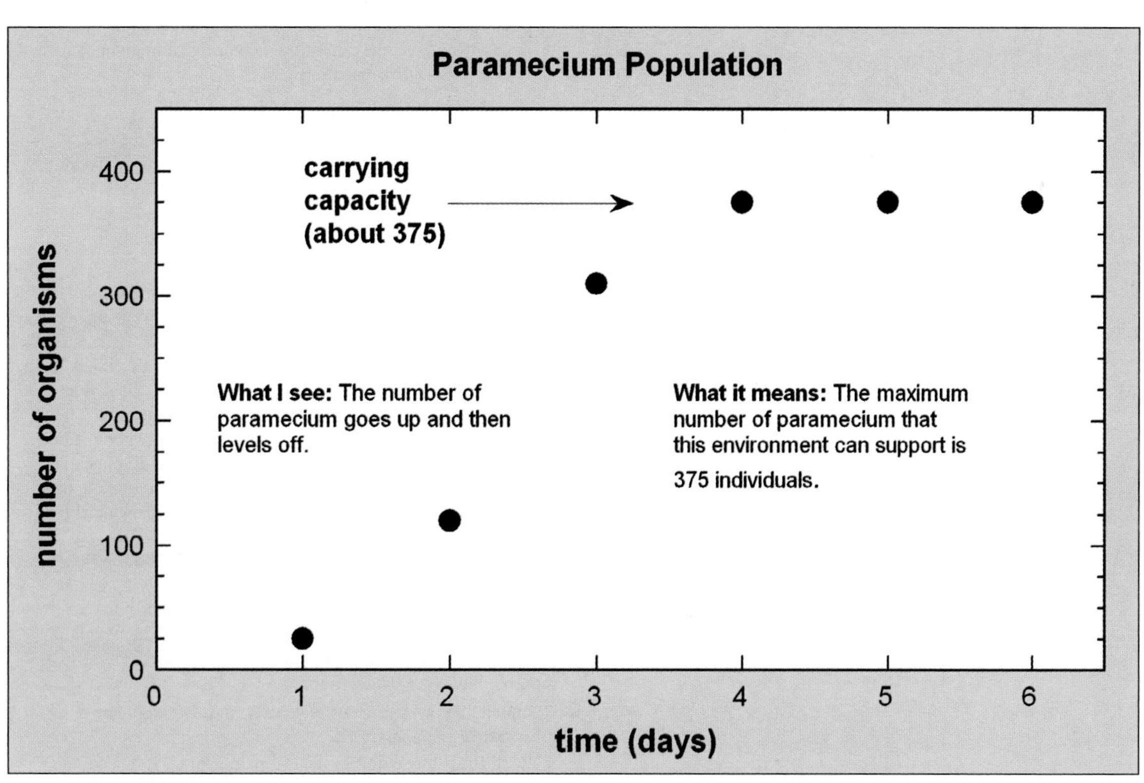

Figure T14.10 Sample graph of paramecium growth. Students' highlight comments should mention that the population size levels off.

NOTES:

Answers to Steps 1c–e, 2–4 are on TE pages 721a–b.

c. Notice how the population doubles every 30 min. What does the 2 in the right-hand column represent? What does n represent?

d. Now calculate the bacterium population after 24 hr. Show your work. Consider rounding the number and giving your answer in scientific notation.

For example, the scientific notation for 5,869,481 is 5.9×10^6.

e. Draw a graph of this bacterium population for a 12-hr period. Include highlight comments on your graph. Your graph represents 1 type of population growth curve.

2. Read the following 2 paragraphs to learn about exponential growth. Then write an answer in your science notebook for the question in the second paragraph.

   The graph of the bacterium population is an example of **exponential growth.** Exponential growth happens when an increase occurs at a constant *rate* per unit of *time.* At first, the population grows slowly, then it increases progressively faster and faster. The number of individuals added to the population gets larger and larger across time. This occurs because the constant rate of growth applies to a larger and larger population. Eventually, the population reaches a very large size. Exponential growth occurs in other situations as well. For example, compound interest makes the money in your savings account grow quickly. The amount your money grows depends on your interest rate.

   Think about this. Would you rather start with $1 in your savings account and have it double every month for 1 year, or get $100 each month for a year? Calculate the total for your savings account for both situations after 1 year. Then explain why you would choose $1 that doubles every month or $100 a month. Show your calculations.

3. Complete the tasks in Steps 3a–c to learn how exponential growth affects populations.

   a. Read the information in the following paragraph. You will use it to create a graph showing the relationship between population growth and population density.

   Why hasn't exponential growth resulted in enormous numbers of organisms that completely overwhelm Earth's resources? In reality, populations rarely grow exponentially. As a population grows, its **population density** increases as well. Population density is the number of individuals per unit of land area or water volume.

Answers to Steps 5–6, SE pages 723–725

5b. See figure T14.11.

6a. The completed equation follows:

$$\text{population size}_{\text{year 1}} = [\text{population size} + (\text{births} + \text{immigration}) - (\text{deaths} + \text{emigration})]_{\text{year 0}}$$

6b. The population size of least bitterns follows:

year 1 = 36, year 2 = 33, year 3 = 30, year 4 = 26

Term	How it is related to the focus question
birthrate	*An increase in birthrate increases population size.*
mortality rate	*An increase in mortality rate decreases population size.*
immigration	*Immigration increases population size.*
emigration	*Emigration decreases population size.*
limiting factor	*Limiting factors affect the maximum population size for an environment.*

◀ **Figure T14.11 Completed table for Step 5b.** Examples in italics show how students might describe the relationship between the term and the focus question.

b. Look at the data in figure 14.13. Decide how you will label the axes of your graph. Then graph the data to see how the growth of a paramecium population changes as the population density increases. Include highlight comments on your graph.

c. How is the paramecium graph similar to the bacterium graph? How is it different?

4. Add a horizontal line to your graph indicating the *carrying capacity* of the paramecium population. Read the following 2 paragraphs to learn what carrying capacity is.

The pattern of a population's size growing slowly, then rapidly, and finally leveling off is called **logistic growth.** You are familiar with logistic growth in other situations. For example, wages increase steadily when you begin working. Then they level off as you approach retirement.

Let's look at what happens in natural systems. As a population's density increases in an environment, the amount of space and resources decreases. Competition within the population increases as nutrients and other resources are used up. Toxic bodily wastes may build up in the environment. Predators and parasites may become common. All these factors reduce reproduction and increase the number of deaths in the population. This slows population growth. A population that develops in a new environment may begin to grow exponentially. But it soon slows and eventually approaches a maximum size. This maximum is called the **carrying capacity.** Carrying capacity is the largest population of a species that the environment can support in a given period of time. Carrying capacities are not fixed.

Time (days)	Number of organisms
1	25
2	120
3	310
4	375
5	375
6	375

Source: G. F. Gause. (1934). *The struggle for existence.* Baltimore: Williams and Wilkins.

▲ **Figure 14.13 Paramecium population data.** Paramecia are single-celled organisms. How will a graph of these data compare with the graph of the bacterium population in Step 1?

5. Read *Population Growth* to learn what causes populations to change size.

a. Use this question to focus your reading: "How is population size related to births, deaths, immigration, and emigration?"

b. Fill in the T-table in figure 14.14 as you read.

Term	How it is related to the focus question
birthrate	
mortality rate	
immigration	
emigration	
limiting factor	

▲ **Figure 14.14 Relationship to population size.** Describe how each term on the left is related to the focus question. Add any terms to the T-table that you think are important.

NOTES:

Population Growth

Imagine a park with 125 oak trees. Thirty years later, the park has only 115 oak trees. What does the decrease of 10 oak trees represent? Because trees cannot wander away, they must have died or been cut down. In this situation, the decrease represents the death rate, or **mortality rate**, of the oak tree population. The number of deaths in the oak tree population per unit of time is the mortality rate. Mortality is not the only change that can affect a population, however. While some of the trees may have died, some young oak trees may have started to grow from seed. Death decreases a population; reproduction increases it. The rate at which reproduction increases the population is called the **birthrate**.

Immigration and emigration are two other ways that change population size in organisms that can move. Imagine you studied the pigeon population in your city. You discovered that in 1 year a certain number of pigeons flew into the city and a certain number flew out. **Immigration** occurs when one or more individuals move into an area where others of their type can be found. Immigration increases the population. **Emigration** occurs when individuals leave the area. Emigration decreases the population. A simple way to remember the difference is that during *immigration* organisms move *into* an area. During *emigration*, organisms *exit* an area.

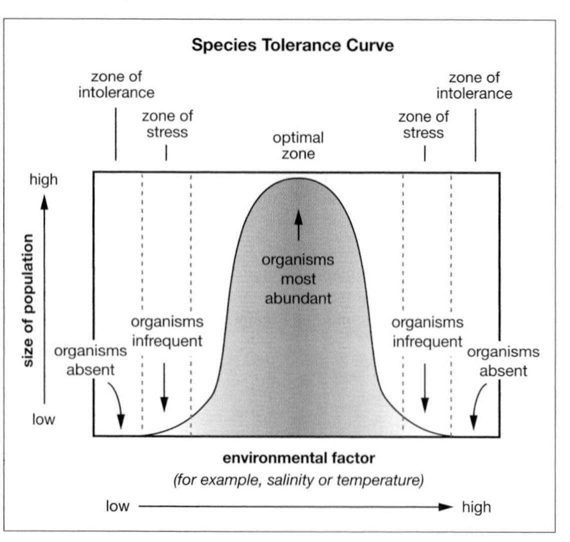

▲ **Figure 14.15 Species tolerance curve.** There are maximum and minimum levels of environmental factors that affect where an organism can survive. These levels might be determined by abiotic factors such as salinity or temperature. Can you think of other environmental factors that will affect where an organism lives?

NOTES:

Answers to Step 6 are on TE page 723.

In any population that can move, birthrate and immigration increase the population. And mortality and emigration decrease the population. Thus, a population's size is the result of the relationships among these rates.

What are some things that might decrease population growth? That is, what could reduce the birthrate or increase the mortality rate? Are there factors that could increase emigration? How does the environment influence population growth?

The **environment** is everything that surrounds and affects an organism. The environment has two parts. The living part is called the **biotic** environment. The biotic environment for a wolf on Isle Royale includes all the plants, animals, and microorganisms that live or once lived on the island. The nonliving part is called the **abiotic** environment. The abiotic environment includes such things as sunlight, water, nutrients, and physical structure.

The environment affects individuals. The environment may slow the individual's growth, kill it, or stimulate its growth and reproduction. Any biotic or abiotic factor that can *limit* the growth of a population is a **limiting factor**. For example, predators like coyotes are biotic limiting factors for a population of rabbits. Temperature is an example of an abiotic limiting factor. Many plants and animals only survive in a specific range of temperatures. Figure 14.15 shows a species tolerance curve. This graph illustrates how environmental factors affect the abundance of organisms.

Topic: population growth
Go to: www.scilinks.org
Code: 2Inquiry725

6. Complete the following 2 tasks to show your understanding of population growth.
   a. Finish the following equation to show how population size is related to births, deaths, immigration, and emigration.

      population size = ______________

   b. Calculate the size of a population of least bitterns (see figure 14.16) over a period of 4 years using data in figure 14.17.

▲ **Figure 14.16 Least bittern and chicks (*Ixobrychus exilis*).** Least bitterns are secretive marsh birds that live in wetlands with tall vegetation.

Time	Starting population	Birthrate (chicks/ year)	Mortality rate (birds/ year)	Immigration (birds/year)	Emigration (birds/ year)
Begin	30	4	6	10	2
year 1	?	3	3	2	5
year 2	?	3	3	2	5
year 3	?	3	4	3	6
year 4	?				

◄ **Figure 14.17 Information about a least bittern population.** How does the population change from one year to the next?

Answers to Stop and Think—Part I, SE page 726

1. Four things that determine population size are birthrate, mortality, immigration, and emigration.
2. See figure T14.12.

3a. The yeast population showed logistic growth because the population size leveled off after several days.

3b. The carrying capacity should match the plateau on the graph of the yeast population.

3c. The carrying capacity is likely to differ with the different environmental conditions students created. Students should explain that the environments created different limiting factors such as food, acidity, and alcohol content.

4a. Birthrate and mortality affect the moose and wolf populations. Immigration and emigration do not because moose and wolves rarely cross to and from the mainland and island.

4b. Students should refer to figure 14.5 in the student book. Students might say the carrying capacity for moose is anywhere from 500 to 1,500 and the carrying capacity for wolves is anywhere from 10 to 30. Accept answers that fall within the range of population sizes shown in the figure.

4c. Students might list balsam fir abundance, tick abundance, wolf abundance, and temperature or precipitation (abiotic).

4d. The carrying capacity might be reduced if the abundance of fir continues to decline because less food will be available for moose.

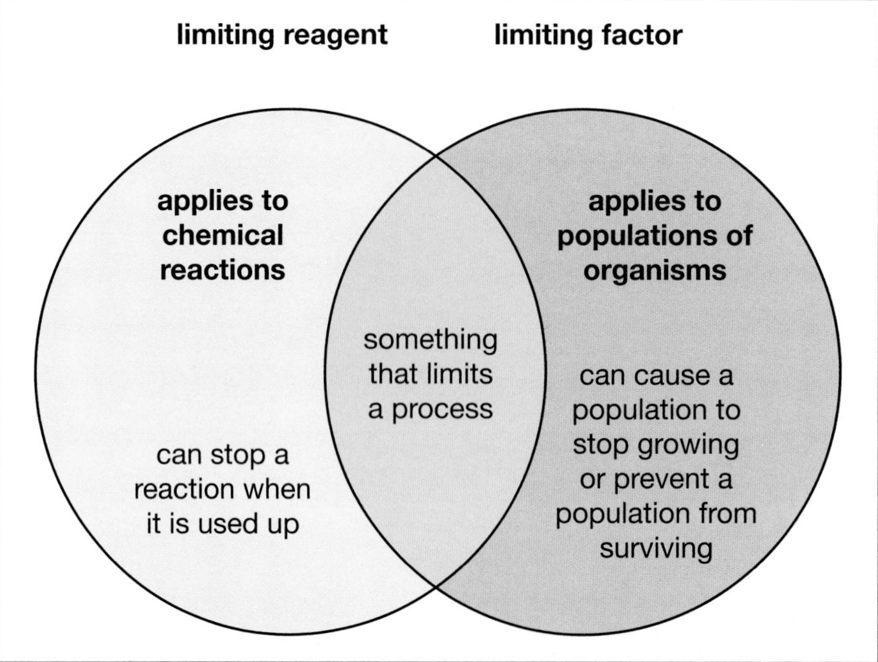

▲ **Figure T14.12 Answer to *Stop and Think* Question 2.** Students' Venn diagrams should show how limiting reagents are similar to and different from limiting factors.

Stop & THINK

PART I

Work alone or with a partner to answer the following questions in your science notebook.

1. What are the 4 factors that determine population size?
2. How is a limiting reagent in a chemical reaction similar to a limiting factor for a population? How is it different? Use a Venn diagram to show the similarities and differences.
3. You have learned about exponential and logistic growth. Apply this new knowledge to the yeast investigation from the explore activity, *Changing Populations*, and answer Questions 3a–c. Refer to your graph of the yeast population and the graphs from other teams.
   - **a.** What growth pattern (exponential or logistic) did the yeast population have? Explain your answer.
   - **b.** What was the carrying capacity of your team's yeast population? Provide evidence for your answer. If your yeast population did not reach carrying capacity, then estimate what the carrying capacity might have been if you had continued to monitor the yeast population. Provide an explanation for your estimate.
   - **c.** Was the carrying capacity for your team's yeast population different from the carrying capacity for other teams? Explain why or why not, and discuss possible limiting factors in your response.
4. Answer Questions 4a–d about the moose and wolf populations on Isle Royale. Review the text and graphs from the explore activity as necessary.
   - **a.** Which of these factors affect the moose and wolf populations: birthrate, mortality rate, immigration, and emigration?
   - **b.** Predict the carrying capacity for moose and wolves on Isle Royale.
   - **c.** List 4 limiting factors for the population of moose. At least 1 of the factors must be abiotic.
   - **d.** How do you think the change in the balsam fir population will affect the carrying capacity for moose on Isle Royale? Explain your answer.

NOTES:

Part II: Ecosystems

Materials

none

Process and Procedure

The world around you consists of more than populations of living organisms. How do the conditions in an environment influence populations? In Part II, you will work with a partner to learn about the systems that affect and are affected by living organisms. You also will relate what you learn about these systems to the cycling of matter and the flow of energy.

1. Think about what kind of relationships you have with the people you encounter. You also have relationships with organisms other than people. In fact, organisms are constantly interacting with other organisms. Work with your partner to consider these relationships.
   a. Read *Relationships among Populations* to learn about some of these interactions.
   b. Look ahead to Steps 2 and 3 to guide your reading. Take turns talking about your ideas. Revise your responses if you get new information after talking with your partner. Remember, this is the think-share-advise-revise (TSAR) strategy.

READING

Relationships among Populations

All populations of organisms, including human populations, interact with one another. The interactions form a complex web of relationships. These interactions can be beneficial or harmful. But all involve the cycling of matter and the flow of energy.

All the populations of different species in a designated area make up a **community**. Each environment has a community of different organisms. Many types of relationships help form a community's web of life. Each relationship involves at least two different organisms. The most obvious relationship between organisms is who eats whom. This is called a feeding relationship. Most organisms get their food from many sources.

We can use a food web to illustrate the feeding relationships in a community of

Chapter 14 Population Interactions 727

Process and Procedure

Part II: Ecosystems

Materials

none

In Step 1, instruct students to use the think-share-advise-revise (TSAR) strategy as they complete the reading *Relationships among Populations*. They should look ahead to the tasks in Steps 2 and 3 to help guide their reading. They complete another reading in Step 4. Encourage them to use a literacy strategy here as well—either the same one or a new one—to guide their reading. They should also look ahead to the task in Step 5.

NOTES:

Relationships among Populations, continued

organisms. Figure 14.18 shows one example of a food web. Notice how many of the relationships are between predators and prey. Also notice the decomposers that break down the dead bodies of plants and animals. There are other common relationships between organisms besides predator-prey relationships. These include competition and mutualism (see figure 14.19).

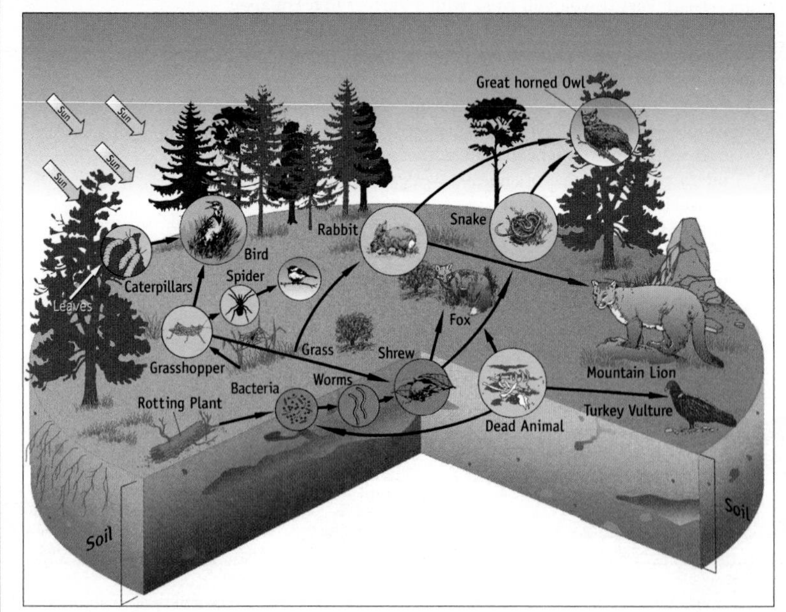

▲ **Figure 14.18 Food web.** Food webs show the feeding relationships among different species within a community. Arrows in the diagram show the direction of energy flow. The arrow points from the organisms getting consumed to the consumer. For example, worms get eaten by shrews, which in turn get eaten by foxes. Recall that producers are organisms that make their own food and consumers obtain their food by eating or breaking down other organisms. Can you think of other arrows that you would include for the organisms shown in this community?

NOTES:

Relationship	Effect of the relationship	Description
Mutualism	+ / +	A relationship among organisms in which both organisms benefit. For example, lichens often consist of an alga and a fungus that live in close association. The alga produces food through photosynthesis and the fungus provides moisture and nutrients. Another example is the relationships between some plant species and insects. Insects eat pollen or nectar provided by the plant and the insect helps the plants reproduce through pollination.
Predator-prey	+ / −	One organism (predator) eats another (prey). This relationship is lethal to the prey but is not an intimate association.
Parasitism	+ / −	One organism (parasite) lives on or in another organism (the host), using it as a food source. The relationship between the two species is more intimate, but not usually as lethal as predator-prey.
Herbivory	+ / −	The consumption of living plant material by a consumer (grazers). The relationship is usually not as lethal as predator-prey and is not intimate.
Competition	− / −	Organisms may compete for such things as food, space, sunlight, nutrients, or water. The competition is often for a resource that limits the growth of a population. In competition, both organisms are harmed.

▲ **Figure 14.19 Relationships in ecosystems classified by effects of the relationship.** In figure 14.18, organisms were classified by feeding relationships. It is sometimes useful to classify species in a community by the effect they have on each other. The survival or reproduction of a species may benefit from the presence of another species (+) or be harmed by it (−). In the table, + / + indicates that both species benefit from a relationship, + / − indicates that one species is harmed and the other benefits, and − / − indicates that both species are harmed.

SCILINKS NSTA
Topic: food webs
Go to: www.scilinks.org
Code: 2Inquiry729

2. After completing the reading, identify the following relationships as predator-prey, parasitism, herbivory, competition, or mutualism. Justify your response and record it in your science notebook. You will use your responses in a class discussion.
   a. A hummingbird getting nectar from a flower and getting pollen on its back
   b. Prairie dogs and bison feeding on grass
   c. Wolves and moose on Isle Royale
   d. Leeches on a fish
   e. A bird removing seeds from a pinecone

Answers to Steps 2–5, SE pages 729–732

2. Students should identify the relationships as follows:
   a. A hummingbird getting nectar from a flower and getting pollen on its back: symbiosis (mutualism)
   b. Prairie dogs and bison feeding on grass: competition
   c. Wolves and moose on Isle Royale: predator-prey
   d. Leeches on a fish: symbiosis (parasitism)
   e. A bird removing seeds from a pinecone: predator-prey

3a. Predators depend on the prey. A predator population will increase or decrease in response to the size of the prey population. Prey populations also change in response to predator populations. Prey populations can potentially decrease in size with larger predator populations and increase in size with smaller predator populations.

3b. Competition reduces the maximum population size for both populations because the 2 organisms use the same resources.

5a. Ecosystems contain more primary consumers than secondary consumers because organisms must use some of their energy to survive. Therefore, there is progressively less energy to pass from one trophic level to another (primary consumer to secondary consumer) and less energy supports fewer organisms.

5b. See figure T14.13.

5c. See figure T14.14.

5d. Herbivores must use some of the energy they get from their food (plants) for metabolism and movement.

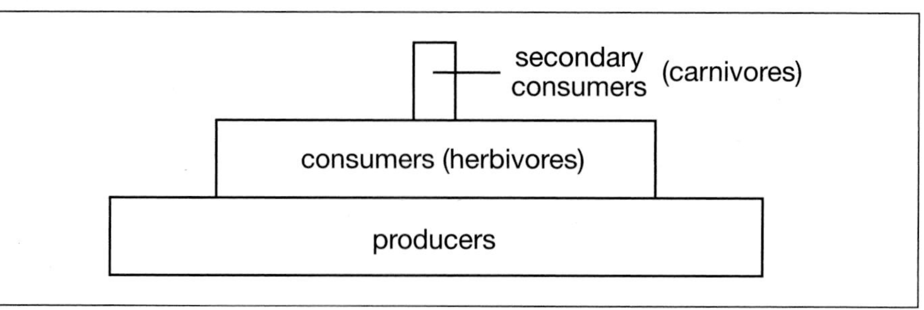

▲ **Figure T14.13 Example of the biomass in trophic levels for Step 5b.** The diagram shows the relative amounts of biomass in different trophic levels.

NOTES:

3. Answer Questions 3a–b about how relationships can affect population size. Provide a brief explanation for each answer.
   a. How does a predator-prey relationship affect the population size of the 2 organisms involved?
   b. How do you think competition between 2 organisms affects their population sizes?
4. Read *Structure of an Ecosystem* to learn what characteristics ecosystems have and how energy and matter move into and out of ecosystems. Look ahead to Step 5 to guide your reading.

READING

Structure of an Ecosystem

A community (the biotic environment) and the abiotic environment make up an ecological system, or **ecosystem**. You learned that the biotic and abiotic environments influence populations. Scientists look at the abiotic and biotic environments to understand how natural systems work. Suppose a trout population in one river ecosystem is wiped out. Yet a trout population in a different river ecosystem flourishes. You may wonder why. So you would compare the abiotic environments in the two ecosystems. From that, you would learn that the first ecosystem had water temperatures above the trout's tolerance limit. As a result, the temperatures wiped out the trout in that ecosystem. Read FYI—*Climatic and Topographic Effects* to learn how climate and topography affect the biotic and abiotic environments in ecosystems.

Ecosystems are open systems. Things constantly enter and leave them. Energy is one of the largest inputs into ecosystems. The Sun is the ultimate source of energy for most ecosystems. Other sources include wind, rain, water flow, or fuel (for ecosystems with humans). Energy outputs can be in the form of heat and organic matter (food and waste products). Other fluxes for ecosystems include water, air, nutrients, and organisms. If you find learning about ecosystems interesting, you might enjoy a career in ecology. You can learn more about careers in ecology in the sidebar *Working for the Environment*.

All organisms require energy. Thus, the amount of energy and material entering and leaving an ecosystem determines the size and diversity of the biotic community. The flow of energy and the cycling of matter from one organism to another tie organisms together. The flow of energy begins with producers. Producers convert light energy from the Sun into food (chemical energy). The conversion occurs through photosynthesis, which involves a series of chemical reactions.

How does energy flow through an ecosystem? The answer is in the ecosystem's trophic structure. The trophic structure is made up of the feeding relationships among the producers and consumers. Each step in a food web is a trophic level. The relationships between trophic levels determine the flow of energy and the cycling of matter in the ecosystem.

Producers make up the trophic level that supports an ecosystem. Consumers are another trophic level. Consumers can depend directly or indirectly on producers for energy and matter.

730 Unit 4 Sustaining Earth Systems

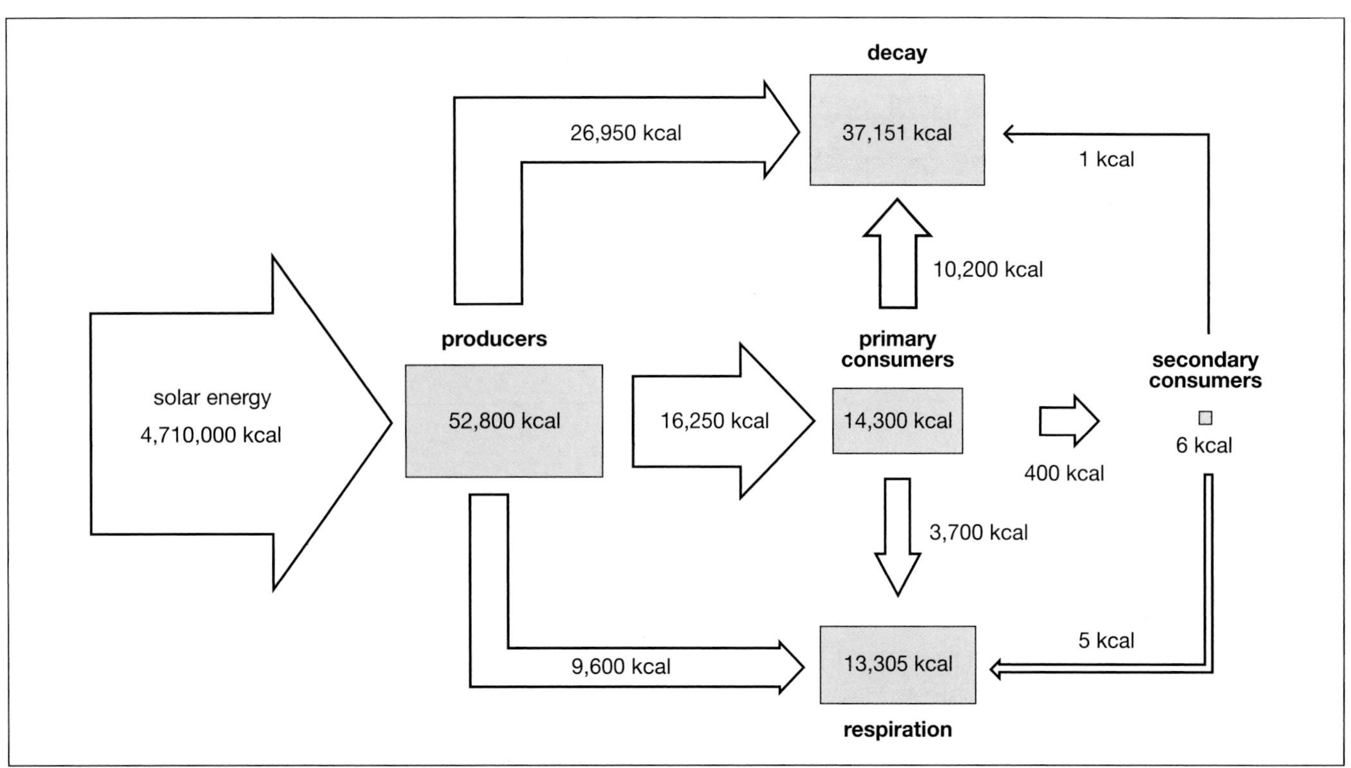

▲ **Figure T14.14 Sample student drawing of energy flow for Step 5c.** Make sure students include solar energy in their diagrams.

Herbivores (organisms that consume plants or algae) are the primary consumers. Deer, grasshoppers, and garden snails are primary consumers. Carnivores that eat herbivores are secondary consumers. Carnivores that eat other carnivores are tertiary (third-level) consumers. Finally, decomposers consume organic material and dead organisms from all trophic levels. Can you identify the trophic levels of the organisms in figure 14.18?

You can use trophic levels to illustrate the amount of energy entering and leaving an ecosystem. Study figure 14.20 to see how energy is distributed from one trophic level to another. Notice that primary producers are the foundation. Each trophic level above them receives less energy. In many ecosystems, each trophic level receives about one-tenth the energy of the level below it. Where does the energy go? Most of the energy is lost to the environment as heat and also to activities needed to keep an organism alive.

You know that the available energy declines at higher trophic levels. So does **biomass**. Biomass is the total amount of living organic matter for a given area of the environment. Living organic matter includes all the living organisms in an area such as plants and animals. Recall that all organisms are composed of organic molecules.

The rate at which new biomass forms, or the **productivity**, is highest among producers. Consumers at higher tropic levels generate less biomass and so are less productive. Therefore, an ecosystem can sustain far fewer top-level carnivores than low-level consumers and producers. For example, the total mass of the coyotes in a grassland is much less than the total mass of rabbits and other prey. The total mass of the coyotes also is less than all the mass of the grass.

In the next chapter, you will learn how the productivity of different ecosystems and agricultural systems has implications for humans.

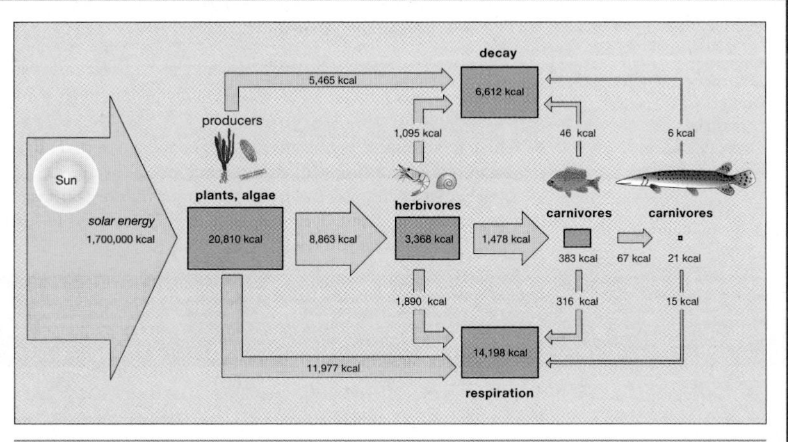

▲ **Figure 14.20 Energy flow diagram for Silver Springs, Florida.** How does the amount of energy (in kilocalories, or kcal) differ from one trophic level to the next? Can you calculate what percentage of energy is transferred from producers to herbivores (primary consumers)?

NOTES:

Answers to Step 5 are on TE pages 730–731.

5. After completing the reading, answer Questions 5a–d about ecosystems.
   a. Would you expect most ecosystems to contain more primary consumers or more secondary consumers? Explain your answer.
   b. Imagine a grassland ecosystem with mice, other herbivores, and predators, such as weasels, which eat mice. Use a sketch or diagram to represent the relative biomass of different trophic levels in this ecosystem. For example, trophic levels often are shown as horizontal, stacked bars inside a pyramid. The lowest trophic level is on the bottom.
   c. Figure 14.21 shows how energy might be distributed in the different trophic levels for the grassland ecosystem described in Step 5b. Create a diagram like the one in figure 14.20 to show the flow of energy for the grassland. Your diagram should include the following:
      - Inputs and outputs of energy
      - Three trophic levels that are labeled
      - The total energy lost through cellular respiration and the energy stored in the remains of organisms

Calculate the total energy lost based on the information in figure 14.21.

      - Sizes of boxes and arrows that are scaled to represent the relative amount of energy

For example, the box for producers should be larger than the box for consumers.

   d. Why is only *part* of the chemical energy produced by plants available for use by herbivores?
6. The interactions of organisms in ecosystems ensure that all organisms have a supply of energy from food. The abiotic environment continues to supply the matter that organisms need to survive. Read *Cycling of Matter in Ecosystems* to learn how. Take notes as you read.

Topic: ecosystem
Go to: www.scilinks.org
Code: 2Inquiry732

▼ **Figure 14.21 Energy for a grassland.** Calculate the total energy lost through cellular respiration and the energy stored in the remains of organisms. Where does the energy input for plants come from?

Part of the ecosystem	Energy input (kcal)	Energy produced (kcal)	Energy loss from cellular respiration (kcal)	Unused energy from the remains of organisms that later decay (kcal)
Plants (primarily grass)	4,710,000	52,800	9,600	26,950
Mice and other herbivores	16,250	14,300	3,700	10,200
Weasels and other predators	400	6	5	1

732 Unit 4 Sustaining Earth Systems

NOTES:

READING

Cycling of Matter in Ecosystems

How are conditions in ecosystems maintained for hundreds or thousands of years? A constant recycling of materials between the biotic and abiotic environments is required. Recall that the amount of chemical elements on Earth is fixed. Essentially, the same atoms and molecules are used over and over. Many of the processes that allow atoms and molecules to be used again occur in ecosystems. In chapter 3, *Collisions—Atomic Style*, you learned about the law of conservation of matter. This law states that matter is conserved in ordinary chemical and physical changes. In other words, matter is transformed, but it doesn't disappear. It cycles endlessly.

You learned about the cycling of water and carbon in unit 3. You know that water cycles between global reservoirs. But it also cycles through ecosystems. Plants absorb water from the soil. Land animals, other consumers, and decomposers absorb water from food or drink it directly. Aquatic organisms are constantly bathed in water. Water returns to the atmosphere through cellular respiration, transpiration (water loss by plants), and evaporation, mostly from the oceans.

Carbon is important for ecosystems. It must cycle through ecosystems to provide the raw materials living organisms need. Living organisms are made up of organic molecules that are based on a skeleton of carbon atoms. Recall from chapter 11 and Level 1 of this program that plants take in carbon dioxide during photosynthesis. Then a series of chemical reactions makes organic molecules. Some of the carbon remains in the bodies of producers and consumers. The carbon leaves them when their bodies decay on a forest or ocean floor. The remaining carbon returns to the air as carbon dioxide through cellular respiration in producers, consumers, and decomposers.

Reflect and Connect

Complete the following tasks individually in your science notebook.

1. Explain how an abiotic factor can affect biotic factors in an ecosystem.
2. Why is energy said to *flow through* an ecosystem in one direction, whereas matter such as carbon *cycles* through an ecosystem? Think about what the source of energy and matter is for ecosystems.
3. Explain why ecosystems typically have so few top-level consumers such as tigers, eagles, and sharks. Think about what you learned about the amount of energy that flows through the different trophic levels in ecosystems.

Answers to Reflect and Connect, SE page 733

1. Abiotic factors determine the types of organisms that can live in an environment because organisms have different tolerances for abiotic factors such as light, temperature, and water. Abiotic factors also affect the population size of organisms because these factors often limit population growth.
2. The Sun is the source of energy for ecosystems. Only producers can convert the energy from the Sun into energy they can use to meet their needs. Consumers must get their energy by eating other organisms. As a result, energy moves in 1 direction, or flows, from one organism to another through a series of feeding relationships.

   Chemicals such as carbon are part of the abiotic and biotic environments in ecosystems. Processes such as photosynthesis and cellular respiration cycle, or move carbon back and forth, between the biotic and abiotic environment.
3. The amount of energy is less at the higher trophic levels. There are smaller numbers of top-level consumers such as tigers because there aren't enough prey organisms to provide the energy needed for more tigers to survive.

NOTES:

Climatic and Topographic Effects

Climate

Climate is an important abiotic factor that shapes ecosystems. Climate is the weather conditions in an area over long periods of time. Climate depends on factors such as temperature, precipitation, humidity, and wind. For example, the climate of a tropical rain forest ecosystem is hot and humid year-round. This ecosystem also receives a lot of precipitation. In contrast, a desert ecosystem can have hot or cool temperatures depending on the time of year. This ecosystem gets very little precipitation.

Topography

Topography, the elevation and shape of Earth's surface, contributes to climate. For example, mountains cause rain shadows. Rain shadows are dry areas on the leeward (downwind) slopes of mountain ranges (see the illustration). Topography also affects temperature. Have you ever driven up a mountain? You probably noticed that the air gets colder as you go up in elevation. Similarly, temperatures are cooler at higher latitudes. Solar radiation is less at the poles than at the equator because of the angle of incoming radiation.

Topography affects the location of water reservoirs. Remember that water is an important abiotic factor in ecosystems. Contours of the land, such as ridges and valleys, determine where water accumulates in ponds or lakes and runs in rivers. Different species of plants grow depending on the availability of water. For example, you will never find lily pads growing in a desert. Changes in elevation also determine how fast water flows in rivers. Have you ever noticed that water seems to run faster in mountain streams? There is more dissolved oxygen in fast-flowing rivers than in slower rivers. Water temperatures are also colder in mountain streams, allowing more oxygen to dissolve. As a result, trout only survive in cold, fast-flowing rivers because they need higher levels of oxygen to survive. Oxygen is an important abiotic factor for many organisms.

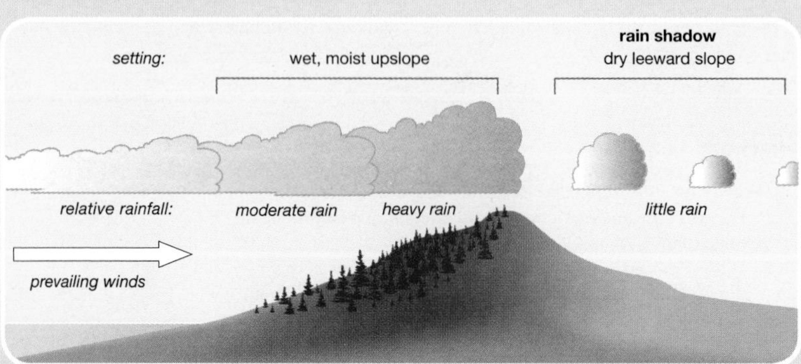

▲ **Rain shadow effect.** Rain shadows are areas of low rainfall on the leeward (downwind) slope of a mountain range. They form as warm, moist air rises to higher elevations where temperatures are cooler. Cool air holds less moisture than warm air, causing precipitation to fall on the windward side. The air has lost most of its moisture by the time it reaches the leeward slope.

734 Unit 4 Sustaining Earth Systems

ELABORATE

Finding Your Niche

Activity Overview

In *Finding Your Niche*, students look at the traits of different shorebird species and identify their niches. Students then think about how competition between organisms such as shorebirds could lead to more specialized individuals and eventually new species.

Before You Teach

Background Information

A habitat is any part of the environment where organisms live. For example, the Chesapeake Bay contains many different types of habitats that are home to more than 2,000 species of organisms. These habitats include islands, wetlands, freshwater tributaries, shallow-water areas, and open water. Habitats provide organisms with the particular resources and conditions they require for survival, such as food, water, shelter, and acceptable physical conditions.

A niche is a species' role in its habitat. A niche describes the relationship that a species has to all the abiotic components of its environment. It includes all the resources and physical conditions that the species requires for survival and reproduction, as well as how a species conducts its life.

Every ecosystem contains a variety of habitats that support a variety of different species with different niches. In nature, species coexist in the same area as long as they have different niches. The greater the overlap of niche between two species, the more intense the competition can be for limited resources. If the niches of two species are too similar, then the intense competition between them can result in one of them being excluded from the area. However, natural selection results in the niches diverging. The competing species use slightly different portions of a resource or even different resources, which reduces competition and permits coexistence. Natural selection is a process where individuals with traits that make them well adapted to an environment survive and reproduce. Individuals without beneficial traits are less likely to survive and reproduce. Across time, selection favors individuals that do not compete for the same resource. Eventually, individuals in a population that were competing may become specialized and cause subpopulations of a single species to diverge into separate species (see figure 14.24 in the student book).

Materials

For the teacher

1 copy of copymaster 14.1b, *Shorebird Habitat Answer Key*

For each student

colored pencils

1 copy of copymaster 14.1a, *Shorebird Habitat*

Advance Preparation

Make 1 copy of copymaster 14.1a, *Shorebird Habitat* for each student.

Earth is a patchwork of distinctive ecosystems called **biomes**. Biomes are large habitats created by major types of climates. They feature a characteristic type of vegetation. For example, warm, arid climates are associated with desert vegetation. Semiarid climates usually are covered with grassland. Moist climates support forests. Each type of plant life, in turn, supports a characteristic variety of animal life. The resulting community of plants and animals forms the biome.

Scientists benefit from studying the physical surroundings that organisms live in. They can better understand the ways that matter and energy are stored or move between parts of an ecosystem. They also learn how an ecosystem works by studying its organization and function.

SIDEBAR: Working for the Environment

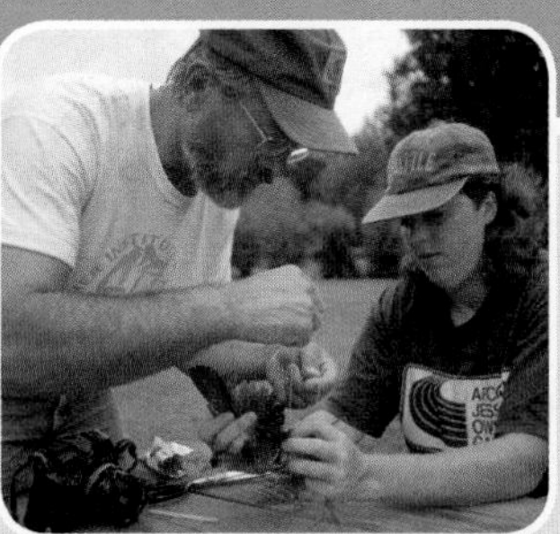

Careers in ecology are diverse and often fun and rewarding. The type and location of the work depend on the job. Ecology jobs can take place indoors in the lab or outdoors in a unique ecosystem. The work can be solitary or with a team of people. Recall that ecology is the study of how living things interact with one another and their environment. People who work in the ecology field are curious about the natural world, enjoy investigating problems, and often want to contribute to society. Their work adds to our understanding and preservation of the natural world.

People with ecology careers need a background in science and certain skills. Ecology involves biotic and abiotic systems. Thus, ecologists need to understand all fields of science. These sciences help them study the links between living things and their environment. Mathematics is also important for making measurements and predictions about the natural world. Sometimes researchers use mathematical models to study processes in ecosystems. Computer skills are important for using tools to analyze data. Communicating ideas in written and oral form is another needed skill. Finally, some ecological issues involve more than the natural world. They may require an understanding of economics or engineering.

Careers in ecology exist for different interests and levels of education. If you like being outdoors, you can find a job that involves fieldwork. Fieldwork can be sampling plants or taking soil samples in a local ecosystem. It can take place far away in a rain forest or on an ice field. Fieldwork involves research. However, research can also take place in the laboratory. With a two-year associate's degree, you can be a field technician, lab assistant, or teaching assistant. With more training, you could become a

As You Teach

Outcomes and Indicators of Success

By the end of this activity, students should

1. be able to explain how natural selection contributes to the diversity of organisms on Earth.

   They will demonstrate their ability by

   - describing that different traits in shorebirds help reduce competition between species;
   - describing that competition might reduce the survival of some individuals in a population and cause the population to consist of more specialized individuals, which eventually might become different species; and
   - describing how interactions between shorebirds might have led to diverse species of shorebirds.

2. be able to interpret information about shorebirds and niches to generate a graph showing the relationship of two shorebird niches.

   They will demonstrate their ability by

   - predicting where different shorebird species might feed in a wetland habitat based on information about their body size and feeding habits,
   - describing how shorebird species might be minimizing competition between one another, and
   - graphing the niches of two shorebird species relative to a resource.

Strategies

Getting Started

Ask students what they think generalists and specialists are and ask for examples. Explain that they will learn about specialized species in this activity.

Process and Procedure

Materials

For the teacher

1 copy of copymaster 14.1b, *Shorebird Habitat Answer Key*

For each student

colored pencils

1 copy of copymaster 14.1a, *Shorebird Habitat*

In Step 1, students look at pictures of shorebirds and read some information about them. Students should begin thinking about whether the shorebirds are competing for the same resources. In Step 2, distribute copies of copymaster 14.1a, *Shorebird Habitat.* In Step 3, students should predict which parts of the wetland habitat each species might use based on what they learned in Step 1. They do this by creating a guide on copymaster 14.1a, *Shorebird Habitat* that shows where each shorebird feeds. Students may feel uncomfortable overlapping the areas that each shorebird uses. Help them realize that different shorebirds may use some of the same habitat and that it is necessary to show this by overlapping shaded areas on their handouts.

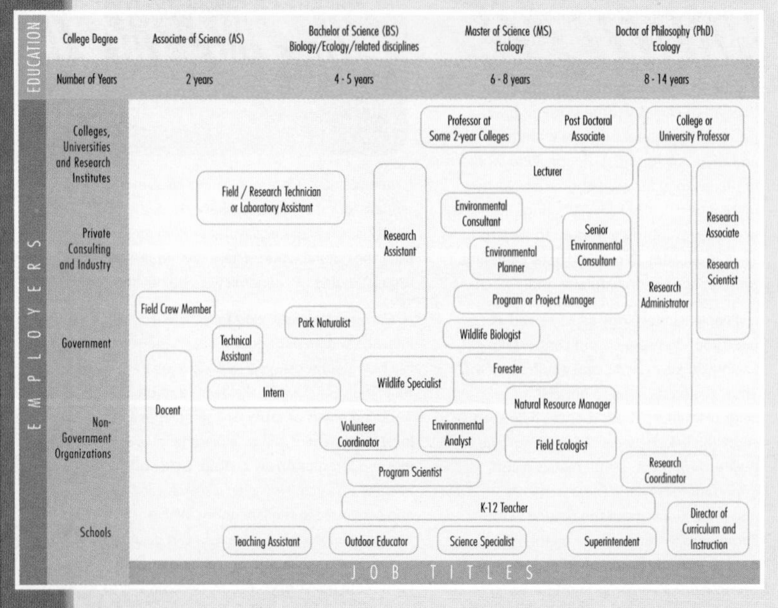

Working for the Environment, continued

wildlife biologist or an ecologist. Maybe you are more interested in managing or restoring populations and ecosystems. Then you could become a manager for a state park or a wildlife refuge. If you enjoy teaching as well as ecology, you could work at a high school, museum, or college or university. Some people bring their teaching interest outdoors by working as an educator at a nature center or as a naturalist at a park. To help solve environmental problems or influence policy makers, you could become an environmental consultant, environmental planner, or even an environmental lawyer.

Ecological and environmental jobs will always be available because we depend on ecosystems. Disturbances to ecosystems are likely to increase because humans will continue to interact with ecosystems. Thus, more people with ecological backgrounds will be needed to better understand how ecosystems work. They will also need to educate the public and develop management plans to sustain and restore ecosystems. Job opportunities are expected to grow in private companies, nongovernment organizations, and precollege schools. The number of jobs with universities and the federal government is expected to stay the same.

▼ **Careers in ecology.** Do any of these careers interest you?

736 Unit 4 Sustaining Earth Systems

NOTES:

Finding Your Niche

ELABORATE

How do you think species' interactions influence the traits of species? Could interactions be important for evolution? Competition for limited resources is a common interaction among species in ecosystems. For example, foxes and coyotes compete for some of the same food resources, such as rabbits. Because they compete, foxes are less abundant in areas where coyotes also live. Foxes and coyotes are species in the same trophic level that coexist because they do not use the same resources entirely. Scientists have evidence that the great diversity of organisms on Earth is a result of interactions.

In *Finding Your Niche*, you will think about how six species of shorebird use the same habitat in a way that minimizes competition. Shorebirds are a group of birds that are adapted to live near water. You will work alone and with your classmates to discover how interactions may have led to diverse species of shorebirds.

Materials

For each student

colored pencils 1 *Shorebird Habitat* handout

Process and Procedure

1. Read about the shorebirds shown in figure 14.22. Are these shorebirds competing for the same resources? Why or why not?
2. Shorebirds live in a variety of habitats. A **habitat** is the specific environment where an organism lives. Shorebirds live in habitats such as seashores, coastal wetlands, inland wetlands, and grasslands. Wetlands are just as they sound—areas that are saturated with water for at least part of the year. Obtain the *Shorebird Habitat* handout from your teacher to see how a wetland habitat for shorebirds might look in South Dakota.
3. Use the *Shorebird Habitat* handout and Steps 3a–d to create a guide that shows where each shorebird in figure 14.22 feeds.
   a. Use a different-colored pencil to shade in areas for each shorebird.
   b. The shaded areas should indicate if shorebirds find food in different depths of soil or different parts of the water. Some of the shaded areas may overlap.
   c. Create a key for your guide.
   d. Use the TSAR strategy to compare your guide with the guides of 2 other classmates. Revise your guide if you learn something new after talking with a classmate. Continue using this strategy throughout the activity.

Answers to Steps 3–4, SE pages 737–739

3. See copymaster 14.1b, *Shorebird Habitat Answer Key* for an example of how students might indicate how different species of shorebirds use a habitat differently.

NOTES:

4. The shorebirds are competing for the same kind of food resource, invertebrates. However, they use different parts of the same habitat to get their food. For example, the shorebirds may all use the shallow water, but some pick food off the water, others pick food off plants, and others probe their bills into the soil.

In Step 5, students read about niches. As they read, they should answer the questions in Step 5 and use the TSAR strategy to refine their answers. You might want to spend a little time reviewing evolution and natural selection from chapter 6, *Exploring Change*, before students complete the reading. In Step 6, students should create a graph that shows the niches of 2 shorebirds relative to habitat type.

Semipalmated plovers (*Charadrius semipalmatus*) are small shorebirds. They are about 18 centimeters (cm) long, with short legs and a very short bill. They feed by picking invertebrates off the soil's surface or off plants.

Wilson's phalaropes (*Phalaropus tricolor*) are small shorebirds. They are about 22 cm long, with short legs and a medium-length bill. They feed by wading in shallow water or swimming in deeper water and picking invertebrates off the water's surface. In deep water, they use their legs to churn up the water and bring invertebrates closer to the surface.

Greater yellowlegs (*Tringa melanoleuca*) are medium-sized shorebirds. They are about 30 cm long, with long legs and a long, thin bill. They feed by wading in water and picking invertebrates off the water's surface or plants.

Baird's sandpipers (*Calidris bairdii*) are small shorebirds. They are about 15 cm long, with medium-length legs and a short bill. They feed by probing their bills into soil to find invertebrates. They search for food on wet mud and in shallow water.

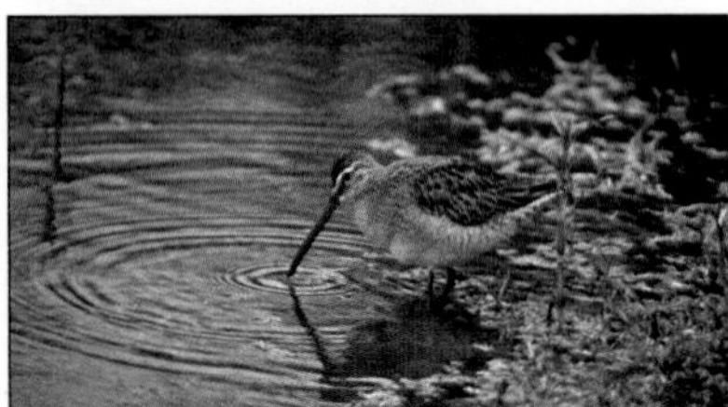

Dowitchers (*Limnodromus sp.*) are medium-sized birds. They are about 30 cm long, with medium-length legs and a long, straight bill. They feed by probing their bills into soil to find invertebrates. They search for food on wet mud and in shallow water.

Pectoral sandpipers (*Calidris melanotos*) are medium-sized shorebirds. They are about 20 cm long, with medium-length legs and a medium-length bill. They feed by probing their bills into soil to find invertebrates or by picking invertebrates off wet mud or water. They search for food on wet mud and in shallow water.

▲ **Figure 14.22 Shorebirds found in shallow wetlands.** How do you think natural selection might have led to so many species of shorebirds?

738 Unit 4 Sustaining Earth Systems

NOTES:

Answers to Steps 5–6, SE pages 739–743

5a. Shorebirds are specialists because they occupy a narrow niche within a wetland habitat.

5b. Shorebirds use different parts of the same habitat by using a different technique to find their food (probing into soil, picking off the surface, or stirring up water) and by having different leg and bill length to reach different parts of the habitat.

5c. If 2 populations of the same species are competing for the same resource, some individuals in each population will be more likely to survive because they have traits that are slightly different from the other population. The differences in traits reduce the amount that those individuals compete. As the more successful individuals survive and reproduce, the populations become more specialized. Eventually, the 2 populations might become different species.

4. Are the shorebirds using different parts of the same habitat? Based on your guide, describe how these 6 shorebird species interact in a wetland habitat.
5. Read *An Ecological Niche* to learn how scientists describe the different roles of species in habitats. Answer Questions 5a–c in your science notebook as you read. Then use the TSAR strategy to refine your answers.
   a. Are shorebirds generalists or specialists? Explain your answer.
   b. How are shorebirds minimizing competition in the same habitat? Include in your answer how the traits of the species differ.
   c. Suppose 2 populations of the same species are competing for the same resource. Both populations have variations in their traits that make them use resources slightly differently, as shown in figure 14.24. Describe how natural selection could result in a new species.

Remember that natural selection occurs when members of a population with the most successful adaptations to their environment are more likely to survive and reproduce than members of the same population with less successful adaptations.

READING

An Ecological Niche

The role that each species plays in the community is its **ecological niche**. A habitat is an organism's address, and a niche is its profession. A niche includes where an organism lives, what it eats, how it obtains its food, and how it interacts with other species. Some species are specialists and occupy a narrow niche. For example, black-footed ferrets (*Mustela nigripes*, see figure 14.23a)

Figure 14.23 Specialist (black-footed ferret) and generalist (long-tailed weasel). (a) Black-footed ferrets have a narrow niche that is limited to habitats containing prairie dogs. (b) Long-tailed weasels have a broad niche that includes different habitats and foods.

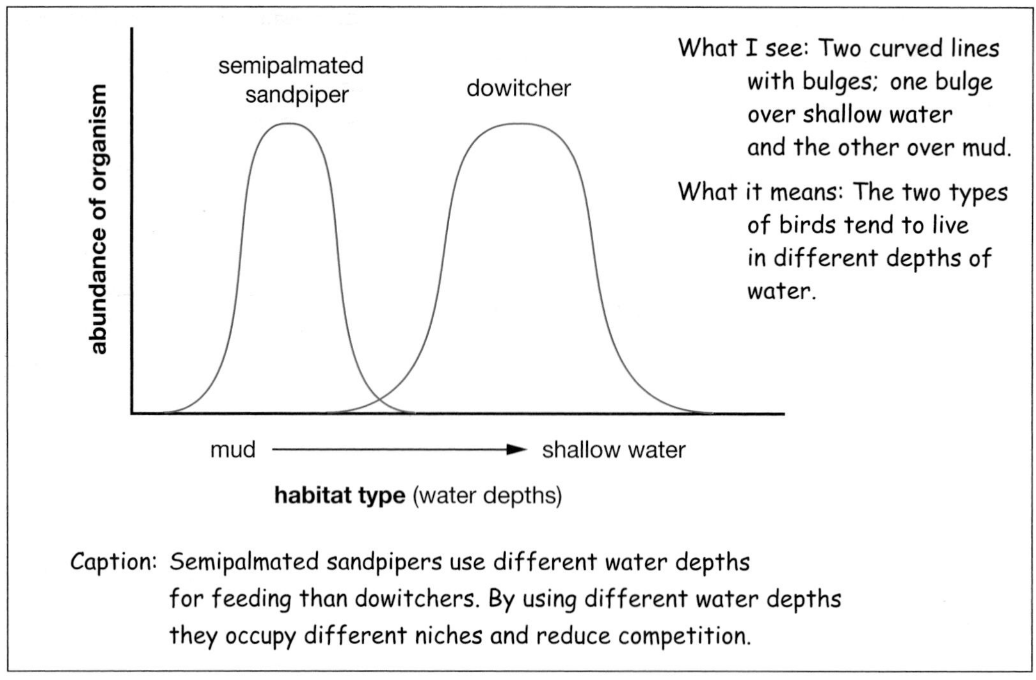

▲ **Figure T14.15 Example of the niches for 2 shorebirds for Step 6.** Students might choose a different resource for the *x*-axis, but all graphs should show very little overlap between the 2 niches.

6. See figure T14.15.

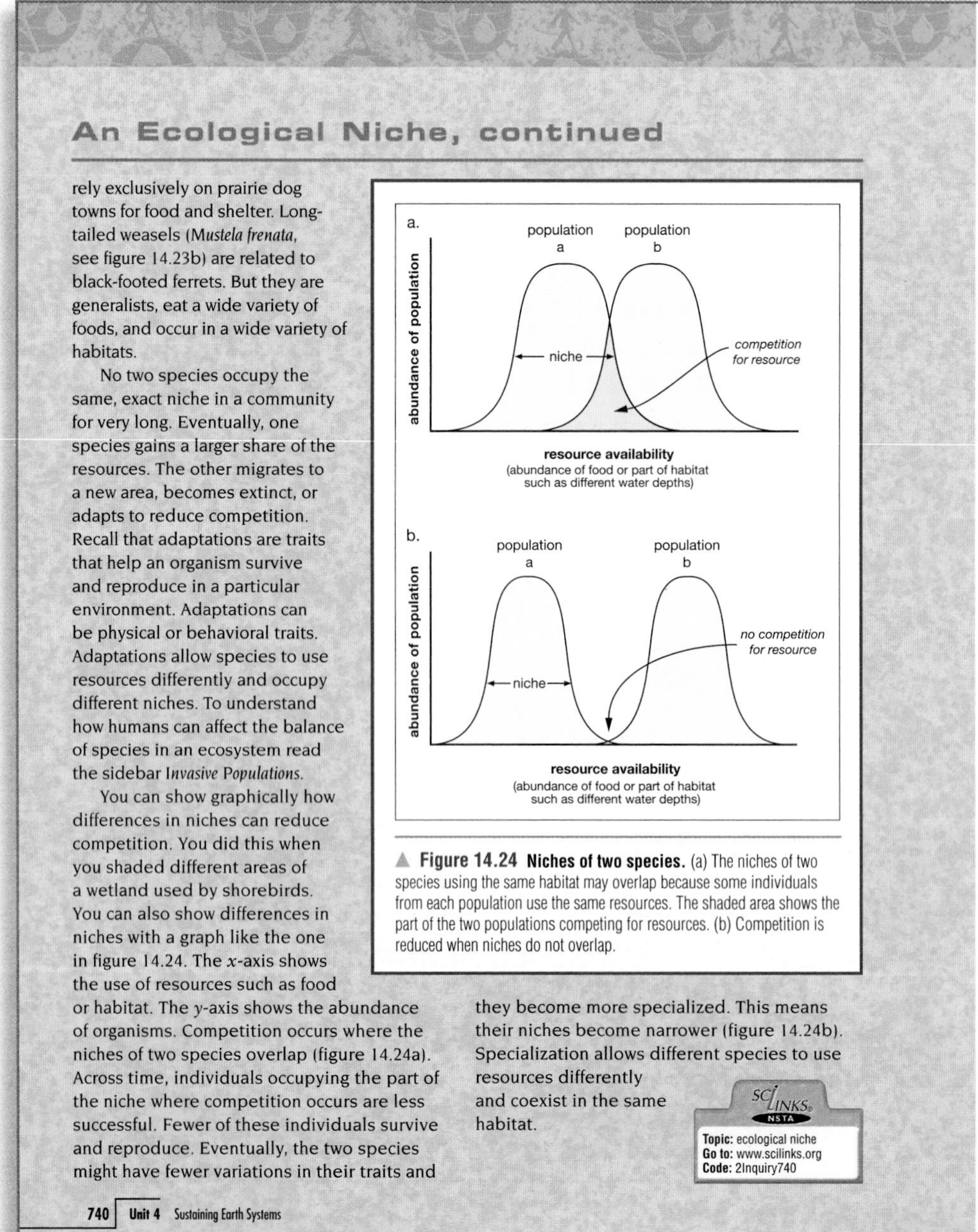

NOTES:

SIDEBAR

Invasive Populations

You have been learning about how plant and animal populations interact in ecosystems. Humans also interact with these populations. In fact, human populations can unintentionally disrupt the balance of species in an ecosystem. Humans can affect the balance by introducing a new species or changing the conditions in an ecosystem in a way that favors some species over others.

Humans transport plants and animals to new locations for food or enjoyment, and sometimes by accident. Arriving with the plants and animals are the bacteria, fungi, and diseases associated with those species. In most cases, when organisms are moved away from their native habitat, they die out once humans no longer use them. Sometimes, however, the limiting factors that were present in a species' natural habitat are not present at a new location. Or a species might invade a new niche that didn't exist in its natural habitat. If non-native species thrive, they can potentially cause harm. These introduced species are called invasive species. Some well-known examples of invasive species are purple loosestrife, zebra mussels, fire ants, and whirling disease.

Purple loosestrife (*Lythrum salicaria*) is a plant brought to the wetlands in northeastern North America from Europe in the 1800s. Immigrants may have brought the seeds because of their value as an herb and ornamental plant. Although purple loosestrife is attractive, it outcompetes and replaces native wetland plants (see the photographs). It produces abundant nectar, but it is a poorer source of nutrition for wildlife than native plants.

Zebra mussels (*Dreissena polymorpha*) are small, fingernail-sized mussels native to the Caspian and Black Seas between Europe and Asia. They are now found in the United Kingdom, western Europe, Canada, and the United States. In 1988, they arrived in the Great Lakes in the ballast water of a transoceanic ship. Ballast water is water held in a ship's ballast tanks and cargo holds to provide stability. This water is taken from a coastal port area and transported to the next port, where it may be discharged. Zebra mussels breed prolifically and live and feed in many aquatic habitats. They filter large amounts of food from the water. This action reduces

Before and after purple loosestrife establishment. (a) The photograph shows a wildlife refuge in New York in 1968. (b) Ten years later, the native vegetation has been replaced by purple loosestrife.

Answers to Reflect and Connect, SE page 743

1. A habitat is where an organism lives, but a niche includes where an organism lives and how it lives. For example, a niche describes how an organism gets its food or interacts with other organisms.
2. In the past, different populations of shorebirds might have had a lot of variation in leg, bill, and body size, and in how they got their food. The birds with the largest differences in size or the way they ate might have survived better than the shorebirds with traits somewhere in between. As the individuals with these traits survived and reproduced, more of the shorebirds became specialized in size or feeding strategy. Eventually, the differences might have become so great that the birds became different species.

EVALUATE

Interpret the Interactions

Activity Overview

In Part I of *Interpret the Interactions*, students will demonstrate what they have learned by revisiting their responses to the engage activity, *What Do You Know about Populations?* They then will be able to revise their responses. In Part II, students will analyze data from scientific research and answer a series of questions to show what they have learned.

Before You Teach

Background Information

See the background sections for the previous activities.

Materials—Part I

For each student

1 copy of copymaster 14.2, *Scoring Rubric for Interpret the Interactions*

answers from the engage activity

Materials—Part II

For the teacher

1 copy of copymaster 14.3b, *Analyzing Research Answer Key*

Answers to Step 6 are on TE page 740.

Invasive Populations, continued

the food supply for other organisms and causes some animal populations to decline.

Black and red fire ants (*Solenopsis sp.*) were accidentally brought to the United States from South America in the early 1900s. As of 2006, they have spread to 14 states. Fire ants sting their victims repeatedly. The sting injects venom that causes a burning sensation. Fire ants sometimes attack and kill newborn domestic animals as well as pets and wildlife. They can also damage some crops.

Whirling disease was brought to North America from Europe in the 1950s. Whirling disease is caused by a parasite (*Myxobolus cerebralis*) that penetrates the head and spinal cartilage of trout and salmon. It does not infect humans. Fish infected with the parasite swim erratically (whirl) and have difficulty feeding and avoiding predators. Water sources with severe infections result in high mortality rates of young fish. This disease is one of the biggest threats to native trout populations.

Some problem populations are viruses that need a host organism such as a bird or human to reproduce and spread. For example, West Nile virus and the avian flu are viruses that mainly infect birds but can spread to humans. West Nile was found in North America in 1999. It is common in Africa, Europe, the Middle East, and west and central Asia. The virus might have arrived in the United States through illegally imported birds, a person who was infected with the virus, or mosquitoes trapped on a plane or boat. Mosquitoes spread West Nile between birds and to humans. When a mosquito feeds on the blood of an infected individual, it can transmit the virus to an uninfected individual during its next feeding. Most cases of West Nile virus in humans occur in people who are immune compromised—their immune systems are not strong.

The avian flu is an infection caused by avian flu viruses. There are many subtypes of avian flu viruses. These viruses occur naturally in birds worldwide. Wild birds usually do not get sick from the viruses, but the viruses are very contagious and spread quickly. The avian flu virus can cause domesticated birds such as chickens, ducks, and turkeys to become very sick and die. Avian flu viruses occur mainly in birds, but occasionally they infect humans. Most human infections result from direct contact with infected domesticated birds. These infections usually do not pass from person to person. However, because flu viruses are constantly changing, they might adapt over time to infect and spread among humans.

New species from other countries are introduced in the United States every year. They may be introduced intentionally or accidentally, but their introduction can potentially create problems for native populations and human health.

6. Create a graph like figure 14.24. Show the niches of 2 shorebirds that you choose. Your graph should have the following:
   - An x-axis labeled "habitat type"

For each student

1 copy of copymaster 14.3a, *Analyzing Research*

Advance Preparation

Make 1 copy of copymasters 14.2, *Scoring Rubric for Interpret the Interactions* and 14.3a, *Analyzing Research* for each student.

As You Teach

Outcomes and Indicators of Success

By the end of this activity, students should

1. demonstrate their understanding that births, deaths, emigration, and immigration contribute to population growth or decline.

   They will demonstrate their understanding by

   - explaining what contributes to the growth of a population and
   - describing how the size of a population of sea otters could increase.

2. demonstrate their understanding that population growth is controlled by limiting factors that determine the carrying capacity of an environment.

   They will demonstrate their understanding by

   - describing possible limiting factors for kelp, sea urchins, and sea otters and
   - applying the concept of limiting factors to explain the control of household insect pests.

3. demonstrate their understanding that ecosystems are composed of biotic (interacting populations) and abiotic components such as nutrients and water.

   They will demonstrate their understanding by identifying abiotic resources that might be important for a kelp forest ecosystem.

4. demonstrate their understanding that organisms interact in different ways in ecosystems.

   They will demonstrate their understanding by

   - describing the relationship between two microorganisms as competition and
   - describing the relationship between organisms in a kelp forest ecosystem as predator-prey.

5. demonstrate their understanding of how energy flows and matter cycles through an ecosystem.

   They will demonstrate their understanding by

   - drawing an energy flow diagram for a bog and
   - describing the role of ecosystems in carbon cycling.

6. demonstrate their understanding of how natural selection led to the diversity of organisms on Earth.

   They will demonstrate their understanding by explaining how evolution through natural selection affects plants and animals in different abiotic environments.

7. demonstrate their understanding of how to interpret graphs and data and develop explanations.

   They will demonstrate their understanding by

   - describing relationships between organisms based on data trends on graphs and
   - identifying limiting factors for populations based on information in text and graphs.

Answers to Reflect and Connect are on TE page 742.

Choose the appropriate habitat type depending on which shorebirds you graph.

- A *y*-axis labeled "abundance"
- Each curve labeled with the names of the shorebirds
- A caption and highlight comments

Reflect and Connect

Work alone to answer the following questions in your science notebook.

1. Describe how a niche is different from a habitat. Use an example in your answer.
2. Describe in a short paragraph how interactions between populations of shorebirds in the past might have led to diverse species of shorebirds.

Interpret the Interactions

EVALUATE

One of the important parts of doing science is reviewing data that other scientists have collected. In *Interpret the Interactions*, you will use what you have learned about populations and ecosystems to *interpret* the results from different real scientific studies. For example, you will look at data from a study of populations in a kelp forest ecosystem (see figure 14.25). As you analyze and interpret the results of these studies, you will be acting like real scientists.

In Part I, you will work alone and with your classmates to revisit the true-false statements from the engage activity, *What Do You Know about Populations?* You will decide whether your responses have changed now that you have completed the activities in this chapter. Then in Part II, you will take a test that asks you to analyze data from current and past research and answer a series of questions about how the populations change and what interactions are taking place in the ecosystems.

▲ **Figure 14.25 Sea otter.** This sea otter is eating a sea urchin. Sea urchins are marine invertebrates that feed on kelp, a type of alga. Sea otters and sea urchins live in kelp forest ecosystems in coastal waters.

Part I: What Have You Learned about Populations?

Materials

For each student

1 *Interpret the Interactions Scoring Rubric* handout

answers from the engage activity

Strategies

Getting Started

Ask students if they think their ideas about populations and ecosystems have changed. Explain that they will have an opportunity to revisit the true and false statements from the engage activity.

Process and Procedure

Part I: What Have You Learned about Populations?

Materials

For each student

1 copy of copymaster 14.2, *Scoring Rubric for Interpret the Interactions*

answers from the engage activity

Distribute copymaster 14.2, *Scoring Rubric for Interpret the Interactions* to the students and discuss it as a class. Then instruct students to review the answers from the engage activity. Students use the TSAR strategy to compare their answers with those of at least 2 other students. After students have had an opportunity to revise their responses, go over the answers as a class.

Process and Procedure

Part II: Analyzing Research

Materials

For the teacher

1 copy of copymaster 14.3b, *Analyzing Research Answer Key*

For each student

1 copy of copymaster 14.3a, *Analyzing Research*

Decide how much time you will allow students to complete the test. Distribute copymaster 14.3a, *Analyzing Research* to students and give them one class period to answer all the questions. Students should write highlight comments for each question as directed by the instructions. Interpreting the numerous graphs in the test may be challenging and time consuming for some students. If you feel you need to shorten the test to reduce student time and grading time, skip questions 3, 4, and 7. The content in these questions overlaps with some of the other questions.

NOTES:

Process and Procedure

1. Get a copy of the *Interpret the Interactions Scoring Rubric* handout from your teacher. Review it with your class.
2. Review your true or false answers to the statements from the engage activity.
3. Use the TSAR strategy to decide whether to change any of your answers based on what you and your classmates have learned in the chapter. Consult with at least 2 other students. Record any evidence you have for keeping or changing each answer.

Even though your answers may not have changed, your reasoning may have. You should have more knowledge now and be able to write better explanations than you did in the engage activity.

Part II: Analyzing Research

Materials

For each student

1 *Analyzing Research* handout

Process and Procedure

1. Get the *Analyzing Research* handout from your teacher and see what you have learned. Steps 1a–c will help you.
   a. Review the graphs carefully before answering each question. Focus on any changes you see.
   b. Write and mark on the graphs as necessary to show what you understand about the data.
   c. You must complete the test in the time allotted by your teacher.

CHAPTER 15

Earth's Capacity

Chapter Overview

Students focused on plant and nonhuman animal populations in chapter 14, *Population Interactions*. They learned how different factors affect population growth and how interactions between the biological and physical environment are part of functioning ecosystems. In chapter 15, *Earth's Capacity*, the focus changes to human population growth and the interaction between human populations and ecosystems. Students will learn how they depend on ecosystems for resources as well as about the natural processes that occur in ecosystems.

Students will become engaged in their dependency on ecosystems by thinking about how much land is necessary to provide all the resources they need. They will get an estimate of this area by calculating their ecological footprint. Then students will map the distribution and consumption of resources for 10 world regions. They will discover that some regions consume more resources despite having smaller populations.

After students learn how humans consume resources today, they will learn how human populations have changed across time. Graphs and readings will show students that changes in the way humans use the environment have caused dramatic increases in population size in recent history. Students will study graphs of birthrates, mortality rates, and fertility rates to see how each is related to population growth. They will learn that the world population is continuing to increase even though the growth rate is decreasing. They will revisit our dependency on ecosystems by reading about how we use ecosystems for resources and services. Students will learn that all resources are finite because we can potentially use them at rates faster than they can be replenished. They will find that the carrying capacity of Earth is determined more by how people on Earth live than by how many people there are. To learn how management of an ecosystem can help sustain it, students will role-play fishermen who must decide how to change their fishing practices to sustain a fish population for future generations. Students will demonstrate their understanding of the chapter concepts by proposing the carrying capacity for a space station the size of Earth. They will describe the ecosystems on the stations as well as population and consumption characteristics.

Goals for the Chapter

The overarching goals for this chapter are that students will understand that human populations grow in response to various factors and that human consumption affects the function of natural systems and thus the availability of resources. By the end of chapter 15, students will understand the following:

- Various factors influence birthrates, fertility rates, and mortality rates in human populations, including social issues, cultural and religious issues, and technology.
- Human populations rely on natural systems for resources that maintain and improve their existence.
- The consumption of resources stresses the natural processes that renew resources and depletes those resources that cannot be renewed.
- Changes in technology can cause either positive or negative changes in the capacity of earth systems to provide resources for human populations.

The chapter organizer uses graphic design principles to help students connect one activity to another. It uses reminders of key concepts, linking questions, and the spatial arrangement of activity titles to foster the sense of a conceptual flow, connecting each activity. Explicitly ask students to locate their position within its flow at the beginning of each activity. This action reinforces the connection among the activities, thus enhancing long-term memory.

Chapter 15 Organizer

EARTH'S CAPACITY

Major Concepts

- **Various factors affect human birthrates, fertility rates, and mortality rates.**
- **Human populations rely on natural systems for resources.**
- **Earth does not have infinite resources.**
- **Human consumption places pressure on natural processes, which renews some resources and depletes resources that cannot be renewed.**
- **Technology can cause either positive or negative changes in the capacity of earth systems to provide resources for human populations.**

ENGAGE — Your Ecological Footprint ★

Key Idea: • Humans rely on resources to support their daily lives.

Activity: Students identify resources they rely on and estimate their ecological footprint, which is a way to visualize the resources we use.

LINKING QUESTION: How are the resources we use distributed across the world?

EXPLORE — Eat, Drink, and Be Merry ★ ★

Key Idea: • Humans and resources are unevenly distributed across the world. People in different parts of the world consume resources at different rates.

Activity: Students create world maps showing the distribution of resources, consumption, and populations. They compare consumption of resources with their distribution in world regions.

LINKING QUESTION: How are human populations changing across time and how will this affect ecosystems?

EXPLAIN — Too Much Is Never Enough: Consumption and Human Population ★ ★

Key Idea: • Human population growth is influenced by a variety of factors such as birthrate, mortality rate, fertility rate, and life expectancy.

Activity: Students analyze graphs of birthrates, mortality rates, and fertility rates to see how each is related to population growth.

LINKING QUESTION: Where do the resources come from that support human populations?

EXPLAIN — Limits to Growth ★

Key Ideas:
- Ecosystems provide resources and services for humans.
- Consumption affects the capacity of ecosystems to provide resources and services.

Activity: Students document how humans use ecosystems for resources and services.

LINKING QUESTION: How are resources managed for sustainability?

★ = One Class Period ☆ = ½ Class Period *Note:* Based on a 50-minute class period.

ELABORATE — Managing an Ecosystem ★★

Key Idea: • Limits are often placed on consumption to make ecosystems sustainable.

Activity: Students play the role of Pacific halibut fishermen and decide how to manage a halibut population.

LINKING QUESTION: How can I use what I have learned to demonstrate my understanding of human populations and natural resources?

EVALUATE — Sustaining Human Populations ★★

Key Ideas:
- Human population growth is affected by many factors.
- Humans rely on ecosystems for resources and natural processes.
- Consumption affects the number of people Earth can support.

Activity: Students compare artificial systems in Biosphere 2 with ecosystems on Earth. They predict how three populations will fare on a space station based on characteristics of each population. Finally, they create a poster that proposes how many people could live comfortably in a space station the size of Earth.

★ = One Class Period ☆ = ½ Class Period *Note:* Based on a 50-minute class period.

NOTES:

Standards Covered by Chapter 15

EARTH'S CAPACITY

STANDARD F: Science in Personal and Social Perspectives. As a result of activities in grades 9–12, all students should develop understanding of

population growth

- Various factors influence birth rates and fertility rates, such as average levels of affluence and education, importance of children in the labor force, education and employment of women, infant mortality rates, costs of raising children, availability and reliability of birth control methods, and religious beliefs and cultural norms that influence personal decisions about family size.
- Populations can reach limits to growth. Carrying capacity is the maximum number of individuals that can be supported in a given environment. The limitation is not the availability of space, but the number of people in relation to resources and the capacity of earth systems to support human beings. Changes in technology can cause significant changes, either positive or negative, in carrying capacity.

natural resources

- Human populations use resources in the environment in order to maintain and improve their existence. Natural resources have been and will continue to be used to maintain human populations.
- The earth does not have infinite resources; increasing human consumption places severe stress on the natural processes that renew some resources, and it depletes those resources that cannot be renewed.
- Humans use many natural systems as resources. Natural systems have the capacity to reuse waste, but that capacity is limited. Natural systems can change to an extent that exceeds the limits of organisms to adapt naturally or humans to adapt technologically.

environmental quality

- Natural ecosystems provide an array of basic processes that affect humans. Those processes include maintenance of the quality of the atmosphere, generation of soils, control of the hydrologic cycle, disposal of wastes, and recycling of nutrients. Humans are changing many of these basic processes, and the changes may be detrimental to humans.

Prerequisite Knowledge

Students should be familiar with terminology associated with populations such as birthrates, mortality rates, limiting factors, and carrying capacity.

Commonly Held Misconceptions

- Renewable resources are in infinite supply.

Although renewable resources can be replenished through natural processes, high rates of consumption can use the resources faster than they can be replenished.

ENGAGE

Your Ecological Footprint

Activity Overview

In *Your Ecological Footprint*, students will work individually and in teams to think about the resources they use and then calculate their ecological footprint. Students compare their footprints with each other's and with the average footprints of other countries. An ecological footprint is an estimate. Emphasize the ecological footprint as a tool that students can use to help them understand more about how earth systems provide the resources they use.

Before You Teach

Background Information

In 1996, William Rees and Mathis Wackernagel published a book titled *Our Ecological Footprint: Reducing Human Impact on the Earth*. They developed the concept of an ecological footprint as a way to visualize the resources required to sustain our households. The footprint estimates are based on data on consumption and trade flows in the United States. Information about consumption is then translated into the land area required to produce the resources consumed and to assimilate the wastes generated. Energy use is translated to land area by calculating how much land area is needed to absorb carbon dioxide produced from energy generation. The data used in the calculations were acquired from United Nations agencies and the Intergovernmental Panel on Climate Change.

The ecological footprint is criticized for several reasons. The translation of energy use to land assumes that all energy is generated from fossil fuel sources. It does not take into account nuclear power, hydropower, or other renewable energy sources. Also, the carbon absorbed by the ocean is not taken into account, and the ocean is the largest sink for carbon. The footprint only counts each area once. It does not count multiple uses of land. For example, a forested area is both a carbon sink and a source of timber. The footprint excludes human activities where there is insufficient data such as recycling or composting. It also excludes human activities that degrade natural processes in ecosystems such as pollution, changing water flow, and deforestation. Because the footprint only looks at the current consumption of a household, it is biased toward households with more children. The footprint does not account for the fact that each child will potentially form another household in the future.

Despite the potential problems, an ecological footprint is a useful tool for educating people about their resource use. Today, most people are disconnected from the resources they consume. The footprint can be powerful because it provides a way to account for human consumption of renewable resources such as food and forests that are usually considered in infinite supply. Humans can potentially use resources faster than they are replenished in ecosystems.

Materials

For the teacher

world map

For each team of 3 students

3 copies of copymaster 15.1, *Ecological Footprint*

Advance Preparation

Make 3 copies of copymaster 15.1, *Ecological Footprint* per team. Display a world map that can be referenced throughout the chapter.

ENGAGE **Your Ecological Footprint**

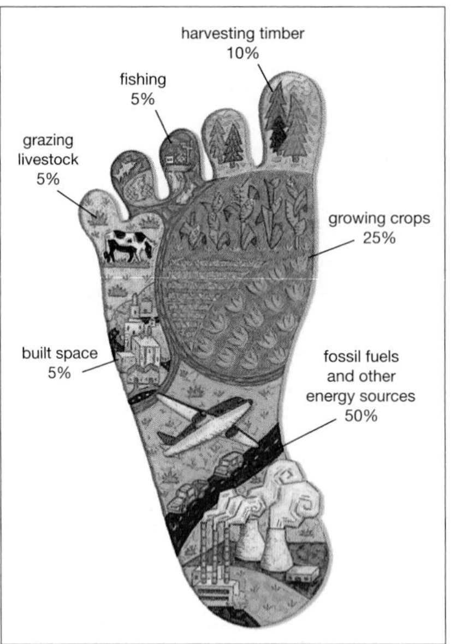

▲ **Figure 15.1 An ecological footprint.** In this activity, you will estimate how much land you need in order to provide all the resources you use.

What do you need to live? For animals like humans, perhaps you think of their needs for food and shelter. How much space do you need to live comfortably? You might be thinking about the amount of space in your dream apartment once you are on your own. Would you include the acres of land needed to provide the food you eat or the materials in your bedroom or home? What about your trash and sewage? Would you set aside space for that? In *Your Ecological Footprint*, you will work with your classmates to think about all the resources you use every day. Then you will work alone to estimate your ecological footprint (see figure 15.1). An ecological footprint is a measure of how much land you need to support what you use (inputs) and what you discard (outputs).

Materials

For each team of 3 students

3 *Ecological Footprint* handouts

Process and Procedure

1. Write down things that you use every day. In your science notebook, record at least 3 things in each of the following categories.
   a. Food
   b. Shelter
   c. Clothing
   d. Transportation
   e. Communication and entertainment
2. Work in a team of 3 and identify what resources are necessary to make or supply the things on your lists from Step 1. Record all the resources you identified.

Make sure you include energy in your list of resources. Write down the different sources of energy that might be necessary for the things on your list. For example, coal might be used to generate the electricity that heats or cools your home.

As You Teach

Outcomes and Indicators of Success

By the end of this activity, students should

1. begin to think about the resources they rely on in their daily lives and how natural systems provide those resources.

   They will demonstrate their thinking by

   - listing items they use every day for food, clothing, shelter, communication, and entertainment;
   - describing the resources needed to produce items they use every day;
   - describing what processes in natural systems might provide the resources they need;
   - predicting how much land is necessary to provide all the resources they use; and
   - filling out a worksheet to estimate the amount of land necessary to provide all the resources they use.

2. become aware of their resource use compared with the resource use of people from other countries.

   They will demonstrate their awareness by

   - comparing their ecological footprint with the footprint of people in other countries and
   - considering how people from other countries might feel about the size of their ecological footprint compared with the ecological footprint of someone from the United States.

Answers to Steps 6–8 are on TE pages 751–752.
Answers to Reflect and Connect are on TE page 752.

3. Make a T-table with the headings "resource" and "natural system." Match the resources from Step 2 with the natural system that provides the resource by aligning them in the T-table. For example, water is a resource that everyone uses daily, and it might come from a natural system such as a river, lake, or groundwater reservoir.
4. Predict how much land area is necessary for the natural systems to supply the resources you use. Give your answer as the number of bedrooms it would take.

An average bedroom is around 11 × 10 feet (ft), or 110 square feet (ft^2). To give you some perspective, you could fit about 524 bedrooms of this size in a soccer field or 396 bedrooms of this size in an acre.

5. Fill in the *Ecological Footprint* handout on your own and complete the calculations.
6. Compare the size of your ecological footprint with those of your teammates. Then follow Steps 6a–b to compare each teammate's footprint with America's average footprint of 9.7 hectares.

1 hectare (ha) = 10,000 meters squared (m^2)

A hectare is an area 100 × 100 meters (m), which is about the size of a soccer field.

   a. Use a ratio to compare your footprint with America's footprint. Then write a sentence that explains what the ratio means.
   b. Discuss what factors make your team's footprints similar to or different from the average American's footprint. Write at least 2 factors in your science notebook.

7. How does your prediction from Step 4 compare with the ecological footprint you calculated in Step 5?
   a. Make the comparison by converting your footprint in hectares to the number of bedrooms: 1 ha = 10,000 m^2, 1 m^2 = 10.76 ft^2.
   b. Does the size of your ecological footprint surprise you? Why or why not?
8. List 3 ways you could make your ecological footprint smaller. Provide an explanation for each way.

Reflect and Connect

Answer the following questions by yourself. Record your answers in your science notebook.

1. Why does footprint size matter? Why might a smaller footprint be advantageous?

Strategies

Getting Started

Read the introduction together as a class. Facilitate a brief discussion of students' ideas about how much land is necessary to meet all their needs. Consider taking students through an example of the resources needed to produce a resource such as an egg they might eat for breakfast. List these resources on the board to provide students with an idea of how to get started for this activity.

Process and Procedure

Materials

For the teacher

world map

For each team of 3 students

3 copies of copymaster 15.1, *Ecological Footprint*

TRCD

In Step 1, students should work individually to make a list of everyday items in 5 categories. Then divide students into teams of 3. Circulate as students discuss the resources necessary to make the items on their lists and match the resources to a natural system. Provide students with examples of resources and systems if they need help. In Step 4, students should show how much land area, as the number of bedrooms (1 bedroom equals 110 square feet, [ft^2]), it would take to provide the resources they need.

In Step 5, distribute copymaster 15.1, *Ecological Footprint* to each student. Students should determine their footprint individually because in Step 6 they compare their own ecological footprint with those of their teammates.

Answers to Steps 6–8, SE page 751

6a. If a student has an ecological footprint of 10.9 hectares (ha), the ratio would be 1.1 (10.9/9.7).

6b. Students are likely to have footprints that are similar to one another and to the average American's since the footprint calculations are based on consumption in the United States. Factors that might make footprints similar include similarities in eating habits, family size, home size, and traveling habits. The same factors might make footprints different.

7a. Converting hectares to the number of bedrooms gives students a better sense of how big the area is.

7b. Look for answers that show that students are becoming interested in how Earth provides the resources they use.

8. Some examples of ways that students might make their ecological footprint smaller are eating less meat, eating locally grown food, living in a smaller home or apartment, using energy-efficient lightbulbs or appliances, riding in a more fuel-efficient car, and generating less waste or recycling.

Answers to Reflect and Connect, SE pages 751–752

1. This question gets students thinking about why they should care about the resources they use. Later they will learn that resources are limited.

2a. Look for answers that are supported by students' current understanding. Animals must consume a lot of other plants or other animals to meet their energy needs. It takes more space to support an animal than it does plants. Help students recall the difference in kilocalories between plants and herbivores and plants and carnivores. Ecosystems can sustain more herbivores than carnivores.

2b. Students are likely to predict that the footprint of an Aborigine would be smaller than 9 ha. They should provide justification such as Aborigines live off the land and do not use as many goods and services.

3a. Students should recognize that many countries import the resources they need.

3b. This question has students think about how the resources that Americans use might affect people from other countries. For example, people from India or Kenya might feel that Americans are taking more than their share of Earth's resources and that these resources could be used by people who need them to survive.

4. This question should help students think about consumption and how countries could reduce the amount they consume. Factors that might make a footprint smaller include encouraging people to eat fewer meat products, eat less-processed food, live in a smaller home, use more energy-efficient appliances and cars, take public transportation more often, and travel less.

5. Some limitations of the "footprint model" might include how the footprint is estimated by translating goods, services, and energy use to land area. For example, land provides very different kinds of resources and amounts of resources depending on where the land is located and what plants and animals are found on the land.

2. How do personal and cultural differences affect ecological footprint size?
   a. Why would a vegetarian's footprint be smaller than a meat eater's footprint? (Assume that they have the same lifestyle except for their differences in diet.)

Use what you know about the amount of energy transfer between trophic levels. Think about how much energy it takes to produce vegetables compared with the amount of energy to raise a chicken or a cow.

   b. Predict the ecological footprint size for an Aborigine from Australia. Provide your reasoning for your answer.
3. Study figure 15.2 and compare the ecological footprints of different countries with the amount of biologically productive space.

Biologically productive space is the amount of land and water area that has a large amount of photosynthetic activity. As a result of this activity, it has a lot of plant and animal matter.

   a. Some countries have an ecological footprint that is greater than their biologically productive space. How do they get the resources to sustain the footprint?
   b. How do you think someone from India or Kenya might feel about the impact Americans are having on the global environment?
4. If a country wanted to make its ecological footprint smaller, how could it do that? List at least 3 things a country could do. Then explain how you think each would make the footprint smaller.
5. What are some limitations to the "footprint model"?

Country	Ecological footprint per person (ha)	Biologically productive space per person (ha)
Australia	7.6	14.6
Germany	4.7	1.7
India	0.8	0.7
Kenya	1.1	1.1
Mexico	2.5	1.7
United States	9.7	5.3

Source:

▲ **Figure 15.2 Ecological footprints and biologically productive space for 6 countries.** The values in this table are based on data from 2002.

EXPLORE

Eat, Drink, and Be Merry

Activity Overview

Calculating their ecological footprint helped students begin thinking about the resources they use. They also compared their resource use with that of other countries. In *Eat, Drink, and Be Merry*, students will explore how some of the resources they use are distributed across Earth. Then they will compare consumption of the resources with resource distribution in world regions. Working in teams, students will use data provided in the text to create their own distribution and consumption maps for analysis.

Before You Teach

Background Information

This activity focuses on resources rather than on populations because, in many ways, consumption has grown more than populations. Between 1980 and 1996, car ownership worldwide increased at a rate of 2.8 percent annually. Population growth only accounts for half the growth in car ownership. Similarly, television ownership grew at a rate of 5.7 percent annually, only a third of which can be explained by world population growth. During the same time period, population growth rates declined from 1.5 percent to 1 percent. As the world becomes more industrialized, family size moderates but consumption consistently increases. As consumption has grown, people in industrialized countries such as the United States have become increasingly separated from the ecosystems that provide the resources they consume. This activity will help connect students to the resources they use and help them understand how resources and consumption differ across the world.

Data for this activity were acquired from the Food and Agriculture Organization of the United Nations and World Resources Institute. See *Educational Technologies* for the corresponding Web sites.

Materials

For the teacher

- 1 transparency of copymaster 15.3, *World Region Map in Color* TRCD
- 1 transparency of copymaster 15.4, *Mean Annual Precipitation*

For each team of 2 students

- 3 copies of copymaster 15.2, *World Region Map*
- colored pencils
- transparent tape

Advance Preparation

Gather examples of maps that use different strategies to represent information. For example, some maps use colors or icons to represent different things.

Make 3 copies of copymaster 15.2, *World Region Map* for each team of 2. This copymaster is 2 pages, and students will need to tape the pages together.

Gather transparent tape and colored pencils. You could also ask students to bring colored pencils to class.

Educational Technologies

If students would like to find out information about resources and consumption, they can query the data provided on the Web sites of the following organizations:

- Food and Agriculture Organization of the United Nations Statistical Databases

---

Eat, Drink, and Be Merry

EXPLORE

Have you ever thought about where the resources you use come from? The resources that plants and wild animals use must be in their immediate area (see figure 15.3). They get their resources from the surrounding environment. Some animals such as birds migrate to get their resources. Other animals such as mountain lions have home ranges that extend up to 260 kilometers squared (km^2), which is 26,000 ha or about 100 square miles (mi^2). Even so, these animals must come into direct contact with the resources they use.

How do humans in modern urban, suburban, and rural societies get their resources? For example, do you gather the food you eat or the water you drink? Humans in many societies transport resources to where they need them. In *Eat, Drink, and Be Merry*, you will work with a partner to map where some of the resources originate. Then you will compare the locations of those resources with population size and the consumption of those resources.

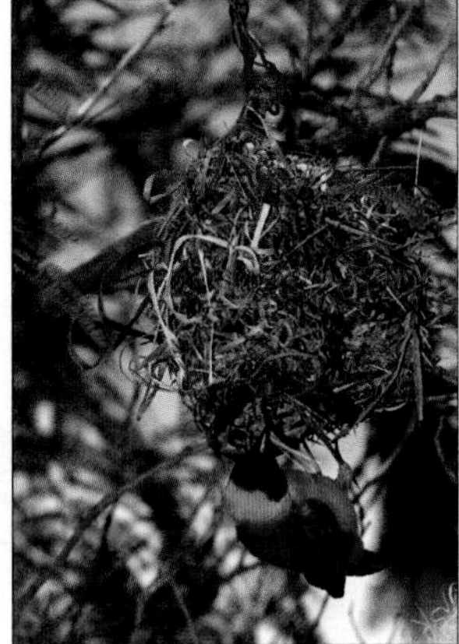

▲ **Figure 15.3**
Resources. The resources birds need to survive, such as nest-building material and food, are in their immediate environment. Where do the resources that you use come from?

Materials

For each team of 2 students

- 3 *World Region Map* handouts
- colored pencils
- transparent tape

Process and Procedure

1. Divide into teams of 2 and get 3 copies of the *World Region Map* handout.
2. Study figures 15.4–15.7. Discuss as a team how you could represent the amount of each resource on a world map.

For example, sometimes maps use color or patterns to represent different values. Other maps use icons such as water drops or trees to represent a specific unit of material.

3. Create world maps showing the available resources and resource consumption. Steps 3a–c will help you.
   a. Meet with another team and divide the work so that each team generates 2 different maps from the data shown in the 4 tables in figures 15.4–15.7. For example, one team could create maps of figures 15.4 and 15.6 and the other team could create maps of 15.5 and 15.7.

Chapter 15 Earth's Capacity 753

- Food and Agriculture Organization's Information System on Water and Agriculture
- International Energy Agency Energy Statistics

As You Teach

Outcomes and Indicators of Success

By the end of this activity, students should

1. be able to manipulate data and display them spatially on maps to make comparisons.

   They will demonstrate their ability by

   - deciding how to represent numerical data from different sources on several maps,
   - calculating the density of resources and population per region, and
   - calculating the consumption of resources per person.

2. be able to interpret that the consumption of resources varies in different parts of the world.

   They will demonstrate their ability by

   - explaining why some regions get more food calories from animal products than other regions,
   - comparing maps showing resource consumption with maps of population density,
   - identifying the biggest and smallest consumers of oil, and
   - describing their position on whether population size or lifestyle has a bigger influence on consumption.

3. begin to understand that human populations rely on natural systems for resources.

   They will demonstrate their understanding by

   - describing how differences in ecosystems might explain differences in the availability of resources,
   - identifying the relationship between precipitation and the availability of some resources, and
   - describing ways that ecosystems provide resources for humans.

Strategies

Getting Started

Get out a world map and ask students to predict which parts of the world have the most water and oil resources. Then ask students to predict which parts of the world use the most water and oil resources. Ask students to explain the basis of their predictions. Consider having students write this in their science notebooks for a record of their ideas. For example, they might have seen or read things about populations on TV or in magazines. Explain that they can compare their answers to actual data on world resources as they complete this activity.

Process and Procedure

Materials

For the teacher

1 transparency of copymaster 15.3, *World Region Map in Color*

TRCD

1 transparency of copymaster 15.4, *Mean Annual Precipitation*

For each team of 2 students

3 copies of copymaster 15.2, *World Region Map*

colored pencils

transparent tape

Divide students into teams of 2 and distribute 3 copies of copymaster 15.2, *World Region Map*. The *World Region Map* is split in half and comes on 2 separate pages. Teams must line up the 2 and tape them together.

Region	Total freshwater resources (km^3/yr)	Total forest area (km^2)	Total agricultural area (km^2)
North America	6,709	5,257,690	5,869,030
Central America and Caribbean	787	232,650	344,960
South America	12,380	8,856,180	6,424,820
Western and central Europe	2,181	1,617,430	2,108,110
Eastern Europe	4,693	8,776,800	2,761,640
Africa	3,950	6,498,660	11,109,740
Near East	491	257,520	3,220,080
Central Asia	289	206,260	3,195,150
Southern and eastern Asia	11,720	5,320,160	10,432,910
Oceania and Pacific	911	1,670,220	4,656,180

Source: Food and Agriculture Organization of the United Nations, "Review of World Water Resources by Country, 2003", "State of the World's Forests, 2005", http://faostat.fao.org

▲ **Figure 15.4 World resources by region.** Total freshwater resources are calculated as the average flow of rivers and groundwater from precipitation. They also include the amount of water flowing into the region from other regions. Total forest area is the land area covered by natural or planted stands of trees. Agricultural area is the land area covered by crops or pasture.

Region	Oil reserves (billion tons)	Coal reserves (million tons)	Natural gas reserves (trillion m^3)
North America	8.0	254,432	7.3
Central America and Caribbean	0.3	2,690	0.7
South America	14.1	17,203	6.4
Western and central Europe	3.6	60,467	7.2
Eastern Europe	9.9	191,163	49.1
Africa	14.9	50,336	14.1
Near East	100.0	4,605	78.2
Central Asia	5.5	31,279	7.8
Southern and eastern Asia	4.9	217,506	11.4
Oceania and Pacific	0.6	79,383	2.84

Source: Putting Energy in the Spotlight: BP Statistical Review of World Energy June 2005

▲ **Figure 15.5 World energy resources by region.** Geologists and engineers estimate the amount of reserves there are. They estimate how much oil, coal, and natural gas can be recovered based on the use of current technology and the cost of extraction. Their estimates may change if new technologies are developed.

754 Unit 4 Sustaining Earth Systems

Display a transparency of copymaster 15.3, *World Region Map in Color* during this activity. The colors will help students distinguish the regions.

In Step 2, teams discuss how they could represent the amount of each resource from figures 15.4–15.7 in the student book on a world map. If you have collected examples of maps, suggest that students review them. In Step 3, teams should work with another team to divide the task of creating 4 maps from the data in the figures. Each team should create 2 maps on separate *World Region Maps* (copymaster 15.2). Teams must include a title and legend with each map they create.

Once teams have paired up with another team in Step 3, they will continue to work together to complete the remaining steps. Teams should share their work in Step 4. Listen to teams as they describe their maps and make sure they are recording ideas from the other teams in their science notebooks.

Answers to Step 4, SE page 756

4. Teams should notice the following patterns for the maps showing available resources. North America, South America, eastern Europe, Africa, and southern and eastern Asia seem to have more resources. Western and central Europe, the Near East, central Asia, and Oceania and the Pacific seem to have fewer resources, with the exception of the large amount of oil in the Near East.

   Teams should notice the following patterns for the maps showing resource consumption. North America, western and central Europe, and southern and eastern Asia seem to consume more resources. North America and southern and eastern Asia also consume the most energy resources. Central America and the Caribbean, and Oceania and the Pacific seem to consume the least resources, including energy resources.

   Teams should notice the following things in common for the maps showing available resources. Students might explain that all the regions have each type of resource. They might also explain that the agricultural area is the most consistent among the regions.

   Teams should notice the following things in common for the maps showing resource consumption. Students might explain that all the regions use each type of resource, with the exception of Africa, which does not use a significant amount of coal. They might also notice that all the regions use more oil than any other energy resource.

Display the transparency of copymaster 15.4, *Mean Annual Precipitation* for Step 5. Teams should work together to complete the remaining steps.

Answers to Steps 5–10, SE pages 756–758

5a. Water resources tend to be located where precipitation is greater, and agricultural land tends to be located where precipitation is moderate. However, the relationship between precipitation and forests is less clear.

Students should notice that water resources are more abundant where precipitation is greater, such as Central America and the Caribbean and South America. Water resources are less abundant where precipitation is less, such as the Near East and central Asia. For most regions, forests appear more abundant

Region	Total water withdrawal (km^3/yr)	Total wood products (1,000 m^3)	Average food calorie supply (kcal)	Food calories from animal products (%)
North America	603	719,615	3,432	23
Central America and Caribbean	22	109,018	2,489	15
South America	165	186,112	2,845	21
Western and central Europe	289	502,018	3,368	27
Eastern Europe	120	137,549	2,943	23
Africa	161	73,761	3,034	9
Near East	210	27,903	2,840	14
Central Asia	163	3,012	2,386	18
Southern and eastern Asia	2,004	374,074	2,477	12
Oceania and Pacific	26	48,037	2,865	24

Source: water data and wood product data: Food and Agriculture Organization of the United Nations, AQUASTAT database, "State of the World's Forests, 2005". World Resources Institute. 2006. food calorie data: EarthTrends: The Environmental Information Portal. Available at http://earthtrends.wri.org. Washington, DC: World Resources Institute.

▲ **Figure 15.6 World water, wood, and food consumption.** Water withdrawal includes any water use, such as industrial, agricultural, and residential uses. Total wood products include wood used for building materials, but does not include paper products. The average food calorie supply is the average amount of food available (in kcal) per person per day.

Region	Oil (thousand million tons)	Coal (million tons)	Natural gas (trillion m^3)	Wood fuel (million m^3)
North America	1,122.4	603.8	784.3	114
Central America and Caribbean	58.3	1.0	17.6	45
South America	163.4	17.7	100.3	190
Western and central Europe	756.4	340.0	560.5	55
Eastern Europe	148.4	145.5	475.9	57
Africa	124.3	0	68.6	546
Near East	282.9	32.1	264.3	8
Central Asia	20.5	28.7	50.0	1
Southern and eastern Asia	1,025.2	1,425.3	331.8	778
Oceania and Pacific	65.3	81.0	35.9	7

Source: Putting Energy in the Spotlight: BP Statistical Review of World Energy June 2005

▲ **Figure 15.7 Annual world energy consumption for 2004.** The oil, coal, and natural gas totals include energy used for all purposes, such as electricity and gasoline. Wood fuel includes charcoal and wood cut directly from forests and used for heating or cooking. Why do you think some regions use more wood fuel than others?

Chapter 15 Earth's Capacity 755

where precipitation is greater. However, eastern Europe does not have as much rain as South America, but it has almost the same percentage of forest cover. This might be because less forest area has been cleared in eastern Europe compared with South America.

5b. Temperature is an important factor that affects what plants grow. Plants are more productive in higher temperatures, and in lower temperatures fewer species will thrive.

6a. North America and southern and eastern Asia consume the most water and wood products. Students might explain that this is because these regions have larger populations or because these regions consume more per person.

6b. Looking at the percentage of food calories (kcal) from animal products gives a better idea of how many resources the region is consuming for food production. Regions with a higher consumption of calories from animal products are consuming more resources than regions with a lower percentage of calories from animal products.

6c. Students might explain that Africa and southern and eastern Asia have higher populations and that food is sometimes scarce, forcing people to eat less meat. They might explain that the United States and Europe have bigger economies (more money) that allow the population to invest more in livestock production or to import animal products.

6d. Students must provide reasoning for their responses. They are likely to explain that lifestyle explains the amount of oil, coal, and natural gas used because North America uses a similar amount of resources to southern and eastern Asia, which has a larger population.

6e. Students might recognize that less industrialized areas in Africa and central Asia use more-accessible or easily available resources such as wood.

7a. Students might notice that Africa and South America have plentiful resources but seem to consume fewer than other regions. They might also notice that North America and Europe have a lot of resources and consume a lot of resources.

7b. Low-resource regions consume a lot of resources by importing them. For example, Central Asia and the Near East have fewer water resources than many regions, but consume as much water as many other regions.

7c. High-resource areas often consume fewer resources because they don't have the technology to use the resources. For example, South America has more water resources than many regions but consumes less water. Similarly, Africa has more forest resources than many regions but consumes fewer wood products.

8a. A completed data table is shown in figure T15.1.

8b. South America and Central America have the most water. The Near East and central Asia have the least water and forest cover. All regions except eastern Europe have at least a third of the land area in agriculture. The Near East has over 100 times more oil reserves than most of the other regions.

Answers to Step 4 are on TE page 755.
Answers to Steps 5–10 are on TE pages 755–759

b. Use the strategy you developed in Step 2 to generate the maps.

For the data in figure 15.6, you might use a different color to show the percentage of food calories (kcal) from animal products.

c. Include a title and legend on each map.

4. Examine the maps your team of 4 created. What patterns do you see? Why might these patterns be important? Discuss the patterns and other important things you notice and record what you learn in your science notebook.

Consider using highlight comments to describe the patterns and to explain what the patterns mean.

5. Study the world precipitation map that your teacher displays. Compare the amount of precipitation with the availability of resources for each region.
   a. Describe the relationship between precipitation and where water, forest, and agricultural land resources are located.
   b. Identify any factors that might influence the availability of water, forest, and agricultural land resources.
6. Consider how human populations in different parts of the world can affect Earth's resources.
   a. Which 2 regions have the greatest water withdrawal and consumption of wood products? Why do these regions consume more water and wood products? See figure 15.6.
   b. Why might it be important to look at the percentage of food calories (kcal) from animal products in addition to the total kcal? See figure 15.6.
   c. The United States and Europe have a higher percentage of food calories from animals than Africa and southern and eastern Asia have. What factors might explain this observation? See figure 15.6.

The average daily food supply for Americans is 3,754 kcal, of which 28 percent is composed of animal products.

   d. Each region uses different amounts of oil, coal, and natural gas. Is the usage affected more by the size of the population or by the kind of lifestyle people have? Figure 15.7 should help you answer this question. Be sure to explain your answer.
   e. Why do you think Africa and southern and eastern Asia use more wood fuel than other regions in the world? See figure 15.7.
7. Compare the maps showing the available resources with the maps showing resource consumption. Steps 7a–c will help you do this. See also figures 15.4–15.7.

Region	Freshwater resources by area (m^3/km^2)	Percent area covered by forest (km^2)	Percent area covered by agricultural land (km^2)	Oil reserves by area ($tons/km^2$)
North America	30,635	24%	27%	364
Central America and Caribbean	105,057	31%	46%	397
South America	69,340	50%	36%	791
Western and central Europe	44,525	33%	43%	736
Eastern Europe	25,935	49%	15%	547
Africa	13,147	21%	37%	492
Near East	7,735	4%	51%	15,970
Central Asia	6,208	4%	69%	1,182
Southern and eastern Asia	55,306	25%	49%	229
Oceania and Pacific	11,304	21%	57%	74

▲ **Figure T15.1 Distribution of resources across total land area.** This table shows the values students should calculate for Step 8a.

a. Discuss with your partner the similarities and differences in where the resources are located and where they are used. Record at least 1 similarity and 1 difference.
b. Identify which regions seem to consume more resources than are available. How might you explain this?
c. Identify which regions seem to have more resources than they consume. How might you explain this?

8. Use Steps 8a–b to help you determine how resources are distributed for the total land area of each region. Use the total land area given in figure 15.8 to make your calculations.
   a. Create a data table to record the following in your science notebook:
      - Amount of freshwater resources (cubic meters, m^3) per km^2 for each region
      - Percentage of area covered by forest per total km^2 for each region
      - Percentage of area covered by agricultural land per total km^2 for each region
      - Amount of oil reserves (tons) per km^2 for each region
   b. Describe the patterns you see.
9. Complete Steps 9a–e to help you think about how human populations are distributed across the world.
   a. Predict which 3 regions have the largest population densities. Provide your reasoning in your answer.
   b. Calculate the population density for each region using the data in figure 15.8. Give the population density in people per kilometers squared ($people/km^2$).

Region	Total area ($\times 10^6$ km^2)	Total population (millions)
North America	22.0	429
Central America and Caribbean	0.8	78
South America	17.8	362
Western and central Europe	4.9	513
Eastern Europe	18.1	213
Africa	30.3	851
Near East	6.3	250
Central Asia	4.7	82
Southern and eastern Asia	21.4	3,497
Oceania and Pacific	8.1	27

◄ **Figure 15.8 Total land area and population for each region.** The total land area includes the area under inland water bodies. How does the population size compare with the total area of each region?

Source: Food and Agriculture Organization of the United Nations, http://faostat.fao.org, AQUASTAT database

Chapter 15 Earth's Capacity 757

9a. Students should make predictions based on their prior knowledge of world populations.

9b. Students should divide the total population by the total land area to get population density. Population densities are given in figure T15.2.

Region	Population density ($people/km^2$)
North America	19.5
Central America and Caribbean	102.5
South America	20.3
Western and central Europe	105.0
Eastern Europe	11.8
Africa	28.1
Near East	39.9
Central Asia	17.5
Southern and eastern Asia	163.4
Oceania and Pacific	3.3

▲ **Figure T15.2 Population density for each world region.** This table shows the population densities students should calculate for Step 9b.

9c. Teams should map the population densities they calculate on their third copy of copymaster 15.2, *World Region Map*. Make sure student maps have a title and legend.

9d. Students should notice that the densest populations are in Central America and the Caribbean, western and central Europe, and southern and eastern Asia. These regions have good supplies of freshwater, forest cover, and agricultural land. Their supply of oil reserves is less compared with some other regions.

9e. Some of the greatest resource use occurs where the largest populations are. Southern and eastern Asia has the largest population and also uses large amounts of water, forest products, and energy. However, Africa also has a large population and uses considerably fewer resources than other regions. North America uses large amounts of all resources even though its population size and density is less than other regions. Students should recognize that many parts of the world must transport resources to where they are used.

10a. Students should divide the total water withdrawal and oil consumed by the total population to get consumption per person. Consumption per person is shown in figure T15.3.

10b. Water: North America, central Asia, and Oceania and the Pacific are the biggest consumers. Africa, Central America and the Caribbean, and South America are the smallest consumers.

Oil: North America, central Asia, and the Near East are the biggest consumers. Africa, central Asia, and southern and eastern Asia are the smallest consumers.

Answers to Reflect and Connect, SE pages 758–759

1. This question helps students look ahead to the next activity. Based on what students learned in chapter 14, they might provide answers such as the following. "Ecosystems are different depending on soils, temperature, and precipitation. Each of these factors has an effect on whether land is forested or could be used for agriculture. The distribution of precipitation and groundwater sources influences where water resources are located."

   Based on previous knowledge, a few students might say that fossil fuels formed in swamps or marine ecosystems millions of years ago and that those energy resources are located where these ecosystems existed in the past. Other students might simply explain that millions of years ago fossil fuels formed in some ecosystems. The location of these ecosystems is where fossil fuels are located today. Students will learn about the relationship between fossil fuels and ecosystems in the next activity.
2. Ecosystems provide resources such as lumber, clean water, food, wood as fuel, and soil. Students might also mention processes that occur in ecosystems such as the carbon cycle and the water cycle.
3. Students should explain that consumption of energy is mostly related to the lifestyle of people. This is because North Americans use more energy per person than any other region, and North America has a smaller population than several other regions.

Answers to Reflect and Connect are on TE pages 758–759.

c. Create a human population map that shows the relative population densities of each region. Include a title and a legend with your map.

d. Compare the human population map with the maps of resources. Are the densest populations located where the resources are most plentiful? What does the pattern of human populations and resources mean?

e. Compare the human population map with the maps of resource and energy consumption. Does the greatest consumption occur where the largest populations are? Why or why not?

10. Determine which regions consume the most water and oil resources per person.

    a. Create a data table to record the following in your science notebook:
       - Amount of water withdrawal per person in cubic meters per year (m^3/yr) for each region
       - Amount of oil consumed per person in tons per year (tons/yr) for each region

    b. Describe which regions are the biggest consumers and which are the smallest consumers.

Reflect and Connect

Answer the following questions by yourself and write your answers in your science notebook. Check your answers with those of another student and revise them if necessary.

1. How might the differences in ecosystems explain the differences in resource availability? Provide an explanation for both energy and nonenergy resources.

   Remember that ecosystems include both the biotic and abiotic environments and that ecosystems change across time.

2. Describe at least 2 ways that ecosystems provide resources that support human populations.

   Use what you know about populations and some of the processes that occur in ecosystems.

3. Review your answer to Step 6d. Has your position changed? Is consumption of energy related more to the size of the population or the lifestyle people have? Use evidence to explain why or why not.
4. Consider what would happen if other regions consumed oil at the same rate per person that North America does.

Region	Water withdrawal per person (m^3/year)	Oil consumed per person (tons/yr)
North America	141	2.6
Central America and Caribbean	28	0.8
South America	46	0.5
Western and central Europe	56	1.5
Eastern Europe	56	0.7
Africa	19	0.1
Near East	84	1.1
Central Asia	200	0.3
Southern and eastern Asia	57	0.3
Oceania and Pacific	98	2.5

◀ **Figure T15.3 Water withdrawal and oil consumption per person for each world region.** This table shows the consumption of water and oil that students should calculate for Step 10a.

Answers to Step 2 are on TE page 761.

a. Calculate the amount of oil (thousand million tons) that southern and eastern Asia would use annually if it consumed the same amount per person as North America.
b. Describe how the world's oil resources would be affected if regions such as southern and eastern Asia started using more oil.

EXPLAIN

Too Much Is Never Enough: Consumption and Human Population

Population size is one factor that affects the quantity of resources a country uses. What do you know about human populations? You learned in the explore activity, *Eat, Drink, and Be Merry*, how human populations are distributed across Earth. In *Too Much Is Never Enough*, you will look at world population data and learn the factors that affect human population growth. Then you will learn about the different goods and services ecosystems provide. You will use what you know about human populations and resources to propose a carrying capacity for Earth.

Materials

For each student

1 *Age Structure* handout

access to a computer and the Web

Process and Procedure

1. Read the following paragraph to learn about a prediction made in 1798 about the future of human populations.

   In 1798, Thomas Malthus published *An Essay on the Principle of Population as It Affects the Future Improvement of Society*. He said that human populations tend to grow at an exponential rate. But food is produced at a stable or slowly increasing rate. He predicted that, as a result, the world would face famine and misery. He argued that the only way to stabilize human populations was for wars or disease to increase mortality rates or for birthrates to decrease.

2. Explain why you think Malthus's prediction about human populations was right or wrong. Steps 2a–e will help you form your explanation.
   a. Read *History of Human Population Growth* to learn how human populations have changed across time. Use this

4a. Students should multiply North America's consumption rate by southern and eastern Asia's total population.

2.6 tons/person/yr × 3,496,794,000 people = 9,091,664,400 tons per yr or 9,091.7 million tons per yr

4b. If southern and eastern Asia consumed this much oil, it would deplete the oil reserves much faster. It would be more than twice the world consumption of oil today.

EXPLAIN

Too Much Is Never Enough: Consumption and Human Population

Activity Overview

After students learn how humans consume resources today, they will learn how human populations have changed across time. Graphs and readings will show students that changes in health care and changes in the way humans use the environment have caused dramatic increases in population size in recent history. Students will study graphs of birthrates, mortality rates, and fertility rates to see how each is related to population growth. They will learn that the world population is continuing to increase even though the growth rate is decreasing.

Before You Teach

Background Information

The global human population has shown a J-shaped (exponential) pattern of growth for the past 1,000 years. This is unlike other populations, which usually show S-shaped (logistic) growth. For most of human history, the world's population has been less than 500 million people (see figure 15.9 in the student book). The dramatic growth of human population in the last 200 years is a product of the agricultural and industrial revolutions. Recent developments such as increased crop productivity, though, have helped food production keep pace with a doubling of the population since 1960. Because population growth rates are declining (see figure 15.19 in the student book), many scientists think that the steep curve we are in right now will level out in the next few decades. Slowed growth can be attributed to changes in age structure and fertility rates as countries become more industrialized.

Data for this activity were acquired from the Population Division of the United Nations Department of Economic and Social Affairs; World Resources Institute; Population Reference Bureau; and International Programs Center, which is part of the Population Division of the U.S. Census Bureau.

Materials

For each student

1 copy of copymaster 15.5, *Age Structure*

access to a computer and the Web

Advance Preparation

Reserve time in a computer lab for students to do research on the Web or give students the organizations listed in *Educational Technologies* to do the research on their own at home.

Make 1 copy of copymaster 15.5, *Age Structure for each student.*

Read the student book and be prepared to help students who struggle with reading.

Educational Technologies

Students are given the opportunity to ask their own questions about population. They are directed to search the Web for the information they need to answer their questions. The following organizations provide statistics on world populations that can be queried:

- U.S. Census Bureau International Data Base
- United Nations Population Division
- Population Reference Bureau

As You Teach

Outcomes and Indicators of Success

By the end of this activity, students should

1. understand that social and cultural issues affect fertility rates.

   They will demonstrate their understanding by

   - describing how different cultures value having children for different reasons and
   - describing how higher levels of education often delay the age when women have children and reduce the number of children women have.

Answers to Step 2 are on TE page 761.

question to focus your reading: "What factors have affected human population growth?"

b. What aspects of Malthus's argument have merit or value?

c. What things have happened across time that he didn't predict?

d. Describe in your science notebook at least 3 reasons why human populations have not collapsed as Malthus predicted. Include justifications from the reading in your answer.

e. Predict what you think the graph in figure 15.9 will look like in another 200 years. Make your prediction by drawing a new graph in your science notebook. Include a caption describing what changes, if any, have occurred that account for the population size.

Consider using the think-share-advise-revise (TSAR) strategy to compare your graph with another student's.

READING

History of Human Population Growth

More than 6.5 billion people live on Earth today. The human population wasn't always this large. It became large only recently. Scientists estimate that the world's population around 8000 BC was near 10 million. The current population size of Los Angeles County, California, is about the same.

Around 8000 BC, many human cultures changed from hunting and gathering societies to farming communities (see figure 15.9). This agricultural revolution provided a more dependable food supply. The food supply allowed human populations to grow and groups of people to live in one place. By 200 BC, the human population had increased to as many as 200 million people. The human population didn't reach 1 billion until the 1800s. Since then, it has increased rapidly.

Many technological changes took place in the 1700s. These changes were the start of the industrial revolution. The technology developed at this time brought about many of the conveniences we enjoy today. Machines and factories became widespread. Many people left agricultural lifestyles and moved to cities. Railroads improved transportation. The telegraph improved communication. Scientific discoveries and technological advances improved medical care and sanitation. People began living longer and healthier lives.

As the human population grew, some countries began having food shortages. In the 1940s, scientists began to research ways to improve crop yields. They used selective breeding to develop grains that were resistant to pests and diseases. The new plants yielded two to three times more grain. New agricultural techniques also were developed. Some of the techniques used fertilizers, pesticides, and herbicides. Irrigation methods improved. Machines replaced human labor in almost every agricultural process (see figure 15.10).

760 Unit 4 Sustaining Earth Systems

2. understand that technology affects human population growth.

   They will demonstrate their understanding by

   - describing how the agricultural revolution and the industrial revolution resulted in increases in human populations and
   - explaining how medical advances have increased the average life span.

3. be able to interpret graphs to help them see trends in human population size and factors that affect population growth.

   They will demonstrate their ability by

   - making predictions about human population size for the next 200 years;
   - identifying patterns in graphs of birthrate, mortality rate, and population size and explaining why these patterns exist; and
   - explaining how changes in fertility rate and age structure are related to population growth.

Strategies

Getting Started

Ask students to recall what factors determine population size. They should remember from chapter 14 that birthrate, mortality rate, immigration, and emigration determine population size. They also might mention limiting factors such as environmental conditions or predators. Ask students to predict what factors will most influence human population size.

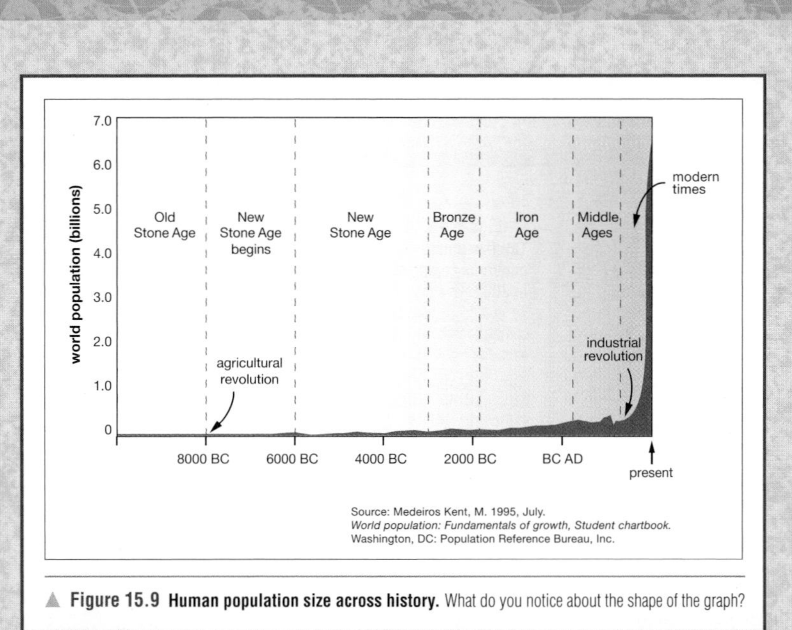

▲ **Figure 15.9 Human population size across history.** What do you notice about the shape of the graph?

▲ **Figure 15.10 Resource extraction.** How does technology influence the extraction of resources? Consider whether different techniques yield the same amount of resources. How do the techniques affect the surrounding environment?

Process and Procedure

Materials

For each student

1 copy of copymaster 15.5, *Age Structure*

access to a computer and the Web

The tasks and questions help guide students to the important parts of many of the shorter readings in this activity. For students who have more trouble with reading, choose a literacy strategy such as a turn-and-talk protocol where students read a passage or view a graph and then talk about it with a classmate.

In Step 1, students read the paragraph describing Thomas Malthus's views on human populations. In Step 2, students should read *History of Human Population Growth* and explain why Malthus's predictions have merit.

Answers to Step 2, SE pages 759–760

2b. Malthus's argument has merit because the human population has grown at an exponential rate in the last 200 years. He was also correct that an increase in mortality rate or a decrease in birthrate would slow population growth.

2c. Malthus did not predict that food production would increase at a rate that would keep up with population growth.

2d. Reasons that human populations have not collapsed include improvements in medical practices and sanitary conditions that increased how long people lived, machines and factories that could produce more goods that people needed, improvements in transportation that could bring resources to larger numbers of people, and changes in agricultural practices that increased crop productivity.

2e. Make sure students' graphs extend to 2205. The graphs must have a caption that describes what accounts for the changes they predicted. The graphs should give you an idea of what students think are the most important factors affecting population growth.

NOTES:

History of Human Population Growth, continued

All these changes increased efficiency. This period of technological advances is referred to as the green revolution.

Today, more than 6.5 billion people live on Earth. The most populous countries are shown in figure 15.11. The world continues to become more urbanized. In 1950, most people lived in rural areas. Now the number of people living in rural and urban areas is nearly equal (figure 15.12).

Although the rural and urban populations are about the same size, more of the world's population lives in developing regions than in developed regions (figure 15.13). Developing regions have a low standard of living and are not very industrialized. Standard of living is a measure of income per person. It includes the availability of health care, education, and goods such as appliances.

▶ **Figure 15.11 The five most populous countries in 2003.** How does the population density compare for these countries?

Source: Food and Agriculture Organization of the United Nations, http://faostat.fao.org

Country	Population size in billions ($\times 10^9$)	Density (people/km²)
China	1.31	137
India	1.07	324
United States	2.94	31
Indonesia	2.20	115
Brazil	1.78	21

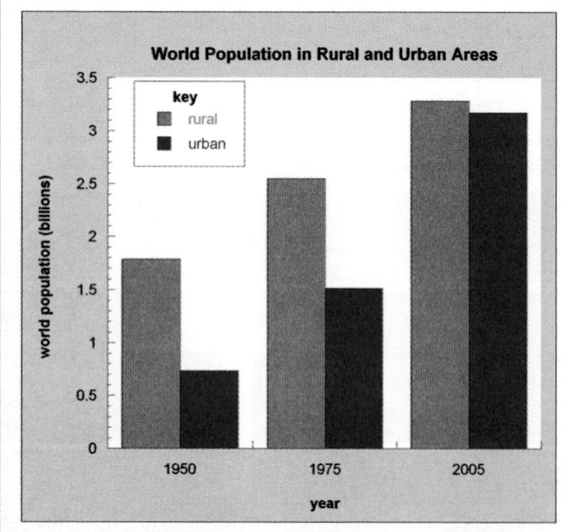

Source: Food and Agriculture Organization of the United Nations, http://faostat.fao.org

▲ **Figure 15.12 Total world population in rural and urban areas.** What effect on the environment do you think the shift of the population to urban areas has had?

762 Unit 4 Sustaining Earth Systems

In Step 3, the reading *Birth and Death* introduces students to a graph with 2 *y*-axes (figure 15.14 in the student book). To help students read this type of graph, instruct them to begin by looking at the *y*-axis on the left. They should see that this axis is for birthrate and mortality rate. Then instruct students to look at the *y*-axis on the right. This axis is for population size. Spend some time with your students to ensure that they are interpreting the graphs correctly.

Answers to Steps 3–4, SE pages 763–765

3. In 1950, birth- and mortality rates were twice as much in developing than in developed countries. At present, developing countries have mortality rates similar to developed countries but the birthrates are still twice as high. At present, developed countries have birthrates and mortality rates that are nearly equal.

3b. This question helps you learn what ideas students already have about factors that affect population growth. The pattern for developed countries is that birthrates have declined, mortality rates have remained relatively the same, and the population is growing slowly. Students might explain that birthrates have declined because people want fewer children. The pattern for developing countries is that birthrates and mortality rates have declined and the population is growing relatively quickly. Students might explain that improvements in health care might reduce mortality rates and contribute to an increasing population size.

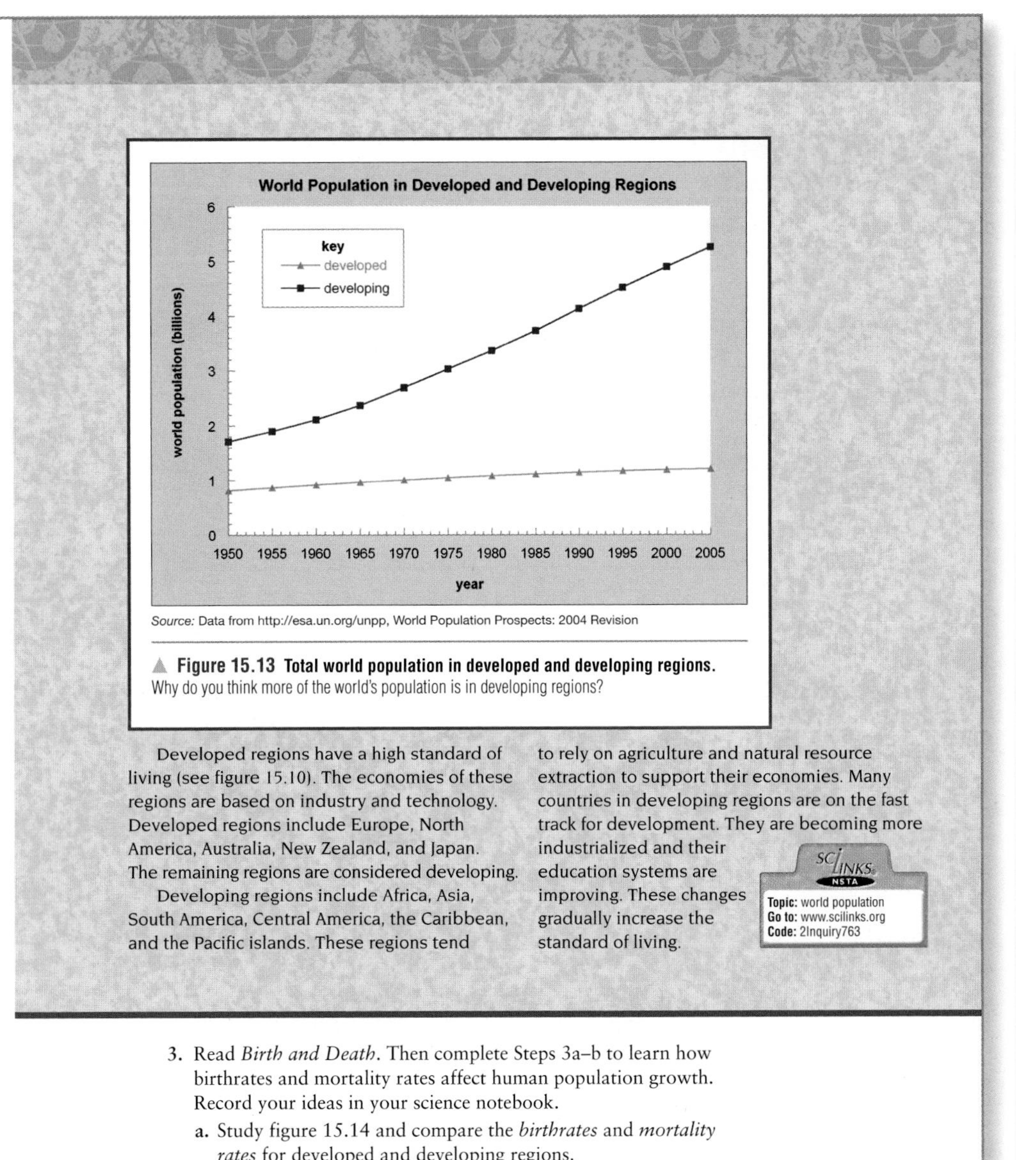

Source: Data from http://esa.un.org/unpp, World Population Prospects: 2004 Revision

▲ **Figure 15.13 Total world population in developed and developing regions.** Why do you think more of the world's population is in developing regions?

Developed regions have a high standard of living (see figure 15.10). The economies of these regions are based on industry and technology. Developed regions include Europe, North America, Australia, New Zealand, and Japan. The remaining regions are considered developing.

Developing regions include Africa, Asia, South America, Central America, the Caribbean, and the Pacific islands. These regions tend to rely on agriculture and natural resource extraction to support their economies. Many countries in developing regions are on the fast track for development. They are becoming more industrialized and their education systems are improving. These changes gradually increase the standard of living.

SCLINKS NSTA
Topic: world population
Go to: www.scilinks.org
Code: 2Inquiry763

3. Read *Birth and Death*. Then complete Steps 3a–b to learn how birthrates and mortality rates affect human population growth. Record your ideas in your science notebook.
   a. Study figure 15.14 and compare the *birthrates* and *mortality rates* for developed and developing regions.
   b. What patterns do you see and why do you think these patterns exist?

NOTES:

NOTES:

READING

Birth and Death

Recall that mortality rate is one important factor used to determine the growth rate of a population. Mortality rate is the number of deaths in a year per 1,000 people. From the 1700s to 1900, the mortality rate for the world's population was 35–40 deaths per 1,000. Since then, the mortality rate has declined dramatically. It is now around 10 deaths per 1,000.

Another factor in population growth is birthrate. Birthrate for humans is the average number of births in a year per 1,000 people. From the 1700s to 1900, the birthrate for the world's population was 35–45 births per 1,000. Like the mortality rate, the birthrate began declining dramatically after 1900. Now the birthrate varies around the world. It ranges from 10 to 22 births per 1,000. Figure 15.14 (a) and (b) show how birth- and mortality rates in developed and developing countries have changed during the last 55 years.

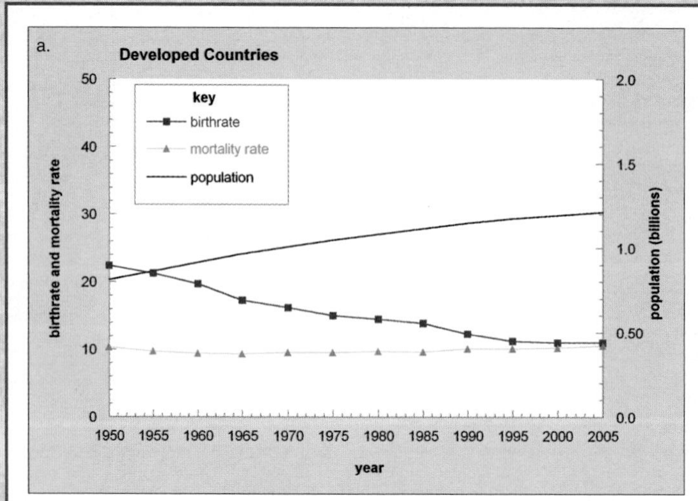

Source: Data from http://esa.un.org/unpp, World Population Prospects: 2004 Revision

▲ **Figure 15.14 Birthrates, mortality rates, and population for developed and developing countries.** Birthrates and mortality rates are on the left axis. Population is on the right axis. How does the slope for the population compare with the change in birthrates and mortality rates?

764 Unit 4 Sustaining Earth Systems

NOTES:

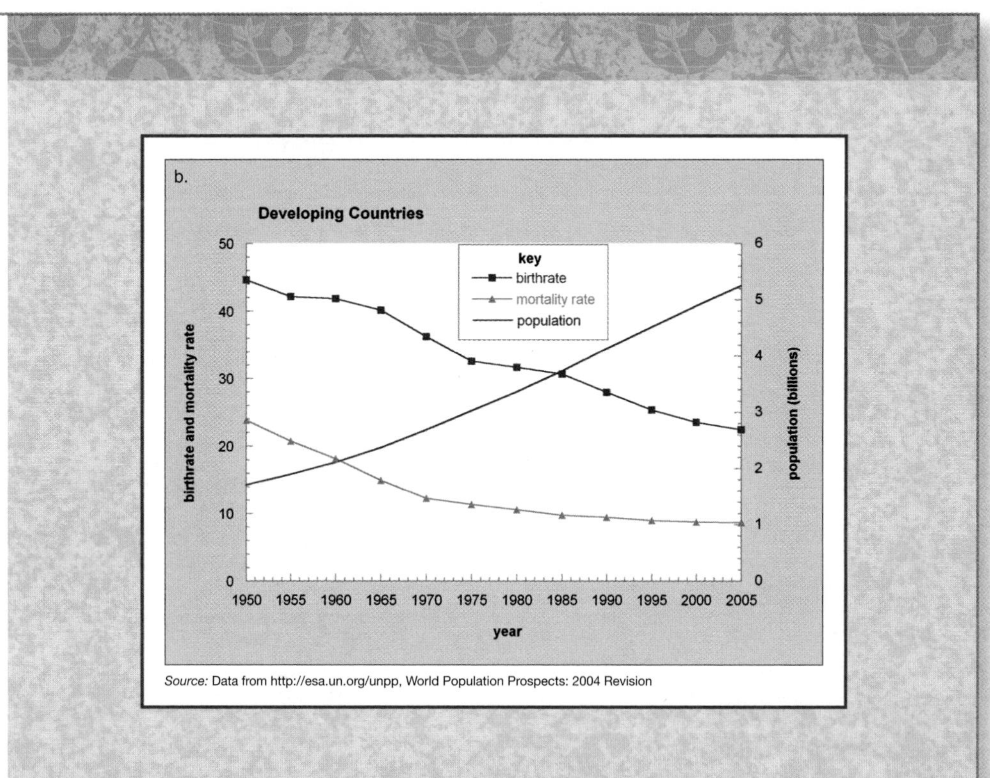

Source: Data from http://esa.un.org/unpp, World Population Prospects: 2004 Revision

4. Answer the questions in Step 4a–c in your science notebook to show your understanding of how birthrates and mortality rates affect human population growth.
   a. Why might there be a difference between birthrates and mortality rates for developed and developing countries?
   b. How does the change in population size compare for developed and developing countries? Discuss the rate of increase (slope) in your answer.
   c. How can you explain the difference in the rate of increase for developed and developing countries? Use what you know about birthrate and mortality rate to explain the rate of population increase.

Recall this equation: *population size = population size + births − deaths + immigration − emigration.*

4a. Students might explain the difference in birthrates by saying that people in developed countries have only a couple of children, but people in developing countries have more children to help work or because they don't have access to birth control. Students might say that developing countries have higher mortality rates than developed countries because people in developing countries have less access to health care than people in developed countries or that they don't have access to as much food.

4b. The population of developed countries has increased very little; the slope is small. The population of developing countries has increased a lot; the slope is large.

4c. The difference in birthrates and mortality rates is small for developed countries, so the rate of increase is small. Birthrates are almost twice as much as mortality rates in developing countries, so the population is increasing.

NOTES:

In Step 5, students discuss with a partner their own ideas about fertility rates. They should record their ideas about how fertility rates are related to population growth. They should develop questions about fertility rates and then spend time gathering information from the Web to answer their questions. See the organizations listed under *Educational Technologies*. In Step 6, students read about fertility to help answer their questions. Suggest that students use a literacy strategy such as a T-table that lists factors that affect fertility and how each factor affects population growth. In Step 7, students answer questions about fertility rates and population growth.

Answers to Steps 5 and 7, SE pages 766–768

5. Student responses will vary depending on the questions they have and the data they find. Make sure they record their questions, the data they collect, and how the data they collect help them understand population growth.

5. Work with a partner to discuss and investigate how fertility rates affect population growth. Record your ideas in your science notebook. Use Steps 5a–e to help you.

Fertility rate is the average number of children a woman will have in her lifetime.

   a. How do you think fertility rates are related to population growth?
   b. What questions do you have about fertility rates?
   c. What information do you need to answer your questions? Discuss which of your questions can be answered with information you might find on the Web.
   d. Look for information on the Web to answer one of your questions. Document what you find.

Remember to document your references. For information on citing other people's work, see *How to Cite References and Avoid Plagiarism* in the *How To* section in the back of the book.

   e. Describe how what you learned is related to population growth.

6. Read *Fertility* to learn how fertility rates are related to population growth. To help guide your reading, consider using a strategy such as a T-table. List factors that affect fertility and how each factor affects population growth.

READING

Fertility

To predict how populations will change, you need to know the number of children born and the number of women who are of reproductive age. The fertility rate provides this measure. Total fertility rate is the average number of children born to a woman during her entire reproductive life. The total fertility rate has remained fairly constant for developed regions since 1975. During this same time period, the fertility rate in developing regions has decreased by half (see figure 15.15).

Many factors affect how many children a woman has. In the past, families may have had many children because infant mortality rates were high. Children often have been, and in some countries still are, important for providing income and helping with chores. For example, they might work in factories, take care of animals and siblings, help grow crops, and gather water and firewood. Some couples have more children in an attempt to have a son because boys may be given special social status. Religious or cultural beliefs may dictate that families should not control fertility and that they should have as many children as possible. In some societies, women's status is tied to children. In these societies, a woman without children has no financial support.

766 Unit 4 Sustaining Earth Systems

NOTES:

Other factors tend to reduce fertility. Women with higher educations often choose to have fewer children (see figure 15.16). Similarly, women who enter the workforce are less likely to stay home and have many children. Women have more freedom to make their own choices when they have their own source of income. The choice of how many children to have also is different for developed and developing countries. In developing countries, adding a child doesn't cost a lot more for the family and may provide additional income or labor that will help the family. However, the cost of raising a child in a developed country such as the United States is high. In 2004, the U.S. Department of Agriculture estimated the cost of raising a child to age 17 averaged about $10,000 a year. With a high cost of raising children, many families in developed countries choose to have only one or two children.

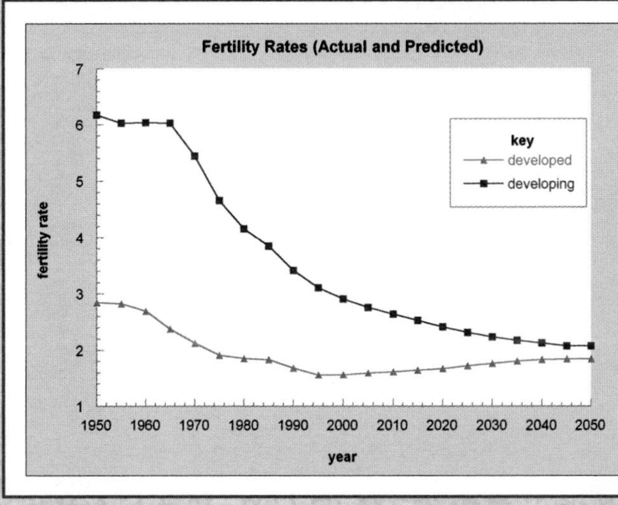

Figure 15.15 Actual and predicted fertility rates for developed and developing regions. The United Nations uses current data to project future fertility rates. What do you notice about the fertility rates predicted for 2050?

Source: Data from http://esa.un.org/unpp, World Population Prospects: 2004 Revision

Fertility rate and education statistics	Developed regions	Developing regions
Total fertility rate	1.6 births per woman	3.0 births per woman
Literacy rate for women aged 15–24	100%	81%
Secondary school enrollment of women	100%	55%

Source: Data from http://esa.un.org/unpp, World Population Prospects: 2004 Revision

Figure 15.16 Fertility and education statistics for women in developed and developing regions. For a woman to be literate, she must be able to write, read, and understand a short, simple statement about her everyday life. Why do you think literacy rates and secondary school enrollment are different for developed and developing countries?

7a. Fertility rates have decreased in the last 50 years.

7b. Both fertility rates and birthrates have decreased because the fertility rate determines what the birthrate will be. The number of children a woman has influences the number of births there will be per 1,000 people.

7c. Fertility rate is influenced by the need to replace children when infant mortality rates are high, the need for children to help with household chores, religious or cultural reasons, the need to gain social status, education level, desire to have a career, and the cost of raising a child.

7d. The trend is for fertility rates to continue decreasing in developing countries and level off or slightly increase in developed countries. As developing countries become more industrialized, fertility rates might decrease because women become more educated, more women choose to work, and it becomes more expensive to have a child.

7e. The fertility rate would be around 2 to replace 2 parents.

In Step 8, students continue to investigate factors that affect population growth, this time looking at age structure. In Step 10, distribute copymaster 15.5, *Age Structure* to each student. If they are interested, students can create age structure diagrams, also called population pyramids, on the U.S. Census Bureau Web site.

Answers to Steps 8 and 10, SE pages 768–769

8. Make sure students record their questions, the data they collect, and how the data they collect help them understand population growth.

10a. Life expectancy has increased to around 70 years old in more developed countries and around 60 in less developed countries.

10b. Life expectancy is increasing because medical technology has changed, people now die later in life from different conditions, and the standard of living has increased.

10d. Kenya has more young people. Italy has more old people.

10e. Kenya's population is increasing because a large portion of its population is made up of young people who could have children. A small portion of Italy's population is composed of young people who could have children.

10f. Students' age structure diagrams should look similar to the one for Italy on the handout, with 2–3 million males and females in the 20–65 age range and less than 1 million males and females over age 65.

10g. Kenya's birthrate is higher than Italy's because Kenya has a higher percentage of people of childbearing age than Italy.

7. Complete Steps 7a–e to show your understanding of what influences fertility rates and how fertility affects human population growth.
   a. Study figure 15.15 and describe the change in the fertility rate during the past 50 years.
   b. Compare the fertility rate with the birthrate shown in figure 15.14. Do both rates show the same trend? Justify your answer using evidence.
   c. Describe at least 3 things that influence fertility rate.
   d. Look at the fertility levels predicted for 2005 to 2050 in figure 15.15. What is the trend? Use evidence from the reading to explain your answer.
   e. What do you think the fertility rate would be if there were zero population growth? Explain your answer.

Zero population growth is the number of births that keep the population size the same. At zero population growth, the birthrate equals the mortality rate.

8. Work with a partner to discuss and investigate how age structure affects population growth. Record your ideas for Steps 8a–b in your science notebook.

Age structure is the distribution of individuals in a population according to age. Age structure varies among populations.

   a. How do you think the age of people is related to population size?
   b. Repeat Steps 5b–e. Make sure you describe how the age structure of a population helps explain population growth.

9. To learn more about how life expectancy affects population size, read *Aging Populations* and study figure 15.17.

READING

Aging Populations

Life expectancy has been increasing in many countries in the past 50 years (see figure 15.17). Life expectancy is the average number of years a person in a given society can expect to live. For much of human history, life expectancy was from 35 to 40 years. Now the average life expectancy for the world as a whole is 65 years. The increase in life expectancy can be attributed to improved health conditions. In the past, most people died from infectious diseases and parasites. Now many people die from chronic conditions and diseases that cannot be passed from one individual to another. These conditions tend to show up later in life. This health transition has occurred as countries become more modernized and the standard of living increases.

768 Unit 4 Sustaining Earth Systems

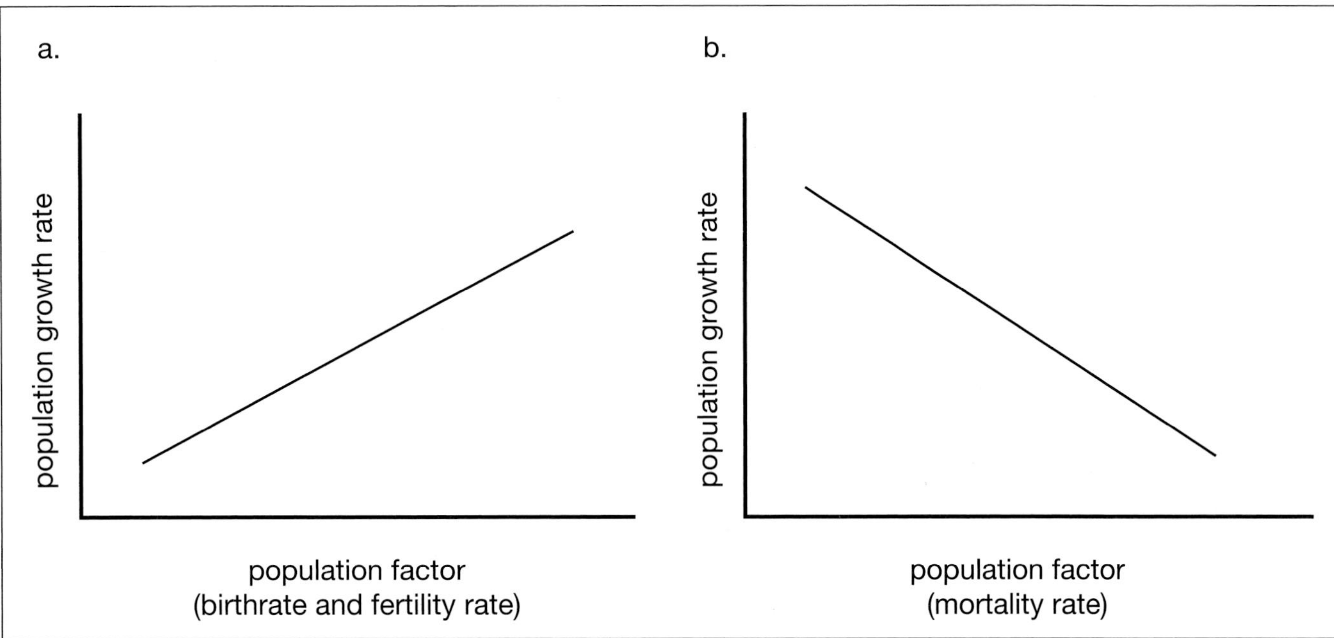

▲ **Figure T15.4 Graphs showing the relationship between population factors and population growth.** (a) Birthrate and fertility rate have a direct relationship with population growth. (b) Mortality rate has an inverse relationship with population growth.

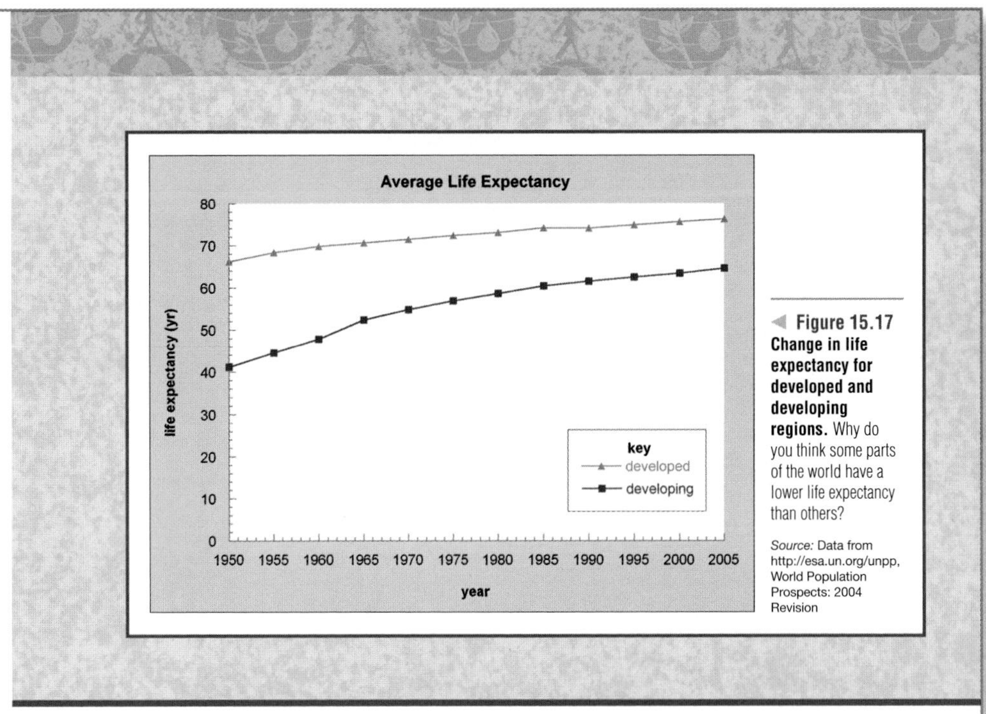

◀ **Figure 15.17 Change in life expectancy for developed and developing regions.** Why do you think some parts of the world have a lower life expectancy than others?

Source: Data from http://esa.un.org/unpp, World Population Prospects: 2004 Revision

10. Consider how the age structure of a population is related to population growth.
    a. Study figure 15.17 and describe how life expectancy is changing across time.
    b. List 2 reasons why life expectancy is increasing.
    c. Get the *Age Structure* handout from your teacher.
    d. Which population (Kenya or Italy) has more young people? Which has more old people?
    e. Use the diagram on the *Age Structure* handout to help explain why Kenya's population size is increasing and Italy's population size stays the same.
    f. Suppose the average life expectancy for Kenya increased to 65 years. Draw how you think its age structure diagram would look.

The current average life expectancy is 50 years in Kenya and 80 years in Italy.

    g. Use age structure to explain why Kenya's birthrate is higher (40 births per 1,000) than Italy's (9 births per 1,000).

In Step 11, students draw graphs showing the relationship between human population growth and the factors that affect human populations. Make sure they draw 3 graphs, one for each factor (birthrate, mortality rate, and fertility rate).

Answers to Step 11, SE page 770

11. The graph for birthrate should show a direct relationship, where birthrate increases as population growth increases. The graph for fertility rate should look the same. The graph for mortality rate should show an inverse relationship, where mortality rate increases as population growth decreases. See figure T15.4. Make sure students include highlight comments and a caption with their graphs.

In Step 12, students calculate growth rate and doubling time for the world's population at different times in history.

Answers to Step 12, SE pages 770-771

12a. Students should calculate growth rate as follows. Make sure students show their work.

$$1700\text{–}1800 \text{ growth rate} = \frac{0.8 \times 10^9 - 0.6 \times 10^9}{(0.6 \times 10^9) \times 100} = 0.003 \times 100 = 0.3\%$$

$$1800\text{–}1900 \text{ growth rate} = \frac{1.6 \times 10^9 - 0.8 \times 10^9}{(0.8 \times 10^9) \times 100} = 0.01 \times 100 = 1\%$$

$$1900\text{–}2000 \text{ growth rate} = \frac{6.1 \times 10^9 - 1.6 \times 10^9}{(1.6 \times 10^9) \times 100} = 0.028 \times 100 = 2.8\%$$

12b. Students should calculate the doubling time for each of the growth rates as follows:

$$\textit{doubling time} = \frac{0.7}{0.003 \text{ per yr}} = 233 \text{ yr}$$

$$\textit{doubling time} = \frac{0.7}{0.01 \text{ per yr}} = 70 \text{ yr}$$

$$\textit{doubling time} = \frac{0.7}{0.028 \text{ per yr}} = 25 \text{ yr}$$

Answers to Step 11 are on TE page 769.

NOTES:

11. Draw 3 graphs showing the relationship between human population growth and the factors that affect human populations. Steps 11a–c will help you.

Population growth rate is the percentage change in a population in 1 year. It reflects the number of births and deaths and the number of people moving to and from a region.

a. Use figure 15.18 as a template to create a graph showing the relationship between birthrate and population growth rate.
b. Add highlight comments and a caption to the graph.
c. Repeat Steps 11a–b for mortality rate and fertility rate.

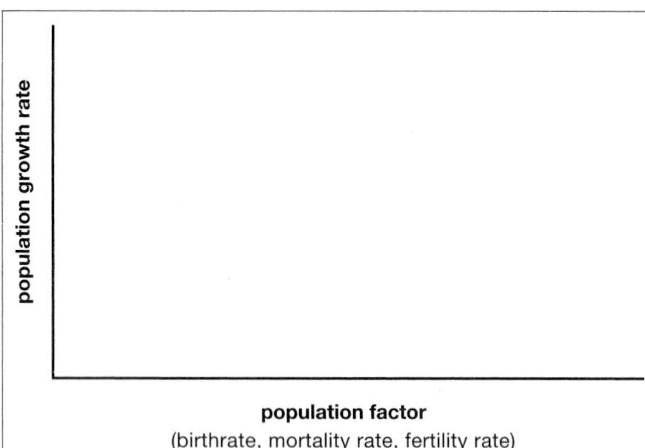

▶ **Figure 15.18 Graph template for showing the relationship between population factors and population growth.** Is the relationship between birthrate and population growth rate direct or inverse? What about mortality rate or fertility rate?

12. Calculate growth rate and doubling time for the world's populations at different times in history. Show your work.

a. Calculate the growth rate from 1700 to 1800, 1800 to 1900, and 1900 to 2000 using the data in figure 15.19. Average growth rate is calculated as

$$\textit{growth rate (percent)} = \frac{\textit{population at time 2} - \textit{population at time 1}}{\textit{population at time 1} \times \textit{number of years}} \times 100.$$

b. Calculate the doubling time for each growth rate in Step 12a. Doubling time is the amount of time required for a population to double in size.

$$\textit{doubling time} = \frac{0.7}{\textit{growth rate}}$$

Year	Population ($\times 10^9$)
1700	0.6
1800	0.8
1900	1.6
2000	6.1

▲ **Figure 15.19 World population.** How has the growth rate changed each century since 1700?

770 | Unit 4 Sustaining Earth Systems

In Step 13, students study a graph of the population growth rate across time. Students may struggle with the idea that the world's population is growing while the world's population growth rate is declining. Keep emphasizing that a population will grow even with a small growth rate.

Answers to Step 13, SE page 771

13a. The growth rate increased from 1950 to 1955. Then it decreased until 1960. It increased from 1960 to 1965, and since then the growth rate has been decreasing.

13b. The 2005 population will double in 2066. The population will be 12.9 billion that year.

$$\textit{doubling rate} = \frac{0.7}{0.0115 \text{ per yr}}$$
$$= 60.8 \text{ or } 61 \text{ yr}$$

13c. One reason that the population has continued to increase is that birthrates in less developed countries are still twice as high as mortality rates. Also, the growth rate is greater than zero.

13d. The growth rate will continue to decline because the fertility rate will continue to decline.

Answers to Reflect and Connect, SE page 772

1. Disease, lack of access to food, lack of access to clean water, and exposure to toxic pollutants could all be considered limiting factors for humans.

2a. The graph shows exponential growth for the last 1,000 years because the population has been increasing at a fast rate.

2b. Limiting factors have not stopped exponential growth in human populations because humans have developed ways to counter limiting factors. Medical technology helps people live longer, healthier lives. Agricultural technology increases crop productivity and provides more people with food. Humans make elaborate shelters and clothing to live in climates that otherwise would be too harsh. Humans can live in places where resources aren't plentiful because we move the resources to where they are needed.

2c. This question gets students thinking about a carrying capacity for Earth. Look for answers that are supported by what they have learned about human populations and resource consumption in this chapter.

Consider spending time facilitating a brief class discussion around the question presented in figure 15.25 of the student book. Students should provide evidence for why they think the low, middle, or high prediction for the future world population is more accurate.

EXPLAIN

Limits to Growth

Activity Overview

Students will revisit our dependency on ecosystems by reading about how we use ecosystems for resources and services. Students will learn that all resources are finite because we can potentially use them at rates faster than they can be replenished. They find that the carrying capacity of Earth will be determined more by how people on Earth live than by how many people there are.

If the annual growth rate is 7 percent, the doubling time is 10 years $\left(\frac{0.7}{0.07/\text{yr}} = 10 \text{ yr}\right)$.

13. Study figure 15.20 to learn how the world population growth rate has changed and is expected to change in the future.
    a. Describe the trend in the world's population growth rate from 1950 to 2005.
    b. In what year will the 2005 world population double? What will the population size be in that year? In 2005, the population was 6.45 billion and the growth rate was 1.15 percent.
    c. Give 3 reasons why you think the growth rate has decreased even though the total population has increased since 1950. Include quantitative evidence in your answer.
    d. Explain why you think the world's population growth rate will continue to decline in the future.

Remember, population growth rate and population size are not the same. Even with a low population growth rate, the population will continue to grow.

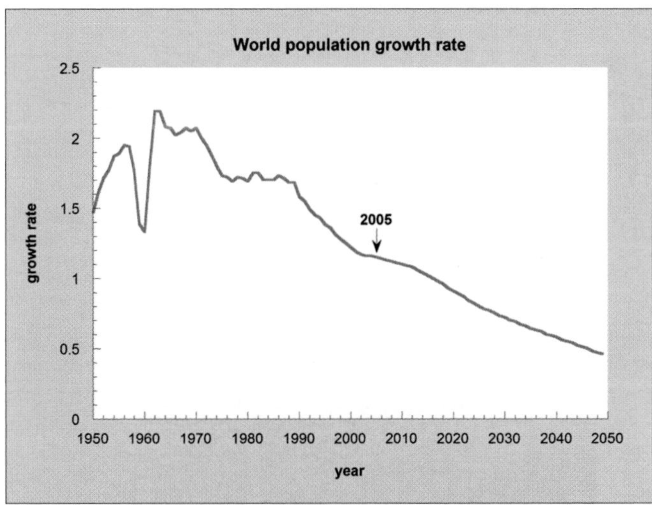

▲ **Figure 15.20 World population growth in the past and future.** This graph shows actual population growth measured from 1950 to 2005. Population growth declined from 1965 to 2005. Scientists predict that population growth will continue to decline in the future.

Before You Teach

Background Information

Human populations are linked closely with the productivity of ecosystems. Ecosystems provide us with what we need, including the water we drink, the food we eat, and the oil that fuels our cars. Ecosystems also provide critical functions such as purifying air and water, maintaining biodiversity, cycling carbon, and decomposing and recycling nutrients.

The resources we get from ecosystems fall into two categories: renewable and nonrenewable. Renewable resources can be replenished, but the capacity of ecosystems to replenish resources is limited. If we use resources faster than ecosystems can replenish them, then the resource is depleted or we damage the ability of the ecosystem to replenish the resource. Some resources are nonrenewable, such as fossil fuels and minerals. Because these resources formed over millions of years through geologic processes, they will run out eventually.

Materials

none

As You Teach

Outcomes and Indicators of Success

By the end of this activity, students should

1. understand that human populations rely on ecosystems for resources.

   They will demonstrate their understanding by

   - explaining that ecosystems are the source of resources such as the coal, oil, and natural gas used for energy;
   - explaining that ecosystems provide materials used for clothing, shelter, and other uses; and
   - describing the importance of ecosystems for natural processes such as purifying air and water.

2. understand that consumption affects the availability of resources.

   They will demonstrate their understanding by

   - explaining how some resources such as oil are nonrenewable because once they are depleted they can never be replenished or can only be replenished over long periods of time and
   - explaining how resources such as water and timber are renewable but can be used faster than they can be replenished.

3. understand that technology can cause either positive or negative changes in the capacity of earth systems to provide resources for human populations.

   They will demonstrate their understanding by explaining that advances in agricultural technology have increased food production, but at the expense of using more fertilizers that pollute water systems.

4. be able to develop explanations using evidence.

   They will demonstrate their ability by using information from a reading to explain the relationship between resources and ecosystems.

Strategies

Getting Started

Facilitate a brief class discussion about the resources and services that ecosystems provide.

Answers to Reflect and Connect are on TE page 771.

Reflect and Connect

Answer the following questions by yourself in your science notebook.

1. List at least 3 limiting factors for human populations and describe why each is a limiting factor.

Recall from chapter 14 that limiting factors such as availability of resources and space, predators, and environmental conditions keep plant and animal populations in check.

2. Look back at the last 1,000 years shown in figure 15.9.
   a. Does the graph show exponential growth? Why or why not?
   b. Explain why you think limiting factors have not stopped human populations from getting larger. Include the role of technology in your answer.
   c. Do you think there is a carrying capacity for humans on Earth? Why or why not?

Recall that carrying capacity is the maximum number of a species that an environment can support.

EXPLAIN

Limits to Growth

We rely on many natural processes and resources to support human life. Ecosystems provide important services such as air and water purification (see figure 15.21), nutrient cycling, climate control, and soil production. You might be more familiar with the resources that ecosystems provide, such as food and water. Recall the list of resources you developed in the engage activity, *Your Ecological Footprint.*

Figure 15.21 Wetland. Wetlands play an important role in purifying water. Plants and soils in wetlands effectively remove nutrients such as phosphorus and nitrogen. These nutrients are commonly found in agricultural runoff and when in large amounts can pollute streams. Many wetland plants can also remove toxic substances from industrial waste and mining activities.

Ecosystem	Resources	Natural processes and services	Threats to the system
Marine	Fish Shellfish	• Air circulation and ocean currents for climate • Carbon sink • Spawning areas for fish • Pollutant filtration • Nutrient absorption	• Population growth • Pollution • Overharvesting of fish and shellfish
Freshwater	Water Fish	• Water filtration • Flood control • Transportation • Hydropower • Carbon storage in wetlands • Habitat for many species	• Population growth • Alteration of water flow • Non-native species
Forest	Timber Fuelwood Food New drugs	• Carbon sink • Water filtration • Erosion and sedimentation reduction	• Conversion to agriculture and roads
Grassland	Food Livestock Genetic diversity	• Carbon sink	• Agriculture • Urbanization • Road building • Intense grazing

▲ **Figure T15.5 Resources and services of ecosystems and threats to ecosystems.** Students fill out this table for Step 2 by using information from the reading *Our Dependency on Ecosystems.*

You thought about the resources needed to provide everyday things such as food, shelter, clothing, and transportation. Now you will consider where those resources come from. In *Limits to Growth*, you will examine how four types of ecosystems support human life.

Materials

none

Process and Procedure

1. Identify 1 question you have about the resources and services that ecosystems provide. Record your question in your science notebook.
2. Read *Our Dependency on Ecosystems*. Then complete Steps 2a–e to show your understanding of how ecosystems sustain human populations.
   a. Work in a team of 4 and divide the reading into 4 sections. Each teammate should read about 1 type of ecosystem, as directed by your teacher.
   b. Draw a table in your science notebook with these 4 headings: "ecosystem," "resources," "natural processes and services," and "threats to the system."
   c. Fill in the table with examples as you read about your ecosystem.
   d. Meet with the other classmates who read about the same ecosystem. Discuss your findings and add new information to your table or revise your examples based on what you learn.
   e. Meet again with your team of 4 and read the information from your table. Then add information about the other ecosystems to your table.

READING

Our Dependency on Ecosystems

Ecosystems provide direct and indirect benefits. Direct benefits include things that can be harvested, such as crops, fish, livestock, and wood. Indirect benefits come from interactions and feedback. The interactions and feedback occur among organisms. They also occur between organisms and the abiotic environment. Some familiar examples are water purification, pollination, erosion control, and seed dispersal. There are four types of ecosystem—marine, freshwater, forest, and grassland. Each type provides a unique set of benefits through its resources and natural processes.

Process and Procedure

In Step 1, students should record a question they have about the resources and services that ecosystems provide. In Step 2, students read *Our Dependency on Ecosystems.* Use a jigsaw strategy to help students through this reading. Divide students into teams of 4 and have each team member read about 1 of the ecosystem types (marine, freshwater, forest, and grassland). As they read, they should fill in a table to show what resources and services ecosystems provide. Have the students who read about the same ecosystem meet to compare and revise their tables. Then ask students to join their original teams to report about their ecosystem. Students should add what they learn about the other ecosystems into their tables. Another option would be to assign the reading and questions as homework, which you follow up with a class discussion.

Answers to Step 2, SE page 773

2. See figure T15.5 for a completed table.

NOTES:

Our Dependency on Ecosystems, continued

Marine Ecosystems

Marine ecosystems include the open ocean and coastal areas. The ocean is important for climate. The heat stored in the ocean drives air circulation and ocean currents. Circulating air carries water vapor from the ocean over land surfaces, where it falls as rain or snow. Ocean currents also affect climate because they redistribute heat. For example, the Gulf Stream makes western Europe much warmer than Canada, which is at similar latitude. In unit 3, *Moving Matter*, you learned that the ocean is important for the global water cycle and the global carbon cycle.

One group of organisms, called phytoplankton, is very important to the carbon cycle. Phytoplankton are microscopic algae that live suspended in the water column, which extends from the ocean's surface to the bottom. Phytoplankton take in the carbon dioxide dissolved in the ocean during photosynthesis. They give off oxygen. As primary producers, they are the basis for the ocean's food chains. Although phytoplankton are an important food source for many organisms, most phytoplankton die before being consumed and sink to the bottom of the ocean. The calcium carbonate in their shells accumulates on the ocean floor. The accumulation of organic matter from phytoplankton makes the ocean a carbon sink. Remember that a carbon sink is a reservoir of carbon that has inputs of carbon greater than the outputs.

Most organisms in the ocean live in coastal areas. More organisms can survive in shallower water where light can penetrate and nutrients are more plentiful. As a result, as much as 95 percent of the world's fish and shellfish supply comes from coastal areas. Almost 40 percent of the world's population lives along the coast. Fish and shellfish account for one-sixth of the animal protein consumed by the world's population. Many small countries, such as Iceland, Bangladesh, Ghana, Indonesia, and Japan, depend on fish as their main source of protein.

Coastal areas are areas up to 200 m deep, tidal areas, and the nearby land areas. Habitats such as mangroves, estuaries, coral reefs, and tidal wetlands are found in coastal areas. Tidal wetlands are wetlands that are flooded with tidal waters. Mangroves are coastal, forested wetlands. Estuaries are wetlands where freshwater and ocean water meet. Some well-known estuaries are located in Puget Sound in Washington state and Chesapeake Bay in Maryland and Virginia. Mangroves and estuaries provide spawning areas for fish. Mangroves also provide wood for building materials and fuel. In the United States, mangroves are found mainly along the Atlantic and Gulf coasts of Florida (see figure 15.22). In December 2004, large mangrove forests in Malaysia and India protected some people from the tsunami that hit southeast Asia. Coral reefs provide areas for small-scale fishing.

Coastal areas also help maintain water quality. These ecosystems filter toxic pollutants and absorb large amounts of nutrients that run off agricultural and urban areas. All the habitats in coastal areas help protect coastlines from storm damage. For example, plants help decrease erosion. Unfortunately, the loss of estuaries along the coast leaves cities more exposed to hurricanes. This happened when New Orleans, Louisiana, was hit by Hurricane Katrina in 2005.

Some of the biggest threats to marine ecosystems are population growth, pollution, and overharvesting. As human populations grow, rivers deliver more pollutants to coastal waters. Increased use of fertilizers on crops has brought more nutrients to coastal areas. The extra nutrients cause harmful algal

NOTES:

▲ **Figure 15.22 Mangrove swamps.** Mangroves are coastal, forested wetlands. The roots of mangrove plants stabilize surrounding mud and sand.

blooms. Overharvesting has become more of a problem as the fishing industry has grown. New equipment allows one fishing vessel to capture many more fish than in the past. Coastal areas are producing less fish because of overfishing, damaging fishing techniques, and the destruction of nursery habitats.

Freshwater Ecosystems

Freshwater ecosystems contain a fraction of Earth's water. But most ecosystem services depend on a consistent supply of freshwater. Freshwater is essential for people to consume as well as for agriculture and industry. Freshwater ecosystems maintain water quality by breaking down contaminants and organic waste. Many species live only in freshwater ecosystems or depend on freshwater ecosystems for a part of their life cycle. Inland fish are an important source of protein for much of the world's population, especially the poor.

Wetlands are an especially important part of freshwater ecosystems. Wetlands are habitats that are flooded for a given period of time and contain water-loving plant species. Wetlands include flooded forests, river floodplains, shallow lakes, and marshes. Wetlands provide flood control; water filtration; carbon storage; and goods such as fish, shellfish, and timber. At least half the wetlands in the world have been drained for settlement or agriculture. Wetlands once covered much of Iowa, for example, but they were drained and filled in. Now most of the area is cultivated for crops.

Freshwater ecosystems are threatened when humans alter them and pollution enters them. Rivers have been disconnected from their floodplains to control the flow of water for human uses. Dams capture 14 percent of the world's runoff. Altered freshwater ecosystems have increased agricultural output, made water transport easier, and provided hydropower. But the alteration has dramatically changed where and how much water flows. As population increases, reduced water flows and increased inputs of nutrients and pollutants affect water quality. Changes in water flow have made it easier for non-native species such as zebra mussels and exotic fish to invade freshwater ecosystems. Non-native species compete with native species, and thus threaten or endanger many native species.

Forest Ecosystems

Forests have provided humans with food, shelter, fuel, and building materials throughout history. Today, millions of people still rely on forests for all their needs. Commercial timber

NOTES:

Our Dependency on Ecosystems, continued

production is a major global industry. North America and Europe produce more timber than less developed countries. However, many less developed countries depend on timber to support their economies. For example, wood fuels account for at least half the energy consumed in less developed countries.

Forests are also important for reasons other than for food and shelter. Forests help maintain water quality by filtering water and reducing erosion and sedimentation. Forests are a much smaller reservoir for carbon than the ocean. However, forests are an important part of the global carbon cycle tied to land. They store 39 percent of the carbon in terrestrial ecosystems. Carbon is stored in the living plant matter and the organic matter in forest soils. Forest ecosystems have the highest biodiversity of any ecosystem. The diverse species found in forests are sources of new drugs and nontimber products such as resins, fruits, and mushrooms.

▲ **Figure 15.23 Cleared trees.** Using forest resources for timber and other purposes affects natural processes in forests. For example, how does clearing trees affect a forest's ability to filter water?

Less than 40 percent of Earth's forests are undisturbed by humans. Forest cover has been reduced 20–50 percent since pre-agricultural times (figure 15.23). Since 1980, forest cover has increased slightly in more developed countries. But it has decreased by 10 percent in less developed countries. The biggest threats to forests are converting the forest land for agriculture and building roads. In Africa, only 49 percent of the forest area consists of large forest blocks (10,000 km^2 or larger). If there were no roads there, large forest blocks would make up 83 percent of the area.

Grassland Ecosystems

Grassland ecosystems cover 40 percent of the land on Earth's surface and are crucial for the world's food supply. These ecosystems include grasslands, savanna, shrublands, and tundra. More grasslands have been converted for agricultural use than any other ecosystem. All of the grains, such as wheat, rice, rye, and corn, were selectively bred from wild grasses. Grasslands will continue to be a source for genetic material to improve crops in the future. Grasslands support grazing livestock such as cattle, sheep, and goats. They also are a source of animals for hunting and for medicinal plants. Grasslands store 33 percent of the carbon in terrestrial ecosystems. Like forests, carbon is stored in the living plant matter as well as in the organic matter in grassland soils. The amount of carbon stored in grasslands is

NOTES:

about half that of forests because grasslands cover twice the area of forests.

Humans have also modified grasslands. Agriculture, urbanization, and road building fragment grasslands into smaller, disconnected areas. Agriculture is important for providing food for human populations, but some farming practices can deplete soils and negatively affect the environment. To learn about farming techniques that have less impact, read the sidebar *Sustainable Agriculture*. Grazing techniques can help maintain grassland ecosystems or degrade them. Grazing cuts back vegetation and prevents bushes and trees from replacing grasses. However, when many animals graze in an area, they destroy vegetation, compact the soil, and increase soil erosion. For example, some grasslands in northern China are becoming deserts (figure 15.24). Growing populations that farm and graze intensively are overusing the land. In addition, they are misusing water resources.

▲ **Figure 15.24 Desertification.** Desertification is the spread of desert conditions in once fertile land. A well-known example of desertification occurred in the 1930s. Drought and poor farming practices turned the grasslands (the Great Plains) in the United States into a dust bowl until rain brought back vegetation. Improvements in land and water management have prevented this from occurring again in the United States.

3. Did the information in the reading answer your question from Step 1 about the resources and services that ecosystems provide? If so, document your answer here. Otherwise, describe what information you need to answer your question.

You can also look for information on the Web to answer your question.

4. Provide a 1- or 2-sentence definition of renewable resources. The resources described in *Our Dependency on Ecosystems* are considered renewable resources.
5. Read *Energy Resources* to learn how ecosystems have provided energy in the form of fossil fuels.

Topic: limits to growth
Go to: www.scilinks.org
Code: 2Inquiry777

In Step 3, students revisit their questions from Step 1. They should either document the answer to their question or describe what information they need to answer their question. In Step 4, students write a definition for renewable resources.

Answer to Step 4, SE page 777

4. A renewable resource is a resource that can be replenished through processes in ecosystems.

In Step 5, students read about how ecosystems provide energy resources. Students answer questions about the reading in Steps 6–7. In Step 8, students answer questions about the relationship between consumption and the availability of resources. Then in Step 10, students answer questions about what limits population size.

NOTES:

Answers to Steps 6–8, 10, SE pages 778–779

6. Fossil fuels formed in wetland and coastal ecosystems millions of years ago. Without the plant matter and marine organisms that accumulated in those ecosystems, fossil fuels would not have formed.
7. A nonrenewable resource is a resource that cannot be replenished except on a geologic timescale.

8a. Altering freshwater ecosystems to redirect water for human consumption has made it easier for non-native species to invade water systems. Use of fertilizers has loaded marine and freshwater ecosystems with nutrients and caused harmful algae blooms.

8b. Consumption of nonrenewable resources will eventually deplete the supply of those resources. The supply of renewable resources can be sustained by ecosystems if consumption is moderate. If consumption is high, the processes that replenish resources may be compromised and renewable resources may be depleted as well.

8c. Renewable resources are finite because they can be used faster than they can be replenished.

READING

Energy Resources

The industrialization of the world created a need for energy to power machinery. Historically, people used wood for fuel. During the industrial revolution, people began using fossil fuels such as coal. By the early 1900s, oil and natural gas were used as well.

Coal, oil, and natural gas form where organic matter was abundant millions of years ago. Coal formed where plant matter accumulated in large amounts, such as in wetlands. Waterlogged soils in some wetlands create anaerobic conditions (conditions without oxygen). Most decomposers require aerobic conditions to break down organic matter. As plants died, they accumulated and gradually turned into peat. Across time, peat was buried under more and more plant matter or sediment. Burial compressed and heated the peat. After millions of years, chemical changes in the peat, which was already high in carbon, transformed it into coal. Coal is 70–90 percent carbon, depending on the conditions in which it was formed.

The formation of oil and natural gas is similar to the formation of coal. Oil and natural gas form in coastal areas where marine organisms were abundant in the past. Many of the marine organisms were buried under sediment before they decomposed. After millions of years, higher temperatures and chemical reactions transformed some of the organic matter into oil and natural gas.

Many countries depend on sources other than fossil fuels for their energy. Nuclear energy provides 7 percent of the world's energy. Nuclear energy requires uranium, which is present in very small amounts on Earth. One problem with nuclear energy is that scientists are still working on the best way to dispose of nuclear waste. Some renewable sources of energy are hydroelectric, solar, geothermal, wind, and tidal energy. These account for less than 1 percent of the world's energy use.

6. Describe the connection between fossil fuels and ecosystems.
7. Provide a 1- or 2-sentence definition for nonrenewable resources. Fossil fuels are considered nonrenewable resources.
8. Think about the relationship between consumption and the resources and services ecosystems provide.
   a. How does consumption of resources affect the natural processes that occur in ecosystems? Look at the table you created in Step 2 to help you.
   b. How does consumption affect the supply of renewable resources differently from nonrenewable resources?
   c. Why are renewable resources finite (limited) even though they can be replenished?

NOTES:

d. Why are fossil fuels considered nonrenewable even though they were made from plant material?

e. Predictions of how long nonrenewable resources will last keep changing. For example, in 1989, reserves of oil and natural gas were estimated to last for 41 years of production. By 1998, the estimate had increased to 57 years. Why do you think the predictions change?

9. Read *Earth's Carrying Capacity* to learn what limits the population size that Earth can support.

READING

Earth's Carrying Capacity

Scientists estimate Earth's carrying capacity to be from 7.7 to 12 billion people. Estimates of Earth's carrying capacity have increased across time. Scientists use factors such as water, energy, food, and the things needed to produce food to make their estimates. Their estimates are often based on the minimal needs of humans. For example, one estimate is based on the fact that the world currently produces enough grains to feed 10 billion people. This estimate assumes that all people on Earth live on a vegetarian diet.

Calculating the carrying capacity of Earth is difficult. The factors affecting carrying capacity depend on one another. For example, crop productivity may decrease if agricultural land is converted to urban areas or if fertilizers become scarce. If water is scarce and energy is abundant, then it may be possible to transport water or remove salt from salt water. If energy is scarce or too expensive, then it may be impractical to make water available in these ways. People might face water shortages. Carrying capacity for humans depends less on the number of people and more on the choices societies make. Although many parts of the world have unused land, this land may not provide the resources that humans use. Recall what you learned in the engage activity. We need land not only to provide space to live, but also to provide the resources we use.

10. Consider how land area and consumption are related to Earth's carrying capacity. Use Steps 10a–b to help you.

a. Explain why the amount of space (land) doesn't determine how many people Earth can support.

b. Based on what you have learned about population and resource consumption, describe 2 ways you think the carrying capacity of Earth could be increased. Explain why these changes would make a difference.

8d. Fossil fuels are nonrenewable even though they are made of plant material because it takes millions of years for the plant material to become a fossil fuel.

8e. Predictions of how long oil resources will last keep changing because new technologies are developed that use oil more efficiently or other technologies replace the use of oil.

10a. The amount of space doesn't determine how many people Earth can support because space alone does not account for how many resources we use.

10b. The carrying capacity of Earth could be increased by reducing our consumption of resources. This might be accomplished by using technology to reuse more of our resources or to use the resources we have more efficiently. The carrying capacity of Earth could also be increased if everyone consumed fewer resources.

Answers to Reflect and Connect, SE page 780

1. Fossil fuels are considered nonrenewable resources because fossil fuels take millions of years to regenerate.

2a. Look for answers that are well reasoned. Water might be in short supply because, as the population grows, more people need water and water pollution might also increase. Fossil fuels are likely to be in short supply because there is only a limited supply of fossil fuels and consumption of fossil fuels is likely to increase. Food might be in short supply in some places because of shortages of water or because the population is high in a location where food production is low.

2b. Students might mention that the ability of water systems to filter water will be affected. They also might mention that the ability of forests to reduce erosion will be affected if more forests are cut down.

2c. The changes are most likely to affect populations in less developed countries where there are more people.

3a. Medical technology has increased the number of people by reducing mortality rates. Agricultural technology has increased the number of people by providing more food and reducing mortality rates. Machines and advances in transportation have made it possible for more resources to be extracted and distributed to new places, which support the livelihood of more people and increase the population.

3b. Machines have a negative effect on Earth by increasing pollution. Agricultural technology has a negative effect by increasing the amount of nutrients that get into water systems and by cultivating more land. Technology allows resources to be consumed at faster rates.

4. This question gives students an opportunity to reflect on what new things they have learned in this activity. For example, students may never have considered the processes that occur in ecosystems that are important for supporting human populations.

ELABORATE

Managing an Ecosystem

Activity Overview

Humans manage ecosystems in a variety of ways to protect the resources and services that ecosystems provide. In *Too Much Is Never Enough*, students learned that one of the biggest threats to marine ecosystems is overexploitation of fish and shellfish populations. Most countries have established harvest limits to prevent overexploitation.

In *Managing an Ecosystem*, students will work in teams to play the role of Pacific halibut fishermen. They will predict how overexploitation affects the future population of Pacific halibut. Then they will propose a management plan that allows fishing to continue and ensures survival of the halibut population.

Before You Teach

Background Information

The world's marine fish harvest more than doubled from 1961 to 1990, reaching around 70 million tons a year. There have been improvements in fishing vessels, nets, and tracking equipment. However, the harvest has remained stagnant since 1990. Many fish populations are being exploited at or beyond

Reflect and Connect

Work individually to answer the following questions in your science notebook. Then check your answers with another student and revise them based on anything new you learn.

1. Why are fossil fuels considered nonrenewable resources?
2. Study figure 15.25 and predict how human populations and ecosystems will be affected if the world population reaches 7.7, 9, and 10.6 billion, respectively, in 2050. For each answer, use evidence from the chapter to justify your answer.

   Notice that this graph of world population size looks different from earlier graphs. This graph only shows population size since the year 2000.

   a. Which 3 resources do you think will be in shortest supply? Explain.
   b. Which natural process in ecosystems do you think will be affected the most?
   c. Where will the human populations that are affected the most by the changes be located?
3. How does technology affect the carrying capacity of Earth? Technology includes new equipment and techniques used in medicine, agriculture, and industry.
   a. List 2 ways technology has increased the carrying capacity for the number of people on Earth. Explain why.
   b. List 2 ways that technology negatively affects the capacity of Earth to support human populations. Explain why the technology has this effect.
4. Has this activity changed your opinion about human population issues? If so, how? If not, why not?

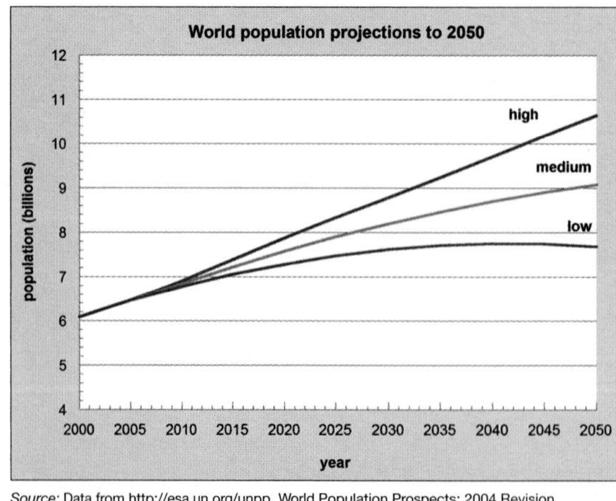

Source: Data from http://esa.un.org/unpp, World Population Prospects: 2004 Revision

▲ **Figure 15.25 World population projections to 2050.** The United Nations has 3 different predictions for the future of the world's population. Each prediction makes different assumptions about how mortality rates and fertility rates will change in the future. Which prediction do you think will be more accurate: a conservative (low) estimate, a high estimate, or an estimate somewhere in between?

the point that harvest will begin to decline. Countries use different management strategies to prevent overexploitation and to aid in the recovery of populations that have already been depleted. The United States and Canada impose annual harvest limits for each licensed fisherman or vessel. Scientists use information about the life history of a fish species, population data, and catch data to determine harvest limits. In 2002, the International Pacific Halibut Commission set a fixed harvest rate of 20 percent of the estimated population size for Pacific halibut.

Students will model a Pacific halibut population in this activity. Students are given assumptions about halibut reproduction to model the population growth across time. The values given to students were chosen to make calculations easier and ensure a certain outcome. Accurate information about halibut reproduction is provided in the following paragraph.

Maturity varies with sex and fish size. Halibut size depends on abundance. When halibut abundance is high, growth rate is slower. Currently, halibut abundance is high so fish are smaller than fish of the same age were 10 years ago. Males usually mature around eight years of age. Females mature around 12 years of age. The number of eggs a female can produce is related to size. Smaller females (23 kilograms, or kg) produce about 500,000 eggs. Larger females (over 113 kg) can produce as many as 4 million eggs.

SIDEBAR

Sustainable Agriculture

Sustainable agriculture produces an abundance of food, while it conserves resources and minimizes pollution. It combines some aspects of existing agricultural systems with new agricultural techniques. It is based on systems for raising crops that are self-sustaining, just as natural systems are. For example, sustainable agriculture takes advantage of local climates, soils, and resources. Sustainable farms use smaller amounts of fossil fuels than farms that use most of the existing agricultural techniques. Sustainable farms conserve topsoil and water. And they control pests with little, if any, use of pesticides. A common practice is low-till or no-till farming, where crop residue is left as cover for new crops being planted.

Most agriculture practices in developed countries focus on the short-term productivity of one crop. That is, they focus on how much crop is produced in a growing season. Sustainable agricultural systems focus on the long-term condition of the soil. Instead of producing a single type of crop, sustainable systems produce a diverse mix of fruit and vegetable crops. These systems also use organic fertilizers made from animal and crop wastes. Special fast-growing trees are planted along with the food crops. The trees supply fuelwood and add nitrogen to the soil. Whenever it is affordable, sustainable farmers use locally available alternatives to fossil fuels. Such alternatives include wind energy and solar power.

A central part of sustainable agricultural systems is crop rotation. Crop rotation is the planned planting of various crops, one after the other, on one field. Rotation provides better weed and insect control. It also improves nutrient cycling, which improves crop yields. Rotating crops reduces disease and insect pests. Since both tend to be linked to specific plants, planting different crops disturbs the life cycles of many insects and diseases. Rotating nitrogen-fixing crops such as legumes (beans and peas) with other crops helps increase the amount of nitrogen available in the soil. This supports soil fertility and helps provide nutrients needed by the next crop.

▲ **No-till farming.** No-till farming prevents erosion and helps soil retain moisture. This photo shows young soybean plants growing in the residue of a wheat crop.

A second component of sustainable agricultural systems is the addition of organic matter, such as crop waste and manure, to the soil. Organic matter improves the soil in many ways. It builds topsoil, increases the ability of soil to store water, and enhances soil fertility. Soil in good condition is easier to till, and it allows seedlings to emerge and root more easily. Water readily seeps into rich soil, thus reducing surface runoff and erosion. Organic materials also provide food for earthworms and other soil organisms. These organisms in turn improve the condition of the soil.

Chapter 15 Earth's Capacity 781

Materials

For each team of 4 students

1 bag of "halibut" (20 small paper clips, 30 large paper clips)
1 stopwatch
1 calculator
access to a computer and spreadsheet software (optional)

Advance Preparation

Gather paper clips, bags, and stopwatches. Place 20 small and 30 large paper clips in each bag. Locate calculators or have students bring calculators to class. Review the student book to learn what values students should use and what assumptions they should make when modeling the halibut population across time.

Educational Technologies

Students must do some repetitive calculations in this activity. Consider setting up a spreadsheet with the formulas in place so that students can simply input their data. Students with more experience with spreadsheets could set up the spreadsheets and formulas themselves. If you take this approach, require students to show all their work with unit cancellations for 1 set of data; then the spreadsheet can handle the rest.

As You Teach

Outcomes and Indicators of Success

By the end of this activity, students should

1. be able to apply their understanding of populations, consumption, and natural resources.

   They will demonstrate their understanding by

   - role-playing as halibut fishermen and calculating their profits from an annual harvest,
   - calculating the size of the halibut population for a 15-year period based on the same annual harvest, and
   - developing a management plan to maintain a population of Pacific halibut.

2. be able to develop an explanation based on evidence.

They will demonstrate their understanding by writing and revising a management plan based on the results of their fishing simulation.

Strategies

Getting Started

Ask students to think of examples where resource use is restricted.

Process and Procedure

Materials

For each team of 4 students

1 bag of "halibut" (20 small paper clips, 30 large paper clips)
1 stopwatch
1 calculator
access to a computer and spreadsheet software (optional)

Divide students into teams of 4 and make sure they read the information in Step 2. Students should set aside 1 large paper clip that represents mature fish that are too difficult to catch. Then in Step 4, students use both hands to harvest as many paper clips as they can in 20 seconds (sec). Students must use both hands because each hand represents a separate fishing vessel. Remind students to keep the paper clips from each hand separate. Teams can monitor the time themselves using a stopwatch, or you can be the timekeeper for the class so that all teams harvest simultaneously. Some students might try to sweep all the paper clips into another hand. Ask teammates to describe how this behavior affected their ability to fish. Use this as an opportunity to discuss how someone exploiting all of the resource affects other people trying to use the same resource. Then tell the teammates to repeat the harvest using both hands separately. In Step 5, teams should record the catch for each fishing vessel (hand) in their science notebooks.

NOTES:

Sustainable Agriculture, continued

A shift to more sustainable agriculture is difficult to accomplish. Some experts believe that the government's support of research, subsidies and tax breaks, and training programs may encourage some farmers to adopt these practices. However, no agricultural practice is sustainable unless it is also profitable. Sustainable agriculture may be best for smaller family farms that serve local markets. Creating new markets for sustainable agriculture will be one of the challenges for increasing its use.

ELABORATE

Managing an Ecosystem

You learned in the explore activity *Limits to Growth* that human populations depend on and affect ecosystems. In some cases, humans have a direct effect on populations of organisms. For example, overfishing threatens the future supply of fish. U.S. fishermen know that the Pacific halibut is one of the most profitable fish species to harvest. Pacific halibut are large flatfish that weigh up to 200 to 300 kilograms (kg) and grow up to 2.7 m long (figure 15.26). They are found along the continental shelf from California to the Bering Sea in Alaska. Larval halibut feed on plankton. Adults are carnivorous. They feed on octopuses, crabs, clams, and fishes such as cod, pollock, rockfish, and sablefish. Halibut are occasionally eaten by marine mammals, but are rarely eaten by other fish.

▲ **Figure 15.26 Halibut.** Halibut have flattened bodies that make them well suited to live on the ocean floor. They typically have both eyes on the right side or "top" of the body.

Commercial fishing began in the early 1900s. Today, fishermen catch halibut by long-lining. Long-lining uses hundreds of baited hooks on a line that can be many miles long. Fishing for Pacific halibut is concentrated off Alaska and the west coast of Canada (figure 15.27).

Like most countries, the United States limits the number of halibut and other fish species that can be caught each year. In *Managing an Ecosystem*, you will experience this firsthand.

782 Unit 4 Sustaining Earth Systems

Answers to Steps 6–7, SE pages 783–784

6. Check student calculations.

   For a student who harvested 15 paper clips (fish) in 1 hand, the profits are calculated as follows:

$$1 \text{ paper clip} = 1{,}000 \text{ fish}$$

$$\frac{15 \text{ paper clips}}{\text{fish}} \times \frac{1{,}000 \text{ fish}}{\text{paper clip}} \times 10 \text{ kg} \times \frac{\$2.40}{1 \text{ kg}} = \$360{,}000$$

NOTES:

You will play the role of a Pacific halibut fisherman in Alaska. First, you will model how fishing affects the halibut population. Then you will propose different ways to manage your fishery to keep your income while sustaining that halibut population.

Materials

For each team of 4 students

1 bag of "halibut" (20 small paper clips, 30 large paper clips)

1 stopwatch

1 calculator

▲ **Figure 15.27 Sampling the commercial catch.** A portion of the halibut caught by commercial fisherman is sampled by the International Pacific Halibut Commission. This group gathers information about age and size to set limits on halibut fishing. This photo shows a large halibut caught by a sport fisherman being weighed.

Process and Procedure

1. Get into teams of 4.
2. Read the following information to become familiar with the halibut you will harvest. Each teammate will act as a Pacific halibut fisherman in this activity.
   - Each paper clip represents 1,000 halibut.
   - Large paper clips represent mature fish that can reproduce.
   - Small paper clips represent immature fish.
   - Fish mature at 10 years.
   - Each mature female can produce 50 eggs.
3. Get the bag of fish from your teacher and scatter all but 1 of the large paper clips across the table or floor. This 1 paper clip represents the mature fish that are hidden; you will not be able to catch these 1,000 halibut.
4. Harvest as many fish as you can by grabbing with both hands for 20 seconds. Remember that as a fisherman, catching fish is your livelihood. This round of "fishing" represents an annual harvest.
5. Record the catch for each fishing vessel in your science notebook. Each hand represents a separate fishing vessel.

Remember to keep the paper clips in each hand separate.

6. Calculate your gross income for each fishing vessel, counting each hand as a fishing vessel. Show your calculations in your science notebook.
   - An average harvested fish weighs 10 kg.
   - The standard price a fisherman in Alaska received in 2004 was about $2.40 per kilogram.

Year	Starting population	Numer of fish harvested	Population after harvest	Reproduction
1	30,000 mature 20,000 immature	29,000 mature 20,000 immature	1,000 mature	500 females × 50 eggs each = 25,000 immature
2	1,000 mature 25,000 immature	0 mature 25,000 immature	1,000 mature	500 females × 50 eggs each = 25,000 immature
3	1,000 mature 25,000 immature	0 mature 25,000 immature	1,000 mature	500 females × 50 eggs each = 25,000 immature
4	1,000 mature 25,000 immature	0 mature 25,000 immature	1,000 mature	500 females × 50 eggs each = 25,000 immature
5	1,000 mature 25,000 immature	0 mature 25,000 immature	1,000 mature	500 females × 50 eggs each = 25,000 immature
6	1,000 mature 25,000 immature	0 mature 25,000 immature	1,000 mature	500 females × 50 eggs each = 25,000 immature
7	1,000 mature 25,000 immature	0 mature 25,000 immature	1,000 mature	500 females × 50 eggs each = 25,000 immature
8	1,000 mature 25,000 immature	0 mature 25,000 immature	1,000 mature	500 females × 50 eggs each = 25,000 immature
9	1,000 mature 25,000 immature	0 mature 25,000 immature	1,000 mature	500 females × 50 eggs each = 25,000 immature
10	1,000 mature 25,000 immature	0 mature 25,000 immature	1,000 mature	500 females × 50 eggs each = 25,000 immature
11	1,000 mature 25,000 immature	0 mature 25,000 immature	1,000 mature	500 females × 50 eggs each = 25,000 immature
12	1,000 mature 25,000 immature	0 mature 25,000 immature	1,000 mature	500 females × 50 eggs each = 25,000 immature
13	1,000 mature 25,000 immature	0 mature 25,000 immature	1,000 mature	500 females × 50 eggs each = 25,000 immature
14	1,000 mature 25,000 immature	0 mature 25,000 immature	1,000 mature	500 females × 50 eggs each = 25,000 immature
15	1,000 mature 25,000 immature			

▲ **Figure T15.6 Estimated population size for halibut over 15 years.** Students must calculate the size of the halibut population for Step 7a.

7a. Check student calculations.

It is likely that students will harvest all 29 large paper clips and 20 small paper clips during 20 sec of fishing. If students harvested all 49 paper clips (fish), the fish population for the next year would only consist of the 1 large paper clip (1,000 fish) that was set aside, and the immature fish added to the population through reproduction. An example of the calculations is shown in figure T15.6.

7b. After the first harvest, the fish population might consist of 1,000 mature fish and no immature fish.

7c. This harvest rate removes all the fish except the ones that were set aside because they were too difficult to catch. There are fewer fish for the fishermen to catch. Each fishing vessel would make less than it did during the first harvest.

In Step 8, teams read the team goal and discuss how they could adjust the harvest to continue to make money and to have a fish population survive and sustain itself. Teams write a management plan after deciding how they might adjust the length of the harvest, the number of fishing vessels, or another variable.

In Step 10, teams should repeat the harvest while following their management plan. Make sure students calculate income after the harvest and the halibut population size over the next 15 years. They should use this information to decide whether they have met the team goal. If not, they should revise their management plan and repeat the harvest and calculations. Check that they are documenting revisions to their management plan. Once they have met the team goal, they must provide evidence explaining why their management is effective.

Answers to Steps 10–11, SE pages 784–785

10c. If teams restrict the harvest so that 20 percent of mature and 20 percent of immature fish are caught, the population would change as shown in figure T15.7. Students should keep in mind that immature fish take 10 years to become mature fish.

Year	Starting population	Numer of fish harvested	Population after harvest	Reproduction
1	30,000 mature 20,000 immature	6,000 mature 4,000 immature	24,000 mature 16,000 immature	12,000 females × 50 eggs each = 600,000 immature
2	24,000 mature 616,000 immature	4,800 mature 123,200 immature	19,200 mature 492,800 immature	9,600 females × 50 eggs each = 480,000 immature
3	19,200 mature 972,800 immature	3,840 mature 194,560 immature	15,360 mature 778,240 immature	7,680 females × 50 eggs each = 384,000 immature
4	15,360 mature 1,162,240 immature	3,072 mature 232,448 immature	12,288 mature 929,792 immature	6,144 females × 50 eggs each = 307,200 immature
5	12,288 mature 1,236,992 immature	2,458 mature 247,398 immature	9,830 mature 989,594 immature	4,915 females × 50 eggs each = 245,760 immature
6	9,830 mature 1,235,354 immature	1,966 mature 247,071 immature	7,864 mature 988,283 immature	3,932 females × 50 eggs each = 196,608 immature
7	7,864 mature 1,184,891 immature	1,573 mature 236,978 immature	6,291 mature 947,913 immature	3,145 females × 50 eggs each = 157,286 immature
8	6,291 mature 1,105,199 immature	1,258 mature 221,040 immature	5,033 mature 884,159 immature	2,516 females × 50 eggs each = 125,829 immature
9	5,033 mature 1,009,988 immature	1,007 mature 201,998 immature	4,026 mature 807,990 immature	2,013 females × 50 eggs each = 100,650 immature
10	4,026 mature 908,640 immature	805 mature 181,728 immature	3,221 mature 726,912 immature	1,610 females × 50 eggs each = 80,500 immature
11	3,221 mature 807,412 immature	644 mature 161,482 immature	2,577 mature 645,930 immature	1,288 females × 50 eggs each = 64,400 immature 2,577 mature + 600,000 immature from year 1 = 602,577 mature
12	602,577 mature 710,330 immature	120,515 mature 142,066 immature	482,062 mature 568,264 immature	241,031 females × 50 eggs each = 12,051,550 immature 482,062 mature + 480,000 immature from year 2 = 962,062 mature
13	962,062 mature 12,051,550 immature	192,412 mature 2,410,310 immature	769,650 mature 9,641,240 immature	384,825 females × 50 eggs each = 19,241,250 immature 769,650 mature + 384,000 immature from year 3 = 1,153,650 mature
14	1,153,650 mature 28,882,490 immature	230,730 mature 5,776,498 immature	922,920 mature 23,105,992 immature	461,460 females × 50 eggs each = 23,073,000 immature 922,920 mature + 307,200 immature from year 4 = 1,230,120 mature
15	1,230,120 mature 46,178,992 immature			

▲ **Figure T15.7 Estimated population size for halibut managed over 15 years.** Students must calculate the size of the halibut population for Step 10c.

NOTES:

Answers to Step 7 are on TE page 783a
Answers to Step 10c are on TE page 783b.

Gross income is the amount of money earned before operating costs and taxes are subtracted. Your calculations do not represent profits because they do not include your business costs, such as the cost of the equipment, fuel, and paying people to fish and run the vessel.

7. Describe the effect of your harvest on the halibut population by completing Steps 7a–c. Record your answers in your science notebook and show your calculations.
   a. Use the information in Step 2 to calculate the size of the halibut population for the next 15 years. Give your answer in the numbers of mature and immature fish. Assume that each year
      - you set aside 1 large paper clip from the population, which represents those fish you could not catch;
      - half the fish are male and half are female;
      - all mature females reproduce (50 eggs per female); and
      - you caught the same number of fish each year.
   b. Calculate the size of the fish population after your first harvest. List the number of mature and immature fish in your answer.
   c. Explain what effect this harvest rate has on the fish population and on the fishermen. Discuss whether each fishing vessel would make as much money after the first harvest.
8. Discuss as a team how you could adjust your harvest to continue to make income and to have a population survive and sustain itself. Use this goal as a guide:

   Goal: Allow halibut fishing to continue while ensuring the survival of the halibut population.

Think about whether the length of your harvest, the number of fishing vessels, or other variables should be adjusted.

9. Write a management plan in your science notebook. Then record your team's ideas for adjusting your harvest based on your management plan.
10. Carry out and adjust your management plan by using Steps 10a–f as a guide.
    a. Repeat the harvest you did in Step 4, but this time restrict your harvest according to your management plan.
    b. Calculate the income for each fishing vessel.
    c. Calculate the size of the halibut population for the next 15 years based on your management plan.

10f. Circulate around the room and listen as teams discuss whether their management plan meets the goal. Make sure students understand that to meet the goal, their plan should leave enough immature and mature fish each year to replace the population through reproduction. This approach should keep the population sustainable while providing income for fishermen. Once teams have decided their plan meets the goal, they should use evidence such as population size and income from fishing to justify their plan.

11. Factors that might affect the halibut population include pollution from fishing boats, toxic pollutants, nutrients from coastal populations, and destruction of coastal habitat.

In Step 12, facilitate a class discussion about managing a fishery. Each team should be prepared to describe how harvests affect the fish population and describe its final management plan. Teams should compare the results of all the management plans and discuss potential advantages and disadvantages of each management plan.

Answers to Reflect and Connect, SE page 785

1. Students should mention criteria such as the size of the halibut population and the number of fishing vessels or the amount of income that the halibut population can support.
2. Students should support their ideas. Some students might explain that open access will always lead to overexploitation because all the fishermen want to earn as much money as possible. Other students might explain that open access will not lead to overexploitation if there aren't many fishermen or if fishermen don't have the equipment and technology to harvest large numbers of fish.
3. Water is managed in some cities to make sure supplies aren't depleted. Water is managed by placing restrictions on when people can water their lawns and wash their cars and by increasing the cost of water for large consumers. Students might explain that water management is effective now, but could become less effective as populations increase.

   Forests are managed to make sure trees are available for habitat, to reduce the chance of forest fire, and to make sure trees are available for commercial purposes. Forests on public land are managed by planning the number, location, and types of trees to be removed. In the past, forests were managed by preventing fires. Now forests are sometimes managed using prescribed fires. Students might mention that management has preserved many forests. If they remember what they learned about wildfire in Level 1 of this program, they might also mention that prevention of forest fires has actually hurt some forests by reducing diversity and making them more vulnerable to devastating fires.

   Animals are managed to make sure populations survive and sometimes to reduce populations. Animals are managed by not allowing hunting, by designating how much and when people can hunt, and by setting aside land for habitat. Some animal populations recover because of management; others continue to decline.

---

d. Decide as a team whether your management plan meets the goal in Step 8.
e. Use evidence to explain why your management plan is effective if you decide not to revise it.
f. Repeat Steps 10a–e if you revise your management plan. Document all revisions of your plan, especially *why* you made a change.

11. Make a list of at least 4 factors, other than removing fish, that might affect the halibut population. Your list should include the influence of other aspects of fishing as well as nonfishing activities.
12. Participate in a class discussion about managing a fishery. Be prepared to do the following.
    a. Describe how harvests affect fish populations.
    b. Describe your team's final management plan.
    c. Compare the advantages and disadvantages of your management plan with other teams' plans.

Reflect and Connect

Answer the following questions on your own in your science notebook.

1. What criteria did you use to decide on a final management plan?
2. Do you think open access to resources will always lead to overexploitation? Explain why or why not.

You modeled an open-access fishery during the first round of fishing in Step 4. An open-access fishery has no limit on the number of fishermen or the number of fish caught. Overexploitation is using a resource beyond its capacity to regenerate. In this case, overexploitation means that reproduction cannot replace the number of fish caught.

3. Think of another example where resources are managed. For example, consider the resources you mapped in the explore activity such as water and forests. Explain why you think the resource is managed, how the resource is managed, and the effectiveness of the management.

In the United States, management of resources may occur at the level of the city, county, state, or federal government.

Your values and attitudes toward nature probably influence how you would choose to manage a resource. Read the sidebar Environmental Ethics and You to learn about different views of humanity's relationship to the natural world.

Topic: managing ecosystems
Go to: www.scilinks.org
Code: 2Inquiry785

EVALUATE

Sustaining Human Populations

Activity Overview

In *Sustaining Human Populations*, students will demonstrate what they have learned about human populations and resource use. In Part I, they will begin identifying how the artificial Biosphere 2 did and did not act like ecosystems on Earth. Then they will decide how well 3 different populations will fare in a space station. In Part II, they will work in a team to create a poster that proposes how many people could live comfortably in a space station the size of Earth. They will describe the ecosystems on the station and how resources are used.

Before You Teach

Background Information

Consult the student book and *Background Information* for previous activities.

Materials—Part I

For each student

1 copy of copymaster 15.6, *Sustaining Human Populations Scoring Rubric*

1 copy of copymaster 15.7, *Population Description*

Materials—Part II

For each team of 2 students

materials for creating a poster

Advance Preparation

Make 1 copy each of copymaster 15.6, *Scoring Rubric for Sustaining Human Populations* and copymaster 15.7, *Population Description* for each student.

As You Teach

Outcomes and Indicators of Success

By the end of this activity, students should

1. understand how birthrates, fertility rates, and mortality rates affect human population growth.

   They will demonstrate their understanding by

   - explaining that growth rates are higher for populations with more young than old individuals and lower for populations with individuals evenly distributed in all age groups,
   - analyzing data from 3 populations and using graphs to predict how the populations will change across time,
   - describing that the population with the highest birthrate would reach a higher population than the other 2 populations with lower birthrates and similar mortality rates,
   - drawing a graph on their posters showing the growth rate of a space station population and why the population has this growth rate, and
   - drawing a graph on their posters showing how the space station population changes across time and what the carrying capacity of the space station is.

2. understand that social and cultural issues affect human population growth.

SIDEBAR

Environmental Ethics and You

Environmental ethics is a branch of ethics that considers the relationship between humans and the natural world. People have different perspectives about humanity's relationship to nature. Their perspectives are based on different values, beliefs, and attitudes. People's values, beliefs, and attitudes about nature are formed by a variety of influences, including the values and attitudes of their culture. People's attitudes about nature also are influenced by their personal experiences, the people they talk to, and the books they read. Together, these values influence how people behave toward the environment. Our behavior has a major impact on the state of the natural world around us.

Brief descriptions of two distinctive ethics follow that show how different people's perspectives can be. How similar or different is your personal environmental ethic from the two views described here? What factors have influenced your environmental ethic? What other environmental ethical views are you aware of?

- *The human-centered environmental ethic.* People who support a human-centered environmental ethic take the position that humans dominate the natural world. People with this view see humans as different from all other life-forms and separate from nature. The value of nonhuman organisms is tied to their usefulness to humans. People with this ethic tend to view Earth as a collection of natural resources that can be used to promote economic growth. People who support this position also think that Earth is vast and has many resources in abundant supply. They point out that human history has been characterized by continual progress. Through technology, people find solutions to all problems (including those of resource depletion and pollution), and progress continues.
- *The deep ecology environmental ethic.* The deep ecology ethic is a life-centered ethic. People who support this view think that all life-forms on Earth have inborn value regardless of their usefulness to humans. From this view, humans have no right to reduce Earth's resources except to satisfy essential needs. People who support this position think that Earth's resources are in limited supply. They think that resources are for all life-forms, not just for humans. This view takes the position that human population growth must be reduced for both human and nonhuman life to flourish. People with this view think that the human impact on Earth's environment must be minimized. People must make economic and technological changes and changes in the way they think in order to promote a sustainable lifestyle. A sustainable lifestyle protects the function of earth systems.

Most people's views are somewhere in between the two ethics described here. Where you fall depends on how you answer questions such as, "What value does the natural world have?" This question has become increasingly important because we have more decisions to make about the fate of the natural environment. For example,

786 Unit 4 Sustaining Earth Systems

They will demonstrate their understanding by

- explaining that people may have larger families because of the need for labor, support during old age, or religious reasons and
- explaining that women with more education tend to have fewer children.

3. understand how technology affects human population growth.

   They will demonstrate their ability by

   - explaining that medical technology can reduce infant mortality rates and increase the average life span and
   - explaining that agricultural technology can increase agricultural production.

4. understand that human populations rely on natural systems for resources and natural processes.

   They will demonstrate their understanding by

   - comparing how natural processes occurred in natural systems with how those same processes occurred in Biosphere 2,
   - explaining that Biosphere 2 was not a self-sufficient system since carbon dioxide and pollutants built up because natural processes did not occur in the same way they do in natural systems,
   - explaining that Biosphere 2 is different from Biosphere 1 (Earth) because natural systems on Earth can compensate for excessive inputs (carbon dioxide or pollutants) to a greater extent, and
   - including labeled sketches on their posters of ecosystems and the resources and services that ecosystems provide.

5. understand that consumption affects the availability of resources.

   They will demonstrate their understanding by

   - describing that the population with higher water and energy use is most likely to run out of resources before the other two populations and
   - describing on their posters how the population on the space station manages its resources and maintains the function of ecosystems.

6. understand how to create graphs, interpret graphs and data, and develop explanations.

   They will demonstrate their understanding by

   - explaining the characteristics of different populations based on graphs and data tables and
   - creating a graph of population growth for a fictional population.

should we consider drilling for natural gas on public lands? Where will we dispose of hazardous waste? Technological advancements that increase our capacity to take advantage of Earth's resources force us to make choices about our responsibility to nature.

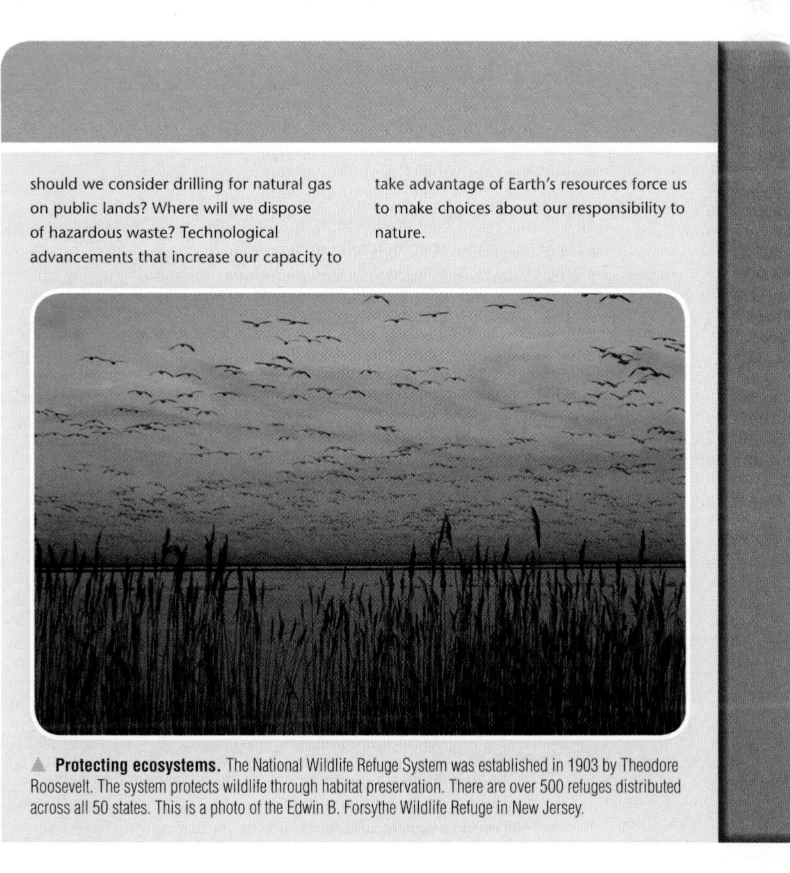

Protecting ecosystems. The National Wildlife Refuge System was established in 1903 by Theodore Roosevelt. The system protects wildlife through habitat preservation. There are over 500 refuges distributed across all 50 states. This is a photo of the Edwin B. Forsythe Wildlife Refuge in New Jersey.

Sustaining Human Populations

EVALUATE

You have investigated human populations in a large open system called Earth. The resources we need are provided by the natural processes occurring on Earth. What if humans were to live in space or on the Moon? One such project is going on right now. The International Space Station is a joint project of six space agencies from different countries. The space station can support two to four people and has 425 m^3 of living space. For comparison, an average bedroom has around 31 m^3 of living space and an average house (2,000 ft^2) has around 1,900 m^3 of living space. Even with its small size, assembly of the station is still in progress, and it requires many inputs from outside sources.

Chapter 15 Earth's Capacity 787

Strategies

Getting Started

Read the introduction to the activity as a class. Facilitate a short discussion of the things scientists need to consider before designing a space station.

Part I: Analyzing and Evaluating Biosphere 2

Process and Procedure

Materials

For each student

1 copy of copymaster 15.6, *Sustaining Human Populations Scoring Rubric*

1 copy of copymaster 15.7, *Population Description*

Distribute copymaster 15.6, *Sustaining Human Populations Scoring Rubric* to the students and answer any questions that the students have about the expectations for this activity. In Step 2, students read about Biosphere 2. As they read, they should work individually to fill in a T-table similar to figure T15.8 and to answer the questions in Step 3.

Answers to Steps 2–3, SE pages 788–790

2b. Figure T15.8 provides an example of what students might record in their T-tables.

Science fiction stories often describe humans colonizing the Moon or living in space. The people live in space stations that provide everything they need. Based on what you know about how Earth sustains human populations, do you think it might be possible for space stations to be self-sustaining in the future? What decisions would people living in a space station face?

In *Sustaining Human Populations*, you will begin by reading about an attempt to create a self-sustaining ecosystem called Biosphere 2. You will discover the challenges its designers faced to keep the system functioning without outside inputs. Then you will apply what you learned about human populations on Earth to decide how well three different populations will fare in a space station. Finally, you will work in a team to propose how a human population could sustain itself and its resources in a space station.

Part I: Analyzing and Evaluating Biosphere 2

Materials

For each student

1 *Sustaining Human Populations Scoring Rubric* handout

1 *Population Description* handout

Process and Procedure

1. Review the *Sustaining Human Populations Scoring Rubric* handout to understand all the evaluation expectations *before* you begin the activity.
2. Complete Steps 2a–b to show your understanding of how natural systems on Earth provide the resources and conditions we need to survive. Remember that natural systems are self-sustaining.
   a. Read *An Experimental Earth System* to learn what happened when scientists tried to create a self-sustaining system.
   b. As you read, compare how natural processes occur in a natural system with how the same processes occurred in Biosphere 2. Show your ideas by filling in a T-table with the 3 headings "natural process," "how it works in a natural system," and "what happened in Biosphere 2."

Natural process	How it works in a natural system	What happened in Biosphere 2
Oxygen cycling	Oxygen levels remain stable in the atmosphere.	Oxygen had to be added because levels got too low for humans. Plants and other photosynthetic organisms did not give off enough oxygen to compensate for the large amounts of oxygen consumed during microbial respiration.
Carbon cycling	The ocean and forests act as carbon sinks, which reduce buildup of carbon in the atmosphere.	Carbon dioxide levels were high because microbial respiration released large amounts of carbon dioxide. Concrete released carbon dioxide as well.
Maintenance of plant and animal populations	Ecosystems provide the biotic and abiotic conditions that plants and animals need to survive.	All the insect pollinators died and vines grew aggressively, making it difficult to grow food.
Water purification	Water is filtered when it passes through forests, wetlands, and other parts of ecosystems.	Water became polluted because it was overloaded with nutrients.
Climate regulation	Air circulation over the ocean and currents in the ocean regulate temperature and moisture over continents.	Temperature and humidity were higher than intended in the original design.

▲ **Figure T15.8 Comparison of processes in a natural system and in Biosphere 2.** Students fill out this table for Step 2b.

READING

An Experimental Earth System

In the late 1980s, Biosphere 2 was built in the southern Arizona desert. (Biosphere 1 is Earth itself.) Biosphere 2 is a glass enclosure containing living ecosystems (figure 15.28). Biosphere 2 was designed to grow food and recirculate air and water without exchanging materials with the outside world. The only inputs into the system were energy for external supporting systems (air pressure, cooling, and other utilities) and information (radio, television, and telephone). The intent was to see if humans could live self-sufficiently in a closed environment. It was designed with connected buildings containing different environments including rain forest, ocean, desert, agriculture, and human habitat.

In 1991, eight people entered Biosphere 2 to live for 2 years without outside intervention. After 1 year, the oxygen level in the closed atmosphere fell from 21 percent to 14 percent. This oxygen level was barely enough to support the residents. Oxygen was added to the closed atmosphere from outside to fix the problem. At the same time that oxygen levels were decreasing, carbon dioxide levels were increasing. Scientists later discovered that

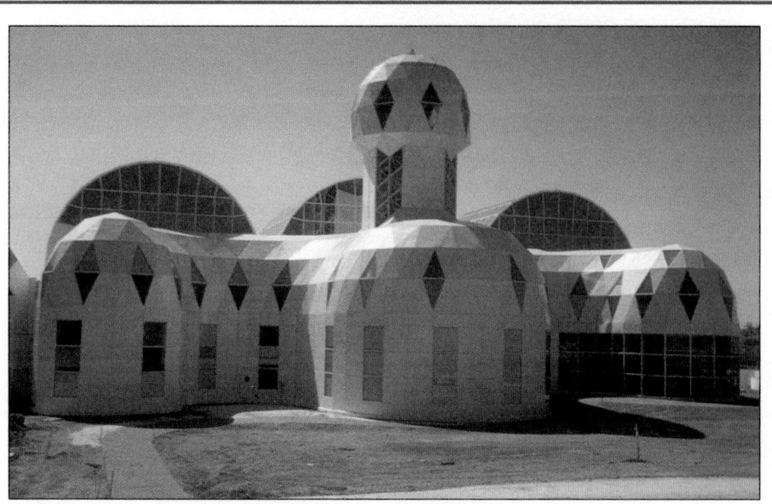

▲ **Figure 15.28 Biosphere 2.** Biosphere 2 is located on about 100 ha in Arizona, 56 km northeast of Tucson.

NOTES:

NOTES:

3a. Biosphere did not accomplish its purpose because oxygen had to be added, insect pollinators died, and the water supply became polluted. The artificial systems did not act like ecosystems that can sustain themselves.

3b. Biosphere 2 required special systems for air pressure and cooling that Biosphere 1 (Earth) does not need. Unlike Earth, Biosphere 2 did not have the conditions necessary to support human life.

3c. Scientists learned that it is difficult to create systems that act like ecosystems. They did not anticipate how the structure itself would make conditions such as sunlight, temperature, and humidity different. They learned that each part of a system is important for it to function properly.

3d. Students might have a variety of ideas. They might mention making their own biosphere bigger to accommodate more organisms and possibly keep nutrients and carbon dioxide from building up. They might suggest including more plants and algae to contribute more oxygen to the atmosphere. They might want to bring in more insects to reduce the chance that all the pollinators died off. To make sure plants are getting enough light, they might suggest using a different glass or supplementing sunlight with artificial light.

An Experimental Earth System, continued

respiration from microbes living in the fertile soils was responsible for the changes. The microbes were consuming large amounts of oxygen and releasing large amounts of carbon dioxide. The concrete used in the structure was releasing carbon dioxide as well.

There were other unexpected problems in Biosphere 2. All the insect pollinators died off, which caused food supplies to decline. Without pollination, flowering plants cannot produce seeds. Vines introduced to absorb carbon dioxide grew aggressively. Residents had to spend a lot of time weeding to keep the vines from overrunning food plants. Water pollution also became a problem as water systems became loaded with nutrients. Excessive nutrients cause blooms of harmful algae. Air temperatures in the upper parts of the facility were higher than anticipated, but light levels were lower because glass cut the sunlight by nearly half. Areas designed to be deserts became grasslands or chaparral filled with shrubby plants. The humidity inside was much higher than outside in the Sonoran Desert.

Biosphere 2 cost nearly $200 million to build. Energy costs were about $1 million per year to keep pumps, fans, and other systems running. In 1996, Columbia University began managing Biosphere 2 for scientific research and educational programs. From 1996 to 2003, scientists studied how high carbon dioxide levels affected forest ecosystems and coral reef communities in the artificial environment. In 2003, Columbia ended its contract and research stopped. In 2006, Biosphere 2 was for sale while tourists continued to visit the unusual facility. A developer made an offer to purchase the facility. The developer is likely to build a community of homes on the site. We will have to wait and see what happens to the Biosphere 2 facility.

3. Think carefully about Questions 3a–d regarding Biosphere 2. Record your best ideas in your science notebook, and then use the TSAR strategy with another classmate to compare answers.
   a. Did Biosphere 2 accomplish its purpose of acting as a self-sustaining environment? Use evidence to explain why or why not.
   b. How is Biosphere 2 different from Biosphere 1 (Earth)?
   c. What do you think scientists learned from Biosphere 2? Use evidence from the reading to describe your thoughts.
   d. If you tried to create your own biosphere, what would you do differently? Document *why* you would make the changes you mention.
4. Read the following paragraph to apply your understanding to a space station.

   Only eight people lived in Biosphere 2. Now imagine you are in the future and scientists have designed a space station that 1,000 people will live in. Your job is to compare

In Step 5, distribute copymaster 15.7, *Population Description* to each student. Students should read about the conditions on a space station and review the copymaster. In Step 6, they should work individually and record their ideas about the populations on the 3 space stations. After students answer each question, suggest that they use the think-share-advise-revise (TSAR) strategy with another student to check their answers. Make sure they record any changes they make to their answers.

Answers to Step 6, SE pages 791–792

6a. Medical technology can reduce mortality rates by reducing the number of people who die from diseases. Agricultural technology can reduce mortality rates by increasing crop production and providing food for more people.

6b. Religious and cultural ideas are likely to make the birthrate higher because children give people status in some cultures and religions and because some religions discourage limiting the number of children.

6c. The fertility rate in space station 2 should be the lowest because more women are educated and the birthrate is lower. The fertility rate should be higher for both space stations 1 and 3 because fewer women are educated and the birthrate is higher.

6d. Space stations 1 and 3 are fast-growing populations because their populations are composed mostly of young people who are or will be at reproductive age. The population of space station 2 probably is remaining stable because it has a similar proportion of young and middle-aged people.

6e. The graphs for space stations 1 and 3 should show the population increasing with a steep slope. Students should include comments that describe that the population is increasing because birthrates are higher than mortality rates.

The graph for space station 2 should show the population increasing slightly. Students should include comments that describe that the population increases slowly because the birthrate is only a little higher than the mortality rate.

6f. The population on space station 2 will run out of water and oil before the other space stations because its population uses at least twice the amount of these resources. Cereal yield on space station 2 might decrease as well if water becomes scarce.

6g. The population on space station 3 will reach the highest numbers because it uses the least amount of resources and has a higher birthrate.

6h. Space station 1: Since this population is growing and uses more resources than space station 3, its biggest challenge will be providing food, water, and oil resources for its growing population.

Space station 2: This population isn't growing but uses a large amount of resources. If resource use remains high, the water and oil resources might eventually be depleted.

Space station 3: This population's biggest challenge will be providing food for its growing population since its cereal yield is lower than the other stations.

---

three populations and their resource use on different space stations. You will decide what the biggest challenge facing each population would be. The following list explains the same conditions for all three populations.

- A starting population of 1,000 people
- Identical resources including water, soils, plants, animals, microorganisms, and energy sources used for fuel
- Identical environmental conditions such as physical space, available area for growing crops, temperature, and sunlight

Keep in mind that these things may change after people colonize the space station.

5. Get the *Population Description* handout from your teacher and begin reviewing the characteristics of the 3 populations.
6. In your science notebook, document your ideas about the populations by thinking carefully about Questions 6a–i. Then record your answers. After answering each question on your own, use the TSAR strategy to review your responses with another student.
   a. Technology can affect populations in different ways. How are differences in mortality rates and agricultural production related to the availability of technology?
   b. How do you think religious or cultural ideas affect the birthrate?
   c. Consider the difference in the education of the women in each population. How would the fertility rate of each population compare?

Remember that fertility rate is the average number of children born to each woman, and birthrate is the number of births in a year per 1,000 people.

   d. What does the age structure of each colonizing population tell you about how the populations might change across time?
   e. How would each population change across time? Draw graphs to show your prediction. Include highlight comments and a caption with each graph.
   f. Which population do you think will run out of resources first? Explain why.
   g. Which population do you think will be the largest while resources are still plentiful?
   h. Each population will face its own struggle to live comfortably while growing. What do you think will be the biggest challenge for each population? Describe the challenge in your science notebook.

Part II: A Space Station Challenge
Process and Procedure

Materials
For each team of 2 students
materials for creating a poster

In Step 1, students should read the team goal. The goal is to propose the maximum number of people (carrying capacity) who could live comfortably on a space station the size of Earth. To help them understand the expectations, they should review the statements in Step 2 and the scoring rubric. Guiding questions are provided in Steps 3 and 4 to help students discuss the characteristics of the space station they propose. Make sure students record ideas from the discussion.

In Step 5, teams prepare a poster that outlines their proposal. The poster should demonstrate what they have learned about populations and resources during this chapter. Make sure the poster includes each of the items listed in Step 5a–e. Make sure students take time to compare their proposed space station to Earth in Step 7.

i. How might the space stations manage their resources to support their populations?

Part II: A Space Station Challenge

Now that you have thought about the difficulties that populations might face on a space station, it's time to confront those challenges with your team.

Materials
For each team of 2 students
materials for creating a poster

Process and Procedure

1. Read and discuss the following team goal:

   Goal: Propose the maximum number of people (carrying capacity) who could live comfortably on a space station the size of Earth.
2. Review the scoring rubric and the following considerations as you develop your proposal:
   - Your team must agree upon an operational definition for "living comfortably." Remember that how a population lives determines its influence on ecosystems.
   - The conditions you describe must apply to everyone in the human population. Everyone must be able to use resources at the same rate.
   - Ecosystems on the space station must operate in the same way as ecosystems on Earth. In other words, you can't create ecosystems that function differently from ecosystems on Earth.
3. Discuss as a team the resources and ecosystem services your space station needs. Use the questions listed here as a guide for your discussion. Record ideas from the discussion.
   - What ecosystems are present?
   - What resources are supplied by each ecosystem?
   - What natural processes are supplied by each ecosystem?
4. Discuss as a team what characteristics you think the population should have. Use the questions listed here as a guide for your discussion. Record ideas from the discussion.
   - What is the growth rate of the population?
   - What are some of the resources the population uses?
   - How will the population get the energy it needs?

792 Unit 4 Sustaining Earth Systems

Answers to Step 5, SE page 793

5a. Teams should include marine, freshwater, forest, and grassland ecosystems. Students should list resources and services similar to those listed in figure T15.5.

5b. Teams should mention restricting consumption of resources, reducing pollution, and minimizing the alteration of ecosystems to help keep them functioning. How they manage resources and ecosystems should be related to the growth rate and carrying capacity they choose. If they choose a high growth rate or carrying capacity, then they must explain how they will manage resources to make sure there are enough for a large population.

5c. Teams must justify whatever growth rate they choose. For example, they should explain how birthrates and mortality rates contribute to the growth rate they choose. They should also explain what influences the fertility rate on their space station and how these influences affect the birthrate.

5d. The graph should reflect the growth rate of the population. Make sure teams indicate the carrying capacity on the graph. The highlight comments and caption should explain how they decided on this carrying capacity. Teams should be making connections between population size and the consumption of resources.

5e. Teams must show how each part of the poster is connected. They should demonstrate how they used their understanding of ecosystems, populations, and consumption to develop their proposal for the carrying capacity of a space station.

- Will the population be made up of individuals who consume a lot or those who consume less? Why?
- How does the population affect the ecosystems?

5. Prepare a poster to share your proposal with the class. Your poster should include the following:
   a. Labeled sketches showing the ecosystems on the station and the resources and services that the ecosystems provide
   b. A description of how the population manages its resources and maintains the function of ecosystems
   c. The growth rate of the population and an explanation of why your population has this growth rate
   d. A graph showing how the population will change across time and the carrying capacity for the space station; include highlight comments and a caption
   e. A logical flow from one idea to the next made clear with graphic features
6. Work with a partner to critically review your posters.
   a. Read your poster and provide explanations for your sketches and graphs.
   b. Listen as your partner describes his or her poster. Note any parts that are confusing or could be improved.
   c. Revise your poster based on your partner's comments.
7. Describe how your proposed space station is similar to or different from Earth today.

NOTES:

CHAPTER 16

Sustaining Earth's Environmental Quality

Chapter Overview

So far in unit 4, *Sustaining Earth Systems*, students have learned about basic processes in ecosystems, populations, and natural resources. In this final chapter, *Sustaining Earth's Environmental Quality*, students apply their understandings to investigate how human activities influence environmental quality. The entire chapter prepares students to gather information for and present recommendations at a Global Conference on Environmental Quality in the evaluate activity, *A Meeting of the Minds*. Students generate their own questions about environmental quality and then use the Web and other resources to gather evidence to answer their questions. Then they use the evidence to develop recommendations for sustaining environmental quality. As students go through this process, they learn that science is essential in making informed decisions, but science cannot resolve environmental quality challenges.

Goals for the Chapter

The overarching goals for this chapter are that students will understand that human activities influence environmental quality and that science and technology are essential to address global challenges such as sustaining global environmental quality. By the end of chapter 16, students will understand the following:

- Humans affect basic processes in ecosystems such as quality of the atmosphere, generation of soils, control of the hydrologic cycle, disposal of wastes, and recycling of nutrients.
- Many factors such as population growth, resource use, and overconsumption influence environmental quality.
- Science and technology can only indicate what can happen, not what should happen.
- Policy decisions should be based on scientific knowledge; however, science alone cannot resolve global challenges.

The chapter organizer uses graphic design principles to help students connect one activity to another. It uses reminders of key concepts, linking questions, and the spatial arrangement of activity titles to foster the sense of a conceptual flow, connecting each activity. Explicitly ask students to locate their position within its flow at the beginning of each activity. This action reinforces the connection among the activities, thus enhancing long-term memory.

Chapter 16 Organizer

SUSTAINING EARTH'S ENVIRONMENTAL QUALITY

Major Concepts

- **Humans affect basic processes in ecosystems.**
- **Many factors such as population growth, resource use, and overconsumption influence environmental quality.**
- **Science and technology can only indicate what can happen, not what should happen.**
- **Policy decisions are based on scientific knowledge; however, science alone cannot resolve global challenges.**

ENGAGE — Think Globally ★

Key Idea: • A variety of environmental issues affect Earth.

Activity: Students research environmental conferences and environmental issues on the Internet. They generate ideas about the global conference and questions about environmental issues.

LINKING QUESTION: How are populations, resources, and lifestyles related to environmental issues?

EXPLORE — Pay Me Now, or Pay Me Later ★ ★ ★

Key Ideas:
- Humans affect ecosystems.
- Many factors influence environmental quality.

Activity: Students choose one environmental issue to present during the global conference. They generate scientifically testable questions about the environmental quality issue. They use their questions to guide Internet research into how populations, resources, and lifestyles influence environmental quality. They also research how the issue affects air, water, and soil quality.

LINKING QUESTION: How can evidence be used to improve environmental quality?

EXPLAIN — The Times, They Are a Changing ★ ★

Key Ideas:
- Science and technology help us understand how humans affect environmental quality.
- Policy decisions should be based on scientific knowledge, but are influenced by societal issues and funding as well.

Activity: Students organize the evidence they have collected about the environmental issue. Using the evidence, they develop a set of recommendations for the global conference.

LINKING QUESTION: How can recommendations be effectively communicated?

ELABORATE — Be Prepared ★ ★

Key Idea:
- Communicating scientific knowledge involves organizing information, developing explanations, and making revisions based on comments.

Activity: Students prepare segments of their presentation for the global conference. They rehearse their presentation in front of their team and revise it based on their feedback.

LINKING QUESTION: How can I use what I have learned to demonstrate my understanding of environmental quality?

EVALUATE — A Meeting of the Minds ★ ★

Key Ideas:
- Humans affect ecosystems.
- Many factors influence environmental quality.
- Science and technology can only indicate what can happen, not what should happen.
- Policy decisions should be based on scientific knowledge; however, science alone cannot resolve global challenges.

Activity: Students share their recommendations at a global conference. They revisit their questions from the *Think Globally* activity and agree on a set of top recommendations for the class.

★ = One Class Period ☆ = ½ Class Period *Note:* Based on a 50-minute class period.

Standards Covered by Chapter 16*

SUSTAINING EARTH'S ENVIRONMENTAL QUALITY

STANDARD A: Science as Inquiry. As a result of activities in grades 9–12, all students should develop

abilities necessary to do scientific inquiry

- Formulate and revise scientific explanations and models using logic and evidence. Student inquiries should culminate in formulating an explanation or model. Models should be physical, conceptual, and mathematical. In the process of answering the questions, the students should engage in discussions and arguments that result in the revision of their explanations. These discussions should be based on scientific knowledge, the use of logic, and evidence from their investigation.
- Communicate and defend a scientific argument. Students in school science programs should develop the abilities associated with accurate and effective communication. These include writing and following procedures, expressing concepts, reviewing information, summarizing data, using language appropriately, developing diagrams and charts, explaining statistical analysis, speaking clearly and logically, constructing a reasoned argument, and responding appropriately to critical comments. [See Teaching Standard B in Chapter 3]

understandings about scientific inquiry

- Scientific explanations must adhere to criteria such as: a proposed explanation must be logically consistent; it must abide by the rules of evidence; it must be open to questions and possible modification; and it must be based on historical and current scientific knowledge.

STANDARD C: Life Science. As a result of their activities in grades 9–12, all students should develop understanding of

the interdependence of organisms

- Human beings live within the world's ecosystems. Increasingly, humans modify ecosystems as a result of population growth, technology, and consumption. Human destruction of habitats through direct harvesting, pollution, atmospheric changes, and other factors is threatening global stability, and if not addressed, ecosystems will be irreversibly affected.

STANDARD F: Science in Personal and Social Perspectives. As a result of activities in grades 9–12, all students should develop understanding of

environmental quality

- Natural ecosystems provide an array of basic processes that affect humans. Those processes include maintenance of the quality of the atmosphere, generation of soils, control of the hydrologic cycle, disposal of wastes, and recycling of nutrients. Humans are changing many of these basic processes, and the changes may be detrimental to humans.
- Materials from human societies affect both physical and chemical cycles of the earth.
- Many factors influence environmental quality. Factors that students might investigate include population growth, resource use, population distribution, overconsumption, the capacity of technology to solve problems, poverty, the role of economic, political, and religious views, and different ways humans view the earth.

science and technology in local, national, and global challenges

- Science and technology are essential social enterprises, but alone they can only indicate what can happen, not what should happen. The latter involves human decisions about the use of knowledge.
- Understanding basic concepts and principles of science and technology should precede active debate about the economics, policies, politics, and ethics of various science- and technology-related challenges. However, understanding science alone will not resolve local, national, or global challenges.
- Humans have a major effect on other species. For example, the influence of humans on other organisms occurs through land use—which decreases space available to other species—and pollution—which changes the chemical compositon of air, soil, and water.

* *Note:* Bracketed portions of the standard are addressed elsewhere in the program.

Prerequisite Knowledge

Students should be familiar with natural processes in ecosystems, human populations, and natural resources from the previous chapters in this unit.

Commonly Held Misconceptions

- Human animals are not part of ecosystems.

Students often fail to realize that they are a part of ecosystems. As a result, they do not recognize the effect that human activities have on environmental quality.

ENGAGE

Think Globally

Activity Overview

The first activity in this chapter, *Think Globally*, introduces your students to an environmental conference, which they will plan and participate in. Students gather information about scientific conferences in general and about environmental issues facing our world today. Students organize and group articles they find to help them generate questions and make recommendations for actions to sustain Earth's environmental quality. Use this activity to introduce your students to scientific conferences in general and to scientific presentations specifically. As part of this activity, your students review the scoring rubric you will use to evaluate their work at the conclusion of the chapter. This way, they will understand your expectations for their work from the beginning of the chapter, which will also help to foster better performances from your students.

Before You Teach

Background Information

At first glance, you may think this chapter lacks scientific content. Upon further examination, however, you will see that it is rich in leading your students through a process in which they will gain a deeper understanding of doing science. Perhaps even more important, students will have the opportunity to experience science in a compelling context that will help them understand firsthand why science is so important now and will continue to be in their future.

In the process of doing science, students immerse themselves in rich science content and synthesize the information to arrive at some type of conclusion about environmental quality. They will draw from what they have learned in previous chapters to convene a scientific conference. This will engage students in the following tenet from the *National Science Education Standards*: "Understanding basic concepts and principles of science and technology should precede active debate about the economics, policies, and ethics of various science- and technology-related challenges. However, understanding science alone will not resolve l ocal, national, or global challenges" (p. 199). Students may not have grasped the idea yet that an understanding of science is important not only to scientists, but also to government officials, engineers, and even ordinary, tax-paying citizens. This understanding is necessary to making informed, lifetime decisions that will contribute to sustaining Earth's environmental quality.

Materials

For each student

access to the Web

scientific or environmental articles in journals or newspapers

1 copy of copymaster 16.1, *A Meeting of the Minds Scoring Rubric* TRCD

Advance Preparation

Make 1 copy of copymaster 16.1, *A Meeting of the Minds Scoring Rubric*, for each student. Your class will need at least 3 days in the computer lab for this engage activity and for the other activities to follow. Make arrangements ahead so that your students may use the computer lab. If you want to narrow the range of Web sites that your students can access, spend some time looking up environmental conferences and select a small number of sites to recommend to your students.

Educational Technologies

Students will need access to the Web for this activity. You will decide if students will work individually or in teams during the first part of the activity in which they will be accessing the Web. This will determine how many computers are required for your class.

As You Teach

Outcomes and Indicators of Success

By the end of this activity, students should

1. become engaged in the idea of an environmental conference on how humans affect global environmental quality.

   They will become engaged by

   - working with a team to generate ideas about how their class can model an environmental conference;
   - collecting articles from a variety of sources that pertain to the environmental quality of Earth, which prepares them for making recommendations for sustaining environmental quality; and
   - beginning initial preparations for holding a mock global environmental conference in their class or school.

2. develop their awareness that many factors influence environmental quality.

   They will develop their awareness by

   - analyzing articles about environmental issues on local, regional, national, and global levels and
   - identifying trends in these issues in *Reflect and Connect* questions.

3. develop their awareness that science requires contributions of individuals from many different disciplines.

   They will develop their understanding by

   - researching different scientific conferences and the topics presented and
   - discovering the range of backgrounds of individuals that participate in scientific conferences.

Strategies

Getting Started

If your community has companies or organizations that hold conferences, contact them for placards or signs from old conferences. Display these in your classroom. Students will be curious about the signs' intent, and their questions can lead in to the activity. If you cannot acquire these signs, consider making posters to put around the room. Posters can say things like Presenters Pick Up Name Badges Here; Registration; Key Note Speaker: Dr. Green, Professor of Environmental Science, University of North America; Welcome to the 1st Annual Earth High School Environmental Conference; and so forth. You might also want to decorate a bulletin board in the hallway to get the school involved in this conference.

Process and Procedure

Materials

For each student

access to the Web

scientific or environmental articles in journals or newspapers

1 copy of copymaster 16.1, *A Meeting of the Minds Scoring Rubric*

ENGAGE

Think Globally

You and your classmates are invited to attend the upcoming Global Conference on Environmental Quality. This conference will be held in the evaluate activity, *A Meeting of the Minds*. The conference will address environmental issues related to sustaining environmental quality on Earth. Before you can participate in the conference, however, you have some work to do. Work individually or in teams, as instructed by your teacher, as you prepare for this conference.

Materials

For each student

access to the Web

scientific or environmental articles in journals or newspapers

1 *A Meeting of the Minds Scoring Rubric* handout

Process and Procedure

1. Become familiar with conferences that address our environment. Use the Web to search for environmental conferences. Then complete Steps 1a–d.
   a. Find a conference that you think addresses global environmental issues and access the conference program.
   b. Record in your notebook the sponsor of the conference. Consider if there are any biases that would be apparent in the conference with this particular sponsor. Record your ideas in your notebook.

Bias is an unfair preference for or dislike of something. Depending on the sponsor of the conference, the invited speakers could show bias toward the environmental issue.

   c. Make a list of the types of presenters who are participating in the conference. Examples include college professors, scientists, business leaders, and government officials.
   d. Consider whether or not there are any special requirements for the presentations. If so, what are they? You might find this type of information in a "call for papers" or with other preliminary arrangements for the conference.

If you do not find this information for the conference you selected, choose a conference that is scheduled for some time in the future.

2. Think about the conference that your class will hold in a few days as you complete Steps 2a–c.

In Step 1, students investigate the many scientific conferences that are publicized on the Web. Decide if students will work individually or in teams and provide enough computers accordingly. Later in the activity, students will form teams if they do not do so here. This step engages students in the idea of a scientific conference on how humans are affecting global environmental quality. They should find a variety of conferences by using the key words *environmental conferences*. There are even Web sites that have collections of conferences across the world. Search for *conference alerts* for an example. You will have to select *environment* to get a list of environmental conferences.

Students will also research specific conferences to identify the different types of presenters that participate in these conferences. They will find presenters who range from the typical university research scientist to policy makers and business leaders. Students are also asked to find any requirements for presenters. Many conferences require a paper and/or a poster. Students should look at the format and requirements for the paper as well as for a poster presentation. Finding conferences that will be held at future dates will increase your chances of finding these requirements posted on the Web site.

Students are asked to note the host of the conference and to consider any bias that may be introduced. Take time to have a class discussion about bias. For example, students should realize that an environmental conference on water quality issues sponsored by a chemical company that produces pesticides is likely to be biased toward the views of the chemical company.

In Steps 2 and 3, students think about how they might model a scientific conference in their class. They will write down their ideas and share them in a class discussion. Use this time to work out some of the logistics of the conference that your students will plan and conduct. You should decide (based on available time and resources) if you want to include student committees to organize different aspects of the conference. These could include a committee in charge of the program, decorations, publicity, invited guests, and so forth. You should also decide at this time if you want different students or teams to assume the role of different individuals in the conference. You may want your students to take on the roles of policy makers, scientists, business owners, city council members, or diplomats from foreign countries, for example. and fashion their presentation according to their role. If you decide to add this additional layer of detail to the activity, then you will need to add appropriate addendums to the scoring rubric.

In Step 4, students begin to gather articles about environmental issues at local, regional, national, and global levels. In addition to the Web, students should also use magazines and newspapers. Discuss with your students options for printing or copying these articles for classroom use. Also, discuss with the students how to find scientific articles on the Web from universities and reputable organizations and agencies such as the Environmental Protection Agency (EPA). Decide on the amount of time to give your students for this part of the activity. Communicate this clearly to students in Step 4a. Also, discuss the requirements of Step 4b. Students may need clarification of environmental issues at the regional, national, or global levels.

Students group the articles in Step 5 to look for patterns. This step also serves as a way for teams of students to analyze a smaller group of articles. At this point, think ahead

a. In what ways might you model the environmental conferences that you read about on the Web?
b. Think about the logistics of the conference as well as the presentations. Which conferences appeal to you and why?
c. Write down at least 3 ideas you have for your class conference. Be prepared to share them in a class discussion.

3. Share your ideas about the conference in a class discussion led by your teacher.
4. Gather information related to environmental issues in Steps 4a–b. These should be issues that affect environmental quality on a local, regional, national, or even global level.
   a. Use the Web and your library to find articles about environmental issues. Your teacher will assign a time frame for you to complete this step.
   b. Collect 3–5 articles about different environmental issues. Be sure to collect articles about local, regional, national, and global issues.

You should be able to describe how each issue you choose affects some natural system. For example, say you choose the overuse of pesticides or pesticide runoff. These issues would affect the water system.

5. Display the articles collected in Step 4b around the room. Arrange the articles in groups according to topic, region, or another factor that your class identifies. Review the articles in their groups.
6. If you have been working individually, choose a team of 2 or 3 other classmates and complete Steps 6a–c.
   a. Choose 1 of the groups of articles that the class collected. Review the articles in that group.
   b. Generate at least 3 questions related to environmental issues that can be answered by science. These questions may relate to population growth, resources, lifestyles, or another issue linked to how humans affect the environment. Record these questions in your science notebook.

You may want to visit other teams and review their articles.

   c. Be prepared to share your questions in a class discussion.
7. Participate in a class discussion and complete Steps 7a–c.
   a. Record the categories your teacher has written on the board.
   b. Share your questions with the class and listen as other teams report their questions.
   c. Decide as a class how to group the questions in 1 of the categories on the board.

to the number of teams that your class will have and orchestrate the number of groups of articles to match the number of student teams. Allow the students to choose how to group the articles. Help them to realize that there are multiple ways to group things and that the way you group things depends on what patterns or trends you are trying to see.

Students use the articles to generate questions in Step 6. The questions do not have to come specifically from the articles, but they should be general in nature and be questions that can be answered by science. Students will have the opportunity to refine their questions in subsequent activities, so they do not have to be in their final form at this point.

Teams will share their questions in a class discussion in Step 7. Consider giving students long strips of paper (old adding machine tape works great) on which to write their questions. Make sure they write their question large enough for the class to see. You will divide the regions of the world into groups that your students will use to categorize their questions. One such grouping could be the United States, other developed western nations; other developed eastern nations; and other developing nations such as in Asia, Africa, and South/Central America. Write your categories across the board where everyone can see. Have students decide in which category their question would fall. If they have questions that fit in multiple categories, have them wait and place their question in a category that does not have many entries. If, at the end of the discussion, there are categories with no questions, ask your students if they can reword a question to make it fit in one of the empty categories. Students will use these questions as a springboard for future activities, as they refine their questions, research possible answers, and make recommendations that they will present at the conference.

In Step 8, students review the scoring rubric for the evaluate activity. Discuss with the students any questions they might have about the rubric. In Step 9, students listen as you discuss a timeline for the project. Consider using class input for the deadlines for different parts. It is possible for each team to work at its own pace throughout the entire chapter up to the presentations in the evaluate activity. You may want to set intermediate deadlines for your class based on the 5E activities. That way teams will know the deadline for completing each activity.

Answers to Reflect and Connect, SE page 802

1a. Answers will vary here, but students should be able to identify a pattern. Patterns may include specific environmental issues related to air quality, the soil, or water pollution. They may also see patterns in what causes certain environmental problems such as chemical contamination or wastewater control. The main pattern that you want them to see is that humans are involved in the environmental issues they have researched.

1b. Students should see that even though issues may appear different on a global scale, they are only different in degree not in kind. Local environmental issues often have an effect on the global environment. Students may also recognize that local problems often have a global counterpart.

Answers to Reflect and Connect are on TE pages 802–803.

8. Review the handout *A Meeting of the Minds Scoring Rubric*. This is the rubric that your teacher will use to evaluate your performance throughout this chapter. Think about what is expected of you to receive the highest credit for your work.

If you have questions about the scoring rubric and how your teacher will use the rubric to evaluate your work at the conference, be sure to ask them now.

9. Listen as your teacher discusses the timeline you will follow as you work toward the goals in the rubric. Record important due dates in your science notebook.

Reflect and Connect

Work with your team to answer the following questions. Record your best ideas in your science notebook.

1. Look at the group of articles that your team selected in Step 6 and answer Questions 1a–b.
   a. What patterns do you see in your group of articles?

Examples of patterns you should look for include the types of issues; issues that relate to the same natural system, for example, all the articles concerning water quality; patterns that indicate that environmental quality is improving or declining; and patterns of issues that all target the same industry.

   b. Are the issues the same or different for articles at a local level compared with those at a regional, national, or global level? Justify and explain your answer.
2. Use the scoring rubric to answer Questions 2a–d in your science notebook.
   a. What constitutes "sound evidence," which is referred to in the first task on the rubric? Where will you find this evidence?
   b. What questions do you have about the science principles listed in the second task on the rubric?
   c. What are your initial ideas about how you will present your recommendations?
   d. Consider the strengths of each member of your team. What types of presentation aids can you use that will draw on these strengths? For example, you may have a team member who is an artist or is very good at designing computer presentations. Use these strengths to select the type of aids you will use in your presentation.

2a. Students should support their recommendations with evidence reported in scientific articles and/or journals. This evidence should be backed up by sound data. The evidence should come from qualitative and/or quantitative data that are collected in a reliable way. Students should recognize that sound evidence is both reproducible and reliable. In this age of the Web, it is often easy for students to come across a collection of claims with no sound evidence to support them. Make sure that your students have not only collected scientific articles but that they have also examined them carefully to determine if they represent sound evidence.

2b. Answers will vary, but should reflect questions students have about science principles of population, resources, and environmental quality, including air, water, and soil. You will want to discuss these questions with students so they are clear on the expectations indicated on the rubric.

2c. This question gets students thinking about their presentation. Expect a list of ideas that will undoubtedly change throughout the chapter.

2d. Look for a list of specific strengths. Encourage the team to list each member. Examples might include, "Juan is a good talker, so he would be good at leading the oral presentation."

Pay Me Now, or Pay Me Later

EXPLORE

You have discovered that many environmental issues affect Earth. Each of these issues is tied to a human activity (figure 16.1). For example, exhaust from cars contributes to air pollution, and some farming practices cause loss of topsoil. These actions result in reduced air and soil quality. As you prepare for the Global Conference on Environmental Quality, you will focus on this relationship between human activity and environmental quality. In *Pay Me Now, or Pay Me Later*, your team continues its preparation by deciding what environmental quality issue it will address. Then you will generate questions about that issue and collect evidence to answer your questions. Throughout your preparations, focus your work to answer the question, "How is this environmental issue related to global environmental quality?"

▲ **Figure 16.1 Center-pivot irrigation.** Agriculture has become a vital way for humans to produce the food that we need. In what ways do you think agriculture and food production relates to ecosystems?

Materials

For each team of 3 students

access to the Web

3 *A Meeting of the Minds Scoring Rubric* handouts

Process and Procedure

1. Get into your team and read over the articles and questions collected by the class in Steps 4 and 6 of the engage activity, *Think Globally*. Discuss what environmental issues interest you the most and briefly describe them in your science notebook.
2. Choose 1 environmental issue related to environmental quality to present at the conference. Remember, you are participating in a global conference, so the issue must be common to people in all parts of the world or be a local issue of global concern.

Examples of issues include managing waste, contaminants from industry, road or agricultural runoff, and clearing forests or grasslands for other uses.

3. Generate at least 3 questions about the environmental issue that can be answered by science.

EXPLORE

Pay Me Now, or Pay Me Later

Activity Overview

In *Pay Me Now, or Pay Me Later*, teams decide what environmental issue they will present at the Global Conference on Environmental Quality. Then they refine questions about the environmental issues that can be answered by science. Team members work together and plan what evidence they will collect to answer their questions. As specified by the rubric, their evidence must reflect scientific knowledge about how populations, resources, and lifestyles are related to the environmental issue and how environmental quality is affected. Students gather their evidence using the Web and/or library resources.

Before You Teach

Background Information

As students research information about an environmental issue, they can draw on what they have learned in earlier chapters of this unit. They can use their understanding of interactions among organisms, populations, and natural resources to help them learn how humans affect environmental quality. Students' own research should reemphasize concepts introduced in the student book.

Materials

For each team of 3 students

access to the Web

3 copies of copymaster 16.1, *A Meeting of the Minds Scoring Rubric*

Advance Preparation

Collect headlines from magazines or newspapers showing the relationship between human activity and environmental quality. You might choose articles that show both a negative effect and a positive effect on environmental quality. For example, a headline might read "Increased use of public transportation reduces carbon emissions by 10%."

Educational Technologies

Reserve the computer lab for students to conduct Web searches. Consider asking a school librarian to help students conduct library searches. Many library searches offer access to the full text of magazine and newspaper articles.

The following organizations have Web sites with good sources of information:

- Worldwatch Institute Environmental Information Portal
- NOVA World in the Balance
- U.S. Environmental Protection Agency
- EPA High School Environmental Center
- Fish and Wildlife Division of Environmental Quality
- Scientific American Environment Channel
- U.S. Census Bureau International Data Base
- United Nations Population Division
- Population Reference Bureau
- Food and Agriculture Organization

As You Teach

Outcomes and Indicators of Success

By the end of this activity, students should

1. develop scientifically testable questions.

   They will demonstrate their ability by generating questions about an environmental issue that can be answered by science.

2. be able to gather evidence about populations, resources, lifestyle, and environmental quality related to a specific environmental issue.

   They will demonstrate their ability by

   - deciding what evidence to collect to answer questions about an environmental issue and
   - using the Web and the library to locate evidence about an environmental issue.

Strategies

Getting Started

If you have gathered headlines about environmental quality, use them to facilitate a brief discussion about the relationship between human activity and environmental quality.

Process and Procedure

Materials

For each team of 3 students

access to the Web

3 copies of copymaster 16.1, *A Meeting of the Minds Scoring Rubric*

In Step 1, students review the articles and questions the class developed in the engage activity, *Think Globally*. They should discuss as a team what environmental issues interest them the most. In Step 2, check to make sure that teams select an issue that has an effect on environmental quality. The issue should affect a natural system. Another option to consider is to have all the teams focus on one environmental issue such as car emissions or environmental quality issues associated with food production. This would give your conference a specific theme and all teams would focus on various aspects of that issue.

Answers to Reflect and Connect are on TE page 805.

You might be able to adjust or improve upon one of the questions from the engage activity. Be sure that your questions are related.

4. Have your teacher approve your questions.
5. Discuss as a team what information you need to answer your questions. Record your ideas in your science notebook.
6. Develop a plan for gathering evidence for the global conference by completing Steps 6a–e.
   a. Review the *A Meeting of the Minds Scoring Rubric* handout.
   b. Discuss what evidence you need to gather about populations, resources, and lifestyles.
   c. Discuss what you need to know about how the issue you chose affects air, water, and soil quality.
   d. Decide as a team which member will gather what evidence from Steps 6b–c.
   e. Record your plan in your science notebook.

Recall that an important part of this conference is justifying your recommendations with evidence.

7. Carry out your plan and collect evidence about the environmental issue you chose by completing Steps 7a–c.
   a. Use the Web and your library to find evidence about the environmental issue. Your teacher will assign a time frame for you to complete this step.
   b. Keep a list of references including the Web sites and other sources you use.
   c. Record in your notebook a summary of each article that you will use for your presentation. Include the reference for the article.

▲ **Figure 16.2 Group of students working.** Work with your team as the students in this investigation are doing.

Reflect and Connect

Answer the following questions individually in your science notebook.

1. Describe what you have learned about the environmental issue you chose by completing Steps 1a–c.
   a. Give 1 example of the relationship between human activity and environmental quality. Use something you learned while researching information about your environmental issue.
   b. Explain how humans affected environmental quality.

Examples of possible environmental issues include the following:

- Car/factory emissions
- Effluent from feedlots
- Herbicides/pesticides and water quality
- Fertilizer runoff and water quality
- Runoff in storm sewers in urban settings
- Deforestation
- Draining or filling wetlands
- Mining coal or drilling for natural gas or oil
- Managing waste (household or industrial)
- Soil degradation such as erosion or contamination

In Step 3, students generate questions about the environmental issue that can be answered by science. Encourage students to approach these questions in the same way that they would approach questions for a scientific investigation. The difference here is that students investigate by collecting evidence from other sources instead of by collecting the data directly. Approve the teams' questions before they begin discussing how to answer them. Assist teams that are having difficulty developing questions.

In Step 5, teams discuss what information they need to gather to answer their questions, and then in Step 6, they develop a plan for gathering the evidence. They should use the scoring rubric to guide their discussion. Circulate among the teams as they discuss their plans and keep emphasizing the importance of gathering scientific evidence about the environmental issue. Let students know how much time they will have to conduct their research.

Starting in Step 7, students spend the rest of the activity collecting evidence from the Web and library. They can also use information from the last 2 chapters in this unit, *Population Interactions* and *Earth's Capacity*. Check in with students during this process. Remind teams of the time allotment you set for this step. There is a lot of interesting information out there, but students need to follow their plan and focus on gathering information that is pertinent to the conference and that comes from reliable sources. Students should summarize the information they have gathered in their own words. Check to make sure that students aren't just turning in pages they have printed from the Web. Students who do this have not processed the information in a meaningful way.

Answers to Reflect and Connect, SE pages 804–805

1a–b. Answers to these 2 questions will vary depending on the environmental issue that a team chooses. Look for responses that show that students understand how humans impact the environment.

1c. This question gets students thinking about recommendations for the global conference. Look for responses that use knowledge about populations, resources, or lifestyle.

2. This question points out to students that additional questions often arise as we learn more about an issue. Questioning is an important part of the process of scientific inquiry.

---

c. Propose what humans could do differently to improve environmental quality.

2. List 1 or 2 new questions you have about the environmental issue after having gathered your evidence.

You do not need to search for evidence to answer these questions. Simply reflect on what you have learned and what you are curious about.

The Times, They Are a Changing

EXPLAIN

Soon you will be making decisions about your life after high school. Will you go to college? If so, what information do you need to make the best decision? You would probably investigate the colleges and universities that interest you. You may base your decision on location, academic programs, or cost. Even if you know everything there is to know about the university, the decision is yours. You likely will make that decision based on information you have gathered.

Policy makers go through a similar process when addressing global challenges such as sustaining environmental quality (figures 16.3 and 16.4). Science provides society with information about what *can* happen, not about what *should* happen. In *The Times, They Are a Changing*, you will go through this process as you continue to prepare for the conference. You will work in your team to develop a set of recommendations based on the evidence you gathered in the explore activity, *Pay Me Now, or Pay Me Later*.

▲ **Figure 16.3 Oil rig.** An oil rig is a structure used to drill for and extract oil. How do you think this process of oil extraction affects environmental quality?

◄ **Figure 16.4 Growing populations.** As populations in cities increase, how will they affect consumption rates and pollution?

EXPLAIN

The Times, They Are a Changing

Activity Overview

In *The Times, They Are a Changing*, teams analyze and organize the evidence they have gathered about their environmental issue. Then students model the process that policy makers use to make recommendations for sustaining environmental quality.

Before You Teach

Background Information

In this explore activity, students bridge their understanding of science concepts with decision making. Taking part in the decision-making process often helps students better understand how science is relevant to their lives. Use this activity as an opportunity to help students understand the role of science in society. Keep going back to the standards addressed in this chapter. Students should begin to understand that science and technology are important sources of information, but humans must decide how to use the information.

Materials

For each team of 3 students

access to the Web

3 copies of copymaster 16.1, *A Meeting of the Minds Scoring Rubric*

Advance Preparation

Gather examples of environmental policies such as the National Environmental Protection Act, city regulations, wetland remediation, and the Kyoto Protocol. The Kyoto Protocol is an international treaty on climate change. Use these policies as key words to search the Web.

As You Teach

Outcomes and Indicators of Success

By the end of this activity, students should

1. be able to use tools to organize evidence.

   They will demonstrate their ability by
   - sorting evidence into categories and
   - using tables, graphs, and other visual strategies to arrange data in a useful way for the presentation.

2. understand that collecting scientific evidence should precede making recommendations but does not resolve environmental quality challenges.

   They will demonstrate their understanding by
   - agreeing on a set of recommendations based on scientific evidence,
   - explaining how evidence helped them to develop recommendations for sustaining environmental quality, and
   - explaining that scientific evidence cannot resolve environmental quality issues because science can help indicate what can happen, not what should happen.

Materials

For each team of 3 students

access to the Web

3 *A Meeting of the Minds Scoring Rubric* handouts

Process and Procedure

1. Review the evidence you collected in Steps 7a–c in the explore activity and cross-check it with the plan you developed.
   a. Do you have evidence showing how populations, resources, and lifestyles are related to the environmental issue?
   b. Do you have evidence showing how the environmental issue affects environmental quality?

You might have found that the issue affects air, water, and soil quality, or only 1 of these. Perhaps the issue affects environmental quality in another way such as reducing biodiversity—the diversity of organisms in an area.

   c. Decide whether you have enough evidence to meet the needs of your plan. If you do, continue with Step 2. If not, spend some more time gathering information.

Consult with your teacher before going on to Step 2.

2. Organize the evidence you have gathered about the environmental issue by following these guidelines.
   a. Use tables, graphs, or other visual strategies to arrange any data you have collected.
   b. Decide as a team how you can sort the evidence into types or categories of evidence.

Be sure to document your decisions in your notebook, as well as any discussions you have as a team.

3. Revisit the questions you developed in Step 3 of the explore activity. Use the evidence you gathered to answer your questions. Record your answers in your science notebook.

Consider collecting more information if you were unable to answer one of your questions.

4. Review the scoring rubric handout, specifically the task of making a set of evidence-based recommendations.
5. Read *Making London a More Sustainable City* to learn about the strategies of the mayor of London for sustaining environmental quality. This short reading might give you some ideas to develop in more detail when making your recommendations.

3. be able to use evidence to justify a recommendation.

They will demonstrate their ability by

- using tables, graphs, or other visual displays of data to make recommendations and
- referring to information about populations, resources, and lifestyles in their recommendations.

Strategies

Getting Started

Facilitate a brief class discussion about what information government officials need to develop environmental policies. If you have gathered examples of environmental policies, use these to guide the discussion.

Process and Procedure

Materials

For each team of 3 students

access to the Web

3 copies of copymaster 16.1, *A Meeting of the Minds Scoring Rubric*

In Step 1, teams review the evidence they have gathered. They cross-check the evidence with their plan to make sure they have evidence about populations, resources, lifestyles, and environmental quality. If students lack evidence in some areas, provide them with additional time to gather more evidence. This mimics the process of scientific inquiry.

In Step 2, teams begin organizing their evidence. If they collected data from on-line sources, they should use tables, graphs, or other visual strategies to make viewing the data more accessible. They should also spend time categorizing their evidence. They can use categories from the rubric such as populations, resources, lifestyles, and environmental quality of air, water, and soil. They can also create subcategories under these subjects or create categories of their own.

In Step 3, teams revisit their questions from the explore activity. They should use the evidence they have gathered to answer the questions. This starts students thinking about how to form recommendations. Have teams look over the scoring rubric again. Make sure they understand the task for making a set of evidence-based recommendations. In Step 5, students read some of the strategies that the mayor of London is proposing to reduce greenhouse emissions. This helps them get an idea of what recommendations might look like.

In Steps 6 and 7, teams discuss and then agree on a set of 3 or 4 recommendations to sustain environmental quality. Circulate as students work on this task and make sure that they use the evidence they gathered to justify their recommendations.

READING

Making London a More Sustainable City

In October 2005, representatives from 20 world cities met at the World Cities Leadership Climate Change Summit. The summit brought together city leaders to discuss climate change and how to reduce greenhouse emissions. Some of the mayor of London's strategies are outlined here.

Air quality

- Reduce traffic by charging a fee for traveling roads in central London during business hours and by improving public transportation and conditions for walking and cycling.
- Reduce emissions by targeting reductions in the most polluting vehicles and by increasing the use of cleaner fuels and vehicles.

Biodiversity

- Increase open space in new housing developments and along transport routes.
- Improve water quality and maintain wildlife habitat.

Energy

- Use less energy.
- Use renewable energy sources.
- Investigate more efficient energy production.

Water

- Install water meters in households that currently don't have them.
- Provide the public with tips on water conservation.

Waste

- Strategically build new waste management facilities and provide equal access to reuse and recycling centers (figure 16.5).

▲ **Figure 16.5 Recycling.** This photograph shows paper and cardboard packed at a recycling center. Recycling paper and cardboard reduces waste in landfills. What other measures could be taken to reduce waste?

Answers to Reflect and Connect, SE page 808

1. Responses should reflect what students learned about environmental quality from the evidence they gathered.

2a. Students should understand that without collecting evidence their recommendations would be based only on opinion. They should realize that in order to sustain environmental quality they need to know what affects environmental quality and how.

2b. Students should understand that the evidence they gathered helps them understand environmental quality issues, but the evidence does not provide a solution.

3. Be open to all occupations and professions that contribute to London becoming more sustainable. Some example professions by category include the following:
   - Air quality
     - Air quality engineer
     - Transportation engineer
     - Traffic planner
   - Biodiversity
     - Urban planner
     - City park worker
   - Energy
     - Chemical engineer
     - Mechanical engineer
     - Geologist
     - Public transportation worker
     - Public utilities worker
   - Water
     - Water system engineer
     - Public water utilities worker
     - Wastewater treatment worker
     - Hydrologist
   - Waste
     - Chemical engineer
     - Wastewater treatment worker
     - Microbiologist

NOTES:

6. Discuss with your team what recommendations you might want to consider after completing your research. Recommendations you plan to present at the conference should describe what steps could be taken to sustain Earth's environmental quality. Record your team's ideas for recommendations in your science notebook.
7. Agree as a team on a set of 3 or 4 recommendations for the Global Conference on Environmental Quality. Your recommendations
   - must be based on the evidence you gathered about environmental issues,
   - should be challenging but feasible, and
   - should reflect the relationship between human activity and environmental quality.

Reflect and Connect

Answer the following questions individually in your science notebook.

1. Describe how 1 of your recommendations would change human activities and improve environmental quality.

   Each team member should choose a different recommendation.

2. Answer Questions 2a–b about making and justifying recommendations to sustain environmental quality.
   a. How did gathering scientific evidence help you develop your set of recommendations?
   b. Can scientific evidence and technology alone solve environmental quality issues? Why or why not?

   To learn more about science and technology, read the sidebar *Science and Technology*.

SciLINKS NSTA
Go to: www.scilinks.org
Topic: sustainability
Code: 2Inquiry808a
Topic: environmental quality
Code: 2Inquiry808b

3. Recall the reading about making London a more sustainable city. Write in your science notebook a profession or occupation for each of the five categories of recommendations that would help London be more sustainable (air quality, biodiversity, energy, water, and waste).

   Be prepared to share your list of professions with the class.

NOTES:

Science and Technology

SIDEBAR

Certainly you've heard the phrase "science and technology." You see it in the news and hear it at school. And you've heard a lot about science and technology in this program. These two words often appear together. But what do we really mean by science and technology, and how does this relate to you? Are there important distinctions? You bet.

Both science and technology are vital to understanding our physical world and to solving human problems. Science begins in questions about the natural world. This is shown in the figure below. Those who use science get information by inquiring and by proposing and testing explanations about the natural world. Examples of broad fields in science include the life, physical, earth, and space sciences.

In contrast, technology stems from problems and challenges that humans face in their environment. Technology is more than shiny equipment or computers. Technology is a process of using problem-solving strategies to propose and develop solutions (see figure). Examples of technology fields include areas

▲ **Relationship between science and technology.** This diagram shows that science focuses on explaining the natural world, whereas technology centers on solutions to human problems. Both science and technology join to solve problems of society.

ELABORATE

Be Prepared

Activity Overview

This elaborate activity helps students make their final preparations for the conference. Students review and connect their questions, information, and recommendations into one coherent presentation.

Before You Teach

Background Information

Draw on your own personal experiences of making presentations to guide students at this point. In general, getting students to review the set of expectations in the scoring rubric should lead them to a stronger presentation. The scoring rubric gives students the benefit of having clear outcomes and goals ahead of their performance.

Materials

none

Advance Preparation

Think through how much guidance you want to give students. You might want to offer graph paper, poster board, and computers for word processing. If this is the case, then take time to procure these materials and have them in class.

Educational Technologies

You likely will want the students to use a computer for word processing, graphics, mathematical modeling, and simulations, all of which can enhance presentations.

As You Teach

Outcomes and Indicators of Success

By the end of this activity, students should

1. develop their portion of a team presentation, perform it for the team, and respond to feedback.

   They will demonstrate their ability by

   - reviewing the presentation requirements,
   - developing their individually assigned portion of the presentation, and
   - revising their individual segment based on team feedback.

2. receive and respond to feedback from their team.

   They will show their response by

   - presenting the full presentation within their team,
   - providing feedback to teammates based on criteria in the scoring rubric, and
   - adjusting presentations accordingly.

Strategies

Getting Started

Effective presentation is a skill that requires time and practice. Many students can collect information, but not all students know how to cull through the information and make decisions about the quality of the data. In this day of the Web, some students think "more is better." Consider reminding students how important it is to filter the information they have collected through the scientific principles they have learned. Students should be able to trace each recommendation to valid and reproducible research from reputable researchers or institutions. Remind students of the focus question stated in the introduction to the explore activity, *Pay Me Now, or Pay Me Later.*

Science and Technology, continued

of computer science, information technology, and engineering. Thus, technology complements science. Using science and technology together helps you solve different kinds of problems for society. And each can also generate engaging new questions.

The Apollo missions to the Moon are a great example of science and technology. The missions were undertaken to answer very fundamental scientific questions. These included questions about lunar geology, the origin of the Moon, moon-planet systems, and the evolution of our solar system.

Answering these questions required that we obtain rocks from the Moon. To do that, many technological challenges would have to be solved to get astronaut-geologists to the Moon, collect the lunar rocks, and return the samples and astronaut-geologists safely to Earth. Virtually all obstacles were cleared for a series of successful missions. Technologies developed and tested in the 1960s formed a foundation for the many exciting NASA missions occurring today.

ELABORATE

Be Prepared

You're moving forward on your preparations for the big conference. Your team has formed questions, collected information, reached conclusions, and is ready to present its recommendations. Each of these tasks is crucial to effective scientific communication. They represent the substance of what you want to convey about the effect of human activity on environmental quality.

Now it's time to share your findings and recommendations with a larger community of concerned scientists. To do this, your team will make a presentation at the conference. But presentations require preparation to be effective. So in this activity, you and your team will prepare for your presentation.

Materials

none

Process and Procedure

Effective team presentations demand strong team communications. This involves ensuring that each member understands his or her responsibilities, performs those responsibilities, and gets feedback from team members. You will begin by working individually and in a team to assemble a first draft of your presentation. Then you will use team feedback to improve the presentation.

Process and Procedure

In Step 1, specify how long students' presentations should last. As students are reviewing the rubric and considering Steps 1a–c, you might want to give additional examples of each form of communication. You can include other forms of communication or rename these forms. The point is to help students gain practice in representing their ideas in multiple ways and to translate among these forms of representation fluently.

In Steps 2 and 3, decide how much time to give students to prepare for their segments.

In Step 4, remind students of the importance of active listening. Part of active listening is the ability to formulate questions. Students should record their questions in their notebooks and share them with the team member who is presenting.

If time allows, and you have a sufficient number of teams to make the process worthwhile, consider adding another step at this point. Have students share their presentations with another team to help them further refine their presentations. This will allow students to work cooperatively in increasingly larger groups, and to obtain feedback in an iterative fashion. Both of these acts should result in a more polished final presentation. This layered approach to multiple forms of feedback models common business and industry practice, especially on large projects.

In Steps 5 and 6, remind students to record both what they changed based on feedback and why they changed it.

Answers to Reflect and Connect, SE pages 811–812

1. Answers will vary, but look for answers that demonstrate students' ability to make connections. For example, if a student chooses a local environmental issue, look for evidence that the student can see the bigger picture of how this local issue can affect the global environment.
2. Again, answers will vary, but look for answers that reflect the degree to which students have thought about their particular issue. Are they thinking about connections to other seemingly unrelated environmental issues? Do they want to find evidence for changes that they may predict in the environment due to the issue they are investigating?

1. Review the handout *A Meeting of the Minds Scoring Rubric* again to be clear about the goals and requirements of your presentation. To help you focus your presentation even more, consider the criteria in Steps 1a–c.
   a. The presentation will demonstrate the connection between findings and recommendations.
   b. The presentation will include 3 forms of communication:
      - Language (written reports and oral presentation)
      - Spatial representation (graphs, charts, models, demonstrations, and posters)
      - Mathematical representation (formulas, data, spreadsheets, and proofs)

   There can be some overlap of forms. For example, graphs should have labels and captions, which involve language.

   c. The presentation will last no more than 10 minutes or a time specified by your teacher.
2. Decide as a team which member will be responsible for each segment of the presentation.
3. Develop each segment of the presentation according to an agreed-upon time schedule.
4. Present your individual segment to your team, using the following team roles:
   - Listeners: Nonpresenting team members listen to the presentation and generate questions they think audience members might ask. Listeners also use the scoring rubric to evaluate this segment of the presentation.
   - Presenter: Answers questions posed by the listeners in his or her science notebook and adjusts the segment of the presentation appropriately.

   Remember that responses should be based on what you know about populations, resources, and environmental quality.

5. Meet as a team and reach consensus on what changes to make based on feedback from Step 4.
6. Record how and why you made changes to your original presentation.

   Remember, it is a good practice to record any changes to your original ideas in a different-colored pen or pencil.

Reflect and Connect

1. Answer the focus question from the introduction to the explore activity: "How is this environmental issue related

EVALUATE

A Meeting of the Minds

Activity Overview

In *A Meeting of the Minds*, your students participate in the Global Conference on Environmental Quality. Since they have been working toward the conference in a number of ways throughout the chapter, they should be well prepared. The students will take their cue from you, so to the extent that you convey the possible richness of this experience and the high expectations that you have, the more likely the conference will be a success.

Before You Teach

Background Information

None.

Materials

assorted presentation aids per team

copymaster 16.1, *A Meeting of the Minds Scoring Rubric*

TRCD

Advance Preparation

In the engage activity, you and your students discussed different ways in which conferences of this sort are organized and hosted. At that time, you began to plan for the type of conference that you wanted to host. You may have decided to confine the conference to your class or you may be planning to convene several classes together in the auditorium for a larger conference. Perhaps you have invited school and district administrators or parents and community leaders. Don't forget the local news media. They may be interested in covering the conference, so be sure to let them know when and where it is happening.

Consider contacting a local scientist to come and give the opening remarks for the conference.

As You Teach

Outcomes and Indicators of Success

By the end of this activity, students should

1. demonstrate their ability to present at a conference a coherent set of evidence-based recommendations for sustaining Earth's environmental quality.

   They will demonstrate their ability by

   - presenting a set of recommendations that is based on sound scientific evidence they collected and
   - presenting recommendations that represent a coherent package, which taken together could help sustain environmental quality.

2. demonstrate their understanding of the many interrelated aspects of sustaining Earth's environmental quality.

   They will demonstrate their understanding by

   - presenting appropriate and accurate detail about how population growth, use of natural resources, and human behavior and lifestyle potentially threaten Earth's environmental quality and
   - using presentation aids that help make a compelling case for their position.

3. demonstrate their ability to use principles of science and technology to justify their set of recommendations.

   They will demonstrate their ability by ensuring that each recommendation they present is supported by sound science and technology content.

4. demonstrate their understanding of the importance of science and technology in resolving environmental issues, but realize that science and technology alone will not resolve global challenges, and that human societies have a responsibility to act in ways that will contribute to sustainability.

   They will demonstrate their understanding by presenting their recommendations in ways that underline the responsibility that

Answers to Reflect and Connect are on TE page 811.

to global environmental quality?" Base your answer on the environmental issue that you have chosen for your presentation.

2. If you had more time to spend researching an environmental issue, what other information would you want to gather?

EVALUATE

A Meeting of the Minds

The opening day of the conference has arrived! During the next few days, think about the significance of your findings and recommendations. You interact with the environment every day of your life and make important decisions about sustaining Earth. Keep this in mind as you participate in the conference and learn from your classmates.

Materials

For the entire class

assorted presentation aids

A Meeting of the Minds Scoring Rubric handout

Process and Procedure

Scientists frequently present their ideas and recommendations to their peers (figure 16.6). You and your classmates are ready to participate in the conference for which you have been preparing during the last 2 weeks. Make the most of your experience as a conference participant.

1. Meet with your team to go over the last-minute details of your presentation. Be sure you are ready when it is your team's turn to present.

Figure 16.6 Scientist making a presentation. What are some important things to consider when making a presentation?

2. Listen to the introductory comments that launch the conference. Record the big ideas that you hear.
3. As each team presents, listen carefully to its recommendations. Record the important ideas along with the justification from science and technology for each idea the team presents.

humans have in protecting and helping to sustain Earth's environmental quality.

Strategies

Getting Started

Be sure that everything is ready for the conference; double-check with others that you may have invited to participate. Have the students help set up for the conference the day before if possible.

Process and Procedure

Materials

assorted presentation aids per team

copymaster 16.1, *A Meeting of the Minds Scoring Rubric* TRCD

In Step 1, circulate among the teams to ensure that each group is ready to present.

In Step 2, you will welcome all participants and provide the opening remarks to launch the conference. Be sure to paint a compelling picture of the importance of this type of collaboration and focused discussion of problems and solutions related to Earth's environmental quality. Your comments at this point will set the tone for the entire conference. Review the procedure for the conference and any other logistics that you want the students to attend to during the conference. As an alternative, you can arrange for a scientist to kick off the conference.

In Step 3, remind students to record the important ideas in their notebooks.

In Step 4, guide the level and quality of the questions and discussion. Make comments or redirect questions to keep the discussion at a rigorous level.

In Step 5, you might walk around the room to see how the students are scoring each of the teams. Do you see some consistency across the scores? If not, you might want to convene a short class discussion about the rubric itself.

In Steps 6–8, be sure to keep these discussions at an appropriate level for the end of the conference. The use of the criteria listed in Step 6 should help focus the discussion and keep it on track. You might want the class to develop a rubric or other system for keeping track of the level of support for each recommendation. Be sure the recommendations in Step 8 constitute a coherent set of ideas; each recommendation should complement the others.

4. When each team finishes, think about 1 or 2 questions you might have about something you heard. Participate in a brief class discussion of the group's presentation.
5. Using the scoring rubric, assign each team a score, based on what you heard.
6. When all teams have presented, participate in a class discussion of the best ideas that you heard. Use the following criteria as a guide:
   - The recommendations are based on principles of science and technology.
   - There is evidence that these recommendations have a good chance of working.
   - The recommendations are feasible.
7. At the end of the class discussion, revisit the questions that each of you asked in the engage and explore activities. Discuss as a class whether you are better able to answer these questions now than you were before you began this chapter.
8. As a class, agree on the top 3–5 recommendations from across the teams and a convincing set of justifications (figure 16.7).

Reflect and Connect

Answer the following questions individually in your science notebook.

1. If you could add 1 more recommendation to the set of recommendations that the class agreed on, what would it be and why?
2. Think about the set of class recommendations, including the one you added from the last step. What might the world look like 50 years from now if people began implementing the recommendations next year?
3. What might the situation be 50 years from now if none of these recommendations is implemented? Cite evidence to support your prediction.

▲ **Figure 16.7 Working together.** How does communicating with your teammates and class help you decide on the best recommendations?

Answers to Reflect and Connect, SE page 813

1. This question gives the students an opportunity to think beyond what the class came up with to focus on something they feel is important, but perhaps overlooked. Remember to have the students justify their answer.
2. Answers will vary depending on what issue students selected. At this point, however, you should expect students to provide a significant and in-depth answer to this question. If you see answers that lack the depth you expect, be sure to ask the students to spend more time on their answers.
3. Again, the answers will vary, but you should see evidence of a deep understanding of the principles by this point.

Use Chapter Organizers

Knowledge is more coherent if it is organized. Organized knowledge gives students a sense of the big picture. And having a big-picture view of knowledge leads to more enduring understanding.

Often, though, it is difficult for students to see the overall organization of knowledge in a unit or a chapter, especially at a glance. Because of this, *BSCS Science: An Inquiry Approach* provides students with a two-page graphic organizer for each chapter. These charts use graphic design principles to map the connections among activities and concepts. Each chapter organizer helps students see the flow of activities in a chapter within the context of important concepts. Progress from one activity to another is represented by linking questions. Thus, chapter organizers use questions to drive students' construction of the big picture—the contextualized set of conceptual relationships inherent in a topic.

Both the student book and teacher edition have chapter organizers. As you might expect, the chapter organizers in the teacher edition contain planning features to help you document your progress through the unit. The teacher version gives you a summary of each activity, the order of activities, the estimated completion time, and room for you to include your notes.

How to Use Chapter Organizers is designed to take your students through their version of the chapter organizers. These organizers give the students a sense of how each activity in the chapter is connected to the previous activity and to activities they will complete later in the chapter. The organizers include key ideas of each activity along with linking questions to show the connection between activities.

Take your students through the activity in the student version of *How to Use Chapter Organizers* so that they have a sense of the purpose and design of these organizers. Then, as you lead your students through each chapter, refer to the organizers several times as you work through the activities of the chapter. There are multiple ways to use these organizers. Here are just a few:

1. Make a "blowup" of the chapter organizer to hang at the front of your class. Do the same for the concept map that is included on the *Student Resource CD* (*SRCD*). Use colored string or chalk to indicate connections between concepts on the map and sections of the chapter organizer. Lead a class discussion to focus on these connections.

2. Use the linking questions from the chapter organizers as a pre-engage exercise to the next activity. Have students think of possible answers to the linking questions and then use collaborative learning interactions to share answers. Students record dialogue in their science notebooks.
3. Use the chapter organizer as an alternative assessment. Have students convert or translate the organizer into a short story so that the reader can recognize key concepts, linking questions, and activities. The big ideas of the chapter should be recognized as the moral of the story.

In the activity for *How to Use Chapter Organizers*, students examine many of the features of the chapter organizers as well as some features of the entire program.

1 HOW TO Use Chapter Organizers

Some of the skills you will improve this year will be your skills of organization. You know that an organized room or file system is easier to work with than one that is disorganized. Knowledge can be organized as well. You will work this year at organizing your thoughts and knowledge in a science notebook. In addition, you will learn to use the organizational tools that the student book provides. You will notice one of these tools as you look through your student book. You will see that we have included a chapter organizer at the beginning of each chapter. This organizer will help you see the big picture. Your understanding will deepen and strengthen as you see that what you have learned today connects to what you will learn tomorrow.

Work with a partner to complete the following tasks. Record your answers and thoughts in your science notebook. Organize your science notebook by including the title "using the chapter organizers."

1. Look through the table of contents of your student book and find a chapter title that most interests you. Do not turn to your chapter yet; just look at the title. Make sure that you and your partner choose *different* chapters. If you both like the same one, work out a plan to have 2 different chapters. Learning to compromise in a group is another skill you will develop this year. Complete the following tasks based on the chapter you select.
   a. Explain to your partner why you think this chapter will be interesting to you. Listen as your partner explains his or her thinking to you. Record the title of your chapter and at least 1 statement explaining why you think this chapter will be interesting.
   b. Think of as many concepts and ideas as you can that might be included in your chapter. List these concepts in your science notebook.
   c. Share your list with your partner and listen as your partner shares with you. Think about your partner's chapter selection. Can you add to his or her list of topics? Add new topics to your list that emerge during this discussion.
2. Turn to your chapter and find the chapter organizer. It is found at the beginning of the chapter. Look at it carefully. All the chapters in this book follow the BSCS 5E instructional model. The 5Es provide a structure for active learning that will have you *doing* and *understanding* science, not just reading about it. Taken together, the

The answers to the nine steps and accompanying questions are included here. This would be a good activity to begin the year.

In Step 1, students look through their books at the table of contents. Students are working in pairs, and this may be the first collaborative learning activity they have done this year. Encourage teamwork and praise groups that work well together. Students have to decide on 2 different chapters to look at. Watch for their ability to make decisions and to compromise if needed.

Students use a collaborative technique in Step 1a called *turn and talk* to explain to their partners why they are interested in the chapter they selected. Watch for students who don't participate or cannot explain why they might be interested in a particular topic. There are many topics that students should find interesting, from genetic engineering to the physics of amusement park rides. Encourage shy students to share their ideas and praise all students for their participation. You should be able to gauge your students' ability to work in small groups. They will use and develop this skill all year.

In Step 1b, student pairs think of and list concepts in their science notebooks. Accept all reasonable answers. Encourage those who have difficulty getting started by asking probing questions such as, "What does this topic make you think of?" "What would a scientist in this field study?" "What have you seen on TV or in newspapers or magazines about this topic?"

Students share with their partners and add to their lists in Step 1c. Encourage them to think about their partner's topic and to add to their lists. Make sure that they are recording their ideas in their science notebooks.

In Step 2, students identify the 5Es. The 5Es are (in order) engage, explore, explain, elaborate, and evaluate. All chapters have these 5Es. Some chapters may have more than one particular *E*, for example, 2 explore activities, or they may contain a combination such as an explore-explain activity.

In Step 3, students record their ideas about each *E*. You may want to have a more detailed class discussion at this point and use the tables describing the BSCS 5Es that are located in *Program Overview* in the teacher edition.

Accept all reasonable answers for the question in Step 4. The linking questions are designed to connect one activity to the next. The linking question is the question scientists or even students might ask after completing the current activity. The linking question supplies the learner with the reason for learning the next concept or the reason for doing the next activity.

In Step 5, students revisit the lists they made in Step 1b–c and compare them with the topics they see on the chapter organizer. They should circle the ideas they listed that appear to be addressed in the chapter, and highlight topics that appear to be addressed in other chapters of the same unit. The student book is divided into 4 units: unit 1, *Interactions Are Interesting* (chapters 2–5); unit 2, *Inside Life* (chapters 6–9); unit 3, *Moving Matter* (chapters 10–13); and unit 4, *Sustaining Earth Systems* (chapters 14–16). Students who choose chapter 1, *Investigations by Design*, have chosen a chapter designed to teach them about scientific inquiry; it is the only chapter in this "unit."

Students may say the chapter title, key ideas, or linking questions were helpful in determining the topics covered in the chapter they selected. However, the key ideas should be the most helpful.

5Es will help you build a strong understanding of science. Can you find each of the 5Es included in your chapter organizer? List them in your science notebook.

3. What do you think each *E* represents in the learning sequence? Record your ideas in your science notebook.

   Include in your answer what you think you should be doing in each activity. For example, what will you be doing in the explore activity? How will you be interacting with your teacher and with your teammates?

4. Every *E* is an activity that builds on the previous one and helps prepare you for the next one—the next *E*. Do you notice that between each activity there is a linking question? Discuss with your partner what you think the purpose of the linking question might be. Record your best ideas in your science notebook.

5. Look back at your original ideas from Steps 1b–c about the concepts you thought would be included in your chapter.
   a. Circle the ones that appear to be covered in this chapter.
   b. Look at the other chapters in this same unit. Highlight topics that will be covered in those other chapters.
   c. What feature of the chapter organizer helped you determine the topics covered in your chapter?

6. Look at another chapter organizer from your book. Discuss with your partner how this organizer can help you with your learning. Record at least 3 ways that you can use the chapter organizers to enhance your learning.

7. Look at your list. Are there things that you will do at the beginning of the chapter, during the middle of the chapter, and at the end of the chapter? Add them to your list so that you have at least 1 from each place.

8. From the chapter organizer that you chose in Step 1, record what you think is the main idea of that chapter. Try to sum it up in 1 sentence.

9. What part or parts of the chapter organizer did you use in Step 8 to write your main idea sentence? What part of the organizer helped you the most?

816 How to Use Chapter Organizers

In Step 6, students look at another chapter organizer. Students should recognize that the chapter organizer shows a path for their learning throughout a chapter. It will show where they are, where they have been, and where they are going. It gives reasons for studying the next topic through the linking questions. Students can use it to help organize their science notebooks and assignments. It summarizes the key ideas for each activity and the major concepts for the chapter to help them see the big picture. Students can also use the organizer to review what they have done in previous activities and prepare for future ones. It can also serve as a review template for their evaluate exercises.

In Step 8, students try to formulate a main idea from the chapter they chose. Students will practice this skill throughout this year. Accept all reasonable answers that are based on the information found in the chapter organizer. Encourage students to look at the complete organizer for their answers.

In Step 9, students describe the part of the organizer that helped them the most. Accept all answers that use the chapter organizer. The major concepts section should help students formulate their answers.

Use the Science Notebook

What is the best indication of student learning: a test score or evidence of steady growth over a long period? It's a loaded question. Both are important. So why doesn't documenting students' ongoing progress get the attention it should?

One reason is the perceived difficulty of assessing the daily, incremental changes in students' minds that form the evidence for growth. In *BSCS Science: An Inquiry Approach*, however, there is a well-researched and successful method for documenting ongoing learning. It is the science notebook.

The student version of *How to Use the Science Notebook* describes how to use the science notebook effectively. The version here is for you. Described in this section are strategies for you to get the most out of your students' science notebooks and to be able to assess them effectively and efficiently. Factors leading to the success of the science notebook fall into two general categories, pragmatic and philosophical.

In *BSCS Science: An Inquiry Approach*, you will use a science notebook on a regular basis. Science notebooks serve many purposes. They provide a place to record data, take notes, reflect on your progress, or respond to questions. This science notebook will become your permanent record of your work, and you will refer to it often during discussions and assessments. The more complete your science notebook is, the more valuable it will be for you.

Your science notebook should be a spiral notebook or a hardcover book that is permanently bound. (Do not use a loose-leaf notebook or a spiral notebook with perforated pages that tear out.) A notebook with square-grid (graph paper) pages will make any graphing that you do much easier.

The following sections describe the major ways in which you will use your science notebook in this program.

Recording Data

Science depends on accurate data. No one—not even the original observer—can trust the accuracy of confusing, vague, or incomplete data. Scientific record keeping is the process by which you maintain neat, organized, and accurate records of your observations and data. Use a pen to record data. Although your interpretation of the data may change, *the original data are a permanent record*. If you learn new or additional things and your thinking changes, make changes in your science notebook in a different-colored pen or pencil. That way, both you and your teacher have a record of your ongoing learning.

Keep records in a diary form, and record your name and the date at the beginning of each entry. Keep the records of each activity separate. Be brief but to the point when recording data in words. It may not be necessary to use complete sentences, but single words seldom are descriptive enough to represent accurately what you have observed or done.

Sometimes the easiest way to record data is in the form of a drawing or sketch. Such drawings need not be works of art, but they should be accurate representations of what you have observed. Place your sketches or drawings in the middle of the page, leaving room for captions, revisions, and highlights. Keep the drawings simple, use a hard pencil, and include clearly written labels. Often, the easiest way to record numerical data is in the form of a table. When you record data for counts or measurements with numbers, include the units of the measurements you used, for example, degrees Celsius or centimeters.

How to Use the Science Notebook 817

Pragmatic Issues

Pragmatic issues often limit the success of science notebooks. These issues revolve around the teacher time allotted to grading. Clearly, teachers must find ways to assess student notebooks efficiently. Some tips that address the pragmatic issues follow:

1. **Limit time spent per notebook.** On average, take no more than 3 *minutes* per science notebook. For a class of 25, that is well over an hour.
2. **Distribute grading time.** Spend no more than 2 minutes for key figures, sketches, diagrams, important *Stop and Think* answers, significant *Reflect and Connect* answers, plus answers to pivotal questions within procedural steps. For checking general completeness, notebook organization, and documentation of ongoing learning, spend 1 minute. At first, you'll require more time, but work toward these time averages. Don't let fatigue due to the time requirements of assessing science notebooks force you to discard this valuable form of formative assessment.

3. **Determine the frequency.** Pick up and grade notebooks at least every 2 weeks. More time in between increases your grading burden per class and fails to provide the needed reinforcement of proper thinking habits for your students.
4. **Decide what to grade.** Don't read everything. Use your professional judgment to select one to two key sketches, graphs, or charts; two to five *Stop and Think* or *Reflect and Connect* answers; and one to three answers to questions from procedural steps.
5. **Insist on notebook organization.** Grading goes much faster if science notebooks are organized in predictable ways. Consider enforcing the following format:
   - the date and name appear on each activity;
   - a bold double line separates days;
   - answers to questions are in different-colored pens or pencils (or highlighters set answers apart visually);
   - changes and modifications are in different-colored pens or pencils (which helps you quickly find them);
   - graphs, charts, tables, sketches, and other spatial representational forms of knowledge are placed toward the center of a new page with plenty of room for highlight comments and captions.
6. **Have a contingency plan.** What if the student
   - forgets the science notebook: Use loose paper that can be taped or glued into the notebook.
   - has special needs: Accommodate the student with the help of support staff; consider an electronic version of the science notebook.
   - loses the science notebook: Difficult situation; use professional judgment and your knowledge of the individual student to decide on fair but instructive action.

Philosophical Issues

Philosophical factors include teachers' attitudes about grading, what constitutes knowledge, and the role of teachers in teaching process skills versus content. These tips will help you with philosophical issues that arise.

1. **Determine grading categories. Narrow grading categories usually involve assigning points for every detailed response. Final scores distribute over a continuum from low to high with many steps along the way. Broad grading categories often use a check-mark system (check, check+, check–). Final scores fall into one of a few groups. Broad grading categories take less time**

Do not record your data on other papers and then copy them into your science notebook. Doing so may increase neatness, but it will decrease accuracy. Your science notebook is your book, and blots and stains are a normal circumstance of field and laboratory work.

You will do much of your laboratory work as a member of a team. Your science notebook, therefore, will contain data that other team members have contributed. Keep track of the source of those observations by circling (or recording in a different color) the data that others reported.

Responding to Questions

When you answer discussion or activity questions in your science notebook, record the date and the activity title. Then number each response. You also may find it useful to record the questions. Sometimes you will respond to questions individually and sometimes with your team; indicate whether your responses are your own or those of your team. As you are writing your responses, practice writing in complete sentences; this will help you when you synthesize and present ideas. After each answer that you write, leave a blank space where you can add questions or comments that arise as your understanding grows.

Taking Notes

Always begin with the date. Then record the source of information. Often, this is a person or a book, but it could be a video, a Web site, or a computer program. When recording notes, start each new idea on a new line. Try to group related ideas under broad headings that will help you remember the important ideas and how they are connected. Write down more than you think you will need; it is hard to make sense of a few words when you look back at them later. Include diagrams and charts to clarify ideas.

It is often valuable to take notes during team and class discussions as well as when your teacher is presenting ideas or instructions. In addition, taking notes in your science notebook as you read helps you better absorb the written information.

You can use the information in your science notebook to prepare for discussions or to review what you have learned. At times, you also will use the information that you have recorded in your science notebook to complete assessment activities.

Keeping Track of Your Questions

Often, as you read or work through an activity, a question will come to mind or you will find that you are confused about something. If you cannot talk with your teammates or your teacher right away, jot down

818 How to Use the Science Notebook

because you do not have to add up points from several items, but they seem more subjective. Select a method that suits your approach and fits into your schedule.

2. **Assess ongoing learning.** "Real-time" learning can be documented and assessed in a valid and reliable way. Science notebooks are a key source of data. Here are examples of the type of information to look for and evaluate in order to document ongoing learning:
   - **Writing.** Look for changes in grammar and syntax, the amount of writing, logical constructions in written form, the number of details included, the ability to discern important facts from surface features, and links between cause and effect. Also look for decreases in hedging, teacher-pleasing comments, and the use of imprecise terms such as "some," "a few," and "a number of."
   - **Representation of knowledge.** Flexible thinkers represent knowledge in many ways. Look for students' use of language (written and oral), mathematics (equations and logic), and dimensions (graphs and sketches). Students should demonstrate a growing ability to reconfigure what they know and understand in multiple forms and to translate fluently among these forms.
   - **Organizing knowledge.** Experts organize knowledge differently than novices do. Look for changes in the way students record, display, and annotate experiences. For example, novices tend to draw graphs too small and place them on a page in a way that prevents including highlight comments and captions. You can monitor how this and other organizational tendencies change over time.
3. **Model ongoing assessment.** Students learn from effective modeling. You can model ongoing assessment by practicing it in front of them often. During activities, for example, walk around the room and talk to small groups of students about what they are doing. Ask questions like, "How does this step connect to the focus question?" "Why did you use those labels on the graph?" or "How do the data you have so far affect your hypothesis?" After some conversation, make a note in the student's science notebook, recording how he or she showed progress.

your question or confusion in your science notebook so that you will remember to ask about it when you have the opportunity. You also may use this technique to record questions that you want to answer yourself.

Keeping Track of Your Responsibilities

Because you will use your science notebook every day in science class, this notebook is a good place to record your class assignments and responsibilities. Each day, you may want to record these in red in the upper corner of your science notebook page.

Using Your Science Notebook during Assessment

At times throughout this program, you will use your science notebook during assessments—both ongoing assessments, such as class discussions and team presentations, and more formal, end-of-unit assessments. Your teacher will collect your science notebook periodically to assess your progress. Using a science notebook for assessment will be a rewarding experience if your entries are complete, detailed, and well organized. Remember to make it easy for someone else reading your science notebook to understand what you have recorded. Use blank space to separate activities, notes, and data. This will make your science notebook easier to assess, and it will provide space for you to add new information if needed. Keep this in mind as you make entries in your science notebook.

How to Use the Science Notebook 819

NOTES:

Learning Strategies Introduction

Much of what students learn comes in the form of printed text or graphical images such as charts, tables, graphs, and diagrams. A literate student moves fluidly among these forms of information, acquiring, interpreting, and applying knowledge. Few students are born with this level of literacy. They must be explicitly taught literacy strategies (Thier, 2002).

BSCS Science: An Inquiry Approach includes research-based, effective learning strategies for day-to-day progress through each chapter. You'll better recognize each strategy and be able to use them more effectively if you read an overview of each one before the lessons begin.

Use Multiple Forms of Representation

Not every learner sees things the same way (Gardner, 1983; Eisner, 1982). We don't expect them to. But we do expect them to see the value of looking at ideas and concepts from multiple perspectives. It is a natural part of building a rich context around anything new. To encourage this, we help students learn from multiple perspectives.

Four ways broadly represent the knowledge commonly encountered in school. These ways are the linguistic, the mathematical and logical, the spatial, and the performance forms.

Learning Strategies

Use Multiple Forms of Representation

Sometimes what you're asked to do in school seems like a waste of your time. How do you evaluate whether it's worthwhile? One way is to examine the evidence. Does what you're being asked to do benefit you now and in the future?

Using multiple forms of representation for the same information is an example. That is, your teacher asks you to make a sketch of what you read, convert a line graph into an equation, or write a paragraph about lab observations. Why represent what you know in more than one way?

Generating different ways to represent knowledge helps you solve problems, enhances your memory, and improves your ability to communicate. Just think how these outcomes affect your performance in school and ultimately in your chosen profession. You can start learning now how to represent knowledge in a variety of ways. First, become aware of the common forms of representation. Second, know which situations use what forms of representation. Third, practice translating among the forms.

1. Read the table in figure H3A.1 and study the example it contains.
2. Practice generating your own tables, similar to this one, for the following scenarios.
   a. A comparison of the number of males to females in your classroom
   b. The force of wind needed to move a sailboat
   c. How fast trees grow

820 Learning Strategies: How to Use Multiple Forms of Representation

Students construct knowledge in these forms during activities such as investigations, readings, mathematical exercises, graph generation, and authentic assessments. They also encounter knowledge in these forms throughout the text. As they assimilate and process these experiences, they continue to construct a deeper understanding. Then students show what they know by representing knowledge in one of these forms.

Any overemphasis on one form over the other produces students with a narrow perspective on knowledge. Such narrowness limits students' ability to solve authentic problems, the ones they find in an increasingly complex work world. For example, a student who is asked to explain the relationship among gas volume, gas pressure under constant temperature, and the number of particles might fail if the only way he represented this relationship was in a formula he couldn't remember. But the student who could sketch a graph *and* include highlight comments with a caption (not necessarily with numbers) could pass even though he had no equation.

Good problem solvers exhibit a balanced ability to represent what they know (Eisner, 1982). That ability in turn leads to increased problem-solving capacity and transfer. On an ongoing basis, this program requires students to draw, sketch, chart, and *do* science in equal proportions to writing, formulating, and speaking. Moreover, it helps students connect the meaning of these multiple forms of representation into a coherent conceptual framework. That framework results in students with the intellectual flexibility requisite to solving today's problems.

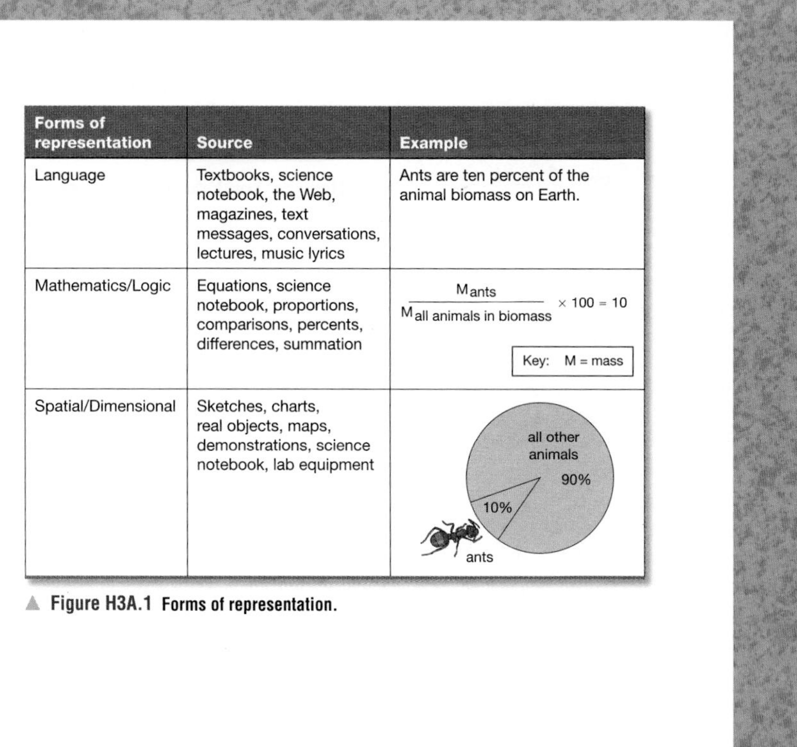

Forms of representation	Source	Example
Language	Textbooks, science notebook, the Web, magazines, text messages, conversations, lectures, music lyrics	Ants are ten percent of the animal biomass on Earth.
Mathematics/Logic	Equations, science notebook, proportions, comparisons, percents, differences, summation	$\frac{M_{ants}}{M_{all\ animals\ in\ biomass}} \times 100 = 10$ Key: M = mass
Spatial/Dimensional	Sketches, charts, real objects, maps, demonstrations, science notebook, lab equipment	

▲ **Figure H3A.1 Forms of representation.**

NOTES:

Learning Strategies: How to Use Multiple Forms of Representation | 821

Use the Think-Share-Advise-Revise (TSAR) Strategy

Talking about what you read helps you *understand* what you read (Rosenshine & Meister, 1994; Lemke, 1990). That is because reading involves input, and speaking involves generating (Wittrock, 1990), hallmarks of information processing. When we generate sentences in speech, we reconfigure knowledge based on its meaning to us. Other people listen to what we say and give us feedback on whether our explanations make sense. That feedback tells us if we need to reread or rethink. This back-and-forth process is essential to constructing understanding (Vygotsky, 1962).

BSCS Science: An Inquiry Approach asks students to read a passage or view a graph, then *turn and talk* to a classmate about the reading or graph. As you would expect, the rules of discussion are explicit and aimed at improving students' ability to acquire, interpret, and apply written and graphical information. You will see these turn-and-talk strategies as part of every aspect of the activities, including laboratory work, text questions, and team projects. These strategies form a major component of the collaborative learning and problem-solving strategies integral to this program.

In Level 2 of this program, students use a specific turn-and-talk strategy developed for students called *think-share-advise-revise* (*TSAR*). In TSAR, we assume that students do not automatically know what you mean by "share." Actually, to share effectively is a complex cognitive task requiring expertise that comes with experience and training. TSAR represents one of a family of teaching techniques used to help students learn how scientists share what they are thinking in a way that promotes learning and understanding.

Chapter 2, *Collision Course*, provides a context-rich example of the TSAR strategy. Refer to it and the student version of *How to Use the Think-Share-Advise-Revise (TSAR) Strategy* as you read the remainder of this section.

In Steps 1 and 2, students use the example from the engage activity in chapter 2, *Forces Make a Lovely Pair*, to compare each step in the TSAR strategy to a table of descriptions of student behavior for the strategy. This table is set up similar to the 5E descriptions given in *Program Overview* in the front of the teacher edition. Following are sample prompts from each stage of the TSAR strategy and hints for you to make the process run more smoothly in your classroom.

1. Sample *think* prompt: "Review silently and *think* about the connection between what you sketched and what you wrote. Look for the most important ideas you represented."

Students need explicit prompts to elicit their prior knowledge. Steps 1 and 2 begin that thinking process. But asking them to connect 2 forms that represent the same information takes it further by promoting reconfiguration of knowledge. That is, students have to examine each answer, map or associate one answer to the other, and determine if the answers are consistent. In effect, they translate between forms of representing what they know. Translation involves reconfiguring knowledge in one form to knowledge in another. As this occurs, students may note discrepancies or differences, which engender

Learning Strategies

Use the Think-Share-Advise-Revise (TSAR) Strategy

Does learning stop when your paper comes back with a grade on it? It shouldn't. The same is true for experiences *during* class. That is, you get the most out of school when you get ongoing feedback on your thinking, then revise your original ideas to reflect what you've learned. This cycle of thinking on your own, sharing your ideas, getting advice from others, and revising what you think is essential in the workplace as well as in school. Work with a partner to learn about the think-share-advise-revise (TSAR) strategy.

1. Chapter 2, *Collision Course*, has an example of using the TSAR strategy for answering a science question. Find it in the engage activity, *Forces Make a Lovely Pair* (p. 52), and read through the process.
2. Match each step from chapter 2 to the descriptions listed in the table in figure H3B.1. You'll see generalized tasks in the table and specific examples in chapter 2. The combination of the tasks and the examples provides you with why, what, and how to use the TSAR process. Use this strategy for any problem, especially in team situations.

822 Learning Strategies: How to Use the Think-Share-Advise-Revise (TSAR) Strategy

reexamination of their prior experiences. Naturally, you encourage students to work to resolve these discrepancies or differences. The end effect is each student thinking about his or her answer in a rich mix of contexts—prior personal experience and school experience.

It is crucial that students work through this *think* step individually. Ultimately, it's how individuals grow that counts as meaningful achievement. Foster a classroom climate of respect for individual thinking time. Usually, this means a few minutes of quiet reflection.

2. Sample *share* prompt: "Share your sketch with your partner and discuss each feature of it, including labels and explanations."

Model for students how to hold sketches and display them to each other as they share information about the sketches. This may seem overprescriptive, but it is not. An important part of sharing is making sure the other person can see or hear clearly. For example, act out holding a sketch in a science notebook at an angle in front of an observer and using a pencil to point out each important aspect. Mimic a minipresentation in which you explain a feature and pause for a reaction, then proceed to the next feature, and so on, until the sharing is complete. If you do not show students how to share explicitly, many will gloss over the details of the sketches. Further, verbally articulating spatial and dimensional representations of knowledge is another chance for students to reconfigure knowledge.

3. Continuation of *share* prompt: "Read your answer aloud as you wrote it."

Emphasize this step strongly. Reading aloud helps students self-diagnose problems with logic and evidence. And when you help them learn how to catch their mistakes, you effectively shrink the size of the class because you are no longer the only source of corrections. This ability to self-monitor represents an essential feature of adult, independent learning—a key goal of this program. Further, reading aloud gives you important assessment information about abilities that affect performance in science, such as reading level and information processing. Finally, reading aloud is a part of how students learn effective scientific communication through giving and receiving feedback.

4. Sample *advise* prompt: "Ask for advice on how to make either the sketch or the answer better."

Learning from feedback is very important to lifelong learning. But students may not know how to listen to advice from peers. You can help them learn by calling attention to the role of peer feedback in successful learning. Remind them that advice is one way for a peer to communicate how his or her prior knowledge applies to a situation. Thus, peer advice is a way to broaden students' perspective, an essential part of effective problem solving. Also, learning how to pay attention to peer feedback reinforces good observation skills.

Pay attention to inappropriate feedback. Examples include, "That's dumb," "No way!" and "You've got to be kidding." Let students know how common it is for scientists to disagree, but remind them that the focus should be on the thoughtful analysis of each position, not on

Step	What you do	What others do
Think	• access what you already know and understand and the skills you already have • work individually • pinpoint what you do and don't know • generate questions • document your thoughts in your science notebook	• respect your private thinking time
Share	• read aloud your thinking to a teammate • explain any diagrams, charts, or sketches • respond to requests for clarification	• listen attentively • ask questions respectfully
Advise	• offer suggestions, elaborations, or alternative explanations to what your teammate read • respond to questions about your advice	• listen to your advice without interruption • ask for clarification if needed
Revise	• record what you changed in your original answer in response to advice • record why you changed your original answer in response to advice (remember, not all advice leads to changes)	• respect your private time to revise your first thoughts

▲ **Figure H3B.1 TSAR table.**

Learning Strategies: How to Use the Think-Share-Advise-Revise (TSAR) Strategy 823

personalities, hurt feelings, and interpersonal politics.

5. Sample *revise* prompt: "Revise your work if you think your partner's understanding is better than yours."

   Show how important this step is to you by giving students time to accomplish it. But they probably are not used to having class time to consider the advice of peers by revising their science notebooks. So students may need some initial encouragement to make this step part of effective scientific communication. Be sure to inform them that such revisions are part of the evidence you use to assess their ongoing progress toward increased scientific thinking. Learning from mistakes and keeping a careful record of the what and why of mistakes or miscues is a mark of successful scientists. Consider providing different-colored pens or pencils for students to record their revisions. This will make it easier to assess the evolution of your students' learning. It will also reinforce and set apart this learning event for you and your students.

6. Sample *role-switching* prompt: "Switch roles and listen carefully to your partner."

   Monitor role-switching very carefully. It can be done after each step in TSAR or after one student has completed the entire process. Some students may not want to share after the first student has done so. This reticence can be due to low self-esteem, fundamental bashfulness, or any number of phenomena that pop up instantly in a teenager's life. Regardless of the reason, develop strategies to ensure each student's full participation in the full gamut of feedback techniques. Learning how to express what is in your mind is not easy. Starting with relatively "low-pressure" feedback environments, as with peers within an activity, helps. Eventually, students use their experiences from methods such as think-share-advise-revise as a bridge to increasingly formal forms of scientific communication such as scientific papers and public presentations.

   Some classes will need more explicit teacher modeling of the TSAR strategy than other classes. Based on your professional judgment, act out the role of each team member during each step. When you play the role of listener, for example, model a respectful, attentive posture. But also scrunch up your face or raise your eyebrows occasionally to model questioning. Explain how the person sharing must look for such body language clues and think of them as part of the feedback. Model proper techniques of expressing and working through differences in explanations. Most important, use an overhead or flip chart to model your expectations of documentation. Write an example of an initial student response and then show the revisions to students' original thinking.

Learning Strategies

Organizing information helps you see patterns and better understand text materials. There are many different kinds of organizing tables. For example, you can use tables to organize data in an investigation, to make comparisons and analogies, and to show relationships between information in reading passages. Here are 3 common organizing tables you might use.

1. *T-tables* show relationships between information listed in the horizontal rows. T-tables can have 2, 3, or even 4 columns. You can use T-tables to show similarities or differences or to organize what you know before or after you read.

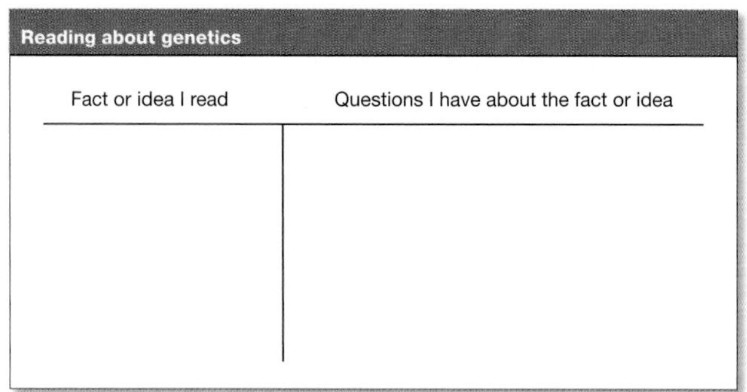

Reading about genetics	
Fact or idea I read	Questions I have about the fact or idea

▲ **Figure H3C.1 T-table example.** This is an example of a T-table you could use as you read about genetics. As you read a passage, record your ideas in a table to help you organize your thoughts.

824 Learning Strategies: How to Use and Create Organizing Tables

Use and Create Organizing Tables

Organizing and relating information helps readers form coherent meaning from text materials (Fisher, Frey, & Williams, 2002). For example, when students read a passage about cell division, they read many new words. Completing a T-table with the headings "feature" and "function" helps students pinpoint what is new to them, then connect it to the essential meaning. In this way, students learn to parse text materials into important relationships. Students represent these relationships in the horizontal rows of a T-table. Further, vertical organization can show a hierarchy of ideas—what is most important and why. Often, a third column allows students to keep track of questions they have from readings. Used in conjunction with turn-and-talk protocols, T-tables consistently increase students' ability to learn from text-based material (Block & Pressley, 2002). A variety of T-tables are used in this program: reading comprehension, prereading, analogy mapping, similarities and differences, and observation and interpretation.

NOTES:

2 *Analogy maps* are a special type of table that allows you to connect new ideas with ideas you are familiar with.

Feature of a road trip	is like . . .	aspect of scientific inquiry . . .	because . . .
A detour on the road	is like . . .	getting unexpected results from an investigation	when you encounter something you do not expect, you change the way you approach your investigation.
Circling back on a portion of the road to look for a turn	is like . . .	adjusting the design of an investigation	you return to your design and adjust it to get the results you need to answer your question.
Trying different routes on a road trip	is like . . .		
Encountering car trouble and returning home	is like . . .		
Abandoning your car on the road	is like . . .		
Starting your trip and changing the destination	is like . . .		

▲ **Figure H3C.2 Analogy map example.** This analogy map is one you could use to compare a road trip you might take with the process of scientific inquiry.

3 *Data tables* provide a place to record observations or data from an investigation. You can create graphs from the information in these tables or interpret your data directly from the tables themselves.

Material	Volume of liquid sample (mL)	Mass of cylinder with liquid sample (g)	Mass of cylinder alone (g)
Sample A	100	142.54	2.54
Sample B	100	93.21	2.54
Sample C	100	83.44	2.54

▲ **Figure H3C.3 Data table example.** Data tables are a place to record both qualitative and quantitative observations or data from an investigation. This data table shows data recorded as students conduct an investigation about density. The data can be used to make a graph or do calculations.

Learning Strategies: How to Use and Create Organizing Tables 825

Use and Create Venn Diagrams

Venn diagrams are a type of graphic organizer used to compare topics or concepts. They visually show similarities and differences. Students can use them to compare processes they have observed in an investigation or read about in a reading. Venn diagrams consist of two or three overlapping circles, each representing a topic or concept. The regions inside the circles provide characteristics of the topics or concepts. In most cases, your students will have information to put where the circles overlap—this overlap represents characteristics that both concepts have in common. However, when three circles overlap, students may not be able to find commonality for all three topics. If your students have little experience with Venn diagrams, consider providing time for them to practice by giving them a few simple topics to compare.

Make Better Observations

What does it mean to your students when you ask them to make observations? Chances are "to observe" means something different to them than it means to you. That causes problems when you expect them to link evidence to interpretations. And when they can't link evidence to interpretations, they can't do science.

Students need explicit training in how to make observations. This doesn't mean telling them exactly what they were supposed to see. Instead, you help them form good habits, all of which together lead to high-quality observations. These habits are not a step-by-step procedure. Rather, they are generalized guidelines that can be accomplished in a variety of sequences and methods.

Example

A set of observation guidelines is printed in chapter 4, *Physics Is Moving*, of the student book and are reproduced here. Read through each guideline and the commentary that follows. Add or subtract guidelines to meet your students' needs. Regardless of your student group, insist that each student improve his or her ability to make scientific observations.

Observation Guidelines

- How is each procedural step related to the focus question or problem you are investigating?

The purpose of this guideline is twofold. One, it links actions to goals. Two, it fosters self-monitoring. When students can't connect their actions to goals, they rarely attain those goals. They might collect a lot of data, but they tend not to know why they collected it. This situation makes generating meaningful interpretations very difficult. Too often, teachers resort to telling students what they were supposed to see and what they were supposed to conclude. To prevent this, teachers need to reinforce how each action students take relates to the general goal of the investigation. Teachers can reinforce the link between actions and goals by informal monitoring during the investigation. Simply asking students what a certain step has to do with the goal gives valuable instant feedback that you can apply to instructional decisions.

Learning Strategies

Use and Create Venn Diagrams

Venn diagrams are a powerful strategy for comparing topics or concepts. You can use them to visually show similarities and differences. A Venn diagram is made up of two or three overlapping circles. Each circle represents one topic or concept. The region inside each circle lists characteristics of the topic or concept. The part of the circle that overlaps contains characteristics common to both concepts. See the example in figure H3D.1. Then try creating your own Venn diagrams using Steps 1–5 to help you.

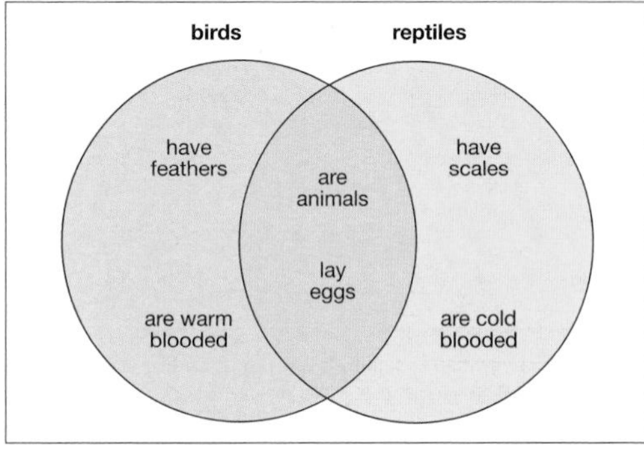

▲ **Figure H3D.1 Venn diagram comparing birds and reptiles.**

Venn Diagram Guidelines

1. Draw 2 overlapping circles like the ones shown in figure H3D.1. Use at least a half sheet of paper for the circles to give you enough room to write inside the circles.
2. Label each circle with the topics or concepts you are comparing.
3. Identify the important characteristics of the topics or concepts.
4. Write the characteristics that are specific to only 1 of the 2 topics or concepts in the circle, outside the overlapping area.
5. Write the characteristics that are common to the topics or concepts in the area where the circles overlap.

826 Learning Strategies: How to Use and Create Venn Diagrams

Linking actions to goals fosters self-monitoring (metacognition). This means students learn how to recognize and troubleshoot problems during lab activities. Students who know how each action links to an overall goal notice when results are contrary to the goal. These students tend to make corrections on their own, freeing you to work with other students.

- What is the best way to represent the initial conditions (with tables, sketches, graphs, equations, or sentences)?

This guideline, along with the next three, calls attention to documenting change. Without changes, few conceptual relationships can be discerned. Of course, the first requirement for noting change is to record the initial conditions fully and accurately. The method of representation should fit the type of information. For example, sketches using colored pencils might be best for an acid-base indicator lab in which color changes are the major observation.

- What is the best way to record the final conditions?

Use appropriate means to document the final condition of an investigation. Students should note when a change resulted in the final condition. Thus, they should record when the independent variable stopped affecting the dependent variable. Only data between the start and finish should be analyzed.

- What is the best way to record what happens *during* the investigation?

This guideline requires the most coaching from you. It is difficult for students to anticipate the most efficient configuration of data tables. They often do not think about the measurements (what type, how many, and how often) they need to make in order to accomplish the investigation's goal. Help them develop this skill by prompting them with questions like, "What would you have to measure in order to answer the focus question?" or "What should the data table look like in order to hold all the data you anticipate collecting?" As the year progresses, decrease these prompts and assess whether students have made this guideline a habit.

- How do you know that the changes you see are the result of the variable you are manipulating and not other variables?

This guideline gets at an understanding of controls. Not every investigation will have only one independent and one dependent variable. But in high school, investigations frequently do. Most students will understand the link between these two variables. But often, they don't recognize or they fail to account for variables that also change during the course of the investigation. You should expect to take extra time, especially during the first few investigations, to help students control these other variables.

- Will multiple trials increase your confidence in what you see?

Reliability is a crucial feature of sound conclusions. If an effect can be reproduced, it increases the confidence in any interpretation from the investigation. Students might complain about doing the same thing over again. Think of everyday situations in which reliability is important and help students see the connection to lab data. Then help them determine

Learning Strategies

Make Better Observations

You were not born knowing how to make good-quality scientific observations. But you can learn. Effective scientists have made good-quality observations for centuries. The following questions related to making observations are not a step-by-step procedure. Rather, they are guidelines (in the form of questions) to help you *think* your way through observations. When done well, observations help you link what you see to what it means—the very heart of science.

Observation Guidelines

- How is each procedural step related to the focus question or problem you are investigating?
- What is the best way to represent the initial conditions (with tables, sketches, graphs, equations, or sentences)?
- What is the best way to record the final conditions?
- What is the best way to record what happens *during* the investigation?

You need to focus on what is happening during the investigation, but sometimes changes occur very quickly. In these cases, you must plan carefully so that you are not distracted by writing down your data.

- How do you know that the changes you see are the result of the variable that you are manipulating and not other variables?
- Will multiple trials increase your confidence in what you see?
- What is the best way to keep a record of your initial ideas and how those ideas change during the course of the investigation?

Learning Strategies: How to Make Better Observations 827

NOTES:

efficient ways to document multiple trials in their science notebooks.

- What is the best way to keep a record of your initial ideas and how those ideas change during the course of the investigation?

Investigations produce more than data in number form. Labs force students to see nature in ways they may never have experienced. This results in a potentially powerful learning opportunity. But students can't monitor and therefore cannot be confident of their progress if they do not have a clear record of how their thinking changed. As with lab data, students should record their initial and final ideas, then compare them. Often, they will produce evidence of significant learning. In this way, students link their high-quality observations to increases in their learning.

Write Highlight Comments and Captions

Graphs, tables, charts, and diagrams are not always easy for students to interpret. Explicit strategies that include these forms of information can help broaden students' scientific literacy. Highlight comments and captions represent two such strategies.

BSCS Science: An Inquiry Approach regularly asks students to interpret information from

Learning Strategies

Write Highlight Comments and Captions

How do you make sense of charts, diagrams, graphs, and sketches? You do what scientists have been doing for centuries. You note what you see, then you try to say what it means. This process helps you connect evidence to interpretations—a hallmark of scientific inquiry.

Highlight comments help you link observations from graphs, charts, and other spatial forms of representation to possible interpretations. Captions assemble highlight comments into sentences that form a coherent paragraph. This paragraph tells the story of the graph, chart, or sketch and communicates the "executive summary" of the essential understandings displayed. The combination of highlight comments and captions helps you communicate scientific information with increasing effectiveness, improving your performance and deepening your understanding of the natural world.

Suppose you investigated the uptake of a nutrient by a tree over 24 hours. How would you make sense of the data? Follow the steps in figure H3F.1 and use them as a general guide for any graph, chart, diagram, or sketch you make.

828 Learning Strategies: How to Write Highlight Comments and Captions

graphs and charts by answering two highlight questions: "What do I see?" and "What does it mean?" Students answer these questions *on their graphs* near a trend line or key information. In this way, students make physical and conceptual connections between graphical information and interpretation (Sweller, 1988). They accomplish this by linking highlight comments to graphical information, thus building cause-and-effect relationships. From these relationships, they are able to construct a meaningful caption.

The student book requires students to write captions under each graph, chart, or diagram they generate. Captions help students assemble highlight comments into a coherent, short paragraph that explains what is important in the figure. In effect, the combination of highlight comments and captions is a reverse literacy strategy compared to T-tables. That is, with T-tables, students reconfigure what they know from text into organized structures or tables; with highlight comments and captions, students generate meaning by shifting from dimensional structures (graphs, charts, and tables) to text. The built-in, back-and-forth process among these various strategies makes for more literate, intellectually flexible students.

NOTES:

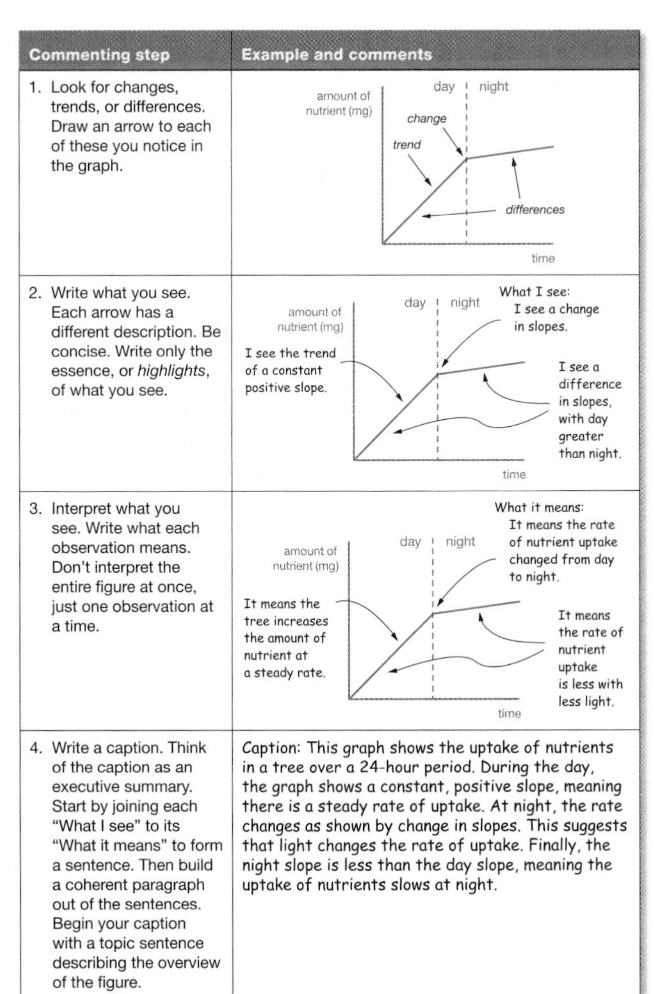

Commenting step	Example and comments
1. Look for changes, trends, or differences. Draw an arrow to each of these you notice in the graph.	amount of nutrient (mg); day; night; change; trend; differences; time
2. Write what you see. Each arrow has a different description. Be concise. Write only the essence, or *highlights*, of what you see.	amount of nutrient (mg); day; night; What I see: I see a change in slopes. I see the trend of a constant positive slope. I see a difference in slopes, with day greater than night. time
3. Interpret what you see. Write what each observation means. Don't interpret the entire figure at once, just one observation at a time.	amount of nutrient (mg); day; night; What it means: It means the rate of nutrient uptake changed from day to night. It means the tree increases the amount of nutrient at a steady rate. It means the rate of nutrient uptake is less with less light. time
4. Write a caption. Think of the caption as an executive summary. Start by joining each "What I see" to its "What it means" to form a sentence. Then build a coherent paragraph out of the sentences. Begin your caption with a topic sentence describing the overview of the figure.	Caption: This graph shows the uptake of nutrients in a tree over a 24-hour period. During the day, the graph shows a constant, positive slope, meaning there is a steady rate of uptake. At night, the rate changes as shown by change in slopes. This suggests that light changes the rate of uptake. Finally, the night slope is less than the day slope, meaning the uptake of nutrients slows at night.

▲ **Figure H3F.1 Steps for writing highlight comments and captions.**

Learning Strategies: How to Write Highlight Comments and Captions 829

Use the *Learn from Mistakes (LFM) Protocol*

Mistakes are information. But many students have been conditioned to think mistakes reflect something negative about them. A scientific view of mistakes suggests that they represent understanding in process. That is, mistakes help us learn. But how do we teach students how to learn from mistakes?

Like many complex cognitive skills, learning from mistakes requires explicit instruction for most students (Bruer, 1994). *BSCS Science: An Inquiry Approach* helps you teach this important, lifelong skill to students by making learning from mistakes a natural part of evaluations.

The *Learn from Mistakes (LFM) Protocol* used in this program is particularly effective with conceptually oriented, multiple-choice test questions, the kind often used in various high-stakes tests. The *LFM Protocol* helps students perform better on these kinds of tests without forcing you to "teach to the test" (Pinkerton, in press). The procedure uses the common sense steps of (1) representing the original question in an alternative way, (2) identifying the mistake, (3) describing the conceptual reason it was wrong, and (4) generating the correct solution. In conjunction with other cognitive skill techniques, the *LFM Protocol* allows you to teach by using inquiry methods and still meet the content demands of state and national standards.

In this program, students learn the *LFM Protocol* early so that you can build on its effectiveness when you opt for constructing tests using our test bank questions. This way, you foster student use of active learning and simultaneously enhance their ability to take an important type of test.

NOTES:

Learning Strategies

Use the *Learn from Mistakes (LFM) Protocol*

School isn't just a place to deposit right answers. Sometimes we make mistakes. In fact, most humans make mistakes when they try to learn something, especially when the subject is difficult or new. When you learn to identify and explain what's incorrect about a wrong answer, you have a better chance of avoiding that mistake next time.

The *Learn from Mistakes (LFM) Protocol* was designed to help you learn from wrong answers. You will use it after you take certain tests. For each of the questions you missed on the test, perform the following steps. If you do, you can earn up to 50 percent of the difference between your raw percentage score and 100 percent. Be sure to write your raw percentage score at the top of the test along with a list of the numbers of the questions you missed.

Learn from Mistakes Protocol

1. Represent the original question in a different way than it was represented on the test. For example, if the question was mostly words, represent it as a sketch. If it was mostly a sketch, represent it in words. When you use words, paraphrase the question in your own words. Do not copy the question word for word. Label any sketch with all the variables, especially the unknown. If the problem mentions any change in condition, then show a before-and-after sketch.
2. Identify and explain the mistake you made in the answer you selected. Focus on explaining any conceptual misunderstanding. When you explain what is incorrect, show how the misconception would lead to a contradiction with what you see in nature. Explanations like, "I read the problem wrong" and "I pushed the wrong button on the calculator" will receive no credit.
3. Show the correct solution or answer. When necessary, show all governing equations, first in symbol form, then followed by substitution with number values. Always place proper units and labels on answers. Include why the answer is reasonable.

830 Learning Strategies: How to Use the *Learn from Mistakes (LFM) Protocol*

NOTES:

Solve Problems

Many times students get "stuck" and cannot get their brains going to solve a problem. This can happen when they are trying to solve a math problem, answer a question, or manipulate lab equipment. *How to Solve Problems* gives students guidelines to get going when they are trying to solve problems.

Learning Strategies

Solve Problems

Humans aren't born knowing how to build dams, determine why a baby is crying, or understand when *i* comes before *e*. We have to learn how to solve these problems. That's one of the primary benefits of school. You learn how to solve problems.

Every problem seems different. But successful problem solvers use a general approach that works for a large variety of everyday and school problems. Read the following problem, then learn how expert problem solvers find a solution. Try to use this approach with the next problem you're asked to solve. An example follows.

Problem-Solving Guidelines

1. *Read the problem.* Often, reading the problem aloud helps you to understand what the problem is asking you to do.

   Example problem: You push a 20-kilogram (kg) box across the floor at 3.0 meters per second (m/sec) with a constant force of 10 newtons (N). What force does the box exert on you?

2. *Adjust your mind-set.* Your attitude toward problem solving matters. The brain that thinks, also feels. Get rid of fears of failure or incompetence. Don't allow resentment or anger to cloud your thinking.

   Example mind-set statements to avoid: "I can't do science, so I'm not going to try." "I never get these right. I give up." "I'll never use this. Why should I do the problem?" "I hate not knowing what to do, so I'm not going to do it."

3. *Sort the problem.* Read the problem and use your prior experiences to determine what you know and don't know in the problem. This step clears your mind so that it can focus on the important features of the problem. It starts you thinking about the real question, not the things that distract you from the solution. The following table is an example of a way to organize your thoughts.

NOTES:

What I know, understand, or assume	What I don't know or understand
I pushed with 10 N force.	How does the box exert a force?
The box has a mass of 20 kg.	How do I find out the amount of box force?
The velocity is 3.0 m/sec.	Why is the box force "pushing back" on me?
The box moves in the same direction as the push and doesn't leave the floor (my assumption).	

▲ **Figure H3H.1 Problem-solving table.**

4. *Represent the problem.* Translate what you know and don't know into some form other than writing. Sketches, graphs, charts, and lists are examples. Be sure to transfer the items from your problem-solving table to the representation.

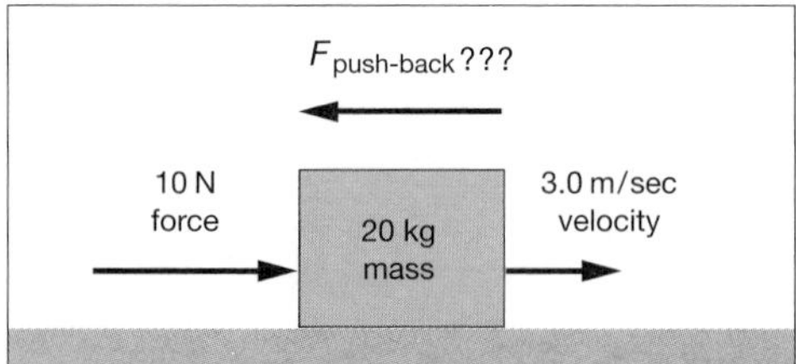

▲ **Figure H3H.2 Example representation of forces on mass.**

5. *Apply a strategy.* Expert problem solvers use a variety of methods, not just one. Successful methods include applying key concepts, using logic, trying to guess and then check, finding a pattern, working backward, and acting it out. Don't let yourself get stuck! If one method isn't working, try another.

   Example application of the key concepts to the strategy: "I remember learning that all objects push back if you push on them. That makes me think of Newton's third law—forces come in pairs that are equal in size and opposite in direction. So if I push with 10 N, that means the box pushes back with 10 N. The velocity isn't important in the problem."

832 Learning Strategies: How to Solve Problems

NOTES:

6 *Check for reasonableness.* Build confidence in your answer. Check it against your everyday experience or scientific theory. If there's a contradiction, then repeat the problem-solving steps as needed.

Example: "I feel something when I push on a box or a wall. That must mean the object pushes back. I remember that a net force causes acceleration. Since the box has a constant velocity, the net force must be zero. That means the push-back force has to be equal to my force. If I thought my force was greater, then the box would accelerate, which contradicts the problem statement."

Learning Strategies: How to Solve Problems | 833

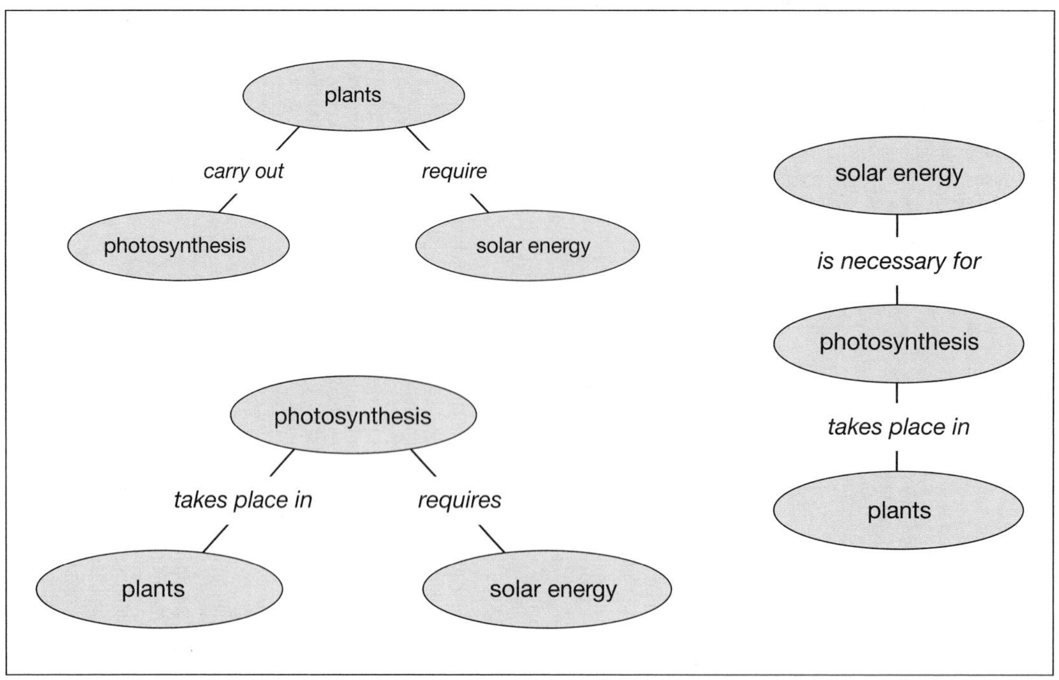

Figure H4.1 Simple concept maps.

Construct a Concept Map

Adapted from BSCS. (2006). *BSCS biology: An ecological approach* [Green Version] (10th ed.). Dubuque, IA: Kendall/Hunt, p. T27.

Success in learning depends on the motivation and effort of each student. No method or process alone can guarantee meaningful learning; the students themselves must make the effort. Concept mapping is a tool that can help students learn by building on what they already know.

Concept maps demonstrate meaningful relationships between concepts through propositions. A concept is a mental image, such as plant, photosynthesis, or solar energy. A proposition consists of two or more concepts linked by words in a phrase or thought. The linking words show how the concepts are related. In developing a concept map, concepts and propositions are linked in a hierarchy, progressing from the more general and inclusive concepts at the top to the more specific at the bottom. The three concepts mentioned above could be linked in several ways (see example in figure H4.1).

Concept maps are tools that help you organize ideas in a way that shows the relationships among them. There is no one right concept map for a body of information. But together, the concept words, connecting lines, and linking words should be an accurate representation of the content. To create a concept map, follow these steps.

Concept Map Guidelines

1. Identify the major concept that you will map. Then list several words or phrases that are important to understanding this concept. These should be words or phrases that identify parts of your major concept, such as parts of a system, a key idea, or an important process.
2. On a new page in your science notebook, write the major concept that you will map at the top of the page and draw a box around it. Arrange the related words or phases below this box. Arrange these words so that the bigger ideas are near the top and the more specific ideas are near the bottom. Draw boxes around these words as well.
3. Draw lines between the boxes to show relationships between the concept words. Lines can crisscross to show complex relationships.
4. Label the lines with linking words that describe the relationships.

Study the sample concept map in figure H4.1 of AIDS concept words, connecting lines, and linking words on the map.

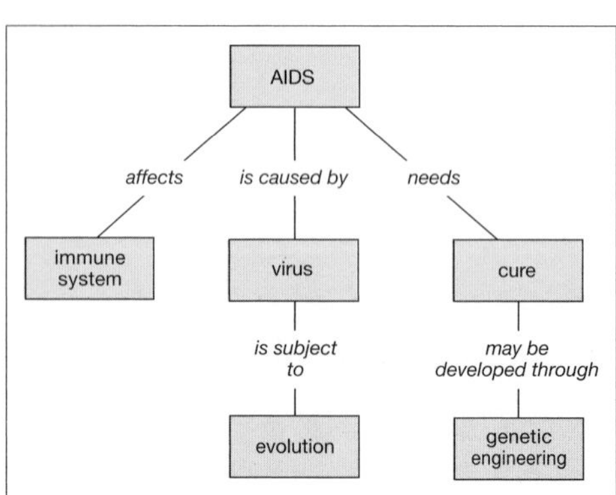

Figure H4.1 AIDS concept map.

834 How to Construct a Concept Map

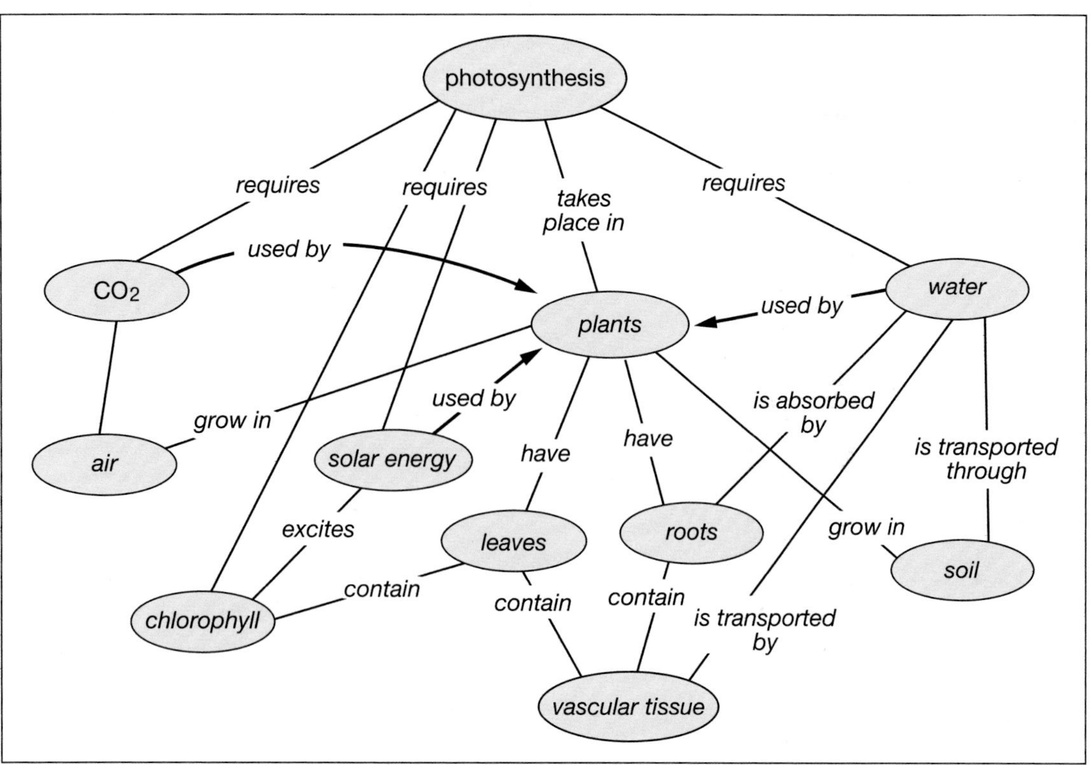

Figure H4.2 Complex concept map about photosynthesis.

As much as possible, links should be functional rather than descriptive (for example, "plants *use* energy" rather than "plants *such as* trees"). Using these three concepts, it is possible to construct a useful concept map with the addition of a few related concepts, such as leaves, chlorophyll, water, air, carbon dioxide, roots, soil, and vascular tissue (see figure H4.2).

There is no single correct way to develop or use a concept map. You may choose to use a concept map to see what your students already know about a concept. Or you may use it as a review of concepts or as an assessment. In *BSCS Science: An Inquiry Approach*, concept maps are used in several different ways and you are free to add them whenever you see fit.

The student version of *How to Construct a Concept Map* describes a simple, step-by-step method for constructing concept maps. As you assess student concept maps, look for meaningful connections and linking language. Note the choices students make for the most general and inclusive concept. Is it the big idea of the chapter? Or have they selected a specific concept? Students should be able to explain their maps and add details in their discussion. In this way, you can assess their understanding of the concept.

Improving Math Skills

Use Graphs, Measure Slopes, and Estimate Uncertainty

Do you like sports? Do you follow how certain teams or players do in football, baseball, or basketball? Or do you note how the price of music CDs or snack foods changes? Perhaps you need to show results from an investigation in a business, science, or math class.

For these and other cases, it is important to be able to show observations or data in graphs and plots. This skill helps you show a bigger picture of trends in data. Similarly, you also need to be able to read and interpret a few basic types of charts and graphs. This is true for many professions and for fields besides science.

The Basics: Labels and Limits

For most graphs, you typically show a variable across the bottom of the graph. This direction of the graph is called the *x-axis*, or *horizontal axis*. The amount that this variable changes is shown in a horizontal direction. The amount that a variable changes in the vertical direction is shown on the *vertical axis*, or *y-axis*. The axes have these names because you often plot data points with x and y values. The data points are also called the *xy coordinates*, written as (x,y). Examples of this follow.

An important next step in plotting a group of data is deciding the limits for the x-axis and the y-axis. To do this, examine your data and write down the high values and the low values for the x and y variables. Your axes must extend a little bit beyond the highest number, typically about 10–20 percent further. For a variable you measured, the difference between the high value and the low value is called the *spread*, or w. Starting the x- and y-axes at the value of zero is useful, depending on the data you are plotting.

You will see examples where the x-axis represents a category of a thing. The section titled *The Bar Graph* shows this. The type of thing is on the x-axis, while the amount of each thing is shown on the y-axis.

Let's look at examples of types of graphs that you will use in science and other fields.

Improving Math Skills: How to Use Graphs, Measure Slopes, and Estimate Uncertainty 835

NOTES:

Improving Math Skills

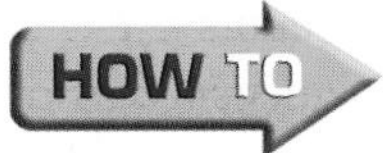

Use Graphs, Measure Slopes, and Estimate Uncertainty

All of the information for this *How To* appears in the student version.

The *xy* Plot

The *xy* plot is a simple plot where pairs of *xy* data are plotted as data points in a graph. Sometimes people call an *xy* plot a scatter plot. As you will see, this name really isn't appropriate because the data can define very straight lines (correlations) rather than scattered points.

For example, the table in figure H5A.1 shows the population densities of two kinds of squirrels that live in the ponderosa pine forests in northern Arizona. The population density is the number of squirrels counted for an area 100 × 100 meters, about the area of two soccer fields. By examining the table, you can quickly see that red squirrels are more common overall than Kaibab squirrels in these forests. Note the shading on the high and low values in the table. You can see that the spread, w, for the red squirrel is about 1.1 (= 1.38−0.31) and the spread for the Kaibab squirrel is about 0.23 (= 0.26−0.038).

Red squirrel	Kaibab squirrel
0.3685	0.0844
0.4955	0.1931
0.5317	0.1083
0.4739	0.0993
0.9713	0.1671
1.0529	0.1263
1.3779	0.2607
0.3126	0.0657
0.3770	0.0377

▲ **Figure H5A.1 Data on red and Kaibab squirrels.**

The values in the table help you decide the limits for the graph. You have some options, but the values of $x = 1.6$ and $y = 0.4$ work well for plot limits in this example.

The *xy* plot in figure H5A.2 helps you see relationships much better than the data table. The *xy* plot shows clearly that as the number of red squirrels

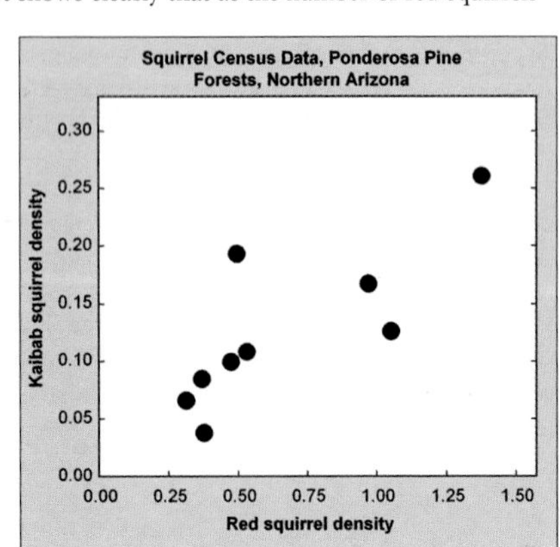

► **Figure H5A.2 Plot for red and Kaibab squirrels.** *xy* plot showing the relationship between the density of red and Kaibab squirrels in northern Arizona ponderosa forests.

836 Improving Math Skills: How to Use Graphs, Measure Slopes, and Estimate Uncertainty

NOTES:

increases, the number of Kaibab squirrels also increases. We say that such data show a *correlation* between red and Kaibab squirrel populations. But why would that be? After viewing these data, a biologist might be interested in further exploring the factors that might cause the number of red and Kaibab squirrels to change together. In Level 1 of *BSCS Science: An Inquiry Approach*, you actually learn about the culprit behind why the numbers of red and Kaibab squirrels are correlated in these ponderosa forests.

Determining the Slope

An important feature of *xy* plots is that they show relationships between pairs of *x* and *y* values. When *xy* pairs define a line, you can calculate the slope to find out how much the *y* value changes for each change in the *x* value. You are probably familiar with this as rise over run, or $\frac{\Delta y}{\Delta x}$. When the variable on the *x*-axis is time, slope is very important because it gives you a rate of change. You have seen that this is part of calculating velocities.

Take an example of a car. You have a record of the total distance that the car has traveled at certain points in time. The data are shown in the graph in figure H5A.3. For example, after about 3 hours (hr), the car has traveled about 190 miles (mi). On average, what is the velocity of the car?

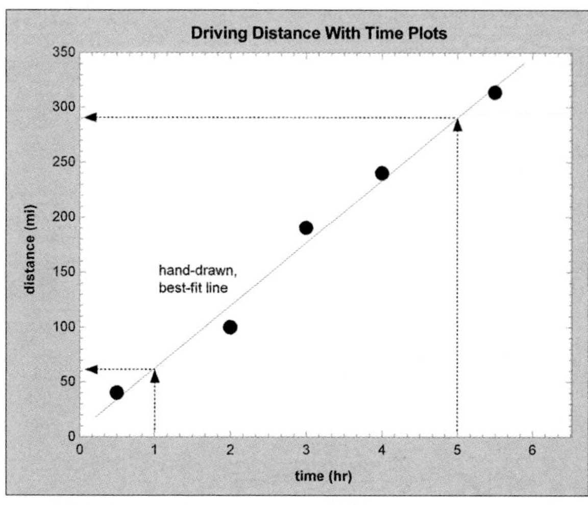

▲ **Figure H5A.3 Driving distance with time plots.**

Improving Math Skills: How to Use Graphs, Measure Slopes, and Estimate Uncertainty | 837

NOTES:

You can determine the average velocity by finding the slope using Steps 1–5.

1. Draw a line that goes as closely as possible through the points.
2. Pick any 2 values on the x-axis, even if they do not have actual data points. You can select values of 1 and 5 hr from the graph in figure H5A.3.
3. Project these points up to where they intersect the best-fit line that you have drawn.
4. Read the y-axis value where the x-axis intersects the slope. By doing this, you obtain the xy coordinates of 2 locations on the line. You can show these locations in a T-table or designate them as x_1,y_1 and x_2,y_2.
5. You calculate the slope with a series of points on the line. By being careful to keep units for the x- and y-axes, this example shows that slope also tells you velocity when time is on the x-axis.

$$slope = \frac{\Delta y}{\Delta x} = \frac{(y_2 - y_1)}{(x_2 - x_1)}$$

$$= \frac{(290 - 61)\text{ mi}}{(5 - 1)\text{ hr}} = \frac{229\text{ mi}}{4\text{ hr}} = 57.3\,\frac{\text{mi}}{\text{hr}}$$

You'll want to remember a few extra points. First, the slope, $\frac{\Delta y}{\Delta x}$, is a rate when the change in the denominator of the slope, Δx, is time. For example, the car's velocity was a rate with units of miles per hour. Second, at times you can draw a best-fit line, but keep in mind that not all physical relationships are linear. You'll see a nonlinear example using radioactivity in the next section, *The Time-Trend Plot*. Other examples in this program use acceleration, population growth, erosion of mountains, and cyclical changes. Thus, slope is only valid for lines, or nearly linear relationships.

The Time-Trend Plot

The *time-trend plot* is a kind of xy plot where the x-axis has the units of time. These types of plots are used for testing whether a variable changes in a predictable way as a function of time. The measured variable is shown on the y-axis, with time on the x-axis.

838 Improving Math Skills: How to Use Graphs, Measure Slopes, and Estimate Uncertainty

NOTES:

Take records of monthly temperatures in Denver, Colorado, for example. Figure H5A.4 shows temperature data for 5 years from 2000–2004. Temperature is on the *y*-axis, with year and month on the *x*-axis. The bold line shows the average monthly temperature. This line is bound by the average high temperature (the average of daily high temperatures for the month) and the average low temperature (usually the average of daily low temperatures for the month). The plot shows annual temperature cycles. Moreover, the graph shows differences among the years.

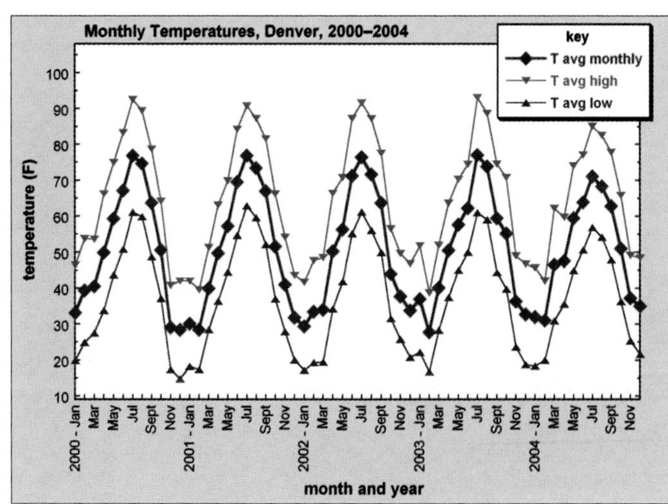

Figure H5A.4 Temperature plot for Denver, Colorado.

Improving Math Skills: How to Use Graphs, Measure Slopes, and Estimate Uncertainty 839

NOTES:

Another useful type of *xy* plot is called a "double *y*" plot. This plot uses both the left and the right *y*-axes to show the values for two variables against a common variable on the *x*-axis. Double *y* plots are useful for time trends, as shown in figure H5A.5 for temperature and rainfall over 5 years in Denver. (Note that low rainfall in winter correlates with snow.)

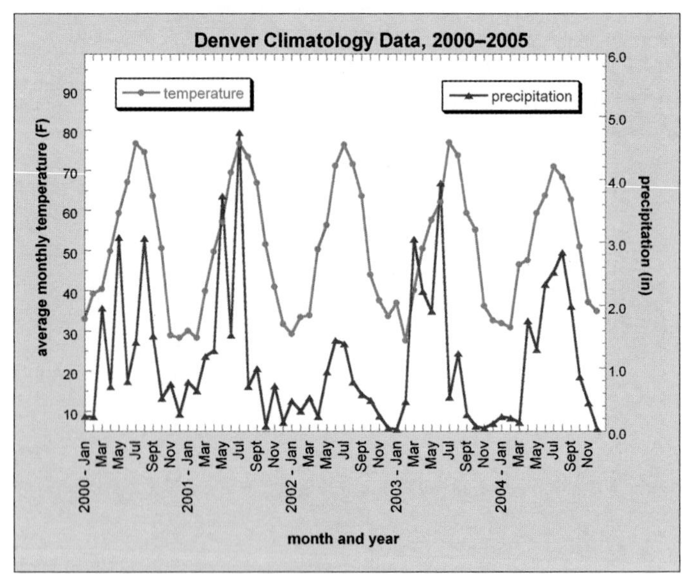

▲ **Figure H5A.5 Denver temperature and precipitation using a double *y* plot.**

The *xy* graph can also be used to show another technique for graphing. Often, we use a regular scale for tick marks on the axes. These plots are *linear.* At other times, the major tick marks on the axes are compressed and show factors of 10. Usually, these axes denote a logarithmic pattern. We call these *log* axes.

Consider a nuclear disaster. A product of nuclear reactions with the element uranium (U-235) is radioactive atoms of strontium-90 (Sr-90). Authorities have been concerned about radioactive Sr-90 because it is similar

840 Improving Math Skills: How to Use Graphs, Measure Slopes, and Estimate Uncertainty

to calcium and it lodges rapidly in the bones of humans. Human bodies use calcium for bones. Radioactive atoms of Sr-90 in your bones are not good.

The mass of radioactive Sr-90 in a sample decreases by one-half (50 percent) in about 30 years (28.8 years, to be exact). This is the *half-life* of Sr-90. The table in figure H5A.6 shows that starting with an initial mass of 100 grams (g) of Sr-90, the mass of Sr-90 decreases by half, or 50 percent, every 30 years.

The data from the table are much easier to see and examine in a graph. For every 30 years that pass, the mass of Sr-90 decreases by about half. For example, after 60 years (two half-lives), only about 25 percent of the initial Sr-90 atoms remain. It appears from the plot in figure H5A.7 that the Sr-90 is gone after about 240 years. But on this linear scale, how would you tell if amounts still existed that were too small to show up on this graph? Even a gram or less of Sr-90 can be a health hazard.

Years	Mass of Sr-90 (g)
0	100.0000
30	50.0000
60	25.0000
90	12.5000
120	6.2500
150	3.1250
180	1.5625
210	0.7813
240	0.3906
270	0.1953
300	0.0977
330	0.0488
360	0.0244
390	0.0122
420	0.0061
450	0.0031
480	0.0015
510	0.0008
540	0.0004
570	0.0002
600	0.0001

▲ **Figure H5A.6 Sr-90 decay table.**

Improving Math Skills: How to Use Graphs, Measure Slopes, and Estimate Uncertainty 841

NOTES:

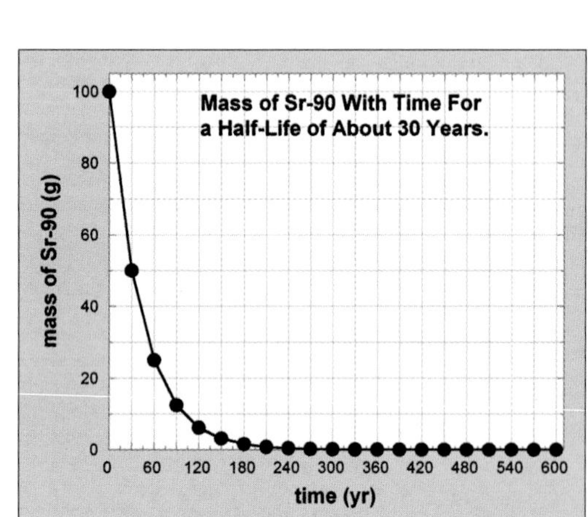

▲ Figure H5A.7 Linear plot of Sr-90.

You would use a log scale on an axis in what's called a *log plot*. In a log plot, the scale of the *y*-axis is modified so that increments are divided for each factor of 10. In general, values increase from 0.01, 0.1, 1.0, 10, 100, 1,000, and so on.

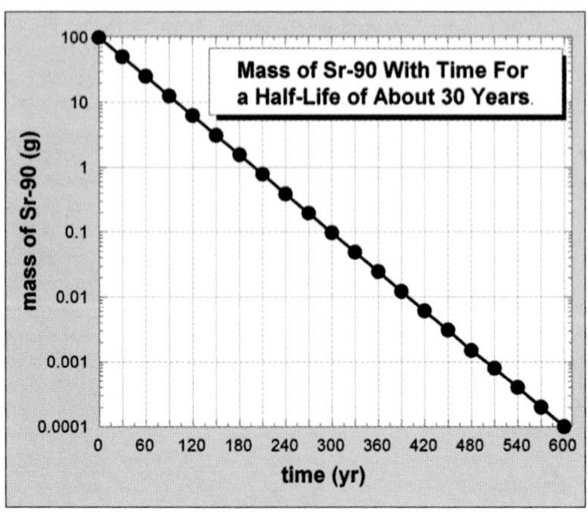

▲ Figure H5A.8 Log plot of Sr-90.

842 Improving Math Skills: How to Use Graphs, Measure Slopes, and Estimate Uncertainty

A key feature of the log plot is that the *y*-axis never goes to zero. Also, a value halfway between factors of 10 is roughly three, compared with five (between 0 and 10) on a linear scale. The graph in figure H5A.8 shows the same Sr-90 data in a log plot.

The Bar Graph

Bar graphs show the values or frequencies (on the *y*-axis) as a function of categories of things (on the *x*-axis). The *x*-axis does not have a numeric scale, either linear or log.

How could we show the frequency by month of tropical storms or hurricanes for the Atlantic Ocean in 1998? Bar graphs are perfect for this. Figure H5A.9 shows that for 1998, tropical storms occurred from July to September, with hurricanes occurring from August to November. Hurricanes also had a pronounced peak in September. Given such data, a scientist could then examine other years to test whether the pattern applies to those years.

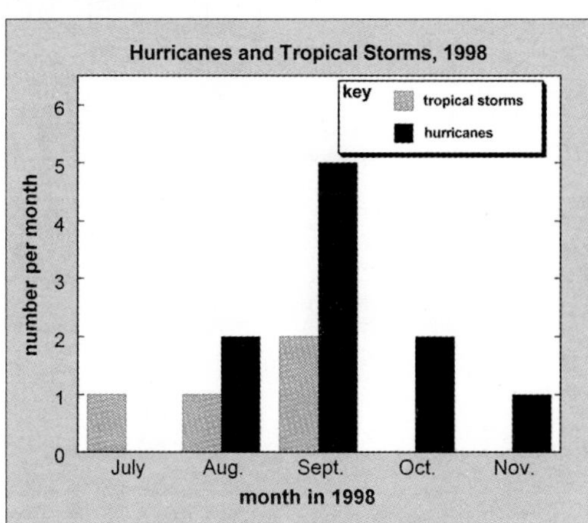

▲ **Figure H5A.9 Hurricanes and storms bar graph.** This bar graph shows the frequency in 1998 of tropical storms and hurricanes in the Atlantic Ocean.

Improving Math Skills: How to Use Graphs, Measure Slopes, and Estimate Uncertainty 843

NOTES:

The Histogram

Histograms are another type of graph. They show how often a result occurs. Let's take an example showing scores in geology class. The following histograms show the scores for 27 students on a final mapping project for a geology class. The first histogram (figure H5A.10) shows compartments, or *bins*, where the scores are tallied. Bin sizes of two and five are shown for the same set of scores. The average score is 88.1, which falls in the bar with the highest value in figure H5A.10. The histograms show the *variability* of data about the mean.

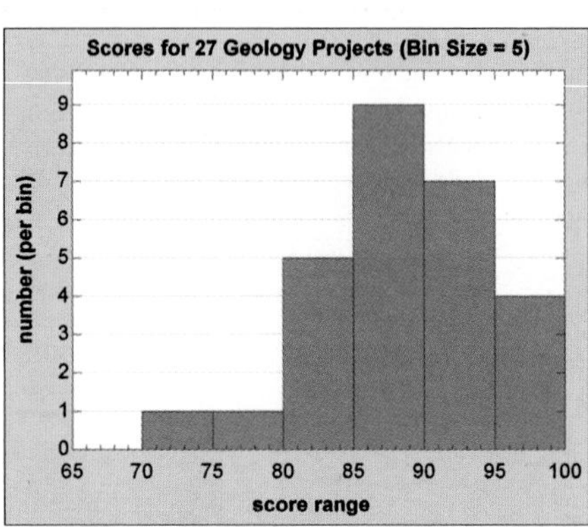

► **Figure H5A.10 Geology scores histogram where bin = 5.** This histogram shows scores for 27 geology projects with a bin size of five.

Scores for 27 Geology Projects (Bin Size = 2)

number (per bin)

0 1 2 3 4 5 6

70 72 74 76 78 80 82 84 86 88 90 92 94 96 98 100

score range

► **Figure H5A.11 Geology scores histogram where bin = 2.** Histogram of scores for 27 geology projects with a bin size of two.

844 Improving Math Skills: How to Use Graphs, Measure Slopes, and Estimate Uncertainty

NOTES:

For comparison, the second histogram (figure H5A.11) shows the same scores (n = 27) using a finer bin size of two. The result is similar, but shows two distinct peaks on each side of the mean of 88.1. You may wish to test different bin sizes to show important points in a histogram that you wish to make.

Note several things about histograms. In the histogram where the bin size equals five, values are distributed about a peak in the center. Sometimes this is called a *bell-shaped curve*. This happens when the number and positions of observations to the right and to the left of the peak are approximately equal. You might see a pattern like this by plotting a histogram of the heights of all students in your class. Your graph might have a peak value around 5.5 feet (ft), with a smattering of values in bins above and below 5 ft, 6 inches.

The key to making histograms is to first record your data or observations in a long column. Then decide the size of your bins. Finally, tabulate how many values in your column fall in each bin. Following these suggestions will help you successfully plot your histogram.

The Pie Chart

Another way to represent measurements or data is with a *pie chart*. This type of graph is called a pie chart because categories are spread around a circle, rather than along an x-axis, and look like slices of pie. The amount per category is given as a percentage of a total. Your teacher can show you how to take percentages for categories and divide them proportionately into a circle of 360 degrees.

Consider the human body. You may have heard statements such as, "Most of the human body is water." But what elements are in the human body? The pie chart in figure H5A.12 shows clearly that we are about 92 percent oxygen, carbon, and hydrogen.

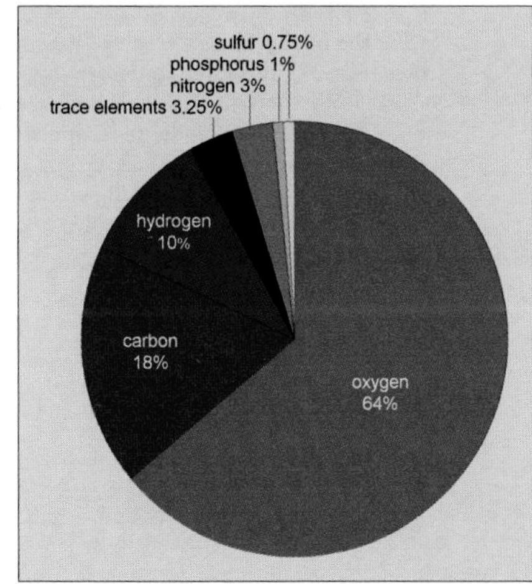

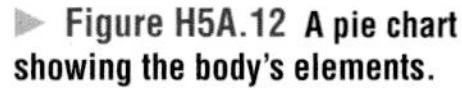
Figure H5A.12 A pie chart showing the body's elements.

NOTES:

Showing Uncertainty (or Error) in Measurements

A good experimental design often requires that you repeat a measurement several times. Because experiments are not perfect, it is unlikely that you will get the same exact measurement in each trial. An average, $\bar{x}$ or "mean," is one way to estimate the actual value from your measurements. You are used to calculating averages. But how would you show the variability of your measurements around that mean? There are several ways to do this.

One way is to show all measured values around the average. Consider the scores on the final project in the geology class from the section *The Histogram*. The plot in figure H5A.13 shows all 27 student scores, along with a large symbol for the mean. For comparison, individual scores with means are plotted for two prior assignments (a quiz and a midterm) in that geology class.

A second way to represent all measured values is to calculate an indicator of uncertainty around the average. This is a quick way to estimate the standard deviation, another term that you might have heard. First, calculate the spread, w, between the high and low values. Next, to estimate the uncertainty (or error), e, divide the spread by the square root of the number of measurements, n.

$$e = \frac{w}{\sqrt{n}}$$

For the final project, the spread is $w = (98.3 - 73.1) = 25.2$. For 27 scores ($n = 27$), this gives an uncertainty of ± 4.8. The $\pm$ sign shows that the uncertainty in scores extends both above and below the mean. This estimate of uncertainty indicates that about 60–70 percent of the scores will have values bracketed by $\bar{x} \pm e$. With the geology final projects, this is 88.1 ± 4.8. (That is, about 60–70 percent of the scores fall in a range from 83.3 to 92.9.) This can also be shown graphically by error bars on the graph in figure H5A.14.

NOTES:

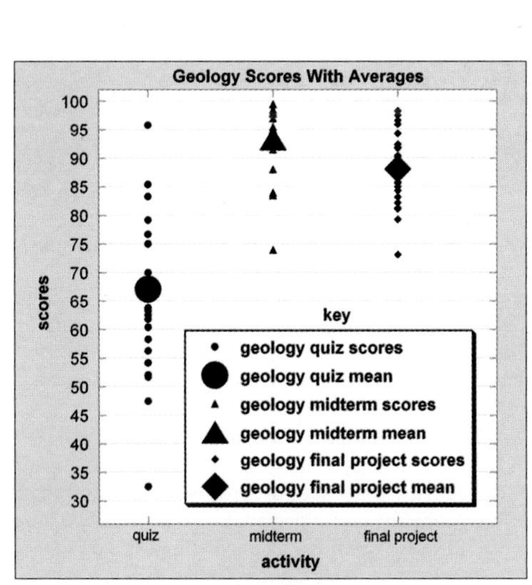

▲ Figure H5A.13 Geology scores with averages.

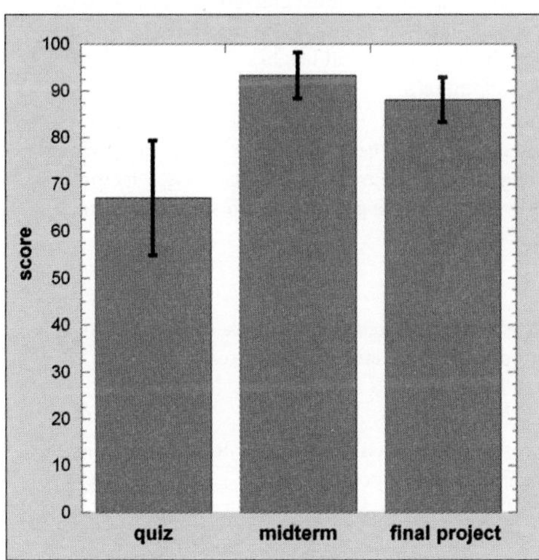

▲ Figure H5A.14 Geology scores with errors.

Improving Math Skills: How to Use Graphs, Measure Slopes, and Estimate Uncertainty 847

Do Unit Conversions

Converting units is an essential skill, whether in science, business, or your finances. The key in all the examples and questions in the *How to Do Unit Conversions* activity is for students to carefully write out all units and conversions. If units don't cancel and give the desired units, then it is a clue to the student that there may be an error.

Another tip is to draw a slash through units in the numerator and denominator that cancel. This helps students see which units have canceled each other, and which units remain. For example, here's how you would show that 86,400 seconds is the same as 1 day:

$$(86{,}400\ \cancel{\text{sec}}) \times \left(\frac{1\ \cancel{\text{min}}}{60\ \cancel{\text{sec}}}\right) \times \left(\frac{1\ \cancel{\text{hr}}}{60\ \cancel{\text{min}}}\right) \times \left(\frac{1\ \text{day}}{24\ \cancel{\text{hr}}}\right) = 1\ \text{day}$$

Seconds (sec), hours (hr), and minutes (min) are on both the top and the bottom, so they cancel, leaving just days. You can use the same method to show that 259,200 seconds is the same as 3 days. Similarly, you can show that a foot (ft) is 30.48 centimeters (cm).

$$(1\ \cancel{\text{ft}}) \times \left(\frac{12\ \cancel{\text{in}}}{1\ \cancel{\text{ft}}}\right) \times \left(\frac{2.54\ \text{cm}}{1\ \cancel{\text{in}}}\right) = 30.48\ \text{cm}$$

For additional practice, see the practice set in the *Toolbox* activity, *Conversions*, on the *Teacher Resource CD (TRCD)*.

NOTES:

Improving Math Skills

Do Unit Conversions

When you measure something, you always need to indicate what units you are using. For example, suppose someone told you that her cat had a weight of "20." That doesn't mean much without units. Does the cat weigh 20 pounds, 20 newtons, 20 ounces, or 20 tons? Distance measurements (length) also need units such as feet, inches, meters, kilometers, and miles. If you are measuring time, you use units such as seconds, minutes, hours, and years.

Converting between units is also very important. For example, what if a friend told you that he would phone you in 86,400 seconds (sec)? When would that be? After this activity, you will be able to show that this is the same as 1 day. Unit conversions are also important for comparing two measurements made with different units. For example, suppose a person who is 5 feet (ft) 8 inches (in) tall has a hat on that is 0.30 meters (m) tall. What is the total height of the person, including the hat? Unfortunately, you cannot simply add the lengths. You must convert all of them to the same unit, and then you can add the lengths. You may have to convert again to a more reasonable unit. The total height of the person would be 79.8 in, 6 ft 7.8 in, or 2.03 m tall.

How do you make these conversions? The method is called unit analysis (or dimensional analysis). These terms may sound complicated, but the method is pretty simple. The method uses conversion factors to convert units step-by-step, canceling units at each step. Using these guidelines, unit analysis is simple.

Unit Analysis Guidelines

1. Conversion factors relate different units and are different ways of expressing the number 1. For example, there are 12 in in 1 ft, or 12 in = 1 ft, or $\left(\frac{12\ \text{in}}{1\ \text{ft}}\right) = 1$.
2. Conversion factors can be flipped (inverted) as long as the units stay with the number. For example, you can write $\left(\frac{12\ \text{in}}{1\ \text{ft}}\right) = 1$, or $\left(\frac{1\ \text{ft}}{12\ \text{in}}\right) = 1$. This is the same thing.

848 Improving Math Skills: How to Do Unit Conversions

NOTES:

3 Units behave as numbers do when you multiply fractions. The units in the numerator of fractions will cancel the same units in the denominator of fractions. For example, $\left(\frac{12\ \cancel{\text{in}}}{3\ \cancel{\text{in}}}\right) = 4$.

4 In unit analysis, your goal is to cancel the same units in the numerators and denominators until you end up with the units you want.

5 When you convert between units, follow these steps.
a. Identify the units that you have.
b. See which units you want.
c. Note the conversion factors that get you from Steps 5a and 5b.

6 Work through the following example to practice using the guidelines for unit analysis from Steps 1–5.

How many inches are there in 1 mile (mi)?

Conversion steps (from Step 5)	Answers
What unit do you have now?	1 mi
What unit do you want?	"How many inches"
What are the conversion factors?	$1\text{ mi} = 5{,}280\text{ ft}$ or $\left(\frac{5{,}280\text{ ft}}{1\text{ mi}}\right) = 1$ $1\text{ ft} = 12\text{ in}$ or $\left(\frac{12\text{ in}}{1\text{ ft}}\right) = 1$

▲ **Figure H5B.1 Conversion table for miles to inches.**

To convert miles to inches, start with what you know (1 mi). Then use conversion factors (figure H5B.1) to cancel units as you go until you get to the units that you want (inches). When the same units are on both the bottom and the top, they cancel. Work with your teacher to see how to cancel these units on the top and bottom.

$$(1\ \cancel{\text{mi}}) \times \left(\frac{5{,}280\ \cancel{\text{ft}}}{1\ \cancel{\text{mi}}}\right) \times \left(\frac{12\text{ in}}{1\ \cancel{\text{ft}}}\right)$$

The units cancel, so you are left with units of inches. You can then multiply the numerator numbers together for the answer in inches.

$$(1\ \cancel{\text{mi}}) \times \left(\frac{5{,}280\ \cancel{\text{ft}}}{1\ \cancel{\text{mi}}}\right) \times \left(\frac{12\text{ in}}{1\ \cancel{\text{ft}}}\right) = \left(\frac{1 \times 5{,}280 \times 12\text{ in}}{1 \times 1}\right) = 63{,}360\text{ in}$$

NOTES:

The unit conversions in Step 8 of the activity show whether your students understand the concept and significance of unit conversions. This is because they have not worked with the units, such as zips, sliffs, or lampos.

Answers to Step 8

8a. The answer for the conversion from lampos to sliffs follows.

$$(1\ \cancel{\text{lampo}}) \times \left(\frac{12\ \cancel{\text{vole}}}{1\ \cancel{\text{lampo}}}\right) \times \left(\frac{3\ \text{sliff}}{4\ \cancel{\text{vole}}}\right) = 9\ \text{sliff}$$

8b. The answer for the conversion from voles to zips follows.

$$(1\ \cancel{\text{vole}}) \times \left(\frac{3\ \cancel{\text{sliff}}}{4\ \cancel{\text{vole}}}\right) \times \left(\frac{5\ \text{zip}}{1\ \cancel{\text{sliff}}}\right) = 3.75\ \text{zip}$$

8c. The answer for the conversion from slinks to flies follows.

$$(1\ \cancel{\text{slink}}) \times \left(\frac{7\ \cancel{\text{zip}}}{1\ \cancel{\text{slink}}}\right) \times \left(\frac{1\ \cancel{\text{sliff}}}{5\ \cancel{\text{zip}}}\right) \times \left(\frac{4\ \cancel{\text{vole}}}{3\ \cancel{\text{sliff}}}\right) \times \left(\frac{1\ \cancel{\text{lampo}}}{12\ \cancel{\text{vole}}}\right) \times \left(\frac{7\ \text{fly}}{8\ \cancel{\text{lampo}}}\right) = 0.136\ \text{flie}$$

7 Work through a more complicated example using dimensional analysis. Suppose that you want to convert 75 miles per hour (mph) into feet per second (ft/sec).

Conversion steps (from Step 5)	Answers
What unit do you have now?	$75\ \frac{\text{mi}}{\text{hr}}$ (mph)
What unit do you want?	$\frac{\text{ft}}{\text{sec}}$ (ft/sec)
What are the conversion factors?	1 hour (hr) = 60 minutes (min) 1 minute (min) = 60 seconds (sec) 1 mi = 5,280 ft

▲ **Figure H5B.2 Conversion table for miles per hour to feet per second.**

Now what? Take your conversions (figure H5B.2) one step at a time, canceling units as you go until you arrive at the units you want.

$$\left(\frac{75\ \cancel{\text{mi}}}{1\ \cancel{\text{hr}}}\right) \times \left(\frac{5{,}280\ \text{ft}}{1\ \cancel{\text{mi}}}\right) \times \left(\frac{1\ \cancel{\text{hr}}}{60\ \cancel{\text{min}}}\right) \times \left(\frac{1\ \cancel{\text{min}}}{60\ \text{sec}}\right) =$$

$$\left(\frac{75 \times 5{,}280\ \text{ft} \times 1 \times 1}{1 \times 1 \times 60 \times 60\ \text{sec}}\right) = \left(\frac{396{,}000\ \text{ft}}{3{,}600\ \text{sec}}\right) = \left(\frac{110\ \text{ft}}{1\ \text{sec}}\right) = 110\ \frac{\text{ft}}{\text{sec}}$$

8 Try the conversions in Steps 8a–c on your own. Use the following conversion factors, and show your calculations for each conversion.

1 slink = 7 zips
1 sliff = 5 zips
4 voles = 3 sliffs
8 lampos = 7 flies
12 voles = 1 lampo

a. How many sliffs are in 1 lampo?
b. One vole is how many zips?
c. How many flies are in 1 slink?

850 Improving Math Skills: How to Do Unit Conversions

Understand Very Large and Very Small Numbers

When thinking about the universe, it is difficult to imagine its size and mass. There are hundreds of billions of stars in our galaxy and then billions of galaxies in the universe. Distances in the universe are trillions of kilometers. Temperatures in the universe were once billions of degrees Celsius. The age of the universe is billions of years. Sometimes numbers like millions and billions are used often enough that people do not realize how large these quantities really are. In the activity in *How to Understand Very Large and Very Small Numbers*, students experience how immense million and billion are.

Materials—Part I

calculators, rulers, or meter sticks (optional)

1 Becker "One in a Million" bottle (optional)

Materials—Part II

stopwatch or clock with second hand

calculators

Advance Preparation

In Part I, students may wish to use a calculator or some way of measuring. Have calculators, rulers, and meter sticks available. Next, look around your classroom, hallway, and outside to get an idea of what students might want to use as their "million of something." Items they might find include blades of grass on the football field, little dots on ceiling tiles, grains of sand, the number of colored fibers in a carpet, and the number of letters (or words, pages, and so on) in a textbook.

If you choose to show the students a Becker "One in a Million" bottle, locate it or order it. It can be purchased from Flinn Scientific, Inc., at http://www.flinnsci.com/ or toll free at 1-800-452-1261.

In Part II, students will need a timer and calculators. Gather stopwatches or check if your classroom clock has a second hand that students can easily view.

Part I: How Many Is 1 Million?

Have the class read the introduction and work in pairs. You may wish to pair students who have different ability levels in math. You might ask them, "If a rich uncle left you an inheritance of $1 million, how long would it take you to count that much money if it were in $1 bills?" Pose the same question as if it were $1 billion. Explain that astronomy involves enormous numbers. This activity will help them understand how large the numbers 1 million and 1 billion are.

Circulate to help the students with their math or to give them hints on what objects they might use. The way that the students likely will approach the task is to find a pattern that is repeated. They count the number in one area and then divide 1 million by that number to determine how much area they would need to get a million of that item. For example, if they counted 200 dots in one ceiling tile, they could assume that ceiling tiles had an average of 200 dots on them (or they could get the average of a few tiles). They then would divide 1 million by 200 to determine that they would need 5,000 ceiling tiles to have 1 million dots. They likely would not find 5,000 ceiling tiles, but their method would prove how to get 1 million ceiling tile dots.

Understand Very Large and Very Small Numbers

When it comes to studying the universe, scientists must work with very large and very small numbers. Scientists use numbers in the millions and billions because quantities, distances, timescales, and temperatures in the universe are so vast. Consider this:

- Our galaxy has billions of stars, and the universe has hundreds of billions of galaxies.
- Distances between objects in the universe can be greater than billions of miles; it would take light over 10 billion years to travel across the universe.
- Astronomers measure time spans of the universe in billions of years.
- Temperatures in the universe once were hotter than billions of degrees Celsius.

You know that 1 million is a lot—but how much is it? For instance, if someone offered you a million dollars in a pile, you'd sure take it. But how could you test that the pile actually had 1 million dollar bills in it? Would you count dollar bills one by one? How long would this take? Now suppose that someone gave you a billion dollars in $1 bills. How much more is this, really?

In *How to Understand Very Large and Very Small Numbers*, you'll explore how big the numbers million and billion really are. Get ready to share your ideas with your classmates.

Part I: How Many Is 1 Million?

Materials

none

1. With your teammate, find or think of a million of 1 type of item. You do not need to actually collect the items, but decide how you will convince the rest of the class that you could gather 1 million of the item. Think through this step carefully. You can change items to arrive at the best example.

When finished, have the pairs share what they found and how they can prove it. Again, it is best if they can use numbers to prove their approach convincingly. Having groups show and argue their evidence and a proof (with numbers) is likely the most important point.

Part II: Millions or Billions: What's the Difference?

It's quite a bit different talking about 1 billion of something than 1 million. The difference is 1,000, but your students might not yet get this point, particularly if they are unfamiliar with scientific notation. Have them work through the estimate of how long it would take to count to 1 million, then 1 billion.

In Step 1, students predict how long they think it will take them to count to 1 million. Any student prediction is OK at this point. Students will time each other saying "383,262" in Step 2a. This number takes about 3 seconds (sec) to say. In Step 2b, students calculate how long it takes to count to 1 million based on their answers to Step 2a. This should be 3 sec times 1 million, or 3 million sec.

In Step 3, students should convert their answer to days. Three million seconds might not make a lot of sense, even though the answer is accurate. Convert seconds to an appropriate unit, which in this case is days. Check that all students show their calculations. This shows why the answer is about 35 days.

$$(3{,}000{,}000\ \cancel{\text{sec}}) \times \left(\frac{1\ \cancel{\text{min}}}{60\ \cancel{\text{sec}}}\right) \times \left(\frac{1\ \cancel{\text{hr}}}{60\ \cancel{\text{min}}}\right) \times \left(\frac{1\ \text{day}}{24\ \cancel{\text{hr}}}\right) = 34.7\ \text{days}$$

There are practice sets in the *Toolbox* activities, *Decimals, Exponents*, and *Conversions* on the *TRCD* if your students need additional practice working with large and small numbers, exponents, decimals, or unit conversions.

NOTES:

2. Work with your partner on a method to prove that you have 1 million of the objects. You will share your ideas and prove your work to your classmates.
3. Discuss these questions in your class and write your answers in your science notebook.
   a. What were some of the difficulties you had finding a million of something?
   b. What were some different methods that groups used to prove their findings?

Part II: Millions or Billions: What's the Difference?

Materials

stopwatch or clock with second hand

calculators

In Part I, you had to prove that you have 1 million of an item. This might have seemed difficult at first, but you probably quickly figured out how to meet the challenge. As you worked, you should have seen how big 1 million of something really is. You also probably saw that counting every single item would not work too well.

Astronomers work with numbers even larger than 1 million. In fact, numbers in the billions and larger are quite common in astronomy. You will work again with your partner to better understand the real size of 1 billion (1,000,000,000).

1. Individually, predict how long you think it would take you to count to 1 million saying each number aloud without stopping. Write this prediction in your science notebook and title it "prediction." What did your partner predict?
2. With your partner, calculate how long it takes to count to 1 million (1,000,000).
   a. Have one person say the number 383,262 ("three hundred eighty-three thousand two hundred sixty-two") while the other person times how long it takes to say the number. Record the time in your science notebook.

   You said this number because most numbers between 1 and 1 million are in the hundred thousands.

852 Improving Math Skills: How to Understand Very Large and Very Small Numbers

In Step 4, students predict the time needed to count to 1 billion. Check that students record in their science notebooks their prediction for the time to count to 1 billion.

In Step 5, students calculate the time it takes to count to a billion by ones. They use the same method as before by timing how long it takes to say "504,394,568." This takes about 5.1 sec to say. Multiplied by 1 billion, it takes 5,100,000,000 sec to count to 1 billion. You can show that this is about 162 years.

$$(5{,}100{,}000{,}000\ \cancel{\text{sec}}) \times \left(\frac{1\ \cancel{\text{min}}}{60\ \cancel{\text{sec}}}\right) \times \left(\frac{1\ \cancel{\text{hr}}}{60\ \cancel{\text{min}}}\right) \times \left(\frac{1\ \cancel{\text{day}}}{24\ \cancel{\text{hr}}}\right) \times \left(\frac{1\ \text{year}}{365.25\ \cancel{\text{days}}}\right) = 161.6\ \text{years}$$

In Step 6, students share and compare their answers with the class. In Step 7, students answer 3 questions about the activity. Note that the difference between 1 million and 1 billion for objects is just 1,000. However, the difference in time for counting is somewhat larger because it takes longer to state the numbers in the hundreds of millions. The differences above are a factor of about 1,700 (161.6 years / 34.7 days = 161.6 years / 0.095 years = 1,700).

Be open to all ideas as students discuss their answers to Step 7b. In Step 7c, see whether students are noting uncertainties in the time it takes different students to say the number. This factor would lead to different results.

b. It took you a certain number of seconds to say that single number. How many numbers are there between 1 and 1 million? Using multiplication, calculate how many seconds it would take you to say all these numbers and, thus, count to 1 million. Record your calculations and this number in your science notebook.

3. You probably calculated many millions of seconds, which probably doesn't make a lot of sense. Convert your answer from seconds to a more appropriate unit. Show your calculations in your science notebook. What did others in your class find?

4. You now know that it takes a significant amount of time to count to 1 million. But many measurements in the universe need billions or even hundreds of billions. Let's see how 1 billion compares with 1 million. Predict how long it would take you to count to 1 billion by ones. Record your prediction in your science notebook.

5. Calculate how long it would take you to count to 1 billion (1,000,000,000) by ones. Use the same method you used in Step 2 and record your answer in the units that make the most sense. Review the unit conversions as necessary.

A good number to say is 504,394,568 (pronounced "five hundred four million three hundred ninety-four thousand five hundred sixty-eight") because most numbers from 1 to 1 billion are in the hundreds of millions.

6. Share your calculation from Step 5 with the class. What did you find?

7. Discuss Questions 7a–c with your class and write your answers in your science notebook.
   a. Were you surprised at how long it would take you to count to a billion versus counting to a million? Explain your thoughts.
   b. How did measuring 1 million of an object help you to understand the enormity of 1 million?
   c. What was the range of values your class had for counting to 1 billion? What might account for this range of results?

NOTES:

Use Very Large and Very Small Numbers

Astronomy is again used as the context. If your students used Level 1 of *BSCS Science: An Inquiry Approach*, this information will be familiar from unit 3, *The Earth and Beyond*. Astronomy is a study that uses extreme numbers. The distances, times, masses, and temperatures are very large, yet atomic masses, diameters, and radiation wavelengths can be incredibly small. Scientific notation is how you and your students will represent the sizes of these things. In this *How To* activity, students learn how to use scientific notation to express numbers. They also read about some of the units astronomers use to measure distances in the universe.

Materials—Part I

calculators
video player and video *Powers of Ten* (optional)

Materials—Part II

calculators

Advance Preparation

Have calculators available for student use. Students can start learning how to key in exponents on calculators. If you have access to the video *Powers of Ten*, it is helpful to show. Your math department may have a copy, or you can order it from Eames Office (search for Eames Office on the Web).

Part I: Big Numbers

Have students read the activity, the table, and the questions in Part I. Be prepared to help them move decimals back and forth. This is an important skill. You can practice this with your class by writing any number students say on the board, and then have one student come up to express the number in scientific notation. It's good to have students do a lot of examples moving decimals in both directions.

There are *Toolbox* practice sets on the *Teacher Resource CD (TRCD)* if your students need additional practice working with large and small numbers, exponents, decimals, or unit conversions.

NOTES:

Improving Math Skills

By now, you understand numbers like million and billion better. Astronomers have to work with numbers in the billions—and bigger—all the time. For example, how many stars are in the sky? Are there more stars that you cannot see? All stars that you see are part of the galaxy in which we live, the Milky Way Galaxy. A galaxy is an enormous group of stars in a massive cluster. The Milky Way has more than 100 billion stars. The universe contains hundreds of billions of different galaxies, many of which are made up of hundreds of billions of stars. How do astronomers know this?

Astronomers are scientists who study the matter in outer space, particularly the many types of stars. When they cannot count stars or galaxies, they need to calculate estimates based on what they can clearly see and count. For example, astronomers cannot see each star in our galaxy because some stars are behind other stars or clouds of gas and dust. So astronomers base their estimates on mass. The laws of physics also allow astronomers to estimate the mass of the Milky Way Galaxy. Dividing this by the mass of an average star like the Sun gives estimates of up to several hundred billion stars in the Milky Way Galaxy.

Part I: Big Numbers

Materials

calculators

You have seen how large numbers can be difficult to manage. It would be awkward for astronomers to use terms such as a million billion billion or to write out numbers like 1,000,000,000,000,000,000,000,000. Rather, astronomers (and other scientists) use a special way of expressing numbers called scientific notation.

Scientific notation is a way to abbreviate numbers to make them easier to work with. To show numbers with scientific notation, you must first be comfortable with exponents. Exponents are shorthand for the number of times a number, called the base, is multiplied by itself. A base with an exponent is said to be "raised to the power" of that exponent. For example, the number 2^4 means $2 \times 2 \times 2 \times 2$, or 16. Here, 2 is the base and 4 is the exponent. In scientific notation, the base number is always 10. Having

NOTES:

10 as the base works well because the exponent shows how many zeros you would need to write out in the long form of the number. So 10,000 is expressed as 10^4, because $10 \times 10 \times 10 \times 10 = 10{,}000$.

Numbers in astronomy work best with powers of 10. With scientific notation, you simply move the decimal point of a number to obtain a more manageable number. Then you write the number of places you moved the decimal as an exponent of 10. For example, you would write the number 4,600,000,000 as 4.6×10^9 with scientific notation. The second number is a lot simpler, and it says the same thing as the first. You write it like this because you moved the decimal nine places to the left to get to the numeral 4.6. This is shown in figure H5D.1.

Other large numbers are also easy to write using scientific notation. You would write the number 34,000 as 3.4×10^4. You would write the number 286,000,000 as 2.86×10^8. You might remember that the metric system is based on multiples of 10. The table in figure H5D.2 shows how large numbers convert to powers of 10. It also shows prefixes for these numbers in the metric system. Using the example above, 286,000,000 is also the same as 286×10^6, or just 286 million.

Figure H5D.1 Example of moving decimals for positive exponents. This diagram shows the conversion of the number 4,600,000,000 to scientific notation, 4.6×10^9. The illustration in the center shows the decimal place moving left nine times. The table in figure H5D.2 explains why 4.6×10^9 is the same as 4.6 billion.

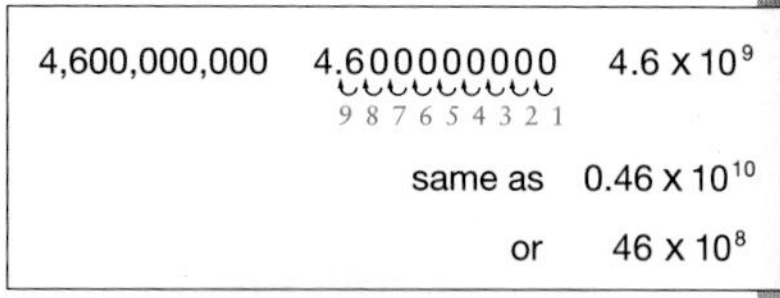

4,600,000,000 4.600000000 4.6×10^9
9 8 7 6 5 4 3 2 1
same as 0.46×10^{10}
or 46×10^8

Pronounced	Number	Powers of ten (scientific notation)	Unit prefix in the metric system (SI)
Trillion	1,000,000,000,000	10^{12} or 1×10^{12}	tera-
Billion	1,000,000,000	10^9 or 1×10^9	giga-
Million	1,000,000	10^6 or 1×10^6	mega-
Thousand	1,000	10^3 or 1×10^3	kilo-
Hundred	100	10^2 or 1×10^2	hecto-
Ten	10	10^1 or 1×10^1	deka-
One	1	10^0 or 1×10^0	
Three hundred twenty-seven thousand	327,000	3.27×10^5	

Figure H5D.2 Table for large numbers.

Improving Math Skills: How to Use Very Large and Very Small Numbers 855

NOTES:

Answers to Steps 1–4

Student answers for these steps include the following.

1. 1,000 meter (m) = 1×10^3 m, or 10^3 m.
2. The exponent on 10 indicates the number of times that the decimal moves. This is the same as the number of zeros. Thus, a googol is 1×10^{100}, or 10^{100}.
3. 3.0×10^8 meters per second (m/sec) = 300,000,000 m/sec.
4. \$87 billion = 87×10^9 dollars, or 8.7×10^{10} dollars;

   248 million stars = 248×10^6 stars, or 2.48×10^8 stars.

Work through these problems individually and write your answers in your science notebook. When you finish, join with another student and compare your answers. Discuss and resolve any differences you have in your answers.

1. One kilometer (km) is the same as 1,000 meters (m). How would you write 1,000 m using scientific notation?
2. A googol is one of the biggest named numbers. It is written as the number 1 followed by 100 zeros. Write this number using scientific notation.
3. The speed of light is 3.0×10^8 meters per second (m/sec). What is this value written without using scientific notation?
4. Use scientific notation to write \$87 billion and 248 million stars.

Part II: Small Numbers

Materials

calculators

Astronomers often work with countless billions of stars and galaxies, but they also work with extremely small numbers. For example, you will see that a key property of light is wavelength. Wavelengths of light are commonly about 1 billion times shorter than a meter.

You write numbers less than 1.0 in scientific notation in the same general way that you write large numbers. The key difference is that the power of 10 is a negative exponent. The exponent still tells you how many places the decimal is from the number 1.0, but the decimal is moved in the other direction (to the right). When writing small numbers using powers of 10, you imagine moving the decimal to the right. The number of places you moved the decimal is the power of 10 expressed as a negative number. We would write the number 0.0000001 in scientific notation as 1×10^{-7} because the decimal moves seven places to the right to get to the number 1.0. Another example is shown in figure H5D.3 for 0.00000035, which is the same as 3.5×10^{-7}.

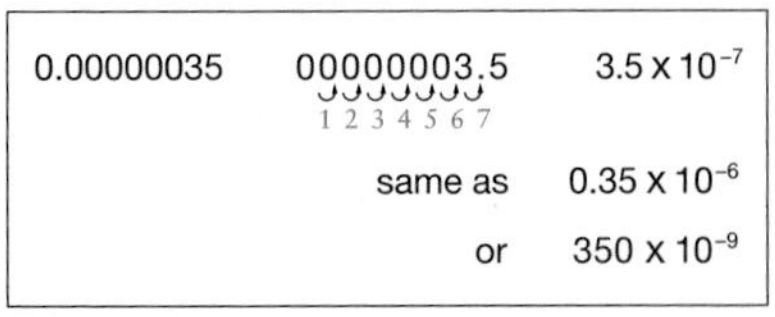

0.00000035	00000003.5 (1 2 3 4 5 6 7)	3.5×10^{-7}
	same as	0.35×10^{-6}
	or	350×10^{-9}

Figure H5D.3 Example of moving decimals for negative exponents. This diagram shows the conversion of the number 0.00000035 to scientific notation, 3.5×10^{-7}. The illustration in the top center shows the decimal place moving to the right seven times.

856 Improving Math Skills: How to Use Very Large and Very Small Numbers

NOTES:

Pronounced	Number	Powers of ten (scientific notation)	Unit prefix in the metric system (SI)
Tenth	0.1	1×10^{-1} or 10^{-1}	deci-
Hundredth	0.01	1×10^{-2} or 10^{-2}	centi-
Thousandth	0.001	1×10^{-3} or 10^{-3}	milli-
Millionth	0.000001	1×10^{-6} or 10^{-6}	micro-
Billionth	0.000000001	1×10^{-9} or 10^{-9}	nano-

▲ **Figure H5D.4 Prefixes for small numbers.**

Work through these problems individually and write your answers in your science notebook. When you finish, join with another student and compare your answers. Discuss and resolve any differences you have in your answers.

1. A micron is an abbreviation for the term micrometer (μm). How would you express 1 μm using scientific notation? Look at the prefixes in the table in figure H5D.4.
2. How many meters are in 1 millimeter (mm)?
3. Scientists often measure wavelengths of light in units called nanometers (nm). A nanometer is 0.000000001 m. Write this number using scientific notation.

Part II: Small Numbers

The key with small numbers (< 1) and scientific notation is remembering the negative sign with the exponent of 10. You might also recall that you can move an exponent from the numerator to the denominator by switching the sign of the exponent. This is a useful manipulation, but remember that units must stay put.

$$\left(\frac{1}{10^3\ \text{m}}\right) = \left(\frac{10^{-3}}{1\ \text{m}}\right) = 10^{-3}\ \text{m}^{-1}$$

There are practice worksheets included in the *Toolbox* on the *TRCD* if your students need extra practice with these skills. See *Exponents*.

Answers to Steps 1–3

Student answers for these steps include the following.

1. 1 micron (μm) = 1 μm = 1×10^{-6} m (or just 10^{-6} m).
2. 1 millimeter (mm) = 10^{-3} m = 0.001 m.
3. 1 nanometer (nm) = 1×10^{-9} m (or just 10^{-9} m).

Conduct an Effective Web Search

In *How to Conduct an Effective Web Search*, students are given guidelines on how to search the Web more efficiently for information. Caution students about plagiarism and refer them to *How to Cite References and Avoid Plagiarism*. Also discourage students from printing out entire Web sites that they find that relate to their topic. Sometimes clicking on the print icon will cause the entire Web site to print, which could print several pages. Encourage students to filter their information and only print what is necessary. Yu might also have students record summaries of the Web sites in their science notebooks, complete with the proper citations.

Conduct an Effective Web Search

Searching for information on the Web can be rewarding as well as frustrating. It may take hours to sift through the thousands of sites that pop up from a poorly designed search. *How to Conduct an Effective Web Search* gives you a few pointers for using any search engine to look for information on the Web. There are times when you want to broaden the search to include more documents, and there are times when you will want to narrow the search to return fewer documents. The following 7 steps will give you a balanced search that is broad enough to find documents that pertain to your topic, but narrow enough to be useful.

Web Searching Guidelines

1. **Choose your keywords carefully.** You will type keywords that relate to your topic into a search engine. Choose nouns and objects as your keywords. For example, if you were searching for information about new planets discovered outside our solar system, using the keyword *planet* or *planets* would be a good start. Verbs, adjectives, adverbs, and similar terms will either be thrown out by the search engine or will be too variable to be useful.
2. **Use several keywords in your search.** Using six to eight appropriate keywords can greatly reduce the number of documents that are returned with your search. Using the example in Step 1, the keywords *new*, *planet*, *solar*, *system*, and *discovery* would return useful documents.
3. **Use appropriate variations in your words connected by OR.** For example, use *planet OR planets* to make sure the search engine picks up both variations of the word "planet."
4. **Use synonyms connected by OR where possible.** *Discovery OR find* is an example of using 2 synonyms connected by *OR* that will cover the different ways a concept can be described.
5. **Combine words into phrases where possible and place phrases in quotation marks (" ").** For example, *"solar system"* is a phrase in our example that should be combined and put in quotation marks. This will restrict the search to exact matches of the phrase.

858 How to Conduct an Effective Web Search

NOTES:

6. **Combining 2 or 3 concepts in 1 search, distinguished by parentheses, will narrow your results and possibly give you just what you want.** For our current example, using *("solar system")("new planet")(discover OR find)* would be the best selection.
7. **Order your concepts with the main subject first.** Search engines tend to rank documents that match the first keywords in the search higher than those that match the later keywords. For our example search, you would order the concepts as *("new planet")(discover OR find)("solar system")*.

NOTES:

Write a Lab Report

In *How to Write a Lab Report*, students are given a set of sections and criteria for a scientific lab report. You may have your own method of writing lab reports that reflects your school or state science standards. Feel free to modify or add to this set of guidelines. Students are asked to write a lab report in chapter 1, *Investigations by Design*, of this program. You should choose additional times throughout the year to incorporate this requirement for your students.

Write a Lab Report

Adapted from BSCS. (2006). *Biological perspectives laboratory manual: Thinking biologically* (3rd ed.). Dubuque, IA: Kendall/Hunt.

When scientists have enough information, data, and evidence about a particular scientific matter, they summarize their results in a formal, scientific paper and submit it for publication in a professional journal. These papers are organized in specific sections as required by the particular journal. You, too, will be writing lab reports this year, and your report should have sections similar to a scientific paper. Those 5 sections are listed here with a brief description of what you should include in each section.

Lab Report Guidelines

1. **Introduction.** The introduction includes background information from scientific papers, textbooks, newspapers, or magazine articles. Be sure to cite your references at the end of your paper. (See *How to Cite References and Avoid Plagiarism.*) The introduction should also include the purpose of your investigation or the question you are trying to answer.
2. **Materials and methods.** List the materials that you used in the investigation. Also include your step-by-step procedure.
3. **Results.** Describe your results in written form in this section. You should also include appropriate tables, graphs, and diagrams with captions.
4. **Discussion.** This section is where you discuss the results of this particular investigation. How do the results relate to what you already know?
5. **Conclusion.** Summarize the findings of your investigation in the conclusion. Try to answer questions such as, "What trends do I see in the data?" "What general statement can I make about the results?" "What do the data mean?" "What do they tell me about what is happening with the object, organism, or phenomenon?"

860 How to Write a Lab Report

NOTES:

Cite References and Avoid Plagiarism

When doing research in your classes, you'll quickly find that you will need to rely on the results and work of others. These are usually professionals who have had the chance to consider a topic in much more detail than you. You will gain insight from their work, and their work will even make yours much stronger. The important thing is to review with your teacher how to reference that work in your write-up or presentation.

Sometimes students may forget to list sources, or they may even use other people's work without a clear reference. Claiming someone else's work as your own is cheating.

Using the creative work, scientific results, or ideas of other people without a specific reference is a form of stealing. This form of stealing is called *plagiarism.* It's easy to be sure not to plagiarize—*just cite in all your work any sources of information, data, creative work, or ideas that you are borrowing from someone else.* It's fine to borrow, but you have to be clear about when you are doing so.

Referencing any materials or facts that you use in your work is a key part of writing a good paper. Accurate references will actually make your work a lot better. If you have questions, be sure to check with your teacher on his or her methods for documenting references. Your teacher should also be able to tell you the policies at your school for plagiarism.

It is common practice to use the Web to do research on school projects. The Web sites that you use in your report must be cited just as you cite a book or an article from a journal. Your teacher can provide you with the format for citing Web resources.

When doing research or projects in any of your classes, it is vital to keep a list of all references that you use. This convention is part of doing research. It is the official way to recognize the results and prior hard work of others, and it is the proper way to confirm your research and interpretations. Two steps are needed to have accurate references.

1. *Clearly indicate, or cite, the prior research or findings directly within your text or write-up.* This is called a *citation*, and it includes the last names of the authors plus the year the work was published (see the following example). Some results in your work may be widely known facts in science (for example, the speed of light and the atomic masses for elements of the periodic table). These facts don't need text citations.

8 HOW TO

Cite References and Avoid Plagiarism

Proper citing of references is often neglected in high school science classes—especially in the age of the Web. Students often simply print off information and cut and paste bits and pieces together to form a report. Take time to instruct your students on how to give proper credit for scientific work.

How to Cite References and Avoid Plagiarism shows students how to document their sources and prevent plagiarism. Examples are given, but you may want students to use a different reference style.

How to Cite References and Avoid Plagiarism 861

NOTES:

But suppose that you are researching changes in the rates of cigarette smoking among adults over the past 20 years. Here's an example of citing resources directly in your text:

> Recent data show that smoking rates are decreasing somewhat, and that about one-fourth (22.5 percent) of all Americans still smoke (Centers for Disease Control and Prevention [CDC], 2004). Factors related to smoking rates include the socioeconomic status of the person (Adler, Boyce, Chesney, Folkman, & Syme, 1993; Sorenson, Barbeau, Hunt, & Emmons, 2004), or where the person works (Nelson, Emont, Brackbill, Cameron, Peddicord, & Fiore, 1994). Another factor is where the person learns about quitting smoking, such as at work or by television or radio (CDC, 1999; Haviland et al., 2004).

2 *Each of the resources you cite must be listed in a reference section at the end of your report.* Your teacher may have a preferred format. The following example cites the resources for the short reading on smoking in adults.

Reference List

Adler, N. E., Boyce, W. T., Chesney, M. A., Folkman, S., & Syme, L. S. (1993). Socioeconomic inequalities in health: No easy solution. *Journal of the American Medical Association, 269*, 3140–3145.

Centers for Disease Control and Prevention. (1999). *Best practices for comprehensive tobacco control programs.* Atlanta, GA: U.S. Department of Health and Human Services, Centers for Disease Control and Prevention.

Centers for Disease Control and Prevention. (2004). Cigarette smoking among adults—United States, 2004. *Morbidity and Mortality Weekly Report, 53*, 427–431.

Haviland, L., Thornton, A. H., Carothers, S., Hund, L., Allen, J. A., Kastens, B., et al. (2004). Giving infants a great start: Launching a national smoking cessation program for pregnant women. *Nicotine and Tobacco Research, 6*, S181–188.

Nelson, D. E., Emont, S. L., Brackbill, R. M., Cameron, L. L., Peddicord, J., & Fiore, M. C. (1994). Cigarette smoking prevalence by occupation in the United States: A comparison between 1978 to 1980 and 1987 to 1990. *Journal of Occupational Medicine, 36*, 516–525.

Sorensen, G., Barbeau, E., Hunt, M. K., & Emmons, K. (2004). Reducing social disparities in tobacco use: A social-contextual model for reducing tobacco use among blue-collar workers. *American Journal of Public Health, 94*, 230–239.

862 How to Cite References and Avoid Plagiarism

NOTES:

The human eye cannot distinguish objects much smaller than 0.1 millimeter in diameter. The compound microscope is a technology often used in biology to extend vision. It allows observation of much smaller objects. The most commonly used compound microscope is monocular (that is, it has one eyepiece). Figure H9.1 shows a binocular microscope. Light reaches the eye after it has passed through the objects being examined. In *How to Use a Compound Microscope*, you will learn how to use and care for a microscope.

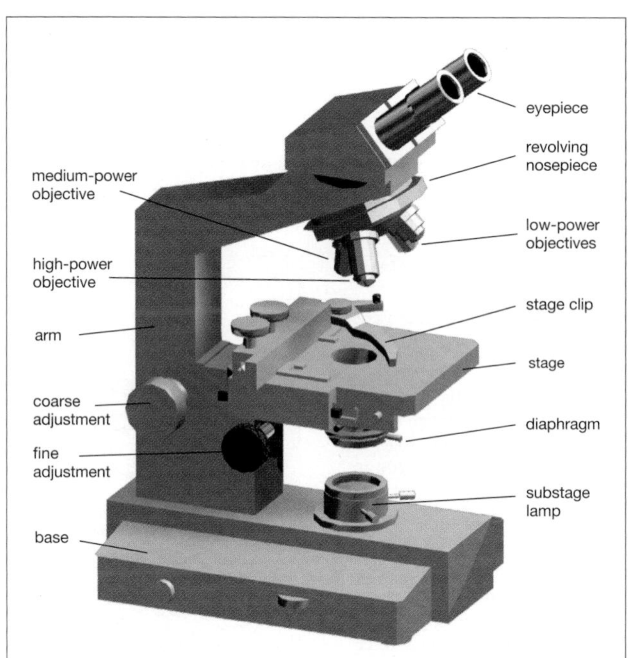

▲ **Figure H9.1 Compound microscope.** Use this figure to help locate the parts of a compound microscope.

How to Use a Compound Microscope | 863

Use a Compound Microscope

Several investigations and activities in *BSCS Science: An Inquiry Approach* involve observing microscopic materials. It is to the students' advantage to learn to use a microscope efficiently at the beginning of the school year. Even students who have used a microscope before will find it useful to take part in this investigation along with inexperienced students.

Materials—Part I

For each team of 2 students

3 coverslips
3 microscope slides
1 100-mL beaker or small jar
1 dropping pipet
1 compound microscope
1 pair of scissors
1 transparent metric ruler
lens paper
newspaper
water

NOTES:

Materials—Part II
For each team of 2 students
supplies from Part I

Materials—Part III
For each team of 2 students
supplies from Part I
1 light-colored hair
1 dark-colored hair

In Part I, students become familiar with the basics of caring for a microscope and the parts of a microscope. In Step 1, review the reading describing how students should care for a microscope. Students need to know how to avoid dropping the microscope or damaging the lenses. In Steps 2–4, students become familiar with the parts of a microscope. Encourage them to use the labeled illustration of a microscope to help them locate all the parts. They should try adjusting the lenses and mirror or diaphragm for light. Provide lens paper for students so that they can practice cleaning the lower-power lenses.

Part I: Setting Up the Microscope

Materials
For each team of 2 students

3 coverslips	1 pair of scissors
3 microscope slides	1 transparent metric ruler
1 100-mL beaker or small jar	lens paper
1 dropping pipet	newspaper
1 compound microscope	water

1. Read *Care of the Microscope* to learn how to properly care for a microscope.

Care of the Microscope

- The microscope is a precision instrument that requires proper care. Always carry the microscope with both hands. Put one hand under its base, the other on its arm (see figure H9.2).
- Keep the microscope away from the edge of the table. If a lamp is attached to the microscope, keep its cord out of the way. Move everything not needed for microscope studies off your lab table.
- Avoid tilting the microscope when using temporary slides made with water.
- The lenses of the microscope cost almost as much as all the other parts put together. Never clean lenses with anything other than the lens paper designed for this task.
- Always return the microscope to the low-power setting before putting it away. The high-power objective extends too close to the stage to be left in place safely.

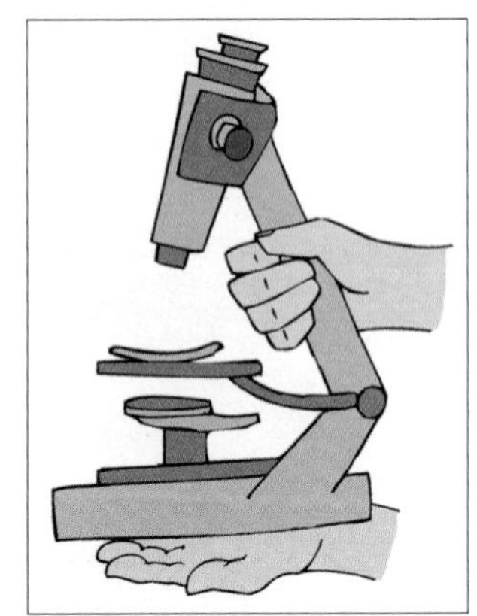

▲ **Figure H9.2 How to carry a microscope.** Always place one hand under the base and the other hand on the arm.

NOTES:

2. Rotate the low-power objective into place if it is not already there. When you change from one objective to another, you will hear the objective click into position.
3. Move the mirror so that you obtain even illumination through the opening in the stage. Or turn on the substage lamp. Most microscopes are equipped with a diaphragm for regulating light intensity. Some materials are best viewed in dim light, others in bright light.

Cautions

Never use a microscope mirror to capture direct sunlight when illuminating objects under a microscope. The mirror concentrates light rays, which can permanently damage the retina of the eye. Always use indirect light.

4. Make sure the lenses are dry and free of fingerprints and debris. Wipe lenses with lens paper only.

Part II: Using the Microscope

Materials

For each team of 2 students

supplies from Part I

1. In your science notebook, prepare a data table similar to the one in figure H9.3.

Object being viewed	Observations and comments
Letter *o*	
Letter *c*	
Letter *e or r*	

▲ **Figure H9.3 Microscope observations.**

2. Cut a lowercase letter *o* from a piece of newspaper. Place it right side up on a clean slide. With a dropping pipet, place 1 drop of water on the letter. This type of slide is called a wet mount.

In Part II, students practice using a microscope and making wet mounts. In Step 1, they create a data table to record their observations. In Steps 2–3, students make a wet mount of a piece of newspaper. First, they cut letters from a newspaper, and then they follow the steps illustrated in student figure H9.4 to make the wet mount. To give them more control with the dropping pipet, students should let it rest in the palm of their hand and gently squeeze with their thumb and forefinger. It is important that they use only 1 drop of water for their wet mount. Too much water will cause the coverslip to float off the slide.

NOTES:

After placing the slide on the microscope stage, students should adjust the focus of the low-power objective until the letter is in focus. Check to make sure students understand how to get the letter into focus. They may have difficulty making small adjustments with the fine focus. Once they have the letter in focus, students record observations in their data table during Step 7. In Step 8, they record the magnification of their view. Make sure they multiply the magnification of the eyepiece by the magnification of the objective lens.

Students repeat Steps 1–7 with the letter *c* and the letter *e* or *r*. In Steps 10 and 11, students answer questions about what they see. Make sure students take time to sketch the letter *e* or *r* in Step 12. Their sketches should include changes in image and in the movement that takes place under the microscope.

Answers to Steps 10–11

10. Students will see that the letter *e* or *r* looks upside down compared with the position they placed it in for the wet mount.

3 Wait until the paper is soaked before adding a coverslip. Hold the coverslip at about a 45-degree angle, with the bottom edge of the coverslip touching both the slide and the drop of water. Then slowly lower the coverslip. Figure H9.4 shows these first steps.

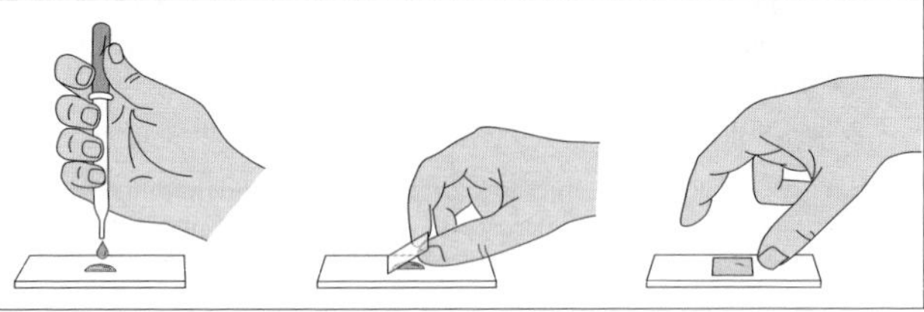

▲ **Figure H9.4 Preparing a wet mount.** This figure shows the steps to prepare a wet mount with a microscope slide and coverslip.

4 Place the slide on the microscope stage. Clamp it down with the stage clips. Move the slide so that the letter is in the middle of the hole in the stage. Use the coarse-adjustment knob to lower the low-power objective to the lowest position.

5 Look through the eyepiece. Use the coarse-adjustment knob to *raise* the objective slowly, until the letter *o* is in view.

6 If you cannot find the *o* on the first try, start the process again by repeating Steps 4 and 5.

7 Once you have the *o* in view, use the fine-adjustment knob to sharpen the focus. Position the diaphragm for the best light. Compare the way the letter looks through the microscope with the way it looks to the naked eye. Record your observations in your data table.

8 To determine how magnified the view is, multiply the number inscribed on the eyepiece by the number of the objective lens being used. For example:

eyepiece (10×) × objective lens (10×) = total (100×)

9 Follow the same procedure with a lowercase *c*. Describe in your data table how the letter appears when viewed through a microscope.

10 Make a wet mount of the letter *e* or the letter *r*. Describe how the letter appears when viewed through the microscope. What new information (not revealed by the letter *c*) is revealed by the *e* or *r*?

866 How to Use a Compound Microscope

NOTES:

11 Look through the eyepiece at the letter as you use your thumbs and forefingers to move the slide slowly *away* from you. Which way does your view of the letter move? Move the slide to the right. Which way does the image move?

12 Make a sketch of the letter as you see it under the microscope. Label the changes in image and in movement that take place under the microscope.

Part III: Using High Power

Materials

For each team of 2 students

supplies from Part I

1 light-colored hair

1 dark-colored hair

1 Make a wet mount of 2 different-colored hairs, 1 light and 1 dark. Cross 1 hair over the other. Sketch the hairs as they appear under low power.

2 With the crossed hairs centered under low power, adjust the diaphragm for the best light.

3 Turn the high-power objective into viewing position. Do *not* change the focus.

4 Sharpen the focus with the *fine-adjustment knob only. Do not focus under high power with the coarse-adjustment knob.* The high-power objective will touch the slide if it is in its lowest position. So you must not make large adjustments toward the slide. *Doing so can damage the objective and the slide by driving the objective into the slide.*

5 Readjust the diaphragm to get the best light. If you are not successful in finding the object under high power the first time, return to Step 2. Repeat the entire procedure carefully.

6 Using the fine-adjustment knob, focus on the hairs at the point where they cross. Can you see both hairs sharply at the same focus level? How can you use the fine-adjustment knob to determine which hair is crossed over the other? Sketch the hairs as they appear under high power.

11. When students move the slide away from them, the image moves toward them. When they move the slide to the right, the image moves to the left.

In Part III, students learn how to use the high-power objective of the microscope. In Step 1, they make a wet mount of different-colored hairs and sketch what they see with the low-power objective. They should adjust the mirrors or diaphragm for the best light. In Step 3, students move to the high-power objective without changing the focus. Tell them to use the fine-adjustment knob to get the hairs in focus. Emphasize that large adjustments will make it difficult to focus and could damage the lens if they drive the lens into the slide. For Step 6, they sketch the hairs once they are in focus.

NOTES:

Answers to Reflect and Connect

1. Images are larger when viewed through a microscope. Type is grainier and shows a dot pattern. Objects are inverted and reversed. They appear to move in the opposite direction of the actual motion of the slide.
2. The high-power objective can focus on only a portion of the depth of the object at any one time.

Reflect and Connect

Work with your partner to answer the following questions in your science notebook.

1. Summarize the differences between an image viewed through a microscope and the same image viewed with the unaided eye.
2. When you view an object through the high-power objective, not all of the object may be in focus. Explain why.

868 How to Use a Compound Microscope

Guidelines for Laboratory Safety

Overview

Safety must be a major consideration in a science laboratory. The safety information in this teacher edition is not intended to be a complete guide but rather to help you organize your own laboratory safety program for which you are ultimately responsible. Consult your school authorities and local and state regulations for complete information about safety requirements in your state or district and for more detailed information about any safety concerns you might have. Keep informed of new safety data made available by government agencies, educational organizations, and other sources, and update your safety programs as necessary.

Before each laboratory experience, anticipate possible accidents and take steps to prevent them. Preventing an accident is, after all, the goal of a safety program. Base your conduct and expectations on the students' age, background, and intelligence. Do not expect them to behave as responsible adults.

Post laboratory rules in a conspicuous place in the laboratory. Insist on a safety contract between the student and the school. Devise your own, or use the Laboratory Safety Agreement presented in this overview.

Instruct students in techniques of laboratory safety and give them the opportunity to demonstrate their knowledge of proper safety practices. When students learn what is expected of them, and when you show that you are safety conscious, they will be more likely to follow appropriate safety procedures. A list of basic safety considerations follows.

1. Have a thorough understanding of each activity and the potential hazards of the materials, equipment, and procedures required.
2. Before conducting an activity, be sure that all safety and personal protective equipment is present and in good working order. Before students begin an activity, review specific safety rules and demonstrate proper procedures.
3. Never permit students to work in or be present in the laboratory without supervision. No unauthorized activity should be conducted, and no unauthorized materials should be brought into the laboratory.
4. Lock the laboratory and storeroom when you are not present. Do not allow students to enter the storeroom at any time.
5. Mark locations of, and call students' attention to, eyewash stations, safety showers, and fire blankets in the laboratory and storeroom. Also mark locations of chemical spill kits, fire extinguishers (ABC triclass), and first aid kits.
6. Post an evacuation diagram and procedure by each exit.
7. Provide for separate, labeled disposal containers for glass and sharp objects and separate, labeled disposal containers for individual waste chemical reagents.
8. For safety and economy, use small hot plates with an on/off switch and indicator light whenever possible. Do not use alcohol lamps.
9. Do not allow food or beverages and the application of cosmetics in the laboratory. Guard against toxic exposure by providing adequate ventilation. Remind students not to ingest or touch chemicals, and identify plants or animals that may cause irritation or poisoning by contact or by bite. Caution students to keep their hands and fingers away from their faces and to wash their hands with soap and water before leaving the laboratory.
10. Know the location of the master shutoff for laboratory electrical circuits, gas, and water.
11. Notify those in authority of the existence or development of any hazard.
12. Remind students that they must report directly to you any accident, no matter how trivial. Keep written records of events related to accidents.

Laboratory Safety Agreement

I, ____, agree to abide by the following laboratory safety regulations whenever performing a biology activity. I will

1. use the science laboratory for authorized work only.
2. remove contact lenses and wear safety goggles when instructed to do so.
3. know the four hazard categories and control measures.
4. study the laboratory activity before coming to the lab. (If in doubt about any procedure, I will ask the teacher.)
5. know how to use the safety equipment and know the location of the fire extinguisher, eyewash station, safety shower, and fire blanket.
6. alert the teacher in case of fire and leave the laboratory.
7. check carefully for the presence of any ignition source (such as open flames and electric heating coils) before using flammable materials such as alcohol.
8. place broken glass and disposable materials in their designated containers.
9. report any incident, accident, injury, or unsafe procedure to the teacher at once.
10. never taste, touch, or smell any substance unless the teacher specifically directs me to do so.
11. handle chemicals carefully, check the label of every bottle or jar before removing the contents, and never return unused chemicals to reagent containers.
12. make sure that the mouth of the test tube points away from other people and away from myself when heating a substance in a test tube.
13. use proper equipment to handle hot glassware.
14. tie back long hair, remove dangling jewelry, roll up loose sleeves, and tuck in loose clothing.
15. clean the work area at the end of the lab, wash and store all materials and equipment, and turn off all water, gas, and electrical appliances.
16. wash my hands thoroughly with soap and water before leaving the laboratory.

______________________________ Student's Signature

______________________________ Parent's or Guardian's Signature

______________________________ Date

Personal Protective Equipment

Whenever chemicals or laboratory equipment are used, everyone in the laboratory should wear safety goggles and laboratory aprons. Loose clothing, full blouses, ties, bows, and so forth should be tucked in. Long hair should be tied back securely. If a chemical spill occurs on someone's clothing or soft cloth shoes, the individual should remove the article and wash the skin thoroughly with running water. Do not attempt to wash off a harmful chemical while the clothing is on the body. Use the safety shower in such cases. (See the Safety Shower section for details.) Contaminated shoes rarely can be reused; contaminated clothing must be laundered separately before reuse.

When corrosives are used, students should wear safety goggles, as well as a laboratory apron and impervious gloves (nitrile rubber). A safety shower and eyewash station should be within a 30-second walking distance. Specifications for protective equipment follow:

- *Lab apron.*Gray or black rubber-coated cloth, Tyvek, or vinyl (nylon-coated), halter-type aprons are recommended when working with corrosives or solvents. Disposable polyethylene is recommended only to prevent physical contact with water-based reagents that are not, in themselves, corrosives or solvents.
- *Gloves.* Nitrile or neoprene rubber is recommended when handling acids, caustics, or organic solvents. Polyethylene or natural latex gloves should be used only for protection against water-based reagents that are not corrosives or solvents.
- *Safety goggles.* Clear, high-impact polystyrene splash goggles should be used; they must meet ANSI Standard Z87.1.
- *Contact lenses.* Liquids can be drawn under a contact lens by capillary action and into direct contact with the eyeball. Therefore, wearing contact lenses for cosmetic reasons should be prohibited in the laboratory. Students who must wear contact lenses prescribed by a physician should wear eyecup ANSI Z87.1–approved safety goggles. These are similar to the goggles sometimes worn when swimming underwater. If an accident occurs (despite the protection of safety goggles), the student should immediately remove the safety goggles and the contact lenses and flush the eyes, including under the eyelids, at the eyewash station for at least 15 minutes. Roll eyes from side to side and up and down while flushing. Meanwhile, call a physician.
- *Eyewash station.* The eyewash station must meet ANSI Standard Z358.1 and be within a 30-second walking distance from any spot in the room. The device must be capable of delivering a gentle but full flow of water to both eyes for at least 15 minutes. Portable liquid supply devices are not satisfactory and should not be used. A plumbed-hose attached to a plumbed-in outlet and designed for use as an eyewash fountain is suitable if it meets ANSI Standard Z358.1. Demonstrate the use of the eyewash station to your students. Follow the procedure described in the First Aid section. You should test the eyewash station weekly to ensure it is in proper working order.
- *Safety shower.* The safety shower must meet ANSI Standard Z358.1 and be within a 30-second walking distance from any spot in the room. Students should be instructed in the use of the safety shower in the event of a fire or chemical splash on clothing. Chemicals should be flushed off the bare skin for at least 15 minutes while under the safety shower. Make certain students understand that contaminated clothing, shoes, wristwatches, and so forth *must be removed while under the shower.* False modesty is a poor exchange for permanent injury. Call a doctor while the student is still under the shower.

No safety shower is referred to in the cautionary statements that accompany each activity because the quantities of chemicals used in this laboratory program are kept sufficiently small. A safety shower should be present in the laboratory, however, as a precaution against fires or chemical spills related to other laboratory procedures. You should test the safety shower weekly to ensure it is in proper working order.

Understanding Chemical Hazards

General Information

Some degree of hazard or risk is associated with every chemical that you or your students will handle. Using chemicals safely means understanding the hazards and taking the appropriate measures to prevent harm. A hazardous chemical is any substance likely to cause injury if precautionary measures are not taken. The hazards presented by any chemical can be grouped into the following categories: flammables, poisons (toxins), corrosives, and reactives. A particular chemical may present more than one hazard.

When dealing with chemical hazards, be aware of and follow general safety procedures regarding storage, disposal, spills, and first aid, as listed in this section. Detailed information about specific chemical categories follows this listing.

Signal Words

This program uses the signal word *Caution* specifically to inform both you and the students about a risk associated with a particular material or activity.

Chemical Hazard Labeling

Any container used by students must be labeled accurately with the following information:

- The *name of the material* and its concentration (if in solution)
- The *names of individual components* and their respective concentrations (if a mixture)

- The appropriate *signal word*
- An affirmative *statement of the potential hazard* or hazards
- *Precautionary measures* to be taken to avoid the hazards
- Immediate *first aid measures*

For example, a stock 70 percent isopropyl alcohol solution should be labeled as shown:

70% Isopropyl Alcohol
CAUTION: Flammable liquid
Avoid open flame, heat, or sparks.
Do not ingest. Avoid skin and eye contact.

Flush spills and splashes with water
for 15 minutes; rinse mouth with water.
Call the teacher.

Small student-use containers such as dropping bottles must be labeled with the name of the chemical and the caution statement. Reagent bottles must have complete labels as shown in the example.

Refer to the introduction material for each activity for appropriate safety information when writing label warnings.

Storage

Specific information about chemical storage may be found in the Management of Chemicals section. In general, chemicals should be stored in a cool, dry place away from direct sunlight and local heat and segregated according to storage colors.

Spills

These directions are generic and may not be appropriate in all types of spills. Refer to the Material Safety Data Sheets (MSDS) for specific instructions.

- *Solids.* Sweep up the material; avoid dusting; place it in a suitable container; wash the area with water and discard the water.
- *Liquids.* Check the pH with litmus or another indicator; if necessary, adjust pH to neutrality with small amounts of 1M acid or base; wipe up with absorbent material and discard; wash the spill area with water.

Disposal of Chemicals Used in This Program

Recommended disposal procedures are included in the *Advance Preparation* section of an activity for all prepared solutions that require special disposal steps. Keep in mind that these procedures may be preempted by state or local regulations. Consult the MSDS for specific procedures for stock reagents before disposal.

- *Aqueous liquids.* Test the pH with litmus or another indicator; if necessary, adjust pH to neutrality by adding small amounts of an acid, base, or other reagent as required. (Exceptions are noted in *Advance Preparation.*) In all cases, dilute aqueous liquid waste material at least 1:20 with water and flush to a sanitary sewer (not a drain that leads to a septic tank).
- *Solids.* Dissolve small amounts of the material completely in water; dilute this volume 1:20 with water again; flush to a sanitary sewer. (Exceptions are noted in *Advance Preparation.*)
- *Biological materials.* Actively growing culture materials should be autoclaved or steam-sterilized in a pressure cooker at 15 psi for 15 minutes. Use autoclavable bags. If an autoclave or pressure cooker is not available, aseptically add (in a fume hood) just enough full-strength chlorine laundry bleach or 70 percent isopropyl alcohol to cover the growing surface. Cover the container, close the hood door, and allow at least 8 hours contact time before disposal. **Caution: Alcohol is flammable. Extinguish all flames and avoid other ignition sources.** Wear safety goggles, gloves, and a lab apron. Dilute with water 1:20 and flush using copious amounts of water to a sanitary sewer. Autoclave or steam-sterilize contaminated objects, or place them in the hood in covered pans or trays containing liquid chlorine laundry bleach. Allow 24 hours contact before diluting with water 1:20 and discarding the bleach to a sanitary sewer. Wash decontaminated objects with soap and water.

First Aid

Before using any chemical, read the label and the MSDS and follow the recommended procedures. In case of spills or splashes, carry out the following immediate first aid measures:

- *Eyes.* Immediately flush eyes, including under eyelids, with flowing water for at least 15 minutes at an eyewash station. Roll eyes from side to side and up and down while flushing. Call a physician.
- *Skin.* Wash with flowing water for at least 15 minutes. Contact a physician if redness, blisters, continued irritation, or painful symptoms develop.
- *Clothing.* Remove any contaminated clothing within 5 minutes and wash skin as above. (For concentrated chemicals the teacher uses, go to the safety shower immediately and remove clothing while under the shower.) Launder or decontaminate any article before wearing. Contaminated clothing includes shoes, belts, watches and watch straps, jewelry, and so forth. If laundering or decontamination is not possible, discard.
- *Inhalation.* Remove victim to fresh air. Begin CPR if the victim has stopped breathing. Get immediate medical attention.

- *Ingestion.* For mouth contact, spit out and wash the mouth with running water for at least 15 minutes. Contact a physician immediately.

Poison (Toxins)

> **Protective equipment:** Gloves, safety goggles, lab apron, container for sharp objects, chemical fume hood, secured storage ventilation sufficient to keep breathing-air concentrations well below the threshold limit value (TLV) and permissible exposure limit (PEL)

Typically, toxic chemicals can injure the body through one or more exposure routes: inhalation, ingestion, injection, and absorption through intact skin or through a break in the skin.

There are two types of toxic effects: acute and chronic. An acute effect usually occurs on exposure or within a few hours following exposure. A chronic effect is noted only following repeated exposures or after a prolonged single exposure.

Important information about toxicity in the MSDS for each substance is provided by the supplier. (See the section titled Health Hazard Data, or similar title, on the MSDS.)

Prevention and Control Measures

1. Treat all chemicals as potentially toxic. Use barriers, cleanliness, and avoidance when handling any chemical.
2. Wear eye protection.
3. Handle contaminated glass and metal carefully. Sharp objects are vehicles for injecting substances into the body.
4. Provide enough ventilation to keep vapor, mist, and dust concentrations well below the TLV or PEL as stated in the MSDS. Use a chemical fume hood if required.
5. Recognize symptoms of overexposure for each chemical used during an activity. These are usually described in the MSDS.
6. Become familiar with immediate first aid measures for each chemical used during an activity. See the MSDS and label.
7. Be scrupulous in housekeeping and personal hygiene.
8. Never consume food or beverages or apply cosmetics in the laboratory.
9. Wash your hands thoroughly with soap and water before leaving the laboratory.
10. Post the phone number of the nearest poison control center and consulting school physician on your telephone.

Flammables

> **Protective equipment:** Safety goggles, approved flammable-liquid storage cabinets, fire blanket, safety shower, fire extinguishers (ABC triclass)

Flammable substances are solids, liquids, or gases that will burn readily. The process of burning involves fuel, oxidizer, and an ignition source. For burning to start, all three components must be present. To stop a fire or prevent it from starting, remove or make inaccessible at least one of those components.

Prevention and Control Measures

1. Store away from oxidizers.
2. Store only in approved containers in an approved flammable-liquid storage cabinet. Minimize the quantities available in the laboratory—usually 100 millimeters (mL) per bottle and 600 mL per room.
3. Remove ignition sources. Extinguish lighted burners. Check for and eliminate sources of ignition, such as sparks from static charge, friction, or electrical equipment, and hot objects such as hot plates or incandescent bulbs. Keep all ignition sources 30 feet (ft) away. If the ignition source is 6 ft above, a distance of 15 ft away is usually sufficient. (Flammable vapors are usually heavier than air and can travel long distances before being diluted below ignitable concentrations.)
4. Electrically bond and ground all metal containers before and during the dispensing of flammable liquids. Check with your local fire department for the correct procedure.
5. Ensure that ABC triclass fire extinguishers are present in the laboratory and storeroom and that you have used these in at least one practice drill, supervised by a firefighting official, within the past year.
6. Drill students in exactly what should be done if clothes or hair catch fire. Practice "stop, drop, and roll" techniques. Be sure a safety shower is available and is in working order. A fire blanket should be available to cover a prone victim but should not be used to wrap smoldering or burning clothing, except in emergencies.
7. Conduct a fire inspection with members of the local fire department at least once a year. Practice fire drills at least annually.
8. Provide adequate ventilation to keep breathing-air concentrations well below the TLV and the PEL.
9. Prepare for spills by having absorbent, vapor-reducing materials close at hand. (These are available commercially.) Plan to have enough absorbent material to handle the volume of flammables on hand.

Reactives

> **Protective equipment:** Safety goggles, lab apron, gloves, segregated storage location

Reactives are chemical substances that undergo violent reactions, generating heat, light, flammable and nonflammable gases, and toxicants under certain ambient or induced (by mixing, shock, or disturbance) conditions. Categories of reactives include, but are not limited to, the following:

- Acid-sensitives—react with acids or acid fumes
- Water-sensitives—react with moisture
- Oxidizers—promote rapid burning or explosion in materials that can burn
- Unstable—spontaneously explode when handled, moved, exposed to sunlight or rapid temperature changes, and so on

Prevention and Control Measures

1. In storage, isolate compounds of a given hazard class away from other hazard classes. Consult color storage codes. Note that certain chemicals classed "white" or "red" should be stored separately—away from other chemicals with the same storage code color. Chemicals requiring special storage assignments are identified in the *Advance Preparation* sections of the activities.
2. Protect reactives from physical shock.
3. Provide a ready water source for dilution (except for water-sensitives).
4. Keep water away from water-sensitives.
5. Store in a cool, dry place away from sunlight and localized heat.
6. Familiarize yourself with any incompatibilities for *all* chemicals used or stored.

Corrosives

> **Protective equipment:** Safety goggles, lab apron, nitrile rubber gloves, safety shower, eyewash station

Corrosives are solids, liquids, or gases that, by direct chemical action, destroy body tissues. Irritants are a group of chemicals that cause less serious injury. Sensitizers are allergenic. Hence, injury may range from sensitization or irritation to actual physical destruction of body tissues. Categories of corrosives include the following:

- Corrosives—cause destruction and irreversible alterations in living tissue
- Irritants—cause reversible inflammation in living tissue
- Sensitizers—cause allergic reaction in normal tissue of a substantial number of individuals after more than one exposure

Prevention and Control Measures

1. Store corrosives below eye level. Keep containers closed.
2. Always wear safety goggles and a lab apron. Also wear gloves when handling any corrosive material above 1M.
3. Have at least one eyewash station and safety shower in close proximity. Be sure they are in working order.
4. Never wear cloth-covered, woven-leather, or open-toed shoes in the laboratory.
5. Prepare for spills by having neutralizing kits readily available in sufficient quantity for the corrosives on hand.
6. Always wash hands with soap and water after working with corrosives.

Management of Chemicals

Note: The following section about storage is for your general information. If you have any questions about the storage of chemicals, call the safety consultant with your materials supplier.

Storage

Never store chemicals alphabetically unless they have been segregated into color-coded storage areas (see the following). Alphabetical storage greatly increases the risk of promoting a violent reaction. A list of storage suggestions follows:

1. Store chemicals in a cool, dry place, away from sunlight and rapid temperature changes.
2. Never store chemicals on the floor or above eye level.
3. Firmly secure all shelf assemblies to the wall.
4. Use only shelves that have antiroll lips.
5. Use permanently fixed, not adjustable, shelves.
6. Store flammables in a dedicated flammable-storage cabinet.
7. Store poisons in a locked, dedicated poison-storage cabinet.
8. Store chemicals by a color-code classification, in separate dedicated storage areas as described in the following paragraph.

Many chemical and biological supply companies use color codes to designate general hazards and to facilitate handling and storage of chemicals. These codes are present on reagent labels, but each chemical or biological supplier uses a different color-code scheme. Many, but not all, of the supplier color codes *appear* to be based on single hazardous characteristics, such as flammability or corrosivity. In fact, they are based on multiple reactivity characteristics. Be sure you are familiar with the color codes for the chemicals used in this program and make appropriate arrangements for safe storage.

Chemical Inventory

It is important to compile an inventory and location map of *all* chemicals and reagents in the school as well as to obtain an MSDS for each. Together, these form a critical database for protecting your own health and safety and those of your students. Have this information available in a central location in the science area and also give it to your local fire marshal or fire chief. Your inventory form should include the following categories: substance, protective equipment, storage color code, hazards, amount on hand, and location.

Material Safety Data Sheets

The purpose of a Material Safety Data Sheet (MSDS) is to protect users and others from harm by supplying readily accessible information about hazards and precautionary measures. Typically, an MSDS is organized into sections that include the following: manufacturer and material identification, hazards, physical data, fire and explosion data, reactivity data, health hazard information, spill and leak procedures, special information, exposure, guidelines, and special handling precautions.

Under federal requirements, all manufacturers and suppliers of hazardous chemicals must provide MSDS. Most biological supply houses include MSDS with the chemical at the time of shipment. To request an MSDS, simply call or write the supplier, giving the product name and catalog number.

MSDS should be kept on file and referred to *before* handling *any* chemical. The MSDS also can be used to instruct students about chemical hazards and to evaluate spill and disposal procedures and incompatibilities with other chemicals or mixtures.

Emergency Procedures

What would you do if a student dropped a 1-liter bottle of isopropyl alcohol or hydrochloric acid? Are you prepared? Could you have altered your handling and storage methods to prevent or lessen the severity of the incident? Plan now how to react effectively *before* you need to. Some planning tips include the following.

1. Post the phone numbers of your regional poison control center, fire, police, and hospital on your telephone.
2. Practice fire and evacuation drills as well as what students must do in case of fire or chemical contact or exposure.
3. Ensure that all personal and other safety equipment is available and tested, if appropriate.
4. Compile an MSDS database and inventory of all chemicals.
5. Prepare in advance for spill-control procedures.
6. Under no circumstances allow students to fight fires or handle spills.
7. Appoint a hazardous material response team of knowledgeable individuals who are prepared to handle spills or leaks. Agree beforehand who in the school has the ultimate decision-making authority for evaluating a hazardous material incident. Know who to call for help and when *not* to handle an incident yourself.
8. Be trained in first aid and basic life support (CPR) procedures. Have first aid kits readily available.
9. Fully document *any* incident that occurs. Documentation is a critical tool in helping to identify areas of laboratory safety that need improvement.

Additional Safety Notes

1. Use only nontoxic marking pens. Many types of permanent marking pens release hazardous vapors.
2. Use nonmercury or digital thermometers in the laboratory. Mercury vapors from broken thermometers are poisonous. In the event a mercury thermometer is broken or if mercury is spilled, collect all droplets and pools at once with a suction pump and aspirator bottle with a long capillary tube (commercially available). Cover fine (invisible) droplets in inaccessible cracks with calcium polysulfide and excess sulfur. Combine all contaminated mercury in a tightly stoppered bottle. Contact a registered and approved disposal agency.

Note: If the mercury in a small clinical thermometer were dispersed in a closed 30 × 30 × 4 meter room, the TLV would be exceeded. Thermometer mercury spills are insidious and potentially dangerous.

3. When treating a student who has a bleeding cut, follow the recent Occupational Safety and Health Administration (OSHA) standard regarding bloodborne pathogens. At a minimum, wear safety goggles and impervious gloves.
4. Electrical sockets in the laboratory must be protected with a GFI (ground fault interrupter) type of circuit breaker. Each electrical outlet in the lab must be a three-hole outlet, and each set of three holes must be checked with a circuit tester before any use to make certain that the wiring has been correctly connected to the three holes. (That is, there should be no "open ground," "open neutral," or "open hot" wiring and no "hot/ground reverse" and no "hot/neutral reverse" wiring. The circuit tester indicates these wrong conditions by various configurations of red and green lights. Circuit testers can be purchased at RadioShack or an equivalent retailer for less than $5.)
5. All electrical equipment should have a three-wire code with an attached three-prong plug.

Safety Information Resources and References

American Chemical Society Health and Safety Service. American Chemical Society. 1155 16th Street NW, Washington, DC 20036, 202-872-4511. This service refers inquiries to appropriate resources to help find answers to questions about health and safety.

Committee on Hazardous Substances in the Laboratory. National Research Council. (1995). *Prudent practices in the laboratory: Handling and disposal of chemicals.* Washington, DC: National Academy Press.

Council Committee on Chemical Safety. (1990). *Safety in academic chemistry laboratories* (4th ed.). Washington, DC: American Chemical Society.

Hazardous Materials Information Exchange (HMIX). HMIX can be accessed on the Internet (http://hazmat.dot.gov/). HMIX is sponsored by the Federal Emergency Management Agency and the U.S. Department of Transportation and serves as a reliable on-line database, accessed through an electronic bulletin board. It provides information about instructional material and literature listings, hazardous materials and emergencies, and applicable laws and regulations.

Lefèvre, M. J. (1989). *The first aid manual for chemical accidents.* [Revised by Shirley A. Conibear.] Stroudsburg, PA: Dowden.

New York State Environmental Facilities Corporation. (1985). *A guide to information sources related to the safety and management of laboratory waste from secondary schools.* New York: Author.

O'Neil, M. J., et al. (2003). *The Merck index* (13th ed.). Rahway, NJ: Merck.

Pipitone, D. (Ed.). (1991). *Safe storage of laboratory chemicals* (2nd ed.). New York: John Wiley.

United States Department of Health and Human Services. (2003). *NIOSH pocket guide to chemical hazards* (DHEW [NIOSH] Publication No. 78-210). Washington, DC: United States Government Printing Office.

Young, J. A. (Ed.). (1991). *Improving safety in the chemical laboratory: A practical guide.* New York: John Wiley.

Special Guidelines for the Biology Laboratory

Because biology involves the study of organisms, both living and preserved, certain safety considerations are unique to the biology laboratory.

Safety When Using Animals

A double safety standard must be maintained when live animals are used in the laboratory for observation and experimentation. The humane treatment of the animals is one objective, and the safety of the student is the other. We recommend that you follow the recommendations outlined in *The Use of Animals in Biology Education* from the National Association of Biology Teachers (NABT), which is available from its Web site.

In addition to the NABT guidelines, observe the following cautions for student safety.

1. All mammals used in the biology laboratory should have been inoculated for rabies unless they were purchased from a reliable biological supply house or pet dealer.
2. Wild animals never should be brought into the laboratory.
3. Any student who is scratched or bitten by an animal should receive immediate attention by the school nurse or a physician.

Safety When Using Plants

1. Become familiar with poisonous plants common to your area.
2. Have students observe the following rules:
   - **a.** Do not eat any parts of plants intended for use in laboratory work.
   - **b.** Do not rub sap or plant juice on the eyes, mucous membranes, skin, or an open wound.
   - **c.** Do not inhale or expose skin or eyes to the smoke of any burning plant.
   - **d.** Do not pick wildflowers or cultivated plants with which you are unfamiliar.
   - **e.** After handling any plants, wash your hands thoroughly with soap and water before leaving the laboratory.
3. Do not work with plants that may have been sprayed with insecticides.
4. If any student exhibits signs of plant poisoning, such as headaches, dizziness, nausea, constriction of pupils, sweating, muscle tremor, or indications of convulsion, call the school nurse or a physician. The poison control center may be able to offer suggestions for first aid.

The following is a partial list of potentially dangerous plants developed by the National Safety Council. Add to the list any dangerous plants specific to your area.

- *House and garden plants.* Autumn crocus, bleeding heart, castor bean (seeds), daffodil (bulbs), dieffenbachia, Dutchman's-breeches (foliage, roots), elephant's ear (all parts), foxglove (leaves), hyacinth, iris (underground stems), larkspur (young plant, seeds), lily of the valley (leaves, flowers), mistletoe (berries), monkshood (fleshy roots), narcissus, oleander (leaves, branches), poinsettia (leaves), rhubarb (leaf blade), rosary pea, star-of-Bethlehem (bulbs)
- *Trees, shrubs, and vines.* Azalea (all parts); black locust (bark, sprouts, foliage); cherries, wild and cultivated (twigs, foliage); daphne (berries); elderberry (shoots, leaves, bark); golden chain (capsules); jessamine (berries); lantana (green berries); laurel; oaks (foliage, acorns); poison ivy (leaves and berries); poison oak (leaves); poison sumac (leaves); rhododendron; wisteria (seeds, pods); yew (berries, foliage)
- *Wildflowers.* Jack-in-the-pulpit (all parts, especially roots), mayapple (apples, foliage, roots), moonseed

(berries), nightshade (all parts, especially the unripe berry), poison hemlock (all parts), thorn apple (all parts), water hemlock (all parts)

Pollen and Mold Spores

Handle pollen-producing plants and spore-producing fungi carefully so that pollen and spores are not spread throughout the classroom. Many people are allergic to pollen, spores, or both.

Safety When Using Microbes

1. Pathogenic bacteria, fungi, protists, or helminths are not appropriate activity specimens in the high school laboratory and should never be used.
2. Demonstrate correct aseptic technique to students before conducting an activity. Never transfer liquid media by mouth or mouth suction. Flame wire loops before and after transferring bacterial cultures.
3. Treat all microorganisms as pathogenic. Use tape to seal plates containing bacterial cultures. Do not use blood agar plates and never attempt to cultivate flora from a human or animal source.
4. Never allow students to clean up bacteriological spills. Keep a spill kit on hand that contains 500 mL of chlorine laundry bleach, biohazard bags (autoclavable), forceps, and paper towels. In the event of a bacteriological spill, cover the area with a layer of paper towels. Wet the paper towels with the disinfectant solution; allow to stand for 15–20 minutes. Wearing gloves and using forceps, place the residue in the biohazard bag. If broken glass is present, place the bag in a suitably marked container.
5. Consult with the school nurse to screen students who may be receiving immunosuppressive drug therapy that could lower immune response. Such individuals are extraordinarily sensitive to potential infection from nonpathogenic microorganisms and should not participate in laboratory activities involving microorganisms unless permitted to do so by a physician. Do not allow students with cuts, abrasions, or open sores to work with microorganisms.
6. Never discard microbe cultures without first sterilizing. Wear safety goggles, a lab apron, and gloves. Autoclave or steam-sterilize all used cultures and any materials that have come in contact with them at 15 psi for 15 minutes. If these devices are not available, flood or immerse these articles in either chlorine laundry bleach or 70 percent isopropyl alcohol for 30 minutes and then discard. While sterilizing the cultures, keep them covered and in a fume hood. **Caution: Alcohol is flammable. Extinguish all flames and avoid other ignition sources.** Do not allow students to use a steam sterilizer or autoclave.

Caution

7. Wash the lab surface with a disinfectant solution before and after handling bacterial cultures. Wear safety goggles, a lab apron, and gloves.

Safety When Using Preserved Materials

Biological supply firms use dilute formalin-based fixatives of varying concentrations (0.9–5 percent) for initially fixing zoological and botanical specimens. Usually it is the practice to posttreat and ship specimens in holding fluids or preservatives that do not contain formalin. Ward's Natural Science Establishment, Inc., provides specimens that are freeze-dried and rehydrated in a 10 percent isopropyl alcohol solution. In these specimens, no other hazardous chemical is present. Many suppliers provide fixed botanical materials in 50 percent glycerin.

Because your lab supplies may contain specimens fixed with formaldehyde (in formalin), you should be aware of the following safety precautions. Be sure the formaldehyde concentration in the air is less than the permissible exposure limit. (Currently, the PEL is 0.75 parts per million [ppm] with an "action level" of 0.5 ppm.) To be sure that exposure levels do not exceed acceptable standards, you can measure the concentration of formaldehyde in the air. Your lab supplier can suggest appropriate measures and technical equipment.

The following personal protective safety equipment is mandated when handling preserved specimens or when in contact with preserving fluids: safety goggles, protective gloves (nitrile, polyethylene, latex, or neoprene), and a lab apron or smock.

To reduce free formaldehyde, prewash specimens in a container left ajar in running water for 1–4 hours to dilute the fixative. Formaldehyde also may be chemically bound to reduce off-gassing by immersing washed specimens in a 0.5–1.0 percent (by mass or volume) potassium bisulfate solution overnight.

The following safety practices are recommended when handling or dissecting any preserved material specimen.

1. Never dissect roadkills or nonpreserved slaughterhouse material. Doing so increases the risk of infection.
2. Have students wear prescribed personal protective equipment (see above). Additional safety equipment includes eyewash stations within a 30-second walk from any location in the lab.
3. Do not allow the preserving fluid to come into continuous contact with the skin. Follow the supplier's recommendations for treating prolonged contact, ingestion, or eye contact.
4. Conduct dissections in an area sufficiently ventilated to keep hazardous substances well below their PEL in the air.

Disposal of Specimens and Preserving Fluids

Neither preserved specimens nor preserving fluids are considered by the Environmental Protection Agency to be a "hazardous waste" under the Resource Conservation and Recovery Act (RCRA), but local regulations may take precedence. Contact your supplier for recommended disposal procedures for the specific fluids provided.

Release of Biological Organisms

Nonindigenous species and certain microorganisms should not be reintroduced into local habitats. The responsible handling of life-forms requires that you be informed of their specific habitat requirements or potential for negative impact on local fauna or flora. The acquisition of any exotic or nonindigenous life-form requires preplanning to assure that it can be properly maintained throughout the entire year. See the Care and Release of Life-forms table at the end of this section for specific information about life-forms that may be used in *BSCS Science: An Inquiry Approach*.

Use the following guidelines in making a decision about the release of any organism into a local habitat.

1. Certain organisms, particularly insects, are specifically regulated, and you must have a permit to possess or release them. Check with your local office of the Animal and Plant Health Inspection Service (APHIS), U.S. Department of Agriculture, or contact your biological supplier. Examples of regulated organisms include cockroaches and termites.
2. Bacteria, fungi, yeasts, growth media, or materials that have been in contact with these organisms should never be discarded without prior sterilization (see Safety When Using Microbes). For certain microorganisms (*Agrobacterium, Erwinia,* and others), you will need a permit (in certain states) before shipment. Check with your biological supplier for restrictions before ordering.
3. Certain aquatic plants, particularly *Anacharis* (elodea), should not be introduced into local habitats. This plant is regulated as a pest in Canada and certain northern U.S. locales.
4. Ornamental plants should not, as a rule, be introduced into native habitats but instead should be kept indoors. Some states (California and others) have strict rules regarding procurement or introduction of plants containing root-bearing soils from outside the state that may contain plant-damaging nematodes. Usually, plants shipped from outside these states must pass an inspection or have a shipping permit. Check with your biological supplier before purchasing plant materials outside your state. Locally cultivated plants, as a rule, may be reintroduced by replanting if desired.
5. Nonindigenous macroinvertebrates and vertebrates should not be introduced into native habitats. In many cases, these organisms will not survive local climates or may compete or otherwise interfere with local fauna and flora. Contact your local APHIS office or your biological supplier for specific information about whether a particular organism is considered nonindigenous in *your* area. In extreme cases, when release or continued maintenance of an organism is impossible, the animal must be humanely destroyed. A recommended resource for the care and handling of invertebrate and vertebrate animals is *Animal Care from Protozoa to Small Mammals* (F. B. Orlans, 1977, Menlo Park, CA: Addison-Wesley). Biological supply companies usually provide information regarding proper euthanasia for animals supplied.
6. Most microinvertebrates and protists may be freely released in aquatic environments. Nematodes should never be introduced but should be destroyed by sterilization. Marine forms should be released only into marine habitats.

Care and release of life-forms

Life-form	Care	Release
Anacharis (elodea)	Place in established freshwater aquarium. Provide photoperiod of 16 hours light: 8 hours dark using plant grow lights (fluorescent or incandescent). Light source should be placed approximately 16–18 in over plants.	Do not release.
Bacteria (eubacteria)	Store slant or broth cultures for extended periods (up to 6 months) at refrigeration temperatures.	Discard only after autoclaving cultures or contaminated materials.
Butterflies, moths	House in perforated box covered with muslin netting. Keep caterpillars dry. Provide continuous supply of fresh leaves. Use egg cartons as surface for population. Keep humidity at 60 percent.	Require permit for release.
Chaetopterus	Require either established 25-gal marine aquarium or equal amount of conditioned seawater. Acclimate the animals to seawater. Aerate. Feed by introducing hatched brine shrimp. If care is exercised, animals may be returned to their tubes and left in aquarium following conclusion of investigation. Do not attempt to maintain these animals except in established marine aquarium.	Release only in Florida gulf area. Otherwise, euthanize using MS-222 (tricaine methanesulfonate).
Coleus, geraniums	Pot in potting soil. Maintain 16 hours light: 8 hours dark photoperiod. Use of plant grow lights is recommended.	May be transplanted.

Care and release of life-forms		
Life-form	**Care**	**Release**
Crickets, grasshoppers, small insects, termites	House in plastic containers that are sealable. Screen in airholes. Use egg cartons as "apartments." Keep temperature between 21–31°C, humidity at around 60 percent. Feed dried food pellets. Provide a number of watering devices (pieces of wet sponge or cotton in plastic petri dish).	Do not release. Euthanize by freezing.
Earthworms, other worms	Place commercial earthworm bedding or rich soil in plastic washtub. Introduce worms. Allow approximately 150 cm^3 per worm. Cover with sphagnum moss or leaves. Keep moist. Cover container with muslin. Long-term storage is best under refrigeration.	May be freely released.
Frogs	Southern species (*RanaBerlandieri*): Place up to 5 animals in 10-gal aquarium or similar container that is slightly tilted. Provide about 1–2 in of water in lower end. Feed crickets 2–3 times per week. Keep tank covered to prevent escape. Place tank in suitable location away from direct sunlight and excessive temperature. Change water daily. Northern species (*R. pipiens*): Store at refrigeration temperature for no longer than 5 days. May be housed for longer periods as described above.	May be released in appropriate habitat.
Gerbils	For up to 3 gerbils: Provide commercial enclosure or use plastic washtub with screened cage top. Use commercial water bottle introduced through cage top. House at room temperature of 21–23°C. Use sawdust bedding changed at least weekly. May be fed commercial pellet food (for rats or mice) or a mixture of seeds and cereals.	Not recommended. Usually pet stores will accept these animals.
Goldfish	House in 15–25-gal aquarium; allow 1 gallon per inch of water for each fish. Use aeration. Maintain water at 20–24°C. Use of aquatic plants recommended. Goldfish are omnivorous; feed them commercially prepared food daily. Remove uneaten food.	Not recommended. Usually pet stores will accept these animals.
Guppies	House in 10–25-gal aquarium: allow 10 cm^2 for each fish. Use aeration. Maintain water at 24–27°C. Use of aquatic plants recommended. Guppies are omnivorous; feed them commercially prepared food daily. Remove uneaten food.	Not recommended. Usually pet stores will accept these animals.
Hermit crabs	Place in plastic disphan with 1–2 in of dry aquarium gravel. Add 2 finger bowls, one containing dry pellet rat chow and the other filled with moderate-sized rocks submerged in water. Hermit crabs eat apples, will climb on small branches, and need some cover under which to hide.	Release only in southern United States, in subtropical climates.
Hydra	Store in jars at refrigeration temperature: change water (spring or pond) weekly. Feeding is not necessary unless animals are stored at room temperature; animals can be stored safely for up to 3 weeks at refrigeration temperatures. If stored at room temperature, feed weekly by introducing small *Daphnia* into jar.	May be freely released.
Mice	For up to 3 mice: Provide commercial enclosure or use plastic washtub with screen cage top. Use a commercial water bottle introduced through the cage top. House at room temperature of 21–23°C. Use sawdust bedding changed at least weekly. May be fed commercial pellet food (for rats or mice) or a mixture of seeds and cereals.	Not recommended. Usually pet stores will accept these animals.
Microinvertebrates	Short-term holding: Unscrew jar caps and place in cool area of lab away from direct sunlight. Long-term culture: Place in jar containing ½-in of pond mud that also contains sprigs of *Anacharis* (elodea). Place in area that will receive southern light exposure but not direct sunlight. Gentle aeration may be appllied.	May be freely released.
Planaria	Store in jars at refrigeration temperature; change water (spring or pond) weekly. Feeding is not necessary unless animals are stored at room temperature; animals can be stored for up to 3 weeks at refrigeration temperatures. If stored at room temperature, feed weekly by introducing small strips of fresh liver into jar.	May be freely released.
Protists	Short-term holding: Unscrew jar caps and place in cool area of lab away from direct sunlight. Refer to instructions for long-term care in microinvertebrates.	May be freely released.

Care and release of life-forms. Consult this figure when dealing with the various living organisms and read each activity's detailed instructions for care and handling of these creatures.

Glossary

A

abiotic [abiótico]: The physical and chemical (nonliving) components of an environment, such as light or water.

acceleration (*a*) [aceleración (*a*)]: The time rate of change in velocity; it is represented by the symbol *a*. The mathematical relationship describing acceleration is $a = \dfrac{\Delta v}{\Delta t}$.

acid [ácido]: A chemical compound that increases the concentration of hydrogen ions (H^+) in solution. This definition represents one of several views of acids.

acre-feet (af) [acre-pie (ap)]: The volume of water that covers 1 acre of land with water that is 1 foot deep.

activation energy (E_a) [energía de activación (E_a)]: The energy associated with the particles formed with the highest potential energy during a chemical process.

adaptations [adaptaciones]: Characteristics that help an organism survive and reproduce within a particular environment.

aerobic respiration [respiración aerobia]: A type of cellular respiration that requires the presence of oxygen.

agarose gel electrophoresis [electroforesis de gel de agarosa]: A process in which scientists separate DNA fragments by size. An electric current is used to propel the DNA through a porous gel matrix.

allele [alelo]: One of two or more possible forms of a gene. Each allele affects the hereditary trait a little differently.

amino acid [aminoácido]: The building blocks of polypeptides and proteins. Amino acids are organic compounds. They are composed of a central carbon atom to which are bonded a hydrogen atom, an amino group ($—NH_2$), an acid group (—COOH), and one of a variety of other atoms or groups of atoms.

anaerobe [anaerobio]: An organism that lives in the absence of oxygen.

anaerobic respiration [respiración anaeróbica]: A type of cellular respiration that does not require oxygen.

ancestral [ancestral]: Something from which a later generation or form is derived.

anion [anión]: A negatively charged particle typically associated with redox reactions.

anode [ánodo]: The electrode of an electrochemical cell, where oxidation takes place.

anticodon [anticodón]: A three-nucleotide sequence in a transfer RNA molecule. It is complementary to, and base-pairs with, a specific codon in mitochondrial RNA.

asexual reproduction [reproducción asexuada]: Any method of reproduction that requires only one parent or one parent cell.

atmospheric mixing [mezcla atmosférica]: The process of transporting and mixing components of the atmosphere on a regional or global scale.

autosome [autosoma]: A chromosome that is not directly involved in determining sex.

B

base [base]: A chemical compound that increases the concentration of hydroxide ions (OH^-) in solution. This definition represents one of several views of bases.

bioethics [bioética]: The study of ethical issues that are raised by developments in life science technologies, such as new medical technologies.

biologic carbon cycle [ciclo biológico del carbono]: A carbon cycle that consists of *active* or *mobile* carbon that moves between reservoirs on timescales of days to hundreds of years. This part of the carbon cycle operates largely at the surface of Earth and involves organisms.

biomass [biomasa]: The dry weight of organic matter that makes up a group of organisms in a particular habitat.

biome [bioma]: The distinctive plant cover and the rest of the community of organisms associated with a particular physical environment; often the biome is named for its plant cover. Some examples of biomes include tundra, tropical rain forest, desert, and temperate grassland.

bioremediation [biorremediación]: The use of microorganisms to degrade waste.

biotechnology [biotecnología]: A solution to a problem that involves technology *and* living organisms. Recombinant DNA technology has created many new forms of biotechnology.

biotic [bióticos]: The living or recently living components of an ecosystem.

birthrate [índice de natalidad]: The rate at which reproduction increases the population; often expressed as new individuals per 1,000 or 10,000 in the population.

boundaries [límites]: The limits of a system within which interactions occur.

C

carrying capacity [capacidad máxima]: The maximum population size that can be supported by the available resources of a given area.

catalyst [catalizador]: A chemical species that increases the rate of a chemical reaction without being changed permanently by the reaction.

cathode [cátodo]: The electrode of an electrochemical cell, where reduction takes place.

cation [catión]: A positively charged particle typically associated with redox reactions.

chromosome [cromosoma]: A long, threadlike group of genes found in the nucleus of all eukaryotic cells. Chromosomes are most visible during mitosis and meiosis. Chromosomes consist of DNA and protein.

climate [clima]: The general atmospheric conditions that repeat over long periods of time.

codon [codón]: The basic unit of the genetic code; a sequence of three adjacent nucleotides in DNA or messenger RNA.

community [comunidad]: All the organisms that inhabit a particular area.

complementary base pairing [formación de pares de bases complementarias]: The predictable interaction between nitrogen bases on opposite strands of DNA and between DNA and RNA. Adenine pairs with thymine and guanine pairs with cytosine in DNA; in RNA, adenine pairs with uracil.

concentration [concentración]: A means of expressing the number of particles per unit of space. A common unit of concentration in chemistry is molarity. It has the units of moles per liter (mol/L).

conservation of mass [conservación de la masa]: The concept that the mass of the reactants in a reaction must equal the mass of the products.

constant [constante]: A factor or attribute that remains unchanged during the course of an investigation. A constant can also be a quantity or value that is assumed not to vary for the purposes of a theory or experiment, for example, the speed of light.

continental crust [corteza continental]: The varied, basic rock material that is 40–70 kilometers thick and makes up continents.

continental drift [deriva continental]: The hypothesis proposed in 1912 by Alfred Wegener that, at one time, Earth's landmasses were joined in a supercontinent that broke up to form the present continents. Continental drift is now considered part of the broader theory of plate tectonics.

control [control]: In an investigation, the control is the individual thing, or group designated to receive no treatment (the unchanged group). All other groups are compared against the control.

convergent zones [zonas convergentes]: Regions where tectonic plates crash together.

cubic feet per second (cfs) [pies cúbicos por segundo (pcs)]: Units of water flow that measure 1 cubic foot of water moving past a point in 1 second.

D

daughter element [elemento derivado]: The chemical substance on the product side of a radioactive decay equation. The nuclei of daughter elements are produced from parent elements.

deoxyribonucleic acid (DNA) [ácido desoxirribonucleico (ADN)]: The hereditary material of most organisms. DNA makes up genes and contains deoxyribose, a phosphate group, and one of four DNA bases.

diploid [diploide]: Refers to a cell that contains both members of every chromosome pair that is characteristic of a species.

dissolved inorganic carbon (DIC) [carbono inorgánico disuelto (CID)]: The component of carbon derived from inorganic sources, such as bicarbonate and carbonate ions, that is dissolved in natural waters.

dissolved load [carga disuelta]: The elements and molecules in an ionic form that are dissolved in natural waters.

dissolved organic carbon (DOC) [carbono orgánico disuelto (COD)]: The component of carbon derived from organic matter, such as plant leaves, that is dissolved in natural waters.

divergent zones [zonas divergentes]: Zones where tectonic plates move apart, forming rifts on continents or on the ocean floor.

DNA polymerase [polimerasa de ADN]: An enzyme that catalyzes the synthesis of a new DNA strand by using one of the original strands as a template.

DNA replication [replicación del ADN]: The process of making a copy of a chromosome in a cell nucleus as well as other genes in certain organelles outside the nucleus, particularly chloroplasts and mitochrondria. The process is different from duplication because each gene and each chromosome in the double set contains new parts and parts of the old gene or chromosome.

dominant [dominante]: Refers to alleles or traits that mask the presence of another allele of the same gene in a heterozygous organism.

E

eccentricity [excentricidad]: Refers to the shape of Earth's orbit around the Sun. Eccentricity varies on timescales of about 100,000 years.

ecological niche [nicho ecológico]: All the adaptations an organism uses to survive in its environment. These include what its role in the community is, what it eats, and what interactions it has with other organisms and with its environment.

ecology [ecología]: A field in biology that studies organisms and their relationship to their environment.

ecosystem [ecosistema]: The biological community and its abiotic environment.

elastic collision [choque elástico]: A collision that occurs when the energy and momenta of objects in a system remain the same before and after collisions. Elastic collisions can occur when colliding objects rebound or bounce off each other.

electric current [corriente eléctrica]: The flow of charge in a particular direction.

electrolytic cell [célula electrolítica]: An electrochemical reaction such as electrolysis. This reaction is characterized by using electrical energy to reverse a spontaneous redox reaction.

embryo [embrión]: An organism in its earliest stages of development.

emigration [emigración]: The departure of individuals from a population; emigration decreases the size of the population.

endemic [endémico]: Animals or plants that are restricted to a specific region.

endothermic [endotérmico]: Processes that absorb heat from the surroundings, resulting in a temperature decrease. Endothermic reactions have a positive net enthalpy ($+\Delta H$).

enthalpy [entalpía]: The net energy ($E_{final} - E_{initial}$ = net energy) associated with a chemical reaction. Its symbol is ΔH.

environment [medio ambiente]: Everything living and nonliving in an organism's surroundings, including light, temperature, air, soil, water, and other organisms.

enzymes [enzimas]: Any chemical species, usually proteins or molecules that include proteins, that catalyze, or speed up, biological reactions. Enzymes are made by an organism.

equilibrium [equilibrio]: A description of the state of any reversible chemical reaction in which the rate of its forward reaction equals the rate of its reverse reaction.

equilibrium position [punto de equilibrio]: An indication of the relative amounts of reactants and products present for a chemical system at equilibrium. When more products are present, the equilibrium position favors the products. The equilibrium position is to the right. When more reactants are present, the equilibrium position favors the reactants. The equilibrium position is to the left.

erosion [erosión]: The process where weathered rock fragments and soils are transported and moved downward due to gravity. Erosion of mountains occurs along steep slopes and river valleys.

erosion half-life [período de semidesintegración por erosión]: The time for the elevations of a topographic profile to decrease by about half.

ethics [ética]: Refers to the morals of individuals and society. Morals are values and beliefs about what is acceptable behavior.

evaporation [evaporación]: The change when molecules of a liquid absorb heat and change into the vapor phase.

evapotranspiration [evapotranspiración]: The total loss of water from land settings due to evaporation and to transpiration from plants.

evolution [evolución]: A cumulative change in the characteristics of organisms or populations from generation to generation.

exothermic [exotérmico]: Processes that release heat to the surroundings, resulting in a temperature increase. Exothermic reactions have a negative net enthalpy ($-\Delta H$).

exponential [exponencial]: A way to describe a line on a graph that is curved. The equations that generate these lines have exponents in them and represent the changing rates of some phenomenon.

exponential growth [crecimiento exponencial]: Growth that occurs at a rate proportional to its size.

F

flux [flujo]: The rate at which matter enters or exits a reservoir or system. Fluxes are typically given as rates relative to a duration of time, such as days or years.

foraminifera (forams) [foraminífera (forams)]: Single-celled, photosynthesizing organisms that live in the ocean. Forams form the base of the marine food web.

fossil fuels [combustibles fósiles]: Fuels that consist of hydrogen and carbon compounds from geologic deposits of organic carbon. They are a primary energy source for humans.

G

gamete [gameto]: A sex cell, either an egg or a sperm, formed by meiosis. Gametes have half the number of chromosomes that body cells have.

gene [gen]: The fundamental unit of heredity, which transmits a set of specifications from one generation to the next; a segment of DNA that codes for a specific product.

gene therapy [terapia de genes]: The insertion of normal or genetically altered genes into cells as part of the treatment of genetic disorders.

genetic engineering [ingeniería genética]: The experimental technology developed to alter the genome of a living cell for medical or industrial use. Genetic engineering introduces new traits to organisms.

genome [genoma]: All the genetic material in any given species or complement of a haploid cell from any given species.

genotype [genotipo]: The genetic makeup of an organism.

geochemical cycle [ciclo geoquímico]: A term that describes the storage and movement of a chemical, element, or nutrient such as carbon, water, phosphorus, or calcium through the earth systems.

geologic carbon cycle [ciclo geológico del carbono]: A carbon cycle that consists largely of *inactive* or *immobile* carbon that moves between reservoirs on timescales of hundreds to millions of years. Carbon in geologic reservoirs is stored mainly inside Earth.

glacials [glaciaciones]: Also known as **ice ages.** Periods where the overall global climate is cold. Glacials are characterized by low sea level and the widespread extent of ice sheets.

H

habitat [hábitat]: The place where an organism lives. Even in the same ecosystem, different organisms differ in their habitats.

half-life [período de semidesintegración]: The length of time it takes for exactly one-half of the parent atoms to decay to daughter atoms. Half-life reflects the time rate of decay.

half reactions [semi-reacciones]: Either the oxidation or reduction portion of a redox chemical reaction.

haploid [haploide]: Refers to a cell that contains only one member (n) of each chromosome pair characteristic of a species.

heterozygous [heterocigoto]: Refers to having two different alleles for a given trait.

homozygous [homocigoto]: Refers to having two identical alleles for a given trait.

humus [humus]: Decayed litter on forest floors and within soils.

hydrocarbon [hidrocarburo]: An organic substance made of hydrogen and carbon.

hypothesis [hipótesis]: A statement that is based on current knowledge and suggests an explanation for an observation or an answer to a scientific problem. A hypothesis suggests that there is a cause-and-effect or an if-then relationship for the observation or problem.

I

ice sheet [capa de hielo]: Thick, glacial ice that accumulates on continents and can be up to several kilometers thick.

immigration [inmigración]: The arrival of new individuals into a population; immigration increases the size of a population.

impulse [impulso]: The product of force and change in time ($F\Delta t$).

independent assortment [muestreo independiente]: The inheritance of the alleles for a trait.

indicator [indicador]: A chemical substance that undergoes a measurable change. A color change during a chemical reaction is an example. The change signals a point of interest during a particular reaction.

inelastic collision [colisión inelástica]: An inelastic collision occurs when the energy of the objects in a system is less after the collision than before the collision. A common example occurs when objects hit and stick together after the collision.

input [entrada]: The amount or mass of material entering a reservoir or system.

interglacials [períodos interglaciares]: Periods where the overall global climate is warm. Interglacials are characterized by high sea level and a limited extent of ice sheets.

isotopes [isótopos]: Atoms of the same element that have different numbers of neutrons.

L

land bridge [puente terrestre]: A bridge of land above sea level that links two continents.

Last Glacial Maximum (LGM) [Máximo de la Última Glaciación (LGM por sus siglas en inglés)]: The most recent of many glacials. The LGM has a strong influence on geology and occurred about 21,000 years ago.

law of conservation of matter [ley de conservación de la materia]: A principle of nature that states that matter is neither created nor destroyed during ordinary chemical and physical changes.

law of conservation of momentum [ley de conservación de la energía]: A principle of nature that states that, in any interaction, the momentum of the system before the interaction will be the same as the momentum of the system after the interaction.

Le Châtelier's principle [principio de Le Châtelier]: A way to predict shifts in equilibrium position. The method depends on changes imposed on a system at equilibrium. Imposed changes such as temperature, concentration, pressure, and volume cause shifts in the equilibrium position. The shift always moves in a direction that lessens the imposed change and restores equilibrium.

ligase [ligasa]: An enzyme that assists in the formation of bonds between adjacent, complementary DNA segments.

limiting factor [factor limitante]: An environmental condition such as food, temperature, water, or sunlight that restricts the types of organisms and the population numbers that an environment can support.

litter [materia]: Litter is the buildup of leaves and plant limbs beneath trees on forest floors. Forming litter moves carbon from trees to the forest floor. When litter starts to decay, it is sometimes called humus.

logistic growth [crecimiento logístico]: Growth that starts as exponential growth then slows and eventually stops. In logistic growth, a population levels off at the carrying capacity of the environment.

M

mantle [manto]: The layer of Earth that lies beneath Earth's crust. The mantle consists mostly of the minerals olivine and pyroxene, and the elements magnesium, iron, silicon, and oxygen.

meiosis [meiosis]: Meiosis is the process in which two cell divisions, including division of the nucleus, produces gametes (in animals) or sexual spores (in plants). The gametes or sexual spores have one-half of the genetic material of the original cell.

messenger RNA (mRNA) [ARN mensajero (ARNm)]: A class of RNA molecule that is complementary to one strand of DNA; mRNA is transcribed from genes and translated by ribosomes into protein (see transcription and translation).

microbe [microbio]: A general term for microorganism.

mid-oceanic ridges [dorsales oceánicas]: Areas of high topography on the ocean floor that form due to the rifting of tectonic plates. They were originally linked with the mid-Atlantic ridge.

millions of gallons (Mgal) [millones de galones (Mgal)]: A standard unit for the volume of water in systems.

millions of gallons per day (Mgal/d) [millones de galones por día (Mgal/d)]: A standard flux for water in systems.

mitosis [mitosis]: The replication of the chromosomes and the production of two nuclei in one cell; mitosis is usually followed by the division of the cytoplasm in the cell; it forms new cells.

molar mass [masa molar]: The average atomic mass of any element (found on the periodic table) in grams. Molar mass is equal to the amount of mass in grams in 1 mole (mol) of that element.

molarity [molaridad]: One of several ways to communicate the concentration of a substance. Molarity has the units of moles per liter (mol/L) and is abbreviated M.

mole (mol) [mol (mol)]: A unit that refers to an amount of a substance associated with 6.02×10^{23} particles of that substance.

momentum (*p*) [cantidad de movimiento (*p*)]: The product of mass and velocity (mv); it is represented by the symbol p. Momentum can be thought of as mass in motion.

monohybrid cross [cruce monohíbrido]: A mating between individuals that differ in one allele.

mortality rate [índice de mortalidad]: Death rate, measured as the proportion of deaths to total population over a given period; often expressed as the number of deaths per 1,000 or 10,000 individuals.

mutation [mutación]: A chemical change in a gene that results in a new allele or a change in the portion of a chromosome that regulates the gene. In either case, the change is hereditary.

N

natural selection [selección natural]: A mechanism for biological evolution. In natural selection, members of a population with the most successful adaptations to their environment are more likely to survive and reproduce than members with less successful adaptations.

net force [fuerza neta]: The force resulting from the vector addition of all forces acting on an object.

Newton's laws [leyes de Newton]: History reports three governing principles of nature called Newton's laws. (1) The law of inertia is often used to describe Newton's first law. It states that there will be no change in an object's motion unless acted upon by an outside force. (2) Newton's second law states that the net force on an object is equal to the product of the object's mass and acceleration. It is represented by the equation $F_{net} = ma$. (3) Newton's third law is the principle of nature that states that forces come in pairs, equal in magnitude and opposite in direction. These forces always act on two different objects.

nucleotide [nucleótido]: A subunit or building block of DNA or RNA. It consists of a 5-carbon sugar, a nitrogen base, and a phosphate group.

O

oceanic crust [corteza oceánica]: The outer part of Earth that resides beneath oceans. Oceanic crust is attached to several continents to form tectonic plates.

output [salida]: The amount or mass of material leaving a reservoir or system.

oxidation [oxidación]: A reaction in which electrons appear on the product side of the reaction or half reaction. That is, electrons are lost by the half reaction.

oxidation-reduction reactions (redox reactions) [reacciones de oxidación-reducción (reacciones redox)]: A chemical process involving the transfer of electrons to produce new chemical substances.

oxidized [oxidado]: A description of atoms or ions that have lost electrons.

oxidizing agent [agente oxidante]: A particle involved in a redox reaction that gains an electron or electrons. Oxidizing agents are reduced in redox reactions.

P

paleoclimatology [paleoclimatología]: The study of past climates.

parent element [elemento precursor]: The original chemical substance on the reactant side of a radioactive decay equation. The nuclei of parent elements decay radioactively into daughter elements and other particles.

pathogenic [patógeno]: Microorganisms that cause disease.

pedigree [pedigrí]: A diagram showing the occurrence of heritable traits across many generations.

peninsula [península]: A long spit of land surrounded by water.

phenotype [fenotipo]: The expression of a genotype in the appearance or function of an organism; the observed trait.

pheromone [feromona]: A chemical signal that functions in communication between animals. Pheromones act much like hormones to influence physiology and behavior.

phytoplankton [fitoplancton]: Very small aquatic organisms, many microscopic, that carry on photosynthesis. Phytoplankton form the basis of aquatic food webs.

plasmid [plásmido]: A small ring of DNA in bacteria. Plasmids carry genes separate from those of the chromosome.

plate tectonics, theory of [tectónica de placas, teoría de]: Plate tectonics is the theory that 12 or so rigid *plates* move slowly over Earth atop the mantle. Plates interact in many ways and affect all systems on Earth.

population [población]: A group of organisms of the same species that lives in the same place at the same time.

population density [densidad de población]: The number of organisms per unit of habitat area.

precession [precesión]: *See* wobble (precession).

principle of independent assortment [principio del muestreo independiente]: A principle that states that the inheritance of alleles for one trait does not affect the inheritance of alleles for another trait.

principle of segregation [principio de segregación]: A principle that states that during meiosis, chromosome pairs separate so that each of the two alleles for any given trait appears in a different gamete.

probability [probabilidad]: The chance that any given event will occur.

producer [productor]: Any organism that produces its own food using matter and energy from the nonliving world.

productivity [productividad]: The amount of available solar energy that is converted to chemical energy by producers during any given period.

products [productos]: The new substances that form as a result of a chemical reaction.

projectile motion [movimiento de proyectil]: A motion in the horizontal plane (often parallel to the ground) and in the vertical plane (perpendicular to the ground). In projectile motion, the horizontal motion and the vertical motion are independent of each other, that is, neither motion affects the other.

proxy [representante]: Something that stands in for, or represents something else.

proxy data [datos de representación]: Data as records that represent and stand in for other patterns of change. For example, the thickness of tree rings is an important proxy for annual climate.

Q

qualitative [cualitativo]: Something is qualitative if it describes features, characteristics, observations, or relative comparisons.

quantitative [cuantitativo]: Something is quantitative if it represents measurements or specific numbers, amounts (quantities), or ratios.

R

radioactive decay [desintegración radiactiva]: The spontaneous breakdown of one kind of nuclei into nuclei of different elements.

reactants [reactivos]: The starting ingredients for a chemical reaction.

recessive [recesivo]: Refers to alleles or traits that are masked by a dominant allele or trait.

recombinant DNA technology [tecnología de recombinación del ADN]: A technique used to cut apart segments of DNA and then put different segments of DNA together. Usually DNA segments from one organism are introduced into a different organism for genetic research, genetic engineering, or medical treatment.

reduced [reducidos]: A description of atoms or ions that have gained electrons.

reducing agent [agente reductor]: A particle involved in a redox reaction that loses an electron or electrons. Reducing agents are oxidized in redox reactions.

reduction [reducción]: A reaction in which electrons appear on the reactant side of the reaction of half reaction. That is, electrons are gained by the half reaction.

reservoir [depósito]: A volume or container that holds a given mass of matter.

residence time [tiempo de residencia]: The average length of time that matter in a system is in a reservoir. This value is estimated when there is no long-term change in the system. Residence time is the mass of material in the reservoir divided by either the flux in or the flux out ($residence\ time = mass\ /\ flux_{in}$ or $residence\ time = mass\ /\ flux_{out}$).

resource [recurso]: In ecology, a supply of one or more of an organism's requirements from the environment (light, food energy, water, oxygen or carbon dioxide, living space, protective cover, and so on). In human society, a resource may be anything useful.

restriction enzyme [enzima de restricción]: An enzyme that recognizes specific nucleotide sequences in DNA and breaks the DNA chain at those points.

restriction site [punto de restricción]: Restriction enzymes that cut at a unique DNA sequence.

ribonucleic acid (RNA) [ácido ribonucleico (ARN)]: RNA is the material coded by the DNA of cells to carry out specific genetic functions; for example, messenger RNA and transfer RNA carry out different functions. It is also the hereditary material of certain viruses.

ribosomal RNA (rRNA) [ARN ribosómico (ARNr)]: A class of RNA molecule found, together with characteristic proteins, in ribosomes; it is involved in the process of translation.

rift valley (rift) [valle tectónico (grieta)]: Zones where plates separate or move apart to form a deep valley. Examples are the East African Rift and the Rio Grande Rift.

S

salinity [salinidad]: A measure of the mass of dissolved ions in natural waters.

salt [sal]: The ionic compound formed when acids and bases react to neutralize each other.

satellite [satélite]: Any object that orbits another object.

scientific inquiry [enfoque científico]: The approach to learning used in this program, in which learners ask questions about the natural world and seek answers based on evidence, logic, and interaction with others. In scientific inquiry, students learn science in the way that science is practiced.

selective pressure [presión selectiva]: A biotic or abiotic factor that drives natural selection. Selective pressures influence an organism's ability to survive and reproduce.

sex chromosome [cromosoma del sexo]: One of a pair of chromosomes that differentiates between and is partially responsible for determining the sexes.

simulation [simulación]: A small-scale model or test of a much larger physical process.

sink [vertedero]: A reservoir that accumulates and gains matter with time.

soil [suelo]: The organic and bacteria-rich layer between the geosphere and the biosphere and atmosphere.

solar radiation [radiación solar]: The external source of energy coming to Earth's surface from the Sun. This energy fuels photosynthesis and food cycles.

solubility [solubilidad]: An indicator of the mass of a substance that will dissolve into a liquid.

source [fuente]: A reservoir that loses matter with time.

species [especies]: A group of organisms that successfully reproduce with individuals of the same type.

spectator ions [iones espectadores]: Charged particles that are not changed during a chemical reaction.

strong acid [ácido fuerte]: An acid that dissociates completely or nearly completely.

subducted [subducido]: Pushed down.

subduction zones [zonas de subducción]: Regions where slabs of oceanic crust sink into the mantle.

subsystems [subsistemas]: Smaller systems within a larger system that have distinct boundaries, inputs, and outputs.

suspended load [arrastre en suspensión]: The fine particles of silt, clay, organic matter, and microorganisms carried by rivers or streams.

system [sistema]: A collection of things that interact within given limits or boundaries. *Open systems* exchange both energy and matter with their surroundings; *closed systems* exchange only energy with their surroundings.

T

tectonic plate [placa tectónica]: The outer, rigid layers of oceanic and continental crust. Tectonic plates move on the order of several centimeters per year over Earth's surface.

terminal velocity [velocidad terminal]: The maximum constant velocity of an object that is moving through a fluid. Terminal velocity occurs when the forces of motion in one direction balance each other after some initial acceleration.

terrace [terraza]: A flat surface formed by ocean waves eroding a surface or plane. When geologists date terraces, the dates can be used to determine the rates of tectonic uplift.

terrestrial [terrestre]: Found on land.

tilt [inclinación]: Refers to the angle of Earth's rotation axis relative to incoming solar radiation. Tilt changes by several degrees every 41,000 years.

trait [rasgo]: An inherited characteristic; a trait is determined by genes.

transcription [transcripción]: The assembly of an RNA molecule that is complementary to a strand of DNA. The product may be messenger RNA, transfer RNA, or ribosomal RNA. Transcription is part of protein synthesis, the process of making proteins.

transfer RNA (tRNA) [ARN de transferencia (ARNt)]: A class of RNA molecule with two functional sites. One site is for the attachment of a specific amino acid. The other site is for carrying the three-nucleotide sequence (anticodon) for that amino acid. Each type of tRNA transfers a specific amino acid to a growing polypeptide chain.

transform fault [falla de transformación]: A zone where two tectonic plates move past each other. Examples are the San Andreas Fault in California and the North Anatolian Fault in Turkey.

transgenic [transgénico]: Refers to when one or more genes, usually from another species, are added to an organism; the organism being changed is called a transgenic organism.

translation [traducción]: The assembly of proteins on ribosomes, using messenger RNA to direct the order of amino acids. Translation is part of protein synthesis, the process of making proteins.

transpiration [transpiración]: The loss of water to the atmosphere by plants through the stomates in their leaves.

trenches [fosas submarinas]: Linear regions of deep water where oceanic crust sinks into the mantle. *See* subduction zones.

U

uplift [alzamiento]: The process of land moving vertically relative to sea level.

V

variable [variable]: A factor or attribute that can be measured or described. Scientific investigations look for changes in variables.

variation [variación]: Small differences among individuals within a population or species that provide the raw material for evolution.

vectors [vectores]: In physical science, vectors are variables that have both magnitude (size) and direction. Force, velocity, and acceleration are vectors as well as any change in these quantities. In biology, researchers use vectors to carry a gene to an organism. A plasmid can be used as a vector.

volcanic arcs [arcos volcánicos]: Curved chains of volcanoes residing above subduction zones.

volcanic degassing [desgasificación volcánica]: The movement of gases, such as carbon dioxide and water, from Earth's interior to the atmosphere.

voltaic cell [pila voltaica]: A spontaneous chemical reaction that generates an electric current by the physical separation of redox half reactions.

W

watershed [cuenca hidrográfica]: The area of land that drains into a body of water.

weak acid [ácido débil]: An acid that does not dissociate readily.

weather [tiempo]: Environmental conditions experienced over periods of time from hours to days, such as an afternoon thunderstorm, a cold front, or a persistent heat wave.

weathering [meteorización]: The process of natural, chemical alteration of minerals in rocks.

wobble (precession) [giro excéntrico (precesión)]: The cyclic motion of Earth's rotation axis in a circular motion, like a spinning top. The period of precession is about 21,000 years.

Z

zygote [cigoto]: The diploid product of the union of haploid gametes during conception; a fertilized egg.

Glosario

A

abiótico [abiotic]: Componentes físicos y químicos (no vivientes) de un medio ambiente, como la luz o el agua.

aceleración (*a*) [acceleration (*a*)]: Rapidez con que cambia la velocidad vectorial; se representa con el símbolo *a*. La relación matemática que describe la aceleración es $a = \dfrac{\Delta v}{\Delta t}$.

ácido [acid]: Compuesto químico que aumenta la concentración de los iones de hidrógeno (H^+) en una solución. Esta definición es una de las diversas formas de concebir los ácidos.

ácido débil [weak acid]: Ácido que no se disocia fácilmente.

ácido desoxirribonucleico (ADN) [deoxyribonucleic acid (DNA)]: Material hereditario de la mayoría de los organismos. El ADN forma los genes y contiene desoxirribosa, un grupo de fosfatos, y una de las cuatro bases de ADN.

ácido fuerte [strong acid]: Ácido que se disocia totalmente o casi totalmente.

ácido ribonucleico (ARN) [ribonucleic acid (RNA)]: El ARN es el material codificado por el ADN de las células para llevar a cabo las funciones genéticas específicas; por ejemplo, el ARN mensajero y el ARN de transferencia llevan a cabo diferentes funciones. También es el material hereditario de ciertos virus.

acre-pie (ap) [acre-feet (af)]: Volumen de agua que cubre 1 acre de tierra con agua y posee 1 pie de profundidad.

adaptaciones [adaptations]: Características que ayudan a que un organismo sobreviva y se reproduzca dentro de un medio ambiente determinado.

agente oxidante [oxidizing agent]: Partícula que participa en una reacción redox que gana un electrón o electrones. Los agentes oxidantes se reducen en las reacciones redox.

agente reductor [reducing agent]: Partícula que participa en la reacción redox que pierde un electrón o electrones. Los agentes reductores se oxidan en las reacciones redox.

alelo [allele]: Una de las dos o más formas posibles de un gen. Cada alelo afecta al rasgo hereditario de forma levemente diferente.

alzamiento [uplift]: El proceso de movimiento de la tierra en sentido vertical con respecto al nivel del mar.

aminoácido [amino acid]: Los componentes básicos de los polipéptidos y proteínas. Los aminoácidos son compuestos orgánicos. Están compuestos por un átomo central de carbono unido a un átomo de hidrógeno, un grupo de aminos ($—NH_2$), un grupo de ácidos ($—COOH$), y un átomo de una variedad de otros átomos o grupos de átomos.

anaerobio [anaerobe]: Organismo que vive en ausencia de oxígeno.

ancestral [ancestral]: Algo de lo cual proviene una generación o forma posterior.

anión [anion]: Partícula cargada negativamente, típicamente asociada a las reacciones redox.

ánodo [anode]: Electrodo de una célula electroquímica donde tiene lugar la oxidación.

anticodón [anticodon]: Secuencia de tres nucleótidos en una molécula de transferencia de ARN. Se complementa y forma pares de bases con un codón específico en el ARN mitocondrial.

arcos volcánicos [volcanic arcs]: Cadenas curvas de volcanes que residen por encima de las zonas de subducción.

ARN de transferencia (ARNt) [transfer RNA (tRNA)]: Clase de molécula de ARN con dos lugares funcionales. Un lugar es donde se anexan los aminoácidos específicos. El otro lugar es donde se halla la secuencia de trinucleótidos (anticodones) para ese aminoácido. Cada tipo de ARNt transfiere un aminoácido específico a una cadena de polipéptidos en crecimiento.

ARN mensajero (ARNm) [messenger RNA (mRNA)]: Tipo de molécula de ARN complementaria de una cadena de ADN; el ARNm se transcribe desde los genes y los ribosomas lo traducen a proteínas (ver transcripción y traducción).

ARN ribosómico (ARNr) [ribosomal RNA (rRNA)]: Clase de molécula de ARN que se encuentra en los ribosomas, junto con las proteínas características de éstos; participa en el proceso de traducción.

arrastre en suspensión [suspended load]: Partículas finas de limo, arcilla, materia orgánica y microorganismos que son transportadas por los ríos o arroyos.

autosoma [autosome]: Cromosoma que no está directamente involucrado en la determinación del sexo.

B

base [base]: Compuesto químico que aumenta la concentración de los iones de hidróxido (OH^-) en una solución. Esta definición es una de las diversas formas de concebir las bases.

bioética [bioethics]: Estudio de los temas éticos que se plantean a raíz de los acontecimientos que se desarrollan en las tecnologías de las ciencias biológicas, como las nuevas tecnologías médicas.

bioma [biome]: Conjunto formado por la cubierta vegetal característica y el resto de la comunidad de organismos asociados a un medio ambiente físico en particular; a menudo el bioma recibe el nombre de la cubierta vegetal que lo recubre. Algunos ejemplos de biomas incluyen la tundra, el bosque tropical, el desierto y la pradera de clima templado.

biomasa [biomass]: Peso seco de toda la materia orgánica de un grupo de organismos dentro de un hábitat en particular.

biorremediación [bioremediation]: El uso de microorganismos para degradar los desechos.

biotecnología [biotechnology]: La solución a un problema que involucra a la tecnología *y* a los seres vivos. La tecnología de recombinación de ADN creó varias formas nuevas de biotecnología.

bióticos [biotic]: Los componentes vivos o recién nacidos de un ecosistema.

C

cantidad de movimiento (p) [momentum (p)]: El producto de la masa por la velocidad (mv); se representa con el símbolo p. La cantidad de movimiento puede concebirse como la masa en movimiento.

capa de hielo [ice sheet]: Hielo glaciar grueso que se acumula sobre los continentes y puede tener un espesor de incluso varios kilómetros.

capacidad máxima [carrying capacity]: El mayor tamaño de una población capaz de abastecerse con los recursos disponibles de una cierta zona.

carbono inorgánico disuelto (CID) [dissolved inorganic carbon (DIC)]: Componente del carbono que deriva de fuentes inorgánicas, como los iones de bicarbonato y carbonato, que se disuelve en el agua natural.

carbono orgánico disuelto (COD) [dissolved organic carbon (DOC)]: Componente del carbono que deriva de la materia orgánica, como las hojas de plantas, que se disuelve en el agua natural.

carga disuelta [dissolved load]: Elementos y moléculas en forma iónica que se disuelven en agua natural.

catalizador [catalyst]: Especie química que aumenta la velocidad de una reacción química sin que la reacción lo altere en forma permanente.

catión [cation]: Partícula cargada positivamente, típicamente asociada a las reacciones redox.

cátodo [cathode]: Electrodo de una célula electroquímica donde tiene lugar la reducción.

célula electrolítica [electrolytic cell]: Reacción electroquímica, como la electrólisis. Esta reacción se caracteriza por usar la energía eléctrica para revertir una reacción redox espontánea.

choque elástico [elastic collision]: Choque que se produce cuando la energía y el impulso de los objetos de un sistema se mantienen inalterados antes y después de los choques. Los choques elásticos pueden producirse cuando los objetos que chocan rebotan o colisionan repetidamente entre sí.

ciclo biológico del carbono [biologic carbon cycle]: Ciclo del carbono que consiste en carbono *activo* o *móvil* que se mueve entre los depósitos en lapsos que abarcan desde días a cientos de años. Esta parte del ciclo del carbono opera fundamentalmente sobre la superficie de la tierra e involucra a los organismos.

ciclo geológico del carbono [geologic carbon cycle]: Ciclo del carbono que consiste principalmente en el carbono *inactivo* o *inmóvil* que se desplaza entre los depósitos en escalas temporales de cientos a millones de años. El carbono en los depósitos geológicos se almacena principalmente dentro de la Tierra.

ciclo geoquímico [geochemical cycle]: Expresión que describe el almacenamiento y movimiento de una sustancia química, elemento o nutriente como el carbón, el agua, el fósforo o el calcio a través de los sistemas terrestres.

cigoto [zygote]: El producto diploide de la unión de los gametos haploides durante la concepción; el óvulo fertilizado.

clima [climate]: Condiciones atmosféricas generales que se repiten a lo largo de lapsos prolongados.

codón [codon]: Unidad básica del código genético; secuencia de tres nucleótidos adyacentes de ADN o ARN mensajero.

colisión inelástica [inelastic collision]: Se produce una colisión inelástica cuando la energía de los objetos de un sistema es menor después de la colisión que antes de ella. Un ejemplo común se da cuando los objetos se golpean y se quedan adheridos después de la colisión.

combustibles fósiles [fossil fuels]: Combustibles que constan de compuestos de hidrógeno y carbono de los depósitos geológicos del carbono orgánico. Son una fuente de energía primaria para los seres humanos.

comunidad [community]: Todos los organismos que habitan en una zona en particular.

concentración [concentration]: Medida para expresar la cantidad de partículas por unidad de espacio. Una unidad de concentración muy frecuente en química es la molaridad: indica las unidades de moles por litro (mol/L).

conservación de la masa [conservation of mass]: Concepto por el cual la masa de reactivos de una reacción debe ser igual a la masa de los productos.

constante [constant]: Factor o atributo que permanece inalterado durante el curso de una investigación. Una constante también puede ser una cantidad o valor que se asume no variará a los efectos de una teoría o experimento, por ejemplo, la velocidad de la luz.

control [control]: En una investigación el control es el individuo o el grupo designado para no recibir tratamiento (el grupo que no cambia). Todos los demás grupos se comparan con el grupo de control.

corriente eléctrica [electric current]: El flujo de la carga en una dirección en particular.

corteza continental [continental crust]: Material variado, de roca básica, que posee un espesor de 40–70 kilómetros que forma los continentes.

corteza oceánica [oceanic crust]: La parte externa de la Tierra que yace bajo los océanos. La corteza oceánica está unida a varios continentes y forma las placas tectónicas.

crecimiento exponencial [exponential growth]: Crecimiento que ocurre a una velocidad que es proporcional a su tamaño.

crecimiento logístico [logistic growth]: Crecimiento que comienza como un crecimiento exponencial y luego se hace más lento hasta finalmente detenerse. En el crecimiento logístico la población alcanza su nivel ideal en la capacidad máxima del medio ambiente.

cromosoma del sexo [sex chromosome]: Uno de un par de cromosomas que se diferencia y es parcialmente responsable de la determinación del sexo.

cromosoma [chromosome]: Grupo de genes largos y en forma de hebra que se encuentra en el núcleo de todas las células eucariotas. Los cromosomas son más visibles durante la mitosis y la meiosis. Los cromosomas están formados por ADN y proteínas.

cruce monohíbrido [monohybrid cross]: Apareamiento entre individuos que difieren en un alelo.

cualitativo [qualitative]: Algo es cualitativo si describe los rasgos, características, observaciones o comparaciones relativas.

cuantitativo [quantitative]: Algo es cuantitativo si representa las mediciones o números, montos (cantidades) o índices específicos.

cuenca hidrográfica [watershed]: El área de tierra con drenaje hacia una masa de agua.

D

datos de representación [proxy data]: Datos de registros que representan y están en lugar de otros patrones de cambio. Por ejemplo, el grosor de los anillos de un árbol es un dato de representación importante para el clima anual.

densidad de población [population density]: La cantidad de organismos por unidad o superficie de hábitat.

depósito [reservoir]: Volumen o recipiente que contiene una determinada masa de materia.

deriva continental [continental drift]: Hipótesis propuesta en 1912 por Alfred Wegener según la cual, en un momento determinado, las masas terrestres de la Tierra estaban unidas, formando un supercontinente que luego se separó para dar lugar a los continentes actuales. Ahora se considera que la deriva continental es parte de la teoría mayor de la tectónica de placas.

desgasificación volcánica [volcanic degassing]: El movimiento de los gases, como el dióxido de carbono y el agua, desde el interior de la Tierra a la atmósfera.

desintegración radiactiva [radioactive decay]: La descomposición espontánea de un tipo de núcleos en núcleos con diferentes elementos.

diploide [diploid]: Se refiere a una célula que contiene miembros de cada par de cromosomas que le es característico a una especie.

dominante [dominant]: Se refiere a los alelos o rasgos que enmascaran la presencia de otro alelo del mismo gen en un organismo heterocigoto.

dorsales oceánicas [mid-oceanic ridges]: Zonas de topografía elevada en el suelo oceánico que se forman debido a las grietas de las placas tectónicas. Estaban originalmente unidas a la dorsal meso-Atlántica.

E

ecología [ecology]: Campo de la biología que estudia los organismos y su relación con el medio ambiente.

ecosistema [ecosystem]: La comunidad biológica y su entorno abiótico.

electroforesis de gel de agarosa [agarose gel electrophoresis]: Proceso en el cual los científicos separan los fragmentos de ADN por su tamaño. Se utiliza una corriente eléctrica para impulsar el ADN a través de una matriz de gel poroso.

elemento derivado [daughter element]: Sustancia química del lado de los productos de una ecuación de desintegración radiactiva. Los núcleos de los elementos derivados se producen de los elementos madre.

elemento precursor [parent element]: Sustancia química original del lado de los reactivos en una ecuación de descomposición radiactiva. Los núcleos de los elementos precursores se desintegran radiactivamente para formar elementos derivados y otras partículas.

embrión [embryo]: Organismo en las etapas iniciales de desarrollo.

emigración [emigration]: Partida de los individuos de una población; la emigración disminuye el tamaño de una población.

endémico [endemic]: Animales o plantas cuya presencia se restringe a una región específica.

endotérmico [endothermic]: Procesos que absorben el calor del entorno, provocando una disminución de la temperatura. Las reacciones endotérmicas tienen una entalpía neta positiva ($+\Delta H$).

energía de activación (E_a) [activation energy (E_a)]: Energía vinculada a las partículas que se forman con la energía de mayor potencial durante un proceso químico.

enfoque científico [scientific inquiry]: El abordaje del aprendizaje que se usa en este programa, en el cual los estudiantes formulan preguntas acerca del mundo natural y buscan las respuestas basándose en la evidencia, la lógica y la interacción con los demás. En el enfoque científico, los estudiantes aprenden ciencia en la forma en que se ejerce la ciencia.

entalpía [enthalpy]: Energía neta ($E_{final} - E_{inicial}$ = energía neta) asociada a las reacciones químicas. Se representa con el símbolo ΔH.

entrada [input]: La cantidad de masa o material que ingresa en un depósito o sistema.

enzima de restricción [restriction enzyme]: Enzima que reconoce las secuencias de nucleótidos específicas en el ADN y descompone la cadena de ADN en esos puntos.

enzimas [enzymes]: Cualquier especie química, generalmente proteínas o moléculas que incluyen proteínas que catalizan o aceleran las reacciones biológicas. Las enzimas son producidas por un organismo.

equilibrio [equilibrium]: Descripción del estado de cualquier reacción química reversible en la cual la velocidad de su reacción directa equivale a la velocidad de su reacción inversa.

erosión [erosion]: Proceso por el cual se transporta tierra y fragmentos de roca sometidos a la meteorización y se desplazan hacia abajo debido a la acción de la gravedad. La erosión de las montañas se produce a lo largo de laderas pronunciadas y de valles de los ríos.

especies [species]: Grupo de organismos que se reproducen satisfactoriamente con los seres de su mismo tipo.

ética [ethics]: Se refiere a la moral de las personas y la sociedad. La moral son los valores y creencias sobre lo que se considera un comportamiento aceptable.

evaporación [evaporation]: El cambio producido cuando las moléculas de un líquido absorben calor y cambian a la fase de vapor.

evapotranspiración [evapotranspiration]: La pérdida total de agua del entorno terrestre debido a la evaporación y a la transpiración de las plantas.

evolución [evolution]: Cambio acumulativo en las características de los organismos o poblaciones de generación a generación.

excentricidad [eccentricity]: Se refiere a la forma de la órbita de la Tierra alrededor del Sol. La excentricidad varía en escalas temporales de alrededor de 100,000 años.

exotérmico [exothermic]: Procesos que liberan calor al entorno, provocando un aumento de la temperatura. Las reacciones exotérmicas poseen una entalpía neta negativa ($-\Delta H$).

exponencial [exponential]: Forma de describir una línea en una gráfica curva. Las ecuaciones que generan estas líneas contienen exponentes y representan los cambios de velocidad de algunos fenómenos.

F

factor limitante [limiting factor]: Condición ambiental como alimento, temperatura, agua o luz natural que restringe el tipo de organismos y la cantidad de habitantes que un medio ambiente puede sustentar.

falla de transformación [transform fault]: Zona donde se superponen dos placas tectónicas. Ejemplos de ello son la Falla de San Andrés en California y la Falla de Anatolia del Norte en Turquía.

fenotipo [phenotype]: Expresión del genotipo en el aspecto o función de un organismo; el rasgo que se observa.

feromona [pheromone]: Señal química que funciona en las comunicaciones entre los animales. Las feromonas actúan en forma similar a las hormonas para influir en la fisiología y el comportamiento.

fitoplancton [phytoplankton]: Organismos acuáticos muy pequeños, muchos de ellos microscópicos, que llevan a cabo la fotosíntesis. El fitoplancton forma la base de las redes alimentarias acuáticas.

flujo [flux]: La velocidad a la cual la materia ingresa o egresa de un depósito o sistema. Los flujos generalmente se expresan como velocidades relativas al transcurso del tiempo, como pueden ser días o años.

foraminífera (forams) [foraminifera (forams)]: Organismos unicelulares con capacidad fotosintética que viven en el océano. Las forams forman la base de la red alimentaria marina.

formación de pares de bases complementarias [complementary base pairing]: Interacción predecible entre las bases de nitrógeno de las cadenas opuestas de ADN, y entre el ADN y el ARN. Los pares de adenina con timina, y los pares de guanina con citosina en el ADN; en el ARN, los pares de adenina con uracil.

fosas submarinas [trenches]: Regiones lineales de agua profunda donde la corteza oceánica se hunde en el manto. *Ver* zonas de subducción.

fuente [source]: Depósito que pierde materia con el paso del tiempo.

fuerza neta [net force]: La fuerza que resulta de la suma de los vectores de todas las fuerzas que actúan sobre un objeto.

G

gameto [gamete]: Célula sexual, ya sea un óvulo o esperma, formada por la meiosis. Los gametos poseen la mitad de la cantidad de cromosomas que poseen las células del cuerpo.

gen [gene]: Unidad fundamental de la herencia genética, que transmite un conjunto de especificaciones de una generación a la siguiente; segmento de ADN que codifica un producto específico.

genoma [genome]: Todo el material genético de una especie determinada o el complemento de una célula haploide de cualquier especie.

genotipo [genotype]: Composición genética de un organismo.

giro excéntrico (precesión) [wobble (precession)]: El movimiento cíclico del eje de rotación de la Tierra en sentido circular, como el de un trompo. El lapso de precesión es de alrededor de 21,000 años.

glaciaciones [glacials]: También conocidas como **edades del hielo** o **períodos glaciales**. Son épocas en que el clima global general es frío. Las glaciaciones se caracterizan por el bajo nivel del mar y la presencia de capas de hielo sobre grandes extensiones de la superficie terrestre.

H

hábitat [habitat]: Lugar donde vive un organismo. Incluso en el mismo ecosistema los diferentes organismos difieren de hábitat.

haploide [haploid]: Se refiere a una célula que contiene solamente un miembro (n) de cada par cromosómico característico de una especie.

heterocigoto [heterozygous]: Se refiere a poseer dos alelos diferentes para un rasgo dado.

hidrocarburo [hydrocarbon]: Sustancia orgánica compuesta por hidrógeno y carbono.

hipótesis [hypothesis]: Enunciado que se basa en el conocimiento actual y sugiere una explicación para una observación o una respuesta a un problema científico. Una hipótesis sugiere que hay una causa y un efecto o una relación del tipo "si...entonces" para la observación o problema.

homocigoto [homozygous]: Se refiere a poseer dos alelos idénticos para un rasgo dado.

humus [humus]: Materia descompuesta en el piso de los bosques y dentro del suelo.

I

impulso [impulse]: El producto de la fuerza y el cambio en el tiempo ($F\Delta t$).

inclinación [tilt]: Se refiere al ángulo del eje de rotación de la Tierra relativo a la entrada de la radiación solar. La inclinación cambia en varios grados cada 41,000 años.

indicador [indicator]: Sustancia química que sufre un cambio medible. Un cambio de color durante una reacción química es un ejemplo. El cambio señala un punto de interés durante una reacción en particular.

índice de mortalidad [mortality rate]: Índice de muerte, medido como la proporción de muertes con respecto a la población total a lo largo de un lapso dado; a menudo se expresa como la cantidad de muertes por cada 1,000 ó 10,000 personas.

índice de natalidad [birthrate]: La velocidad con que crece la población a través de la reproducción; a menudo se expresa en función de los individuos nacidos por cada 1,000 ó 10,000 en la población.

ingeniería genética [genetic engineering]: Tecnología experimental desarrollada para alterar el genoma de una célula viva para uso médico o industrial. La ingeniería genética introduce nuevos rasgos en los organismos.

inmigración [immigration]: Llegada de nuevas personas a una población; la inmigración aumenta el tamaño de una población.

iones espectadores [spectator ions]: Partículas cargadas que no cambian durante una reacción química.

isótopos [isotopes]: Átomos del mismo elemento que poseen diferentes cantidades de neutrones.

L

ley de conservación de la energía [law of conservation of momentum]: Principio de la naturaleza que indica que, en toda interacción la energía del sistema antes de la interacción será la misma que la energía del sistema después de la interacción.

ley de conservación de la materia [law of conservation of matter]: Principio de la naturaleza que indica que la materia no se crea ni se destruye durante los cambios físicos y químicos comunes.

leyes de Newton [Newton's laws]: La historia da cuenta de tres principios que rigen la naturaleza, llamados leyes de Newton. (1) La ley de la inercia se utiliza a menudo para describir la primera ley de Newton. Enuncia que no habrá cambios en el movimiento de un objeto a menos una fuerza externa actúe sobre él. (2) La segunda ley de Newton enuncia que la fuerza neta de un objeto es igual al producto de la masa por la aceleración del objeto. Se representa con la ecuación $F_{neta} = ma$. (3) La tercera ley de Newton es el principio de la naturaleza que describe que las fuerzas se presentan en pares, iguales en magnitud y opuestas en dirección. Estas fuerzas siempre actúan sobre dos objetos diferentes.

ligasa [ligase]: Enzima que contribuye a la formación de enlaces entre los segmentos adyacentes y complementarios de ADN.

límites [boundaries]: Fronteras que delimitan un sistema dentro del cual se producen interacciones.

M

manto [mantle]: La capa de la Tierra que se encuentra debajo de la corteza terrestre. El manto consiste principalmente en los minerales olivino y piroxeno, y los elementos, magnesio, hierro, sílice y oxígeno.

masa molar [molar mass]: El promedio de masa atómica de cualquier elemento (de la tabla periódica) en gramos. La masa molar equivale a la cantidad de masa en gramos en 1 mol de ese elemento.

materia [litter]: Materia es la acumulación de hojas y ramas vegetales debajo de los árboles en el suelo de los bosques. La materia en formación moviliza el carbón de los árboles hacia el suelo del bosque. Cuando la materia comienza a descomponerse, a veces recibe el nombre de humus.

Máximo de la Última Glaciación (LGM por sus siglas en inglés) [Last Glacial Maximum (LGM)]: La más reciente de muchas glaciaciones. El LGM tuvo una fuerte influencia en la geología y se produjo hace alrededor de 21,000 años.

medio ambiente [environment]: Todos los seres vivos y no vivos del entorno de un organismo, incluyendo la luz, temperatura, aire, suelo, agua y demás organismos.

meiosis [meiosis]: La meiosis es el proceso en el cual las divisiones de dos células, incluyendo la división del núcleo, producen gametos (en los animales) o esporas sexuales (en las plantas). Los gametos o esporas sexuales poseen la mitad del material genético de la célula de origen.

meteorización [weathering]: El proceso de la alteración química natural de los minerales en las rocas.

mezcla atmosférica [atmospheric mixing]: Proceso de transportar y mezclar componentes de la atmósfera en una escala global o regional.

microbio [microbe]: Término general para microorganismo.

millones de galones (Mgal) [millions of gallons (Mgal)]: Unidad estándar del volumen de agua en los sistemas.

millones de galones por día (Mgal/d) [millions of gallons per day (Mgal/d)]: Unidad estándar del flujo de agua en los sistemas.

mitosis [mitosis]: Replicación de los cromosomas y producción de dos núcleos en una célula; la mitosis está generalmente seguida de la división del citoplasma en la célula; se forman nuevas células.

mol (mol) [mole (mol)]: Unidad que se refiere a una cantidad de una sustancia asociada con 6.02×10^{23} partículas de esa sustancia.

molaridad [molarity]: Una de las diversas formas de expresar la concentración de una sustancia. La molaridad posee las unidades de moles por litro (mol/L) y se abrevia M.

movimiento de proyectil [projectile motion]: Movimiento en el plano horizontal (a menudo paralelo al suelo) y en el plano vertical (perpendicular al suelo). En el movimiento de proyectil el movimiento horizontal y el movimiento vertical son independientes entre sí, es decir que ninguno afecta al otro.

muestreo independiente [independent assortment]: La transmisión hereditaria de los alelos para un rasgo.

mutación [mutation]: Cambio químico en un gen que da como resultado un nuevo alelo o un cambio en la porción de un cromosoma que regula a ese gen. En cualquiera de los casos el cambio es hereditario.

N

nicho ecológico [ecological niche]: Todas las adaptaciones que un organismo utiliza para sobrevivir en su medio ambiente. Éstas incluyen su función dentro de la comunidad, lo que come y las interacciones que posee con los demás organismos y su medio ambiente.

nucleótido [nucleotide]: Subunidad o componente de ADN o ARN. Consta de un glúcido de 5 carbonos, una base de nitrógeno, y un grupo de fosfatos.

O

oxidación [oxidation]: Reacción en la cual los electrones aparecen del lado del producto de la reacción o semi-reacción. Es decir, los electrones se pierden en la semi-reacción.

oxidado [oxidized]: Descripción de los átomos o iones que perdieron electrones.

P

paleoclimatología [paleoclimatology]: El estudio de los climas del pasado.

patógeno [pathogenic]: Microorganismos que provocan enfermedades.

pedigrí [pedigree]: Diagrama que muestra la aparición de rasgos hereditarios a lo largo de varias generaciones.

península [peninsula]: Punta larga de tierra rodeada de agua.

período de semidesintegración [half-life]: También conocido como vida media. El tiempo necesario para que la mitad exacta de los átomos originales se degraden hasta convertirse en átomos derivados. La vida media refleja la constante de degradación.

período de semidesintegración por erosión [erosion half-life]: El tiempo que debe transcurrir para que se reduzcan a la mitad las elevaciones de un perfil topográfico.

períodos interglaciares [interglacials]: Lapsos en los cuales hay un clima global general cálido. Los períodos interglaciares se caracterizan por el elevado nivel del mar y la presencia limitada de capas de hielo.

pies cúbicos por segundo (pcs) [cubic feet per second (cfs)]: Unidades de flujo de agua que miden 1 pie cúbico de agua y se desplazan en 1 segundo con respecto a un punto.

pila voltaica [voltaic cell]: Reacción química espontánea que genera una corriente eléctrica mediante la separación física de las semi-reacciones redox.

placa tectónica [tectonic plate]: Las capas externas rígidas de la corteza oceánica y continental. Las placas tectónicas se mueven en el orden de varios centímetros por año sobre la superficie terrestre.

plásmido [plasmid]: Pequeño anillo de ADN en las bacterias. Los plásmidos transportan los genes separados de los genes de los cromosomas.

población [population]: Grupo de organismos de la misma especie que habitan en el mismo lugar al mismo tiempo.

polimerasa de ADN [DNA polymerase]: Enzima que cataliza la síntesis de una nueva cadena de ADN utilizando una de las cadenas originales como plantilla modelo.

precesión [precession]: *Ver* giro excéntrico (precesión).

presión selectiva [selective pressure]: Factor biótico o abiótico que fomenta la selección natural. Las presiones selectivas influyen en la capacidad de un organismo para sobrevivir y reproducirse.

principio de Le Châtelier [Le Châtelier's principle]: Forma de predecir los cambios en el punto de equilibrio. El método depende de los cambios que se le impongan a un sistema en equilibrio. Los cambios impuestos como temperatura, concentración, presión y volumen provocan cambios en el punto de equilibrio. El cambio siempre se desplaza en la dirección que disminuya el cambio impuesto y restablezca el equilibrio.

principio de segregación [principle of segregation]: Principio que enuncia que durante la meiosis los pares de cromosomas se separan de forma tal que cada uno de los dos alelos que determinan cualquier rasgo aparece en un gameto diferente.

principio del muestreo independiente [principle of independent assortment]: Principio que enuncia que la herencia de los alelos para un rasgo no afecta la herencia de los alelos para otro rasgo.

probabilidad [probability]: La posibilidad de que tenga lugar un acontecimiento dado.

productividad [productivity]: La cantidad de energía solar que los productores convierten en energía química durante cualquier período dado.

productor [producer]: Todo organismo que produce su propio alimento utilizando materia y energía del mundo no vivo.

productos [products]: Las nuevas sustancias que se forman como consecuencia de una reacción química.

puente terrestre [land bridge]: Puente de tierra por encima del nivel del mar que une a dos continentes.

punto de equilibrio [equilibrium position]: Medida de las cantidades relativas de reactivos y productos que deberán estar presentes para que un sistema químico se encuentre en equilibrio. Cuando hay más productos presentes, la posición de equilibrio favorece a los productos. El punto de equilibrio está a la derecha. Cuando hay más reactivos presentes, la posición de equilibrio favorece a los reactivos. El punto de equilibrio está a la izquierda.

punto de restricción [restriction site]: Enzimas de restricción que efectúan un corte en una secuencia única de ADN.

R

radiación solar [solar radiation]: Fuente externa de energía que llega a la superficie de la Tierra y proviene del Sol. Esta energía alimenta a la fotosíntesis y los ciclos alimentarios.

rasgo [trait]: Una característica que se hereda; los rasgos son determinados por los genes.

reacciones de oxidación-reducción (reacciones redox) [oxidation-reduction reactions (redox reactions)]: Proceso químico que involucra la transferencia de electrones para producir nuevas sustancias químicas.

reactivos [reactants]: Ingredientes iniciales de una reacción química.

recesivo [recessive]: Se refiere a los alelos o rasgos que quedan enmascarados por un alelo o rasgo dominante.

recurso [resource]: En ecología, el abastecimiento por parte del medio ambiente de uno o más de los requisitos de un organismo (luz, energía de los alimentos, agua, oxígeno o dióxido de carbono, espacio vital, cubierta protectora, y demás). En la sociedad humana, un recurso puede ser cualquier cosa que resulte útil.

reducción [reduction]: Reacción en la cual los electrones aparecen del lado de los reactivos de la reacción o semi-reacción. Es decir, se ganan electrones en la semi-reacción.

reducidos [reduced]: Descripción de los átomos o iones que ganaron electrones.

replicación del ADN [DNA replication]: Proceso para fabricar una copia de un cromosoma en el núcleo de una célula, así como en otros genes de ciertos organelos fuera del núcleo, particularmente los cloroplastos y las mitocondrias. El proceso es diferente de la duplicación porque cada gen y cada cromosoma en el doble par contiene partes nuevas y partes del antiguo gen o cromosoma.

representante [proxy]: Algo que representa o está en lugar de otra cosa.

reproducción asexuada [asexual reproduction]: Cualquier método de reproducción que requiera únicamente de un progenitor o una célula madre.

respiración aerobia [aerobic respiration]: Tipo de respiración celular que requiere de la presencia de oxígeno.

respiración anaeróbica [anaerobic respiration]: Tipo de respiración celular que no requiere de oxígeno.

S

sal [salt]: Compuesto iónico que se forma cuando los ácidos y las bases reaccionan para neutralizarse entre sí.

salida [output]: La cantidad de masa o material que sale de un depósito o sistema.

salinidad [salinity]: Medida de la masa de iones disueltos en aguas naturales.

satélite [satellite]: Todo objeto que orbita en torno a otro objeto.

selección natural [natural selection]: Mecanismo de la evolución biológica. En la selección natural los integrantes de la población que posea el mejor poder de adaptación al medio ambiente tendrán mayores probabilidades de sobrevivir y reproducirse que los integrantes con menor capacidad de adaptación.

semi-reacciones [half reactions]: La porción de oxidación o reducción de una reacción química redox.

simulación [simulation]: Modelo o prueba a pequeña escala de un proceso físico mucho mayor.

sistema [system]: Conjunto de cosas que interaccionan dentro de ciertos límites o fronteras. Los *sistemas abiertos* intercambian energía y materia con su entorno; los *sistemas cerrados* intercambian solamente energía con su entorno.

solubilidad [solubility]: Indicador de la masa de una sustancia que se disuelve en un líquido.

subducido [subducted]: Algo sometido a una fuerza que lo empujó hacia abajo.

subsistemas [subsystems]: Sistemas más pequeños dentro de un sistema mayor que poseen límites bien delineados, elementos de entrada y de salida.

suelo [soil]: Capa orgánica rica en bacterias entre la geoesfera, la biosfera y la atmósfera.

T

tecnología de recombinación del ADN [recombinant DNA technology]: Técnica utilizada para recortar segmentos de ADN y luego unir diferentes segmentos de ADN. Generalmente se introducen los segmentos de ADN de un organismo en diferentes organismos a los efectos de realizar investigación genética, ingeniería genética o tratamientos médicos.

tectónica de placas, teoría de [plate tectonics, theory of]: La tectónica de placas es la teoría que expresa que hay alrededor de 12 *placas* rígidas que se mueven lentamente sobre la Tierra por encima del manto. Las placas interactúan de muchas formas y afectan a todos los sistemas de la Tierra.

terapia de genes [gene therapy]: Inserción de genes normales o genéticamente alterados en las células como parte de un tratamiento de los trastornos genéticos.

terraza [terrace]: Superficie plana formada por las olas oceánicas que erosionan una superficie o plano. Cuando los geólogos determinan la antigüedad de las terrazas, las fechas pueden utilizarse para determinar la frecuencia del alzamiento tectónico.

terrestre [terrestrial]: Que se encuentra sobre la tierra.

tiempo de residencia [residence time]: El lapso promedio en el cual la materia de un sistema permanece en el depósito. Este valor se estima cuando no hay cambios a largo plazo en el sistema. El tiempo de residencia es la masa de material en el depósito dividida por el flujo entrante o el flujo saliente ($tiempo\ de\ residencia = masa / flujo_{en}$ o $tiempo\ de\ residencia = masa / flux_{sal}$).

tiempo [weather]: Condiciones ambientales que se experimentan a lo largo de lapsos que abarcan desde horas a días, como una tormenta eléctrica vespertina, un frente frío o una ola de calor persistente.

traducción [translation]: La formación de proteínas sobre los ribosomas, utilizando el ARN mensajero para dirigir el orden de los aminoácidos. La traducción es parte de la síntesis proteica, el proceso para la fabricación de las proteínas.

transcripción [transcription]: La formación de una molécula de ARN que complementa a una cadena de ADN. El producto puede ser el ARN mensajero, el ARN de transferencia o el ARN de los ribosomas. La transcripción es parte de una síntesis de proteínas, el proceso para fabricar las proteínas.

transgénico [transgenic]: Se refiere a cuando uno o más genes, generalmente de otras especies, se agregan a un organismo; el organismo que se altera recibe el nombre de organismo transgénico.

transpiración [transpiration]: Pérdida de agua de las plantas hacia la atmósfera a través de los estomas que poseen en las hojas.

V

valle tectónico (grieta) [rift valley (rift)]: Zonas donde se separan o se desplazan las placas para formar un valle profundo. Los ejemplos son la grieta del Este de África y la grieta del Río Grande.

variable [variable]: Factor o atributo que puede medirse o describirse. Las investigaciones científicas buscan cambios en las variables.

variación [variation]: Pequeñas diferencias entre los individuos dentro de una población o especie que proporcionan la materia prima para la evolución.

vectores [vectors]: En la ciencia física los vectores son variables que poseen magnitud (tamaño) y dirección. La fuerza, la velocidad vectorial y la aceleración son vectores, al igual que cualquier cambio en esas cantidades. En biología los investigadores utilizan vectores para transportar un gen a un organismo. Un plásmido puede utilizarse como vector.

velocidad terminal [terminal velocity]: La máxima velocidad constante de un objeto que se desplaza a través de un fluido. La velocidad terminal ocurre cuando las fuerzas del movimiento en una dirección se contrarrestan entre sí después de cierta aceleración inicial.

vertedero [sink]: Depósito que acumula y gana materia con el paso del tiempo.

Z

zonas convergentes [convergent zones]: Regiones donde chocan las placas tectónicas.

zonas de subducción [subduction zones]: Regiones donde las placas de la corteza oceánica se hunden en el manto.

zonas divergentes [divergent zones]: Zonas donde las placas tectónicas se separan, formando grietas en los continentes o en el suelo oceánico.

Unit 1 References

Activation energy. (n.d.). Retrieved June 13, 2006, from http://chemed.chem.purdue.edu/genchem/topicreview/bp/ch22/activate.html

Biological Sciences Curriculum Study (BSCS). (1963). *High school biology: BSCS green version*. Skokie, IL: Rand McNally. Currently in its 10th edition, © 2006, Kendall/Hunt.

Biological Sciences Curriculum Study (BSCS). (2001). *BSCS biology: A molecular approach* (8th ed.). Chicago: Everyday Learning Corporation.

Biological Sciences Curriculum Study (BSCS). (2006). *BSCS biology: A human approach* (3rd ed.). Dubuque, IA: Kendall/Hunt.

Brown, L., Mulvihill, C., Stolz, J., Thiel, H., Adamo, J. A., Foos, K. M., et al. (1999). *Microbeworld activities*. Reston, VA: National Association of Biology Teachers.

Case, C. L. (n.d.). *Handwashing*. Retrieved August 16, 2000, from http://www.accessexcellence.org/AE/AEC/CC/hand_background.html

Chemistry misconceptions. (n.d.) Retrieved June 2, 2005, from http://educ.queensu.ca/~science/main/concept/chem/c07/C07CDTL1.htm

Department of Physics and Astronomy. (2005). *Batteries*. Retrieved March 13, 2006, from http://hyperphysics.phy-astr.gsu.edu/hbase/electric/battery.html

Duma, S. M., Manoogian, B. S., Bussone, W. R., Brolinson, P. G., Goforth, M. W., Donnenwerth, J. J., et al. (2005, January). Analysis of real-time head accelerations in collegiate football players. *Clinical Journal of Sport Medicine, 15*(1), 3–8.

Ericksen, A. B. (2001) *Jobs off the beaten track*. Retrieved May 12, 2006, from http://www.graduatingengineer.com/articles/feature/09-04-01b.html

Freudenrich, C. C. (n.d.). *How breathalyzers work*. Retrieved July 20, 2005, from http://science.howstuffworks.com/breathalyzer.htm/printable

Gilstrap, M., Kleyn, J., & Nester, E. W. (1982). *Microbiology experiments: A health science perspective*. Philadelphia: Saunders College Publishing.

Harris, T. (n.d.). *How luminol works*. Retrieved July 20, 2005, from http://science.howstuffworks.com/luminol.htm/printable

Hewitt, P. G. (1992). *Conceptual physics: The high school physics program teacher's edition* (2nd ed.). Menlo Park, CA: Addison-Wesley Publishing.

Jones, E. R., & Childer, R. L. (1990, May). *Contemporary college physics*. Reading, MA: Addison-Wesley Publishing.

Koch, G. H., Brongers, M. P. H., Thompson, N. G., Virmani, Y. P., & Payer, J. H. (2002, July). Corrosion: A natural but controllable process. *Supplement to Material Performance, 3*.

Koch, G. H., Brongers, M. P. H., Thompson, N. G., Virmani, Y. P., & Payer, J. H. (2002, July). Cost of corrosion study unveiled. *Supplement to Material Performance, 2*.

Kotz, J. C., & Purcell, K. F. (1991). *Chemistry & chemical reactivity* (2nd ed.). Philadelphia: Saunders College Publishing.

Lienhard, J. H. (n.d.). *No. 622: Ignaz Philipp Semmelweis*. Retrieved September 6, 2000, from the University of Houston, College of Engineering Web site: http://www.uh.edu/engines/epi622.htm

McMurry, J., & Fay, R. C. (1998). *Chemistry* (2nd ed.). Upper Saddle River, NJ: Prentice Hall.

Munro, K. (1997, July 21). *Why does bruised fruit turn brown?* Retrieved July 20, 2005, from http://www.sciam.comprint_version.cfm?articleID=0006947D-57E8-1C72-9EB7809EC588F2D7

NACE International. (2002, July). *Historic congressional study: Corrosion costs and preventive strategies in the United States* [supplement to Materials Performance]. Retrieved May 23, 2006, from http://www.nace.org/nace/content/publicaffairs/images_cocorr/ccsupp.pdf

National Institute of Allergy and Infectious Diseases. (2000, June). *Antimicrobial resistance*. Retrieved August 16, 2000, from http://www.niaid.nih.gov/factsheets/antimicro.htm

Naunhelim, R. S., Standeven, J., Richter, C., & Lewis, L. M. (2000, May). Comparison of impact data in hockey, football, and soccer. *The Journal of Trauma: Injury, Infection, and Critical Care, 48*(5), 938–941.

Nester, E. W., Pearsall, N. N., Roberts, J. B., & Roberts, C. E. (1982). *The microbial perspective*. Philadelphia: Saunders College Publishing.

Newman, J. A., Beusenberg, M. C., Shewchenko, C., Whitnall, C., & Fournier, E. (2004, June 19). Verification of biomechanical methods employed in a comprehensive study of mild traumatic brain injury and the effectiveness of American football helmets. *Journal of Biomechanics, 38*, 1469–1481.

Oxtoby, D. W., Gillis, H. P., & Nachtrieb, N. H. (1999). *Principles of modern chemistry* (4th ed.). Forth Worth: Saunders College Publishing, Harcourt Brace College Publishers.

Scientific inquiry: Chapter 1: Introduction: What is scientific inquiry? (2001, January 16). Retrieved August 24, 2001, from http://acept.la.asu.edu/courses/phs110/si/chapter1/main.html

Summerlin, L. R., & Ealy, J. L., Jr. (1988). *Chemical demonstrations: A sourcebook for teachers* (2nd ed., Vols. 1–2). Washington, DC: American Chemical Society.

Swartling, D. J., & Morgan, C. (1998). Lemon cells revisited-The lemon-powered calculator. *Journal of Chemical Education, 75*(2).

Vonderbrink, S. A. (1995). *Experiments for advance placement chemistry*. Batavia, IL: Flinn Scientific.

Weise, E. (2003, September 15). Green's peroxide catalyst could help clean up the world. *USA Today*.

Weisstein, E. (n.d.). *Newton, Isaac (1642–1727)*. Retrieved February 27, 2006, from http://scienceworld.wolfram.com/biography/Newton.html

Zumdahl, S. S. (1993). *Chemistry* (3rd ed.). Lexington, MA: D. C. Heath and Company.

Unit 2 References

About NOAH. (n.d.). Retrieved May 7, 2002, from http://www.noah-health.org/english/about.html

About Regenesis. (n.d.). Retrieved May 23, 2001, from http://www.regenesis.com/About/about.htm

About the Biogroup. (n.d.). Retrieved May 23, 2001, from http://www.bioremediationgroup.org/AboutUs/Home.htm

About the human genome project. (n.d.) Retrieved May 5, 2006, from http://www.ornl.gov/sci/techresources/Human_Genome/project/about.shtml

Age of the Earth. (1997, October 9). Retrieved December 10, 2002, from http://pubs.usgs.gov/gip/geotime/age.html

An overview of hemoglobin. (2002, April 10). Retrieved July 30, 2002, from http://sickle.bwh.harvard.edu/hemoglobin.html

Association of genetic technologists: What we do. (n.d). Retrieved May 5, 2006, from http://www.agt-info.org/Jobdesbod.aspx

Bellenir, K. (1996). Genetic disorders sourcebook. Detroit, MI: Omnigraphics.

Bellis, M. (n.d.). Fax, fax machine & facsimile invention. Retrieved August 23, 2002, from http://inventors.about.com/library/inventors/blfax.htm?terms=fax+machine+history

Benton, M. J. (1991). *The rise of mammals*. London: Eagle Editions.

Berger, L. R. (2001, December 4). *Viewpoint: Is it time to revise the system of scientific naming?* Retrieved July 30, 2002, from the National Geographic News Web site: http://news.nationalgeographic.com/news/2001/12/1204_hominin_id.html

Bio-engineering. (n.d.). Retrieved April 30, 2001, from http://library.thinkquest.org/18258/bioengintro.htm

Biological Sciences Curriculum Study (BSCS). (1990). *Biological science: A molecular approach* (6th ed.). Lexington, MA: D.C. Heath.

Biotech applied. (n.d.). Retrieved May 17, 2001, from http://www.accessexcellence.org/AB/BA/

Biotechnology's impact on society. (1990). Retrieved May 8, 2001, from http://www.accessexcellence.org/AB/IE/Biotechnologys_Impact.html

Blumberg, R. B. (1997, February 22). *MendelWeb*. Retrieved September 17, 2002, from http://www.mendelweb.org/

Breakfast for the birds. (1988, April 24–30). *National Science & Technology Week*.

Brining, L., Chan, V., Choi, E., De Sosa, M., & Lee, C. (2000, May 1). *Introduction to the lyginopterids: Primordial seed plants*. Retrieved August 7, 2001, from the University of California-Berkeley, Museum of Paleontology Web site: http://www.ucmp.berkeley.edu/ seedplants/lyginos.html

Career in genetic counseling. (n.d.) Retrieved May 5, 2006, from http://www.nsgc.org/career/index.cfm#as_a_profession

Careers in genetics and biosciences. (n.d.) Retrieved May 5, 2006, from http://www.ornl.gov/sci/techresources/Human_Genome/education/careers.shtml

Carroll, R. L. (1988). *Vertebrate paleontology and evolution*. New York: W. H. Freeman.

Cleaning up wastes. (1992). Retrieved May 17, 2001, from http://www.accessexcellence.org/AB/BA/Cleaning_Up_Wastes.html

Colby, C. (1996, January 7). *Introduction to evolutionary history*. Retrieved October 26, 2001, from http://www.talkorigins.org/faqs/faq-intro-to-biology.html

Csongradi, C. (n.d.). *Why the topic of bioethics in science classes? Definitions of some key terms*. Retrieved May 8, 2001, from http://www.accessexcellence.org/21st/SER/BE/definitions.html

Cutter, M. G., Drexler, E., Friedman, B. E., McCullough, L. B., Mclnerney, J. D., Murray, J. C., et al. (1997). *The puzzle of inheritance: Genetics and the methods of science*. Colorado Springs, CO: Biological Sciences Curriculum Study.

Dalrymple, B. G. (1991). *The age of the Earth*. Stanford, CA: Stanford University Press.

Darwin's visit. (n.d.). Retrieved September 12, 2000, from http://www.terraquest.com/galapagos/history/darwin/darwin.html

Dennis, C., & Gallagher, R. (Eds.). (2001). *The human genome*. New York: Nature Publishing Group.

DNA map opens doors: Breaking gene code will bring advances in science, medicine. (2001, February 12). *The Gazette*, p. A1, A7.

Drexler, E., Hinchee, M. A., Lundberg, D. T., McCullough, L. B., Mclnerney, J. D., Murray, J., et al. (1989). *Advances in genetic technology*. Lexington, MA: D.C. Heath.

Edwards, L. E., & Pojeta, J., Jr. (1997, August 14). *Fossils, rocks and time*. Retrieved July 26, 2001, from http://pubs.usgs.gov/gip/fossils/contents.html

Facsimile & SSTV history. (n.d.). Retrieved August 23, 2002, from http://ourworld.compuserve.com/homepages/hffax/toc28.htm

Fossil horse cybermuseum. (n.d.). Retrieved November 1, 2001, from the Florida Museum of Natural History Web site: http://www.flmnh.ufl.edu/natsci/vertpaleo/fhc/firstCM.htm

Gene therapy. (n.d.). Retrieved May 8, 2001, from http://www.accessexcellence.org/AB/WYW/wkbooks/PAP/therapy.html

Genetic disorders. (n.d.). Retrieved May 7, 2002, from http://gslc.genetics.utah.edu/units/disorders/

Genetic traits. (1999). Retrieved May 7, 2002, from http://k12science.ati.stevens-tech.edu/curriculum/genproj/traits.html

Geologic age: Using radioactive decay to determine geologic age: Background. (2001, October 16). Retrieved October 18, 2001, from http://interactive2.usgs.gov/learningweb/teachers/geoage.htm

Grant, V. (1985). *The evolutionary process: A critical review of evolutionary theory*. New York: Columbia University Press.

Hardy, J. K. (2000, April). *General, organic and biochemistry*. Retrieved July 8, 2002, from http://ull.chemistry.uakron.edu/genobc/title.html

Hardy-Weinberg equilibrium made easy. (n.d.). Retrieved May 8, 2001, from http://library.thinkquest.org/18258/noframes/hweinberg.htm

Harter, R. (1998, June 1). *Changing views of the history of the Earth*. Retrieved July 25, 2002, from http://www.talkorigins.org/faqs/geohist.html

Haynes, G. (1991). *Mammoths, mastodonts, and elephants: Biology, behavior, and the fossil record*. New York: Cambridge University Press.

Hill, J. W. (1992). *Chemistry for changing times* (6th ed.). New York: Macmillan.

History of the human genome project. (n.d.). Retrieved February 9, 2001, from http://www.ornl.gov/hgmis/project/hgp.html

Horton hears a genome: Human genes are small ecosystems. (2002, February 11). *The Gazette*, p. A26.

Hunt, K. (1995, January 4). *Horse evolution*. Retrieved November 1, 2001, from http://www.talkorigins.org/faqs/horses/horse_evol.html

Industry Canada – Life Sciences Branch. (2000, October 16). *Transgenic microorganisms overview*. Retrieved May 23, 2001, from http://strategis.ic.gc.ca/ssg/tc00039e.html

Information about a new strain of Clostridium difficile. (2005, July). Retrieved May 26, 2006, from http://www.cdc.gov/ncidod/dhqp/id_CdiffFAQ_newstrain.html

Japikse, C. (2000, May 1). The Irish potato famine. *EPA Journal*, [1994, Fall]. Retrieved May 7, 2002, from http://www.epa.gov/history/topics/perspect/potato.htm

Landmark gene studies released. (2001, February 12). Retrieved February 13, 2001, from http://www.cnn.com/2001/HEALTH/02/12/humangenome/index.html

Lemonick, M. D., Dorfman, A., & Robinson, S. (2001, July 23). One giant step for mankind. *Time, 158*, 46–54.

Levin, H. L. (1999). *Ancient invertebrates and their living relatives*. Upper Saddle River, NJ: Prentice Hall.

Lewin, B. (1990). *Genes IV*. New York: Oxford University Press.

Lieberman, D. E. (2001). Palaeoanthropology: Another face in our family tree. *Nature, 410*, 419–420.

LifeWorks: Explore medical and health science careers. (n.d.) Retrieved May 5, 2006, from http://science.education.nih.gov/LifeWorks.nsf/alpha.htm#P

Lister, A. M., & Sher, A. V. (2001). The origin and evolution of the woolly mammoth. *Science, 294*, 1094–1097.

MacFadden, B. J. (1992). *Fossil horses: Systematics, paleobiology, and evolution of the family equidae*. New York: Cambridge University Press.

MacRae, A. (1998, October 2). *Radiometric dating and the geological time scale: Circular reasoning or reliable tools?* Retrieved October 26, 2001, from http://www.talkorigins.org/faqs/dating.html

Marantz Henig, R. (2000). *The monk in the garden: The lost and found genius of Gregor Mendel, the father of genetics*. Boston: Houghton Mifflin.

Marzano, R. J., Gaddy, B. B., & Dean, C. (2000). *What works in classroom instruction.* Retrieved July 18, 2002, from the Mid-continent Research for Education and Learning Web site: http://www.mcrel.org/products/learning/whatworks.asp

Mayr, E. (2001). *What evolution is.* New York: Basic Books.

Mendel. (1998). Retrieved September 17, 2002, from http://www.cs.bham.ac.uk/~idm/mendel/ index.html

Mendel Museum of Genetics: The exhibition on-line. (n.d.). Retrieved September 17, 2002, from http://www.mendel-museum.org/eng/1online/

Micklos, D. A., & Freyer, G. A. (1990). *DNA science: A first course in recombinant DNA technology.* Burlington, NC: Cold Spring Harbor Laboratory Press.

Mulheisen, M., & Berry, K. (1999, December). *Eptesicus fuscus: Big brown bat. Retrieved January 4, 2001, from the University of Michigan, Museum of Zoology Web site: http://animaldiversity.ummz.umich.edu/accounts/eptesicus/e._fuscus$narrative.htm*

Muscular Dystrophy Association. (2003, April 11). *Myotonic dystrophy fact sheet.* Retrieved August 26, 2002, from http://www.mda.org.au/specific/mdamyt.html

National Academy of Sciences. (1999). *Science and creationism.* Retrieved August 23, 2002, from http://www.nap.edu/html/creationism/index.html

National Institutes of Health. (2000, September). *The chemistry of health* (NIH Publication No. 00-4121). Washington, DC: U.S. Department of Health and Human Services.

National Institutes of Health. (2000, November). *The structures of life* (NIH Publication No. 01-2778). Washington, DC: U.S. Department of Health and Human Services.

National Research Council. (1996). *A "tasteless" tasty test.* Retrieved May 7, 2002, from http://www.freyscientific.com/lessons/middle/life_genetic.html

Novak, G. A. (1999, April). *Radioactive isotopes – the "clocks in rocks": Numerical and relative ages for rocks.* Retrieved July 25, 2002, from http://www.sciencecourseware.com/VirtualDating/files/1.0_ClocksInRocks.html

Ohio Division of Wildlife. (n.d.). *Life history notes: Big brown bat.* Retrieved January 4, 2001, from http://www.dnr.state.oh.us/wildlife/resources/wildnotes/pub372.htm

O'Neill Skinner, P. (2000, October 30). *Ethical decision making framework.* Retrieved April 30, 2001, from http://genetics-education-partnership.mbt.washington.edu/cool/tools/ethics.html

Onion, A. (2002, April 11). *To be human: Scientists zero in on what distinguishes people from chimps.* Retrieved July 31, 2002, from http://abcnews.go.com/sections/scitech/dailynews/chimphuman020411.html

Part F: A closer look at...: Adenine-requiring mutants. (1999, August 14). Retrieved March 30, 2001, from http://www.phys.ksu.edu/gene/f_1.html

Pasternak, J. J. (1999). *An introduction to human molecular genetics: Mechanisms of inherited diseases.* Bethesda, MD: Fitzgerald Science Press.

Peace, W. E. (2001). *DNA for dinner?* Retrieved May 8, 2001, from http://www.gis.net/%7epeacewp/webquest.htm

Pharmacogenomics. Retrieved May 5, 2006, from http://www.ornl.gov/sci/techresources/Human_Genome/medicine/pharma.shtml

Pojeta, J., & Springer, D. A. (2001). *Evolution and the fossil record.* Alexandria, VA: American Geological Institute.

Radiometric time scale. (2001, June 13). Retrieved October 26, 2001, from http://pubs.usgs.gov/gip/geotime/radiometric.html

Russell, P. J. (1996). *Genetics* (4th ed.). New York: HarperCollins College Publishers.

Savage, R. J. G. (1986). *Mammal evolution: An illustrated guide.* New York: Facts on File Publications and The British Museum of Natural History.

Scott, E., Kirkner, L., Shin, J., Desai, V., & Chan, J. (2000, May 5). *Localities of the Cambrian: The Burgess Shale.* Retrieved August 7, 2001, from the University of California-Berkeley, Museum of Paleontology Web site: http://www.ucmp.berkeley.edu/cambrian/burgess.html

Seibert, T. (2002, July 16). Site offers mammoth discovery. *Denver Post*, p. 1A, 10A.

Sherman, F. (2000, September 19). *The yeast genome.* Retrieved November 16, 2001, from the University of Rochester, Department of Biochemistry and Biophysics Web site: http://dbb.urmc.rochester.edu/labs/sherman_f/yeast/5.html

Shoshani, J. (1998). Understanding proboscidean evolution: A formidable task. *Trends in Ecology and Evolution, 13,* 480–487.

Shoshani, J. (Ed.). (1992). *Elephants.* New York: Checkmark Books.

Shoshani, J., Golenberg, E. M., & Yang, H. (1998). Elephantidae phylogeny: Morphological versus molecular results. *Acta Theriologica, Supplement, 5,* 89–122.

Shoshani, J., & Tassy, P. (Eds.). (1997). *The proboscidea: Evolution and paleoecology of elephants and their relatives.* New York: Oxford University Press.

Simison, W. B. (1996, January 22). *Introduction to the crinoidea: Sea lilies and feather stars.* Retrieved August 7, 2001, from the University of California-Berkeley, Museum of Paleontology Web site: http://www.ucmp.berkeley.edu/echinodermata/crinoidea.html

Speer, B. R., & Waggoner, B. (1995, December 4). *Chiroptera: More on morphology.* Retrieved January 4, 2001, from the University of California-Berkeley, Museum of Paleontology Web site: http://www.ucmp.berkeley.edu/mammal/eutheria/chiromm.html

Stanhope, J. (1994). *Hardy-Weinberg equilibrium.* Retrieved July 12, 2001, from http://www.woodrow.org/teachers/bi/1994/hwintro.html

Stassen, C. (1997, April 22). *The age of the Earth.* Retrieved December 10, 2002, from http://www.talkorigins.org/faqs/faq-age-of-earth.html

Suzuki, D. T., Griffiths, A. J., Miller, J. H., & Lewontin, R. C. (1986). *An introduction to genetic analysis* (3rd ed.). New York: W. H. Freeman.

Thomas, M. G., Hagelberg, E., Jones, H. B., Yang, Z., & Lister, A. M. (2000). Molecular and morphological evidence on the phylogeny of the elephantidae. *Proceedings of the Royal Society of London, Series B, 267,* 2493–2500.

Tissue engineering. (n.d.). Retrieved May 1, 2001, from http://www.whitaker.org/95_annual_report/tissue95.html

Trilobite. (2002). In *The new encyclopaedia Britannica* (Vol. 11, pp. 925–926). Chicago: Encyclopaedia Britannica.

United States Department of Agriculture. (1994, June). *Biomining.* Retrieved May 17, 2001, from http://www.accessexcellence.org/AB/BA/Biomining.html

United States Department of Energy, Human Genome Program. (1992). *Primer on molecular genetics.* Retrieved February 9, 2001, from http://genome.rtc.riken.go.jp/hgmis/publicat/primer/toc.html

United States Department of Energy, Natural and Accelerated Bioremediation Program. (2000, August 24). *Scientists combine chemistry and bioremediation to clean cadmium from soil.* Retrieved May 23, 2001, from http://www.eurekalert.org/pub_releases/2000-08/BNL-Scca-2308100.php

United States Food and Drug Administration. (2000, January). *Methods for genetically engineering a plant.* Retrieved May 1, 2001, from http://vm.cfsan.fda.gov/~dms/fdbioenc.html

United States Geological Survey. (1997, April 1). *Bioremediation: Nature's way to a cleaner environment* (Fact Sheet FS-054-95). Retrieved May 23, 2001, from http://water.usgs.gov/wid/html/bioremed.html

Well, W. (1997, December). *Extreme chemistry*. Retrieved May 23, 2001, from http://www.accessexcellence.org/AB/BA/1297xtremo.html

What Darwin didn't know: Gregor Mendel and the mechanism of heredity. (2001). Retrieved September 17, 2002, from http://www.pbs.org/wgbh/evolution/library/06/1/l_061_01.html

Whitfield, J. (2002, January 22). Human genome pioneer steps down. *Nature*. Retrieved January 19, 2002, from http://www.nature.com/nsu/020121/020121-9.html

Zimmer, C. (2001, September). How old is it? *National Geographic, 200*, 78–101.

Zimmer, C. (2001). *The triumph of an idea*. New York: Harper Collins.

Unit 3 References

Ahnert, F. (1970). Functional relationships between denudation, relief, and uplift in large mid-latitudine drainage basins. *American Journal of Science, 268*, 243–263.

Anderson, D. L. (2001). Top-down tectonics? *Science, 293*, 2016–2018.

Bennett, R. A., Davis, J. L., & Wernicke, B. P. (1999). Present-day pattern of Cordilleran deformation in the western United States. *Geology, 27*, 371–374.

Berner, E. K., & Berner R. A. (1987). *The global water cycle: Geochemistry and environment*. Englewood Cliffs, NJ: Prentice Hall.

Berner, E. K., & Berner R. A. (1996). *Global environment: Water, air, and geochemical cycles*. Upper Saddle River, NJ: Prentice Hall.

Browning, K. A., & Gurney, R. J. (Eds.). (1999). *Global energy and water cycles. New York: Cambridge University Press.*

Clark, P. U., Mitrovica, J. X., Milne, G. A., & Tamisiea, M. E. (2002, March 29). Sea-level fingerprinting as a direct test for the source of global meltwater pulse IA. *Science, 295*, 2438–2441.

Clemens, S. C., & Prell, W. (1990). Late Pleistocene variability of Arabian Sea summer monsoon winds and continental aridity: Eolian records from the lithogenic component of deep-sea sediments. *Paleoceanography, 5*(2), 109–145.

Coates, A. G. (Ed.). (1997). *Central America: A natural cultural history.* New Haven and London: Yale University Press.

Colorado Springs Utilities. (n.d.). *Colorado Springs water system*. Retrieved January 15, 2002, from http://www.csu.org/water/h20system.html

Colorado Springs Utilities. (2000). *Water: Colorado Springs lifeline* [Brochure]. Author.

Colorado Springs Utilities. (2001, May). *2001-2002 fact book* [Booklet]. Author.

Cutler, K. B., Edwards, R. L., Taylor, F. W., Cheng, H., Adkins, J., Gallup, C. D., et al. (2003). Rapid sea-level fall and deep-ocean temperature change since the last interglacial period. *Earth and Planetary Science Letters, 206*, 253–271.

Deep-sea sample repository: A long history of coring the ocean floor. (2000, July 20). Retrieved February 4, 2002, from the Columbia University, Lamont-Doherty Earth Observatory Web site: http://www.ldeo.columbia.edu/CORE_REPOSITORY/RHP1Head.html

Environmental Protection Agency. (n.d.). *Water supply & demand: United States water budget*. Retrieved December 18, 2001, from http://www.epa.gov/seahome/groundwater/src/supply.htm#budget

Etheridge, D.M., Steele, L. P., Langenfelds, R. L., Francey, R. J., Barnola, J. M., & Morgan, V. I. (1998). Historical CO_2 records from the Law Dome DE08, DE08-2, and DSS ice cores. In *Trends: A compendium of data on global change*. Oak Ridge, TN: Carbon Dioxide Information Analysis Center, Oak Ridge National Laboratory, U.S. Department of Energy.

Faure, G. (1998). *Principles and applications of geochemistry*. Upper Saddle River, NJ: Prentice-Hall.

Friends of the Great Salt Lake. (n.d.) *Friends of the Great Salt Lake Web site*. Retrieved November 11, 2002, from http://www.fogsl.org

Gwynn, J. W. (Ed.). (1980). *Great Salt Lake: A scientific, historical and economic overview* [Utah Department of Natural Resources Bulletin 116]. Salt Lake City, UT: Utah Geological and Mineral Survey.

Gwynn, J. W. (1998). Great Salt Lake, Utah: chemical and physical variations of the brine and effects of the SPRR Causeway, 1966-1996, In J. K. Pitman & A. R. Carroll (Eds.), *Modern and ancient lake system: New problems and perspectives* (pp. 71–90). Salt Lake City, UT: Utah Geological Association.

Gwynn, J. W. (2001). *A lake divided: A history of the Southern Pacific Railroad Causeway and its effect on Great Salt Lake*. Retrieved November 11, 2002, from the Utah Geological Survey Web site: http://www.ugs.state.ut.us/utahgeo/gsl/lakedivided.htm

Herbert, T. D., Schuffert, J. D., Andreasen, D., Heusser, L., Lyle, M., Mix, A., et al. (2001). Collapse of the California current during glacial maxima linked to climate change on land. *Science, 293*, 71–76.

Hoorn, C. (2006, May). The birth of the mighty Amazon. *Scientific American, 294*(5), 52–59.

Imbrie, J., Boyle, E. A., Clemens, S. C., Duffy, A., Howard, W. R., Kukla, G., et al. (1992). On the structure and origin of major glaciation cycles. *Paleoceanography, 7*, 701–738.

Imbrie, J., & Palmer Imbrie, K. (1979). *Ice ages: Solving the mystery.* Cambridge, MA: Harvard University Press.

Intergovernmental Panel on Climate Exchange. (2001). *Climate change 2001: The scientific basis. Chapter 3: The carbon cycle and atmospheric carbon dioxide*. Retrieved June 13, 2006, from http://www.grida.no/climate/ipcc_tar/wg1/095.htm

Jouzel, J., Barkov, N. I., Barnola, J. M., Bender, M., Chappelaz, J., Genthon, C., et al. (1993). Extending the Vostok ice-core record of paleoclimate to the penultimate glacial period. *Nature, 364*, 407–412.

Keeling, C. D., & Whorf, T.P. (2005). Atmospheric CO_2 records from sites in the SIO air sampling network. In *Trends: A compendium of data on global change*. Oak Ridge, TN: Carbon Dioxide Information Analysis Center, Oak Ridge National Laboratory, U.S. Department of Energy.

Kious, W. J., & Tilling, R. I. (1996). *This dynamic Earth*. U.S. Geological Survey.

Lambeck, K., & Chappell, J., (2001, April 27). Sea level change through the last glacial cycle. *Science, 292, 679–686.*

Loving, B. L., Waddell, K. M., & Miller, C. W. (2000). *Water and salt balance of Great Salt Lake, Utah, and simulation of water and salt movement through the causeway, 1987–98.* (Water-Resources Investigations Report 00-4221). Salt Lake City, Utah: United States Geological Survey.

Lyle, M., Heusser, L., Herbert, T., Mix, A., & Barron, J. (2001). Interglacial themes and variations orbital forcing, global warming and associated responses from the terrestrial and marine biosphere, 0-500 ka in the Pacific Northwest. *Geology, 9*(12), 1115–1118.

McCrae, J. (1996). *Oregon developmental species: Brine shrimp*. Retrieved October 15, 2002, from the Oregon Department of Fish and Wildlife Web site: http://www.hmsc.orst.edu/odfw/devfish/sp/brine.html

Murray, M. H., & Segall, P. (2001). Modeling broadscale deformation in northern California and Nevada from plate motions and elastic strain accumulation. *Geophysical Research Letters, 28*, 4315–4318.

Oskin, M., & Stock, J. (2003). Marine incursion synchronous with plate boundary localization in the Gulf of California. *Geology, 31*(1), 23–26.

Petit, J. R., Jouzel, J., Raynaud, D., Barkov, N. I., Barnola, J. M., et al. (1999). Climate and atmospheric history of the past 420,000 years from the Vostok ice core, Antarctica. *Nature, 399*, 429–436.

Planetary Photojournal. (n.d.). *PIA07236: Mosaic of river channel and ridge area on Titan*. Retrieved July, 18, 2005, from http://photojournal.jpl.nasa.gov/catalog/PIA07236

Potter, E. K., Esat, T. M., Schellmann, G., Radtke, U., Lambeck, K., & McCullouch, M. (2004) Suborbital-period sea-level oscillations during marine isotope substages 5a and 5c. *Earth and Planetary Science Letters, 225*, 191–204.

Press, F., & Siever, R. (2001). *Understanding Earth* (3rd ed.). New York: W. H. Freeman.

Quay, P. (2002, December 20). Ups and downs of CO_2 uptake. *Science's Compass, 298*, 2344.

Quinn, T. M. (2000). Shallow water science and ocean drilling face challenges. *Eos, Transactions of the American Geophysical Union, 81*, 397–404.

Ruddiman, W. F. (2001). *Earth's climate: Past and future*. New York: W.H. Freeman.

Ruxton, B. P., & McDougall, I. (1967). Denudation rates in northeast Papua from K-Ar dating of lavas. *American Journal of Science, 265*, 545–561.

Sarmiento, J. L., & Gruber, N. (2002). Sinks for anthropogenic carbon. *Physics Today, 55*(8) 30–36.

Shackleton, N. J., Berger, A., & Peltier, W. R. (1990). An alternative astronomical calibration of the lower pleistocene timescale based on ODP site 677. *Transactions of the Royal Society of Edinburgh: Earth Sciences, 81*.

Siegenthaler, U., Stocker, T. F., Monnin, E., Lüthi, D., Schwander, J., Stauffer, B., et al. (2005, November 25). Stable carbon cycle-climate relationship during the late Pleistocene. *Science, 310*, 1313–1317.

Stephens, D. (1998). Salinity-induced changes in the aquatic ecosystem of Great Salt Lake, Utah. In J. K. Pitman & A. R. Carroll (Eds.), *Modern and ancient lake system: New problems and perspectives* (pp. 1–8). Salt Lake City, UT: Utah Geological Association.

Stephens, D. W. (1990). Changes in lake levels, salinity and the biological community of Great Salt Lake (Utah, USA), 1847–1987. *Hydrobiologia, 197*, 139–146.

Tiedemann, R., Sarnthein, M., & Shackleton, N. (1994). Astronomical timescale for the Pliocene Atlantic delta18-O and dust flux records of Ocean Drilling Program site 659. *Paleoceanography, 9*, 619–638.

Tomkins, S. (2000). A review of the use of the brine shrimp, *Artemia* spp, for teaching practical biology in schools and colleges. *Journal of Biological Education, 34*, 117–122.

United States Geological Survey. (2001, May 3). *Great Salt Lake, Utah*. Retrieved December 11, 2001, from http://ut.water.usgs.gov/greatsaltlake/index.html

Utah Water Research Laboratory. (n.d.). *The Utah water atlas*. Retrieved May 29, 2002, from http://www.engineering.usu.edu/uwrl/atlas/

Waddell, K. M., & Barton, J. D. (1980). *Estimated inflow and evaporation for Great Salt Lake, Utah, 1931-76, with revised model for evaluating the effects of dikes on the water and salt balance of the lake*. Utah Department of Natural Resources, Division of Water Resources.

Wright, J. D. (1998). Global climate change in marine stable isotope records. In J. M. Sowers, J. S. Noller, & W. R. Lettis, (Eds.). *Dating and earthquakes: Review of quaternary geochronology and its application to paleoseismology* (NUREG/CR 5562) (pp. 671–682). U.S. Nuclear Regulatory Commission special publication.

Wurtsbaugh, W. A., & Berry, T. S. (1990). Cascading effects of decreased salinity of the plankton, chemistry, and physics of the Great Salt Lake (Utah). *Canadian Journal of Fisheries and Aquatic Sciences, 47*, 100–109.

Unit 4 References

2005 World population data sheet. (2005). Retrieved on June 5, 2006, from http://www.prb.org/pdf05/05WorldDataSheet_Eng.pdf

Bybee, R. W., Buchwald, C. E., Crissman, S., Heil, D. R., Kuerbis, P. J., Matsumoto, C. & McInerney, J. D. (1989). *Science and technology education for the elementary years: Frameworks for curriculum and instruction*. Washington, DC: National Center for Improving Science Education. 121.

Calinvaux, P. (1993). *Ecology 2*. New York: John Wiley and Sons.

Cunningham, W. P., & Woodworth Saigo, B. (1999). *Environmental science: A global concern* (5th ed.). Boston: McGraw-Hill.

Dreissena polymorpha (mollusc). (2005, June 22). Retrieved May 27, 2006, from http://www.invasivespecies.net/database/species/ecology.asp?si=50&fr=1&sts=sss

Duggins, D. O., Simenstad, S. A., & Estes, J.A. (1989). Magnification of secondary production by kelp detritus in coastal marine systems. *Science, 245*, 170–173.

Ecological footprint analysis. (n.d.). Retrieved June 5, 2006, from http://www.rprogress.org/newprojects/ecolFoot.shtml

Ecological footprint of nations, 2005 update. (2005). Retrieved June 5, 2006, from http://www.rprogress.org/newpubs/2006/Footprint%20of%20Nations%202005.pdf

Expenditures on children by families. (2005). Retrieved June 5, 2006, from http://www.usda.gov/cnpp/Crc/crc2004.pdf

Glig, O., Hanski, I., & Sittler, B. (2003). Cyclic dynamics in a simple vertebrate predator-prey community. *Science, 302*, 866–868.

Global aging: The challenge of success. (2005). Retrieved June 5, 2006, from http://www.prb.org/pdf05/60.1GlobalAging.pdf

Global population profile: 2002. (2004). Retrieved June 5, 2006, from http://www.census.gov/ipc/www/wp02.html

Harper, J. L., & Clatworthy, J. N. (1963). The comparative biology of closely related species of clover in mixed and pure culture. *Journal of Experimental Botany, 14, 172–190.*

Hoagland, M. (1995). The way life works. New York: Times Books.

Imported fire ants: An agricultural pest and human health hazard. (1999, April). Retrieved May 27, 2006, from http://www.aphis.usda.gov/lpa/pubs/fsheet_faq_notice/fs_phifa.html

Invasive species information node. (n.d.). Retrieved May 25, 2006, from http://invasivespecies.nbii.gov

Kates, R. (2000). Population and consumption: What we know, what we need to know. *Environment, 42*, 10–19.

Kent, M. M. (1995). *World population: Fundamentals of growth* (Student chartbook). Washington, DC: Population Reference Bureau.

Key facts about avian influenza (bird flu) and avian influenza A (H5N1) virus. (2006, May 5). Retrieved June 1, 2006, from http://www.cdc.gov/flu/avian/gen-info/facts.htm

Kormndy, E. J. (1996). *Concepts of ecology* (4th ed.). Upper Saddle River, NJ: Prentice-Hall.

Lindeman, R. (1942). The trophic-dynamic aspect of ecology. *Ecology, 23*, 399–418.

McComas, W. F. (2002). The ideal environmental science curriculum: I. history, rationales, misconceptions & standards. *The American Biology Teacher, 64*, 665–672.

McComas, W. F. (2003). The nature of the ideal environmental science curriculum; advocates, textbooks and conclusions (Part II of II). *The American Biology Teacher, 65*, 171–178.

Munson, B. (1994). Ecological misconceptions. *Journal of Environmental Education. 25*, 30–34.

National wildlife refuge system fact sheet. (n.d.). Retrieved June 7, 2006, from http://www.fws.gov/refuges/pdfs/2004_NWRSfactSheet.pdf

Odum, E. (1992). Great ideas in ecology for the 1990s. *Bioscience, 42*, 542–545.

Odum, E. P. (1993). *Ecology and our endangered life-support systems* (2nd ed.). Sunderland, MA: Sinauer Associates.

Overview of the ecology and research of wolves and moose on Isle Royale. (n.d). Retrieved May 26, 2006, from http://www.isleroyalewolf.org

Peterson, R. O., & Vucetich, J. A. (2005). *Ecological studies of wolves on Isle Royale, Annual report 2004-2005.* School of Forest Resources and Environmental Science, Michigan Technological University.

Press, F., & Siever. R. (2001). *Understanding Earth* (3rd ed.). New York: W. H. Freeman.

Short history of the refuge system. (n.d.). Retrieved June 7, 2006, from http://www.fws.gov/refuges/history/over/over_hist-a_fs.html

State of the world's forests 2003. (2003). Retrieved on June 5, 2006, from http://www.fao.org/documents/show_cdr.asp?url_file=/DOCREP/005/Y7581E/Y7581E00.HTM

The challenge of whirling disease. (n.d). Retrieved May 27, 2006, from http://www.whirling-disease.org/disease.html

The state of food and agriculture 2003–2004. (2004). Retrieved on June 5, 2006, from http://www.fao.org/documents/show_cdr.asp?url_file=/docrep/006/Y5160E/Y5160E00.HTM

The state of world fisheries and aquaculture 2004. (2004). Retrieved on June 5, 2006, from http://www.fao.org/documents/show_cdr.asp?url_file=/DOCREP/007/y5600e/y5600e00.htm

Turchin, P. (2003). *Complex population dynamics: A theoretical/empirical synthesis.* Princeton, NJ: Princeton University Press.

Van Den Bergh, J., & Rietveld, P. (2004). Reconsidering the limits to world population: meta-analysis and meta-prediction. *Bioscience 54*, 195–204.

Vucetich, J. A., & Peterson, R. O. (2004). Long-term population and predation dynamics of wolves on Isle Royale. In D. Macdonald & C. Sillero-Zubiri (Eds.), *Biology and conservation of wild canids* (pp. 281–292). Oxford University Press.

West Nile virus. (n.d.). Retrieved May 27, 2006, from http://westnilevirus.nbii.gov/index.html

What is sustainable agriculture? (n.d.). Retrieved June 7, 2006, from http://attra.ncat.org/

Women of our world 2005. (2005). Retrieved June 5, 2006, from http://www.prb.org/pdf05/WomenOfOurWorld2005.pdf

World population prospects: The 2004 revision. (2005). Retrieved June 5, 2006, from http://www.un.org/esa/population/publications/WPP2004/2004Highlights_finalrevised.pdf

World resources 2000–2001: People and ecosystems: The fraying web of life. (2000). Retrieved June 5, 2006, from http://pubs.wri.org/pubs_description.cfm?PubID=3027

World resources 2002–2004: Decisions for the Earth: Balance, voice, and power. (2003). Retrieved June 5, 2006, from http://governance.wri.org/pubs_pdf.cfm?PubID=3764

How To References

Bergman, M. K. (2004, December). *Guide to effective searching of the internet – 2005.* Retrieved May 10, 2006, from http://www.brightplanet.com/pdf/SearchTutorial.pdf

Biological Sciences Curriculum Study (BSCS). (1994). *Middle school science and technology implementation guide.* Dubuque, IA: Kendall/Hunt.

Biological Sciences Curriculum Study (BSCS). (2000). *Making sense of integrated science: A guide for high school.* Colorado Springs, CO: Author.

Block, C., & Pressley, M. (Eds.). (2002). *Comprehension instruction: Research-based best practices. Solving problems in the teaching of literacy.* New York: The Guilford Press.

Bransford, J. D., Brown, A. L., & Cocking, R. R. (1999). *How people learn: Brain, mind, experience, and school.* Washington, DC: National Academy Press.

Bransford, J., Brown, A., & Cocking, R. (Eds.). (2000). *How people learn: Brain, mind, experience, and school.* Washington, DC: National Academy Press.

Bromley, K. (1999). *Journaling: Engagements in reading, writing, and thinking. Teaching strategies.* New York: Scholastic.

Bruer, J. (1994). How Children Learn. *Executive Educator, 16*(8), 32–36.

Bybee, R. W. (1997). *Achieving scientific literacy.* Portsmouth, NH: Heinemann.

Cohen, E. G. (1986). *Designing groupwork: Strategies for the heterogeneous classroom.* New York: Teachers College Press.

Cohen, E. G. (1994). Restructuring the classroom: Conditions for productive small groups. *Review of Educational Research, 64*(1), 1–35.

Corcoran, T., & Hansen, B. (1983). *The quest for excellence: Making public schools more effective.* Trenton, NJ: New Jersey School Boards Association.

De Lisi, R. (2002). From marbles to instant messenger: Implications of Piaget's ideas about peer learning. *Theory into Practice, 41*(1), 5–12.

Dvorak, J. D., & Buchanan, K. (2002). Using technology to create and enhance collaborative learning. *World Conference on Educational Multimedia, Hypermedia and Telecommunications,* (1), 459–464. Retrieved February 7, 2005, from http://www.eric.ed.gov/

Eisner, E. (1982). *Cognition and curriculum.* New York: Largman.

Fisher, Frey, & Williams. (2002). Seven literacy strategies that work. *Educational Leadership, 60*(3), 70–73.

Gardner, H. (1983). *Frames of mind.* New York: Basic Books.

Johnson, D. W., & Johnson, R. T. (1991). Group assessment as an aid to science instruction. In G. Kulm and S. M. Malcolm (Eds.), *Science assessment in the service of reform* (pp. 283–289). Washington, DC: American Association for the Advancement of Science.

Johnson, D. W., & Johnson, R. T. (1999). *Learning together and alone: Collaborative, competitive, and individualistic learning* (5th ed.). Boston: Allyn and Bacon.

Johnson, D. W., Johnson, R. T., & Holubec, E. J. (1986). *Circle of learning: Cooperation in the classroom.* Edina, MN: Interaction Book.

Johnson, D. W., Johnson, R. T., & Taylor, B. (1993). Impact of cooperative and individualistic learning on high-ability students' achievement, self-esteem, and social acceptance. *The Journal of Social Psychology, 133*(6), 839–844.

Kagan, S. (1994). *Collaborative learning.* San Juan Capistrano, CA: Kagan Collaborative Learning.

Kimmelman, P., Kroeze, D., Schmidt, W., van der Ploeg, A., McNeely, M., & Tan, A. (1999). *A first look at what we can learn from high performing school districts: An analysis of TIMSS data from the first in the World Consortium.* Washington, DC: National Institute on Student Achievement, Curriculum, and Assessment (ED/OERI).

Krol, K., Janssen, J., Veenman, S., & van der Linden, J. (2004). Effects of a cooperative learning program on the elaborations of student working dyads. *Educational Research and Evaluation, 10*(3), 205–237.

Lavoie, D. R., (Ed.). (1995). *Toward a cognitive-science perspective for scientific problem solving.* NARST

Monograph, Number Six, ED454060, National Association for Research in Science Teaching.

Lavooy, M. J., & Newlin, M. H. (2003). Computer mediated communication: Online instruction and interactivity. *Journal of Interactive Learning Research, 14(2), 157–165.*

Lemke, J. (1990). *Talking science: Language, learning, and values.* Norwood, NJ: Ablex Publishing.

Lundgren, L. (1993). *Collaborative learning resource guide.* Lake Forest, IL: Glencoe Division, Macmillan/McGraw-Hill School Publishing.

Mandel, S. M. (2003). *Cooperative work groups: Preparing students for the real world.* Thousand Oaks, CA: Corwin Press.

Marzano, R. (2003). *What works in schools: Translating research into action.* Alexandria, VA: Association for Supervision and Curriculum Development.

McGarrigle, M., & Lamb, T. (2004). *Inquiry III Earth-space science and science & technology chapters.* BSCS Evaluation Report (ER-2004-22, November, internal document).

McGilly, K. (1996). *Classroom lessons: Integrating cognitive theory and classroom practice.* Cambridge, MA: The MIT Press.

Merrienboer, J. (1997). *Training complex cognitive skills: A four component instructional design model for technical training.* Englewood Cliffs, NJ: Educational Technologies Publications.

Moore, J. E. (2003). The art of sorting: Using Venn diagrams to learn science process skills. *Science Activities, 39*(4), 17–21.

National Research Council. (1996). *National science education standards.* Washington, DC.

National Research Council. (2000). *Inquiry and the national science education standards.* Washington, DC.

Novak, J. (1990). Concept maps and Venn diagrams: Two metacognitive tools to facilitate meaningful learning. *Instructional Science, 19(1), 29–52.*

Pellegrino, J., Chudowsky, N., & Glaser, R. (Eds.). (2001). *Knowing what students know.* Washington, DC: National Academy Press.

Peterson, P. L., & Fennema, E. (1985). Effective teaching, student engagement in classroom activities, and sex-related differences in learning mathematics. *American Educational Research Journal, 22*(3), 309–335.

Pinkerton, D. (in press). Learning from mistakes. *The Physics Teacher.*

Rosenshine, B., & Meister, C. (1994). *Reciprocal reading: A review of the research. Review of Educational Research, 64*(4), 479–530.

Rubin, C. (1999). *Self-esteem in the classroom.* Master's Research Action Project, Saint Xavier University and Skylight Professional Development. Retrieved February 14, 2005, from http://www.eric.ed.gov

Slavin, R. E. (1987). *Collaborative learning: Student teams.* Washington, DC: National Education Association.

Sleeter, C. E., & Grant, C. A. (1988). *Making choices for multicultural education: Five approaches to race, class, and gender* (2nd ed.). New York: Merrill Publishing.

Sweller, J. (1988). Cognitive load during problem solving: Effects on learning. *Cognition and Instruction, 12*, 2258–285.

Thier, M. (2002). *The new science literacy: Using language skills to help students learn science.* Arlington, VA: University of California, Berkley.

Vygotsky, L. (1962). *Thought and language.* Cambridge, MA: Harvard University Press.

Wang, M., Poole, M., Harris, B., & Wangemann, P. (2001). Promoting online collaborative learning experiences for teenagers. *Education Media International, 38*(4), 203–215.

Wentzel, K. R., & Watkins, D. E. (2002). Peer relationships and collaborative learning as contexts for academic enablers. *School Psychology Review, 3*(3), 366–377.

Wiggins, G., & McTighe, J. (1998). *Understanding by design.* Alexandria, VA: Association for Supervision and Curriculum Development.

Wittrock, M. (1990). Generative processes of comprehension. *Educational Psychologist, 24*(4), 345–376.

Master Materials List

For information on standard and custom kit availability, please contact your Kendall/Hunt representative at 1-800-542-6657.

Type	Chapter	Item Description	Kit Qty.
Consumable Items			
C	1	Agar Plates, Pkg/10	4
C	3, 5, 11, 13	Aluminum Foil, Roll	1
C	5	Ammonia, 100 mL	1
C	5	Antacid, Alkamints, Bottle/75	1
C	1, 5	Antibacterial Soap, 236 mL	3
C	3, 5, 11	Baking Soda, 454 g	2
C	12	Bamboo Skewers, Pkg/100	1
C	5	Battery, 9 V	8
C	1	Biohazard Disposable Bags	1
C	8	Cheesecloth, 2 m	1
C	12	Clay, Assorted Colors, 1 lb.	10
C	7	Clay, Blue, 1 lb.	4
C	2	Clay, Green, 4 oz. Stick	2
C	7	Clay, Red, 1 lb.	4
C	12	Clear Plastic Straw	1
C	12	Clear Plastic Straw	10
C	2	Coffee Filter, Flat Bottom, Pkg/100	1
C	1, 9, 10	Colored Markers, Pkg/10	10
C	frequent use	Colored Pencils, Set/12	15
C	6	Colored Tape, Blue	1
C	6	Colored Tape, Green	1
C	6	Colored Tape, Red	1
C	6	Colored Tape, Yellow	1
C	9	Construction Paper, Colored, Pkg/50	2

Type	Chapter	Item Description	Kit Qty.
C	8	Construction Paper, White, 12×18″	1
C	3	Copper Shot, Box/1500	1
C	5	Copper Wire, 454 g	1
C	13	Corn Syrup, 474 mL	1
C	3	Cotton Swabs, Pkg/180	1
C	frequent use	Dropper Pipets, pkg/500	1
C	7, 14	Dry Yeast, 7 g	2
C	1	Filter Paper, pkg/100	1
C	3, 10, 13	Food Coloring, 4 Colors	10
C	5	Galvanized Nail	1
C	5	Gelatin, Box/4	3
C	1	Germ Simulator	15
C	frequent use	Graph Paper, pad/100	2
c	13	Highlighters	30
C	3, 5	Hydrogen Peroxide, 3%, 230 mL	1
C	8	Index Cards, 5×8″, Pkg/100	1
C	1, 3, 7, 8, 9	Index Cards, Blank, Pkg/100	5
C	7	Inoculating Loops, Sterile, pkg/25	2
C	3	Iron Filings, 100 g	1
C	5	Iron Nail	1
C	5	Iron Wire, 25 M	1
C	12	Large Styrofoam Ball	10
C	5	Lead Fishing Weight	1
C	5	Lemon Juice, 500 mL	1
C	5	Magnesium Ribbon, 6 cm	1

Master Materials List

For information on standard and custom kit availability, please contact your Kendall/Hunt representative at 1-800-542-6657.

Type	Chapter	Item Description	Kit Qty.
C	frequent use	Markers, Black, Pkg/30	1
C	frequent use	Masking Tape	10
C	5, 11, 13	Matches, 10 Boxes	1
C	8	Meat Tenderizer	1
C	14	Molasses, 350 mL	1
C	11, 12	Nails, pkg/500	1
C	5	Pan, Aluminum Foil	1
C	6, 7, 8, 9	Paper Bags	56
C	13	Paper Plates	1
C	9	Paper, Roll, 18″×30′	1
C	5	Pencil Lead, Pkg/12	3
C	3, 5, 7	Petri Dish, Pkg/25	3
C	13	Red Pen	30
C	6	Sand, 2.5 kg	1
C	6	Sandwich Bags, Pkg/80	1
C	8	Seeds, Pinto Bean, 1 lb.	1
C	7	Sodium Benzoate Tasting Paper, 100 Strips	1
C	5, 8	Sodium Chloride, 737 g	1
C	8	Split Peas, 1 lb.	1
C	3	Starch, Soluble, 100 g	1
C	1	Sterile Cotton Swabs, Pkg/100	1
C	1, 3, 8, 11	Sticky Notes	4
C	frequent use	Ball of String, 430’	2
C	12	Styrofoam Balls	100
C	5, 6	Sugar, 354 g	1

Type	Chapter	Item Description	Kit Qty.
C	frequent use	Tagboard, 24×36″	95
C	4	Thread, White, 200 yds.	1
C	3, 5, 6	Toothpicks, Pkg/250	1
C	frequent use	Transparent Tape	15
C	3, 5	Vinegar, 473 mL	2
C	11, 13	Votive Candle	11
C	3, 14	Wax Pencil	10
C	5, 8	Wooden Splints, Pkg/25	1
C	8	Yarn	1
C	3, 8, 12, 15	Zip-Lock Bag	65
Live Items			
C	7	Live Coupon, Yeast, A2, HAR	1
C	7	Live Coupon, Yeast, A3, HBT	1
C	7	Live Coupon, YED Agar, 6 Bottles	2
Chemicals			
C	5	Ammonium Hydroxide, 0.1 M, 50 mL	1
C	3	Anhydrous Calcium Chloride, 500 g	1
C	11	Bromothymol Blue, 500 mL	1
C	3	Cobalt Cloride, 50 mL, Concentrated	1
C	5	Copper II Chloride, 100 g	1
C	3	Copper II Nitrate, 50 mL	1
C	8	Ethanol, 500 mL	1
C	3, 5	Hydrochloric Acid, 1.0 M, 1 L	1

Master Materials List

For information on standard and custom kit availability, please contact your Kendall/Hunt representative at 1-800-542-6657.

Type	Chapter	Item Description	Kit Qty.
C	5	Hydrochloric Acid, 3 M, 500 mL	2
C	5	Magnesium Ribbon, 6 cm	1
C	5	Manganese Dioxide, 5 g	1
C	14	Methylene Blue (optional)	1
C	5	Phenolphthalein, 50 mL	1
C	3	Potassium Bromate, 50 Ml	1
C	3	Potassium Chromate, 50 mL, Concentrated	1
C	5	Potassium Ferricyanide, 50 mL, Concentrated	1
C	3	Potassium Iodide, 50 mL, Concentrated	1
C	5	Silver Nitrate, Capsule, Quick Mix	1
C	11	Sodium Hydrogen Carbonate, 500 g	1
C	5	Sodium Hydroxide, 0.1 M, 50 mL	2
C	3	Sodium Hyroxide, Concentrated, 30 mL	1
C	3	Sodium Thiosulfate, 50 mL, Concentrated	1
C	3	Sulfur, 100 g	1
C	3	Sulfuric Acid, 3.0 M, 1 L	1
C	5	Universal Indicator, 50 mL	1
Nonconsumable Items			
N	6	Aquarium Gravel, 1 kg	1
N	5	Battery Clip	8
N	frequent use	Calculator	30
N	5	Clear Aquarium Tubing	1
N	6	Clothespin, Spring Type	8

Type	Chapter	Item Description	Kit Qty.
N	2	Collision Ball, Steel, 19 mm	8
N	2	Collision Ball, Steel, 25mm	8
N	3	Corks, Size 11, Pkg/6	5
N	2	Cup Hooks	24
N	6	Dinosaur Bone (Jurassic)	1
N	12	Drop Cloth	5
N	6	Fern Fossil	6
N	6	Forceps (optional)	24
N	7	Forceps, Medium Point	15
N	6	Fossil Assortment, Set/8	6
N	13	Friction Block with Hook	1
N	10	Glass Dropper	1
N	11	Jar	20
N	2, 15	Jumbo Paper Clips, Box/100	2
N	6	Lentils, 1 lb.	1
N	11	Lid to Jar	20
N	4, 6	Marbles, Pkg/30	2
N	11	Metal Tablespoon	10
N	7, 14	Microscope Slides and Coverslips, Set/72	1
N	3	Microwell Plate, Pkg/10	8
N	12	Model of Earth	1
N	6	Navy Beans, 1 lb.	1
N	4, 6	Packing Peanuts, Pkg/200	1
N	8	Paper Clips, Assorted, Pkg/800	4
N	6, 7, 8, 10	Plastic Cups, Pkg/50	1

Master Materials List

For information on standard and custom kit availability, please contact your Kendall/Hunt representative at 1-800-542-6657.

Type	Chapter	Item Description	Kit Qty.
N	6	Plastic Spoons, Pkg/24	1
N	2, 12	Protractor	30
N	12	Push Pins, Pkg/100	1
N	6	Red Beans, 1 lb.	1
N	frequent use	Ruler	30
N	5	Small Alligator Clip	16
N	13	Small Plastic Animal	10
N	6	Split Peas, 1 lb.	1
N	4	Spring	10
N	4	Spring Scale — 20 N	15
N	frequent use	Stopwatch	15
N	8	Strainer	15
N	13	Syringe, 60 cc	1
N	2, 6	Tape Measure	8
N	2	Tennis Balls	24
N	3	Thermometer	6
N	5	Tin Foil, 100 g	1
N	5	Tin Roofing Material	1
N	12	Top	10
N	2	Toy Cars	16
N	14	Transparent Metric Ruler, Pkg/10	3
N	2	Velcro Strip, Hook, 1 yd.	1
N	2	Velcro Strip, Loop, 1 yd.	1
N	2	Weights	
N	5	Zinc Shot, 100 g	1

Type	Chapter	Item Description	Kit Qty.
Equipment			
N	2, 3, 8, 12	Balance	6
N	8, 14	Blender	1
N	7, 14	Compound Microscope	15
N	5	Conductivity Meter	15
N	3, 13	Hotplate, Single	1
N	1, 7	Incubator, 37 C	1
N	14	Spectrophotometer (optional)	1
N	5, 8	Stereomicroscope, 20×	15
N	1	UV Light Source	15
Safety Items			
N	frequent use	Disposable Nitrile Lab Gloves, Box/100	4
N	frequent use	Lab Apron	30
N	frequent use	Safety Goggles	30
Labware			
N	13	1000-mL Beaker	1
N	6, 10	100-mL Graduated Cylinder	10
N	8, 10	10-mL Graduated Cylinder	10
N	5, 10	150-mL Beaker	80
N	10, 12	25-mL Graduated Cylinder	10
N	3, 10, 11	400-mL Beaker	20
N	3	500 mL Graduated Cylinder	1
N	8	50-mL Beaker	15

Master Materials List

For information on standard and custom kit availability, please contact your Kendall/Hunt representative at 1-800-542-6657.

Type	Chapter	Item Description	Kit Qty.
N	10	50-mL Graduated Cylinder	10
N	8	600-mL Beaker	15
N	4	Ring Stand	15
N	4	Slotted Weights, Set/13	15
N	4	Support Rod	15
N	5, 8, 14	Test Tube Rack	15
N	14	Test Tube with Screw Cap	21
N	1, 3, 5, 8, 14	Test Tubes, 18 mm×150 mm	24

Local Items

These items are needed to complete the activity and are available locally.

Type	Chapter	Item Description
	8	½ Banana
	8	½ Cup of Chicken Liver
	4, 10	1-Liter Bottle
	8	200-mL of Water
	15, 16	Access to a Computer and the Web
	15	Age Structure Handout
	5	Assorted Fruits
	16	Assorted Presentation Aids
	4	Ball
	1, 7, 8	Bleach Solution
	6	Box Top
	7	Bucket
	5	Card Pack 1
	5	Card Pack 2
	2	Chair
	8	Clock or Timer
	8	Coded Message
	3, 4, 6	Coins
	2	Collision Grid
	3	Container for Water Bath
	14	Density Indicator Strips (optional)
	3, 5, 11	Distilled Water
	11	Dry Ice, 2-cm Cubes
	15	Ecological Footprint Handout
	11	Glass Container with Cover
	11	Glass Container without Cover
	5	Gold and Silver Jewelry
	11	Hammer
	4	Hardcover Book
	11, 12	Ice Cube
	7, 8, 10	Large Sheet of Paper
	1	Magazines, Newspapers, etc.
	5	Marshmallows
	4, 6, 13	Meter Stick
	5	Milk
	8	Nucleus Sign
	3	OverheadProjector
	frequent use	Paper
	11, 13, 14	Paper Towels

Master Materials List

For information on standard and custom kit availability, please contact your Kendall/Hunt representative at 1-800-542-6657.

Type	Chapter	Item Description
	14	Peas, Frozen
	2	Pen Cap
	frequent use	Pencil and Eraser
	6	Pictures of Diverse Organisms
	2, 12	Piece of Cardboard
	11	Piece of Wood
	3	Pipette Holder or Cassette Box
	6	Plastic Bin of Water
	15	Population Description Handout
	1, 15	Presentation Materials
	5	Property Cards
	5	Rain Water
	6	Raisins
	2	Ramps
	13	Red Toothpaste
	8, 16	Reference Materials
	frequent use	Scissors
	16	Scoring Rubric for a Meeting of the Minds
	15	Scoring Rubric for Sustaining Human Populations

Type	Chapter	Item Description
	5	Scoring Rubric Handouts
	11	Seltzer Water, 2 Liters
	12	Shallow Box
	15	Small Paper Clips
	1	Source of Bacteria
	5	Sparkler
	9	Stapler
	3	Staples
	8	Summary Materials
	8	Term Chart Completed Handout (optional)
	15	Transparency of Mean Annual Precipitation
	15	Transparency of World Region Map in Color
	6	Uncooked Elbow Macaroni
	3	Water
	8	Woolite Liquid Detergent
	15	World Map
	15	World Region Map Handouts
	6	Wrapping Paper

Credits

CHAPTER 1: None

Unit 1

CHAPTER 2: None

CHAPTER 3: None

CHAPTER 4: None

CHAPTER 5: None

Unit 2

CHAPTER 6: **T6.13** © Weldon Owen, Inc. Adapted with permission.; **T6.14** (elephant molar) Phil Myers, University of Michigan Museum of Zoology and Animal Diversity Web, http://animaldiversity.org, (mammoth molar) Sarah Rieboldt and the University of California Museum of Paleontology.

CHAPTER 7: **T7.6** Biophoto Associates/ Photo Researchers, Inc.

CHAPTER 8: **T8.1** Genetic Science Learning Center.

CHAPTER 9: None

Unit 3

CHAPTER 10: None

CHAPTER 11: **T11.9** (Law Dome) D.M. Etheridge, L.P. Steele, R.L. Langenfelds, R.J. Francey, J.-M. Barnola and V.I. Morgan. 1998. Historical CO_2 records from the Law Dome DE08, DE08-2, and DSS ice cores. In Trends: A Compendium of Data on Global Change. Carbon Dioxide Information Analysis Center, Oak Ridge National Laboratory, U.S. Department of Energy, Oak Ridge, Tenn., U.S.A., (Mauna Loa) Keeling, C.D. and T.P. Whorf. 2005. Atmospheric CO_2 records from sites in the SIO air sampling network. In Trends: A Compendium of Data on Global Change. Carbon Dioxide Information Analysis Center, Oak Ridge National Laboratory, U.S. Department of Energy, Oak Ridge, Tenn., U.S.A. **T11.10, T11.11, T11.12** Sarmiento, J.L., & Gruber, N. (2002)

CHAPTER 12: **T12.8** Data source: Shackleton, Berger, & Peltier (1990).

CHAPTER 13: **T13.11, T13.12** Map image from ARC Science Simulations Inc.'s "Face of the Earth" produced on UNAVCO's map server http://jules.unavco.org.

Unit 4

CHAPTER 14: None

CHAPTER 15: None

CHAPTER 16: None

Student Edition Index

Page numbers in bold print indicate item was in bold in the text; italic indicates a chart, table, graph, or illustration.

A

B

C

D

E

F

G

H

N

O

P

R

U

V

W

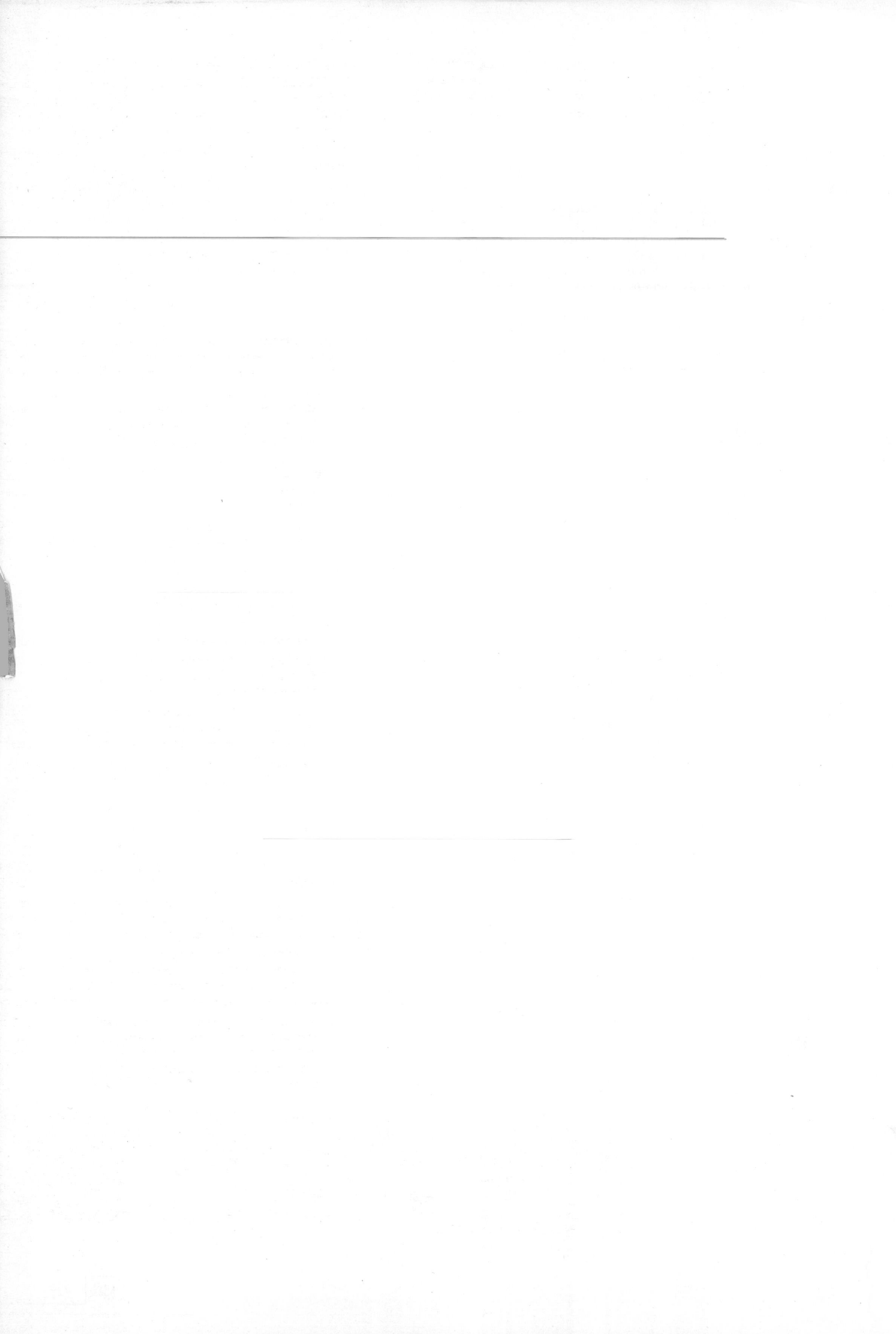